WORLD NAVAL WEAPONS SYSTEMS

The Naval Institute
Guide to

WORLD NAVAL WEAPONS SYSTEMS 1997–1998

Norman Friedman

Naval Institute Press
Annapolis, Maryland

© 1997 by the U.S. Naval Institute
Annapolis, Maryland

Library of Congress Cataloging-in-Publication Data

Friedman, Norman, 1946–
    The Naval Institute guide to world naval weapons systems,
1997–1998 / Norman Friedman.
        p.   cm.
    Includes index.
    ISBN 1-55750-268-4 (alk. paper)
    1. Weapons systems—Handbooks, manuals, etc.   2. Ordnance,
Naval—Handbooks, manuals, etc.   I. Title.
VF346.F75   1997
359.8—dc21   97-3768

Printed in the United States of America on acid-free paper ∞

04 03 02 01 00 99 98 97   9 8 7 6 5 4 3 2
First printing

CONTENTS

INTRODUCTION   **vii**
  ACKNOWLEDGMENTS   xi

PREFATORY NOTES   **xiii**
  RADAR   xiii
  ELECTRONIC WARFARE (ESM AND ECM)   xviii
  SONAR   xxiii
  OPTRONICS AND INFRARED DEVICES
    (PHOTONICS)   xxx
  LASERS   xxxiv
  IFF   xxxv
  MISSILE GUIDANCE   xxxvi
  COMPANY CONSOLIDATIONS   xxxvii

  DESIGNATION SYSTEMS   xxxix

  ABBREVIATIONS   xliv

SURVEILLANCE AND CONTROL   **1**
  COMMAND ADVICE SYSTEMS   1
    Australia 2, France 2, Germany 2,
    International 3, Russia 3, Sweden 4, United
    Kingdom 4, United States 5

  SATELLITE SENSOR SYSTEMS   16
    France 16, Russia 17, United States 17

  SURFACE RADAR/ELINT (ELECTRONICS
    INTELLIGENCE) SYSTEMS   19
    Australia 19, Canada 19, Russia 19, United
    Kingdom 19, United States 20

  STRATEGIC UNDERWATER SENSOR SYSTEMS   21
    Canada 21, China 21, Finland 21,
    Germany 21, Indonesia 21, Japan 21,
    Russia 21, Sweden 22, Taiwan 22,
    Turkey 22, United States 22

  TACTICAL COMMUNICATIONS SYSTEMS   25
    RADIO SYSTEMS   25
    Denmark 25, France 26, Germany 26,
    India 26, International 26, Italy 30, Japan 30,
    Netherlands 30, Russia 30, South Africa 31,
    Sweden 31, Taiwan 31, United Kingdom 31,
    United States 32
    SUBMARINE COMMUNICATIONS SYSTEMS   41
    Russia 42, United Kingdom 42, United
    States 43

  COMPUTERS   45
    Canada 48, France 48, Israel 49, Italy 50,
    Netherlands 50, Norway 51, Sweden 52,
    Taiwan 52, United Kingdom 52, United
    States 53
    DATA BUSES   67
    Canada 67, France 67, Germany 67, Italy 68,
    Netherlands 68, United Kingdom 68, United
    States 68

TACTICAL DATA SYSTEMS   **70**
  SURFACE SHIP COMBAT-DIRECTION
    SYSTEMS   73
    Brazil 73, Canada 73, Chile 74, China 75,
    Denmark 75, France 76, Germany 82,
    India 85, Israel 86, Italy 86, Japan 90,
    Netherlands 90, Norway 95, Russia 98,
    South Africa 101, Spain 103, Sweden 104,
    United Kingdom 107, United States 116

  SUBMARINE COMBAT-DIRECTION SYSTEMS   138
    Denmark 139, France 139, Germany 141,
    Italy 143, Netherlands 143, Norway 144,
    Russia 146, South Africa 146, Sweden 148,
    United Kingdom 149, United States 151

  AIRCRAFT TACTICAL DATA SYSTEMS   165
    France 166, International 167, Israel 167,
    Italy 167, Russia 168, South Africa 171,
    Sweden 171, United Kingdom 171, United
    States 173

STRATEGIC STRIKE SYSTEMS   **186**
    China (PRC) 186, France 186, Russia 188,
    United States 188

STRIKE/SURFACE WARFARE   **190**
  RECONNAISSANCE SYSTEMS   190
    AIRCRAFT-CARRIED SENSORS   190
    United States 190
    UAVs (FORMERLY RPVs)   192
    Germany 192, Israel 192, United States 192

  AIRBORNE SENSORS   193
    Australia 193, Canada 193, China 193,
    France 194, Israel 197, Italy 197, Russia 198,
    Sweden 200, United Kingdom 200, United
    States 203

  AIR FIRE-CONTROL SYSTEMS   216
    France 216, Russia 216, United States 216

  SURFACE MISSILE FIRE-CONTROL SYSTEMS   217
    Russia 217, United States 218

  MISSILES AND GUIDED BOMBS   220
    Brazil 220, China (PRC) 220, France 223,
    Germany 228, India 229, International 229,
    Israel 229, Italy 230, Japan 232,
    Norway 233, Russia 234, South Africa 246,
    Sweden 246, Taiwan (ROC) 247, United
    Kingdom 248, United States 249

  UNGUIDED BOMBS AND AIR-LAUNCHED
    ROCKETS   261
    France 261, Russia 262, United
    Kingdom 263, United States 263

  AIRCRAFT GUNS   266
    France 266, Germany 266, Russia 266,
    United Kingdom 267, United States 267

  COAST-DEFENSE GUNS AND ROCKETS   267
    Brazil 267, Finland 267, Germany 268,
    Norway 268, Portugal 268, Russia 268,
    Spain 269, Sweden 269, United
    Kingdom 270, United States 270,
    Yugoslavia 270

BOMBARDMENT ROCKETS 271
Italy 271, Russia 271, United States 272

ANTIAIRCRAFT WARFARE **273**
SHIPBOARD RADARS AND FIRE-CONTROL
SYSTEMS 273
Bulgaria 273, Canada 273, Chile 275, China
(PRC) 275, Denmark 280, France 280,
Germany 293, India 294, Israel 295,
Italy 298, Japan 309, Netherlands 313,
Poland 324, Russia 325, South Africa 341,
Spain 342, Sweden 342, Switzerland 346,
Taiwan (ROC) 348, United Kingdom 348,
United States 365

SURFACE-TO-AIR MISSILES 395
China (PRC) 395, France 396, India 399,
International 399, Israel 401, Italy 401,
Norway 402, Poland 402, Russia 403, South
Africa 408, Sweden 408, United
Kingdom 409, United States 411

AIR-TO-AIR MISSILES 421
France 421, Germany 422, Japan 423,
Russia 423, United States 426

SHIPBOARD GUNS AND GUN SYSTEMS 431
Australia 431, China 431, Finland 432,
France 432, Germany 434, Israel 435,
Italy 436, Netherlands 440, Norway 441,
Russia 441, South Africa 448, Spain 448,
Sweden 449, Switzerland 454, Taiwan 458,
United Kingdom 458, United States 460

ELECTRONIC WARFARE **472**
Australia 472, Brazil 473, Canada 474,
Chile 474, China (PRC) 474, Denmark 475,
France 475, Germany (West) 487, India 491,
International 492, Israel 492, Italy 497,
Japan 503, Korea 504, Netherlands 505,
Norway 507, Poland 507, Russia 507, South
Africa 516, Spain 516, Sweden 517,
Taiwan 519, United Kingdom 520, United
States 535

ANTISUBMARINE WARFARE **576**
SONARS AND UNDERWATER
FIRE-CONTROL SYSTEMS 576
Australia 576, Canada 577, Chile 579,
China 579, Finland 579, France 579,
Germany 591, India 596, International 597,
Israel 597, Italy 597, Japan 599,
Netherlands 600, Norway 602, Russia 603,
South Africa 608, Sweden 608, United
Kingdom 609, United States 615

SUBMARINE PERISCOPES 638
France 639, Germany 641, Russia 641,
United Kingdom 642, United States 643

SONOBUOYS AND SIGNAL PROCESSORS 644
Australia 646, Canada 647, China 648,
France 648, India 650, Italy 650, Japan 651,
Korea (South) 651, Russia 651, Sweden 652,
United Kingdom 652, United States 654

NONACOUSTIC ASW SENSORS 662
Australia 662, Canada 662, France 662,
Japan 663, Russia 663, United States 663

MISSILES 664
China (PRC) 664, France 664,
International 665, Russia 665, United
States 667

TORPEDOES 668
China (PRC) 670, France 671, Germany 673,
India 675, International 675, Italy 676,
Japan 678, Korea 679, Russia 679,
Sweden 684, Taiwan 686, United
Kingdom 686, United States 689

UNGUIDED WEAPONS (MORTARS
AND DEPTH CHARGES) 697
Chile 697, China (PRC) 697, Italy 697,
Spain 699, Sweden 699, United
Kingdom 701, United States 701

COUNTERMEASURES 702
China 703, France 703, Germany 706,
India 706, International 706, Israel 707,
Italy 707, Russia 707, Sweden 708, United
Kingdom 708, United States 709

MINES AND MINE COUNTERMEASURES **713**
MINES 715
Argentina 715, Brazil 716, Chile 716,
China 716, Denmark 716, France 717,
Germany 717, Iraq 718, Italy 718, Japan 719,
Korea (North) 719, Korea (South) 719,
Norway 719, Russia 720, South Africa 724,
Spain 724, Sweden 725, Taiwan 726, United
Kingdom 726, United States 727,
Yugoslavia 732

MCM/MINEHUNTING SONARS 732
Australia 732, Canada 733, China
(PRC) 733, Denmark 733, Finland 733,
France 734, Germany 740, Hungary 741,
International 741, Italy 742, Japan 743,
Netherlands 743, Norway 744, Poland 745,
Russia 745, Sweden 746, United
Kingdom 748, United States 751,
Yugoslavia 760

INDEX **761**

ADDENDUM **777**

INTRODUCTION

We are living in a period of transition, from an ordered (but extremely threatening) Cold War, through a period of instability in which many of the certainties of the past, such as the stability of NATO, seem less and less sure. We cannot yet know whether the current age of instability will end with the creation of relatively stable rival great powers, as it did after the Napoleonic wars of the early nineteenth century. In any case, the sense of randomness and unpredictability in world politics, which was once common, disappeared during the Cold War; we gained a false sense of certainties and also of a slow pace in international affairs. Now we are back in the world as it existed before World War II, or even before World War I. For example, forms of nationalism that were suppressed during the long communist domination of Central Europe are now quite active. The mess in the former Yugoslavia is one consequence. It is far from unique. Indeed, much of Asia is seeing a second wave of nationalism (the first wave freed countries from their European overlords after World War II) which is likely to fuel numerous border disputes.

Current naval developments mirror these trends. Flexibility is increasingly prized because it is no longer possible to believe in a set of fixed scenarios for conflict, let alone for tension short of war. Navies that once designed themselves mainly for blue-water sea control (which usually meant ASW in some form) must now seek the ability to attack an enemy ashore, albeit on a far smaller scale than was contemplated during the Cold War.

Political uncertainty is mirrored by technological uncertainty. Without a Cold War driving weapon developments in the superpowers, new weapons are more likely to appear in the Third World. In some cases they may be related to abortive superpower projects, just as German jet-fighter designers managed to realize their wartime dreams after 1945 in Argentina, Egypt, India, and Spain. Too, the superpower defense establishments no longer drive some of the most important technology, that of information processing.

Anyone looking ahead must take into account the commercial forces driving not only microelectronics hardware, but also the software that it runs. For example, with the rise of multimedia, considerations other than number-processing speed may become paramount in processor chip design. In that case, relatively inefficient techniques, such as writing programs so that they can easily be rehosted, may prove embarrassing; in the past, they seemed acceptable because it was assumed that processing speed would continue to increase explosively. For that matter, the demand to connect many different computer applications is driving military systems to use commercial operating software environments such as Windows, which may contain obscure quirks that may prove far more embarrassing for military than for civilian applications. Inefficiencies in these systems, accepted because they allow multiple (more or less simultaneous) operation of different programs, are also becoming evident.

More generally, as resources available for purely military development decline, many military programs may be driven by what the civilian economy is willing to develop for its own purposes. That is not new. For example, U.S. programs to develop closed-cycle submarine powerplants after World War II failed largely because they had no civilian application and therefore attracted no civilian resources outside a tightly constrained military budget. This situation was contrasted at the time with nuclear power, whose civilian advocates were more than willing to finance research in hopes of nonmilitary rewards.

At present, Northern Telecom of Canada is participating enthusiastically in the Canadian-Dutch-German APAR active radar program because it believes that the solid-state transmitter-receivers involved have vital civilian applications, most likely in a new generation of S-band cellular telephones. Conversely, the U.S. 5in guided shell may now finally become a reality mainly because Detroit mass-produces miniature gyros and accelerometers for antiskid car braking systems. Both cases suggest that future military programs that exploit civilian technology have far better prospects than those whose components seem to have no important civilian applications. Of course, predictions are always tricky. The U.S. government spent heavily on lasers for military applications, but now they are probably most widely used in computer printers and in telephone system repeaters.

Political uncertainty affects many weapons systems currently in use. Communication (as in the digital data links) and identification (IFF) systems were both conceived within alliance rather than national boundaries. Indeed, allied forces could not fight together without sharing these systems. What happens now, when alliances may lack real force, and when military action may be taken by ad hoc coalitions? For example, aircraft can be extremely effective ship-killers. A ship that spots an approaching low-flying airplane has very little time to react; yet shooting down an airplane operated by a coalition partner may literally destroy the coalition. The very elaborate measures adopted during the Gulf War seem to have succeeded in sparing coalition aircraft, but probably were acceptable only because the Iraqis proved so docile. Other Third World opponents may behave very differently.

As available reaction time has shrunk since the early 1950s, the solution has generally been more and more automation, hence (since the late 1950s) greater and greater reliance on computer-to-computer links. What happens when a coalition partner lacks any equivalent to our links, when the partner's combat-direction system is really not analogous to ours? Would we prefer to exclude that potential partner, or would the political goal (of including the partner in some operation) outweigh anything else? Surely that would be the case with Russian warships.

The extent to which the details of command and control (C^2) have invaded the realms of policy, which once seemed so innocent of technical issues, is striking. Perhaps that is not so different from the way in which apparently abstruse issues of interface protocols (such as Link protocols) have given the Microsoft Corporation, at least temporarily, so much power in the world of microcomputers, in a way that may not be amenable to U.S. government antitrust action. It may literally be almost impossible for NATO navies and air forces to divorce themselves from Link 11 and its successors.

As an example of the way details of Link operation now count, it now appears that USS *Vincennes* shot down the Iranian Airbus in 1988 partly because two separate Link 11 nets in effect merged, probably due to ducting. When the same track number, originally used for the Airbus, was used by another ship (HMS *Manchester*) for a different airplane, far away, this data became available on the net used by *Vincennes*. When the wrong question was asked (what is the altitude of the aircraft with the Airbus's original number?), the answer was that it was diving—and that seemed to show that the Airbus was attacking *Vincennes*, when in fact it was climbing out of its takeoff.

Combat identification is likely to become increasingly difficult because the usual alternative to the standard interrogator-transponder combination, physical identification, is no longer particularly attractive. Russian-supplied equipment may well be operated by states friendly to the old Western powers, and many former Western client-states may at times be enemies. Iran was a good example of this problem. For example, the ESM operator on board the frigate *Stark* mistook the French-supplied Agave radar of the Iraqi airplane that attacked the ship for a U.S.-supplied AWG-9 operated by an Islamic Iranian air force (U.S.-supplied) F-14A.

Navies are likely to see considerable action because, as is usual after a major war, local ambitions and grievances are coming to the fore. In many cases, such as the U.S. and British escort missions during the Iran-Iraq War, the naval contribution may be to try to restrain local combatants in order to protect vital trade. In other cases presence may be vital either to encourage a friendly regime or to dissuade an unfriendly one from particularly unfortunate actions. All such persuasion is ultimately a tacit threat (or promise) of using force, so it will always be important for ships or groups on presence missions to offer both the potential for effective attack and the ability to ward off local forces.

These missions are likely to arise very suddenly and, to most observers, unpredictably. The Third World is far too varied for anyone to foresee local crises terribly accurately. In some cases, major-power governments will not want to react at all; in others they will want to limit their involvement. Naval forces are the obvious mechanism for intervention in these ambiguous times, simply because they can be deployed without local consent and easily withdrawn at will. It is many centuries since Roger Bacon wrote that he who commands the sea can take as much or as little of a war as he likes, but it is still true. Deploying a carrier risks far less, particularly in prestige, than deploying a wing of fighters to a local air base, and withdrawing it costs even less. Too, multilateral naval operations create far fewer human problems than multilateral ground operations, since it is not necessary for large numbers of troops to work together intimately. Also, many potential host governments surely find assistance by naval forces far less destabilizing than accepting the presence of large ground forces.

Presence means far more than operating a visible, handsome ship off a port to influence the local government. The ship must present a realistic threat, and it must be able to stand up to the locals' weapons. In the past, the classic form of presence was a British nineteenth-century cruiser. When the ship arrived in some Third World port, she carried enough Marines to form a respectable landing party, and enough firepower to blow away the local ruler's palace. Almost certainly the locals had never invested in enough firepower to sink the cruiser, particularly if she remained offshore.

The flexibility navies provide is likely to become more important because the relationships between countries will probably change relatively quickly and suddenly. Our experience of Cold War calculations of friendship and enmity, which were predicated on the fight between the Soviets and the West, are unlikely to remain valid. For example, in East Asia the United States is friendly with both South Korea and Japan. In both cases, military support was provided to hold back communist expansion. Many Americans assume that the main threat in the area is a North Korean attack on South Korea. They may be correct, but it is also true that Korea and Japan are separated by very deep enmity. What would (or should) American policy be if that enmity escalates?

As for China, the American friendship that began in the 1970s was predicated partly on hopes that the "China card" would force the Soviets to divide their forces, and thus would relax pressure in Europe. Now the Cold War is over, and China is a major U.S. trading partner. As the Chinese government applies pressure to other U.S. partners in South Asia (in pursuit of domination of the South China Sea), who is the enemy? Is there a clear enemy present, or is the United States' national interest to prevent a clash?

The Cold War provided simple answers: those who supported us against the Soviets were our friends. From time to time we discovered, generally painfully, that not all of our friends were each others' friends, and that we sometimes had to choose. Examples of such problems included Britain versus Argentina in the Falklands, Greece versus Turkey, and, from time to time, China versus Taiwan. Generally, there is no longer any obvious indicator of national interest, not even the flawed one so useful during the Cold War.

Some Third World governments incapable (for political reasons) of achieving prosperity for their countries managed to survive through the Cold War by becoming clients of one superpower or the other, or by playing off the two superpowers to gain both economic support and breathing space. With the Cold War over, neither combatant has much interest in continuing to support governments that controlled strategic spots in the World War III that might have broken out had the Cold War turned hot. Examples surely include both Cuba and the Philippines. One might see the Iraqi invasion of Kuwait, in effect a bank robbery, as an early example of post–Cold War measures a government might take to compensate for the loss of subsidies. Some will argue that governments will now find it impossible to resist a conversion to something approaching a free economy, simply to make the money they are no longer receiving as subsidies; but to many dictatorial governments a free economy is merely one step down a slippery slope to a free polity, and thus to the loss of the raw power that they crave.

Navies are likely to find themselves quite busy, albeit frequently without the resources they need. In particular, we may find that our current U.S. standard for measuring our military requirements—the ability to fight two major regional wars nearly simultaneously—dangerously misleading.

To fight two big wars (say, in the Gulf and in Korea), the United States would need large ground and ground-based air forces, since each war would be a sustained conflict. Naval forces are useful, but mainly for quick reinforcement and to insure access to the theater of war. On the other hand, a future of numerous simultaneous (but relatively small) crises demands the ability to show some form of credible presence in many places simultaneously. Forces capable of sustained operations are not nearly as important. The mismatch is quite unfortunate. For example, naval forces built up to fight the two "major regional conflicts" (MRCs) are sized by the number of carriers and major amphibious ships and then by the number of escorts they need. As the blue-water threat recedes, the number of escorts also declines. On the other hand, to provide presence in numerous places simultaneously, the Navy needs many surface action groups (carriers can never be operated in sufficient numbers). The current plight of the Royal Navy, which has barely enough frigates to cover its assigned overseas stations (principally the Armilla Patrol in the Gulf and the antidrug guardship in the West Indies), may indicate our own future problems. Although frigate/destroyer numbers were dictated mainly by affordability, the absolute minimum was what was needed to cover the two carriers and the amphibious group. At present the Royal Navy is concentrating on replacing its carrier escorts.

These political considerations carry very real technological (and tactical) implications. It is most unlikely that crises arising randomly will occur in places with nearby base facilities. Too, it is unlikely that plans have been prepared to deal with crises which, according to Murphy's immutable law, will happen where least expected. In this case plans include intelligence assessments and missile targeting profiles. Information badly needed by tacticians may be available at home, in effect, in archives. Getting that information to deployed forces, in a form usable in timely fashion, becomes extremely important. It motivates projects like the U.S. Challenge Athena experiment, which make it practical to transmit targeting photographs to the deployed fleet. The need for flexibility also explains the U.S. shift away from terrain-comparison guidance (which required elaborate digital mapping) toward GPS (which requires almost no preparation) for the very important Tomahawk missile. Surprise deployments also require quick updating of EW libraries, for example; note how many RWR libraries can now be changed on the flight line (limitations on such changes proved embarrassing during the Gulf War).

Naval combat is likely to become more common not merely because the world is less stable but also because nuclear deterrence is unlikely to be effective against Third World states, even as retaliation against chemical or biological attack. Thus it is quite likely that many current beliefs, for example, in the lethality of antiship cruise missiles, will be tested in the next decade or two. The result may be new weapons. In the past, it was considered quite impressive that a missile flew and homed on its target; missile characteristics were usually set by launcher design, hence overall missile envelope. Many existing weapons do not seem particularly lethal; the usual claim that they can exact a mission kill is merely an admission that they cannot sink a ship. That may be enough; many modern combat systems are quite fragile. However, the technology now exists to build extremely robust distributed combat systems. Combat demonstration that modern Western missiles simply lack killing power might cause wholesale replacement.

After all, much the same thing happened during the nineteenth century. That was a time, like ours, of largely cold war (between Britain and France) but also of rapid technological development. Many thinkers tried to draw conclusions as to the consequences of the new technology, but the small fund of actual experience seems to have had disproportionate impact, perhaps simply because it was not conjectural. For example, quick-firing guns and surface-launched torpedoes became really important only after they proved effective in action (at the Yalu in 1894 and in the Brazilian civil war of 1891). In this century, the full implications of antiship missiles apparently were appreciated only after the sinking of the Israeli destroyer *Eilat* in 1967.

The effective end of nuclear deterrence carries enormous, and largely unrecognized, implications. It may seem trivial to remark that nuclear weapons offer enormous explosive power in a very compact package, but the reader should reflect on where the withdrawal of nuclear weapons leaves the small number of missiles and aircraft now available. One popular answer is that extraordinarily precise weapons are nearly as good as nuclear ones, but that is hardly believable. Surely there is some difference between the effect of a 500- or 1000-lb bomb, no matter how cleverly placed, and a vast, radiating, smoking crater. There may be even more difference in a prospective victim's appreciation of the threat the two weapons pose, particularly if the conventional bomb cannot penetrate the deep bunker in which he resides.

Certainly the experience of the Gulf War brings the value of precision weapons into question. Perhaps the single most important mission of the massive strategic bombing offensive against Iraq was to eliminate Iraqi nuclear and chemical-biological weapons. After the war was over, UN inspectors discovered that virtually none of the important Iraqi sites had been hit, not because they were so cleverly defended, but because they were largely unknown to the attackers. Even the most precise weapon cannot hit such targets. Now there is a major U.S. program to detect buried targets (as a means of halting nuclear proliferation), but it is unlikely to succeed. Decoying should be relatively easy, and the number of available U.S. warheads will be limited.

The implication seems to be that we will often find ourselves making hit-and-run raids (something like the 1986 Libyan strikes), with the goal of demonstrating our ability to overcome local defenses without bringing into question our ability to find and destroy the most important targets. If we do in fact want to disarm a country, we probably have to invade and (at least briefly) occupy it. The bombing solution no longer seems valid.

Hit-and-run in a very unpredictable world requires very flexible forces. They cannot really be tied to local bases, because crises will break out in places for which bases were not built. Planning must be extremely fast, using intelligence quickly gathered as a crisis unfolds. If the operation involves landing Marines, it may well be unwise to land their command/control, since the entire ground operation may be extremely quick. Much of the U.S. reaction to this requirement can be seen in the Surveillance and Control section of this edition.

During the Cold War, the major navies naturally emphasized what was needed either to maintain or to deny sea control. The end of the Cold War is the end of great-power conflict at sea, at least for the next few decades (it does leave considerable potential for local naval warfare). That leaves the very real question of how many Western warships conceived mainly for ASW can be adapted to the demands of presence. Little of their missile armament can be changed, and many are far too small to accommodate operations spaces for troop or air control ashore. Perhaps the most likely route is via the weapons the nearly ubiquitous helicopters can carry. After all, an aircraft carrier is by far the most adaptable kind of warship because her aircraft can be changed more or less at will. The Royal Navy has demonstrated as much with its *Invincible* class, conceived as ASW support ships carrying mainly Sea King helicopters. Their air groups have been changed dramatically to emphasize Sea Harrier strike aircraft (the Sea King successors, the Merlins, will operate from the accompanying Type 23 frigates).

It seems likely that weapons, sensors, and C^2 systems, rather than platforms such as ships and aircraft, are likely to dominate military budgets, at least in the near term. Existing platforms can often be retained in service for many decades, but they need upgrades to keep them competitive. For example, several navies now operate ex-U.S. *Knox*-class frigates, designed about 1963 and transferred without anything resembling a computer combat-direction system (CDS). Yet their hulls and machinery plants are surely good for several more decades of service; indeed, a few navies still operate U.S. destroyers completed in 1944–45. As electronics become more compact, the possibilities for upgrades become more interesting.

The CDS largely determines how closely a given ship or airplane can approach the potential implied by its platform performance and by the visible weapons and sensors on board. At a higher level, a fleet command/information system may determine how closely the collection of ships and aircraft can come to their joint potential. Surely, then, it is far less expensive to integrate a ship or a fleet than to buy new ships or even (in some cases) new weapons.

This book includes some interesting examples of this thinking. The Chilean navy operates a variety of relatively dated British warships. Its modernization program includes buying the Israeli Barak defensive missile, but much more effort seems to have gone into the SP-100 C^2 system, which embraces both intra- and interplatform integration. Pakistan bought new 9LV Mk 3 command systems for its ex-British Type 21 frigates. Taiwan has already rebuilt ex-U.S. *Gearing*-class destroyers with, among other things, a rather sophisticated Hughes-built C^2 system. Conversely, British Type 23 frigates were not deemed capable of surviving in hostile environments such as the Gulf until their C^2 woes had been solved. Their modern AA missile batteries would have been useless in any sort of realistic situation until the missiles were linked with automated C^2 systems.

Combat-direction systems lack the appeal of the more visible weapons or even of the sensors that direct them. Yet, more and more, they seem to be the focus of new development. For example, the major new U.S. Navy programs for ship defense against missiles are not new weapons, but rather new ways of linking weapons and sensors together, such as SSDS (ship self-defense system) and CEC (Cooperative Engagement Capability).

Similarly, much of the U.S. effort toward greater effectiveness in littoral warfare has gone into making information concerning the situation ashore more available to local commanders, and to make retargeting of existing weapons quicker and easier. A comparison with the previous edition of this book will show that the weapons have changed very little, but that the descriptions of C^2 systems have changed radically.

To be effective, C^2 must extend beyond a single ship or aircraft. That may seem obvious, but it carries real dangers and real problems. Last year it was announced that an Air Force officer had managed to "hack" into the computers controlling U.S. warships via an ashore telephone line. The Air Force gleefully announced that the hacker had gained total control over a ship. Although such a victory might have done much for interservice warfare, it seems likely that the reality was that the hacker had gained control over information in the ship's JMCIS computer, which is generally *unable* to command the ship or group via its own CDS. The hacker would have been able to do real damage, but only by manipulating the OTH database available to the command aboard; actually firing weapons would have been a different proposition. As for maneuvering, that is not even a computer function, at least not yet.

The world arms market is changing. The United States is currently going through a series of drastic amalgamations of defense producers, which will probably leave a few very powerful companies capable of competing quite effectively on the world market. Europe is unlikely to do the same. No Cold War European producer operated on the scale of, say, Lockheed or Martin-Marietta, partly because none enjoyed the same sort of domestic market. The Europeans were far more effective exporters, and it is still an open question whether U.S. companies can do as well in the foreign market. Some have suggested that very stringent limitations on payoffs often cripple U.S. sales efforts in much of the world.

Although the European Union is larger than the United States, its net military budget (hence its internal market) is substantially smaller. No European government seems very willing to abandon national producers in favor of some sort of transnational military production machine. Any expectation of merging European armed forces into some sort of European Union force

is even further away. Efforts to develop pan-European programs, such as the Project Horizon frigate and the Eurofighter, have been plagued by very high costs and gross delays as minor details are negotiated at endless length. The results, at least in the past, have usually been obsolescence and low performance (due to the insistence on always buying European, even when no satisfactory European unit existed). Very high costs were acceptable only because they were spread among several governments. With the end of the Cold War and the consequent crash in defense orders, international consolidation suddenly seems almost inevitable. Some companies will probably have to go. For example, it seems unlikely that the French government will be able to continue its policy of maintaining the full range of military production capacity.

In 1996 the French and German governments formed a European arms purchasing agency, which in theory would improve efficiency by fostering mass purchases. However, the British, invited to join, charged that its real purpose was to protect European manufacturers by closing Europe to foreign, mainly U.S., competition, and thus would contribute to a decline in European capabilities. For their part, the French were happy to acknowledge that the agency would exercise European preference wherever possible.

Russia and the other former Soviet republics have now joined the open world arms market, and it is finally possible to describe their products in some detail. The Soviet Union invested very heavily in defense (by one account, at the end the military accounted for 70% of Soviet industrial activity), and the results show in the variety and inventiveness of naval weaponry. Thus far the Russians have largely failed to achieve the level of sales their ingenuity seems to deserve, probably largely because of a widespread feeling that the country is far too unstable to support products after they have been bought. In some cases, too, the Russians suffer from the perception that their equipment failed dismally during the Gulf War. Ironically, they can now argue that it failed partly because, until the end of the Cold War, the best equipment could never be exported. For many potential buyers, the acid test of support is probably to be the Malaysian experience with MiG-29s.

In the past, the Soviet export market generally meant arms assistance, financed by the Soviet government (although some wealthy client-states were forced to pay hard cash). The Cold War determined which governments had to buy from the Soviets, so salesmanship was often unimportant. Now the climate is drastically different. Reportedly, Russians often returned from shows in (for example) the Gulf area believing that expressions of interest could easily be converted into contracts. Now they know better: selling is extremely difficult and tortuous. Programs often die when a minister loses favor or when a government falls—or when someone else offers better offsets or better paybacks. The Russian case is particularly difficult because so much money has to be brought in merely to keep the immense military industry alive at all. The only saving grace is that the ruble is still so undervalued that relatively small hard-currency operations can keep industry alive in the short term.

The future of this defense industry has enormous political implications. So much of the Soviet economy was devoted for so long to defense that demobilization ("conversion") must be traumatic in the extreme. Yet the current Russian government lacks the resources to support even a fraction of that industry. In order to trade with the rest of the world, it must cut defense spending (in terms of budget percentage) to the sort of level common in the West. To do that means shutting down very large industrial units. To survive, the defense industry, the modern part of Russian industry, ought ideally to convert to producing vital civilian goods, yet conversion has not, apparently, as yet been particularly successful.

It seems likely that individuals, rather than organizations, will convert, in the sense that a particularly enterprising (often young) engineer will quit a moribund weapons-maker to seek employment in the growing private economy. That leaves large numbers of administrators, engineers, and production workers whose whole lives have revolved around the weapons plant, and who may not be able to imagine alternatives. Inevitably they must recall a time, not too distant, when they were valued and, after a fashion, prosperous. Bringing back that time would probably mean bringing back some kind of Cold War. The situation is not unlike the chaos wrought by corporate downsizing in the West, except that it is happening on a much larger scale, and that it carries much more serious political consequences.

Major arms sales might mitigate those consequences, though of course they would carry dangers of their own. At present, U.S. insistence on limiting the spread of ballistic missiles is making some sales difficult (and causing considerable resentment in Russia). Too, the departure of the enterprising engineers will probably sap the creativity of the Russian arms makers, and will also make overseas sales far more difficult (those remaining in the companies may find it impossible to adjust to the new climate, in which the Russian government can no longer afford to give away weapons to client-states).

The other manufacturer largely invisible during the Cold War was South Africa, a pariah regime due to its racist internal policy. With the end of apartheid, the South Africans are now very interested in selling their wares to a welcoming world. For them, as for the Russians, sales are urgent because there is no longer a very large internal market. Unless the substantial defense industry built up during the pariah years can find sufficient markets, the South African government may have no option but to close it down in favor of buying foreign equipment.

Finally, the reader cannot help noticing how many familiar weapon systems are suddenly gone, as older ships have been discarded en masse, often to save operating costs. Many of the major deep-water ASW programs of the past have been scrapped or drastically reduced. In the United States, the emphasis in air defense has shifted from the long-range Outer Air Battle against hordes of incoming Backfire bombers to the very demanding short-range problem of dealing with missiles on boats, fighter-bombers, and trucks ashore. At least for the present, there is also substantial interest in missiles for shore bombardment.

As in the past, this book attempts to describe all current and prospective naval weapons systems. Systems are dropped only when they have been discarded, or (if they have not yet been sold) when the manufacturer has abandoned hope. All entries have been reviewed and, in most cases, rewritten.

Compared to previous editions, this book has been somewhat rearranged. Combat-direction systems (CDSs) now have their own section. Submarine CDSs have been moved into it to take their rightful place alongside surface-ship CDSs. In some cases, the line between combat direction and fire control is difficult to draw, so some systems on the border between the two remain in the ASW chapter, alongside sonars. Electronic warfare systems, both airborne and shipboard, have been consolidated into a separate section, in part because several systems have alternative air and surface (or subsurface) versions.

Weapons and related systems of the former Soviet Union have all been grouped under Russia. Although I am well aware that not all Soviet military production was concentrated in the Russian Republic, it is still too early to say where particular weapons or other components were made, and Russia is likely to operate the bulk of the former Soviet fleet remaining in CIS hands.

Dimensions are given, wherever possible, as diameter × length (wingspan or fin span as a separate item). For radars, the first dimension is the horizontal one, which determines the hor-izontal beamwidth. Dimensions are generally in the units (English or metric) used by the country of origin. Where that is metric, English units are given in parentheses. Dimensions for a few Russian systems are given in English units (feet and inches), even though the weapons have certainly been designed in metric terms, because the published data come from U.S. sources and are surely approximate rather than exact. Ranges are in meters and yards (sometimes in thousands of yards, or kiloyards, abbreviated kyd). Although a nautical mile is 6080 feet (6053 feet in British measurement), it is commonly approximated to 2000 yards, so that a range of 17.5 nautical miles is probably actually 35,000 yards.

An important note on sources. Readers should keep in mind, above all, that this is an *unclassified* book, a compilation of information from the open literature, from declassified documents, and from brochures provided by the manufacturers of the equipment. I have chosen data on the basis of the plausibility of the source, and also on the basis of their conformity to the known characteristics of similar weapons for which data are better established. In some cases I have identified equipment from available photographs. Official documents generally are not declassified for some considerable time after their origination, typically at least 12 years in the United States, but often as long as 30 in Britain. Because systems change (not only to be improved) over time, data correct at the time the documents were compiled are often only approximately correct when the documents are declassified. Data should, therefore, be taken as typical rather than precise.

ACKNOWLEDGMENTS

I could not have written this book without considerable assistance. I am particularly indebted to A. D. Baker III, the editor of the companion volume, *The Naval Institute Guide to Combat Fleets of the World*; to Larry Bond; to Chris Carlson; to Raymond Cheung; to Jim Christley; to Eric Grove; to Chuck Haberlein; to Josh Handler; to David Isby; to Dave Markov; to Fu S. Mei; to Anthony Preston (editor of the invaluable newsletter *NAVINT*); to David Reade; to Dr. R. S. Scheina; to Stuart Slade of Forecast International/DMS; to David Steigman; to Mark Wertheimer; to Armin Wetterhahn; to C. C. Wright; to Steven J. Zaloga; and to my extremely patient editor, Therese Boyd. The U.S. Navy Office of Information provided invaluable information on current systems. I am also grateful to the Freedom of Information Office of the U.S. Army Communications-Electronics Command, which answered queries concerning standard U.S. electronic equipment. The U.S. Navy Operational Archives and the British Public Record Office provided invaluable historical material, which remains relevant because a great number of the systems described here have been in service for so long. Many of the manufacturers represented here have been extremely generous with material, both factual and photographic. I would emphasize, however, that the descriptions and analyses of equipment are my own, and that the manufacturers should not be held responsible for the conclusions I have drawn.

I would like especially to thank my wife, Rhea, for her loving support, her encouragement, and her direct assistance.

Any book of this type is inevitably incomplete, and some inaccuracies will slip in. Additions and corrections for the next edition are most welcome; please submit them to the author c/o Naval Institute Press, Annapolis, MD 21402.

PREFATORY NOTES

RADAR

Radar signals bend slightly around the earth, so maximum radar range is $\frac{4}{3}$ of the visual horizon. However, under some conditions evaporation off the sea will form a duct (a waveguide) just above the surface; similar ducts can form in the atmosphere. Radar signals can travel extraordinary distances through such ducts. However, the top of the duct (or the bottom, in the case of an airborne duct) will reflect signals from outside, creating a radar "hole." Ducting particularly affects microwave (S- and X-band) radars, but it can also operate at lower frequencies (e.g., L-band). Duct heights (over water) can be calculated. Ducting also occurs over land, but in that case it is much more difficult to predict. Although propagation through a duct is always described as anomalous, ducting is found as much as 80% of the time in areas such as the Baltic, the Eastern Mediterranean, the Indian Ocean, and the South China Sea, hence the importance of combining surface radars with airborne ones to avoid holes, and also the possibility that fast-attack boats may detect (and fire at) radar emissions far beyond their nominal horizons.

At very low radar frequencies (HF in radio terms) vertically polarized signals will travel up to about 180 nm over water as "ground waves"; the corresponding "sky waves" bounce off the ionosphere to reach very great ranges. Most over-the-horizon (OTH) radars exploit sky-wave propagation, but in recent years surface-wave HF radars have emerged. In effect, such radars use the space between the surface of the water and the ionosphere as a waveguide.

The antenna, the visible element of the radar, is usually a reflector. At long wavelengths several elements (typically dipoles) radiate in front of a wide-mesh screen. Microwave radars customarily employ horns radiating into reflectors. Generally the radar signal's polarization turns when it is reflected (it will pass right through a mesh whose wires run along the direction of polarization, and will be completely reflected by a mesh whose wires run at right angles to the direction of polarization). There are, therefore, twist-Cassegrain antennas in which the signal radiates out from the center of the reflector. It is then reflected by a secondary flat reflector, which sends it back into the main reflector. The re-reflected signal has had its polarization turned so that it passes through the secondary reflector. The advantage of this arrangement is that it reduces the blockage in the radar beam due to the structure supporting the radiator. Many such antennas can be recognized by their enclosed form with a flat or even convex front panel. Yet another alternative is a slotted waveguide, a series of radiating slots whose signals add up to a fairly narrow beam (slotted waveguides are common in surface-search radars). In each of these cases, the mechanical form of the antenna in effect determines the form of the radar beam.

In many cases it is important to be able to move a radar beam much more quickly than is possible mechanically. The standard solution used to be frequency scanning, in which the direction of the beam emitted by a special (serpentine) slotted waveguide depended on the frequency (actually, on the phase difference between the slots). A quick change in frequency scanned the beam. Examples are the Russian Fregat series and the U.S. SPS-52.

The step beyond is a phased array, in which the phase of the signal emitted from each element of the radar is individually controlled. Phased arrays became inexpensive as the price of electronic components (in this case, ferrite phase shifters) fell and reliability increased. They are exemplified by the U.S. SPY-1 of the Aegis system. Such antennas are still somewhat complex, because a signal must be fed to each radiator. Thus the back of each SPY-1 panel reveals elaborate microwave "plumbing." The Russians developed an alternative, a space-fed phased array. This is, in effect, a combination of the usual phased array and the older reflector technology. As in the older antennas, a single feed illuminates a reflector. However, in this case each element of the reflector contains its own ferrite phase shifter, which is individually controlled. Clearly such technology is inappropriate for a fixed surveillance radar, but it is apparently quite useful in fire-control sets such as the Cross Swords of the SA-N-9 system, or, apparently, the Front Dome (Orekh) of the SA-N-7 illuminator. As of 1995, the Russians were promoting this hybrid technology as a much less expensive alternative to full phased arrays. They were showing a 35-GHz radar with 3600 reflector elements.

Cheap phased arrays offer more than quick beam movement. A single antenna can be used to transmit a variety of beams for different purposes, such as long- and short-range air search (e.g., in the German TRS-3D). In the Italian EMPAR, control of the beam in both the vertical and the horizontal makes it possible to sweep it across the rotating antenna face, so that the beam scans at either the mechanical rate or at a much slower rate, for longer-range search. Beam control on this scale makes it possible for airborne radars, such as the U.S. APG-73, to provide search, air-to-air fire control, and exotic ground-mapping modes.

Radars are generally described by their frequency bands, peak power, pulsewidth, and pulse-repetition frequency (PRF).

Frequency (which is inversely proportional to wavelength) determines how precise the radar beam can be, since beamwidth (in radians) is approximately equal to the inverse of the antenna size in wavelengths. The larger the antenna, the narrower the beam. Moreover, the larger the antenna, the higher the gain: the larger the fraction of the returning echo the radar will detect. Frequency (or wavelength) also determines the kind of technology required to produce the radar signal, and the extent to which that signal will be absorbed by the atmosphere, for example, by rain.

There are two quite distinct systems of coding frequency bands. One, developed during and after World War II and currently used by the U.S. government, describes the physical characteristics of the signals and is almost certainly mnemonic. It is used in this book. A second, more recent system is a more systematic division of the possible radar bands. It was developed for electronic intelligence, and it reflects the fact that other nations (particularly the Soviets) use radar frequencies very different from those common in the West. This ECM system was adopted by NATO; it is used in this book primarily to describe ECM equipment. Details of both systems are given in Table 1.

Table 1. Radar Frequency Designations

The boundaries between bands in the classic radar system have changed over time, but the approximate positions of the bands have not. 1000 MHz is 1 GHz, and older references use cycles rather than Hertz, i.e., Mc/s instead of MHz.

Frequency	U.S. Radar Designations	ECM Bands
30–250 MHz		A
100–150	I-band	
150–225	G-band (World War II IFF)	
225–390	P-band	
250–500		B
390–1550	L-band	
500–1000		C
1000–2000		D
1550–3900	S-band	
2000–3000		E
3000–4000		F
3900–6200	C-band	
4000–5000		G
5000–8000		H
6200–10,900	X-band	
8000–10,000		I
10,000–20,000		J
15,250–17,250	Ku-band	
33,000–36,000	Ka-band	
20,000–40,000		K (K-band embraces Ku through Ka)
36,000–46,000	Q-band	
40,000–60,000		L
46,000–56,000	V-band	
56,000–100,000	W-band	
60,000–100,000		M

NOTE: In radio parlance, HF extends up to 30 MHz; VHF is 30–300 MHz; UHF is 300–3000 MHz; SHF is 3000–33,000 MHz. These boundaries approximate wavelengths of, respectively, 10 m, 1 m, 10 cm, 1 cm, and 1 mm.

The original wartime radar-band system consisted of a metric P-band (P for pulse, as in the U.S. APS and SPS designations), and an S-band for short (or centimeter) wavelengths (about 10 cm). An X-band (for exotic) was added during World War II for a newer generation of 3cm radars. After the war, radar development shifted to a long centimetric wavelength (L-band, about 20 cm), and a new compromise band (C, about 5 or 6 cm) was developed. C-band radar could use a small antenna (like X-band) and could penetrate rain better than X-band. K-band wavelength was shorter than X-band (about 1 cm: K probably for *kurz*, "short" in German). Some radars are characterized as UHF, meaning a frequency range somewhat higher than P but lower than L (the term *UHF* is used slightly differently in radio).

The beamwidth of a linear array, such as a slotted waveguide, is about 1 divided by the array length (in wavelengths), in radians. A similar consideration applies to a circular antenna, uniformly illuminated. At X-band, the beamwidth (in degrees) of such an antenna is about 70 divided by antenna diameter in inches. Many such antennas use tapered illumination, which gives a slightly wider beam but much lower sidelobes; in that case beamwidth is about 85 divided by antenna diameter.

Because seawater conducts electricity, signals reflect off the sea (and, similarly, off a ship's metal superstructure and masts). At low frequencies (e.g., P-band), reflected and direct signals interfere constructively and destructively, forming a lobe pattern. The lowest lobe can be at an elevation angle well above the sea surface; as a result, P-band radars generally cannot detect low-altitude targets. On the other hand, at higher angles, interference can be constructive, and radar range can be greater than it might be in free space (or, for that matter, over land). The lobing phenomenon itself causes targets to fade in and out of detection as they approach; the ranges at which fading occurs are a crude measure of target altitude. At higher frequencies, lobing is much less significant because the areas of constructive and destructive interference are very narrow and tend to wash out as a ship rolls.

At low altitudes and high frequencies (and short pulse widths) the main effect of sea reflection is multipath: the radar signal travels both directly to and from the target and indirectly via the surface of the sea. In effect the radar sees both the target and a reflected target image, at two ranges and two elevation angles. It may "nod" instead of tracking. Several antisea-skimmer systems claim special antinodding or antimultipath features.

The radar beam will intersect the sea at some range, and thus the radar will see a patch of sea clutter. That may well be larger than a sea-skimming missile. The solution is usually Doppler processing, to filter out anything but a fast target.

Because a ship is relatively small, and because it must carry numerous antennas in close proximity to its superstructure, its radars may often be affected by reflection off the ship and off other antennas. For example, a whip antenna vibrating near a radar antenna may impose a modulation on the radar signal through its sidelobes.

The higher the frequency, the narrower the beam, and the less attention need be paid to problems like multipath and sea clutter (the beam points off the sea even at a very low elevation angle) and sidelobes (the beam is very narrow). However, at very high frequencies, molecules (mainly oxygen and water) in the atmosphere absorb most radiation. There are five windows (Ku-band is about the upper limit of easily transmitted or windowless operation):

> 35 GHz (8mm wavelength)—Ka band
> 94 GHz (3.2mm wavelength)—M band in the ECM system
> 140 GHz (2.3mm wavelength)
> 220 GHz (1.4mm wavelength)
> 360 GHz (0.8mm wavelength)

The current upper limit on reasonable radar power generation is probably 94 GHz. Millimeter-wave radar touches the far infrared part of the spectrum. In the infrared, which is closer to light, there are windows at 8–14 microns (0.008–0.014 mm) and 3–5 microns (0.003–0.005 mm). (The term *micron* is typically used for one-millionth of a meter, or one-thousandth of a millimeter.) Visible light wavelengths are a smaller order of magnitude, around 0.5 micron, or 0.0005 mm.

Radar power determines how well the radar is able to detect an individual echo. Because detection is cumulative, a large number of relatively weak echoes will have the same net effect as a small number of strong ones. Moreover, the detectability of an individual echo depends not only on its peak energy but also on how long it lasts. Thus maximum radar range is commonly equated to average radiated power, that is, to the product of peak power, pulse duration, and pulse-repetition rate or frequency (PRF). The product of pulse duration and PRF is the duty cycle, the amount of time (as a fraction or percentage of the total time) that the radar is transmitting. For example, a radar transmitting pulses of 1 microsec at a PRF of 500 pps has a duty cycle of 0.0005; if peak power is 1 MW, average power is 500 W.

Because a radar measures distance by measuring the time between sending and receiving a pulse, it cannot distinguish a distant echo, returned after the next pulse has been sent, from a close-in echo, returned soon after that next pulse has gone out. Because of this second-time-around (STA) problem, unambiguous or maximum radar range is commonly equated to half the time interval between pulses, that is, to the inverse of the PRF. This is not the same as the range the radar will actually achieve on a given target, but it is often the figure listed as radar range. Since the radar designer maximizes the probability of detection by maximizing PRF, a designer will generally try (but possibly fail) to match PRF range with a realistic range on the target of greatest concern.

Some radars eliminate many STA echoes by jittering the PRF around an average value: the apparent range of STA echoes will vary with PRF. Jittering cannot, however, eliminate the STA echoes of large objects, such as land masses. So PRF remains a measure of effective range.

Radar signals travel at about 186,000 mi/sec (about 162,000 nm/sec, or 300,000 km/sec), so the unambiguous range for a 1000-pps radar is about 81 nm (162 nm between pulses, for a pulse to go out and return). Thus 2000 pps corresponds to about 40 nm, and 500 pps to about 162 nm.

There is one important exception to this idea. Pulse-Doppler radars use very high PRFs and typically detect targets at ranges considerably beyond their unambiguous range (because actual detection range depends on the average power sent out, i.e., on the product of peak power, pulse width, and PRF). Due to the Doppler effect, the frequency of the echo from a moving target is shifted proportional to its velocity (actually, to twice the component of velocity in the direction of the radar sending out the pulse, once for the path out to the target and once for the path back).

Just as a pulse radar can be limited in its unambiguous range, a pulse-Doppler radar is limited in its range of unambiguous velocities. The radar signal is a mixture of pure signals of different frequencies spaced around the nominal radar frequency (separated by the radar's PRF). Each such subsignal is Doppler-shifted in frequency by target radial velocity as a fraction of the speed of light. Just as the radar cannot distinguish echoes that return after the next signal has been sent (i.e., whose delay times exceed the pulse-repetition interval), a pulse-Doppler radar cannot recognize velocities whose Doppler shifts exceed the PRF. For example, a velocity of 1000 km/hr (620 mph, 540 kt) shifts an X-band signal (10,000 MHz) by about 18.4 kHz. Typically the first speed that cannot be distinguished is called the first blind speed. These considerations explain why Doppler radars often use extremely high PRFs, for example, 20 kHz (corresponding to an unambiguous range of only 4 nm).

The higher the PRF, the worse the associated ambiguity in pulse range. High-PRF radars typically measure range by varying their carrier (radio) frequency with time, associating a particular range with a particular frequency. For example, frequency can rise up to a maximum, then fall back to the initial frequency. The frequency shift associated with range is mixed with the frequency shift associated with target Doppler, and the radar must sort between them. One solution is to insert a constant-frequency segment at the end of each period of changing frequency; the frequency shift of this segment is the target Doppler shift. Another is to vary frequency smoothly up and then down. The

target Doppler adds to the rising frequency on one half-cycle and subtracts on the other. This scheme also uses a flat (constant-frequency) segment to measure target Doppler.

Doppler data may be important in itself if the radar is being used to predict target motion. It is also the most important means by which the radar distinguishes among multiple targets. Given measurements of the target Dopplers, the radar can associate the appropriate rising and falling frequency segments for the different targets (de-ghosting). Since a target must be detected on all three segments of the frequency cycle, maximum detection range is shorter than in the pure-Doppler case. Fighter radars, therefore, generally have a separate velocity-search mode, operating at a pure high PRF. They can switch to a range-while-search (FM-ranging) mode.

Some fighter radars, such as the AWG-9 of the F-14 Tomcat, have an additional raid-counting mode. Beyond some particular range, several aircraft will fit within each radar resolution cell. Raid counting protects a fighter from locking on to the raid as a whole and, hence, losing the ability to deal with any particular airplane before it is too late. Between search scans, the radar spotlights (scans narrowly) the radar target(s) representing the raid for precise Doppler measurement. Several aircraft flying together will have slightly different Doppler shifts, and the spread in the radar return is measurable. A multiple-aircraft symbol appears on the display. As the range closes, and the target covers a larger angle, the radar automatically widens the spotlight scan.

FM-range accuracy is limited by the precision with which the frequency of the returned signal can be measured, that is, by the width of the filters (real or mathematical) making up the Doppler filter bank; that width in turn is limited by the integration time, the length of time during which frequency ramps up or down (this time interval is also a measure of maximum unambiguous range). The total extent of frequency change is limited by the requirement that the lowest Doppler targets be distinguishable from clutter. All of these considerations greatly limit the accuracy of FM ranging for a high-PRF (Doppler) radar.

High PRF is attractive partly because it can give a high probability of target detection even at a relatively low peak power. Since counterdetection generally depends on the strength of the particular pulse picked up by the target's radar detector, the high-PRF/low-peak power solution may amount to a somewhat stealthy radar.

Anywhere near the ground an airborne radar will pick up the echo of its sidelobes (and, in cases in which the radar points down, its main lobes). Operation over the sea is easier, because the relatively flat sea tends to reflect the beam forward, away from the radar. That is one reason why AEW radars generally have better over-sea than over-land performance. There are two main solutions to the over-land problem: range and Doppler. The range solution eliminates very short range echoes (in the sidelobes, which point almost straight down) and it tries to distinguish main lobe echoes by their range difference from real low-flying targets, using very narrow pulses. A Doppler radar will experience two kinds of clutter: strong but narrow-band (in velocity) clutter from the main lobe, and weak (but wide-band) clutter from the sidelobes (corresponding to a range of velocities from 0 almost up to the platform's velocity). The narrow-band main-lobe clutter is relatively easy to exclude.

An airplane flying nose-on toward the radar will have a very high relative velocity and a large corresponding Doppler shift, well away from the shifts of the ground clutter. The plane can, therefore, be detected at long range. On the other hand, an airplane flying away will have a very small relative velocity, hence a small Doppler shift, and it may be swallowed in the ground clutter. Modern fighter radars typically operate at very high PRFs (often hundreds of kHz) so that they can effectively and unambiguously detect nose-on (closing) targets. At very high PRFs, it is difficult to resolve range ambiguity, and available methods reduce the detection range. For this reason, for example, the longest-range mode of the AWG-9 radar (used to control the Phoenix missile) is velocity, that is, Doppler search.

A medium-PRF mode is often available as a compromise to permit detection of tail-aspect (low-relative velocity) targets.

Both range and Doppler are ambiguous. The strong main-lobe peaks in frequency are far enough from one another (because the PRF is great enough to keep the signal components well part) that target signals can be distinguished. On the other hand, there is still enough range precision to separate the close-in sidelobe clutter. Range measurement in general is easier than with high PRFs. Both high- and low-speed targets still have to compete with sidelobe clutter.

Doppler blind zones are eliminated by shifting among several quite different PRFs, each maintained for a brief period. Such switching limits maximum range because there is never very much time to integrate over numerous pulses. One common scheme is 3:8, the cycle consisting of eight PRFs covering overlapping Doppler ranges, any three of which must be clear for detection. An earlier alternative is to use three widely separated "major" PRFs. Each is flanked by two "minor" PRFs. Range ambiguity is avoided by switching from the major PRF to the two minor ones in succession (one for resolution, the other to eliminate ghosts). The problem is that because the minors are close to the major, their blind zones may be adjacent. Using a cycle of widely spaced PRFs (without minors) eliminates the problem.

ISAR (inverse synthetic-aperture radar) is a very different application of the Doppler effect. ISAR uses the motion of the ship target (roll, pitch, yaw) to form an image. The image lacks the quality associated with a synthetic-aperture radar (SAR), which uses the motion of the airplane to form its effective high-resolution aperture, but it may suffice for crude ship recognition and for attack assessment (comparison of before and after images). Crude recognition may even be automated, and thus applicable to future antiship missiles.

The key is that the single angular velocity of the target as a whole equates to different linear velocities (which means different Doppler shifts) at different distances from the line around which the target is rolling or pitching. Thus the top of the mast of a rolling ship is associated with a greater Doppler shift than, say, the top of the bridge below it. The line about which the target moves becomes a reference line, and an image of distances above it (or to each side of it) can be built up.

ISAR is now being applied to several airborne radars, but it has also been tried on shipboard (see APS-137).

Most shipboard radars exemplify the low-PRF case, and the big AEW radars also employ low PRFs, for long unambiguous range. Fighters generally use high-PRF transmitters that can switch to medium PRF. Radars for close-in weapons such as Phalanx are generally high-PRF pulse-Doppler types.

Pulse width determines resolution, the ability to distinguish between two targets that are close together. Radar signals travel at about 300,000 km/sec, so a pulse length of 1 microsec corresponds to a distance of about 300 m. Resolution is generally slightly greater than the length associated with one pulse length, since the radar cannot quite distinguish two pulses end to end.

Waveguides and other radar components can carry only a limited amount of energy. If that limit is exceeded, they break down. For example, an overloaded coaxial or waveguide may arc (spark), so that no signal at all is transmitted. Since radar range depends on average power rather than on peak power, one alternative is to spread that power over a pulse varying in frequency (a chirp). The returned echo can be compressed ("pulse-compressed") into the equivalent of a very energetic short pulse. Pulse coding is another approach to the same problem. Different portions of the extended pulse are differentiated, for example, by polarization. The resulting pulse bears, in effect, a coded signature that can be distinguished from the surrounding noise. In either pulse compression or pulse coding, the key is that the radar can distinguish between different parts of the long returning pulse, so that it can be made equivalent to a much shorter pulse.

Pulse compression or coding has another advantage: stealth. A pulse-compression radar spreads its energy over a series of frequencies, using a short pulse in each. Although total average energy may be considerable, there may be relatively little peak energy in any one pulse; therefore, a countermeasures receiver

may find such pulses difficult to detect. The longer the train of pulses, the lower the peak power (for a given average power, i.e., for a given detection range). Recent pulse-compression radars with very low peak power, such as the Canadian SPS-503 and the French DRBV 26C, are designed specifically for low probability of intercept. Ultimately the pulse train (extending across different frequencies) could occupy nearly all the time between initial pulses. Such a radar could be described as frequency-modulated continuous wave (FMCW) or as spread-spectrum (for low probability of intercept), and the only current public examples are the Dutch Scout and the Swedish Pilot.

In general, low probability of intercept (LPI) seems achievable mainly by using spread-spectrum techniques, in which signal strength at any one frequency at one time is quite low, because power is always spread over a wide frequency range, possibly in a pseudo-random pattern. Such patterns become easier to implement as computing power increases, that is, as it becomes easier to provide the appropriate template in the receiver to match the spread-spectrum pulses.

Radar beam dimensions are horizontal × vertical; the horizontal dimension measures how accurately the radar can locate a target in bearing without concentrating on that particular target (e.g., by beam switching or monopulse techniques). Antenna dimensions are, similarly, width × height. Scan rate or data rate is the rate at which the antenna spins and, therefore, the rate at which data about the location of any particular target are renewed. The faster the scan, the higher the target speed with which the radar can cope. On the other hand, the faster the scan, the shorter the time during which the radar dwells (stares) at any particular target and, therefore, the lower the probability that a target will be detected.

Radar *detection* is the act of deciding that a given received signal represents a target. In the past, that was done by a radar operator looking at an analog display, that is, at a direct representation of the strength of the signal, and deciding when a particular strength (e.g., brightness) represented a real signal rather than noise. In effect, the operator converted the signal from analog to digital (range and bearing) form. Most modern radars perform the same function automatically. Given noise, the receiver sees some signal strength at virtually any range. The range is divided into segments, and received signal strength in each segment is measured; the radar applies some cutoff to decide whether what has been received at a given range (as it listens while some set number of pulses go out) is indeed a valid detection (the number of pulses, i.e., the integration time, must be as long as possible, yet short enough that the radar has not turned very far during detection; otherwise the radar would lose angular accuracy). The criterion can be varied according to the noise level, to present a constant false-alarm rate (CFAR). Such operation is called automatic target detection (ATD). The operator sees *synthetic* video (points representing detected targets) rather than *raw* video (analog). A very good operator can often decide that a target is present before the ATD picks it up, so some radars have alternative raw-video modes. On the other hand, ATD maintains its level of alertness continuously, hence can make up for fatigue. ATD may also be more effective in a dense environment, where an operator might miss targets appearing in very close sequence.

The step beyond ATD is automatic detection *and tracking* (ADT), in which the radar associates sequences of detections to form tracks. However, it may be preferable for automatic detections (plots, in British terminology) from several radars (which have different beam shapes and thus different characteristics) to be combined in a computer before tracks are formed. Hence many radars have progressed from ATD to ADT and then back to ATD for track combination.

Typically, a distinction is drawn between search and tracking radars. A search radar scans continuously. A pure tracking radar follows a particular target. Any scheme for associating successive target locations (as detected by a search radar) to establish an approximate target track blurs this distinction. The quicker the scan, the more accurate the track. Very quick scanning radars with the appropriate associated memory are, therefore, described as track-while-scan (TWS) radars. As more and more search radars are associated with computers for ADT, TWS operation is becoming more universal. TWS is very common in surface-gun fire-control systems. The Russians are probably unique in using very fast scanners for TWS of air targets.

Radar tracking generally requires the radar to compare several beam positions, that is, to measure when it is off the correct direction. One method is conical scanning (conscan), in which the beam spins. Each position of the spinning beam is somewhat off the proper radar direction, but the beam is symmetrical about the direction at which the radar antenna is pointed. Thus, if the radar return is constant while the beam spins, the radar is pointing right at the target. Any variation shows that the radar is pointing off, and the variation itself can be used to generate the appropriate correction signal. The 2D equivalent of conscan is a nodding radar, pointing its beam alternatively to left and right (or above and below) the target. Conscan is simple to design, but it is subject to a relatively simple countermeasure. If a strong signal is sent back out of sequence, the tracker may pick it up in a sidelobe. The tracker will associate the signal not with its actual location but with a direction associated with its place in the scanning pattern; it can capture the tracker and lead it astray. This technique is called angle-stealing or angle-gate pull-off using inverse conscan. Moreover, a conscan radar may be confused by a target whose apparent cross-section varies very quickly (fluctuates).

Some radars put out a consistent beam but use a conscan receiver (the technique is called COSRO, conscan on receive only). Such operation preserves the simplicity of conscan tracking, but denies an enemy knowledge of the conscan cycle, hence the possibility of easy deception.

The usual solution is monopulse, a technique in which the radar simultaneously puts out multiple beams, continuously comparing their signals. Since there is no cycle associated with this sampling, there is no way for a point jammer to insert a deceptive signal out of sequence. The tracker can be led astray only by signals from several distinct sources, separated in location, a technique called "cross-eye."

Monopulse operation generally requires that the radar be fed by a cluster of horns, one for each sub-beam. Since the cluster is fairly large, such a radar will generally use an inverse- or twist-Cassegrain antenna, so that the feed does not block the main beam.

Some radars described as monopulse may really be COSROs; the two would be difficult to distinguish externally.

Russian FCS radars generally use scanners; they never adopted conscan, and most probably do not use monopulse. Most likely, they use a form of scanning called scanning with compensation (SWC) which is mathematically almost equivalent to monopulse. However, it is presumably subject to inverse conscan-type countermeasures, and presumably it suffers from target fluctuation.

Five current technical developments deserve brief mention here. One is the rise of solid-state transmitters (see, for example, the French DRBV 26C and the U.S. SPS-40). This trend is distinct from the much earlier shift from vacuum-tube to solid-state technology for radar control and data processing. That left one big vacuum tube, the radar transmitter, which had to be cooled and protected. Now solid-state transmitters are powerful enough to be used, in combination, in place of the tubes. The solid-state transmitters are more reliable; they require less power (and emit less heat); and they cannot burst. Moreover, since numerous transmitters are used together, the failure of any one does not put the entire radar out of action. For the U.S. Navy, the first major solid-state transmitter is that replacing a klystron in some SPS-40 radars. This transmitter is expected to achieve a mean time between failure (MTBF) of 10,000 hr. It uses 112 2500W modules, each of which uses eight 400W peak-power transistors working in parallel. However, a plan to replace the transmitting tube in SPS-49 radars was quashed when it was realized that the existing tube already had an MTBF of 5 yr, and that development of a solid-state equivalent would be extremely expensive.

A second major technical development is the active-array radar, which combines the promise of inexpensive solid-state transmitters with the reality of inexpensive phase shifters. In such a radar, the elements of the antenna themselves transmit the signal. There is no need to apply a phase shift to a signal produced by a separate unitary transmitter; there is no longer any microwave plumbing reaching into the radar; only LF electrical power and waveform information (probably sent by optical fiber) would come up from below. The new Japanese OPS-24 is the first active-array radar to have entered operational service. The British MESAR and the Dutch-German-Canadian APAR also fall into this category. Major issues in this development are how to cool the array without creating a hot spot attracting IR missiles, and how to reduce the cost of the transmit-receive modules. As in many other forms of electronics, the latter depends on whether there are nonmilitary applications for the modules. In the case of APAR, a Canadian company, Northern Telecom, hopes to develop them primarily for microwave communications, in which case mass production would drastically reduce unit cost.

One interesting aspect of phased-array antennas, both active and passive, is that their faces may have much smaller reflecting radar cross-sections than conventional reflector antennas. That may explain why the French low radar–cross-section *La Fayette*–class frigates are equipped with Sea Tiger Mk 2 radars using flat phased-array antennas, rather than the conventional reflectors of the earlier Sea Tiger Mk 1s. These antennas also have end baffles, presumably consisting of radar-absorbing material, to cover the ends of the antenna, which might otherwise reflect radar radiation. Phased arrays do have one signature problem: their numerous elements all generate heat, which must be dissipated either at the antenna or below decks. For example, the German TRS-3D reportedly has a considerable thermal signature. It is unlikely to be unusual in that regard.

A third development is the software-controlled waveform. In most radars, pulse characteristics are determined by the physical character, including dimensions, of the signal generator. They are extremely difficult to change. There may be special wartime operating characteristics, but they, too, are hard-wired; even when compromised, they cannot easily be changed. However, a number of current airborne radars, such as APG-65, are software-controlled, so their signal characteristics are quite easily changed. This ability will potentially allow the system to counter current methods of radar recognition by pulse analysis. It may still be possible to recognize a radar by the detailed structure of its pulses, but that type of recognition is several orders of magnitude more difficult.

Fourth, as computers become much more powerful, signal processing is changing radically. A waveform traditionally associated with one radar function may be processed to provide a very different sort of information. For example, a U.S. EW training unit recently found that better signal processing could extract sea-search data from a standard airliner weather radar, without any modification to the waveform the radar produced, that is, without any external cue. Of course, more powerful processors also make it easier to exploit pseudo-random (e.g., spread-spectrum) waveforms, which are far more difficult to counter-detect than their relatively simple forebears.

Finally, there is growing interest in ultra-wide-band (UWB) or impulse radars, which are usually defined as radars in which the signal bandwidth is at least a quarter of the frequency. The word *impulse* is used because the greater the frequency range, the narrower the pulse. Instead of lasting many carrier wave cycles, the impulse lasts only a few (e.g., three cycles provides an impulse with a bandwidth of a third of the carrier frequency). If the pulse is short enough, it can pass through many materials, such as foliage, because their molecules cannot react quickly enough to absorb the pulse. Too, the pulse will contain so wide a range of frequencies that at least some are likely to generate strong returns as parts of the target resonate. These radars have become practical in recent years because the technology to produce ultrashort signals is now available. High peak power can be achieved because there is so little time during the pulse's duration for electrical breakdown to begin.

The major types of radar scope in current use are:

A-scope: Range versus signal strength, with range measured horizontally. This was the first type of radar display. The great remaining advantage of the A-scope is that jamming can more easily be distinguished from a real signal, both appearing as spikes. FCS radars often use an A/R-scope, a precision version in which a portion of the range is magnified. A range notch can be moved onto the target to gate it for tracking. In effect, ATD uses a digitized internal A-scope to decide whether a target has been detected.

B-scope: Range versus bearing, distorted so that all signals at a given bearing are in a single vertical line. This reduces the spread of signals at long range and is often used for gunfire control. In some cases only a portion of the full range-versus-bearing field is shown, for example, an area centered on the estimated target position.

PPI: Plan position indicator, the classic maplike radar display. Usually the ship or airplane is at the center, but PPIs can be off-centered. A PPI is, in effect, a rotating A-scope in which the spikes of the former are replaced by brightening on the face of a CRT. The British term for a synthetic-video PPI is LPD (labeled plan [position] display).

RH: Range-height indicator, in effect a PPI showing range and altitude instead of range and bearing. It is the natural display for 3D radars.

ELECTRONIC WARFARE (ESM AND ECM)

ESM (electronic support measures) are means of locating and identifying an emitter passively, such as to target a weapon (in theory, the target identifies itself). For example, an antiradar missile uses ESM guidance. The targeting requirement explains attempts to achieve significantly better angular resolution, for over-the-horizon targeting (OTH-T). Typically the goal is to determine target direction within a degree or two. The only current alternative is to use an LF towed array sonar, and that is unlikely to be nearly as precise. ESM systems concentrate on identifying a particular emitter. Their relatives, radar-warning receivers (RWRs), concentrate instead on quick warning of likely threats. A very precise ESM system designed to measure emitter parameters may be called an ELINT (electronic intelligence) system.

ECM (electronic countermeasures) are means of neutralizing radars, usually by emitting deceptive or blanking signals. Such signals can be divided into those intended to flood the emitter's receiver (jamming) and those intended to deceive, for example, by creating false targets. Deception is often based on the fact that, although a radar beam may be fairly narrow in the intended direction, the same beam must also include *sidelobes* pointing in other directions. The radar cannot distinguish signals it receives along its main lobe from those it receives along its sidelobes; all appear (to it) to come from the same direction. Many radars use auxiliary omnidirectional receivers to detect sidelobe signals, which can be subtracted from the main signal. Deception measures include passive physical decoys such as chaff; there are also active decoys.

It might be argued that surface ESM range cannot exceed the range of a radar signal, or $\frac{4}{3}$ the visual horizon. However, ducting is quite common, albeit intermediate. It can yield much longer ranges, as long as the ESM system can pick up short transients. The North Atlantic is apparently particularly good for intermittent ducting. The record may be held by a British frigate off Gibraltar, which detected a Russian ship in the Norwegian Sea. The Russian Rum Tub is specifically intended to make use of this phenomenon to target SS-N-12 and -19 missiles.

For ESM systems, the first great divide was between precision and wide-open types, both in direction and in frequency. In both cases, precision equates to higher gain but also to lower probability of intercept, since the narrow window (in either direction or frequency) may well not be pointed at the incoming signal.

Wide-open antennas have limited gain, hence limited range. A few older systems use rapidly spinning high-gain antennas. They are likely to find signals at very long ranges, but may well miss transient ones, for example, from fast-moving aircraft or missiles. Modern systems are generally wide open. Older U.S. systems (still used by a few navies) used a spinner in conjunction with an omnidirectional antenna (the ultimate wide-open case). The spinner generally offers the best DF precision. Some modern systems use a trainable directional dish to measure the precise direction of a signal detected and tracked by a wide-open system, mainly to target antiship missiles.

The lower-gain (higher probability of intercept) antennas are usually cavity-backed spirals for monopulse DF. They work by comparing signal strength in different antennas. Each antenna generally has to have a broad beam, so gain cannot be very high. The main current exception is a lens antenna (as in SLQ-32), in which each of several beams in effect shares the gain of the entire large antenna. In analog systems, the signals from four antennas at right angles are often used to drive four plates of a CRT, so that the strobe representing the signal comes out at the appropriate direction. The simplest systems do not compare signals from the different antennas; they merely indicate which antenna picks up any signal at all. This approach is exemplified by aircraft RWRs, which often merely show the quadrant or octant from which a threat signal has been received (the better ones show direction by forming a vector from signal strengths).

Shipboard monopulse systems sometimes have a higher-directivity mode in which the phases of the signal acquired by different antennas are compared (interferometry). Phase comparison is done by comparing signals over time, whereas monopulse is instantaneous (often called instantaneous direction-finding, IDF). Interferometry is also used at lower frequencies (HF and VHF).

In at least some cases, all or part of the ship or airplane is considered an antenna element, the ESM system using a probe to sample the induced current on it. The sampling may be implicit, in the form of calibration. For example, deck-edge antennas (as in the U.S. Classic Outboard) measure the angle of incidence of an HF sky wave. They are calibrated by measuring the response of scale antennas on a scale brass model ship, because the effect of the ship outside the antenna proper has so much effect on the behavior of the antenna.

Spiral antennas are common because they can receive signals with both horizontal and vertical polarization. In some recent airborne systems, such as ALR-67ASR, the usual single spirals are replaced by pairs of distorted spirals running in opposite directions. Because any polarization can be represented as a combination of right- and left-hand circular polarizations, antennas such as AEL's ''ambidextrous'' units can measure polarization (by comparing right- and left-handed components). Moreover, a spiral running the wrong way may not detect a circularly polarized signal at all, whereas the ambidextrous unit will detect such a signal (which is quite common in air-to-air radars).

Shipboard HF/DF sets generally use open-loop or dipole (Adcock) antennas, which cannot distinguish signals 180 deg apart (in higher-frequency ESM systems, the masthead or the airplane body blocks a signal from one side, so no spiral is confused by signals coming from its rear sector). They therefore use a secondary-sense antenna (an omni) to distinguish signals by phase, and thus to resolve the usual 180-deg ambiguity. Purely navigational HF/DF antennas may lack a sense antenna because they use cross-fixes (combatant DF operates against a single target).

The direction of the signal can be detected in several ways. A single-loop antenna can be rotated physically or, equivalently, a pair of loops can be rotated electrically (as a goniometer). Generally the antenna is so arranged that the signal strength falls to 0 when the antenna points directly at the target. Many World War II systems, for example, used headphones, and the operator detected the target when the sound vanished. The alternative is to use a pair of separate loops at right angles, the signals from which drive the two pairs of plates of a CRT, showing the angle of any intercepted signal instantaneously. The latter technique was invented in the 1920s by Robert Watson-Watt, who also invented the British form of radar.

A single rotating loop takes about 10 sec to find a direction; a rotated goniometer takes about 3. World War II experience showed that an instantaneous CRT system could cut DF time to half a second or less. That capability was particularly important after the Germans drastically reduced the duration of their signals to defeat conventional DFs, and, of course, it would be important in a DF attempting to deal with short radar pulses. A modern system would replace the CRT with a computer comparator and would do better because the computer would sense the presence of a signal much more quickly than would a human operator. On the other hand, the instantaneous system requires that the various receivers be balanced perfectly and tuned to the same signal, whereas a rotating loop or goniometer requires only a single receiver.

The stage beyond the Watson-Watt system is to form more than two beams, using what amounts to a phased array. The first major application of this principle was the German Wullenweber circularly disposed array of World War II; coincidentally, the Germans applied much the same technique to their wartime GHG passive sonar. It was adopted postwar by both the Soviets (as Krug) and the United States (as the circularly disposed antenna array, CDAA). Compared to an Adcock, a Wullenweber provides better directivity because its more numerous elements give a much narrower beam pattern. In the Wullenweber, about a third of the elements were used at any one time, the relative delays being fixed to form a narrow beam. A goniometer selected the appropriate third and applied the delays; it rotated among the elements of the array. This operation was exactly analogous to the use of a commutator in early scanning sonars. As in a scanning sonar, this technique suffers from the weakness that it does not stare in all directions simultaneously. A modern array would use preformed beams; it would sample all directions simultaneously and would form beams in all directions at the same time, via a computer memory.

Many modern systems use Doppler DF, in which the Doppler shift of signal frequency, rather than the signal amplitude, is used to measure direction. When the antenna points at the target, the Doppler shift is 0. The advantage of Doppler DF (as compared to the older technique) is that it can be integrated with a frequency-measuring receiver, hence easily digitized. Other modern HF/DF systems use interferometry.

In all shipboard cases, the antennas are far smaller than the ideal half wavelength, so gain is very low. For very small antennas, such as those used by submarines, amplifiers are integrated into the antenna itself; these devices are called active antennas.

If signal characteristics are broadly known, a system can trade off size (for instantaneous directivity) against time (to achieve directivity using a small antenna), using a superresolution technique. The outputs of the different wide-beam (because they are small compared to wavelength) antenna elements can be characterized as mixtures of signals from different directions. The mixtures change over time because the signals are not quite in phase. Several mathematic techniques have been developed to this end (e.g., MUSIC [multiple signal classification], and MEM [maximum entropy method]). In theory, this technique can resolve signals arriving simultaneously from different directions, whereas simple monopulse DF will merely yield the average direction of the signals. Superresolution can be considered a relative of the interferometry used in some fine-DF systems for missile targeting. Superresolution does entail much more computation than conventional approaches to DF (typically 10 to 100 times as much in a digital system), so its success depends on the availability of very fast digital processors.

Some recent HF/DF systems offer SSL (single station location; as opposed to the usual triangulation) by measuring the angle of incidence of the sky wave. For example, phase differences across an array of receiving antennas can be measured. At shorter ranges, out to about 300 km (about 160 nm), it is probably possible to compare the times of arrival (ToA) of the surface and near-vertical angle of incidence sky waves (NVIS). The angle of arrival (AoA) depends on the structure of the ionosphere, which can be measured either by periodic sounding or by periodically measuring the AoA of signals from known locations. Accuracy is not as good as from triangulation (AWA of Australia claims 5% for its new CELTIC), but SSL does offer a single ship a fully

passive means of location. The new French HF/DF systems (such as Altesse) provide SSL. The use of an extended hull array in the U.S. Classic Outboard suggests a similar capability. Current SSL producers include AWA of Australia, Rohde & Schwartz and TST of Germany, Thomson-CSF of France, and South West Research Institute (SwRI) and TCI in the United States.

Airborne systems also offer a sort of SSL if they can accurately measure the depression angle to the target. Since the altitude of the airplane is known, range is given by triangulation. In the case of aircraft flying above the sea, range can be measured by the timing difference due to multipath (direct path vs. signals reflected off the sea, with some imprecision because the altitude of the target is not known). An alternative form of passive ranging against fixed targets is provided by a series of bearings taken as the airplane flies past. It was used during the Vietnam War by A-6s delivering antiradar missiles.

Receivers fall into two categories: superheterodynes (superhets or SHRs) and crystal video receivers (CVRs). The superhet scans a narrow (hence sensitive) tuning window through the system's frequency spectrum, thus both detecting incoming signals and measuring their frequency fairly precisely. On the other hand, it may not be able to scan quickly enough to capture a very short signal, such as a radar pulse. The superhet is so called because it mixes (heterodynes) a local oscillator (LO) signal. The mixer's output includes a signal whose frequency is that of the original signal minus that of the mixing signal, as well as a sum signal at about twice the original frequency, which can be filtered out. The original signal superimposed some information (e.g., audio) on a carrier wave; the superhet in effect replaces that carrier with an intermediate frequency (IF) signal of much lower frequency, more amenable to processing.

The LO is tuned with the system as a whole to preserve a constant IF. Amplifiers work best over the relatively narrow ranges represented by the IF rather than over the whole frequency range of the system. A typical superhet might mix a 10.5-MHz signal with an incoming signal at 10 MHz, leaving the original signal superimposed on a 0.5-MHz IF carrier (in effect, -0.5 MHz, but the sign does not matter). In a radio, the IF signal is amplified and then detected (filtered) to separate out the audio, which is then amplified for use in headphones or in a speaker. Much the same can be said of the signal passed through for display on a CRT or for analysis by a computer.

In fact, the incoming carrier signal might not be at exactly 10 MHz. The 10.5-MHz IF can handle signals some distance above and below 10 MHz; 10.5 MHz would be just above the upper limit, since the IF would subtract out the whole carrier. In any case, the combination of the sort of signal involved and the bandwidth needed to carry it would determine just how much effective bandwidth the 0.5 MHz represented. The wider that passband, the wider (in effect) the instantaneous tuning window of the system.

The superimposed signal, which the SHR seeks to recover, has a certain bandwidth; the IF frequency must be greater. For example, in a radar the pulses are the signal superimposed on the carrier, which is at a frequency far above that of the signal. The signal proper is at multiples of the radar PRF, so the baseband needed to make sense of it must be several times the radar PRF.

The lower the IF frequency (i.e., the narrower the tuning window), the less noise (outside the frequency range represented by the signal proper) the superhet mixes with the desired signal. Too, there is an optimum ratio between IF and LO frequencies. At radar frequency, for example, that may require an IF far beyond that needed to carry the radar pulses. The system may therefore use several heterodyne stages to get to an IF not too far above what is needed for optimum amplification. For example, a radar receiver operating at S-band (3 GHz) might drop to 160 MHz in one stage, then down to 21 MHz, and then to 7 kHz for radar pulse work.

The IF signal is usually further filtered to reduce unwanted noise interference. For example, a 500-kHz IF might be passed through a 10-kHz filter. Many receivers have multiple filter widths; in a radio it would be 1 kHz for Morse, wider for AM speech, much wider for FM speech if in VHF-UHF band. These filters are generally tunable to exclude unwanted signals.

Typically, a mechanical tuner may sweep a few GHz per second, and an electronic tuner may improve this to a GHz per microsecond. However, typical radar pulse widths are also on the order of microseconds. On the other hand, the SHR is extremely sensitive, so it may be able to pick up not only the main lobe but also the sidelobes of a radar. In that case some radar signal will always be present, and it can be argued that the scanned SHR is likely to detect it, hence the use of such devices in the early models of British postwar systems like UA-1/4 and UA-8/9/10 (they were later replaced by modified CVRs). Some modern systems, such as the U.S. WLR-1H, use channelized SHRs, with numerous parallel settings. Electronic tuning offers high enough tuning rates to give a good probability of detection.

Some recent superhets, such as the British Falcon RX-740/RX-750, offer wide instantaneous bandwidth. In effect, the maximum IF passband is the width of the tuning window. Watkins-Johnson displayed a wide-bandwidth system at the U.S. 1995 Navy League exhibition. These devices do not match CVR bandwidths, but they do offer great sensitivity. It is not entirely clear how they overcome the additional noise associated with greater bandwidth. In at least some cases, the system may stack a series of IFs at slightly different frequencies.

In most aircraft systems, superhets are typically used to detect pulse-Doppler radar emissions and the CW signals of missile-guidance radars, both of which combine frequency stability with low peak power.

Loral's RWRs represent a very different concept. Loral argues that the essential requirement is to recognize threats early enough to choose effective reactions. The company values the superhet's sensitivity. It argues, too, that proper identification using a wide-open receiver requires a means of instantaneous frequency measurement (IFM). IFMs are limited in bandwidth. A shipboard system generally uses several to cover several bands. Airborne systems cannot afford the weight and complexity of multiple IFMs, so they either scan a single IFM over their bands or else down-convert all signals to the IFM's baseband. The system must then scan through what is received to find threats. Loral argues that it is easier to use a superhet front end, which scans rapidly through the threat library, since it will almost automatically identify the threats as it detects them (and since point-to-point scanning can be extremely fast). Loral is apparently unique in using this sort of architecture. The main objection would presumably be that a narrow frequency window might miss a frequency-hopping radar; Loral has a proprietary solution.

Loral is not alone in continuing to use superhets. It is now possible virtually instantaneously to synthesize a signal of a given frequency, using computer-controlled solid-state devices. If the threat frequencies are known, a superhet can now jump among them. Litton now argues that, using this technique, it can exploit the very high sensitivity of the superhet to detect threats from their back- and sidelobes, not merely their main lobes. The superhet receiver thus enjoys many more detection opportunities than a conventional receiver, balancing off any time lost through hopping among threats. Of course this technique fails in the face of unknown threats.

The classic wide-open receiver is a CVR, which detects all signals over its bandwidth but is relatively insensitive. In the early 1960s, for example, aircraft radar warners used CVRs because they were sure to detect strong signals of any frequency (within the band) pointed continuously at the detector, such as those from fire-control radars. CVRs would be far less likely to detect search radars, but they were much less important. Later it became possible to provide good sensitivity in CVRs by adding broad-band front-end amplifiers (and by reducing CVR bandwidth); swept superhets fell out of use in most ESM systems. Because it is a broad-band receiver, a CVR can identify a signal by frequency band, but it cannot tell where in the band that signal is located.

Channelized receivers are a sort of compromise between a wide-band CVR and a narrow-band superhet. Their narrow channels offer better sensitivity than a CVR, hence offer better detection range. For example, a channelized receiver may be able to detect a threat radar's sidelobes, whereas the corresponding CVR may only barely detect the main lobe. Since the sidelobes are present most of the time, the channelized receiver has a better chance of detecting the threat in time for the potential victim to react. The main lobe may be detected far too late.

At the 1994 Old Crows meeting Westinghouse showed a channelized receiver it was developing to handle future very dense signal environments, including truly simultaneous pulses. Incoming signals are down-converted to a baseband before analysis. Since the down-conversion can be varied, the receiver can be tuned to one of several bands. This is not a new concept (see, e.g., the U.S. WLR-1). What is new is channelization (rather than, e.g., superhet reception) after down-conversion. Earlier attempts failed because the channels were not truly repeatable. In effect, channelization eliminates any need for an IFM. Signals can be further analyzed within a channel by a superhet, which can scan quickly enough to cover the entire channel.

Superhets have survived in applications where sensitivity is essential. For example, CW and pulse-Doppler radar signals have very low peak power, so they may be missed by CVRs. On the other hand, they are generally very stable in frequency. Many systems include superhets specifically to detect them. Superhets are also virtually standard in COMINT systems, in which signals are also relatively weak (in maximum power) compared to conventional radars.

Other approaches have been tried. Microscan (or microsweep, or compressive) receivers are, in effect, superhets that scan a bandwidth in a time shorter than the duration of the pulse, using a chirped (or ramped) signal in place of a constant IF. As in any superhet, the time at which a response is received gives the frequency of the signal. Resolution (to separate several pulses received simultaneously) and response are good, but such receivers are complex and expensive, and they can handle only a limited bandwidth.

There are also hybrids, such as superhets feeding IFMs.

A dish/SHR system will detect signals at great ranges, but with only a very low net probability. It is essentially an ELINT device. The monopulse/CVR combination is tactical, in that it enjoys a high probability of intercept, albeit at somewhat shorter ranges. It is sometimes pointed out that the tactical combination can be extended to ELINT, but that the ELINT combination is almost impossible to modify for tactical purposes.

The simplest analog systems indicate signal direction and band. The detected signal switches on and off as it pulses, and it can drive a headphone or a loudspeaker. Radar PRFs (for anything but pulse-Doppler sets) are generally at audible frequencies. When radars were few and types were reasonably well known, this combination sufficed for tactical purposes. A pilot, for example, could see a strobe on an RWR and hear a characteristic tone through earphones, hence the NATO nicknames of some Soviet radars, redolent of the sound associated with their pulse rates, such as Owl Screech (high PRF for gunnery fire control).

RWRs typically used four cavity-backed spiral antennas. They did not have to produce detailed information; they were designed to tell the pilot to launch chaff and try violent evasion. Thus it sufficed for the rough direction (often the quadrant) of any sustained received signal to be displayed, often with PRF converted into an audio signal that the pilot might recognize (PRF is a good way to distinguish a long-range search radar, which is not an immediate threat, from a fire-control radar, which is). Some RWRs provided a bit more detail in visual form or somewhat better directional information. For example, the U.S. ALR-45 (Vector IV) gave a signal at an angle given by the vector sum of the received signals (in effect, it used monopulse DF). RWRs could not originally afford to do any analysis because in analog systems that was a protracted manual task. A minute or so of analysis was often a minute or two too long—better to accept a high false-alarm rate.

Much the same logic applied to early chaff launchers aboard ship. Many such systems are triggered directly by RWRs, such as Matilda. Similar RWRs could be used to warn a submarine commander to pull down his snorkel and dive in the face of an approaching maritime patrol airplane.

A typical modern RWR tries to identify an incoming signal first by its frequency band and then by PRF (actually pulse-repetition interval, or PRI) as listed in its mission data software. Because many radars may have similar PRIs, many RWRs call up a separate operational flight program (in the airplane's central tactical system) which uses characteristics such as scan rate and the pattern of PRI variation (stagger pattern).

The next step up in complexity is pulse analysis. The goal is to determine a signal's frequency, pulse width, and pulse rate, and (if possible) scan rate. Typically an omnidirectional (omni) antenna, wide open in both direction and frequency, fed a pulse analyzer (a CRT literally displaying the pulse structure), sometimes through an SHR. The ESM operator scanned the frequency band until a radar was detected; the tuner setting gave its frequency. The panoramic receiver (CRT) showed PRF and pulse width. The rate at which the signal reappeared and its duration gave scan rate and beam width. Given all these parameters, the signal could be identified. The analysis of a single signal would take at least a minute. Such systems cannot automatically recognize incoming signals; the operator must look up known characteristics in a table. Moreover, they cannot analyze signals very quickly, and therefore they cannot deal readily with a dense thicket of signals.

A variation on this theme, introduced in the 1960s, was a digital analyzer. The ESM operator chose a particular signal on the display. That signal could be fed into the digitizer, which measured various parameters. The signal could then be compared automatically to a short list of known radar parameters, typically about 15. This was called manual analysis, even though it was more automated than the pure CRT technique.

As in other forms of naval electronics, the great divide in ESM was the shift from analog to digital electronics. It is worth distinguishing between wholly analog systems, those that digitize pulses one by one, and those that de-interleave. In a wholly analog system, a signal can be selected (strobed) by bearing and by band for further manual analysis using a CRT. In some cases a separate omni antenna is used for this purpose. The next step is to digitize the incoming pulse (measuring pulse width, ToA, and, using an IFM, frequency; bearing can also be measured pulse by pulse). The operator still selects (strobes) a signal (by bearing and band) and measures PRF manually.

The final step is radically different from the analog approach. The ESM set is typically "wide open" in frequency (it uses CVRs) and in angle. Each individual pulse is preprocessed: ToA, direction of arrival (by strength or phase comparison between the antennas), pulse width, and band (which CVR receives the signal) are all measured within microseconds. These data go into a central processor, which sorts (de-interleaves) the pulses into separate trains, to associate them with different emitters and measure PRFs (by examining the ToAs of subsequent pulses in a train). Some systems measure direction in the computer by associating different ToAs (from different antennas) with the same pulse. This is intermediate between monopulse and phase comparison.

The sorting process is complicated by distortion of the original radar signal, for example, by multipath reflection off the sea and off parts of the ship around the ESM antennas. For example, apparent pulse width may stretch out, or additional pulses (multipath versions of the original pulse) may appear. Bearing may be the only clear discriminator between truly different signals.

Frequency is clearly an important parameter, but the wide-open approach measures, in effect, only band. Most systems therefore add an omnidirectional IFM antenna, which separately feeds the processor with a stream of ToAs and measured frequencies (the IFM antenna is often the "pimple" on top of a wide-open DF array). The processor uses ToA to associate a frequency with each pulse. Originally, IFMs were fairly elaborate. In some recent systems, a separate IFM is associated with each directional antenna. Such operation eliminates errors due to misassociation of an IFM pulse and a directional pulse.

The IFM was invented in the early 1960s, probably by the Phil-

ips Laboratory in England. IFMs rely on the fact that the *phase* of a signal coming out the end of a delay line depends on its frequency (which is why frequency-scanning radars work). Because phase is periodic, no single delay line can measure frequency unambiguously. However, a series of parallel delay lines of different lengths (e.g., 1, 2, 4, 8, 16) can resolve the ambiguities. Each line compares the signal with a delayed version. The output is a 1 (the two add) or a 0 (the two are completely out of phase), that is, a bit. Each line contributes a bit toward the digital "word" describing the signal's frequency; modern systems typically use 12 lines to form a 12-bit frequency indicator. An IFM can measure frequency to within about 0.1%, but it cannot deal with two different signals simultaneously present, and it can be drowned out if a strong CW signal overlays pulses.

IFMs tend to be less sensitive than the SHR because they have to respond to so broad a range of frequencies (sensitivity is generally inversely proportional to channel width). They are becoming common in shipboard systems, but are rarely used in aircraft. The main drawback of an IFM is that it cannot deal with several signals in close succession since it requires a finite time to process each signal. An IFM presented with several signals simultaneously at different frequencies within its band will be captured by the strongest among them; it will miss the others altogether. This is not an unsolvable problem, but it does increase the complexity of the equipment.

The output of the computer is a stream of emitter characteristics, mainly frequency, pulse width, and PRF. Naturally, a stream of pulses cannot be converted instantaneously into a series of digital words, nor can frequency be measured truly instantaneously. The power of the computer determines just how fast it can sort pulses. The system has a finite capacity, generally measured in number of pulses per second, but also in limits on the parameters it measures.

As in the old manual system, the computer can notice when a signal reappears (and for how long) to estimate scan rate (and type) and beamwidth. All of these digital data are suitable for library look-up and thus for quick emitter identification—and for automated reaction. By opening and updating a file, a computer can track a signal by observing its direction over time (always associating the same signal with the same parameters). Clearly such tracking becomes difficult if a radar frequency-hops or shifts PRF or pulse width over time. Since the signal characteristics and other data are all digital, they can be used to control jammers and to feed a combat-direction system.

Library look-up systems need libraries of radar parameters. To assemble them, the major powers have invested heavily in ELINT. ELINT is by no means the same as ESM. Its role is to ferret out radar parameters *and identify them with specific emitters.* Thus an ELINT set must provide precise directional information; otherwise an emitter on one ship or airplane may be confused with one on another. In many cases the only way to guess which radar is under a given radome is to examine the signals that emerge.

Many systems have two libraries, a small tactical one against which signals are automatically compared, plus a larger one for manual look-up. For example, the Canadian CANEWS has a 128-mode tactical library and a 2000-mode main library.

The CVR/IFM system will find it difficult to deal with CW or pulse-Doppler signals, so it may be supplemented by one or more superhets. More generally, many systems incorporate special receivers to handle complex or difficult (e.g., spread-spectrum) signals.

An ESM or ELINT system may have a very different architecture, in which a series of narrow-band monitor receivers are set by one or more master acquisition receivers scanning the spectrum. Each monitor receiver analyzes an assigned signal. An additional special receiver may be supplied to provide additional information about a particular signal being processed by one of the monitoring receivers.

Many modern radars, particularly those developed by the Soviets, have alternative peacetime and wartime modes (the latter are called WARMs, war reserve modes). Clearly, the electronic library data are wasted if they omit the WARMs; just as clearly, the Soviets had no incentive to exercise WARMs in international airspace and seaspace in peacetime, hence the vital importance of ELINT platforms and techniques capable of probing interior training areas in peacetime, preferably without revealing their missions. That is one reason for the deep secrecy surrounding ELINT spacecraft: an emitter may be left on if the satellite passing overhead can be dismissed as, say, a pure photo or communications satellite. It also explains the use of ferret aircraft, which run toward a border in order to set off local radars *in their WARM modes*. Allied aircraft operated in just this way along the Iraqi borders during the week prior to the Gulf War, specifically to capture WARM modes so that the radars could be countered successfully once the war began. This activity should be distinguished from merely locating potential threat radars.

It seems unlikely that a neutral lacking special resources can build up much of a national emitter library; it must depend on what it can buy from the ESM manufacturer, and that library will surely omit locally modified radar modes and war reserve modes. Thus sheer library size may not always buy much in the way of ESM or threat-warning capability. Even for the major powers, equipment in areas they tend not to cover may be absent from the libraries of their ESM/ECM systems. Of course ELINT also provides strategic intelligence, such as warning of imminent hostilities, and ELINT platforms are used to track ships and aircraft passively. By way of contrast, ESM is primarily a tactical sensor, used by a commander in possession of ELINT data to develop a tactical picture.

Digital techniques became necessary as radars multiplied, and as false-alarm rates became less and less acceptable. That happened first with aircraft. The first such system was apparently ALR-53 (Giraffe), the system that inspired the design of the EA-6A/B. ALR-53 had a simple computer with a magnetic drum memory; periodically it closed down its signal-collection element to sort through its library to identify the emitters it would jam. Some early systems used the airplane's main computer as a time-shared ESM processor (as in the U.S. ALQ-78 and ALQ-99; the latter was probably the first airborne computer-driven ESM system in general service). However, the need to digitize RWRs was more urgent. An airplane could carry only so much chaff, and once that was gone, so was the airplane's main protection.

As digital computers shrank, it became possible to package them into RWRs. A digital version of the U.S. ALR-45 (which became the current ALR-67), probably the first such device, appeared about 1978. Such systems often lack an IFM; they rely on other pulse characteristics (such as PRF and scan type) to characterize emitters. Digital processing can also improve DF accuracy since the outputs of the antennas can be compared on a more subtle basis, closer to interferometry. Thus RWRs tend to evolve toward radar homing and warning receivers (RHAWRs), which may help locate surface targets. They may even provide useful electronic intelligence. The ALR-67 upgrade program is a case in point.

As the sheer number of radars increases, it becomes more and more difficult to identify them, to filter out irrelevant signals so that only the important threats cause alarms. The distinction between an RWR and an ELINT system loses much of its relevance. It seems likely that next-generation tactical aircraft systems will incorporate IFMs and even channelized SHRs. Matters are further complicated by the radar's ability to hop frequencies and to vary its PRF.

That may not kill off ESM. Radars using pulse compression modulate their pulses (a process called IMOP, intentional modulation on pulse). That modulation probably does not change from pulse to pulse, so it may be used to follow a radar-hopping frequency or varying PRF. Too, each radar transmitter is slightly different, and it imposes some unintentional modulation on each pulse (UMOP), a characteristic that may not change much with frequency. At the least, emitters may be sortable on a UMOP basis. At best, if electronic reconnaissance has fingerprinted an enemy's radars, they may be individually recognized. Such fingerprinting is sometimes called specific emitter identification (SEI); it was a major feature of U.S. Cold War efforts to track specific Soviet naval units. Note, however, that to exploit such complexity requires a great deal of the processor behind the precision receiver used to detect IMOP/UMOP.

Shipboard systems evolved in parallel fashion. Probably the first to incorporate computers were automatic reaction systems developed to combat missile threats in Vietnam. Some of them time-shared the central NTDS computer for emitter identification. Similarly, in many Soviet systems, ESM data were used directly to identify radar tracks within a "second captain" computer. Given such identifications, other elements of the shipboard electronic combat system could, in theory, automatically engage threats.

Within a few years, shipboard computers were cheap enough and compact enough that they could be packaged into self-contained ESM systems. Early examples were the British Racal systems and the Italian Farad/Newton series. The U.S. equivalents were SLQ-17 for large ships and then SLQ-32, the "design to price EW suit" (an earlier threat-reactive system, Shortstop, proved too elaborate and too expensive).

Like airborne RWRs, the RWRs used to trigger shipboard chaff launchers were afflicted with false-alarm problems. The solution was often to combine them with more sophisticated ESM systems.

The most important distinction within ECM is probably between simple noise jamming, which seeks to blot out a signal, and deception. Noise jamming can cover a wide range of frequencies (barrage jamming), or it can be directed to a particular narrow frequency band (spot jamming). The best counter to spot jamming is frequency agility (the signal's frequency moves away from the jammer's). The higher the basic frequency, the broader the range of frequencies a barrage jammer must cover. Noise jamming is sometimes screening, in which an escort produces a strong enough signal to make it impossible for a targeter to distinguish a nearby high-value unit. This is distinguished from self-screening.

Deception generally depends upon some measurement of the radar PRF, scan rate, and pulse width, since the jammer must send back a false echo. The echo may appear to be a false target. It may confuse the radar in range (e.g., range-gate pull-off), in velocity (e.g., velocity-gate pull-off to counter a pulse-Doppler radar), in bearing (via the sidelobes), or in tracking angle (e.g., versus a conscan radar). Jittered or varied PRF is a counter-countermeasure because the radar may reject signals that do not conform to the precise pattern of its variation in PRF.

There are also simple repeater jammers, which rebroadcast samples of the radar signal in hopes that the radar will not be able to distinguish the jamming from a real signal or real noise. A strong enough repeater will capture the radar's automatic gain control circuit, causing it to reduce receiver gain to the point at which real signals go unnoticed.

A jammer may either repeat the received signal directly, or it may construct a new signal in response to the received signal, for example, at a different frequency (to indicate a Doppler shift, or to mimic the next hop of a frequency-hopping radar). Because direct repetition (a TWT amplifies the replica signal) is so simple, a repeater can be extremely quick; the new signal can be sent in as little as 100 nanosec. A repeater is, therefore, a natural counter to a tracking radar, with its high pulse rate.

In a repeater, a frequency-memory loop (FML) stores an exact replica of the received pulse. The analog version is typically a coaxial, a waveguide, or an acoustic delay line. The radar pulse is fed into the line, whose memory switch closes a set time after the beginning of the pulse is detected. The pulse energy then circulates within the delay line. It picks up noise on each circulation, and thus the information in it is gradually lost. The jammer taps it and amplifies it to produce a replica signal. A typical FML has a frequency range of 8–16 GHz, carrying a signal accurate to within 3 MHz (distortion would be introduced by the characteristics of the delay line), with a duration of 7.5 microsec. The line itself is 150 nanosec long (duration measures how quickly a signal in the line would decay to uselessness). There are also dual-delay memory loops. A typical example can switch between lengths of 150 and 300 nanosec, with a 15-microsec duration.

In some cases a digital RF memory (DRFM) replaces the FML, for better reliability and for variable storage time. It does not process the signal in the sense that an ESM set does. The DRFM can be filtered to exclude the jammer signal, and thus to avoid feedback. A typical DRFM, proposed for an abortive Canadian ULQ-6 upgrade, sampled incoming signals at a rate of 120 M/sec, representing amplitude by 4 bits, with an instantaneous bandwidth of 10–550 MHz within an operating bandwidth of 2–18 GHz. Memory capacity was at least 340 microsec. This DRFM used a four- or eight-channel receiver; the four-channel version used a frequency divider to double the effective bandwidth of the DRFM, so that a frequency-agile radar could be kept within a single channel. Each signal channel contained 11 parallel processing channels.

A responsive jammer must set an oscillator to create the jamming signal. Delay time is set by the turn-on time of the oscillator. Current linear hyperabrupt transistor oscillators can tune over 25 GHz/microsec, over a total bandwidth of 4.5 GHz, with a settling accuracy of 2 MHz in 100 nanosec. Total response time is longer; current technology can provide a response accurate to within 2 MHz within 250 nanosec.

Effective jamming operation typically requires that jamming energy be concentrated on the target; jamming antennas are, then, typically paired with target trackers. In some cases, as in Scimitar, the tracker (receiver) antenna is identical to the jammer antenna. SLQ-32 is unusual in using the same antenna for initial detection, target tracking, and jamming. More generally, although the tracker can function as a search antenna, it has too narrow a beam for efficient search. Ships, therefore, generally have separate coarse DF for initial detection.

There are also chaff or decoy launchers, as well as a few towed or floating decoys. A chaff launcher can have one or more of three distinct functions. Firing at long range, the launcher can provide a targeting radar or an incoming missile with multiple targets. If all targets must be engaged, the attack is diluted, and close-in weapons have a better chance of dealing with those weapons that do lock onto the ship herself. The usual counter-countermeasure is MTI (moving-target indication). A radar easily distinguishes an airplane from chaff because the real target is moving so much faster. Such a distinction is much more difficult to make if the target is a ship. The second, intermediate-range function is to seduce the missile seeker away from the ship target onto a decoy cloud.

The missile seeker is designed to avoid seduction by using a range-gate, that is, by reacting only to signals within a narrow band of ranges around the expected target's position. An active ECM transmitter (range-gate stealer or range-gate pull-off) is used to move the missile's seeker into the chaff cloud some distance from the ship.

Finally, there is a last-ditch tactic, centroid seduction. The missile's seeker generally homes on the centroid of the target's return, seeing the ship target as a complex array of point and corner reflectors. If a large chaff cloud is added, it moves the centroid up and away from the ship target, and the missile may pass overhead or to the side. Success in this mode depends upon the reflective cross-section of the chaff cloud compared to that of the ship proper. If the cloud is designed merely to move the centroid up, that countermeasure may be countered by a radio altimeter that keeps the incoming missile at low altitude.

Chaff (and IR decoys) may be launched by rocket or mortar. Rockets provide longer range (for the dilution role) and do not impose any load on the surrounding deck. However, they are relatively large, and a designer must protect against their back blast. Mortars are more compact, as is their ammunition. Both types exist in considerable variety.

SONAR

At this writing, the only ASW sensors effective beyond a few hundred yards are acoustic. Numerous (and expensive) attempts to develop nonacoustic sensors have not succeeded, except under very specialized conditions, and there is every evidence that the world's navies must continue to rely on acoustics. Nonacoustics is attractive because, at least in theory, a nonacoustic sensor can be operated continuously by an airplane or even a satellite. Acoustic sensing demands that the sensing platform put something in the water, either an expendable sonobuoy or a hull or towed sonar. Because sonobuoy fields must be of limited size and density, an airplane's search rate is inherently limited. In addition, the finite supply of sonobuoys always limits possible searches.

Generally there is a surface layer in the sea, kept at constant temperature (hence constant sound velocity) by mixing due to weather; this surface layer acts as a waveguide. The surface layer is about 300–600 ft deep in the North Atlantic, for example, depending on weather conditions. Within this layer, sonar acts much like radar, with signals propagating in nearly straight lines. For a hull-mounted sonar, the maximum (direct-path) range in the surface layer is about 20,000 yd, and ranges are often considerably shorter. Whether a given sonar can realize such maximum performance depends upon the sonar's power and frequency.

Below the layer, the velocity of sound varies with the depth, so rays of sound tend to bend, just as light passing through a complex medium will be refracted. One effect of this bending is to limit drastically the detection range of a surface ship against a submarine below the surface layer.

If the sonar's signals can propagate far enough, and if the water is deep enough, they bend down to a region of minimum sound velocity and then refract back up. The signals focus in a convergence zone around the ship, at a range set by water conditions. The convergence zone forms an annular ring around the ship, and additional convergence zones form at multiples of this first range. The typical range to the first convergence zone in the North Atlantic, for example, is 35 nm, and additional zones are found at 70, 105, 140, and so on. Each zone may be 5 nm wide, and the sonar detecting a submarine in a convergence zone cannot distinguish positions within that zone. As a result, weapons cannot be fired on the basis of very long range detection. Instead, some platform must search the area in the zone within which the submarine may be located, to reacquire the target before attacking.

Two other acoustic paths deserve mention here. One is bottom (or surface) bounce: both the bottom and the surface can function as acoustic mirrors. In the late 1950s it appeared that bottom-bounce propagation could help fill the gap between relatively short direct-path ranges and long convergence-zone ranges; maximum bottom-bounce range was about 40,000 yd. Bottom bounce later lost much of its popularity because the sea bottom in much of the world turned out to be much more absorptive than had been expected.

A submerged submarine (or, in theory, a submerged variable-depth sonar) can use surface-bounce propagation. Presumably, U.S. submarine sonars are spherical (i.e., can both depress and elevate their beams) specifically to exploit surface- as well as bottom-bounce propagation. Most Russian submarines, such as Victors, have bow torpedo tubes and are presumably, therefore, limited to chin sonars, which are unlikely to make much effective use of surface-bounce propagation. That limitation in turn may be related to an emphasis on operation at shallow depths. Surface-bounce propagation is somewhat limited by weather, since reflection will be much less efficient if the surface is rough on the scale of sonar wavelengths, that is, several feet.

Both bounce paths are inherently limited in range because the sound ray must pass steeply enough through the various layers to avoid refraction and trapping, a phenomenon equivalent to that of the critical angle in optics. Actual range must depend on the bottom depth (or, in the case of surface-bounce, on the depth of the source), but for surface ships under average conditions the usual assumed maximum range is 40,000 yd. That figure may be based in part on an estimate of the loss to be expected in reflection off the bottom.

The other alternative is the reliable acoustic path (RAP), essentially the vertical path from bottom to surface or vice versa. No matter what the acoustic layering of the sea, a signal propagated perpendicular to the layers should pass through without distortion. There is also a small angle around the vertical in which signals can pass with little loss or distortion. If the sound source or detector is deep enough, even that small angle can subtend a very considerable distance at the surface. RAP is hardly new, as it explains the successful operation of echo-sounders. However, the widespread application of RAP to sonar operation is relatively recent because a RAP sonar generally has to be quite deep.

In relatively shallow water, inside the 100-fathom (600ft) curve, convergence-zone propagation is impossible. Hull sonars suffer from multiple bottom bounces, so detecting real targets is very difficult. However, a very high frequency upward-looking RAP sonar can function effectively. A sonar source well below the surface, moreover, can send out a horizontal beam at a shallow grazing angle to bottom and surface.

Sonar may be active or passive. Active operation has the advantage of imposing a signature on a submarine, and thus of overcoming silencing, but active operation reveals the presence of the searcher, and range is limited by the amount of energy that can be poured into the water. Passive operation depends upon picking up relatively faint sounds against the background of a relatively noisy ocean. When passive signals can be picked up, extraordinary ranges can be achieved because of multiple convergence zones. In most cases, success with passive sonar was the key to NATO's ASW dominance, with active operation virtually limited to homing torpedoes. That situation may now be changing.

The major development of the late Cold War was the Soviets' progress in countering Western sonars. Countermeasures consist of both silencing submarine noises to reduce passive ranges and applying anechoic coatings to absorb active pings, thus making active detection more difficult. The anechoic coatings cannot be very thick, so they are likely to be most effective against relatively high frequency sonars, that is, against the sonars on board homing torpedoes. Western navies have now widely adopted anechoic coatings, which are sometimes called special hull treatment (SHT).

The basis of passive operation, that is, of all signal processing, is that the submarine's signals are regular, whereas the background noise is random. There are two fundamental approaches: the signal may be analyzed in spectral (frequency) terms, on the theory that over time the constant signature of the submarine will emerge; or the sonar can look instead at small volumes (cells) of ocean, choosing a particular cell that is consistently louder than its neighbors on the assumption that it contains a noise source. Mathematically, the two approaches are Fourier-transform alternatives. Spatial processing (i.e., concentration on a cell or on a volume defined in terms of bearing angle) is equivalent to adding up (integrating) signals over a broad band of frequencies from sources within that cell or angular range. Spatial processing is, therefore, often described as broad-band. The alternative (spectral processing) is, naturally, described as narrow-band.

Narrow-band noise is produced by rotating devices such as machinery and propellers or, for a diesel, the regular firing of the engine. In practice, each line of noise is accompanied by harmonics, weaker repetitions of the sound at progressively higher frequencies. A signal processor may concentrate on a harmonic, even though it is weaker, because it occurs in a quieter part of the background noise. Moreover, because listening arrays are limited in size, they will have better gain (i.e., better discrimination in direction) at higher frequencies. The better that discrimination, the less background noise is mixed with the signal of interest.

Broad-band noise is much less well defined. Examples might include the flow noise over the submarine's hull and the gurgling of piping inside the submarine.

The appropriate choice for analysis depends on several factors. The fainter the submarine's sounds (i.e., the better it is silenced), the longer the period of integration required to separate a regular acoustic signature from the surrounding noise. If the signature is not really constant, integration time is limited, perhaps below what would be required to overcome noise. In that case broad-band (spatial) processing may be a much better choice.

Many systems combine the two types of analysis, forming beams (i.e., processing spatially) and then breaking down the signal in each beam by narrow-band processing. The greater the computing power of the system as a whole, the more easily it can conduct this two-step analysis. Given sufficient processing power, the user must cope with an enormous amount of data; typically, then, the user needs some semiautomated means to indicate the presence of a real signal in a narrow frequency band of one of many beams.

Conversely, a computer-based combat system can track an enormous number of targets simultaneously. There will generally be relatively few real ones, but analysis of the motion of the others will often allow them to be disregarded. This is also true of decoys, and it explains the need for a modern torpedo, such as Impact, to track numerous targets simultaneously.

To deal with quieter and more distant targets, arrays have grown in complexity and in area; in one typical case, the number of separate hydrophones (in several arrays on board a submarine) quadrupled. Since all the array data are digital, they can all be processed together, a single system forming beams out of all the array data. This type of processing can be very powerful (e.g., it can form nulls to cancel out self-noise and jamming), but it also entails a very high data rate, in this case more than an order of magnitude greater than in the past. This output in turn is needed to improve resolution, both in space and in frequency, to detect quiet targets more effectively amid the surrounding noise. The associated system has over 200 channels of track information: 12 passive broad-band trackers, 12 DEMON trackers, 4 adjustable spectral window trackers, 8 passive-ranging trackers, 5 active track channels, and 164 high-quality automatic trackers. Such numbers would overwhelm an operator at a display; the system must make many of the decisions as to how the targets it detects are to be tracked, the operator monitoring the process and intervening when necessary.

Both types of processing can be quite sophisticated, and both represent alternatives to active operation. After World War II, when submarines (particularly those snorkeling) were relatively loud, passive operation entailed essentially no integration: a sonobuoy (or, for that matter, a homing torpedo) had only to seek a noise noticeably louder than its surroundings. That operation was very simple broad-band processing. That era ended in the mid-1950s, partly because submariners learned not to snorkel for protracted periods. Too, by the late 1950s the British had demonstrated that careful sound-mounting could drastically reduce snorkel sound levels. The question then was whether passive ASW was still practical.

The solution turned out to be LF narrow-band processing and integration, which the U.S. Navy code-named LOFAR (LF analysis and recording). In theory, the sound a submarine emits is a combination of discrete LF tones (tonals or lines created by rotating machinery) and broad-band noise (e.g., due to flow over the hull or through piping). Because the lines are regular, they stand out from the random noise of the sea. To detect them, the listener periodically breaks down a sample of sound into its frequency components (the breakdown can only be carried out on sound received over a finite, if relatively short, period). If the strength at each frequency is added up over a longer time, the regular features eventually stand out, even if they are quite weak, since the random noise cancels out.

LOFAR was the basis for Western passive acoustics from the mid-1950s on, and for many years it was a closely guarded secret (the name was invented to safeguard it; as applied to sonobuoys, LOFAR was called Jezebel). The success of LOFAR depended in part upon knowledge of the detailed acoustic signatures of potential enemy submarines because signal processing could be much more effective if specific features of a target submarine's acoustics were known. During the 1970s Soviet recording devices began to turn up in areas where NATO submarines operated, such as Norway and Puget Sound. Such devices are useful only in a LOFAR-acoustics context. We now know that the Soviets had developed their own version of LOFAR.

Many modern passive sonars use waterfall displays, in which the vertical ordinate is time. The horizontal scale is either frequency or bearing. In either case, the data flow down from the top of the display, which shows the short-term history of what the sensor receives. The bearing version, therefore, shows relative target motion. Signals that are constant in frequency stand out in a frequency waterfall (a LOFARgram, often shortened to "gram"). The observer integrates the data visually to separate the stable signals (which appear as more or less continuous vertical lines) from the surrounding noise. The LOFARgram is, in effect, a spectrogram. Some systems record relative intensities at different frequencies at time intervals and then integrate over time to form a true spectrogram that is usable, for example, for automatic or semiautomatic target recognition.

The original grams were paper records, equivalent in theory to waterfalls. The new signal appeared across the top of the paper and moved down as the paper moved. Marks on the paper indicated the intensity of the signals picked up at various frequencies. The electronic form of a gram shows signals over only a short period; the associated system generally relies on its memory to pick up long-term but weak signals. A paper gram can be spread out and integrated, in effect, by eye, and sometimes that is superior to the mathematical analysis. For example, a line varying slightly (e.g., due to Doppler) can be picked up by eye. Some current systems provide both CRT and paper readout specifically so that signals missed on the CRT will be picked up when the paper gram is spread out.

The hard-copy printer is inherently limited by the speed at which a record can be written, usually 1.25 sec/line. Hence the paper recorder must show signals as they are processed and thus cannot easily switch from channel to channel. A CRT can switch rapidly, so it can show all the historical data in the processor. The CRT can simultaneously display several portions of a frequency spectrum to emphasize harmonic relationships between lines. This technique is specially valuable in deciding whether particular lines are related to submarine speed or to machinery gear ratios. The CRT can also be used to designate a particular line to the system to begin, for example, a tracking or bearing measurement algorithm. Hard copy, however, is more useful to regain a lost contact since the operator's eye can bridge a vertical gap in a line, whereas a gap may break the computer's track.

Waterfalls are not suitable for active sonar displays since a waterfall cannot show range and bearing simultaneously. Therefore, active scanning sonars generally use PPIs or B-scans. In cases of omnidirectional transmission (ODT), the display often uses an expanding ring to represent the outgoing omnidirectional pulse; in contrast, in a radar PPI, a line representing the directional pulse and its echo revolves around the face of the scope. Many active sonars use B-scans, rectangular displays of range (vertical) versus bearing. Compared with a PPI, a B-scan has the advantages of compressing distant targets into a limited space, yet showing nearby targets clearly. Searchlight sonars use an A-scope and bearing indicator.

Armed with knowledge of the primary Western signal-processing technique, and probably driven by revelations of the effectiveness of NATO's submarine detections, the Russians achieved considerable silencing in their latest classes. The question, again, is whether passive signal processing has much of a future.

Three possibilities emerge, and as yet it is impossible to choose between them. One is that improvements in LOFAR technology (e.g., by adding more spatial discrimination, by tightening discrimination between nearby frequencies, or just by increasing integration time) can solve the problem. The United States' new LOFAR array sonobuoys and continued investment in towed passive arrays typify this approach. If this approach succeeds, the current situation—that Russian submarines can generally be detected at long range without revealing the presence of NATO forces—will basically continue.

Another possibility is that LF narrow-band passive sonar will lose its capability, so that passive operation will be reduced to MF flow noises. In that case, it will pay to abandon expensive signal processing in favor of mass-producing relatively simple (broad-band) sensors of flow noise and strewing them about the estimated position of a submarine. This approach was the basis of the abortive low-cost sonobuoy. An intermediate possibility would be to distinguish regular features of broad-band noise and,

thus, to retain longer-range operation at a cost in processing complexity.

The third alternative is to abandon passive operation in favor of very low frequency (VLF), that is, very long range, active operation. In that case, the existing LF systems would be retained, but they would function as the receivers in bistatic sonars, receiving echoes from the pings of relatively simple noise sources. Several active towed arrays, described in these pages, typify this approach.

Driving the development of ASW weapons, sensors, and tactics are the basic facts of sonar operation: sound propagates farthest at low frequency, and sound tends not to propagate in straight lines. Lower frequency means longer wavelength, and a sonar operating at that lower frequency must be larger to maintain the same gain (directionality). World War II sonars operated at high frequency (20–30 kHz) to assure directionality even with relatively small transducers. Medium frequency might loosely be defined as the 5–15-kHz range, and low frequency as about 1–5 kHz. However, some navies regard 5–7 kHz as low frequency and so describe their sonars. Operation below about 1 kHz generally requires devices, such as towed arrays, different enough from conventional sonars for another differentiation to be made, for example, very low frequency (sometimes 1–10 kHz is considered MF, so that 1 kHz and below is LF). Another way to draw this distinction would be to associate high frequency with short direct-path ranges and with sonars essentially limited to the surface layer. MF sonars can detect submarines below the (surface) layer at useful ranges, and, if properly designed, they can use the bottom-bounce path. Low frequency means convergence-zone propagation, at least potentially. On this basis 5 kHz is low frequency in the Mediterranean, but about 3 or 3.5 kHz is required for LF operation in the Atlantic and the Norwegian Sea. The history of sonar since 1945–50 has been a series of jumps down in frequency and, therefore, up in range. The velocity of sound in water is about 4700 ft/sec, so 30 kHz equates to a wavelength of about 1.8 in. A typical World War II maximum operational range was 2500 yd. Postwar sonars, such as the U.S. SQS-4, operated at about 10 kHz (about 5.5in wavelength) and could achieve ranges of about 5000 yd. A drop to about 5 kHz (wavelength about 1 ft) bought twice the range in sonars such as the U.S. SQS-23. Sonars such as the U.S. SQS-26 and -53 operate at still lower frequencies, about 3 kHz (wavelength about 1.5 ft), and are credited with direct-path ranges of about 20,000 yd. All of these figures are nominal, keyed to specific idealized conditions and useful more for comparisons between sets than for predictions of actual performance. Actual performance depends not only on water conditions but also on such considerations as the energy output of the sonar, the efficacy of its signal processor, and the character of the dome through which the energy must pass. SQS-26/53, whose dome is about the size of a 60ft personnel boat, represents an upper limit for conventional hull sonars.

Beyond increasing the size of the dome, there are two choices for increasing a sonar's performance. One is to spread the sonar over a longer portion of the ship's hull, as a conformal array. That configuration has been tried, but so far it has not been effective. The other possibility is to remove the sonar from the hull altogether and tow it astern in the form of a linear or towed array.

It may be much more difficult for submarine designers to eliminate the lowest-frequency narrow-band sound, so longer arrays, working at lower frequencies, may effectively counter silencing. In that case, the practical limit on frequency is probably the array length that can be towed without kinking, that is, without losing beam coherence. For a surface ship, there is really no effective limit on the array's length, although a very long array would be relatively heavy and, hence, difficult to pull back on deck. For submarines, a very long array may be too bulky to house. That bulkiness is a particular problem in many Western submarines, which have either a single hull or else very limited space between their double hulls: hence the vital importance of thin-line arrays, which can be substantially longer than the existing thicker array.

The technological problem here is twofold. First, the thicker the array, the less flow noise per unit area that the array must overcome. Therefore, for a thinner array to be effective, it must be backed by better signal processing. Second, the array must accommodate both a string of transducers and the wire(s) carrying their signal(s) back to the ship. Conventional thick-line arrays, which have been in service since the late 1960s (at least in the U.S. Navy), are built up of transducer elements in an oil-filled casing. Each element has its own output wire, and the wires are fed back through the multicore towing cable. A thin-line array needs more compact elements and, ideally, a multi-plexed-signal transmitter cable. Recently there have been suggestions that fiber optics can solve both problems. The optical path through the fiber changes if it is subjected to distortion, for example, by a passing sound wave. This path can, moreover, be monitored by maintaining a standing optical wave in the fiber (using a laser). Optical fibers are much smaller than conventional wires, so multiplexing might be unnecessary. It is also possible that the optical signals so produced could be processed optically, using an array of fibers in a specialized computer; thus, many or all of the usual signal converters could be eliminated.

Arrays and their associated processors are generally described in terms of the number of octaves they cover. As in music, an octave is the range between a tone and the one having twice the first's frequency (i.e., half the first's wavelength). For example, different versions of the Ferranti processor cover either two or five octaves. Each octave may surround a single line, so that a two-octave system may be intended to seek two particular lines in a target's spectrum. The number of octaves is increased by adding hydrophones to each end of the two-octave array (to achieve the same sort of directionality at a lower frequency). One subarray will typically cover one octave, for example, 50–100 Hz, centered on 75 Hz. The center frequency will be chosen in the expectation that useful signals will occur nearby. If the signals are narrow-band, they are often accompanied by higher harmonics, that is, by signals at multiples of the original frequency. Thus a line at, say, 70 Hz might be accompanied by others at 140, 210, 280 Hz, and up. Peculiarities of transmission might even make some of the higher harmonics stronger than the original signal. Thus, it is important to provide a towed array with capability at several ranges of frequency, and also with the software to correlate a line at one frequency with its possible harmonics.

Useful (i.e., directional) reception at very different ranges of frequency is achieved by nesting the transducers, each of which has a very broad range of frequency responses. A single unit of the array may be long enough to provide good directionality for signals at the highest frequency (i.e., shortest wavelength) with which the system deals. That unit becomes the middle subunit of a second, longer subarray used at a lower frequency. Typically, all the subarrays are built of identical basic units, so in this case the second subarray is three times the length of the first, operating at a third of the first's base frequency. The two are nested, the units of the first subarray working simultaneously at both frequency ranges. Forming the middle of the lower-frequency array, the first is said to nest in the second. Adding two more units to the ends of the three-unit array gives a third array five times the length of the first, operating at a fifth its frequency.

If the first subarray was designed to work in the range around 600 kHz, the second would be centered on 200 kHz and the third on 120 kHz. The U.S. SQR-18A reportedly consists of eight identical subunits, two of which form the highest-frequency subarray. The combination of those two with the two at their ends forms the next lower-frequency subarray (at half the highest frequency). If the next two are counted, then the next-lower subarray consists of six basic units, at one-third the highest frequency. All eight basic units form the lowest-frequency receiver, working at a base frequency a quarter that of the highest-frequency subarray.

In each case, the subarray is imagined as built out fore and aft from the center of the array as a whole. That design greatly simplifies beam-forming. Beams are formed by adding the outputs of the subelements of the subarrays in proper phase, and that addition changes least from frequency to frequency when the array is handled symmetrically.

Current towed arrays are passive receivers of sounds made by submarines; but as the submarines become quieter, it becomes attractive to provide an active sound source, generally in the form of a flex-tensional transducer operating at about 150–600 Hz (wavelength about 7.5–30 ft). The array would then act as the receiver of a VLF sonar.

Systems vary from navy to navy partly because different navies operate under very different acoustic conditions, and partly because navies perceive their missions very differently. For example, the Royal Navy operates its frigate-towed arrays largely for surveillance. They must, therefore, be relatively long (to work at the low frequencies at which sound propagates most effectively); and the ships must be very carefully silenced. In contrast, the U.S. Navy operates separate surveillance arrays (the SURTASS program) and separate tactical arrays, the latter for defending battle groups or convoys. U.S. tactical arrays can, therefore, be shorter, and they can tolerate worse acoustic conditions.

Sea conditions modify sonar choices. In summer, the surface layer in the Mediterranean, for example, may be only about 50 ft deep, so hull-mounted sonars become nearly useless. That condition explains the long-standing interest of the French and Italian navies in variable-depth sonars, which can operate under the layer. In the Mediterranean, too, the deep sound-channel is much shallower than in the Atlantic, and the convergence zone is much closer. In consequence, there is little point in using VLF sonars, and neither the French nor the Italians have gone as far as the U.S. Navy in the development of lower-frequency sonars. Other warm areas, such as the Arabian Sea, also have shallow surface layers, heated by the sun and often not mixed with deeper, cooler water. The Baltic is notorious. Because so many rivers empty into that sea, its acoustics are dominated by alternating layers of different salinity, from which sonar pings reflect. That condition is one reason the Swedish navy effectively abandoned ASW in the 1960s, and also one reason why it was so difficult to determine whether the Soviets really were operating midget submarines in shallow Swedish waters. On the other hand, the Arctic Ocean is at a nearly constant temperature, so that the surface layer extends down to the bottom, making for much longer effective ranges. Presumably, the only problem is the reflection and refraction of sound in the presence of large masses of ice. Special sound conditions may also be caused by particular marine life or particularly heavy shipping lanes or fishing areas. Other special conditions obtain in other areas, such as the South China Sea or the waters around Australia.

Some technological points require explanation. Virtually all modern sonars scan. They may send out directional pings, but they do not wait for the ping to return before looking in another direction. Reception is separated from transmission: the sonar either scans very rapidly (with a scanning cycle much shorter than the ping's length, so that the sonar is in effect looking in all directions all the time) or actually simultaneously. Because the sonar need not continue to stare in one direction before looking elsewhere, the scanning rate is independent of the expected time between ping and echo (i.e., independent of range), and a sonar can search a large volume with a reasonable probability of detecting a target.

A scanning sonar consists of an array of more or less omnidirectional transducers, achieving directionality by combining the signals from several adjacent transducers in the appropriate phase relationship, much as a phased-array radar works. This idea is not new: as long ago as World War I, linear hydrophone arrays formed beams using delay lines (which were sometimes called "artificial" or "electrical" water because the lines corresponded to effective water paths to different elements of the array).

Scanning sonar was developed in parallel by the United States, Britain, and Germany during World War II. In older U.S. (and many other) scanning sonars, a commutator carrying the appropriate (beam-forming) phase relationship scans physically. Each transducer stave feeds a stator element, and the commutator (rotor) spins within this external stator to form a series of successive listening beams that, in effect, sample the returning echoes.

The listening beam must scan quickly enough to pick up at least part of the echo from any target within range, so the emitted pulse should be about as long as the scan period. The shorter the pulse, the faster the scan must be. For example, a pulse 33 msec long would be associated with a scanning rate of 1800 rpm.

The usual display for such a sonar is a radar-like PPI, in which the point of light indicating a possible target describes a spiral, sweeping simultaneously around and outward at a rate proportional to the local speed of sound. Sometimes a circle indicating the outward motion of the omnidirectional ping is superimposed.

The transmitting beam can be rotated by a second stator within which another rotor spins. Each transducer stave is connected to one stator pole in an oscillator programmer (in U.S. terminology) in the sonar control room. The scanner rotor turns continuously and is energized only when the sonar transmits. It, in turn, energizes the stator poles and thus forms the rotating beam. The faster the rotor speed, the shorter the pulse, since each stator is energized for a shorter time. The rotor carries low-energy signals that are amplified between stator and transducer stave.

It might seem simpler to spin a commutator within the transducer itself, but the separate stator arrangement makes it possible to provide one or more additional beams that need not turn continuously. The main examples are a tracking beam using left-right comparison and a separate audio beam, which the sonar operator can place atop a target of interest. The audio beam picks up target sound for classification; at least until very recently audio was the chief means of target identification. The U.S. SQS-4 and -23 series have separate video (continuously scanning) and audio beams. ASPECT (see below), a sonar echo technique, was one attempt to find an alternative means of target classification.

The use of an external rotor extended to the big spherical bow sonars used in submarines, such as BQS-6.

The commutator has several disadvantages. It inevitably adds to the noise of the system. Because it samples all the transducer outputs, it cannot listen continuously; therefore, it misses some transient sounds. It also cannot fully exploit the strength of a long pulse since it listens in the appropriate direction for only part of the received pulse. Finally, the mechanically scanned system is really most appropriate to a cylindrical (or, in modified form, a spherical) sonar since the commutator must treat every group of adjacent staves alike. In a sonar transducer without such symmetry, the same transducers require different delays or phases to form beams pointing in different directions.

The parallel British approach was to provide appropriate networks of delay lines from groups of transducers to form separate beam patterns simultaneously (the prototype used 72 elements and formed 72 beams). Each beam was provided with a separate amplifier and rectifier, the charge on the rectifier representing the strength of the signal from the direction in which that particular beam was pointed. It, therefore, stored the whole of the returning ping. The array of 72 rectifiers could be scanned periodically. This arrangement was more complex than the U.S. commutator, but it could be applied relatively easily to shapes other than a simple cylinder. Because scanning rate was unrelated to ping length, the sonar could get the full benefit of each ping.

This British system could be called beam preforming, and it was more closely analogous to radar technology than was the U.S. system. The British verdict was that the faster scanning possible with preformed beams allowed for better contact-keeping. Moreover, because such a sonar could be other than cylindrical, it could concentrate sonar energy (and listening capability) on a narrower sector, for greater range. This view led to the development of the flat-plate Type 177. To the extent that the Soviet spy rings at Portsmouth were obtaining uniquely British sonar technology in the mid- to late 1950s, they were presumably obtaining the sector-scan/preformed-beam technology of Type 177.

The wartime German GHG passive submarine sonar (which led postwar to most of the major Western—and, probably, Soviet—passive submarine sonars) was broadly analogous to the British scanner, using a network of delay lines (compensators, also sometimes called "artificial water") to form its beams. Typically, a compensator switch was combined with a series of delay lines. Turned into a position corresponding to a given beam direction, the compensator switch sampled only certain delay line outputs.

Modern sonars use preformed beams, which make better use of the entire transducer array than any commutator system. Unlike the British wartime and postwar sets, however, they are not hard-wired, and they do not scan through the outputs of the beams. Instead, the beam-forming phase relationships are stored electronically. Individual transducer outputs are digitized, and beams are formed arithmetically, these outputs being added and subtracted with the appropriate multipliers. The sonar signal processor can then deal with all of the beams simultaneously. In effect, the sonar stares in all directions at once. This type of processing explains the very high computing power required in modern sonars.

Such digital operation is called DIMUS (digital multibeam steering). Beam preforming is clearly easiest for a symmetrical sonar but can also work for a more complex shape, such as that of a conformal array. In any case, it has the great advantage of making full use of the arriving signal, eliminating scanning loss. In addition, the relationships between outputs from the different transducers can be adjusted to meet changing operational or water conditions (adaptive beam-forming) since the relationships may be software-controlled rather than hard-wired. Thus, beam preforming is a prerequisite for building complex conformal sonar arrays.

Beam preforming can also be used to project or to receive multiple beams, just as a phased-array radar can produce several beams simultaneously. A commutator sonar requires a separate commutator for each such beam. Physically, beam preforming generally involves the replacement of a mechanical commutator by a digitizer and the associated digital computer(s). The effect is to increase greatly the number of targets that can be handled simultaneously.

The first scanning sonars sent out omnidirectional pulses (ODT, omnidirectional transmission). These sonars had the advantage of effectively matching their transmissions with omnidirectional reception, but the power available in any one direction was limited. One modern alternative is RDT, rotationally directed transmission, the sonar sending out concentrated pulses along each bearing while scanning through all transmission directions, like a 360-deg radar. The drawback to simple RDT is that it does not scan through all directions quickly enough; it offers too low a data rate. Some sonars employ tribeam transmission, scanning three transmitting beams that are 120 deg apart. An alternative to tribeam is to use multiple RDT beams scanning separately, perhaps at different frequencies to make them easily distinguishable, providing the sonar with several chances (in close succession) to detect a target in a given sector, and with several independent Doppler measurements.

Sonars are sometimes classified as search or attack, or a single sonar may operate in both modes. Attack always implies a narrower beam capable of tracking a target sufficiently well for weapons to be aimed. The required standard of aiming depends on the lethal envelope of the weapon. A mortar or rocket launcher, whose bomb has only a very limited lethal range, generally requires 3D ballistic information, including the underwater equivalent of height-finding. A homing torpedo, delivered either over the side or by rocket or missile, may need little more than an initial range and bearing, although the target's depth may still be important for predicting a target's position.

Most ASW surface ships armed with mortars or rocket launchers in the early postwar period were provided with separate search and attack sonars, and some ships still show this distinction. On these ships, the attack sonar has a narrow beam that can both train and elevate. In more recent sonars, the beam can be depressed electronically, since each vertical stave (an element that resembles and is named after a barrel stave) consists of several fairly nondirectional transducers that can be phased relative to each other. In large sonars the beam can be elevated fairly precisely. However, in a few cases there is only one fixed elevation or perhaps two alternative elevations. For example, a 24-stave sonar credited with 48 beams probably produces a fan of 24 beams at one elevation and 24 at another. It is impossible for any modern stave sonar to depress its beam continuously so as to match the motion of a target precisely.

A few sonars still employ searchlight operation, which was standard through the end of World War II: they concentrate their energy in a single directional pulse and have only a single receiver. They must ping in one direction and listen for an echo before they shift to another direction. That requirement severely limits the search rate. All specialized attack sonars are searchlights capable of depression.

There is also an intermediate case, a flat-plate sonar that scans a limited sector. Compared to an ODT scanner, the flat-plate sonar provides a stronger ping and may achieve a tighter beam over the scanned sector. Such sector scanning might be justified for a ship operating as one of several escorts in a screen.

Many of the sonar entries mention alternative range scales. They equate to alternative pinging rates. As in a radar, a sonar cannot easily distinguish a ping returning from a very distant target (after another has been sent out) from the echo of a nearby object: the problem of the second-time-around echo (STAE). Therefore, a sonar operator will set the ping rate beyond the maximum range he or she expects to achieve. On the other hand, the operator will try to get as many pings as possible to increase the probability of detection, typically using some type of sonar-performance predictor to set the ping rate.

As in radar, the length of the sonar's pulse determines the precision with which nearby objects can be distinguished. The length of sonar pulses is typically measured in msec (thousandths of a sec), compared to microsec (millionths) for radar pulses.

Early sonars produced only CW pulses (tones). As in radar, a longer pulse provided more energy on the target and hence offered better range performance. However, it could be affected by reverberation, and it reduced precision. A Doppler shift in the echo indicated target velocity and could be used for target classification and for tracking. Later, coded pulses (FM) were introduced. Again, as in radar, they can be pulse-compressed; they are also useful for overcoming reverberation. Variations on this theme are linear FM (slides) and hyperbolic FM. There is also FSK, a succession of short single tones (called a Costas, after its inventor) to obtain both range and rate. Pulses can be transmitted either singly or, if there appears to be a target, as a train. FM, which amounts to frequency diversity, can also be used to reduce the probability of interception.

Many current search sonars can generate very short pulses for a form of target imaging for classification; in the U.S. Navy this is called ASPECT (acoustic short-pulse echo classification technique). ASPECT first appeared about 1960, and was applied to U.S. sonars through the following decade. Several short pulses are sent in rapid succession. Like longer pulses, they are reflected not by the target as a whole, but mainly by a series of highlights. Because they are very short, the pulses produce separate echoes from the separate highlights (the echoes that longer pulses produce from the different highlights overlap). The combination of short echoes is a sort of target image, and it can indicate both the character of the target (for classification) and even its heading (target aspect, hence the name) relative to the sonar. ASPECT initially used a paper recorder similar to that of a LOFARgram; the echoes printed as a series of dots on horizontal lines.

Submarines (and now many surface ships) operate entirely passively. By about 1950 it was understood that submarine-on-submarine engagements would be conducted passively. Triangulation ranging was definitely a short-range proposition, so bearings-only ranging techniques (by analysis of plots) were developed. They were called target-motion analysis (TMA).

TMA was applied in two very different areas. One was fire control, in which the listener had to gauge target position, course, and speed closely enough to get a torpedo within homing range. Another was the initial approach to the target, to get the listener to within fire-control range (or to stay well outside the target's fire-control range). TMA for fire control itself was implemented in many torpedo fire-control computers. The approach form of TMA initially involved paper plots. Later it was incorporated in computer-driven submarine CDSs. It differs from short-range or fire-control TMA in that bearings change much more slowly, and also in that multiple targets are more likely to be involved. The mathematics of the two is much the same.

At the least, the listener knows target bearing, bearing rate (the rate at which bearing changes), and target Doppler. Often the target may be a member of a class, acoustic characteristics of which have been collected. Too, the submarine has generally collected local acoustic data from which its own sonar performance can be estimated. Thus the received sound level may allow the listener to make an initial range estimate (although individual members of the target class may be louder or quieter than average). A turn count may indicate target speed. Too, the listener's own maneuvers change bearing and bearing rate in a way that depends on target range, course, and speed. All of the data are approximate, and the art of TMA is to turn that mass of data into an estimate accurate enough for tactical decision-making and also for fire control.

Working primarily with bearing data was nothing new. Periscopes rarely could give accurate ranges on surface targets. World War I submariners appreciated that the closer the target, the higher its bearing rate. The bearing rate reaches a maximum at the closest point of approach. The sole exception is an unchanging bearing, indicating that listener and target are on a collision course or are on exactly parallel courses at the same speed. Early in TMA development it was observed that the quickest bearings-only solution could be obtained when target bearing changed most rapidly.

Initially it was understood that three bearings, taken at intervals, accompanied by either a target range or a target speed, would suffice to solve for steady target motion. Later it was discovered that a series of four bearings, two of them separated by a maneuver, would also suffice. (This technique, apparently no longer common in the U.S. Navy, is called Speiss ranging.)

A simpler method, Ekelund ranging, is to move back and forth across the line of sight/sound to the target. The ratio of own-ship speed in the direction across the LOS to bearing rate gives a range, the assumption being that the target has not moved much during the maneuver. Part of the art of Ekelund ranging is to determine the time, t*, associated with the range. The appropriate time is not obvious, since the act of ranging (the maneuver back and forth across the LOS) takes some time. The quicker the maneuver, the more precise the range. That is why WAA, with its very precise bearing measurement, is so valuable. Ekelund ranging is probably the most common fully automated form of TMA. For example, a U.S. Mk 117 or CCS Mk 1 system constantly performs Ekelund ranging on all available contacts. It does so by mathematically smoothing (typically by Kalman filtering) the bearings measured by the submarine's sonar, then estimating the bearing rate. The U.S. Navy designation for this automatic technique is KAST.

KAST is not terribly accurate, but it is easy to automate. A combination of KAST and bearing-rate measurement can be used to filter out distant contacts of limited interest. KAST solutions are also used as starting points for more elaborate forms of TMA, such as MATE.

Modern digital sonars can automatically track a target both in bearing and in the frequency of a chosen tonal, using mathematical trackers (automatic target followers, ATFs, or frequency-line integration trackers, FLITs). ATFs provide bearing data. FLITs provide the associated Doppler data, which give the component of target speed along the LOS. For example, if a turn count gives overall target speed, Doppler tracking gives target course. If a target moves steadily, the way its Doppler changes depends on range and course, so a sophisticated analysis can extract those data. Reportedly, the French navy prefers Doppler-based TMA techniques, whereas the U.S. Navy prefers bearing-based techniques such as Ekelund ranging.

Techniques include the strip or navigational plot, the time-bearing plot, and the relative motion plot. A strip plot is a navigational (true-motion) plot, showing bearing lines from listener to target at regular intervals, as the listener moves. Generally the bearing lines are not parallel, since the target is not moving at exactly the same course and speed as the listener. The name of the technique derives from the way the plot was initially used. Plastic strips with distances per minute corresponding to various possible target speeds were moved along the lines of bearings (taken each minute). At the appropriate target course and speed, the marks on the strip would fall exactly on the bearing lines. This type of plot measures course quite accurately, but errors in target speed estimate make for range errors. If the target and listener move in the same direction, bearing rate falls off and bearing lines become almost parallel; course but not range can be obtained. However, if the target does not maneuver, a maneuver by the listener (e.g., across the LOS) can make a speed error quite evident as a "range break" (a result mathematically equivalent to the concept of Speiss ranging): the range seems to jump if the speed is wrong, and the direction of the jump indicates the direction of the error (estimate too high or too low). Too, the strip plot may erroneously detect a target zig if small errors are made in timing bearing measurements at high bearing rates, that is, when the target is nearby. Thus a strip plot is probably most useful early in an approach, to develop initial estimates of target course, speed, and range. Target zig-zags can be detected because in that case the tracks do not connect.

Current U.S. practice is often to automate the strip plot. The MATE (manually aided TMA evaluator) display is a vertical series of dots representing the intersections between measured bearings, taken periodically, and the assumed target course. The horizontal positions of the dots indicate divergence between actual target bearings and those that the assumed target solution would have predicted. Dots move sideways as parameters are adjusted (the computer does the plotting, in effect), and the human operator seeks to line them up vertically. Apparently some operators can recognize a maneuvering target, which should correspond to a slightly curved line of dots.

The Royal Navy equivalent to MATE was Cross Range Error Minimization (CREM). As more powerful computers became available, the Royal Navy added Kalman (Filter) Analysis and Track Evaluation (KATE).

A time-bearing plot (Barnard plot: relative bearing against time, a waterfall) could be faired to filter noise out of the bearings used in the strip plot. The slope of the fairing line at any one time measures the bearing rate; kinks in that line (when the listener maintains constant speed and course) indicate that the target is zig-zagging. The shape of the curve indicates approximate target course, and hence can be fed back into a strip plot. Too, for a very distant target (effectively motionless relative to the listener), bearing rate is a measure of target range (as in Ekelund ranging).

The third type of plot developed during the 1950s was relative-motion or bearing rate (Lynch plot). The concentric circles on a maneuvering board were marked to indicate bearing rates, for example, 2 to 60 deg/min. Each bearing was plotted with its associated instantaneous bearing rate, as measured by time-bearing plot. A line through several such points gave the direction of relative motion. Assuming a target speed, a simple vector construction yielded target course. Relative speed and bearing rate gave a range. Using manual techniques, plotters in the 1950s could get excellent target course solutions at ranges inside 5000 yd and good ones inside 10,000. The course solution was completely independent of range, and could be used to test the solution reached on the strip plot, and to get more accurate range data.

U.S. experience seems to have favored the strip plot and similar navigational techniques, since early attempts to mechanize submarine plotting led to installation of navigational (Mk 19) rather than relative-motion plotters. A proposed bearing-rate plotter (Mk 18) presumably was not introduced because existing sonar displays (paper and then waterfall) already gave bearing rates.

Under many circumstances the fact that sound travels over several paths in the sea can be used to estimate target range (by comparing transmission paths from target to listener: the target is located where the paths cross). To do such depression/elevation ranging requires detailed knowledge of local sound paths, which generally involves a computer.

By 1960, a new problem was arising. If it took a skilled team considerable time to deal with a single contact, how was a submarine commander to handle the multiple contacts that really long-range passive sonars might make? The new programmable digital computers seemed to be the answer. The more complex the tactical situation, the greater the need for a usable tactical picture (for situational awareness). Sonar would probably detect numerous targets, but only a few would be worth tracking and considering attacking, that is, worth subjecting to fire-control analysis. On the other hand, a clear tactical picture might also make it easier to deal with escorts and other hazards.

For the U.S. Navy, the issue first arose with the advent of Subroc, a long-range ASW missile. Suddenly the long-range plotting realm and the short-range torpedo-data computer (TDC) realm seemed to coalesce. In the *Thresher* class the Mk 113 FCS was designed to use simple TMA techniques to localize four contacts simultaneously. It seemed that, at least in this form, TMA was little more than an extension of earlier TDC techniques, although now a programmable digital computer was needed. The computer was so arranged that the four targets were processed separately, in effect by four subcomputers. The analogy was strengthened when the system was modified to handle only a single target. The target solution was passed to what amounted to the TDC element of the FCS. Mk 113 worked with analog sonars. As in the contemporary NTDS, sonar operators entered data into the computer memory, in effect performing analog-to-digital conversion. Because the autotrackers of the associated sonar were analog devices (reduced-scale models of the sonar), the number of tracks the system could handle at any one time was limited by available space in the submarine (in fact, to two targets).

Digital sonars offered something quite different. They stared constantly in many directions, and could report many target bearings roughly simultaneously, as sets of numbers tagged with time, frequency, and other identifiers. As in radar, any such series could be broken down into track files, in this case series of time-tagged bearings. At least in theory, as the submarine maneuvered, the way the bearings changed over time could be used to determine target course, speed, and range. Once that had been done for many targets, a computer could plot them and project ahead their probable motion. Tactical decisions could be made on that basis.

In some cases, sonars produce only a stream of detections (plots). The associated CDS embodies the trackers, which are in effect computer slots. Other sonar systems have embedded trackers, and send only track files to a CDS computer. The distinction parallels that between ATD and ADT radars. There are also obviously sonar parallels to the track combiners used in air defense systems.

Current U.S. practice is to combine computer and manual operation. A Mk 117 or CCS Mk 1 system contains three Mk 81 tactical consoles, each of which can be used for MATE (in a CCS Mk 1, a fourth Mk 81 is devoted to Tomahawk/Harpoon targeting). Typically one is used for a commanding officer's tactical (summary) display (COTD). There is also a pair of Mk 19 automatic plotters (dead-reckoning tracers), one of which is typically used for navigation (quartermaster plot) and the other for the geographic plot. These are in addition to totally manual plots maintained around the attack center on rolls of graph paper: typically the contact-evaluation plot (CEP), time-frequency plot, and expanded time-bearing plot.

The CO acts as approach officer; the officer of the deck (OOD) drives the submarine. The most experienced subordinate officer, typically the executive officer, acts as fire-control coordinator, supervising a plot coordinator, a weapons-control coordinator, and a sonar coordinator.

The sonar puts out bearing data in two forms: as discrete raw bearings of the primary target, displayed on a bearing-recorder indicator (BRI) in the attack center, and as smoothed (integrated) bearings of all contacts sent to the computer and then to the Mk 81s (and called FIDUs, [target] follower integrated data units). Alternatively, FLIT data can be sent (the FLIT technique is called FLIT MATE).

Typically, one MATE Mk 81 is devoted to the primary target (Prime MATE), the other to other contacts or to a backup MATE solution.

The CEP is the primary situation plot, a true-bearing plot of own-ship course (down the middle), with all known contacts (in effect, a waterfall). It shows which contacts are approaching (those on the right will draw left, and vice versa), hence can be used to decide which contacts are of greatest interest.

Watching the BRI, the bearing-recorder calls out a bearing every 15 sec with a time mark and writes down the bearing. It is plotted by the expanded time-bearing plotter. The time mark cues the geoplotter to mark own-ship position every minute.

Each plot has a plot evaluator. The expanded time-bearing plot evaluator fairs bearing data using a ruler, to determine a bearing rate. A pair of bearing rates (at either end of a cross-LOS maneuver) gives an Ekelund range. The fairing line also gives faired bearings, which are fed back into the geoplot, associated with own-ship positions, and used for a strip plot laid out by the geoplot evaluator. Typically a strip plot starts with pairs of ranges and speeds set by the plot coordinator, which may be based on water conditions (giving the range of the day) and on a turn count or assumed speed. For each, opening and closing solutions are tried.

The fire-control coordinator chooses between the geoplot and MATE solutions available in the attack center. Once a solution has been accepted, it is inserted into the submarine's computer and the target position projected ahead on the solution course and speed. Targets for which MATE or manual solutions have not been worked out are shown according to the computer's KAST solutions. The COTD shows these solutions as a PPI-like display of the estimated current tactical situation.

Current U.S. interest in littoral operations is apparently leading toward a more automated form of TMA intended to promote situational awareness: there may be far too many close-in targets for a submarine commander to have them processed even semimanually. Similar considerations may apply to automated or semiautomated evasive action in the event a submarine finds herself under attack.

Sonobuoys and their processors are the airborne equivalents of surface-ship or submarine sonars. Most modern passive buoy systems use LOFAR analysis. CODAR is a correlation-display analyzing recorder, which measures the time difference between reception of the same signal by two buoys. As in the PUFFS passive ranger for submarine fire control, CODAR can obtain the direction of a signal relative to the two omni hydrophones that pick it up, given knowledge of the spacing of the buoys (which were dropped at specified points by intervalometer). If the time of the signal's origination is known, CODAR also gives a range.

The U.S. Navy adopted LOFAR (Jezebel) as an alternative to explosive echo-ranging (Julie), in which a signal depth charge was dropped, CODAR measuring the range from the timing of the echo of the explosion. Julie was conceived as a way to use existing passive buoys despite the expected silencing of Soviet submarines in the late 1950s. (Reportedly, the name "Julie" honored a stripper who could "make a passive buoy [pronounced like "boy"] active.") It was largely abandoned in favor of the new passive LOFAR. The necessary signal-processing technology has survived, however, and Julie concepts are being revived as E²R, officially Extended Echo-Ranging. Reportedly the Russians are enthusiastic users of explosive echo-ranging.

A LOFAR processor concentrates on frequencies around a particular line of interest. Although a submarine may emit strongly at only a very few frequencies, acoustic conditions on a given day may make it easier to detect some harmonic of one of those lines. Typically, a searching airplane drops XBT and background noise buoys, and then the LOFAR processors are set for the line sought. Analog processors handle only a narrow band, throwing out any other data reported by the buoy. Digital ones, such as AQA-7, can store the buoy's entire output for later analysis at alternative frequencies. Too, the flexible digital processor can offer either narrow- or broad-band analysis, LOFAR or CODAR (Julie-Jezebel).

DIFAR is directional LOFAR. A DIFAR buoy has two beam patterns at right angles to each other; it therefore measures two components of the signal it detects. It sends two LOFAR signals (corresponding to its two beams) up to the monitoring airplane, plus an omni sense signal to resolve the 180-deg ambiguity in the two beams (much as in HF/DF). Thus, from a signal-processing point of view, one DIFAR buoy equals two LOFAR buoys. Signal processing includes comparison of the two signals, generally using an arctan function to derive an angle. The resulting direction is not precise because the two beams overlap to a limited extent, but target direction can generally be found within about 10 or 15 deg.

DEMON (demodulated noise) extracts VLF signals that are reflected in the modulation of flow noise. LOFAR/DIFAR typically detects machinery noise (including noise made by auxiliaries), whereas DEMON is generally used to extract blade rate (i.e., propeller turn counts) from flow noise (direct LOFAR analysis is impossible because there is too much random noise).

DIFAR cardioid processing is a more sophisticated directional technique than conventional DIFAR processing, in which the directional beams are processed separately (incoherently). The alternative is to add or subtract each directional signal from the omni signal before processing, forming four cardioid (heart-shaped) beams, each pointed in a direction with a null opposite. That more than doubles the processing load, but the null excludes enough noise to add about 2 dB of processing power.

ANODE is a noise-measurement technique (ambient noise omnidirectional evaluation) using a DIFAR buoy. The pure omnidirectional signal is compared with a root-mean-square average of the two directional signals. If the noise is really not directional, the two should match exactly, but directional noise (e.g., from nearby shipping) will unbalance the two. Typically the comparison is matched against frequency, largely to determine which frequency ranges are best for buoy operation (i.e., which do not suffer from highly directional ambient noise). ANODE is commonly used by airborne ASW platforms, but more rarely in postmission analysis.

There are also command-activated pinging buoys, either omnidirectional (range-only, or RO, also called CASS, for command-activated sonobuoy system) or directional (e.g., the U.S. DICASS and the British CAMBS). Typically they can produce either CW or FM pulses, and pulse length can be varied by command.

Sonobuoys require a number of settings. When they are launched from within an airplane's pressure cabin (as in the British Nimrod, for example), the crew sets them at launch time. The U.S. P-3C carries them externally, in sonobuoy launch containers set before flight time. If the launchers are inside the pressure cabin, then the cabin must be depressurized if multiple buoys are to be launched (the Nimrod uses a 6-rnd launcher) or else launched one by one through a special pressurized launcher. An airplane intended to launch buoys from high altitude (e.g., while monitoring a large field) must almost inevitably use external launchers.

In the case of the P-3C, the aircraft tactical system is aware of which buoys are set in which way and selects the ones it wants. This method becomes less satisfactory as the number required to prosecute a contact grows toward the total on board, and as the buoys themselves become more flexible in their operation (so that setting involves more tactical judgment, made at the scene of prosecution). The two available solutions are a command downlink and remote setting on board the airplane.

OPTRONICS AND INFRARED DEVICES (PHOTONICS)

An increasing number of naval sensors (including missile seekers) operate passively, either in the visible band (optronics) or in the infrared (IR). Optronics is the combination of optics and electronics, as in a television; optronic devices are sometimes also called electro-optical (EO) for the means by which they convert light signals into usable electronic ones. Since both optronics and IR generally involve the detection of photons (which produce electrical signals by knocking electrons from one energy level to another), optronic and IR devices are sometimes lumped together under the heading "Photonics," as in the coming generation of submarine masts.

Optical wavelengths are about 0.4–1.1 microns (commonly 0.7–0.95 microns). This is all reflected light, due to the sun, moon, or stars. By way of contrast, IR is typically radiation produced by a body. Any body above absolute zero radiates; the strength (and the strongest wavelengths) depends on its temperature.

IR radiation is defined as wavelengths too long to be visible, that is, from 0.8 or 0.9 microns up. IR devices operate in a few "windows" through which radiation easily passes: 1.5–1.8, 2.1–2.4, 3–5, and 8–14 microns. The last two are the most commonly used in military and naval systems. The different windows are sometimes called different IR "colors," so that a two-color IR device generally works at both the 3–5- and 8–14-micron bands. Typically the 3–5-micron range is defined as mid-wave IR (MWIR), and the 8–14-micron band as long-wave IR (LWIR). Devices intended to detect very hot objects, such as jet engines and active guns, often operate in the MWIR; they include missile seekers. Imagers intended to detect cooler sources operate best in the LWIR region, although many operate in both bands.

The hotter the source, the shorter the wavelength at which it provides maximum radiation. The shape of the curve of emissions also changes, so that the ratio of the strength of emission at one wavelength to that at another will also change. The farther apart the two readings, the more drastic the change in their ratio as the temperature changes. IR flares and flashers rarely work at the same temperature as the targets they are masking; they rely on sheer energy to swamp out the detector. As a counter-countermeasure, some IR seekers work in two "colors" (IR bands) or "shades" (wavelengths within one band), measuring the ratio of strengths. Such operation can also help the seeker distinguish its target from the sun.

A jet pipe radiates most strongly at 3.75 microns, and early air-to-air missiles homed on this radiation. Because an airplane's jet pipe is visible only within about 30 deg of dead astern, violent maneuvers often sufficed to break the locks of such missiles. The hot plume of exhaust gas radiates most strongly at 3 microns (carbon dioxide) and at 4.2 microns (water vapor), and extension of the seeker to these wavelengths greatly enlarges the area astern within which a missile seeker can operate. This is still a signature visible largely from astern, although some IRSTs (such as the French VAMPIR) can detect the rising plume of a missile exhaust from ahead. Forward-aspect IR-guided missiles generally detect the exhaust plume from ahead. A fast airplane or missile is heated aerodynamically, and its skin will glow in the infrared; it can, therefore, be detected from ahead. A supersonic target, flying at Mach 1.25 at low altitude, will radiate most strongly in the 8.6-micron range, although some radiation will spill over into the upper end of the 3–5-micron range. Sunlight will glint off glass and even aircraft structure, and the IR portion of this glint can be detected. Because the hot exhaust is the main IR signature of a subsonic airplane or missile, there is some interest in reducing its strength, for example, by mixing it with cool air or by doping it to move its emissions out of an IR window.

Much, of course, depends on how much noise surrounds an IR signal. Thus few IR detectors are likely to be very effective against targets flying out of the sun. Many IRSTs apparently find it difficult to decide whether an IR source is an airplane or a sun-warmed cloud. On the other hand, even a relatively cool airplane is probably very visible from above, silhouetted against a cold sea (or a cold nighttime desert).

There are two classes of IR detectors, cooled and uncooled. The cooled detectors respond to individual photons striking them; cooling reduces the amount of extraneous activity. Most current missile seekers and imagers fall into this category. Uncooled detectors generally measure the heat difference between an object and its surroundings (pyroelectronics). At present they are used primarily in short-range low-resolution devices, such as the detectors firefighters sometimes use to search rubble for survivors. For the future, however, they are attractive because they can operate without bulky cooling systems. Moreover, since they need not wait until they cool to operational temperatures, they can (at least in theory) be used in faster-reacting missiles. The distinction between cooled and uncooled is not altogether precise, however, since even uncooled detectors of standard types can often function to some extent against hot enough sources, such as jet engines.

Current imagers, which work against relatively cool heat sources, must be cooled to well below ambient temperature. Their technology, then, includes not only that of the detector and related signal processor, but also the cooling mechanism. In air-to-air missiles such as Sidewinder, the cooling source may be a bottle of liquid gas that cools by expansion; in many optronic/IR detectors, the mechanism is a closed-cycle refrigerator.

Compared to radar, photonic devices suffer much more severe weather limitations. Generally they cannot penetrate clouds or rain, although IR signals will penetrate haze better than visible light. Variations in temperature and water vapor in the atmosphere will tend to bend both visible light and IR radiation. Generally longer-wave IR will suffer less than shorter wave in haze and fog. Some typical transmission factors are

Visible Light	3–5 Microns	8–12 Microns
1.00 (no fog)	1.0	1.0
0.5 (fog)	0.87	0.97
0.10	0.36	0.66
0.01	0.01	0.22

That is, when only 1% of the light is penetrating, 22% of the LWIR radiation is still available.

Typical IR detectors are lead sulfide (1–3 microns), indium antimonide (3–5.5 microns), mercury-doped germanium (8–13 microns), and mercury cadmium telluride (2–14 microns; photoconductive at shorter wavelengths and photovoltaic and photoconductive at longer ones). Lead sulfide cuts off at about 3 microns when uncooled and at 4 microns when cooled. Indium antimonide does not extend its range when cooled but does become more sensitive. Indium antimonide is much more effective than lead sulfide, since it can detect not only a hot jet pipe and exhaust radiation, but also the shorter-wavelength radiation from aerodynamic heating. For shorter wavelengths, silicon is effective at 0.4–1.2 microns. Television cameras typically use antimony sulfide (0.4–0.7 micron).

Thermal imagers generally have to detect relatively cool heat sources, all of which will radiate at relatively long wavelengths. Typically they detect temperature differences as small as 0.1°C, and differences of about 10°C will be detectable at ranges as great as 10–20 km. In contrast, a missile seeker detects hot tailpipes, with temperatures of hundreds of degrees; even an aerodynamically heated wing leading edge may be 65°C hotter than its surroundings.

A distinction is usually made between a spot tracker and an imager. The output of a spot tracker is the position of the spot in its field of view (FOV). The output of the imager is a representation of an entire scene; software (as in an EO FCS) may then track a feature of that built-up image, often one designated by a human operator. Because spot tracking is inherently far simpler, it came first: IR missiles are spot-trackers.

As in radar, IR missile trackers operate by measuring how far off-center the target is (the tracking error), then correcting. The simplest missile seekers use spinning disks broken up into opaque and transparent spokes. The spokes are triangular, so signals furthest from the center of the FOV are strongest. The rotation of the spokes imposes a time cycle, and the angle of the target (the error angle) corresponds to a point in that cycle. In effect the spokes act as time markers. They chop up the signal, imposing a frequency on it. The output of the chopper is processed like a radio signal to extract a sine wave ("missile video") whose amplitude indicates the size of the tracking error and whose phase indicates the direction. A variation on this theme is to make half the disk 50% transparent, so extended IR sources such as clouds will produce DC signals (which can be stripped from the varying target signal). One problem with spin-scan seekers is that a target near the center of the FOV provides no error signal at all, since all the spokes receive much the same signal simultaneously; the missile therefore cannot fly straight to the target. Nor can it easily reject a bright flare.

The next step is more closely equivalent to radar conical scan. The reticle is fixed; a tilted secondary mirror spins, in effect scanning the viewing beam. As in a radar, the detector produces a signal of constant frequency when the missile is pointing at the target. Errors show up as shifts in frequency. Because the missile tends to come closer to pointing directly at the target, it may reject flares better, since they leave its FOV more quickly than in the simpler spin-scan system. However, like a conscan radar, a conscan IR system still associates position with a point in its scan cycle. The typical countermeasure is to flash an IR source. It is equivalent to the inverse conscan technique used against conscan radar trackers.

The step beyond conical scan is a more elaborate scan pattern, such as a rosette (in-and-out superimposed on rotation), whose pattern consists of a series of lobes distributed around a circle. A target detected in one lobe is unlikely to move very far between complete scans, so the pattern can be gated (like a radar seeker) to reject decoys (which may move quickly into other lobes). As for flashers, although there is still a cycle, it is more complex and hence more difficult to capture. Rosette scanners are sometimes called pseudo-imagers in that they break up the missile's FOV into portions small enough to separate target from decoy.

There are other countermeasures to flares. The seeker can measure the rise time of the source; a sudden increase in illumination indicates a flare. Generally the flare has to provide at least twice the energy of the target to cause the missile to break lock; the missile can reject anything that more than doubles its received signal in less than, say, 40 msec. An alternative is to measure (in effect) the temperature of the source by comparing the return in two colors or two tones. Yet another is kinematics. A missile with a gyroscope measures target motion to some extent, in order to use proportional navigation. It can therefore reject flares that fall back from the target (hence current interest in propelled IR decoys). Kinematics is, however, of limited value in nose-on or stern-on attacks.

The alternative to a scanning seeker is a staring or imaging seeker, consisting of an array of point detectors in the focal plane (focal plane array, or FPA). It might be considered broadly equivalent to monopulse, as opposed to conical-scanning operation, with the same immunity to a time-varying countermeasure. In effect, such a seeker is a simple imager. An elaborate imager can reject a flare because it is a point source (an airplane is an extended IR source).

There are two kinds of imagers: sequential scanners and FPAs (staring imagers). Until very recently, detectors were so large and so expensive that no array could cover more than a few pixels. In a standard television, for example, an electron beam scans a photocathode (in effect) one pixel at a time. IR imagers typically use a linear array of detectors (see below) which is swept across the scene to form a full image. In theory, any such sequential scan is subject to a flashing countermeasure, since the imager will associate a bright enough flash (swamping out the scene) at a given time with the point in its scan with a point in its image, not necessarily with the appropriate position in space. This is much like the effect of jamming through a radar's sidelobes. Sequential scanners are sometimes time-gated (just as radar seekers are range-gated) to avoid jumping from the target to a bright flare moving quickly away from it.

TV-type scanning is a series of horizontal lines rastered vertically to form the full image. Resolution is measured by the number of lines per frame. Although picture brightness will vary continuously along each line, the system is generally arranged so that resolution is the same vertically and horizontally. Picture shape is defined by aspect ratio (or one might say that the appropriate aspect ratio is the one for which horizontal resolution matches vertical resolution). For example, the standard U.S. television frame employs 525 lines, and the aspect ratio is 4:3; it follows that each line consists of 700 picture elements or pixels (four times the number of lines). The entire scene is represented by a total of 367,500 pixels. The television displays 30 such pictures (frames) each second. Just as in radar, this type of sequential scanning defines a data rate that determines just how well the television can detect motion.

There are several alternative television formats, including 625-lines, PAL (576×768 pixels), and high-definition television (HDTV, perhaps 1500×2000 pixels).

Digital televisions (or CRTs) handle (and can process) each pixel separately. That can make for better clutter reduction (the civilian version promises to eliminate ghosts, for example), but the associated computer power can be enormous. After all, the television signal is equivalent to about 1.1 million pixels/sec, and each pixel may be in any of several colors and several intensities. In a computer, each pixel is associated with a certain number of bits of information, so the machine may have to handle many millions of bits/sec.

Imagers track on a frame-by-frame basis. They were first employed in "smart" EO bombs (such as Walleye) during the Vietnam War, and now they form the basis of many airborne trackers (which are used to control laser designators) and shipboard IRSTs (IR search/trackers). Future frame-by-frame trackers will be used in FPA IR-guided missiles.

Most trackers focus on a particularly prominent part of the scene; in air-to-surface weapons it is usually designated by the operator. The overall scene changes slowly enough on a frame-by-frame basis that the tracker can keep pointing at it by measuring changes in its position. Contrast trackers typically follow the centroid of a dark area or an edge. In centroid tracking, an area of the overall scene is defined by gates above and below and to either side. The tracker breaks the gated area into quadrants, calculating the total intensity of each. The intensity is treated like the output of one channel of a monopulse seeker, the tracker pointing toward the most intense quadrant. An edge tracker is a variation on this theme: the edge is detected and then tracked by centroid techniques.

Spot or centroid tracking is simple, although it may become confused if the target passes near some alternative dark object. Edge tracking is simple, and an edge will not change very rapidly as the missile approaches its target and the scale changes. On the other hand, the missile may tend to slide down the edge and onto another dark object should the target pass one (appear to merge with it, from the camera's point of view). For example, if a truck moves past telephone poles, the tracker may find the poles more interesting. Both centroid and edge tracking are most effective against extended targets. Centroid tracking is only fair against point targets (it is easy to confuse because it calculates a centroid over a wide area), and edge tracking is useless in such cases (a point target has no discernible edge).

Correlation tracking is a more sophisticated alternative. If a sufficiently varied area of the television image is chosen, then the tracker can compare the complex profile of that area with alternative areas on the next frame. In many cases, the human operator points the seeker or tracker at the target by enclosing the area to be tracked within gates; the gates define the area of the next frame that must be searched.

Correlation tracking is potentially far more stable than the other alternatives, since the signal being tracked contains much more information and thus is much more difficult to swamp in optical noise (i.e., in false targets). However, correlation also often (though not necessarily) involves much more processing than edge or spot tracking. Typically a correlation target must be inserted by a human operator.

Appropriate circuitry or software can be made to notice important features in a television scene, alert operators to their presence, and then track them. This development is the basis of IRST devices, such as the French VAMPIR. An IRST scans a scene, for example, turning through 360 deg, and searches for particular features. A simple IRST, however, may simply search for hot spots that rise above a set threshold.

Signal processing can, of course, be much more elaborate on a pixel-by-pixel basis. There now exist computer programs for limited image recognition by shape. Images may also be classified, at least tentatively, by their measured temperature (apparent color), their apparent size, and their measured speed. Because the image is very rich in detail, any substantial processing entails very great computing power. The numbers are much like those encountered in television: a signal rate of 5 million pixels/sec might well be encountered. The processor would form images based on whether each of those pixels was above or below some selected threshold, and thus it would have to examine each one every second. Threshold crossings must be correlated from pixel to pixel to decide whether individual pixels were isolated points or were parts of extended images. Moreover, clutter, which may resemble real targets, must be eliminated. Such processing entails the use of numerous parallel channels.

Photonic detectors suffer from two inherent defects. First, the overall scene they observe tends to be much richer in detail than the scene observed by, say, a radar. It may, therefore, be much more difficult for an automatic system, such as a missile seeker or an IRST, to separate out the limited number of features of interest, such as the target itself. The earliest EO devices succeeded because a human operator could select out a sufficiently distinctive aiming point for the tracking circuits to distinguish as the missile flew. However, current IRSTs are worthwhile precisely because they can recognize particular targets before human operators can do the same.

Second, these devices are all passive; therefore, none can measure range to a target. Optronic/photonic fire-control devices often incorporate a ranging laser, whose weather-penetration capability is broadly comparable with that of the passive tracker.

TV cameras typically use either photocathode or CCD detectors. The CCD (charge-coupled device) is a matrix of photosensitive sites on the surface of a solid-state device. The electric charge at each site is proportional to the amount of light (the number of photons) striking it. The charge at each site is turned into an electrical signal, and thus the image focused on the CCD array can be read out electronically. Depending on the material of which it is made and the character of the array elements, a CCD array can be designed to function either in the visible or in the IR spectrum. A CCD array can be considerably more sensitive than a conventional video tube, and thus a camera incorporating it can function at low light levels.

Most low-light-level televisions (LLLTVs) work instead by intensifying the light coming through their lenses. In the simplest such devices, starlight scopes, the light falls on a photocathode, which releases electrons. These electrons can then be processed to produce a stronger signal. Vietnam-era starlight scopes used very large voltages, typically 10 or 30 kV, to accelerate electrons given off by the photocathode. The electrons in turn struck a phosphor screen, which glowed. Such voltages required bulky equipment and large power supplies. In particular, Vietnam-era starlight-scope technology would not be suitable for night-vision goggles (NVGs), which are now common on board airplanes and helicopters.

The key to compactness is an electron multiplier, a microchannel plate (MCP). The initial electrons are accelerated over a short distance via an electrostatic lens. The MCP is an array of glass capillaries (channels) down which electrons are accelerated. They collide with the channel walls, which are coated with secondary electron emissive material. As in the original starlight scopes, these electrons in turn are used to produce a brighter secondary image, typically on a phosphor screen that glows when it is struck by electrons. The MCP does not distort the form of the image, and the entire device can be quite compact. A typical modern set of aviator's NVGs covers the spectrum from the UV to the near IR. The extension into the near IR is important because the night sky is illuminated largely in that region (the day sky is in the visible range). Earlier MCPs operated almost entirely in the visible spectrum. The accelerating voltage is 1–3 kV and the typical light gain is 30,000. Distortion is about 7%, and magnification is close to 1, that is, the final image is very nearly the same as an image of the scene in natural light. The same technology can be used in an LLLTV.

The most sensitive LLLTVs use a starlight scope combined with a CCD.

Modern IR systems generally use detector arrays, across which a rapidly rotating mirror scans the image of the scene. For example, a forward-looking infrared (FLIR) imager typically uses a vertical array of detectors, which scan across the scene. Unlike a television, a FLIR produces all of the lines across the scene simultaneously. They are multiplexed to produce lines in sequence for television viewing. Since it generally cannot accommodate as many detectors as a standard television provides lines, the FLIR image will often not be of television quality. In some cases, even though the detecting array is linear, scanning is not only horizontal but also vertical, so that a smaller and lighter array can still cover a wide FOV.

The U.S. common module FLIR uses 180 detectors in its vertical linear array, scanning across 480 pixels horizontally. Two horizontal scans are interlaced, so that in effect there are 360 vertical positions. The sampling rate per channel is 480 pixels × 30 Hz (frames/sec) × 2 (interlacing), for a total of 29 kHz. There are also 60- and 120-element U.S. common module detectors (DT-591 and -594), both operating in the 7.7–11.75-micron band. Hughes produces a standard 160-element parallel-scanning FLIR module. Current naval aircraft common module FLIR systems are AAQ-16 for the V-22, AAR-50 for the F/A-18 (navigational FLIR), AAS-36 in the P-3, AAS-38 in the F/A-18, and OR-263/AA in the S-3. Some current linear systems are several detectors across, using time-delayed integration to combine the images they see (examples are 96 × 4 and 288 × 4 arrays).

Many British systems use TICMs (thermal-imaging common modules), which are serial scanners using SPRITE (signal processing in the element) detectors. SPRITE is a linear array that is mathematically equivalent to a point detector: the output of each element is added up, with an appropriate time delay, for a net improvement in signal-to-noise ratio. A vertical array of SPRITEs would be equivalent to the arrays in current U.S. FLIRs, scanning a scene in parallel. TICM was first proposed in the mid-1970s and thus represents a later technology than the U.S. common modules.

Class I is a man-portable direct-viewing system made by Thorn-EMI; Class II is a mid-performance module, made by GEC-Marconi (which defeated Barr & Stroud). The Class II TICM is used on board U.S. AV-8B Harrier IIs.

The ultimate detector development is a staring array (FPA) on which the image is focused; it is a full 2D detector on a single chip, generally including its own preprocessor. The image is self-scanned, that is, its subelements are sampled electronically. No mirror is needed, and the system is physically very stable, so that signals can be integrated over a long time to eliminate noise. Such a system may, therefore, be able to operate without much cooling.

The effect of the large number of elements of the FPA is to improve field coverage; their small size makes for better resolution and better signal-to-noise ratio; on-chip processing makes for less noise and faster readout. A typical current chip accommodates as many as 512 × 512 individual detectors in a 12mm square, 16 mm thick. Individual detector elements are tens of microns across. In 1996, Rockwell stated that it could mass-produce big MWIR arrays (1024 × 1024) on sapphire (rather than CdTe) substrates; the advantages of sapphire were its strength and its reflective properties, which made nonreflective coatings unnecessary. A silicon readout integrated circuit (ROIC) is bonded to the sapphire. The ROIC electronically scans the array, using one output for 256 × 256 and 320 × 240 arrays, and four for larger ones. Presumably Rockwell's big arrays are a step toward a U.S. government goal of cutting FPA cost to match those in CCD television cameras.

Generally a current staring array will not cover a very wide area (field of regard) at a reasonable level of resolution. Typically its designer will have to accept either limited resolution or else some mechanical means of stepping to scan over a wider area. In the latter case, the staring array is, in effect, a better version of the linear detector already described. Since the array itself is stepped, it cannot move very quickly, and frame time may be lengthy. Scanning systems tend to be best for wide field coverage; staring systems provide more sensitivity.

In 1990 a 64 × 64-element indium antimonide array cost about $50,000 (in FY86 dollars, the cost per pixel is about $10). This price was far too high to realize the potential advantages of FPAs in tactical weapons. In 1986, for example, a DoD estimate showed a need for more than 340,000 64 × 64-element arrays between 1991 and 1996, which in turn would cost about $17 billion. The Infrared Focal-Plane-Array Initiative was created to reduce the cost per pixel to 10 cents, that is, to 1% of the 1986 figure. The companies involved are Rockwell, Hughes, and Fairchild, and the materials are indium antimonide, mercury cadmium telluride, and platinum silicide. By 1996, the technology developed was being exploited in a wide variety of programs. Foreign equivalents to this initiative include the French SOFRADIR (primarily for a new antitank missile, Trigat) and a Japanese program.

LASERS

Lasers are already very widely used for range finding (as range-only radars) and for target designation; they are beginning to be used for communications and for weaponry. All follow the same basic principle, but at very different wavelengths and power levels. In most cases, the value of the laser lies in its very pure coherent light, easily distinguishable against a very noisy background and thus capable of carrying substantial information. Purity means not only purity of wavelength (frequency), but also coherence: the laser beam is pure in phase as well as in overall frequency. In effect, the laser beam is a single very strong light wave, rather than the usual random mixture of many beams with different phases. This coherence shows in the characteristic speckled (spatial interference) pattern shown by a laser beam in air.

The beam is narrow because it is coherent. If the laser aperture was infinitely wide, the beam would not diverge at all. As with radar, the laser beam diverges (has some width) because the aperture through which it emerges is only a finite number of wavelengths wide. However, because light has so short a wavelength, a laser beam is often only a few mrad in width, so that it is still fairly narrow at a great distance. Inevitably some radiation leaks to the side (in effect, into sidelobes): a laser link cannot be entirely covert.

The basis of laser operation is that atoms (and other atomic systems, such as semiconductors) have well-defined and well-separated energy levels. When they fall from level to level, they emit photons of fixed frequency (wavelength) corresponding to that particular difference in energy levels. The presence of one such photon stimulates an atom to emit another of just the same frequency and phase, hence the coherence of a laser. The laser medium is pumped up into an excited but fairly stable (metastable) state. Then an atom decays to a lower energy level, emitting a photon. That photon causes another atom to emit a second, and the process avalanches. Typically the laser medium is enclosed by mirrors so that the photons (quantized light waves) reflect back and forth, causing further emission. In the simplest arrangement, two flat mirrors are at either end of a solid laser rod; the two mirrors must be an integral number of half-wavelengths apart to form what amounts to a resonant cavity. There are also other mirror arrangements, better suited to gas lasers. In any case, one of the two mirrors is partially (typically 1%) transparent; the laser beam exits through it when enough energy has been built up.

The laser can fire spontaneously (one of the metastable atoms will soon decay), or it can be fired by a master pulse sent through it, along its optical axis, perpendicular to the mirrors (in which case it amplifies that pulse).

Thus the laser consists of a lasing medium and a source of energy that pumps the medium up into the inverted state from which the atoms can fall to release the laser energy. Because there are other ways for the pumped-up atoms to lose energy, a laser generally cannot convert more than a few percent of the pumping energy into output. Solid and liquid lasers are generally optically pumped; semiconductor solid lasers use electric discharge.

Solid lasers are limited in output because the pumping heats them; the motion of the atoms in a hot solid smears out the energy states. The upper limit is about 1 kW/m of length.

Really high power output demands a flowing medium, which can dissipate the pumping energy. Each atom or molecule of the flowing medium is active while it passes through the open laser cavity. For a laser weapon, the alternatives are electric discharge, gas dynamics, and chemical reactions. A gas dynamic laser pumps up its molecules by heating them; collisions in the dense gas convert that energy into molecular energy. In a chemical laser, a chemical reaction leaves molecules in a high-energy state from which they can release photons. Usually the reaction product is hydrogen fluoride. In all of these gas lasers, the gas streams through the laser cavity, perpendicular to the line along which the laser beam resonates and projects. High-powered chemical lasers present special problems for shipboard installation because their exhaust gas is often quite toxic.

Some typical laser materials, with their dominant wavelengths, are

Alexandrite	0.7–0.82 micron. Typical repetition rate 40/sec; typical of many tunable crystal lasers. Used as target designator.
GaAs	0.850 micron (semiconductor laser). Power conversion efficiency can be as high as 57%. Used for signaling in fiber optics and as seeker head.
GaAlAs	0.8–0.95 micron. Used as seeker head.
Ruby	0.694 micron. Typical repetition rate 6/min; now obsolete for military applications. Used as range finder.
Nd: Glass	1.06 microns. Typical repetition rate 10/min; now obsolete. Pulse energy 10 times that for ruby. Used as range-finder, target designator.
NdYAG	1.064 microns. Typical repetition rate 20/sec; low energy (range-finder). Also used as target designator and weapons-guidance data link and as decoy for laser-guided bombs.
CO	4.9–5.7 microns. Typically used as a laser jammer. Output power of 100 kW and efficiency +60% demonstrated.
CO_2	10.6 microns (gas laser). Typical repetition rate 2/sec; pulse energy 40 W in a burst. Can tune 9.6–10.6 microns. Uses: range-finder, target designator, beam-rider, LADAR, laser jammer, laser decoy, high-energy laser (HEL).
DF	3.6–4.2 microns (chemical laser). Used as jammer and HEL.
HF	2.6–3.3 microns (chemical laser: hydrogen fluoride). Typical HEL.
XeCl	0.31 micron (blue-green).
XeF	0.35 micron.

The principal current naval laser applications involve relatively low energies, for target designation, for range-only radar (range finding), for LADAR, and for signaling (as in the case of the experimental air-to-submarine channel, and also within fiber-optic systems). Typically, current laser range-finders operate at 0.6 to about 1 micron, laser designators in the 1.4–1.8-micron band, and laser trackers at longer wavelengths, in the mid-IR (3–5 microns).

Current LADARs (sometimes called LIDARs) are used mainly for ranging because they have very low PRFs, typically about 20/sec. They cannot easily scan over wide fields of regard; a laser equivalent to conventional radar would have to use many lasers in parallel.

Blue-green lasers present particularly interesting possibilities because they can penetrate considerable depths of seawater. As early as the mid-1960s, such beams could reach down as much as 400 ft, and for a time it seemed likely that a shallow-water submarine-hunting LADAR was practicable. The effort was abandoned because insufficient return energy was available, probably because too much was lost to internal reflection when the beam passed through the water surface on the way up. More recently, analogous downward-looking LADARs have been used for shallow-water surveying and for mine location (as in Magic Lantern).

Perhaps surprisingly, blue-green lasers are ineffective *in* water; red is preferred for wholly submerged lasers.

It has been possible to generate very high laser energies for some time, but laser weapons (other than the recent British "dazzler") are still almost as far away as they seemed two decades ago. There are two problems, propagation and actual damage to the target.

The atmosphere is not homogeneous, and the beam bends as it passes through. The beam director, therefore, must adapt to changing atmospheric conditions, some of them caused by the beam itself. At least at present, beam directors for high-energy lasers are quite massive. In addition, the atmosphere absorbs the beam. Water vapor is a particular problem for a beam directed close to the sea surface. As it heats, the air changes its index of refraction, and it bends or spreads the beam (blooming).

The beam can transfer energy either continuously or in a short pulse. A continuous-wave laser heats its target, and there is always some question as to whether evaporation from the target will carry away energy quickly enough to protect it. Alternatively, a short pulse will transfer energy very quickly, almost like a kinetic-energy projectile, smashing into a target. Such a laser has the additional advantage that it may be so short that the air will not heat enough to bloom it as it passes through.

In either case, damage is likely to be limited to a small portion of the target. Many potential targets turn out to be surprisingly survivable. For example, a missile approaching head-on presents few large areas susceptible to damage, and it is not always clear how much (or just what kind of) damage will be fatal. A crossing target is far more vulnerable, but current laser ranges seem insufficient to provide area defense. Explosives are a very different proposition; they cause massive damage distributed over the target, neutralizing it because they are likely to hit something vital, or because the net effect of all that damage is likely to be fatal.

IFF

Because IFF (identification friend or foe) applies to so many radar systems, it seems best to treat it here. Since the middle of World War II, the standard system, both in the West and in the Soviet Union, has been the interrogator-transponder. A radar is fitted with, or associated with, an interrogator with approximately the beamwidth of the main radar. The interrogator sends a coded pulse or pulse train in approximately the same direction as the main radar, but at a different frequency. The transponder on the target sends back a reply at a third frequency. Generally, the reply is coded to indicate the details of the target's identity. Over the years, frequencies have increased and interrogators have become more directional; in some cases, the text gives details for the interrogators associated with particular radars.

All of the many interrogators on board a single ship (not to mention in, say, a fleet) are generally independent, so that all may interrogate the same incoming target. As a consequence, the transponder of any particular target may be unable to reply to all of them, since it can send its code to only one interrogator at a time. The main current exception to this problem is the single integrated IFF antenna used in conjunction with the U.S. SPY-1 radar (see that entry in the Antiaircraft Warfare section): it limits a single ship's interrogations.

Moreover, the interrogator-transponder system can be a liability in combat since an enemy with access to the interrogation codes can use them to trigger transponders aboard approaching targets and thus can use IFF itself to track targets. That makes the coding of interrogators particularly important, and this requirement in turn makes for relatively complex systems.

IFF is not a universal identification system; it is a means of positively identifying some radar targets, leaving all others unidentified (and hence either neutral or foe). Moreover, because a potential target may not reply to a particular interrogator (for example, because it is replying to others at the same time), IFF errors can occur even for friendlies. Additionally, the more complex the coding for security, the better the chance of error. It is commonly assumed that in wartime large numbers of aircraft will fall victim to IFF errors, on both sides of any conflict.

There is also a danger that a nearby ship will receive the reply intended for another, either through the main lobe or through a sidelobe. Such false replies are called "fruit," and they are eliminated or "defruited" by assigning each interrogator its own pulse-repetition frequency (PRF): special circuits eliminate any reply with a different PRF. It is also possible for a single target to receive interrogations from two radars in line, so that the reply intended for one is received by the other, and thus is associated by the other radar with an entirely different, nonreplying target. Multiple interrogation signals can also overlap and confuse a transponder.

The current NATO system, Mk 10, was introduced during the Korean War. There was no Mk 9; Mk 10 was developed as Mk X, the *X* standing for the future system (it replaced Mk V of 1945). This system interrogates at 1030 MHz and replies at 1090 MHz. A coded Selective Identification Feature (SIF) was added in the mid-1950s. Capacity is 4096 identification codes, in three modes (1, 2, and 3). This system is used for both military and civil aircraft, and the responses typically carry coded information. Civil aircraft provide flight call sign and altitude. Military aircraft provide a basic IFF response plus other data. Mode 3 is military, Mode A is joint military/civil (often called Mode 3/A), Mode B is civil (identification), and Mode C is civil (altitude reporting). A further Mode D is not currently used but is available for expansion of the system.

Mk 10A has an Automatic Code Changing (ACC) capability, with more code combinations. Because Mk 10A and the civil ATC system use the same message format, there is always a possibility that an enemy will find it relatively easy to fabricate false Mk 10A messages.

Early in the 1960s the United States added a cryptographic facility, Mode 4. The interrogator as well as the transponder is coded to prevent an enemy from tracking by using a false interrogator to trigger transponders. Mk 10/10A plus Mode 4 is designated Mk 12, which is now standard in much (though not all) of NATO. Mk 12 has never extended throughout NATO partly because it is much more expensive than Mk 10 and partly because its greater degree of coding makes the system as a whole more vulnerable to jamming, which might confuse the codes.

In the early 1970s, NATO set up a working group to define a NATO Identification System (NIS) that would replace Mk 10/ 12. By 1981 Britain, West Germany, and the United States were all developing prototypes. Britain and West Germany favored a higher-frequency (S-band) system, the United States and France an L-band system compatible with Mk 10/12. In April 1985 NATO agreed to adopt the U.S. solution. Britain and Germany had claimed that L-band was too crowded but accepted the L-band system when the United States agreed to add a radar interrogator mode (i.e., interrogation at radar frequencies in the S- and X-bands to supplement the previous standard of 1090 MHz; however, as at present, responses would still be at the standard frequency of 1030 MHz). This scheme meets a requirement stated by the European NATO partners, allowing interrogation by a radar not fitted with a separate interrogator.

This new system, called Mk 15, was to use two types of interrogation, one using spread-spectrum interrogation, the other a radar mode using pulse-position keying. Where possible, the radar mode was to be integrated directly into weapons systems.

The U.S. Air Force decided to opt out of Mk 15 as its budget was cut; in 1992 the U.S. Navy was made lead service for the next-generation U.S. system. It will probably be a less-robust version of Mk 15.

In a larger sense, identification must be based not only on electronic replies but also on observed behavior. For example, schemes for air operations in Europe commonly involve special corridors, including altitude, along which returning strike aircraft can expect to return without being shot down. To avoid funneling enemy strikes into the same areas, the corridors are changed very frequently. Similarly, a fighter returning to a carrier would not only "squawk" or send the proper IFF reply but would also behave in a particular preassigned way. Otherwise, the fighter would probably be shot down. Systems based on flight profiles can help to allow for possible electronic failure or battle damage, but they cannot be perfect.

These inherent problems have prompted considerable work on noncooperative means of identification, using the physical characteristics of the approaching target. In the past, at least in the United States, the most popular have been the measurement of the rates of rotation of jet engines' compressor blades (since the blades make prominent radar returns), and the direct imaging of an approaching airplane. Neither has ever been implemented.

A third alternative is positive tracking of all the aircraft in an area. That was done in the Gulf of Tonkin during the Vietnam War, when a computer-equipped ship tracked literally all air contacts. In theory, much the same thing could be done, say, by an Aegis ship in the Mediterranean. However, identification by tracking requires the cooperation of neutrals, who in effect must identify themselves when they take off. If they do not, identification will fall apart—as in the *Vincennes* incident of 3 July 1988.

The shooting down of the Iranian airliner by the USS *Vincennes* illustrates these points. Because the airliner was not a U.S. military aircraft, it could not send an appropriate IFF signal. The signals it did send seemed to correspond to those the Iranians had used earlier for F-14s, but that was a deduction from observed Iranian behavior, not necessarily a positive identification. After all, the Iranians might well change their own IFF codes quite often. Thus the captain of the *Vincennes* could not be sure what the IFF return meant. He tried to contact the airliner by radio but received no reply, and the airliner itself did not swerve away, as Iranian airliners had in the past. He did not shoot, however, since the negative information he was receiving did not necessarily mean that the airliner was hostile. Then he was told (incorrectly, as it turned out) that the aircraft had begun to descend, to dive. To the captain, that was a positive signal of hostile intent. This reading in turn was based on a series of known Iranian threats and an expectation that the Iranians might well try a suicide attack.

It now appears that the error was due to a quirk in the ship's CDS. It turns out that *Vincennes* was participating in two separate Link 11 circuits, one of which she managed, and one of which, managed by the destroyer *Spruance*, was outside the Gulf. The cruiser initially assigned the Airbus the track number 4475. However, because it had been detected earlier by the frigate *Sides*, the circuit merged the two under the frigate's number, 4131. Meanwhile HMS *Manchester*, operating in the *Spruance* circuit, was tracking an A-6 Intruder which, as it happened, *she* had assigned track number 4475. Captain Rogers was unaware of the reassignment of the Airbus number. Thus, when he asked the system to give him the *altitude* of track number 4475, he received the altitude of the distant A-6. He was not told that this contact was about 110 nm from his ship, that is, that it could not have been the Airbus. Concentrating on track number 4475, those in CIC saw a descending target without realizing that it was an irrelevant one. Presumably the order to shoot was based on "hooking" a target on the display rather than on inserting the track number. Ironically, a system slightly more graphically oriented would not have permitted this error, since altitude would have been given only by marking ("hooking") the appropriate target on the display. The sophistication entailed in asking for data by track number proved disastrous.

The incident well illustrates the central problem of identification: one might be able to determine the physical character of an approaching target, but how can one interpret the intent of the target's operator? Although Captain Rogers undoubtedly believed he was facing an Iranian F-14, in fact his ship could have been crashed just as effectively by an airliner. A system that merely told him what type of airplane was approaching could not have sufficed. This problem will most likely recur in other areas, where several countries might be operating the same or similar equipment.

MISSILE GUIDANCE

The three most common types of missile guidance are inertial, command, and autonomous.

Inertial guidance systems measure the motion of a missile through space, sensing and integrating accelerations to find the missile's velocities. Inertial systems were initially used only in long-range ballistic missiles because these systems were so expensive. There are two types: a hard-wired system, in which the missile attempts to fly a precomputed path, correcting whenever the missile deviates; and a computer-based system, which constantly recomputes the necessary flight path based on the actual flight of the missile. The latter requires less fuel for correction, and thus is suited to greater ranges. It allows for operational flexibility, since only the launch location and the target need be entered into the computer. In the absence of such a system, a missile must be fired at a single preassigned target from a preassigned site.

In recent years inertial sensors, such as gyros, have become much cheaper, and some form of mid-course inertial guidance is now quite common. Often it is described as strapdown, which means that the inertial sensor lacks the full range of measurement, that is, it cannot measure pitching motions. That is acceptable in a short-range missile, or in a missile constrained by a radar altimeter to fly a flat path.

In many cases, inertial guidance seems to be giving way to GPS guidance, in which a simple radio receiver on board the missile determines its position using satellite navigational data. For example, the new U.S. guided 5in shell (Hammer) is intended to fly to a GPS-designated target; the new versions of Tomahawk use GPS guidance; and a projected future cruise missile ("Cheap Shot") is likely to be inexpensive precisely because it relies entirely on GPS. Some critics have pointed out that the extent of U.S. dependence on GPS may be quite dangerous, since GPS signals are weak and thus may be jammed relatively easily. Antijam GPS receivers exist but are expensive, and they are not widely used. Too, GPS suffers from a subtle problem: it is keyed to a datum, and not all maps (or equivalent databases) are keyed to the same datum. Errors can be embarrassing. A British warship, for example, found that her GPS position was several thousand yards ashore, because of a datum error. There may also be problems due to the fact that the earth is by no means perfectly spherical.

A more fundamental problem is that missiles like Tomahawk are guided into specified points in three-dimensional space. Unfortunately, the coordinate least well known is generally altitude, so without good current 3D maps missiles may well fly either into the ground or well over their targets.

Command guidance may be of several forms: commands may be sent through a wire or fiber-optic cable or a radio link; or the missile might be a beam-rider, controlled by the movement of a radar beam (in at least one case, a laser beam). The basic attraction of command guidance is that the intelligence of the weapons system can be concentrated in a director that need not be limited in size or cost, rather than in an expendable missile of very limited size. The main limitation on command guidance is the loss of accuracy as the range increases. An advantage of beam riding is that it is somewhat difficult to jam: the missile's antenna that senses the beam faces rearward instead of forward, toward the target. The jammer must, therefore, concentrate on the more distant (and more sophisticated) tracker, rather than on the nearby missile. That is why Bofors advertises its laser beam-rider, RBS 70, as unjammable.

Much depends on whether the beam tracks the target itself. In most early beam-riders, such as the British Sea Slug and the U.S. Terrier, a single tracking radar generated the beam, and the missile, therefore, continuously pointed at its target. Because it had to follow target maneuvers, it could lose a good deal of its energy along the way. On the other hand, in the contemporary U.S. Talos (now extinct), the beam motion was programmed so that the missile flew along an energy-efficient up-and-over path. It homed semiactively only as it approached the target.

Autonomous or self-sensing guidance takes many forms. It does make the missile more accurate as it approaches its target; on the other hand, the missile seeker is of limited size, and it may not be able to deal with countermeasures. Moreover, it may be difficult to design a seeker that can distinguish some kinds of targets.

Usually missiles incorporate some compromise between these elements. In the case of AA fire, semiactive homing is quite widely used. Semiactive homing is a type of command guidance, to the extent that the missile director tracks the target. However, the missile actually tracks the radiation reflected from the target (usually radar, sometimes laser). The missile's estimate of target position, therefore, becomes more accurate as it approaches the target. The greatest drawback to semiactive homing is that the tracking radar must be powerful enough to provide the missile with sufficient reflected illumination from the moment that it is launched. This requirement limits effective range. One alternative is to use command guidance or inertial guidance (i.e., a preset autopilot) to bring the missile relatively close to the target before turning on the semiactive seeker. That is the solution chosen in the U.S. Aegis and Phoenix systems.

Missile guidance determines missile flight path. Here command guidance has an advantage, since it can bring the missile along the most efficient flight path possible. Any form of full autonomous homing or semiactive homing results in a less energy-efficient path and, therefore, in a shorter range for a given missile.

The simplest and least efficient path is pursuit because the missile turns to fly along the LOS to the target. The missile's rate of turn equals the rate of turn of the LOS, and quite violent maneuvering may be required as the missile approaches its target. Pursuit is effective against slow targets, or against targets approached from the rear (e.g., by IR-guided missiles). It is also effective at very short range. Missiles using command-to-LOS guidance (such as the French Crotale Navale and the British Sea Wolf) follow pursuit paths that limit the system's effective range. For missiles launched from shipboard, command-to-LOS is effective for point defense but not really for defense against crossing targets. To the extent that major Soviet systems such as SA-N-1 and SA-N-3 appear to employ command-to-LOS guidance, they are effective for the defense of individual ships but not of formations of ships.

Proportional navigation requires the missile to measure the rate of change of the LOS and to maneuver at some fixed or variable multiple of that rate of change. The navigation ratio may change during flight to optimize missile performance. Proportional navigation systems require the missile to compare the direction to the target with the direction in which it is flying. That is sometimes done by a Doppler comparison between the reflected energy from the target and a broad reference beam from the launcher. In such cases the missile requires a set of rearward-facing reference antennas. The reference beam has to be broad because the missile generally is not in the tracking beam itself. Proportional navigation improves missile range performance, and also improves performance against a maneuvering target, since the missile need not maneuver violently to follow the details of target motion. In effect, proportional navigation aims the missile not directly at the target but at a computed interception point ahead of the target.

Proportional navigation can also be applied to IR missiles. In these cases the reference is an internal gyroscope. The missile tracks the forward edge of the target. As a consequence, it tends not to be distracted by decoys (flares) dropping away to the rear of the target. The French Mistral is the only publicized example, but for some years Sidewinder has been credited with the ability to hit the forward portion of its target. That suggests that it, too, employs proportional navigation, and that this form of guidance is an important anticountermeasure feature. Presumably the only way to decoy a proportional-navigation missile would be to fire the decoy ahead of the target.

In contrast, command guidance generally involves some quite different flight path. The main alternatives are:

A constant-bearing or collision course, which requires the missile to be fired with a sufficient lead angle to meet the predicted position of the target.

A fixed lead angle path.

An LOS path, which requires the missile to follow the LOS from launcher to target (as in a beam-rider).

These concepts apply not only to missiles flying through the air but also to torpedoes. A straight-running torpedo is inertially guided. Lightweight torpedoes are self-guided, although they may have inertial (preset) run-outs before their homing devices are activated. Most heavy torpedoes are command- (wire-) guided, until they reach a homing basket. In a few cases they are wire-guided all the way.

COMPANY CONSOLIDATIONS

Since the last edition of this book was published, numerous defense manufacturers have merged. The following notes, arranged by country, may be helpful in keeping track of the situation. In some important cases, companies retained their identity after having been bought.

CANADA

MEL Canada was taken over by Lockheed to become Lockheed Martin Canada.

FRANCE

Thomson is to be privatized, which may mean that its divisions will be sold off separately. However, in December 1996 a plan to merge the defense portion of Thomson with Matra collapsed due to French public opposition to the sale of Thomson's loss-making consumer electronics arm to Daewoo of Korea (which presumably wanted entree into the European Community). Note that when Thomson bought Signaal, it had to promise the Dutch government that Signaal would retain its special identity. The likely effect of a Thomson sell-off is unclear. Also in 1996, the Matra missile division joined with BAe Dynamics, although it is not clear whether the result is a single entity. In February 1996 the Minister of Defense announced that Aerospatiale and Dassault will be merged. However, Aerospatiale is a loss-making government-owned entity, whereas Dassault is privately owned (and makes a profit). In January 1996 Aerospatiale and DASA (of Germany) formally announced a merger to create European Missile Systems (EMS), to be headquartered in France, and European Satellite Industries (ESI), to be headquartered in Munich. This deal still required French government approval and some analysis by each company.

In 1995 DCN and Thomson Sintra established Underwater Defense Systems International (UDSI) to develop submarine combat systems, particularly SUBTICS. In April 1996, Thomson Sintra and GEC-Marconi Naval Systems created a new Thomson Marconi Sonar NV company, which absorbed Thomson Ferranti Sonar Systems (TFSS). Thomson-CSF owns 50.1% of the merged company. Apparently this merger will not affect UDSI.

CSEE is now CS Defense.

GERMANY

MBB and the other aerospace companies merged into DASA, which is the aerospace subsidiary of Daimler Benz (also called Daimler Benz Aerospace).

In the fall of 1994 STN Systemtechnik Nord and Atlas Elektronik merged to become STN Atlas Elektronik, both of which were divisions of Bremer Vulkan. However, Bremer Vulkan later went bankrupt, and the profit-making STN arm was bought by a German consortium supplemented by BAe (the German government insisted that control remain in German hands).

ITALY

Many of the Italian companies were actually divisions of the Finnmeccanica Group, which took over the competing conglomerate.

Note that Alenia was formerly Selenia. Elettronica has taken over Alenia's electronic warfare operations.

FIAR has taken over SMA's radar operations.

OTO-Melara and Breda merged as OTOBreda.

Whitehead Motofides merged with MISAR, but both retained their separate names.

NETHERLANDS

Signaal, formerly of the Swedish PEAB group, was sold to Thomson-CSF. It retains its former identity, however. Fokker went bankrupt during 1996, and early in 1997 proposals to buy it were still being entertained. They would presumably affect its Enforcer series of maritime patrol aircraft.

NORWAY

Kongsberg, which became NFT, is now again named Kongsberg.

RUSSIA

Design bureaus are now merging with production organizations to become integrated companies which advertise their products. For example, MiG has now merged into MAPO. These organizations can now do their own advertising and sales, and thus no longer need work through the government sales organization, Rozhvoorouzhenie. However, in the fall of 1996 Rozhvoorouzhenie was still acting as the organizing force for Russian arms exporters.

In the past, although a particular design office was often associated with a particular factory, the two were formally separate. Indeed, in recent years both the design office *and* the factory have often separately claimed exclusive rights to a design. Matters are further complicated in that the old Soviet Union tended to split up production so that many complete systems required major elements from many different republics, which are now independent countries. For example, the main gas turbine plant was in Ukraine, which is why Russian shipyards now produce mainly steam-turbine surface warships.

Note that many factories in Ukraine that produced weapons (such as 53-65 torpedoes and several sonobuoys) designed in Russia are advertising them independently.

SOUTH AFRICA

Armscor, the unifying face of South African defense and long its sales organization, has in effect been eclipsed by the companies it formerly managed: most prominently Denel (whose divisions include Kentron, the missile maker, and Atlas Aviation), Grinaker Electronics, Southern Oceanics, and UEC Projects.

SWEDEN

The PEAB (Philips) group sold off its defense companies (including Signaal and MEL in the United Kingdom). Philips (PEAB) in Sweden was taken over by Bofors (became BEAB). Bofors was taken over by Celsius to become Swedish Ordnance, which then organized into CelsiusTech (electronics) and Bofors (ordnance). Saab remains independent.

UNITED KINGDOM

Dowty sold off its defense arms. Management bought out the sonobuoy arm, which became Ultra Systems. Ultra in turn bought up the assets of a Canadian company, Devtek Applied Electronics, formerly Hermes; the new Canadian company will again be known as Hermes Electronics. Dowty-SEMA, the combat-direction arm, was bought by British Aerospace to become BAeSEMA. SEMA was the former Gresham-CAP Scientific, which developed several British submarine CDSs.

Having bought International Signals Corp (ISC) in the United States, Ferranti fell victim to a massive financial fraud and had to be broken up. In a desperate attempt to survive, Ferranti International tried to sell off noncore sections of its business (to reestablish cash balance). Unable to rectify the situation, the company had to sell major assets including the radar/avionics sections (to become GEC Marconi Avionics). This, too, proved unsuccessful, and the remains were placed in receivership, to be bought in pieces, including by GEC-Marconi (some portions simply died).

This process was complicated by the formation of FTSS, Ferranti-Thomson Sonar Systems, a joint venture between Ferranti and Thomson Sintra of France. The 49.9% Ferranti shareholding was bought by GEC-Marconi, which merged it with its own sonar operations.

MUSL (Marconi Underwater Systems Ltd.) became GEC-Marconi Naval Systems Division. See France (above) for the formation of Thomson Marconi Sonars NV.

Plessey was broken up, its radar division going to Siemens and its combat-direction division and electronic warfare operations to GEC-Marconi Naval and Defence Systems, respectively.

Racal bought the Thorn-EMI defense electronics division (April 1995), which had recently bought MEL. The Thorn-EMI optronics division was sold to Pilkington Optronics, which is in turn part of Pilkington Optical (and which owns Barr & Stroud).

VSEL was bought by GEC-Marconi, which beat out BAe for this prize.

Wallop was reabsorbed back into its parent company, ML Aviation Ltd.

UNITED STATES

Some of the mergers may eliminate competition in important fields. For example, early in 1996, the two competitors for the new attack submarine network were Lockheed Martin and Loral Federal Systems Division (formerly IBM Federal Systems Division).

Alliant, formerly the defense arm of Honeywell, bought Hercules. In December 1996 Hughes bought the Alliant Marine Systems Group (but see below).

Allied Signal Ocean Systems is the former Bendix dipping sonar division. However, Bendix continues to produce radars.

Boeing bought ARGOSystems, an electronic-defense company. Late in 1996 Boeing bought both the Rockwell defense arm and McDonnell-Douglas; Rockwell becomes its North American division.

Condor Systems, which specializes in electronic warfare, bought most of Watkins-Johnson, except for HF communications; it also bought ESSI.

Emerlec's (formerly Emerson Electric's) gun mount business (which produced the Emerlec-30) is now owned by ESCO (Electronics and Space Corp.). ESCO owns Hazeltine (which is important for IFF systems).

FMC and BMY (which makes armored vehicles) merged as United Defense.

Hughes bought General Dynamics' missile business, including the Phalanx gun system; General Dynamics retains the Electric Boat submarine yard (and has bought Bath Ironworks). In December 1995 Hughes Electronics bought Magnavox Electronic Systems, among other things a major sonobuoy maker. Magnavox had been Signaal's U.S. representative (mainly for the Scout radar). Now that role has been taken over by General Atronics, otherwise mainly concerned with data links. Hughes also bought Alliant's Marine Systems Group (see above).

Litton bought General Instruments (ESM) some years ago.

Lockheed and Martin-Marietta merged as Lockheed Martin. Martin-Marietta had already bought Gould (which made towed arrays) and the weapons/electronics side of General Electric (which in turn had bought the RCA electronic defense arm [which made SPY-1]). Lockheed had bought Sanders (EW) and the aircraft production division of General Dynamics.

Loral, initially an electronic warfare company, bought up Ford Aeroneutronics (which made Sidewinder missiles), Goodyear, IBM Federal Systems division, Librascope, the LTV missile division, and Unisys (defense division). In January 1996 it was announced that Lockheed Martin had bought the Loral defense electronics business (everything but the company's satellite communications arm). The merger became effective in mid-1996.

Northrop bought Grumman to become Northrop Grumman; this combination then bought the Westinghouse defense electronics division. Westinghouse had already bought Norden from United Technology.

Raytheon bought E-Systems. Raytheon bought the defense arm of Texas Instruments in January 1997. Later the same month, Raytheon bought Hughes Electronics. Many saw this as the last of the series of major U.S. defense mergers.

Texas Instruments bought Tiburon in 1995.

Tracor bought AEL.

DESIGNATION SYSTEMS

AUSTRALIA

Australia uses the U.S. tri-service (AN) designation system, but numbers are in an 800 series (e.g., the Barra sonobuoy is SSQ-801).

CANADA

The Canadian government uses the U.S. tri-service (AN) designation system, but numbers are in a 500 series. Thus SPS-501 is the first, not the 501st, Canadian naval radar.

FRANCE

The French government uses a unified tri-service electronic designation system, similar in spirit to the U.S. AN system. Each piece of equipment is designated by four letters (the quadrigramme) and a number, with a letter suffix to indicate modifications. The first letter indicates the main function; the second, the process employed; the third, the normal mode of installation; and the fourth, the particular function of the system. In contrast to the AN system, the third and fourth letters can change depending upon the main function.

In addition, in at least some cases, letters are assigned in blocks that further describe the equipment.

Radars in the 10-19 block are X-band; the 20-29 block indicates either L- (20 cm) or P- (2 m) band; the 30-39 block indicates X-band; and the 50-59 block indicates C-band (5 cm).

Sonars in a 20-series are hull mounted; sonars in a 40-series are towed fish; sonars in a 60-series are towed arrays.

MAIN FUNCTION LETTERS (FIRST LETTER)

A Electronic warfare
B Test equipment
C Switchboard (commutation)
D Detection
E Transmitters (emitters)
F Electric generators
G Mine countermeasures
I Information processing
J Imagery (EO)
M Measurement
N Navigation
Q Miscellaneous, not covered in other categories
R Receivers
S Fire-control systems
T Transceivers
V Guidance (for weapons)

PROCESS LETTERS (SECOND LETTER)

A Artillery (fire control)
B Chemical energy (batteries, etc.); ballistic missiles (fire control)
D Doppler
E Wind generators; electricity (measurement)
F Wire (fil, in French)
G Gyroscopic; gas generators
H Magnetic
I Infrared and light intensification
J Inertial; bombing (fire control)
L Laser; mechanical generators
M Mixed; missiles (fire control)
N Nuclear and radioisotope
P Fluidic, hydraulic
R Radio-electric or electronic
S Sound; solar generators
T Thermal generators; television and CRT; torpedoes (fire control)
U Ultrasonic; electric
X Other processes
Z Satellite communication

SPECIAL PROCESS LETTERS FOR INFORMATION PROCESSING (SECOND LETTER)

A Analog
B Magnetic band
C Magnetic card
D Magnetic disk
E Magnetic memory element
G Magnetic drum
K Punched card
M Analog/digital
N Digital (numerical)
O Microfilm; optical memory
P Paper
R Punched tape
S Semiconductor memory
T Cathode-ray tube

MODES OF INSTALLATION (THIRD LETTER)

A Aircraft
B Surface ship (bâtiment)
C Man-carried (cadre)
D Vehicles and man-portable
E Missile
F Fixed
M Mobile
N Surface ships and submarines
P Man-portable (portatif)
R Submerged
S Semifixed
T Portable
U Submarine
V Vehicle

PARTICULAR FUNCTIONS (FOURTH LETTER)

A Analysis (identification); countermeasures; signaling device; attack (sensors and imagery); in generators, 400 Hz; self- (auto-) protection (mine warfare); measurement of voltage and current; landing (atterrisage) in navigation; amplification; direction (asservisement) in fire control
B Jamming; in generators, direct current for battery charging; in mine warfare, buoys; nonelectrical measurements (e.g., acoustic); information processing (fire control)
C Multiplex; fire control; generator control; in mine warfare, classification; calculation (computing); positioning in curvilinear coordinates (navigation) (i.e., Loran-like systems); vector control (fire control)
D Surveillance—alert; detection; power distribution; in mine warfare, sweeping (dragage); coding (computing); detection (imagery); distance measurement (navigation)
E Listening; emission (in test equipment and in guidance); scouting; in generators, 50 Hz for electronic equipment; writing-recording (computer); standards of measurement; illumination (navigation); engagement (fire control)
F Frequency measurement; facsimile; telephone-telegraph (test equipment)
G Direction finding (goniometry); graphics; in generators, 50 Hz for general use; mine warfare (test equipment); signal generators (measurement); electrical distribution (fire control)
H Radio; in generators, 60 Hz for general use; printing (impression) for computers; hyperfrequency measurement (spectral analysis, envelopes, noise factors, etc.); vertical measurement (navigation)
I Identification
J Interception; information transmission; in mine warfare, immunization; accelerometry (navigation)
K Calculator; radioactivity (sensors and imagery); in generators, energy conversion; data conversion (computers); guidance (including autoguidance and wire guidance) in fire control

L Deception; security; in mine warfare, localization; reading (computers); measurement of semiconductor tube and crystal characteristics; localization and pursuit in fire control

M Mixed; also mines; in mine warfare, mine-hunting; input/output (computers); oscilloscopes (measurement); modems (miscellaneous equipment); management (fire control)

N Navigation; also teletype; in mine warfare, neutralization; bearing measurement (navigation); control of nuclear explosives (fire control)

O In mine warfare, obstruction (antisweep)

P Telephony; in generators, production of direct current for various purposes; perforation (computers); pursuit (imagery); bridges for electrical measurement; position in polar coordinates (navigation)

Q Indicators for measurement (galvanometers, magnetometers, etc.)

R Localization, reception; missile guidance (sensors and imagery); reproduction (computers); marking (navigation); reception (fire control)

S Weapons system; also position—altitude (sensors and imagery); translation (computers); analysis of low-frequency signals (measures of distortion, phase, wave analysis, etc.); altimetry (*sondage*; navigation)

T Transceiver; teleprinters; terrestrial objects (sensors); sorting (triage) for computers; marking (imagery); test or multifunction equipment (measurement); position in geographical coordinates (navigation); launching or firing (fire control)

U Regulation of direct current; general functioning (fire control)

V Guidance (command); television; surveillance (*veille*, in sensors); in mine warfare and in computers, imaging (visualization); speed measurement (navigation); display of the tactical situation (fire control)

W Propulsion, energy; visiphone; meteorology; in mine warfare, surveillance; verification (computers); power measurement (wattmeter)

X Special; testing (fire control)

Y Teletype; information storage (computers); miscellaneous, special (fire control)

Z Training

GERMANY

Germany follows the U.S. AN designation system for shipborne sonars, except that all are prefixed D (Deutsch), as in DSQS-21. The serially assigned numbers do not coincide with U.S. numbers and are assigned in blocks (e.g., in sonars, the 11-series for minehunting sonars and the 21-series for search sonars).

ITALY

For naval radars, Italy uses the U.S. tri-service (AN) system of designators, with the prefix MM (Marine Militare), with a 700-series (e.g., MM/SPS-768). There are also company designators. It appears that blocks of numbers within the overall series are reserved for special applications, as some of the numbers are too high to reflect a single sequence. It also appears that all naval radars and other electronic equipment, whether air- or shipborne, are in the same single numerical sequence.

Air force electronic equipment is designated in a 200-series.

JAPAN

Japan uses the U.S. tri-service (AN) system of designators, except for different platform letters:

E Other
H Aircraft (sonobuoy and dipping sonar applications)
L Land-based fixed (corresponds to U.S. F and G)
O Surface ship
R Small, portable (corresponds to U.S. P)
Y General use (corresponds to U.S. U)

Z Undersea (submarines, but also minehunting surface-ship sonar)

The prefix N (as in NOLR-1) indicates a combination of other equipment. In many cases with electronics, the U.S. system is used with the prefix J, as in JVRC or JAN/GRC for a radio transceiver. In some cases U.S.-supplied (or license-built) equipment retains its U.S. designation; in others, it is redesignated with a J prefix.

In some cases a Type number system is used, for example, Type 1 fire-control system. However, most Type numbers indicate the date of designation (not production) in terms of Japanese fiscal years. Thus Type 63 is a designation adopted during Japanese fiscal year 1963. The Japanese fiscal year runs 1 April–31 March and is designated by the calendar year in which the FY begins (e.g., JFY63 began on 1 April 1963). This system corresponds to British practice and is six months away from the U.S. fiscal year (which runs 1 October–30 September).

Finally, equipment under development is given a serial designation, with a prefix: G for torpedo, K for mine, S for sweep gear. Thus a torpedo developed as G-9 was adopted for service as Type 73.

NETHERLANDS

Dutch naval electronic systems are generally developed by Hollandse Signaal Apparaten (HSA), and it is not altogether clear whether the HSA designations are imposed by the Royal Netherlands Navy. Radars are divided into

DA Target indication (*doels aanwijzing*)
LW Air search (*lucht waarschuwing*)
ZW Sea search (*zee waarschuwing*)

Fire-control systems, both for surface ships and for submarines, are designated by the letter M and by a number; in some cases the combination WM is used. The numbers are not in sequence of development, but often indicate alternative (and roughly contemporary) levels of capability.

A few U.S.-style official designations, such as SPS-01 for the big *Tromp* radar and SPRs for ESM, are known; it is possible that all naval equipment is similarly designated.

RUSSIA

All equipment is developed by design bureaus (OKBs), and each bureau maintains an internal designation series. In addition, equipment accepted for service use is given a service designation. The best-known example is aircraft designations. Published histories of Soviet aircraft design provide numerous examples of internal (bureau) and service designators, for example, Tu-95 and Tu-20 for the same bomber (Bear). Many weapons seem to have acquired names either as covers for designations or as popular references.

Soviet economic planning required that each product within the economy be assigned what amounts to a national part number, identifying the item by producing ministry. Few of these industrial designations have ever been made public. All are in the form of a number followed by a letter and a number, as in 4K40 (Styx, which is also P-15). The first number indicates the ministry; the second indicates the type of weapon or system (e.g., K for system, M for missile, R for radar, S for launcher). In many cases all elements of a system will have the same numbers, the letter changing to indicate the element of the system.

Recently many Russian designations have become available; they are used in the text whenever possible. Some of the main series seem to be:

A   Gun
AK Gun
D   Ballistic missile system ("complex")
Kh Air to surface missile (naval and land use)
MG Sonar
MP Naval ESM/ECM
MR Naval radar (including FCS)
P   Naval surface to surface missile; as a suffix, indicates EW

R	Air to air missile
RK	Chaff launcher
RSM	Naval ballistic missile (treaty designation)
RSR	Naval long-range air-to-surface missile
SPS	Aircraft jammer
ZIF	Launcher or gun mount

Numbers frequently are *not* in sequence; they may be assigned by what amounts to a numerical pun. For example, the first tactical air-to-surface missile was Kh-66 (for 1966), but the version for the MiG-23, which entered mass production, was Kh-23. Naval systems are frequently assigned a ship project number as suffix.

In the cases of radar and sonar, the suffix K (Kompleks) indicates an integrated system, as in the MRK-50 radar or the MGK-503 sonar. A U prefix generally means "universal," for example, both antisubmarine and antiship in a torpedo. An M suffix means modernized (upgraded). PL means ASW.

Until very recently, almost no Soviet designations, of whatever type, were public knowledge. Typically, therefore, NATO has assigned reporting names and numbers. The numbers are in a NATO-generated sequence and may not include prototypes or, in some cases, weapons fielded in small numbers or covertly. Since they reflect the dates on which weapons are first observed, the sequence of the numbers may not reflect the development sequence. The chief series are:

AA	Air-to-air missiles
AS	Air-to-surface missiles (both strategic and tactical)
SA	Surface-to-air missiles
SS	Surface-to-surface missiles (both strategic and tactical).
SSC	Surface-to-surface missiles for coast defense

NATO unfortunately applied Soviet-style designators to torpedoes. See the Russian torpedo section for an attempt to assign the actual designations now known to those used by NATO.

NATO's reporting names for Soviet electronic equipment often reflect either signal characteristics or physical appearance. For most naval systems, they combine an animal's name with some physical characteristic.

SWITZERLAND

The first letter in Oerlikon designations indicates a mount (G) or a gun (K, *kanone*). The second indicates the caliber (A for 20mm, B for 25mm, C for 30mm, D for 35mm). The third is a modifier (for guns, typically A, B, or C). Typical gun designations are KAA, KBA, and KBB. A typical gun-mount designation is GCM, with a numerical suffix; the M is not a modifier.

TAIWAN (GRC)

Taiwan uses the U.S. AN system, except that equipment is prefixed CS, as in CS/SPG-24; CS stands for the equivalent of the U.S. Defense Advanced Research Projects Agency.

UNITED KINGDOM

The Royal Navy uses a type number system, originally adopted for radio sets. Equipment is designated in blocks, for example, 900 for naval radars (1945–65, roughly). There is some evidence of blocks within these series, so that numbers are not sequential. For example, Type 992 was developed well before Type 967. In addition, some numbers are left blank, either to allow for improvements or for security purposes. When a block is exhausted, another is designated. Modifications are indicated by suffixes, but not all letters are used. Nor are they necessarily in alphabetical order. Typical radar modification letters are M, P, Q, and R.

Some aircraft-related systems are designated in the NATO triservice AN series, in a 900 block (e.g., the AQS-903 acoustic processor).

The chief current blocks are:

1–99	Radios, etc., through about 1945
100	Sonars up through the 1960s
200	World War II naval radars and IFF
600	Radio transmitters and jammers
700	Hydrophones
900	Radars, post-1945
1000	Radars, from the 1950s on
1200	VHF/UHF radio transceivers (recently opened)
2000	Modern sonars

From 1945 on special designations were used for complete weapons-related systems (with sequence numbers, to indicate versions). Current ones are:

ADAWS	Action Data Automation Weapon System
CACS	Computer-Assisted Command System (ADAWS successor)
CAAIS	Computer-Assisted Action Information System
FPS	Flyplane Predictor (computer) System (GFCS, including radar and director, with Flyplane computer; replaced by MRS)
GDS	Gun-Direction System
GSA	Gun System Automation
GWS	Guided Weapon System. The GWS series is divided into blocks:
GWS 1	Area defense (Sea Slug)
GWS 20 series	Point defense (Sea Cat, Sea Wolf)
GWS 30 series	Area defense (Sea Dart)
GWS 50	Antiship (Exocet)
GWS 60	Antiship (Harpoon)

Subsystems are designated by the overall GWS designator; for example, Sea Slug used a Mk 1 missile launcher, but Sea Cat (GWS 20 series) used Mk 20, and Sea Dart Mk 30.

MDS	Missile-Direction System (MDS 1 for Sea Slug)
MRS	Medium-Range (gun) System
WSA	Weapon System Automation (e.g., gun and missile)

Electronic *outfits* are designated by three letters, the first letter indicating the role. The second letter indicates the category within the role. Second letters were not assigned sequentially; in some cases they are mnemonics (e.g., AWA, for a whip antenna). In a few cases, two letters plus a sequence number are used. Third letters are sequence letters within the series. The main examples are:

A	Antenna (radio and radar), as in ANU
C	Radio receivers, e.g., CUH; includes COMINT (CX series: HF, VHF); CV were radio tubes and their successors (valves).
D	Computer or display system; DA for ADAWS series; DB series for surface ships and DC for submarines. This prefix is also used for decoys (DL series).
F	Radio direction-finders; FH series for HF, FM for MF, FV for VHF, in each case with a numerical suffix, as in FH-4. Radar (SHF) direction-finders are prefixed U, as below.
H	Teachers; but HO indicates a Hull Outfit (sonar dome, always HO with a number)
J	Radar displays, with both two and three letters
K	Distribution control (internal communication switchboard), e.g., Outfit KMY in a Type 23 frigate
L	Radar track extractors (e.g., LFA for Type 996 radar of a Type 23 frigate)
Q	Some displays
R	Data link (e.g., Outfit RBB for helicopter transponder; Outfit RJL[1] is the LAN for the Type 23 frigate command system); also sound recorders and reproducers
T	Transmitters, when part of a larger system
U	ESM, with one or two additional letters, e.g., UAP
Y	Electronic subsystems

In many cases, particularly in electronic countermeasures, the system has a code name, and it is not always clear whether there is any associated designation. More generally, most British weapons have names rather than numerical designators. However, some are described by their Naval Staff Requirement (NSR) or Staff Target (NST) or corresponding Air Staff designators, generally a four-digit figure. Reportedly, these numbers are applied randomly; presumably they are required for computerized accounting. With the amalgamation of service purchasing under a unitary Ministry of Defence, practice has changed and now there are Staff Requirements (Air) and (Naval) (and corresponding Staff Targets), each with a three-digit suffix.

UNITED STATES

U.S. electronic equipment is designated by three letters in an AN (tri-service, originally Army–Navy) series. The first indicates the platform, the second the type of equipment, and the third the function. Numbers run in sequence within each designation, so that there can be both an SPS-49 radar and an SQS-49 sonar. In each case, the full designation is prefixed by the letters AN (multiservice), for example, AN/SPS-49; the first two letters will generally be omitted. In a very few cases, examples of an earlier system survive: Mark numbers applied to fire-control radars (e.g., Mk 13 on board the battleships). These numbers fit the postwar SPG series, with Mk 49 becoming SPG-49, for example. However, they were never retroactively identified within the AN series.

Experimental versions of equipment are indicated by a two-letter code denoting the developing agency. Thus SPS-49(XN-1) would be the first Navy Department (i.e., contractor) prototype of the SPS-49 radar. The other major navy suffixes are XB for the Naval Research Laboratory; SG for the Naval Ocean Systems Center in San Diego; XJ for the Naval Air Development Center, Warminster, Pennsylvania; XU for the Naval Underwater Systems Center, New London, Connecticut; XAN for the Naval Avionics Center, Indianapolis; XCA for the Naval Weapons Center, Crane, Indiana; XCL for the Naval Weapons Center, China Lake, California; XDV for the Naval Surface Weapons Center, Dahlgren, Virginia; XGS for the Ground Support Division (Naval Air Engineering Center), Lakehurst, New Jersey; XIH for the Naval Ordnance Center, Indian Head, Virginia; XMG for Point Mugu, California; XUC for the Naval Undersea Center, San Diego; XPC for the Naval Coastal Systems Laboratory, Panama City, Florida; XWH for the Naval Weapons Station, Earle, New Jersey; and XWO for the Naval Surface Weapons Center, White Oak, Maryland. The suffix XZ was used for the old Bureau of Naval Weapons.

Different versions of systems are indicated in two ways. Originally, each version had its own suffix letter, for example, SPS-6C as compared to SPS-6B or -6D. More recently, a distinction has been made between variable systems, which differ by deletion or addition of subcomponents, and modifications that are interchangeable with earlier versions. Variable systems are indicated by (V) plus a number, as in SPS-49(V)5. Modifications are indicated by suffix letters, as before.

Parts of systems, or subgroups of equipment, receive one- or two-letter designators, for example, CP for a computer or OL for an indicator. Sometimes the designation is written out to include the designator of the associated system, such as TB-16/BQQ, which is a towed body that is part of several BQQ-series submarine sonars. Typically, parts of systems are distinguished from subsystems (groups), but both are designated in this way.

U.S. missiles and rockets are also designated within a tri-service (three-letter) system, but in this case each number is used only once. In some cases, such as Harpoon, the three-letter designator is actually changed to reflect a different application of the same basic weapon. In recent years weapons' designators often have not been made public until very late in the development process (for example, veterans of the Sea Lance program cannot recall ever having seen a standard designator). This practice may have been adopted to conceal gaps in the list denoting highly classified ("black") programs such as stealth weapons. Code names are published for budgetary reasons, but without any indication of their significance, and one name may cover several weapons (or vice versa).

U.S. aeronautical equipment (such as bomb guidance units, missile launchers, and warheads) is designated within a system developed by the U.S. Air Force in 1960. Although it superficially resembles the missile designation series, that Air Force system is entirely different, having been designed to embrace not only equipment carried on board aircraft but also ground-based materiel such as tractors and fuel tanks. This system does not include jet and rocket engines or photographic equipment. As might be expected of so broad a system, it is cumbersome (the Air Force initially wanted to expand the AN system to cover all aeronautical items, but the Office of the Secretary of Defense rejected that as unwieldy). Equipment is denoted by an initial letter A/, then by a three-item code. Aircraft components are designated by three letters, the last of which is K. Aircraft-associated units are designated by three letters, the last of which is U. In the case of ground equipment, the designator consists of a letter indicating the type, a two-digit number, and a letter indicating function, for example, A/S32P-5, the fifth self-propelled (S), mechanical (32), protective (P) device (in this case, a fire truck). The only example in this book is A/N37U, a sweep-control device.

In the case of aircraft or missile units, the first two letters form a code, and designations include a letter after a slash to indicate the installation. The most important two-letter codes and installation codes are indicated below.

This system was not applied retroactively, so designations such as Bomb Mk 82 survive.

Finally, in accordance with older procedures, U.S. naval weapons (and many systems' components) other than missiles themselves are organized by Mark number. Marks are applied, for example, to fire-control systems (and, separately, to gun directors), to gun mounts (in sequence whatever the caliber), to missile-launching systems (and, to add to the confusion, to the launchers proper), to rocket motors, to torpedoes, to warheads, and to weapons systems (built around unified control systems) as a whole. Examples of the latter are Mk 7 for Aegis and Mk 15 for Phalanx (see the table below). In at least some cases, Mark series were blocked to differentiate underwater from surface systems, for example, Mk 101 was an underwater fire-control system, not the 101st fire-control system. However, when the original series reached 100, it continued interleaved with the special underwater series.

All U.S. nuclear weapons are assigned Mark numbers (by the Department of Energy, formerly the Atomic Energy Commission). Any application of a weapon is indicated by a prefix letter; for example, the B77 bomb would be a bomb version of the Mk 77 warhead, and W77 would be the same weapon configured as a missile warhead. Similarly, all reentry vehicles have Mark numbers in a single series.

1. ELECTRONICS (THE "AN"-SERIES)

♦ **Platform Letter**

A   Airplane
B   Submarine ("boat")
C   Air-portable (obsolete)
D   Missile ("drone")
F   Fixed
G   Ground use (general)
K   Amphibious
M   Ground-mobile
P   Man-portable
S   Ship (or water surface)
T   Ground-transportable
U   Universal (land/water)
V   Ground (vehicular)
W   Waterborne (surface/submarine)
Z   Piloted and pilotless airborne vehicle combination

♦ **Type of Equipment**

A   Infrared
B   Pigeon (obsolete)
C   Carrier (wire)
D   Radiac
E   Nupac (obsolete)

F   Photographic (not for U.S. use)
G   Telegraph, teletype
I   Interphone or public address
J   Electromechanical or inertial wire covered
K   Telemetry
L   Countermeasures
M   Meteorological
N   Sound in air
P   Radar (pulsed)
Q   Sonar and underwater sound
R   Radio
S   Special, magnetic, etc. (or combination)
T   Telephone (wire)
V   Visual
W   Weapons
X   Facsimile or television
Y   Data processing (integration of sensors)

♦ Function

A   Auxiliary equipment (e.g., antennas, displays)
B   Bombing
C   Communications (transceiver)
D   Direction finding, surveillance
E   Ejection or release
G   Fire control (gunnery) and searchlight direction
H   Recording/reproducing
K   Computing
L   Searchlight control (obsolete)
M   Maintenance and/or test
N   Navigational
P   Reproducing (obsolete, use H)
Q   Multifunction or special
R   Receive (passive detection)
S   Search
T   Transmit (e.g., jam)
W   Weapons control
X   Identification (IFF)
Y   Multifunction (phased-array radar)

♦ Group Indicators

OA   Miscellaneous
OD   Indicator
OE   Antenna
OG   Amplifier
OH   Simulator
OJ   Consoles
OK   Control (used in towed-array reeling equipment)
OL   Data analysis and data processing
OM   Modulators, demodulators
OP   Power supplies
OR   Receivers
OT   Transmitters
OU   Converters
OV   Generators
OW   Terminals
OX   Coders, decoders, interrogators, transponders
OY   Radar sets (not to be used if more specific indicators apply)
OZ   Radio sets (not to be used if more specific indicators apply)

♦ Component Indicators

AM   Amplifier
AS   Antenna
AT   Antenna (now obsolete)
BA   Battery (primary)
BB   Battery (secondary)
CA   Computer (auxiliary parts)
CD   Controlling device
CP   Computer
CU   Coupler
CV   Converter (e.g., from frequency to frequency, or medium to medium)

CW   Radome
DA   Dummy load
DT   Detecting head (e.g., hydrophone)
F   Filter (electrical or electronic)
FR   Frequency measurement
G   Generator
GO   Goniometer (DF device)
J   Interface
KY   Keying device (used for cryptographic devices)
LS   Loudspeaker
M   Microphone
MD   Modulator, demodulator
ML   Meteorological device
MU   Memory unit
O   Oscillator
OC   Oceanographic device
OS   Oscilloscope
PL   Plug-in unit
PP   Power supply
PT   Mapping and plotting unit (electronic)
PU   Power equipment
R   Receiver
RD   Recorder-reproducer
RL   Reeling machine
RO   Recorder
RP   Reproducer
RR   Reflector
RT   Receiver/transmitter
SA   Switching unit
SB   Switchboard
SG   Signal generator
SM   Simulator
SU   Optical unit (EO)
T   Transmitter
TA   Telephone
TB   Towed body (e.g., in towed array or MAD)
TD   Timing device
TF   Transformer
TG   Positioning device
TH   Telegraph
TR   Transducer
TT   Teletype, facsimile
V   Vehicle

2. MISSILE-ROCKET DESIGNATIONS

♦ Launch Environment

A   Airplane
B   Multienvironment
C   Coffin
F   Infantry
H   Silo-stored (fired from surface)
L   Land (fixed silo)
M   Mobile
P   Soft pad
R   Ship
U   Underwater

♦ Function

D   Decoy
E   Special electronic
G   Surface attack
I   Intercept (antiaircraft)
Q   Target drone
T   Training
U   Underwater attack
W   Weather

♦ Type

M   Missile (guided)
N   Probe
R   Rocket

3. AIR EQUIPMENT DESIGNATIONS

♦ **Two-Letter Code**

BB   Explosive items (not warheads)
BD   Bombs, simulated (dummy)
BL   Bombs, aircraft (live)
BN   Buoys
BR   Bomb racks, shackles
BS   Munitions stabilizing and retarding devices
CB   Cluster bomb unit, consisting of a clustering device or dispenser (SUU) and bomblets (BLU or BDU); may function on board the airplane or after it is dropped
CD   Clustering device containing bomblets to be dispensed from an SUU; may or may not be required to make the BLU/BDU compatible with the dispenser (SUU)
CP   Computer
CY   Cartridge case
DS   Target detector (e.g., in proximity fuze)
DT   Timing device (e.g., intervalometer)
FM   Fuze, munitions
GA   Gun, aircraft (e.g., in gun pod)
GB   Guided bomb
GD   Dummy guided missile (for training)
GP   Gun pod (GA plus SUU)
GT   Gun turret (excludes gun pods)
GU   Guns, nonaircraft
KA   Unfilled clustering device
KB   Simulated cluster bomb unit
KD   Simulated clustering device
KM   Miscellaneous kits (used for early "smart" bombs)
LA   Launcher, aircraft (e.g., missile rails)
LK   Links, ammunition
LM   Launching mechanism, ground
LU   Illumination (light) (e.g., searchlight)
MA   Miscellaneous armament
MJ   Countermeasures munitions (e.g., bombs containing chaff or flares)
ML   Miscellaneous live munitions
PA   External munitions dispensers (e.g., pods, tanks, clip-ins or other devices mounted externally)
PG   Gun ammunition
PJ   Projectiles
PW   Internal munitions dispensers
RB   Rocket and launcher units (combination of LAU and conventional rockets, RLU; excludes CBU)
RL   Rocket, live (e.g., FFAR, HVAR)
RV   Reentry vehicle (dummy or practice type)
RW   Reentry vehicle (live)
SA   Sights, gun-bomb-rocket
SP   Self-protection (as in the SPU-1/W magnetized orange pipe for aerial minesweeping)
SU   Suspension and release unit stores (munitions dispenser); may provide a clustering device (CD) to provide compatibility with the ordnance being transported; also may be a CBU less its BLUs
TD   Target devices
WA   Warhead section
WB   Body section
WC   Control section
WD   Loaded warhead
WE   Empty warhead
WG   Guidance section
WP   Propulsion section
WT   Training or dummy warhead

♦ **Application Code**

A   Aircraft or missile
B   Aircraft or missile transported (mission expendable)
C   Combined air and surface
E   Ground (not fixed)
F   Ground (fixed)
M   Ground movable
N   Aircraft or missile transported (not mission expendable)
P   Personal use
S   Ground, self-propelled
U   Multi-installation
W   Waterborne (surface or submerged)

4. WEAPON SYSTEM MARK NUMBERS

Mk 1   Weapons Control System (Typhoon; abortive)
Mk 7   Aegis
Mk 15   Phalanx (CIWS)
Mks 20–24   TAS (Target Acquisition System; only Mk 23 entered service)
Mk 31   RAM (RIM-116 missile)
Mk 32   Tomahawk (ABL launcher)
Mk 33   DD 963 5in gun system using guided shells
Mk 34   DDG 51–class 5in gun system
Mk 35   SEAL boat gun system (abortive, for SWCM boat) using 25mm gun in EX-90 mount, with remote sighting and control
Mk 36   Tomahawk submarine-launched missile system (Mk 44 launching system) using SWG-2 control
Mk 37   Tomahawk vertically launched missile system, using SWG-3 control
Mk 38   Dragon III assault missile, for marines
Mk 39   *Iowa*-class 5in/38 gun system
Mk 40   *Iowa*-class 16in/50 gun system

Many of these designations were applied ex post facto for convenience in referring to the system as a whole. The significance of missing numbers is unknown.

ABBREVIATIONS

A-scope   radar display (range only)
AA   antiaircraft, also active adjunct (sonar)
AAM   air-to-air missile
AAW   antiaircraft warfare
ACC   attack-control console
ACDS   Advanced Combat Direction System; Automatic C/M-Dispensing System
ACM   air combat maneuvering
ACQ   acquisition
ACTD   advanced concept technology demonstration
ADAC   French airborne radar designation; also U.S. all-digital attack center (in submarines)
ADAR   adaptive receiver for horizontal line array sonobuoy (U.S.)
ADAWS   action data automation weapons system (British)
ADCAP   advanced capability
ADIMP   ADAWS Improvement Program
ADS   Advanced Deployable System; Advanced Display System
ADT   automatic detection and tracking
ADVCAP   Advanced Capability (version of EA-6B aircraft)
AEW   airborne early warning
AFSATCOM   Air Force Satellite Communications system
AGC   automatic gain control (ECCM measure)
AGI   intelligence-gathering ship
AGIS   Automatische Gefechts und Informations-system Schnellboote
AGPO   angle-gate pull-off (ECM technique)
AHEAD   Advanced Hit Efficiency and Destruction (ammunition, Swiss)
AI   artificial intelligence

AIDS	AVP Integrated Display System (UYQ-65, U.S.)	ASW	antisubmarine warfare
AIEWS	Advanced Integrated EW System (U.S.)	ASWDS	ASW direction system
		ASWM	ASW module
AIMS	IFF Mk XII system (U.S.); also Advanced Integrated MAD System (Canadian)	ASWOC	ASW Operations Center
		ATARS	Advanced Tactical Air Reconnaissance System
AIO	action information organization (British term for CIC)	ATAS	active towed-array sonar
		ATC	air-traffic control
ALFS	airborne low-frequency sonar (U.S. program, AQS-22)	ATCD	advanced technology concept demonstrator, formerly a BTI program, a U.S. term denoting a demonstration of advanced nonnuclear technology
ALI	automatic line integration (in sonar processing)		
ALP	acoustic localization plot	ATD	automatic target detection; also advanced technology demonstration, a U.S. program designed to move as quickly as possible from concept to full-scale development
AM	amplitude modulation (as opposed to FM)		
AMDAS	Airborne Mine Detector and Survey System		
Amp	ampere(s)	ATF	automatic target follower
AMRAAM	advanced medium-range air-to-air missile (U.S. AIM-120)	ATLIS	French laser designation pod
		ATM	asynchronous transfer mode
AMTI	airborne MTI	ATO	air tasking order
ANODE	ambient noise omnidirectional evaluation (in sonobuoy processing)	ATT	automatic target tracking; also acoustic target tracker
AoA	angle of arrival	ATW	Advanced Tactical Workstation
AP	armor piercing	ATWCS	Advanced Tomahawk (or Tactical) Weapons Control System
APAM	antipersonnel/antimateriel		
APAR	active phased-array radar (Canadian-Dutch-German)	AUWE	Admiralty Underwater Weapons Establishment (British)
APDS	armor-piercing discarding sabot (ammunition)	AVP	acoustic, advanced, or adapted video processor
APECS	Advanced Programmable Electronic Countermeasures System (U.S. commercial EW system)	B-scope	radar display (rectangular plot of range vs. bearing)
		BAe	British Aerospace
		BB	bottom bounce (sonar)
APFDS	armor-piercing fragmenting discarding sabot (ammunition)	BBC	broad-band chaff
		bbl	barrel (e.g., of a gun)
APFSDS	armor-piercing fin-stabilized discarding sabot (ammunition)	BCH	Bloc Calcul Hybride (French computer)
APHE	armor-piercing high-explosive (ammunition)	BDI	bearing-deviation indicator (for target following in sonar)
API	armor-piercing incendiary (ammunition)	BGPHES	Battle-Group Passive Horizon ESM System (U.S.)
API-T	armor-piercing incendiary tracer (ammunition)	BHP	brake horsepower
		BIP	battle information post (Russian)
APS	Afloat Planning System	bit	binary digit (0 or 1)
ARBS	angle-rate bombing system (U.S. AN/ASB-19)	BIT(E)	built-in test (equipment)
		BMDO	Ballistic Missile Defense Organization (U.S. successor to SDIO)
ARE	Admiralty Research Establishment (British, now part of DRA, Defence Research Agency)		
		bps	bits per second
		BT	bathythermograph, to obtain a temperature profile of the sea
ARM	antiradar missile		
ARPA	Advanced Research Projects Agency (U.S., for a time known as DARPA, Defense ARPA)	BTI	Balanced Technology Initiative (BTI): congressionally mandated conventional munitions program to complement the Reagan-era SDI (strategic defense initiative: "Star Wars"); programs of this type were later renamed ATCDs, advanced technology concept demonstrators, to distinguish them from ATDs.
ASAP	Advanced Systolic Array Processor (U.S.)		
ASAT	antisatellite (weapon)		
ASIC	application-specific integrated chip		
ASM	air-to-surface missile		
ASMA	Air Staff Management Aid (British)		
ASMD	antiship missile defense	byte	hexadecimal digit (eight bits, i.e., base-64 digits)
ASMP	Air-sol Moyenne Portée, French air-launched strategic cruise missile		
		C^2	command and control (C-squared)
ASP	airborne signal processor; also advanced signal processor	C^2P	command and control processor
		C^3	command, control, and communications (C-cubed)
ASPECT	acoustic short-pulse echo classification technique		
		C^3I	command, control, communications, and intelligence
ASPRO	Associative Parallel Processor		
ASRAAM	advanced short-range air-to-air missile	C&D	command and decision
		ca.	circa
ASROC	antisubmarine rocket (U.S.)	CAAIS	Computer-Assisted Action Information System (British)
ASTAB	automated status board		
ASUW	antisurface (ship) warfare	CAC	computer-aided classification

CAD	computer-aided design, also computer-aided detection
CAFMS	computer-aided force management system
CAINS	carrier aircraft inertial navigation system
cal	caliber (either bore in fractions of an inch for weapons of under 1in bore, or length of barrel in multiples of the bore, e.g. 5in54 cal, or 5in/54, is a gun 54 × 5 inches long, 270 in long)
CAMLAC	Computer-Aided Master Launcher Control (U.S., for decoys)
CANE	Computer-Aided Navigational Equipment (British)
CAS	command advice system
CASOM	Conventional Stand-Off Munition (British program)
CASS	command-activated sonobuoy system
CATIC	China National Aero-Technology Import and Export Corp.
CBU	cluster bomb unit
CCA	Captain's Combat Aid (British)
CCC	combined command center
CCD	charge-coupled device (electronic component)
CCS	combat-control system
CCSS	cryptologic combat-support system
CCTV	closed-circuit television
CDC	Combat Direction Center
CDS	combat-data or combat-direction system
CEC	Cooperative Engagement Capability (U.S.)
CEP	circular error probable (half of all shots will fall within this radius); or Cooperative Engagement Processor (U.S.)
CEPLO	Command Electronic Plotting System (Swedish)
CFA	crossed-field amplifier (radar transmitter)
CFAR	constant false-alarm rate (in radar)
CHBDL	Common High-Bandwidth Data Link
CIC	Combat Information Center (U.S.; equivalent to operations room [British])
CIGARS	console internal generation and refresh system, modification to U.S. UYA-4 console of NTDS system
CILOP	conversion in lieu of procurement (U.S. term)
CINCEASTLANT	Commander-in-Chief Eastern Atlantic
CINCIBERLANT	Commander-in-Chief Iberian Area Atlantic
CINCNAVSOUTH	Commander-in-Chief Naval Forces Southern Area
CINCUSNAVEUR	Commander-in-Chief U.S. European Naval Forces
CIS	Commonwealth of Independent States
CIWS	close-in weapons system
CLOS	command to line of sight (missile guidance)
cm	centimeter
CMOS	complementary metal-oxide-semiconductor (type of computer-chip technology)
CMS	contact management system; combat management system
CNO	chief of naval operations (U.S.)
CO	commanding officer
CODAR	correlation-display analyzing recorder (ASW), to obtain position data by correlating the outputs of two or more passive sonobuoys
COEA	cost and operational effectiveness analysis
COMINT	communications intelligence
COMUSKOREA	Commander U.S. Forces Korea
conscan	conical scan (in radar)
COOP	craft of opportunity program (generally in minesweeping)
CORT	coherent receive/transmit (in radar)
COTS	commercial off-the-shelf (for procurement); see also GOTS
CP	command-plotting/plotter
CPA	closest point of approach
CPIC	coastal patrol and interdiction craft (U.S.)
CPMIEC	China Precision Machinery Import/Export Corporation
CPU	central processing unit (of a computer)
CRT	cathode-ray tube (display)
csc^2	cosecant-squared, a typical vertical shape for radar beams; it provides constant power at a given altitude at all ranges. The expression "30 deg csc^2" means a beam that has cosecant-squared shape up to 30 deg of elevation.
CSDC	combat-system display console (U.S.)
CSS	command support system; communications support system
CSU	compact sonar for submarines (U-boats) (German)
CTM	Conduit de Tir Multisensor
CU	control unit, cooperating unit (in U.S. CEC system)
cu ft	cubic foot/feet
CUDIXS	Common User Digital Information Exchange System
CVR	crystal video receiver
CW	continuous wave (nonpulsed); also chemical warfare
CWAT	continuous wave acquisition and tracking
CWC	composite warfare commander
CWI	continuous wave illuminator/injection
CZ	convergence zone (sonar)
DAC	digital autopilot
DAISY	Digital Action Information System (Dutch)
DAMA	demand-assigned multiple access
DANCS	Distributed Anti-Air Naval Control System (Aegis for frigates)
DARO	DoD Aerial Reconnaissance Office
DARPA	Defense Advanced Research Projects Agency (U.S., now ARPA)
dB	decibel, a measure of relative size; it is 10 log (base 10) of a ratio. Thus, 3 dB is a factor of about 2, and 10 dB a factor of 10; −3 dB is about a half. The reference value in the ratio is often implicit, as in radar, when it is the performance of a notional antenna radiating power equally in all directions.
dBm	decibel-milliwatt (measure used in ECM)
DC	direct current; also depth charge
DCC	damage control center

DCNI	Direction Construction Naval Internationale (French)
DCU	damage-control unit
DDS	data distribution system (link in U.S. CEC system)
deg	degree
DELEX	destroyer life-extension program (Canadian)
DEMON	demodulated noise (ASW signal-processing technique)
DEPLO	Danish version of CEPLO
DF	direction finding
DFT	discrete Fourier transform
DFTDS	Data Fusion Technology Demonstrator System (U.K.)
DGA	Delegation Generale pour l'Armament, the French government organization responsible for weapons development for all three services
dia	diameter
DICASS	directional command-activated sonobuoy (ASW)
DIFAR	directional LOFAR (in ASW)
DIMUS	digital multibeam steering (ASW)
DIRCM	directional IR countermeasure
DIWS	Digital Imagery Workstation
DIWSA	DIWS Afloat
DLC	down-link communications
DLPS	data-link processing system (British)
DLRP	data-link reference point
DMA	direct memory access; Defense Mapping Agency
DME	distance-measuring equipment (U.S.: measures distance by transponder [secondary radar or sonar])
DMTI	digital MTI
DoA	direction of arrival
DoD	Department of Defense (U.S.)
DPDS	Digital Processing and Display System
DRA	Defence Research Agency (British)
DRAM	dynamic random-access memory
DRFM	digital RF memory
DRT	dead-reckoning tracer
DSCS	Defense Satellite Communications System (U.S.)
DSMAC	digital scene-matching (cruise-missile guidance); also abbreviated DIGISMAC
DSP	digital signal processor; Defense Support Program
DSTO	Defense Science and Technology Organization (Australia)
DT	directional transmission (in sonar); Developmental Testing
DTCN	Direction Technique Construction Naval (French)
DTS	data terminal set
ECCM	electronic counter-countermeasures
ECM	electronic countermeasures
ECMIU	ECM Interface Unit
ECP	engineering change proposal (U.S.)
EDATS	extra-deep armed team sweep (British)
EDM	engineering development model
EEPROM	electrically erasable programmable read-only memory (in a computer, ROM that can be electrically erased for reprogramming; it cannot be erased by the computer itself, hence is read-only)
EEZ	exclusive economic zone (defined by Law of the Sea Treaty)
EFA	European fighter aircraft (multinational project)
EHF	extremely high frequency
ELF	extremely low frequency
ELINT	electronic intelligence
EMATT	expendable mobile ASW training target (U.S.)
EMCON	emissions control (electromagnetic silence)
EMCU	enhanced memory core unit
EMI	electromagnetic interference; also the name of a British electronics manufacturer
EMP	electromagnetic pulse
EMPAR	European Multi-Purpose Array Radar (SPY-790)
EMR	extended memory reach (in a computer)
EMSP	enhanced modular signal processor (U.S. UYS-2)
EO	electro-optical
EORSAT	ESM Ocean-Reconnaissance Satellite (Russian)
EPROM	erasable programmable read-only memory
ERAPS	expendable reliable-acoustic-path sonobuoy
ERATO	Extended-Range Targeting of Otomat
ERP	effective radiated power (in jamming)
ESGN	electrically suspended gyro, navigational
ESM	electronic support (surveillance) measures
ESSMS	Evolved Sea Sparrow Missile System
est	estimated
ETG	electrothermal gun
EW	electronic warfare; also early warning
EWCM	electronic warfare coordination module
FAAMS	Family of Anti-Air Missiles (Aster system); see also FSAF and PAAMS
FAC	fast-attack craft
FAE	fuel-air explosive
FARS	frigate array radar system (U.S.: Aegis for frigates); Fast Acquisition Receiver System
FCC	Fleet Command Center (U.S.)
FCS	fire-control system
FDDI	Fiber Distributed Data Interface (a type of data bus)
FDDS	Flag Data Display System; Fleet Data Distribution System
FDS	Fixed Distributed System (U.S.)
FEWSG	Fleet Electronic Warfare Support Group (simulating enemy jamming for training) (U.S.)
FFAR	folding-fin aircraft rocket (2.75in caliber)
FFISTS	Frigate Integrated Shipboard Tactical System (U.S.)
FFS	Force Fusion System (U.S.)
FFT	fast Fourier transform
FHLT	Fleet High-Level Terminal (U.S., used at ASWOCs/TSCs)
FIAR	Fabbrica Italiana Apparecchiature Radioelettroniche (Italian manufacturer)
FIR	finite impulse response (type of radar receiver, for ECCM)
FLASH	Folding Light Acoustic System (French)
FLIR	forward-looking IR

FLOPS	floating-point instructions per second (measure of computer speed, as in 1 MFLOPS, i.e., 1 million FLOPS per second)	GRP	glass-reinforced plastic (construction material)
FLTSAT	fleet satellite	GRT	gross registered tonnage (of merchant ships)
FLTSATCOM	fleet satellite communications	HAIS	Hydroacoustic Information System
FLYRT	Flying Radar Target (U.S.)	HALE	high-altitude long-endurance (drone)
FM	frequency modulation (as opposed to AM)	HARM	high-speed antiradar missile (U.S. AGM-88)
FMC	U.S. defense manufacturer, formerly Food Machinery Corp., now part of United Defense	HARP	Horizontal Array Random Position (sonobuoy array, U.K.)
FMCW	frequency-modulated continuous wave	HBX	high explosive (more powerful than TNT)
FMS	foreign military sales (U.S.)	HC	high capacity (as in a shell)
FoM	figure of merit	HCER	high-capacity extended-range
FoR	field of regard (field over which a sensor can scan)	HDW	Howaldt, a German shipbuilder
		HE	high explosive
FOTC	Force OTH-T coordinator or commander	HEAT	high-explosive antitank (shaped charge)
FOV	field of view	HEI	high-explosive incendiary
FPA	focal plane array	HF	high frequency
FPB	fast patrol boat	HF/DF	high-frequency direction finding
FPU	floating-point unit	HOTAS	hands-on throttle and stick
FRAM	fleet rehabilitation and modernization (U.S. program, applied to many destroyers now serving in foreign navies)	HP	horsepower; or high power; or high pressure; or horizontal plotter
		hr	hour(s)
		HS	ASW helicopter squadron (U.S. Navy)
FRAZ	frequency-azimuth	HSA	Hollandse Signaal Apparaaten (also known as Signaal)
FSAF	Family of Surface-to-Air Defense Systems (FAAMS)	HTP	high-test peroxide (concentrated hydrogen peroxide)
FSD	full-scale development	HUD	heads-up display
FSED	full-scale engineering development	HUMINT	human intelligence
FSK	frequency-shift keying (symbols differentiated by different frequencies)	HVAR	high-velocity aircraft rocket (5in caliber)
		Hz	hertz (cycles per second)
ft	foot/feet (12 inches)	I/O	input/output
FTAS	fast-time analyzer (for postmission analysis of MPA data)	IADT	integrated automatic detection and tracking
FTC	frequency translator compressor; false-target canister	IAI	Israeli Aircraft Industries
		ICDC	improved control display console (U.S.)
FTEWA	Force Threat Evaluation and Weapon Assignment (in U.S. CEC system)	IDAP	Integrated Defense Avionics Program (U.S.)
FY	fiscal year (U.S.: 1 October–30 September)	IDECM	Integrated Defensive ECM
		IDF	instantaneous direction-finding
G	force of gravity	IFF	identification friend or foe
g	gram	IFM	instantaneous frequency measurement (in ESM)
GAO	General Accounting Office (U.S.)		
Gbyte	gigabyte(s) (billions of bytes; also GB)	IIR	imaging IR
GCCS	Global Command and Control System	ILS	instrument landing system, often as VOR/ILS
GE	General Electric Company	IMOP	intentional modulation on pulse
GERDSM	French ASW and mine warfare development establishment	in	inch
		INS	inertial navigation system
GFCS	gunfire-control system (U.S.)	IOC	I/O controller
GFCP	generic front-end communications processor	IR	infrared
		IRCCD	IR charge-coupled device
GFLOPS	billions of floating-point operations per second	IRCM	IR countermeasure
		IRDS	IR detecting set
GHG	Gruppen-Horch Gereat (array listening system), the wartime German low-frequency passive sonar from which several postwar systems were derived	IRST	IR search and track (or target designation)
		ISAR	inverse synthetic-aperture radar
		ISDL	intersite data link
		ISUS	integrated-sensor underwater system (German)
GHz	gigahertz (thousands of MHz)		
GOPS	billion (giga) operations/sec (for computers)	ITAWDS	integrated tactical amphibious warfare data system (U.S.)
GOSIP	Government Open Systems Interconnect Profile (a computer specification)	ITT	invitation to tender (British equivalent to an RFP); also International Telephone and Telegraph Corp. (U.S.)
GOTS	government off-the-shelf (for procurement)	IUSS	integrated undersea surveillance system (U.S.)
GPS	global positioning system	IXS	information exchange system

JCS	Joint Chiefs of Staff (U.S.)
JDAMS	Joint Direct-Attack Munitions System (U.S.)
JDISS	Joint Deployable Intelligence Support System
JFY	Japanese fiscal year
JIC	joint intelligence center
JMCIS	Joint Maritime Command Information Strategy/System (U.S.: successor to JOTS)
JMSDF	Japan Maritime Self-Defense Force (navy)
JOTS	Joint Operational Tactical System (U.S.)
JPTDS	Joint Participating Tactical Data System (U.S.)
JSOW	Joint Standoff Weapon (U.S.)
JSTARS	Joint Standoff Airborne Radar System
JTDS	Joint Tactical Data System
JTIDS	Joint Tactical Information Distribution System (U.S., NATO)
k	kilo, thousand. In electronics, a kilobit (or -byte) equals 1024 rather than 1000 bits (bytes).
KAST	Kalman Automatic Sequential TMA (U.S. submarine term)
kbit	kilobit(s)
kbps	kilobits per second
kbyte	kilobyte(s)
kFLOPS	thousands (kilo) of floating-point operations/sec (for computers)
kg	kilogram, 2.204 lb
kHz	kilohertz
KIPS	thousands (kilo) of instructions/sec (for computers)
kloc	thousands of lines of code (for computers)
km	kilometer
KOPS	thousands (kilo) of operations/sec (for computers)
kpps	kilopulses per second
kT	kilotons, thousands of tons (equivalent TNT)
kV	kilovolts
kVA	kilovolt-ampere(s)
kW	kilowatts
kWh	kilowatt hours
kword	thousands of words (for computers)
kyd	kiloyards, thousands of yards
LADAR	laser radar; also rendered LIDAR
LAMPS	Light Airborne Multi-Purpose System (U.S. helicopter)
LAN	local area network (for computers)
LANTIRN	low-altitude navigation-and-targeting IR system for night (U.S.)
lb	pound(s)
LCAC	landing craft air cushion (U.S.)
LCAW	low-cost antisubmarine weapon
LCC	local control center; also local communication controller
LCD	liquid crystal display
LEAP	Lightweight Exoatmospheric Projectile (U.S., for antimissile defense)
LEASAT	Leased Satellite System
LED	light-emitting diode (for electronic displays)
LEDS	Link Eleven Display System (U.S.)
LEIP	Link Eleven Improvement Program (U.S.)
LF	low frequency
LFA	LF adjunct or LF active (sonar)
LFDM	low-flier-detection mode (in radar)

LGB	laser-guided bomb
LIDAR	light (i.e., laser) radar
LIOD	lightweight optronic director
LLLTV	low-light-level television
LOAL	lock-on after launch
LOB	line of bearing
LOFAR	low-frequency analysis and recording (ASW)
LOP	line of position; also local operator plot
LOS	line of sight
LPD	labeled plan display
LPI	low probability of intercept
LRU	line-replaceable unit
LSI	large-scale (electronic) integration
LTV	Ling-Tempco Vought, U.S. manufacturer
LWIR	long-wave IR
m	meter
M	million
MAD	magnetic-acoustic detector (in ASW)
MADOM	MAD of mines
MAGICS	Modular Architecture for Graphic and Imaging Console Systems (Italian)
MAIGRET	Materiel Automatique d'Interception et de Goniometrie des Radio communications en Exploitations Tactique
MAINS	Minehunting Information System (British)
MARS	magnetic array sensor
MARV	maneuverable reentry vehicle
MATE	manually aided TMA evaluator
MATES	Multiband Antiship Cruise Missile Defense Tactical Electronic System
max	maximum
MBAT	multibeam array technology/transmitters
Mbit	megabit, million bits (approximate)
Mbps	megabytes per second (measure of data rate)
Mbyte	megabytes, million bytes (approximate)
MCC	maintenance of close contact (sonar)
MCDV	maritime coastal defense vessel (Canada)
MCM	mine countermeasures
MCOPS	millions (M) of complex operations/sec (for computers)
MCS	Modular Combat System (U.S., Hughes)
MEB	Marine Expeditionary Brigade
MEF	Marine Expeditionary Force
MEKO	modular frigate (by Blohm & Voss)
MEL	British and Canadian electronics manufacturer
MEOSS	Marine Electro-Optical Surveillance System
MEU	Marine Expeditionary Unit
MF	medium frequency
MFCC	multifunction common console
MFCS	missile fire-control system
MFLOPS	millions (M) of floating-point operations/sec (for computers)
MG	machine gun; also motor generator, to transform AC to DC current
mGauss	milligauss (measure of magnetic field)
MHC	minehunter, coastal
MHIDAS	multiple high integration distributed architecture data-bus systems

MHQ	maritime headquarters (German)
MHz	megahertz (millions of cycles per second)
mi	mile(s)
microsec	microsecond, millionth of a second
MIDAS	mine detection-and-avoidance system (U.S.)
MIDS	Multifunctional Information Distribution System
min	minute or minimum
MIPS	millions (M) of instructions/sec (for computers)
MIRV	multiple independent reentry vehicles
MJ	megajoules (energy)
Mk	mark (number, for designations)
MLS	multilevel security
mm	millimeter
MMD	multimode device
MMI	man-machine interface
MMIC	monolithic microwave integrated circuit
mmw	millimeter-wave (length)
MNS	mine neutralization system (U.S., SLQ-48; also Mission Need Statement in U.S. procurement system)
MOC	multifunction operator console
MOCC	mobile miniature operations control center
MoD	Ministry of Defence (e.g., British)
Mod	modification to equipment of a given Mk number, as in Mk 46 Mod 5 torpedo
mOe/s	meter-Oerstads per second
MOPS	millions (M) of operations/sec (for computers)
MOS	metal-oxide semiconductor
MOSS	mobile submarine simulator (U.S.)
MoU	memorandum of understanding
MPA	maritime patrol aircraft
MPC	multipurpose console
mph	miles per hour
MPU	medium-PRF upgrade (for SPS-48 and -49 radars)
mrad	milliradian (thousandth of a radian)
MRBF	mean rounds (fired) before failure
MRV	multiple reentry vehicle
MSB	minesweeping boat
MSC	minesweeper, coastal
msec	millisec, thousandths of a second
MSI	medium-scale integration, as opposed to LSI and VLSI; also minesweeper, inshore; multisensor interface
MSL	minesweeping launch
MSP	modular self-protection; modular signal processor
MSSE	multisensor situation elaboration
MT	megatons, millions of tons (TNT equivalent); also mechanical time, for a fuze
MTBF	mean time between failures
MTI	moving-target indicator (or indication)
MTST	maneuvering target statistical tracker
MTTR	mean time to repair; also multitarget tracking radar
MULTS	multilink terminal station
MUSL	Marconi Underwater Systems Ltd.
MW	megawatt, million watts
MWCS	multiweapon control systems

Mword	megaword, millions of words (for computer)
NAAWS	NATO AAW System
NATO	North Atlantic Treaty Organization
NAUTIS	Naval Autonomous Tactical Information System
NAVAIR	Naval Air Systems Command (U.S.)
NAVSEA	Naval Sea Systems Command (U.S.)
NCA	National Command Authority
NCCS	Naval Command and Control System (U.S.)
NDI	nondevelopmental item
NFT	Norsk Forstvarsteknologi, a Norwegian defense manufacturer, formerly Kongsberg; renamed Kongsberg 1995
NILE	NATO Improved Link Eleven (Link 22)
NIPS	Naval Intelligence Processing System
nm	nautical mile, 6080 feet
NMOS	n-channel metal-oxide semiconductor (type of computer chip technology)
NMR	nuclear magnetic resonance
NOSC	Naval Ocean Systems Center (U.S.)
NPO	cooperative production organization (Russian design bureau [KB] plus factory)
NRL	Naval Research Laboratory (U.S.)
NSA	National Security Agency (U.S.)
nsec	nanosecond (billionth of a second)
NSIS	New Sonar Intercept System (U.S.: WLY-1)
NSR	Naval Staff Requirement (British)
NSSMS	NATO Sea Sparrow Missile System
NSWC	Naval Surface Warfare Center (U.S.)
NTCS-A	Naval Tactical Command System Afloat
NTDS	naval tactical data system (U.S.)
NTU	New Threat Upgrade (U.S. program)
NUSC	Naval Underwater Systems Center (U.S.)
NUWC	Naval Undersea Warfare Center (U.S.)
NVGs	night-vision goggles
OAB	Outer Air Battle; also open-architecture backpanel (Unisys)
OASIS	OTH-T Airborne Sensor Interface System (U.S.)
OBU	OSIS baseline upgrade (U.S.)
OCC	operational control console
ODT	omnidirectional transmission (sonar)
OFD	optical fire director
OKB	design bureau (Russian)
ONI	Office of Naval Intelligence (U.S.)
OOD	officer of the deck
OPV	offshore patrol vessel
OR	Operational Requirement (U.S.)
ORDALT	ordnance alteration (U.S.)
ORTS	operational recording and testing system (U.S.)
OSD	Office of the Secretary of Defense (U.S.)
OSIS	Ocean Surveillance Information System
OSS	Operations Support System
OTC	officer in tactical command
OTCIXS	OTC Information Exchange System
OTH	over the horizon (in radar)
OTH-T	over-the-horizon targeting (U.S. term)
P³I	preplanned product improvement

PADLOC	passive-active detection and localization (sonar, U.S.)
PALIS	Passiv-Aktiv-Link-Lage-Informationssystem
PAP	Poisson Auto-Propulsée (French: self-propelled VDS)
PARIS	Passive/Active Range-and-Intercept Sonar (French/British/Dutch intercept sonar)
PCC	polarity coincidence correlator
PD	probability of detection; also point detonating (fuze)
PDI	pulse-Doppler integration
PEAB	Philips Elektronikindustri AB (Swedish manufacturer)
PFHE	prefragmented high-explosive (ammunition)
PFSS	Pilot Flag Support System (British)
PK	probability of kill
POM	program objective memorandum (U.S. planning document)
POSIX	Portable Operating System Interface (a computer specification)
POST	prototype ocean surveillance terminal
PPI	plan-position indicator (maplike radar display)
pps	pulses per second
PRC	People's Republic of China
PRF	pulse-repetition frequency
PRI	pulse-repetition interval
PROM	programmed read-only memory
PRS	passive ranging sonar
psi	pounds per square inch
PTA	passive-tracking algorithm
PU	participating unit
PUFFS	passive underwater fire control (U.S.)
PVDF	polyvinylidene fluoride
PWO	principal warfare officer (British equivalent to U.S. TAO)
QRCC	Quick-Reaction Combat Capability
R&D	research and development
RAAF	Royal Australian Air Force
rad	radian, measure of angle (1 radian is about 57.3 deg)
RAF	Royal Air Force (British)
RAIDS	Rapid Antiship Missile Integrated Defense System (U.S.)
RAM	random access memory (in computers); rolling airframe missile (U.S.); radar-absorbing material
Ramses	Reprogrammable Advanced Multimode Shipboard ECM System
RAN	Royal Australian Navy
RAP	reliable acoustic path (ASW); rocket-assisted projectile (shell)
Rapids	Radar Passive Identification System
RAWS	Role-Adaptable Weapons System (Australian, for S-70)
RBOC	rapid-blooming off-board chaff (U.S.)
RCS	radar cross-section
RDT	rotationally directed transmission (sonar)
RDT&E	research, development, testing, and engineering
RDX	high explosive (more powerful than TNT)
RECO	remote control of mines
RF	radio frequency
RF/IR	combined radio (or radar) and IR
RFA	Royal Fleet Auxiliary (British)
RFP	request for proposal
RFQ	request for quotation

RGPO	range-gate pull-off (ECM technique)
RHAWR	radar homing and warning receiver
RIS	Remote Influence Sweep
RISC	reduced-instruction-set computer
RMPA	replacement MPA (British)
RMS	root-mean square
RN	Royal Navy (British)
rnd	round(s)
RNEE	Royal Navy Equipment Exhibition
RNLN	Royal Netherlands Navy
RNTDS	restructured NTDS
RNZAF	Royal New Zealand Air Force
ROM	read-only memory (in computer)
ROTHR	relocatable OTH radar
ROV	remotely operated vehicle (generally underwater)
RPG	receiver-processor group (in ECM)
rpm	revolutions per minute
RPV	remotely piloted vehicle; see UAV
RTC	radar track combiner
RTN	Italian (Selenia) radar designator
RVP	radar-video processor
RWR	radar-warning receiver
RWS	range-while-search
Sabre	shallow-water breach system (mine clearance)
SACC	shore ASW command centers; supporting arms coordination center
SACLANT	Supreme Allied Commander Atlantic
SADANG	Système Acoustique de l'Atlantique Nouvelle Génération
Sadie	Segregation, Association, De-interleaving, and Identification Equipment processor
SADOC	Systema Automatico Dirizione della Operazioni de Combattimento
SADS	SubACS active detection system (U.S.)
SAFENET	Survivable Adaptable Fiber-Optic Embedded Network
Sagaie	Système d'Autodefense pour la Guerre Infra-Rouge et Electromagnetique
SAM	surface-to-air missile
SAP	semi-armor-piercing
SAR	synthetic-aperture radar; also search and rescue; also Selected Acquisition Report (U.S.)
SARIE	Selective Automatic Radar Identification Equipment
SATCOMM	satellite communication
SATIN	Système de Traitement Automatique de l'Information Navale
SATIR	System zur Auswertung Taktischer Informationen auf Raketenzerstoren
SAWS	Submarine Acoustic Warfare System
SBC	single-board computer; single broadcast
SCCS	submarine combat-control system
SCEPS	stored chemical energy propulsion system (for torpedoes; see U.S. Mk 50)
SCI	special compartmented information (generally information outside the usual classification system; information is often "sanitized" to remove SCI so that it can more freely be used by operating forces) (U.S.)
SCSI	special compartmented security information; small computer system interface; a type of computer internal bus

SDC	sonar data computer; Système de Defense et de Commandement		SSCS	Surface Ship Command System (British)
SDIO	Strategic Defense Initiative Organization (U.S.), now BMDO		SSDS	ship self-defense system (U.S.)
SDT	steered directional transmission (sonar)		SSES	ship signals-exploitation spaces
			SSI	sector scan indicator (sonar, for target tracking)
SEAL	Sea-Air-Land (U.S. Navy special forces)		SSIPS	shore signal and information processing segment
sec	second		SSIXS	Submarine Information Exchange System
SEI	specific emitter identification			
SEM	standard electronic module (U.S.)		SSK	ASW submarine (nonnuclear)
SENIT	Système d'Exploitation Naval des Informations Tactiques		SSL	single station location
			SSM	surface-to-surface missile
SEPADS	sonar-environment prediction-and-display system		SSN	nuclear submarine
			SSPK	single-shot kill probability
SFCS	submarine fire-control system		SSTD	surface-ship torpedo defense
SFMPL	submarine force mission-planning library		SSTx	solid-state transmitter
			STA	second time around, referring to radar pulses arriving back at the radar soon after the next pulse has been sent
SHF	super high frequency			
SHINPADS	Shipboard Integrated Processing and Display System (Canadian)			
SHR	superheterodyne receiver		STACOS	Signaal Tactical Command and Control System
SIASS	Submarine Integrated Attack-and-Surveillance Sonar (Dutch)		STAE	second-time-around echo (radar)
SID	situation information display		STAP	situation threat-assessment planning
SIDS	sensor interface data system (U.S.)		START	Strategic Arms Reduction Treaty
SIF	Selective Identification Feature		STC	sensitivity time control (ECCM technique)
SIGINT	signals intelligence			
SIMAS	sonar in-situ mode assessment system (U.S.)		STIR	separate track and illumination radar (U.S.); Signaal track and illumination radar (Dutch); surveillance and target-indication radar (British)
SIMD	single instruction multiple data			
SINBADS	Submarine Integrated Battle and Data System (Dutch)			
SINS	ship's inertial navigation system		STM	serial-tone modulation
SISC	Système d'Integration du Système de Combat		STRAP	Sonobuoy Thinned Random Array Processor
SLAM	standoff land-attack missile (modified Harpoon)		STT	shore targeting terminal; submarine targeting terminal
SLAR	side-looking airborne radar		SubACS	Submarine Advanced Combat System
SLASM	Système de Lutte Anti-Sous-Marin			
SLAT	supersonic low-altitude target		SURTASS	surveillance towed-array sonar system
SLBM	sea-launched ballistic missile			
SLCM	sea-launched cruise missile		SVLA	steered vertical linear array (sonobuoy)
SLEP	service-life extension program (U.S.)			
SLMM	submarine-launched mobile mine		SVP	spatial vernier processing; sound-velocity profile
SMA	Segnalamento Marittimo ed Aero (Italian manufacturer)		SWC	scan with compensation (radar tracking technique); also subordinate warfare commander; surface-warfare coordinator
SMCS	Signaal Modular Combat System; submarine multiscreen command system			
			SYS	sensor (radar) integration computer (U.S.)
SMTD	submarine torpedo defense (weapon)			
SNAPS	Smiths Navigation and Plotting System		TACAMO	"take charge and move out" (strategic command/control)
SNIA	French rocket motor manufacturer		TACAN	tactical air navigation beacon (U.S.)
SOBIC	Shore Information and Classification Center (U.S.)		TACCO	tactical coordinating officer
			TACELINT	tactical ELINT
SOR	specific operational requirement (U.S.)		TACINTEL	tactical intelligence, special classified information
SOSUS	sound surveillance system (U.S. and NATO)		TACNAV	tactical navigation system
			TACNAVMOD	P-3A/B modification with TACNAV
SPRITE	signal processing in the element		TADIL	tactical digital link (U.S. and NATO)
sq	square		TADIXS	Tactical Digital Information Exchange System
SR	Staff Requirement			
SRAM	static RAM		TADS	Target Acquisition and Designation System
SRBOC	super rapid-blooming off-board chaff (U.S.)		TADSTAND B	Tactical Digital Standard B
SRDT	steered rotationally directed transmission (sonar)		TALD	Tactical Air-Launched Decoy
			TAMPS	Tactical Aircraft Mission Planning System
SSB	single sideband (radio); also diesel-powered ballistic-missile submarine		TAO	tactical action officer
SSBN	strategic ballistic-missile submarine (nuclear powered)		TAP	towed array processor; torpedo alert processor

TAPS	towed array broad-band processing system (British)
TARP	towed-array range processor/processing for U.S. long thin array
TAS	target-acquisition system (U.S.); also tactical Arctic sonobuoy (U.S.)
TAVITAC	Traitement Automatique et Visualization Tactique
TB	towed body (U.S. designation)
TCC	tactical coordination console
TCG	Track Control Group
TCPA	time to closest point of approach
TCSS	torpedo-control system, submarine (British)
TDA	tactical decision aid
TDC	torpedo-data computer; tactical display console
TDD	target-detection device (proximity fuze)
TDHS	tactical data-handling system (ASW)
TDI	target Doppler or deviation indicator (sonar, for target tracking)
TDLT	Track Data Link Terminal
TDMA	time division multiple access (type of data link)
TDP	tactical data processor
TDS	tactical data system
TDT	target data transmitter
TEAMS	Tactical EA-6B Mission (Planning) System
TEDR	threat-emitter data recorder
TELCOM	two-way wire guidance for Mk 48 torpedo (U.S.)
TENCAP	tactical exploitation of national (intelligence) capabilities (U.S.)
TERCOM	terrain comparison (cruise missile guidance)
TERPES	Tactical Electronic-Reconnaissance Processing Evaluation System
TEWA	threat evaluation and weapons assignment
TFCC	Tactical Flag Command Center
TFCS	torpedo fire-control system
TG	transmitter group (in sonar)
THAAD	Theater High-Altitude Air Defense
3D	three-dimensional
TICM	thermal-imaging common module
TIP	tactical-information processing; track initiation processor
TLAM	Tomahawk Land-Attack Missile
TMA	target-motion analysis (for ASW ranging and fire control)
TMD	theater missile defense
TMDS	Tomahawk Mission Display System
TMS	track management system
ToA	time of arrival
TOR	Tentative Operational Requirement (U.S.)
TOW	tube-launched optical wire-guided missile (U.S., antitank)
TP	target practice (ammunition)
TP-T	target practice tracer (ammunition)
TPI	tactical plotting indicator
TPX	explosive (torpex, more powerful than TNT)
TRDT	tribeam rotationally directed transmission (sonar)
TRE	tactical receive equipment
TRF	tuned radio frequency (wide-band type of receiver)
TRUMP	*Tribal*-class modernization program (Canadian)
TSC	tactical support center (U.S., for ASW)
TSS	tactical surveillance sonobuoy (U.S.); tracking subsystem
TT	torpedo tube
2D	two-dimensional
TWCS	Tomahawk Weapons Control System
TWS	track-while-scan
TWT	traveling wave tube (radar transmitter)
UAV	unmanned air vehicle (this more general term is replacing RPV in many cases)
UDACS	Universal Display and Control System (Boeing ASW system)
UEP	underwater electric potential
UFO	UHF Follow-On Program
UHF	ultrahigh frequency
UMOP	unintentional modulation on each pulse
USCINCPAC	Commander-in-Chief Pacific Fleet
UUV	unmanned underwater vehicle
UVPROM	ultraviolet programmable read-only memory (the read-only feature is disabled when the appropriate ultraviolet light is shined on the memory)
UWB	ultra-wide-band
V	volt
VDS	variable-depth sonar
VERDIN	VLF emergency digital information network (secure radio for submarine broadcasts, U.S.)
VF	fighter squadron (U.S. Navy) (with a number)
VGPO	velocity-gate pull-off (ECM technique)
VHF	very high frequency
VHSIC	very high speed integrated circuit
VLA	vertical-launch ASROC (missile) (U.S.)
VLAD	vertical line array DIFAR (U.S. sonobuoy)
VLF	very low frequency
VLS	vertical launch system
VLSI	very large scale integration (of electronic circuits)
VME	versatile memory Eurobus, a current standard internal computer data bus
VOR	VHF omni-range (for air navigation)
VP	patrol (ASW) squadron (sometimes used for patrol aircraft) (U.S. Navy)
VQ	ECM squadron (U.S. Navy); vector quantization
W	watts
WAA	wide-aperture array (U.S.)
WCC	weapons-control console
WCS	weapons-control system (U.S.)
WDS	weapons-direction system (U.S.)
WRA	weapons replaceable assembly
WWMCCS	Worldwide Military Command and Control System
XBT	expendable bathythermograph
yd	yard(s)
yr	year(s)

SURVEILLANCE AND CONTROL

A fleet's visible elements are its ships, submarines, and aircraft. These elements are tied together by communications links, many of them satellite-borne. Increasingly, a fleet's operations are motivated by external (over the horizon, OTH) sources of operational intelligence data.

Before the advent of the big OTH systems the most important development in naval command and control had been the automation of the Combat Information Center (CIC). The CIC itself was conceived during World War II as a way to concentrate and collate all the information available on board a ship in a single summary plot. Radars detecting post–World War II jet aircraft poured information into CIC faster than it could be plotted by hand. The solution adopted in the early 1960s was to replace the manual plotters with a computer; the U.S. NTDS is the oldest surviving such system. The computer produced a coherent tactical picture in the form of target tracks, from which target motion could be projected, and on the basis of which threats could be ranked. Computers aboard different ships could exchange track information via a digital link, Link 11 in the United States' case. Within any one ship, the track data could be used to cue fire-control systems (FCSs). In some cases, an associated computer carried a duplicate air picture used for target selection and for weapon and sensor assignment. In effect, it was the memory of the antiair system, providing the next target after a target had been destroyed.

The second computer causes some confusion. In the event the main computer fails, it can take over some of the picture-keeping function, so in effect it is a hot spare. On the other hand, it must operate independently for efficient antiair action. It in turn generally feeds a separate fire-control computer. Often descriptions are somewhat garbled, so that, for example, the British ADAWS is described as consisting of a track-keeper, a hot spare (actually the weapons-direction system), and an integrated FCS (actually a third computer).

The next step, which is now being taken, is to add some element of tactical advice (based on preprogrammed doctrine and/ or stored intelligence data), and often a facility to ask "what-if" questions using near real-time computing power to test alternative tactics. Examples are the U.S. Aegis and ACDS and the British Captain's Aid (in ADIMP).

These systems grew up long before OTH targeting (OTH-T) was conceived, at least in the West. Now a major effort is underway in the U.S. Navy to integrate the own-ship/own-group data of CDS with the external data provided by OTH-T. Simple meshing of the two pictures is difficult because the OTH data generally are not quite current. The OTH system cannot provide full-time coverage of the entire ocean; it must generally make do with a few sensors.

Since the Cold War has ended, a key question for the United States is whether to continue to rely heavily on fixed intelligence-gathering systems designed primarily to track the old Soviet fleet. The budget calls for some fixed sites to be shut down, and the planned SOSUS successor, FDS (Fixed Distributed System), has been reduced to R&D status. Money will be spent instead on a deployable system. Satellites, with their global reach, have largely superseded the old land-based HF/DF net.

Deletions: Link America (United States, apparently never implemented), Arcticsat (United States, dropped in 1992 in favor of transponders on existing satellites), Submarine Laser Communications (United States, canceled 1993).

COMMAND ADVICE SYSTEMS

The systems described in this section connect external sensors, and often external commanders, to deployed forces. In several cases their dependence on time-late data distinguishes them from the more or less real-time systems on board ships, which are used for combat direction. In some important cases, such systems are also used for what amounts to off-line command advice (as in the U.S. NTCS-A/JOTS family). In other cases, off-line advice is clearly a separate issue (as in the Royal Navy, or in the U.S. C&D processors). The distinction is often difficult to make, because the advice system (e.g., an air-strike planner) may make use of surveillance information.

Navies oriented toward coast defense necessarily maintain shore-based surveillance systems as the basis of patrol boat and antiship strike operations. In at least some cases the shore headquarters is automated, and connected to deployed seaborne craft and aircraft by data link. Such linkage provides the deployed craft with a common tactical picture, and so may help prevent erroneous attacks on friendly forces. Systems of this type might be termed shore environments, just as automated air-defense information systems are commonly termed air-defense environments. OTH surveillance, generally by aircraft (but also by land-based ESM), is an essential element of any such system.

Probably the first example of such a shore environment was the German navy's AGIS combat-direction system (described below, under shipborne systems). Other NATO navies probably operate similar systems, as do the Swedes. It seems likely that the Israeli navy used a very similar system in the October War of 1973, although details are lacking.

Many Third World countries operate small radar-equipped maritime-surveillance aircraft, often with commercial data links, but it is not clear to what extent these links are used to set up an integrated tactical picture. In at least some cases they are no more than aids to OTH targeting for individual fast-attack craft.

AUSTRALIA

ADI's new N-FOCSS (Naval-Force Command Support System) is a locally developed alternative to the U.S. naval command system (JMCIS), derived from the same company's Joint-Force Command Support System (J-FOCSS). Like the U.S. system, it includes a track manager, formatted message generator, and tactical decision aids. The main features are a current automated General Operations Plot (GOP) generated via formal tactical messages (mainly OTH-T Gold) plus manual entries; a geographic display backdrop; a technical intelligence database; maritime track management functions (manual and automatic track correlation, location history, port movements, logistics information); maritime operations chart overlays; oceanographic and bathymetric data; configurable operator roles for access and control (such as system administrator, releasing officer, picture compiler, track manager); tactical decision aids (spatial aids such as CPA computation, relative velocity, distance and range, trial tracks, furthest-on circles, and ellipsoids of probability, plus plotting of expected way-points for planned movements); general decision aids (including weapon and sensor range circles); an object manager list (for easy separation of objects clustered close together); a naval overlay editor (with NTDS and user-defined symbols); logistics planning aids (such as fuel consumption status); office automation and briefing tools. The system can communicate via both synchronous (digital link) and asynchronous communications channels, producing a Recognized Maritime Picture (RMP) broadcast and having a connection to a Tactical Picture Broadcast (TBP, using Link 11). Software is written in ADA.

FRANCE

◆ SYSCOM NG

SYSCOM NG is a shore-based naval command/control system, broadly analogous to the U.S. Fleet Command Center (FCC) and the British OPCON. The staff objective was written in September 1989, and the system became operational at the end of 1992.

Aidcomer
Aidcomer is the shipboard terminal of the SYSCOM NG naval command/control system, thus broadly analogous to the U.S. TFCC/NTCS-A. On board the carrier *Charles de Gaulle*, a CDS computer will be reserved to exchange information between the two systems. The current version, employing five color UNIX workstations (the system can support up to 15 workstations), was installed in 1992 on the three command ships and on the carriers, to provide at least one installation each in the Atlantic and the Mediterranean. All large warships will ultimately have provision for installing Aidcomer (components will be easy to cross-deck). Units other than carriers have Mini-Aidcomer, which is the same except for aircraft functions (Disopair, Digiraid). OPSMER or SEAO (Système Embarqué d'Aide aux Operations) is a simplified version for AAW frigates and for the *La Fayette* class. Surveillance frigates and avisos will receive the necessary infrastructure for installation; a pool of systems will be established for cross-decking. Submarines will have a simplified tactical advice system, as will major amphibious units (*Foudre* class) and fast-underway replenishment ships (*Var* class).

Aidcomer currently incorporates artificial intelligence to assist battle-group commanders in situation assessment, decision-making, resource management, management of tactical and logistics data, transmission and reception of operational messages, and planning for electronic warfare (EW) and emissions control (EMCON).

Subsystems include: Sachem, to receive or automatically route messages to and from SYSCOM; Sextant, to prepare naval operations, monitoring them in real time and analyzing them later; Disopair, to plan airborne missions and maintain operational readiness; and Digiraid, for aircraft mission planning (e.g., for defense penetration).

The Aidcomer databank contains permanent information (entered before the ship leaves port) but can be modified when the ship is underway, either via a keyboard or via formatted messages. Aidcomer stores a month of SENIT data and a year of intelligence inputs; its database also holds information about world fleets. Other command aids without their own databases, such as Amelie Cristal (operational aspects) and CSGE (EW), are to be incorporated into Aidcomer.

Aidcomer is being developed by Cap Sesa Defense, Syseca Temps Reel, Graphael, and Itmi in collaboration with the French naval programming center. Software, written in LISP, includes a relational database-management system and a cartographic system.

A naval staff objective for *aide du commandement la mer* was issued in December 1987, and the system was first tested on board the carrier *Foch* off Lebanon in September 1989. The second prototype began trials aboard *Clemenceau* in the fall of 1990.

◆ CIRCE 2000

CIRCE is designed to support planning for up to five aircraft missions simultaneously. It was conceived as a land-based system, but a variant was installed on board the carrier *Foch* in November 1988 to plan Super Étendard strikes. Maps for mission planning are digitized by a scanner, with an accuracy equivalent to 25 m; the system uses a 2-Gbyte digital optical disk (30cm diameter) to store a map representing a surface area larger than that of the United States at a scale of 1:5 million–1:250,000. The system database can include more detailed images, including satellite photos and 1:50,000 maps. The same disk stores terrain elevation data. The pilot selects the area to be displayed in high resolution and can change scale, recenter, zoom, and reproduce 3D terrain perspective, and then uses these data to plan the mission. The local library includes such relevant data as aircraft and weapons parameters, stored on a 40-Mbyte disk. CIRCE generates all flight documents, loading two memories for the airplane to carry, a 2-Mbyte magnetic bubble memory to store terrain data and a data-entry module (2-kbyte EPROM) containing navigation parameters such as turning points and fly-by time. For example, it calculates the amount of fuel required and maps a route to take into account enemy defense, finding an optimum route within available fuel allowances.

The follow-on mission-planning system for Rafale, SLPRM, communicates with a carrier's Aidcomer system.

GERMANY

◆ MHQ

The specially built ashore MHQ at Murwik supports the link-equipped fast-attack boats in the Baltic, which use the AGIS and PALIS command systems. Development of the MHQ information system began in 1972; the basic system was ready in 1980.

It used two IBM 370/168 computers, which could handle 40 plots/sec. By 1986, work was proceeding on an enlargement to handle all NATO BALTAP command/control, bringing the modernized coastal-radar chain into the system.

◆ TAICOS

The Tactical Action Information and Command System was developed by Blohm & Voss and Philips System Technik (PST) of Kiel for the Turkish frigate *Yavuz*, the flagship of the Turkish navy. It is the Turkish equivalent of the U.S. TFCC, and is presumably associated with an automated national command center ashore. The other three Track I Turkish MEKOs are fitted for, but not with, TAICOS, but the *Yavuz* installation can be moved rapidly as needed.

TAICOS collects, coordinates, and automatically filters track data, both own-ship and external (presumably from the shore center and from Link 11). Its decision-making database also includes data on both its own and enemy ships and other platforms and weapons, and also about 120 charts, enlarged sections of which can be displayed. It can also display more detailed data (e.g., concerning shorelines, depth). The main system components, in two MEKO modules, are connected by an Ethernet bus.

INTERNATIONAL

◆ NACCIS

The NATO Command and Control Information System is apparently an international version of the U.S. OSS/NTCS-A combination. It became operational 1 January 1995 at SACLANT (Norfolk, Va.), CINCIBERLANT (Lisbon), CINCEASTLANT (Northwood, UK), and currently also at CINCNAVSOUTH (Naples). In addition, the system is being adopted at national naval command centers in the Benelux countries, Denmark, and Norway, and it is being installed in France alongside Aidcomer at Toulon (and is being considered for Brest). The Royal Australian Navy has the compatible OSS system. Canada will probably buy NACCIS for its East Coast operational command center, and may use it to replace its current Maritime Command Operational Information Network (MCOIN II).

SACLANT distributes a sanitized NTCS-A/JMCIS picture to shore headquarters via the NATO SHF satellite system. Ships receive an HF or SHF satellite rebroadcast, presumably incorporating national information.

The sea-based end of the system is the TAC-3/4 JMCIS (NTCS-A) workstation. Users, current and prospective, include Australia (currently buying TAC-4s), Canada (planned to replace current JOTS II), France (*Foch* and *Clemenceau*), Japan (to replace leased JOTS terminals, no longer in service), Netherlands (TAC-4: on *Tromp*, late 1994; to replace JOTS II on *van Heemskercks*, 1995–96; to be installed in *de Ruyter*, 1996, limited facilities to be in all other frigates, 1995–96, and to be installed in the new AOR and LPD), Saudi Arabia, United Kingdom (HMS *Illustrious*), and United States.

RUSSIA

Through the late 1960s it seems to have been assumed that central authorities ashore could direct individual units in these tasks. That was certainly the case in coast defense, where missile or ASW boats would respond to commands from a shore center. Its sensors were close at hand and information could flow quickly. For example, sub-chasers equipped with short-range sonars and RBU-6000 rocket launchers could send their sonar data ashore, where it was filtered by computer. This type of computer control was most likely the basis of the later command systems.

The shore-centered system was tested, apparently with disastrous results, in the Okean 70 (1970) maneuvers. Reportedly, turn-around time for information was far too long; virtually all the ships would have been sunk. At-sea flagships were needed: they were afloat equivalents to the ashore computer developed earlier specifically for ASW (and, presumably, for rocket boat attack). In parallel to the own-ship command system, with its "second captain," these computers might be called "second admirals." Each would accept data from ashore and from a number of ships; each would command those ships via data links. The first full flagships were the *Kirov* (for the rocket cruiser force) and the *Kiev* (for the pro-SSBN ASW force). Two *Sverdlov*-class cruisers were converted to command ships to test the rocket cruiser (*Zhdanov*) and ASW (*Admiral Senyavin*) second admiral command systems. A parallel program produced submarine command ships (converted submarine tenders).

The new flagships were not independent command centers in the Western mold. They did, however, receive vital targeting data from shore centers via special high-capacity links: the Vee Cone (and successor) HF antennas and, later, Low Ball satellite antennas. The result recalls the contemporary U.S. decision to develop shore intelligence fusion centers (FCCs) communicating via satellite (OTCIXS links) with TFCCs afloat.

There were some key differences. Without great computer capacity, it is unlikely that the Soviet shore plots (fusion centers) offered anything like the level of detail available in an FCC. Nor could they project ahead target motion. The Soviet shore center, then, could only provide a series of time-late potential target positions. The deployed flagship and strike units had to rely heavily on reconnaissance assets (e.g., Bear-D and satellites) to establish updated target and threat positions. At least for anti-ship attacks, each strike unit obtained its own final targeting (fire-control) data, although there was apparently a means of relaying data from, for example, a Bear-D between attacking units.

The evolution of submarine command and control for attacks on surface ships seems to have paralleled that of the surface ships. Soviet submarines were organized in brigades, and originally each brigade consisted of three two-boat divisions. The submarine tender/flagships, such as *Volga* and the *Don* class, appeared in the late 1950s. Control must have been by radio (most likely by burst transmission), because the tender would not be at sea, hence would not have been able to transmit acoustic signals, no matter how effective such signals might have been.

On the whole, it could be argued that no distant commander could efficiently control a submarine brigade against fast high-value targets any more than a distant commander could control surface ships. Presumably that was amply demonstrated in Okean 70. As in the surface fleet, the conclusion drawn was that each brigade needed its own nearby flagship. Since submarines, unlike all other warships, could operate in enemy-dominated waters, the flagship had to share their stealthiness: it had to be a *submarine* flagship. The idea was not new, but in the past it was generally rejected on the ground that efficient and secure communication between submerged submarines was impossible.

The external marks of a submarine flagship are a larger Pert Spring satellite communications antenna, a more elaborate Park Lamp VLF antenna, and a larger UHF communications antenna (Shotgun). Presumably the flagship, like a surface flagship, receives overall information via a satellite or long-haul radio. She then processes it and transmits to the other boats via line-of-sight radio, probably using a burst (squash) transmitter. Quite possibly a very simple acoustic signal is used to inform the other boats of the brigade that they should rise to periscope depth to receive their tactical orders via UHF.

Because all the submarines have Pert Spring and Park Lamp, each can function in an alternative solitary mode, receiving instructions directly from home. That most likely applies mainly to submarines operating in a primarily ASW mode, but it does permit single attacks when a full brigade or division cannot be present.

As in the surface flagships, the key piece of technology was a compact computer, which perhaps might be called a "second commodore." It seems likely that the first submarines so fitted were "Victor IIIs," which were also the first to have second captains (used to process contact data from their towed arrays). A modern submarine brigade, then, consists of a flagship and three divisions. Building policy was apparently to construct surplus flagships so that no submarine class appeared in multiples of seven. In peacetime, moreover, only one division per brigade was active; the other submarines were retained for mobilization.

It seems likely that the special communications versions (SSQ) of the "Hotel"- and "Golf"-class strategic submarines were interim or experimental submarine flagships. Submarines intended to operate closer to the coast, such as Kilos and Tangoes, were probably never built in flagship configuration; they could do perfectly well with tenders. Nuclear submarines, with their global reach, were and are a very different proposition.

◆ SOSS

The Soviet Ocean Surveillance System was the generic Western name for the integrated system the Soviets built to detect, track, and target Western ships. A natural outgrowth of the coast-defense system built up from before World War II, SOSS was designed to detect and target ships approaching the country, rather than to protect a moving naval formation from the approach of hostile ships or aircraft. The system, therefore, feeds a central naval command authority, which in turn directs ships and aircraft to intercept the approaching enemy force. The home-defense, rather than formation-defense, role of SOSS is probably reflected in its criterion for target detection. Since there is considerable sea space beyond the frontiers, the system can afford a low probability of detection on a day-by-day basis. In contrast, a surveillance system protecting a moving naval force cannot afford leaks.

In theory, the system is alerted to ships leaving Western bases by a combination of agents (HUMINT) and intelligence-gathering ships (AGIs) offshore. Ships at sea are detected and tracked by passive sensors: by satellites (EORSAT) and by ground HF/DF stations. Passive operation helps filter the vast number of ships at sea down to potential targets, but it also lays the system open to deception. These target acquisition devices in turn are used (by the central command) to cue trackers (such as radar aircraft, mainly Bear-Ds, and tattletale ships) which provide what amounts to fire-control information for missile attacks. Unlike the other system sensors, the trackers and targeters can communicate directly with shooters. The defunct radar satellite (RORSAT) fell into the targeter category, and EORSAT probably straddles the target acquisition and targeter categories.

SOSS was first tested in the Okean 70 exercise.

SWEDEN

◆ STRIKA/SUMP

Ericsson's current coastal-surveillance and weapons-control systems are for Swedish coastal artillery (STRIKA) and for naval command centers (SUMP). STRIKA and SUMP both use the CCIS bus approach of the shipboard tactical data systems; the system computer is a Censor 900E series machine, and the terminal is the Ericsson DS86 alphanumeric display terminal (ADT). A typical one- or two-operator station has one 23in vertical PPI, one to three ADTs, keyboards and rollerballs or joysticks, and a communications terminal.

SUMP supersedes the earlier STINA system (9CSI 500). See the 1991/92 edition for details of STINA, which had a capacity of 200 tracks at each of five regional control centers. The main STINA system sensor was the BEAB coastal radar. It is not clear to what extent foreign buyers of such radars also bought STINA systems.

UNITED KINGDOM

INRI, the company responsible for JOTS software, now has a British subsidiary (set up in October 1992). It offers a form of JMCIS software commercially as Nauticus, using a DRS console. In analogy to JMCIS, INRI's system now forms the core of JOCS (Joint Operational Command System), the British equivalent to GCCS. In 1996 INRI won the contract for CSS (command support system) originally envisaged as an LPD system, but now a British equivalent to the U.S. NTCS-A.

◆ OPCON/FOCSLE

OPCON is the British automated national naval central-command information system, based at the naval headquarters at Northwood. Conceived in 1974, it became fully operational in 1985. OPCON supports 150 local display terminals there, as well as remote workstations aboard deployed flagships and one at SACLANT headquarters in Norfolk, Virginia. As of early 1989 OPCON workstations or terminals were to have been installed in the German naval headquarters at Glucksburg, in the Allied Forces Northern Europe headquarters at Kolsas near Oslo, and in SACEUR headquarters at Brussels. An OPCON terminal was installed on board the U.S. flagship *Mount Whitney* for North Atlantic exercises. The system seems broadly comparable to the U.S. FCC.

The Royal Netherlands Navy has its own OPCON computers at Den Helder, linked to those at Northwood: a Dutch ship can talk to a British ship via radio to Den Helder, the link to Northwood, and Link R to the British ship.

Like FCC, OPCON is a track-keeping system; it is built around two ICL 2966 mainframe computers, with Tandem TXPs for I/O (including local displays). A back-up database at an alternative naval headquarters is periodically updated to match the main OPCON database. The standard workstation consists of an Aydin color graphics display alongside a DRS 20 alphanumeric display, the latter incorporating a badge reader (to control access to sensitive data); both displays have separate keyboards. The graphics display shows past, present, and predicted positions (and tracks) of all British naval vessels, together with maritime air patrols and reported contacts; coastlines and depth contours are also shown. It is not clear to what extent foreign vessels are shown; OPCON currently receives and filters JOTS data.

FOCSLE (Fleet Operational Command System Life Extension) is replacing OPCON 2, under a contract awarded to Siemens Plessey early in April 1995 under the SR(S) 7826 staff requirement. The new open-architecture system (for easier updates) provides a new core operating environment, using INRI Nauticus consoles, a Digital Alpha AXP-based compartmentalized mode workstation secure client/server system, and an MLS+ secure operating system. The existing upgraded DESC NSTN 7126 message-handling system is retained. As of spring 1995, FOCSLE was expected to enter service by the end of the year (thanks to using off-the-shelf equipment) and to have been completed by mid-1997.

British carriers and AAW ships have ASMA, the RAF-supplied Air Staff Management Aid, a text system providing information on air fields (status, readiness) and Opnotes. ASMA is provided via an SHF satellite link to a dedicated terminal. An ASMA terminal is aboard USS *Mount Whitney* (for the commander of the Atlantic Strike Fleet).

◆ PFSS/FOSP/OSCAD

Pilot Flag Support System is the British equivalent of the U.S. TFCC. It uses U.S. JOTS I software running on Hewlett-Packard 330 workstations. The workstation, Outfit PDT, acts as an intelligent data-link terminal with no picture-compilation capability. It has also been installed as an intelligent shipboard Link 11 terminal. The shore sources are OPCON (including the USN JOTS picture, supplied by CINCLANT at Norfolk) and the RAF Air Staff Management Aid (ASMA). SD-Scicon has recently added an extension to PFSS that provides the ASMA picture to Type 42 destroyers. Data are passed via Link R. PFSS is concerned with the surface and air pictures; it does not pass detailed submarine information to the deployed surface force.

FOSP (Fleet Ocean Surveillance Product) is a JOTS extension written in Rocky Mountain Basic, developed by SD-Scicon in the summer of 1990 and delivered that fall to support Gulf operations. It uses JOTS modules, including message-processing for track correlation and dynamic update of on-board databases. It can merge the remote picture with that received via tactical data links, and it can retransmit selected portions of the compiled picture for other local users.

Ocean Surveillance Communications and Display (OSCAD) is the next-generation successor to PFSS/FOSP; it will include the sub-surface picture. SD-Scicon has contracts to study shore connectivity, ship-shore-ship communications, geographical information system, and system security policy.

◆ CCA (Outfit JZZ)

Captain's Combat Aid is a target-evaluation and weapon-assignment system, part of the ADIMP modernization of the carriers and Type 42 destroyers. It is broadly comparable in concept to the U.S. C&D processor of the Aegis and Model 5 combat-data systems. Like Model 5, CCA uses its database to add characteristics to the objects (platforms, weapons) in the tactical picture built up by the ship's combat-information system. This information is used to identify and rank threats; the ship's expected performance against those threats is continuously evaluated. The system has its own dedicated color display. There are four display formats: ship system status, tactical situation, course recommendation, and preview display (projected tactical situation with projected effect of own-ship maneuvers). The course recommendation display shows no-go zones to support its recommendation. Threats are ranked on the basis of filters that can be preset or based on rules (which presumably can be changed as required). For example, CCA may identify incoming objects with nonincreasing aiming errors as threats not dealt with by ECM. The list of threats feeds the list of response planner goals. The system designers rejected a totally rule-based approach because it might have been slowed by excessive computation and by the need to choose among too many alternatives; in a situation corresponding precisely to a script, response can be far quicker. However, an exact match may not exist, so different components of a script can be modified by the system. In effect, the system is script-based at high levels, rule-based at lower levels. CCA also continuously monitors the tactical situation to recommend alternative measures if one fails (e.g., chaff does not distract incoming missile).

MUSL won the production contract in 1991, exploiting experience with Plessey's (now Marconi's) private venture Command Support Tool (CST, in operation since 1986) and the Marconi CAS (Command Advice System). Much CCA operation must involve looking up data; Marconi uses transputers to speed this process. The processors are 68040s.

Presumably CCA is virtually CAS rewritten in ADA rather than in the original LISP. The CAS workstation display was a large PPI showing the overall picture (presumably that compiled by the ship's CDS), with an operator-configured secondary display alongside to show the long-range tactical picture or the perceived air threat. Windows below the main PPI display showed status and own-ship status (course and speed, wind speed and direction), as well as a tote advising of enemy surveillance (e.g., by satellite), and could provide a touch-screen (alternatives are window/icon/rollerball, electroluminescent panel, and hard keyboard). Windows under the secondary display included automatic threat alert and time to closest point of approach (TCPA), an automated display of plan options and time to implement, a display of the plan chosen (with automatic replanning if it failed or if the threat changed), and an optional tote to show own-ship weapon status and target information. The system could be reconfigured at sea. Marconi also offered an option in which CAS built up a tactical picture directly from the ship's sensors, and thus in effect could substitute for the ship's CDS.

CAS differed from conventional combat-direction systems in that it automatically alerted a commander to a pressing threat, and automatically provided a solution, the efficacy of which it assessed continuously and the planned reaction adjusted to suit. CAS also offered tactical planning aids for use outside the combat zone.

◆ MAPS

Ferranti's Maritime Asset Planning System is an AI-based command advice system (TDA). It plans dispositions of ships in a group, automatically taking into account local conditions (e.g., radar propagation). It can also reconfigure a force to take account of the effect of losses or battle damage.

Functions include sector screen calculation, radar/communications propagation, geographic database, and large-scale disposition calculation. Sector screen calculation uses tactical rules to assign stations or sectors for units of a main body, to deal with

an estimated threat, taking into account station requirements (e.g., goalkeepers, inner screen, special stations) and available unit characteristics and capabilities (e.g., towed arrays). MAPS also calculates a numerical measure of effectiveness for the solution it selects. It can explain its reasoning, and it can display the effect of choosing some alternative. Large-scale disposition is a related but larger-scale calculation on a 240 × 240nm grid, allowing for operations well away from the main body. The coverage calculation, based on weather conditions, includes coverage of antimissile systems in the force. Force radar coverage can be calculated for any selected target height, and for any arrangement of serviceable radars within the force. Options include aircraft sortie planning, electronic warfare tasking, search and rescue control, underway replenishment (UNREP) planning, rules of engagement assessment, amphibious-operations planning, sonar-propagation prediction, task-force routing, MCM command planning, and ship safety and damage control. The basic MAPS does *not* include sonar considerations.

The MAPS calculations are supported by an Oracle Relational Database containing characteristics of ships, their sensors, and their weapons; performance data for missiles; performance data for radars; and geographic positions of bases and airfields.

In 1991 MAPS was sold to the JMSDF for integration in their C^2 systems. Ferranti claimed that other Pacific navies were interested.

UNITED STATES

Naval command systems are connected to a global military command system. The current World Wide Military Command and Control System (WWMCCS) was probably conceived primarily as a means of controlling nuclear forces; it is designed mainly to transmit orders to the specified and unified commanders. WWMCCS was necessary for the National Command Authority (NCA) and the Joint Chiefs of Staff (JCS) in Washington to command naval forces as part of strategic or joint operations.

The replacement, the Global Command and Control System (GCCS), is patterned on the decentralized Navy JOTS system (which evolved into JMCIS, the Joint Maritime Command Information Strategy). This is much more a means of providing a deployed commander with sufficient information for war-fighting. The shift reflects the change in conditions due to the end of the Cold War, from relatively simple but very tightly controlled operations with a nuclear emphasis, to very complex and loosely controlled war-fighting, as in the Gulf War.

GCCS can be imagined as a joint version of the naval system in which a combined command center (CCC rather than FCC) communicates with deployed commanders using TCCs (rather than TFCCs). The communication system envisaged is called Copernicus Forward.

Under the new concept of joint-force air operations, a carrier must be able to receive the joint air tasking order (ATO) by radio; that was not possible during the Gulf War. She may have to generate an ATO. The Navy has rejected an Air Force proposal that its ATO-generating computer, CTAPS (a follow-on to the Gulf War CAFMS), be installed on board carriers, on the ground that it adds unnecessary features and is too costly. Too, it is a broadcast system; the Navy prefers two-way operation. Late in 1992 Navy ships off the California coast received an ATO from a CAFMS at Luke AFB, Arizona (Exercise Tandem Thrust).

◆ OTH-T and OAB

The ongoing transformation of U.S. naval command and control was motivated by two concerns: the ability of forces afloat to target Tomahawk missiles beyond the horizon (OTH-T) and the ability of a deployed battle force to engage incoming Soviet missile attack aircraft before they could release their weapons (the Outer Air Battle, OAB). In each case it was vital that organic sensors be complemented by sensors outside the battle group.

Antiship Tomahawk presented a difficult targeting problem. In the past, a commander contemplating a long-range strike could rely heavily on the intelligence of the pilots conducting it. To use Tomahawk, he had to form a much more precise picture of the target and its behavior before attacking. The penalty for error became much greater.

In the case of Tomahawk, the decision was taken, about 1973, not to develop new dedicated (i.e., Soviet-style) ship-tracking sensors. Instead, current ship positions were *deduced* from the mass of information already available to the national intelligence agencies, as well as through intermittent observations (e.g., by patrol aircraft). Thus the new system concentrated on computer analysis of information rather than on new devices to gain new inputs. The picture would be formed at a shore center (FCC). Information would be sent to a tactical FCC, or TFCC, on board a flagship, using a satellite link. In the initial concept, the FCC was to send out only the locations of likely targets or other high-interest units, a technique called a HITS (high-interest targets) broadcast. That limited the load on communications media and also on the receiver.

Unfortunately, a Tomahawk strike planner needed more information, because the missile might not lock on to the right target in a group. It was therefore necessary not only for the FCC to maintain an elaborate shipping picture, but also for the TFCC to do likewise. Under the original HITS concept, the shore terminal would also control the shooters, since they would attack only those targets that had been declared to them on HITS broadcast. Under the later concept, authority in effect was moved to the deployed fleet.

As in the tactical links between shipboard combat-direction centers, the FCC would broadcast a series of updates to similar centers (TFCCs) in the battle groups. The high-capacity satellite link was TADIXS/OTCIXS. The key sensors were signal-intercept systems ashore, in the air (e.g., on EP-3s), and in space.

Initially it appeared that TFCC would be an elaborate system. It required a powerful computer, USQ-81, to assemble a long-range picture from the updates sent over the link. There was no question of cooperative track formation; the link was limited to updates to minimize the load on the receiver computer. However, the 1980s were a time of explosive computer development. Quite soon it was obvious that TFCC functions could be accomplished on a standard DTC I workstation. It became JOTS. JOTS II (hosted on a DTC II) could cooperate with the shore station to help form tracks. Not only were the new computers far more powerful than USQ-81, they were so cheap that virtually all ships could be equipped with them. Ultimately the sea-based nodes were designated the Naval Tactical Command System Afloat (NTCS-A).

The Royal Navy adopted the U.S. FCC-TFCC concept when it abandoned large-deck carriers (which provided the long-range fleet sensor, in the form of AEW aircraft). In effect, the current Sea Harrier was considered a sort of manned Tomahawk, cued to its target beyond the fleet's horizon. The British shared some U.S. sensor data, adding some of their own at Northwood. The British FCC was originally OPCON; it is now being updated under the FOCSLE program. Unlike the U.S. system, OPCON transmitted HITS messages, presumably on the theory that a Harrier pilot could indeed distinguish the targets from the surrounding nontargets.

The OTH-T investment paid off handsomely. The system designed to track Soviet warships was used very successfully to track merchant ships en route to Iraq after September 1990. In this chapter it appears under names such as TWCS (Tomahawk Weapons Control System), JOTS, Outlaw Hunter/OASIS, and ATW (Advanced Tactical Workstation).

In the 1980s, much the same consideration applied to the OAB. This time key sensors included a new relocatable OTH radar (ROTHR) and Slow Walker, a means of extracting information from existing DSP satellites originally intended to sense strategic missile launches. Once again, the issue was the extent to which the forward commander's horizon could, in effect, be extended by using other kinds of sensors.

OAB, like OTH-T, was a consequence of new technology, in this case Aegis. Before the advent of Aegis, it was generally accepted that fighters on patrol were the best counter to Soviet missiles after the latter had been launched. It was pointless to concentrate the fighters on killing Soviet bombers if that con-centration would leave the fleet open to any missiles that had been fired. However, once Aegis was in service, the fleet could afford the gamble of concentrating the fighters against the bombers, both before and after the latter had fired.

Both OTH-T and OAB implied that the traditional easy demarcation between strategic (time-late) intelligence sensors and real-time tactical sensors was breaking down. There are still important barriers, partly because national sensor data is still handled very differently than tactical data. Thus commanders often still need special terminals (TRE) for the special highly classified TENCAP broadcasts (see below). Systems that receive the data must sanitize it before it can be used.

During the Gulf War, another mission, theater (ballistic) missile defense (TMD), claimed considerable attention. Like OAB, it required external input (cueing). For example, satellites such as the DSP system can detect a missile launch, warning deployed units. Other systems may be able to follow the missile some way into its flight, defining a basket through which the missile must fly, and into which a defending weapon must be fired. More recently, cooperative engagement experiments have shown that combinations of sensors aboard ship can greatly help.

This evolution has continued with the increased emphasis on land-attack Tomahawk, which requires considerable imagery support. That is, the missile strike planner needs not only images of the target area, but also images of the areas over which the missile must fly (for correlation, for better accuracy, and to avoid enemy countermeasures and buildings). The need to send imagery to the deployed fleet is likely to lead to a new generation of high-capacity data links, the prototype of which is Challenge Athena. This practice makes data (video) compression extremely important.

For the U.S. Navy, the revolution in command and control is the decision to provide forward afloat commanders with sensor data rather than with instructions based on a reading of that data. This change is often expressed as a desire to improve "connectivity between sensor and shooter" or as a need for Tactical Exploitation of National [Intelligence] Capabilities (TENCAP program, established 1977).

The revolution inspired the new Copernicus communications architecture, which attempts to provide the at-sea commander with something approaching the volume of offboard sensor data needed with minimum delays. Enormous volume is needed simply because the decision is centered on the deployed commander, not on a shore decision-maker.

◆ NCCS/FCC/OSS/NFEP

NCCS is the generic term for the Naval Command and Control System, the basis of which is a shore node (FCC) connected to an afloat node (TFCC) by a high-capacity satellite link, OTCIXS.

Fleet Command Centers (FCCs) are the shore stations (and wartime command centers) of the unified Atlantic and Pacific commanders, the commanders of the Atlantic Fleet (Norfolk) and Pacific Fleet (Pearl Harbor) and the deployed Numbered Fleet commanders (London, Naples, and probably Yokosuka), a total of seven sites. They connect the fleet to the WWMCCS, by means of which the NCA commands deployed forces.

The combination of FCC and links was attractive to the political authorities because it could be used to control deployed naval forces, particularly (presumably) their nuclear weapons. After all, Tomahawk aboard attack submarines was a major dispersal of U.S. strategic nuclear firepower. Thus the FCC was also the naval node of the national-level WWMCCS. More recently NCCS has entered the antidrug war via links to the maritime defense zones.

Initially the TFCC was quite expensive because it was built around an expensive picture-keeping computer, USQ-81. However, with the advent of the powerful but inexpensive DTC-series workstations, shipboard terminals for the FCC-TFCC system could be installed on board virtually all ships. NCCS could be extended from major flagships down to lesser combatants; the afloat element was renamed NCCS-A and then NTCS-A, for naval tactical command system afloat. Because all the system computers were now to be identical DTC/TACs, effort was concentrated on software, including tactical and logistical aids for the FCCs and tactical decision aids for the afloat units. NCCS modernization includes a new DTC-based Navy front-end processor (NFEP) for the FCC, for the communications links that tie the system together.

The Operations Support System (OSS) is the DTC/TAC-based system used in the FCCs to combine, display, and transmit information to the TFCCs (and to provide information for ashore command centers). The OSS Operational Requirement was issued in December 1987. OSS originally ran on a Honeywell DPSS computer. An upgrade (to JOTS II standard, using DTC II computers and large-screen displays) was begun in FY89 (OR December 1987). The baseline system employs the Fleet Command Center Battle-Management Program (FCCBMP) and Operations Support Group Prototype (OSGP).

OSS Increment I (FY91/92) standardizes the centers, providing each with a SAFENET LAN. Each center will ultimately have about 15 workstations. The LAN architecture makes it relatively easy to replace existing workstations with more powerful ones, as the Navy moves from DTC II to TAC-3, TAC-4, and beyond.

The FY91 program included development of a decision aid, CASES (Capabilities Assessment Expert System), and an integrated scheduler using the Force Requirement Expert System Enhancements (FRESH)/PC EMSKED/Fleet Enhancements Scheduling System (FESS).

CASES analyzes combinations of different warfare areas and controls simulations and warfare models running simultaneously on other dedicated computers. Its models are ray mode acoustic propagation, sweep width/search rate acoustic search, ASW barrier, ASW area search, IUSS (integrated undersea surveillance system), OPTAMAS (optimization of the performance of theater ASW mobile acoustic sensors), acoustic detection, battle-group defense, and carrier- and land-based air strike. It also includes two expert systems, OPERA (ASW water management) and ASSESS (to derive conclusions from CASES studies, including generation of summary reports). OPERA bases its recommendations on the expected detection-and-attack potential and expected survivability of the various available ASW platforms (air, surface, submarine). CASES was developed under DARPA sponsorship (under the Strategic Computing Program) and is now operational at CINCPACFLT at Pearl Harbor. It is currently running on a Macintosh and has to be revised for DTC II operation.

Increment II (FY93/95: software releases 93-1 through 95-1) provides an interface with the OSIS baseline upgrade (OBU), as well as to WWMCCS (through the Navy WWMCCS Software Standardization [NWSS] replacement). WWMCCS is to be replaced by GCCS, which uses the standard naval tactical computers and the naval command system architecture. Software added at this stage includes status of forces data (Status of Readiness and Training System, or SORTS), Casualty Reporting (CASREP), Movement Reporting (MOVREP), Employment Scheduling (EMPSKD), Military Sealift Command Movement Report (MSCMR), Submarine Notice (SUBNOT), and the position-processing connection to WWMCCS. The FY93 program included the beginning of an upgrade to TAC-3 computers. Tactical decision aids introduced at that time included route generation and land mass avoidance.

Under Increment III, OSS will incorporate the formerly separate functions of the STT for submarines (at submarine operational command centers) and of the Fleet High-Level Terminal (FHLT) for patrol aircraft (at shore ASW command centers [SACCs]). It will also add a new Information Presentation and Distribution System (IPDS). This version should be complete sometime in 1996 (FY97). Increment IV (FY96/99) will continue the evolutionary development of OSS. Multilevel security (MLS) features will be incorporated as they become commercially available.

There is a related USCINCPAC Command Center Improvement Program (CCIP). The OSS program is involved in several joint programs: Joint Crisis Management System (JCMS)/Joint Crisis Analysis Tools (JCAT) and PAC Crisis Management System (PACCMS). SACLANT shares in the OSS system under a cooperative project agreement of 18 December 1992.

♦ **OSIS/OBU**

Ocean Surveillance Information System is the combination of all the U.S. Navy's existing operational intelligence systems, joined to support tactical operations, particularly for over-the-horizon missile targeting (OTH-T), and also to warn of the approach of enemy long-range missile-firing platforms. The outputs of Navy intelligence systems are combined with inputs from national systems (under a program called TENCAP). The OSIS OTH-T product is disseminated to the Fleet as the OPINTEL broadcast.

OSIS now employs four major sites: two joint intelligence centers (the former Naval Ocean Surveillance Information Center at Suitland, Maryland, and a center at Pearl Harbor), one Joint Intelligence Center Detachment (for the Pacific), and one Fleet Ocean Surveillance Information Facility (FOSIF) at Rota, Spain. There is also a software support activity and a training site.

Dedicated OSIS sensors include a ground HF/DF system, Bulls Eye (and its shipboard adjunct, Classic Outboard), and the Classic Wizard/White Cloud satellite described below, as well as SOSUS and its adjuncts (described below). The DoD Aerial Reconnaissance Office (DARO) now tasks the EP-3s formerly dedicated to OSIS tasks.

The OSIS Specific Operational Requirement was issued in September 1970. Presumably it responded to the expanded Soviet naval surface presence in areas like the Mediterranean. For example, the Rota FOSIF was built at about this time specifically to provide the Sixth Fleet with warning of possible Soviet naval threats.

Late in 1982 TRW was given a contract for an OSIS baseline upgrade (OBU). An OBU Navy Decision Coordinating Paper, presumably laying out the current OBU concept, was issued in May 1987. It was followed by an OSIS Decision Coordinating Paper in January 1990, and by a Program Change Approval Document in January 1992. The dates suggest that the 1987 paper called for OBU development in accord with the new evolutionary acquisition (i.e., continuous computer upgrade) concept and that the later papers integrated new capabilities, such as ROTHR.

At present an OBU site is built around a dual Ethernet bus fed by a series of VAX6000 series computers, serving workstations for the system manager, watchstanders, and analysts. The mainframes in turn can access a common database in the form of a disk farm. OBU is intended to improve OSIS's timeliness to nearly real time (to 95% accuracy) without heavy investment in new sensors, by updating the OSIS database with each satellite pass and each new sensor reading. Given the degree of noise in existing data, this goal is probably somewhat unrealistic. Under the FY90 program a ROTHR Interface Module (RIM) was completed for the Pacific FOSIC (however, the radar in question has now been moved to the Caribbean).

In common with other major command/information systems, OBU is now subject to evolutionary acquisition, meaning periodic upgrades with new computers. As of 1993, it had already completed Phases I and II, and Phase III was in progress. Phase III apparently envisages a file-server architecture, in which powerful workstations handle data and the central computer is reduced to maintaining massive files of information. Both graphics and alphanumeric workstation upgrades were developed under the FY93 program. This program also includes work on a special security architecture for the envisaged open system.

OBU has been sold to the RN (installation and accreditation were completed in FY90), and then to the JMSDF and to the RAN. Presumably these agreements cover the OBU software, not the information content.

♦ **NTCS-A/JMCIS/JOTS/TFCC/USQ-112/USQ-119**

NTCS-A (the Naval Tactical Command System Afloat) is conceived as a unified family of hardware and software for all the major levels of afloat command, from the Numbered Fleet commanders in their FCCs to the officers in tactical command (OTCs) in their TFCCs down to the composite warfare commanders (CWCs), subordinate warfare commanders (SWCs), commander amphibious task force (CATF), commander landing force (CLF), and commanding officers/TAOs. It is hosted on standard desktop tactical computers (currently DTC IIs and TAC-3s). Thus, the TFCC on a carrier is in effect a collection of standard computers running software directly related to the software on, for example, the single machine on a frigate.

JMCIS, the Joint Maritime Command Information Strategy (formerly System), is the concept of using increasingly powerful desktop workstations to merge many formerly separate systems in NTCS-A. The term *JMCIS* was to have superseded *NTCS-A*, but the earlier term proved more popular. Each workstation maintains a series of databases, each keyed to geographic position. The operator can assemble what amounts to an increasingly complex tactical picture by overlaying the databases, within limits set by the system's security filters. This sequence began with JOTS, whose OTH-T database was essentially a map of world shipping patterns. Embedded in JMCIS are the Naval Warfare Tactical Data Base (NWTDB) and the Joint Deployable Intelligence Support System (JDISS). JOTS (Joint Operational Tactical System) was implemented on DTC I and DTC II computers.

JOTS was USQ-112; JOTS II was USQ-112A (1991), running version 1.15 software. The baseline NTCS-A implemented on DTC II computers is USQ-119. The initial upgrade version (with TAC-3 computers), conceived in 1992–93, is USQ-119A. The JMCIS baseline version is USQ-119B. The integrated C^4I version is USQ-119C. The TAC-4 version will be USQ-119D. Variants are designated 1 through 54 and 101 through 126 (e.g., USQ-119A[V]3); 101 through 126 are reserved for NTCSS-unique shore sites. Shipboard systems use low numbers, shore systems higher ones. Each ship or site has its own variant number so that, for example, USQ-119(V)13 is replaced by A(V)13, and so on.

NTCS-A maintains identical databases (OTH tactical pictures) for all its users. The architecture is much the same as in ACDS/Link 11, but on a grander scale: as a user updates the database, the updated data are transferred to other users. A user can, in theory, maintain a global database, but filters generally are used to limit updates to the area of interest. Filters can also limit access to specially classified data. The main NTCS-A net is OTCIXS. Automatic contact data come from up to three Link 14 broadcasts, the OPINTEL broadcast (including BLUFORLOC [Blue Force Location]), OTCIXS Rainform (OTH) Gold broadcast, Link 11 (requires special link-monitor unit), FOTC (OTH-T) and/ or HITS (high-interest target system, via GENSER teletype), FDDS/TWCS broadcast via OTCIXS, TADIXS broadcast, TACINTEL (tactical intelligence, special classified information), and other DTC/TAC-based units (such as TEPEE). For organic data, NTCS-A taps into (but generally does not provide data to) own-ship NTDS and navigational data. It transmits via the OTCIXS and HIT nets.

NTCS-A includes tactical decision aids (TDAs) to answer "what if?" staff planning questions. They were added in the transition from JOTS I to JOTS II (the DTC II computer can support multitasking, so the results of TDA calculation can be displayed as windows over parts of the basic database).

Each workstation is a terminal in the FOTC (force OTH track coordinator) broadcast. It can act as FOTC or as a participant. FOTC is a track manager; it provides consistent track data rather than individual event data (as in NTDS); ships receiving the broadcast can build up their own track files, as the basis for consistent decision-making throughout a force. FOTC serves as a basis for Tomahawk antiship targeting.

The basic JOTS II program consists of 300,000 lines of code, and it can run on any UNIX-based computer with 32 Mbytes of memory, a 500-Mbyte hard disk, and a speed of 7 MIPS or more. The associated bus is Ethernet (generally a fiber-optic bus in U.S. applications). Although DTC II is the usual host computer, JOTS II can also run on some Hewlett-Packard machines and on Silicon Graphics and Sun workstations.

The JOTS software comprises an operator-machine interface and four main programs: a tactical database manager (TDBM), a geographic database (The Chart), communications, and Wizard

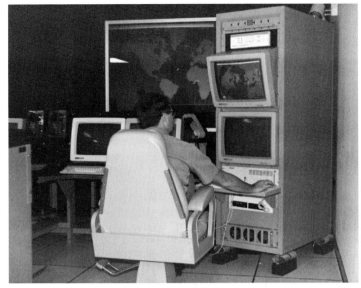

A JOTS station shows typical elements of modern U.S. Navy command systems: the two-screen console at right, typical single screens, and a large-screen display at center. JMCIS has much the same display elements, run by a much more powerful processor. (Larry Welcher, NAVELEX)

X. TDBM fuses available information to form a correlated track database. Typically, one workstation in a ship's system is designated master track-keeper, and its changes are automatically passed around the shipboard network. The ship designated FOTC passes its track database to other ships of its battle group via OTCIXS. With several battle groups (and several different countries' ships) operating together, it becomes necessary to designate a theater-wide FOTC (super-FOTC). This minor enhancement was added late in 1990 and tested early in 1991. The Chart automatically plots TBDM data for display, and it also provides such navigational graphics as projected tracks. It is to be revised to include terrain elevation and other features (to support amphibious operations) and also to support more projections (a total of 15). The communications software configures the system to accept various external inputs, such as OTCIXS messages (primarily OTH-Gold format). The "tool kit" defines such features as buttons, scrolling windows, and pop-up menus, by means of which applications can easily be built.

Version 1.1 (February 1991) includes the following TDAs:
ASW: Barrier search, area search, passive screening, ray trace, propagation loss, sonobuoy field planning
ASUW: Two-track analysis, maneuvering board, closest point of approach (CPA), range/bearing table, surface surveillance, Tomahawk launch, multiunit Harpoon launch, line-of-bearing (LOB) firing
ASUW/ASW: Maneuvering target statistical tracker (MTST) analysis, transit search, contact analysis (tracking algorithms, history plots, contact predictions, constructions of containment areas, and solutions for dynamic bearings/ ranges), aircraft search
AAW: CAP stations, Chainsaw (fighter tactics), vector-grid-logic (fighter tactics), surveillance air intercept, surface ship screening
EW: Satellite vulnerability prediction, integrated radar environment prediction (IREPS), HF spectrum-propagation prediction, EMCON planning
Weather: Prediction using the GOES satellite
Logistics: Refueling-route planning, communications planning, time statistics, position and intended movement (PIM)

NTCS-A now embraces JOTS as well as several formerly independent systems: TFCC, ACS, EWCM, POST, and NIPS (see below). The JMCIS concept (1992/93) was to develop a fully open architecture that could support turnkey applications, using structured interfaces (a common operating environment using common TAC-series hardware). The main elements are the incoming communications manager, outgoing communications manager, chart package, and tactical database manager (TDBM). TDBM acts as a buffer for incoming information, correlating it and automatically sending it to the appropriate section. Information is generally presented in geographically keyed form, called up by the TDBM.

The FY93 NTCS-A software release (2.0) merged EWCM, Advanced Tactical Processor (ATP), and Strike Plot into the space and electronic warfare commander (SEWC) module of NTCS-A. The next step (FY94, release 3.0) integrates all digital imagery (e.g., TAMPS and DIWS) into an NTCS-A Imagery LAN. The FY94 program also integrates the formerly separate Cryptologic Combat Work Station (CCWS, originally the Cryptologic Combat Support Console, SSQ-93) into NTCS-A. The meteorology program, formerly TESS (one of the most stressful of all applications), is now NITES (NTCS-A Integrated Tactical Environment Subsystem). NIEWS is the NTCS-A Imagery Exploitation Workstation. USQ-119 now embraces the OSS (in the FCCs) and the mission support computer in a TSC (formerly ASWOC). As of the fall of 1995, the standard software package was release 2.0.10.5, with 2.2 planned for operational evaluation late in the fall. It is the first cleaned-up version.

ACS (Afloat Correlation System) assembles and correlates track data from off-board and on-board sources to form a consistent tactical picture, sending sanitized data back to the ship's CDS and also sending battle-group track data back to OSIS to help ensure that the larger system carries the same tracks as the fleet at sea. At one time the *unclassified* description of ACS showed an ability to handle 4000 tracks simultaneously. ACS was merged with another program, POST (Prototype Ocean Surveillance Terminal), under which correlation algorithms for external data had been developed. Correlation is by a statistical/heuristic algorithm using such factors as radar emissions (for identification), feasibility of different possible motions between detections, and likelihood of movements. For example, two detections of a ship's air-search radar 30 nm and 15 min apart would have to be taken as separate ships, whereas the system might determine that two such detections 30 nm and 70 min apart came from the same ship. The result of correlation is a picture of the likely positions of ships, a database that can be used, for example, for OTH-T. EWCM (EW Coordination Module) is intended to allow force commanders to evaluate alternative EW tactics on a large scale quickly enough for them to be implemented. Decision aids include selection of optimum power and frequency of communications equipment (to minimize the probability of intercept) and optimum decoy location. The combination of ACS and EWCM forms a Force Fusion System (FFS), to evaluate threats and handle countermeasures.

With the increased emphasis on jointness, recent NTCS-A efforts have included integration of Air Force modules to process air tasking orders and display target locations on naval workstations. For the Marines, NTCS-A now includes interfaces with the Position Location and Reporting System (PLRS) and with the Marines' Intelligence Analysis System (IAS).

A related system is the Joint Worldwide Intelligence Communications System (JWICS), a core architecture for intelligence communications, including video teleconferencing. Another development is Intelink, which became operational in December 1994, for communication from the national level down to Joint Task Forces.

These systems began with JOTS, which was conceived as a "poor man's TFCC" for Adm. Jerry O. Tuttle, who was commanding a carrier division in 1983. At the time commercial workstations were clearly outperforming many Mil-Spec machines. In this case a very powerful desktop computer (HP 9845, a precursor of the HP 9020 bought as DTC I) ran FDDS (TFCC display) software, displaying the OTH-T picture provided over the link from the shore FCC. Admiral Tuttle wanted the OTH picture, but did not want to wait for the major refit required to install TFCC. As it happened, the workstation both outperformed the Mil-Spec computers in TFCC and cost far less. JOTS soon adopted the standard Navy desktop computer (DTC I) as its host machine.

The admiral took JOTS with him when he went to the Atlantic Fleet FCC. It replaced the earlier shore terminal. A JOTS derivative was later adopted by the U.S. national military command authority and by the CINCs.

JOTS II was operationally evaluated on board the *Independence* and *Jouett* in June 1990; more than 200 systems were then hurriedly produced to support Desert Shield. They included JOTS installations on board the Australian, Canadian, and Dutch ships in the Persian Gulf. By early 1991, Japan was considering a version for its P-3 Orions. Rapid production was possible because JOTS II is little more than a standard commercial workstation running software that can easily be reproduced.

JOTS is installed on board British flagships, including the light carriers, in the form of PFSS (see above). JOTS differs from the British OPCON in that it provides graphics. OPCON provides only alphanumeric data, and in this case it is multiplexed with JOTS. The British installations use HP 9020 computers and are to be upgraded with HP 300s.

The current software contractor is INRI (Inter-National Research Institute), which is trying to rewrite the system in ADA.

In accordance with JMCIS concepts, NTCS-A uses a variety of commercial display hardware. As of 1994, the major stand-alone units were the 19in EDL Model 6119 or Sony GDM 1932 high-resolution display, the 27in EDL Model 6127 autosynchronous display, and a large-screen display using a three-color Esprit 2000G commercial projector. In each case, resolution was 1280×1024 pixels, and frame rate was something over 60 Hz. Future systems are to use LCDs.

Simple USQ-119(V) systems use a DTC II computer, which may feed a single 19in high-resolution terminal for the TAO. Inputs into the computer are Link 14, the Fleet Broadcast, and tracks from the ship's own radar set (SPA-25G/RADDS). There is also a navigational input from the charthouse. There is a two-way connection (for cooperative OTH-T) with the HIT/BOSN broadcast. Systems of this type are installed on board major auxiliaries and amphibious ships (AD, AE, AO, AOE, AOR, LSD, LST, LPD, LPH).

FMS variants are similar, with a single TAC-3 either in CIC or in an equipment room, controlling one or more 19in high-resolution monitors with their own keyboards, including at least one in CIC and perhaps also one in a staff space.

Three Coast Guard variants (A1, A2, A3) were approved in 1993 for, respectively, the 210-, 270-, and 378-foot cutters. All use single TAC-3s. In A1, the TAC-3 in CIC receives various navigational inputs directly (commercial GPS, navigational radar, gyro, Loran-C). It also receives tactical broadcasts: the Fleet Broadcast, OTCIXS, and an SBA data link. The A2 version is more elaborate, the radio central containing a separate processor to receive OTCIXS and TADIXS A. The A3 version has a pair of TAC-3s in CIC, with four 25in displays. This may be the version the Coast Guard plans to develop into a next-generation navigation and control system.

A non-Tomahawk FFG has a more elaborate system, USQ-119(V)3A, adding a one-way feed from the ship's combat-direction system (passive link tap, or PLT), and a two-way connection to OTCIXS. This version feeds two 19in screens (with keyboards) in CIC, each connected to a separate DTC II. The corresponding version for the *Kidd* class, (V)4A, adds a connection feeding into the ship's signal exploitation space (SSES), with its own 19in monitor and keyboard. It is shared with any staff riding the ship. The *California*-class version, (V)4B, adds a monitor in a separate staff space, but is otherwise similar to (V)4A. The early *Ticonderoga*-class version, (V)5, is also similar, except that it provides a direct input from the ship's inertial navigation system. Flag-configured LPDs (LPD 7–10, 12, 13) are similar ([V]6 version), except that they add a large-screen display in the staff space and a separate joint intelligence center (JIC) with an imagery support terminal (USQ-109[V]3) fed by a separate SATCOMM link.

Tomahawk shooters require something more, the TADIXS A targeting broadcast. In a *Spruance* a separate TWCS is fed by both the OTCIXS, which feeds NTCS-A, and by TADIXS A, via the generic front-end communications processor (GFCP). This version is (V)8A or 8B, depending on details of the ship. Aegis cruisers' (V)9 version and the *Arleigh Burke*–class and later *Ticonderoga*-class (V)10A and 10C are similar, except for using the inertial navigation inputs. In these cases, too, the paired 19in monitors in CIC are replaced by one (destroyer) or two (cruiser) Aegis color monitors. A video switch chooses between Aegis C&D and NTCS-A video for these monitors.

A submarine is a somewhat simpler case. The submarine version for the CCS systems is A(V)23A. Sonar and the gyro (ESGN) both feed into an automatic data acquisition processor (ADAP) and then to an Ethernet LAN. The SFMPL computer in the submarine sonar room (see the discussion under submarine CDSs) is also connected to this LAN. So is an HP 730 in the attack center, which receives TADIXS B data directly, and OTCIXS and TADIXS B via a GFCP. VERDIN and Link 11 data are sent into a sensory interface unit (SIU), which is connected directly to both a Mk 81 Mod 3 weapons-control console in the attack center and to the GFCP, hence ultimately to the HP 730. That computer in turn controls a pair of 19in monitors with keyboards, one for the fire-control operator. Trident submarines have (V)23B; *Seawolf* is to have (V)23C.

Flag-configured LPHs (LPH 3, 7, 9, 10, and 11: [V]12 version) had three DTC II computers on a fiber-optic LAN. Two were located in the staff space; the other was in CIC. A new crisis action center had its own large-screen display connected to one of the DTC IIs in the staff space (it could also receive data from the machine in CIC). Another was connected to a 19in display in the SSES. The TACINTEL broadcast and similar data were fed into an HP 9020 (DTC I) in that space (operating as a POST) and then into the DTC II in CIC, which maintained the OTH-T picture. Although these ships lacked NTDS, they received the Link 11 broadcast, which was fed into the CIC computer via a passive link tap.

The next step up in complexity is the LHA's USQ-119(V)13B, in which the LAN is connected to no fewer than 11 DTC IIs in CIC (one), the EW module in CIC (one), the NTDS Room (two), Flag Plot (two), the joint intelligence center (three), the Landing Force Ops Center (LFOC) (one), and the SACC (one). An HP 9020 (DTC I) in a separate War Room runs a large-screen display, and is connected to the rest of the system by switchboard. Flag Plot, CIC, and LFOC all have large-screen displays. Unlike earlier systems, this one makes imagery data available on the fiber-optic LAN. A(V)13 Phase I (LHA 4) replaces the DTC IIs in the JIC with TAC-3s and connects them to a local Ethernet LAN carrying 386 workstations. The LHD version, (V)14, has two additional DTC IIs in its JIC (some feeding the TAMPS strike planner), and a Flag EDP (electronic data processing) space replaces the NTDS room of the LHA. A DTC II is placed in the SSES (there is none in the EW module in CIC) and a second is placed in the LFOC, for a total of 14 DTC IIs. They are replaced wholesale by TAC-3s in the A(V)14A version. The A(V)14B version introduces a secondary SCI LAN to connect DTCs in the JIC, in the SSES, and in the Supplementary (ELINT) Plot.

A carrier ([V]16 version) has many more spaces that must be interconnected: the Combat Direction Center (CDC), Flag Plot, TFCC, Supplot or SSES, Intelligence Center (CVIC), War Room, and NTDS Room. CDC contains three computers: one to connect with the ship's CDS, one for the FOTC, and one for the ASWM (ASW module). The FOTC computer connects with a screen and keyboard in the EW module of the CDC. There is also a large-screen display. Flag Plot contains its own computer (presumably mainly for "what-if" calculations) connected to the LAN and to a bridge terminal. TFCC contains two computers: one for the space and electronic warfare commander (SEWC), one to handle the various broadcasts (including TADIXS). There are two large-screen displays and two 27in autosynchronous displays. SSES lives off the LAN, with no computer of its own. CVIC, however, has three computers (typically two TAC-3 and a DTC II), one of them feeding distributed workstations by means of an Ethernet. No TAC or DTC computers are in the War Room or NTDS Room. Thus CV-66, for example, has a total of six TAC-3s and three DTC IIs. Many ships have a triple workstation (command table) in TFCC to replace the two 27in displays with their keyboards. Versions vary. The two newest carriers (CVN-74 and -75 as well as CV-63) have four 19in high-resolution monitors, one 15in TIMS monitor, and one 13in CCTV monitor. An earlier version (CV-62, CVN-68, CVN-72) has the four 19in monitors plus two 15in autosynchronous monitors and two keyboards and trackballs. CVN-76 is not to have a triple table at all. Several of these ships have a separate SCIF (special compartmented intelligence facility) outside the CVIC, with its own special LAN.

The flagship systems (LCCs and AGFs) are (V)17 through (V)20; there is no (V)21, and (V)22 is a shore command center system (22A for JMOCC, 22B for 10 MOCCs, 22C for 4 MAST II, and 22D for 4 MICFAC IIs). (V)23 is for submarines. (V)24 is for the shore command center in Bahrein. (V)25 is for USS *Inchon* (LPH being converted to MCM command ship). (V)27 is for the LPD-17 class. (V)28 is for ARS, (V)29 is for AFS, (V)31 is for Marine air bases, (V)32 is for MCMs, (V)33 is for the *Cyclone*-class PCs, (V)35 is for the CNO command center in Washington, (V)36 is for the CINCPAC command center, (V)37 is for CINCUSNAVEUR, (V)38 is a pair of systems for the command center in Naples, (V)39 is for four systems at Norfolk, (V)40 is for CINCPAC and the Pacific ASW command, (V)41 is for the Iceland Defense Force, (V)42 is for COMSUBPAC, (V)43 is for the submarine commander at Yokosuka, (V)44 is for five intelligence centers, (V)47 is for 14 tactical support centers (formerly ASWOCs), (V)48 is for the Sixth Fleet surveillance center, (V)49 is for the patrol plane commander in Japan, (V)51 is for the Fleet Numerical Meteorology and Oceanography Center, and (V)52 and (V)53 are for various oceanography centers.

See also NACCIS, above.

◆ **AFDS/TIPS**

The Amphibious Flag Data System was originally developed for the two flagships *Blue Ridge* and *Mount Whitney*; the requirements were developed in 1964 by a study group convened for the purpose at San Diego. AFDS combines an integrated operational intelligence center (NIPS, the Naval Intelligence Processing System), an amphibious command-information system (ACIS), and the ship's NTDS. NIPS matches the system on board an aircraft carrier. ACIS is built out of NTDS equipment (based on one CP-642B computer with OL-170 displays) to provide an amphibious commander with force-loading data (so that plans can be changed if, for example, one ship is lost), with the landing plan, with the shore-bombardment and air-support plans, with a bomb-damage-assessment file, and with intelligence data.

Compared to the usual installation, the associated NTDS adds a capability to control aircraft over the amphibious objective area and to coordinate helicopter assault and resupply, close air support, and air defense.

Note that ACIS is not a real-time command system; it cannot order troops to move, or airplanes to attack specific targets. Nor has it any automatic connection to the ship's NTDS (which also uses CP-642B computers, in this case four of them with an EMCU). About 1990 a major refit with UYK-43 computers in both CDS and tactical information processing system (TIPS), equivalent to the system on board LHDs, was planned for FY96 and FY98.

LCC amphibious command spaces are: landing force operations center (LFOC), supporting arms coordination center (SACC), tactical air control center (TACC), helicopter direction center (HDC), joint intelligence center (JIC, containing NIPS and other equipment), and ship signals-exploitation space (SSES). LHAs and LHDs have corresponding spaces. In each case there is also a flag plot. LPHs have similarly designated spaces but lack tactical air control (they do have a troop operations and logistics center). They also lack automation of any kind.

The LHAs (*Tarawa* class) have a new UYK-7-based system, ITAWDS (integrated tactical amphibious warfare data system). The word "integrated" means that the two elements, the ship's TDS proper and the tactical information management (or processing) system (TIPS), are fully integrated, using a common executive/operating system. The computers are a pair of UYK-7s.

TIPS uses UYA-5 displays rather than the UYA-4 of the TDS. TIPS (corresponding to ACIS) manages assault personnel, operational planning, and logistic coordination. It can generate target designation data and updates, transmitting targets to weapons (including close-air-support aircraft) via the combat-direction element of the system. It in turn accepts data from NIPS and can read and store digital intelligence data. Compared to the LCCs, these ships have improved (Phase 2) intelligence centers. They are now being modernized with UYK-43 computers.

The associated TDS is comparable to NTDS, but lacks the usual threat evaluation/weapon assignment (TEWA) and quick-response facilities. It also lacks any ASW element, and does not support strike warfare.

The LHDs have an updated version of the same integrated ITAWDS, this time using UYK-43 computers and UYQ-21 displays. They were completed with large-scale displays, digital data indicators, and automated status boards. These ships also have PLRS (TSQ-129), a means of tracking troops operating ashore (and the basis for a system to control air-cushion landing craft, KSQ-1).

In theory the LHA or LHD has an austere version of the LCC's ACIS, suited only to controlling a smaller scale assault (MEB or MEU level, rather than MEF level). However, the later ships enjoy far more computer power than the LCC. Indeed, the LCCs are currently scheduled for retirement without replacement. They are used as fleet flagships, based at Yokosuka and Norfolk.

To a considerable extent, the advent of massive computer power in the form of NTCS-A (JMCIS) has overtaken TIPS. See the NTCS-A entry for details.

One element is still lacking. None of the amphibious systems is designed to command forces ashore on a sustained basis; there is no amphibious system really equivalent to a naval CDS. Current interest in such a system is, however, considerable. In theory, the Army's digital battlefield concept corresponds to the fleet operating concept reflected in the tactical data links and in systems such as NTDS and ACDS. It is entirely possible that in future littoral operations command will never move ashore with the troops, and thus that the LHA or LHD may have to control forces, including supporting arms, well inland, despite its very limited flag spaces.

♦ **Naval Surface Fire Support Control System/AFATDS**

This system is being developed to replace existing manual systems for answering calls for fire support ashore. One driver is the desire to support the shore battle from beyond the horizon, using weapons with long times of flight; another is the need to integrate a greater variety of long-range systems, such as the projected naval version of ATACMS, guided shells, and close air support aircraft. Presumably it is the advent of GPS, a very precise navigational system, which makes it possible to key OTH fire to battlefield targets. A scheduled May 1996 demonstration will use three ships (*Saipan*, *Mount Whitney*, and *Mitscher*) and a shipboard installation of the standard army AFATDS (Army field artillery tactical direction system, actually a joint Army/Marine program). Although AFATDS is conceived as a fire-direction center, it provides considerable information on terrain and on small-unit movements, and thus provides the situational awareness that might be used to control troop movements ashore. It would also permit rapid replanning.

The Army already sees AFATDS as part of its Force XXI digital battlefield initiative, for which it is developing an Army battle command system (ABCS) including a lower-level Army tactical command-and-control system (ATTCS). AFATDS is one of five battlefield elements of ATTCS, using common hardware and software. The others are the maneuver control system (MCS); forward area air defense command, control, and intelligence system (FAAD C³I); all-source analysis system (ASAS); and the combat service support control system (CSSCS). They are linked by common hardware and software, much as in the current naval command and control systems. Thus ATATDS can display overlays of obstacles taken from ASAS and ammunition supply reports from CSSCS. Presumably amphibious command ships will ultimately have to accommodate some elements of ATTCS,

since command may have to be exercised from afloat for a protracted period.

Plans for ABCS also include a lower-level system, Force XXI Battle Command Brigade and Below (FBCB2), which is intended to provide individual soldiers with digital systems based on the intervehicular information system (IVIS) of the M1 tank. In theory, this system will initially provide ATTCS with the location and status of every vehicle on the battlefield, and ultimately of every individual on the battlefield. Again, in theory that should make for quick and safe fire support, since AFATDS will automatically know where all friendlies are, and will also automatically receive and evaluate all requests for fire support. This sort of intercommunication is promised thanks to a common software operating environment extending throughout the system. The problem is extremely complex. Typical naval CDSs, admittedly using somewhat ancient computers, carry up to about 2000 tracks. A battlefield might easily accommodate several times that many vehicles, not to mention varied terrain features that are extremely significant in ground combat.

An AFATDS system consists of one, two, or three workstations. The display is a map showing targets and fire-support resources, with their coverage. Army practice is to use the workstations to plan fire-support missions that can be integrated into operations plans and operations orders. The system can also receive an ATO, both to request air support and to avoid interference with aircraft (for example, a rocket or guided missile may actually endanger an airplane flying nearby). Because planning is so fast, plans can easily be changed to deal with changing circumstances. AFATDS initial software passed an initial operational evaluation in August 1995 and was then authorized for production. Fielding began in February 1996. It is to be part of the Army's Task Force XXI experiment (February 1997). AFATDS already includes naval fire-support weapons and air attack weapons in its database.

Version 1 of AFATDS replaces the existing initial fire-support automation system (IFSAS) and the tactical fire-direction system (TACFIRE) and adds many new functions. It automatically develops firing orders and reports fire mission status. The planning function includes the choice of weapon, which may include air or naval weapons. Version 2, intended to improve joint operability, should appear in 1998. It automatically develops a logistic support plan and controls maintenance and personnel. Version 3 should automate support for all fire-support tasks (planning, execution, movement control, mission support, and fire direction). From an Army perspective, among the most valuable AFATDS functions is one also familiar in naval operations, the ability to update and disseminate a tactical picture automatically and instantly; at present soldiers constantly manually update their own map boards, with all the possibilities of error that entails (on the other hand, it also protects them from failures of data transmission, and from errors made at the top).

On board *Saipan*, AFATDS is being installed in the current SACC (supporting arms coordination center), a manual space employing 15–30 people, who pass information by handwritten notes. It will be compatible with existing communication systems.

♦ **ASWOC/ASWM (SQQ-34)/TSC/MOCC**

ASW Operations Center supports P-3 ASW aircraft; it has now been redesignated a tactical support center (TSC) to reflect the wider, non-ASW, role of the P-3. A MOCC (mobile-miniature operations control center) is a deployable TSC, transportable on board two standard P-3s. ASWM is the ASW module on board a carrier, which has a similar function (for S-3s). An ASWOC plans P-3 missions, based on ocean surveillance information (such as SOSUS outputs), and also on data brought back by other P-3s and replayed for analysis. It is built around a central tactical computer, with CRT consoles and a manual plot. Console displays can be projected onto large graphic displays for aircrew briefing and debriefing. The ASWOC supports four console stations, so four crews can be debriefed simultaneously. A MOCC can be transported abroad in two fleet-configured P-3s for contingency operations.

The current TSC C^3 modernization program (TMS) replaces the current centralized TSC computer system with a LAN-based system using standard TAC-series computers. The emphasis has now shifted from after-mission ASW analysis to tactical planning based on a wide variety of sensors, including ELINT and imagery. TSC Modernization software release 1.0.4 (incremental release 4) and ISAR radar workstations were installed at selected TSCs under the FY93 program. TSC Brunswick is the operational test site. The FY94 program included development of sensor analysis stations (ISAR, ESM, imagery) and completion of integration with TAC-3 workstations. The TSC was modified to accept OTH-T messages (OTH-Gold and U.S. Message Text Format [USMTF]). Increment 2 (TMS 2.0 software) includes integration of the new sensor workstations, automation of preflight insertion data (PID) and a Link 11 module for the TAC-3 computer. Under the FY85 program, a LAN interface to the acoustic processor (FTAS) was developed, a CUDIXS (Common User Data Information Exchange System) interface was added, and work began on an ESM workstation. The FY96 program adds the completed ESM module, adds access to the naval tactical warfare database (NTWDB), updates the environmental system (TESS), and adds a ground-to-air voice module into the MOCC version of the system. Tactical planning software is also added. The FY97 program adds a TADIXS B interface. TMS 3.0, reflecting these improvements, is to be released to the Fleet early in FY98.

An earlier modernization program updated message and data processing to support simultaneous aircraft missions, improve system availability, connect to NTCS ashore theater databases, improve systems interoperability with U.S. and Allied Naval Operating Forces, and support new aircraft capabilities (presumably P-3C Update IV was intended). This program included an interface with the IUSS and a UYC-8 security filter. The first mission support aid was computer-aided search. Keflavik was the first modernized ASWOC.

The current version of the ASWOC/TSC was developed to an August 1986 OR (117-094-86); the MOCC was developed to a March 1988 OR (208-05-88). Program change documents approved in 1990–91 presumably called for transition to open architectures and the new emphasis on surface operations.

An ASWOC can communicate directly with a naval facility (NAVFAC) (i.e., a SOSUS node) and also (via a dedicated secure link) with the ASW force commander, with other ASWOCs, and with command sites such as FCCs. This digital link operates at 2400 bps and carries both alphanumerics and graphics. The ASWOC also processes information from the merchant shipping and reporting control system. Finally, an ASWOC can also communicate with an airborne P-3C via HF and UHF, linking it to force, fleet, and group commanders and also to lateral commands for quick interchange of ASW information.

Postmission analysis is important because a crew can easily miss a target in flight. That was only a minor problem for aircraft whose crews could monitor only a very few sonobuoy channels, as printed out on their LOFARgram recorders, but a P-3C records many more channels than its crew simultaneously monitors, hence the need for postmission playback and analysis (although it is also true that visual inspection of a spread-out LOFARgram, after flight, can sometimes reveal targets not detected in flight). The ASWOC, therefore, arose with the P-3C, and it includes a fast-time equivalent of the sonobuoy analyzer on board an ASW airplane.

Beside its S-3 function, the ASW module (SQQ-34) on board a carrier controls carrier-based ASW (inner zone) helicopters, and it provides the information on which the force ASW commander relies. Although P-3s or S-3s can in theory function without the support of ASWOCs/ASWMs, in practice they search relatively limited areas and thus have to be directed to areas of likely submarine presence. With a barrier, the ASWOC/ASWM ensures that the search pattern is efficient and that it corresponds to the tactical requirement.

As of mid-1992 18 ASWOCs were operational, but two (at Cubi Point and Guam) were being deactivated. ASWOC is a U.S. designation; NATO uses MAOC (Maritime Air Operations Center), France uses CENTAC (a new system now in development),

and the British use MSS (Mission Support System). The Spanish system is quite rudimentary, using a single center comparable to the U.S. Air-Surface Classification and Analysis Center (ASCAC). Other NATO navies: one or two German, at least one Dutch, two Canadian (one each coast). The RAAF has at least one ASWOC. The Italian system is called SAVAAS.

ASCAC is a straightforward acoustic analysis center, not a C^2 node. It has no means of contact management and no area of responsibility. An ASWOC contains an ASCAC-like sensor analysis section, but it manages contacts over an area of responsibility, and thus has access to other kinds of data.

◆ Coast Guard System

As of 1995, the U.S. Coast Guard is developing a JMCIS-based (TAC-based) CDS to replace its existing navigational system. One screen carries the JMCIS picture; the other shows electronic charts with radar overlay, for navigation.

◆ Maritime Mission Support System

PRB Associates (which makes TEAMS) developed this ASWOC equivalent for the Pakistani navy, to support that service's P-3C UPDATE 2.5 aircraft. It runs on a VAX computer and incorporates Link 11; it does not include a fast spectrum analyzer. The first such system was delivered to the U.S. Navy in August 1991 (for transfer to Pakistan under Foreign Military Sales). Presumably it is under the same embargo as the P-3Cs.

◆ MTST

The standard Navy Maneuvering Target Statistical Tracker is a software package used for OTH tracking in the TWCS, CCS Mks 1 and 2, JOTS II (MTST variant), and ATW/Outlaw Hunter/ OASIS. The basic algorithm, developed by Tiburon Systems, has been written in Fortran, Turbo-Pascal, and ADA for various applications. It can run on a standard 80386 desktop computer. MTST processes contact and line-of-bearing reports and statistically projects ahead target position and area of uncertainty for any requested time. This is the basis for Tomahawk antiship targeting.

◆ NIPS (SYQ-9)/STIP

The Naval Intelligence Processing System (NIPS) is the shipboard intelligence center located aboard carriers and amphibious flagships. This program is also known as STIP (Shipboard Tactical Intelligence Processing). Fed by various offboard systems, including imagery sources, NIPS provides a central intelligence database to the TFCC aboard the carrier and, by extension, to other NTCS-A nodes, as well as to the aircraft and missile strike planning systems (APS, TAMPS, TEAMS, the Marines' TERPES, and the planning system for the SLAM missile). This type of system becomes essential as automated planning systems (such as APS) enter service, and also as shipboard CDSs (such as ACDS Block 1) use such data to supplement operational information. Because not all intelligence data are held at the same security level, a special MLS workstation was tested under the FY92 program. New hardware is used to handle special compartmented information (SCI). The associated imagery terminal is DIWSA (Digital Imagery Workstation Afloat). It receives data from FIST, the fleet imagery support terminal.

NIPS always incorporated its own air strike planner, but pilots distrusted its text output, and it saw little or no use. Modern graphical approaches, such as TAMPS, have been far more successful.

NIPS/STIP works in part as a database file server, maintaining the Naval Warfare Tactical Data Base (NWTDB) which is incorporated in the NTCS-A. Thus, under the FY93 program the NIPS Central Data Base Server/Advanced Message Handler (CDBS/ AMH) was integrated into the standard NTCS-A software (release 2.0). Work began on database support for tactical decision aids used by the naval command system.

SYQ-9 employs a UYK-7 computer and 7 to 17 UYQ-23 displays, plus a single I/O console (OA-7984), one or two disk memories (UYH-2), two to eight teleprinters, and a digital magnetic recorder reproducer (RD-358/UYK). The (V)1 version entered production in FY91. As in many other systems, SYQ-9 is being rehosted to standard TAC-series computers as part of NTCS-A; it will cease to have a separate identity.

The current version of the NIPS OR was released in June 1989; the FIST OR was released in April 1984.

(*above*) DIWSA, the Digital Imagery Workstation Afloat (GDE Systems).

JSIPS-N architecture (*below*), as depicted by GDE Systems in 1995. Note the connection with TAMPS, the tactical planning system, and the need for multilevel security, to separate special compartmented information (special intelligence, SCI) from other secure data (GENSER). The first operational JSIPS-N systems were installed at the Naval Strike Warfare Command and Control Center and at the National Military Training Center under the FY94 program. The next year two carriers (CVN-70 and -73) were fitted. Plans called for two more carriers (CV-64 and CVN-71) in FY96 (plus an installation at Fallon, for training), followed by five carriers in FY97 (CV-67, CVN-68, -69, -72, and -74), then three in FY98 (CV-63, CVN-65, and -75), and CVN-76 in FY99. (GDE Systems)

During FY90 work began on an interface with the Joint Services Imagery Processing System (JSIPS), the new filmless reconnaissance system (see the Strike/Surface Warfare section). The FY90 program also included initial work on NIPS interfaces to the Tomahawk cruise missile afloat-planning system (APS) and to DIWSA. Under the FY91 program techniques of data compression were developed so that digitized images could be transmitted along available communications paths (compression to 1.29 bits/pixel was demonstrated as part of the Challenge Athena project).

Beginning in FY95, DARO is embedding JSIPS into a new Common Imagery Ground/Surface System (CIGSS) from FY95. There it will join several Air Force and Army systems, including Senior Blade (electro-optics from the U-2) and Senior Year (electro-optics, co-located with CARS [Contingency Airborne Reconaissance System] for U-2R electro-optics, IR, and SAR imagery and special intelligence).

By late 1995, plans called for placing JSIPS-N on board 23 ships (12 carriers and 11 large-deck amphibious ships) over the next four or five years. Flagships will have partial installations (later upgraded to full JSIPS-N on four ships). There will also be five rapid deployment suites that can go ashore. SAIC is the systems engineering contractor.

DIWSA was originally intended only to support Tomahawk targeting, as part of the new APS; it then became the image-exploitation element of JSIPS, and is being used to support strike planning. A stereoscopic imagery processor, it is used to generate the DSMAC scenes the missile uses to navigate. The console has a pair of full-width screens alongside each other (one folds out in a frame). Processing power is huge: 163,164 MIPS, with on-line storage of 152 Gbytes, to handle graphics on a vast scale. Processors: two VAX4000, three VAX3500, twenty-six 68030, three Mercury Array Processors, nine bit-slice processors, with 140 custom circuit boards and 67 COTS circuit boards. A typical installation employs three workstations (two screens each) backed by a three-cabinet processor. The manufacturer is GDE Systems Inc. (a Tracor company).

DIWSA contains algorithms corresponding to the various na-

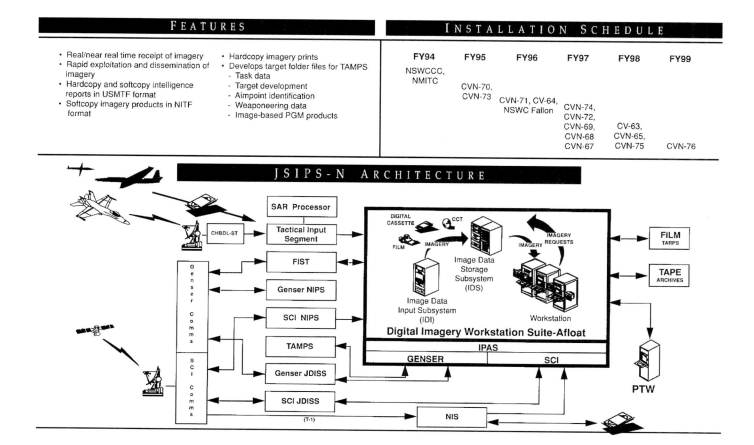

FEATURES	

• Real/near real time receipt of imagery
• Rapid exploitation and dissemination of imagery
• Hardcopy and softcopy intelligence reports in USMTF format
• Softcopy imagery products in NITF format
	• Hardcopy imagery prints
	• Develops target folder files for TAMPS
	  - Task data
	  - Target development
	  - Aimpoint identification
	  - Weaponeering data
	  - Image-based PGM products

INSTALLATION SCHEDULE					
FY94	**FY95**	**FY96**	**FY97**	**FY98**	**FY99**
NSWCCC, NMITC	CVN-70, CVN-73	CVN-71, CV-64, NSWC Fallon	CVN-74, CVN-72, CVN-69, CVN-68, CVN-67	CV-63, CVN-65, CVN-75	CVN-76

JSIPS-N ARCHITECTURE

tional assets (such as satellites), so it can correct the distortions in their raw images; it need not receive processed data. It also has the same mapping, charting, and geodesy functions as Defense Mapping Agency (DMA) equipment, so it can use DMA's point positioning database with current imagery from national and tactical sources in digital form. It can, therefore, locate objects with the same accuracy as can DMA. The system includes the Precision Targeting Workstation (PTW), an electronic light table based on a TAC-4 computer.

By 1997, the system is to be reduced to a single equipment rack, and the workstation modified to support two screens. In 1996–97 an interface with the TEAMS mission planning system is to be introduced.

The entire system is predicated on the new filmless digital imagery systems, such as ATARS. Current types of analog images must be digitized before JSIPS-N can process them. Because development of the input sensors lagged development of the input equipment, the Navy decided to add a common SAR processor to handle SAR imagery (which is now available from the APG-73 radar of the F/A-18).

♦ Outlaw Hunter/Outlaw Viking/OASIS

Outlaw Hunter was conceived as a means of binding the P-3 with its ISAR radar into the overall fleet OTH-T system. It applied accurate target-location data and an area of uncertainty to the target identified by the ISAR imaging radar. Aircraft position was obtained from GPS, and the data thus developed were correlated with the JOTS database (received via OTCIXS) and then transmitted to other platforms (e.g., those using the TWCS) via the OTCIXS link (OTH-T Gold message format).

The new ISAR radar made the P-3 effective (for target identification) against Soviet warships equipped with long-range defensive missiles, particularly SA-N-6. However, the inertial navigation systems (two LTN-72s) were not accurate enough to fix those targets within Tomahawk launch criteria (the missile cannot be allowed to spend much time searching for its target at low speed within the target's self-defense zone; position errors translate into search time). The solution was to use the new GPS navigational satellite system. In Outlaw Hunter, GPS data are assigned a figure of merit for purposes of comparison with inertial navigation fix data; the inertial navigation system takes over when the figure of merit falls below a fixed value. The radar and the navigator are combined with a communications system that can pass targeting information to a Tomahawk platform with the necessary speed and reliability (via OTCIXS).

The fallback to the inertial navigator is necessary until the GPS satellite constellation is completed.

The on-board data processor is the Tiburon ATW (see separate entry, below), a workstation similar in concept to the DTC used for JOTS. As used in Outlaw Hunter, the ATW can display tracks, labels, and areas of uncertainty. The workstation can also play back or fast-forward the tracks it carries, so the operator can analyze target motion and detect trends to predict future actions. The operator can list displayed tracks, read incoming Opnotes, create outgoing Opnotes, control the list of addressees, view the incoming-message log, and select output filters. The operator can designate an area from which all of the updated positions for the contacts, which are being automatically tracked by the aircraft's ISAR radar, can be transmitted either manually or automatically at set intervals. This feature is valuable because it provides a distant commander with a full picture of all shipping in an area, not just the target of interest. Opnotes can indicate the confidence of the ISAR operator in target classification, and they can also send environmental data such as wind speed, direction, and air temperature, all of which are important in Tomahawk launch planning.

Outlaw Hunter was a quick demonstration project; the first conversion (on board a VP-9 P-3C) was completed in August 1989 in nine months at a cost of only $700,000. This figure included all development costs. Further upgrades should take eight weeks, at a cost of $250,000. In tests in 1989–90, tracks or Opnotes transmitted via OTCIXS to ships or to shore sites typically took about 3 min from transmission to verification of receipt. To reach a submarine, data must be routed through a shore targeting terminal (STT; see below), which imposes a 5–8min delay. In the 1989 exercises, Outlaw Hawk successfully cued the submarines *Salt Lake City* and *Omaha*. The system was also used to provide targeting and prestrike surface pictures to a carrier, both to the combined strike warfare commander (Alfa Sierra) and to the aircraft themselves (via voice SURPICS [secure voice]). Outlaw Hunter has also transmitted targeting data over Link 11 and over plain-voice channels, sometimes simultaneously with the OTCIXS and SURPICS channels.

On board the Orion, a single equipment rack just aft of the sonobuoy storage rack accommodates a communications/radar processor (CARP), a generic front-end communications processor (GFCP), a satellite communications controller (ON-143[V]6) with an encrypting unit (KG-84), and the modem and other equipment linking the communications processor to a small satellite antenna (DMC-34) atop the airplane amidships. A second antenna serves GPS. The ATW itself is just forward of the aft observer's station. In addition to its high-resolution display, it has a laptop computer to monitor overall hardware performance and to display raw teletype information.

The Outlaw Hunter P-3C proved very successful in Desert Shield; presumably, it supported maritime interdiction (the embargo) by detecting, identifying, and tracking the very numerous merchant ships in the area around Iraq.

OASIS (OTH-T Airborne Sensor Interface System) is the successor to the 1989 Outlaw Hunter prototype system. OASIS I was assembled quickly to equip an Atlantic Fleet P-3 for Desert Shield. It is Outlaw Hunter with more reliable components and upgraded tactical software. In this version, the OTCIXS channel is the satellite communications system designed for the abortive UPDATE IV. The tactical data processor uses a VME system bus to connect the CARP (which receives both GPS and ISAR radar data) with the ATW and also with a scan converter. The scan converter provides ATW video output to a channel selector, which the tactical coordinating officer (TACCO) can use to display ATW outputs or APS-137 radar video or data from the aircraft's mission computer (CP-901); thus, the main system display has moved to the TACCO station, where it belongs. The TACCO controls the system via trackball and keyboard. Overall system weight is reduced from 1200 to about 150 lb, allowing the airplane to carry a full load of sonobuoys.

OASIS I was ready too late for the Gulf War (the airplane was later assigned to VP-46).

OASIS II is a repackaged (230 vice 550 kg, smaller volume) Outlaw Hunter occupying two racks at the ordnanceman's station of the P-3C. The correlator uses 80486 chips. At present, OASIS II can use its ELINT correlator to cue the ISAR radar operator, and it can project ahead radar tracks to regain false contacts. The combination of active radar and correlated passive (ELINT) data makes an OASIS airplane a source of independent, fully correlated OTH-T data; alternatively, it can feed a larger network of FOTCs. Current plans call for installations on board three S-3s (Outlaw Viking). OASIS is later to be extended to use ALR-66 inputs and satellite data.

As of mid-1993, OASIS II was aboard a P-3C of VP-26. All Outlaw Hunter/OASIS aircraft were brought up to the same standard by the summer of 1992. They have stand-alone equipment in the rear of the cabin, but follow-on aircraft will integrate the system into the TACCO station.

OASIS III is part of the P-3C AIP program; production began October 1994. Plans currently call for 33 aircraft, but up to 68 may receive AIP modifications.

OASIS has also been applied to other aircraft: E-2C (Outlaw Hawkeye), EP-3 (Outlaw Story Teller), and SH-60 (Outlaw Seahawk). Software for Outlaw Hawkeye was developed under the FY92 program. Outlaw Hawkeye and Outlaw Seahawk are both being fielded. Outlaw Seahawk differs from Outlaw Hunter/ Viking in that data is downlinked to the mother ship for onward transmission via OTCIXS.

See also the separate entry for the ATW workstation used in Outlaw Hunter.

◆ RTIC/Talon Sword/Talon Lance/ATIMS

Real Time in the Cockpit is a joint program intended to speed targeting of mobile targets by using reconnaissance data (including satellite data) directly. Talon Sword was an Air Force–led demonstration program (1993–94); Talon Lance is the Air Force's follow-on. For example, in one Talon Sword demonstration an EA-6B launched a HARM missile at a patrol boat on the basis of satellite OTH-T information. In another, an EA-6B combined satellite data with its own sensor data to guide an F-16 firing a HARM at a radar site beyond its own horizon. In yet another demonstration, the satellite data were correlated at an Air Force Constant Source ground station, then transmitted to an F-16. Finally, in July 1994, satellite data cued a long-range electro-optical sensor on board a P-3, which used it to confirm and refine attack data. The satellite data and the P-3 image were transmitted to an F-16. Further satellite data were used for battle damage assessment, to plan a follow-up strike. Key to the program was the improved data modem (IDM) developed for the Navy by Symetrics Industries of Florida.

Talon Lance, begun in mid-1993, envisages an on-board supercomputer for data correlation and display. Loral Electronics is the prime contractor. The goal is a single computer card with the power of two Crays, operating 30 times faster than current computers.

ATIMS (Airborne Tactical Information Management System) is a joint ATD, in effect the naval equivalent to the Air Force Talon programs, managed by the Program Executive Office (PEO) for Tactical Aircraft Programs. The systems integrator is GDE Systems, Inc. (a division of Tracor). ATIMS is part of the Real-Time Support for Joint Power Projection ATD. It apparently embraces both cockpit automation (to reduce pilot workload) and quicker transmission of target information to the cockpit. In theory, modular open architecture should make it possible to use much the same software and hardware at every stage of the mission: in unit level planning and training; in flight; and in mission analysis and playback. Virtual-reality techniques will make it easier for the pilot to interact with mission-planning and situation-assessment tools. On-board features will include improved situation display/aids, mission management, better in-flight replanning, embedded training mechanisms, and integrated C3I. Presumably the displays will include the new helmet-visor displays, perhaps replacing current HUDs, and there will be new high-capacity digital data links, passing images (e.g., for strike operations) as well as numerical data.

◆ STT

The shore targeting terminal provides submarines with Tomahawk targeting data for antiship attack. STT is currently a DTC II using Copernicus/OSS architecture. The communications interface is NFEP, the Navy front-end processor, which runs on a MicroVAX computer; a modernized NFEP (or MNFEP) runs on the DTC II. Currently STT receives its data via OTCIXS and TADIXS satellite links, Autodin, and CLI (communications line interface with ASWOCs via FHLT, and so on). CLI is also used for messages from units that are not OTCIXS-capable. In future, OSS will collect all messages for STT.

STT messages are transmitted to submarines via SSIXS (OTH-Gold format) for their CCS systems.

◆ TAMPS

The Tactical Aircraft Mission Planning System is the standard aircraft planning system for the U.S. Navy and Marine Corps, developed in 1985 and since modified to operate on standard tactical computers, receiving JMCIS data. It is to migrate into later TAC-series computers as they become available. The current Version 6 was developed by TRW. It develops a complete mission package for an airplane, based on topography, threat, and weather data. This version is based in part on experience with earlier forms of TAMPS during the Gulf War.

As the planner "points and clicks" to lay out a candidate flight path to the target on a 2D chart, the system automatically checks in three dimensions to avoid terrain, as well as to avoid

exposure to hostile weapons (taking into account terrain masking of those weapons, and their lethal envelopes). Specific vehicle performance modules can be added to provide the system with aircraft load-outs and maneuverability. The system can display information in three dimensions, rotating and zooming images of the flight path. The system also constructs a preview of what the pilot is likely to see during the mission, to make ingress and egress paths and alternatives familiar before flight time. TAMPS can also fold together a series of flight plans at squadron level to form a strike package. TRW claims that it can be upgraded to force-level (ATO) capability.

TAMPS includes a Stores Planning and Weaponeering Module (SPWM), which provides aircraft computers with essential mission data for using current-generation weapons such as JSOW and SLAM. It also provides data for the Tactical Aircraft Moving Map System (TAMMS). Ultimately all naval aircraft will be programmed using TAMPS. The F/A-18 is probably the main current example, although TAMPS is already the primary means of loading JTIDS data into F-14Ds and E-2Cs. In an F/A-18, TAMPS loads planned flight data (way-points, sequential steering files, air-to-air radar presets, TACAN and radio channel files) into the data storage unit (DSU) of the aircraft computer. TAMPS is to be the means of loading data for GPS-guided weapons. It is to take data from the Forward Area Minefield Planner (FAMP) and the Naval Special Warfare Mission Planning System. Several other air tactical planning tools are to merge into TAMPS, including TEAMS, Map Operator and Maintenance (MOMS), Common Helicopter Aviation Mission Planning System (CHAMPS), the AV-8B Maintenance Data System, the ES-3 Mission Planning System, and TERPES.

Initially TAMPS software ran on a special hybrid computer that separated its two primary processes, mission planning and database administration. In this form it was first delivered on board the *Carl Vinson* in August 1986. During the Gulf War, 26 afloat TAMPS workstations (six carriers, one battleship, and the major amphibious ships) supported Desert Storm. TAMPS was criticized as too slow; it needed flyable quality color copiers and more data storage. The system did not provide advice on weapon choices (weaponeering) and war-at-sea planning; both are to be added as upgrades. It also needed more robust connections to the two other major air planning tools, TERPES and TEAMS.

The first version using standard tactical computers was produced in 1989–90. Further versions are characterized by software release numbers (as of the spring of 1996 the latest to be tested was 6.2). The annual minor software release (6.1, 6.2) is made to accommodate mission planning systems and to integrate new weapon systems. It does not cause design changes to external mission planning modules (MPMs). A major release (7.0 is next) entails core changes requiring changes in MPM software. For example, a major release would be needed to provide dynamic communication between MPMs during mission planning. Major releases are expected every three years.

As of April 1994, TRW's Version 6.0 had just been supplied to six naval warfare and training centers for initial user testing. Version 6.1 includes automatic route construction; the ability to scan maps; to process intelligence database material; training capability; and full duplex security.

Version 6.2, which had just passed its OpEval early in 1996, added some new modules: SWPM, TAMM, an air-to-air warfare module, and an EW module. It also added full capability for secure satellite radio communications via the ARC-210 radio, a mission planning interface for JDAM, and improved system security.

The next step, Version 7.0, is to integrate TAMPS into the JMCIS/GCCS common operating environment, and to provide an interface with DIWSA to provide imagery for precision-guided weapons such as SLAM.

◆ TEAMS (TSQ-142)

The Tactical EA-6B Mission Support system provides an EA-6B squadron on board a carrier or ashore with full mission data (as assembled from the vast amount of intelligence available before flight), and assimilates data collected in flight. TEAMS is unusual in that it actually reprograms three sets of EA-6B mission computers (navigation, ALQ-99, and HARM) on board the airplane by means of a data cartridge inserted at flight time. TEAMS also produces flight plans, kneeboard charts, and 30min strip maps. One cartridge can carry several missions' worth of data, so a mission can be changed even after the EA-6B has taken off. In flight, the airplane's ECM receivers feed their data into the cartridge, whose contents are read back into the TEAMS database after the EA-6B lands. To serve the new ADVCAP version of the EA-6B, TEAMS will program a total of nine aircraft computers (including ALR-67ASR, ALQ-149, and the ALE-47 chaff launcher). TEAMS's databases include the Defense Mapping Agency's computerized maps (including terrain) and several intelligence databases; the system receives tactical intelligence (TENCAP) data directly via OTCIXS nets. TEAMS also includes performance predictions for the airplane, for its ALQ-99 system and for the HARM missile, so it can predict the effect of a particular mission profile or tactic in a specific situation. On a carrier, it runs on paired VAX3800 workstations (each with 32 Mbytes of RAM and about 2 Gbytes of storage). There is also a transportable version for the Marine Corps, and a portable version is currently under contract. The system is being developed into an open architecture that will be suitable to a variety of workstations, such as Sun (DTC II series) or the new IBM RISC stations.

TEAMS was developed by PRB Associates. It entered service in 1984 and was probably the first such mission planner to program the airplane for a particular mission (by reprogramming its computer). The current version carries a database covering 6 to 7 million square miles, with very large lists of friendly and enemy orders of battle. It keeps track of these orders of battle and also of theater assets (such as weapons and expendables). The postflight readouts are used both to update the databases and to reconstruct missions to extract lessons learned and tactically significant intelligence and EW data; the system helps produce postaction messages and reports.

A TEAMS derivative is now being developed to support EW reprogramming for radar-warning receivers and jammers on board other carrier-battle-group aircraft.

◆ TSCM

The Tactical Strike Coordination Module works with TAMPS (see above) and Tomahawk strike planners to provide overall strike plans and route tasking. It takes its data from NTCS-A/JMCIS and from the central database server (CDBS), and was developed on a fast-track schedule. Presumably TSCM was an outgrowth of Gulf War experience; it is intended to support a Navy cell in a JFACC staff, as well as afloat battle group and strike warfare commanders. TSCM is software running on a single TAC-3 computer. The contractor is GDE (a Tracor company).

TSCM is provided with a strike plan (targets, threats, available weapons, and so on), which it feeds into a strike plan (including attack and SEAD elements). Alternative plans are evaluated (including development of measures of effectiveness), and then a candidate strike plan is fleshed out into a detailed plan for each airplane. Each stage is fed back to earlier ones. For example, the strike planning stage may ask for additional data. Plan evaluation may affect individual missions. Plan construction will feed strike plans back into the plan evaluation stage. Once a plan has been developed, text and graphics are prepared for briefing and for further processing by systems such as TAMPS and TEAMS. At this stage, the staff can feed changes back into the system. The TAC-3 used for TSCM carries 128 Mbytes of RAM and a 3-Gbyte hard disk, as well as 4mm and $\frac{1}{4}$in tape drives and a CD-ROM drive. Software is written in a mixture of UNIX, C, ADA, and MOTIF.

◆ USQ-81(V)

USQ-81 was the Lockheed (Austin) terminal developed for OTH-T, built around one or two Rolm 1666 computers. Some survive within Tomahawk weapon systems (those in the TFCC and STT have been replaced by standard DTC/TAC-series workstations). USQ-81 was first developed for Outlaw Shark/Outlaw Hawk. It

was intended as the standard terminal of the OTH-T network linked by satellite, compiling a large-scale tactical picture from a series of reports or preparing surveillance reports for onward transmission to tactical data display systems. As such it was the basis of the Track Control Group (TCG), an OTH detection, classification, and targeting subsystem within the SLCM (Tomahawk) common weapons-control system (CWCS: SWG-2/3). The Lightweight OTH Terminal (for P-3s) was a derivative. Some USQ-81s were probably deployed aboard P-3Cs and EP-3s providing OTH-T information. The display is a cursive CRT supplied with a keyboard and with special-function keys on either side and on top.

◆ JADDIN

In June 1991 Unisys received a contract for a 40-month program to develop and deploy the Joint Air Defense Digital Information Network for Thailand, to provide naval and ground forces with information from the Royal Thai Air Defense System (RTADS). RTADS became operational in 1990.

◆ CTT (TSC-125)

E-Systems' Commander's Tactical Terminal is a multichannel UHF (225–400 MHz, with channels spaced at 5 or 25 kHz) receiver/transmitter intended to handle TENCAP broadcasts in support of systems such as NTCS-A. CTT is a full duplex (receive/transmit) terminal initially developed for the Air Force. The CTT/TEREC version was a multichannel Constant Source (Air Force TENCAP broadcast) receiver with a TIBS (Tactical Information Broadcast Service) interface and receiver. CTT/H-R (Hybrid Receive Only) combines these functions into a single terminal, using open architecture, a VME backplane, and an interface to a standard 1553B bus (for aircraft). It can receive and decrypt the Tactical Reconnaissance Intelligence Exchange Service (TRIXS) or TIBS while simultaneously receiving TADIXS B and the Air Force Tactical Receive and Related Applications (TRAP) broadcasts. It can also receive the Air Force Senior Span broadcast (a U-2 relay, in effect a "poor man's satellite"). CTT can handle data rates of 2400, 4800, 9600, or 19,200 bps. The current version fits a standard 3/4 ATR aircraft enclosure.

The current series is the three-channel CTT(3); it is used, for example, in the Army's Integrated Battlefield Targeting Architecture. CTT/H3 is a full-duplex version in one channel while receiving in two others. CTT/H-R3 receives in three intelligence channels. CTT was exhibited at the 1995 Navy League Show, and is presumably planned for naval air platforms such as the upgraded EP-3E.

CTT is to be part of a new joint intelligence dissemination system, development of which was ordered in 1995. The Navy is now the executive service in charge of dissemination, building on its Copernicus communication architecture. The Air Force is in charge of intelligence broadcasts, and the Army is in charge of the terminals. The current standard terminal, the Commander's Tactical Terminal (CTT), has two channels. The future Joint Tactical Terminal (JTT) will have three, permitting intelligence transmission as well as reception. As of late 1995 an RFP was expected in July 1996, with a contract to follow that December, while specifications for a new Multimission Advanced Tactical Terminal (MATT) were being written. It is to combine CTT and JTT characteristics, using a set of common intelligence broadcast system modules (CIBS-M), which can be mixed and matched. The MATT contract is to be let by the end of 1997.

SATELLITE SENSOR SYSTEMS

FRANCE

◆ Helios

This Matra Marconi imaging satellite, a modified version of the civilian Spot 4, was built for France, Italy, and Spain. It will photograph targets in real time (transmitting by laser cross-link to Syracuse communications satellites), with a resolution of 1.5 m (5 ft), using a pair of linear CCDs (4096 and 2048 pixels) for imaging. Helios 1A was launched on 7 July 1995, and the second is to be launched in 1996. Helios 1 follows a low (450km) sun-synchronous orbit. France is contributing 79% of the program cost (estimated at $1.5 billion), Italy 14%, and Spain 7%. Imaging will not support operations at sea, but is likely to be used for strike support. The satellite has a three-year lifetime.

Although Germany did not pledge support for the second-phase Helios 2, France announced in April 1995 that the project would go ahead. Italy and Spain had already pulled out but said they would return to the program if Germany agreed to help finance it. Germany seemed likely to rejoin the program as of the fall of 1995. Two Helios 2 satellites, with IR sensors, are planned, the first to be launched in 2001. They are to be followed by a digital imagery radar satellite, Osiris, in 2002. The $1.3-billion Osiris is being proposed as a pan-European project. It will use microwave sensors, but is based on the civilian optical Spot Mk 2.

There is also a planned ELINT/tactical communications satellite, Zenon, being developed by Alcatel Espace and Thomson-CSF. Zenon satellites will occupy three geostationary positions at 8 deg W, 15 deg E, 19 deg E. France will gain ELINT experience by launching a 50kg Cerise microsatellite (made by Surrey Satellite Technology of the UK, equipped by Alcatel) with Helios. DGA (the French government's military technology agency) is also working on early-warning and secure-data relay satellites.

RUSSIA

◆ EORSATs

ESM and radar ocean reconnaissance satellites (RORSATs) were conceived as targeters for Soviet warships, probably specifically for the SS-N-19 (Granit) missile. The system was called Kasatka (killer whale). The satellites downlink directly to the missile shooter; the shipboard antenna is Punch Bowl. Satellites can also cross-link their information to a command center ashore, or store it for later dump to an ashore center. Both satellites were probably conceived in parallel, but RORSAT appears to have been canceled as part of the defense cuts of the late 1980s. EORSAT picks up radar sidelobe emissions.

The EORSAT system became operational in March 1980. Satellites occupy near-circular 276–286mi orbits (93.3min period) inclined at 65 deg. They last 22 months. Location accuracy at the surface may be as good as 1.3 nm. The system currently consists of five or six satellites in two orbital planes (so that a second EORSAT follows the first along the same path over the target); pairs of EORSATs replace the former RORSAT-EORSAT combination. The paired fixes give an estimate of target course and speed.

Two constellations of ELINT satellites provide their data only to a ground station: (a) six satellites in six orbital planes spaced 60 deg apart, mean altitude 443 mi, inclination 82.5 deg, launched by SL-14; (b) newer series, larger satellites, 71-deg inclination, 579mi altitude, normally four in orbit (SL-16 booster). There is also a geosynchronous ELINT satellite with a two-year life; reportedly, one operates over the Atlantic to monitor Trident telemetry, downlinking to Lourdes, Cuba. Presumably the ELINT satellites are used for initial detection, cueing shooters and the EORSATs on which they rely.

The RORSATs are no longer operational, but a civilian radar satellite, Almaz, announced in 1991 (and offered for export) suggests their characteristics. It was launched on board the Kosmos 1870 satellite. The 1.3 × 15m slot antennas produced a beam 4 deg wide in the vertical plane, but only 25 min of arc in the horizontal (S-band, 250 kW, 0.1 microsec pulses, 3000 pps). This is a synthetic-aperture radar (SAR), producing images either optically (Almaz) or digitally (Almaz-1). Data are stored on a magnetic recorder for playback on command. Orbiting at 250–280 km (inclined at 73 deg), the satellite radar sweeps out a swath 30–40 km wide on the surface; each frame is 20–240 km long along the satellite track. Range resolution is 15–30 m. Presumably the RORSATs swept out the much wider swath required to have a good probability of intercepting moving ships. They were much more powerful than Almaz, with spaceborne nuclear reactors on board.

UNITED STATES

The U.S. Navy uses nonnaval "national" intelligence sensors, including satellites. One important goal of current command/control systems (Copernicus) is to make it easier to get their data to shooters ("sensor-to-shooter connectivity"). The density of information involved has grown with changing naval priorities.

The "national" intelligence sensor data were always treated as very sensitive, requiring special protection. Data had to be sanitized for tactical use. The sensitivity of this data is a major reason for the intense interest in MLS arrangements in computer systems that handle the wide-area picture used, for example, for OTH-T. Matters are further confused because different agencies operate different sets of satellites, all of which have TENCAP applications.

The Air Force operates the DSP (Defense Support Program) series, which was originally intended mainly to detect Soviet nuclear tests and missile launches. The other two satellite operators are the CIA, mainly for imagery, and NSA, for signal intercepts (including radar intercepts). CIA operates the imagery satellites through the National Reconnaissance Office (NRO). A National Imagery Agency (NIA) was formed in 1992 to prioritize and manage aircraft and satellite imagery requirements, given limited resources.

The current DSP orbits geosynchronously (at 22,500 nm). It employs a 12ft-long Schmidt IR camera (with 6000 detectors) with its line of sight offset 7.5 deg to the vertical axis of the satellite, so that it scans continuously as the satellite rotates about its axis at 6 rpm. Three satellites can cover the entire earth. Combining data from two or more satellites improves launch point accuracy by about a factor of 4. The missile signature involved is its exhaust plume. The satellite's naval significance is that it can also detect a hot booster for a tactical missile and even a hot afterburner from a high-flying airplane. During the Gulf War DSPs detected Iraqi Scud launches. The ground stations are at Alice Springs, Australia, and at Buckley Field, Colorado (data are passed from satellite to satellite and then to the ground station). There is also a mobile ground station (MGS), conceived during the Cold War as a means of improving system survivability. The major current question is whether DSP, which is valuable as a tactical sensor, should transmit to a forward tactical terminal, or whether it should continue to be centrally controlled by the Air Force Space Command.

DSP improvements in recent years have included going from the original 2000 sensors to 6000, enhancing the resolution of the below-horizon array, and adding an above-the-horizon array and a second color array.

In March 1994, of five DSP satellites in orbit, only the shuttle-deployed No. 16 was reported in good condition. No. 12 (launched December 1984), which had been very important during the Gulf War, suffered a power supply failure in 1992. Because it lost automatic control, No. 13 had to have its attitude controlled from the ground (U.S. or Australia). Nos. 14 and 15 (1989 and 1990) suffered blown fuzes in power supplies for their arrays, limiting their capability against missiles that do not burn very brightly or for very long. No. 17 was launched in the fall of 1994, but as of the fall of 1995 No. 18 had not yet been launched. Four more satellites are in storage, and work has begun on No. 23, the last in the series. No. 16 and later units have the fuze problem fixed. Late DSPs may be upgraded with a multispectral sensor proposed by Aerojet/TRW for a classified program canceled when the Soviet Union broke up. It would be mounted in place of an abortive laser cross-link. DoD planned to cancel Nos. 24 and 25 in favor of a new system, but was ordered to keep the No. 24 option open. The planned follow-on program is SBIR (space-based IR), using four satellites in geosynchronous orbit, two in highly elliptical orbits, and a low-altitude constellation of Brilliant Eyes satellites to be used in missile defense.

The main optical imagery satellites are Big Birds, employing KH-series optical systems. The current version is reportedly TRW's KH-11. These satellites report via communications satellites (the satellite data system, SDS) in more or less real time, using television transmission techniques. Given fixed bandwidth, they must presumably trade off transmission rate against resolution, although new data-compression techniques (see the discussion of the LAMPS data link below) may reduce that conflict. In 1995 it was reported that the next to be launched would have reduced resolution so as to increase their data transmission rates. Because lenses have limited resolution, these satellites must operate at relatively low altitude, and thus their coverage is transient. They can be maneuvered to some extent to provide coverage as required, but that costs on-board fuel and thus reduces the satellite's designed lifetime of 5–8 yr.

Recent Big Birds have been launched into 1020×270km sun-synchronous orbits; they appear everywhere at the same local time (reportedly there are morning and afternoon satellite passes, at 1000–1100 and 1300–1400 hours). Differences in shadows on the two passes make it easier to interpret photographs. Reportedly, the satellite produces two kinds of image, survey and detailed. The satellite can also be used to photograph other objects in space (e.g., KH-11-4 was used to inspect the space shuttle *Columbia* in 1982). According to a 1994 Russian article on the KH-11 program, the satellite photographs a 2.8×2.8km strip (resolution 0.15–0.18 m) and a 90×120km strip (resolution 0.5–1.7 m); the resolution figures are met only under ideal weather conditions. A projected Advanced KH-11 (incorrectly called KH-12) adds an IR camera (CCD array) to achieve a resolution of 0.6–0.8 m on a 2.8×2.8km strip; it also uses a Hubble-type camera to compensate for atmospheric distortion (resolutions 0.08–0.1 m in a 2.8×2.8m strip, 0.5–1.0 m in a 90×120km strip in visible wavelengths). According to the article, two such satellites were launched, the second (unsuccessfully) in 1990; a third is planned.

A Russian summary of U.S. satellite programs, published in 1995, lists nine such satellites (plus a tenth lost in a failed launch), of which two are still operational in orbit. The first was retired in 1979, and nos. 6 and 7 were retired in November 1994 and June 1992, respectively. All were launched by Titans.

The survey comments that, with the advent of a very competitive commercial space image market, U.S. wartime requirements may largely be met through commercial U.S. satellites with resolutions on the order of a meter.

Reportedly there is also a radar-imaging program, begun in 1977 as Project Indigo (the satellite was Lacrosse). Reportedly the program calls for a total of six such satellites (Lacrosse-1 was launched in 1988, and Lacrosse-2 in 1991), and ground resolution (using a centimetric radar) may be nearly as good as that available from a Big Bird. The orbit is 704×676 km. The reported manufacturer is McDonnell-Douglas. As in Big Bird, there may be parallel survey and detailed images. Note that Lacrosse is *not* the sort of radar satellite that might be used for real-time aircraft or ship or cruise-missile detection; that would require many more satellites in low orbits, for continuous cover.

There is probably also an IR imaging program, but no such satellite has been reported. Reports of an imaging adjunct to DSP suggest that the arrays involved came out of an abortive black satellite program.

Reportedly, Allied operations during the Gulf War were supported by three Big Birds (KH-11) and by the first Lacrosse. The forces also used unclassified satellite images from LANDSATs and from the French Spot 1 and 2, but presumably their resolution was insufficient for targeting.

The specialized satellites are extremely expensive and, given very limited numbers, net duration over a combat zone is very limited. There have, therefore, been proposals for cheap short-life tactical satellites, but to date nothing has materialized.

There are also NSA-sponsored ELINT satellites. Reportedly they comprise a geosynchronous element and numbers of low-altitude satellites. There may also be ELINT packages aboard other satellites, such as Big Birds.

Reportedly the initial geosynchronous element was the TRW Rhyolite series, first launched in 1973, using a 70ft antenna and also smaller microwave dishes, primarily to detect missile telemetry (but also to pick up radar and even radiotelephone signals). One great advantage of Rhyolite, as compared to earlier low-altitude ELINT satellites, was that its victims could not turn off emitters during the satellite's transient coverage. The ground station was at Alice Springs, Australia. Four satellites were launched. Rhyolite was compromised in 1976, and reportedly that compromise led the Soviets to encode their missile telemetry beginning about 1978. An improved Rhyolite using a dish nearly twice as large (Argus) was planned, but it was dropped in 1975 to release money needed for the Big Bird series. Argus became considerably more important in 1979, when the United States lost access to Iranian facilities used to monitor Soviet missile tests. Work on Aquacade, an updated Argus, began in 1979. It could be made substantially larger because it was designed for shuttle launch (soon it had to be redesigned for Titan launch, the shuttle having failed to meet schedules). Reportedly the first Aquacade was launched by shuttle early in 1985. The names Chalet, Vortex, and Magnum have also been associated with geosynchronous ELINT satellites. It seems likely that there are different programs dealing with different portions of the spectrum.

Jumpseat is apparently a lower-altitude satellite similar in size (about 700 kg) to the SDS satellite-data relay mentioned above. There are also small satellites (reportedly 50 kg) launched from Big Birds, and probably from others as well.

One other sensor system deserves mention here: GPS (Navstar). Because it is so precise, annd because its receiver is so compact, GPS has become an important means of fixing weapon as well as platform positions. Examples include JSOW, JDAMS, and Tomahawk Block III. GPS is now so important that questions of its vulnerability (often meaning the vulnerability of the downlink from the satellite) are now being raised quite prominently. The promise of GPS is that all data can be keyed to a single set of geographic coordinates, which can also be used for weapon delivery.

Each user automatically chooses the four most suitably located satellites, obtaining a pseudorange (time difference) to each. The system then automatically solves a set of four equations involving the pseudoranges. In theory, positions can be accurate to within 30–52 ft, *if* a system can lock on to all four satellites. The system employs a total of 21 satellites (3 spares) broadcasting at 1227.6 MHz (with a coarse signal at 1575.42 MHz).

♦ **Have Gaze**

This previously black program was revealed in the mid-1992 House report of the Defense Authorization Bill; it is used to detect stealthy aircraft from space. Almost certainly it is an IR system. Have Gaze is controlled by the previously black Joint Counter Low Observable Office (JCLO), controlled by the Navy, but the satellite itself is funded by the Air Force; probably it is a follow-on to the current DSP satellite. JCLO involvement suggests that the newer satellite can track relatively cool nonafterburning aircraft, presumably using a better IR sensor and better clutter-rejecting software.

♦ **Slow Walker**

Slow Walker exploits stereoscopic DSP satellite data to detect theater missile launches and aircraft using their afterburners (those objects were called Slow Walkers because they moved slowly across the screens of DSP ground stations). By way of contrast, satellites in low orbit, which were detected by the glint of sunlight, were Fast Walkers. During the 1980s new DSP satellites (5R and 6R) were fitted with sensors intended specifically to detect Slow Walkers. Sensor sensitivity could be increased for a designated area of interest (AOI) on the earth. A Navy collection team first visited the Nurrungar, Australia, earth station in 1983 and the first formal OR was drafted in 1984. At first the DSP system warned the Fleet via voice radio using an AFSATCOM channel. The timing of the Slow Walker concept would seem to tie it to naval interest in the OAB, which in turn required the earliest possible warning of approaching missile-armed bombers. IBM received a contract to develop a tactical ground station for Naval Space Warfare Command, beginning in FY91. The system became operational in FY93, and is to be completed in FY96. Total estimated procurement cost is $10 million, the first $4.5 million of which was spent in FY93. A Navy proposal for an IR satellite for wide-area air surveillance (the Air Force supports an alternative radar system) may be related to Slow Walker.

◆ White Cloud (Parcae)/Classic Wizard

White Cloud is a passive ocean-surveillance satellite system employing clusters of satellites and functioning as the overhead part of the Classic Wizard ocean-surveillance system. Each satellite is reportedly equipped with IR and mm-wave scanners and with receivers for intercepting radio transmissions. Each cluster of three satellites (plus a mother) orbits at an altitude of about 700 nm and can detect emissions from ships 2000 nm away. The cluster is used so that emitters can be located by interferometry, using the distance between the satellites as a baseline.

The first cluster was launched in 1976, and the fifth cluster was placed in orbit in June 1983. As of 1992 at least three were reported operational: Parcae-10, -11, and -12 (launched 1987, 1988, 1989). Satellite lifetime is probably 3–5 yr.

White Cloud seems to have been conceived as an intercept system to catalog Soviet emitters so that units equipped with tactical ESM devices could identify them. The location capability was necessary to pair the emissions with particular Soviet platforms. In the late 1970s a program called Clipper Bow proposed to combine White Cloud with an active radar. Most likely an imaging radar, which could identify emitters very precisely, was intended. Congress killed Clipper Bow in 1980, ordering the Navy to participate instead in similar Air Force/CIA projects (probably Lacrosse).

In 1993 it was reported that an Advanced White Cloud was in service, and that Lockheed Martin had been selected to develop a next-generation system.

SURFACE RADAR/ELINT (ELECTRONICS INTELLIGENCE) SYSTEMS

AUSTRALIA

◆ Jindalee

Jindalee ("Bare Bones") is the Australian OTH radar project for sea and air surveillance. It also monitors sea-state and wind direction and is currently being used to provide wind- and sea-state maps for the area north of Australia. Depending on ionospheric conditions, range may be as great as 4000 km, and target resolution is reportedly 20–40 km. Demonstrated range is about 3000 km. Frequency is about 30 MHz, and transmitter power is about 400 kW.

Jindalee reportedly incorporates special locally developed software for automatic detection and tracking. The main means of detecting aircraft is Doppler, but other methods were developed for ships, and the Australians claim that the latter represent a major advance in OTH radar technology.

The three operational radars of the Jindalee Operational Radar Network (JORN) will be at Hart's Range (140 miles north of Alice Springs; this is the prototype), Kalgoorlie, Western Australia, and Longreach, Queensland. The network center is at Edinburgh, South Australia (RAAF Salisbury). AWA (Amalgamated Wireless of Australia)/CSA (Computer Sciences of Australia)/Transfield/GE won the contract early in 1990, and the first site (Hart's Range) was handed over to the RAAF in April 1992. The others are to be completed in 1996. Plans for two more sites have been abandoned.

CANADA

◆ Integrated Maritime Surveillance System/SWR-503

Raytheon Canada's system is built around an SWR-503 HF surface-wave radar operating at 3.5 to 5.0 MHz at a pulse rate of 250 Hz (peak power 16 kW, average power 2 kW). The bandwidth occupied is 3–80 kHz, and pulses are compressed on reception. The receiver samples the received waveform at a rate of 500 kHz. This combination updates an aircraft position every 10 sec and a ship position every 200 sec (an iceberg location is updated every 20 min). Track capacity of the MHT-500 multiple-hypothesis

tracker is 100 aircraft and 500 surface targets. Small ships can be detected at a range of 200 nm, medium ones at 240 nm, and large ones beyond 270 nm (500 km). Small aircraft can be detected at 110 nm, and large ones beyond 215 nm (400 km). Bearing accuracy: SWR-503-16, 0.35 deg; -24, 0.25 deg; -32, 0.175 deg. Range accuracy: with 20-kHz receiver bandwidth, 375 m; with 40-kHz, 188 m; with 80-kHz, 94 m. Range rate accuracy: ships, 0.2 m/sec; aircraft, 0.8 m/sec. Each site covers a 120-deg sector.

Early in 1996 Canada announced the purchase of two systems to cover the Grand Banks fishing area. They will be placed at former Loran sites, the first at Cape Bonavista. The Integrated Maritime Surveillance System fuses SWR-503 data with that from other sensors, such as those on board coastal surveillance aircraft. Its operations center is at St. John's. Shipping is displayed there on FLAG (Fleet Location and Graphics) displays, with remote displays in Halifax and Ottawa.

RUSSIA

◆ HF/DF Net (KRUG and FIX series)

The Soviets captured the German Wullenweber HF/DF systems at the end of World War II and about 1952 began producing a Soviet version, KRUG, an array about 115 yd in diameter, consisting of 120 equally spaced monopole antennas. DF accuracy is reportedly about 1 deg, over a range of 6–20 MHz. The HF array was later supplemented by an inner concentric ring of monopoles that extended coverage into the VHF range. There is also reportedly a somewhat less accurate land-based HF/DF antenna, FIX-24, consisting of 24 monopoles located at 15-deg intervals around a 150m circle. Since HF/DF is used by all the Russian services, it is not clear from the unclassified literature to what extent, if any, particular networks are intended primarily for naval purposes. Presumably the loss of sites in client states has much affected the Soviet ocean surveillance system.

◆ Irida

This surface-wave HF (7–15 MHz) radar, comparable to the Marconi system described below, was announced in 1993, when it was offered at a unit cost of 12–15 million rubles. It had been developed by the Research Institute of Long Range Radiocommunication (RIAN). The transmit and receive arrays are 500–1500 m apart. A pair of arrays covers a 90-deg arc out to a range of 300 km; it can track 100 targets with a range accuracy of 3–4 km and a bearing accuracy of 3–5 deg. Average radiated power is 16 kW (peak power is 64 kW). The system requires five to seven operators per shift. A prototype was tested in the Black Sea.

UNITED KINGDOM

◆ S124

Marconi's coastal HF surface-wave radar is intended to detect low-flying aircraft out to 150 km and ships out to 370 km within a 120-deg sector. It can plot 400 vessels simultaneously (and can

Marconi's concept for the receiving and transmitting antennas (which in fact would be 1 km apart) of its S124 surface-wave coastal-surveillance radar. (Marconi Radar Systems)

be extended to track 40 aircraft). S124 uses a 50m-wide transmitting antenna array about 1 km from its 800m wide receiving array. Its solid-state amplifiers transmit 32 kW pulses at 4–7 MHz; typical azimuth resolution is 15 km at 200 km, and range resolution is selectable between 0.6 and 2.4 km (depending on bandwidth). Plot accuracy is 3/4 deg, 110m, 1/4 kt (postprocessing). S123 is a companion air search radar, using a 600m receiving array 1 km from a 50m transmitting array. It detects low-fliers at 250 km, and high-fliers at 500 km. It covers a 90-deg sector; power level is 160 kW (6–12 MHz); typical azimuth resolution is 10 km at 200 km (range resolution is 7–20 km). Track accuracy is typically 1 km, 2 kt. Track 100 aircraft, refresh every 10 sec. In both cases, targets are detected by their Doppler returns, so aircraft show up clearly against sea clutter. To detect much slower ships, the radar uses coherent processing over a longer dwell time.

UNITED STATES

♦ Bulls Eye

Shore HF/DF net is generally described as the shore complement to the shipboard Outboard. By 1960, there were three HF/DF nets, two in the Pacific (presumably Western Pacific and West Coast) and one in the Atlantic (East Coast); they were being modernized to deal with very short time-compressed transmissions (the goal at the time was 1 msec). The antennas are presumably large Wullenwebers, the U.S. term for which is Circularly Disposed Array Antennas, operating over the 2–30 MHz range.

♦ ROTHR (TPS-71 [XN-1])

ROTHR is Raytheon's Relocatable Over-the-Horizon Radar, capable of detecting both ships and aircraft. The program was ter-

minated in FY92 after four had been authorized (prototype plus three in FY88/89). Emplaced at Amchitka, in the Aleutians, the prototype became operational in 1985. The Amchitka site was shut down on 15 Sep 1993, and the radar was moved to Virginia to support the drug war. Two more were completed about 1995: one for Texas and another for Puerto Rico, both to support the drug war. A projected Japanese ROTHR seems to have been shelved.

A ROTHR site covers a 64-deg wedge between 500 and 1600nm range (the ionospheric bounce technique rules out shorter ranges). The 200-kW FMCW transmitter uses a 32-element phased array (a 1200ft line of wires strung from short masts); the receive array is 372 pairs of 19ft monopoles in a 1.6mi line, 50–100 nm from the receiver. Beams are formed digitally in the signal processor at the receiver (in an operations control center).

♦ NAVSPASUR

The Navy Space Surveillance System detects and tracks space objects crossing the continental United States, warning the deployed fleets of the approach of hostile reconnaissance and targeting satellites. This role became particularly important as the Soviets shifted from aircraft to satellites to target their large antiship missiles. Clearly it is now less important, but many countries will probably try to loft reconnaissance satellites within the next few years. To the extent that naval forces are most effective when they are least visible, warning of the approach of a satellite is quite important. It is possible to limit surveillance to the area over the United States because most ship-surveillance satellites must fly at relatively low altitude, hence must cross the United States fairly often. Because SPASUR is always active, no satellite

ROTHR coverage of 1.6 million square miles of the Caribbean, from a radar located in Virginia. (Raytheon)

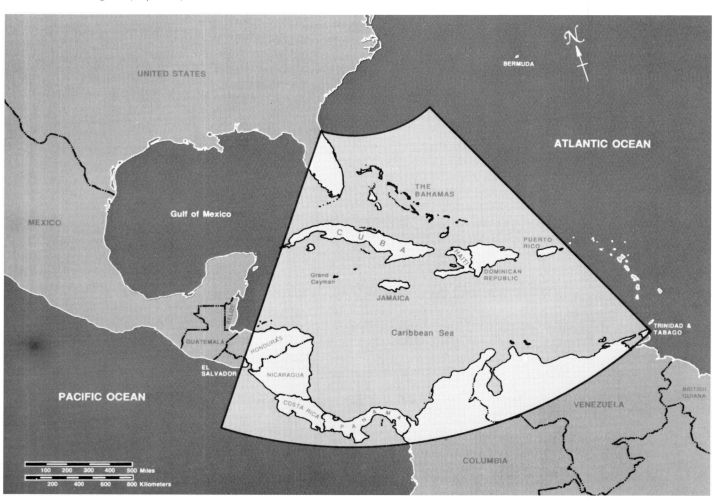

it picks up is likely to receive any indication that it is being detected or tracked. At present NAVSPASUR is the only U.S. space surveillance system that provides satellite vulnerability data (data on when ships are likely to be detected) to the Fleet.

The sensor is a relatively simple bistatic CW radar "fence" employing three transmitters, six receivers, and a computation center, with the transmitters and receivers in a great circle across the southern states. The computation center is at NAVSPASUR HQ in Dahlgren, Virginia.

Current research examines processing alternatives, digital filtering, and other processing of signals, and attempts to improve system performance. A digital signal processing receiver (DSPR) was developed for high-altitude stations, which are presumably conceived as an alternative to the current ground stations. There is also interest in using all-source target data to improve system performance.

STRATEGIC UNDERWATER SENSOR SYSTEMS

CANADA

For some years the Canadian Department of National Defence has been considering an Arctic subsurface surveillance system as a means of controlling access to northern Canadian waters; at times such a system has been advertised as an alternative to further Canadian submarine purchases. Sensors would be located at chokepoints, and they might transmit their data by satellite. Current research reportedly includes work on matched field processing (MFP), a technique that presumably uses templates of likely sound sources. MacDonald Dettweiler developed MFP techniques under a 1993–95 contract, with a follow-on due for completion at the end of 1997.

CHINA

Passive bottom arrays protect harbor entrances, extending out to sea about 20–30 nm.

FINLAND

Nokia Data Systems O/Y has produced an integrated coastal surveillance system, which is probably the one used by Finland. The architecture is similar to that of the Swedish system. Local control centers (LCCs) collect sensor data (radar, TV, night optics, and remote MA 8530 and MA 8560 laser rangefinders). Each LCC has a computer-driven 16in CRT (and can have additional color CRTs). District control centers (DCCs) assemble LCC data into a synthetic video tactical picture. It is not clear whether the DCCs feed into a national command center.

The Finnish underwater detection system is FHS-900/FHS-2000, developed by Elesco Oy A/B and operated by the Coastal Artillery. Groups of hydrophones are deployed in depths of 20 to 300 m, and a single control station can handle up to 32 hydrophone groups. FHS-900, which was deployed in the mid-1980s, apparently used pairs of hydrophones. The frequency range was 0.5 Hz to 100 kHz. Tests apparently showed that they were not sensitive enough and could not determine target bearing unambiguously. After considering solutions including linear arrays, Elesco opted for frequency-domain (LOFAR) processing and three-hydrophone elements (2m baseline) operating at 0.1 to 50 kHz, with integrated 40-dB preamplifiers. Trials in 1989–91 were successful. The current shore processor uses a Pentium CPU and a separate FFT processor. One shore station can handle 32 hydrophone groups located up to 30 km away. The workstation incorporates a pair of 20in high-resolution (1280 × 1024-pixel) monitors, each above a smaller monitor for alphanumeric data. Targets are shown tracked against a digitized map background (with 90% probability of position circles displayed). Fiskars was responsible for the multitarget detection algorithms, which presumably use ALI. The upgrade to this version was completed by early 1996. Elesco expects to improve sensitivity further by increasing sensor integration time.

The Swedish KAFUS is probably a version of FHS-900. Norway may have a similar system in fjords and coastal waters.

GERMANY

◆ AISYS

Atlas' AISYS was the first bottom-surveillance system to be marketed publicly. Reportedly it is used by Germany and Denmark (for the Kattegat). The system uses linear arrays in deep water and cylindrical submarine-type arrays in shallows. Both can be connected to shore either through fiber-optic or microwave (via buoys) links. The associated shore information and classification center is called SOBIC. AISYS may have been entered in a reported NATO competition for Turkish and Greek surveillance systems.

INDONESIA

In 1992 Indonesia signed an agreement with Thomson Sintra to develop bottom arrays. The ultimate goal is to monitor all the Indonesian straits, beginning with the Lombok Strait.

JAPAN

Japan maintains two surveillance centers at the southern and northern entrances to the Sea of Japan (Tsushima Straits and Straits of La Perouse), using a combination of bottom arrays, shore radars, and optical observation. Because they are barrier arrays, the bottom arrays used would not have been long-range SOSUS-type installations; initially, they were probably upward-looking devices. In the late 1960s they were replaced by a total of 19 LQO-3 arrays; the first two of five sets in the Tsushima Straits were installed in 1968; they were upgraded to LQO-3As in the 1980s. An official report suggested that a diesel submarine operating at less than 6 kt had a 70% chance of being detected at a range of 1000 yd and a 15% chance of detection at 3000 yd. Such figures would be entirely acceptable in a barrier, as opposed to an open-ocean, tracking system. In the 1970s development of the lower-frequency long-range LQO-4 began. It initially coordinated operations of P-2J patrol aircraft.

Japan deploys SURTASS-type surveillance towed array ships with U.S. technical crews; Japan and the United States share their surveillance data.

RUSSIA

In 1989 the U.S. Director of Naval Intelligence (DNI) reported that the Soviets had short-range fixed acoustic sensors in the Northern Fleet operating area, and longer-range planar arrays (code-named Cluster Lance) in the Far East, where geography is more favorable to such devices. Presumably, the devices in Northern Fleet waters are, in effect, acoustic fences that indicate that a submarine has actually passed through them. Such fences could be used to cue nearby aircraft or other ASW platforms and could form part of bastion defenses. The sensors would probably use RAP propagation and thus could function even in relatively shallow water. The DNI also stated that the Soviets were testing a towed surveillance array similar in concept to the U.S. SURTASS, and that within a few years they were expected to deploy surveillance platforms equipped with the new array.

None of these systems is likely to be particularly effective against modern very quiet submarines. Presumably Searchlight, described below, is one of the systems previously noted.

◆ Searchlight

This coastal surveillance system was announced by Okeanpribor, which was responsible for most Soviet sonar designs. Presumably it was one of the systems deployed off Soviet coasts. As currently described, it can be used not only for ASW surveillance but also to target surface ships; it is the targeting sensor for the recently advertised shore version of the SS-N-14 ASW/antiship missile. Maximum underwater sensor range is given as 150 km. Searchlight combines passive with active sensors, and includes an underwater telephone capability, presumably to cue submarines to deal with contacts.

The system employs separate transmitters and hydrophones, all at 300m depth; the transmitter can be moored in up to 1300 m of water, but the hydrophone array (1000 t) must lie on the

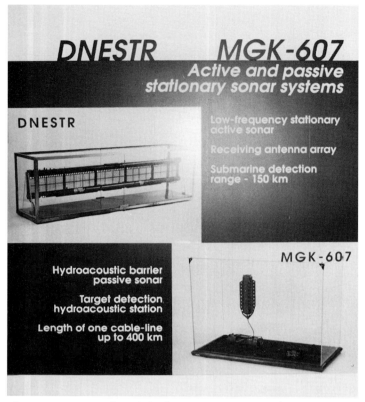

This Russian poster (1996) displays models of elements of the Dnestr (MGK-607) underwater surveillance system; the upper model shows the passive receiver, the lower the active element. Note that stated range is 150 km, but also that the active element can be on a 400km cable. (Dave Markov)

bottom. Each site covers a 110-deg arc. In active mode the system is accurate to within 3 m in range. Doppler can be measured to within 0.5 kt. The arrays can lie as much as 40 km offshore, without boosters on their cables. Okeanpribor claims that the array has a 10-year life in the water, and that it can be repaired there. Each set of arrays requires two or three operators. The power requirement is 110 kW continuous, 250 kW when a pulse is transmitted.

Searchlight is probably the outcome of experiments described by a Soviet emigré in the late 1980s. He stated that work on long-range submarine detection in shallow seas, using active LF (less than 1 kHz) sound sources, dated from the early 1980s or before. Hydropneumatic sources (rubber shell and compressed air) were used at 10–90 Hz (maximum output was 750 W at 50 Hz) and hydraulics were used at up to 100 Hz (maximum 186 dB at 40 Hz). In an experiment in the northwest Pacific in the summer of 1984, with the sound channel at only 100m depth, three radiators (tonals at 100–500 Hz) were towed at up to about 8 kt. A horizontal array was used as receiver. A target was detected at up to 1000 km (about 510 nm) using a narrow-band detector (resolution about 0.002 Hz).

SWEDEN

KAFUS (fixed underwater reconnaissance system) is being completed: it uses hydrophones, magnetic and other sensors, TV and other surveillance sets, linked by fiber-optic communications.

TAIWAN

Taiwan is experimenting with a SOSUS-type surveillance array system; in about 1986 the Chang Shan Institute was commissioned to emplace a small system off the eastern Taiwan coast for a 14-month evaluation (RCA had proposed such a system in 1981, but refused to release source code to Taiwan and hence was rejected). The arrays were laid at 90–300 m (300–1000 ft) depth, probably at Su-Au in northeast Taiwan. As in SOSUS,

data from the arrays are presumably collected at a shore station and used to cue ships and shore-based ASW aircraft. The introduction of such a system might explain the purchase of shore-based S-70C(M) ASW helicopters. A model surveillance system has been displayed at the Chang Shan Institute.

An official paper released in 1990 reported the acquisition of a U.S. Navy experimental harbor defense system, which Taiwan calls Lung Chin (Dragon Eyes). It included harbor nets, and apparently was not entirely satisfactory.

TURKEY

Reportedly, there is some type of underwater surveillance system in the Bosphorus.

UNITED STATES

◆ ADS

Advanced Deployable System is the deployable successor to FDS. It is to be covertly and overtly deployable, and modular so as to be suitable for environments from shallow to deep water. Upward-looking acoustics would work in both cases; in the shallow case the array may be supplemented by short-range non-acoustic sensors, such as magnetic and perhaps UEP. The U.S. Navy already has cooperative programs with France and Norway for magnetic surveillance sensors (the Norwegian system employs fiber optics). There is also some interest in mine-type seismic sensors which might be better than hydrophones in noisy shallow water. The system would have to last at least 30 days, and might have to remain in place for five years. Ideally, portions would be retrievable for refurbishment and later redeployment. Congressional language in the FY93 defense bill characterized ADS as optimized for shallow-water operation against quiet diesel submarines. The Navy thought of ADS as a subset of FDS, using much FDS technology, so it planned to spend about $20 million on development and an at-sea demonstration of the latter. ADS would use existing technology (NDI, nondevelopmental items). A request for proposal (RFP) was released on 8 May 1992.

In hopes of reducing system cost, late in 1994 the Navy dropped the requirement that ADS be air-deployable, and allowed deployment time to increase from three to seventeen days. On this basis, preliminary development (Milestone I) was approved in October 1994. Analysis included parallel studies of more covert and more autonomous systems, the latter being connected by radio rather than by cable (later the more autonomous version would be described as monitored by cellular telephone–type technology).

Loral Federal Systems (formerly IBM Federal Systems), teamed with Alliant, BBN, and E-Systems, won the ADS competition in April 1995. Loral is responsible for integration and dry-end processing; Alliant for the wet end, signal conditioning, signal processing, deployment, and retrieval; and BBN for dry-end signal processing, algorithm development, and analysis. This team won over McDonnell-Douglas/Hughes/Magnavox/Orincon/Western Instrument/Applied Remote Technology, Lockheed Martin/ Planning Systems Inc./Sparton/Texas Instruments, and AT&T/ Westinghouse/Presearch. All of the competitors received development contracts on 17 December 1992. The Naval Research Laboratory conducted a parallel study of all-optical sensor/network technology. As of 1995, it appeared that a production contract would be awarded about the end of FY00, with a system operational about 2004. The dry end is likely to be containerized for easy deployment, and the entire system will use considerable FDS technology. Indeed, the Navy has already developed a demonstration deployable FDS-D, which passed developmental tests (DTIID) in FY94. By September 1995, plans called for two fixed FDS and two deployable FDS-D.

The draft RFP for the integrated undersea surveillance system (January 1992) included a rapidly deployable component with an open architecture and modular design for mission-specific configurations and deployment methods, that is, corresponding to ADS.

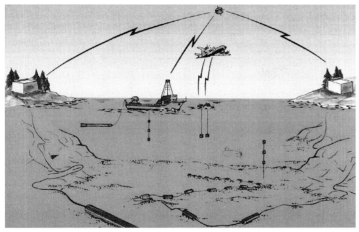

This sketch shows the alternative techniques for long-range undersea surveillance: at bottom left is the large hydrophone array of the type used in SOSUS; at right bottom is a distributed array, as in FDS. The boat at center tows an array and has an active pinger suspended from its hull, as in the LFA version of SURTASS. The P-3 monitors sonobuoys. Not to be neglected is the satellite communications system tying the sensors together to form a coherent tactical picture. None of the sensors has been drawn to anything like scale. (Courtesy of Alliant Techsystems)

◆ FDS

Fixed Distributed System was conceived as a successor to SOSUS, using a large number of upward-looking (RAP) sensors connected by fiber-optic cable, in addition to SOSUS-style large arrays. A single array has been deployed. Estimated lifetime was 24 yr. Much of the technology developed for FDS is likely to appear in the new ADS. IBM received the contract for the FDS SSIPS (shore signal and information processing segment). Its processors were open-architecture VME-based units, generally using Motorola 8800 processors. Each shore site would break its area of operation into sectors, with five desks (on a LAN) per sector (three CRTs with boxes alongside). Three CRTs offer multiple presentations of the acoustic data for correlation or to examine large amounts of data so as to extract subsets for processing.

The associated SDS (see below) uses much the same equipment (six consoles per sector). The consoles may provide support to battle group commanders or to sector ASW commanders, providing some dedicated assets.

The FDS Navy Development Coordinating Paper was approved 13 May 1986, followed by the DoD Decision Coordinating Paper on 10 May 1989 and the Milestone II decision on 22 September 1989. Full-scale engineering development of the underwater element was approved in January 1990, followed by the shore element in June 1991. Because of the decline of the Soviet threat, FDS has been reduced to technology demonstrator status. Planned funding was approximately halved in FY93. Work did continue on the two test arrays built, however, and in September 1995 plans called for maintaining them plus two deployable FDS-D arrays. The two arrays are to be refurbished and expanded by 50% (at less than 10% additional cost) using spare clusters. Underwater component integration is to be completed under the FY96 program.

◆ SDS/IUSS

Surveillance Direction System is the integrating element of the integrated undersea surveillance system (IUSS); the IUSS consists of SOSUS, SURTASS, and the new LFA (low-frequency [active] adjunct [to SURTASS]). SDS is intended to identify a contact in any one system and cue others to seek contacts representing the same object. OR-246-02-89 was issued 5 June 1989.

◆ SOSUS

The designation SOSUS (sound surveillance system) has been applied both to a particular deep-water system and to the full array of fixed detectors, including several technologies, that the United States and its allies possess. Most of the details that follow come from a 1977 history declassified in 1990. SOSUS was inspired by the discoveries, just after World War II, of the deep sound channel and, somewhat later, of LOFAR for signal processing. The first array, at Eleuthra, was installed by January 1952 for tests beginning that April. The goal was to achieve detections at 50–500 mi. In experiments in 1954, such arrays detected submarines as far away as 600 nm, though the average was 300–400 nm. In the late 1950s arrays were credited with 300nm range. In the late 1960s the existing FQQ-1 (Deltic) analog signal processors were replaced by FFT processors (CDC SPEAR).

LOFAR, that is, detection by signature, allows different SOSUS stations to be sure that they are detecting the same submarine (so that they can cross beams to provide range as well as bearing). Moreover, given the signature of the submarine, an airplane using LOFAR buoys should have a better chance of redetection, comparing the known signature to the received signal. This combination (SOSUS plus patrol aircraft) was first extensively (and very successfully) used during the Cuban Missile Crisis in 1962.

SOSUS Phase I (Project Caesar) consists of 1000ft arrays at 1000 fathom depth, to exploit the deep sound channel. That places them well out to sea in the Atlantic, but close inshore on the steeply shelving Pacific coast. Typical arrays comprise 40 hydrophones, forming 5-deg beams. Each beam feeds its own LOFARgram processor; initially detection/classification took about 5 min. By 1958 the program included twelve Atlantic (including Bermuda) and seven Pacific arrays; two more were added the following year. All were operational by late 1960, at which time a shallow-water array was being added at Argentia (to block submarines trying to end-run the deep water line in the Atlantic). An additional (22nd) deep-water array northwest of Bermuda was added in 1962. Further arrays were planned, but this 22-array system is the one generally mentioned officially. Continuously improved, it still exists.

Raw SOSUS data are initially processed by NAVFACs (naval facilities), which pass their products to regional evaluation centers (RECs: one each for Atlantic and Pacific) and then to main evaluation centers (MECs), which have access to information from other sources.

Phase II was the forward-area sites, in the Far East and in the North Atlantic and the Norwegian Sea, inspired by the success of the long-range OBOE array installed at Adak in 1962. This device successfully covered Petropavlovsk as well as the transit area running toward the mid-Pacific. A planned further extension of the original short-range arrays was canceled in favor of a new emphasis on forward-area listening. Arrays covering transit areas often enjoyed greater range because transiters were louder than submarines on patrol: they had to make a substantial speed to reach their patrol areas within a useful time. Early in the 1970s new arrays in North American and Western European waters extended coverage into the Norwegian Sea and also into the Eastern Atlantic (Project Backscratch). At about the same time, arrays were installed to cover areas of the Western Pacific and mid-Pacific.

By the early 1970s interest had increased in using all-source intelligence, properly sanitized, to cue SOSUS arrays. The arrays achieved their maximum range in alerted searchlight mode because in that mode they could accept a higher theoretical false-alarm rate.

A major SOSUS-upgrade program (1971) included sensors moved forward into the deep ocean basins: the abortive SASS, the Suspended Array Subsystem, a tripod, six miles on each side, which supported a directional array in the deep sound channel in water 18,000 ft deep.

In 1973 DoD issued a classified Area Coordinating Paper on Undersea Surveillance that seems to have shaped subsequent policy. The worst problems were prospective Soviet silencing and third-party basing (i.e., basing out of Soviet base areas covered by the forward-area extension). The latter extended to dealing with strategic surprise, for example, the rise in U.S. interest in the Indian Ocean. The solutions included the following: better signal processing (including interarray correlation for lower overall system noise), which the 1973 paper suggested could deal with problems arising over the next 10–15 yr; possible alternative array concepts; and mobility (flexibility) based on towed arrays and deployable moored buoys (the abortive RDSS). The towed array solution was presumably encouraged by the success of the interim array (SQR-14) in the Mediterranean. It became SURTASS. The future possibilities were the FDS (see above), SASS, and coherent signal processing. As of about 1976, the improved signal-processing system was scheduled for operational evaluation in the winter of 1977–78.

Phase III is the current modernization program. The number of shore evaluation sites and the number of personnel per site are being reduced as the system is more highly automated, with better means to assist operators in classifying signals. In view of submarine silencing, it is being adapted to detect nontraditional signals (transients, speed dependent signals, and active sonar emissions; traditional signals are narrow-band, deriving from machinery a nuclear submarine must always run, even at low speed). The FY93 program included installation of all-source automatic detectors in two prototype systems and refining and improving automatic signal classification by combining information from traditional and nontraditional signals. The FY93 program also included development of specifications for a processing architecture that will support real-time automatic detection, classification, tracking and reporting using all sources, presumably including nonacoustic (e.g., signals) intelligence. The results of the FY93 demonstrations will be incorporated into a full-scale engineering development. The SOSUS Phase III system will be designed and developed by a competitively selected contractor and fielded in all SOSUS NAVFACs.

Other current improvement programs are development of an adaptive beam-former (ABF) and an integrated acoustic display/wide-band acoustic recall (IAD/WBAR). Here, wide band is presumably in contrast to the narrow-band operation of the past.

See also SDS, the Surveillance Direction System.

◆ SURTASS (UQQ-2)

Surveillance Towed Array System uses specially designed towing ships (T-AGOS) and a very long array; it is a backup or gap filler for SOSUS. SURTASS replaces the six SQR-15 towed arrays deployed in the 1970s. Signals from the array are partially processed on board the towing ship, but most of the work is done at a shore station after the signals have been transmitted by satellite (DSCS) link. The ships are designed to steam 1500 nm to a patrol area, where they tow their arrays at 3 kt. The arrays are 8575 ft long, towed at a depth of 500–1500 ft; the tow cable is reportedly 6000 ft long.

The main current improvements are the reduced-diameter fiber-optic array (RDA) and the low-frequency adjunct (LFA), a towed sound source. Reduced array diameter should equate to longer array length (as in submarines). LFA is to be on board second-generation SWATH ships (T-AGOS 23 class), presumably suspended from a well between the hulls. In these ships LFA/RDA/UYS-2 amounts to a bistatic sonar. During FY91 the engineering development models of RDA and LFA were installed on board the research vessel *Cory Chouest*. Low rate production began in FY94.

SURTASS was conceived as a strategic system reporting to centers in the United States. Fleet commanders protested that it might very usefully support deployed forces, and this more tactical role has become more important as the Soviet threat has declined. The effort, then, has been to make units more autonomous, capable of evaluating and processing their own data. The signal processor is UYS-2, and it is supplemented by a special acoustic performance predictor, AEAS (ASW Environmental Acoustic Support), a large-area analog to the SIMAS (UYQ-25) of tactical systems. As in the tactical case, performance prediction makes it possible to guess reliably in which convergence zone a target has been detected. UYS-2 on SURTASS ships is being converted from SEM-B to SEM-E standard for greater processing power. These improvements and RDA form the SURTASS Block Upgrade, which was tested on board T-AGOS 21 in FY93.

SURTASS improvements are delivered as "Builds." Build 1 includes automated line trackers and a source auto-detector; Build 2 includes wide-band energy trackers, source-set formation, and analysis tools. Build 3 includes automated localization and tracking, and wide-band/narrow-band feature association. It uses SEM-E rather than SEM-B components. Planned further improvements include a fiber-optic array and a twin-line array.

Hughes Aircraft is responsible for the SURTASS upgrade program.

SURTASS entered service late in 1984. There are three classes of U.S. SURTASS ships: the original monohull *Stalwarts* (T-AGOS 1–18), now being retired; four *Victorious*-class SWATHs (T-AGOS 19 class), and eight projected T-AGOS 23-class SWATHs (one authorized in FY90). In addition, five Japanese surveillance ships (AOS, the first in the 1989 program) will tow UQQ-2 and will reportedly carry U.S. crews to operate the sensors.

◆ LFA/MSS/SALFAS

The Low Frequency Adjunct to SURTASS (see above) is built by Hughes. The Full-Scale Engineering Development contract for LFA was let in 1991. Much the same technology was used in a multistatic sonar (MSS), built as a technology demonstrator (trials were completed in September 1993). Ultimately a tactical stand-alone active sonar (SALFAS), towable by a *Spruance*-class destroyer, may result from this work. For the present, ASW investment is concentrated on relatively short-range systems for shallow (littoral) waters.

By 1993, Hughes was producing the first LFA and had options for 12 more, a figure that assumed that the last three T-AGOS units would be built. The active array proper is made by Lockheed Sanders; the reduced-diameter passive array (RDA) is by AT&T.

Sea trials have been conducted for some years. For example, in bistatic mode LFA managed to detect and track a diesel submarine in the shallow Ionian basin. In this test, the pinger was towed by the oceanographic ship *Cory Chouest*, operating in deep water; the echoes were detected by destroyers, using a new MARS receiver developed by DRS. In this particular experiment a single LFA system in mid-Mediterranean managed to cover the whole width of that sea, from the northern to the Libyan coasts.

The main console has two screens, the upper usually a geographic plot (geosit) with pie wedges showing the generated sonar beams, the lower a waterfall (the output of the signal processor). A window generated below the waterfall allows the operator to query details of a given return, to help identify it. The system simplifies the operator's task by deciding that some echoes are actually undersea terrain. Others are color-coded: yellow for an unknown, red for a target. The screens are overlaid with information processor cues. The operator correlates acoustic data and patterns with the processor.

The operator can switch the upper screen to show the A-scans from three beams. Using them, he can compare an echo with the transmitted wave form, which will generally be either CW (for Doppler) or Hyperbolic FM (HFM) for range. Pulses can be transmitted either singly or, if there appears to be a target, as a train. The system can show how many echoes (hits) are received per opportunity (M of N). The A-scans also show fine target structure. For example, bathymetric (terrain) targets are noncoherent, and show numerous peaks.

Typically a surveillance ship will detect 200 wave trains per minute, so the system includes an information processor to reduce the operator's workload. Ultimately the display shows position and track for each target; this information can be transmitted by various data links (e.g., Link 11, OTH-Gold).

MSS was related to the abortive SQY-1 program. The primary difference from LFA is in energy management, that is, in the ranges to be obtained. LFA uses long pulses over many minutes; MSS uses 2- and 4-sec forms—sweep (FM) and tone (CW)—every 30 sec to 1 min, using a quarter- or half-scale key for more range. With the quarter-scale key, the sonar pings every minute, using four unique ping types and then recycling every 4 min (it gets four looks in that 4 min). Typically the surveillance display shows an FM waterfall on one side and a CW waterfall on the other, indicating Doppler by color and amplitude by intensity, so the operator can correlate the two.

Several different waveforms are used: coded pulses (which can be pulse-compressed) for range, CW for rate, and also FSK (a succession of short single tones to get both range and rate, called a Costas after its inventor). The coded pulses, which are detected by a convolution filter, are HFM, linear FM (LFM), and FM. The returning CW pulses are subjected to FFT analysis to extract frequency shifts.

Tests included both monostatic and bistatic arrangements. In the monostatic *Glover* test, half of the planned planar array was mounted in a bow dome; the receiver was a reconfigurable multiline array (RMES: nine lines in a cruciform arrangement; Hughes also tried a planar arrangement of three lines, each three arrays in length). A lower-frequency towed body (1 to 2 CZ from the receiver) was also tried.

The MSS trials were considered proof of principle; they demonstrated that the sonar source transmitter could be located well enough to track targets precisely enough to attack them.

♦ **Loral Surveillance System**

In 1995, Loral Federal Systems (formerly the IBM Federal Systems Division) announced a new coastal surveillance system. It is probably a commercial equivalent of FDS. Loral offered sensors made by Alliant, acoustic sensor/surveillance technology by BBN, and installation by Cable & Wireless Marine of Southampton, England.

♦ **Sea Sentry/MIUW Upgrade**

DRS's export coastal and harbor surveillance system, announced in 1996, uses the acoustic processor techniques the company developed for towed arrays and then for a COTS-based upgrade for U.S. Mobile Inshore Underwater Warfare units. Sonar data are combined with data from a surface-search radar and with environmental information (to predict sensor performance). The main operator station is a tactical display, flanked by a sonar display. C² elements include a data link similar to OTCIXS.

The radar is a standard slotted-waveguide type, such as a Furuno available under FMS. The sonar is a passive line array,

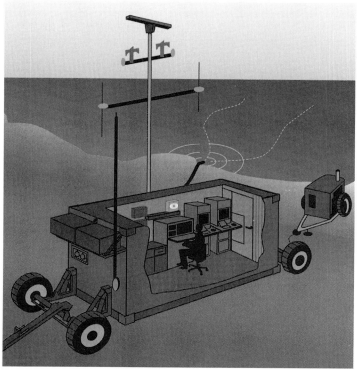

DRS's modular Sea Sentry van shows its surface-search radar and a cable connection to a pair of sea-bottom arrays. (DRS)

typically with 32 elements spaced 1.17 m apart. The beam-former and processor can accept further 32-element arrays added to the initial one, and all can be up to 20 km from the shore station.

The entire system is designed to be accommodated aboard trucks.

As of 1996, possible customers included Saudi Arabia, Taiwan, and the Gulf states.

TACTICAL COMMUNICATIONS SYSTEMS

Radio Systems

Long-haul naval communications may be by LF, using a ground wave, up to 300 kHz, or by MF/HF, up to 30 MHz, using a combination of ground waves and sky waves bounced off the ionosphere. Higher frequencies are inherently limited to line of sight, although most antennas are not directional. All navies use a combination of MF/HF and shorter-wave, higher-frequency communications, and only a few systems can be listed here. UHF is generally used for ship-to-aircraft and aircraft-to-aircraft, and for short-range ship-to-ship (LOS). UHF and higher frequencies are generally used for satellite uplinks.

Current attention to antijam and anti-intercept measures focuses largely on frequency-hopping. Attempts are also being made to overcome the vagaries of the ionosphere, which is affected by, among other things, the 11-yr solar cycle. For HF radio, these two developments are linked because the appropriate transmission frequency depends on ionospheric conditions. In the past, finding the appropriate frequency and making contact was sufficiently laborious that frequency-hopping was inconceivable. Now the radio can automatically repeat the usual manual steps, and it can often achieve a connection in as little as 10 sec. The logical extension of automatic connection is automatic frequency-hopping, typically 10–20 hops/sec (less than 7 millisec/hop). Hopping is unlikely to be fast enough to frustrate interception (hence, HF/DF will remain), since the existing wide-open intercept systems will probably pick up even very short snippets of message. However, hopping can frustrate jamming since it takes some time for an enemy to retune the jammer from one bit of message to the next.

Examples of modern HF systems are the French SPIN and the British ASSAT (Advanced Ship-to-Shore Automatic Telegraph). SPIN emphasizes ECM resistance by frequency-hopping; ASSAT seems more oriented toward reliable long-haul transmissions. In ASSAT, the shore station transmits a standard message for several seconds on each available frequency, and the shipboard receiver measures the signal-to-noise ratio for each and calculates the best frequency to use; this evaluation continues throughout the transmission. ASSAT is currently being tested.

Fading (due to multipath propagation) has long limited effective HF data rates. Only recently has the full Link 11 rate (2.4 kbps) been realized in a single-tone rather than a multiplex system (see the discussion of Link 11 below). In 1994 the U.S. Navy succeeded in transmitting at 4.8 kbps (between the amphibious ships *Duluth* and *Peleliu*).

The current NATO HF naval system, Cross Fox (commissioned 1989), uses 27 ground sites in eight countries.

Automated message processing is an important current trend. A modern system collects all received messages in a computer memory, allowing them to be called up as required and distributed by what amounts to electronic mail (to workstations throughout a ship). In the past, automatic data links have always been differentiated from conventional radio communications. However, it is natural for an automated processing system to merge data links with other radio traffic.

DENMARK

Terma, which manufactures the current Danish naval combat-direction systems (TDS), also manufactures an associated data link; like the Swedish link, the Danish link can transmit both data and text messages. The Terma TDS is intended for use ashore, as part of a coast-defense system. Data-link messages must, therefore, be passed between coastal centers via land telephone lines; they must also be compatible with those used by other land-based command/control systems. Terma developed a Standard Communications Controller to solve the interface problems raised by such operation. The Terma data link operates at about 1.2 kbps.

FRANCE

French SSBNs are controlled via a communications center in Rossnier (Dept of Indre), which can communicate at ranges of up to 9000 km.

◆ ASTARTE

This airborne VLF system, ASTARTE (Avion station relais de transmissions exceptionelles), analogous to the U.S. TACAMO, is based on four Transall aircraft carrying U.S.-supplied VLF equipment. Operated by the French air force, ASTARTE entered service in 1988. It is hardened against EMP.

◆ Link W

This unlicensed copy of Link 11 is associated with the Vega and Tavitac systems, equipment for which is manufactured by SAT (W comes from the letter *w* in *Sawari*, the Franco-Saudi naval arms program for which Link W was developed). Link W is probably also used by China (Luda III and Luhu classes, which are equipped with license-built Tavitac combat systems).

◆ SOLFERINO

The current command link for SSBNs uses the VLF (20-kHz) transmitters at Kerlouan and Rosnay, which were built specifically for the strategic submarine program.

◆ Syracuse

This system employs five repeaters (7–8 GHz, transmitting at 2400/75 baud) in the two French Telecom 1 satellites reserved for military (primarily naval) use, under an agreement made in 1980. Ground coverage extends from the West Indies to the Reunion Islands. Syracuse I became operational in 1987.

The associated shipboard system uses a pair of 1.5m stabilized antennas in radomes, located so that one will always have a clear line of sight to the satellite. The antennas track either using preprogrammed satellite data or homing on the satellite's beacon. As of 1995, 22 ships have terminals.

Syracuse II, which entered service in December 1991, employs three satellites: Telecom 2A (launched 1991), Telecom 2B (launched May 1992), and Telecom 2C (reserve). As in the Telecom 1 system, each carries five X-band military transponders. Dishes are 0.90m dia for surface ships and 0.40m dia for Atlantique Mk 2 aircraft. Telecom 2B and 2C are to incorporate a laser cross-link to the Helios photo reconnaissance satellite (they will downlink to surface units).

France hopes to put a collaborative Syracuse III in service by 1995.

GERMANY

◆ TDLT

Rockwell-Collins GmbH Track Data Link Terminal is a stand-alone Link 11 introduced in 1990, with a capacity for 500 tracks within a coverage area of up to 2048 × 2048 nm. The track capacity is predivided into air, surface, subsurface, EW/ESM, and points tracks. When any one category fills, messages that would initiate further tracks in that category are ignored. TDLT uses data-link track filters (accept/reject based on track type/category, identification/hostility, penetration, geographic area, speed) to avoid overload. TDLT can accommodate information beyond that normally provided in NTDS and similar systems, for example, it can distinguish between a fighter and a strike airplane. The 1280 × 1024-pixel raster-scan color display is driven by a 68020 processor with a math coprocessor; there is also a separate database manager processor. The operator has a keyboard and a rollerball. Typically the screen is divided into a large operational situation display on the left, overlaid with a tote display area. The upper right-hand side is a mini-map, with track data readout (for up to three tracks) and setup tote below it.

Users: Denmark (frigate *Olfert Fischer*), Norway (*Andenes*), Singapore (*Victory* class), United Kingdom (Nimrod aircraft in the Persian Gulf). Denmark and Norway bought TDLT specifically to support Gulf operations, but Norway began a trial in August 1991 to decide whether to buy it for other ships. As of the spring of 1991, 14 TDLT had been sold and 11 delivered, all within a few weeks that year.

INDIA

In spring 1996, Bharat Electronics Ltd. announced a new data link, composite communications system (CCS) Mk 2, to connect Indian warships with each other and with a network of shore stations. Given Bharat's parentage as a Signaal subsidiary, CCS Mk 2 is probably very similar to Signaal's Link Y Mk 2.

INTERNATIONAL

◆ NATO Phase 4

The two satellites (one operational, one spare in orbit) operate at 7–8 GHz, carrying much of the load of the NATO Integrated Communications System (NICS), serving national command authorities and designated NATO CINCs. Each satellite has an area coverage transmitter for the Atlantic and a narrow-beam transmitter pointed at Europe. Channels provide secure voice and data. NATO 4 is a modified British Skynet satellite, and it has an explicit maritime role.

◆ NATO Data Links

Link 1/TADIL-B—The basic NADGE (NATO air defense ground environment) data link (ground-to-ground, between sector observation centers, SOCs), analogous to, but not compatible with, Link 11. In 1978 the U.S. Marine Corps obtained an interface, MANTA, to pass Link 1 data into its own TDS, which uses Link 11 formats for air information. TADIL-B (Link 11B), used by the U.S. Army and Marines, is similar but uses the Link 11 (TADIL-A) format and a different speed of transmission. The NATO SSSB (ship-shore-ship buffer) is used to mediate between Link 1 and Link 11; it is installed, for example, on board the Italian missile cruiser/carrier *Giuseppe Garibaldi*.

Link 2—Link for radar and associated data between land radar stations (successor to Link 1): the projected replacement, LISA (Link In Support of ACCS, i.e., air C² systems) was to have been Link 2, but that designation was rejected, presumably for fear of confusion with Link 11 (11 confused with II, the Roman numeral for 2).

Link 3—Slow teletype link (analogous to Link 14) between SHOCs (operations centers) and strategic early warning evaluation centers. Each center regularly assesses the air picture and sends a message. Link 3 is currently in service as a slow-speed teletype warning link for AAW.

Link 4/TADIL-C—This interceptor-air-control link was used by both France and the United States. It has been replaced in U.S. service by Link 4A, which is used for carrier-controlled (all-weather) approach as well as for air defense. Link 4B is a ground-to-ground land-line link. At least the original Link 4 used 70-bit messages (each bit being 200 microsec in duration, for a total of 14 msec), each of which included a synchronizing pattern, a start pulse, an aircraft address, a message number or label, two information groups, and parity-checking bits. The link operates at a fixed frequency within the 300–325-MHz band by FSK. There is no overall net-control clock; an airplane receiving a message uses the synchronizing pattern to set its own clock to receive. Even so, the finite length of each message sets a practical limit on the number of aircraft that can share a single net. A controlling transmitter must be able to send messages to all its aircraft in sequence, and there must be some allowance for message feedback. There must also be some short time between messages. Practical net size is limited by allowable time-lateness of messages. For example, 20 messages would take something more than 0.28 sec, so 1 of 20 aircraft would have to wait at least that long for an updated enemy aircraft position. The U.S. designation is TADIL-C. This link is not encrypted, nor is it jam resistant.

The current standard U.S. Navy aircraft terminals are ASW-25 and ASW-27. Link 4 originally did not allow for communication between aircraft. However, before the outbreak of the Gulf War Harris Electronics managed to modify ASW-27s (to ASW-27C) aboard F-14As so that groups of four aircraft could communicate via Link 4C, without using any intermediate ground terminal. Fleet-wide installation was completed before the Gulf War. It was the only operational fighter-to-fighter data link then available, and was widely praised.

Harris is now offering a reduced-size ASW-27C, ASW-54(V), which it calls LITDL (Link 16 Interoperable Tactical Data Link), operating at UHF (300–325 MHz) rather than at L-band (as in Link 16). ASW-54 can operate in multiple formats (Link 4 or Link 16). One aircraft is designated as master for timing purposes. Up to 15 aircraft can operate on each of 250 orthogonal nets. A pilot would select the desired channel from the 250 available, insert his tail number and net position, and would be initialized and on-line within 1.5 sec. Gateways aboard C^2 aircraft (such as AWACS) translate the ASW-54 messages into 70-bit JTIDS format for injection into the JTIDS L-band broad-area network. Aircraft equipped only with ASW-54 can communicate among themselves at UHF frequencies. Harris claims that this combination provides up to 85% of overall JTIDS performance at a very low cost (about $100,000 for an ASW-54). ASW-54 was conceived to replace Link 4A terminals on the F/A-18. It was first ordered for the abortive A-12; Harris built eight units plus two with internal funding. The system finished first flight trials on board an S-3 in May 1992. Further tests have involved passing SAR and IR video, which could be used to update strike aircraft en route to their targets.

Link 5—Proposed ship-to-shore link with Link 11 characteristics, overtaken by Link 11 development and abandoned. Link 11 was briefly described as Link 5A.

Link 6—Ground link connecting main control centers, weapon systems or sites, primarily for missile control. In service.

Link 7—Civil and military air traffic control (point-to-point) link, in service in France only.

Link 8—Proposed ship-shore-ship link with Link 13 characteristics. Abandoned. Link 13 was briefly described as Link 8A.

Link 9—Air defense control center/air base link primarily for scrambling interceptors. Abandoned.

Link 10/Link X/Link Y—This British tactical digital data system is broadly equivalent to (but not compatible with) Link 11. Conceived by Ferranti as Link X (hence 10), it was adopted by the Belgian, Dutch, and Greek navies (the latter when it bought the two *Kortenaers* in 1980). It may survive in some British Type 42 destroyers. When operating with other NATO ships, British Link 10 units are fitted with receive-only Link 11 (ROLE); otherwise they rely on Type 42 "gateway" ships, which have both Links 10 and 11. The export version, Link Y, was developed by Ferranti and later made by Signaal. It survives in several navies (see below). Link 10/Link Y is limited to positional information. In effect Link 10 handles information in serial form, Link 11 in parallel. Link 10 carries only a subset of Link 11 messages (it sends only positional information; Link 11 includes engagement tellbacks, ESM, and IFF information). Hence it is suited to small systems, but would be a mismatch for a large one. Link 10 uses a 10sec slot time (6 participants/min, 1.2 kbits/min). This is almost equivalent to Link 11 cycle time. Operating range is reportedly 150–180 nm. Like Link 11, Link 10 uses about 3 kHz of bandwidth. In contrast to Link 11, Link 10 has no net controller.

Link Y can accommodate up to 24 units/cycle (possibly 30 in a current Ferranti version), providing more slots for a smaller number of subscribers. The standard message format is two 24-bit words; standard transmission speed is 300–1200 bps (2400–4800 bps optional). The current Ferranti Link Y processor, based on the company's Argus minicomputer, maintains a track database of up to 120 tracks, comprising both tracks passed by link and own-ship tracks. This figure is presumably typical of the capacity of a Link Y system. The current version uses a color display and can accommodate data points up to 2000 miles from own-ship position. Net modes: time slot, radio silence, terminal net test, system net test. Station modes: net control, dependent station, restricted transmission station, passive station, receive only, single report, range extension relay. Radios: HF SSB, VHF, or UHF standard voice frequency channel.

Signaal now produces a Link Y Mk 2, which has been bought by Kuwait, Malaysia (for the *Lekiu* class and the ex-Italian corvettes; it will probably be in the new OPVs; the earlier *Kasturi* class have the original Link Y), Oman, Pakistan, and Qatar. This version can accommodate up to 31 subscribers at a rate of up to 4.8 kbps, and can handle distances of up to 900 km. It can use both HF and UHF radio.

Link Y users include Argentina (carrier and Type 42 destroyers, possibly also MEKOs), Brazil (YB: carrier and frigates), Egypt (YE: Ferranti receive-only Link Y in Ramadan, *Descubierta*, and Romeo classes, and also in Beechcraft 1900s, to direct OTH missile fire), Korea, Kuwait (CMN FACs and command center or surviving boat), Malaysia, Oman (*Qahir* class), Pakistan (Type 21s), Qatar (*Barzan* class), Thailand (in F27s, specifically to support OTH missile fire). Ships with export SEWACO systems probably have the Dutch version of Link Y, which is not entirely interoperable with the British. Link Y was offered for export on board Tornado aircraft, so it may be in service in Saudi Arabia. See also the Indian CCS Mk 2 system above.

Link 11/TADIL-A—Digital encrypted HF or UHF link for the U.S. NTDS, and the current NATO naval standard. Beside all major NATO surface ships with CDSs, all new NATO (and new Australian) submarines have or will have a receive-only version, so that they can share an overall tactical picture (the U.S. Navy may fit two-way Link 11 to *Los Angeles*–class submarines for better tactical support). Some British ships have receive-only Link 11 (ROLE). Link 11 is also installed on board S-3A and P-3C aircraft. The Italian navy plans to install Link 11 on its new EH-101 helicopters. The AEW version of the EH-101 will have Links 11 and 16. Compared to Link 10, Link 11 carries three times the data per target and requires about four times the dedicated computing power. Link 11 is subject to NATO STANAG 5511. Note that different navies use different subsets of the full Link 11 capability.

The Link 11 net operates in roll-call mode. Subscribers operate either as designated net control station (NCS) or in picket (PKT) mode, and each unit is assigned its own picket or participating unit (PU) number. The NCS calls up each PU in its net in turn, then reports its own message. Alternative modes are broadcast (BC), short broadcast (SBC), net sync (NS), net test (NT), and radio silence. In broadcast mode, a station continuously broadcasts to all net participants and must coordinate with the NCS to avoid jamming (except in the case of USQ-79 users). SBC is a single broadcast. NS is an initializing transmission by the NCS to synchronize the pickets. NT is a test pattern broadcast by the NCS.

Link 11 generally carries a stream of updates to the agreed tactical picture, carried by formatted SBC messages keyed to the standard track table. In the 1970s an alternative broadcast (BC) mode, in which a single unit broadcast the entire picture as a series of Link messages, was tested successfully. It could have been used, for example, to update distant units via a satellite. It did not enter service for that purpose, but it is presumably the mode by which a submarine using receive-only Link 11 quickly obtains a force tactical picture from, for example, an ASW airplane. As currently understood, Link 11 satellite relay operates in normal mode, imposing dummy message frames or participating units to compensate for the time delay inherent in satellite transmission.

Each participating unit is assigned a two-digit octal address code; the data terminal set of the net control station carries all the addresses of its pickets in its own address register. A data terminal set may accommodate more than one such register (e.g., four in USQ-76, for a total of up to 62 picket stations, 16 per register [including own station]).

The Link 11/NTDS network operates with very short time delays between transmissions by different stations; the end of one message signals the next transmitter to start. The transmitter sends a series of synchronizing pulses, then starts sending data. One technical problem in the early versions of the system was that the receiver of the unit that had just transmitted could not start up quickly enough to receive the synchronizing pulses of the next transmission. Because time delays would be so destructive, it was not possible to transmit Link 11 data through a satellite. Even a distance such as that between Rome and Brussels is reportedly too great, in terms of the resulting time delay. However, satellite transmission is extremely valuable, for example, for a submarine that enters the net intermittently. Current work (under LEIP) therefore includes a satellite version of Link 11.

Link 11 currently operates on both HF (2–30 MHz) and UHF (225–400 MHz), the former for use at up to 300 nm, the latter for 25 nm or less (particularly from aircraft). HF operation is AM; UHF is FM. Messages are transmitted as 30-bit data frames, each consisting of 24 bits of encrypted message data plus 6 bits of error-detection code. The system operates at two alternative rates, NTDS fast (2250 bps, 75 frames/sec) and NTDS slow (1364 bps, 44.75 frames/sec).

The current Link Eleven Model Five (LEMF) improvement program adds new waveforms and protocols and is intended to be jam resistant in HF. LEMF (design completed FY88) is part of Phase I of a longer-term Link Eleven Improvement Program (LEIP). A full-scale engineering-development contract for LEIP was let in 1987. LEIP Phase II seeks increased capacity and quicker network access. There is also a new message standard (OPSEC 511). The LEIP OR was issued in February 1982, and the Decision Coordinating Paper for High-Frequency Anti-Jam communications (HFAJ) and LEIP was issued in January 1987. LEIP led to NILE, NATO Improved Link Eleven, which is now termed Link 22 (see below).

LEIP products included SATCOMM Link 11 as well as expansion of Link 11 to non-CDS (non-NTDS) ships via a Link Eleven Display System (LEDS, built around USQ-69, including a low-cost Link 11 terminal with versions capable of forwarding data), MULTS (multilink terminal station), a new common shipboard data terminal set (CSDTS), work on message standards, and the abortive "Link America." There was also a data link for use with foreign navies not equipped with Link 11. As of March 1992, Litton had demonstrated versions of Link 11 using telephone, satellite, and Have Quick radio. LEIP also developed an HF single-tone modulation or serial-tone modulation (STM) alternative to the original Kineplex signal technique employed by Link 11; the new terminals are USQ-111 and the open-architecture USQ-125. Of the entire program, only NILE work continued past FY93. The LEDS upgrade program was completed that year.

The original Kineplex system tried to overcome HF multipath problems by using 15 × 75-baud signals, each with a long tone, in parallel, on the theory that multipath (sky wave/ground wave) could not distort a superimposed combination of long tones, whereas it could smear out a sequence of short pulses, like those sent down a telephone line. The solution was imperfect; in practice not all Link 11 messages are even received, and the elaborate error-correcting code is vital. STM defeats multipath by periodically testing the HF medium by inserting a known set of bits. The receiver can then construct the appropriate filter; coherent reception buys a 20-dB gain. The technique accepts only multipath signals that reinforce the tones, rejecting those which smear one digital bit into another. Past attempts to solve the problem failed because the HF medium changes rapidly; only recently have fast enough signal processors appeared. In theory, STM allows a much higher data rate than Kineplex, and thus is a key to more powerful systems.

There is also a digital UHF mode, used with satellites. A DTS therefore generally has alternative audio (HF) and digital (satellite or wireline) modes. There is also a mixed mode, in which the terminal broadcasts data via both interfaces; anything it receives via one port it retransmits on the other. The first U.S. mixed LOS/satellite net was tested in June 1979. A P-3C transmitted directly (by UHF) to the ASW Operations Center at Rota, which also communicated with a submarine via a Fleetsat.

A DTS can also be split between a local site and a remote site connected by land-line. The local site can include the data-link control element and the encryption; the remote site can be the radio receiver side. The split is necessary because the land-lines cannot handle Link 11 audio (tone) data because of bandwidth or linearity or other limits; time delays in the audio lines can also make circuit operation difficult because they interfere with the usual frame rate. Technology developed to handle such splits, with their delays, can also handle the long delays inherent in satellite operation.

Current splits are: the U.S. Air Force Iceland system (USQ-76; this system includes a "Navy tap" connecting it with the ASWOC in Iceland), the NATO Iceland Air Defense System (NIADS, using an MX-512P), the Royal Saudi Air Force Peace Shield system (USQ-76), the Canadian ROCC (MX-512P with a satellite split), the U.S. Navy CARIBROC operations center (MX-512P with a satellite split), the Italian ship-shore-ship buffer (MX-512P semi-split), and the Spanish ship-shore-ship buffer (MX-512PV).

Link 11 was conceived by a CANUKUS (Canadian-UK-U.S.) Naval Data-Transmission Working Group (NDTWG) formed in 1954. The final proposal was ratified at Ottawa in late November 1957. The Royal Navy proposed a name, TIDE (Tactical International Data Exchange), which was reportedly inspired by that of a popular U.S. laundry detergent; the data link would help clean up a messy tactical picture. At this time the Royal Navy already had a digital link associated with its comprehensive display system; it proposed that the new link be Link II. Hence the choice of Link 11 when other NATO Links were given Arabic numerals. Many contemporary television commercials showed Tide (or some other advertised detergent) as superior to an alternative, less expensive, "Brand X." It seems likely that the much later name Link X (which became Link 10) was inspired by that parallel (Link 10 is, after all, a less capable but also less expensive data link).

Export versions for E-2C aircraft include Link Delta for Egypt (reportedly because Delta resembles a pyramid), Link Pi for Israel (the numeral 11 with a line above it), Link Sigma for Singapore.

Single terminals were tested aboard a Knox-class frigate (1988) and a PHM (1988). It seems likely that four more frigates were outfitted with Link 11 in 1990, and that the other five PHM were fitted in 1991. Some Coast Guard ships were also fitted with Link 11. Link 11 is also installed on board S-3A and P-3C aircraft (and, therefore, at ASWOCs).

Link 11 is also used by the U.S. Air Force and the Royal Saudi Air Force (on board AWACS [E-3A] early warning and control aircraft).

Link 11 usage varies. The naval concept is to maintain a common tactical picture as close as possible to real-time, with minimum net cycle time, since the pickets providing data are also the units being defended (and, in most cases, the shooters). A naval AEW airplane is only one among the pickets. By way of contrast, the Air Force controls only fighters so it concentrates on AWACS as their controlling arm, and its surface radars are quite subordinate. They are responsible only for reporting tracks in their own assigned areas (track production areas, or TPAs). By way of contrast, an Air Force AWACS passes data to ground stations through a strategic link, and those data are usually time-late.

Conversions from Link 10: AEG installed Link 11 on board the Belgian Wielingen-class frigates when they were modernized. The Dutch Kortenaers and van Speijks (now sold to Indonesia, presumably without their Links) all received Link 11 during their big refits, beginning in 1984 (the Tromps were built with both Links, as gateway ships). British Type 42s and early Type 22s had both Link 10 and 11, and the three carriers were "gateways" between the two Links. All British ships now have two-way Link 11.

Norway bought the EDO workstation for Link 11 for the modernized *Oslos*, integrated with their MSI-3100 CDSs. The first (leased) unit was installed on board *Trondheim* to fit her for NATO StaNavForLant service. Link 11 may later be fitted to Norwegian fast-attack craft.

Major recent foreign purchasers (from Litton, a major U.S. DTS supplier) have been:

Australia: 10 USQ-76(V)8 in 1983; 12 MX-512P for ANZAC frigates 1991

Canada: 19 USQ-76(V)6 for ADLIPS program (1980); 7 USQ-76(V)9 for *Halifax* class (1984); 6 USQ-76(V)1 for TRUMP upgrades (1986)

Greece: 2 in 1989 delivered to Signaal for Greek frigates (presumably MEKOs); 5 for surface ships in 1990 (presumably including the other 2 MEKOs)

Korea: 8 MX-512P for Korean Navy program, 1989

Turkey: 4 ROLE (MX-512P, 1988); 1 for naval C² center (1989); 12 in 1990 (possibly only 4 for ships); 13 in 1991 for mobile radars; 2 in 1991 (probably for patrol aircraft). The initial Turkish MEKO frigates were fitted for Link 10, and they presumably received first ROLE and then full Link 11 capacity. Turkish Track II frigates will be delivered with Link 11 capacity.

By early 1995 the Spanish *Descubierta* class had been upgraded to Link 11 capability. The Turkish navy recently bought Signaal MOCs as part of a Link 11 program for *Knox*-class frigates. U.S. users include the Customs Service.

Denmark installed two-way integrated Link 11 on two *Nils Juel*-class frigates (*Olfert Fischer* received the Rockwell unit described above during the Gulf War); the Stanflex corvettes are also to be fitted.

The U.S. Coast Guard bought an EDO workstation, its first Link 11, for the cutter *Dallas*. By 1995 the Coast Guard was developing its own stand-alone Link 11. Two EDO stand-alone Link 11s were installed on board EP-3s for forward-deployed operations (because these aircraft were converted from P-3B airframes, they had no Link 11s).

NATO Link 11 (to STANAG 1241) now includes a neutral category (which the U.S. version lacks). The Royal Navy uses its own symbology (letter only: N for neutral, U for unknown, I for interception, H for hostile, Z for zombie). The Dutch use a combination of NTDS and British practice. The British practice is to display target data; NTDS displays data only when the contact is "hooked" by an operator.

Link 12—Proposal for 9600-bps UHF link based on early USN work in early 1960s, abandoned 1965.

Link 13—This less capable alternative to Link 11 was developed by France, Belgium, and Germany in 1962–64 but was dropped after successful sea trials in 1965. It was the basis for Link 10.

Link 14—Teleprinter data link (75 bps) from computer-fitted to noncomputer-fitted ships. In effect, Link 14 is a formatted text version of a Link 11 message. Formatting makes it possible to reverse the process and use Link 14 messages as computer inputs; apparently only the Japanese did so, in some of their CDSs. In effect they had produced a receive-only version of Link 11. A plan to replace all U.S. Link 14 terminals with receive-only Link 11 was canceled early in 1990. A stand-alone, two-way Link 11 proved less expensive. The latter uses the LEDS (part of which is USQ-69) developed under LEIP.

Link 15—This projected (abandoned) 75-bps link was to have allowed noncomputer ships to send teletype data to Link 11 ships.

Link 16/TADIL-J—Link associated with JTIDS, the U.S. Joint Tactical Information Distribution System. Link 16 is intended to replace Link 4A and to complement (but not replace) Link 11. It is included in the E-2C update plan, the F-14D program, and later versions of the F/A-18 (using the MIDS terminal). JTIDS includes a secure voice channel and it automatically creates a common navigational grid for its users. The first JTIDS networks were delivered in FY90, at which time JTIDS terminals first flew aboard the E-2C and F-14D (F-14D integration was completed in FY91). Beginning in May 1994 the *Carl Vinson* battle group (including the cruisers *Antietam* and *Arkansas* and the submarine *Asheville*) was the first to deploy with JTIDS, making the U.S. Navy the first service to deploy JTIDS-equipped platforms in an operational environment. Only selected E-2C and F-14D were equipped. The shipboard version provides two separate simultaneous voice circuits: each terminal contains two voice decoders that translate to and from digital format to provide voice-recognition-quality communications. The NATO Military Operational Requirement (MOR) for JTIDS, MC 306, was issued in March 1987; the U.S. Multiple Required Operational Capability document, MJCS-194-89, was issued in August 1989. The NATO JTIDS terminal memorandum of understanding was signed on 14 November 1986.

JTIDS operates in Lx-band (960–1215 MHz), hopping frequency randomly over a bandwidth of several hundred MHz on a pulse-to-pulse basis. A JTIDS net is defined by a particular sequence of hopped frequencies. Subscribers in the net are assigned transmission slots within the 12.8min cycle; each slot is 7.8125 msec (1/128 sec) long, so that the cycle contains 98,304 slots. One subscriber is the designated time reference, responsible for maintaining the timing of the net. Within each slot, every other message pulse is redundant, so that messages can be reconstructed even if they are badly jammed. There is also a jitter period at the beginning of each slot, so the actual beginning of the transmission of data varies. The data rate can be doubled (at a price in terms of ECCM), first by eliminating the redundant data (packed-2 structure), and then again by eliminating the jitter (packed-4 structure). This scheme is described as time division multiple access (TDMA).

Time slots are combined into 12-sec frames (1536 slots) and 64-frame epochs (12.8 min), the epoch being the system cycle. Each slot contains up to 12 Link 16 words (75 bits/word), which can be updated on every frame (the basic cycle is the epoch). The transmission waveform uses a 6.4-microsec pulse as its bit and leaves 6.6 microsec between pulses; each pulse is transmitted in sequence at one of 51 frequencies (3 MHz apart) chosen from a pseudo-randomly coded list. Each pulse is subcoded (chipped) by 32 phase modulations; chipping provides additional coding so that a receiver can identify a pulse against background noise. Each net normally supports up to 32 transmitters (each can be allocated more than one slot per frame). Nets differ in their frequency-hopping sequences and time references and can run in parallel. Up to 128 can be stacked with negligible chance that two long words will coincide.

Class 2 terminals use GPS data, and JTIDS can use TACAN (tactical air navigation) data. Each terminal periodically and automatically broadcasts a precise position location and identification (PPLI) message, which identifies the sender. Terminals use the message structure to measure time of arrival, combining this information with the terminal's prior estimate of transmitter range to form a range input for the terminal's Kalman filter. The filter processes a sequence of such inputs to allow each terminal in the net to maximize its own navigational performance. A typical display shows the positions of the transmitters as well as of the targets they detect.

Air and surface terminals send active targeting intent messages through the JTIDS net; in theory, that should reduce redundant targeting. A typical cockpit display shows own position relative to nearby friendly and enemy aircraft, in each case with vectors to show their courses and lines indicating engagements. Both color and shape are used; the graphics do not follow current NTDS practice.

JTIDS LOS range is about 300 nm, a figure probably limited by the time of transmission (which must be allowed for in the slot's length: 300 nm equates to about 1.6 msec); it can be extended to 500 nm. From a user's point of view, JTIDS provides all subscribers with a common tactical picture, much as NTDS does. Link 16 offers about 10 times the target-handling capacity of Link 11.

The initial JTIDS terminals were Class 1 (ARC-181) for AWACS and Class 2 (URC-107) for fighters. Class 1 deliveries began in 1977. Those terminals used the interim message standard, TADIL-I, which was not compatible with either TADIL-J or Link 11. Class 2 is lighter than Class 1 and has a higher data rate (115 rather than 28.8 kbps); it also adds integrated voice, relative navigation (using GPS), and embedded TACAN. It can be used to form up to 20 subgroups, communicating among themselves but not across the whole net. URC-107(V)4 Class 2H (high-power) adds a 1-kW amplifier group, and is to replace Class 1 on E-3s as part of Block 30/35 Upgrade; there is also a smaller Class 2M for the Army. The U.S. Navy is buying Class 2 for the F-14D, and Class 2H for the E-2C, major ships, and the Marine Corps Tactical Air Operations Module (TAOM). Class 2 has suffered from unreliability (in 1993 its MTBF had just risen to 402 hr) and high cost (planned cost in the mid-1980s was $400,000, but in 1993 low-rate units were costing about $500,000).

MIDS (Multifunctional Information Distribution System) is equivalent to the earlier JTIDS Class 2 terminal, but uses VHSIC and MMIC technology to halve the weight and cut volume to one-third. Work began in 1987 for the F/A-18, the French Rafale, and the Eurofighter. Responsibility was transferred from the Air Force to the Navy in FY90 (Joint ORs were issued in January 1981 and in July 1989). That year the study contract was awarded to McDonnell-Douglas (the project also included downsizing the HARM CLC in the F/A-18). Thomson-CSF is a contractor, and the French navy plans to install MIDS in its aircraft. NATO partners are France, Germany, Italy, Spain, and the United States. The program has suffered cost and schedule problems, partly because each partner wants to have all MIDS technology transferred by the others (so it can build the whole system), partly simply because so much has to be done in so small a volume. Thus the target price of $200,000 has risen to $450,000 to $600,000, and as of 1993 MIDS was not expected to enter service before 1997–98. MIDS replaces an earlier French SINTAC program, begun in the 1970s, for a JTIDS terminal (the prototype SINTAC began ground trials in 1985 and naval trials in 1986).

In 1994 Rockwell-Collins advertised a next-generation Link 16 terminal, IDS-2000, which it claimed would be only one-fifth as expensive as the existing Class 2 terminal, and one-third the size. Because the device is modular (built around an internal bus, using SEM-E cards), a user can trade off transmission range against cost, or can choose more or less antijam capability. All interfaces unique to a particular platform are placed on one card, which can be changed if the box is moved to a different platform. The IDS-2000 box can participate in up to 127 nets simultaneously, with 128 time slots/net/sec; data rate is 28.8–238 kbps, and to overcome jamming it can frequency-hop at 77 kHz. Work began in 1990, and IDS-2000 was demonstrated in 1994 as part of a U.S. Air Force Affordability and Manufacturing Technology Demonstration (AMTD) program. Growth options include five-channel GPS, video image transmission, and variable message format; the latter might allow the box to act as a gateway between different link circuits (e.g., Link 4/Link 16).

At about the same time, Hazeltine offered a Universal Data Link (UDL) that could be installed in aircraft to provide them with local networks and with the ability to connect to the larger-scale JTIDS nets. UDL uses J-message (JTIDS) formats in multiple frequency ranges (UHF, L-band, SHF, EHF) and thus acts as a gateway to UHF Link 22.

Link 22 (i.e., double Link 11) is NILE (NATO Improved Link Eleven), which uses JTIDS-type messages and the JTIDS TDMA net protocol, and thus is not compatible with Link 11. In effect it is JTIDS on a different frequency band. It is implemented in three radio media: HF (non-ECCM), UHF (non-ECCM), and ECCM UHF (Have Quick II). HF ECCM may be added. The signal processor controller (SPC) has cards for the different modes; no special Link 22 radio is required. Clearly, however, Link 22 can easily connect to a Link 16 gateway. Too, a single antenna can handle Link 11 and Link 22 traffic, the former (M- rather than J-messages) being separated off before processing. Alternatively, a computer can translate between the two links (it is

called a J- to A-translator). Link 22 does require a new cryptographic device (KG). The system network handles TDMA, net protocols, and so on. Given a frequency-hopping radio (not yet bought for the U.S. Navy), it has much the effect of JTIDS. The new message standard was essential to allow the system to handle more tracks at a faster rate; it also may be possible to give critical information priority (not possible in Link 11). Link 11 is limited to perhaps 200 out of a total of as many as 3000 tracks/ sec that a major command might require in a major war. Track capacity would be particularly stressed in a hot air engagement, when ships would be seeing on their radars and other sensors not only friendly and enemy aircraft and antiship missiles, but also the defending antiair missiles, their boosters, decoys, and perhaps even bursts from close-in defensive guns. In effect, Link 22 is JTIDS without special JTIDS electronics. Existing JTIDS terminals impose difficulties mainly because too much is crammed into a very small space; Link 22 imposes no such problems. In effect it opens out the terminal.

To ensure interoperability, the U.S. is the Lead Technical Nation to the NATO Improved Link Eleven office (the NATO partners are Canada, France, West Germany, Italy, Netherlands, Spain, and the United Kingdom). Reportedly, NATO likes the interoperability with the U.S. Navy on J-messages without having to buy JTIDS terminals.

ITALY

Two Sicral satellites (Sistema Italiana di Communicazione Ricervente Allarmi) were to have been launched in 1995–96, but the program has been delayed due to the advent of Eumilsat (see Skynet).

JAPAN

All Japanese destroyers are equipped to communicate using the Super-Bird B communications satellite. The satellite was launched on 27 February 1992.

NETHERLANDS

◆ VESTA

Signaal's VHF helicopter-to-ship link is used on board MEKO-type frigates. It consists of a transponder, which provides very accurate location data, and a short-burst (approx 1 sec) data link using voice channels (VC). The data link is intended primarily to transmit the position of a ship as seen by the helicopter's radar; digital (not analog) position data sent in FSK form (2100 Hz for a 0, 2400 Hz for a 1) can be inserted directly into a ship's TDS. Each burst consists of fifty 32-bit words. This is not transmission of radar video; it requires that the helicopter-borne radar do automatic target detection. Helicopter position is established by a separate VHF transponder triggered by the ship's 1–10-GHz search radar; the helicopter reply appears on the ship's radar display. The coded pulses are 2.2 microsec long, and typically there are five alternate codes (the system can accommodate up to 64). PRF is 20 kHz without the code. Maximum range is 64 nm.

RUSSIA

◆ Lurch/Altair (Soviet Satellite Data Relay Network, SDRN)

These satellites are data relays between ground stations and satellites and space craft in low earth orbit (e.g., EORSATs). They normally operate at 95 deg East and 344 deg East, have three transponders (1800 W total), and last five years in orbit.

◆ Molniya

The Molniya satellites in high elliptical orbits cover the northern latitudes; each spends about 8 hr over the CIS each day. They have been launched since 1965: Molniya 1, 33 satellites; Molniya 2, 15 satellites from 1971; and Molniya 3, 4 satellites from 1974. Orbital period is about 12 hr, with perigees of about 500 km in the Southern Hemisphere and apogees of about 40,000 km in the Northern. The arrangement was initially 120 deg apart (so that three satellites could cover the Soviet Union for 9 hr each day); but Molniya 2 and 3 were 90 deg apart, and Molniya 1 satellites were moved to positions between the Molniya 2 and 3 satellites in 1976. Molniya 1 is UHF; Molniya 3 and later satellites operate in the SHF range. Molniya 1 is used for government and military traffic; Molniya 3 is a television relay.

◆ Raduga

Geosynchronous communications satellites occupy a total of eight orbital slots; they use six 4-GHz transponders. Two or three launches per year are required to maintain the system. There is also a television relay system, Gorizont.

◆ Data Links

The Soviet Union evidently employed numerous data links, for example, that connecting a Bear-D with the submarine or surface ship for which the aircraft furnishes targeting data. However, apart from some identifications of the antennas involved, few details have been made public. Some radars (certainly Plank Shave and Strut Curve) function as highly directional data-link receivers.

◆ Bell Crown

Ship-ship data link between second captains, probably mainly for radar data, tested 1973–74. The antenna is in a small radome, which implies a directional link at microwave radar frequency. On board *Kiev, Moskva, Kirov, Slava*, Kara, Kresta II, *Udaloy, Sovremennyy* classes. This is a master-slave system, in which the slaves transmit their radar data to the flagship (the master), which replies with commands. The slaves do not share radar data among themselves.

◆ Bell Hop

Data link connecting Bear-D with surface units and submarines; reportedly it is nearly a direct copy of the U.S. postwar AEW link used with APS-20 radars (Big Bulge is closely related to APS-20). The U.S. link was called Bellhop.

◆ Bell Spike

On board *Kirov*- and *Slava*-class cruisers, this may be a surface-to-air link intended to control land-based fighters (Su-27s) operating over the sea. In that case it would be a Russian equivalent of Link 4. The antenna is a very sharp spike resembling a toothpick end.

◆ Bell Strike

Missile video data link receiving antenna on *Sovremennyy* and *Dergach* classes (SS-N-22 missiles).

◆ Bell Thumb

Missile video data link receiving antenna on *Slava*-class cruisers (SS-N-12 missiles).

◆ Fig Jar

Data link used to command-fire RBU-6000s (and presumably to transmit sonar data). See the account of the ASW variant of the second captain. The dedicated antenna, a squat cylindrical radome with a flat top pointing up at the end of an antenna, was probably superseded in small ASW ships by a link in which Strut Curve is the receiver (Grishas, all of which have Strut Curve, lack Fig Jar).

Fig Jar is on board *Moskva*, Kara, Kresta I/II, Kynda, Mod Kashin, Mirka, Petya, and Poti classes. It may be on board *Kiev, Kirov, Udaloy*, and Krivak classes.

◆ Fish Bowl

Command link for SS-N-9 missiles, on board "Nanuchkas." Superseded by Light Bulb.

◆ Light Bulb

Command link for SS-N-22 and other missiles, possibly also used as a ship-to-ship data link.

◆ Shot Dome/Shot Rock

Small radomes, typically located above the bridge, in all modern combatants (and back-fitted in some older destroyers, now dis-carded). They are probably directional antennas for bridge-to-bridge communication, not connected with data links. The size suggests microwave frequency, which would normally limit the system to LOS, and thus make it difficult to intercept.

SOUTH AFRICA

As modernized, the "Minister"-class fast-attack boats and the *Daphne*-class submarines all have TDN (tactical data network) data-link terminals with a reported maximum rate of 16 kbps. Data can be transmitted by HF, VHF, and UHF, and there is a message gateway/repeater facility to link different nets, for example, a shore-to-ship net and a ship-to-ship net connecting several fast-attack boats. One description of the ships' communication systems suggests dynamic choice of communications medium, something like that envisaged in the U.S. Copernicus architecture. The tactical data link is part of a larger Seacom I modular communications system, which includes INMARSAT satellite communications. The system includes some COMINT and SIGINT functions. In 1995, South Africa was reporting interest in TDN by at least one foreign navy.

SWEDEN

Swedish small-craft command/control systems include a PEAB (now BEAB) specialized VHF/UHF TDMA data link (which can transmit text messages), used by the STINA coastal command/control system and by the MARIL shipboard CDS (and probably by other CCIS systems). It has been exported, at least to Yugoslavia.

The TDMA link may be a simple standard point-to-point digital radio link to pass two or three tracks and engagement orders. The operator radios to set up the contact, data being sent via a modem. Since the standard data rate is about 1.2 kbps, this link may be related to Link Y. Reportedly the data links of the Swedish-built Malaysian "Spica-M" class *are* Ferranti Link Ys. In 1995 the Royal Swedish Navy was reportedly considering adopting Link 11.

TAIWAN

◆ Link T (Taching)

This CSIST-developed data link, comparable to Link 11, equips the Wu-Jinn III–class destroyers and the *Perry*-class frigates. The RAT II computer (which carries an encryption card) is the processor, using a 19in Barco color display. Link T embraces the ASN-150 link with the new helicopters.

UNITED KINGDOM

◆ DLPP

Ferranti's data-link preprocessor, for Type 22 frigates (Batches 2 and 3) with CACS CDS, is built around Argus microprocessors. It is analogous to the U.S. C2P. DLPP constructs and maintains a track file (up to 100 tracks) based on Link 11 data; it acts as a buffer. Because DLPP is external to the ship's main CDS, it can be modified relatively easily to accept data from other links, such as Link 16. CACS originally accepted only Link 10 data, and presumably its central computer lacked the capacity to handle Link 11. A Ferranti ROLE (receive-only Link 11) may have been fitted to British minehunters in the Persian Gulf.

◆ DLPS (Outfits RTC and RJJ)

Thorn-EMI/Data Sciences/Dowty Data Link Processing System is being installed in carriers and Type 42 destroyers under the ADIMP program. It is also in frigates. It is an open-architecture system built around an internal Multibus II data bus; the chassis accommodates 20 cards. Processors for each link connect to the bus; the ship's command system connects to the bus through a formatting processor. The processor filters, correlates, and deconflicts the incoming data to form a common track database for the command system. DLPS uses a single-board 80386/80486 processor, part of the Dowty Maritime G-Range Card set, based on those in SMCS and SSCS. Each link has its own processing card; the bus also connects to cards for network control and data forwarding. A central database supports the distributed system.

DLPS handles Links 11 and 14. This contract was let in February 1990. A new software issue (April 1995) rectified problems with ADIMP, in the interface with the ship's combat-system bus. At that time a contract award for a Link 16 element was expected by late 1995. The designation Outfit RJJ has also been reported. As of early 1995, 20 DLPS were in service.

◆ DLPS/DLE (unofficial designations)

This Ferranti Link Y processor/terminal is not to be confused with the Royal Navy's new DLPS. Based on the Military Argus microprocessor, it has a capacity of 120 tracks (both received and own-ship). They are displayed in color on an LPD (PPI), typically 14 in in diameter, which can show a data range of up to 2000 nm from own-ship. DLPS may be fully integrated with the host combat-data system. Interfaces: RS232C, RS422C, NTDS Slow, and 1553B. There is also a DLPS for Link G.

The Link Y airborne DLPS is called DLE (data-link equipment).

◆ Link G

This Ferranti air-ground link (G for Ground) is presumably equivalent to Link 4. The ground station continually polls the aircraft terminals on a cyclic basis. Each aircraft responds automatically by sending its address, position, height, and any other additional information, if available. Normally Link G uses one channel, but it can use two for quicker operation: one for continuous transmission from ground station, the other for transmissions by aircraft. That type of operation avoids time delays due to build-up of power at the ground transmitter and in the AGC circuits of aircraft. In half-duplex mode Link G operates at 1200 baud over VHF/UHF and HF voice networks. It can pass targeting and intercept information as well as aircraft position.

◆ Link R

Link between British central naval headquarters and JOTS at sea.

◆ Links X and Y

See NATO links above (Link 10/Link X/Link Y).

◆ Link Z

Ferranti's non-NATO version of Link 14. This link typically transmits at 75 bps. It is a broadcast system, so one terminal can transmit to any number of subscribers.

◆ Stand-Alone Link 11

This system, built around an FM-1600 series computer, is probably the standard RN Link 11 terminal for ships with CDS designed for Link 10, for example, Type 42 destroyers. It was probably introduced about 1983, when the Royal Navy decided to adopt Link 11 instead of Link 10. This device was also offered as a stand-alone unit accepting manually tracked surveillance radar video and other own-ship inputs. Link-received tracks are displayed and correlated. In a federated configuration (presumably that bought by the RN), data from own-ship sensors are compiled in the ship's AIO/CIC, while the Link 11 picture is compiled within the Link 11 processor and data is exchanged on a computer-to-computer basis; the processor can also provide data directly to a digital WCS. The system consists of a self-contained two-operator console plus an interface cabinet. The complete tactical picture is shown on a 400mm circular CRT (LPD). Each half-console carries its own rectangular CRT, plus a trackball and keypads (they differ in other ways). The system can process up to 300 tracks, make tactical calculations (such as CPA, rendezvous), display radar tracks, NTDS symbols, and full character set, allow for interaction using prompts, allow operator-selected filters to display tracks by category, hostility, and so on, and can be expanded to include Link 14 and/or additional consoles.

◆ Skynet/Star of Siam

BAe's Skynet is the British military/naval communications satellite system, begun in 1967 with the trials of the NEST ship terminal. The current Skynet 4A and 4B were launched in December 1988 and January 1990. By spring 1993 three Skynet 4

were in orbit, with Skynet 4D due for launch in 1997, 4E due for launch in 1998, and 4F in 2000. Skynet has 300 times the power of its predecessor and provides one two-channel UHF transponder (25-kHz bandwidths, mainly for submarines) and one four-channel SHF transponder (60–135-MHz beamwidths, for strategic and tactical communication), and beamwidths down to 3 deg. There is also a single experimental EHF uplink. Estimated satellite lifetime is 7 yr. The program's sponsor is the RAF, but the Royal Navy is the chief user.

The follow-on program (April 1993) is the Anglo-French (Matra-Marconi) Future Military Satellite Communications System (FMSCS) or Bimilsat, the British version being Skynet 5 and the French being Syracuse 3. The first Skynet 5 launch is scheduled for 2003. If the Germans and other Europeans join the program, it becomes the six-satellite Eumilsat program; if the United States joins, it becomes Inmilsat.

Star of Siam is a Skynet 4/5 for Thailand, with important naval applications; it is to be launched about 2000.

The associated ship's terminal is SCOT, operating in the 7–8-GHz (SHF) band (chosen to avoid radar and cosmic interference). Frigates and destroyers use a SCOT 1 (1.1m dish); larger ships use SCOT 2 (1.8m dish). An enhanced SCOT 1A was ordered in 1984 for delivery beginning in 1986: it provides a 1.2m dish for both classes of ships and the equivalent of four secure-voice communications channels. Bandwidth is 500 MHz, compared to 50 MHz for SCOT 1; the 1A terminal can be tuned to any 50-MHz channel. All 17 remaining units of the original 21 SCOT 1 terminals are being brought up to SCOT 1A standards. The larger SCOT 2 terminals are also being modified for greater bandwidths.

SCOT is not far from the X-band missile-seeker and fire-control-radar frequencies, so that it may be necessary to shut down nearby ESM equipment when SCOT is in use. Reportedly, that interference contributed to the loss of HMS *Sheffield* in the Falklands, hence the interest in the EHF uplink.

Users include Germany (*Bremen* and Type 123 classes), Netherlands (*Tromp* class), Portugal (ordered January 1994 for frigate *Vasco da Gama*, for use when a Portuguese commodore takes over StaNavForLant), Spain (*Principe de Asturias*), United Kingdom (carriers, Types 22, 23, and 42, *Fearless* class)

Principe de Asturias uses her SCOT to link her to the Spanish national command authority, via the Sistema Español de Comunicaciones Militares por Satelite (SECOMSAT), which carries two voice, three teletype, and two data channels (1200 bps Sacomar, 9600 bps Simacar) plus a computer data channel. All channels are encrypted. The satellite system is Hispasat (satellites 1A and 1B), which has a 10-yr lifetime. The project originally called for six ship terminals (carrier plus five frigates), but budget cuts reduced that to one. The SCOT terminals aboard the carrier have provision for code division multiple access (CDMA) modems, so they can receive NATO downlink signals. Note that the Spanish *Santa Maria*–, *Baleares*-, and *Descubierta*-class frigates all have commercial Saturn 3S SATCOMM equipment.

UNITED STATES

The U.S. Navy relies on six satellite systems: Fleet Satellite (FLTSAT), Leased Satellite (LEASAT), Defense Satellite Communications System (DSCS), UHF Follow-On Program (UFO), NATO satellites, and the Air Force Satellite Communications (AFSATCOM) system.

The next-generation system is Milstar, the Navy portion of which is the Navy EHF SATCOMM Program (NESP). Existing satellites are transponders: they receive signals, amplify them, and then broadcast them. To some extent their downlinks preserve information about the uplinked data. By way of contrast, Milstar is digital: its broadcast preserves nothing of the uplinked data, except for the intended data content. Milstar also offers LPI antijam signals. As a consequence, it suffers from high cost and a limited data rate, neither of which may be acceptable in the future, particularly if the subtle vulnerabilities inherent in transponders are little appreciated. Milstar is a joint program, and development of user terminals is coordinated by a joint terminal project office (JTPO).

By the spring of 1995, new satellites were badly needed in all three bands (EHF, UHF, SHF). Several cost-cutting options were under consideration:

Combine EHF and UHF in five MLV satellites

Eliminate crosslinks and agile beams from EHF (Milstar)

Eliminate nulling, agile antenna, hard-limit transponders on SHF

Focus on X-band (SHF) only for the DoD Global Broadcast Services (GBS).

The current R&D program develops an afloat automated network (AAN) for high-data-rate transfer of messages within the Navy Modular Automated Communications System (NAVMACS), a stand-alone system for message processing within the battle group. Feasibility design began in FY90. NAVMACS provides mass storage of incoming messages, with retrieval as needed; presumably it is related to the effort to develop paperless ships. During FY92 work began on a LAN for NAVMACS II and for CUDIXS, a high-data-rate interface. NAVMACS was originally hosted on DTC-2 computers; in FY93 work began to rehost it to TAC-3s. The next step was to evolve NAVMACS II so that it fit into the Communications Support System (CSS)/Copernicus baseline. A new volume-responsive high-speed Fleet Broadcast (HSFB) replaces the existing limited-volume Fleet Broadcast; the first EDM system was bought in FY90, with five more in FY91. Under the FY93 program, enough HSFB equipment was bought to equip one communications area and two battle groups for formal testing.

Full CSS production is planned for the year 2000. The submarine version will be SCSS. Some elements will appear earlier; for example, an automated baseband switch should enter service about 1997. Other elements of the future CSS are the EHF satellite terminal (for Milstar and EHF FLTSATCOMM) and DAMA. The central CSS element is the SSQ-33(V)3 semiautomatic computer-controlled switcher (SACCS), which includes the integrated network manager and a series of packet, multiplex, and circuit switches leading to the various media.

In FY93 a testbed for the Navy Theatre Extension Network (TENet) was built. TENet, which is now a tri-service project, is intended to extend the commercial, terrestrial high-data-rate communication network (information highway) employing ATM (asynchronous transport mode) switches and fiber-optic cables to radio communications to the deployed fleet. A tri-service testbed is being developed to evaluate standard protocols and demonstrate the capability to interoperate. It will link Rome Laboratories (Air Force), CECOM (Army), and NRaD (Navy) with commercially based high-data-rate links. The first demonstration showed capability to communicate at 1.544 Mbps (commercial T1 rate). In FY95 that was extended to T3 rates (45 Mbps). The next step is OC-3 rates (155 Mbps). TENet will also demonstrate a multicast (one sender, many receivers) capability (as in the current Fleet Broadcast). Multicast is used extensively by the Navy, but it is not supported by current commercial protocols.

Current policy is to place SHF satellite terminals on every carrier and amphibious flagship and on selected cruisers. The Universal Modem is a joint U.S./UK development to provide U.S. force and Allied satellite communications interoperability. EHF terminals for Milstar are going on surface combatants and submarines. UHF terminals are being added to AEW and maritime patrol aircraft.

The FY91 advanced technology program included an at-sea demonstration of a submarine hull (vice trailing) ELF antenna, tests of the two-way relay buoy, investigation of new wide-band communications modes (such as atmospheric evaporation ducts and troposcatter), and work with the Air Force on covert airborne communications using LPI spread-spectrum waveforms.

The FY92 program began a new next-generation communications system program: (a) automated integrated communications (AICS), applying digital networking techniques to voice, data, and digital communications; (b) translation of developmental communications software into ADA; and (c) an MLS processing system to provide a common operational picture among tactical units. AICS requires a multinet controller and communication will be via AICS waveforms and standard single-channel DAMA

waveforms. This program is being managed by NRL and NOSC San Diego.

The FY93 program included investigation of radar for communications purposes.

A current R&D (6.2) effort explores the use of SHF for the very high-data-rate (1.54 Mbit/sec) ship-to-ship communication required for such programs as cooperative engagement. SHF is usually limited to LOS, but it can refract, and in many cases it can use an evaporation duct to achieve very long ranges. It becomes more viable as ships in battle groups operate closer together (because they no longer face a nuclear threat). SHF is attractive because it can support very high data rates, far beyond those possible with HF systems such as Link 11. SHF satellite communication is currently a very high priority; a new SHF information exchange system (IXS) is being defined. Each carrier is now being fitted with an interim SHF terminal, and new terminals were bought beginning in FY94.

New communications programs include the following:

Radiant Hail is a man-portable multisource tactical intelligence receiver and processor for the Marine Corps.

Radiant Ivory is a downlink receiver to allow a command ship to receive DSP satellite data.

Radiant Tin is a Navy/Marine project to provide imagery to forward users over existing communications links by drastic image compression (e.g., by a factor of 175:1). It uses standard TAC-series computers and is to be used in aircraft cockpits, submarines, and other applications that preclude the installation of new wide-band communications links.

Radiant Mercury was an MLS scheme.

◆ ASN-150

At least in the case of Taiwan Navy S-70s, this includes the helo-ship data link.

◆ CHBDL/USQ-123

Common High-Bandwidth Data Link, for the BGPHES and ATARS programs, was tested in FY90/93. In the future it is likely to work with UAVs. CHBDL has 10 prime mission equipment channels, plus secure voice. The X-band CHBDL downlink operates at high (274 or 137 Mbps) or low (10.71 Mbps) rates or carries voice traffic (CVSD); the uplink operates at 200 kbps. Images are transmitted at 137 Mbps (e.g., from an F/A-18 to JSIPS-N); BGPHES transmits at the low rate. The shipboard USQ-123 system uses two one-meter dishes to handle one full duplex link.

◆ Close Air Support Link (ATHS/TDM-200)

Collins produces these digital links for close air support, replacing earlier voice radios. The advantage of the digital link is that it can provide data directly to the airplane's central tactical system. ATHS (CP-1516/ASQ) is an automatic target handoff system. Data is transmitted in a special nine-line code. The pilot is given target coordinates, which weapon to use, and which areas to avoid, information formerly provided only by voice and written down on a pilot's notepad, hence very much subject to error. ATHS is a secure multiservice data link (the Army calls it the improved data modem, IDM). The forward air controller uses a hand-held radio, and the data show up on the airplane's main display. The airplane's central tactical system can then fly in using the forward controller's target position (latitude and longitude).

ATHS was an Army initiative, based on determination that voice communications and manual target calculations were too slow for a rapidly moving battle. Rockwell was selected in 1980 to develop ATHS, tests followed in 1982–83, and the first production contract followed in 1984. More than 750 CP-1516s were made; applications include the Marine AH-1W attack helicopter and the Army OH-58D, as well as the Air National Guard F-16s assigned to close air support and the S-70B-2 helicopter (RAN Seahawk). It is also in the Apache B and in the Italian Agusta A-109A.

ATHS uses a 96-kbyte computer with 2 kbytes of nonvolatile memory and 8 kbytes of RAM and with an 8-bit bus. It has one modem and four ports for radio access, and it transmits only in FSK mode (75–1200 baud). This version is compatible only with the Army TACFIRE and digital message device (DMD). It can transmit and receive on only a single channel, and it has no space for expansion. It can be programmed on the flight line only with mission data, not with a new operational program. MTBF is 1500 hr.

Rockwell performed a tri-service ATHS evaluation for the Air Force in 1989, and in 1990–91 it developed the improved TDM-200 (tactical data manager) as a private venture. This device was successfully tested on board a Marine AV-8B in 1991; qualification was completed in 1993. The new computer has a 256-kbyte memory, expandable to 1 Mbyte; nonvolatile memory is 32 kbytes and RAM is 64 kbytes. The modem now has a programmable memory (needed for encryption) of 128 kbytes as well as 32 kbytes of RAM. The 8-bit bus can be replaced by a 16-bit bus. Data can be transmitted in digital (75–16,000 baud) as well as FSK formats. Additional transmission formats are added (DCT [digital communication terminal] and digital NRZ). Up to four digital modems can be accommodated, all receiving and transmitting simultaneously. The device automatically recognizes the data rate and protocol of a device transmitting to it, something ATHS could not do. It can be programmed via the 1553 bus by means of which it communicates with other aircraft systems, and it can receive a new mission program on the flight line. Program memory is EEPROM. In contrast to ATHS, there are four to six expansion slots. All of this is achieved within exactly the same weight and volume, with half the power drain, and with twice the MTBF.

Typical messages give multiple target position, type, and identification; time-to-target; present aircraft position, weapons, and fuel status; laser designation codes for laser-guided weapons (so that a surface designator can be used); friendly positions; situation reports; battle damage assessments; and fighter-to-fighter information. Rockwell adds that the TDM-200 data can be read out via a HUD or a helmet-mounted display, so that the pilot need not fly head-down and left-handed while copying critical data on a knee pad.

As of early 1996, Collins was embedding ATHS/IDM, a voice radio (to MIL-STD-188-220A, the new standard verbal message format) with modular communications security devices in an ARC-210 radio. This improved device, which Collins calls DCS-2000 (digital communications system), is to be available for integration into the F/A-18 in April 1997.

◆ Copernicus/FASTT

The new U.S. fleet-level command and control architecture uses very powerful workstation terminals derived from the JOTS/JMCIS program. The object is to reorient naval communications so that the communications links revolve around the users rather than the other way around, hence the name. In this system, the total available communications capacity is split by software into the required set of satellite links (GLOBIXS and TADIXS). The links are virtual, that is, software-defined rather than hardware-defined. Thus, if it needs more capacity, a single link can expand to embrace several satellite channels. In the past, the communications system was easily overloaded because channels could not interchange capacity and, thus, there was very limited surge capacity in a crisis. Much capacity was filled by low-priority administrative messages, because the channels involved could not have been switched to any higher-priority role. One important aspect of Copernicus is the use of intelligent terminals that can filter out (and store) inessential messages so as not to overload the commanders to whom they are addressed.

The major driver is the need to use available channel capacity more efficiently. As the Navy shifts to littoral warfare concepts, detailed imagery of land areas becomes vital, for example, in planning aircraft and Tomahawk strikes. Too, the sheer number of platforms in the combat area increases enormously. According to a recent SPAWAR presentation, the FY93 requirement for throughput to a flag-capable ship was 1.2 Mbit/sec. That in-

creased to 2.0 in FY96, and is expected to reach 6.0 Mbit/sec in FY2000. Milstar 1 offers only about 500 kbps. SHF DAMA can meet the FY93 requirement—by about 1996. A single commercial T1 channel (television channel) carries about 1.5 Mbit/sec.

Copernicus is currently described as the Navy's C4I (command/control/communications/computer/intelligence) post–Cold War architecture, with special emphasis on the ability to shift focus among geographical areas. That is possible because it relies on space-based rather than fixed surface assets.

Copernicus is the current incarnation of the long series of OTH-T efforts begun in the mid-1970s with Outlaw Hawk/Shark and FCC/TFCC/OTCIXS. In the past, data were fused ashore and the results passed to the fleet. Copernicus envisages "distributive fusion," in which information passes freely through the shore/ship network; each node in the network contributes to the same overall tactical picture. This is much the same idea as a fully distributed combat system but on a much larger scale. Just as the distributed combat system is practicable only because shipboard data buses now have sufficient capacity, distributive fusion is possible only because the satellite links now have enormous capacity. That capacity is to be exploited by the new technique of virtual software-allocated links.

Communications capacity is to be handled by a new CSS (communications support system); Harris received a five-year, $5.4-million contract for CSS system architecture, design, and integration. Phase I included a demonstration of the use of SHF to add interoperable bandwidth. Phase II (begun 1993) reportedly includes an extension to UHF/HF and, if available, satellite EHF.

Copernicus is to use a special intelligent terminal, FASTT (Fleet All-Source Tactical Terminal), to streamline the mass of special messages currently in use and also to sanitize them. For example, an OTH-T message (which would contain information limited to special U.S. users) could be filtered to eliminate information limited to NATO users in the Mediterranean. It can also be reformatted to eliminate references to specially classified U.S. sensors. This sort of reformatting is necessary if messages are to be used directly to build the databases (i.e., tactical pictures) in numerous locations.

FASTT is to replace four existing systems: FIST (fleet imagery support terminal), JOTS, TESS (tactical environmental support system), and TMDS (Tomahawk Mission Display System).

Beyond the communication server (FASTT), there are three other main computer building blocks: a desktop series (equivalent to personal computers, not to the DTCs), a tactical workstation series (TAC series), and file servers to handle large databases. One objective of the system is to develop a common (across warfare areas) method of handling and denoting tracks.

The Copernicus project office was established on 1 October 1990, and the first industrial symposium held to announce system architecture was held on 28 January 1991. As of that time, the Copernicus hardware and software program, leading to a 6-yr procurement plan, was to have been completed during 1991.

CSS Phase I Early Operational Capability (EOC) became operational in June 1992; EOC Phase II followed in the summer of 1993, and Phase III in the summer of 1994.

Copernicus Forward is the extension of Copernicus ideas to support a force ashore, as part of the current concentration on littoral warfare. The associated information exchange system is BCIXS (Battle Cube Information Exchange System).

◆ DAMA (TD-1271) and Mini-DAMA (USC-42) Multiplexers

Demand-assigned multiple-access terminals make more efficient use of valuable satellite resources. The usual TDMA technique assigns a single user to a time slot, no matter whether the user needs the whole slot or not. DAMA allows up to 12 users per slot. By examining the protocol of each message, the network controller can determine its length, allowing it to fill the part of the slot it needs.

Surface ships and shore stations already have TD-1271 DAMA multiplexers; the Mini-DAMA is intended to extend the program to submarines and aircraft. Compared to the original DAMA, Mini-DAMA provides eight rather than four half-duplex networks. It also embeds many encryption and data-transfer functions that now require separate equipment. USC-42(V)1 is the submarine ship/shore version; (V)3 is the airborne version. At this time, too, DAMA is being converted from a distributed control (DC) mode to an automatic (Auto-DAMA) mode, via an interim semiautomatic (SAC) mode. Auto-DAMA dynamically assigns DAMA slots to gain a fourfold increase in satellite channel utilization efficiency; the interim SAC provides a twofold increase. SAC entered service in FY95, with AC following in FY96. Integration of (V)3 on board the P-3 (AIP) and the E-2C was completed in FY94, at which time work began on a secure voice version (KG-84 encryption device), and engineering development models of (V)1 and (V)3 were delivered. Mini-DAMA has now led to a joint program (JMINI); JMINI is to be fielded in FY00. The Navy Fleet Broadcast, CUDIXS/NAVMACS, SSIXS, secure voice channel, TACINTEL, TADIXS A, and ORESTES will all use Mini-DAMA.

USC-42(V)2 is a later version of Mini-DAMA intended to provide fully automatic control of the whole network. Components include an embedded modem/receiver-transmitter and a separate power amplifier; the airborne version also includes a remotable operator control/display. Each set has four full-duplex baseband I/O ports, and can therefore provide up to eight half-duplex or simplex channels (5 or 25 kHz wide, spaced 5 kHz apart) through its embedded UHF (225–400 MHz) radio. Most of the software is written in ADA. This unit incorporates three 80386 CPUs and two TMS320C25 digital signal processors. Data rates are 75, 300, 600, 1200, 2400, 4800, 9600, 14.4k, 16k, and 25 kbps. Modulations: BPSK (binary phase shift keying), DPSK (digital phase shift keying), DQPSK (digital quadriphase shift keying), DEQPSK, SOQPSK, BFSK, Shaped BFSK, FM, and AM. It has seven operational modes: 25-kHz UHF SATCOMM (Navy TDMA-1 network and non-TDMA comms); 25-kHz LOS (short-range tactical communications); 5-kHz UHF SATCOMM (Navy non-TDMA, Air Force DAMA net, Air Force non-TDMA net, and AFSATCOM 1). Possible preplanned upgrades include an interface with the SAFENET data bus and embedded AFSATCOM IIR and Have Quick IIA modes.

OTCIXS Phase II and OTCIXS Phase IV/V are versions suitable for a DAMA channel on the satellite. Sending OTCIXS and TADIXS data on DAMA frees valuable satellite channels for other fleet operational use. The DAMA Decision Coordinating Paper was released in July 1972 (with the Joint OR following in January 1975); the Mini-DAMA OR was released in July 1987. The first preproduction Mini-DAMAs were delivered during FY93; integation began into P-3 (ASUW), E-2C, and EP-3E aircraft. Work on a secure voice/KG-84 version of Mini-DAMA began in FY94. OTCIXS II and TADIXS IV became operational (on a limited basis) in FY92. The associated satellite terminal is WSC-6(V)2.

In 1995 a California company, Viasat, announced a DAMA Subnet Controller (SC) for UHF satellite communication channels, using a network of UHF SATCOMM TDMA-1 modems. This technique was demonstrated in December 1994 in an Early Capability fleet exercise. It was able to support simultaneously, for example, Internet Protocol (IP) packets, JOTS, Link Eleven Display System (LEDS), and other tactical data. Apparently Viasat was demonstrating a DAMA implementation of the IXS channels. Its controller could manage two to eight DAMA slots simultaneously, whereas the existing IXS supports one user at a time, and thus requires the whole channel.

The technique, which is also being applied (by other companies) to the New Attack Submarine combat system bus, amounts to packet-switching, as on the Internet and telephone systems: no matter what the message, it is broken down into short packets, which are reassembled at the receiver. The short packets are of standard length, so the same channel can mix long and short messages (which will amount to greater or lesser numbers of packets). Because the channel is broken down into more slots, network members are not locked out of the channel while a long transmission occupies a single slot. Viasat added a priority/precedence scheme for packets, to make the channel highly responsive. Viasat calls its protocol MUST, Multi-User UHF SATCOMM TDMA-1 protocol.

The current world standard for packet-switching (ATM), the Broadcast Integrated Services Digital Network (B-ISDN), is to break data into cells, each consisting of a 5-byte header (address and sequence) and 48 bytes of data. Rates are 256 kbps to 155.52 Mbps and will soon increase to 2.488 Gbytes/sec.

◆ DSCS

The Defense Satellite Communications System is the main high-volume system for the DoD and for diplomatic communications. Users include the fleet commanders, the NCA, and the major U.S. defense agencies. This SHF (X-band) system reportedly carried over 80% of the long-haul communications load during Desert Shield/Desert Storm. Milstar should take over the strategic circuits, DSCS remaining as the link between fixed tactical users.

Work on the initial DSCS system (IDSCS: 28 satellites) began in 1966, followed by DSCS II. Work on the DSCS II satellite was authorized in July 1968. Full capacity requires four satellites plus two in-orbit spares; the full constellation of four satellites was completed in December 1978. Sixteen DSCS II were launched in 1971–88. Eight DSCS III were launched 1982–93, to be followed by six more in 1995–2003. In 1990 three DSCS III and one DSCS II were active, but as of 1993 TRW stated that three DSCS II were active. For example, when DSCS III-1 was disabled, DSCS II-15 was returned to service to replace it. As of 1995, DSCS II satellites are being retained as in-orbit spares but are largely inoperative.

These satellites operate at 7/8 GHz (up/downlinks). TRW's 1300-lb DSCS II handles 1300 duplex (two-way) voice channels or 100 Mbit/sec of data. It has two steerable antennas, and the satellite can be moved within two days to a new geosynchronous position to handle a contingency. DSCS II uses 20W TWT amplifiers (transponders) with 410-MHz bandwidth (increased to 40 W in satellites 13–16). Beams are global (16.8 dB, 18 deg), regional (32 dB, 6.5 deg, footprint 4100 km diameter), and spot (33 dB, 2.5 deg, footprint 1600 km). The narrow beam antenna is steerable within +/− 10 deg.

Lockheed Martin's (formerly GE Astro Space's) Phase III, the current system, uses 2143-lb satellites hardened against nuclear and laser attack. The program began in 1975 and the development contract was awarded in February 1977. DSCS III represented a considerable advance over earlier satellites, which were essentially repeaters with fixed characteristics. It was designed to adapt to user needs, which vary in location, demand, and terminal antenna size. Adaptation is possible because the satellite uses a multibeam lens antenna controlled electronically from the ground. On the other hand, like DSCS II, this satellite uses transponders that reproduce (in the downlink) not only the content but also the waveform of the uplinked signals.

Each DSCS III carries a six-channel SHF transponder (500-MHz bandwidth: 7.9–8.4/7.25–7.75-GHz; up/downlinks: two 40W and four 10W channels, all using solid-state amplifiers rather than TWTs; in later satellites two of the 10W channels are replaced by 16W channels; four channels are 25 kHz wide, but two low-power channels are, respectively, 50 and 85 kHz wide, to support frequency-hopping). Transponder channels can be allocated to either multibeam, earth coverage, or high-gain steerable antennas. Too, the multibeam antennas can null out some jammers. There is also a separate AFSATCOM antijam transponder for strategic nuclear communications (single-channel at 300–400-MHz receive/225–260-MHz transmit). AFSATCOM can also receive at SHF through the other antennas, and it can transmit at SHF through the other antennas. There are four earth-coverage horns (two transmitting, two receiving, for two low-powered channels); a 61-beam waveguide lens receiving antenna; two 19-beam waveguide lens transmitting antennas (29 dB for the two high-power channels, 23 dB for two low-powered, with a 1-deg/34-dB mode for the high-power channels); and a gimballed dish (30.2 dB, 3 deg, for the two high-power channels and one low-powered channel). These satellites have higher power and, thanks to their movable beams, should be more difficult to jam. Nominal lifetime, set by fuel capacity at launch (600 lb of hydrazine), is 10 yr.

The last four DSCS III have a second movable antenna specifically to support increasing naval use of SHF.

◆ FLTSATCOM

FLTSATCOM is a UHF (244–400 MHz) fleet-communications system that provides worldwide high-priority communications between aircraft, ships, submarines, ground stations, the Strategic Air Command, and the NCA. The system, managed by the Air Force System Command (Space Division), uses five 2170-lb satellites (and one spare in orbit). It became operational in 1981, and the final satellite in the series was launched in September 1989. For a time FLTSATCOM handled about 90% of Navy long-haul traffic. Each satellite has an 18-turn-helical UHF receive-antenna and a 16ft-parabolic UHF transmitter antenna. There is also an SHF uplink for the shore transmitters of the Fleet Broadcast. Each satellite supports more than 30 voice and 12 teletype channels or, alternatively, 23 high-capacity channels (one 25-kHz [SHF up/UHF down] for Fleet Broadcast; nine [seven low- and two high-power] 25-kHz wide for Navy relay; twelve [all low power] 5-kHz wide for Air Force narrow-band; and one 500 kHz for the NCA). There are also two piggyback AFSATCOM channels. FLTSATCOM 7 (1986) carried an additional EHF package, which is also on board the last satellite in the series. FLTSATCOM operates with Marisat/Gapfiller (a Navy transponder leased on the civilian Marisat) and LEASAT (see below). This system is being replaced by UFO. Design lifetime was 7 yr, but some satellites are being required to double that; they are retiring from 1994 on due to lack of fuel for stationkeeping. To conserve fuel, controllers allowed them to drift up to 10 deg off their equatorial positions.

◆ GFCP

Tiburon's VME-based, generic front-end communications processor is currently deployed on board ships and at shore stations to support Tomahawk targeting. It is an interface between tactical data processors or a Tomahawk Mission Display System and the ON-143(V)6 satellite interface used for the OTCIXS net during Tomahawk targeting; for example, GFCP is part of Outlaw Hunter/OASIS. It formats and reformats messages, determines and controls data routing to appropriate systems, allows tactical data processors and communications systems with different interface protocols to exchange data, and provides message buffering. Applicable tactical data processors are the USQ-81(V) OTH-T system (formerly Outlaw Shark/Outlaw Hawk), JOTS, the Fleet Data Distribution System (FDDS), the Tomahawk command/control network (CCN), the Tomahawk Mission Data Distribution System (MDDS 1.X and 2.X), the Tomahawk Mission Display System (MDS), TWCS, and OSIS baseline and upgrades (OBS/OBU). Planned applications are to TEPEE, VIDS (visually integrated display system), and TAMPS.

By 1994 over 250 GFCP I were in service. They were Versions 4.0 to 4.3.5 with 5-slot VME backplanes and 8 ports. GFCP II Phase I provides the interface between ON-143(V)6 and sensor interface units on SSNs to allow routing OTH-Gold and Tomahawk mission data updates to multiple tactical data processors. These units are installed on board attack submarines and on AIP-modified P-3Cs. Phase II provides a single interface between an FDDI bus and a satellite modem for OTCIXS, TADIXS A, SSIXS, SKIP/VERDIN, and GPS Almanac data. Versions 1.0 to 3.X have 12-slot VME backplanes and 12 ports.

◆ Copernicus Links (GLOBIXS and TADIXS)

These high-capacity satellite links (GLOBIXS and TADIXS) are associated with the new Copernicus architecture. TADIXS already exists. GLOBIXS connects the FCCs and their sources of data. TADIXS is the FCC-NTCS-A(JMCIS) net, ultimately replacing the current separate OTCIXS and TADIXS and also the current Fleet Broadcast. Administrative traffic will be relegated to a separate NAVIXS net. TADIXS replaces the current series of formatted OTC messages, each of which requires its own dedicated communication net. Because each formatted net is concerned with only one type of sensor, this system does not encourage consolidation of sensor data. The specific combination represented by the OTCIXS nets reflects the requirements of war against the Soviets. The many separate nets also exhaust finite UHF communication capacity. The new philosophy is to structure the nets functionally rather than by data source. All subscribers to the tactical nets have access to the tactical data, which they may need to be able to operate in large (OTH) battle spaces. The current view is that it is far simpler for all tactical subscribers to have full access than to choose which data each subscriber really needs. Subscribers filter data themselves, for example, geographically.

GLOBIXS data are transmitted over the Defense Data Network (DDN) and the Defense Satellite Communications System (DSCS).

The TADIXS/GLOBIXS combination is intended to replace a current system, based on naval communications area master stations (NAVCAMs), with one controlled more directly by the FCCs and afloat NTCS-A nodes. The current Fleet Broadcast mixes operational and administrative signals, which are difficult to disentangle and which fill a limited jam-resistant channel capacity (sixteen 75-bps channels).

Current satellite capacity limits are:

Comsat	1.544 Mbit/sec (T1 link)
EHF	2.4 kbps (Milstar)
SHF	19.2 kbps
UHF	9.6 kbps
HF	1.2 kbps

As an example of communication-load requirements, each tactical report (HIT) of the current type consists of 10 lines (65 characters, each 8 bits), or 5.2 kbits. In a typical 18hr period, a carrier battle group in the Mediterranean might receive 500 such reports (2.6 Mbits) coming from a series of organic and nonorganic sensors. These reports would include indications and warning, cueing, tracking, targeting, engagement, battle damage assessment, and retargeting. Current message capacity in the Mediterranean, in terms of retransmission from the major shore stations, for the battle group is 155.5 Mbits/18 hr, so the overall system has sufficient link capacity (i.e., satellites and radios) *if* that capacity is properly used, that is, if it can be spread across channels. However, the capacity is currently spread among several channels.

As currently envisaged, the Global Information Exchange Systems (GLOBIXS) might embrace eight channels (SIGINT Management, ASW Management, SEW [space and electronic warfare] Management, Command, Imagery Management, Data Base Management, RDT&E Coordination [new secure telephone net], and Navy-wide Administration). The Tactical Data Exchange Systems (TADIXS) might embrace 14 channels (OTC Battle Management, ELINT, SEW Management, ASW Management, AAW [JTIDS], Tactical Intelligence [TACINTEL], Cruise Missile Targeting, High Command, Intelligence Broadcast, the Common High-Bandwidth Data Link, an Intelligence Net, a Combined Broadcast, a Single Integrated Satellite Broadcast, and the administrative channel [NAVIXS]).

These combinations suggest that the future Navy will abandon shore-based HF transmission almost completely, except for minor auxiliaries. One effect should be to eliminate dependence on transmitters on foreign soil, which will presumably have to cease operations with the end of the Cold War alliance structure.

◆ CSDS/Challenge Athena/SUBCOMMS

Commercial SATCOMM Demonstration System (Challenge Athena) uses commercial GTE satellites. SPAWAR's Challenge Athena project demonstrated the impact of a very high-capacity satellite link. The Challenge series are apparently short-term CNO initiatives paid for out of a special fund; it was apparently embarrassing that for a time it seemed that money for the leased satellites would run out just as they were proving particularly useful. High capacity was vital to provide forward commanders with sufficient imagery to target strikes (including Tomahawks) against targets ashore. In this sense Challenge Athena or some similar link has much the same significance for littoral warfare that OTCIXS had for OTH-T. As it happened, the enormous capacity of the link could also be used for numerous simultaneous telephone calls back to the United States, a feature that proved quite popular among deployed sailors. After a six-month demonstration (funded by GTE), in USS *George Washington* in 1992, the Navy competed a contract for a similar system to support Ocean Venture 1993. GTE won, and its system began continuous operation on board the flagship *Mount Whitney* in May 1993. Challenge Athena I used the entire 36-MHz bandwidth of a C-band transponder and a 2.2m (4-GHz) dish receiver antenna. Capacity ranged from 64 kbps to T1 (i.e., one television channel, 1.554 Mbit/sec) in a TADIXS/CCC (formerly FCC) link; the link typically operates at 768 kbps. This bandwidth suffices for simultaneous transmission and reception of voice, full-motion video, and compressed data and imagery.

The carrier was chosen because of her unique internal communications network (a fiber-optic LAN with a capacity of 100 Mbit/sec, which can support more than 300 workstations, the *George Washington* Information System [GWIS]). This combination was able to receive an ATO from Shaw Air Force Base, solving a serious problem encountered during the Gulf War. As important, the T1 link could easily and securely transmit imagery for strikes. It was also used to provide live television for the carrier's crew. The same television capability made it possible to arrange a video teleconference between the Joint Intelligence Center (Norfolk), the National Military Joint Intelligence Center (Washington, D.C.), and the carrier's Strike Planning Center on 16 October 1992. None of these capabilities had been approached in the past.

During Ocean Venture 93, using CSDS, *Mount Whitney* was able to support not only the usual naval force commander, but also an embarked Joint Task Force Commander and the Joint Forces Air Component Commander (JFACC). On the ship, the SATCOMM terminal was connected to a telephone switchboard (12 lines), to the intelligence system LANs (JDISS and imagery) in the ship's secure space, and also to a data server in the space used by the JFACC. In this configuration, the Ku-band link took over the terminals usually used for DSCS and for commercial leased communications satellites. This version increases the number of modes available, including an amphibious node which can be brought ashore.

GTE has nine INTELSAT satellites with the relevant links (C-band shore link, Ku-band ship link). They can operate at up to 2.048 Mbit/sec, compared to 64 kbps for the commercial IN-MARSAT. The *George Washington* shipboard end uses a 1.5m Ku-band antenna (the shore terminal has a 3.6m antenna). The *Mount Whitney* terminal uses a 3m Ku-band antenna.

Challenge Athena II, using the INTELSAT V satellite (COM-SAT experimental wide-band mobile service) was funded by the Congressional Intelligence for Targeting Initiatives program. It used a 2.4m shipboard dish to receive the 36-MHz-wide C-band global satellite beam; data rates were T1 shore to ship and 1.152 Mbit/sec ship to shore (*Mount Whitney* used a Ku-band spot beam steered to follow the ship).

Challenge Athena II was used during a deployment from the Atlantic to the Mediterranean and then to the Gulf during May through November 1994. It was reactivated, at CNO request, as Challenge Athena IIA in the fall of 1995. A projected Challenge Athena III will be fleet-wide, to several ships simultaneously. It will be the first example of the newly established Defense Information Supply Agency (DISA) communications satellite commercial initiative (CSCI).

SUBCOMMS is a parallel submarine-communication project, first demonstrated in May 1994 on board USS *Albany*. Its 64-kbps full-duplex link compared to the current limit of 4.8 kbps (and to the more usual rate of 2.4 kbps). For example, a relatively low-resolution picture (640 × 480 pixels, 64 gray shades, i.e., 6 bits per pixel, or a total of 1.84 Mbits) would take nearly half an hour to transmit at 2.4 kbps, requiring an unacceptable degree of mast exposure. The increased data rate could cut that to 45 sec, minimizing exposure to detection while the submarine has a mast extended above the surface. Quality imagery could be transmitted quickly, for example, for missile targeting. For ex-

ample, a 1274 × 1649-bit image was transmitted in 4.6 min without error. Presumably data compression techniques could further reduce this time. Note that at T1 rates this 2.1-Mbit image could have been transmitted in a few seconds. Mission data updates could be transmitted up to 25 times more quickly, and the submarine could send live periscope video back to command centers. On-board DEC Alpha workstations running GTE DIEP (digital image exploitation and production) software were used to process classified video taken aboard or transmitted by the submarine. The system employed GTE's Ku-band spread-spectrum Portable Submarine Terminal (PoST), which uses a 12in dish, mounted in the existing BRD-7 radome.

◆ EHF Terminal (USC-38)/NECC

These terminals are required for use with Milstar and with EHF transponders piggybacked on UFO satellites (numbers 4 through 9); during Desert Storm (1991) Navy terminals operated with an EHF package on board Fleet Satellite 8. Full rate production was approved in April 1993. NECC, the Navy EHF Communications Controller, establishes EHF networks, controls data transfer over them, and acts as a gateway between networks. The Engineering Development Model was completed in January 1994. A Medium Data Rate (MDR) upgrade to the terminal is being developed to allow operations with Milstar satellites 3 and beyond as well as Army and Air Force MDR terminals (MDR responds to a congressional demand for a higher-rate Milstar mode).

The antennas are a shore pedestal group using a 72in dish in an 86in rigid or 144in inflatable radome, a shipboard pedestal using a 34.5in Cassegrain dish in a 56in radome, and a submarine pedestal carrying a 5.5in stabilized dish in a 7in radome. Frequencies: 44.5 GHz (2.0 GHz bandwidth) uplink, 20.7 (1.0) GHz downlink. Data rates: 75–2400 bps on up to 12 channels.

◆ Have Quick

This Air Force program, now adopted by the Army and Navy, provides antijam UHF/VHF single-channel ground-air LOS radio (SINCGARS) voice communications, primarily by frequency-hopping (over 100 times/sec) across the radio net. The main technical issue is synchronizing clocks in all the radios of the net, so that they hop together. The original Have Quick had to rely on a master radio station; a newer Have Quick IIA takes its timing from a GPS navigational receiver, and so can hop at a higher rate. The primary piece of hardware is the Have Quick A20 control module, which contains the processor, memory, signal interface, and controls. The Navy's initial contracts, awarded in 1981, applied to airborne ARC-182 combination radios (low- and high-power VHF/FM, VHF/AM, UHF/FM, and UHF/AM) with frequency-hopping filters and broad-band antennas. and to shipboard WSC-3s.

In a typical battle group, a carrier and a cruiser might communicate over a Have Quick link; other users would be the E-2C and the F-14D and the Air Force AWACS. Airborne UHF relay pods and VHF relay pallets ("poor man's satellites") are used for communications within the battle group (to limit intercept range). The pod uses four ARC-182s, two of them modified to carry Link 11. Development of the pod was completed during FY87.

A new Have Quick Combination Radio (ARC-210 and Shipboard SINCGARS) program, using a radio already under development for the F/A-18, began under the FY88 program. The VHF/UHF ARC-210 uses Have Quick I/II and SINCGARS waveforms. Shipboard SINCGARS will provide VHF (FM) jam-resistant communications, a digital communications terminal (DCT), and a VHF relay pallet aboard naval gunfire support and amphibious ships.

In May 1991 Collins Radio demonstrated the ARC-210 VHF/UHF AM/FM radio in SINCGARS-V, Have Quick, Have Quick II, and Have Quick IIA modes, showing that it was interoperable for all services in voice communications.

NATO Have Quick II (STANAG 4246) is a parallel VHF-UHF program, currently on board the Dutch *Karel Doorman* class and on all recent French warships (*Foudre*, *Jean Bart*, and so on); at the end of 1993 France bought 30 Have Quick II radio modules for installation in warships, to give the first UHF jam-resistant capability in the French Navy.

♦ **Intelligence Broadcasts: TIBS, TRAP, TRIXS**

These nonnaval broadcasts are increasingly important in joint and littoral operations.

TIBS—Tactical Information Broadcast Service, up to 10 data providers and 240 field (query) terminals using satellite relay (240–320-MHz) or UHF (225–400-MHz) LOS radio. Sources include Air Force Rivet Joint and Army Ground Collection Systems. Data at Secret level is sent in TADIL-J format and filtered by the TIBS host processor. Throughput is over 7300 information bps at a net data rate of 19.2 kbps (alternative rates are 2.4, 4.8, or 9.6 kbps, depending on channel bandwidth).

TRIXS—The Tactical Reconnaissance Intelligence Exchange System, capable of handling up to 5 data producers or subnets transmitting data to 100 unique field terminal addresses via an airborne relay. The network includes Senior Span (U-2R) and can include JSTARS and UAVs. Throughput is over 2800 information bps on each channel, at 225–400 MHz, using four-level FSK modulation at 32 kbps.

TRAP is TADIXS B. Multiple providers provide data to an unlimited number of receive-only terminals via a satellite relay.

Because each system uses unique protocols and formats, no single receiver can interconnect them. Hence the importance of multiple channels in the CTT (see separate entry).

♦ **LAMPS Data Links/TACNAV**

LAMPS I helicopters communicate sonobuoy data to their ships via an AKT-22 FM transmitter, the simplex analog data link that can carry two DIFAR or two DICASS channels, as well as a voice channel. Originally the link could also transmit up to eight channels of LOFAR data. Of the channels, seven had 10–2000-Hz bandwidth, and one had 10–2800-Hz bandwidth. The dynamic range of each channel was 0.16–16 volts (a range of 20 dB). Alternatively, the link could transmit four omnidirectional sonar channels (for active buoys, at 26–38 kHz). The four- and eight-buoy modes were abandoned when the U.S. Navy decided to concentrate entirely on directional buoys. The helicopter antenna (AS-3033) has two sections, one to receive sonobuoy data, the other to transmit to the ship.

Because AKT-22 operates in S-band (2200–2290 MHz, on one of 20 channels), it is limited to LOS range, and thus a LAMPS I helicopter cannot prosecute a target beyond the ship's radar horizon: LAMPS I was intended to operate within 50 nm of the parent ship.

The LAMPS I data link is primarily acoustic. It does not carry radar video from the helicopter's LN-66 radar.

LAMPS III uses a C-band (4435–4535-MHz) duplex digital link (SRQ-4, Hawk Link with ARQ-44 airborne element, in two belly radomes), for sonobuoy data plus radar and ESM data. It cannot transmit radar and sonobuoy data simultaneously. However, the system does carry a full duplex command/control channel parallel with the data channel. Typically, helicopter sensors (ESM and radar) are operated remotely, from the parent ship, and their outputs are presented primarily on board the parent ship. The main data link is line-of-sight, but LAMPS III also has an HF-voice radio link, for distances beyond the horizon. It is intended to operate 100 nm from the parent ship.

A Unisys LAMPS data-link upgrade, emphasizing transmission of video (e.g., from the FLIR), is part of the LAMPS III Block II (SH-60R) program. Unisys claims a video compression rate of 8:1 using a new vector quantization (VQ) technique, which permits simultaneous radar/video downlinks and ISAR downlinking. The image is broken into blocks (vectors) which are encoded together (the alternative is pixel-by-pixel encoding). A limited number of vectors is used to represent all possible vectors (blocks), and the encoder chooses a best match for each vector. That match gives an index number, which is transmitted in place of the vector. Compression is complex, but decompression (reconstruction of the image) is a simple look-up exercise. Band-

width and data-storage requirements are drastically reduced. In addition, some image signal processing can be simplified by being applied to the vector rather than to the original image. In tests, VQ easily outperformed the alternatives, Fourier transform (discrete cosine transform, DCT) and differential pulse code modulation (DPCM, which concentrates on pixel-to-pixel differentials).

The new data link can carry up to 3.1 Mbps in full-duplex mode, an order of magnitude greater than existing ship-to-ship capability. This capability was demonstrated at sea during 1994. It opens up a new possibility, that ships can communicate via their LAMPS links (using the omni rather than the directional antenna). This makes possible such new services as video conferencing, white-boarding, file transfer, and shipboard LAN-to-LAN interconnection.

TACNAV is a new helicopter-to-ship link connected to the ASN-123 system on board a LAMPS I helicopter. It is a LAMPS III-like upgrade to the earlier system, automating information transfer from the helicopter: own position, sonobuoy positions, some other data. The associated EDO TDP (tactical data processor) is the interface between the communications link and the console on the ship using this data.

♦ **LEASAT**

The U.S. Navy leased four Hughes Communications HS-381 commercial satellites, orbited 1984–85, to supplement FLTSAT-COM. A fifth, built as a ground spare, was launched in January 1990. The contract allowed for purchase after 7 yr (the nominal lifetime), and the first three were bought in 1991–92. Lifetime set by fuel capacity is 10 yr, so the first two were retired beginning in 1994. As of January 1994 only two of the four slots in the system were occupied. Each satellite has two helical UHF antennas plus SHF horns (uplink and earth coverage downlink). Channels: six relay (25 kHz wide), one broad-band (500 kHz wide), five narrow-band (5 kHz wide), plus Fleet Broadcast (with on-board processing). The SHF antennas are used for control messages and for the Fleet Broadcast uplink. The Navy also leases a transponder (Gapfiller) on board the Marisat civilian satellites (three transponders, one per satellite). Unlike military satellites, these commercial types almost certainly are not hardened against attack (e.g., against EMP). However, their use indicates the number of U.S. communications satellites that can be turned to military use in an emergency. LEASAT is to be replaced by Hughes's UHF Follow-On Satellite (UFO).

♦ **Link 11 Data Terminal Sets**

The data terminal set connects a ship's NTDS system to other ships or aircraft in the same NTDS net. The DTS accepts digital data (which the KG-40 key generator has already encrypted) and converts them into a series of tones for radio transmission. It also detects and corrects errors, controls link protocol, and controls the NTDS interface. Normally, it operates in half-duplex mode, sending or receiving data, but not both (it operates in full duplex mode only when being tested).

The current major U.S. DTS suppliers are Litton and General Atronics. Different DTS can support different numbers of participating units (PUs). Thus USQ-36, introduced in 1964–66, could support 20. USQ-59, -63, and -79, which are all based on the same CV2969, can each support 15; USQ-79 is on board many AEW and ASW aircraft. These units were introduced in the 1970s. The next-generation USQ-74 and -83 could each support 61 PUs. Submarines and ASWOCs have USQ-76, which is limited to four PUs. The current generation (mainly USQ-125) is based on the open-architecture MX-512P, which can support 80 PUs, and which appeared in 1990. It was derived from MX-512, conceived about 1976 as a low-cost alternative to USQ-76, incorporating a digital modem.

GTE's USQ-83, which entered service in 1992, replaces not only USQ-74 but also the current HF Fleet Broadcast terminal (UCC-1) and the advanced narrow-band digital voice terminal (ANDVT). Development began in 1983; the first four production units were delivered in 1989.

General Atronics has developed several open-architecture DTSs based on MX-512. MX-512P and USQ-111 (1985) were programmable, with menu-driven touch panels. About 1990 MX-512P was modified to support single-tone rather than multitone operation. MX-512PV/USQ-125 (1993) is a one-board VME data terminal set, which could be inserted into a standard enclosure. The related MX-512PA (1993) is a compact airborne version (1/4 ATR Short enclosure); MX-512PL (1995) is a link monitor, and MX-512P(K) (1995) includes an embedded crypto element.

As of late 1994, the total DTS population amounted to 300 USQ-76 (100 U.S. Navy, 50 U.S. Air Force, 30 Canadian navy, 20 Australian navy and air force, 30 Royal Saudi Air Force, and 70 others), 502 USQ-111 and MX-512P (110 U.S. Navy ships and shore stations, 180 U.S. Air Force, 60 U.S. Marine Corps, 23 U.S. Army, 36 Turkish armed forces, 12 Royal Australian and New Zealand navies, 9 Norwegian navy, 15 Royal Saudi Air and Naval Forces, and 57 others), 132 USQ-125 and MX-512PV (102 U.S. Navy combatants and mobile operations centers, 6 U.S. Air Force, 3 U.S. Army, 5 Spanish navy and air force, 4 Italian air force, 3 Danish, and 9 others), and 87 MX-512PA (8 U.S. Air Force, 57 RAF, 9 Singapore maritime patrol aircraft, and 13 others). Presumably the unlisted items include DTS for the Israeli and Japanese E-2 programs.

The DTSs should be distinguished from the data-link terminal, USQ-69, which is an operator interface with the DTS and related components.

◆ EDO Link 11 Consoles

EDO has developed a Link 11 console capable of displaying up to 1024 tracks. An amplification window shows tactical data for a selected (hooked) track. This workstation has been bought by Norway and by the U.S. Navy (for EP-3Es, which lacked their own integral Link 11 capability) and by the U.S. Coast Guard.

EDO also offers a Link 11 computer card which takes data from an Ethernet and translates them into NTDS/ATDS format for a standard Link 11 encrypting device (KG-40).

◆ LRDS

EDO's new Link and Radar Display System merges real-time radar video with data-link symbology to form a single tactical picture. It is, therefore, a potential Link 11 stand-alone terminal. The internal VME backplane carries a RISC processor (with Ethernet and serial interfaces for radar data), optional data-link cards, radar interface cards (scan converter and radar interface, with 40-MHz sampling rate and software-controllable gain and offset), a graphics engine (for 1280 × 1024 pixels, with a 128-Mbps bus connecting the scan converter boards to the graphics engine), and mass memory (a 1-Gbyte hard disk and a 4mm digital tape drive). LRDS can accept up to three radar inputs (two analog, one discrete) and can accept Link 1, Link 11/11B, Link 14, Link 16, and JMCIS (LN2) data, as well as that from a variety of specialized links. Raw radar video is controlled by X-Windows software. Tracks can be manually initiated. There is also a tactical situation window suitable for link data display, using NATO or U.S. symbology. NTDS and 1553 cards can be inserted into the backplane. The system can generate the usual variety of standard Ethernet and link messages, such as those designating areas of probability, data-link reference points (DLRPs), and weapon/engagement status.

Users: Canada (replaced ADLIPS in replenishment ships, installed on submarines and auxiliary minesweepers, under consideration for MCMDVs; also in other roles), Norway (*Oslo* class), U.S. Coast Guard.

◆ Milstar

The Milstar all-service U.S. military antijam communications satellite system is now entering service, the first of six having been launched on 7 February 1994. Milstar is the first U.S. communications satellite designed to allow all the services to communicate using the same network. Unlike earlier communications satellites, which used transponders, Milstar has considerable on-board signal processing capability: it receives, recodes, and transmits, thus eliminating any trace of the uplink

The Milstar satellite shows its cross-link antennas (at the ends of the wings), helical antennas (for UHF), two of its three directional spot beams (circular antennas alongside the boxes), and the box-shaped antennas of its agile beams. (Lockheed Missiles and Space)

waveform in its downlink. This capability is apparently necessary to support the satellite's frequency-hopping anti-intercept/antijam performance. Intersatellite links (cross-links) make it possible for the Milstar system to function without using foreign ground stations. The cross-link functions at 60 GHz, a frequency to which the atmosphere is virtually opaque. Milstar is also the first U.S. satellite to operate at EHF (mm-wave) frequencies (uplink at 44.5 GHz, downlink at 20.7 GHz, nominal bandwidth 1 GHz in both cases). EHF operation drastically reduces dish size for a given gain. It was apparently chosen as well because it was least likely to be interrupted by nuclear blackout (which is strong at UHF) following explosions in the atmosphere. Throughout, the design of the system emphasized survivability (including nuclear hardening) and stealthiness (LPI) over capacity (it actually provides less data per second than predecessors now in orbit). Work began in 1983. Milstar was considered important enough to receive overriding (Brick Bat) priority. It was sometimes described as a nuclear war–fighting tool. With the end of the Cold War, its high cost (paid largely to protect it against nuclear damage and interference) came into question. On-board processing limits total capacity to 0.5 Mbit/sec (192 channels, 75–2400 bps; 100 channels at 2400 bps). One broadbeam (earth coverage) downlink antenna is supplemented by five agile spot beams (five up/one down agile, two up/down narrow spot, one up/down wide spot). Downlinks are steerable and uplinks can be nulled to avoid jamming. There is also a piggyback UHF transponder: two AFSATCOM channels (75 bps, earth coverage) and one Fleet Broadcast channel (1.2 kbps, earth coverage). The satellite weighs 4.67 tons.

With the end of the Cold War, Congress ordered the program restructured, nuclear hardening reduced, and a medium data rate (MDR) added to supplement the existing low-data-rate (LDR) payload. MDR provides 32 more channels (1.5 Mbit/sec, 2-GHz bandwidth) using eight steerable beams. Early plans to include a classified payload (presumably for intelligence gathering) were dropped.

Early expectations of a ten-satellite program (minimum of seven operational) were scaled back to the current six satellites (two Milstar 1, four Milstar 2 with MDR, of which two are still to be authorized). For the system to be operational, four satellites must be placed in geosynchronous orbits. Earlier plans had called for four geosynchronous satellites, three in polar orbits to cover high latitudes, and three spare satellites in very high supersynchronous orbits, which provide hemispherical footprints and a degree of protection against ASAT weapons.

◆ MULTS

This system translates between Link 11 and the NATO Air-Defense Ground Environment (NADGE) data link, Link 1, permitting deployed naval forces to take advantage of the NADGE data. MULTS is generally stationed ashore, in a van on board a light truck (HMMWV), transmitting out to ships offshore. The van carries a workstation connected to an EDO TDA.

◆ Satellite Information Exchange System

The U.S. Navy communications satellites carry a combination of Fleet Broadcast and other nets. The naval communications system as a whole employs a combination of HF radio and UHF/SHF satellite broadcast, plus automated facilities that assemble and retransmit the broadcasts. The shore stations are NAVCAMS (naval communications area master stations) and NAVCOMMSTAs (naval communications stations). The chief nets supported by the satellite information exchange system are:

FSB, the Fleet Satellite Broadcast, using a shore terminal (NAVCAMS/NAVCOMMSTA) broadcasting on 15 channels at 75 bps (teletype rate) on a spread-spectrum SHF uplink to the FLTSATCOM satellite (the downlink is UHF).

BCIXS, the Battle Cube Information Exchange System, is intended to provide shooters ashore with national-level data (for sensor-to-shooter integration). BCIXS is part of the current Copernicus Forward effort to modify the Copernicus approach to meet littoral warfare needs.

BGIXS, the Battle Group Information Exchange System, is a high-data-rate OTH-T net within a battle group, using the satellite links.

CUDIXS, the Common User Digital Information Exchange System, providing RF link control and message processing (for general service [GENSER] messages). The shipboard equivalent is NAVMACS.

OTCIXS, the Officer-in-Tactical-Command Information Exchange System, the battle group's command/control channel, carrying RAINFORM messages (at 2400 bps), teletype (75 bps), and narrow-band secure voice (2400 bps). This net provides both OTH-T data and Tomahawk mission data updates (MDUs) for land attacks. This net uses the ON-143 satellite link controller, which provides automatic crypto synchronization, stores and forwards teleprinter and tactical processor messages, and controls link access.

VINSON (Secure Voice Subsystem) uses a half-duplex (push-pull) link, employing two channels on each FLTSATCOM. VINSON is interoperable with NATO allies.

SSIXS, the Submarine Satellite Information Exchange System, carrying the submarine broadcast messages in unformatted text, plus targeting information in formatted computer-readable standard message formats (RAINFORM formats). One 25-kHz-wide channel on each FLTSATCOM satellite is allocated to SSIXS; up to 120 units can share a net within the satellite's footprint. Transmission rate is 2400 or 4800 bps. SSIXS computers are located at four submarine broadcast controlling authorities and their designated alternates. Besides the satellite broadcast, the SSIXS computers assemble the VLF/LF broadcast, which is stored and transmitted by the Integrated Submarine Automated Broadcast Processing System (ISABPS) for the VLF/LF sites.

TACINTEL, the Tactical Intelligence Network, exchanging special intelligence data, using the USQ-64(V)5, and carrying both RAINFORM and unformatted messages. An expanded TACINTEL II (designed to an August 1987 OR) is becoming operational. It implements the Integrated Special Intelligence Communications (INSICOM) portion of the Copernicus architecture. A related NSA program is the Operational Intelligence Processor (OPINTEL) upgrade (Project Embroidery). TACINTEL II interim capabilities were demonstrated in FY93, and engineering development models (EDM) of TACINTEL Link Control Facilities were bought and installed. Six TACINTEL II Build 1 suites were bought in FY94 for the FY95 OpEval. The FY95 program includes initial work on INTELNET, on the Multiple User Special Intelligence Common (MUSIC) II and on INTELDATA. The TACINTEL net uses one 25-kHz channel on each FLTSATCOM.

TADIXS, the 2400-bps Tactical Digital Information Exchange System, a one-way satellite link, mainly carrying ocean-surveillance data from the FCC to Tomahawk shooters and flagships at sea. The current version is TADIXS Phase IV. TADIXS employs one 25-kHz channel on each FLTSATCOM. TADIXS A carries OTH-T and Tomahawk MDUs. TADIXS B carries real-time intelligence data, and requires a TRE receiver (USQ-101). Typically a ship has a dual-channel receiver with a single processor.

Narrow-band secure-voice channel supporting the High Command Net, linking fleet commanders with battle-group commanders. There is also a Fleet Tactical Net.

◆ SHF Links

SHF satellites are expected to provide a primary channel for large-volume communication, for example, of images for real-time retargeting. As a consequence of Desert Storm, a fleet-wide SHF upgrade was begun, including an interim DAMA capability (Quick-Sat) using the MD-1030A modem in selected flagships and carriers. DSCS SHF satellites and the corresponding shore stations were upgraded. Full fleet SHF capability, as described in a 1992 OR, is to include a new surface ship terminal, a version of WSC-6 using a 4–7ft antenna, and a new Stel 1105A DAMA modem; after the program is complete, surface ships will be able to receive 256–640 kbps, depending on antenna size (i.e., gain).

◆ SPEAKEASY

This is a tri-service effort (joint-service multiband-multimode radio) to develop a common radio that will simultaneously support several waveforms over different frequency bands. The radio can then serve as a gateway between two different radio networks, eliminating the need for some separate internet gateways. The key technology seems to be very fast digital processing. A digital system can easily create a very wide variety of radically different waveforms, switching virtually instantly from one to another. It should also have a superior ability to reject noise. In effect, digital processing allows the designer to create filters that cannot be realized physically. The first stage, in FY93, was to develop an adaptive locally optimum processing algorithm, which could cancel out powerful interfering signals in the processor passband, such as from nearby radio transmitters. The next step (FY95) is to build a UHF Speakeasy to demonstrate that digital processing can greatly increase the radio's data rate. Increased data rate requires more complicated signal processing, including channel equalization and bandwidth-efficient modulation schemes, which become more practical as digital processing becomes faster.

◆ SSR-1

This is the nondirectional receiver for the UHF Fleet Broadcast from the FLTSATCOM, built by Motorola. The antenna is an inconspicuous crossed vertical wire loop. The receiver accepts both frequency- and phase-shift-keyed (FSK and PSK) signals. All surface ships carry this receiver.

◆ TRE (USQ-101)

Tactical receive equipment receives, decrypts, filters, formats, and transfers incoming TADIXS B data to local broadband TDPs (e.g., TAC-series computers in NTCS-A). Full-scale development began in 1986, in response to an OR issued 2 October 1985. See also the E-Systems CTT.

◆ Two-Way Link 11

The standard U.S. Navy two-way stand-alone Link 11 terminal is a DTC II combined with a DTS and an EDO TDP (see separate entry). The 1991 plan was to provide all non-NTDS ships with this capability: the surviving battleships, *Adams*-class destroyers, pre-FFG 7 frigates, amphibious ships, and the large auxiliaries. It would also go to some shore sites. This program superseded receive-only Link 11 (ROLE) because, given advancing computer power, the two-way capability is not much more expensive. Most of the planned combatant ship installations were overtaken by the decommissioning program.

The Whittaker UYQ-61 stand-alone Link 11 terminal is used ashore, by the Army and the Marines, as a way of receiving AEW information. This link is also on board Turkish *Gearing*-class destroyers.

◆ UFO

Hughes' UHF Follow-On satellite replaces FLTSAT and LEASAT. Designed lifetime is 14 yr. The system will consist of nine satellites (two each over the continental United States, the Atlantic, Indian, and Pacific Oceans plus one spare; the FY93 program bought the tenth, and leased three commercial UFO satellites). The first failed to enter its planned orbit (Mar 1993), but a second was successfully launched in Sep 1993, entering service over the Indian Ocean on 2 Dec. Two more were launched in 1994, with six more to follow through 1997. The satellite is Hughes's HS-601, selected at the end of July 1988, six weeks after Australia had chosen that same design. Each satellite has double the capacity of the earlier vehicle: 21 narrow-band channels (5-kHz bandwidth), 17 relay channels (25-kHz bandwidth), and one Fleet Broadcast channel (25-kHz bandwidth). All but the Fleet Broadcast channel use UHF up- and downlinks (the fleet channel uses SHF, 7–8 GHz). The satellites use DAMA technology. Beginning with satellite 4, an EHF capability will be added.

◆ VERDIN/EVS

VERDIN is the strategic submarine VLF/LF link from the TACAMO airborne relay aircraft. It is being upgraded to provide U.S./NATO interoperability with attack submarines (SSNs). EVS is the Enhanced VERDIN receiving system, which improves reliability, maintainability, and performance. It can handle the strategic emergency message (as part of the Minimum Essential Emergency Communications Network) at a new rate of 1600 bps. A new noise-reduction circuit reduces the effects of atmospheric noise. A nonlinear adaptive processor (NONAP) increases submarine flexibility by predetecting differences between the desired VERDIN signal and noise interference (presumably it monitors noise between signals).

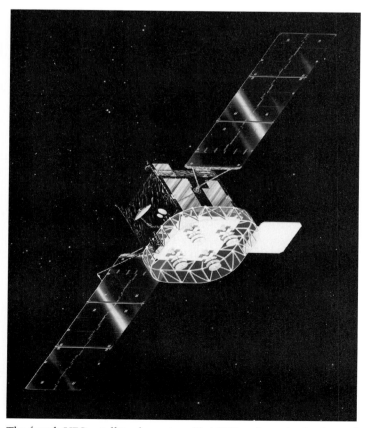

The fourth UFO satellite shows its added EHF package, in the form of small round antennas visible against the black thermal blankets on the side of the spacecraft. (Hughes)

◆ WSC-3/WSC-5

WSC-3, the U.S. Navy's standard UHF satellite-communications terminal, is also the standard LOS radio transmitter/receiver, in part because its modular design made modifications simpler. It supports 7000 channels (20 preset) at 25-kHz intervals. V(2) and V(3) were the original FLTSATCOM terminals. V(6) and V(7), the next to be produced in quantity, were LOS radio terminals. V(8) was a Coast Guard radio, remotely controlled. V(9) was compatible with AFSATCOM's 5-kHz-channel spacing. V(10) and V(11) are Have-Quick upgrades of V(6) and V(7). V(12) is a V(2) adapted for Trident submarine use. V(13) operates from a 400-cycle power supply, and V(14) has an interface compatible with MIL-STD-1553. (V)15, 17, and 18 are DAMA-compatible. ECCM versions are (V)6, 7, and 11. RT 1217 is an LOS WSC-3 for the Danish and Norwegian navies. RT 1217-2 is the relevant Have-Quick version. RT 1244 adds a fast frequency-hopping synthesizer to the WSC-3 used by the Australian and New Zealand navies. The manufacturer is E-Systems.

Users: Australia, Canada, Denmark, Egypt, Germany, Indonesia, Japan, Korea, Morocco, Netherlands, New Zealand, Norway, Portugal, Saudi Arabia, Spain, Turkey, United Kingdom, United States.

Rockwell's WSC-5 UHF terminal has been bought in small numbers (39 as of 1991).

◆ WSC-6(V)

This SHF (7.9–8.4-GHz uplink, 7.25–7.75-GHz downlink) SATCOMM terminal is used for command communications via DSCS II/III satellites. This system is also used on board SURTASS ships, to relay sonar data. It employs dual or single 1.2m radome-enclosed antennas. Originally WSC-6 used an 8-kW klystron, but in 1992 the manufacturer, Electrospace Systems, was awarded an ECP contract to replace the klystron with a 300W TWT, and to replace the earlier spread-spectrum modem (OE-55) with a DAMA modem. A new 2.1m antenna has been tested on board USS *Blue Ridge*, and a more compact version is under contract. Versions: (V)1 uses two modems, (V)2 uses four. As of 1994, 44 systems had been bought, and options were open for 14 more.

◆ TACNET

About September 1995 Comtek Federal Systems Inc. of Buffalo announced a new low-cost tactical data link and display, based on the earlier Link America, using a ruggedized 486-66 computer with 8 Mbytes of RAM made (originally for the Army) by IBI of Florida. The system can forward Link 11 data, but does not use Link 11 formats, and thus is exportable (as of January 1996, two navies were asking for demonstrations). Like Link 11, TACNET passes data at 2400 baud over an HF radio (it can also use VHF or UHF). Data are transmitted in 128-byte packets, 8 bytes per message. The data are less granulated than in Link 11, but throughput is similar (e.g., in terms of tracks per second); data are handled on a byte rather than a bit basis.

Submarine Communications Systems

A submarine's radio communications with surface ships and aircraft are inherently limited because seawater is a barrier to most signals. The primary communications choices for submarines are currently surface radio (HF and above), periscope-depth radio (LF and VLF), and ELF (extremely low frequency) radio.

A submarine must put an antenna either through or very near the surface to receive all of the usual long-haul naval signals (HF or satellite-transmitted SHF, UHF, or EHF). For example, many submarines are equipped with buoys containing wrapped-wire HF antennas. Higher LOS frequencies are useful either for air-to-submarine communications or for submarine-to-satellite communications. One advantage of very short wavelengths (such as SHF or EHF) is that the antennas can be so small that they can be housed atop periscopes.

At lower frequencies (VLF), radio waves can penetrate the water's surface down to 10–30 ft. Typically, reception requires ei-

Standard U.S. Navy submarine communications buoys. (Spears Associates)

A Victor-I-class submarine displays her Park Lamp antenna (open loops on the aftermost mast). Although possibly usable for direction-finding, Park Lamp is almost certainly primarily a VLF receiver, usable at periscope depth, analogous to the U.S. Navy's loop antennas (originally radio direction-finders) of World War II. (U.S. Naval Institute)

ther a wire loop (which may be in a towed buoy) or a towed linear floating antenna. Using a towed wire limits the submarine's depth, speed, and course. Moreover, any method of communicating requires the submarine to place an object near the surface, where the antenna is more visible and marks the submarine's position.

Conventional antennas can transmit signals down to VLF, although VLF antennas can be quite large. For example, the airborne VLF antennas used as backups for communicating with strategic submarines are several thousand feet long and must be trailed from a considerable altitude. The sheer sizes of LF and VLF antennas make it impossible for submarines to transmit at these frequencies; LF and VLF are usable only for communication to submarines.

Only ELF penetrates to great depths, but it requires very large land-based transmitters (which in turn require favorable geological conditions) and has a limited capacity for carrying information (it acts as a bell-ringer, informing the commander that the submarine must come near the surface to receive a more conventional message, e.g., by HF or satellite link). Moreover, because ELF has so great a range, it is subject to jamming, intentional or otherwise, by other nations' ELF systems.

Submarines are generally fitted with underwater telephones; the standard NATO frequency range is 8.3–11.1 kHz Many navies also use their telephone receivers as medium-frequency passive (warning) sonars. Transmission is typically omnidirectional with a secondary directional mode. It can be voice or Morse. Typical rated range is 10 or 20 km.

Major NATO types include:

    Canada: WQC-501 (by Safare-Crouzet)
    France: TUUM-Z (by Safare-Crouzet)
    Italy: TS-200 (and smaller omnidirectional TS-510)
    United Kingdom: Types 185/Graseby G1732, 2008; emergency Types 183, 2073
    United States: UQC-1, UQC-2A (alternative mode: 1.45–3.1 kHz), WQC-2.

RUSSIA

For many years, the Russians have been credited with superior, and probably covert, means of coordinating their submarines and surface ships. The Soviet style of naval command/control required considerable direction from above and would demand an effective system for communicating with submarines. At the same time, because the Soviets tended to use stereotyped tactics, they might have been been able to tolerate a very low information rate, or a very limited repertoire of messages, so that developing a satisfactory secure and covert underwater communications system would be easier. The U.S. Navy appears to have been far less successful in this endeavor, perhaps because the more flexible U.S. tactics require much greater information exchange.

MG-29 (Khost, NATO code-named Fez) was an underwater communications and IFF set probably introduced in the 1960s, for surface ships and submarines. In submarines, it is typically carried behind an array of acoustic windows in the sail. The bow dome previously associated with such devices actually houses an acoustic intercept set. MG-26 was another such set.

Most surface combatants apparently have underwater sound communications systems. An example is MG-35E, on board the export version of the Project 1265 minesweeper ("Sonya"). It is a nondirectional HF/LF set for voice and Morse, which also measures ranges by a DME (transponder) technique. MG-35E operates alternately with the ship's sonar and echo sounder. It is roll- and pitch-stabilized. Presumably there is a submarine equivalent. Some minesweepers have a simpler underwater telephone, MG-16.

◆ Radio Links

The standard mast-mounted VLF/LF receiving antenna is Park Lamp (which is often described as an ECM or navigational antenna). In addition, strategic and some tactical missile submarines (Charlie-II, Oscar) tow buoys, which are often carried in prominent housings. Of the new classes of attack submarines, Akula seems to be unique in towing a communications buoy. Many submarines (including all strategic submarines) also have satellite antennas (Pert Spring).

Bear-J aircraft function as strategic communications links analogous to the U.S. TACAMO. These aircraft entered service in 1985.

In 1987 it was reported that the Soviets were building an ELF station. In 1990, they were credited with nine LF and two VLF transmitters, most operating at 10 kW, but five strategic LF stations at 500 kW.

UNITED KINGDOM

◆ Type 2009

Type 2009 (UARS: underwater acoustic recognition set) is a secure multitone-simplex communications and encoding device. It is IFF and uses G-tone codes for challenge and reply.

◆ Type 2010

Type 2010 (ACUTE) is an acoustic teletype, working with Type 2008 and coding its signals for better resistance to jamming and for automatic error detection. Reportedly, tests showed that the use of an automatic error-detecting code made for 98% accurate reception and ultimately for several-fold improvement in transmission rate and in effective range. Type 2010 was presumably the acoustic data link associated with the British DCA submarine command system, which was conceived for close cooperation with surface units. Both it and 2009 would have been effective if the submarine were nearly directly under the ship with which she communicated, using the reliable acoustic (propagation) path.

◆ ELF

In mid-1987 the British announced that they were building an ELF site in Scotland (Glen Gally Forest, near Fort William).

UNITED STATES

U.S. *Los Angeles*–class submarine radio communications suites are being upgraded in stages, to lead to a suite, SCSS, compatible with the new surface communications support system (CSS): (a) submarine message buffer (SMB) in FY94/97, (b) baseband switch (BBS) in FY97/98, (c) SACCS in FY99 and beyond. Trident radio rooms, which are more expensive to refit, are to be frozen in their current configurations and then fitted with packaged new systems about FY99.

SMB accepts and stores messages as they arrive, using a TAC-3 computer with a color monitor. It includes an ORACLE relational database, presumably to assemble and route messages. BBS uses a nondevelopmental automated switch to provide the first automated internal routing capability for a submarine radio room. SSNs will also receive a Time and Frequency Distribution System (TFDS) to replace the currently overloaded system. TFDS provides elements of the communication system with the precision time and frequency standards they need, for example, to synchronize with a Link 16 net (which is time-divided). TFDS takes its master standard from a cesium beam. It distributes precise sine waves (at 100 kHz, 1 MHz, and 5 MHz) and timing signals.

A new automated antenna distribution system will replace the current manual patches connecting the radio room and the antennas. The prototype is to be tested in FY96. The communications upgrade program includes new HF receiver/transmitters, ultimately with VME-based models; similarly, a submarine LF/VLF VME bus receiver (SLVR) will be installed.

For the attack submarines, the objectives include interoperability with joint forces (i.e., Link 11, Link 16, Link 22, Milstar, and TRE/TADIXS B), an open architecture for future modifications, sufficient throughput to handle the imagery needed for Tomahawk strikes (SSIXS; in future, commercial satellites and Milstar medium data rate [in place of the current low data rate]; minimum capability 64 kbytes/sec), and the ability to receive standard record messages without exposing any mast (VERDIN/EVS). The program includes providing all submarines with receiving equipment for the OTCIXS net and with NTCS-A/JMCIS computers (they currently have JOTS), so that they can receive and display the same large-scale tactical picture as the battle group. This last capability was presumably originally provided when submarines were modified to fire Tomahawk antiship missiles (the TWCS incorporates a USQ-81 picture-keeper). SCSS will also be adapted to special forces communications, currently an ad hoc capability.

New requirements include automatic message distribution, using the submarine message buffer (in future, placing the SMB on a LAN with NAVMACS II), VVFD, and interoperable imagery (currently Cluster Nave, in future via NTCS-A).

Reportedly the United States uses 22 transmitters and 7 special receivers for submarines. For each submarine patrol zone there are at least two transmitters for each of UHF, HF, LF, and VLF bands. They constitute the Fixed Submarine Broadcast System (FSBS). The main LF (14–35-kHz transmitters at 1 MW; Cutler is 2 MW) are at Stockton (Calif.), Adak (Alaska), Okinawa, Sigonella, and Keflavik. Sites at Annapolis and in Hawaii host both LF and VLF transmitters. High-power VLF transmitters are at Cutler (Maine), Jim Creek (Wash.), and in Puerto Rico and Australia. These sites use VERDIN/VALLOR equipment operating at 50 bps. Major FSC-79 ground stations (2400 baud) are at Norfolk, Honolulu, Guam, Diego Garcia, and Naples. VLF sites are being upgraded with solid-state power amplifiers (SSPAs).

NATO is installing its own submarine VLF/LF system. The sites at Cutler and in Puerto Rico are being modified to accept NATO message formats (STANAG 5030). U.S. submarine VERDIN receivers are also being modified.

The U.S. submarine signal buoys (BR series) listed below are ejected from the standard 3in signal ejector.

A 1992 Russian article described Trident submarine communications equipment as follows:

The BRS-1 ELF receiver uses a 530–610m trailed cable antenna to receive signals at 76 Hz at depth down to 120 m and speeds up to 20 kt (note, however, that proponents of ELF generally claim that this equipment can be used at any feasible submarine operating depth, which would be closer to 300 or 400 m). The receiver incorporates a UYK-44 computer, and takes about 5 min to receive a three-letter combination.

The LF and VLF receivers are WRR-3, WRR-7, and BRR-3, operating at 14–60 kHz, with folded-dipole, floating wire, and loop antennas. VLF signals can be read at 67 words/min. The folded-dipole cable antenna is four 20-strand copper wires twisted in pairs and covered with polyethelene and then with fiberglass; the active section, which must float on or near the surface is 300 m long (total length is 900 m). Float-type VLF and LF antennas are trailed at the end of a 450m steel cable. The loop antenna consists of ferrite rods. The trailing antenna can be used at 15–30 m depth and at speeds of up to 10 kt; the float antenna limits the submarine to 40–60 m depth and 5 kt. The loop can receive signals at up to 30 m depth.

HF signals (2–3 MHz) are received using retractable stub antennas on masts; signals can be read by teletype at 100 words/min. Submarines have URT-23 burst transmitters operating at 1000 words/min.

The standard VHF/UHF (240–340 MHz) receiver is SSR-1. It has 15 fixed channels (each 25 kHz wide) and operates at 75 bps. The antenna consists of four 39cm dipoles. The standard transceiver is WSC-3, which is preset to 20 of a potential 7000 channels; power is 100 W and signals are transmitted at 9600 bps. WSC-3 operates with either frequency or phase modulation. This frequency band is used both for LOS and for satellites.

External communications are controlled by five UYK-20s, with a sensor for the submarine's time standard.

◆ Antennas

The current mast antennas are BRA-34 for UHF (including FLTSATCOM), a 5.25in EHF receiver atop the Type 8 Mod 3 periscope, and a sleeve on the Type 18 periscope for VHF. Work on an upgraded BRA-34 began in 1989; it now includes a DAMA capability and can receive at VLF up to UHF frequencies, with transceiver capability in VHF/UHF (LOS and SATCOMM: 10–170 kHz, 2–30 MHz HF, 225–400 MHz VHF/UHF), and carries an IFF transponder and a GPS receiver. A new nonpenetrating mast (NPM) is being developed to carry a 12.25in EHF antenna for the USC-38 Milstar terminal (originally a 9in dish was planned). An SHF antenna is planned, possibly using a 21in multiband antenna, which would be shared with EHF. The antenna, which would support data rates up to 56 kbps in SHF or 128 kbps in EHF, might be mounted either on the BRA-34 mast or on the ESM (BLD-7) mast. EHF and SHF are needed to receive joint imagery via Milstar and commercial satellites. A new VHF capability is needed to communicate with special forces. It is provided by the BRA-34 upgrade.

Tridents and some other submarines have an AT-441/MRC MF/HF mast. Trident submarines also have a pair of OE-207 HF/VLF/LF mast antennas.

U.S. submarines employ towed buoyant cables and towed buoys, both manufactured by Spears Associates. These devices grew in importance during the late 1970s and early 1980s because they appeared to be the best way to provide submarines with the sort of UHF-receiving capability needed for full battle-group integration, that is, the ability to receive Link 11 on at least an intermittent basis (the *Los Angeles*–class submarines, then being built, had been bought as battle-group escorts). UHF also became more important at that time because it was the frequency of the fleet satellite; by 1975 a program was underway to provide all submarines with WSC-3 UHF satellite receivers. The satellite system was so arranged that a submarine could request stored tactical messages at a convenient time, rather than having to put up an antenna for regular fleet transmissions as in the past. UHF does have one major drawback: it requires that the receiver be at or very near the surface. This consideration has led to renewed interest in both cables and towed buoys.

The current buoyant cable LF/VLF/ELF antenna on all types of submarine (towed from the sail) is OE-315/BRC (the system is BRA-24). It is being replaced by an antenna that can be towed at flank speed, HSBCA or OE-315(V). HSBCA will receive VHF, VLF, and ELF messages, and will transmit and receive MF/HF. Work is proceeding on an on-hull VLF/LF antenna. OE-315(V) is to include HF capability.

The standard buoyant cable antenna (BCA) is 2000 ft long (1900 ft of it deploying cable), with a diameter of 0.65 in, allowing for reception at 10 kHz–30 MHz or at 10 kHz–200 MHz, depending on the version. The submarine can also transmit HF signals from the portion of the antenna near the surface. The antenna can be deployed either by an electric winch outside the pressure hull (the "Bustle" device demonstrated on board a U.S. nuclear attack submarine in the 1970s) or by a hydraulic unit inside the pressure hull (which is standard). The cable includes an in-line amplifier, which can operate over the 2–400 or 2–30-MHz range.

The main disadvantage of the towed buoyant antenna is that, as the submarine increases speed, the cable tends to stream directly astern. Since the antenna must lie at or very near the surface to be effective at high frequencies, it is usable (at those frequencies) only at relatively low speed. However, because it is a very broad band device, it can receive VLF signals at higher submarine speeds, when it is well below the surface.

Towed ELF cable antennas are more than 1000 m long (towed below 100 m); LF and VLF are 300–900 m long. On-board antennas can receive VLF at 30m depth.

There are three standard towed buoys:

OE-305/BRR 97.5 × 30 × 24.38 in (height less fin); 41 in high including the fin; air weight 900 lb (buoyancy 750 lb); payload volume 2 ft³ (95 lb).

BRR-6 90 × 36 × 24.38 in; height 35.38 in including fin; 900/750 lb; 2 ft³ (95 lb). This buoy, on Trident submarines only, receives HF down through VLF.

BSQ-6 72 × 26 × 19.5 in; height 31.25 in including fin; 650/300 lb; payload 3 ft³ (200 lb).

All three are proof against 650 lb/in² of sea pressure. They are made of fiberglass-reinforced plastic, and their shape causes them to follow the contour of the sea surface at a shallow depth, to avoid broaching and thus revealing the submarine's presence. Buoys are typically towed at up to 15 kt, and they can contain both receivers and transmitters.

◆ BRC-6 (XSTAT)/OUTPOST/SLATE

Sippican's Expendable Submarine Tactical Transceiver is a two-way buoy for UHF communication between a submarine and an airplane. After launching, a lifting body separates from the buoy, remaining attached to the submarine (and, therefore, to the terminal) by a 40ft tether cable. Very fine wire (0.008in dia, up to 10,000 ft long) unreels from the flying body, maintaining a connection to the rising buoy. When the buoy reaches the surface, it deploys an antenna for two-way radio voice communication. The battery is useful for 45 min, but communication duration really depends on the length of fine wire, which unreels as the submarine steams away from the nearly stationary buoy. Typically, the wire lasts for 8 min at 10 kt, or for 20 min at 4 kt. OUTPOST replaces the wire with a 20km (33,000 ft) optical fiber; it is now in advanced development at NUWC New London.

SLATE was an earlier version.

◆ SLOT (AN/BRT-1/2)

Sippican's submarine-launched one-way VHF (sonobuoy frequency) radio transmitter carries a 4min tape-recorded message (either voice or CW). SLOT can be set to delay transmission either by 5 min or by 1 hr, giving the launching submarine time to get clear. The buoy can function in sea-states up to 5. Having received the message, an aircraft or surface ship can command the buoy to turn off by UHF signal. Selectable buoy lifetime is 1, 3, or 8 hr. Dimensions are 3 × 39.12 in, and weight is 7.25 lb.

BRT-2 is a SLOT buoy manufactured by Electrospace.

◆ BRT-3 through -5

The submarine-launched expendable buoys provide improved bad-weather submarine identification and position. They operate for 30 min; each buoy transmits a characteristic tone: 300 Hz for BRT-3, 2700 Hz for BRT-4, and 900 Hz (pulsed, amplitude-modulated) for BRT-5. These devices date from 1974. Overall dimensions are 3 × 11.5 in (weight 1.4 lb).

◆ BRT-6

Hazeltine's one-way UHF satellite communications buoy carries a tape-recorded message and is usable up through sea-state 5. The satellite channel can be preselected (290–315 MHz). Data are transmitted digitally into the SSIXS system, and one to fifteen transmissions can be made. The buoy is normally preset for 2400 bps; alternatively, 75, 300, 600, 1200, 4800, or 9600 bps can be selected. As with BRT-1, a message transmission delay can be selected (in this case in 5min increments), with output selectable between 25 and 100 W. The buoy scuttles within 30 min after its final transmission. Dimensions are 3 × 40.5 in (9.7 lb). Approved for full production 1983.

Work on a tethered two-way UHF SATCOMM buoy, comparable in concept to XSTAT (BRC-6), began under the FY89 program.

◆ Sanguine

The U.S. ELF system was originally conceived as a means of alerting strategic submarines, using transmitters hardened against an initial nuclear attack. Work on ELF began in 1958, and the concept was first demonstrated in 1962, using a 175km antenna. The project was opposed on political (nominally environmental) grounds, and it was canceled by President Carter in 1978. It was revived, in limited (and vulnerable) form, by the Reagan administration and entered service in 1987. The operating frequency is 76 Hz; wavelength is then about 2500 miles. Radiated power for one transmitter is 2–8 W. The antenna at Clam Lake is 28 miles long, and the one on the Upper Peninsula of Michigan (at Sawyer AFB) is 56 miles long. All attack and strategic submarines have been equipped with receivers.

Sanguine currently reportedly transmits three-letter messages, which have limited content. In the mid-1990s, R&D concentrated on antijam techniques and on means of achieving an enhanced data rate (EDR). Apparently the data rate was very low precisely to overcome jamming, and the new antijam concepts were advanced as a means of achieving a better data rate in the face of possible jamming.

In a test about 1984, Clam Lake successfully contacted a submarine maneuvering in the central Atlantic at 20 kt, at a depth of 100 m (330 ft), also one at 16 kt and 122 m, and it contacted a submarine under 10 m (30 ft) of ice at 16 kt. At this time it reportedly took 15 min to transmit three characters. Work is underway on an EDR modification, which might permit the use of longer messages (4 to 13 times current message length) at slightly shorter ranges in the same time as the current low data rate (LDR) system.

By 1992, two shore transmitters and about 161 submarine receivers (including 20 developmental models) had been produced.

One major current program is installation of ground well arrays for transmission (FY95/96). Submarines currently receive ELF signals using a 2000ft buoyant cable antenna. Work is currently underway on a much more compact on-hull ELF antenna.

R&D is underway on a compact "corona mode" ELF transmitter, which might be deployed in a forward area for direct control of SSNs.

◆ Probe Alert

See SQS-26/53 sonar.

◆ SSQ-71

The air-dropped two-way air-submarine acoustic-communications (ATAC) buoy can be tuned to one of three radio channels. It is in current production. This A-size buoy weighs 25 lb.

◆ SSQ-86

This A-size communications buoy (25 lb) is tunable to one of 99 RF channels.

◆ SUS

Sound Underwater Signal is a small device dropped by an airplane to send signals to a submarine. For example, SUS can indicate an emergency, telling the submarine to stay down; ask an unknown submarine to surface for visual identification; or act as a bell-ringer, asking the submarine to establish radio communications. The current version is the Sippican Mk 84 Mod 1, replacing the earlier Mk 64. An earlier version of SUS was the sound source in the Julie explosive echo-ranging system (see the ASW section).

Mk 84 can be launched at 100–10,000 ft, at speeds of 30–380 kt. It sinks at 14.5 ft/sec, spin-stabilized by its canted tail fins. The signal, which lasts 45–128 sec, consists of two tones (2.95 and 3.5 kHz), coded by pulsing for either 0.5 or 1.5 sec. The tones may alternate at two different pulse lengths, for four signals, or the SUS can transmit steadily at 3.5 kHz, for a fifth signal. The signal's source level is 160 dB. The desired signal is selected before launch by using a switch on the side of the SUS. Dimensions: 3×15 in (6.5 lb).

◆ TACAMO

The national command link to strategic submarines currently operates on E-6A aircraft, which replace the earlier C-130s. Since 1993 these aircraft have also taken over the Air Force airborne command post (ABNCP) mission formerly carried out by EC-135s. The communications suite is designated USC-13; it receives over the VLF-to-UHF range and transmits in VLF, using a dual (long and short) trailing antenna. The OR to incorporate ABNCP capability in the E-6 was issued in March 1994. Messages are received from the Navy's shore bases and from the Air Force emergency headquarters (an E-4) via satellite and other emergency radio links. Ultimately the E-6 must communicate with both submarines and missile silos ashore.

The long trailing antenna is half the wavelength of the transmission; the short antenna, which is active, is trailed at a length tuned to that of the long reflector. About 35,000 ft of long and 5,000 ft of short antenna are available, but typically the long antenna is unreeled to a length of 16,000–20,000 ft. The signal is vertically polarized and can penetrate the sea's surface. Transmitting frequencies are 14–30 kHz. In the 1980s a Soviet article claimed that TACAMO operates at 21–26 kHz at 200 kW, using antennas 3 km and 10 km long. A submarine could receive the signal at an antenna depth of 15 m (50 ft). When the airplane banks at angles greater than 40 deg, the antenna can brush the horizontal tail. Aircraft are being modified to avoid such maneuvers.

The current upgrade program has two phases. Block I provides a high-power transmitter to ensure that the TACAMO aircraft

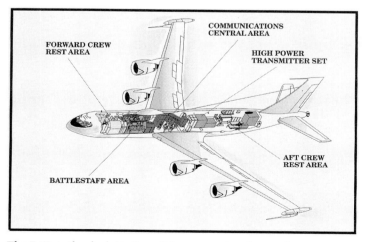

The E-6B is the dual Air Force/Navy strategic relay airplane. Note the addition of an Air Force battle staff area forward. (Chrysler Technologies)

can communicate with U.S. Air Force airborne national command posts over the central United States. It also adds dual trailing-wire antennas (plus a third utility wire antenna) to replace the current obsolete system. Block II improvements include provision for the E-6A to use the Milstar communications and GPS navigation satellites. The existing VERDIN (VLF submarine communications) system (processor and modulator/demodulator) will be replaced in two phases. Phase I is a replacement to host the Phase II Enhanced VERDIN System (EVS), which should improve communications performance. A new compact VLF (CVLF) system will ultimately replace the current receiver/demodulator and transmitter/modulator (except for its high-powered elements) and the VERDIN and EVS processors. A new high-power solid-state transmitter system (HPTS) will replace earlier 200-kW vacuum-tube equipment. Block II also includes the TACAMO Message Processing System (TMPS). Full-scale development of these improvements was originally scheduled for FY90, with TechEval/OpEval in FY91. However, a cut in the FY88/89 budget pushed Block II into FY93, with the exception of the provision for Milstar.

With the wind-down of the emergency communication air fleet, there is a program to improve the range, timeliness, and reliability of shore-to-submarine emergency action communication by the Minimum Electronic Emergency Communication Network (MEECN). A new MEECN message processing mode (MMPM), which reduces transmission time while improving delivery reliability at greater ranges, is being implemented in the MEECN VLF/LF systems. There is also a new high-data-rate (HIDAR) mode, which greatly reduces transmission time while providing the reliability of low-data-rate modes. HIDAR is implemented in the Enhanced VERDIN System (see above); it was certified in FY94. There was some question as to whether HIDAR was truly compatible with the TACAMO Block II system.

The term *TACAMO* derives from the order to a submarine commander to "take charge and move out." Work on the system began in 1962, and the two TACAMO squadrons became operational in 1968. The decision to upgrade to the E-6A was taken in 1977. Although escalating costs prompted some consideration of cancellation, the contract for 15 new E-6A aircraft was awarded in 1986, and the first E-6A flew in February 1987.

◆ Acoustic Data Link

A FY97 ATD (advanced technology demonstration) is to test a new concept for an underwater data link. For many years, attempts to develop really long-range acoustic data links have been frustrated by multipath effects, which smear out the digital data. However, in 1995 Lockheed Martin displayed a concept in which a coherent receiver characterizes the changing medium and thus introduces appropriate time delays. The company claimed that its advanced digital system can recover speech at a range beyond 20 nm. Ultimately such a system would be valuable because it might make it possible for submarines to participate fully in a battle group's digital net.

◆ UTSM

Despite its name, the Underwater Training System, Mobile offers a relatively inexpensive way to maintain continuous two-way communication with a submerged submarine. A series of transponders is laid on the sea bottom, at a spacing of about 20 nm. The submarine has a transducer on its hull, connected to a VME bus. She releases SLOT buoys, which turn acoustic signals into radio signals. As the submarine runs over the field of transducers, she transmits acoustically to them. They in turn activate the SLOT buoys. The process can also be reversed. UTSM was being developed by NUWC Newport in the summer of 1995, and a MENS (Mission Needs Statement) was being written.

COMPUTERS

Modern digital computers have four basic elements: a processor, fast read/write data storage, program storage, and some means of input/output. In civilian machines, the contents of fast read/write storage is volatile, that is, is generally lost when the machine loses power, but many military machines have nonvolatile running memories. Input/output generally includes a connection to some form of mass memory, in nonvolatile form. All of these elements are familiar to users of personal computers: the processor is the basic chip (e.g., an 80486); the fast storage is the RAM (random access memory); the programs actually being executed are stored with the data in the RAM; and the input/output channels are, typically, the computer screen, a printer, and the disk drives.

The computer memory is typically organized in words of fixed length (in bits, the binary digits whose value is either 0 or 1). Each word has its own address, and a program refers to the addresses of the data on which it operates. In theory, then, the maximum size of the memory (in words) is fixed by the largest address that can be written in the form of a single word. For example, the largest 8-bit word is 256; the largest 10-bit word is 1024 (1k). The largest 16-bit word is 64k. Some systems get around this limit either by using longer address words or by dividing memory into pages, within each of which items of data can be separately addressed.

These limits do not apply directly to mass storage, in which data are organized in files (whose names, however, must generally be entered in a file directory). For example, a typical word-processing program, written for 8-bit computers, can accommodate up to 256 files in its mass storage. The length of each file is limited by the overall size of the mass storage.

Because address capacity is necessarily a power of 2, it is generally given in terms of k (units of 2 to the 10th power, 1024). It may be given as a number of words, bytes (units of 8 bits each), or bits. The standard NTDS word length is 30 bits, and some early computers were similarly organized. More recently, the standard length has been an even number of bytes or half bytes ("nibbles"). The current standard is 32 bits.

In many cases a single word does not provide sufficient precision for calculation. Therefore, many machines have a provision for double-precision arithmetic, in which numbers are represented as pairs of words. In the past, the distinction between "scientific" and "business" computers was generally a distinction between machines that could or could not execute double-precision arithmetic. This distinction carries over to the math coprocessors, which generally calculate in terms of longer (multiple-precision) words. The other important distinction is between integer (whole number) and floating-point (including a decimal point) calculations. A floating-point calculator automatically keeps track of the decimal point, whereas in integer calculations the parts of the number before and after the decimal point are handled separately. On the other hand, integer calculators are also used for logical operations, such as decisions to take one or another branch of a program.

Most of the machines described here employ bit-slice processors, capable of handling data in slices shorter than entire words. Typically, there are separate 2-, 4-, and 8-bit processors, so that the processor as a whole can handle anything between 4 and 32 bits. Bit slicing makes for higher speed when less than full precision is needed, but it also makes for complicated programming.

The machines described in this section belong to two distinct generations. In the first, solid-state devices such as transistors were wired together to form a central processing unit (CPU). The U.S. CP-642 and UYK-7 fall into this category. The next step was to miniaturize the components, integrating more and more of them onto a single silicon chip. Integrated circuits (ICs) made possible the first desktop minicomputers (such as the UYK-20 of 1974) with performance similar to that of earlier discrete-component machines. These machines did not yet have a full CPU on a single chip. That took the next step, large-scale integration (LSI), typically defined as the ability to place at least 500 components on a chip. VLSI (very-large-scale integration) is an order of magnitude more (20,000 components per chip). Well over a million components per chip, three orders of magnitude beyond VLSI, is now common in leading-edge commercial chips (this level is sometimes called ULSI, ultra-large-scale integration). Each stage required that devices and their interconnections shrink. Devices are now typically packaged on several layers

within a chip. In such a configuration, even draining heat becomes a serious issue. The great question for the future is whether chip designers are approaching some physical limit, at least as it applies to silicon chips. If that is indeed the case, then the basic architecture of machines may be about to change (presumably to parallel computing). Because a radically different type of computer would be unable to using existing software (or even existing software concepts), it might not replace existing machines, as software itself is now the main expense (both in time and in money) in developing new systems. For example, in the mid-1980s 80–85% of total U.S. DoD computer spending went to software. This figure explains the determination to impose a high-level computer language, ADA, which allows the same program to be executed by many generations of computers (the program must be recompiled, newly translated into machine language, in many cases, however, and the compilers themselves must be tested).

This software barrier helps explain why so many elderly machines are still in service. To adopt a new generation of much higher performance machines is also to adopt new software. At the least, it will be necessary to rewrite existing software. This is so serious a problem that in some cases the new machines are designed specifically to run software developed (and, more important, tested) for their predecessors. This is called upward compatibility. Unfortunately, compatibility must be tested; there may always be nasty surprises waiting in the complexity of a new design. The well-publicized mathematics problems of the early Pentium chips were by no means unique. Testing makes it difficult for navies to exploit new commercial hardware, since the typical hardware development cycle (18 months) is shorter than an adequate test cycle. Testing is one reason why, until very recently, the U.S. Navy was unwilling to use adapted commercial computers for critical tactical tasks.

LSI sufficed to place a CPU on a chip. Thus the first single-chip CPU, the Intel 4004, appeared in 1971. The first general-purpose microprocessor, the Intel 8080, appeared in 1974. It powered the first generation of microcomputers (personal computers). As CPU performance has improved, it has become more and more difficult to distinguish between standard microcomputers and the more powerful workstations, and between workstations and what used to be called mainframes.

Integration drastically cut computer cost, since it was no longer necessary to assemble the components of each CPU produced. IC production is essentially a printing rather than an assembly process. Certainly it is more expensive to produce a more elaborate IC composed of much smaller elements (technology is now measured in element size, in microns), but unit cost (reproduction cost) is still low. Achieving a similar level of complexity in discrete components would be prohibitively expensive. Moreover, because the discrete components are so much larger, it takes more time for signals to travel among them, so they are much slower. Too, the single-chip CPU (and associated chip memory) drastically simplified overal computer design and manufacturing since so few wiring connections were now needed. Reliability improved just as sharply, since there were so many fewer connections between components to fail.

The crash in purchase and operating cost and the dramatic increase in capability explain the current dominance of microcomputers. The microcomputer market, in turn, is now so much larger than the military computer market that it dominates development; although a few special military machines are made, they are based on commercial CPU chips.

A less obvious development, but one quite common in the civilian world, has been a shakeout in the CPU market. Although many manufacturers package computer components, there are few widely used CPU chips, virtually all of which were either designed in the United States or are described as equivalent to (i.e., can run most programs written for) U.S. chips.

The chip is usually described in terms of its published instruction set. However, that set usually is not implemented in the actual hardware of the chip, which may be extremely complex. Typically the chip incorporates a hard-wired microcode, into which the published instructions are translated. The microcode runs on a very fast nanoprocessor (to distinguish it from the microprocessor in which it resides). The use of microcode allows several chip designers to produce nominally equivalent chips; it also allows any one manufacturer to offer quite different hardware as identical chips. On this level, two nominally identical chips may not quite perform identically. That is a major pitfall in the inevitable passage from tightly controlled military specifications to commercial hardware.

Beyond tighter packaging, there are several ways to increase CPU speed. One is to change the instruction set, either adding more complex instructions (each equivalent to several simpler ones). Alternatively, the set can be drastically simplified, on the theory that 80% of the computer's work involves only 20% of its set of instructions. Most current CPUs are variations on this RISC (reduced instruction set computing) theme. Some RISC machines eliminate microcode altogether in favor of hard-wiring their smaller instruction sets.

Typically executing an instruction involves several steps in different parts of the CPU. A *pipelined* CPU can read the next instruction while processing the last (Pentium uses a four-step pipeline, so it is reading the fourth instruction before it completes processing the first). The longer the pipeline, the faster the CPU. However, many programs branch; the choice made down the line really depends on the result of a calculation further up. If the CPU guesses wrong, it may load a series of steps it cannot execute, and the pipeline must be dumped. The current solution is branch-prediction logic, to guess which branch will be chosen so as to fill the pipeline correctly. That makes even seven-stage pipelines useful.

An alternative is superscalar (multiple-issue) architecture. A superscalar CPU tries to execute several parts of a program in parallel; for example, a Pentium chip has two parallel paths. The number of parallel paths is the number of *issues* the computer can handle per machine cycle. As in the case of pipelining, the CPU must judge whether parallel execution is possible. In effect, superscalar CPUs are the first approach to parallel computing, without the pain and expense of adopting radically different kinds of software.

The step beyond superscalar CPUs is parallel computing, in which several distinct CPUs communicate among themselves. The first major example was the Inmos Transputer, which was programmed in a new language, Occam. Several current CPUs (such as Pentium Pro and MIPS R8000) are reportedly designed specifically to support parallel operation, although they can also function alone.

Integration also applied to computer memory. The computers of the 1960s used core, in which each bit of data was stored in terms of the direction in which a small ferrite ring was magnetized. Typically, a core takes 1 microsec to read. The alternative, semiconductor memories (based on transistor technology), appeared in the late 1960s. In 1970 Fairchild introduced a chip, the size of a magnetic core, that could hold 256 bits of memory, each readable in only 7% of the time it took to read a magnetic core. One form of semiconductor storage uses capacitors (which can be charged or discharged), which leak their charges and hence have to be refreshed every few milliseconds (hence the name dynamic RAM [DRAM] for such memory). The alternative is to store information as switch settings, which do not have to be refreshed periodically, and therefore are called static RAM (SRAM). In each case random means that any element of memory can be called up at any time (as opposed to information on a tape or disk, which has to be brought into position in order to be read). Both forms of semiconductor memory survive only so long as current is available, hence are called volatile.

DRAM chips are rated by access time (typically a machine requires two cycles per access). The time for two back-to-back accesses may be two or three times single access time. Current DRAM chips are slightly too slow for 50- or 66-MHz CPUs, so memory-intensive operation sometimes requires that the CPU wait several cycles between memory calls. SRAM is much faster (e.g., 25–35 nsec vs. 60–70 nsec for DRAM) but also more expensive. There are also hybrids. The typical solution to slow DRAM is to provide a cache of very fast SRAM at the CPU. See

the U.S. CPU chip descriptions for examples. Often the cache contains not only data but also the next few instructions the CPU must execute.

Magnetic cores retain their polarity whether or not power is applied. They have therefore lived on in some military applications, and a variety of alternatives have been tried. Magnetic bubbles, which are moved into position to indicate memory state, have had some success, but they are relatively slow. Ferromagnetic and ferroelectric materials (here "ferro" indicates that they retain their magnetic or electric state even when power is lost) are also sometimes used.

Programmable read-only memory (PROM) uses, in effect, fuzes as memory. The chip is programmed by burning out specific fuzes. The step beyond is to be able to clear and reuse the chip, either by shining high-intensity ultraviolet light on it (EPROM) or by using a high-intensity electric field (EEPROM, electrically erasable programmable read-only memory). Unfortunately, EEPROMs last only a finite number of read-erase cycles, so they cannot be used as survivable primary memory. There is also Flash RAM, which can be erased using normal internal computer voltages, but which, like EEPROM, enjoys only a limited lifetime. It is sometimes used as a disk emulator.

Another solution to the problem of memory loss due to power loss is periodically to save the contents of the volatile working memory. Some military computers have backup power supplies that are expected to last long enough for read/write memory to be saved onto a less volatile medium, such as a hard disk.

Computers do have nonvolatile mass memory used for long-term storage (disks and tapes). Many but not all forms of mass memory are designed to be detachable from the computer. For example, U.S. Tomahawk flight plans are carried on board ships and submarines in the form of removable hard disks. To be nonvolatile, mass storage requires powerful read/write devices, which cannot be duplicated by the million or billion within a small machine. Typically, then, the medium is brought mechanically past a few read/write heads. Such scanning cannot be anything like as fast as electronic scanning inside a semiconductor chip, hence the need for fast RAM as working memory. Too, the pressure for more and more nonvolatile storage capacity must equate to pressure to shrink the area devoted to each bit of data. At present, the smallest such area (hence the largest overall storage) is offered by optics: a laser pits the surface of the disk, and another laser detects that shallow pit. On the other hand, that particular technique precludes rewriting, so laser disks are usually described as read-only memory (ROM). However, the sheer size of the disk (many Gbytes) allows many versions of a given series of data to be written onto the disk before it is full.

Denser storage requires greater and greater precision in controlling the read/write head relative to the medium on which data is recorded, and it makes the mechanism as a whole more and more sensitive to shock. For example, at one time it was notorious that the shock of catapult firing would often disable the tape cartridge of the AYK-10 mission computer of the S-3A. In this case the solution was to abandon conventional nonvolatile memory altogether in favor of magnetic bubbles in cartridge form.

Most naval systems must perform several distinct functions nearly simultaneously. For example, a CDS accepts and edits data to form a coherent tactical picture, on the basis of which it ranks threats, assigns weapons, and may even direct those weapons. When computers were massive and expensive, it was obvious that a single machine would have to do everything, even refresh the screens of the display terminals (which had no intelligence of their own). To do that, the CPU had to break its tasks down into modules, spending some of its time on each before storing the relevant data and switching to the next. This type of operation was called time-sharing and, in modern guise, is often called multitasking. The hardware requirement was a special set of registers in which vital data from one module could be stored before switching. Another important hardware feature of central tactical computers is a large number of input-output channels corresponding to the large number of devices with which the computer must communicate. Neither the stack register nor the array of input-output devices is badly needed for most civilian applications, although some degree of multitasking (e.g., in machines running Windows and similar systems) is now quite common.

As the number of separate program modules increases, the system itself runs slower and slower. The only solution is to unload the central processor by relegating some of its functions to separate machines. That may be done by wiring a separate coprocessor to the main CPU, as is common in some microcomputers required to do very intensive computing. A simpler alternative is to connect both the main CPU and subordinate units to a common data bus, allowing all to communicate to some extent. For example, many workstations have both a CPU and a separate graphics processor, because graphics imposes very heavy computer and memory loads. It is also possible to connect separate machines together using a bus.

In theory the single input/output port to the bus replaces the numerous input/output ports of a specialized military computer. In fact that is true only if the relationship between the central computer and the other devices in the system changes drastically. For example, in the original U.S. NTDS system, the central computer literally controlled each console in the system, using it as an input/output device. None of the consoles had any intelligence of its own, so the central computer had to direct the electron gun forming its display image. It had to refresh that image frequently enough to avoid flicker.

Merely providing each console with a character-generating capability, so that the central computer could send a few bits indicating that character (rather than the elaborate controls to form the character), substantially reduced the communication load and, incidentally, the load on the central computer. At this stage the central computer still periodically had to repeat the character indication. The next step was to provide each console with some intelligence, so that the central computer only had to send changes in the picture displayed.

Ultimately very little information actually had to be sent to any particular device in the system, because each device did a great deal of its own computing. As long as each message was properly addressed and as long as messages were not too lengthy, a single input/output port could suffice.

The change from fully centralized to largely decentralized bussed systems can be traced partly to the need to improve system speed. However, it is probably also an inescapable result of the shift toward semicommercial hardware not designed for very large numbers of input/output ports.

Data buses are also widely used inside computers (in workstations the internal bus is called the backplane, so called because it runs up the back of the cabinet). In a personal computer, each circuit board contains high-speed buses connecting elements on that board, such as the CPU and fast memory. The boards themselves usually fit into a bus (backplane) which allows them to communicate among themselves. Finally, the computer itself may communicate with a system bus. In some cases, the local bus (local area network, or LAN) communicates with yet another bus extending through the ship.

The 32-bit VME bus (originally versatile Eurocard, IEEE 1014), introduced in the early 1980s, is probably by far the most popular current backplane, at least at the workstation level. Capacity is 40 Mbyte/sec in asynchronous mode; a typical card size is 233 × 160 mm. VME passes only data. However, in a multiprocessor, the boards would have to be able to communicate, and a future bus standard (such as a developed VME) will probably include some means of passing messages. Thus far, attempts to introduce a new backplane, such as the 64-bit Futurebus+ (3.2 Gbyte/sec), have failed.

CANADA

♦ **AYK-502**

See U.S. AYK-10.

♦ **UYK-502/UYQ-503/UYQ-504**

UYK-502 is a less militarized version of UYK-505 (see below)

with a fast semiconductor memory in place of the slower core memory, used primarily to drive displays. Memory capacity is 16–256k in 16/64 kword (16-bit words) increments. The machine can accommodate four types of memory: NMOS DRAM (65k modules), core (64k module, can be combined with NMOS DRAM in 192k modules), CMOS SRAM (16k modules), and RAM/PROM (4k/12k combinations, 16k total). Typical operating rate is 240 KOPS. There are up to 64 I/O channels. UYK-502 began as an internal Sperry (Unisys) Canada program for a low-cost processor (LCP) compatible with UYK-20 for noncritical tasks. It was selected by the Canadian government as a primary computer for many Canadian systems, including the SHINPADS CDS.

UYQ-504 is a UYK-502 with a SHINPADS embedded node, so it can be integrated into a SHINPADS system. UYQ-503 combines the SHINPADS nodes and the UYK-502 processor in a single unit. It is a joint project with Unisys (U.S.) and began late in 1988.

♦ **UYK-505**

UYK-505 is a Canadian Unisys-manufactured version of the U.S. UYK-20A, which has memory expanded over that of UYK-20 (160 kwords, expandable to 256k). It is the main computer of the SHINPADS CDS of the Canadian "City"-class and "Tribal Update" (TRUMP) frigates and is the basis of the ADLIPS 90 CDS. The UYK-20A design dates from about 1980 and was roughly simultaneous with that of UYK-502 (above).

♦ **UYK-507/UYQ-505**

> **Word Length:** 32 bits
> **Memory Capacity:** Up to 4 Gwords (see below)
> **Speed:** 5 MIPS
> **Instructions:** 516
> **I/O Capacity:** 16 modules

UYK-507, introduced in 1990, is intended to supersede the UYK-502/505 series in such naval systems as SHINPADS. It uses some UYK-44 technology but is a separate development. Existing UYK-502/UYQ-504 computers will be upgraded since their cabinets can accommodate the new cards. UYK-505s will be replaced since their UYK-20 cabinets are not compatible. A UYK-507 can emulate a UYK-44 or -502. It is a hybrid, combining new electronics with an old existing cabinet. Consequently, it is much less expensive than a new UYK-44 (but also less rugged, particularly against threats such as EMP and TEMPEST).

Versions: (V)1 is a newly built computer, (V)2 a refurbished UYK-502 or UYQ-504 with fewer slots. As of 1990, the first six "City"-class frigates were to receive (V)2s (they have already had their SHINPADS installed).

UYQ-505 is a SHINPADS node embedded in a UYK-507, analogous to UYQ-504.

The processor can directly address 4 Gbytes of memory. It includes an extended memory reach (EMR) set of registers, to address further memory (up to 16 Gwords) by paging, with 256 groups of 64-page registers for code and 256 groups of 64-page registers for data. The processor uses a 64-kbyte cache memory.

The minimum configuration is 256 kwords of semiconductor RAM plus 2 kwords of bootstrap EEPROM (for start-up). It can be expanded by another 256 kwords of semiconductor RAM or EEPROM, plus 512k–8M words of RAM in 512-kword increments. The much larger number of directly addressable words refers to mass memory. The processor is pipelined. The instruction set is described as ADA-friendly; it includes instructions beyond those in UYK-44, specifically designed for easy compilation of ADA programs.

FRANCE

The standard military programming language is LTR (Pascal derivative: Langue Temps Reel).

♦ **IRIS 35M**

> **Word Length:** 16 bits
> **Memory Capacity:** 16–256k bytes (ferrite cores); increments are 16–64k bytes (each of 3)

Speed: Memory cycle time, 1.6 microsec; add/subtract time, 5.4 microsec; multiply time, 14.1 microsec
Instructions: 58
I/O Channels: 34–36

This was the smallest of the IRIS computer family, made by CII (Compagnie Internationale pour l'Information, now part of the Thomson group); it was proposed for the small-ship version of SENIT about 1969. It was used in the Pluton tactical-nuclear-missile system; in a land-based command system, ATAC; and in the DLT 4 submarine FCS. IRIS 35M is software-compatible with other IRIS-series computers, such as IRIS 55M (described below). IRIS 35M could be equipped with up to six 1-Mbyte magnetic-disk mass memories. Mean time between failure (MTBF) was 4000 hr.

◆ IRIS 55M

Word Length: 16 bits
Memory Capacity: 512 kbytes, in 32-kbyte increments
Speed: Memory cycle time, 1.2 microsec; add/subtract time, 2.5 microsec; multiply time, 5.3–7.7 microsec
Instructions: 80
I/O Channels: 24

IRIS 55M was the first French SENIT computer, all previous versions having used U.S. computers. I/O channels include an NTDS channel (1300 bytes/sec) and a multiplexing channel (which can accommodate eight external connections) with a rate of 400 bytes/sec. There are four independent memory accesses.

◆ 15M/05 (also called 15M05)

Word Length: 16 bits
Memory Capacity: 32 kwords, expandable to 64k (64–128 kbytes)
Speed: Typical instruction time, 1.2–1.8 microsec
Instructions: 98

CIMSA's minicomputer is typically used for signal processing. It is supplied in board as well as chassis form. This is the minicomputer of the Vega III/Tavitac system.

◆ 15M/125 (also called 15M125)

Word Length: 16 bits
Memory Capacity: 128 kwords, expandable to 512k
Instructions: 128

The 15M/125F (floating point) version has a fast arithmetic processor. The 15M/125S version is used for space applications and has a 64k-memory capacity; it has 135 instructions. The 15M/125X version is the main computer of the Atlantique 2 patrol aircraft. Unlike the earlier machines, it uses 32-bit words. Memory capacity is 1 Mbyte (much the same as in the 125), and throughput is 1 MOPS. The first airworthy prototype was delivered in 1986.

The 125 and 125S versions are made in both full- and half-chassis versions; 125X is made only in a full-chassis version. The 15M/125X version is the one used in the new missile destroyer *Cassard*.

◆ CDE

Thomson-CSF's digital real-time ballistic computer is the current standard French navy type and is installed in export Vega II and related systems; it is also used for tactical functions. Capacity is 64k or 128k 16-bit words. CDE is parallel microprogrammed (16 registers of read-only memory), using the instruction set of the 16/32 bit interdata computer family. There is also program memory written in LTR. Program memory is separated from data memory. There are 256 potential inputs (external interrupts) and 7 internal interrupts. CDE has direct memory access capability via interrupts, an integral A-D converter, a modular structure, and self-test features. CDE can incorporate ballistics for 100mm, OTO-Melara 76mm, Bofors 57 and 40mm, Breda-Bofors 40mm, Sea Vulcan 30mm (in the abortive Satan system), and Oerlikon 30mm (for the Castor IIC system). CDE replaced the BCH hybrid computer, which had an analog ballistic section.

◆ MLX 32

The Thomson-CSF standard military computer is built in three versions: civil, ruggedized, and military. It is built around a VME-M bus, using Double Eurocards. Each processor board has its own local bus, which connects the processing unit, local memory, and any specialized processor; the main processor, local memory, and I/O connect to the VME bus. There are two basic versions: MLX-32/20 (68020 processor, 3 MIPS, 512 kbytes local memory, 10 Mbytes accessible via the bus), and MLX-32/30 (68030 processor, 4 MIPS at 25-MHz clock rate). MLX-32/30 is offered only in civil and ruggedized versions until a militarized 68030 chip is available. In each case, a suffix indicates the number of processors, for example, MLX 32/20 has one 68020 processor, MLX 32/22 has two, MLX 32/24 has four. A further suffix indicates real-time (T) or UNIX (X) or UNIX and real-time (XT. two or more processors only). MLX uses two operating systems: UNIX V for batch processing and MOP-MLX for real-time (e.g., in a CDS); the latter can support programs in LTR 3, C, Pascal, or ADA. Processor cards: 68020 with 68881 and 68882 for real-time, 68020 and 68881 for UNIX, 68030 with 68882 for real-time or UNIX. Memory cards: 2 Mbytes SRAM or mixed SRAM/EPROM, 4 Mbytes DRAM. I/O: four multiprotocol ports (synchronous or asynchronous), two HDLC synchronous ports (X25 level 3), Ethernet, SCSI, 32-bit parallel, 1553B.

The version in the *La Fayette* class is built around 68030/68040 processors with one to four CPUs and up to 4 Mbytes per computer; it has two 40-Mbyte hard disks. Note that DCNI chose a U.S. Hewlett-Packard computer for the SENIT 8 system in *Charles de Gaulle*.

MLX is intended to work with the VLX display system.

◆ SENIT 8 COMPUTER

CSEE-Defense's ruggedized computer uses U.S.-supplied Hewlett-Packard RISC processors (50 MHz PA-VME) and is broadly comparable with the U.S. TAC-3. It is five or six times as powerful as the 15M/125 used in SENIT 6. The version offered to Kuwait about 1994 uses a faster processor (99-MHz HP 743-RT). DCNI's statement that the computers and consoles use the same processors suggests that the *de Gaulle* system may now also use the 743 processor (which is already in the Calisto consoles). The computer has a VME backplane carrying a single main processor (PA-VME) connected to a four-port I/O device: one port to mass memory (300 Mbytes fixed, 300 Mbytes removable), one to the external Recital/Ethernet bus (SCSI), one to remote control (RS422), and one to the front panel (RS232). This combination is connected to the backplane. So is a separate I/O communication device (for data links, with two RS232 and two RS422. The backplane also carries three high-data-rate couplers to the Recital network (one net per coupler) and six slots for further function integration (AI, multiprocessor I/O, or memory extension).

◆ CALISTO

CSEE-Defense's console is on board the *Charles de Gaulle* and is presumably offered for other versions of SENIT 8. It is a ruggedized version of Hewlett-Packard's HP-9000 series 700 UNIX (HP-UX) workstations, using Barco RGD 651 19in color displays, packaged and ruggedized by CSEE Defense. There are single- and dual-screen, one- or two-operator versions using 19in Barco color raster screens and paired programmable coded-action keyboards, plus trackballs and joysticks. Typically the left-hand keyboard is for one-touch quick-action commands, the right for inputs of specific system data. Applications run on the Hewlett-Packard 743RT (PA-RISC) 99-MHz RISC processor (capable of 124 MIPS), and there are also dedicated display processors. Memory is 16 + Mbytes, with a 500-Mbyte hard drive. A console can mix synthetic and raw video in real time, displaying up to three live IR, TV, or radar images. In the SENIT 8 system on board the *Charles de Gaulle*, the graphic user interface employs X-Windows, OSF-Motif, and Starbase software packages. These consoles are broadly equivalent to the U.S. UYQ-70.

ISRAEL

The 32-bit Elta EL/S-9000 is the standard naval mainframe computer. It is based on the 68020 CPU. Throughput is 8.4 MOPS.

◆ EL/S-8600 Series

Word Length: 16 bits
Memory Capacity: 64 kbytes, expandable to 2 Mbytes
Speed: Load, 1.34 microsec; add/subtract, 0.66 microsec; multiply, 6.56 microsec; divide, 9.26 microsec
Instructions: 90

These are standard Elbit 16-bit computers for air, land, and sea applications. Data apply to EL/S-8610, which has 15 modules. Another member of the family, EL/S-8611, has only 4.

ITALY

◆ CDG-3032 (CP-7010)

Word Length: 32 bits
Memory Capacity: 128 kwords (four memory modules)
Speed: Memory cycle, 0.7 microsec; half-word memory cycle, 0.15 microsec
Instructions: 112
I/O: Four modules, 250 kwords/sec/channel

This Selenia machine is the main computer of the IPN series. It was introduced about 1973. Memory is semiconductor (MOS), and operation can be in full- or half-words (16 and 8 bits). The memory can be addressed simultaneously by the main processor and by the I/O channels.

◆ MARA Series

Word Length: 16 bits
Memory Capacity: Up to 16 Mbytes
Speed: 0.8 MIPS

The Alenia Modular Architecture for Real-Time Applications computer is the basis of the new Italian combat systems: IPN-S, NA-25 and -28, the MAGICS consoles (which are also used in FAAMS). It is a tightly coupled multiprocessor computer with a configurable backplane; it separates software into cooperating but protected functions. MARA is based on 80x86 series microprocessors. It is built of Standard Double Eurocards, and uses a VME bus. The main current naval version is MARA 286, that is, MARA using an 80286 microprocessor. Data apply to the version using a single such processor; there are also MARAs with two or three, with maximum memory capacities of 24 and 32 Mbytes and with throughputs of 1.6 and 2.4 MIPS.

MARA can be fitted with circuit boards for a RISC processor (MRU, microprogrammable RISC unit), for either a multiprocessor (MUL) or a monoprocessor (MON, 0.5 Mbytes of RAM), a fixed-program processor (MAU, micro-programmed arithmetic unit), a bubble memory (BSU1, 0.5 Mbytes), a nodal RAM memory (NDR), EPROM (ERM, 64 kbytes of EPROM plus RAM plus battery), ERB (768 kbytes), and ECM memory extension (2 Mbytes of RAM). Other boards can connect it to either an Ethernet or a Selenia MHIDAS bus.

The airborne version of this machine is SL/AYK-204/1; 204/2 and /3 are the multiprocessor versions. SL/AYK-203 is a slower version (0.3 MIPS), using an 8086 processor, with a maximum memory capacity of 1 Mbyte.

Note that as of 1992 Alenia announced that the next-generation Italian naval CDS would abandon MARA in favor of a more open architecture. It is not clear to what extent this decision affects other Alenia systems.

◆ NDC-160/E

Word Length: 16 bits
Memory Capacity: 64 kwords (core or semiconductor)

NDC-160/E is the standard minicomputer of the Italian SADOC and related systems; it is being superseded by the MARA series described above. There are two operating systems, a Disk Operating System and a Time-Sharing Executive. NDC-160/E has a synchronous architecture for both the processor and the I/O-bus, choice of multilayer boards for high noise immunity, timeout and error interrupt features, a maximum of 256 indirect instruction levels, special instructions for analysis after an error, and restart instructions that permit the writing of resident application software.

◆ Elsag Computers

The Dardo FCS employs an 18-bit computer, probably designated ESA-18. It adds in 2.4 microsec, multiplies in 8.7, and divides in 10.5. Capacity is 20 kwords, there are 82 instructions, and programming is in Assembly language. Dardo-E, NA-18, and NA-30 employ the later 24-bit ESA-24, with a 250-microsec memory access time and 21 I/O channels. Presumably both machines were conceived as alternatives to the standard Italian navy computers described above.

NETHERLANDS

JOVIAL is the high-level language for the SEWACO systems.

◆ SMR

Word Length: 24 bits
Memory Capacity: 8 kwords (0.5-mm ferrite cores); maximum 64k
Speed: Load or store word, 2 microsec; memory cycle time, 1 microsec; add/subtract time, 2 microsec; multiply time, 12 microsec; divide time, 22 microsec
Instructions: 60
I/O: Autonomous control; maximum transfer rate, 168 kwords/sec

SMR is the main computer of Signaal SEWACO/DAISY systems. The first unit was delivered in 1970 to a program generation center. The SEWACO I unit, for the *Tromp* class, was first delivered in 1973; it is the 64k version. The 32k version was delivered to Canada in 1970 for ASWDS (together with two 24k units, presumably for training). The Belgian frigates' SEWACO IV system (1974) uses the 64k version.

SMR (and the later Signaal computers) uses bit-slice arithmetic, in which the 24-bit word is broken down into six 4-bit subwords that are processed in parallel.

In 1971 Signaal estimated MTBF as 4000+ hrs. In a typical 24k configuration, SMR weighs 310 kg; dimensions are 53.5 cm (width) × 62 cm (depth) × 169.7 cm (height). SMR means Signaal Micromin Reckoner (computer).

◆ SMR-4

Word Length: 24 bits
Memory Capacity: 1 Mword internal, 1 Mword external
Speed: Memory cycle time, 0.416 microsec; effective cycle time with pipelining and interleaving, 0.250 microsec (can be as little as 0.166 microsec)
Instructions: 273
I/O: Up to 256 peripheral devices; maximum rate 230 kwords/sec; up to 1 Mword/sec with DMA

SMR-4 was the last Signaal mainframe computer, the basis of the current versions of the SEWACO or STACOS combat-direction systems, for example, in the Turkish MEKO frigates. It is a development of SMR-MU; the -4 indicates fourth generation in the Signaal series (SMR/SMR-S, SMR-S1, SMR-MU, SMR-4).

The main processor is designed for multiprocessing (timesharing). There are 16 levels of process priorities, and for each level there is a 256-entry register. Each process (each time-shared program) is defined by hardware context (the contents of 11 process registers), software context (e.g., two process stacks), and the setting of the memory-management unit (MMU). The contexts and the MMU settings are saved when the processor switches to the next process. SMR-4 incorporates memory pipelining to reduce the waiting time involved in reading memory during the shifts from process to process. Memory is organized into 16 logical pages/process, each of 4k, 16k, 18k, 32k, or 64k words.

The memory bus, which connects the central processor to the main memory, can also be connected directly to an Ethernet LAN (in a CDS) and to direct memory access (DMA) controllers; external devices can also be coupled directly to the memory bus. There is a separate input/output processor that transfers data to and from the main memory without direct reference to the main processor. Memory access by the application software is controlled by the MMU, which also prevents illegal access to specified parts of the memory (e.g., to provide special protection to specially classified data).

Signaal estimates the MTBF as 2653 hr; MTTR is 5 min, using line-replaceable units. Weight is about 23 kg; dimensions are 176 mm (width) × 536 mm (height) × 672 mm (depth). SMR-4 was announced in 1987.

◆ SMR-MU

Word Length: 24 bits
Memory Capacity: 16–64 kwords
Speed: Memory load time, 2.25 microsec (12 microsec for double precision); add/subtract time, 2.25 microsec (16.125 and 16.875 microsec in double precision); multiply time, 11.25 microsec (19.875 microsec in double precision); divide time, 10.875 microsec (19.5 microsec in double precision)
Instructions: 146
I/O: Up to 62 devices can be connected; maximum I/O rate 120,000 words/sec; maximum DMA rate 400,000 words/sec

Announced in 1978, SMR-MU is a minicomputer superseding SMR-S and is upwardly compatible with the earlier machine (i.e., it can run programs written for SMR-S, but SMR-S cannot run some SMR-MU programs). DMA is optional; it allows a high-data-rate device to be connected directly to the memory. The higher-memory version can have 48 kwords in either 16k modules of read/write memory or in 4-kword modules of PROM (permanently programmed read-only memory). An earlier version had a basic 4-kword configuration, expandable to 64k, with the 60k in 4k read/write memory modules or else in 4k PROM modules. This version was credited with 151 instructions. In the latest version (1984) the basic configuration is 64 kwords, and the maximum is 2 Mwords, addressable in 8k pages. In 1979 Signaal estimated MTBF as 21,000 hr for the 16k version.

◆ SMR-S

Word Length: 24 bits
Memory Capacity: 4k, expandable to 64k in 4k modules (RAM or ROM)
Speed: Load or store word, 4 microsec; add full word, 4 microsec; multiply, 16 microsec; divide, 28 microsec; sin/cos (optional), 8 microsec
Instructions: 56
I/O: Six channels (up to 64 peripheral devices); data transfer rate 100 kwords/sec

SMR-S is a minicomputer derived from the SMR, using the same word structure, the same instruction set, and the same flexible I/O system. The memory is solid-state MOS (Intel 1k chips) rather than ferrite cores. SMR-S was introduced in 1973. At that time Signaal estimated MTBF as 13,000 hr. SMR-S weighs 20 kg, and its power supply adds another 20 kg.

◆ SMR-S1

Word Length: 24 bits
Memory Capacity: 4 kwords, extendable to 64k in 4k modules
Speed: Load or store, 2.7 microsec; add, 2.7 microsec; multiply, 10.7 microsec; divide, 18.7 microsec; trigonometrical functions, 8.0 microsec (optional)
Instructions: 56
I/O: Autonomous I/O control; maximum transfer rate, 150 kwords/sec; HSDC rate, 700 kwords/sec

Introduced in 1975, SMR-S1 is a faster replacement for SMR-S. An optional high-speed data channel (HSDC) allows direct connection of a device with a high data rate to the memory. Memory is solid-state. Signaal estimated MTBF at 13,000 hr. The mainframe, including 32 kwords of memory and 6 I/O channels, weighs 20 kg. Dimensions are 170 mm (width) × 600 mm (depth) × 540 mm (height), matching those of the earlier SMR-S.

NORWAY

The current standard high-level language is Mary.

◆ KS500

Word Length: 16 bits
Memory Capacity: 64 kwords, expandable in modules of up to 32 kwords each
Speed: 164 KIPS (Wheatstone test)
Instructions: 130

KS500 is the standard computer of Kongsberg command/control systems (such as NAVKIS and MSI-3100); it is being superseded by KS900. Because it is used to integrate a very wide variety of weapons and sensors, many of them designed in the 1950s, it can be connected to an unusually large variety of interface modules. KS500 is also the basis of the early Racal CANE command/control systems, and probably of the first generation of Racal high-capacity ESM systems, such as Cutlass. A Racal-built single-board version of KS500 was used as an interim replacement for the next-generation SADIE processor.

◆ KS900

Word Length: 16 bits
Memory Capacity: Up to 4 Mbytes per board, total of up to 128 Mbytes, plus up to 256 kbytes of EPROM for processor programs
Speed: Clock frequency, 15 MHz; typical memory access time, 0.270 microsec
I/O: See below

KS900 is the main computer of the current NFT command/control systems. It is conceived as a process control computer for use in particularly difficult conditions, for example, in North Sea oil rigs, as well as for military applications. Therefore, application programs are described as processes rather than in more conventional language. The first user was the MSI-90U submarine command/control system.

The main processor is a Motorola 68020, with a 68881 math coprocessor. The computer uses separate microprocessors to control its I/O functions, and its operating system kernel combines the power of the central processor and the subprocessors. KS900 is built around a 32-bit bus with a secondary 180-kbaud serial bus for built-in testing. The bus (backplane) carries a processor card (characteristics above), a Budos interface to the external system bus, a console interface, a mass memory module, an interface to instruments, a serial interface, a graphics interface, and an interface to the built-in test equipment. Each I/O board has its own local microcomputer (68000-series) for local control. Because the modules are all united by a bus, individual microprocessors controlling input/output can load their own programs directly from the mass memory, without intervention by the main processor. Module functions are largely controlled by EPROM software. All of the modules are in extended euroboard module format, 233.4 × 220 mm.

The memory listed above is accessed as local memory by the main processor and as system global memory (via the bus) by the I/O boards. This type of direct access is not too different from the access that allows modular operation in the Hughes Modular Combat System; see the description of that system.

KS900 can accommodate up to 63 user processes and one system process, expandable to 255 user processes with additional memory. Each process memory consists of up to 16 segments, each of up to 512 kbytes.

Although the system as a whole has a bus width of 32 bits, the processor operates on a normal word of 16-bit length, counting 32 bits as a long or double word.

Mass memory is up to 28 Mbytes of magnetic bubble memory, in 512-kbyte capsules (eight to a board). Data transfer rates are 100 kbytes/sec (average) or 400 kbytes/sec (maximum), and data are stored as pages of 128, 256, or 512 kbytes.

◆ SM-3/Mk 157

Word Length: 16 bits
Memory Capacity: 64 kwords
Speed: Memory cycle time, 0.8 microsec
Instructions: 32

Kongsberg computer, used in the Penguin system and then in the NATO Sea Sparrow; the U.S. designation is Mk 157. It has NTDS-compatible I/O channels and a teletype for on-line data entry (printed at 10 characters/sec). Mod 0 had 16k memory, and paper-tape input (300 char/sec). Mod 1 (1981) had a 24k memory and a magnetic tape reader (1200 char/sec). In Mod 2, memory was increased from 24 k to 32 k. In Mod 3, ferrite cores were replaced by CMOS chips, and memory capacity was doubled (to 64 kwords, i.e., to 128 kbytes). Processing efficiency increased at least 25%. This computer is used in FCS Mk 91 Mods 2 and 3 for the RIM-7M missile.

SWEDEN

As of 1988, ADA was the standard language of all future defense projects.

◆ Censor 908

Word Length: 4 bytes (32 bits)
Memory Capacity: 16 kbytes (ferrite cores), expandable in 16k increments to 128k
Speed: Memory cycle time, 1.0 microsec

Censor 908 is a Standard Radio & Telefon (now Ericsson) minicomputer, part of the Censor 900 series (ca. 1971). It was designed to operate either as a central computer or as a satellite to a Censor 932; the main memory can be accessed independently by the main computer. Up to four 908s can be connected to one 932. In such a system, a common main memory can serve both the 908s and the 932 master.

◆ Censor 932

Word Length: 4 bytes (32 bits)
Memory Capacity: 4–128 kwords (16–512 kbytes), in 4-kbyte increments up to 128k
Speed: Memory cycle time, 1.0 microsec (also given as 750 nanosec); average execution time is 2.5 microsec; clock speed is 1.3 MHz
Instructions: 80

Censor 932 is a Standard Radio (now Ericsson) main computer, originally designed for use in air-defense centers, and then used in shipboard command/control systems. Its architecture allows for 64 priority interrupts, compared to 32 in the Censor 908 minicomputer. Memory can be supplemented by up to 2 Mwords of ferrite core mass storage.

◆ Censor 932E

Word Length: 32 bits
Memory Capacity: 512 kwords
Speed: Memory cycle time, 0.525 microsec; add word, 2.4 microsec; multiply/divide time, 16 microsec

Censor 932E is the current standard Swedish navy tactical computer, in the Maril CDS. Operations can be conducted with half- or double-length words. Typical dimensions are 500 mm (height) × 530 mm (width) × 230 mm (depth); weight is 35 kg.

◆ D80

Ericsson's 32-bit unit is the mission computer of the JA39 Gripen and of the Sea Harrier FA. 2. Typical speed is 1 MIPS (instruction execution time is 125 microsec or more). The prototype was delivered in 1987.

◆ P800

Word Length: 32 bits
Memory Capacity: 64–256 kwords
Speed: Memory cycle time 0.5 microsec, memory access time 0.3 microsec, typical execution speed, 0.5–2 microsec

The Philips P800 is the standard distributed minicomputer of the 9LV Mk 2 system. It is sometimes described as a 16-bit computer. In the 9LV Mk 3 system, it is replaced by a single-board CPU using a 68020 microprocessor, with up to 4 Mbytes of onboard memory (and 256 kbytes of EPROM-carrying programs).

TAIWAN

ACER makes several IBM clones that are used in naval systems. RAT II (ruggedized AT, using an IBM AT internal bus, with 20 slots and a 486 processor) is the basis for the Link T terminal. Current plans are to replace the old UYK-19 computers of the Wu-Jinn III destroyers with RAT IIs, at least for fire control.

There is also a ruggedized graphics workstation (RGW 1000A), using a 486-33 processor. It is used in the Tien Kung AA missile system.

Development of a wholly Taiwanese CDS has been hampered by the lack of a real-time operating system. However, ACER claims that the problem can be solved by using multiple 486 chips in parallel, achieving near real-time performance. ACER already has a design for a multi-486 LAN server (currently with two processors).

UNITED KINGDOM

The standard high-level language is Coral 66, structured similarly to Algol, with some features taken from JOVIAL and Fortran. Coral 66 is now being superseded by ADA (which became mandatory in British defense projects on 1 July 1987). Fixpac is the assembly language of the Ferranti FM 1600 series computers.

The current standard minicomputer is the Argus F700, and the standard microcomputer of the 1980s was the F100.

◆ Argus M700

Word Length: 16 bits
Memory Capacity: Up to 256 kwords
Speed: 250 KIPS (M700/40: 1.6 MIPS)
Instructions: Over 120

These Ferranti minicomputers are typically used in combination with FM 1600-series main computers. In the basic version, 64 kwords are directly accessible, and total memory (including bus memory) is 256 kwords. M700/20 incorporates a memory-management card and can access all 256 kwords directly. M700/40 is an LSI version, with a 4k cache memory. M700/42 incorporates up to 256 hardware-implemented subroutines, such as conversion between fixed- and floating-point formats, square root, and trigonometric functions.

Argus 700 supersedes the earlier Argus 400, introduced in 1966, with 4–12 kwords of memory in ferrite core. Word length is 24 bits, as in the larger Ferranti computers; there are 38 instructions. Speed: Add/subtract, 12 microsec; multiply, 18–162 microsec; divide, 162 microsec.

◆ F100-L/F200-L

Word Length: 16 bits
Memory Capacity: 32 kwords (see below)
Speed: Clock rate, 8.5 MHz (13.5 MHz in commercial version); multiply time, 9–13.5 microsec; divide time, 12–16.2 microsec
Instruction Set: 153

F100-L is a standard Ferranti microprocessor, developed for the British MoD. It can address up to 32 kwords. The microprocessor, clock-generator, multiply/divide unit, and two bus buffers are available as a single hybrid chip (FBH 5092).

F200-L is a faster (300 KIPS) improved version, which can address 64k–1M words, and which has on-chip multiply/divide.

◆ FM 1600B

Word Length: 24 bits
Memory Capacity: 4 kwords, expandable to 64k in 4k increments
Speed: Memory cycle time, 1 microsec; add/subtract time, 2.7–4.3 microsec (fixed point), 6.3–7.0 microsec (floating point); multiply time, 11.3–13.3 microsec (fixed point), 14.0 microsec (floating point); divide time, 13.0–16.0 microsec; clock rate, 3 MHz
I/O Channels: 20 (maximum)

Dimensions are 19 × 16 × 7 in. FM1600B was used in CAAIS tactical data systems as well as in submarine tactical systems; some were exported for use by the Royal Netherlands Navy. The original version used 1-microsec memory, but in 1969 a 600-nanosec (0.6-microsec) memory was introduced. Modules for automatic radar-data extraction and for analog-to-digital conversion for synchros were designed for FM 1600B.

◆ FM 1600D

Word Length: 24 bits
Memory Capacity: 4 kwords, expandable to 64k in 4k or 8k increments
Speed: Memory access time, 1 microsec; add/subtract time, 4.7–14.0 microsec; multiply time, 0.9–137.0 microsec; divide time, 68.0–98.0 microsec; typical throughput, 350 KIPS
Instructions: 325
I/O Channels: Up to 16

This version of FM 1600 appeared about 1972. Its 8-bit processor handles its 24-bit words in slices. It is also capable of double-precision arithmetic. Capacity is at least equivalent to that of FM 1600B but 1600D is less expensive. FM 1600D is a standard airborne computer, in the Searchwater radar processors of the Nimrod and the Sea King early-warning helicopter. It is also used in some ESM systems.

◆ FM 1600E

Word Length: 24 bits
Memory Capacity: 32–256 kwords
Speed: Clock rate, 12 MHz; floating point divide, 9.6 microsec (from main store); conditional jump, 2.1 microsec; read or write to memory, 0.75 microsec (read-modify-write, 1.05 microsec); processing speed 650 KIPS
I/O Channels: 28 (four high priority)

Introduced about 1977, FM 1600E is a larger equivalent to FM 1600D; both embody medium-scale integration technology. The FM 1600 series instruction set is expanded to include double-length floating point operations and block transfers. Both computers are small enough to be integrated into the display consoles themselves, so that there is no need for a separate computer room. FM 1600E uses a cache (kernel) plus main storage, and there is provision for program protection through memory partitioning. Of the input/output channels, the four high-priority ones have their own buffers and can transfer a word in 6.5 microsec. The other 24 channels are multiplexed in two groups; transfer rate is one word in 9.0 microsec. The semiconductor memory (DRAM) is in modules of up to 128 kwords each. FM1600Es used in CACS may have been upgraded to a 1.2-Mword memory capacity.

◆ F2420

Word Length: 24 bits
Memory Capacity: 3 Mbytes (1 Mword)
Speed: 3.8 MIPS

F2420, originally named FM 1600F, is the successor to the FM 1600 series, with four times the computing speed and much more memory. The 3-Mbyte memory can be extended to 24 Mbytes using external addressing. As in the U.S. UYK-20/44, the faster and more powerful machine can run programs originally written for the smaller and slower one. F2420 is used in the enhanced version of the Ferranti CAAIS/WSA 400 series, and it replaces FM 1600s in the CACS tactical data system. F2420 is sometimes described as enjoying six times the computing power of its predecessors.

◆ GEC-Marconi 920ATC

Word Length: 18 bits
Memory Capacity: 64 kwords, plus up to 192 kwords externally (ferrite cores)
Speed: Internal memory access time, 0.42 microsec; cycle time, 1.0 microsec
I/O: Up to 16 peripherals, including magnetic tape and bootstrap loader; nominal data-transfer rate, 1 MHz (64 and 500 kHz rates are also available)

This is the central tactical computer of the Nimrod MR.2 and the computer of the MR.2's AQS-901 acoustic system. The computer is housed in a single ATR Short case; maximum weight is 37 lb.

◆ RDP

Thorn-EMI's Ruggedized Data Processor was chosen for RN Outfits LFC (radar track combiner) and RTC (link processor for ADIMP). It incorporates a 21-slot VME bus frame with dual backplanes. Overall dimensions 700 mm (width) × 690 mm (depth) × 520 mm (height) (less than 55 kg). As applied to LFC, the chassis carries a communications processor, a track update processor, and a track correlation processor.

◆ Transputer (T400/T800)

Inmos's Transputer is a single-chip 32-bit processor specially designed for parallel computing using the Occam language; it can communicate both with the unusual I/O channels and also with other Transputer chips. T800 has four standard Inmos links (to other chips). Cycle time is 57 nsec, peak instruction rate is 17 MIPS, 2.5 MFLOPS; it includes 4 kbytes of on-chip RAM (*not* a cache) for high-speed processing, and a configurable memory interface. The chip includes a 64-bit floating-point unit. In a typical application, T800 is credited with a speed of 1.75 MFLOPS, or 12 MIPS of scalar (single-number) processing power. T800M

is the military version. Reportedly, a single Inmos T800-20 has about five times the performance of a 68020 combined with a 68881 floating-point processor. There is also a T400 rated at about a third of the peak power of T800. Transputers are used in the new British surface-ship and submarine command systems (SSCS and SMCS).

T800 was eventually outperformed by RISC CPUs. In 1994 Inmos announced a new T-9000 based on T800 but designed to regain the advantage. Clock speed is up to 50 MHz. The chip contains four main units: the CPU, the VCP (to communicate with other chips; previous Transputers used software in this role), the memory manager (PMI), and a scheduler. The main cache (16 kbytes) allows three reads and one write simultaneously, presumably corresponding to the four connections to other T-9000s. A separate workspace cache consists of 32-word rotating buffers (two reads and one write simultaneously). The chip incorporates a five-stage pipeline.

UNITED STATES

The current standard large computers are UYK-7 and its successor, UYK-43; the corresponding minicomputers are UYK-20 and the successor UYK-44. In a few cases, UYK-19 is used instead of UYK-20. The standard airborne computer is AYK-14. AAYK-14 (advanced AYK-14) is a much faster successor. Some special output channels are NTDS slow (41,667 words/sec), NTDS fast (125 kwords/sec), and A-NEW (125 kwords/sec); the last refers to the A-NEW ASW system introduced in the P-3C airplane. AYK-14 has an additional high-capacity digital channel, Proteus (10 Mbit/sec), for communication with a separate on-board acoustic-signal processor.

The minicomputers are available as SEM (standard electronic module) boards, suitable for embedding in other devices.

The current standard naval programming language is CMS-2 (second-generation Compiler Monitor System programming language, adopted in the mid-1960s). This language exists in several versions (dialects), -2M, -2Q, and -2Y. ADA is used in recent systems. There is also a special signal-processing language, SPL/1, which is also suitable for graphics display processing. Like ADA, SPL/1 is related to the Pascal civilian language.

Standard Mil-Spec computers are increasingly being supplemented by very powerful ruggedized commercial machines (DTC, now TAC, series) for semitactical applications such as JOTS and FDDS. These machines have been programmed in the C and UNIX commercial languages, although ADA is now taking over. Senior officers' skepticism has reportedly been overcome by demonstrations that different C compilers do not often produce exactly the same code from a high-level program, whereas ADA provides reproducible (if cumbersome) results.

There is increasing interest in flat liquid crystal displays (LCDs) using ruggedized commercial technology. For example, in 1995 Lockheed Martin (Sanders) displayed IP-1553X, a dual-screen (side-by-side) Aegis display employing color active matrix LCD technology to provide a 10 × 8in viewing area (1280 × 1024 pixels), with 16 million colors and 256 shades of gray. A major selling point was that the display was unaffected by magnetic fields (a conventional color display can have its colors interchanged in a stray magnetic field, a common problem in CICs).

◆ ASQ-114

See CP-901/ASQ-114, below.

◆ ASQ-212

See CP-901A/CP-2044/ASQ-212, below.

◆ AYK-10 (Univac 1832)/AYK-502

Word Length: 32 bits
Memory Capacity: 64 kwords (expandable to 96k)
Speed: Memory cycle, 0.75 microsec
Instruction Set: 133
I/O Channels: 18

The Sperry (Unisys, now Loral) AYK-10 is the central tactical computer of the S-3A, analogous to the ASQ-114 of the P-3C; as

AYK-502 it is the central tactical computer of the Canadian CP-140. It was first delivered in 1971. There are two independent central processors, two I/O controllers, and two I/O interfaces, all of them cross connected. Both processors have access to the entire memory, which is in 32k units (normally two, with a growth option to three). Each 32k unit contains two 16k memory banks. There is also a magnetic drum mass memory, separated into two halves (one fed by each I/O interface). Each I/O interface has six Type I channels, four Type II, one Type III, and one spare. Type I channels are multiplexed (up to seven devices/channel). Devices include the sensor operator inputs, the FLIR, ESM data, and navigational data. Type II channels communicate with the tactical display system (four/interface, or eight/computer). Type III channels communicate with the mass (drum) memory. One of the Type I channels is reserved for growth; the spare is presumably also a Type I channel. Another Type I channel is reserved for test purposes. The 18 channels listed above presumably omit these and the drum memory channels.

The drum memory functions both as auxiliary storage for the computer and as the memory of the S-3A's OL-82 acoustic-data processor. It stores most of the operational subprograms used by the AYK-10. The computer runs 21 concurrent programs, as well as four displays; it uses a 1553B data bus.

Total weight is 410 lb, with a power consumption of 2.3 kW.

An AYK-10A version was developed for the S-3B, which uses the UYS-1 acoustic processor in place of the earlier OL-82 integrated with the AYK-10 in the S-3A.

♦ AYK-14/AAYK-14

Word Length: 16 bits (can operate on 4-, 8-, 16-, 32-bit data)
Memory Capacity: 4 Mwords in 32-kword (semiconductor) or 64-kword (core) modules
Speed: Typically, 300 KIPS–2.3 MIPS; add/subtract time, 0.6 microsec; multiply time, 1.9 microsec; divide time, 3.9 microsec; clock rate, 1 MHz
Instructions: 307
I/O: Up to 16 modules (see below)

Data apply to the product-improved AYK-14. The original AYK-14 is the current standard aircraft computer (in the AV-8B, F/A-18, and SH-60B); about 5000 are in the Fleet. It was the first truly standardized U.S. Navy airborne computer, all previous machines having been purchased as part of a total aircraft systems package. Development began in 1976, initially for the F/A-18 and LAMPS programs; the new computer uses a superset of the UYK-20 set, so it can emulate the earlier machine. Versions are used in weapons such as the Mk 50 torpedo. Control Data was the original manufacturer (AYK-14 was developed from that company's 480 microcomputer). It entered series production in 1980. Reliability has improved from an MTBF of about 200 hr in 1981 to above 1500 in 1989, and cost has fallen about 8.2%/yr, from $185,000 in 1981 to $80,000 in 1989. Unisys is now the second-source producer.

A standard AYK-14 can accommodate up to 16 I/O modules, up to five of them smart modules incorporating their own on-board controllers, to execute chain programs and initiate data transfers using DMA. The other (standard) modules require the central processor to intervene to move data in and out. An AYK-14 expansion chassis can provide additional I/O bus ports. The computer uses two memory buses, even (EMEMBUS) and odd (OMEMBUS), for efficient overlapping memory access; they are controlled by a memory-control module interface.

The AYK-14 was designed to be functionally and physically partitioned into replaceable modules so that it could be upgraded. In 1987 Control Data received a contract for a preplanned product-improved (P³I) version, and deliveries began that year. In this version three of the cardlike processor modules are replaced by a single module with twice the processing power and 8 times the memory (using 0.5M- and 4M-memory modules). The single-card processor incorporates both a 16-bit central processor and a 32-bit math coprocessor, the EAU (extended arithmetic unit). There is also a cache memory, and the card has an extended instruction set. This version is used in the F-14D, V-22, Mk 50 torpedo, and new-production F/A-18 and SH-60B aircraft.

Control Data has also been developing a VHSIC processor module (VPM) for the AYK-14 since 1986. This plug-in module quadruples the processing power of the P³I version and also substantially increases memory. It incorporates a 64k cache memory. Reliability should also be greatly improved; expected MTBF is about 9000 hr. Speed of the modified computer is up to 18 MIPS. Other required improvements are (a) a 50-MHz serial high-speed data bus (HSDB) to overcome F/A-18 I/O deficiencies, and for future computer standards; (b) an interactive voice I/O module for the AV-8B (to control the mission computer, radios, and weapon system); (c) an embedded video processor module to reduce aircraft weight (by 43 lb) and reduce video latency (up to 10 sec) when switching between display formats; and (d) a 32-bit AYK-14(V) configuration with an embedded coprocessor. There is also an embedded GPS module.

The first experimental VPM was delivered in September 1989, and production deliveries began in 1991. Ultimately, VPM will be inserted in most fleet P³I AYK-14s.

CDC's follow-on is the Advanced AYK-14 (AAYK-14). Its core processor set has been selected as the integrated mission processor (IMP) for the LAMPS III Block II upgrade, and it may be incorporated in the F/A-18E/F. The Navy sees AAYK-14 partly as a bridge to a future open-architecture system more amenable to technology insertion. AAYK-14 employs a commercially based RISC processor module (RPM) using a MIPS R4400SC multichip module working at 100 MHz. RPM operates at up to 45 MIPS (60 SpecMARKS) and the module carries 32 Mbytes of DRAM and 4 Mbytes of EEPROM memory. It can connect to either a planned 32-bit Futurebus+ backplane or to the existing 16-bit M-prime bus of the original AYK-14, for interoperability with the earlier VPM. Predicted MTBF is 14,700 hr. RPM supports communications between existing AYK-14 16-bit programs (written in CMS-2) and AAYK-14 32-bit ADA modules. Total weight is 2.1 lb.

As of the spring of 1996, a laboratory version of AAYK-14 was running both at the manufacturer, CDI, and at a Loral laboratory. Low-rate initial production was expected in mid-1998.

Meanwhile, CDI has developed an alternative replacement for AYK-14, a single-board AOSP (advanced open-source processor) carrying a PowerPC 603E CPU and the required I/O devices. It made a test flight on board a TAV-8B Harrier owned by McDonnell-Douglas on 29 March 1996, and was expected to fly on board an F/A-18 late in April or early in May 1996. It has also flown as an AYK-14 replacement on board a Harrier GR.7. In this case the card carries a 1553B interface as well as an Ethernet interface for fast loading on the flight line; it has 64 Mbytes of flash memory on board.

The card can replace the AYK-14 altogether, or it can be mounted inside an existing AYK-14 (as in the F/A-18), acting as a coprocessor, and thus preserving the existing system architecture and much of the existing code.

♦ CP-642B/USQ-20

Word Length: 30 bits (can operate in 15-bit half words)
Memory Capacity: 32 kwords (ferrite cores)
Speed: Memory cycle time, 4 microsec; typical execution time, 8–12 microsec; time to add and store (fixed point), 24 microsec; time to multiply and store (fixed point), 56–72 microsec; time to divide and store (fixed point), 80 microsec
Instructions: 62
I/O Channels: 4, 8, 12, or 16 rapid channels; can have NTDS interface

CP-642, which entered service in 1961, was the central computer used in the original NTDS installations. The initial version, CP-642A, had a memory cycle time of 8 microsec, and a typical instruction-execution time was 13 microsec. There were 12 input and 12 output channels for external equipment, plus two input and two output channels for intercomputer communication. In addition to the main memory, there was an auxiliary 16-word memory to store critical instructions and constants for automatic recovery in the event of program failure (crash). CP-642B (1962) introduced a control memory (32-word read-only magnetic thin film with a faster cycle time, 2 or 3 microsec), and a -3-volt I/O interface. These features increased data transfer rates to 125 kwords/sec/channel.

Dimensions are 72 in (height) × 38 in (width) × 37 in (depth) (2400 lb).

USQ-20, the computer system of the early version of NTDS, combined CP-642 with a separate control console (C-3413) and mass storage in the form of tape drives. System software, the Dynamic Module Replacement (DMR) program, allows the system operator to insert or delete particular program modules into the running operational program. For example, an ECM module can be inserted when needed, then deleted to leave more memory space, without stopping the system. USQ-20 is a modular system in which individual CP-642s can be run in parallel for increased total processing power.

Groups of CP-642As and -642Bs were eventually fitted with CDC's enhanced memory core unit (EMCU: MU-602), typically with a capacity of 262,144 words (each 32 bits long), so a typical combination of three CP-642 and an EMCU has a capacity of 360,160 30-bit words. Each unit has four-port access (to accommodate up to four CP-642s) on a first-come, first-served basis. Access time is 0.75 microsec (cycle time is 1.05 microsec). The added memory suffices to accommodate the entire NTDS program, so the capability to add or delete modules while running (dynamic system reconfiguration) becomes unnecessary. The EMCU was probably first ordered in 1974.

Users: CP-642B: France (*Suffren, Clemenceau* classes), Italy (*Vittorio Veneto*), Japan (destroyers), United States (unmodernized carriers, *Mount Whitney* class).

◆ Mk 152 and CP-848/UYK (Univac 1219B)

Word Length: 18 bits
Memory Capacity: 8, 16, 32, or 64 kwords
Speed: 1.8 microsec typical execution time; clock rate, 1024 Hz
I/O: 4, 8, 12, or 16 channels

CP-848 is a second-generation 18-bit computer. I/O modes are (Univac) 1218 normal, 1218 NTDS, and 1219B. This computer was an early application of preassembled circuit boards, what might be called very-small-scale integration (the individual devices are quite visible).

Mk 152 was the U.S. naval ordnance designation for this machine; it was the first U.S. standardized digital fire-control computer. In this form it has 16 I/O channels plus a slow interface; memory capacity is 32 kwords, plus a separate 256-word control memory. Mod 1 (1966) had eight I/O channels (1070 lb). Mod 2 (1400 lb, 1968) was similar to Mod 0 but had eight fast and eight slow I/O channels, with two paper tapes bootstrapped to channel 13, and modified input on channels 11 and 17. Memory access time was 2 microsec. It was part of FCS Mk 86. Mod 5, for digital Tartar (FCS Mk 74 Mod 8, 1100 lb, 1972) had a 48k memory and was otherwise similar to Mod 1. Mod 6, for later versions of the Tartar (Mk 74) system and for shore sites, was a Mod 5 with 16 I/O channels (1460 lb). Mod 7 was a modified Mod 5 with a 64k memory for FCS Mk 74 Mod 8 (1050 lb, 1980). It added four memory stacks and the associated printed cards. In several cases, more capable versions of systems employing Mk 152 computers have UYK-20s instead.

◆ CP-855/UYK (Univac 1230)

Word Length: 30 bits
Memory Capacity: 32 kwords (ferrite cores)
Speed: Memory cycle time, 2.0 microsec; add/subtract time, 2–4 microsec; multiply time, 8 microsec; divide time, 14 microsec; clock rate, 1024 Hz
Instructions: 78
I/O Channels: 16

CP-855 was designed as a successor to the CP-642 series, as a second-generation 30-bit computer. Originally designed for NASA (for the Apollo program), CP-855 was not used in the U.S. NTDS system, but it was used in the French equivalent, SENIT 3 (on board the frigate *Aconit* and the *Georges Leygues* class).

The 32k memory operates as two parallel 16k memories, and there is a separate 128-word control memory (expandable to 256 words). There is also 80 k of mass storage. Two memory banks,

operating in parallel, allow two simultaneous references for I/O, instruction extraction, or operand processing during one cycle. This architecture later appeared in UYK-7 and its successor, UYK-43. Special registers permit expansion of memory to 128 kwords, for use with the Univac 1503 expanded memory unit (EMU) and the hardware floating-point option. Typically, an EMU would be connected to a pair of 1230 computers, providing each with two or three banks of additional memory (16k per bank) and up to four I/O channels.

Compared to CP-642B, CP-855 has a larger instruction set, including 15 logical instructions and a hardware square-root instruction. The control memory includes seven 15-bit (17-bit in expanded mode) index registers (CP-642B had seven 15-bit registers). There is a 64-word ROM plus a 128-word fast (0.4 microsec magnetic thin film) control memory. Dimensions: 72 in (height) × 38 in (width) × 37 in (depth), 2200 lb.

◆ CP-901/ASQ-114 (Univac 1830A)/Univac 1830B

Word Length: 30 bits
Memory Capacity: Up to 64 kwords in 16-kword banks; can address up to 128 kwords; 512-word bootstrap (start-up) memory
Speed: 2-microsec cycle time without overlap; 1-microsec memory cycle with overlap; clock rate, 1024 Hz; typical performance, about 275–300 KOPS
Instructions: 70 basic
I/O: 4, 8, 12, or 16 channels

The Unisys tactical computer for the P-3C has been in service since 1968. It performs a function analogous to that of the central computer in a shipboard NTDS system. CP-901 is not the aircraft sonar-signal processor but maintains the current tactical picture, integrating data from the various sensor stations.

The mass memory media are a magnetic drum and a digital magnetic tape set, the latter to retain data for postmission analysis. ASQ-114 is connected to the aircraft sensors by the GE AYA-8 data-analysis programming group.

CP-901(V)6 is a modernized CP-901 developed in 1988, with an extended memory unit (64k increased to 4 Mwords of CMOS and bubble memory) and 16 I/O channels. I/O address capability is increased from 32 to 128 kwords.

The Unisys designation for CP-901 is Univac 1830A. Univac 1830B (1970) is the main computer of the German AGIS fast-attack boat command/control system. Compared to CP-901, 1830B can accommodate up to eight memory modules (total 128 kwords). It has increased power-supply capability, optional I/O control memory (48 words), and nonbussed output channels. There are 76 basic instructions, and the clock rate is 102.4 kHz. Addresses beyond 32 k are written in page mode.

CP-901 performance is broadly equivalent to that of the Univac 1230 (CP-855) adopted by the French navy. Further development of such 30-bit computers was abandoned when 32 bits became the commercial standard.

◆ CP-901A/CP-2044/ASQ-212

Word Length: 32 bits
Memory Capacity: 1 Mword (see below)
Speed: 10.5 MIPS throughput
Instructions: 68030 set
I/O Channels: 34 (see below)

This entirely new central computer for P-3Cs fits within the same space, weight, and power requirements as the earlier CP-901 (the mission computer system is designated ASQ-212 rather than ASQ-114). 901A uses a dual memory bus like that of other current Unisys naval computers. Instead of a single central processor, it has three Motorola 68030 microprocessors (with card slots for four more). Throughput can be increased to 14 MIPS by using the four additional microprocessors.

Each of the three microprocessors has a local memory of 256 kwords, which can be increased to 1 Mword/processor. The 1 Mword listed above is the global memory available to all three processors. It can be doubled, for a total of 5 Mwords. All of these are volatile memories (CMOS); there is also a 3-Mword bubble memory for fast mass storage. In addition, each microprocessor has 32 kbytes of bootstrap and diagnostic memory (EEPROM);

Unisys has proposed replacement of this memory by 32 kwords (128 kbytes) of UVPROM. The total global memory (1 Mword CMOS and 3 Mwords of bubble mass memory) can be doubled within the cabinet dimensions.

The I/O channels are two 1553B buses (64 users), four ARINC 575 serial channels, 10 synchro-to-digital channels, four digital-to-synchro channels, 10 A-NEW channels (MIL-STD-1397C), and four stroke-display (i.e., cursive video) channels; there are also three manual-entry-system (keyboard) interface cards. Growth options are one video input channel and four color raster display channels.

The equivalent upgrade kit to CP-901 is designated CP-2044. CP-901A and -2044 will use ADA software, but they also have a CMS-2 compiler for compatibility with existing software.

CP-901A incorporates the functions of the AYA-8 logic units and the CV-216 signal data converter, previously separate equipment, in its cabinet. The cabinet is 52 × 13.5 × 17.7 in and weighs about 380 lb; it uses 6 × 9in printed circuit cards.

Users: Korea (new P-3Cs), Netherlands (P-3C CUP upgrade), Norway (P-3C upgrade), United States (P-3C Update III upgrades).

◆ CP-1469 (ASPRO)

This Goodyear (now Loral) Associative Parallel Processor was designed to upgrade the Grumman E-2C. A 1979 demonstration showing that ASPRO was the best solution to the E-2C upgrade led to a fully militarized ASPRO in 1982. Tested at sea on board an attack submarine for OTH-T (targeting) January 1988, it reduced system-level targeting solution execution time by a factor of 10 over the existing system; in June 1989 Loral was awarded a contract for 10 to support OTH-T by nuclear attack submarines.

ASPRO is a single instruction multiple data stream (SIMD) computer: it executes one instruction at a time, but does it in parallel against many different data items; that makes for 100-MOPS speed. A large database can be searched in a few cycles. The computer consists of an execution controller (EC), buffer memory, array control, and an associative array of 4096 1-bit processing elements (PEs) synchronized by the array control. The array control broadcasts instructions to the PEs. The EC carries the program (total EC storage is up to 2 Mbytes of RAM) and uses a RISC processor (MIPS R3000) for operations not suited to parallel execution. It also contains a high-speed cache, 4 Mbytes of main memory, external Ethernet connection, and two RS-232 interfaces.

Each PE contains an arithmetic logic unit (ALU) and local registers for temporary data storage, so it can perform both logical and arithmetic operations on the data. The PEs are connected to array memory by a high-speed data bus (over 1.1 Gbytes/sec). The array memory is up to 4096 words (1 per PE) × 64 kbits (total 32 Mbytes); each word is bit-addressable, for variable-length operands.

Buffer memory (64 kbytes static RAM) is triple ported to allow access by ASPRO as well as by two other devices. Each port can transfer 5 Mbytes/sec (total 10 externally).

For example, in aircraft tracking, each of the 4096 words would be the array of attributes of one aircraft. Thus each aircraft word could be interrogated simultaneously for, e.g., range or speed match with a new radar plot (which would be part of the 64-kbit word). If a match is found, the relevant entry is updated.

In 1991 Loral announced a version of ASPRO suitable for mounting within a larger 6U VME-backplane computer. The upgradable family of parallel processors offers from 150 MFLOPS (with 512 processing elements) to 2.4 GFLOPS (8192 processing elements). The basic processor resides on three boards (one array memory with 512 processing elements, one array control, and one control processor). The control processor is a MIPS R3000. Each custom VLSI processor chip contains 32 processing elements; each element contains a high-speed, word-parallel arithmetic unit and a bit-serial logic unit. The associated scalar processor is a MIPS R3000/R3010 RISC processor. Memory is 128 kbits/processing element (8 Mbytes/array memory board) expandable to 1 Mbit/element. Scalar memory is 2 Mbytes on

the control processor board, expandable to 32 Mbytes. Array memory to processing element sustained transfer rate is 640 Mbps (512 processing elements) to 10.2 Gbytes/sec (8192 processing elements). PEs are interconnected by a "FLIP" network for multidimensional access.

◆ CP-1820 (MECA 43)

Teledyne's tactical computer (of the ASN-150 aircraft tactical system) is used in SH-2G, SH-60, and export ASW helicopters and aircraft. Its arithmetic is arranged for 8-bit slices so that it can work with 16-, 24-, or 32-bit words. Memory options are magnetic core (18-mil cores, 16k 16-bit words, cycle time 1.0 microsec; or 13-mil cores, 16k 16- or 24-bit words, cycle time 0.8 microsec); CMOS RAM (2k or 4k 16-bit words, cycle time 0.2 microsec); bipolar RAM (2k 16-bit words, cycle time 0.05 microsec); or PROM (8k 16-bit words, cycle time 0.2 microsec). The central processor can address up to 64 kwords, expandable to 1M. Speed: fixed-point add/subtract, 1.625 microsec (floating-point, 7.531); fixed-point multiply, 4.375 microsec (floating-point, 12.531); fixed-point divide, 7.125 microsec (floating-point, 19.781). Floating-point numbers are represented by 16 or 32 (or 24 or 48) bits. This computer differs from most others in using only 2 parity bits for 24-bit words. There are 103 instructions (88 basic instructions).

◆ OL-77/ASQ

See L-304.

◆ USQ-69B

This Unisys device, an intelligent version of the USQ-69 datalink terminal, incorporates an 80386 (16-MHz) chip with an optional 80387 coprocessor. The architecture is much like that of a civilian PC, using the MS-DOS language (i.e., an IBM PC-AT clone); it has a seven-slot backplane (with 32-bit bus) accommodating a single-board computer (including 1 Mbyte of DRAM memory), a memory expansion board (with 512k or 1-Mbyte disk emulator, up to 4 Mbytes of memory, and a connection to an SCSI [small computer system interface] bus), two general-purpose expansion slots, two I/O slots, and one RS-170 (video) card slot. The chassis can accommodate 9 Mbytes with SCSI and/or a disk emulator, or up to 40 Mbytes without. The CPU board carries 384 kbytes of UVEPROM and 298 bytes of NVRAM. The green phosphor monitor displays a 640 × 480-pixel picture. The chassis can accommodate a 3.5in high-density disk.

USQ-69B can function as a stand-alone computer. It can replace an existing USQ-69, fitting into the latter's logic drawer. The marines connect 12 on an LAN on board an LHD for trooplocation planning. Preproduction deliveries began in June 1990, and production deliveries in March 1991.

◆ UYK-7

> **Word Length:** 32 bits (can do double-precision arithmetic)
> **Memory Capacity:** 262 kwords (ferrite cores)
> **Speed:** Memory cycle, 1.5 microsec; add/subtract time, 1.5 microsec; multiply time, 10.0 microsec; divide time, 17.0 microsec; clock rate, 1024 Hz
> **Instructions:** 130

Unisys' UYK-7, which appeared in 1969, was conceived for three programs: Aegis, the *Spruance*-class destroyer, and the *Los Angeles*–class submarine. It is being replaced by UYK-43. UYK-7 can operate either as a single or as a multiple processor. The single-cabinet version has a capacity of 48 kwords of memory and up to 16 I/O channels. Up to thirteen 16-kword modules can be added. Such additions are described as multibay configurations (one-, two-, three-, or four-bay). UYK-7(V) is an upgraded version.

UYK-7 has two unusual features. The main memory can be read as several parallel memories, for faster processing (speed is increased by a factor of 2 in the single-processor version, and by a factor of up to 8 when several processors are used together). UYK-7 has a bus connecting the memory modules, and up to three central processors can be connected to the same bus.

The standard UYK-7 cabinet is 40.88 in (height) × 19.80 in (width) × 22.34 in (depth) (excluding handles); total weight is 527 lb, including the cooling blower.

◆ UYK-15 (Univac 1616)

Word Length: 16 bits
Memory Capacity: 8–64 kwords in 8k increments
Speed: Add, 0.750 microsec; multiply, 3.75 microsec; divide, 3.75 microsec
Instructions: 64
I/O: 16 parallel channels; or 8 parallel and 8 serial; or 4 parallel and 16 serial channels

This is the Unisys computer of the SPS-52 through -52B radars; SPS-52C has a UYK-20 instead. The memory banks (increments) are independently addressable. Dimensions: 14.4 in (height) × 20.75 in (width) × 25.75 in (depth) (approx 170 lb). UYK-15 appeared about 1970. It was unusual in that there was no separate accumulator for arithmetic results; instead, all computation was conducted from register to register, and the large number of registers could accommodate numerous parameters. Compared to UYK-20, UYK-15 has an independent I/O controller and a time-sliced memory, whereas UYK-20 uses an emulator in its processor for handling I/O. Hence, to maintain the same throughput, two UYK-20s are equivalent to one UYK-15.

◆ UYK-19

Word Length: 16 bits
Memory Capacity: Up to 128 kwords (32k modules); 512-kbyte ROM
Speed: Clock rate, 20 MHz; memory cycle time, 2 microsec; add time, 1 microsec; floating-point add time, 4.6–10.1 microsec; floating-point divide time, 20.95–29.95 microsec
Instructions: 101
I/O: Up to 7; transfer rate, up to 1.32 Mbps

This Rolm computer competed with UYK-20. UYK-19 is used mainly in electronic-warfare systems; it beat out the UYK-20 for application to both the SLQ-32 ESM system and also the Tomahawk missile targeting system. UYK-19 is also the standard computer of the Hughes Modular Combat System (H930) and drives displays of the TFCC. The processor of the USQ-81 display (which was part of the Outlaw Shark and Outlaw Hawk predecessors of TFCC) was an enlarged UYK-19.

UYK-19 is a militarized version of the Data General NOVA computer and first appeared about 1974. There are five versions, which Rolm designates 5605, 1603A, 1650, 1602B, and 1666B; the last is also designated UYK-64 and uses an expanded instruction set. Data above refer to Model 1602B. Hughes tested a Model 1666 as an upgrade to its MCS; details of this computer are given below. See also UYK-64 (Rolm 1666B), which is intended as the UYK-19 successor, in analogy to UYK-44, the UYK-20 successor.

See UYK-64, below.

◆ UYK-20

Word Length: 16-bit words (can operate on 4- and 8-bit subwords)
Memory Capacity: UYK-20: 8–64 kwords; UYK-20A: 32–262 kwords (32k increments) (ferrite cores)
Speed: Memory cycle time, 0.75 microsec; add time, 0.84 microsec; multiply time, 3.6 microsec; divide time, 6.6 microsec
Instructions: 283
I/O Channels: 16

Unisys introduced this minicomputer in 1974; the development contract was awarded in March 1973. As built, UYK-20 outperformed the original version of UYK-7. The processor was of MSI (medium-scale integration) design. UYK-20A is a more powerful version, capable of addressing a larger memory. Typical dimensions are 20 in (height) × 19 in (width) × 24 in (depth) (230 lb). UYK-20 is also supplied as a set of 6 × 2in SEM-B cards, which can be embedded in another system.

In 1984 MTBF was reported as 2000 hr.

UYK-20 was the first of the series of 16-bit standard naval computers, which now includes UYK-44 and AYK-14.

◆ UYK-43

Word Length: 32 bits (can do half word and double-precision arithmetic)
Memory Capacity: 4 Gwords (see below)
Speed: Throughput, 2.25 MIPS; cycle time, 150 nanosec; add time, 150 nanosec
Instructions: 258
I/O Channels: 64

The Unisys UYK-43 replaces UYK-7 as the standard U.S. Navy shipboard mainframe computer. UYK-43 was designed to be compatible with the earlier machine, so that programs written for UYK-7s could be run on -43s with minimal modification. However, because UYK-43 is so much more powerful, programs written for it can add capability not practicable with the earlier machine. Applications include the Advanced Combat-Direction System (ACDS), which is replacing NTDS. UYK-43 uses VLSI technology. The German navy now uses the UYK-43 (in the new Type 123 frigate), and Taiwan uses it in its new *Perry*-class frigates.

UYK-43 is modular, produced in A and B versions (enclosures). The A enclosure (20 × 22 × 69 in, 950 lb) has a single central processor, one I/O controller (throughput 3 MIPS), and five memory modules and is about four times as powerful as a UYK-7. The B version (20 × 22 × 72 in, 1795 lb, when water-cooled, or 29 × 22 × 72 in, 1865 lb, when air-cooled) has two central processors, two I/O controllers, and 10 memory modules and is about nine times as powerful as a UYK-7. The A enclosure is designed to pass through a 25in-dia submarine hatch; it has the same footprint as a UYK-7. Ferrite-core memory is 32 kwords; semiconductor memory is available in 64k, 128k, 256k, and 512k, 1- and 2-Mword modules. The last was first offered in 1987 as a direct replacement for the 512k module. At least in the case of the 512k and larger modules, a battery backup within the module saves data for 30 min in the event of power failure. Module read/write time is 450 nanosec, and the modules are built out of 256k memory chips. Presumably, larger modules will soon be offered, using the newer 1M memory chips.

Because the B version is equivalent to two independent computers sharing a common memory, it replaces a pair of UYK-7s in upgraded *Perry*-class frigates. The B enclosure can also accommodate two I/O controllers (throughput 3 MIPS each), and up to 10 memory modules. None of the existing memory modules allows the system to approach its theoretical capacity of 4 Gwords; the current maximum within the enclosure is 20 Mwords.

Unisys claims that UYK-43 is the most reliable military computer yet developed, with an MTBF of 56,000 hr. The original requirement was for a 6000hr MTBF (MTTR of 15 min).

Sperry (Unisys) and IBM were awarded competitive contracts for UYK-43 prototypes in December 1980. Engineering development models were delivered in March 1983, and Sperry was chosen in May 1983. Deliveries began in December 1983. Control Data was chosen as second-source producer in 1988, to compete for 1990 production.

Although the addressing scheme of UYK-43 allows for up to 4 Gwords, the original central processor was limited to 2 Mbytes (512 kwords). Unisys developed an expanded memory reach (EMR) central processor, which expanded memory reach to 2 Gbytes (512 Mwords). This modification adds 52 instructions to the original instruction set, and extends eight of the existing instructions.

A UYK-43/44 upgrade program was begun in December 1988. Plug-in upgrades were phased in during 1990–94. UYK-43 gets a new high performance CPU with four to six times more speed, a math coprocessor, and additional memory improvements (new standard mass-memory storage, i.e., a small disk drive). There will also be software upgrades. The coprocessor in UYK-43 was originally provided to improve self-noise monitoring in Trident submarines.

A preplanned product-improvement program added a 32k cache memory (16k instructions, 16k data) and 1024k and 2048k semiconductor memory units. The central processor was modified so that it could address more memory.

The math coprocessor (Time-Critical Subfunction Coprocessor, or TCS) carries a multifunction processor (MFP) and a vector processor (VP), plus independent memory, use of which does not conflict with the use of the main UYK-43 memory. The two processors are connected to the memory and to an interface adapter by a local bus. The MFP consists of a Motorola 68030 microprocessor, a Motorola 68882 floating-point coprocessor, cache memory, EEPROM, and the associated memory interface. Calculations are done in single (32-bit) or double (64-bit) precision, at 0.5 MFLOPS. The vector processor consists of an AT&T WEDSP32C digital signal processor and 1.5 kbytes of local memory. It can operate at up to 25 MFLOPS (sustained rate, 5 MFLOPS) and is under the control of the MFP, operating in parallel with it. TCS carries its own 8-Mbyte memory (expandable to 16 Mbytes). TCS is intended specifically for operations such as FFTs; up to four can be installed in a UYK-43 B enclosure. The standard form is three printed circuit assemblies: one for the processor, one for memory, and one for the interface adapter. A higher-performance version consists of four: two memories and two processors.

Access by the multiple processors and I/O controllers to the same memory module can present a problem as processor execution times drop below the memory-bus cycle time, since then the memory cycle becomes the limiting factor in computer speed. In 1991 Unisys announced a high bandwidth memory (HBM) to overcome this problem. HBM employs eight 1-Mword memory blocks, each separately addressable; total memory is split into two groups of four blocks each, each with its own scheduler. Scheduler rotation time is 0.3 microsec, but each scheduler has access to four separate blocks, so overall effective request time is 0.0375 microsec (as long as no two devices try to access the same word or the same subblock). In addition, HBM reads from (or writes to) the memory in four-word bursts. Such bursts require five memory bus cycles (one address, four data) rather than the current eight, for a 58% improvement in speed. The bursts write into the cache memory of the central processor. Overall memory performance is improved by a factor of up to 12.

In March 1991 Unisys also announced a new open-architecture backpanel (OAB) accommodating fiber optics and LAN connections. The new OAB would allow connection of existing—for example, commercial—equipment into a UYK-43, and would thus allow for rapid prototyping. Unisys presented it as a bridge to a next-generation computer, since massive improvements could easily be accommodated. The next stage of this proposal was VME Lowboy, in which open system modules, which can accommodate 6U VME cards, are connected to the UYK-43. They can carry a Concurrence Maxion multiprocessor or an HP single-board computer (as in a TAC-3 or -4). External CIC cabling and input/output devices would be retained, and the UYK-43 and VME-based elements could work in parallel, interchanging messages at their own very high speed.

As of 1995, Loral Unisys was still marketing a VME-upgraded UYK-43. None had yet been sold to the U.S. Navy, but it is by no means clear that existing UYK-7 and UYK-43 ships will all be upgraded to distributed UYQ-70-based systems. A Navy program to upgrade existing UYK-43s passed its preliminary design review in March 1993 and its critical design review in November 1993. HBM passed its developmental test in November 1992. The Navy program also includes a new mass memory storage device (MMSD), on which tests were completed during FY93.

◆ UYK-44

Word Length: 16 bits
Memory Capacity: 256 kwords (core); 4 Mwords (semiconductor memory)
Speed: Throughput, up to 0.94 MIPS
I/O Channels: 16

Unisys' UYK-44 is the current standard U.S. Navy minicomputer (i.e., 16-bit computer). It will replace UYK-20. In addition to stand-alone functions, UYK-44 is embedded in other devices, such as the UYQ-34 multimode display and the SQS-53 and SQQ-32 sonars, as the Militarized Reconfigurable Processor (MRP) and the Militarized Reconfigurable Computer (MRC). The MRP is designated OL-335(V) Data-Processing Group. The

UYK-44 instruction set matches that of the AYK-14 airborne computer, which UYK-44 may ultimately replace. Actual word length, including check bits, is 22 bits.

Three alternative semiconductor memories can each be accommodated on a standard electronic module (SEM) card: 8 × 64k (512k), 8 × 256k (2M), or 4 × 1M (system maximum). Greater capacity means slower operation: the 64k SEM has a cycle time of 120 nanosec; the 256k, 250 nanosec; and the 1M, 350 nanosec. With the 64k SEM, the processor limits overall speed to about 0.930 MIPS; the 256k version runs at 0.934 MIPS, but the 1M version runs at 0.894 MIPS.

The original central processor directly addresses up to 64 kwords of memory. It uses four sets of 64 (256) -page registers (1 kword each) to address further memory via an executive mode program. Thus the maximum addressable memory is 256 kwords.

Unisys offers an expanded memory reach (EMR) version of UYK-44, which doubles the direct addressing ability of the computer by differentiating between instruction and data addresses. Using EMR, the computer can address 256 groups each of 64 code (instruction) pages plus 256 groups each of 64 data pages; each page consists of up to 1 kword. This is a total of 32 kpages (32 Mwords), 16 Mwords of data, and 16 Mwords of instructions. Four of the 64 data-page groups are reserved for I/O, so that I/O page address registers can be manipulated independently of central-processor page address registers.

EMR is standard in embedded versions of UYK-44 delivered after August 1989. The change requires 20 new instructions.

Unisys won the UYK-44 contract in competition with IBM. Both companies received prototype contracts in September 1980, and Unisys (then Sperry) won the contest in March 1983. Several Allied navies, including the Japanese, now use UYK-44. Raytheon, GE, and Microlithics have all qualified as second sources for the SEMs out of which the UYK-44 is built.

Unisys claims that MTBF is 13,000 hr.

An upgrade program began in December 1988. UYK-44 will be fitted with an enhanced processor with five to six times greater processing speed, plus memory improvements. The improved processor meets requirements of the SQQ-89 program.

As of November 1988 Unisys was offering a UYK-44EP (enhanced performance), which is probably the upgraded UYK-44. UYK-44EP can operate in either 16- or 32-bit mode and can address 8 Mbytes of memory (configured in words of either length). Using a page addressing scheme, it can address up to 32 Mbytes. The existing nine UYK-44 processor cards are replaced by two UYK-44EP cards, and there is a new instruction set, by means of which the machine can emulate the UYK-20A, UYK-502, AYK-14, and UYK-44. The processor cards carry 64 kbytes of cache memory, as well as 32 kbytes of UVPROM (read-only memory, which can be reprogrammed when scanned with ultraviolet light) for its microcode. Speed is 5 MIPS.

As in the case of UYK-43, a Navy upgrade program is intended ultimately to produce an open system; the UYK-44 Open Systems Module (OSM) design was completed during FY93 (developmental tests were completed in December 1992).

◆ UYK-64(V)/Rolm 1666B

Word Length: 16 bits
Memory Capacity: Core: 128 kbytes internal/1920 kbytes external; semiconductor: 2048 kbytes internal (1024 kwords)
Speed: Memory access time, 0.4 microsec internal, 0.7 microsec external; core cycle time, 1 microsec internal, 1.1 microsec external; effective memory cycle time (four-way interleave), 0.1 microsec (1 microsec core); semiconductor cycle time, 0.4 microsec; add time, 0.2 microsec (1.0 core); multiply time, 4.4–7.4 microsec; divide time, 4.4–7.4 microsec; floating-point divide, 5.0 microsec (9.8 in double precision); typical single-precision throughput, 0.441 MOPS (core 0.268 MOPS)
Instructions: 230
I/O: 59 addressable devices; I/O time: 1.25/0.25-Mbps core, 1.7/ 1.25-Mbps semiconductor

UYK-64 is a second-generation UYK-19. Performance figures are given for two versions, one using ferrite-core memory and one using semiconductor memory of the type now common in small computers. The basic core version has 64 kbytes of internal memory, expandable to 128 k; additional memory is contained in external I/O devices or memory chassis. The semiconductor version is built up from 512-kbyte modules. Memory is allocated on the basis of 2-kbyte pages.

The 1666B is upward-compatible with existing UYK-19s, just as the UYK-44 is upward-compatible with UYK-20s. See below for details of the Rolm 1666, a related machine that has been used in TFCC and in the upgraded version of the Hughes Modular Combat System. The 1666B or UYK-64 can be upgraded to the Rolm MSE/14 by replacement of one CPU board and one optional floating-point unit (FPU) board.

◆ UYS-1/2

See the ASW section. These are specialized signal processors.

◆ Next-Generation Computer Resources (NGCR: TADSTAND B)

For its next generation of computers, the Navy wants to shift from a limited number of special designs to open standards that can be met by any number of functionally equivalent and interchangeable modules. No prototype has been built, but NGCR program recommendations have been adopted for several commercial standards, including a backplane (Futurebus+, ultimately to replace VME) and an instruction-set architecture (IEEE 1003 POSIX operating system). The ADA language is also becoming standard for some civilian mission-critical systems, such as the fly-by-wire system in the new Boeing 777. Apparently one of its advantages is that it produces very consistent machine code when it is compiled, whereas some commercial languages, such as C, do not.

◆ BuOrd/NavOrd Computers

The Bureau of Ordnance and its successors gave computers Mark numbers; these devices are outside the normal AN series. Many are still in use, covering the entire range from electromechanical analog devices to digital machines. Stabilization and other secondary computers are omitted in the list that follows (see the 1991/92 edition for details). True general-purpose computing came only with Mk 152. The number of distinct computers declined sharply with the introduction of general-purpose types (many FCSs use such standard machines as UYK-7 and UYK-20).

Mk 1 Electromechanical analog computer of the Mk 37 gun fire-control system (FCS). Total weight is 3200 lb (2900 lb in some versions). Available ballistics, in the Mk 37 system, were 8in/55, 6in/47, 5in/54, and 5in/38. Maximum computing range was 18,000 yd. Maximum speeds: 400 kt horizontally, 250 kt vertically. Mk 1 introduced fully automatic rate control to U.S. practice, and the Mk 37 FCS was the first U.S. naval ordnance application of closed-loop servo practice (initially experiencing severe problems because its feedback made it unstable). Most U.S. ships used the Mk 1A version.

Mk 42 Ballistic analog computer of the Mk 56 gun FCS. One computer was needed for each set of ballistics to be computed. It operates by a mechanical linkage of five mechanical inputs, one manual and the others by servo. The results were converted into electrical analog form by the rotation of potentiometers, for introduction into an electric computing network. The unit for primary ballistics weighed 640 lb; the secondary ballistics unit weighed 550 lb, the saving presumably being the result of avoiding duplication between the two. Ballistics included fuze time computation. Available ballistics were 6in/47, 5in/54, 5in/38, and 3in/50. Computing range was 15,000 yd.

Mk 47 Electronic/electromechanical analog computer of the Mk 68 gun FCS, successor to FCS Mk 37. Surviving examples control 5in/54 guns. Computing range is 18,000 yds. Mod 5, the earliest surviving version, was simplified and repackaged (weight was approximately halved, to about 2700 lb). It entered service about 1958. Mod 7 (1961) extended the computing range to beyond 72,000 yd so that Mk 68 could control missiles. Mod 8 (1961) had transistors in place of the electronic tubes of earlier versions, as well as new plug-in electronic units (for easier maintenance). This version was part of the Mk 68 Mod 4 FCS. Weight was 2450

lb. In this version, maximum target range was 35,000 yd, and maximum range for gun orders was 20,100 yd. CG 26 and later ships had Mod 9, similar to Mod 8 but modified to work with computer Mk 116 Mod 4. Mod 10 (1965) time-shares horizontal relative target bearing, star shell gun-train order, gun-train order, gun-elevation order, and star shell-elevation order computations and so eliminates the need for a Mk 116 computer. It allowed for ballistics for a new reduced-charge 5in/54 round. It was used in the Mk 68 Mod 13 FCSs of FF 1078-class ships. Mod 11 (1969) included ballistics for RAP shells. It was equivalent to ORDALT 6948 applied to the Mod 10.

Mk 116 Computer (750 lb) to supplement Mk 47 (and thus part of the Mk 68 FCS), to produce star-shell orders. Mod 3 was installed on *Charles F. Adams*–class destroyers. Mod 4 was the solid-state-electronics version, part of Mk 68 Mod 8 FCSs (1962). It could provide surface control only, for 3in/50 guns.

Mk 118 Analog computer producing missile and launcher orders for Tartar (later SM-1MR) missiles, 1956; installed on board frigates. It was part of missile FCS Mk 74. The Mod 2 version (1963) eliminated the gun-order section and changed the launcher blind-zone computed output.

Mk 119 Computer of the Mk 76 Terrier (later SM-1ER) missile FCS. It survives only on board the Italian missile cruiser *Vittorio Veneto*.

Mk 152 See CP-848, above.

Mk 157 See Norwegian SM-3, above.

Mk 160 Current standard gunfire-control digital computer. It incorporates a UYK-20(V) computer and is in the modernized Mk 68 gun FCS. Mod 4, for the *Arleigh Burke* class (1985), incorporates a UYK-44.

◆ DTC I

Hewlett-Packard HP 9020A/C (Model 500) workstation/computer, adopted as a standard naval machine in July 1984. The two versions differ primarily in the quality of their color monitors, 9020C offering higher performance. The 32-bit microprocessor is a proprietary Hewlett-Packard chip containing 450,000 transistors, which was an order of magnitude greater than the level of integration achieved by competitors when the machine was introduced. Internal (RAM) memory: 2-Mbyte basic version, expandable to 14 Mbytes (naval versions typically carry up to 8 Mbytes). The machine normally accommodates two 5.25in floppy disks and one or more (up to seven) hard disks (initially 20 Mbyte, but now typically 55 or 130 Mbyte; the final version [1989] could accommodate 304-Mbyte hard disks). HP 9020 was the first multiple-CPU 32-bit workstation; it can accommodate up to three floating-point math chips. Each CPU can directly address up to 500 Mbytes. Speed of the single-CPU version is 1.5 MIPS (based on an industry-standard mix of instructions, in which a VAX 11/780 runs at 1 MIPS); the two-CPU version runs at 2.9 and the three-CPU version at 4.3 MIPS. Other measures of speed: microinstruction cycle time, 55 nanosec; addition of two 64-bit floating-point numbers, 1.17 microsec; multiplication of two 32-bit integers, 1.25 microsec; multiplication of two 64-bit floating-point numbers, 1.28 microsec; load a register from memory, 550 nanosec.

DTC I was sold to the Navy by Tetratech, which added software and some minor hardware to the basic HP 9020. About 2500–3000 DTC Is were bought, for programs including FFISTS (see separate entry), ICADS (integrated carrier ASW prediction system), JOTS I, POST (prototype ocean surveillance terminal), SCATS (squadron-commander ASW tactical system), SIMAS (sonar condition prediction for SQS-53 sonars), SFMPL (submarine force mission-planning library), SPAR, TASWIT (tactical ASW interim trainer), and TEPEE (see separate entry).

◆ DTC II (CP-2137)

DTC II is the desktop tactical computer of the Flag Data Display System (FDDS) and JOTS II, a ruggedized C3–4/110 manufactured by C3, Inc., of Herndon, Virginia. DTC II is based on the Sun Series-4/110 32-bit SPARC (RISC technology) microprocessor and has a VME internal bus (backplane) with nine slots and a patented memory-management unit (MMU). The MMU supports rapid switching among eight register-resident processes for multitasking. The original microprocessor was capable of 7.5 MIPS when operating on integers (see below for upgrades). Clock rate was 14.28 MHz. Memory is 8, 16, 20, or 32 Mbytes; memory cache is 16 kbytes. The address bus is 28 bits wide (the data bus is 32 bits wide). The computer can support 15-, 19-, and 25in monitors. Resolution is 1152×900 pixels, with a refresh rate of 66 frames/sec and a bandwidth of 93 MHz. It can display 256 colors.

DTC II was chosen to succeed DTC I in applications such as JOTS because it was adapted to a much more widely used language (UNIX rather than Rocky Mountain Basic) and because it incorporated a standard VME backplane. As in the commercial world, the backplane made it possible to incorporate special-purpose boards. For example, the version of DTC II used in FDDS has perhaps only one board in common with a standard DTC II computer. Reportedly, however, DTC II has proven less than sufficiently rugged in service. The successor is TAC-3 (rather than DTC III).

The total DTC II contract was for 3000 computers (total cost $115 million), of which more than 1800 had been delivered by the beginning of 1991. There are currently several versions based on different Sun workstations: Sun 4/110 (7.5 MIPS), Sun 4/300 (16 MIPS), and Sun 4/470 (22 MIPS—may be used for the NIPS program; it is a powerful file server, with up to 6 Gbytes of storage). These machines can also accept special graphics and applications processors on internal boards, for example, the CSPI Supercard 2 array processor (a 6U VME board using the 40-MHz i860 RISC microprocessor, with total throughput of 80 MFLOPS) used in the SURTASS and LFA programs.

Current standard characteristics: 25-MHz clock rate, SPARC C47C601 processor with 32 Mbytes of RAM, 128-kbyte cache memory, and Sun 4/300 floating-point processor. Graphics processor: Sun CG-6/Megatek one or four channels. Mass storage: one or two 500-Mbyte hard disks, 150-Mbyte tape drive, 1.2-Mbyte floppy drive.

The standard single-screen workstation is OJ-683(V); the twin-screen (one atop the other) workstation is OJ-684(V); and the unattended computer cabinet is OL-529(V) or the extra-height OL-531(V). OL-530(V) is a console with a 14- or 15in rather than the standard 19in screen. An A suffix (as in OJ-683A) indicates a TAC-3 rather than a DTC II workstation.

◆ TAC-3 (CP-2184/CP-2231) and TAC-4

This next-generation workstation, renamed TAC (Tactical Advanced Computer), embodies much more powerful graphics. Specified processing rate was 22 SPECmarks, with a bonus for each SPECmark above 22. An alternative measure was 50–100 MIPS (as in DTC I/II, on a scale on which a VAX 11/780 has a speed of 1 MIPS). The three specified configurations were: A, full-height dual-screen for 19in shipboard racks, B, a single-screen desktop or rack-mounted workstation (disk optional), and C, an unattended file server. The machine had to be adaptable to a Futurebus backplane and to GOSIP and POSIX specifications.

HBC, a joint venture of Hughes Data Systems and BTG Inc., won the TAC-3 competition in March 1992. The new machine is based on the Hewlett-Packard HP 9000 Model 700-series workstations equipped with the company's PA-RISC chips: HP720 (50 MHz, 57.5 MIPS, 17.9 MFLOPS) and HP730/750 (60-MHz, 76.7 MIPS, 23.7 MFLOPS). The current standard high-end TAC-3 processors are 735/125 (124 MIPS, 40 MFLOPS) and 755/125 (154 MIPS, 51.3 MFLOPS). There are three configurations: System A, the maximum expandable workstation; System B, a small desktop computer; and System C, a disk and computer server. System A can be either a desktop machine or one of two rack-mounted machines (one or two color monitors). System C can be desktop or rack-mounted. System A uses an HP750 with 32 Mbytes of RAM (expandable to 192 Mbytes), and three full-

height 5.25in disk-drive bays. The rack carries one or two 19in color monitors. System B uses the HP730 and 32–64 Mbytes of RAM. System C uses the HP750 and 64–192 Mbytes of RAM, plus a seven-slot VME chassis and three full-height 5.25in disk-drive bays. Any monitor is external. The standard CRT is a CRX Color 2D/3D (1280×1024 pixels, $8 + 8$ double-buffered color planes, that is, images that can be displayed simultaneously, plus one color lookup table). The optional extension is a CRX-24 (1280×1024 pixels, 24 color planes and eight overlay planes, plus five color lookup tables).

About 4000 TAC-3s were purchased. Some use an HP755 workstation; there is also an upgrade, HP 755+, with a 125-MHz clock rate, credited with about 170 SPECmarks.

Current standard characteristics:

CP-2184: 66-MHz PA-RISC processor (76.7 MIPS, 77.5 SPECmarks, 23.7 MFLOPS in double-precision, 34.3 MFLOPS single-precision arithmetic). G2 dual-display graphics controller (up to four RGB color outputs). Storage: 192-Mbyte RAM (32 Mbytes in System A plus three or five 32-Mbyte RAM upgrades); 256-kbyte instruction cache, 256-kbyte data cache. Mass storage: 1.3- or 2.0-Gbyte hard drive, 1.2-Gbyte tape drive; can accommodate a 1.44-Mbyte floppy and a CD-ROM drive.

CP-2231 (TAC-3 System D): 99-MHz PA-RISC processor, 320 Mbytes of RAM, 256-kbyte instruction cache, 256-kbyte data cache, 2.0-Gbyte hard disk, 1.44-Mbyte floppy, 2.0-Gbyte tape drive, CD-ROM drive. RAM upgrades are in units of 64 Mbytes.

There are still HP-730 TAC-3s in service.

Single-monitor workstation versions are OJ-683A and OJ-685A, the latter with a larger cabinet below the keyboard (total height 70 in rather than 54.125 in).

TAC-4 is the follow-on. Hewlett-Packard (teamed with SAIC and the Harris Corp.) won the competition in January 1995, and plans call for buying 42,000 of these computers.

TAC-4 was required to have at least twice the performance of TAC-3 (credits were offered for higher performance, to avoid buying a low-cost low-performance machine). Unlike TAC-3, TAC-4 also had to include a low-end rugged portable version. Despite some interest in making TAC-4 a multiprocessor machine, all competitors used single RISC processors. The Navy had decided that compilers were not yet sufficiently developed to take advantage of multiprocessing. Minimum internal storage is 1 Gbyte. The hard drive is a RAID (redundant access device): the same data can be put on five drives (to protect against drive failure), or it can be broken up for faster access, using multiple drives simultaneously. Typical RAID capacity is 10 to 15 Gbytes.

The failed competitors used PowerPC (Hughes Data Systems, teamed with IBM and BTG) and Alpha AXP (DEC, teamed with Allied Signal, CACI, Codar, CSI, GTE, Miltope, and Syscon) CPUs.

Like TAC-3, TAC-4 is based on HP 9000-series workstations, in this case using Model 712, 743i, and J210 (formerly Model 770) processors. Different versions are adapted to different environments: white (benign office), red (mission-critical on board ships and submarines), blue (peacetime installations at sea), gold (transit, in a shipping case), green (wheeled and tracked vehicles, for expeditionary warfare), and tan (outdoors combat environment on land).

Model 712 runs at 60, 80, or 100 MHz (Models 712/60, 712/80, and 712/100). All versions use the PA 7100LC CPU. Performance, respectively: 73, 92, 125 MIPS; 12.9, 27.6, 34 MFLOPS. All use 48-bit virtual memory addresses. Caches are shared; size (total/typical data in kbytes): 64/32, 256/128, 256/128. Cache bus performance varies: 480, 680, 800 Mbps for a 4-byte instruction fetch or an 8-byte second load data fetch. Inherent memory capacity is 16–192 Mbytes (70-nsec DRAM), with a 64-bit data bus. These workstations can support a 14-, 17-, or 19in color monitor, up to 128 Mbytes of RAM (192 Mbytes in the 712/100 version), internal 1- or 2-Gbyte hard disks, 3.5in floppy disks, keyboard, mouse, or trackball.

HP Series 700i (including 743i, 743irt, and 748i) is a real-time processor intended for tactical tasks such as those in CDSs. HP743i is a single-board (6U VME) computer incorporating a

7100LC processor running at 64 or 100 MHz with a 256-kbyte instruction/data cache. Performance: 743i/64 runs at 77.7 MIPS or 25.3 MFLOPS; 743i/100 runs at 121.6 MIPS or 37.8 MFLOPS. Peak cache performance is, respectively, 512 and 800 Mbps; the cache bus is 64 bits wide and the main memory bus is 64 bits wide. Unlike Model 712, these units use 60-nsec DRAM. Model 748i is an enclosure for Model 743i.

J210, the high end of the family, uses one or two HP 7200 PA-RISC CPUs (see PA entry below) running at 120 MHz. The associated memory management unit uses 48-bit memory addresses. Primary caches are 256 kbytes of instructions and 256 kbytes of data; bus width is 64 bits. Main memory is 32–1024 Mbytes (60-nsec DRAM). Main memory bus width is 128 bits (plus parity bits). Performance: 176 MIPS, 57 MFLOPS. HP J210 supports one or more 19in monitors, internal hard disks, and removable storage devices, including 3.5in and 5.25in floppy disks.

Particular combinations of processors and other hardware are called *bundles*. Principal basic versions are:

Processors A and C: High-performance workstation and server, respectively, using Model J210. The ruggedized rack-mounted workstation uses either one or a pair of 19in ruggedized monitors mounted one above the other. The rack-mounted server lacks its own monitor. There are also desk versions (for a White environment) using vertical-format chassis.

Processors B and D: Medium-performance workstation and server, respectively. Like A and C, they use J210 processors (D is equivalent to C but has 32 rather than 64 Mbytes of RAM).

Processors B and D: Portables (normal and rugged, respectively): Model 712/60. RAM is 16 Mbytes, expandable to 128 Mbytes, and the ruggedized version includes a 1-Gbyte hard disk and a 1.44-Mbyte floppy. The display is 640 × 640 pixels (9.4in diagonal).

Processor G: Low-cost workstation (desktop personal computer configuration): Models 712/80 and 712/100. RAM capacity is up to 128 Mbytes.

Processor H: Real-time processor, using Model 743i.

Note that the French SENIT 8 system in the new carrier *Charles de Gaulle* uses the HP 743i processor.

The next-generation TAC-5 contract is due in 1997 (as of 1995 SPAWAR was developing requirements).

◆ TDP/MDAU

EDO's tactical data processor provides standard U.S. Navy DTCs with an interface to tactical data, both own-ship (EW and sonar) and via Link 11/14 and formatted intelligence broadcasts (OTCIXS, for example). The DTC provides tactical decision aids and displays the real-time multisource tactical picture built up in the TDP. A single TDP can connect multiple DTCs, as in FFISTS. The TDP can also measure force Link 11 performance through a combination of information derived from link management messages and observation of network events; observation and tracking of originators of messages can determine who is actually active on the link. Displays of operational performance are: number of tracks by each participant, time duration of each track, detection range from a reference point, engagement statistics, identity and classification, and invalid PIFs. Interfaces are MIL-STD-188, NTDS Slow and Fast, 32-bit data, and IEEE 488 (to DTC). The TDP is built around an Intel 8635 board (comparable to an 80286) with EDO-supplied frontware. It has no AN designator.

TDP is the basis for tactical applications of the DTC I and II. Major current applications are FFISTS, JOTS I and II, two-way Link 11, MULTS, TACNAV, and JVIDS. About 120 are currently in service, mostly for the Link 11 connection to JOTS.

The Multi-Source Data Acquisition Unit (MSDAU) consists of a TDP, a DTC I, and related software to manage and display the data acquired by the TDP. To EDO, multisource data acquisition means automatic sensor input (radar/sonar), automatic intelligence input (using machine-readable formatted identification and location information from intelligence broadcasts), and force sensor information via TADIL-A (most likely Link 11). The associated C^2 processing system architecture is used for data distribution, for database management (including sensor correlation, track updates and support, geographic displays, air track intercept planning, dispersed planning, weapons planning, range sensors, Kalman filtering prediction, TMA, sensor performance prediction, and satellite vulnerability), and to support graphic displays (large-screen displays, multiterminal operation, and remote multi-pen plotters). MSDAU has now been overshadowed by DTC II systems such as FFISTS.

◆ L-304/OL-77

Word Length: 32 bits
Memory Capacity: 4 kwords, expandable to 128k in 4k or 8k increments (ferrite cores)
Speed: Memory cycle time, 1.6 microsec (4 kwords) or 1.8 microsec (8 kwords); add/subtract time, 14 microsec; multiply time, 44–72 microsec
Instructions: 62
I/O Channels: 64 (maximum transfer rate, 312 kwords/sec)

Two L-304s form the central tactical computer of the E-2C, OL-77/ASQ. The architecture of this machine is similar to that of the somewhat earlier U.S. CP-642 series, which performed an analogous role in NTDS. L-304 was announced in mid-1965.

L-304F has five memory modules, each containing 8k 32-bit words (only four of the five may be addressed at a time, a software instruction activating or deactivating a given module). I/O is in 4kword blocks (32- or 8-bit), the length of the word depending on the number of data lines in the particular interface. The system uses nine-track magnetic tape as its mass storage.

◆ Rolm 1666

Memory Capacity: Up to 1024 kwords in 16-kword modules (plus 512-word ROM)
Speed: Add time, 1.1 microsec; multiply, 5.3–5.5 microsec; divide, 9.3–12.7 microsec; floating-point divide, 15.9–16.7 microsec (single precision)
Instructions: 234

This microcomputer replaces the earlier UYK-19 in the current upgraded version of the Hughes Modular Combat System. It is used in the U.S. TFCC (initial version) and in USQ-81. There are three degrees of precision: 32-bit single precision, 48-bit, and 64-bit double precision.

Memory can be divided into up to eight distinct sections: the operating system, the DMA processor, and six user memories (up to 64 kwords each). These memory areas may be shared or they may be limited to each user. Of the total 1024 kwords, 64 kwords are 1-microsec core memory.

◆ System/4 Pi

The IBM military and space-program computer series was introduced in 1966; at that time it was unusual because it was an off-the-shelf modular series. System/4 Pi computers are used in the A-6E (TC-3 and now TC-4), EA-6B, and AV-8B ARBS (SP-1); the LAMPS III display is run by an embedded System/4 Pi CP-3. These are all basically 16-bit machines (17 bits including the parity bit). There are three families: tactical computer (TC), customized processor (CP), and extended-performance computer (SP). A more powerful 32-bit Advanced System/4 Pi was introduced in 1970 and is used in the F-14. The advanced series consists of three families: advanced processor (AP), command/control (CC), and subsystem processor (SP). Applications include the space shuttle (AP-101) and the E-3 AWACS (CC-1), the latter being the most powerful of the series.

Characteristics (as originally announced, 1966):

	TC	CP	SP
Data Word	16 or 32 bits	16 or 32 bits	16, 32, or 64 bits
Instruction	8 or 16 bits	16 or 32 bits	16, 32, or 48 bits
Memory	16–64 kbytes	8–32 kwords[a]	16–128 kwords[a]
Memory cycle	2.5 microsec	2.5 microsec	2.5 microsec
Add time	9–18 microsec	5–10 microsec	2.1–5.0 microsec

continued on next page

	TC	CP	SP
Multiply time	48–54 microsec	29.6–34.6 microsec	9.2–10.4 microsec
Instructions	54	36	70
Interrupts	1 level	4 levels	2 levels (one 6-level)
MTBF	7500 hr	2500 hr	Not given

[a]32-bit words

Machines within families were differentiated in part by the addition of microprogrammed special-purpose processors. For example, a special sine-cosine calculator reduced computation time for these functions by 60%. IBM claimed that time for data correlation, for example, in tracking, could be reduced by better than an order of magnitude. From the first, System/4 Pi was designed to run programs that could be written and tested on commercial Series 360 computers.

♦ **Univac 1230**

See CP-855, above.

♦ **Univac 1830A and 1830B**

See CP-901, above.

♦ **VAX**

Some current machines are described as MicroVAX types. VAX itself is a DEC 32-bit minicomputer series replacing the earlier 16-bit PDP-8 and -11 series. MicroVAX refers to a word length and an instruction set; one advantage of a MicroVAX is that its software can be developed on a standard VAX machine. The current VAX 8842 accommodates 0.256–1 Gbytes of memory and executes instructions at a rate of 22 MIPS.

VAX appeared in 1978, and single-chip versions of the VAX followed about 1984. In many ways VAX 11/780 is used as the standard for 1 MIPS (though actual running speed was apparently closer to 0.5 MIPS). The machine is designed for multitasking, using a special 64-bit word to keep track of the program modules (processes) it executes, and reserving a pair of 1-Gbyte parts of memory to each process (one for data, one for instructions). VAX 11 has an 8-byte instruction prefetch register (VAX 8600 has a six-stage pipeline).

♦ **DEC Alpha AXP**

This DEC microprocessor (also designated 21064) was introduced in 1992. It is a pipelined (seven-stage) superscalar (two-issue) RISC chip using 64-bit data and address buses, and a 128-bit data bus between processor and memory; it also has a built-in floating-point unit (FPU) and 8-kbyte instruction and data caches. This chip contains 1.7 million transistors. The original version ran at 150 MHz (300 MIPS peak), but a newer version runs at 200 MHz (400 MIPS peak rate). There is also a low-cost 21068 (1993: 66 and 100 MHz).

A new Alpha 21164 was introduced in 1995; it was then the fastest microprocessor in the world. It is to be followed by a 21164A early in 1996. These chips incorporate 9.3 million transistors, most of them used for cache memory: 8 kbytes of data and 8 kbytes of instructions, with a 96-kbyte secondary cache feeding into both primary caches and fed by a bus interface unit carrying 40-bit addresses and 128-bit data. There are two separate parallel integer and two separate parallel floating-point arithmetic units (three stages for the integers, five for floating point), and a four-stage instruction pipeline fed from the instruction cache. Target clock speed for 21164A is over 300 MHz.

The Alpha CPU was conceived to modernize the DEC VAX computer series, so it is designed to run both the usual VAX-series VMS operating system and also the UNIX system popular in workstations. One unusual feature is hardware error correction, using an addition 14 bits for each 64-bit word, for a total of 78 bits per word; another 2 bits are used to check parity of bus transfers. Alpha can handle 32-bit data, but it loses performance when it emulates DOS and handles 16-bit data. It also generates considerable heat due to its very high performance.

♦ **Hewlett-Packard PA-RISC Series**

Hewlett-Packard introduced the Precision Architecture (PA) series in 1985. Although classified as a RISC machine, it has a considerable number of instructions. Many, such as multiply-and-add, combine two operations in one, increasing speed (by executing the whole instruction in one clock cycle) at a cost in hardware complexity. There are 32 registers, with pipelining to minimize the number of cycles per instruction. Some versions have multiple parallel arithmetic logic units (ALUs). Addresses consist of a 32-bit linear offset and a 16-, 24-, or 32-bit space identifier.

These are the CPUs of the TAC-3 and TAC-4 and also of the French SENIT 8 system.

The main current series is PA7100, which uses 850,000 transistors on its chip and runs at up to 100 MHz. It can execute two instructions simultaneously, but only if one is an integer operation and the other a floating-point operation. This chip has a 64-bit data bus in and out of it. Because the cache is external, it can be quite large, up to several Mbytes. The chip has three bus outlets: I/O, instruction cache, and data cache. The data cache can be 4 kbytes to 2 Mbytes and the instruction cache 4 kbytes to 1 Mbyte.

PA7100LC operates at up to 75 MHz. It adds a second ALU, hence can execute two integer operations simultaneously. It employs a unified (vice dual) off-chip cache, 8 kbytes to 2 Mbytes. The object of the design was to reduce cost (hence the LC) without cutting performance.

PA7150 is an upgrade to 125–150 MHz.

PA7200 has enhanced cache management.

PA8000 offers 96-bit operation in 32-bit segments, with a dual FPU, higher bandwidth memory interconnect, and speculative execution (in which the machine in effect guesses at the result of one instruction so as to execute a later one). PA8000 has also been described as a 200-MHz 64-bit machine.

PA9000 is a planned version with more parallelism.

In June 1994 Intel and Hewlett-Packard announced a technology-sharing agreement, under which Intel would eventually shift to PA-based designs, closing out the current CISC series. The first fruit of this cooperation is PA8000.

♦ **Intel Chips (iAx86 Series)**

Intel produced the 8-bit microprocessor chips that began the personal-computer industry (8080, 8085). Most military machines use 16- or 32-bit chips, which offer more processing power and also a larger number of potential memory addresses. The entire series is designed so that each later version can use programs written for the earlier ones. Intel is now alone in continuing to develop new CISC CPUs. The important chips are the following:

8080 is the original 8-bit microcomputer chip. It appeared in 1974 and had 111 instructions. The bus bandwidth, a measure of maximum operating speed, is 0.75 Mbps, and register-to-register add time is 1.3 microsec. The chip has 256 I/O ports.

8085 is an 8-bit microprocessor, software compatible with 8080 but faster, with a 1.3-microsec instruction cycle.

8086 (introduced 1978) has the same architecture, addressing modes, and instruction set as 8088 (see below), but it has a 16-bit external data bus and incorporates data pipelining for simulated coprocessing (time-sharing). Bus bandwidth is 5 Mbps, and register-to-register add time is 0.3 microsec. This chip is the basis of the IBM PC XT. As a measure of relative speed, the clock rate of the XT, which has an architecture similar to that of the original PC, is 4.77 MHz, for an 8088-2 chip. Maximum clock rates: 5 MHz for 8086, 8 MHz for 8086-2. There is also a 10-MHz version. The associated math coprocessor is 8087.

8088 is the chip of the IBM PC and its clones. Although it connects to an 8-bit external data bus (rather than the 16 of the 8086), its internal bus is 16 bits wide. The chip uses a 20-bit address field so that it can address up to 1 Mbyte. There are 165 instructions. As a measure of speed, clock rate of the original PC was 2.0 MHz. Chip clock speeds are 4.77 and 8 MHz.

80186 is a faster version of 8086, made in 6- and 8-MHz versions. It enjoys twice the overall throughput of the 8086, partly because it has a faster bus interface (4 Mbps). It combines 15–20 of the most used 8086 system components into one. Compared to the earlier machines, it adds 10 new instructions. The associated math coprocessor is 8087.

80286 (introduced 1982) is related to 8086 but uses 24-bit addresses and thus can directly address up to 16 Mbytes. Memory management (paging) allows 80286 to address up to 1 Gbyte in all. The instruction set has 24 instructions added to that of the 8088/8086. This chip is the basis of the IBM-PC AT and AT clones. As a measure of relative speed, the clock rate of these machines is 8 MHz, although some clones have speeds as high as 12 MHz. Intel calculated that an 8-MHz 80286 has at least six times the throughput of a 5-MHz 8086. A special memory-protection feature (protected, as compared to real, mode) separates data from system code and permits the separation of programs and data from different tasks running through the processor.

80386 is a full 32-bit microprocessor, capable of handling 32-bit words as units rather than as double-precision entities. It can, therefore, address 4 Gbytes of memory. This chip has a virtual 8086 mode, in which it can emulate several 8086s running simultaneously, each with its own 1 Mbyte of memory. Bus bandwidth is 32 Mbps, and register-to-register add time is 0.125 microsec. There are 154 instructions. 80386 is the processor of the IBM PS/2 Model 70. In comparison with the earlier 8088, the Model 70 has an overall clock rate of 20 MHz. The Intel 80386 was introduced in 1985. The original version was later redesignated 80386DX. A new low-cost 80386SX was introduced in 1988; it is basically 80386DX with a 16-bit data bus, for use in PC AT systems, as a 286 replacement. The associated math coprocessors are 80387 and 80387SX.

80486 is an even faster chip, introduced in 1989, in which an improved 80386 processor is combined with an improved 80387 coprocessor and 8 kbytes of cache memory, the total requiring 1.2 million transistors. The original 80486 runs at 25 MHz, compared to 33 MHz for the fastest version of the 80386; however, it has a much greater capacity because of integration within one chip. The chip carries both an integer (arithmetic logic) unit and an integral FPU (equivalent to an 80387 coprocessor). It is pipelined (five stages), using a branch taken/not taken predictor to decide how to load the pipeline (if the prediction is wrong, the pipeline must be reloaded). It carries an 8-kbyte combined data and instruction cache (in effect four 2-kbyte caches). Too, the bus inside the chip is double-width (64 bits). Thanks to the cache and the wider bus, data are transferred to the processor twice as quickly as in a 386 (one vs. two clock cycles). Clock speed, originally 20 MHz, was increased to 25 MHz (April 1989), and then to 33 MHz (May 1990).

In June 1991 Intel announced a new 80486DX, to run at 50 MHz. The next step was clock-doubling (to 40, 50, or 66 MHz) in the 486DX2 (1992), which otherwise matches 486DX. Then clock speed was tripled in the 486DX4 (March 1994), which was offered in both 75- and 100-MHz versions, to replace the 25- and 33-MHz versions of the original 486. The main change was to double the cache to 16 kbytes. There were also changes in chip technology to limit power consumption (hence heat production), so that a 486DX4 could fit into an existing 486 socket.

The next chip in the series, Pentium (P5), introduced in March 1993, is similar to 80486 in using an integral FPU and a 64-bit internal bus. However, unlike the 386 and 486, it has a 64-bit external bus and thus cannot fit a 486 socket. On the other hand, it can run all x86-series software. It has two arithmetic units and is a superscalar processor (two-issue). It has dual 8-kbyte caches (data and instructions). There are two parallel instruction pipelines (five stages, the last three of which branch into the two parallel lines) and an FPU pipeline with individual add, multiply, and divide FPUs. Both integer pipelines have direct simultaneous access to the data cache. Splitting the pipeline enables the chip to set up both alternatives of a branch before the choice has been made. Compared to 80486, Pentium adds a layer of devices

(three vs. two layers) which contain 3.1M rather than 1.2M transistors (80386 had 275,000 transistors).

Pentium was designed to perform about twice as fast as a 486 running at the same clock rate (thanks to its superscalar design and double-width external bus), but most software does not make full use of its paired processors. Intel also claims that the Pentium coprocessor is 3 to 5 times as fast as the 486 coprocessor.

The 1993 Pentiums were rated at 60 and 66 MHz. Pentiums released in March 1994 had a 1.5-fold clock multiplier, so a 90-MHz Pentium could plug into a 60-MHz board, and a 100-MHz Pentium into a 66-MHz board. They were not fully compatible, however, because they used a different voltage. By late 1995, Intel was offering a 110-MHz version, with a 150-MHz version (P55) due in the near future. A shift to more compact technology (0.35 rather than 0.6 micron) may increase speed to 167–180 or even to 200 MHz.

Reportedly, Intel abandoned the 80586 designation after it discovered that many of its rivals were using 86-series designations for competitive chips (there is at least one 586).

The next in the family, P6 (Pentium Pro), is a two-chip, 14-stage CPU/cache module. It is superscalar (three-issue) and pipelined (12-stage) with dual 8-kbyte caches and a secondary 256-kbyte cache. As in P5, there are two integer units and an FPU. There is also a jump execution unit, presumably for multitasking. Plans originally called for a clock speed of 133 MHz, but prototypes performed better than expected, and some units may reach 166 or even 200 MHz. A redesign using more compact technology may take clock speed to 231 MHz by late 1996. Note that Pentium Pro has been described as a Pentium chip specially adapted to parallel computing. A P7 using very long instruction words is due in 1997.

Intel also produces a series of math coprocessors: 8087, 80287, 80387.

8087 is the two-chip math coprocessor intended to work with the 8086. 8087 adds hard-wired arithmetic, trigonometric, exponential, and logarithmic functions, amounting to a total of 68 more instructions. It is a bit-slice processor, operating on numbers represented by 8-, 16-, 32-, and 64-bit integers and on 32-, 64-, and 80-bit floating-point numbers (the internal architecture of the chip is arranged in terms of 64-bit words). It has eight 80-bit individually addressable register stacks and 14 general-purpose registers. The net effect of 8087 is to multiply the arithmetic performance of 8086 by a factor of 100.

80287 is the coprocessor intended for the 80286. It operates on 32-, 64-, and 80-bit floating-point numbers and on 32- and 64-bit integers. It incorporates over 50 mathematical instructions beyond those in the 80286 repertoire. Clock rate is 6, 8, or 10 MHz, and it incorporates eight 80-bit registers (internal architecture uses 80-bit words).

80387 is the coprocessor intended for the 80386. Total capacity is 108 bytes.

◆ Intel RISC Chips

About 1987–88 Intel introduced a pair of 32-bit RISC chips, i860 (formally announced in 1989) and i960. The former was intended to replace the company's CISC series (i86 chips), the latter for high-end and embedded applications. Apparently only the latter was particularly successful, although i860 is used for some signal processing applications, for example, in electronic warfare.

The i860 chip contains a RISC core (the arithmetic logic unit, ALU), an FPU, a memory-management unit (MMU), a 3D graphics unit attached to the FPU (the first in a microprocessor), and separate data (8 kbytes) and instruction (4 kbytes) caches. There are separate data (128-bit) and instruction (64-bit) buses, and the chip can accommodate 4 Gbytes of memory. The bus to external memory is 64 bits wide. The CPU can operated in both scalar and superscalar (two instructions per cycle) modes. The size of the instruction set, 85, is well down from those of its predecessors, but quite comparable with total instruction sets of the late 1960s. Instructions include a multiply-and-add floating-point instruction, equivalent to three conventional instructions, executed in a single clock cycle. Integers are normally handled as 32-bit data, but the CPU can handle 64- and even 128-bit data. The graphics element always operates on 64 bits of pixel at a time.

Speed is achieved partly by pipelining (using up to four pipelines in parallel) and partly by multiple-issue operation (which was not available in any contemporary single-chip CPU). This CPU has achieved 66 MFLOPS at a clock speed of 33 MHz (it has performed at up to 50 MHz). Operating at 40 MHz, it is faster than a standard VAX (see below), executing instructions at 33 MIPS. At peak (which cannot be sustained with a normal program) it executes 80 MFLOPS in single-precision mode and 60 MFLOPS in double-precision. It can execute a single-precision 1024-point FFT in 1 msec, which is only slightly slower than a contemporary specialized IBM FFT chip.

The i860 is used mainly as a coprocessor, because it is fastest in very limited mathematical or graphic applications. It has difficulty handling interrupts, which may cause the pipelines to lose their data.

The latest version, i860XP, has dual 16-kbyte caches and adds a few instructions. Compared to the earlier i860XR, it has more than twice as many transistors (2.55M vs. 1M).

The more successful i960 is a family of processors with four distinct architectures. All have a RISC core. The simplest architecture is limited to the core (80960KA and 80960CA). The next step up is a numeric processor (960-kbyte), which adds an FPU. Above that is the protected architecture (960MC), which adds an on-chip MMU and has the multitasking capability required by the ADA language. The final step up is the extended architecture (960XA), for object-oriented computing; it provides object addresses and protection using a thirty-third tag bit on the data bus (it defines a 32-bit word as either a data word or a pointer to an object in memory). The tag bit also improves data security by making it impossible to forge pointers to protected objects within memory. The extended architecture was chosen by the Joint Integrated Avionics Working Group (JIAWG) as a 32-bit Instruction Set Architecture standard for military avionics. See the ALR-67ASR in the Electronic Warfare section for an application of JIAWG standards.

The processor is pipelined. The integer execution unit (equivalent to an ALU) has access to 16 "global" registers and a 16-word local register cache. The FPU operates on 80-bit words and uses four registers of its own. There is also a 512-byte instruction cache.

◆ MIPS RISC Chips

Some of these chips are used in current U.S. programs, such as the AAYK-14. MIPS is a commercial version of a RISC architecture developed at Stanford University, and first announced about 1981. The competing Berkeley RISC architecture inspired the Sun SPARC series described below. MIPS is an acronym for microprocessor without interlocked pipeline stages. Silicon Graphics, which bought MIPS, produced Iris-series graphics workstations using MIPS processors. One was used in the U.S. CCS Mk 2 system.

MIPS was the first company to offer a commercial RISC chip, its 32-bit R2000. Addresses are 32 bits long, so addressable memory is 4 Gbytes. There is a five-stage pipeline. The chip carries two processors, a system control processor (which also manages memory), and an integer unit. The CPU is designed to operate with four coprocessors: the control unit, an FPU, and two others. The cache unit (4k to 64k) is separate from the main chip. The integer processor has 32×32-bit general-purpose registers and a pair of 32-bit registers to hold multiplication and division products; the control processor has a 32-bit program counter. R3000 is a modified version that handles its cache differently.

R4000 is a 64-bit equivalent to R2000/R3000 (instructions are still 32 bits long). An FPU is integrated into the main chip. The pipeline is lengthened to eight stages, on-chip data and instruction caches hold 8k to 32k each, and secondary cache capacity is 128k to 4 Mbytes. Addresses can be up to 36 bits long. R4200 is a low-power portable version.

R4400, which is used in military applications, is a high-performance version with a 200-MHz clock speed. R4400SC runs at 100 MHz with a 32-kbyte cache memory, a 128-kbyte secondary data cache, and a 128-kbyte secondary instruction cache. Integrated Device Technology produces R4600 (Orion), a comparable chip with a shorter pipeline and different cache operation, which the maker claims outperforms R4400 by 35% for integer calculations and by 8% for floating-point calculations.

R6000 is a 32-bit RISC chip with 36-bit words (4 bits for parity checking) and a 36-bit memory bus. As in R2000/3000, the pipeline has five stages. The primary data cache (on the chip) is 16k, and the instruction cache is 16 to 64k; secondary cache size is 512k or 2M.

The current R8000/R10000 are MIPS superscalar RISC machines using a two-chip package to double up power: two integer units, two FPUs, two load/store pipes, and one branch unit that can process up to four instructions per clock cycle. There is a five-stage pipeline. There are twin 64-bit buses for the integer and FPUs. Primary caches for floating-point operation are external, with 16k each of internal instruction and data integer caches. R10000 is intended to achieve a 200-MHz clock rate.

◆ Motorola Chips (68000 series)

The Motorola chips were first mass-produced as the basis of the Macintosh personal computers; their high speed made possible extensive graphics. All of the chips in the series are upward compatible (e.g., 68030 can execute 68000 programs, but not necessarily the other way around). The important chips in the series are the following:

68000, the first in the series, could bit-slice, handling data in segments of 8, 16, and 32 bits. The basic word is 16 bits, but the chip also operates on long words (32 bits). The chip is unusual in having two different operating modes, a supervisor mode and a user mode. Supervisor-mode instructions, which are used to run the screen in a Macintosh, take priority over user instructions, such as those for computation. Presumably, the bit-slicing is designed for fast graphics since the screen pixels generally are not specified by full 32-bit (or even 16-bit) words. Heavy use of the supervisor mode would slow computing, as many Macintosh users have found. There are 203 instructions. As an indication of speed, the original Macintosh ran at a clock rate of 8 MHz. This chip has a 16-bit data bus and a 24-bit address bus; it is a 16/32-bit microprocessor. The 24-bit address bus suffices for 4 Mwords (although the original Macintosh was limited to 512 kbytes). There are two other versions, 68008 (8-bit data bus, 20-bit address bus) and 68010 (which introduces virtual addressing and uses some different instructions).

68020 was the first full 32-bit microprocessor in the series. It could directly address up to 4 Gbytes of memory. The chip includes a 256-byte instruction cache for higher operating speed, and it uses pipelining. Alternative processing speeds are 12.5, 16.67, 20, 25, and 33.33 MHz. This chip can be combined with the 68881 and 68882 math coprocessors and also with the 688851 paged MMU. Up to eight coprocessors can be accommodated.

68030 is a faster equivalent to 68020, with both instruction and data caches (256 bytes each), and it has more sophisticated pipelining compared to that of 68020. There are 256-byte data and instruction caches. Processor speeds are 16.67, 20, 25, and 33.33 MHz. This chip can be combined with the 68881 and 68882 math coprocessors, up to eight of which can be accommodated.

68040 combines a main (integer) processor comparable to 68030 with an FPU, which in effect replaces a coprocessor; MMUs; and 4-kbyte instruction and data caches. The chip uses multiple independent pipelines and multiple internal buses. The main processor operates at 20 MIPS, and the FPU operates at 3.5 MFLOPS.

68060 was announced in 1993 and appeared in 1994 (the 68050 was never released). As of 1995, 68060 was being described as a 50-MHz chip with a planned 66-MHz version. It is compatible with earlier chips in the 68000 series, but it is a two-issue (two instructions fetched and executed in parallel per cycle) superscalar processor using a four-step pipeline (actually a four-stage instruction fetch pipeline followed by a pair of four-stage pipelines). There are separate 8-kbyte instruction and data caches, twice the size of those in the 68040.

These chips incorporate a hard-wired graphic user interface (GUI), which makes it relatively easy to run an elaborate display, but which cannot be eliminated (by editing computer code) in order to increase running speed for elaborate calculations.

68881 is a floating-point coprocessor designed to operate with 68020 or 68030. It uses two kinds of extended-precision data, a long word (80 bits: 15-bit exponent, 64-bit mantissa, 1-bit mantissa sign) and a shorter word (67 bits), the latter for intermediate-precision operation at very high speed. The chip uses 46 instructions (including 35 arithmetic operations), and it carries 22 constants in on-chip ROM (e.g., pi, e, and powers of 10).

68882 is an alternative math coprocessor that operates nonconcurrently with the main chip; it can control the bus in the chip independent of the main processor, a feature that can make for higher overall performance.

◆ Motorola RISC Chips (88000 series)

The MC88100 CPU (including an FPU) is typically connected to two and the 88200 cache and memory-management units (CMMU) by a 100-Mbps bus; the two 88200s provide separate 16-kbyte caches of instructions and data. Motorola calls the integer and floating-point arithmetic units special-function units (SFUs), and the instruction and physical architecture of the 3-unit chip are designed to accommodate up to 8 SFUs, some of which may be special purpose. Up to eight CMMUs can be attached, for a total cache of 128 kbytes. Other current RISC chips do not have on-board floating-point capability; typically, the central processor and a separate FPU are paired. The 88100 processor has 51 instructions (and uses 7 data types). It has 4 separate buses: a 30-bit data address bus (1G addresses), a 32-bit data bus, a 32-bit instruction address bus, and a 32-bit instruction bus.

In a typical application, the 88100 runs at 20 MIPS (microcomputers using it run at 25- or 33-MHz clock speed). Motorola has indicated that in the future it may redesign the basic RISC chip with a 64-bit bus for faster floating-point arithmetic. It may also move a 16-kbyte cache onto the basic chip.

In 1991 Motorola announced a second-generation RISC microprocessor, the 88110, which uses 0.8 micron HCMOS technology, with more than 1.4 million devices on a chip. It combines the functions of the current 88100 CPU and 88200 cache and memory-management unit; it runs at 3–5 times speed of previous units. It also incorporates multiple integer, floating-point, and graphics execution units, and an 80 bit wide internal data path.

In 1993 the 88000 series was abandoned in favor of an alliance with IBM to produce the PowerPC chip.

◆ PowerPC

The RISC chip was developed by Apple, Motorola, and IBM. It is used in the new Cooperative Engagement Capability (CEC) system and also by Ford as a car microcontroller. PowerPC was intended to execute (by emulation) both 68000-series and i86-series programs, unifying the IBM PC and Apple product lines. IBM considered Power an acronym for Performance Optimization with Enhanced RISC, and the chip is related to POWER-series chips developed for IBM's System/6000. The POWER1 CPU contained five or seven separate chips: branch unit, fixed-point unit, FPU, and two or four cache chips (separate instruction and data caches). The branch unit makes superscalar operation possible; POWER1 could execute up to four at once. This unit dispatches instructions (which may be out of order) to the various units of the CPU, keeping track of their status; too, each unit has its own instruction buffer. Like some other very fast processors, this one predicts which way a program will branch, pipelining the appropriate instructions and canceling them if the program takes the other branch. Eventually a single-chip version of POWER1 appeared as PowerPC; there is also a POWER2 (1993, using eight chips, including a 256-kbyte data cache). Despite a relatively low clock speed, such parallel chips can achieve very high throughput, so that a 71.5-MHz POWER2 is considered faster than a 200-MHz DEC Alpha 21064.

PowerPC is a superscalar (three-issue) using compound instructions (equivalent to more than one basic operation, as in the Hewlett-Packard PA series) as well as single dedicated instructions for floating-point arithmetic (most machines use several per operation). PowerPC uses a 64-bit data bus and a 32-bit address bus (as in Pentium).

Versions:

PC601 (three-issue, 50, 66, or 80 MHz; 100 and 135 MHz versions were announced late in 1994). Integer operations use 32-bit data (32 registers) but floating-point calculations use the full 64 bits (32 registers). The computer executes up to three instructions per cycle by using three separate units: integer, branch, and floating-point. However, most of the processing is done in the integer unit. The chip simultaneously executes branch and floating-point instructions out of order, before the integer unit executes earlier ones, then collates the results, to keep the branch and floating-point pipelines full. There is a single 32-kbyte cache for both instructions and data, operating in either read-only or write-back or disabled modes; the machine can stack two entries to read or three to write between cache and external circuits (the cache is connected to the queue by a 256-bit bus). The chip fits 2.8 million transistors onto its chip. This is the chip in the Apple Power Macintosh.

PC602 (two instructions/cycle, 66 or 80 MHz; 603e announced February 1995 for 100 MHz), optimized for portable operation. The design in simplified; it requires only 1.6 million transistors on the chip. Caching and buffering arrangements are entirely different from those in the PC601, with 8k in each of separate instruction and data caches. With the two types of caches separated, the chip need not make special arrangements to maintain the integrity of the cache. Nor is there a special memory queue, as in the PC601, between cache and external circuits. Design for energy conservation includes the ability to shut down the processor while preserving its contents.

PC604 (four instructions/cycle, 75, 100, 120, 133 MHz), a faster enhanced 601 with some 603 features for general-purpose computing. This version has at least two integer processors (hence four rather than three instructions executable per cycle) and a total of six execution units. Like a PC603, it has separate instruction and data caches, but they are 16 kbytes wide. The chip accommodates 3.6 million transistors.

PC620 (75, 100, 125 MHz), the highest-power version, for data servers and calculation-intensive requirements. This is the first true 64-bit member of the family. Like the 603 and the 604, it has a dual cache (32 kbytes). It is described as a higher-issue superscalar, so it must execute more than four instructions per cycle. It employs very long instruction words. Elements are two integer, two floating-point,and two branch branch/jump units.

PC630 will use a multichip CPU comprising a core, cache, and controller.

The 603, 604, and 620 represent a pure PowerPC architecture, whereas the 601 combines some elements of the earlier IBM POWER architecture with those of the PowerPC series.

◆ Sun SPARC Series

SPARC (Scalable Processor Architecture) is a specification to which CPUs are designed, rather than a proprietary series. Sun Microsystems was the first to make SPARC CPUs, but SPARC-compatible CPUs are made by several other companies. SPARC specifications are developed by an independent SPARC consortium, which tests chips to insure that they meet its requirements. A SPARC processor has separate integer and floating-point processors, each with its own 32-bit registers, and an optional coprocessor. The two processors act entirely independently, even simultaneously. Each has its own path to memory, although the integer unit sets memory addresses for both units. The main innovation in the architecture is a windowed set of registers which limits the need to go back to memory; Sun claims that this design cuts memory access from the usual 30 to 40% of instructions to about 20%.

The word "scalable" refers to the way in which the window can be scaled up to reduce loading and saving between functions, or scaled down to reduce switch time in multitasking, when the entire window must be saved.

The initial SPARC processor, the Sun-4/200, operated at 16.67 MHz and was announced on 8 July 1987. The instruction set was limited to 55 integer and 13 floating-point instructions. Current SPARC specifications (Version 9) describe 64-bit machines, although existing machines are 32-bit types. The typical SPARC operating system is UNIX. Presumably Sun won the DTC II competition largely because its RISC processor, SPARC, outperformed the CISC processor Hewlett-Packard was then offering.

♦ **Texas Instruments TMS320C Series**

These standard commercial digital signal processors (DSPs) use CISC architecture. They are very widely used in military programs such as radar systems and missiles. A DSP differs from a conventional CPU in that it is optimized for fast mathematical operation, particularly for matrix multiplication. Unlike a math coprocessor, it can be used independently of a CPU, using the program in its ROM. For FFTs, these DSPs have a special MAC instruction (multiply and add into the accumulator, i.e., accumulate). Unlike most CPUs, instructions are hard-wired into the chip; in the interest of speed, there is no microcode.

The original fixed-point 16-bit 32010 was developed for military purposes about 1981, using NMOS technology and ruggedized for a wide temperature range. TMS320C10 (1982) was a redesign using faster CMOS technology. It was the first commercial Texas Instruments DSP chip. A second militarized chip, SMJ32020, was also developed, but it is no longer made; TMS320C20 superseded it.

TMS320C10 and related chips (C1x series) all have 12-bit address buses (16-bit external and internal data, 32-bit accumulators). Running speed is about 5 MIPS. As a measure of complexity, these chips have 40 pins. TMS320C10-25 has 144 words of RAM and 1.5 kwords of ROM; C16 has 256 and 8 kwords, respectively. Members of the associated TMS320E family have EPROM in place of ROM. These chips have six or eight parallel ports, each 16 bits wide. C17 and E17 have six parallel ports but also have an interprocessor port to support parallel operation. Speed is measured by the time to load and store, for example, 114 nsec for TMS320C16 or 280 nsec for TMS320C10-14. C10 and C14 run at 25.6 MHz; C16 runs at 35 MHz, and C17 at 20 MHz.

The next series (C2x) has a 16-bit address bus and 16 parallel ports and one serial port. There are more instructions than in the C10 series. These chips use a Harvard architecture, in which there are separate program and data memory areas (64 kbytes for each), so that both can be fetched simultaneously. The arithmetic logic unit (ALU) is a parallel 32-bit device including a carry bit. TMS320C25 can load/store in 100 nsec. On-chip memory is 544 words of RAM and 4 kwords of ROM (C26 has 1.5 kwords of RAM and only 256 words of ROM). As a measure of increasing complexity, these chips require 68 pins. These chips run at 40/50 MHz (about 20 MIPS).

SMJ32020 is described as having twice the throughput of SMJ32010. Like the C25 described above, this 68-pin chip has 16 parallel and one serial ports, and a 16-bit address bus; memory is 544 words of RAM with no ROM, and load/store time is 200 nsec.

There is also a C2xx series intermediate between C2x and C5x (described below). Unlike C2x, these chips can perform a MAC operation in a single cycle. Like a C5x, a C2xx can access 64,000 16-bit parallel ports. Versions (speed in parentheses): C203 (40/57/80 MHz), C204 (40/80 MHz), C205 (40/80 MHz), F206/207 (40 MHz), F209 (40/57 MHz).

The next 16-bit generation is TMS320C50, running at up to 100 MHz (20-nsec instruction cycle). There are two parallel functional units feeding off the data bus: an ALU and a bit-logic processor. There is a hard-wired MAC circuit with a 16×16-bit multiplier feeding a 32-bit accumulator. There are 9 kwords of

RAM and 2 kwords of ROM, and eight parallel ports plus two serial ports. Clock speed increases to 100 MHz (50 MIPS), and there are more instructions (a total of about 125) than in C25. Load/store time is slashes to 35–50 nsec. This series of chips (which includes C51 and C51-57) requires 132 pins. C51 carries 1 kword of RAM and 8 kwords of ROM. Versions (with speeds): C50 (40/57/80 MHz), C51 (40/57/80/100 MHz with 4-kbyte RAM, 16-kbyte ROM), C52 (40/57/80/100 MHz; only member with 100 pins; 2-kbyte RAM, 8-kbyte ROM), C53 (40/50/80 MHz, 8-kbyte RAM, 32-kbyte ROM), LC56/LC57/LC57S (57/80 MHz with 14-kbyte RAM, 64-kbyte ROM).

There is also a C54x family, the company's highest-performance 16-bit DSPs, using 40-bit accumulators. Versions: C541 (80/100/133 MHz, 5 kwords RAM, 28 kwords ROM), C542/543 (80/100/133 MHz, 10 kwords RAM).

TMS320C30 (1988) is a 32-bit floating-point digital signal processor running at 33 MFLOPS. The arithmetic unit is separate from the logic control unit, and there is a four-stage pipeline. Buses: 32-bit external, internal, and address. There are 16 parallel ports. Memory: 2 kwords RAM (in two blocks, each with its own bus), 4 kwords ROM. Load/store time is 60 nsec. C30 runs at 33 to 50 MHz. Related versions include C31 (60 nsec, 33 to 50 MHz) and C32 (40 to 60 MHz).

TMS320C40 is another 32-bit floating-point DSP, the most important difference being that it is designed for parallel computing. It therefore has six high-speed ports for interprocessor communication, running at 20 Mbps (32 bits wide). Buses: 32 bits external and internal, 31 bits address. Memory: 128-word cache, 4 kwords of boot ROM, 2 kwords of data RAM. Load/store time is 40 nsec. This CPU runs at 40/50/60 MHz (25 MFLOPS sustained, 50 peak). Target applications for C40 include radar and sonar. Texas Instruments makes dual and quad C40 modules for the military, containing the chips plus additional memory, all in a compact package. They are used, for example, in missile guidance systems, which must package enormous computing power in a very small space. The related C44 runs at 50/60 MHz (4 kwords of boot ROM, 2 kwords of data RAM).

The next stage up, TMS320C80 (1994), has four fixed-point (16-bit) digital signal processing cores on a single chip, for a kind of parallelism. There is also an FPU. C80 was conceived for high-performance graphics. It is also used in multichannel modems, which are important for computer network servers (and are presumably also important for distributed data systems). The fixed-point units were specially designed for this application; they can operate on three numbers at the same time (for example, adding two and comparing the result with a third). C80 operates at 50 MHz.

The less expensive C82 (1996) combines a pair of 32-bit processors on its single chip with a RISC master processor, a 100-MFLOP FPU (with 4-kbyte data and instruction caches), a transfer controller (400 Mbps off-chip transfer rate), a crossbar switch, and 44 kbytes of SRAM. Each DSP has 4 kbytes of instruction cache and shares a 12-kbyte data memory (with the other digital signal processor and the master processor) via the crossbar. Special 64-bit long-word instructions are used to support many parallel operations in a single cycle. Texas Instruments claims that the C82 can exceed 1.5 BOPS (billions of operations/sec), 10 times the operating rate of any existing general-purpose processor.

♦ **VisiBridge**

VisiCom Labs' series of VME-backplane COTS processors replaces standard naval computers (UYK-7, -20, -43, -44, ON-143(V)6/(V)11, and AYK-14). Because these systems interpret existing CMS-2 code, they do not require new software, except in cases in which machine timing is critical. Each version uses a 68040 system control processor and a RISC processor (originally a Motorola 88100, currently a Motorola 88110) for each UYK-series machine replaced (because it has two processors, a UYK-43 requires a pair of RISC processors). For example, the VisiBridge version of the Army's EPLARS requires four 88110s to replace a UYK-7 and 3 UYK-44s, for a total throughput of 125 MIPS. The RISC processor is provided with 4 or 1 Mbytes of

DRAM, with two cache and memory-management units, and with a read-only memory which is used to interpret the CMS-2 program. The system control processor initializes the system, and controls system timing and contains code to control input/output. The chassis also carries an I/O control processor (an 88100/88110), an intelligent serial I/O board (carrying a 68020 I/O controller processor) for every 8 MIL-STD-118C/188-144 I/O channels and proprietary NTDS (one per channel) and 1553B boards, the latter controlling up to 8 channels. In some cases no I/O control processor is needed. Typically the chassis is an 18-slot ruggedized VME; a Futurebus+ replacement is being developed. The most elaborate version of VisiBridge produced to date is a UYK-43 replacement for the Aegis surface training and test center at Dahlgren.

The 88110 offers about 105 percent of the running speed of a UYK-43. VisiCom chose it because of its large cache memories and integrated floating point unit. As of the spring of 1996, VisiCom plans to shift to a new RISC processor, either a PowerPC 604 or a MIPS 4700 or 4800, to achieve about 5 times the throughput of a UYK-43. VisiBridge also offers a new graphic user interface (GUI) compatible with standard UNIX-based workstations. Existing connections to the interface in the CMS-2 program are automatically redirected to the GUI. Similarly, a computation-intensive part of a program can be extracted from the original CMS-2 onto a more powerful COTS computer running in ADA. VisiBridge is compatible with the commercial SCSI (small computer system interface) standard for I/O peripherals such as disk drives.

Applications to date have included the front-end communications processor of NAVMACS Mod 2 (eight delivered before the shift to a higher-order language), CUDIXS (replacing all shore terminals), the Coast Guard ON-143V(6) communications processor for JMCIS (about 20 delivered), the shore station of the British submarine tactical data system, RNSSIXS (eight delivered; the submarines have ON-143s), and the Aegis shore system (three delivered). As of the spring of 1996, VisiBridge was being tested as a UYK-7 replacement for the *Spruance* class, inside a Loral (Unisys) Lowboy. Vitro envisages a similar application for its proposed *Perry* class upgrade.

♦ Zilog Z80/Z8000

Z80 is an 8-bit microprocessor developed by former Intel engineers, descended from the 8080 and capable of running 8080 programs (it also has 80 more instructions, and can operate on 1, 4, 8, and 16-bit data). It has a 16-bit address bus, and thus can handle up to 64 kwords of addresses. Another unusual feature is that the CPU generates its own RAM refresh signals, simplifying any design using it. Clock speed, originally 2.5 MHz in an NMOS version, rose to 10 MHz in a CMOS version. Z80 was used in the Tandy TRS-80 computer. Z8000 was Zilog's later full 16-bit CPU, developed slightly later than Intel's 8086/8088. It can address up to 23 bits. Like Z80, it is designed for bit-slice arithmetic, with 8, 16, or 32-bit data (and it has a hardware instruction to multiply two 32-bit numbers into a 64-bit number). This was one of the first CPUs with two modes, one for the user and a protected mode for the operating system, to keep a user from directly affecting interrupts and other system functions. Z8000 ran into initial problems because it was very complex and did not use microcode. A later Z80000 was expanded to 32 bits and was among the first micro-CPUs to be pipelined, but it found few buyers. Z80 and Z8000 can be found in several British systems.

Data Buses

Buses are now used either to transmit data within a CDS or within a larger combat system. They are generally separate from a ship's internal communication system, which carries voice and analog signals. However, as bus capacity has increased, it has become attractive to merge the data bus and internal communication functions. Examples are the German DAVONET and the version of USQ-82 used on board the Australian *Collins*-class submarines.

CANADA

♦ SHINPADS (UYC-501)

This bus, equivalent to ten 1553Bs, can accommodate up to 256 users, with a maximum length of 300 m; maximum throughput is 9.5 Mbps. Up to 16 users can be given priority access, if their functions are particularly time-critical. For example, fire-control equipment requires updated information about every 50 millisec (i.e., about 20 times/sec). That rate can be achieved because the average user's access time is less than 100 microsec. An analysis of typical frigate requirements showed that the data bus would have to pass at least 3 million bps, and the design capacity is over twice that rate (actually 8 million bps [10-MHz clock rate]) to prevent delays. The standard message is up to 127 words (32 bits each) plus a 32-bit header and a 16-bit CRC word. A special block mode allows much longer messages to be sent.

The bus uses a pair of triaxial cables (control and data channels) plus up to four reserves; any two cables can be selected to form the primary bus. Access is via bus access modules (BAMs), each of which can accommodate up to four users. Typically each user is connected to a BAM on each bus cable. Bus control can be assigned to any node (user interface); if the control node fails, another can replace it.

FRANCE

♦ DIGIBUS/GINABUS

DIGIBUS, which is now standard in the French military (specification GAM-T-101) and is a proposed NATO standard. Originally called GINABUS (*Gestion des Informations Numeriques Aéroportes*, i.e., airborne digital data management), it was developed jointly by Dassault and ESD in 1973–76; the Bus Standard Marine was developed from it in 1975–77. It employs two twisted, shielded cable pairs, one carrying data and the other protocol messages; it can accommodate up to 32 ports, including bus-control ports. Maximum length is 100 m. Bus repeaters are now being developed to extend this length to 300 m, plus sub-bus couplers for sub-buses of up to 100 m length, each accommodating 31 more ports. Operating at 1 MHz, DIGIBUS has a capacity of 40 kword/sec (16-bit words).

♦ Recital (ED.103)

Reseau Ethernet Temps Reel, by Dassault Electronique, shown at Bourget Naval 1989, is a fiber-optic next-generation Ethernet LAN for the *Charles de Gaulle*. Each port requires an electro-optic transceiver (Bach) which handles data in Manchester frames at 10 Mbit/sec (it is downrated from the usual 30 Mbit/sec). Recital uses a multimode fiber (100/140/500-micron diameter; wavelength 850 nm). It can handle up to 128 ports along a 1500m cable. In contrast to the standard Ethernet, Recital switches from the standard random-message mode to a priority (deterministic) mode as message density increases. In this mode the latency delay for a priority message is 500 microsec.

GERMANY

♦ DAIL

Blohm & Voss has specified this Ethernet bus (Data Information Link) for MEKO Mk 3 frigates, the first of which are the Portuguese MEKO 200 PN frigates of the *Vasco da Gama* class. Although DAIL currently uses coaxial cable (at least two, up to eight), it can also use a fiber-optic cable. Each weapon and electronic functional unit is connected to DAIL via a Multi-Interface Computer Unit (MICE). A MEKO has two separate networks, A for command/control and B for navigation and own-ship data. They are interconnected, so one can take over the other's function. In the case of the Portuguese frigates, the single DAIL bus connects the STACOS command/control system, the EW system, the NATO Sea Sparrow, the 100mm gun, the double STIR, the weapons-control system, the radars, and the sonar. Blohm & Voss calls each system element, including its MICE interface, an intelligent functional unit (IFE). MICE/DAIL has been under development since 1981. An experimental network, using three MICE, was tested in 1984.

◆ DAVONET

Data and Voice Optical Network is the Siemens/Philips fiber-optic network for secure transmission of data (periodic, time-critical, and packet-oriented), voice, and narrow-band video. It combines the FOCON and SIFONET developed independently by Philips and Siemens, meets German MoD requirements, and should be usable by all branches of the service. It is a triple-redundant ring (which can be meshed). Capacity is 34 Mbit/sec (usable rate 33 Mbit/sec). DAVONET uses TDMA (time division multiple access): data is segmented in time, fed into path time slots in accord with a 34.8-MHz system clock providing 1088 channels (8 bits/channel, 32 kbps each), up to 1056 of which can be used either individually or in groups. General network management takes up less than 3% of overall capacity, hence the usable capacity of 33 Mbit/sec. Access delay to any user of a fixed channel is less than 10 microsec. Alternatively, channels can be assigned dynamically. In this case the channel is reserved only for the duration of a transmission. Channels are made available to each user every 250 microsec after connection setup. This mode is particularly good for voice/intercom. Another alternative is a token-passing mode with priority control. The three different access modes (fixed, dynamic, priority) can be used in parallel. Each bus station (BAU) can accommodate up to 10 individual user interfaces (BIUs, or bus interface units). The net can accommodate 128 BAU (expandable to 256), or it can be limited to a single BAU (up to 64k logical addresses).

ITALY

◆ MHIDAS

Alenia's multiple high integration distributed architecture data-bus system is the bus of the new SADOC/IPN systems. A single bus can be up to 300 m long, with branches up to 50 m long; it can support up to 64 bus-access modules. Each module can couple up to four users to the bus, for a total of 256 per bus. Data are transmitted in TDMA form, at up to 10 Mbit/sec, each word 1–4 bytes long (and each message 16–1024 bytes in length). Messages can be assigned three levels of priority, the bus providing priority 1 messages an average access time of 50 microsec (100 for priority 2, 200 for priority 3). Expected average throughput is 5 Mbit/sec, or 5000 messages/sec (100 bytes each, on average). MHIDAS is normally a cable bus; Alenia also offers a fiber-optic version.

NETHERLANDS

◆ SINCOS

Signaal's bus for STACOS systems is based on the Ethernet principle, and can use up to four triaxial cables in parallel to transmit at 10 Mbit/sec each. One cable handles the data load of a frigate combat system. Signaal equipment is connected to the bus via bus interface control logic (part of the equipment); other equipment is connected via a stand-alone bus interface unit (BIU) containing serial and parallel interfaces. Access to the bus is organized by a local communication controller (LCC) using the carrier sense multiple access/collision detection (CSMA/CD) procedure; controller is a VLSI chip integrated in the bus interface control logic of each user. The LCC senses whether the bus is free to allow the user to send a message.

Maximum length is about 250 m; 64 taps with two users per tap, or 128 per cable. Message length is variable up to 1500 bytes.

UNITED KINGDOM

◆ D3

Thorn-EMI's third-generation shipboard data distribution system (DDS) accepts information from a variety of ship sensors, including navigational units, translates it into standard format, and manages its distribution by data bus; similarly, it connects consoles with weapons. The effect of using a common bus is to provide nontraditional data, such as pitch and roll, to all ship sensors. Data from or for each sensor or weapon are passed through a data corrector/translator; those data may be further translated before being passed into the system bus. The intelligence in the corrector/translator may be used to enhance data prior to onward transmission, for example, to correct radar bearing data from an unstabilized antenna, using pitch and roll data on the combat-system bus. Thorn-EMI points out that uncorrected data may cause tracking errors as great as 3 deg.

D3 uses four standard configurations of 19in Double Eurocard racks, each carrying a master rack and zero, one, or two slave racks. The master rack contains the unit's CPU, communications controller (to the dual 1553B bus), and one to three buffers (Watchdog Interfaces, WIs). Each WI connects to a series of I/O units via an internal bus (the main WI directly, the others via bus extenders, BEs). The WI isolates data and converts and generates signals for self-monitoring. Standard modules include processor/memory, WI, BE, high-power digital to synchro converter, three-channel digital to synchro converter, two-channel synchro to digital converter, analog to digital converter, digital to analog converter, digital to torque synchro converter, 1553B, RS 422/232, DEF 0019, and NTDS. The rack can also accommodate an embedded data-bus remote terminal or bus controller. One rack can selectively (software-controlled) combine and repackage data from several sources for transmission into the ship system bus. A special small-ship D3 unit accommodates six synchro inputs, nine synchro outputs, one high-power synchro output, one digital (RS-422) input/output (to connect to the system bus) and an integral power supply in 50 kg.

Thorn-EMI states that 400 of its DDSs have been supplied over the last 20 years to 18 navies. That includes the combat-data distribution systems of the British Trident (*Vanguard* class) submarines and the Danish *Narvahlen* class, plus all or part of the DDS for the Norwegian *Kobben*, *Oslo*, and *Nordcap* classes. Thorn-EMI is responsible for navigational data distribution (including depth) for the British *Upholder*, Type 23, and *Sandown* classes, for translation and data format handling in Type 22, and for data bus control in the Canadian TRUMP program. Equipment is also in service in the Far East, Middle East, South America, and Europe, including the Brazilian *Niteroi* class.

◆ DEF STAN 00-19 (ASH)

The newest British official system is DEF STAN 00-19, previously known as ASH or the ASWE (Admiralty Surface Weapons Establishment) Serial Highway. At present it is limited to British surface warships. The transfer rate is 1.5 Mbit/sec (16-bit words), using a screened single twisted-cable pair. Up to 63 computers can be accommodated in a total length of 300 m.

◆ PLANET

Racal's naval version of PLANET (Private Local Area Network) can communicate both voice and digital data. The data interchange rate is 19.2 kbps (normally 9.6 kbps). The company, however, claims that PLANET easily carries digitized voice data at 64 kbps.

UNITED STATES

◆ ARINC 429

This standard commercial aircraft bus is used in some aircraft TDSs. Adopted for civil aircraft (large airliners) in 1977–78, ARINC 429 is a screened twisted-wire pair connecting a single transmitter to up to 20 receivers, with a data rate of 100 kbps or an alternative low rate of 12–14 kbps, always in 32-bit words.

◆ Ethernet (IEEE 802.3 and Ethernet 2 standards)

This is the standard of many shipboard LANs. Information is transmitted in packets. All devices listen to all packets, but accept only those addressed to them. To minimize collisions (simultaneous transmission by two devices), Ethernet uses carrier sense multiple access/collision detection (CSMA/CD): the hardware detects when two devices transmit at the same time. Even so, collisions (in which data are wiped out) apparently begin to occur at a small fraction of theoretical capacity. Ethernet is, however, attractive because below this point it offers extremely short latency: messages arrive much more quickly than in networks in which each device is allocated a time slot. Devices are connected to the Ethernet via media attachment units (MAU: transceivers or modems). Multiple-port transceivers (concentrators) permit several devices to share the same MAU.

There are various possible cables. The thick coaxial transmits at 10 Mbps with a maximum length of 500 m; the thin coaxial transmits at 10 Mbps with a maximum length of 185 m. Both are baseband cables. There are also 2, 5, and 10 Mbps broadband coaxials (max length 3600 m), an unshielded twisted pair (baseband, 10 Mbps, 100 m), and a multimode fiber-optic cable (baseband, 10 Mbps, 5000 m). Ethernet generally means thick Ethernet cable. Broadband is necessary if video, voice, and data are to be shared. Installations can be full duplex (one transmit and one receive cable).

◆ MIL-STD-1553B

The best-known Western data bus, defined in 1978 (1553A dates from 1975), is a single twisted-cable pair carrying data in 16-bit words (with a parity-checking bit and two synchronization pulses) at up to 50 kword/sec (800 kbps) at a frequency of 1 MHz. The maximum length of the cables is 100 m, and a terminal can carry up to 32 stubs (I/O points), one of which is allocated to a bus controller; the bus controller keeps signals from different systems separate. It is rare for the cables to approach the maximum length or for the terminal to have all 31 stubs. The 1553B differs from 1553A in having a broadcast mode (one sender, multiple receivers) and dynamic bus control (control can shift between terminals, for graceful degradation). In British service, MIL-STD-1553B is called DEF STAN 00-18.

MIL-STD-1773B is the fiber-optic version of MIL-STD-1553B.

MIL-STD-1760 is the standard aircraft bus controlling underwing stores.

A higher-capacity standard U.S. bus is under development; it will probably have a capacity of 20 Mbit/sec, split-channel operation (as in the French DIGIBUS), 64 remote terminals, and a maximum message length of 4000 words, compared to 32 words for MIL-STD-1553B.

◆ UDICON/USC-40(V)

FMC's Universal Digital Communications Network can accommodate 2 to 256 terminals. It is rated at 10 or 20 Mbit/sec using a single twisted-cable pair or fiber optics, in redundant ring configuration. Access can be controlled by token passing or by setting time slots; each terminal has four programmable priority levels. In either case control is distributed, so there is no single point of failure. Data can be stored and forwarded in packets of fixed size, or in real time in variable-length packets. UDICON is installed (in 14-terminal form, with 80 users) on a foreign frigate (probably the Israeli *Eilat* class).

USC-40(V) is a U.S. Navy derivative used in New Threat Upgrade (NTU) ships, distributing inertial navigation data to weapon system equipment, such as the integrated tracker and missile FCS. A two-terminal version is used on board *Seawolf* to collect and display own-ship information.

◆ USQ-82 (SDMS/ES-SDMS/FODMS)

Rockwell's Shipboard Data Multiplex System (SDMS) uses up to five copper coaxials in parallel, for redundancy. The current system uses copper cables; the future upgrade would be the fiber-optics FODMS, using two sets of dual counter-rotating fiber distributed-data interface (FDDI) rings to replace the current linear copper buses. It would be adaptable to the projected SAFENET architecture (see below). Adoption of fiber optics would eliminate 21 major units, but would not affect user interfaces to the system. Fiber optics reduce overall system weight to only 6–25% of the weight of the copper system.

ES-SDMS, adopted for the Australian *Collins* class, is the expanded service SDMS, encompassing combat-system data rather than ship-system data (e.g., damage control, rudder orders).

USQ-82 is a 16-bit digital system designed to handle all existing shipboard analog signals, including synchros and discrete ones (such as on/off). They are passed through 8- or 16-slot I/O module enclosures (IOMEs). User signal interface adapters collate mixed types of ship signals, aggregating common signal types to common I/O modules. The variety of I/O modules reflects the great variety of signal types aboard a ship. As of 1991, 18 types of I/O module interface were in full-scale development: two types of DC analog (high and low resolution), three synchro, seven discrete, five digital, also a switching control module (no external interface). Another 32 types had been specified but had not yet been developed: AC analog, demand digital input, solid-state power controller interface, STANAG 4153 (direct), time code output, EM log input, noise and vibration monitoring input, dual-speed synchro input (gear-locking), DC current input, and synchronous/asynchronous communications interface.

The eight-channel low-resolution DC analog I/O converts between step voltages ($+/-$ 10, 20, 40, 80 volts) and 12-bit channels. Each synchro I/O spans two slots (four channels in all, single or dual-speed inputs or outputs), converting to 10-bit data; limits are 1000 deg/sec and an acceleration of 500 deg/sec^2. A discrete data I/O handles 16 channels (eight for trilevel rather than on/off). Data are handled in Ethernet form at NTDS Fast (first-in/first-out output buffer, 60,000 $\times$ 16-bit words/sec) or Slow rate (256 $\times$ 16-bit word buffer). SDMS handles 8/16/24/32-bit words.

SDMS transmits 16-bit words at 2.4 Mbit/sec at up to 60,000 words/sec in either of two modes (A: data only; B: control plus data).

Each line of the transmission group has its own traffic controller, and is connected to area or area/remote multiplexers. The number of bus cables is not limited by system design. The system can accommodate up to 32 area/remote multiplexers, up to 16 area multiplexers, up to 112 remote multiplexers, up to 448 controller converters, and up to 7168 I/O modules; it can carry up to 114,688 user signals.

USQ-82 was chosen for the DDG-51 (TechEval/OpEval on board DD 972 1983, in production 1986) and LHD-1 (chosen for combat system 1984, operational 1990) classes. A derivative is used in BSY-1 (chosen 1979, first hardware delivered 1985). SDMS was tested for the Australian *Collins* class in 1986, and entered production in 1990.

◆ SAFENET

Survivable Adaptable Fiber-Optic Embedded Network has been chosen as the next-generation U.S. naval LAN data bus. Work began in June 1984, and in 1987 SAFENET became part of the NGCR (next-generation computer resources) program. This token-ring bus was designed so that the same hardware could be adapted both to current software (protocols) and to evolving, more sophisticated software, which could support features such as multicast (messages transferred to several users simultaneously), and which has a higher inherent capacity: SAFENET I (IEEE 802.5 standard) is to operate at 16 Mbit/sec among 64 users, and SAFENET II (FDDI standard) at 100 Mbit/sec among up to 256 users. SAFENET can be configured to carry two separate data streams. For example, in the TFCC system (FDDS) one carries secret-level data (GENSER), the other specially classified (compartmented) data.

TACTICAL DATA SYSTEMS

Tactical data-handling systems (TDSs), or combat-direction systems (CDSs), perform two related functions. First, they integrate available sensor data into a meaningful tactical picture, generally in the form of a 2D summary (or compiled) plot of the surrounding sea and air area. Such a plot includes some attempt to identify the occupants of that surrounding area, at least as friendly versus enemy. In this sense TDSs are command-decision aids.

Second, they often partially or completely automate the results of decisions taken by means of the plot. For example, using an electronic plot, an officer may designate a target for attack. This designation at a console in CIC will result automatically in the proper orders being given to, say, a surface-to-surface missile launcher. In some systems automation extends further. The combat system identifies particularly urgent threats and initiates reactions (such as missile firings) against them. In such cases the display allows the monitoring officer to abort the reaction while it is being made.

In some systems, an effort is made to provide tactical advice based on preprogrammed criteria; there may also be sufficient computer capacity for the TAO (or the system itself) to ask "what if" questions. Systems with these facilities are sometimes called combat-direction systems (to differentiate them from combat information systems) or combat management systems (CMS).

The sensors provide instantaneous data: current locations of targets or, in the case of passive sensors (ESM and sonar), lines of bearing. In many cases automatic combination of different sensor data (including data from off-board sensors, such as radars or passive devices on other ships or aircraft) can materially improve the total picture. However, *no* instantaneous picture is really useful for tactical decision-making since the essence of the tactical situation is its dynamic. The value of the plot is that it shows not only where everything is at any precise moment, but also enough of the history of the movement of any target to permit projection ahead. Integration of ESM and active-sensor data may also be valuable as a means of *identifying* given tracks.

Much of the purpose of the system is often threat evaluation and weapons assignment (TEWA). Many current systems claim to offer a degree of TEWA, but their capabilities often entail little more than a comparison of range and rate of approach, on the theory that a fast-moving inbound object is likely to be a more serious threat than a slower object farther out. That assumption is relatively naive. The next stage is for the system to try to identify targets by type and then to use an internal database to advise the monitoring officer (in U.S. practice, the TAO) of what threat each target represents.

Plots long antedated electronics, and the development of computerized TDSs was driven initially by the need to compile tracks more rapidly than could be done by hand. That requirement particularly applied to complex air situations, which developed very rapidly and demanded rapid decision-making and quick responses. Surface and ASW automation were slower to develop, and indeed many modern frigates lack automated plots of any type. It may be that the driver toward automation in smaller ships, such as large fast-attack boats, is primarily the need to limit manpower while still taking advantage of external sources of data, such as data links both to shore and to airborne radars. Only in recent years has automation become so inexpensive that it can easily be applied to fast-attack boats.

The big digital TDSs (such as the U.S. NTDS, the British ADAWS, the French SENIT, and the Italian SADOC) began as air-defense systems, oriented toward the control of interceptor aircraft. They, therefore, emphasized the ability to keep track of numerous relatively distant airborne targets and could tolerate some imprecision in tracking since the pilot (usually assisted by the aircraft's radar) could make up for inaccuracies of a few miles.

A separate line of development came out of gun (and then missile) fire control. Typical World War II practice was to assign one director (one fire-control channel) directly from CIC or the operations room to a target. That practice made for good tracking, but reassignment of the fire-control channel after a target was shot down was necessarily slow since the long-range air-search radars feeding the CIC had broad beams. The solution, adopted particularly by the Royal Navy, was to provide a separate narrow-beam target-indication radar. It could feed a series of separate tracking (memory) channels. When any fire channel (weapon plus director) destroyed a target, it could be reassigned (designated) from a tracking channel. This type of system is exemplified by the British GDS 3, with its associated Type 992 radar. When this type of system was digitized, the tracking channels were all carried together in a single computer, which the U.S. Navy would term the basis of a weapons-direction system (WDS).

Similarly, many weapons-control systems of the 1960s combined a search radar with a single tracker, which would control an engagement. The search radar inserted targets into a TWS memory, from among which the tracker selected. Examples include the French Vega, the Dutch WM20 series, the Italian NA 10, the Swedish 9LV, and the U.S. Mk 86. Predigital TWS placed each target in a separate channel, but the digital solution was generally to provide the system with a rudimentary short-range picture-keeper. Certainly the Dutch and French system designers quickly took the next step, adding a second computer to maintain a more elaborate tactical picture, as in the French Vega CDS and the Dutch minicombat system.

Both types of system share a common architecture. Typically the picture-keeping and weapons-system functions are carried in separate, often identical, computers. The picture is used for overall tactical decisions. The track picture in the weapons-control system is used to choose targets and perform fire control. In a ship with long-range missiles, both computers carry much the same overall picture, and the weapons-direction computer is often described as a hot spare (if the main picture-keeper crashes, it can take over the whole system). Matters are further complicated in that often the weapons-direction computer is considered part of a separate weapons system outside the combat information or TDS.

For example, a precomputer British air defense ship would have a main air plot based on the output of its long-range radar, and a separate gunnery plot based on the output of the shorter-range, higher-definition target acquisition radar. When ADAWS was introduced, each radar fed its own computer. The long-range air picture was generally used to cue the weapons system built around the shorter-range picture, but the latter used its own separate computer. Fire control itself absorbed the attention of a third computer. Ships without long-range radars had only a single air picture, hence a single picture-keeping computer (as in the CAAIS system).

The U.S. approach was different, perhaps because before the advent of missiles and their 3D radars the U.S. Navy did not use target-indication radars. The U.S. NTDS systems therefore combined all radar data in a single computer (actually, two to four linked computers) and embedded the WDS function in them. Only later did separate U.S. WDS computers appear, as in the missile cruisers and (in effect) the *Perry*-class frigates. (See the U.S. CDS entry below.) European navies that did use target-indication radars but which adopted NTDS either continued to use separate computers to service those radars or ultimately adopted separate WDS computers.

The U.S. Navy transferred expertise to France and Italy; early French SENIT and Italian SADOC systems are essentially NTDS clones. In each case a national naval programming center was set up. The West Germans initially collaborated with the French, and their SATIR can be considered a second-generation NTDS clone. The newer Spanish TRITAN is also essentially NTDS. All of these systems employ (or originally employed) standard U.S. Navy or Unisys computers. The Dutch SEWACO system is broadly analogous to NTDS but differs considerably in computer configuration.

These systems were conceived before the advent of inexpensive microcomputers. Generally the picture-keeper, for example, supplied video to all the system consoles. Consoles, sensors, and weapons were connected directly to the computer in a star architecture. Change required a combination of rewiring and reprogramming.

Compared to a conventional automated combat-direction system (CDS), a fire-control-oriented system tends toward more precise track data but also toward much shorter ranges and a smaller track capacity. The ultimate development of this type is the Aegis CDS, built around a fire-control-grade phased array radar, SPY-1. The SPY-1 Aegis radar has a very narrow beam because it is primarily a weapons-designation and -control radar. That characteristic in turn makes for very effective air surveillance, since the radar rarely sees two objects in any one search cell (range × bearing × altitude) and thus rarely confuses tracks.

Any central computer is limited partly by the number of different functions between which it must shift. One solution is to unload functions onto peripheral computers, ultimately leaving only the vital one of picture compilation. This shift to federated processing initially exploited the minicomputers introduced in the late 1960s and early 1970s. It is still continuing. For example, U.S. systems have recently unloaded their central computers by splitting off data-link processing (into a separate C2P computer) and, now, by pulling graphics out into separate smart workstations (of the Advanced Display System, ADS). Other navies have gone much further.

In theory, each separate unit can be programmed independently, so new systems and new functions are relatively easy to fit into the system. Only the channel between the unit and the central picture-keeping computer is firmly specified (e.g., the protocols by which the unit changes the central picture and by which it taps that picture). In fact, existing systems generally still require considerable integration between the programs in the different computers, so that they can act together (and also, usually, so that one machine can take on additional duties in the event of a failure).

A federated or distributed system is ultimately limited by a combination of bus capacity and the message-handling capability of its elements. These limits appear to have been felt in distributed systems such as the Malaysian version of Nauticus, the British SSCS, and the Rockwell system in the Australian *Collins* class. The solution is generally to be found in greater computer power at the element level, which (as of mid-1996) is not yet a serious problem.

The United States was the last major Western holdout favoring a central-computer system. ACDS Block 1 Level 3 is to be fully distributed. At present, all U.S. systems are centralized, as are many foreign ones reflecting U.S. Navy practice, for example, in Japan and Germany. France and Italy have opted for federated systems (TAVITAC, IPN series). Britain, which in the past favored centralized systems, has opted for fully distributed ones. Of the major foreign buyers, Taiwan has used the H930 modular (distributed) system for some time, and it appears that Korea has similar views. At least in the case of Taiwan, the survivability of the system is an important consideration in making a modular system attractive.

As minicomputers became more powerful, a greater degree of distribution became attractive. The main exemplars are probably the Canadian SHINPADS, the U.S. (Honeywell/Hughes) H930 Modular Combat System, and the British NAUTIS. These systems operate without any central computer at all. The consoles all link to a high-capacity data bus, and all benefit from database modifications initiated by any console. This scheme is similar to that employed in fleet-level NTDS, in which all ships share a common tactical picture, but the picture as a whole is not refreshed periodically. Instead, changes are propagated through the system. For details of the operation of such a distributed system, see the discussion below of the U.S. H930/ MCS.

There are two quite different distributed architectures. In one, weapons, sensors, and processors all ride a common ship bus. Examples are the Hughes H930 and the Plessey NAUTIS. Such a system has no bottlenecks at all. Each processor can execute any function (e.g., track-keeping or gunfire control), since all share the same stream of data and messages.

The alternative is to arrange the processors in a LAN, a special-purpose data bus. This bus in turn connects to the weapon/sensor bus or buses. The LAN acts as a central computer complex but, unlike a single-computer system, it degrades gracefully. Each machine in the LAN carries its own version of the tactical picture, updated by actions taken by the other processors (and transmitted within the LAN). Such a system has the advantage that intra-LAN message traffic need not compete with the traffic along the weapon and sensor buses, so picture updates can be quicker and more complete. On the other hand, the nodes at which the LAN connects to the weapon/sensor bus(es) form points of vulnerability. The LAN type of architecture is typified by the BAe-SEMA SSCS (British) and by the Contraves CoSys 200 (Swiss).

Aside from computer power, perhaps the single central issue in combat-system design is the operator-machine interface. Information must be presented in a manner best suited to very rapid decision. Just as a computer is limited in its throughput, a human operator is limited in the ability to process data presented visually. Different manufacturers have had markedly different responses to this problem. In the case of online data, there is a real question as to just how much supplementary data an officer in combat can or should absorb.

Both in Britain and in the United States, the service or the associated defense ministry was the system integrator. It selected contractors for the components, such as the computers and displays, but it retained responsibility for overall system design. Programming was a particular problem, especially since the early systems had to be written in machine language rather than in higher-level language. As a result, program maintenance was extremely difficult: machine-language programs are difficult to understand and thus to debug.

The U.S. approach was to accept commercial software production, with maintenance by naval personnel. However, because so much programming was done in machine language, maintenance was a serious problem, and contractor personnel had to remain at the Fleet Programming Center for many years. The Royal Navy used a team of naval officers to set down specifications for ADA and then ADAWS clear enough to enable contractors to program. That approach proved extremely laborious, and the result was inflexible and difficult to maintain. The Canadians later opted to teach naval officers to write the required software.

Console displays have gone through three generations. The first are radar (analog displays), on which some digital symbols can be superimposed. They can be described, then, as analog with digital injection. The electron guns creating the analog and digital symbols are entirely separate, and the only connection is through the brain of the operator. Many early NTDS consoles exemplify this type of operation. Some early ESM (strobe) displays, on which signal digital data could be superimposed, are of this type.

Pure synthetic-video displays are equivalent to early personal-computer displays. These displays are often described as *cursive* because each symbol is separately written out. They can show symbols and line elements, but they cannot address each pixel of the screen and thus cannot easily combine pictures from alternative sensors. Such displays cannot easily fulfill multiple functions since they cannot be used to dissect or display raw video of any type. Most current displays are of this type.

In pure raster-scan displays, the display computer can separately address each pixel on screen. Unlike the earlier radar-cum-symbol displays, raster-scan displays are not synchronized to any particular mechanical radar scan rate. Instead, radar-video data are scan-converted to a form compatible with raster display. After such conversion, two dissimilar radar pictures can be displayed simultaneously (e.g., superimposed in different colors). A fully rastered display can show different pictures side by side (windowing) in different scales. Such displays are probably ideal for cross-matching sensor data and are the current trend. They require vast processing power since there are no (physical) hardware character generators.

An important current issue is the value of color. It is argued that the use of color greatly increases the density of information that can be presented, and that monochrome displays cannot begin to provide enough. On the other hand, many people are moderately color-blind, and it may be that a very complicated display overloads the brain of the observer. This is a very difficult practical problem since the issue is one of overload *in combat*, that is, under great stress that cannot readily be duplicated in a peacetime experiment.

Current color displays all use electron beams sweeping across closely spaced triplets of color dots on the CRT face. Very precise beam alignment is used to illuminate the particular dots desired. It follows that stray electromagnetic fields, by no means unknown in shipboard spaces, can not only distort the tactical picture, but can also interchange the colors displayed, which may be embarrassing. That having been said, the recently adopted NATO standard calls for color coding of data in combat-direction displays.

Another issue in combat direction is symbology. The current standard U.S. NTDS symbols, which are widely used within NATO, were adopted partly because they were very easy to generate. Their meanings are not intuitively obvious. With enormous increases not only in computing power but in display sophistication have come calls for more natural symbols, such as airplane silhouettes oriented in the direction of flight (to replace the current abstract static symbols with vector tails). The British DFTDS demonstrator tested such ideas (its symbols were color-coded). A new NATO symbology standard is to replace the older NTDS set.

There is also the much larger issue of man-machine interface in the combat system as a whole. The displays are there to help operators compile a tactical picture usable by a decision-making officer (a TAO in U.S. parlance, a PWO in British parlance). That officer may want a composite or summary display physically large enough so others, such as the CO, can discuss the tactical situation. It is difficult to build very large CRTs; this is the same limit that applies to large-screen televisions. At least as of a few years ago, the effective limit on CRT diameter was about 22 in, which is why 22in displays are so common in the catalog that follows. The current U.S. solution, as manifested in the Aegis system, is a projection screen, similar to that used in current large-screen televisions. Its lines of sight will vary because of vibration, so the image may not be clear, especially during a hot action. Some other systems, such as TAVITAC, drive an electronic plotting board that becomes a summary display. The ultimate solution to this problem, a large flat-screen television using LCDs, is still some time in the future.

There are also important ergonomic issues. Before computers, the summary plot was a horizontal plotting table, marked up in grease pencil. Generations of naval officers became familiar with it and expected its electronic equivalent to look roughly the same. Numerous systems, therefore, employ horizontal displays, sometimes with several operator positions arranged around them. On the other hand, when CICs were invented, so were vertical plots. A vertical glass board was easier to plot against, and the plotters could work on one side while the tactical officers read the other.

It is probably easier for a single operator to read a vertical plot while seated at an associated keyboard. As long as each operator has a personal console, then, vertical CRTs (similar to those in computer workstations) are probably preferable. Certainly U.S. and U.S.-inspired systems are so configured. As soon as multiple operators must interact at a single summary display (e.g., to save CIC space), then presumably the horizontal or near-horizontal display comes into its own. This choice might be exemplified by the Swedish CEPLO (but note that the Danes are replacing CEPLO with a Terma TDS incorporating vertical screens).

Recent combat experience suggests that CIC personnel should always wear antiflash gloves. That presents a problem, since such gloves are far too clumsy to allow the wearers to use conventional keyboards (as in U.S. systems) efficiently; they are limited to one-finger typing. That is why the British, who have long demanded that all personnel wear antiflash gear, prefer light pens.

Deletions: CCS-280 (Canadian, discarded when "Tribal" class was rebuilt; report that it survived in two older ships was incorrect, as this modernization was never carried out), SEN-100/

SER/TBA (Italian: no sales), WSA 4 (British, only on Type 21s, removed by Pakistan when ships were purchased), HYCATS (U.S., used only on PHMs, now extinct), W-1200 (U.S., never sold as an all-up system; only elements entered service), CWS (U.S. Color Workstation, OJ-666[V]/USQ-88[V]: contract canceled).

SURFACE SHIP COMBAT-DIRECTION SYSTEMS

BRAZIL

◆ Siconta

This CDS, Sistema Controlo Tactica, developed by the Brazilian navy and by local industry (the Instituto de Perquisas da Marinha) with assistance from Ferranti's Brazilian subsidiary, SFB, now equips the carrier *Minas Gerais*. Siconta 2 has been selected for the *Niteroi*-class modernization. Siconta entered service in 1993. It uses a main processor (using 68030 and 68040 CPUs with a VME backplane) which feeds up to eight workstations via an Ethernet bus. Radar and data-link data are preprocessed by plot extractors (using 8086/8087 chips with 1 Mbyte of local memory); there are no detector/tracker operators. The mainframe uses a VRTX 32 (versatile real-time executive) operating system, and applications programs are written in C. The workstations, developed by EMGEPROM, use 68020 and 68030 processors and VME backplanes. There are two alternative consoles: a one-man vertical type with large and small screens (the latter alongside buttons) and with a keyboard and rollerball; and a nearly horizontal version with larger screens, still using a one-man keyboard and trackball.

CANADA

◆ SHINPADS/Mk 200X

Shipboard Integrated Processing and Display System is the combat-direction system (CDS) of the new "City"-class frigates and of rebuilt "Tribals" (under the TRUMP program). In the latter ships it supersedes an earlier centralized system, CCS-280.

SHINPADS was developed as the result of a 1974 study of alternative architectures for combat systems. It was one of the earliest fully distributed (data bus) systems, chosen because digital equipment was no longer so expensive that all processing had to be concentrated in a single central computer. All users have access to the entire database, and consoles are interchangeable (for graceful degradation in case of damage or breakdown). There is still a central database (tactical picture), divided into two elements, with primary and backup storage. The data bus itself was designed to be transparent to standard NATO interfaces; thus, existing equipment could be connected to the bus.

SHINPADS installed on board a TRUMP-class destroyer, showing standard multifunction displays. Note that although both the TRUMP and "City" class use the same SHINPADS hardware, there is very little software commonality between them. (Loral Unisys)

The system operates in three modes: automatic, semiautomatic, and manual. The normal mode is semiautomatic; the tactical situation usually changes relatively slowly. The automatic mode is for very fast engagements (the command can control engagements by veto). In the fall-back manual mode, the operator assigns weapons, begins engagements, and reconfigures the system to account for failures or damage to its components.

The 32 computers (UYK-502s, UYQ-504s, UYK-505s) of a "City"-class SHINPADS system are linked by four triaxial cables, only two of which need be active for 100% capability. Each cable can carry either system data or electrical control messages. The 10-Mbit/sec UYC-501(V) serial bus, equivalent to ten 1553B buses, was developed especially for SHINPADS. It uses only about 10% of its 10-MHz bandwidth. Similarly, 60% of total computer power could be lost without the loss of full system capability. All of the display consoles are interchangeable. SHINPADS is unique in its direct integration of EW (including chaff launching) into the combat system's data bus. The current word length is 16 bits (sometimes ganged to 32). All the computers are to be upgraded to UYK-507s (SHINPADS currently uses a mix of UYK-502s and -505s).

A "City"-class frigate has 13 SHINPADS standard display consoles (UYQ-501s) in the operations room and another on the bridge, plus a U2049 display used to monitor and reconfigure the system after damage or when changing modes, and two STIR (FCS) consoles. The operations room (CIC) is divided into two teams, AAW/Surface (led by a sensor weapons controller) and ASW (led by the assistant sensor weapons controller). The AAW/Surface group includes the two STIR operators, the track supervisor (with two radar tracker operators), and the EW supervisor (with an ESM operator and a communications-intercept operator). The ASW group includes a sonar-control supervisor (to supervise the operators of the hull sonar, towed array, and sonobuoy processor [Jezebel]) and the ASW-aircraft controller. The teams in the operations room are supervised by the operations room officer, who stands at an additional standard console. There is also a standard console in the operations room for the commanding officer (but the communications-intercept console is not a standard console).

The separate, integrated, machinery-control system (SHINMAX) has its own SHINPADS data bus. Very early on (late 1970s, certainly before 1983) there was some interest in integrating the operations room with machinery control, but that idea was dropped, and a different (CAE) system monitors the machinery and ship's condition. SHINMAX does use SHINPADS hardware, so that a hardware transplant is possible in the event of damage to one system or the other.

The TRUMP version of SHINPADS employs nine UYK-502 processors driving nine standard displays (the displays can also receive raw video directly). The bus is also connected to an EWS processor (UYK-502), a CCS data processor (UYK-505), and a system controller (a pair of UYK-502s, which are also connected to the system mass storage and other peripheral devices). The EWS is the interface to the ship's ECM system (CANEWS, SRD-501 HF/DF, and the ULQ-6 jammer). CCS is connected to the sensors, weapons, and the data links (11 and 14). CCS connects to the underwater FCS and the ship's CIWS via a data converter. A separate sonobuoy processor is provided for the ship's helicopters. Note that because the "City"- and TRUMP-class SHINPADS projects were separate, they use completely different, incompatible, software.

The SHINPADS display is the Computing Devices Company UYQ-501(V), a navalized version of the company's MSD-7001. UYQ-501 is part of a standard Canadian navy family of digital equipment, using a 19in, 1024 × 1024-pixel CRT, with 4 Mbits of RAM to service its display. It can, therefore, show complex overlays. The associated graphics processor has 8 Mbits of RAM and can operate in eight colors. Alternative modes are 525, 625, 875, and 1025 lines of television resolution. This standard console is also used in the DELEX program.

MSD-7001 is one of a line of MAGICS (Multimode Advanced Graphics and Imaging Systems) consoles for command and control. The next version, MAGICS 2, is built around 68020 processors, which allow for simultaneous display of up to 14 outputs on a 19in screen. Two screens are accommodated vertically in a 24in console, with a standard VME-bus chassis below. MAGICS 2, intended for the German requirement won by AEG (see the German section below), began tests early in 1989.

The Link 11 data terminal set in this system is USQ-76.

Mk 200X is a Unisys (Loral) commercial version of SHIN-PADS, announced in 1994.

◆ ADLIPS

The Automatic Data Link Plotting System, a "poor man's NTDS," survives on board two pairs of elderly frigates, *Annapolis* and *Nipigon* and *Gatineau* and *Terra Nova*. The latter pair are likely to retire relatively soon, and all four will be retired to provide operating funds if Canada buys the British *Upholder*-class submarines. ADLIPS on board replenishment ships have been replaced by EDO LRDS consoles (see the control/surveillance section above). The system employs a UYK-20 central computer, limiting computing load by avoiding target evaluation and relying on external EW and ASW systems; the only weapon controlled by the UYK-20 is the gun. The main display is the situation information display (SID), a 20in horizontal CRT showing raw video, IFF data, and synthetic video. Each of three operating stations around the SID has its own trackball and alphanumeric keyboard. This type of display was chosen to minimize space requirements in a crowded operations room. In addition, plasma displays show synthetic video only on the bridge and in the EW room. As in NTDS, the operators at the consoles detect the targets, so that each SID can insert three targets simultaneously into the system. System capacity is 25 local and 75 remote tracks plus 40 static points, with 6min track-position histories for 25 local targets and vectors for all 100 tracks. ADLIPS can pass 10 tracks (7 dynamic) to the associated ASW direction system (ASWDS); it can accept 16 dynamic tracks from ASWDS.

A follow-on system using a UYK-44 computer, ADLIPS 90, attracted no customers. See the 1991/92 edition for further details of ADLIPS and of its planned successor.

◆ MSDF

Unisys Canada developed this multisensor data fusion device for exploratory research in target tracking and classification, but it may be incorporated in the "City"-class software update planned for 2005. It is broadly analogous to the British DFTDS described below in that it takes contact data directly from the ship's combat-system bus, assembling it automatically into a tactical picture by associating contacts from different sensors at the plot or contact level, rather than at the vector level (as in a current CDS). In a sense, too, it is analogous to the U.S. SYS series, except that it accepts nonradar data.

MSDF employs four parallel UNIX processes: information management (IM), data fusion (DF), performance evaluation (PE), and display management (DM). It is designed to read "City"-class bus data (SPS-49, Sea Giraffe, IFF, and ESM) without any design modifications to the ship, although the sensors and bus were not originally designed to support a track management function that fuses information at the contact level. It excluded Link 11 and STIR, but they will be added later. Tracks are automatically associated with each other and automatically identified using a Unisys approach that relies on speed and emitter category (if emitting), and also by associating radar and ESM data. Compared to existing systems, MSDF offers four improvements in identification: it is automatic, requiring no operator intervention; it is continuously updated from multiple correlation of all sensor data; all proposed identifications show the degree of confidence; and the system offers alternatives for low-confidence cases.

MSDF provides some features not available on the frigate, such as a one-line explanation of each QAB (quick action button) from the right mouse button; visual evaluation of track quality through optional display of an ellipse of probability of hooked track; optional time history of the last N contacts ($N = 10$ on the actual configuration); a map of the tactical situation area;

and scrolling windows in the data amplification read-out part of the display.

MSDF tests to date (since 1991) have shown that data fusion makes for better target location, velocity measurement, and identification. It is currently set up to compare the "City"-class combat system and MSDF track performance on a real-time basis, displaying frigate and MSDF data using an operator-machine interface based on that of the frigate.

MSDF began as a private venture in January 1991, but one-third has been funded by Maritime Command since April 1991. As of spring 1995 Unisys was negotiating with MARCOM to supply a version of MSDF based on the "City"-class C^2 system. This version uses SunSPARC 10 workstations with Barco display processors, linked to a SHINPADS bus, using software in Fortran and C. A production version could be available 1998–99.

CHILE

◆ SP-100

This fully distributed system was developed by SISDEF (Compania de Ingeria de Sistemas de Defense Ltd.), a joint venture of Ferranti International and ASMAR. It is equipping Chilean "County"-class cruisers (*Blanco Encalada* began sea trials in the summer of 1993; the new system replaces ADAWS-1 as ships are modernized) and *Leander*-class frigates (the first ship fitted was *Condell*; these ships previously lacked any CDS). A miniaturized version, SP-100C, was developed for maritime patrol aircraft, submarines, and fast-attack craft, but it is not clear whether it has been deployed.

The system's Ethernet LAN links fully autonomous tactical consoles (Consolas Tacticas, or CONTACs), each with four dedicated 80486DX-66 processors and a TMS34020 signal processor, running software written in ADA, on Cheapernet backplanes (internal buses). Each processor has a separate function and runs its own software module: LAN manager, graphic module, link tracker, operator module, and coordinator. The LAN manager establishes communications between the software modules and the other system elements, including other consoles. The graphic module (running on the TMS34020 graphic host) connects to the radars and to the LAN manager, as well as (via a separate graphic Cheapernet) to the CRT and the trackball. The operator module connects to the touch screen and to the keyboard. One element connects the internal Cheapernet to the Ethernet. The console Cheapernet carries a graphic host and the link tracker. In the link tracker reside the programs associated with administering the tactical database: track and point tables, geometrical elements, reference points, and so on.

There are both vertical (one-operator CONTAC-V with 19in screen) and horizontal (three-operator CONTAC-H with 27in screen, alphanumeric screen, and three trackballs) versions. The tactical picture, carrying up to 512 tracks (as well as 64 reference points, 100 vectors, 8 tactical grids, and 64 acquisition sectors), is duplicated in each console, so there is no central computer. The standard screen (1600 × 1200 pixels) accommodates a synthetic- or raw-video PPI alongside a 1024 × 1024 window for information and video and two windows for totes. Range scales: 4, 8, 16, 32, 64, 128, 256, and 512 nm.

A typical destroyer system uses up to five vertical and horizontal workstations. All are connected to an Ethernet LAN. Each sensor is connected to the LAN via an operator console and a tactical preprocessor. For example, a surface search radar (Radar Rebusca) feeds a plot extractor, which feeds a multitracker (which is connected to the LAN). The LAN also carries the data link (with its own computer) and the CONTACs. The same LAN is also connected to the weapons via weapons preprocessors and fire-control systems. Own-ship sensors (GPS, log, gyro) feed the same LAN through their preprocessor. Beside the CONTACs there are service computer feeding services: a printer, a plotter, and an optical disk.

SP-100C is a compact version using MDL, the module data link, a minimum-capacity console for airplanes, helicopters, or minor units. The screen can be as small as 14 in, and this version may carry only 100 tracks. It is not clear whether it has ever been deployed.

All versions of the system use a digital data link (19,200 bps, using error-correcting codes). There are two channels, roll-call and TDMA.

CHINA

Weapons systems, at least in frigates and smaller ships, each consist of a dedicated sensor connected to the weapon via a standard 2KJ-series console. It apparently displays the dedicated sensor picture and also performs ballistic calculations; presumably it is a digital workstation carrying alternative cards for different sensors and weapons. The tight coupling between sensor, control station, and weapon mirrors Soviet practice. The console suffix gives its role, for example, 2KJ-3 is used with the Type 352 radar (and C801 antiship missiles), 2KJ-5 is used for ASW, and the Chinese version of Newton Beta uses 2KJ-8. Each console carries a vertical green or black screen (ca. 10 × 12 in) and an IBM-style QWERTY keyboard; there is no trackball. Presumably all are standard workstations. Reportedly they incorporate 80286 or clone chips. These workstations may be related to the Italian MARA 286 family. The PRC tried to buy Dardo and was looking at IPN-S (which incorporated MARA) about 1985.

Systems as a whole have their own designations. Thus the ASW system on board a "Jianghu" is SJD-5, consisting of a searchlight sonar coupled to a 2KJ-5 console, which in turn controls a rocket launcher. There is probably no separate sonar console.

According to a recent Chinese official account, the second-generation missile destroyers (later "Luda" class, the first of which was delivered in December 1989) have a computer CDS. Work on the concept study (by the Seventh Academy, 701, 709, 716, and 724 Institutes) began in 1983, presumably after the decision had been made not to buy a British system employing Sea Dart missiles. No. 701 Institute was designated primary organization for destroyer combat systems. The Chinese account states that this was the first time the CDS was designed first; in the past, equipment was selected, and the CDS developed later (however, there is evidence that at least in the case of frigates, there were no CICs at all prior to the "Jiangwei" class). Land tests of the new system began in December 1986.

A photograph of the system elements shows six vertical consoles, each carrying a circular CRT with a small rectangular TV-type screen above and to the left. There are also the usual switches and keyboard below. The configuration suggests the French TAVITAC, which was reportedly sold to China.

"Luhus" (Project 051HT), which may be considered third-generation "Ludas," apparently have a Chinese equivalent of TAVITAC 2000. In their case it is described as an improvement on previous CDS, with "higher automation and faster reaction," which would tend to confirm that the earlier system was something like TAVITAC (Vega III).

The same Chinese account indicates that "Type II antiship frigates," which may mean the "Jiangwei" (Project 055) class, have a simplified CDS in an enlarged CIC, room for which is made by enclosing the main deck amidships. Other reports indicate that the "Jiangwei" system is designated CCS-3 and is associated with a digital data link. It seems unlikely that Type II refers to the "Jianghu II" class (Project 053HT), because ships of this type exported to Thailand lacked not only computers but also, reportedly, spaces for CICs. It seems likely that the link in Project 055 is the French Link W, which is associated with the TAVITAC family of systems.

DENMARK

◆ StanFlex 300 System (StanFire)

This is the first CDS designed specifically for rapid reconfiguration. StanFlex 300 consists of three standard two-position multipurpose consoles (each including its own ruggedized commercial-type VLSI computer) on a data bus that also connects the consoles to modular weapons and sensors. The latter can be replaced, using only dockyard cranes, in 24 hr, and the system

reconfigured by software substitution. Up to three additional consoles can be added to control additional weapons or other systems. All weapons control is centralized in the operations room (there is no local control at all in a classical sense). This type of operation requires very high computing capacity at each machine; the Danish navy states that the total computing capacity of a StanFlex is 30,000 times that of the first Danish small-ship system, which entered service as recently as 1978. A fiber-optic data bus was considered and tested, but instead a conventional 10-Mbit/sec shielded cable has been used. The bus is duplicated to ensure its reliability.

The number of operator stations was dictated by the MCM requirement: assisting the minehunting officer during the detection and classification phases are two sonar operators, one classification operator, and one surface drone operator. Another console is needed for the operator of the minehunting/killing submersible. The boats also function as missile- or torpedo-armed fast-attack craft, roles that in the past have been altogether incompatible with mine countermeasures. In this case, minehunting is possible only because the ship can deploy and control remotely operated vehicles.

It was originally expected that the machinery would be monitored and controlled from the single data bus so that the ship could operate with an unmanned engine room. The full integration of machinery with the command/control system proved too difficult, and instead the machinery forms a separate subsystem that feeds into the main data bus.

The StanFlex program began as a feasibility study in 1982; project definition followed in 1983, and funds for seven ships were approved in 1984. The first ship, *Flyvefisken*, was delivered in December 1988. The number "300" is the nominal displacement of the ship (actual displacement depends upon which weapons and sensors are installed at any time). A similar system has been installed on board the *Thetis*-class frigates.

Terma was responsible for much system hardware; this system is a variant of the Swedish (CelsiusTech) 9LV 200 Mk 3.

◆ TDS/PDS

Terma's TDS grew out of a plot data system (PDS) developed for fishery protection frigates; the prototype was aboard the *Vaedderen* in 1982. The Royal Danish Navy saw PDS as a possible approach to a low-cost TDS (much like the British CANE) and let a contract in December 1984. The first unit was installed on the fast patrol boat *Bille*. TDS replaced the CEPLOs on board *Willemoes*-class attack boats and *Hvidbjornen*-class fishing pro-

The Terma tactical data system, with two local operational plots (LOPs) flanking a general operations plot (GOP). Each LOP has a system terminal (ST) underneath; the ST consists of a pair of plasma displays, a rollerball, and a keyboard. The console between the two LOPs handles the data link. (Terma)

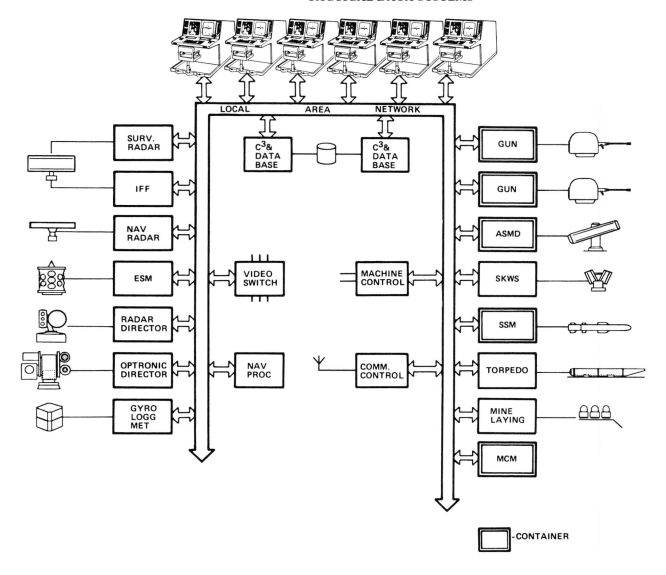

The StanFire system of the *Flyvefisken* class is based on the Swedish 9LV Mk 3. It is unusual in its ability to reconfigure to accommodate a wide variety of containerized weapons. The two boxes marked C3 and Data Base are two system database computers that carry the system track file. All applications software is run in the processors in the consoles. (CelsiusTech)

tection frigates; it has been installed on board *Falster*-class mine-layers (the first in 1990, then one per year).

The system uses a Motorola 68000-series microprocessor, a VME bus, and Pascal and C-language software. The main elements are the local operator plot (LOP) and the general operational plot (GOP). In a typical installation (*Hvidbjornen*), the GOP is flanked by two LOPs, each of the latter incorporating a system terminal (ST) for data entry.

The LOPs are the operating consoles; the GOP is the summary plot. The latter is a 20in, color, raster-scan CRT, showing up to 240 tracks (including those received via data link). It stores one large and up to eight small maps, and up to 400 mine positions. Because the GOP is a summary display using external data, it incorporates a latitude-longitude grid (rather than a polar grid centered on the ship). It can display data in eight colors, and range scales are 2–512 nm.

Each LOP carries a 16in CRT showing both raw and super-imposed synthetic video and up to 50 tracks. Its memory can store up to eight small maps, each composed of up to 20 vectors. The display also incorporates two vectors for measurement purposes and two index lines for navigational purposes, as well as optical sight lines and helicopter approach patterns. There are eight range scales (0.5–128 nm). The associated ST is a keyboard

with dedicated function keys, a rollerball, and two alphanumeric plasma displays (totes).

TDS-2000, the export version, uses a different (Scanter) work-station using 68030/68040 processors and a 21in (1280 × 1040) raster-scan display. These workstations are used as backups in the *Nils Juel* and *Flyvefisken* classes.

Denmark is the only user. PDS is used in the *Beskytteren*-class frigates, in the *Falster* class, and in the *Lindorman* class; TDS is in the *Willemoes* class.

FRANCE

◆ SENIT/TAVITAC

Système d'Exploitation Naval des Informations Tactiques (SENIT) was originally equivalent to and derived from the U.S. NTDS. As with NTDS, SENIT is a national system developed by the government laboratory system. The associated CPM (navy programming center) was established in 1963. TAVITAC (Traitement Automatique et Visualisation Tactique) is the Thomson-CSF export equivalent to SENIT. The term *TAVITAC* is also used for the tactical picture-keeper in Vega (now Thom-sea) combat systems for fast-attack boats. As of 1996 DCNI (which is responsible for SENIT) is competing with Thomson-CSF (which now markets TACTICOS, but which in the past was responsible for TAVITAC).

Versions:

SENIT 2 was conceived as a destroyer-size version of SENIT, using the Univac 1212 (CP-642) computer and UYA-4 console of the U.S. NTDS system, developed in collaboration with West Germany and thus leading to the German SATIR system. There were two versions, one for Tartar missile destroyers (three computers), and one for radar pickets (one computer). Tartar ships had their fire-control systems converted from analog to digital for SENIT compatibility; SENIT is responsible for many FCS functions.

Users: Initially eight destroyers (three radar pickets, four SAM destroyers, and the ASW destroyer *Duperre*). The carrier *Clemenceau* has the SENIT 2 of the discarded destroyer *Jaurreguibery* (refit September 1977–November 1978). *Foch* has the system of the discarded destroyer *Tartu* (refit July 1980–December 1981). The carriers were to have had SENIT 4. This version replaced the earlier SENIT 1 installed on the *Suffren* class during September 1989–March 1991 refits. The carriers have nine consoles and a V6 TER horizontal display; the *Suffrens* have 10 consoles. Like its U.S. equivalents, this system can maintain 128 tracks.

SENIT 3 employs two Univac 1230 computers (with memory extensions) for ASW ships; it also handles a tactical air picture (128 tracks). There are eight tactical consoles in *Aconit* (10 in the *Tourvilles* plus a PLAD automatic plotting table) corresponding to the sensors, plus weapons consoles and a computer-driven plotting table. The displays are UYA-4s. This system is on board the destroyer *Aconit* and the three F67 (*Tourville*)-class frigates.

SENIT 4 is a French-designed system built around the French IRIS 55M (P2MS) computer programmed in ADA and a new Vizir display with 16in CRT, keyboard, and trackball. The software language is Maxiris or LTR 2. There are seven consoles, each of which can display all 130 system tracks, plus up to 12 lines each of 18 alphanumeric characters, and 23 lines of target vectors. There are also two Precilec E8000 automatic plotting tables.

Users: Georges Leygues class.

SENIT 6 is shown as installed on board *Cassard*-class frigates. Dashed lines indicate future capabilities (the ships now have their jammers). Each circle indicates a computer (15M/125X, 256 kwords, 16-bit words) serving an element of the system. The sixth computer is backup and provides growth potential. GE is guerre électronique, EW in French. DO is Designation d'Objectif (target designation). (DCN)

SENIT 5 was an abortive small-ship (2000–6000 t) version announced in 1976. The design initially called for an IRIS 15M computer (total capacity 60 tracks), but the version finally proposed was built around an IRIS 35M computer (16–256k) with two to five Vizir displays, each of which could show 40 tracks. SENIT 5 was planned for the A69-class corvette, but it was never used. Vega IIIC (TAVITAC; see below) is an export version, using a less-capable central computer (15M/125F, with a capacity of 128k, expandable to 512k), exported to Saudi Arabia and possibly to China. TAVITAC 2000 (see below) is a very different distributed system.

SENIT 6 is a federated system for the *Cassard*-class AAW frigates, built around six 15M/125X minicomputers programmed in ADA. A seventh computer is kept in reserve, and ships have sufficient space to add an eighth (which will be required to handle Link 16). The computers are located in two separate rooms, fore and aft. The ship is arranged in six subsystems, each served

SENIT 6 aboard the destroyer *Cassard*, showing standard Vista consoles. (DCN photo by Jean Biaugeaud)

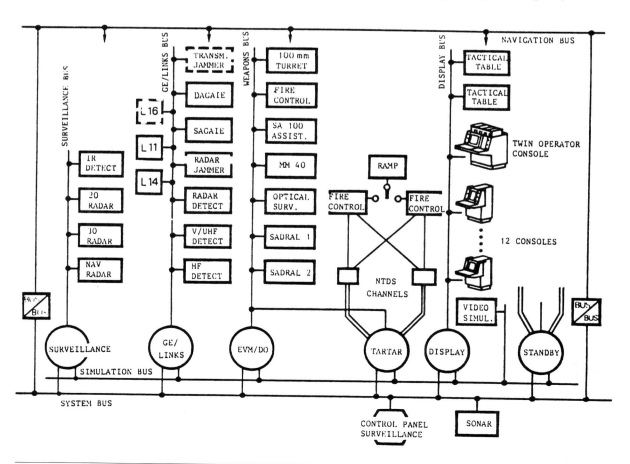

by one of the six running main computers. Each subsystem has several 15M05E computers for local processing and constitutes a LAN. The subsystems, in turn, are linked by a 1-Mbit/sec Digibus (BSM).

One of the main computers carries the tactical picture and runs the display subsystem, and is connected to 11 single-operator consoles, one two-operator console (for CO and TAO), and two Precilac navigational tables (for ASW: each can carry up to 20 tracks).

The other main computers are dedicated to sensor processing, TEWA (for self-defense), area air defense, ESM/ECM, and the data links. The ASW function is autonomous, linked to the system bus. Much of the processing for each weapon and sensor is done locally, outside the system bus. Total capacity is 400 tracks.

The GVM console carries a 16in (40 cm) monochrome CRT with variable-action and fixed-action buttons and a trackball.

SENIT 6 incorporated multisensor tracking from the outset, and will include a Link 16 terminal (possibly MIDS, for which the French navy has bought 100 terminals) from 1995.

Note that the CDS of the Atlantique 2 maritime patrol aircraft is a version of SENIT 6.

SENIT 7 is the French navy's designation for TAVITAC 2000, which is installed in the *La Fayette* class. This system is also called SACEIT (Système Automatise de Commandement et d'Exploitation des Informations Tactiques). For details, see TAVITAC 2000 below.

SENIT 8 is on the carrier *Charles de Gaulle*. It was the first French CDS to use an open systems approach. It employs eight main 32-bit Hewlett-Packard computers (ruggedized by CSEE-Defense, equivalent to the U.S. TAC-3). Each of four computer cabinets contains two processors (one a spare) and shelf space sufficient for a third. Functions include weapons control, search, link handling (Links 11, 14, and 16; presumably also Link 22), and command/control. There is apparently a separate air-control center. The 24 operator workstations (15 dual-screen system-operator consoles, 9 single-screen picture compilation consoles; with space for one more console) are CSEE-Defense's Calistos. These workstations are equivalent to the U.S. UYQ-70 used in ACDS Block 1. They are all carried on a dual-redundant Ethernet bus (ED.103, using the Dassault Electronique Recital real-time deterministic network protocol). The main system bus feeds the main computers, which have separate links to the SENIT consoles (which are also fed by a bus connected to the main bus). The system uses a separate Ethernet bus to connect with AIDCOMER.

Software was written by ISC (Integration de Systèmes de Commandement, now absorbing the French navy programming center), CSEE-Defense, Hewlett-Packard, and Dassault Electronique. About 1 million lines of ADA code were required for tactical applications, with another 400,000 lines of C software in console-based graphics processing. DCNI credits SENIT 8 with a capacity of over 2000 tracks.

System functions include automatic fusion of IRST tracks with 2D and 3D radar data. In this application, four horizontal bands of IR imagery (each covering a 90-deg sector) are shown on the console screen, with radar track symbology overlaid on the horizontal margins above and below.

Work on the infrastructure kernel, which includes the tactical database, graphical interface, and bus software, began in mid-1993. All coding is due for completion by end 1996.

This system is also called SISC (Système d'Integration du Système de Combat), SDC (Système de Defense et de Commandement), and SENIT PAN (PAN is Porte-Avions Nucleaire). The architecture is similar to that of SENIT 6, but with more air-control capability. The system includes a dedicated computer (with standby) for the interface to the AIDCOMER system (see separate entry).

DCNI now offers a range of distributed combat-direction systems based on SENIT 8, competing with the Thomson-CSF/Signaal Tacticos series. As announced in 1995, they are:

SENIT 801	Non-offensive; self-defense add-on
802	Gunboat
803	Corvette
804	Frigate
805	Carrier, destroyer

SESIT is a requirement issued in July 1989 for a simplified data-handling system for A69-class corvettes, and possibly also the *Foudre* class and at least some *Floreals*. It must be based on a commercial workstation, and it must process Link 11. Thomson-CSF proposed a TAVITAC 2000 variant; the French navy programming center was considering off-the-shelf systems, including British ones. As of 1996, no such system had been selected, and it seemed likely that the A69s would be limited to a stand-alone Link 11, if that. The A69s (including those for Argentina) lack any integrated computer-driven CDS. They have, in effect, a Vega I system, without any computer-driven tactical table. It comprises two surveillance consoles, one fire-control console (with a BCH computer), and one ASW fire-control console (with a second BCH); there are a manual plotting table and an ASW plot. A SENIT version for small combatants, SENIT Petit Batiments, was apparently also abandoned in the early 1990s, possibly in favor of a version of SENIT 8 (see above).

◆ **Vega/CTH/Canopus/TAVITAC**

Vega is a series of modular, small-ship, weapons-control systems and tactical data systems grown from gunfire-control systems

The side-by-side Calisto console of the SENIT 8 system shows an array of fast-action buttons at right and a plasma touch-screen, the buttons on which are software-defined, to the left. There is also a version with one 19in screen (1024 × 1280 pixels) above the other, with two coded-action (fast action) keyboards (40 software-driven buttons), and a trackball. Performance, which probably matches that of the side-by-side console, is 124 MIPS, to produce over 1 million vectors per second. The console contains a 99-MHz HP 743-RT RISC processor plus specialized video processors. Consoles can be initialized in less than 3 min after a cold start (less than 2 min after a hot start). A tactical screen shows a new object less than 0.1 sec after it has been detected, and a tactical screen can be redrawn in less than 0.3 sec (to show up to 1000 objects, 400 coastlines, 3900 characters, 100 zones). The system can carry a tactical picture for an area up to 1024 × 1024 nm, and can handle up to 1000 tracks after fusion/correlation. The system reconfigures instantaneously after network failure, and in less than 3 sec after computer failure. (DCNI)

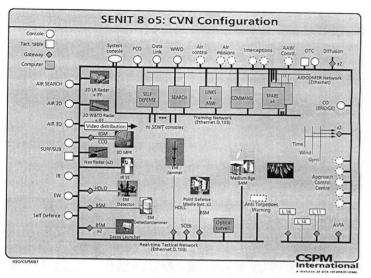

SENIT 8 as installed on board the carrier *Charles de Gaulle*. The deterministic Ethernet bus (STANAG 4254 extended to ISO 802.3) can handle
up to 100 subscribers with a sustained data rate of 8 Mbyte/sec. Maximum length is 1.5 km. Slots are 51.2 microsec long, each frame of data
being slightly shorter than the slot. The modular tactical software, such
as that used to update the tactical picture or to conduct TEWA, is written
in ADA, and is intended to be independent of hardware, buffered from
the hardware by the real-time operating system (to POSIX standards) and
the graphics software (X-Windows-CGI, written in C + +). (DCNI)

(GFCSs). It is comparable in concept to the contemporary Dutch
M20/WM20 series (and to their extensions as minicombat systems), to the Swiss Sea Hunter, and to the Swedish 9LV 200
series. In each case a dedicated air tracker (Castor, Castor II, or
Pollux) is combined with a surface-search radar (Triton). In the
basic version, targets detected by the main search radar are designated to the dedicated tracker. Versions designed to control
Exocet missiles and/or wire-guided torpedoes use the surface-
search radar in TWS mode, the main system computer conducting the associated calculations.

Thomson-CSF chose a nonstabilized TWS antenna (Triton) because it can be mounted higher in a ship, for a gain of about 4
km in range, equivalent to 3 min of warning on a 40kt target.
Overall, the system's ECCM benefits from the use of two dissimilar radars (Triton and Castor/Pollux). Doppler filtering is used

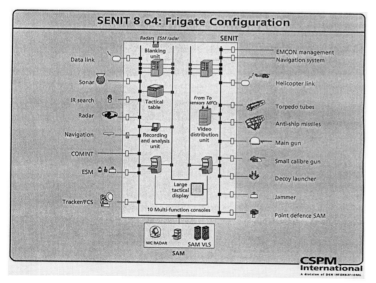

SENIT 8 as it would be installed on board a frigate equipped with
FAAMS/Aster. Presumably this is the French proposal for the Project
Horizon CMS. The inner bus carries video; the outer one is the digital
Ethernet. The two boxes near the top are tactical cabinets, each contain-
ing three computers. The small console shown at bottom as part of the
SAM system is dedicated; the others are multifunctional. (DCNI)

TAVITAC II is shown on board a fast-attack boat. The vertical console
in the background is fed by the ship's radar and is connected to her missile system. The "tactical table" in the foreground carries a wider tactical
picture, and is used by the ship's CO. Note the trackball toward the front
of the display; targets can be designated electronically and transmitted
automatically to the FCS. TAVITAC grew out of the Vega digital FCS,
much as did the Dutch minicombat system and, on a far grander scale,
the U.S. Aegis system. (CMN)

to reject clutter, and the system is partly digital. Some versions
may have used an optical target designator, DIDON. The large-
ship versions (for Colombia and Saudi Arabia) use Sea Tiger in
place of Triton.

The TAVITAC picture-keeper accepts manual detection of air
and surface targets, providing rate-aided tracks, automatically
integrates IFF responses to these initialized targets, and can accept OTH targets manually entered according to radio-telephone
information (e.g., from aircraft or from shore). It can accept sonar
data as well. Target identities are manually entered and the appropriate symbols displayed. For air targets, the threat is automatically assessed. Self-defense can be partially or fully automated, including ECM and decoy launching. TAVITAC also
conducts navigational calculations.

Different generations of Vega (I, II, III) are defined by their computers: BCH for Vega I, CDE for Vega II, 15M for Vega III. BCH
(Bloc Calcul Hybride) is a hybrid computer (analog ballistics, digital track-keeping). The next step was the all-digital CDI (each
letter advanced by one; this is *not* an acronym); CDE was the
extended (i.e., double-precision) version of CDI. CDE is all-digital, but has separate ballistics (ROM, i.e., effectively hard-wired)
and track-keeping sections. Vega I and II were both conceived in
one- and two-computer versions. The second computer was used
to operate a tactical table (showing a compiled tactical picture).
The single-computer version has a limited track-keeping (rate-
aided tracking) capability, required so that the system can engage
surface targets (using the search radar in TWS mode). Other basic
computer functions include stabilizing the display (i.e., compensating for ship motion), stabilizing the tracker radar in autonomous search mode, compensating for ship speed in MTI receivers, and tracking radar control.

BCH has a typical operating time of 2–5 microsec. It was the
hybrid element of the CTH fire-control system (in the French
navy it has been replaced by CDE). A single-computer BCH system can carry six air or surface tracks, one sonar track, and one
ESM strobe. It can handle two gunnery targets simultaneously.
A second BCH computer (in the abortive SATIN version) can
carry 16 tracks and can automatically extract plots (ATD); it
reverts to rate-aided manual tracking if it is confused by clutter.

The CDE version carries 16 fire-control tracks; the second
computer can handle 16–64 tracks (typically 32). The two-computer version is also called TAVITAC (a name associated with
all the later full CDS versions). CDE memory capacity is 64k or
128k 16-bit words. It has an integral A-D converter, so that in
effect it can emulate BCH for gunfire control and stabilization.
Thomson-CSF argued that using a single type of computer

throughout a system (for weapons control, tracking, and radar management) made the system modular and homogeneous, for easier maintenance.

The Vega III version with 15M computers can handle up to 128 tracks. It automatically evaluates the threats posed by air contacts, and it can automatically engage targets.

Before Vega II appeared, Thomson-CSF designated different versions by which search radar and which weapons they used. The simplest Vega Triton versions (later renamed Vega Canopus) lack any tracking radar, relying instead on a Lynx optical director. Vega Canopus A is the single-computer version, Canopus B (which did not sell) the two-computer version. Canopus C adds a Pollux tracker (which shares a transmitter with Triton), and thus is designated Vega Pollux PC. Vega Pollux PCE controls Exocet (E), and thus requires extended track-keeping. Vega Pollux PCET (Exocet/Torpedo) lacks the Lynx optical director.

Users:

>   Canopus: Ghana (A version in PB-57 class; possibly in FPB 45 without radar)
>   PCET: Greece (Combattante II and first four Combattante III)
>   PCE (Vega I/43): Ecuador (*Quito* class), Germany (S 148 class; first major customer), Malaysia (Combattante IID)
>   CTH: France (in many warships, with CDE computers), Greece (*Jason* class), Portugal (*Baptiste de Andrade* class)

The Portuguese *Baptiste de Andrade* class uses a Vega system (with AWS-2 search radar and Diodon sonar; they can be fitted with Exocet missiles). The optical director is Panda. These ships are so large that they may have the two-computer version of the system.

Vega, presumably surplus, is being installed on board the five Greek *Jason*-class landing ships. These units may be adapted French navy CTHs, some from ships now being discarded.

Vega II:

Vega II/12: Probably the one in the Libyan *Ibn Ouf*–class landing ships.

Vega II/43: Greece (Combattante III, with Pollux); Libya (Combattante IIG, with Castor IIB [probable version]); Peru (PR72 class).

Vega II/53 (II/43 plus TAVITAC): The tactical table, one-operator vertical console, and fire-control console are all on a data bus; the search radars and IFF all feed a common video processor/plot extractor that is connected to the tactical table. The table is also connected directly to the SSMs, ESM, ECM, and data link. The bus is connected to the gunfire-control computer (in turn connected to the guns) and to the receiver and servo of the Castor II radar. It is used by Qatar (Combattante IIIM).

Vega II/73 (for automatic antimissile capability: II/53 with two-man operational console rather than single-man console): Nigeria, Tunisia (Combattante IIIB). The Tunisian system is sometimes described as II/83, but it cannot be the II/83 described below.

Vega II/83 (for automatic engagement capability against all targets, including missiles: also called TAVITAC; two directors [Castor II and Canopus optronic director], hence two fire-control consoles; two tactical tables, three vertical display consoles): Colombia (*Almirante Padilla* [FS 1500] class). This version was sometimes called II/89.

Vega III is the large-ship version, essentially II/83 with the more powerful 15M125 computer. It is suitable for helicopter control, ASW, missile control, and multitarget self-defense. The Saudi *Al Madinah*–class version has six GVM consoles (one on the bridge) plus an E7000 tactical table. Each console consists of a CRT plus a second display (alphanumeric, television, or plasma), a keyboard, a rollerball, and a video-display panel. The CRT can be monochromatic or color, circular or rectangular. It can carry up to 200 tracks and 100 symbols (but note the central-computer limitation to 128). Brochures, which may refer to a Chinese version, show one new three-operator horizontal console (each op-

erator has his own keyboard and rollerball and a small rectangular CRT mounted vertically, a tote), a tactical table, two FCS consoles, and three vertical consoles (of a new type with a larger screen). The associated fire-control system(s) use 15M05 computers.

Note that Vega III was in effect an export version of the abortive SENIT 5. It was also called TAVITAC (Traitement Automatique et Visualisation Tactique).

Users: China (updated "Luda I" and "Jiangwei" classes), Saudi Arabia (IIIC version in *Al Madinah* class). The Chinese offer a CDS for export, CCS-3, which is probably their version of Vega III.

◆ TAVITAC 2000/TAVITAC-FD

The next-generation development of Vega/TAVITAC is TAVITAC 2000. It retains the centralized picture-keeper of earlier systems but—in common with many contemporary CDSs—places it on a LAN, with intelligent workstations in place of the earlier dumb terminals. It abandons the traditional combination of a 15M-series minicomputer, LTR language, and Ginabus. This system was developed by Thomson-CSF, working with the French navy programming center. It uses hardened civilian equipment instead of specialized military types. Reportedly, TAVITAC 2000 costs half as much as an equivalent system using specialized computers. Economies are so great that Thomson-CSF claims that the cost of the new *La Fayette*–class frigate's command/control system will be less than 5% of total cost.

Like earlier SENITs and TAVITACs, TAVITAC 2000 is a federated system built around one or two (in the *La Fayette* class, two) MLX 32 tactical picture-keeping (creation, correlation, central control of tracks) computers. They are placed on a dual triaxial-cable Ethernet LAN, which also connects to the standard multifunction display consoles. Operator aid functions, such as zone creation, are executed locally by the Vista consoles. All the subsystems are linked to the LAN either directly or via a net interface unit (NIU) derived from an MLX 32 computer (the system uses one or two for this purpose). The system can accommodate 15 identical Thomson-CSF VISTA RM color consoles; a *La Fayette* has five (air picture compilation, air supervisor [who also has access to the ESM console], surface/ASW picture, weap-

A TAVITAC 2000 command-and-control console with random-scan CRT. (Thomson-CSF)

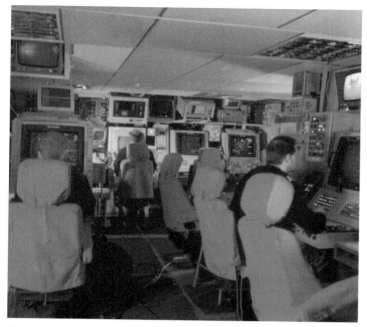

TAVITAC 2000 on board a *La Fayette*–class frigate. (DCNI)

ons control, TAO), with space for a sixth. Helicopter, ECM, and Exocet control employ separate consoles. Because all of the consoles are software-configured, they are interchangeable. The system also accommodates a Precilac E8000 tactical table. It is programmed in ADA.

Applications software is written in ADA. Computers and NIUs are accommodated in a standard tactical cabinet (containing an MLX computer, an NIU, and a free space alongside the NIU).

Users: China ("Luhu," and possibly "Jiangwei" classes), France (*La Fayette* class and trials ship *Monge*, as SENIT 7), Kuwait (new PBR-37BRL patrol vessels; version with Calisto consoles), Saudi Arabia (*La Fayette* class), Taiwan (*La Fayette* class). The Taiwan version uses RISC processors. Note that it appears that China bought both this version and the earlier TAVITAC.

As of the spring of 1996, Thomson-CSF was calling its CDS TAVITAC-FD, in analogy to SEWACO-FD.

◆ **VISTA**

In a TAVITAC 2000, each VISTA RM console contains several 68020-series microprocessors and carries up to three displays stacked vertically: two 19in, high-resolution, raster-scan units (1024 lines × 1280 pixels) and, below them, a smaller CRT for alphanumeric data. In a *La Fayette*, each VISTA console has a single color screen, areas of which are reserved for alphanumeric data (alerts, scale, image characteristics, weapons status, data concerning the hooked track and console operational mode). There are also two software-defined touch-sensitive keyboards, and a 32-bit processor (which can process up to 800 tracks over

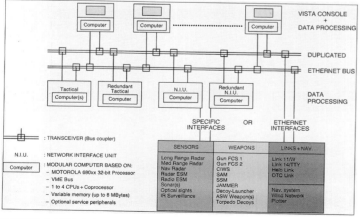

TAVITAC 2000. (Thomson-CSF)

a 512nm radius). Up to 32 ESM and 5 local sonar tracks can be carried and displayed as synthetic video. Each console can handle the entire track file, and the tactical picture is updated through a double buffer (the system need not wait while the picture in the central computer is being updated). A full picture (300 tracks, 30 circles, 30 ellipses, 500 vectors, 2000 shoreline elements, and 1800 characters) can be built up in less than 0.3 sec. Refresh time is typically 0.3 sec (0.85 sec for the maximum data load). Raw radar video can be superimposed on the synthetic video of the displays.

The console can use 256 colors, and has windowing and zoom capability. The console carries a rolling trackball with four or five press-buttons (to hook tracks, activate and control a marker on the screen, recenter the marker, hook certain types of track sequentially, and to drop a hooked track); there are also two function keyboards (plasma panels with software-controlled labels), an alphanumeric keyboard, and an auxiliary panel (brightness and contrast controls).

Vista Mk 2 has a 25in screen (2048 × 2048 pixels) providing twice the surface area of the Vista screen and three times the graphic information. It can function as an X-Windows terminal. With a 25in screen, it is 700 mm wide (600 mm with 19in screens); depth is 1300 mm and height is 1500 mm (with a 25in screen; 1400 mm with one 19in or 1600 mm with 2 × 19in screens). Internal RAM is up to 256 Mbytes, with RISC tactical and graphics processors. Screen memory is 8 to 16 bit-planes, for superimposed or windowed images. The X-windows element has a memory of up to 184 Mbytes and uses a T2000X processor to handle the full screen. The digital converter can handle a radar, a sonar, and two television channels simultaneously.

◆ **Grand X**

Matra Defense–developed large-screen interactive display for the French navy. Its first application is to the new-generation SSN. It is supplied in 1–36-sq-m sizes (probably with 2:1 aspect, like a television).

◆ **Minehunting Systems (Skubermor, Ibis)**

Thomson Sintra minehunting systems are derived from the French navy's Skubermor series: the Breton name means "sweeper of the sea." The associated computer-driven plotting table is EVEC (Ensemble de Visualisation et d'Enregistrement de la Chasse Aux Mines), installed in the minehunter's CIC. EVEC processors in French MCM craft are to be modified to accept GPS satellite navigational data. This system will not replace the current Syledis but will permit overseas deployments of MCM forces when shore stations cannot be emplaced.

EVEC 10 was the first version, followed by EVEC 20 (with a 20-kb computer) in Skubermor III/Ibis III in the "Tripartite" minehunters. EVEC 20 could track 200 mine contacts. EVEC 20 has automatic navigational radar input. The action display shows a 100m safety circle around the minesweeper/hunter; 10 previous contacts can be recorded and displayed. Next-generation systems all use TSM 2060 (NAVIPLOT), which has a 15M05 computer and can display 256 contacts plus planned and actual ship track. NAVIPLOT has a 22in four-color display showing both symbology and raw video (for navigation near shore). All data are recorded for later review.

Current systems are all built around a TSM 2061 command (tactical data) system using a pair of 19in high-resolution color raster-scan screens, 68020 chips, a removable hard disk, a keyboard with a trackball, a printer, and an X-Y plotter. TSM 2061 can replace TSM 2060 in Ibis V.

Skubermor I (in the minehunter *Circe*) had DUBM 20 and an EVEC 10 computer-driven plotting table. It used radar and Ragep-Toran for navigation, and PAP 104 and divers for mine classification and destruction.

Skubermor II (in the converted ocean sweeper *Dompaire*, now discarded) used the DUBM-21 sonar and an EVEC 11 plotting table.

Skubermor III (Ibis III) had the two-array DUBM 21 and EVEC 20. This system equipped the "Tripartite" minehunters. The as-

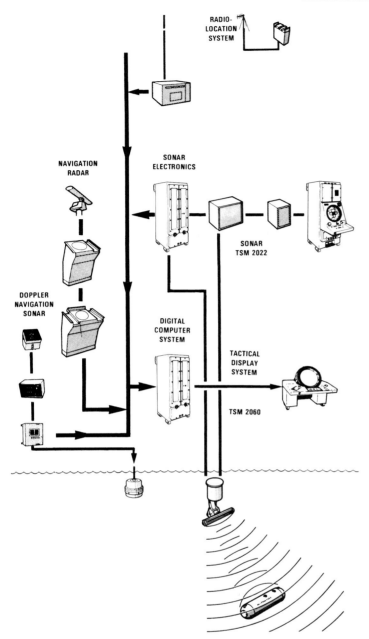

Ibis V. The sonar and tactical display consoles are normally mounted side by side. The system can carry 256 contacts. The four-color tactical CRT has a diameter of 22 in, with a refresh rate of 30 to 50 Hz. In later versions of Ibis, it is replaced by a Colibri console with rectangular raster-scan CRTs. (Thomson Sintra)

sociated navigational system is Syledis-Toran (Dutch and Belgian Tripartite minehunters use Decca Hi-Fix). *Users:* Belgium (10 Tripartite class), France (10 Tripartite class), the Netherlands (15 Tripartite class), and Pakistan (3 Tripartite class). Belgium and the Netherlands use a Signaal SEWACO combat system rather than NAVIPLOT.

Ibis III Mk II: DUBM 21B sonar (simultaneous detection and classification, using two arrays; TSM 2061 system; for mines at depths of 7 to 80 m). *User:* Norway (five new minehunters)

Ibis V: Lightweight (1.4 vs. 6 tons) version of Ibis III with TSM 2022 sonar (in some cases possibly a lightweight version, TSM 2026) and NAVIPLOT, announced 1980. Typically Ibis V includes a Thomson Sintra Doppler bottom log (TSM 5721 or 5730). *Users:* Egypt (COOP minehunters; sonar made by Thoray [Thomson-Raytheon joint venture]), Indonesia (two *Almaar* class), Malaysia (four *Lerici* class), Nigeria (two *Lerici* class), Sweden (seven *Landsort* class), Yugoslavia (two in updated *Sirius* class). The Swedish ships substitute a 9MJ400 combat system for NAVIPLOT or its equivalent.

Ibis V Mk II: TSM 2022 Mk II sonar (sequential detection and classification, using one array) and TSM 2061; it adds a new 19in high-resolution color display. Mk II incorporates the new Colibri console, used by both the sonar operator (one 19in display) and the tactical officer (who has two screens). It provides computer-aided detection and classification and includes a sonar-performance indicator. This version was selected for the four new Norwegian minesweepers and for the four Singapore navy *Land-sort*-class ships. Presumably this is the system planned for the three Pakistani Tripartite minehunters. The Norwegian ships embed this system in a MICOS combat system. Thomson Sintra reported that a total of 31 TSM 2022 and 2022 Mk II had been ordered for seven navies as of 1992; the lists above account for 28 of them in eight navies, so several are probably missing.

Ibis V NG (Nouvelle Generation): TSM 2022 NG sonar (paired line arrays, for sequential, semisequential, or simultaneous detection and classification) and TSM 2061.

Ibis VII: PVDS (propelled variable depth sonar, carrying the TSM 2022 NG sonar) and TSM 2061, developed for the abortive *Narvik*-class ocean minehunter (BAMO). Under development by DCN, the fish is fitted with TSM 2023. Ibis VII is to replace Ibis-42.

Ibis 42: DUBM-42 side-scan sonar and TSM 2061, for intermediate and deep water (down to 300 m). *User:* France (*Narvik*)

Ibis 43: TSM 2054 side-scan sonar and TSM 2061 for shallow and intermediate water depths (60 to 200 m), announced 1989. *User:* Denmark (*Flyvefisken* class). Ibis 43 differs from the French DUBM-42 in having a shorter (3 m) towfish to suit smaller MCM craft, dedicated software to suit Danish seabed conditions, higher maximum tow speed (15 kt), shorter range (due to shorter array), and obstacle-avoidance capability. The Danish corvette uses two remote-controlled 15m craft, each towing a fish at up to 15 kt, in the Q-route (600 yd wide) surveillance role. There are also Ibis III/43 and Ibis V/43, combining hull and towed sonars. Depth 6 to 200 m, speed 4–15 kt, altitude over the bottom 3 to 15 m, range 2×50 m and 2×100 m (10 and 20cm constant transverse resolution). Mk II, announced in 1991, adds a database of past bottom surveys.

Ibis 51: TSM 5451B compact mine hunting sonar with a short array which can be oriented horizontally or vertically; TSM 5451A is the relocation and identification sonar for the PAP 104 mine neutralization vehicle.

    As of October 1992, Thomson Sintra had supplied over 80 hull sonars, over 30 variable depth sonars, 10 mine surveillance sonars, and 10 mine avoidance sonars.

GERMANY

◆ AGIS

This command/control system for fast-attack boats (Automatische Gefechts und Informations-system Schnellboote, i.e., automatic combat evaluation and WCS) was the second generation of German CDSs, after SATIR I. AGIS was conceived for S143-class missile boats, which were intended to lead flotillas of Types 142 and 148. It uses Link 11 to exchange data with shore stations, with SATIR-equipped surface ships, and with surveillance aircraft. AGIS entered service in 1976, providing a link with the central German maritime headquarters (MHQ) ashore. The link was probably most significant because it permitted fast-attack boats lurking behind Baltic islets to engage targets detected and tracked by other targets. It permitted MHQ to form mixed battle groups, including both fast-attack craft and aircraft, because MHQ could be sure of the precise location of each during combat. Otherwise, the aircraft might well have killed the fast-attack boats by mistake. The expectation was always that the fast-attack boats would operate passively in wartime, although the link also made it possible for them to feed MHQ's overall surface picture. The system has been criticized as too complex operationally, and as taking too long to learn.

    The system has two Univac 1830 computers: one (the command/control computer, or FUR) to maintain the tactical picture, one for fire control (the Feuer Leit Rechner, FLR). The FUR/FLR combination is reminiscent of the roughly contemporary French Vega II system, but with a different radar and different computers. Fed by the boat's WM27 radar and her ESM set, the FUR runs a computerized tactical table (horizontal plot). It also feeds into the FLR. The latter has one output/gun control console. The original S143 version also has a pair of consoles to control wire-guided torpedoes. S143A lacks the torpedo tubes and therefore the two special-purpose consoles. The CIC space thus freed was ultimately used for a vertical display console (multipurpose display console, Mehrzweckdarstellungskonsole, or MDK). This version is called AGIS II; the MDK makes possible combined helicopter-boat attacks. The deck space freed aft was used for the installation of the RAM self-defense missile. Boats with AGIS II have active and passive ECM integrated into their combat systems.

Installations of AGIS II are associated with the program to modify 20 German Sea King helicopters from the SAR role to fire Sea Skua antiship missiles. The helicopters provide OTH-T for the missile boats, via Link 11.

A third AGIS computer (a UYK-7) processes Link 11 data (terminals are USC-27 in S143, TE-905 in S143A boats).

Originally all 10 S143s were to have been converted to S143A configuration, with RAM defensive missiles and ECM, as the S143B class. However, those plans have been abandoned, leaving only the 10 S143As with the full capability.

♦ MWS-80/DSQS-11/DDQS-11

STN Atlas Elektronik's MWS-80 minehunting system comprises the SATAM command/control system (based on the British Ferranti 500), the DSQS-11 hull sonar, the DDSX-11 sonar on the minehunting vehicle, and the NBD navigation and track control system. A bus connects the sonar, SATAM, and NBD; both sonar and SATAM use the new standard German navy consoles (one for sonar, tactical and supervisor for SATAM). A fourth console, of a different type, is used to control the system's Pinguin RoV. In the Type 332 minehunter, the navigation/control element is designated NCE.

DSQS-11, STN Atlas Elektronik's standard German minehunting sonar, generally is integrated into the MWS-80 minehunting combat system. The entire system costs about $11.5M, of which $2.5–$3M is the sonar proper. As initially conceived, DSQS-11 was unusual in using the same sonar for both detection and classification. The narrow classification beam was formed by phase-shifting (beam pre-forming), that is, by an application of submarine sonar technology already highly developed by STN Atlas. Too, DSQS-11 was conceived from the first as a digital sonar suitable for integration into a computer-driven command system. Problems with the scanning sonar arrangement led to later versions with more conventional combinations of separate detection and classification sonars. One writer described DSQS-11 as an unfortunate attempt to combine five conventional sonars into one electronically scanned unit.

The original DSQS-11H uses a cylindrical detection array and a separate flat classification array, both operating at the same frequency, 103 kHz, in a retractable hull dome. The detection array covers a 90-deg sector in RDT mode (a sequence of 1-msec pulses, each covering 2 deg) with preformed-beam reception (45 fan beams, each 2 deg wide). The detection sector can be switched to any one of five preset center bearings 72 deg apart, the sectors overlapping by 18 deg. The square flat classification array can be trained through 130 deg in azimuth, and it can be tilted to measure target depth. It transmits 20 vertically stacked beams (0.1-msec CW pulses) within a 2-deg horizontal width. Classification is in two stages: first depth, then shape; up to five classification images can be stored. DSQS-11 has a variable pulse rate and uses a PPI display whose video is processed to suppress noise returns. The full array projects 0.9 m below the keel, and the assembly above it is 2.5 m high.

Experience with DSQS-11H has apparently been less than happy. For example, the Royal Thai Navy had to use its new minehunters as patrol craft, retaining older U.S.-built "Bird"-class sweepers with UQS-1 sonars for mine countermeasures. The Royal Australian Navy, too, was unable to use DSQS-11H effectively. The German navy is replacing DSQS-11H with a new version, DSQS-11M. Reportedly, the problem was undue reliance on electronic scanning, a technology with which KAE had been very successful in lower-frequency submarine sonars.

DSQS-11A and the improved -11H both use a single software-controlled array for both detection and classification. The much more successful -11M adds a lower-frequency linear array for long-range detection and long-range classification (the original higher-frequency array is retained for high-resolution detection in clutter and for echo- or shadow-mode classification). The Australian version of -11M has a longer linear array (2.0 vice 1.5 m) and filtering to cope with local seabed and temperature conditions.

For the Royal Australian Navy, DSQS-11M was provided with an additional lower frequency mode, to search for buried mines.

MWS 80-4 (with DSQS-11M sonar) was accepted by the German navy in 1991 for the Type 332 class, and will probably be retrofitted to Type 343 (*Pegnitz* class). MWS 80-5 is the containerized version for the Royal Australian Navy (one container for the operations room, one for the sonar). The version with the VLF sonar, first tested on board HMAS *Shoalwater* in 1995, is designated MWS 80-5/VLF.

Besides DSQS-11, MWS-80 comprises Tactical Command and Documentation (TCD) equipment, a precision navigation system, and the Active Identification Sonar (AIS-11, with the German naval designation DDSX-11) on board the Pinguin B3 mine disposal vehicle. The TCD uses two consoles to plan and present track and mine data, and to prepare data for evaluation and for follow-on mine hunting. This system is a version of the Ferranti SATAM (MC500) command system.

MWS 80-4 offers simultaneous detection and classification supported by CAD/CAC, for one-man sonar operation. The MCM CIC typically contains three dual-screen consoles: two side by side, a third in front of them with a large screen on top and a much smaller one below. The two side-by-side SATAM consoles are for track planning, presentation of status information, presentation of maneuver data to the helmsman, control of sonar and navigational equipment, contact management; correlation of new and existing targets; documentation of all results for evaluation and follow-on; and data logging. The third presumably controls the RoV, displaying its sensor picture. Sonar modes: LF long-range detection and classification (echo mode); HF high-resolution detection in high-clutter environment, HF classification (echo and shadow modes); depth classification. At least this version (with the DSQS-11M sonar) employs pulse compression. There are alternative conventional detection and detection magnifier displays, the latter like a 2D A-scan, like a square in perspective, with height showing echo strength.

DDQS-11 is the drone version of DSQS-11, as in the SVDS system.

Users: Australia (three *Rushcutter* class; -11M replacing -11H), Germany (DSQS-11M in Types 332 and 343, -11A in Types 331 and 351 [-11H in *Fulda*, trials ship]), Sweden (-11H in last four *Landsort* class, replacing Thomson-CSF TSM 2022), Thailand (two M48 class).

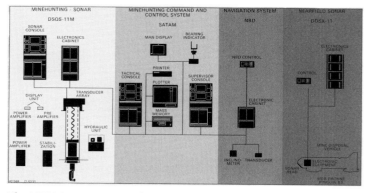

The MWS 80-4 system, including its SATAM CDS core. (STN Atlas)

◆ MWS-90

The follow-on to MWS-80, announced about March 1995, uses a self-propelled RoV (an ECA drone based on PAP 104) carrying a DDQS-11M sonar to complement the hull-borne DSQS-11M, to fill the gap in sonar coverage near the bottom. Presumably this is an alternative to the fish planned for MA 2000, since it employs a rotatable linear array for horizontal detection and classification (DDQS-11M). The associated depth array is integrated behind a dome in the vehicle's head and allows simultaneous depth classification of contacts within the horizontal sector. It is expected to be effective down to 300 m and to function at up to 8 kt. A fiber-optic core in the umbilical power cable transmits sonar data and vehicle control data. The linear array can be stabilized; the depth array normally follows it.

◆ PALIS

Passiv-Aktiv-Link-Lage-Informationssystem is a lightweight TDS for fast-attack boats (S148 class), for the *Hamburg*-class destroyers (Z101A class as modernized, now discarded), and for the new fast minehunters (M343 class). In each case PALIS is built around a UYK-20A computer. S148 and Z101A use the same version, with Sanders Mk 95 and Mk 95 Mod 1 consoles and with TE 905 and TE 237 data terminal sets. The minehunter version uses the new KAE BM 802-61 console and the TE 237 data terminal set. PALIS's functions are navigation, tactical navigation, target tracking, identification, indication of special (fixed) points, tactical bearing indication, ESM integration, weapons designation, Link 11, alerts, and data extraction. In each case, PALIS is not connected directly to the weapon system.

PALIS was developed during the AGIS program to unify the tactics of the German fast-attack boats. With PALIS, any fast-attack boat could cooperate with other units, even dissimilar ones such as destroyers, and with MHQ. Given this system, Link 11 information for the construction of a current tactical picture could be relayed, stored, and correlated with own-ship sensor information. Reaction time could be drastically reduced.

PALIS was installed on board Type 148 boats from 1982 on.

◆ SATIR

System zur Auswertung Taktischer Informationen auf Raketenzerstoren is a command/control system for the three German *Lutjens*-class missile destroyers and for the Type 122 *Bremen*-class frigates. As developed for the *Lutjens* class (which entered service in 1969–70), SATIR was the first NTDS-like system on a destroyer, proving sufficiently successful for the German navy to choose a derivative for its *Bremen*-class (Type 122) frigates. It inspired the U.S. JPTDS/JTDS systems in missile destroyers and

SATIR on board a German Type 122 frigate. The consoles are taken from the U.S. UYA-4 display system. This system differs from U.S. frigate systems in that there is no larger-screen summary display for the TAO. (German Navy)

frigates. SATIR is based on experience with NTDS and with its French equivalent, SENIT.

The associated data link is SATIR-1, presumably Link 11. There are three versions:

SATIR I for *Lutjens* (modified *Adams*)-class (Z103-type) destroyers, which have now been modernized (Z103B class). Although SATIR originally used a USQ-20B computer, the current (modernized) version uses a UYK-7. It incorporates a version of the SYS-1 integrated ADT (IADT). SATIR I incorporates three OJ-194(V)3/UYA-4 PPI consoles (two for SYS-1, one for the FL1800S ECM system), 11 OJ-7979(V)/UYA-4 multipurpose consoles (each with an associated digital indicator), a disk memory unit (U 1647/1, with 500k 32-bit words; data rate is about 127 kwords/sec), and a USQ-69 data terminal set. SYS-1 includes a range-height indicator (IP-1117/UYA-4). This equipment is typical of contemporary U.S. NTDS practice. The Z103B combat system includes an SPS-67(V)1 surface-search radar in place of the earlier SPS-10F and a DSQS-21B sonar in place of the earlier SQS-23L. The MFCS is Mk 74 Mod 6, and the GFCS is Mk 86 Mod 8. This version controls two RAM missile launchers.

The SATIR I operational program was written by German officers at the U.S. naval programming center at San Diego. SATIR originally corresponded to the U.S. NTDS. It tracked the ship's position automatically and conducted navigational calculations (such as collision points and CPAs). It kept track of (and provided rate-aided projection of) radar-target data entered manually. It provided computer assistance to maintain a radar and sonar plot and could pass target data to the weapons-control system (and calculate whether particular targets were engageable). It also exchanged data with other units via Link 11. It was not integrated with the ship's ESM system or with the ship's underwater FCS. The Z103B system enjoys improved AAW performance through automatic radar-target detection and tracking (SYS-1), incorporates a new GFCS (Mk 86), can control a long-range antiship missile (Harpoon) and a new AAW weapon (RAM), and is integrated with the ship's ASW FCS (it mediates between the ship's sonar and her Mk 114 underwater FCS) and with her ECM system (FL1800S; it mediates between the FL1800S sensor and its transmitter).

SATIR II for the *Bremen* (F122) class is built around a UYK-7 computer, which is powerful enough to handle all shipboard sensors and weapons (Z103 had a separate Mk 114 underwater FCS and separate missile and gun FCSs). All weapons and sensors operate through multifunction consoles (MZKs). SATIR II differs from SATIR I in using digital links to sensors, weapons, the integrated navigation system, and CIC displays. This version incorporates automatic radar-target detection and tracking and can engage air targets automatically (it chooses the weapon most appropriate to a given target). It supports ASW using both shipboard weapons and the embarked helicopters. Like the Z103B system developed somewhat later, SATIR II integrates ESM with other shipboard sensors. The German ships are very similar to the Dutch "Standard" frigates, but reportedly the introduction of a wholly new combat system (instead of the Dutch SEWACO) was extremely expensive, equivalent to the cost of two ships. This version uses nine OJ-194 consoles: TAO, AAW supervisor, track coordinator/supervisor, helicopter controller, gun FCS, Mk 91 SAM system, ASW officer. There is a separate sonar console. The absence of radar detector/trackers presumably reflects the use of ADT radars.

SATIR III (SATIR F123) for the new *Deutschland* (F123) class is built around a UYK-43 computer. It has 12 Atlas Elektronik DG 802-52 consoles, each with two raster-scan color monitors; there are also two Link 11 data terminal sets. SATIR III was formally accepted in July 1992.

As in the case of NTDS, the navy is the system integrator, and a special official organization is responsible for programming. The developers were the Bundesamt fur Wehrteknik und Beschaffung (BWB) and the Kommando Marine Fuhrungssysteme (KdoMFuSys).

◆ CoSys

CoSys is a collaborative effort among Contraves, Siemens Plessey, and STN Atlas Elektronik, the system integrator. The name suggests that Contraves is the lead company, and that the system is an outgrowth of that company's Seaguard ship point-defense system. Plessey contributes the system's target acquisition radar, as in the Turkish Seaguard system. Versions have numerical suffixes corresponding to the versions of the MEKO frigate for which they are intended. Thus CoSys 200 is intended for a MEKO 200 or similar ship. CoSys 100 was announced in September 1991, for a new MEKO 100 corvette. CoSys 90 is intended for OPVs. Thus far (mid-1996) the system has not yet been sold, although elements may appear in the new German AAW frigate (Type 124). A reported sale to Turkey (1992) was abortive, and in 1993 Korea opted for the British SSCS after having chosen a 10-console CoSys 200 (CoSys 2090K1) initially for the new KDX.

CoSys 200 is a federated system, using a pair of DEC KAV 30 computers on an Ethernet LAN carrying Krupp tactical data consoles like those in the German *Brandenburg*-class frigates. They are similar to those in the existing Seaguard system. All elements of the system use 32-bit processors. In CoSys 100, the picture-keeper is apparently the Link Y terminal (128 tracks). Track capacity is not altogether clear, however, because a CoSys brochure evaluates it in terms of the total capacity of all the elements (e.g., it includes the six rate-aided tracks in the multifunction tracker, the one in the TMEO, the two in the target designation sights, and the 100 datums, fixes, special points, and so on, carried in the system, to reach a total of 237 tracks). Similarly, tracks carried by an ADT radar (30, in the simplest version) can be added, the Link Y terminal presumably being limited to externally supplied tracks and not including those generated internally. Apparently each console can take track data from any source, and each replicates the overall system picture.

◆ MICOS

This modular CDS was first offered in 1989 as MTDS, the modular tactical data system, for warship modernization. MICOS was tested on board a Type 343 minesweeper (possibly *Hameln*) and has been proposed for the new Bremer-Vulkan export corvette. At present it is essentially a digital FCS associated with the Radamec 2400 optronic director. As offered in the past, MICOS employed a central computer on a data bus with up to four displays, a data link (HF and UHF), radar and navigation interfaces, and a general-purpose interface to a ship's weapons and sensors. The central computer time-shared most functions. No particular computer or workstation has ever been identified, so presumably the bulk of the work undertaken has been software development.

Telefunken Systemtechnik began to advertise MTDS late in 1989. The system is currently offered by STN. No sales have been reported.

◆ BM 802

Atlas Elektronik's workstation console, announced in 1990, has been standardized by the German navy as the QKM (Querschnitt Konsole Marine). It employs 16-bit EPR 1300 and 32-bit MPR 2300 single-board microcomputers, the latter based on 68000-series processors. There are four series:

BM 802-1/2: 15in random-scan color screen (1440 × 1120 pixels)
BM 802-3/4: 14in raster-scan screen (respectively, 720 × 560 and 1365 × 1024 pixels)
BM 802-51/52: Two 20in color, superimposed raster-scan screens (1365 × 1024 pixels). -52 has two MPR 2300 (68030 processors) with 4 Mbytes of memory plus a 68020 for graphics processing. Dimensions: width 70 cm, height 1.59 m, weight 370 kg. This is the display of the SATIR system on board the new *Deutschland* class.
BM 802-61: Single 20in raster-scan screen (940 × 700 pixels)

INDIA

Bharat Electronics (BEL) is to supply Shikari CDS for the new Indian Type 16 frigate. Reportedly this is an improved IPN-10 using three workstations linked by a Unicom-type LAN, as supplied by UDI (ex-FMC). The workstations use Barco 19in raster-scan displays plus alphanumeric displays, QWERTY keyboards and numeric pads. This system may also be installed on the destroyer *Delhi*. Note that the name *Shikari* has also been associated with a Contraves Seaguard–type FCS for the *Delhi* class. That implies that Shikari may actually be related to CoSys.

The Bharat Electronics system on board the *Khukri* class, which is a license-built mini-SADOC, is designated Vympal. The first Indian-built unit was on board the second unit, *Khutar*, commissioned in 1990.

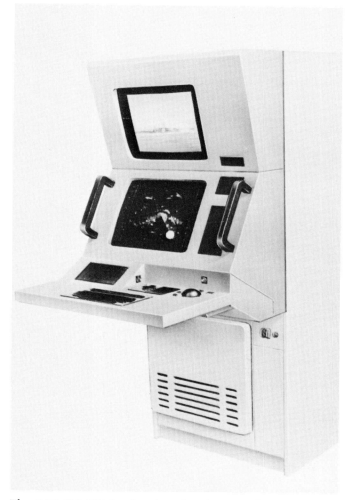

The KAE BM 802 family of workstation consoles is now standard throughout the German military; they are used in the SATIR system of the new Type 123 frigates and also in the CoSys system. BM 802-52 is a double-screen CIC console. This photograph shows it with a medium-sized CRT (14 in) above a larger (20 in) CRT. Both are raster-scan color CRTs (1365 × 1024 addressable pixels, equivalent in clarity to a 2000-line display). The console is driven by a 32-bit KAE multiprocessor computer (MPR 2300) using 68030 chips. Others in the series differ in the number and type of displays. BM 802-1/2 have 15in cursive color CRTs (1440 × 1120 addressable locations on screen, equivalent to 4000 lines); -3 has a 14in raster color CRT (720 × 560 pixels, 1000 lines equivalent); -4 has the full 14in raster color CRT. Of these versions, BM 802-2, -3, and -4 can have either one or two displays. BM 802-51 and -52 each have two displays, and BM 802-61 has one. All but -51 and -52 use both 16- and 32-bit microprocessors (KAE EPR 1300 and MPR 2300). EPR 1300 has a throughput of about 0.3 MIPS and can be expanded to 8 Mbytes. BM 802-51 and -52 can be further upgraded by adding plug-in processor assemblies. All versions have trackballs and keyboards. In addition, the upper and lower screens can be flanked by control panels carrying keys, pushbutton switches, rotary switches, potentiometers, shaft-encoders, annunciators, and an audio channel (not visible in the console illustrated here). (STN Atlas)

BM 802-61 is the new standard German CIC display console, for tactical display, assessment of the tactical situation, and weapons-control planning. It can accept both digital computer data and raw radar video (it incorporates a radar scan converter). It carries a 20in monochrome raster-scan CRT (940 × 700 pixels, equivalent to 700 lines). (STN Atlas)

ISRAEL

At least initially the *Sa'ar* 2/3 class (as typified by the South African boats) apparently had no computer CDS at all. Then IAI introduced digital technology, using their own design computer, with ferrite cores. Then they adopted more advanced models, with some integrated circuits, mainly for gun and missile fire control. Upgrades were gradual, aimed toward surface capability, not toward a fully integrated system (which did not appear until *Sa'ar* 5, *Eilat*). There were also different versions of the tactical displays. These upgrades were gradual and continuous; the separate generations delineated below are, then, somewhat misleading.

◆ Elbit CDS Systems: TADS/Reshet/NTCCS

There are three generations, all Gabriel-oriented. The first is TADS/Reshet (Reshet is the large-ship version). TADS is a Gabriel-and-gun FCS with secondary track-keeping capability. A separate automatic tracking computer maintains 20 tracks, 10 of them rate-aided from the boat's own search radar. The TADS computer also performs gunfire control and all other system calculations. The console operator classifies and identifies radar targets. The system as a whole is intended to localize targets with an accuracy of 70 m in range and 0.5 deg in bearing. A second computer in the TADS console can service a data link. This combination is similar to Vega II with TAVITAC or to NA-10; it probably incorporates some NA-10 technology, such as the plot extractor/tracker and the multiweapon calculator.

TADS is probably the CDS on board *Sa'ar* 2– and 3–class boats in Israel and Chile (as well as Chilean *Sa'ar* IVs); it was probably also the system exported to Ecuador (*Manta* class), Kenya (32m and 37.5m classes), and Singapore (FPB 45 class). A specially compact version of TADS, designed for the *Dvora* class, was exported to Taiwan (*Hai Ou* class).

In a TADS-equipped *Sa'ar* 4, the three-man TADS console was supplemented by a four-man EW console, a search radar operator's console, and a manual surface plotting table.

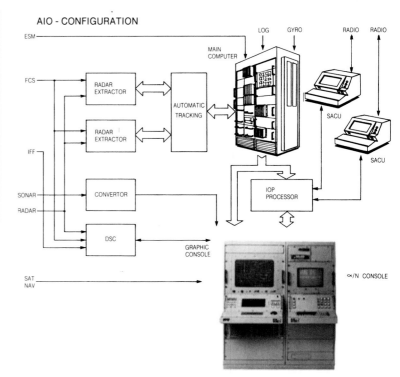

Elbit's NTCCS employs the company's Navscon dual console, shown at bottom. This system can handle up to 200 tracks. The SACUs shown are Elbit's basic data-link terminal; note that this system can handle two links simultaneously. Each SACU-2000 can receive messages from up to six different HF channels. It is a small computer with dual-language and graphic capability, and can operate in stand-alone or integrated mode. Elbit also advertises OVERSEA, an integrated sea-shore command and control network, presumably employing a digital data link, to provide a commander ashore with a current correlated tactical picture from ships, aircraft, coastal stations, and other sources. Filtered information from the shore headquarters is distributed automatically to deployed users. Presumably this or a similar system is currently employed by the Israeli navy. (Elbit)

Reshet is an extended TADS for destroyers, bought only by Taiwan, for Wu-Jinn II destroyers (three *Gearing* FRAM I, one *Gearing* FRAM II). A typical system consists of a central processor, TAD console, a tactical editor (track supervisor) console (tactical display station, TDS), and a commander's tactical console. The TDS uses a color raster-scan monitor to show the tactical picture in synthetic video form. This console also accommodates the system's picture-keeping computer. At least in the Taiwanese case, organic system capacity is 12 tracks (it can engage three); overall reaction time is about 20 sec. In the Taiwanese ships the sensors are SPS-29, EL/M-2208, RTN-10X, the two-man version of the OG.R7 direction, and the SQS-23 sonar. Probably the long-range air search radar and the sonar are not actually tied into the Reshet system, although one account claims that the system includes ASW processing and display functions. The Taiwanese version apparently also includes a data link.

IAI has also advertised a simpler version, in which the TDS can be replaced by a tabular track list (a data-management terminal). It is possible that this version is the one used by the Israeli and other navies; the choice would depend on the available space in the boats' CICs.

The follow-on is Elbit's NTCCS (Naval Tactical Command-and-Control System). It is installed on board Israeli (but not South African) *Sa'ar* 4 (*Reshev* class) missile boats. NTCCS probably appeared in the late 1970s, after the first series of *Sa'ar* 4s were completed. Early *Sa'ar* 4s (including those in Chile) are probably limited to an unintegrated system based on TADS. Reportedly NTCCS was originally built around a U.S. UYK-20 computer, which receives ATD radar data and is connected to a separate data-link unit (SACU). The current version probably uses a pair of EL/S-9000 computers (one a hot spare) using 68000-

series processors, as in the *Sa'ar* V system described separately below.

Current descriptions of the NTCCS show a single main computer fed by a plot combiner (fed by radar plot extractors). The computer in turn feeds a two-man Navscon intelligent console. Track capacity is probably several hundred (the standard Navscon console used has a capacity of 300 tracks). NTCCS is a true tactical picture-keeper, designating targets for the TADS and for any other FCS. It is directly responsible for chaff rocket patterns (and thus probably for evasive maneuvers after chaff firing). Reportedly the Singapore navy has had trouble integrating NTCCS with Harpoon.

Navscon itself is a two-man console containing a radar video-scan converter (to show a radar picture on its raster-scan screen), as well as graphics display processor and generator. It probably also contains 16-bit applications processors. The main (left-hand) 19in screen (1280 × 1024 pixels) is complemented by a smaller screen on the right (probably 16 in, 640 × 512 pixels) and by a small alphanumeric screen. There are a plasma touch-screen (32 × 8 soft-keys), a trackball, and fixed-action keys.

There are two separate data links, one to the other deployed units and one to the naval headquarters ashore. Both are serviced through a SACU, the Elbit stand-alone communications link. Thus an NTCCS boat can act as a gateway and as a group leader. Two *Aliyah*-class (*Sa'ar* 4.5) boats, with OTH-T helicopters on board, were described as group leaders; presumably they, too, have NTCCS.

◆ *Sa'ar* V System (Elbit AIO III)/NAIS

The new *Sa'ar* V corvettes have a more distributed combat system using a pair of Elta EL/S-9000 computers (based on 68040 microprocessors), probably mainly as picture-keepers, connected by LAN with the system's intelligent consoles. The commercial version, announced in Paris in 1993, is the Naval Action Information System (NAIS). The 17 multifunction consoles of the AIS Mk III system are connected to all own-ship data by multiple triple Ethernet buses (Tadiran's Shipboard Databus, SDB-2). Reportedly AIO Mk III was the first fully integrated Israeli CDS; the others were all piecemeal upgrades.

The *Sa'ar* V design includes a secondary (emergency) CIC aft, and the main CIC is buried in the hull for survivability. The combat system can also be operated, to some extent, from the bridge, although it appears that the CIC is the CO's battle station. The system can also accommodate a unit commander. The main CIC is divided into "attack" and "defense" areas, the former including positions for the CO and navigator (Exec). The latter includes the link processor.

The workstation console is the operational control console (OCC) developed by Astronautics Corp. of America, Ltd., under Israeli navy contract. It incorporates a 19in screen (1280 × 1024 pixels) plus either a second such screen or 2 × 9in screens for 60-Hz raster-scan data. The workstation is built around a VME backplane carrying three 68040 display processors: operator-machine interface, display, and a dual graphics engine. Each graphics engine contains three processors operating in parallel to generate 6 million pixels/sec of random graphics. The workstation can accept 40-Hz digital data or analog video (e.g., raw radar video).

The main display includes the current tactical picture and alphanumeric data. One of the small displays carries information required to cooperate with other consoles or operators; the other carries system status information.

The limited published descriptions of NAIS indicate that it may be limited to a single computer and that it uses OCC workstations with paired 19in raster-scan displays plus paired subpanels tailored to customer requirements. Besides the usual capability to store photographs and drawings (such as maps), this system is said to have the ability to store synthetic and recorded voices of compact disc quality, presumably to generate prompts and alarms. The NAIS data-link system can handle up to six separate nets.

In mid-1996 it was reported that problems had been encountered integrating the Barak missile system with the Elbit CDS.

The existing CDS consoles may be replaced by COTS units. The lead ship, *Eilat*, is now not expected to become operational before 1997 or 1998.

ITALY

Software is developed by the programming center, MARICEN-PROG, established in 1970.

◆ SADOC (IPN-10 and -20) Series

SADOC 1 (Systema Automatico Direzione della Operazioni di Combattimento) was the general designation for the Italian version of NTDS, using the standard U.S. CP-642B computer and SYA-4 displays. Presumably it corresponded to contemporary U.S. cruiser systems in which the WDS was embedded in the main computers. Ships fitted with this system had analog FCSs cued by the CDS. NTDS was adapted to Italian needs by Selenia (now Alenia). Conceived in 1968, this system was first installed in 1970. *User: Vittorio Veneto.*

SADOC 2 was essentially NTDS with an Italian CDG-3032 (CP-7010) central computer (comparable to and slightly faster than a UYK-7) and Italian SVC-16 displays. This system was initially installed on board the two *Impavido*-class missile destroyers, probably about 1975 (under the 1974/75 and 1976/77 budgets); it paralleled the U.S. JPTDS, the French SENIT for destroyers, and the German SATIR. SADOC 2 was installed on board *Lupo*- and *Maestrale*-class frigates in 1978. These ships introduced a digital weapons-control system (NA-10), which presumably included a computer-driven close-in WDS. There are two types of multifunction consoles, a single-operator vertical console with a 16in CRT (SVC-16) and a three-operator horizontal console with a 22in console (MHC-22). Export *Lupos* (IPN-10 system) have five consoles (four SVC, one MHC) and one CDG-3032; Italian *Lupos* and *Maestrales* have six (an additional MHC), and two CDG-3032s. Aside from WDS functions, the second computer may provide sufficient power for Link 11, which export *Lupos* lack. Thus when the Italian navy bought the *Lupos* originally built for Iraq, they had to be relegated to coast guard functions because they lacked the capacity for Link 11, hence the capacity to be integrated into the Italian fleet. The star topology of their combat systems prohibited any addition as radical as a second main computer.

An uprated (federated) version built around two CDG-3032 (one functioning as WDS computer), using a 10-Mbit/sec dual serial fiber-optic data bus, was installed on board the *Giuseppe Garibaldi* in 1987. All the consoles (each with its own 16-bit NDC-160/E, or CP-7020, microcomputer) show both synthetic and raw video at a refresh rate of more than 30 Hz (range scales 2 to 512 nm, with off-center capability up to 512 nm in all range

A standard horizontal display, part of the SADOC system, on board an Italian warship. The consoles in the background are for weapon control; they are not part of SADOC. (Italian navy)

scales). They also have 7in alphanumeric displays (16 × 40 matrix). The export version of the federated system is IPN-20. Uprated SADOC 2 was installed on board *Audace*-class destroyers in 1989. A further uprated SADOC 2 was installed on board *Mimbelli*-class destroyers in 1992. The final *San Marcos*–class amphibious ship is to be the last equipped with SADOC 2.

In the carrier *Garibaldi*, this system incorporates two MHC (supervision, command/control) and nine SVC (EW, track management, air operations control) to handle 200 tracks. In this case SADOC 2 supports Links 1 (to NADGE, the NATO shore-based air-defense system), 11, 14, and 16; the NADGE link permits the ship to control shore-based aircraft. The *Mimbelli* version has two MHC and ten SVC consoles; the SVCs are in three separate banks in CIC (air picture compilation, AAW warfare, and surface warfare/picture compilation). Separate consoles control SM-2MR and Otomat missiles. The four Dardo E consoles are outside CIC (two one deck below, two in the aft superstructure). Presumably this dispersion is to avoid losing close-in defense in the event CIC is hit.

A corvette version was developed for the *Wadi M'ragh*–class corvettes, built around an NDC-160 central computer, with one MHC and one SVC. It also went on board the Taiwanese *Lung Chiang* class. A revised version using a command system LAN is on board the *Minerva* class. In this version, each display (two SVC and one MHC) incorporates its own NDC-160 computer. The two SVCs are typically used for radar surveillance, EW coordination, and data-link control. The MHC is assigned to weapons control, helo/aircraft control, navigation/maneuvering, and ASW operations/tactical situation assessment.

SADOC 3 is the future system (IPN-S) described separately below.

The SVC-16 console incorporates a keyboard and rollerball and can be used as an independent radar repeater. MHC-22 has three flat screens, at least one of which is used for alphanumerics, and three keyboards with rollerballs. The typical SVC is 870 (width) × 1415 (height) (460 kg); a full depth of 1703 mm is needed to withdraw the CRT. The MHC is 1160 (width) × 1085 (height) × 1879 (depth) (560 kg). Equipment drawers pull out to the side to a maximum width of 1825 mm. The CPU is 744 (width) × 900 (height) × 392 (depth); two can be stacked vertically for the larger systems.

IPN-10/SADOC users: Ecuador (*Wadi M'ragh* class), India (*Vikrant*, *Godavari*; mini-SADOC in "Tarantul," "Kashin," and *Khukri* classes), Iraq (*Wadi M'ragh* class, for sale), Italy (*Garibaldi*, *Mimbelli*, *Audace*, *Maestrale*, *Lupo*, *San Giorgio* classes and *Vittorio Veneto*; mini-SADOC in *Minerva* class), Malaysia (mini-SADOC in *Wadi M'ragh* class), Peru (*Lupo* class), Venezuela (*Lupo* class). Some elements of IPN-10 may have been sold to China about 1985, perhaps in connection with the Dardo purchase. IPN-10 may also have been exported as the basis of a ground air defense system. Mini-SADOC may equip the Taiwanese *Lung Chiang*, which is reportedly equipped with an NA-10 FCS.

◆ SADOC 3 (IPN-S)

IPN-S is the next-generation successor to the IPN series, under development since 1984. The system is federated rather than fully distributed, since it retains a system computer and a central mass memory. However, the system computer need not be very powerful, since much of the system computation is done in the MAGICS workstations. A typical frigate might have six two-screen MAGICS consoles, a bridge console (one screen), and a command console (like three bridge consoles side by side). A corvette might have four two-screen workstations, and a fast-attack boat three.

IPN-S is to be built around the new 32-bit combat system elements (such as the NA-25 FCS and EMPAR), standard MAGICS vertical consoles, and MARA 286-series computers, all connected by a dual-MHIDAS bus. Software is written in a new System Configuration Language (SCL) which can describe hardware and software configurations separately, allocating software modules to the hardware modules in a way separate from the development process.

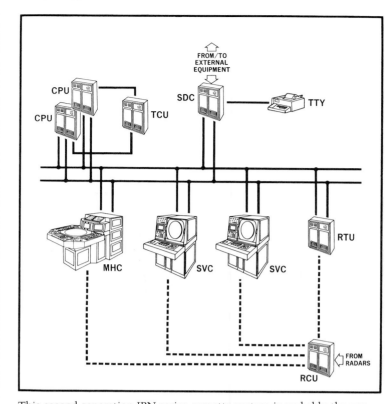

This second-generation IPN series corvette system is probably the version in the Italian *Minerva* class, with one MHC and two SVCs. The MHC is typically used for weapon control; helicopter/aircraft control; and navigation, maneuvering, ASW operations, and tactical situation assessment. The two single vertical consoles would be used for roles such as radar surveillance, EW coordination, and data-link control. The two NDC-160/E CPUs function as the system's central computer. They carry the system's tactical picture and are also responsible for system resource management. Their tape-cassette unit (TCU), with three sets of tape reels, loads the tactical program into the CPUs and records system data for later retrieval. Unlike a first-generation central computer, the CPUs do not have to refresh display screens continuously. That is done by the NDC-160/Es in the separate consoles. This degree of unloading is associated with the shift from a star to a LAN architecture, since the LAN cannot carry as much data as the set of separate connections from a central computer to peripherals. Instead, much of the data stream has to be reduced to computer-to-computer instructions (macros). That is generally the case with systems that are modernized by shifting to LAN arrangements. The RTU is a radar video target extractor and automatic tracker (it presumably incorporates at least one NDC-160/E). The RCU (radar central unit, or switchboard) distributes radar video directly to the consoles and also to the RTU. The SDC shown at top is an I/O expander and converter unit allowing the system to communicate with analog weapons and other equipment. Bus capacity is 10 Mbit/sec. The corresponding small-ship system has a single MHC and can accommodate a single SVC. As in the version shown, it is connected to a pair of CPUs. An interface and digitizer unit (IDU) atop the MHC connects the system to analog equipment. This version is the LAN equivalent of the *Wadi M'ragh* system. (Alenia)

Elsag, the developer of SADOC 3, announced in mid-1992 that it would be redesigned for a more open architecture; the MARA computers (with 80386 or 80486) processors may be discarded. The planned 32-bit family of equipment, such as the NA-25 FCS and EMPAR, will be retained, as will the dual-MHIDAS bus.

A typical combat system (for a frigate) would use a dual-MHIDAS system bus (for weapons, sensors, and consoles) and a separate video-distribution bus for raw radar, IFF, and ESM video (they feed synthetic video [extracted plots and strobes] into the main system bus). Fire-control radars feed the main bus via a FCS processor and ADT. Optronics and the navigational radar feed only the video bus. The system bus connects to the navigational sensors and the weapons via a special interface (TAU). Fire-control functions are conducted at fire-control devices, not at the main console level (e.g., by an SSM processor or a torpedo control box).

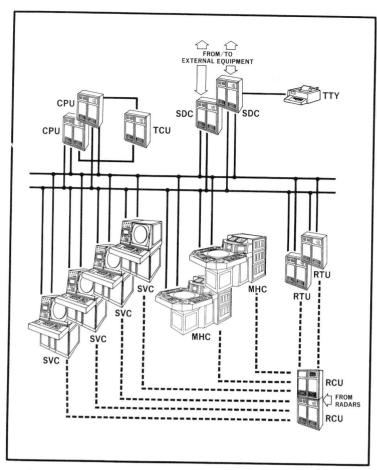

This is the frigate version of the second-generation IPN system. Although it was never built, it is not too different from the version on board such ships as the carrier *Garibaldi* and the *Audace*-class destroyers. It is essentially a distributed version of the system in *Maestrale*-class frigates. As in the corvette, this version has NDC-160/E central computers; the Italian navy version uses the much more powerful CDG-3032, the central computer of the original SADOC 2 series. The two MHCs provide the main command facilities for air, surface, and underwater warfare. The SVCs are used for selected operational tasks such as surveillance (air and surface), EW coordination, situation management (presumably meaning picture compilation), and helicopter/aircraft control. (Alenia)

There is some expectation that SADOC 3 will use a new universal (voice/data) fiber-optic bus (100 Mbit/sec) compatible with the U.S. FDDI standard.

The first SADOC 3 will probably be aboard the second Italian carrier, an improved *Garibaldi*; this system will also be on board the new classes of ASW and AAW frigates.

◆ SSN-715

The SMA automatic navigation and tracking system for hydrofoils and light naval craft uses navigation data and targets from the ship and displays the naval tactical situation for surface navigation.

◆ MAGICS

MAGICS is Selenia-Elsag's new Modular Architecture for Graphic and Imaging Console System workstation, used in SICS, in the NA-25 fire-control system, in the Italian version of FAMS, in Alenia's Submarine Integrated Combat System (SISC), and in SADOC 3/IPN-S command/control systems. MAGICS uses the same YMS operating system as the Digital VAX computers; the language is ADA. The standard console accommodates one or two 19in color monitors (1280 × 1024 pixels), each driven by a MARA 286 computer. The MARA acts as display processor/controller, carrying application software and providing data to the internal graphic resources of the console. There are also a video processor and a graphics unit. The video processor accepts raw sensor data to form radar (PPI, A-scope, B-scope) and sonar (B-scope) images, and also provides an image memory. The separate graphics unit does geometric processing, produces geometric shapes (such as lines, cones, and polygons), can transform sensor data from format to format, can digitally mix two video channels (for windowing or mosaic-type image superposition), and pro-

A SADOC 3 for frigates shows the full range of current and near-term Alenia systems. Note that the old horizontal console has been replaced by a triple vertical command console. The old single-screen vertical consoles have been replaced by dual-screen MAGICS consoles, with only a single screen on the bridge. The single video extractor/tracker of the past has been replaced by a series of separate ADT processors associated with individual radars. Note that the navigational radar is unique in feeding only the video bus; it has no target extractor. This is a federated rather than a fully distributed system, in that it still retains one or more C^2 computers ("CCS computers") on the bus, with separate mass storage. (Alenia)

COMBAT SYSTEM FOR FRIGATES

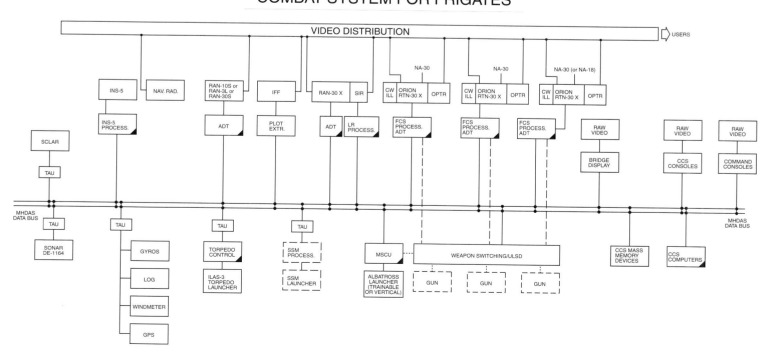

vides an image memory. This unit can also function in other image formats, from 580 × 780 pixels interlaced (equivalent to 625-line European television) to 1280 × 1530 pixels (60 frames/sec).

MAGICS can function directly as a sensor display. It can accept radar data at a PRF of up to 16 kHz centered, or 8 kHz off-centered. Radar video-sampling rate is up to 25 MHz, with 8 bits/sample (analog-to-digital conversion). Standard television and IR video can be accepted at 512–1024 lines/frame, and in this case video sampling rate is up to 40 MHz (6 bits/sample). Range scale can be 0.5–1024 km or nm. Time to change a pixel is 6 nanosec (0.006 microsec).

The basic MAGICS console carries a magnetic-tape cartridge. There is also a tabletop configuration for limited space. The keyboard can have programmable flat panels, a joystick, or a trackball.

MAVID is the associated architecture for video- and image-distribution system.

◆ CTI

This new family of ruggedized tactical consoles (1995) is built around the new PowerPC processor, which has a capacity greater than 60 SpecMarks. The console carries 16 Mbytes of RAM (expandable to 128 Mbytes). Its backplane is a VME; it connects to an Ethernet LAN. It carries a radar scan converter, hard drive (over 500 Mbytes) and DAT (2-Gbyte tape cassette) mass memory units, and a 20in, 1280 × 1024 pixel raster-scan color screen. The keyboard has illuminated buttons plus a trackball. It can accept two analog and eight digital videos. Different windows can simultaneously show PPI or B-scan; A/R (altitude/range) presentation; PPI or B-scan plus B sector of same radar; and PPI or B-scan plus A/R for search radar and fire-control unit.

JAPAN

An unusual feature of early Japanese computer CDSs was that they used Link 14 to form their tactical picture, interpreting and automatically plotting its formatted messages. Japanese naval tactical data systems are designated in an OYQ series.

An integrated data system, NYYA-1, was developed in the 1960s using the U.S.-supplied CP-642B (USQ-20B) computer. It apparently formed the core of later systems, which added weapon control. This system was probably analogous to a contemporary frigate version of NTDS then being installed on board the U.S. frigates *Koelsch* and *Voge*. It employed a single CP-642B with memory expansion, four OA-7979/UYA-4 consoles, and one summary console (OJ-195). This system could handle 64 local tracks and 96 remote tracks, and thus was roughly equivalent to the Spanish Tritan-1 using a single UYK-20 computer.

The first generation of Japanese CDSs comprised OYQ-1B (1978) and OYQ-2B (1979) for the missile destroyers *Tachikaze* and *Asakaze* and OYQ-3 (1979–80) for *Shirane*-class helicopter destroyers. OYQ-1B and -2B are described as a weapons-entry system. The name suggests that actual missile fire control was not integrated with the TDS that assigned targets to the missile system. It probably follows that these systems were broadly equivalent to slightly earlier U.S. missile cruiser systems built around a pair of USQ-20 computers and UYA-4 displays, with a capacity of 128 local and 128 remote tracks. OYQ-3 is described as a tactical data processing system (TDPS). The new designation seems to imply actual weapons control, in this case of ASW helicopters. It was probably occasioned by the addition of a third computer, a UYK-20. These systems employed USQ-20 and UYK-20 computers and UYA-4 displays. The DDH version was eventually modernized with a UYK-44 computer (to replace the UYK-20) and UYQ-21 displays.

The next generation comprised OYQ-4 (missile destroyers: *Sawakaze* and *Hatakaze* class, 1982–87) and OYQ-5 (new-construction *Hatsuyuki*-class destroyers and modernized destroyers *Takatsuki* and *Kikuzuki*, 1981–86). OYQ-4/5 appeared at the same time as the FCS-2 system. OYQ-4, described as a full CDS, is equivalent to slightly earlier missile destroyer systems such as the U.S. JPTDS; it is built around a UYK-7 computer (in effect, replacing the paired CP-642Bs, as in a *Spruance*), a UYK-20 mini-

computer, and UYA-4 displays. All air defense sensors (radar and ESM) feed directly into the central computer, which also receives both Link 11 and Link 14. Only sonar data bypasses it to feed directly into the underwater FCS (SFCS-6A). Apparently the main difference between OYQ-4 and OYQ-2/3 is the presence of the UYK-20, which would be used for missile fire control.

In nonmissile destroyers, OYQ-5 (one UYK-20, four or five OJ-194B displays, and one weapons-control panel [WCP-1A]) superseded the earlier NYYA-1 tactical navigation and target designation system. OYQ-5 is described as a TDPS. It is probably broadly equivalent to the Spanish Tritan-1.

The next-generation OYQ-6 is a full destroyer CDS (as opposed to a destroyer target designation system). Introduced in 1987, it is aboard modernized *Haruna*-class DDH, on board the eight *Asagiri*-class destroyers completed from 1988 on, and on board the six *Abukuma*-class frigates completed from 1989 on. The associated underwater FCS, in the *Asagiri* class, is SFCS-6B. Note that although the NOLR-6C ESM system feeds the CDS, the other major ESM sensor, OLR-9B, feeds directly into a jammer (OLT-3) and does not feed into the main CDS computer at all. In a helicopter destroyer, OYQ-6 employs two CP-642Bs, one UYK-20A, five OJ-194Bs, and one weapon control panel (WCP-1A).

The frigate version of OYQ-6 may be redesignated OYQ-7, in which case the current OYQ-7 (see below) will become OYQ-9.

The current generation comprises OYQ-7 (*Murasame* class) and OYQ-8 (*Kongo* class). OYQ-7 is apparently to be redesignated OYQ-9. Both systems employ UYK-43 main computers and UYK-44 minicomputers. In a *Kongo*, OYQ-8 comprises the usual combination of Aegis computers: the Mk 8 Aegis system computer (tactical picture and fire control), the C&D computer, the SPY-1D computer, and the Mk 2 display system computer. The main fire-control computer also controls underwater weaponry through the underwater FCS (OQA-201), which receives data directly from the sonar (OQS-102) and the towed array (OQR-2). This system is adaptable to Link 16. The new feature in a *Murasame* is the fixed-array FCS-3.

TDSs are also designated in a Type series, so that, as modernized, the *Takatsuki*-class destroyer has TDS 3-2 with provision for Link 14.

Submarine CDSs are designated in a ZYQ series.

NETHERLANDS

Officially the SEWACO (Sensor, Weapon, Control System) designation is limited to the Royal Netherlands Navy. Signaal applied other designations to systems, often unofficially called SEWACO, for other navies. DAISY is the standard program, produced in modular form by the RNLN Center for Automation of Weapon and Command Systems (CAWCS). The current edition, common to all SEWACO versions, is Mod 3. Note, however, that Signaal distinguishes between SEWACO (which includes sensors and weapons) and DAISY (Digital Action Information System), which is the control system proper. At one time Signaal described DAISY as a computer plus its proprietary combat information display system (CIDIS). FORESEE is the combination of DAISY hardware with the appropriate command/control software. The name is a pun on 4C: command, control, communication, and coordination. However, both the command/control system *and* the full-up combat system are generally denoted by the term SEWACO.

As of 1995, Signaal was developing a large-screen projection display similar in concept to the U.S. system, but somewhat smaller, about 3 × 4 ft.

◆ SEWACO/DAISY/FORESEE/EASY/STACOS

Like NTDS, SEWACO was originally based on a single central computer. Later versions were first federated (using a LAN) and then fully distributed. DAISY and FORESEE are export designations. EASY is a corvette derivative, apparently an alternative to the minicombat system described below.

SEWACO was developed in the mid-1960s, entering service in 1975–76 on board the two *Tromp*-class missile destroyers, serv-

Standard horizontal display consoles of the missile-control system on board a Dutch L-class air-defense frigate. (Signaal)

ing their elaborate 3D radars. Architecturally it was much like the contemporary U.S. NTDS, but the symbology and the program architecture were quite different. SEWACO uses alphanumeric track identifiers.

The detailed data that follow describe the original form of the system. SEWACO VII and the related STACOS use a later-generation SMR-4 computer and workstation consoles (SIGHT, Signaal general-purpose high-resolution tactical) incorporating some local processing capability in the form of 68000-series chips.

The standard computer is the Signaal SMR (the smaller but compatible SMR-S1 in some versions). At least in the original SEWACO, radar-video data were automatically extracted and inserted into the computer memory; early versions of SEWACO differed in the number of separate radar-video extractors and in

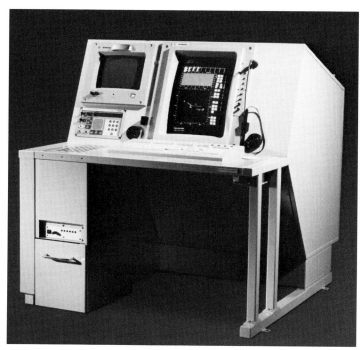

General-purpose operator station (GOS) of an M-class (*Karel Doorman–class*) frigate. Several such stations are arranged side by side in the frigate's operations room. (Signaal)

the number of consoles. In some cases the system also served a DES electronic plotting table. Physically, the system is built around a data-handling cabinet and consoles. The cabinet contains the tactical computer, the sensor-data distribution unit or SDDU (which feeds sensor data to the consoles), a computer-data distribution unit or CDDU (which feeds synthetic video to the consoles), and one or more radar-video extractors. The video extractor takes radar information from the SDDU and feeds it to the computer via the CDDU. Up to 10 consoles can be served.

In all versions of SEWACO, the computer interfaces with both the weapons and the sensors, using 24-bit I/O channels.

The design concept was to build different systems around a common core, so that about 75% of the software modules and database (tactical-picture) elements of any version of DAISY would be identical. This modular programming concept made it relatively easy to develop new members of the family and to ensure their reliability and efficiency. Signaal also claimed that its modular programming approach made later modernization relatively simple. Such programming should, however, be relatively inefficient in terms of core usage.

The system carries two types of tracks: 225 point tracks (i.e., tracks of objects for which range and bearing are both known) and 30 bearing tracks (ESM, passive sonar, and visual bearings). Tracks can be automatic, manual, or dead reckoned. For air tracks, the system maintains a track history over the last 2 min, and for surface and subsurface tracks over the last 40 min. In each case the track file includes course and speed (and height for an air target, depth and Doppler for a subsurface target), as well as link status/correlation and ESM-bearing association data. Bearing tracks are characterized as ESM/ECM, ASW/torpedo, or visual.

Threats can be ranked in relation to own-ship, escorted high-value unit, or vital area center. Calculations are based on target hostility criteria, including category, identity, position, course, and speed; target identity can be derived from the target electronic signatures, IFF responses, or data from external sources. DAISY automatically computes the best pairing of targets with the highest threat rank with own-ship or own-force weapons (including missiles and fighters). Free-fire boundaries are entered manually, and some versions of the system can respond automatically within those limits. Up to two airborne weapons systems can be controlled locally by a DAISY system, the shipboard controller selecting the mode of attack (e.g., frontal, rear, up-and-over). A version of DAISY was developed for carrier use, presumably for the Dutch carrier *Karel Doorman*, but it seems not to have been installed. It included facilities for carrier-controlled approach.

DAISY is designed to operate with Link 10 or 11, incorporating manually set filters that restrict linked information to an area of interest and thus protect the system from overloading. Filter categories are the number of automatically accepted tracks, target category, and range. The software is designed to accommodate up to 24 units in the data-link net. The system is also designed to format its own data for rebroadcast on Link 14 (teletype link); up to 45 tracks can be broadcast in this way.

There are two types of multifunction consoles, a vertical display console (VDC) and a horizontal type (HDC). Each carries a 16in-diameter, labeled position display (CRT). The VDC also carries a 7in alphanumeric display. The HDC can carry a 16–20in PPI as an alternative to the labeled 16in display, and there are one or two 7- or 15in alphanumerics. Such a display normally accommodates a supervisor and two operators. These displays carry keyboards, programmable quick-action (i.e., special-function) keys, rollerballs, and handwheels for communication with the system. Each console can be configured for any system task simply by changing the overlay (designation) of its special-function keys. There are two types of vertical display consoles, one for radar and one for sonar video. The HDC is a radar display console.

Signaal also describes the HDC as a tactical display console; it is an analog/cursive device (LPD) capable of displaying video from three radars. Range scales are 2–256 nm. The VDC offers similar ranges.

Signaal currently offers a new general-purpose workstation, SIGHT, with raster scan. It can use laser disks to store maps, manuals, and procedures. SIGHT can have up to four system functions linked to it. It uses a multiple version of Ethernet with a total capacity of 40 Mbit/sec.

Versions of SEWACO:

SEWACO I (ordered 1971) was for *Tromp*-class AAW destroyers. Reportedly, the SEWACO project was started when a Dutch-British joint-development program, which included the SPS-01 radar, died with the cancellation of the British carrier CVA.01 in 1966. The radar had been planned for the *Bristol* (Type 82)-class missile destroyer and would have served a complementary ADAWS TDS. The Dutch decided to continue work on the radar and to develop their own TDS. Thus, SEWACO almost certainly shares a common architecture with ADAWS. Presumably it employs a separate computer to run its radar, and a separate weapons-direction computer (not normally considered part of SEWACO).

SEWACO II (ordered 1975) is for the Dutch "Standard"-class frigates (ASW version). There are two horizontal and five vertical radar displays, one vertical sonar display, separate WM25 and STIR (Signaal tracker/illuminator) weapons-control consoles, and a separate ESM-control console. This is probably much the version in the Argentine *Almirante Brown* and Nigerian *Aradu* classes (both MEKO 360s). System architecture probably broadly matches that of the contemporary U.S. *Perry* class, with linked and identical picture-keeping and weapons-system (WM 25/STIR) computers, corresponding to the U.S. WSP and WCP. ASW fire control is presumably cued by the picture-keeping processor (WSP analog).

SEWACO IV (ordered 1974) was for the Belgian *Weilingen*-class frigates. There are three horizontal displays, a sonar display, and a radar plotting table (with true-motion indicator). There are separate fire-control consoles for missiles, guns, and ASW rockets. The SEWACO MA in the Malaysian FS 1500 class may be similar to this system.

SEWACO V (ordered 1976) was for the midlife modernization of the Dutch *Van Speijk* class (now sold to Indonesia). There are four horizontal tactical displays and a plotting table.

The SEWACO VII system of the M-frigate (*Karel Doorman* class). (Signaal)

SEWACO VI is for Dutch "Standard"-class frigates (AAW version). There are six vertical consoles, two horizontal consoles, and a sonar display console. This version includes both primary and secondary radar-video extractors and was ordered in 1985.

SEWACO VII, for Dutch *Karel Doorman*–class (M-class) frigates, was designed beginning in 1985. In effect it is a LAN derivative of the earlier star-topology systems, similar in concept to STACOS (see below). It retains the two picture-keeping SMR-4 computers (one for the weapons-engagement picture) of the earlier system, but unloads much of the tactical processing onto the system consoles (workstations). These two SMR-4s are described as data-handling computers (DHCs). Sensor data (other than sonar) feed into both via a sensor management computer (SMC), a track manager. Sonar data feed directly into the ship's data bus. The two data-handling computers communicate directly with an interface computer (INC), an SMR-Mu, which receives Link 11 data and is used for Harpoon and Goalkeeper fire control (it also receives and processes bathythermograph data). This computer runs existing DAISY software. In effect it is the remains of the original SEWACO architecture, most functions having been unloaded into other computers or into intelligent workstations.

Sea Sparrow and gunfire control are the province of a separate multiweapon control system (MWCS) fed with track data by the two DHCs. Some elements of the ship's combat system are entirely off-line: the Scout stealthy surface-search radar, torpedoes, decoys (both Nixie and SRBOC), the 20mm guns, the underwater telephone (UT-2000), and the 2013 fixed bathythermograph. A DEC VAX4500 is connected to the bus interface unit for the APECS II ECM system; another is connected to the bus interface unit for the Anaconda towed array. The two DEC computers maintain an elaborate database (e.g., of charts and intelligence data) on 14 optical disks. The database will ultimately feed an AI system comparable to the U.S. C&D computer or to the British CCA.

A third SMR-4 runs the ship's external communications system (Signaal's SINCOS-1200), and a fourth runs the ship's internal data bus (a dual-redundant fiber-optic FOCON-A). These two are called communications control computers (CCCs). The CDS is tied together by a triple Ethernet, with separate TV/IR and fiber-optic audio (internal communications) networks. This version uses over 10 times as much software as earlier SEWACOs. SEWACO VII uses 16 standard GOC consoles, 15 in the CIC and 1 in the communications room (as a communications management console). There are also 13 video/data displays. The computer/software core of the combat system, replacing DAISY, is

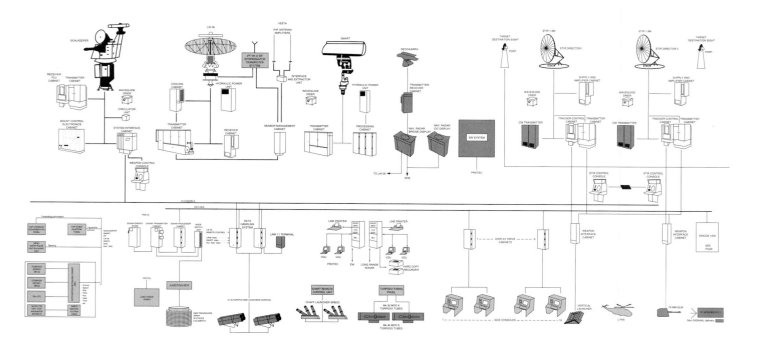

called SPIDER (Ships Processor Interconnection and Data Exchange Resource). The initial version, without SMART, is SEWACO VIIA; VIIB is the ultimate version, first appearing in the fifth ship of the *Abraham van der Hulst* class (completed December 1993).

Reportedly Korean *Donghae*- and *Po Hang*–class frigates (hulls 756–65) have SEWACO VIIK CDSs. The later units of this class (766–82) have the Ferranti WSA 423. The *Ulsans* (951–56) have the simpler Signaal minicombat system built around a WM-series FCS. Later *Ulsans* (957–58) have WSA 423.

SEWACO VIII is for Dutch *Walrus*-class submarines and was ordered in 1979.

SEWACO IX: SEWACO-M, for Tripartite minehunters (except French): Belgium, Indonesia, Netherlands, Nigeria. SEWACO IX was derived from SEWACO VII.

SEWACO X: For the projected Dutch-Belgian-Portuguese deepwater minesweeper, subsequently reduced to a Belgian class (KMV) intended to replace the old U.S.-supplied *Aggressives*. This version uses a data bus with two main processors (on a fiber-optic LAN): weapon and navigation. The weapon computer controls sweep winches and incorporates the system's mine signature database. The navigation computer controls the ship's autopilot, and carries the system's map database. There is a separate dual sweep planning and evaluation system (SPES) for tactical planning. All sensors and any other weapons connect to the system via the ship's bus.

SEWACO XI: Long-range AAW FCS module to be added to SEWACO VII elements, for the Dutch LCF frigate replacing the *Tromp* class. The Germans, who are partners with the Dutch in the frigate project, plan to use SEWACO FD/TACTICOS instead. Both versions will have a common AAW core employing APAR, SMART-L, and the new SIRIUS IRST. SEWACO XI uses Sun/SPARC hardware (over 100 MIPS in each console), programmed in ADA (also in C, UNIX, with X-WINDOWS graphics).

SEWACO XII: SEWACO VII plus SEWACO XI, for the Dutch LCF frigate.

STACOS: Signaal Tactical Command and Control System is a commercial designation for a LAN-based version of SEWACO built around an SMR-4 computer. Mods 1 and 2 have relatively dumb consoles; Mod 3 (redesignated TACTICOS, see below) has smart consoles and is roughly equivalent to SEWACO VII. This version can handle 512 tracks. The Turkish MEKO version has three vertical displays for tactical-picture compilation, a horizontal conference display for command decision making, and an automatic plotting table. The Greek and Portuguese ships have a Signaal digital dual directive weapons-control system (DDWCS, using two STIRs), an independent, redundant C² unit.

Unit cost of a current SEWACO is probably about $2 million, based on extrapolation from the stated costs of equivalent systems rather than from Signaal published data.
Users: Argentina (MEKO 360, with DAISY-AR system and three SMR-MU computers; DAISY-AR in carrier *25 de Mayo*; EASY-AR in MEKO 140s), Belgium (SEWACO III in *Weilingen* class, SEWACO IX in minehunters), Greece (SEWACO II in *Kortenaer* class, STACOS Mod 2 in MEKO frigates), Korea (SEWACO VIIK in *Donghae* and *Po Hang* classes), Indonesia (SEWACO V in *Van Speijk* class, SEWACO IX in minehunters), Malaysia (DAISY-MA in *Rahmat* and in FS1500s), Netherlands (SEWACO I in *Tromp* class, SEWACO II in *Kortenaer* class, SEWACO VI in *van Heemskerck* class, SEWACO VII in *Karel Doorman* class, SEWACO VIII/GIPSY in *Walrus*-class submarines, SEWACO IX in *Alkmaar*-class minehunters), Nigeria (MEKO 360, with DAISY-BV system, with two SMR-MU computers; SEWACO IX in minehunters), Peru (*Almirante Grau*, with projected FORESEE-PE system employing three SMR-MU computers), Portugal (STACOS Mod 1 in MEKO frigates), Thailand (*Makut Rajakumarn* with FORESEE-TH system, PF 103 with FORESEE-TH system, and *Ratanakosin* with FORESEE-TH system), Turkey (STACOS Mod 1 in Track I frigates; contract for Mod 3 in Track II changed to TACTICOS). The Thai ships probably actually have the minicombat system.

◆ TACTICOS (SEWACO FD) and MOC Console

This new fully distributed Signaal-Thomson CDS supersedes both TAVITAC 2000 and the distributed form of STACOS. TACTICOS/STACOS was formerly called SMCS (Signaal Modular Combat System). System consoles are MOCs (multifunction operator consoles), formerly called SIGHT for export applications. Each MOC maintains its own copy of the tactical picture. The basis of the system is a new fully modular hardware/software architecture, Sigma-Splice. Sigma-Splice acts as a buffer between various system functions and the dual Ethernet data bus (there is a separate video bus). Software functions are all written as separate modules, running within a TACTICOS "Kernel" which includes Sigma software interfaces.

The interfaces make it possible for TACTICOS to use commercial software, such as database managers. The system can also support nontraditional programming concepts (e.g., expert systems, blackboard systems, neural networks) and special processors (e.g., for acoustics).

For example, a sensor is connected to a preprocessor, which feeds the bus via Sigma-Splice (the combination of preprocessor and Sigma-Splice is a Sigma-Node). Similarly, a combat system console (MOC) conducts some system application function, which feeds (and is fed by) the bus via Sigma-Splice (the combination of system application and Sigma-Splice is a Sigma-Node). The weapon system connects to its own control processing and interface, which is combined with a Sigma-Splice in a third kind of Sigma-Node. Each MOC carries all software files in its own mass memory, so it can shift functions very quickly. System management software is distributed over the nodes. The system automatically (or manually) reallocates programs to processors in case of failure or battle damage. It automatically reroutes functional and database information via semantics-based connections. Ultimately TACTICOS will use a fiber-optic bus, which has greater capacity than the Ethernet bus of the M-class frigates.

Software is written in ADA and C; graphics are in X-Windows and OSF/MOTIF. The MOC consoles use VME backbones with double Eurocards and UNIX-based hardware.

Each MOC (formerly SIGHT) carries one or two 20in CRTs (1024 × 1280 pixels, 50–72-Hz refresh rate, 120-MHz video bandwidth), a graphics engine, two 400-Mbyte hard disks, and a

A MOC Mk 2 console. (Signaal)

keyboard with rollerball or joystick. Its backbone is a 25-slot VME, carrying multiprocessor boards, dual Ethernet interface boards, and graphics processor(s). Other boards may be radar- or TV-scan converters (RACO [up to three raw radar videos simultaneously], TVCO [for optronic trackers and for conventional RGB television]), a videobus interface (for RACO and TVCO), a graphics accelerator, a Z-buffer memory (for 3D-oriented graphics), and support for a second CRT. The application host processor is a Sigma multiprocessor node using SPARC (RISC) architecture, two to seven SUN-1S processor boards (each 12.5 MIPS with 16-Mbyte onboard RAM), one nodal resource module plus an S-Bus Ethernet interface, a 200-Mbyte Winchester (hard) disk, and a 60-Mbyte tapestreamer (backup for the hard disk). The graphics host processor is a MIPS R3000 CPU (32 bits, 20 MHz, with 32-kbyte data cache and 64-kbyte instruction cache), a MIPS R3010 FPU, 16 or 32 Mbytes of RAM, four RS 232 and eight RS 422 interfaces, a 200-Mbyte hard disk, and a 60-Mbyte tapestreamer; the operating system is IRIX. Graphics hardware provides 24 bitplanes, four Window/ID bitplanes, four Overlay/Underlay bitplanes, and a 12-bit color look-up table (4096 out of 16.7 million colors available). A second combination (with another 200-Mbyte drive) would be added to support a second CRT. The radar-scan converter (RACO) can handle up to 16 kHz (with 20% stagger) PRF; maximum range setting is 256 nm or 512 km; maximum antenna scan rate is 1.1 Hz (66 rpm). Output code is 4 bits/pixel (so intensity can vary by a factor of 16). Each console can be linked directly with up to four subsystems.

The MOC is also used in the new Sintra submarine command system, SUBICS, and it is used as a Link 11 terminal which may form the basis of a new CDS (see Stand-Alone Link 11 below).

A typical SEWACO FD system, showing its TACTICOS core (as defined by the dashed line). BTS are bus connection units. Vesta is a helicopter video link. (Signaal)

In some cases MOC is called a general-function operator console, GOC.

Turkish Track IIA frigates use eight MOC Mk 2 consoles; in Track IIB two more MOCs replace the usual pair of dedicated FCS consoles. The Turkish *Dogan*-class FPBs use five MOCs. The associated combat system includes a Vesta link modified with voice component so helicopters can support OTH-T. Qatar uses a four-console version.

At Bourget Naval 1992 (October 1992) Thomson-Signaal displayed a mocked-up triple command console: a 29in Barco MX2500 screen (2,560 × 2,048 pixels) flanked by two standard 17in TACTICOS displays with their standard controls. The 29in screen is repeated in a large-screen display (over 1 sq m), the first in Europe. This may or may not be a fixture in future TACTICOS systems; it was intended to provoke comment.

The designations TACTICOS and SEWACO FD are so very nearly equivalent that they are difficult to distinguish. Signaal appears to distinguish among the combination of CDS, sensors, and weapons (SEWACO) and the CDS core (TACTICOS).

Users: Oman (Vosper-Thornycroft corvettes), Qatar (Vosper-Thornycroft fast-attack boats), Turkey (repeat *Dogan*-class and Track II frigates). This system may be used in the new Kuwaiti offshore patrol vessels ("Combattante I" class). In the Omani corvettes, the system employs three MOC Mk 2 consoles: one for the PWO, one for the air/surface picture compiler, and one for gunfire control. A slave display is on the bridge.

◆ Signaal Mini- and Compact Combat Systems

These systems are extensions of the WM-series FCSs described in the Antiair Warfare section. In a minicombat system, a standard Signaal horizontal tactical display (described above under SEWACO) is connected to the weapons-control console, which contains the SMR-S1 computer (the same type as in the corresponding WM-series FCS). Signaal also offered a compact system

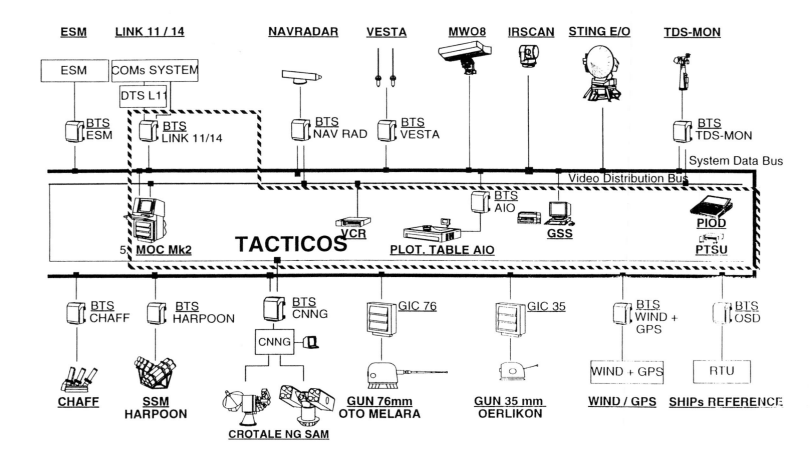

This standard Signaal horizontal console (HDC) is the main display element of the company's Mini-Combat System. Systems based on particular versions of the "egg" are denoted by a /41 suffix, as in WM28/41. In most cases, the vertical weapons-control console is supplemented by a horizontal tactical display console of the type shown. This HDC is part of a larger SEWACO system on board the Dutch air-defense frigate *Jacob van Heemskerck*. (Signaal)

in which the computer fed feeds two or three horizontal consoles. The latter may be the version in the Spanish *Descubierta* class. In each case, the computer is installed in the standard Signaal weapons-control console. These systems correspond broadly to the French Vega/TAVITAC, but with the search and fire-control radars unified rather than separate.

Users: Argentina (*Espora* class), Egypt (*El Suez* class, 1978), Korea (*An Yang Ho* or KCX class with WM-28 FCS), Morocco (*Errhamani* class, 1979), Norway (*Storm*-class fast-attack boats [probable]), Singapore (110ft Type B fast-attack boats [probable]), Spain (*Descubierta* class, 1974), Thailand (*Ratanakosin* with WM-25). Reportedly two minicombat systems were on board Greek *Gearings*, though they lacked the "egg" usually associated with this system.

◆ Stand-Alone Link 11

Signaal produces a two-way Link 11 system built around a MOC smart console. Since the MOC houses, in effect, a picture-keeper, it can become the kernel of a full-blown CDS. In December 1994 Signaal received a contract to fit three such systems aboard the Portuguese *Joao Belo* (*Commandante Riviere*)-class frigates (presumably as a follow-on to a prototype installation). Portugal ordered a full CDS for installation from 1996 on. The MOC-based Link 11 is also going aboard Turkish *Knox*-class frigates. No other sales have been reported. However, as of early 1996 another *Knox*-class operator and a Far Eastern navy (which does not operate the *Knox* class; probably Korea) were reportedly showing interest.

NORWAY

◆ MICOS

Simrad's MCM mission-control system was adopted for the Norwegian minesweeper/minehunter (*Alta* and *Oksoy* classes) program. It is fully distributed, tied together by a dual Ethernet, using standard ATC900 single-screen (20in screen) tactical consoles. Each console contains two SBC3000 processors (using 80386 CPUs). The minimum configuration, in the minesweeper,

has three bridge consoles (CO, dynamic positioning/navigation, and officer of the watch) and two main CIC consoles (tactical console and mine warfare officer console). These consoles are not independent. Thus the tactical console is connected directly to the officer of the watch console (which is itself connected directly to the navigational radar). It is used to plan the mission, managing large databases, including electronic charts. The CO console is connected directly to the officer of the watch console and to the mine warfare officer console, and not directly to the data bus. The mine avoidance sonar also feeds the data bus, through its own processor (its console is connected directly to the processor, to obtain raw as well as processed video). In the expanded minehunter version of the system, the tactical console in CIC is grouped alongside an ROV control console, and there are separate detection and classification sonar consoles. The dynamic positioning console is duplicated in CIC, alongside a pair of mine warfare officer consoles. (see page 96)

The contract for the air cushion MCM craft was signed in February 1990, and the first system was delivered in March 1992. The associated sonars are the Simrad SA 950 in the minesweepers and the Thomson Sintra TSM 2023N in the minehunters; the ROV is Gayrobot Plus. The sweepers can tow an Agate acoustic countermeasure. (see page 96)

◆ MSI-80S/PFCS 2

MSI-80S is a fast-attack (missile) boat tactical system manufactured by NFT. It employs a single three-operator tactical console (tactical operator, weapons-control operator, and passive-sensor operator); the officer in tactical control occupies a fourth position. The tactical operator initiates and controls target-data calculations and updates the tactical situation display. The system entered service in 1977 on board Norwegian *Hauk*-class fast-attack boats.

The computer is a KS 500, using the Mary language. Some of the software is based on that developed for the MSI-70U submarine system (see below). The console itself incorporates a 23in horizontal (main tactical) display that shows raw and synthetic video, plus a 12in CRT. The latter normally shows alphanumerics but can act as a backup for the main display. Displays are manufactured by GEC Sensors.

The associated sensors are twin Decca TM 1226 navigational radars and an EO tracker (GEC V334 LLLTV camera, laser rangefinder, IR scanner), optical sights, and ESM.

Penguin FCS System 2 (PFCS 2), a radar-based derivative of the EO MSI-80, has equipped the Greek "Combattante III"–class missile boats for many years. It may also be on board the Turkish *Kartal* class.

MSI-80S on board the Norwegian fast-attack boat *Hauk*. A smaller derivative is used on board Greek "La Combattante"–class fast-attack boats. (NFT)

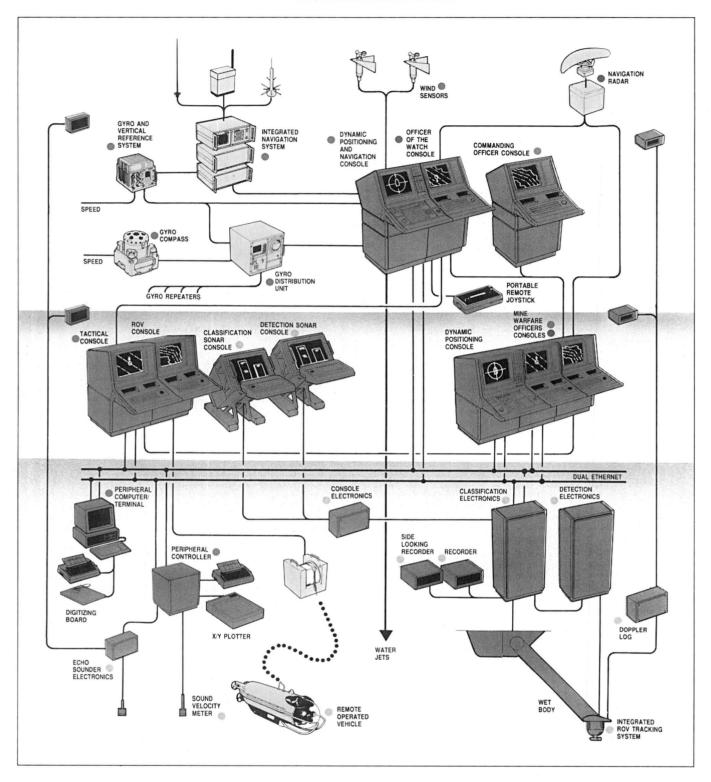

MICOS as installed in Royal Norwegian Navy *Oksoy*-class minehunters. (Simrad)

◆ MSI-3100

This combat system for the modernized *Oslo*-class frigates was first installed in February 1987. The contract was awarded in 1985. MSI-3100 incorporates two two-operator KMC 9000 consoles, one for tactical control and one for weapons control. Tracking can be manual (via trackball) or automatic, the former mode permitting the operator to modify raw-video inputs. In the latter mode, radar data are inserted by an REX II radar plot extractor. As a whole, the system can handle up to 99 self-generated and 48 link-reported tracks. The two consoles communicate

via a Budos data bus. There are no dedicated FCSs as such because all directors feed the weapons-control console, which in turn connects to the guns and missile launchers.

Each console accommodates two KS 500 computers, one for general operation (256k) and one dedicated (128k). A KS 800 is used as a scan converter and display controller. In the weapons console, the dedicated computer is used for Terne (ASW mortar) fire control; in the tactical console, it is used for air defense and antiship fire control. All use the Norwegian Mary computer language. Taken together, the consoles amount to a federated system.

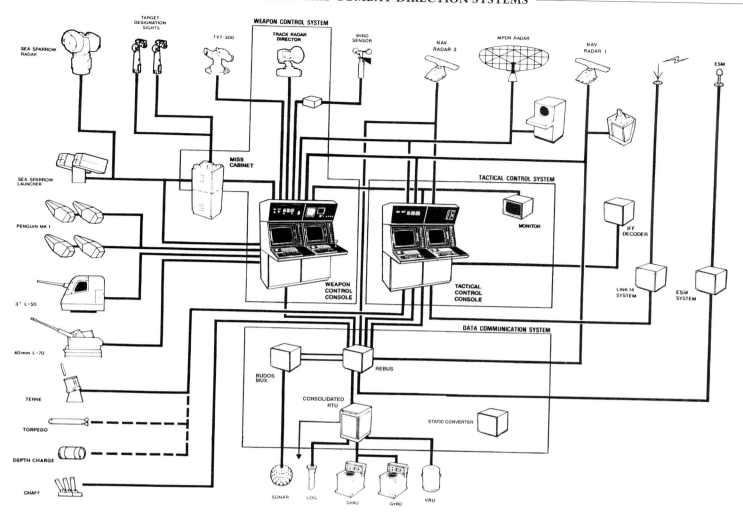

MSI-3100 as installed on the *Oslo* class. The current modernization substitutes an air defense system based on the British Odin for the MPDR radar shown here. (Kongsberg, formerly NFT)

The same KMC 9000 multipurpose console is used in MSI-3100, in the MS-90U submarine system, in the NOAH ARCS control system for the improved Hawk missile, and in the FENRIS radar data-integration system.

◆ MSI-340/350

This development of MSI-3100 was announced in 1987. It employs the same KMC 9000 two-operator console, with either KS 500 or KS 900 processors. The software is written in either Mary, Pascal, or ADA. MSI-340 is a single-operator system with a 20in CRT; it uses the NFT REX II radar plot extractor. MSI-350 is a two-operator extension of -340. Generally, the console accommodates one weapons operator and one tactical (command/control) operator.

Reportedly, MSI-340/350 is the tactical command system envisaged for the next generation of Norwegian fast-attack craft. Units intended for group command will have two-console installations.

◆ NAVKIS

Kongsberg's (now NFT's) Navigation Command Control and Information System is installed in the *Nordkapp*-class coastal-patrol ships (EEZ enforcement ships). The system was ordered in November 1978. Priorities were (a) accurate navigation, so that the borders of the EEZ could be maintained; (b) command/control; (c) air surveillance and gun control. Each function is served by its own console (two in the case of navigation: one in CIC and one on the bridge), and the consoles are connected by a data bus, which also receives sonar data directly.

The main console is the Command and Control Information System (CCIS), which can identify and automatically track 16 targets and identify and automatically plot up to 64 fixed points. It can display the air targets picked up by the air surveillance console, and it can define and display local geography (including fishery grid, oil block, and similar data). This console is also responsible for antisubmarine weapons control (sonar input, drop-point calculation and plotting for mining, and target-intercept calculation for torpedoes), and it provides a navigation backup (correlates data from the ship's sensors with known geographical points in the display of navigation data). The air-search radar feeds into the CCIS console, as does the ESM receiver.

Navigation was considered particularly important because radio-navigational-aid coverage of the Norwegian Sea is relatively poor. The ships therefore use three-axis main gyros, two-axis secondary gyros, a passive log, TRANSIT (satellite), Decca, Loran C, an echo-sounder, X-band navigational radars, and GPS. A navigational computer monitors the receivers and sensors, filtering their data to produce a best estimate of ship's position. The navigational computer also has access to surveillance radar, LLLTV, and optical-sight data normally fed to the CCIS console.

Finally, the air-surveillance and gun-control console directly controls air engagements and the ship's helicopter. Up to eight air, surface, or subsurface targets can be tracked manually, and the air display includes IFF data. This console receives data from the air-search radar via a radar switchboard, which also feeds data to the CCIS.

The data bus is Budos, operating at about 30 MHz (bandwidth 10 MHz), with a capacity of 1–3 Mbits/sec.

◆ Sea Command

Kongsberg's (formerly NFT's) COTS-based fully distributed command system uses an MFC2000S standard console (or MFC2000C twin-screen compact [because only one console is needed per system] console, or MFC2000M mobile console) with a VME backplane and Sun SPARCStation architecture. The system employs two different operating environments: the MMI (and all tasks not requiring fast real-time processing) is written in UNIX, using OSF/Motif graphics. Tactical (real-time) applications, which interface with weapons and sensors, are written in ADA. The standard console shows two superimposed 20in color raster-scan screens, the lower one tilted up (1280 × 1024-pixel raster-scans). The interfaces are a QWERTY keyboard, trackball, and a programmable touch-screen (the compact version adds a joystick). The high-speed LAN is not specified.

Sea Command was first announced in 1994 as a weapons-control system, interfacing via its VME backplane with a missile, gun, surveillance radar, and EO director, and using a dual-workstation weapons-control console. The full CDS was announced in 1995.

RUSSIA

◆ "Second Captain," "Second Admiral," and CDS Architecture

The "second captain" computer is the basis of the Russian equivalent of Western CDS. This computer carries both track data and data on ships, aircraft, and weapons. Its software includes routines to deal with various tactical situations in the optimum manner. The CO fights his ship through the second captain computer system, which communicates with weapons controls. Typically a ship has a second captain console on the bridge, and another in a secondary plot (battle information post, BIP) adjacent to a weapons-control space, which may have a console used to designate air targets. The BIP may also contain a vertical plot. Originally BIPs were comparable to Western CICs, containing radar consoles whose operators fed the vertical plot with target data. Current units apparently use automatic target trackers associated with a single main radar, to feed the central computer with a single set of unambiguous target data.

Because the ship is fought through the second captain, it appears that a flagship can control a ship by sending commands via the Bell Crown data link to the second captain computer. The likely structure of the Bell Crown signal (data sent, command returned, acknowledgment) would seem to support such a contention.

In many ships when in AAW mode the second captain cues a secondary radar directly associated with the ship's weapons. That is the case, for example, in a *Slava*, which has both a Top Sail (long-range, for the second captain) and an associated Top Steer shorter-range set to cue its SA-N-6 system. The *Sovremennyy* class is unusual in having only a single air-search radar. That would seem to imply that digital radar data are distributed to both the second captain and the weapons system, perhaps via a data bus.

Typically the weapons-control area is divided by function. Visitors who are told that this is the ship's CIC are given the impression that the ship must be fought warfare area by warfare area, without any coordination. In action the ship's executive officer apparently generally stands in the weapons-control space, and must give approval before targets can be engaged. This practice limits the ship's ability to engage multidimensional threats, but it is not inherent in the design of the system.

There is one important exception to the concentration of weapons-system controls in a below-decks space: controls for antiship missiles are generally on the bridge, with a duplicate set in the secondary bridge (BIP). Presumably antiship engagements often require external cueing and use the vertical plot in

The command system of a Krivak-I (Project 1135) -class frigate is typical of pre–second captain practice. It is clear that the tactical aid was added well after the ship was completed because it is not connected in any way to the main plot. Unlike Western naval summary plots, this one is horizontal, targets being indicated by markers rather than by grease pencil. This practice is much like that in World War II air-defense filter centers, the shore equivalents of CICs. (Stuart Slade, DMS/Forecast International)

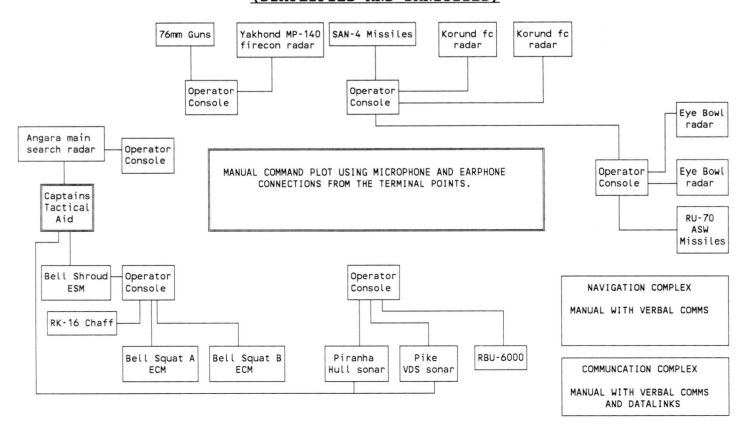

PROJECT 1135 COMMAND SYSTEM
(SIMPLIFIED AND SANITIZED)

PROJECT 1135P COMMAND SYSTEM – SIMPLIFIED AND SANITIZED

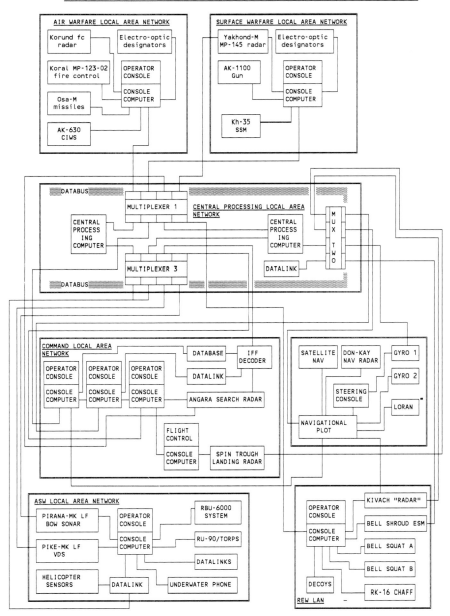

A Krivak-III (Project 1135P) has a fully integrated command system using a second captain and a data bus (the single bus has been somewhat distorted to simplify the diagram). This is now a federated CDS using LANs. Note that the Kivach radar is associated with the ECM (radio-electronic warfare, or REW) LAN because it can function as a precision radar direction-finder. The ships were designed as ASW units but taken over as border-patrol craft. This diagram reflects the original design concept, in which the ship's helicopter acted as an ASW sensor, reporting (like a U.S. LAMPS) through a data link into the ASW LAN. This version of the Krivak could dispense with SS-N-14 missiles because SS-N-15s (RU-90s) could be fired from the torpedo tubes. There was also provision for SS-N-25 (Kh-35) antiship missiles, though none have been seen to date. (Stuart Slade, DMS/Forecast International)

BIP, whereas AAW and ASW engagements can be fought using the main air-search radar.

It appears that in flagships there are two levels of control. A computer, which might be called the "second admiral," maintains a track picture and decides the priority of different warfare areas. It commands ships in company through their second captains using the Bell Crown data link. On board the flagship, the second admiral feeds track data and commands to specialized second captain computers primarily concerned with specific warfare areas. The main flagship classes in question are *Kiev* (to support pro-SSBN ships) and *Kirov* (to control groups of rocket cruisers, RKRs, attacking surface targets). The two *Sverdlov* flagship conversions tested these two systems. In both cases, the main sources of data are the Vee Cone long-haul HF antenna and the Big Ball satellite antenna. Submarine tender/flagships are probably also equipped with the second admiral, using lower-powered HF and MF transmitters of their own.

These flagship systems were developed from the very first second captain installations, on board the *Moskva* and the flagship-tender *Volga*. Presumably these ships used single computers for both flagship and combat-system tasks, and they were overloaded.

The *Moskva* (and probably the *Volga*) version initially passed information to other ships via a burst transmitter, Akula, sending data from a tape punched by the computer. Only later was a Western-style data link, Bell Crown, added to the AAW ships. Own-ship radar data were entered by a radar operator using a foot pedal (i.e., the system carried tracks rather than raw video).

Second captains form a family of versions emphasizing different warfare areas. Apparently the *Moskva* and Kresta II versions share a common technology, although the latter is much less capable. Reportedly, the Kara class, construction of which began two years after that of the Kresta II class, has a next-generation version, which can handle more tracks and can form a net with more ships. Kara was also apparently specifically designed to work closely with May patrol aircraft, using a ship-to-air link (Kresta II appears to lack this feature).

The main series of second captains are probably:

Rocket Cruiser (RKR), initially on board the Kresta I, primarily concerned with target selection, discrimination, and engagement. The main sensor is presumably the Big Bulge radar of a Bear D bomber. This computer also processed Bell Tap ESM data and controlled the Side Globe jammer, which the Russians thought of as a means of holding off counterattack until the SS-N-3 missiles could be fired. There was probably no intership data link. The latest version of this system is on board the *Slava* class.

Rocket Cutter (MRK) on later Nanuchkas, to control their own SS-N-9 missiles and (probably later) also to coordinate the fire of accompanying Osa-class missile boats. The next-generation system is on board the surface-effect boat *Dergach*, to work with Tarantuls. Reportedly the transmitting section of the system does not yet work.

ASUW for submarines, on the "Charlie" class; it may be related to the Nanuchka system, which fires a related missile. Note that the earlier "Echo II" submarine had no such system.

ASW short range, on board a destroyer controlling groups of smaller ships firing RBU-6000s. This was probably the first approximation of a second captain to go to sea, on board the Kashin-class destroyer *Odarenny* (ca. 1965). The computer also processed ESM data from the ship's Watch Dog B. Ships fitted with RBU-6000 generally have this fire-control computer on board. It is actually a shore-based computer brought to sea to control the RBU-6000 projectors on board small ASW craft such as Mirkas and Petyas. Given sonar data from the hunters, the computer evaluates the probability that the target is within a circle of a given size. Once the probability is high enough, the hunters are commanded to saturate the circle with projected depth bombs. Such computers were initially ashore, but then they were moved to sea aboard command ships (BPKs). Command was probably exerted via a data link (Fig Jar) to a bridge console aboard each hunter. The combination of a maintained tactical picture and a tactical calculation is a primitive form of the second captain.

ASW medium range, controlling SS-N-14 missiles, first installed in the Kresta II, and then in Kara-class cruisers and Krivaks. The main sensor is the Bull Nose sonar. In the Krivaks, this second captain is also used to control Grishas operating in company. In Krivaks, the same computer handles the ESM/jammer combination (the evidence that the combination is computer controlled is the IFM pimple on top of the Bell Shroud ESM antenna: an IFM is useless unless it is connected to a computer for pulse de-interleaving). Presumably the *Udaloy*-class introduced a later version of this system, with a later longer-range sonar.

ASW for submarines, first in the Tango (Project 641BUKI) class, and probably also in "Victor II"–class submarines. The system in the "Kilo" class may be related.

AAW, controlling SA-N-3 missiles, in Kresta II and Kara-class cruisers. The main sensor is the Top Sail radar; the same computer probably handles the Bell Tap/Side Globes combination. SA-N-6 and -7 ships have their own versions of the second captain, using Top Pair. The associated data link is Bell Crown.

ELINT ships probably have their own version of the second captain. There are also second captains on board submarines and on later versions of the Bear F ASW aircraft.

Craft too small to accommodate second captain computers have command consoles adjacent to their bridges. In a Tarantul, the ship's captain fights using the console (which displays Plank Shave radar data), or the console can be used as a terminal for a data link. In this case the link sends the boat's radar data back to a shore command post, and carries back the order to fire. Because the boat lacks a computer, the link back cannot control the boat in detail, for example by taking over her autopilot. Using the data-link setting also made it possible to insert received data into the missile fire-control computer, which normally would obtain its data directly from the Plank Shave radar.

In the case of AAW, dedicating the long-range search radar to compiling the tactical picture (and reserving a shorter-range search set for target acquisition) would not be too different from British practice. In the past, it has generally been assumed that the Russians paired their search radars as insurance against failure. The effect of running the ship's ESM suite through the central computer is automatically to provide it with a means of identifying targets through their emissions. It appears that in at

least some cases the tactical picture displayed to the CO or admiral includes this identification, perhaps in icon form.

◆ *Slava*-class CDS

A *Slava*-class cruiser has second captain workstations both on her bridge and in the BIP below decks. Near the bridge workstation is a console to designate targets to the ship's SS-N-12 (Bazalt) antiship missiles. A similar console, with further SS-N-12 consoles, is in the BIP. Presumably one workstation carries the ship's tactical picture, formed automatically by her main radar and by her sonar; the other may carry the OTH-T data provided for long-range missile firing. The separate weapons-direction space contains launching consoles for the ship's SA-N-6 defensive missile system. It acquires targets using a secondary radar (Top Steer), in effect a higher-frequency equivalent to the main radar (Top Pair) feeding the second captain. Gun and ASW targets are presumably engaged from the weapons-control space.

◆ *Sovremennyy*-class CDS

Sovremennyy is unusual in amalgamating the BIP and weapons-direction spaces below decks. Recent photographs of this space show both a missile (SS-N-22) command console and AAW control consoles, as well as standard second captain workstations. As in the *Slava* BIP, there is a vertical plot (in this case, a pair of perspex boards in the center of the space).

The AAW module comprises a circular horizontal console (S-170AM), a vertical console (S-170M), and a separate SAM-control section (one OK-10V situation display and one OE 3-1/5 target-engagement console). It is probably not too far-fetched to imagine that the vertical console is the radar scope used to enter

One of two second captain multifunction consoles on the bridge of the *Slava*-class cruiser *Marshal Ustinov*; the other is to the left. The curtains are to screen off ambient light; in addition, the entire area is curtained off from the front of the bridge. Another pair is in the ship's BIP. The ship has a total of about 20 such consoles. This type of console appears to be standard in recent ships, such as *Udaloys* and *Sovremennyys*. (Author)

SS-N-12 control console in the BIP of the *Marshal Ustinov*. Standard practice seems to be to place such consoles only on the bridge and in BIP, never in a weapons-control space. (Author)

plots into the tactical system; the horizontal console would then be the target designation console (perhaps a second captain readout). When working from the BIP, the commanding officer uses an additional air picture console (S-170M), which can be used to direct friendly aircraft.

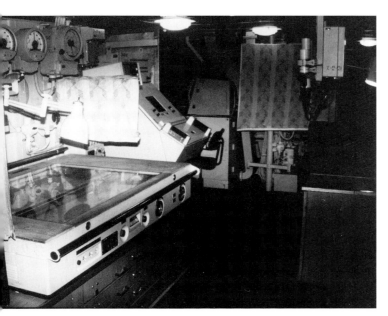

BIP area aboard the *Sovremennyy*-class destroyer *Gremyashchiy* (1993), showing the SS-N-22 control console behind the dead-reckoning tracer (for navigation). This space is directly under the optical periscope forward of the bridge; the periscope eyepiece is visible at right. The console in shadow in the background is probably a second captain terminal. Although this space was not physically separated from the rest of the command space, it was screened off. (R. L. Scott)

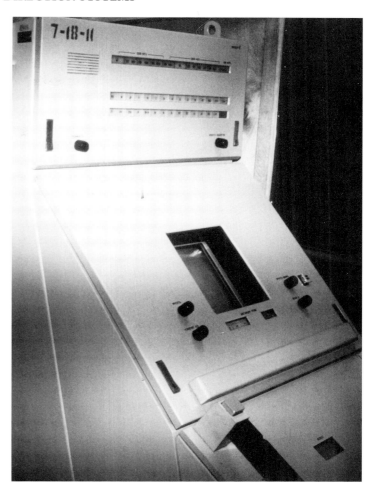

SS-N-22 console aboard *Gremyashchiy*. The small rectangular screen apparently displays the ISAR target image produced by the missile's radar. The small windows below indicate data-link performance. Buttons on the hand-holds lock on or destroy the missile. (R. L. Scott)

The ASW module consists of a single passive/active sonar display (PREBOR 6) connected to a separate sonar room. There are also a separate navigational radar console, EW and, apparently, CW modules in CIC.

Controls for the guns (130mm and 30mm) are reportedly local; it appears that their radars presumably are not tied into the air picture in any way. Again presumably, targets are designated in the BIP. Such an arrangement would satisfy the supposed Soviet requirement that a ship degrade gracefully in combat. It would correspond to Western World War II and early postwar practice.

There is also a secondary control position containing a ship's wheel and manual (grease-pencil) status boards, used primarily for damage control.

SOUTH AFRICA

UEC Projects of Durban (part of Altech Defence Systems [Pty] Ltd) produces a "versatile housing" console for use in CDSs. It is now marketing extended versions of the distributed system used in the fast-attack craft upgrade described below.

There is also a minehunter system, which plans search patterns, compiles a mine plot (working with detection and classification sonars), and coordinates and controls the detection of detected mines. It also supports a data link. This system is probably intended for the "Ton"-class upgrades.

◆ Kingfisher/Seawatch

UEC's proposed OPV system is intended to allow an OPV to identify vessels outside the likely range of their weapons, 1500 m (20mm-gun range). The company argues that existing OPV ra-

S-170M SA-N-7 vertical console, *Gremyashchiy*. Dials (presumably to show director orientation) and the side-by-side rows of eight vertical square lights match those on the horizontal console. Note, however, that there is a third vertical row of circular lights between the square ones—which is *not* in the horizontal consoles. Each magazine holds 24 missiles, but the use of only two rows of lights suggests that only 16 are ready-service rounds. (R. L. Scott)

dars can generally detect a target perfectly adequately, but cannot identify it. It would therefore add both a plot compilation facility and an optical tracker capable of identification outside 1500 m range. The system can also lock a gun onto a suspicious target so that it can be engaged (for forced arrest or, if need be, destruction).

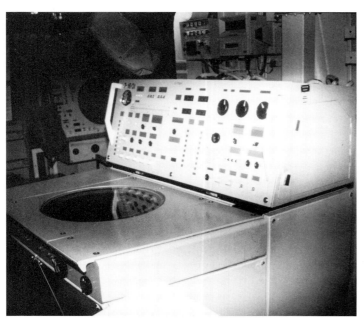

S-170AM horizontal console for SA-N-7 missile control, on board *Gremyashchiy*. Each is associated with an S-170M vertical console, one of which is visible in the background. The ship has two horizontal consoles, probably one for each of the two launchers, each associated with three Front Dome (Orekh) radars. (R. L. Scott)

The system is controlled by a tactical weapon console (TWC) on the extended bridge of the OPV. The TWC can be connected to a shore-based vessel management system by data link. Normally it is connected by RS422 wiring to the ship's radar, and to a stabilized video tracker by video bus. The tracker, TWC, and a gun are all connected to a system LAN (the gun is connected through a gun drive unit and through a gun control unit, which in turn is connected to a stabilizer). The LAN can also be connected to a Seawatch vessel management system.

System performance: It is assumed that a standard X-band radar can detect a vessel at 15,000 m and that two scans suffice to establish track data (course, speed, CPA). The system is expected to identify a 10m boat moving at 15 to 25 kt at a range of about 2700 m by day or 1200 m by night.

The preferred gun option is the South African-made GA35 35mm rapid-fire cannon, but the system can also accommodate 20mm and 40mm weapons. A dual-tube 68mm flare launcher (range 5600 m) can be fitted to the gun's elevating mass (under the cradle).

UEC designed a special optical tracker (tracking subsystem, TSS) for Kingfisher to carry a FLIR, a high repetition rate laser range-finder, and a TV camera.

Seawatch is an alternative coast guard system, also intended for installation aboard ship. Its processor includes embedded GPS. A navigation option interfaces to the ship's radar, autopilot, and various navigation sensors; it displays the ship's radar targets on an electronic chart. A communications option connects the ship to a maritime headquarters, allowing quick downloading of data from shore. The shipboard element of the system includes fuel management. All hardware is commercial.

The system includes a shore terminal, which displays a complete operational picture on an electronic chart. Seawatch has been sold to the South African Police Service for new patrol boats, and it has been marketed in the Middle East and in the Pacific Rim region.

Both Kingfisher and Seawatch use standard commercial PCs.

◆ NAVTAC

UEC has been selected as systems design and integration contractor for studies of a new corvette for the South African navy. The company calls its standard warship CDS NAVTAC (Naval Tactical Command System). It is designed to use an embedded data link for all tactical communication. It employs two to five standard operator consoles connected to each other by a LAN. Normally consoles would be used for the following separate roles: picture compiler, command (summary), ASUW director, AAW director, OTC. The command-systems LAN is also connected to the data link and printer. There is also the usual video bus connecting the consoles to a video distribution box (which is itself connected to the LAN) and to radars, optical trackers, and navigational equipment. All other systems are connected to the LAN via IFUs (standard interface units). The system can handle up to 400 tracks. Target classification is linked to a platform characteristics database. The system database, including track data, is replicated in each console; there is no central computer. TDAs include submarine avoidance tools (calculation of limited lines of submerged approach, torpedo danger zones, cones-of-courses, and furthest-on circles). The system as a whole includes provision for expert system-based decision support.

The standard LAN is an Ethernet (FDDI is an alternative). Software is written in ADA and C. Consoles use dual 20in color raster screens (1280×1024 pixels), and weigh about 350 kg (dimensions are $1.6 \times 0.7 \times 1.2$ m). The processors are 32-bit COTS units. The interface units also use 32-bit COTS CPUs.

UEC also offers a shore-based command/control facility and a shore-based planning and debriefing workstation, to work with ships equipped with NAVTAC.

◆ SAIS

Altech's Surface Action Information System was designed for the "Minister" class (Israeli *Sa'ar* 4) service life extension program. Studies began in the late 1980s, with a project definition contract let in 1992. Equipment deliveries began in 1994, with initial trials on board SAS *Frederic Creswell* following in 1995. Six of the nine ships are to be modernized under this Project Caliban, which is to keep them in service through 2007. A production contract for the remaining five ships is expected in 1997. It will include any work required to bring the prototype system up to full production standard. The system is fully distributed, using a pair of UEC's standard multifunction consoles, each carrying two 21in rectangular screens (one above the other) to replace the original plotting table. One is normally the command workstation, the other the tactical picture compiler. They are connected to each other and to ship sensors, EW, and weapons control by a Plessey Tellumet fiber-optic Ethernet LAN. Track capacity is over 100. Symbology is standard NATO, with color threat classification. The system offers plot zooming, panning, centering, and de-clutter. It includes TDA functions: overlays for planning, target detection, weapon-firing data, expert-system-based tactical recommendations, and plot annotation. Electronic and sonar emissions can be triangulated for passive tracking. The integrated EW system offers automatic threat alarms.

Installation of a fully digital system presumably required automation of radar functions (via ADT) and of EW detection and identification functions. Fire control also had to be updated so that targets could be passed automatically from the two-console CDS. There are now two WCS consoles side by side; the original Israeli console is now flanked on its right by a Target Designation Assembly Mk III (with a large circular CRT) connected to the CDS, the optical director, and the FCS radar.

The ships' 76mm guns fire new ammunition developed by Fuchs in South Africa, and the mounts are being converted to electric power. The South African navy claims that a new target Trigger Burst Function offers the gun an 80 to 85% chance of shooting down an incoming antiship missile. Presumably that prediction is based largely on the improvements in target acquisition and fire control included in the CDS modernization.

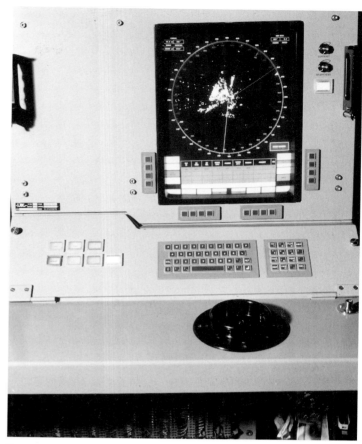

Target Designation Assembly of a modernized "Minister"-class fast-attack boat. It is part of a three-console array; it is installed adjacent to the original Skorpioen FCS console. This version replaces an earlier one with a large circular CRT. (Altech)

The new navigation subsystem includes integrated GPS and an inertial platform, as well as the usual elements (gyro, speed log, echo-sounder, anemometer).

The standard console assembly is also used in other SAN applications. Dimensions: $0.68 \times 1.25 \times 1.61$ m (320 kg).

UPC is currently working on a corvette CDS, and reports interest by at least one other navy in its fast-attack craft system.

SPAIN

Sainsel is now responsible for all Celsea-Inisel naval CDS. It supplied the three-operator CONAM display systems for the *Santa Maria*–class frigates *Navarra* and *Canarias*, and will supply the CDS for the new M51-class minehunters.

◆ Alcor

Alcor is Bazan's small-ship combat system. Development reportedly began early in 1986, with shore trials early in 1988 and sea trials late that year. The initial-production version provides optronic fire control for 40mm guns, but an expanded Alcor M is intended for corvettes and frigates. It incorporates a radar-video extractor and uses two parallel redundant data buses. The Alcor project is being funded largely to develop a combat system–architecture capability at Bazan.

The small-ship version consists of a COAR weapons console and a CONTAC tactical console; the current fire-control sensor is a stabilized television connected to a video tracker. The ship also carries navigation and surface-search radars, as well as an auxiliary optical target designator.

The system is tied together by a Cormonet data bus, which reportedly differs from the usual type in that it takes into account the priority of each user.

The CONTAC console contains two ruggedized IBM PC/AT-compatible computers, one carrying the tactical picture and the other providing the general-purpose computing power of the system. In this particular case, the second computer is responsible

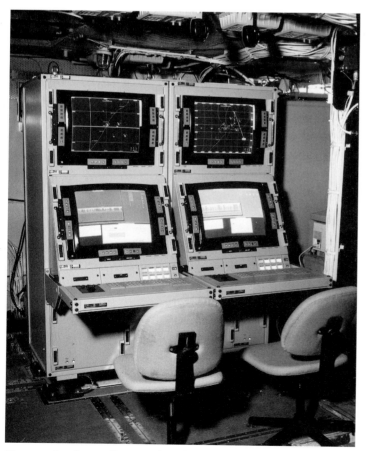

Command and compiler consoles of the SAIS fast-attack boat system. Typically they are located alongside and abaft the fire-control consoles. Across from them is the communication-system console. (Altech)

for gunfire control. The main tactical display, on the right-hand side of the console, is a 20in (diagonal) high-resolution color monitor (1024 × 800 pixels); it is flanked by a 9in monochrome display, presumably for raw sensor video. The operator communicates with the system by means of software-defined keys plus a standard keyboard and a rollerball. The programming language is Pascal 86.

The COAR console carries two monochrome monitors, one for alphanumerics and the other for video (e.g., television monitor video). Three separate keyboards control the video tracker, the configuration of the FCS, and data entry; the data-entry keys can be used to reconfigure the system, for example, for stand-alone gun operation in the event that the system cannot obtain fire-control solutions from the tactical console. It seems unlikely that the COAR console has any local computing capability at all.

Alcor was developed as SPCVZ (Sistema de Combate para-Patrullero de Vigilancia de Zona) for offshore patrol vessels. It is the optronic FCS of the Spanish *Serviola*-class patrol ships, having entering service in 1991.

♦ Tritan

Tritan is the Spanish navy's TDS, developed by the Spanish Naval Observatory at Cadiz. It was installed on board the carrier *Principe de Asturias* and the last two *Santa Maria*–class frigates as built, and on board the *Baleares*-class frigates as part of their modernization. Tritan will also be installed in the modernized *Descubiertas*. It is essentially NTDS plus Italian- and Spanish-built components. Selenia IPN-10 series consoles are provided to control the Meroka close-in weapons and to act as monitors for Selenia radars. There are also separate Elettronica ECM consoles. The main consoles are OJ-194/UYA-4s, built under license.

The *Principe de Asturias* has a Tritan-2 system, using a UYK-7 central computer, supplemented by UYK-20s. She has ten OJ-194 operations consoles, two OJ-197 command/control consoles, four Selenia IPN-10 consoles (for Meroka), three Elettronica consoles for that company's ESM, ECM, and ELINT systems, and communications consoles.

As modernized, the *Baleares*-class frigates have Tritan-1, incorporating a Spanish-built UYK-20 central processor (U 1600, with a 256k memory), five OJ-194 consoles, U.S.-type target engagement and weapon assignment consoles, an ASW console, four Selenia tactical and weapons-control consoles (MHC and SVC), a radar-data integrator (apparently broadly analogous to the U.S. SYS-1), and a Rockwell two-way data link (for Link 11). The associated EW system is also new: it is Deneb, manufactured by Ceselsa.

System capacity: own ship, 64 local and 64 remote tracks, 26 local and 14 remote special points, one local and one remote DLRP, one local and one remote PIM, four local and four remote ASW vectors (strobes), four local torpedo vectors, four local and four remote acoustic points (presumably sonobuoys), 16 local and 8 remote ESM strobes, and four local and four remote ESM positions. The CIC crew includes an air intercept controller, an air antisurface controller, and an air ASW controller.

SWEDEN

♦ CCIS/CEPLO/DEPLO/MARIL

CCIS (Command Control Information System) is a DataSAAB (later Ericsson, now CelsiusTech) tactical system, for frigates, corvettes, and fast-attack boats. It is typically integrated with a 9LV 200 series Mk 2 FCS (9LV Mk 3 absorbs the CDS function) and has probably been supplied to all buyers of 9LV 200 Mk 2 systems. Other designations: CEPLO (Command Electronic Plotting System), DEPLO (Danish version of CEPLO), MARIL (Swedish: Marinen Eldlegnings), MARIL 880 (extended version for Royal Swedish Navy), and MARIL 890 (*Landsort*-class minehunters). MARIL 880a equips the *Norkopping* class, MARIL 880b equips the *Stockholm* class, and MARIL 880c equips the minelayer/training ship *Carlskrona*.

A MARIL 880 missile-boat installation, showing the horizontal local-operations console and the vertical-screen general operations plot (GOP) behind, above the two alphanumeric plasma displays. The screen in the background is a vertical operations console with a 21in split-screen phosphor, to display synthetic video (a radar PPI) above alphanumerics. (Ericsson)

As EPLO, this system entered service in 1973 on board the Swedish *Norkopping* class (it was replaced in 1984 by the related but greatly upgraded MARIL 880). The Royal Danish Navy adopted a similar system as DEPLO in 1972 for the *Willemoes* class (it entered service in 1976). A next-generation version was announced in 1975 as the Ericsson CCIS; the Royal Danish Navy bought it as CEPLO to upgrade the *Peder Skram* class (now discarded) and later for the *Nils Juel* class.

CCIS is responsible for TEWA and for direct management of ECM (including chaff firing) and for torpedo fire control (replacing the TORCI system of earlier Swedish fast-attack craft). It displays weapon danger zones and conducts such navigational calculations as CPA and time to arrive. Maneuvering assistance may include maneuvering advice upon firing chaff.

This system was originally built around two Censor-900E series 32-bit computers, each of which suffices to run a two-console system (one is a spare). The extended MARIL 880 (in the *Spica II* and *Stockholm* classes) uses a Censor 932E, and can accept OTH-T data from helicopters and from a shore command center (the SUMP system, see above) via a digital data link (earlier versions may require a separate data-link terminal). A system bus connects CCIS with the 9LV FCS. Thus raw radar video (as well as communications, ESM, and the output of a radar warning receiver) is normally fed directly into the radar plot extractor of the CCIS. The CCIS in turn assigns weapons and commands the 9LV systems. However, in the event the central computer fails, raw radar video can be fed instead into the 9LV plot extractor, and thus into the combat-system bus.

The 16in- or 23in-diameter horizontal PPI display (LOP console) is used for target detection (manual plot extraction, for surface targets) and tracking, the three operators using their rollerballs and keyboards. It includes two alphanumeric plasma displays. There is also a single-operator, 21in rectangular, LOP (PPI) display, in which the lower part of the screen (coated with a different phosphor) shows alphanumeric information, while the rest of the screen is reserved for raw video. This console also has a roller- or joyball and a keyboard. The 16- or 23in vertical, command-decision display (GOP) shows only synthetic video. Tracking can be automatic or rate-aided. The PPI area shown can be magnified by a factor of up to 128. There is also a standard data-link terminal with an alphanumeric screen and a keyboard.

In a medium ship (a missile attack boat, such as a *Spica II*), the three displays are typically combined into a four-operator command center, the GOP standing above the flat LOP, with the two alphanumeric displays under it and the keyboard on one side. In a *Spica II* the LOP (16in PPI) is manned by the tactical-picture compiler, the weapons officer, and the (antiship) missile-control officer. The weapons officer assigns targets to the separate gun and torpedo FCS operators of the 9LV 200 system at their one-man consoles. RBS-15 antiship missile orders are sent directly and automatically to the missile control panel. In a larger ship, such as the Danish *Nils Juels*, the command center has paired GOPs, with alphanumeric displays and keyboards between them, and paired LOPs (a total of four, for local air, surface, and subsurface plots and for weapons coordination and control) to either side.

The simplest version, in the Swedish *Hugin* class (and probably in the Yugoslav *Rade Koncar* class), probably has only a single vertical console.

Target positions are updated cyclically, every 2 min for 24 tracks, or every 30 sec for six tracks. In the semiautomatic (rate-aided-tracking) mode, the operator can correct the estimated target position by means of a trackball; the PPI then shows the new position plus a track history. All targets are generally shown with vectors (course and speed). Charts used on the displays are built up of vector lines, typically 1000 of them. Several can be stored on a tape cartridge and called up as needed. In addition, the operators can use their keyboards and rollerballs to mark areas of special interest (such as minefields) onto the electronically stored maps.

The Swedish *Hugin*-class upgrade program, begun in 1991 (to complete 1997), replaces the tape program loading units with PROMs. Sonars are installed for ASW. The MARIL 880 CDS of the earlier *Spica II* class was upgraded when these boats were armed with RBS-15 missiles. Consoles were upgraded with new raster-scan screens and alphanumeric displays (TEP 200 display system) and software was added. The CDS was integrated with the missile control console for quicker reactions. At least six will be further upgraded to remain in service through 2010. The improved MARIL 880 in the *Stockholm* class is to be modernized beginning in 1997.

The modernization of the Danish *Nils Juel* class (begun 1995) includes replacement of CEPLO by a 9LV Mk 3 CDS (as in the *Flyvefisken* class); the 9LV Mk 2 FCS will remain.

Users: Bahrein (FPB 62 and TNC 45 classes), Denmark (CEPLO: *Nils Juels* class; see above), Finland (*Helsinki* class), Iraq (probably *Ibn Khaldum*), Kuwait (FPB 57, TNC 45 classes), Malaysia (Spica-M class), Oman (probably "Province" class), Sweden (as MARIL/MARIL 880: *Carlskrona, Hugin, Spica II, Stockholm* classes), UAE (FPB 38 and TNC 45 classes), and Yugoslavia (*Rade Koncar* class).

◆ ERIMIS

The Ericsson Maritime Information System was selected in 1994 for the new YSB-class MCM ships: four ship-sets plus a training set are to be supplied 1995–98. Eiva, the Danish company responsible for the MCM core of the system, is acting as subcontractor to Erisoft of Sweden (an Ericsson company). This is *not* the COOP system supplied to FMV in 1991 (and described above). Its LAN carries five Sun SPARC 20 workstations (CO, navigator, helmsman, sonar officer, and minehunting officer) and a printer and a plotter. The LAN is fed by the navigation, command, and control computer, and by an EG&G DG-1000 digital fish (side-looking sonar). The minehunting officer console is separately connected to the Terma Reson mine-avoidance sonar, the sweep, and the remotely controlled SAM I/II. The navigation/control computer controls the ROV (a Sutec Eagle, using a Tritech 6000 sector-scan sonar).

◆ 9LV Mk 3 Series/Base System 2000/Sea Viking

Base 2000 is a series of CelsiusTech (formerly PEAB) multipurpose (naval and other defense applications) distributed command/control systems; some naval applications may refer to it as FS 2000 (FS is the Swedish equivalent to Ship System). This series replaces the earlier combination of 9LV and CCIS; 9LV Mks 1 and 2 were FCSs (see the Antiair Warfare section). Sea Viking is the stand-alone FCS version of 9LV Mk 3, presumably offered as a one-for-one replacement for 9LV Mk 2.

Software is written in ADA, an object-oriented language specially adapted to such modular applications. BEAB argues that it is therefore possible to achieve a high degree of commonality (as much as 80%) in systems for very different purposes since, for example, a track-keeping module need not be rewritten for reuse. On this basis it has sold 9LV Mk 3 systems for both surface ships (e.g., ANZAC frigate, *Goteborg*-class corvette) and the current

The standard workstation of the 9LV Mk 3 system. (BEAB)

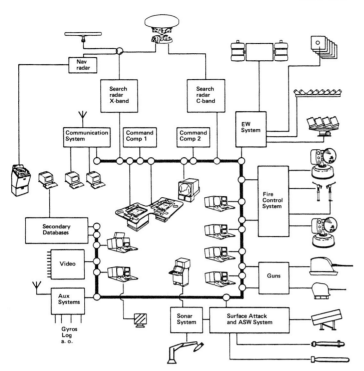

This sketch shows 9LV Mk 3 as installed in the Swedish *Goteborg*-class corvettes. In addition to the usual single-operator stations there is a large-screen display and a paired horizontal conference-type display (actually two separate items). The two command computers carry the system track database and other databases. (CelsiusTech)

Swedish submarine (A19 class). Base 2000 has also been adopted for the new Swedish national air defense system (STRIC).

Unlike the earlier CCIS/9LV systems, 9LV Mk 3 uses a dual Ethernet data bus (10 Mbit/sec per line) to connect the sensors (including the EW system, with its own subprocessor), weapons, FCS stations, multipurpose consoles, and the dual system computer. All data pass through the bus; for example, the FCS stations are not directly connected to the weapons. This is still an AAW-oriented system; at least in the *Goteborgs*, the ASW system is separately fed by the sonars. The two system computers still carry the tactical picture.

Each node on the bus (including each workstation) has its own Motorola 68020 processor (CPU), in the form of a single circuit board, associated with 4 Mbytes of RAM memory (as well as 256 kbytes of read-only EPROM memory carrying instructions for that node). For example, a radar node includes an automatic plot extractor (raw video would overload bus capacity). Note that the ANZAC version has a second (video) bus specifically to provide the consoles with raw rather than synthetic (plot-extracted) video as an alternative. The bus can accommodate up to 100 users per segment. Quite aside from the modularity inherent in ADA, the separation of the software in the different nodes makes the system relatively easy to expand (for example, the *Goteborg* class was intended for later installation of a point-defense missile, such as VLS Sea Sparrow).

The standard VME-backbone/double Eurocard workstation, SPL 85, made by the Danish company Terma exists in two forms, Type IIA (single monitor, as in ANZACs) and IID (double monitor, as in *Gotland*). Monitors have 20in color or monochrome monitors (1280 × 1024 pixels, refreshed at 60 Hz, using the upper 1024 × 1024 for a radar or tactical picture, and the lower 256 × 1024 for a menu read-out). Type IIA has a smaller 12in raster-scan display on its upper right, to display television, radar, graphics, and text, and a second 12in raster-scan on its lower right for television, A-scan radar data, or text. Operators call up functions by means of two touch input screens showing menus, and they also use keyboards and one or two rollerballs. The *Goteborg* version uses the earlier CCIS workstations (two standard horizontal displays, connected together, and a vertical command display [GOP]).

The first versions to use SPL 85 consoles are for the Australian/New Zealand ANZAC frigate (9LV 453 Mk 3) and for the Finnish *Helsinki II* class. The 9LV 453 Mk 3 uses six SPL 85 consoles, for the CO/PWO (equivalent to the U.S. TAO), the surface-warfare coordinator, the ASW director, the helicopter controller, the air-picture controller, and the surface-picture controller. An additional console can be provided for the EW director. Compared to the *Goteborg* system, the ANZAC frigate requires six or eight rather than five operators/controllers. There are three separate buses: a combat-system bus, a video bus (to supply the consoles with raw video), and a command/control bus (consoles and computers). Presumably the single bus of the simpler versions would not have sufficed. Reportedly this version required some software redesign because it was not fully compatible with Link 11 (it did not automatically report some actions back into the Link), because its man-machine interface did not use standard NATO symbology, and because it could not accommodate the usual fast-action buttons.

In the Finnish *Helsinki II* class, 9LV Mk 3 employs two SPL 85 consoles, plus two navigational radar consoles and a fire-control console. The Danish Standard Flex 300 (Stanfire) version has six command consoles with daylight screens (the CIC is on the bridge). The version in the *Thetis* class has four consoles.

As a measure of system complexity, BEAB claims that it has produced a software library amounting to one to two million lines of code for the *Goteborg* (missile-corvette) installation.

As of 1996, CelsiusTech and its Australian subsidiary CTA were working on a COTS version of 9LV Mk 3, using RISC processors, a fiber-optic LAN, and X-Windows/MOTIF graphics. Hopefully any such system would be able to use much of the existing software (500,000 lines of C and 1.5 million of ADA). It would appear, then, that the CelsiusTech approach is to emulate existing 9LV Mk 3 computers and consoles on the much more powerful commercial machines, so that much software could be used directly. CelsiusTech began work on a prototype system in the fall of 1994, using an IBM RS/6000 (with a Power CPU) and a UNIX operating system; a future version might use Pentium or DEC Alpha CPUs. In 1995 CTA developed a prototype COTS console to run the version of 9LV Mk 3 provisionally selected for the RAN offshore patrol combatant. It has a pair of 1280 × 1040 pixel flat-screen (LCD) displays, one for the tactical picture and the other for four alphanumeric windows. Unlike CelsiusTech in Sweden, CTA apparently did not try to emulate the earlier 9LV Mk 3 hardware. Instead, it wrote new interface software which could be hooked to portable elements (written in ADA) of the earlier software. Now CelsiusTech is trying to unite the two approaches.

Users: Australia (ANZAC class), Denmark (StanFlex 300 and *Thetis* classes, to be on board *Nils Juel* class), Finland (*Helsinki II* [two SPL 85 consoles]), New Zealand (ANZAC class), Oman (OPVs, single-console version planned), Pakistan (modernized Type 21 frigates; there is also an associated shore command center), Sweden (*Goteborg* class). This system has probably been adapted for coastal defense (it is presumably the new Swedish system). The command system of the new Swedish submarines (A19 class) is derived from 9LV Mk 3; see the Underwater Warfare section.

◆ 9MCM200

CelsiusTech's new-generation mine warfare TDS incorporates post–9LV Mk 3 COTS technology. It is a fully distributed system employing one-man general operator's consoles, without the tactical table employed in 9MJ400. The same type of equipment is to be used ashore, at an MCM operations center. It may be the system recently sold to Australia for shore MCM control.

◆ 9MJ400

The BEAB-Racal-Decca minesweeping direction system of the Swedish *Landsort* class is related to the 9LV series. It can control up to three SAM vehicles. The main sensor is the French TSM 2022 sonar, and 9MJ400 is integrated with a 9LV 100 optronic FCS (which uses the electronic plot of the 9MJ400 system for target detection). This is a centralized system built around two computers, a main processor and a minehunting computer. The main processor feeds the displays (one horizontal tactical console and two navigational PPIs). It is fed by the optronic director, target designators (pointers), the navigational radar, the wind sensor, and radio data links. It in turn is connected to the separate minehunting computer. The latter is connected to the minehunting sonar, automatic chart table, helm indicators, printer, and gyro compass. The integrated navigation and minehunting functions are based on the British Decca MAINS/CANE systems. During mine search the ship is controlled by an integrated autopilot for maximum track accuracy. The autopilot hovers it in the optimum position during mine disposal.

UNITED KINGDOM

In May 1990 the U.K. Ministry of Defence requested bids for the combat management system (CMS) for the next-generation air-defense destroyers, which by 1992 was an Anglo-French program. As of mid-1992 three alternative CDSs were being considered: the Dutch-French SEWACO 11, an upgraded version of the BAeSEMA SSCS, and a Ferranti System 700 descended from the earlier System 500. No choice had yet been made as of mid-1996.

◆ ADAWS/ADIMP

Action Data Automation Weapons System is an Admiralty-designed CDS incorporating weapons control. It equips the *Invincible*-class light carriers and Type 42 destroyers; the original ADAWS is now being superseded by ADIMP (ADAWS Improvement), which replaces each FM1600-series computer with an F2420. ADAWS was redesignated ADAWS Mod 0; ADIMP is ADAWS Mod 1. The initial ADIMP software was ADAWS Edition 20, built on the ADAWS Edition 12 baseline introduced aboard HMS *Exeter* in 1993. All systems are built around two computers, one for general processing and one for weapon control. In the event of a casualty, either computer can carry the system load.

The displays are analog Plessey Mk 8s with digital injection, analogous to early U.S. UYA-4s or SYA-4s. The standard vertical display is the LPD (labeled plan display), with a 12in circular monochrome CRT, for specific sensors and weapons. The JZ horizontal (tactical) display, used to create the merged tactical picture, is a 20in-dia monochrome CRT with an attached 12in vertical alphanumeric display. Typically, there are three associated keypads and three rollerballs. Most systems have two horizontal displays (ADAWS 10 has four).

Early ADAWS differed from NTDS in using only alphanumerics and vectors, where NTDS uses standard symbols to distinguish among friendly, unknown, and enemy (and air, surface, and subsurface). In later versions, which have better symbol generators, ADAWS and other British command/control systems revive the earlier standard symbols (icons) for ship types, which

The Outfit JZ horizontal display is used in ADIMP. (Royal Navy)

had been used in manual plots at least since the late 1930s. Thus, current British TDSs provide the operator with both a vehicle (type) identification (e.g., a triangle for a cruiser) and a letter track identifier alongside it.

Control is a problem, because instead of variable-action buttons or fast-action buttons the designers preferred alphanumeric commands; experience in Falklands combat showed that under stress complex operators often made errors or forgot coding altogether. Worse, the keyboards were not the common QWERTY type, so operators had to be specially trained. These problems were addressed in the ADIMP upgrade. It also afflicts other British CDS, such as the WSA 400 series and CAAIS.

ADAWS incorporates ATD (plot extraction). Usually a human operator opens a track file by designating a target. In local area extraction (LAX), the system applies its plot extractor to the area of the display immediately around this initial plot. The operator resolves ambiguities, such as crossing tracks. The faster the target, and the smaller the probability of detection on a per-scan basis, the larger the local area and the greater the human input. In the alternative limited area/full extraction (LFX), ATD is conducted, but only in a limited designated area. Only in later versions is there full ADT, as in current U.S. systems. Generally, the operator or the system decides which radar to use for tracking.

The earliest surviving version is ADAWS 4 (Outfit DAD), for Type 42 destroyers, aboard two Argentine ships. This version was limited to Link 10 (Link X in the Argentine ships).

The modernized ADAWS 7 (DAF, 1988) adds a separate data-link processor, providing it with full Link 4 and Link 11 capability; better threat evaluation; and a separate captain's console so that the captain no longer has to look over the PWO's shoulder. ADAWS 8 (DAG), for Type 42 Batch 3 destroyers, accommodates the Type 2016 digital sonar, which presumably has its own FM1600-series computer. Near-term post-Falklands improvements included a second Sea Dart control position and SNAPS (the Smiths Navigation and Plotting System, which can keep track of up to 128 targets).

ADAWS 10 is the last pre-ADIMP carrier system, installed as ships were modernized. It employs 32 LPDs, and has full ADT.

ADIMP (DAH) introduces a Captain's Combat Aid (CCA, Outfit JZZ) and some discrete preprocessors. An F2420 computer replaces each FM1600E of the earlier ADAWS 8 system. Each F2420 enclosure also contains a tote engine, based on a Z-80, to drive the alphanumerics on the JZV totes.

As in many other upgrades, the picture-keeper is now connected to a combat-system bus, which carries data from the sensors. The dual-redundant combat-system highway (bus) uses triple-screened coaxial cable pairs running along the port deck edge and starboard waterline. Because it is on the main bus, the CCA receives sensor data in real-time. The point-to-point topology of the weapons-control computer (WDS computer) remains.

The picture-keeper uses a "recognized air and surface radar picture" produced by Thorn-EMI's LFD track combiner, which takes track data from the ship's radars (each radar has its own ADT: Thorn-EMI LFB for Type 1022 and LFC for Type 1007, and Ferranti LFA[2] for Type 996). LFD feeds its picture onto the bus, not directly into the picture-keeper.

Both computers feed a pair of display central equipment (DCE) processors via a single bus. They also receive raw radar video, digitizing it and mixing it with synthetic video from the tote engine and processor before distribution to an individual display. This system seems analogous to the U.S. UYQ-21.

As modernized by GEC-Marconi, the displays are designated JZV; a Type 42 has 24 LPD (PPI) displays, two horizontal tactical displays, and an additional LPD in the computer room for engineering reference, diagnostics, and configuration management. LPDs have raster-type alphanumeric displays in place of the earlier cursive units (using 68000-series processors) plus a TV tote on the right-hand side of each console (driven by the tote engine described above), and the horizontal displays are provided with additional alphanumeric displays. Scan compression improves synthetic-video displays. QWERTY keyboards replace the original type.

The system includes an auxiliary link processor comparable in concept to the U.S. C2P, DLPS (Outfit RJJ), by Data Sciences with Ultra Electronics and Control Systems, for Links 10, 11, 14, and later 16 and 22.

ADIMP Sea Dart control improvements are comparable in concept to the U.S. NTU. ADIMP includes provisions for Goalkeeper and also for the 2050 sonar in Type 42 destroyers.

Manchester completed 18 months of proof trials in October 1994; as of early 1995 *Gloucester* and *Illustrious* had also completed the ADIMP upgrade.

Modernization includes additional units. Outfit INB correlates data for ship direction, speed, pitch, and roll and feeds them into the combat-system bus. A new ECM interface unit (ECMIU) connects the ESM and jammer to each other without passing their data and commands through the central computer. In effect, it federates the system.

In 1991 a British parliamentary paper estimated that 19 AD-IMP systems (three carriers, 12 destroyers, two shore facilities for each version), which would become operational from 1993 on, would cost a total of £115M.

◆ ADAWS 2000

Ferranti's (now GEC-Marconi's) CDS has been selected for the British LPH. It is based on ADIMP, using a picture-keeping computer rather than a fully distributed architecture. Indeed, it was first demonstrated in December 1992 with two F2420s. The four-console version was judged 25% less expensive than the alternative, NAUTIS, even though at the time of contract award the console vendor (for open-architecture commercial-standard units) had not yet been chosen. It is expected to be able to handle up to 1000 tracks with over 100 track updates/sec. Unlike AD-IMP, ADAWS 2000 employs an open architecture, using a UNIX operating system and standard graphics (X-Windows, MOTIF). Console applications software, which is inherently modular, is written in ADA and C (input/output software is in ADA and Assembler, with a limited amount of Coral). The dual-redundant Ethernet local network connects to the ship's combat-system highway (data bus) via a processing unit. There is also a separate video bus. Presumably one workstation will function as picture-keeper.

◆ CAAIS (DBA) and WSA Series

Ferranti's Computer-Assisted Action Information System (CAAIS) was conceived as a less-expensive alternative to ADAWS using the same first-generation FM1600B computer. The picture-keeping and weapons-direction functions were amalgamated into a single computer, so targets were designated and weapons and sensors assigned directly from the central computer. The associated fire-control computer was retained where needed; it became a WSA (weapon-system automation, the Royal Navy term). The result was often described as decentral-

WSA 422 console, showing the video screen and the two flanking radar scopes. (Ferranti)

ized only because descriptions of ADAWS omitted the fire-control computer, which was generally associated with the ship's weapons system. Amalgamation of picture-keeping and weapons-direction functions greatly reduced track capacity and much simplified the system.

As in older versions of the U.S. NTDS, plots are manually entered but are projected ahead by the central computer on a rate-aided basis. The system automatically processes IFF data and vectors an associated helicopter. The 1966 Naval Staff Requirement (for CAAIS in Type 21 frigates) called for a unit cost of £100K.

Production began in 1969. The first CAAIS went to sea on board *25 de Mayo* (the Argentines wanted compatibility with the ADAWS/Link X on board their Type 42s).

In all, the five versions of CAAIS accounted for 23 editions of software, mainly written in Coral.

Versions:

DBA (1) in *Leander*-class frigates (32k FM1600B). This version, which entered service in 1974, survives only on board Ecuadorian *Leander*-class frigates. It employes six two-operator Decca CA 1600 horizontal displays and is compatible with Link 10.

DBA (3) in HMS *Hermes* (carrier) as modernized (now the Indian *Viraat*). This is probably much like the version the Argentine navy bought for its *25 de Mayo*.

DBA (4) in "Hunt"-class minehunters. This version uses two horizontal displays, one for the minehunting director and one for the operations officer. The minehunting director is responsible for details of minehunting operation, particularly sonar and ROV operation. This system had the first approach to automatic ship control in an MCM ship. The ship has a conventional autopilot, whose set course can be changed via the CAAIS system. Capacity was originally 64 contracts, updated continuously; it has now been increased to 5000. The later NAUTIS system in a *Sandown* provides direct control. Note that the British system differs from the French Ibis in that the Royal Navy separates sonar and command functions; in Ibis command system synthetic video can be overlaid directly on sonar video. Early in 1993 Ferranti Naval Systems was awarded a contract for an upgrade to allow integration of the Navpac positioning aid. In November 1994 Ferranti was awarded an 18-month feasibility study as integration contractor for the Hunt Mid-Life Upgrade (HMLU).

The operations room (CIC) of the Brazilian frigate *Liberal* (Vosper Mk 10), showing vertical consoles and a standard two-operator horizontal display. This ship is equipped with two WSA 400–series systems and CAAIS 400. (Ferranti)

DBA (5) in Type 22 Batch 1 frigates, to control Sea Wolf missiles (GWS 25) and Type 2016 sonar. The computer is a FM1600E (128k of memory); system capacity is 60 tracks. DBA (5) uses six identical JHA(1) horizontal displays in the operations room, plus two video display units mounted at the EW director and CO/PWO positions, and a bridge JUD display. It is not clear whether the Brazilian navy, which bought the Batch 1 frigates, will replace DBA (5) with a version of its own Siconta.

CAAIS 400/450 is the export version. CAAIS 400 uses the FM1600B computer and works with WSA 400–series WCS. The follow-on CAAIS 450 works with the WSA 420 series. It uses the FM1600E computer and new vertical displays (12in CRT for the single console, 16in for the command console, all monochromatic and incorporating keyboards and rollerballs). It performs threat evaluation and can connect directly to a data link and to on-board ECM systems.

Although in receivership, in 1994 the Ferranti Defence Systems Integration division (now taken over by Marconi) outlined CAAIS 2000, a proposed modernization of existing CAAIS systems, partly for the "Hunt"-class midlife upgrade. Computing options are as follows: a 64k block-step module added to an FM1600E computer; replacement by F2420, offering fourfold increase in throughput; or introduction of a full workstation-based COTS system. The display update would introduce a new keyboard, color screens, and additional VU703 minitotes. Alternatively, the existing JHA(1)s could be replaced with four double-headed multifunction workstations, significantly reducing manpower and freeing up space. The replacement consoles had already been prototyped. Ferranti also proposed a link upgrade and integration of remaining stand-alone peripherals.

Ferranti's WSAs are the weapons-control elements associated with CAAIS, using the same type of computer. The WS 400 series used by Brazil is derived from the now-extinct WSA 4 of the British Type 21 frigate, which controlled a 4.5in gun and the Sea Cat missile (the export version is WSA 403, used on board the general-purpose version of the *Niteroi*-class frigate). CAAIS is responsible for the tactical picture; the CAAIS operator designates targets and assigns tracking radar(s) and weapons; the dedicated WSA console is responsible for gun ballistics or missile tracking. WSA 4 was built around a single Ferranti FM1600B computer, the same type as that in CAAIS itself. It had two identical consoles, for gun and Sea Cat control, both linked to a one-operator horizontal console of the CAAIS automated AIO, manned by the missile-and-gun director. WSA 4 was sometimes denoted GSA 4/GWS 22 for its separate gun and missile elements.

From one console, the single gun controller could track targets on two Type 912 (Orion RTN 10X) radars, watch them on television, and fire as many as 20 rounds from the Mk 8 gun. The Sea Cat controller could fire as many as four Sea Cats (without reloading). The gun controller at the WSA console initiated the fire-control calculation and ordered the gun or missile to aim and fire. Normally, the director received track data before fire began, but in special cases the gun controller could open fire by closing the safety switch and pressing the firing pedal.

The two-operator WSA console has two main electronic data displays (EDDs) with light pens, each showing data in graphical and alphanumeric form on a page-by-page basis. The correct page is chosen by light pen, using a list running along the bottom (TCD, WCD, NGSA, NGSB, WIND, SEACAT, for target-control display, weapons-control display, naval gunfire-support channel A and B, wind, and Sea Cat, respectively, in a Type 21). TCD, for example, shows the status of the trackers, the track number of the target, the weapons mode (e.g., GAA, for gun antiaircraft), and the target's heading, range, speed, and height.

The WSA computer stabilizes the tracking radar antennas and predicts future target position. It holds the basic range tables; information such as mean sea-level pressure and measured muzzle velocity (gun wear/ammunition temperature) is entered by light pen. Because the combination of computer and radars acts like a TWS radar, shifting from target to target while firing at both is relatively easy; and spotting corrections from both targets can be applied. In essence, the computer executes two fire-control solutions simultaneously. This technique takes advantage of the shell's 30–50-sec time of flight to provide the equivalent of two gunfire channels. Splash spotting is semiautomatic, the gun controller entering splashes via a trackball applied to a B-scan scope. For indirect fire, the ship's and the target's coordi-

nates are entered into the computer in metric grid form; the computer automatically tracks the ship using log and compass data and tidal data. During surface fire, if the director calls for AA fire, the system can shift over within a few seconds.

Ferranti then developed a series of private-venture CAAIS 450/WSA 420 combinations based on CAAIS and WSA 4 experience, using FM1600D computers, and working with Link Y (Link 14 was an option). The CDS element selects the biggest threat and can control ECM.

The minimum CAAIS employs two consoles (command/picture supervisor, surface picture supervisor/EW, and data-link supervisor), each carrying a 16in CRT, and a third carrying two 12in CRTs (in effect, two single-operator consoles joined together, for the weapons director and the air-picture compiler). This configuration can be expanded with one- and two-operator units to a total of 8 CRTs and 16 operators. Typical range scales are 4 to 64 nm. The displays are refreshed 16 times/sec. Total system capacity is 120 tracks, 100 of them automatic.

The simplest associated WCS, WSA 421, uses two trackers, a radar (with coaxial television camera) and a visual sight (with laser range-finder), and (as an option) a Decca range-only radar. Targets can be provided by the AIO system (from its search radars), or they can be acquired by the tracker radar (in search mode) or by the visual sight. Thus it can simultaneously track two targets while maintaining a third track from AIO; it can also fire at a grid point in space (for shore bombardment). The computer can slew the visual sight (the optical fire director) onto the target, controlling it either in train or in train and in elevation. Alternatively, the operator can control the sight by joystick, either fully manually (emergency mode) or in stabilized mode. Two guns can be controlled.

The standard weapons-control console carries a 12in-dia CRT on its left (TAU: target acquisition unit) side, and a 7in-diagonal alphanumeric display (tote) and a closed-circuit television monitor on its right (gun controller's position). Displays are run by F-100L microprocessors, for flicker-free operation. They provide 128 stroke-written (cursive) standard characters and 16 programmable characters. The CRT on the left is used as a PPI (for air search), as a B-scan (for surface tracking and splash spotting), and as a split A/R-scope.

One operator can run the system in cruising condition and two in action stations (four for a double version). An extra radar tracker requires an additional console.

Typical acquisition time, from target indication with the tracking radar parked, to slew 90 deg to a target 10 deg above the horizon, is about 4 sec. An initial gunfire-control solution is available half a second after tracker acquisition, and the gun can be aimed at the target half a second later (albeit not fully accurately). Ferranti claimed significantly improved gun accuracy from that in earlier systems; a 4.5in Mk 8 gun made 19 proximity-fuzed bursts out of 19 rnd fired at a Rushton target closing from 7000–1500 yd (speed not given).

WSA 422 is a full CDS grown out of the two-operator console, adding a one-operator surveillance, tracking, and target-indication section, which can provide CIC services. It can accept search- and navigation-radar inputs and can provide manual rate-aided contact tracking. However, WSA 422 can be modified to extract radar data automatically for automatic tracking. The one-operator surveillance section carries a 16in-dia CRT (labeled radar display) and a 7in-diagonal alphanumeric display (tote). Typical range scales are 1 to 32 nm. The display is refreshed at a rate of 16 times/sec. The system can handle up to 60 tracks, although the weapons director's capacity is 10–12. Typical output accuracy is sufficient for target indication (1 deg in bearing, 1000 m in range).

Like WSA 421, WSA 422 can hold three gun-control-quality tracks simultaneously, two of them queued. However, because the AIO performs as a TWS radar, sufficient information is available to support surface-to-surface missiles separately.

Both WSA 421 and WSA 422 were built around FM1600D computers.

WSA 423, built around an FM1600E computer, is a three-operator CAAIS 450 command console (third position for weapons director) plus a two-operator weapons-control console. In this case both CRTs of the weapons-control console are 12 in in diameter. A larger version has double-headed weapons control and a seven-operator AIO console (duplicating the full CAAIS 450). Gun-control-quality track capacity matches that of WSA 421 and 422. As in CAAIS 450, the AIO subsystem can maintain 120 tracks, 100 of them automatic. Accuracy matches that of CAAIS 450, given above.

Users (CAAIS and WSA series): Argentina (*25 de Mayo*), Brazil (CAAIS 401/402/403 in *Niteroi* class: WSA 401 controls a 4.5in gun and a Bofors 375mm rocket launcher; WSA 402 controls the Ikara [now defunct] and Sea Cat missiles; WSA 403 controls the 4.5in gun and a Sea Cat system in the general-purpose version of the frigate); CAAIS 450/WSA 421 in *Inhauma* class; DBA [5] in Type 22 Batch I frigates), Ecuador (*Leander*-class frigates), Egypt (*Ramadan* class, probably first WSA 422), India (*Viraat*: DBA [3] version), Kenya (*Nyayo*: CAAIS 450/WSA 422), Oman (CAAIS and all-optical WSA 422 in *Al Sharquiyah* [her sisters have 9LV 300–series systems]), South Korea (CAAIS 450/WSA 423 in fourth and later *Ulsans* and later KCX classes), United Kingdom ("Hunt"-class minehunters). Samsung makes WSA 423 under license in South Korea; the first contract was awarded in 1986, and by September 1989 12 ships had been completed, a further batch was on order, and a third under tender. The South Korean version is almost certainly the single-headed version (two trackers). The Egyptian CAAIS system was reportedly derived from an earlier, previously undescribed, Marconi mini-AIO for the Egyptian *October* class (see below). Pakistani Type 21 frigates are having their CAAIS systems replaced by 9LV Mk 3.

◆ CACS (DFA)

The Computer-Assisted Command System was intended as the CAAIS successor for Type 22 Batch 2/3 and Type 23 frigates; it was rejected for the latter because of insufficient capacity. CACS was first proposed by Ferranti in 1977 as a replacement for the CAAIS system then installed aboard Type 21 frigates, but the concept was soon extended to the new (and much more demanding) Type 22. Unlike ADAWS, CACS was contractor developed; Ferranti was the first British firm to get a full command/control-system contract. The first installation was aboard HMS *Boxer* (1982).

CACS introduced what Ferranti called a prompt interface to overcome the limitation inherent in the ADAWS command structure: the display at each console shows a menu, from which the operator chooses via light pen or the keyboard. Like equiv-

CACS AAW/ASUW consoles on board a Type 22 frigate. They differ from the ASW consoles shown in that the round CRT is larger, and it is tilted back. Note the light pens used to communicate with the system (gloved operators cannot easily manipulate a keyboard). (Royal Navy)

alent menu-driven software in civilian computers, this approach becomes practical as computer power increases. Ferranti developed its version as a private venture.

CACS failed because its centralized system could not be modified to meet rapidly changing and growing requirements. Ferranti wanted to shift to a distributed system (like its System 500), but the Royal Navy refused, hoping instead for some commonality with ADAWS. Unlike the CAAIS of Type 22 Batch 1, CACS was intended as the first British command system to handle passive ESM and passive sonar data. The use of long-range data implied long-range air control, hence maintenance of an elaborate air picture. CACS 1 was installed in 1984–86, but it did not become fully operational until 1991.

Compared to CAAIS, CACS reverts to an ADAWS architecture in that it uses separate picture-keeping and air weapons-system computers, close-coupled so that they share a common memory (mainly the tactical picture). The second computer is sometimes described as a running spare. A third (auxiliary) computer deals with the long-range sonar and ESM pictures. This architecture is not too different from that of a U.S. FFG 7 with a towed array and LAMPS III; in both cases the long-range ASW computer is described as an auxiliary processor. The computers were originally FM1600Es, but they have been replaced by F2420s.

CACS ASW consoles on board a Type 22 frigate. Each round CRT is associated with four small rectangular alphanumeric CRTs. Behind the operator, not visible in this photograph, is a line of AAW/ASUW consoles.

CANE on board the Cameroon missile boat *Bakassi*, with a Naja console to its left, in the RADOP integrated system. (Racal)

Unlike ADAWS, CACS uses a command-system LAN (command display highway) carrying its computers and consoles. This LAN (ASWE serial highway) connects to the combat-system bus carrying weapons and sensors (a triple-serial ASWE bus). The command-system LAN also carries the three types of Plessey Mk 9 console: conference console, twin operator console, and maintenance console. The conference or command (PWO summary: Type A) two-operator console carries a single 400mm monochrome cursive LPD (PPI), two prompt displays, two 7in raster-scan tote (or video) input displays, two light pens (the main means of communicating with the system), two keyboards (probably QWERTY), and two rollerballs. The twin-operator console (Type B) is similar but with 1 × 300mm LPDs and two totes for each operator. The maintenance console is a single-operator version of the twin-operator console with computer-controlled monitoring facilities. Each Type B console contains two (three in the updated version) Argus M700/20 microprocessors handling displays, sensors, and fire control. There are also several F100L microprocessors. CACS software is written in Coral 66.

CACS 1 has 12 Argo M700/20s in six Type B consoles split between surface/air and underwater warfare, with a Type A console for the PWOs (surface and subsurface). Including sensor operators, the Type 22 Batch 1 operations room has 16 displays requiring 26 personnel when at action stations. In 1985 CACS was described as capable of maintaining over 500 tracks.

CACS 5, the command system for Type 22 Batch 3 frigates (*Cornwall* class), probably survives mainly because it was always considered a relatively simple modification of CACS 1.

Other versions of CACS died: CACS 2 would have replaced ADAWS in Type 42 destroyer midlife refits, CACS 3 would have equipped the abortive Type 43 destroyer, and CACS 4 would have equipped the Type 23 frigate. The plans for the destroyers make it clear that CACS was in effect a renamed ADAWS.

According to a 1991 British parliamentary paper, total estimated cost of nine CACS 1 systems (three ashore) was £217M; four CACS 5 (operational in 1992) cost a total of £67M. About £30M was spent on replacing the original FM1600E computers with F2420s (first contract let September 1988).

◆ CANE/DBE/DEA/600 Series/MAINS/QX3

Racal's (formerly Decca's) Computer-Aided Navigational Equipment is a CDS for patrol craft and minecraft built around a plot maintained by a Racal version of the Kongsberg (NFT) KS500 computer (DS500), in effect a precursor to current ARPA systems; it appeared in 1978. It is also a precision navigational system, using the Decca and Loran systems (hence its adoption for intelligence-collection ships). The simplest existing version, CANE II (DEA-2), can maintain 38 rate-aided surface tracks, which it displays as synthetic video. A rollerball on the automated chart table is used to trace out a coastline and convert it into synthetic video. Alternatively, a light spot on the CRT can be transferred to the chart table, for example, to identify a buoy. All CANE systems retain this interaction between chart and display. There is also a 40-character × 12-line interactive display. CANE conducts navigational calculations (e.g., CPA and intercept), and can transmit track data to an FCS. DEA-2 has three consoles (two driven by the main plotter) and an automatic chart table. It is installed on board British "Isles"- and "Castle"-class OPVs. In this form it is essentially an antismuggler CDS.

The current generation is a fully distributed version; sensors, fire controls, consoles, an automatic plotter, and an automatic chart table all ride a LAN with intelligent I/O nodes incorporating 68000-series chips. In this form the system evaluates and classifies threats, displays weapon status, and designates targets to separate fire controls. It can also direct and control aircraft. That is a less radical change than might be imagined since the original centralized system was really only the tactical-picture element of the usual CDS. The distributed versions add separate consoles for other functions, and the data bus carries the tactical picture among them.

Each tactical-control console (TCC) or control display unit (CDU) is run by a DS500 and has 1 Mbyte of internal memory;

software is written in Coral 66. The interactive display carries a 12- or 16in CRT, which can combine raw video with cursive characters (synthetic video); it also uses a 40-character × 12-line data screen. These consoles use resident bubble memory.

There are also unintelligent terminals (operations-display units, ODUs). Each ODU carries a large PPI, either analog or scan-converted (raster-scan); it can also display synthetic video superimposed on raw video.

As in other British command systems, the command bus (LAN) itself connects to a separate combat-system "highway," in this case a dual serial bus.

CANE 100/200 are export versions, announced in September 1981. CANE 100 (for fast-attack craft) uses an integral Kongsberg KS 590 computer and a table-mounted CDU. CANE 100 incorporates an automatic chart table and an automatic plotter. CANE 200 is intended for corvettes and larger ships.

600 Series (presumably CANE 600) was announced at RNEE 1991. It uses full-color 20in digital displays (1344 × 1010 pixels, 60-Hz refresh rate) which can show a 12in-dia PPI. This time the architecture is new: the consoles use 68030/68040 chips (instead of DS500s) and VME buses, and the LAN is Ethernet (possibly to be replaced by fiber optics). Inputs will be radar (surface and air), ESM, and sonar. Racal is developing an MCM version with new software. 600 Series uses some of the same consoles as SSCS. Racal claimed that this system would be significantly less expensive than NAUTIS and System 500, its main competitors. It is intended for small ships such as light frigates and corvettes.

MAINS (Minehunting Information System) is a minehunting version of CANE. It is integrated with 9MJ400 on board Swedish *Landsort*-class minehunters. The PPI shows the current radar plot as well as the sonar search plan and current underwater contacts.

MAINS consists of a Racal Integrated Navigation System (RINS) and a Racal Action Display System (RADS). RINS suffices for minesweepers, which need only to know precisely which channel they have swept. RADS is required for minehunters and sweeper/hunters. A typical RADS display shows the known bottom features, the vessel's track, a safety circle around the vessel, the location of a suspected mine (with its danger circle), and the locations of other suspected mines.

In MAINS, RINS and RADS share a common central computer. The RINS inputs are various positioning systems, including the log and gyro; RINS exchanges data with the autopilot. RADS inputs are from sonar and radar; RADS exchanges data with the minehunting vehicle proper and provides data to the chart table and to tactical displays. RINS can be used to guide the helmsman, or it can control the ship automatically for great track precision.

In theory, the minehunter can make an initial route survey using a side-scanning sonar; RADS/RINS can locate any contacts precisely so that the hunter can revisit them later. The system also incorporates a track plotter, so the results of minesweeping or -hunting can be charted for use by other vessels. These charts also show whether coverage of an area is sufficiently complete.

Users: Korea ("Swallow" class), and Sweden (*Landsort* class).

QX3 is a related minesweeper support system, presumably RINS. It can store up to 80 km of route, with 60 contacts/km. The tactical display shows a real-time ground-referenced plot, with land masses, navigational markers, underwater pipelines, and wrecks. The centerline of the task route, annotated with waypoints and the location and classification of sonar contacts, is superimposed over this background.

QX3/1 was installed on board British "River" class; it is also on board the U.S. *Avenger* class (as URN-30).

Users: Cameroon (*Bakassi*: first CANE 100), Denmark, Germany (Type 443 intelligence collectors), Finland (*Tursas*), Hong Kong (450-ton police command craft *Sea Panther* and *Sea Horse*), Indonesia (PB 57), Jordan ("Hawk" class), Korea ("Swallow" MCM), Sweden (probably intelligence collector *Orion*), the United Kingdom ("Isles"- and "Castle"-class OPVs, *Argus* [DBE(1), distributed three-console version], *Sir Galahad*, and "River"-class minesweepers), United States (QX3 in *Avenger* class, as URN-30), and Yugoslavia (*Vukov Klanac* MCM).

◆ CSA

Thorn-EMI's system provides advice on course to steer, using a standard Navy intercom and four buttons. It is built around a single-board 68040 computer with 16-Mbyte memory, a graphics card (supporting a 1280 × 1024-pixel picture), and a VME bus.

◆ DFTDS/RRASL

DRA's (formerly ARE's) Data Fusion Technology Demonstrator System uses 600 knowledge-based rules to filter and associate data, particularly tracks, to form automatically the compiled tactical picture; in effect, it is a next-generation CDS without any weapon-control functions. For example, knowing that a helicopter has been assigned to patrol a given zone, DFTDS will tentatively identify a helicopter-like radar contact there. Knowledge of the position of land masses limits the possible area from which a line of bearing (such as an ESM strobe) can originate. DFTDS evaluates sonar propagation to estimate passive ranges. The system automatically gives its reasoning and the basic data for any particular identification. The inputs are messages (mainly tracks) from own-ship and force sensors (via Link 11); DFTDS handles 1000 messages/sec, all from the ship's combat-system bus.

DFTDS differs from existing systems, such as SSCS (DNA), in taking its data directly from the ship's combat-system highway (data bus); it has no LAN. Raw sensor plots are automatically processed into tracks in the DFTDS system rather than being processed into tracks before being used to construct the tactical picture. Too, the correlation between on-board and off-board track data has been automated. The effect of such automation is a drastic decrease in the number of CDS personnel.

The system uses five VAXserver 4500 (originally 3800) computers on a fiber-optic Ethernet LAN: front-end interface (to the ship's combat-system bus) and user interface processors and three modules: database, data fusion, planning (including situation assessment for a force). The latter associates threats with their likely targets and lists which weapons can react. The user-interface VAXserver drives the five displays (ACT Sigmex AS 6264s): three in an operator array in the port console bank, one alongside the command radar display on the starboard side, and one at the after end of the operations room between the missile director and the EW operator. The system uses two databases, one for geography, the other for equipment/platforms (including performance data). DFTDS is to be extended to time-stale (JOTS) data. Weather data (e.g., for ducting) will probably also be added. DFTDS was installed on board HMS *Marlborough*, a new Type 23 frigate (as yet without any installed CDS) in March 1991, for 1992–93 sea trials.

The use of developmental software was acceptable because DFTDS does not include any weapons-control functions, hence could not make lethal errors.

Ferranti (now absorbed by Marconi) provided a combat-system TDA, RRASL (Reactive Resource Allocation—Single-Ship Level), to DFTDS; the contract was signed in August 1990. RRASL is based on System 500; in effect, it is a next-generation CCA. RRASL automates the TEWA process to advise the CO

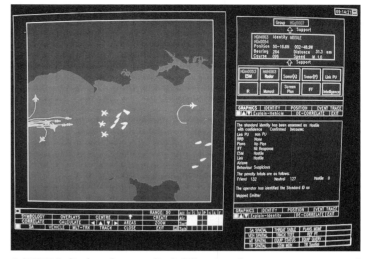

A DFTDS display shows radical differences from more conventional CDS displays. Symbols are more intuitively shaped, and they are oriented in the direction of motion, with curved lines to show track history. The system attempts to identify each target, and it displays its reasoning at right. Land mass is colored green; water is blue; targets are yellow and white. (DRA)

and PWO of the likely consequences of different courses of action. It goes beyond the DFTDS to take into account the potential for mutual interference between different defensive measures, both hard- and soft-kill, basing its recommendations on a library reflecting current tactical doctrine and system characteristics. Ferranti has also defined an operational variant, presumably for the next-generation frigate. It combines rule-based and knowledge-based technology. Ready access to the rule base is useful both to see the rationale for a choice and also to change rules at sea. Ferranti had designed the DFTDS's data-fusion engine.

The full system consists of three modules: DFM (data fusion), SAM (situation assessment), and RAM (resource allocation, developed from RRAS). The laboratory prototype of the latter ran on a pair of Sun SPARCStations, one for the knowledge-based system node and the other for the graphics node.

The next stage is a Weapons Coordination System Demonstrator, under development by DRA, EDS Defence, and BAe-SEMA. It models possible alternative attacks to produce running weightings for alternative defense ploys. For example, an approaching group of airplanes may launch missiles using a variety of tactics. Some defensive ploys may be effective only against some of those tactics, so appropriate choices must entail considering all likely enemy actions. Ploy selection is based on both the existing database and knowledge of incoming platform movements and identities. BAeSEMA is also developing an FTEWA as part of its bid for the "Project Horizon" combat management system. Its demonstrator uses a Symtactics object-oriented battle modeling software tool and Intellicorp's Knowledge Engineering Environment.

◆ Kelvin-Hughes SCTD System

Kelvin-Hughes has developed a ships combination tactical display (SCTD) based on several of its color tactical displays (CTD), each with its own processor, on a fiber-optic LAN. Each CTD can track 20 contacts (a more powerful processor, to be introduced in 1994, will probably double that); five or six can share a common track file. Software in the CTD processors solves the relative velocity problem, so targets can be designated to an FCS (the CDS can indicate weapon-bearing and range limits inside which the weapon will be effective; an alarm sounds or shows when a target is in range). An IFF can be controlled from the CTD screen. KRIS (Kelvin-Hughes Radamec Integrated System) for patrol boats combines CTDs with Siemens-Plessey Lookout and 1007 radars and a Radamec 2300 (for a 40mm gun) or 2400 (for a 57mm gun). The CTD system may cost about half as much as CANE (say £125,000).

DFTDS as set up on board HMS *Marlborough* (1992). (DRA)

Users: Indonesia (Presidential Escort Ship), Ireland (*Peacock* class), Netherlands (new AOR: four-console version), Singapore (*Victory* class), Spain (new AOR: three-console version).

◆ Mini-AIO

Marconi's system in Egyptian *October*-class missile boats uses a single AD16L surface display, with a 16in CRT. The operator can track and allocate four targets. Markers show targets being tracked (with rate-aiding), and automatic track-sequencing allows the operator to update tracks quickly using a trackball. A second AD16L alongside the surface display controls the Otomat missile. The operator detects the target, plots its course, and allocates it to the fire-control computer. The more elaborate surveillance and fire-control system in the Egyptian *Ramadan* class was adapted from this system. The associated gunfire-control system is Sapphire.

◆ Odin

Siemens-Plessey Air Defence Division announced this COTS-based CDS in 1994 (it was formally launched in 1995). It employs a standard LAN (preferably FDDI) with ruggedized 64-bit DEC Alpha AXP computers and other DEC COTS products running ADA software modules derived from Siemens-Plessey's proprietary Controller (ATC, air defense) product. A dual-screen display is standard (a single-screen version and a workstation-based captain's monitor are also available). Odin will first be employed with AWS-9(2D) radars installed on board Norwegian *Oslo*-class frigates. In this case the radar and Odin will form an air warning subsystem interfaced with the existing MSI-3100.

This NAWS (Norwegian Air Warning System) uses both dual- and single-screen consoles, and integrates IFF plot extraction with that of the AWS-9 radar.

Radar and IFF video are piped directly into the display system, which has its own scan conversion channels. IR and EO data are distributed by a separate TV distribution system (TVDS) which is connected to all the consoles; they can display its video either as windows or in full-screen format. Raw radar video can be overlaid with selected system synthetic video, and tracks (for example, for surface combatants) can be manually initiated. The LAN generally communicates with external systems via communications servers which act as buffers. Presumably the buffers are the reason Odin could be integrated into the Norwegian frigates without a major reconstruction. Link data, however, may be coupled directly to the LAN via an Alpha Server. Provision is also made for special interface processors to handle external sys-

tems, such as target designation sights and navigational sensors, whose interfaces do not comply with the usual digital standards.

Odin is optimized for above-water applications, including air defense. It uses software derived from the earlier Controller 1 series of software modules for air defense and air traffic control. However, Controller 1 was written in RTL 2 software. Controller 2, the basis for Odin, was rewritten in ADA as a private venture. It also includes modules beyond those in Controller 1. Among numerous Controller 1 applications, the NATO Missile Firing Installation (NAMFI) system led to development of windowed raster displays, as well as of buffers allowing integration of sensors other than those produced by Plessey. In the Air Defence Workstation (ADW), Controller software was hosted on COTS equipment. Controller 2 and a DEC Alpha computer were combined in Agincourt, a system currently in production for the Royal Air Force. This software was also used in FATMI, the Finnish Air Traffic Management system, which uses DEC Workstations and VAX central servers, and thus might be imagined as analogous to a distributed (36-site) combat-direction system.

◆ SSCS (DNA)/SUCCESSOR

The Surface-Ship Command System is the BAeSEMA DNA(1) system for the Type 23, to replace the failed CACS. SSCS was selected in August 1989. Planned installation of a DNA(2) version in the new *Fort*-class replenishment ships was canceled. SUCCESSOR is the BAeSEMA family of command systems, including SSCS and the submarine system, SMCS, from which it was developed. The command-system consoles are distributed along a fiber-optic LAN (IEE 802.5 standard), with two I/O nodes (transmit and receive) linking it to the ship weapon/sensor bus. Each console contains a full copy of the applications software, so that it can perform any system function. The system master database (the tactical picture) is carried in the two I/O nodes (with 80386-based microprocessors). They also do some preprocessing. They broadcast information into the consoles, each of which holds copies of the database. A hard disk holds permanent or slowly changing data, such as geography.

The Racal multifunction consoles (MFCs) are described separately below. Type 23 employs 12 identical consoles, including separate ones for the captain and the PWO. The Type 23 system as a whole contains 220 microprocessors and 478 Mbytes of memory, plus 3.2 Gbytes of online storage; these figures include the parallel processors (Intel transputers, rather than the Inmos T800 series of SMCS). System software amounts to 1.5 million lines of code, compared to 1 million for the earlier SSCS.

DNA installed on board the Type 23 frigate *Westminster*. (BAeSEMA)

NAUTIS monochrome consoles on board HMS *Fearless*. (Marconi)

This view of the operations room of HMS *Westminster* shows a large vertical plot, the DPIP (dual parallel index plot), used with the Type 996 radar to triangulate jammers. Below the DPIP are standard SSCS consoles. (Stuart Slade, DMS/Forecast International)

BAeSEMA claims that the Type 23 command system can handle 1000+ tracks simultaneously. As installed, reportedly it has 70% excess capacity.

In this version, four consoles are mounted in line in front of the operation officer's (PWO's) chair, for the long- and short-range air, surface, and subsurface track supervisors (the computer room is on the other side of the bulkhead behind them). On the officer's right are a pair of consoles (CO and PWO). The other six consoles are in a row behind the PWO, facing the other way: typically two for weapons, two for sonar, and one each for radar and EW operators. Because the system is modular and the consoles interchangeable, this distribution can be changed as required.

This is the first Royal Navy color-command system. It is expected to use red for enemy, blue for friendly, yellow for unknown, green for neutral, and white for unidentified or supporting. The symbology and colors were tried out on the operations room crew of HMS *Norfolk*. There is some problem with colors (staring).

Software is written in ADA; as of September 1991 the estimated size of the program was 200,000 lines of code (200 kloc). The fiber-optic token-passing ring LAN was adopted because it was considered more predictable than an Ethernet.

SSCS encountered some problems in its first two years with its distributed operating system (Infrastructure Software), which was built from that designed for SMCS, but had to operate in a faster environment. There were reportedly also problems with the color displays. The redesigned version was also fed back into the submarine SMCS system. Both programs were delayed one to two years as a result. SSCS might have gone into the seventh ship, HMS *Montrose*, but had to start with the eighth, HMS *Westminster*. The ninth and tenth completed with SSCS. The first seagoing software version, Phase II, began sea trials in HMS *Westminster* in the fall of 1994, on schedule. It provides about half of the required capability. The remainder will be provided in Phase III (Phases IV and V are not as critical). All non-SSCS ships were to have had their systems installed by the end of 1995. DNA is to replace CACS 5 on board Type 22 Batch III frigates.

A British 1991 parliamentary paper estimated that eight shipboard systems plus four shore systems would cost a total of £345M.

SSCS Mk 7 was adopted in 1994 for the Korean KDX program in preference to CoSys 200 K1. It employs a dual-redundant fiber-optic LAN to link its eight Racal consoles (MFCC), two independent Signaal FCS consoles (WCC, for the two STIR 1.8 trackers), an MW08 radar, and the combat-system highway (bus). BAeSEMA expects to use about 60% of the software written for DNA(1); KDX will require well over 1 million lines of ADA source code. Samsung Electronics is prime contractor for ship 02 and beyond; it license-produces the command-system hardware and the combat-system bus. Goldstar makes the Signaal FCS. As of 1994, sensors already selected include the SPS-49 (V) ADT radar, the SPS-55M radar, UPX-27 IFF, APECS II ECM, Dagaie Mk 2, DSQS-21BZ hull sonar, RIM-7M (16-cell Mk 48 VLS), Block 1C Harpoon (eight canisters), two Goalkeeper, and an OTO-Melara 5in/54 gun. At that time a towed array was planned for ship 02. The Korean Advanced Development Agency has been working on a passive system, although it may shift to an active array. There are also plans for a stretched KDGX area air defense version, perhaps as early as ship 04.

◆ NAUTIS/SYQ-15

Plessey's (now GEC-Marconi's) decentralized command/control system (Naval Autonomous Information System) was based on a standard NAUTIC (Naval Autonomous Intelligent Console). NAUTIS was announced in 1983. Development of the first version, for the single-role minehunter (*Sandown* class) began in 1984.

The console employs iAPX-286 microprocessors, typically dual 80286s in a multibus. Additional iAPX-286s are used for intelligent interfaces to sensors and weapons. RAM is typically

NAUTIS color consoles, probably on board an RNZN *Leander*-class frigate. A chart table is in the foreground. The latest version of the workstation has a plasma touchscreen under the main screen, and a joystick rather than a trackball. (Marconi)

4 Mbytes, expandable to at least 16 Mbytes, with additional non-volatile memory for program and database retention (typically 2 Mbytes, expandable to at least 4 Mbytes). Presumably, the running tactical picture is periodically dumped into the bubble memory. The console can accept video from up to three separate radars, as well as up to eight separate digital inputs, including IFF, helicopter transponder, and data-link plots and tracks. There is an RVP with scan conversion for the raster display. The console also includes a radar-plot extractor with multiple thresholds for constant false-alarm rate, clutter mapping, and windowing. Each console accommodates up to 54 double Eurocards (circuit boards).

Each standard console (workstation) accommodates either a 20in, 1500-pixel × 1200-line color raster (announced at RNEE in September 1989), or a 4096 × 4096-pixel, 16in cursive monochrome display. The new raster display can show raw radar video, graphics, or alphanumeric tables (totes); the cursive display is limited to synthetic video. The standard console can be supplemented by a separate tote display (alphanumerics) alongside; the enlarged console functions as a command/tactical suite. Each console has 32 software-defined special-function keys, as well as a standard keyboard and a trackerball.

Consoles are connected to two data buses (command-system LAN and combat-system bus), both dual 1553Bs or Ethernets.

The database, replicated within the consoles, covers a 2000 × 2000nm area (range scales 0.125–1000 nm) and includes radar and sonar tracks, route/search plans, user-designated tactical maps, and synthetic charts. Early system descriptions included a capacity for six user-designated tactical maps, 15 synthetic charts, 200 labeled reference points, 5000 underwater contacts, and 32 labeled bearing lines. The system can maintain at least 200 tracks (radar and sonar). In minimum configuration, it can automatically track 20 targets.

Although NAUTIS is designed to operate as a modular system, with each console carrying the full tactical picture, at least one buyer has chosen to economize by deleting the full tactical processor from all but one console, in which case NAUTIS is effectively a central-computer system with outlying workstations, architecturally equivalent to ADAWS or NTDS. Later installation of the missing processor boards converts this centralized system back into a decentralized one. In this case the deciding factors were the requirements for computing power and reliability; there was no question of combat survivability since in either case all the consoles were concentrated in one restricted space.

NAUTIS can function either as a command data system or as a full combat system, including weapons-control consoles; the degree of decentralization can vary radically in this way, as in the question of console content. A drawing of a typical possible NAUTIS-P installation shows that both the central system (two consoles) and the two gun-control consoles would be connected to a common video bus, fed by the navigation and air-search radars and connected to the EW suite. However, the gun-control radar and the optronic director would have their own consoles, connected directly to the gun consoles rather than to the system bus. This arrangement is broadly equivalent to CAAIS.

A next-generation version, first installed on board the Malaysian *Lekiu* class, has a pair of 68040 processors on Radstone Technology PME 6842 boards in each VME-backplane console; one is used for applications, the other for graphics. Software has been written in C and ADA, for portability, so the system can use other 32-bit CPUs. The consoles use a variety of displays, including a Barco 27in 1600-line raster-scan screen. Track capacity is 800 to 1000, compared to 200–300 in earlier versions. Each screen can be windowed to show up to two LPDs (PPI-like displays) with alphanumerics. The *Lekiu* version has a total of eight consoles, including three for weapons control.

This version has reportedly encountered weapons-integration problems; delivery of the ships has been delayed about a year (as of mid-1996).

Seeing a big derivative market in U.S. sealift ships, amphibious ships, and so on, for which NTDS would be much too massive, Plessey has teamed with Raytheon Equipment Division, on a

NAUTIS-M on board HMS *Sandown*, with two monochrome consoles (large circular CRTs) and sonar/ROV consoles. (GEC-Marconi)

project-by-project basis. NAUTIS forms the basis for a Raytheon proposal for an export surface-ship combat system, and the company may ultimately manufacture it in the United States under license.

Past references to different versions with different suffixes, such as NAUTIS-F, have been dropped in favor of a generic NAUTIS designation (although the MCM version is still called NAUTIS-M).

Users: Australia (*Huon* class: four consoles in CIC, one on bridge; uses the same console for both the 2093 sonar and the combat system), Greece (reported, but not confirmed, in new "Osprey 55" class), Malaysia (*Lekiu* class), New Zealand (two *Leander* class; five-console version), Saudi Arabia (*Sandown*-class minehunters, three-console version), Spain (new minehunters, three-console version), Thailand (*Kamronsin* class: three console version), United Kingdom (*Sandown* class [three-console version] and *Fearless* class [seven-console version]), United States (*Avenger* class, as SYQ-15; uses three color consoles). The MCM version has at least three consoles: bridge control, mine-warfare director, and operations officer. In a *Sandown*, the mine-warfare director console is placed between the two two-screen Type 2093 sonar displays, with the operations officer console on the right of one of them. An additional console can be used to control the mine-disposal vehicle. This system provides automatic track-keeping and hovering, as well as manual control via a joystick. However, a planned facility for automatic circling of a contact at a set range was eliminated during development.

◆ CTC/WAMS

Racal Marine Radar's Command Tactical Console (CTC), announced in 1985, is a very simple command system based on the company's ARPA radars, themselves introduced in 1983 and now mandatory in many merchant ships. Plots are locally extracted (radar gain is optimized separately for different sectors; Racal claims that such operation makes small-target detection, e.g., of periscopes, possible), and CTC can carry up to 20 target tracks, acquired either automatically (in predesignated guard zones) or by joystick. They can include aircraft at up to 600 kt. Target data are stored in true- rather than relative-motion form, which should make coordination with other ships easier. CTC computes and displays time to CPA. It can pass data to up to three weapons.

Wartime Adaptation of Merchant Ships (WAMS) is a proposed wartime adaptation for merchant ships taken up from trade in an emergency (as in the Falklands).

Users: Chile, China, Netherlands, Norway, Spain (*Milano* class, with 2459 radar).

◆ WS 500/GP 250

Ferranti's next-generation System 500 was a fully distributed combat-direction/weapons-control system. Apart from the SATAM element of the German MWS-80 minehunting system, it did not sell as such, but may have formed the basis for the Chilean SP-100 and perhaps also for the Brazilian Siconta. GP250, which did sell, was conceived as its gun-control element. The GP250 predictor (software embedded in a series of extended double 68000 VME Eurocards, using 68020 processors programmed in ADA) is designated GP250P. GP250P initializes the gun system, predicts ship and target motion, filters/smooths the data it receives both from own-ship sensors (wind and log, gyro and vertical reference) and from the target tracker (e.g., a radar), and calculates aim points. The system can accommodate ballistics for guns from 25 mm up to 5 in or 155 mm. Target-track prediction is based on Kalman-filtered data, and the method of prediction can be either a straight line (SLP), goal-oriented prediction (GOP, for initial engagement of long-range air targets), or SLP with maneuver detection. The system is sensitive to pop-up targets, and it takes into account such corrections as deck movement (roll and pitch), the curvature and movement of the earth, and sensor and gun offsets (parallax). Ship velocity, wind, air temperature, humidity, and air pressure are all taken into account automatically. Splash spotting is inserted via a manual data entry, and fixed gun aim-offs can be provided for warning shots. One or more guns can be controlled. The algorithms used are based on those developed for Ferranti large-ship systems, the 400- and 500-series. The customer supplies the man-machine interface (MMI) and final gun drive. GP250M adds a color MMI. GP250L is the land-based coast-defense version. GP250T, the total gunfire-control system, adds a gun synchro drive, gun tellbacks, gun status indication, and a control/display unit.

Users: Denmark (GP250 in coast defense), Finland (GP250 in coast defense), Germany (MC500 SATAM in Type 332 minecraft), and Hong Kong (GP250 for police, presumably to track small craft).

◆ MFC/MCS

Ultra's (formerly Dowty's) multifunction console is used in the new surface ship (DNA) and submarine (SMCS) combat-direction systems. Both use the same main display, but SSCS uses a menu display, QWERTY keyboard, special function keys, and a rollerball. SMCS uses two plasma displays, a graphics pad, a touch-sensitive panel, and dedicated fire-control buttons. The main display is a 20in raster-scanned color CRT in landscape format (1344 × 1010 pixels, frame rate 60 Hz, 40% modulation depth). Above it are two auxiliary displays (plasma panel neon orange) for text and graphics (512 × 256 pixels, all separately addressable, normally controlled through an MFC card). The operator has a plasma touch panel and a graphics tablet. The submarine (SMCS) version adds a puck (mouse). The surface-ship (DNA) version adds a joyball (trackball with adjustable gearing), a QWERTY keyboard, and a special-purpose keypad. Future versions will probably eliminate the keypad altogether in favor of soft keys only, to reduce the time an operator shifts his eyes down from the screen.

The processor drawer under the operator controls can accommodate 18 (applications version) or 21 (graphics version) extended double Eurocard PECs plus a hard disk (60 Mbytes in DNA; Dowty offers 20 to 100 Mbytes). Card functions include: CPU (80386), display processor (68030 or 68040), fast (array) processor (Inmos T800 in SMCS, Intel transputer in DNA), interface to MMI devices, interface to storage devices, interface to other MFCs, and interface to other systems. There are two parallel VME buses. Each console can accommodate up to four 68040 boards (8 Mbytes each), though in practice two is more usual. Maximum video RAM memory is 2000 × 2000 × 12 bits deep, some of which is used to handle windows. The console can handle, simultaneously, 4-bit radar video, 8-bit graphic video, and 8-bit TV video. The graphics processor is a Texas Instruments TMS320C20 with a math coprocessor. Dimensions: 1.42 m (height) × 0.65 m (width) × 0.65 m (depth) + 0.33 m for desk; weight approx. 250 kg.

In 1994 Ultra began advertising a Modular Console System (MCS) carrying one or two (superimposed) screens (51 cm, 1280 × 1024-pixel color) above a plasma touch screen, a trackball, and a conventional keyboard. System electronics are housed in the cabinet below the screens. Dimensions: 550 × 1020 (depth) × 1360 mm (single-screen version). Processors would be RISC types; the backplane is VME. Details are too vague to describe the display completely, but apparently it uses COTS VME cards and is to be delivered with integrated COTS software, including a UNIX/POSIX open-architecture operating system, X-Windows, MOTIF, LAN drivers, data highway (bus) drivers, graphics drivers, and the usual boot-up software. Presumably the company sees MCS as the basis of a next-generation open-architecture CDS which might compete with SUCCESSOR (Ultra/Dowty is no longer involved in the BAeSEMA systems).

UNITED STATES

NTDS and successor systems are now termed CDS, combat-direction systems. U.S. CICs have been renamed CDCs (combat-direction centers).

The Unisys CDS division was briefly renamed Paramax, incorporating the Canadian company that developed SHINPADS. It then reverted to the Unisys name before being bought by Loral in 1995. Now that Lockheed Martin (which is responsible for Aegis) has bought Loral, it appears that some SHINPADS concepts may be incorporated into the future fully distributed version of Aegis.

◆ Aegis (Weapon System Mk 7)

Aegis is the overall weapons system that uses a SPY-1 radar to control SM-2 AA missiles. The system was initially conceived to deal with long-range saturation attacks; it was the first to use missiles with commandable autopilots, which could be launched and then guided into "baskets" near their targets without continuous radar illumination. Once the missiles were close enough, slaved illuminators were turned on. In this way a single illuminator could be time-shared among several missiles. Aegis was also designed for very quick reaction, since the air search and fire-control radar functions were unified in one set (SPY-1). With the end of the Cold War, the quick-reaction element has become more important. It seems likely that ships with vertical launch systems (VLS) will ultimately be armed mainly with Evolved Sea Sparrow Missiles (ESSMs) quad-packed for greater numbers to deal with short-range littoral threats.

The system has four operating modes: automatic, automatic special, semiautomatic, and casualty. In the automatic special mode, the system automatically engages targets that meet preset criteria unless the engagements are manually vetoed. In peacetime ships tend to operate in fully manual mode, for fear of accident. Ironically, in the case of *Vincennes*, the system probably would *not* have engaged in automatic mode, since it would have

The large-screen display area on board the cruiser *Philippine Sea* (CG 58, Baseline 2) at Kiel, June 1995. The single screen in the center is a JMCIS display. (H&L van Ginderen)

been aware that the approaching Iranian Airbus was climbing rather than diving. However, manual mode was selected partly because the ship's role was far more to keep track of air traffic over the Persian Gulf than to engage that traffic. Too, it must have seemed likely that many air targets apparently approaching the ship were actually nontargets.

In practice, the very clear air picture provided by the system has proven more important than actual engagement. For example, an Aegis cruiser controlled the air interception of the Libyan terrorists flying over the very crowded Mediterranean from Egypt at night in 1986. It also turned out that the clear Aegis picture made it far easier to stage missile training shots in Mediterranean waters because the controllers could be much surer of whether civilian aircraft were within range.

The extremely good radar performance associated with the system inspired experiments in controlling missiles fired by other ships, ultimately leading to the current cooperative engagement capability (CEC).

Mod 0 equipped the first *Ticonderoga*-class cruisers. Mod 1 (CG 49–51) added LAMPS III. Mod 2 was planned for the abortive U.S. strike cruiser (CSGN). It was later also applied to VLS cruisers without SQQ-89. Mod 3 is the VLS version for cruisers with SQQ-89(V)3, Mod 4 is Baseline 3 with SQQ-89(V)3, and Mod 5 is the cruiser version with UYK-43 computers. Mod 6 equips *Arleigh Burke*–class destroyers. Aegis replaces the NTDS/WDS combination of earlier U.S. missile cruisers. In a cruiser, Aegis is built around Command and Decision System Mk 1, Aegis Display System Mk 1, and Weapons Control System Mk 1, the first and last replacing, respectively, NTDS and a WDS (the original Aegis test ship, USS *Norton Sound*, had WDS Mk 12). Destroyers have C&D Mk 2, Aegis Display System Mk 2 (with two screens rather than four), and WCS Mk 8. The SPY-1 radar has its own UYK-7.

The display system has the four very large (42 × 42 in) paired projection screens of the UYQ-21 system. In principle, one pair of screens is for the ship's captain and one for the embarked group commander. Each pair of large screens is supported by two command-display consoles, a data-input console, and five automated status boards (ASTABs). In addition, two ASTABs are on the bridge. Aegis destroyers (*Arleigh Burke* class) lack group commander facilities and thus have only one pair of screens.

The large screens display processed rather than raw radar video as tracks, NTDS symbols, and Aegis symbols, in white on a blue background. Each screen can operate individually, at its own

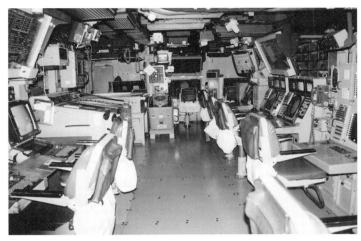

UYA-4 displays, including the large nearly horizontal summary, on board the Aegis cruiser *Philippine Sea* at Kiel, June 1995. The display in the foreground at left is for a TAC-series computer. This is presumably the ASW/ASUW area of the ship's CIC. In the foreground at right is a UYQ-21 display. (H&L van Ginderen)

range scale; controls allow for irrelevant tracks to be suppressed, for tracks to be tagged (track numbers or alphanumeric labels of up to 24 characters in three lines), and for offsets from a display centered on the ship. Additional information is supplied on the associated command-display consoles and the ASTABs above the large screens. In principle, the CO and TAO sit at the two command-display consoles, with a data-input assistant at the adjacent input console.

Because the two displays of either group can show the same situation at radically different scales (calling up the same computer database), operators can position their ball tabs on either large-scale display (LSD), and operators working to different scales or in different warfare areas can share the same target data without changing screens or even manually pointing (as in standard NTDS systems). Important tracks and symbols can be highlighted without being tagged.

The display system can also store up to 40 patterns, such as formation diagrams, anchorages, and amphibious boat lanes. It can automatically initiate up to 16 simultaneous track histories until ordered to stop doing so. It can also provide digital maps of the area in which the ship is operating, refreshing own-ship position every 2 sec.

The CIC contains 18 consoles, some of which can read off data for targets shown on the large screens. For example, height versus range can be read off for a hooked target. There is, however, no graphic display of range versus altitude, as there might be in an earlier system. That proved very unfortunate in the case of USS *Vincennes*, when a badly shaken officer in CIC apparently mistook range for altitude and imagined that the approaching Iranian Airbus (for which range was rapidly decreasing) was diving toward the ship when altitude was actually increasing.

The UYK-7 version of Aegis as a whole is credited with the ability to handle 128 tracks. The SPY-1 radar can actually handle more, the extra capacity being used to avoid overflow. The most important limit on track capacity is the interface with the track file in the associated command/control system. The margin in the radar prevents overflow when numerous long-range tracks of little immediate interest are present. A track initiation processor (TIP) is now being added to help filter out extraneous tracks.

The original Aegis system employed four UYK-7 computers: one picture-keeper (the Aegis Display System), one C&D processor, one to control the SPY-1 radar, and one for the WCS. The Mk 99 missile FCS is considered a separate entity. Ships have two more UYK-7s for ASW (for the SQS-53 sonar and the associated Mk 116 FCS). There are also 11 UYK-20s: one for the Operational Readiness and Test System (ORTS), six in the WCS, one for the link to the SQS-53 sonar, and units for gun (Mk 86), missile (Mk 99), and Tomahawk FCS (with a UYK-19 for Tom-

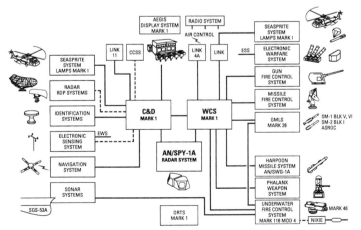

Baseline 0 was the original Aegis system for cruisers, with a mechanical launcher (Mk 26). Note that the first Aegis cruisers have provision only for LAMPS I helicopters; LAMPS III would have added too much topweight. The main difference between Aegis Display Systems Mk 1 and Mk 2 is that the latter has only two screens; the cruiser has another two screens, for a unit commander. Note, too, that the cruiser has an SPS-49 radar in addition to its surface search set, whereas the destroyer has only the SPS-67 surface search set. Total combat-system weight in this version is 610 t; in Baseline 3 it is 650 t, and in Baseline 4 (CG 65, *Chosin*) it is 656 t. The original Baseline 0 program amounted to 802,500 words, which grew to 1,010,000 (with more than a third changed) in Baseline 3. (U.S. Navy)

ahawk targeting). These devices are apart from the UYK-7s used for the ship's sonars and underwater FCSs. In Baseline 4 the UYK-7s were replaced, one for one, by UYK-43s and two more were added (an on-board trainer [in effect a spare] and a UYK-43 for the Mk 86 system). Baseline 5 adds a seventh UYK-43 for link processing (C2P). Destroyers have five UYK-43s. Their C&D systems receive ASW inputs from SQQ-89s, and they have gunfire control integral with Aegis, rather than separate (as in cruisers, which have Mk 86 FCS).

The FY90 program included integration of the SPS-49(V)7 air-search radar, the Mk 86 Air Gun Mode, and Ship Signal Exploitation System (SSES) upgrades into the Aegis combat system.

Current efforts to improve the existing Aegis system include the development of new computer algorithms to deal with deceptive ECM. The wording of the official description suggests that the perceived threat includes deception jammers carried by incoming missiles.

Versions (Aegis baselines):

Baseline 1 (CG 47–51): Original version with UYK-7/20 computers and UYA-4 CIC displays.

Baseline 2 (CG 52–58): VLS, Tomahawk, ASW upgrades. Demonstrated at the Aegis land test site in FY86; the ASW upgrade was added to the program in September 1986. Tomahawk was integrated into Baseline 2 in FY87. This version has UYK-7/20 computers and UYA-4 CIC displays. Baseline 2A is a planned upgrade with UYK-43 computers and possibly OJ-194B consoles.

Baseline 3 (CG 59–64): SPY-1B; retained some UYA-4 displays and the UYK-7 computer system (apparently a planned upgrade of the tactical display system to UYQ-21 could not be carried out completely). Baseline 3 was demonstrated in June 1987. Ships are being upgraded to Baseline 3A to make their computers and displays identical to those of the later cruisers and destroyers. The first to be modernized is *Monterey* (CG 61). UYK-7 computers are replaced by UYK-43 lowboys and displays are being replaced by UYQ-21s. The last two ships in the group, CG 59 and CG 64, may receive UYQ-70 displays. Baseline 3A also includes installation of Link 16.

Baseline 4 (CG 65–73, DDG 51–67): Version based on Baselines 2/3, that converts computer programs to UYK-43/44 computers and provides increased battle-group capability in the Aegis display system (force doctrine and OTH-T upgrades). This version includes a UYK-43 version of the Mk 86 FCS. The Japanese DDG version is Baseline J1. Baseline 4 cruisers are being modernized to Baseline 5 Phase III configuration.

Baseline 5 (FY92: DDG 68–78): DDG 51 modernized with JTIDS/C2P, Combat DF (display only), tactical graphics capability, TADIXS B (with ATWCS), SLQ-32A(V)3, computer upgrades, and the Aegis ER missile. Originally this was to have been the DDG 51 Flight III version; presumably it became the Flight IIA version when Flight III was abandoned. There are three phases: Phase I integrates the ER missile and provides an initial operational capability; Phase II integrates all planned improvements except JTIDS, so that they can be backfitted into Baseline 4 ships (the new programs are to be operable in Baseline 4 ships whether or not the new equipment has been added); and Phase III adds JTIDS/Link 16 and the OJ-663 color display. Phase I software was completed in FY93; that year the Phase II critical design review was completed. Phase II improvements include TIP, the track initiation processor which sensitizes or desensitizes the SPY-1 system, screening transients to reduce processor load and improving detection of small targets in sea clutter; and associated track load control algorithms. TIP employs a UYK-44 computer. Tactical Graphics Capability provides reference data for the combat display consoles, using 22 TAC-4 computers connected by an FDDI bus. Beginning with DDG 68, a ruggedized COTS unit with 68040 chips replaces the UYK-44 in the SGS (gridlock) element. Beginning with DDG 72, Combat DF uses TAC-3 processors, saving $800K. Some of the planned improvements were not available in time. Phase III currently adds ATWCS for Tomahawk and SLAM control, Combat DF, color

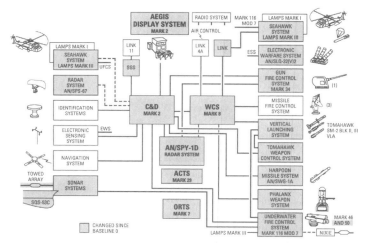

Baseline 4 was the first Aegis destroyer version. Shading indicates the many elements changed since Baseline 0. GFCS Mk 34 is fully integrated with the Aegis system and its SPY-1D radar, whereas the cruiser has a separate SPQ-9A surface gunfire-control radar. This was the version in which UYK-43/44 computers replaced the earlier UYK-7/20s. What the drawing does not convey is that computer programs grew enormously (to 3,420,500 words), partly to transfer modules formerly carried on disk to core, for much faster execution. Another improvement was to carry duplicate copies of the program in core, to protect against partial computer failure. On-line systems supporting computer program testing and maintenance also grew enormously. Development of Baseline 4 cost about 28% as much as the original Aegis program (all cruiser baselines together cost about 20% as much as the original program). ACTS is the Aegis Combat Training System, occupying a separate UYK-43 computer. If one of the main computers fails, the ACTS computer can be connected to the combat system to take its place; it can carry the Aegis tactical picture while running the training program. The program simulates sensors but does not stimulate them, so that it does not provide radar operator training. As adjunct computers and new capabilities are added, the boundaries between computers will begin to fade, since the same machines may host several different programs. For example, some programs will be moved into adjuncts to make room for capabilities such as TBMD. ACTS will combine with the battle force tactical trainer (BFTT). (U.S. Navy)

displays, TADIXS B, and Link 16. The combat system program grows to more than 6.5 million lines, compared to about 4 million in Baseline 4.

Baseline 6 (begins with the last FY94 ship, DDG 79, the prototype of DDG 51 Flight IIA): it integrates SPY-1 upgrades into the Aegis combat system. This version corresponds to ACDS Block 1 Level 2, that is, it replaces the UYQ-21 display system with UYQ-70 (beginning with DDG 81, *Churchill*). DDG 80 introduces a new COTS large-screen display, CLSD. This version includes provision for embarked helicopters and for the ESSMS missile (to replace Phalanx; but at least the first few ships will retain Phalanx, as ESSMS will not be ready for some years). There are also a fiber-optics bus (the data multiplexing system, DMS), and a fiber-optic interior voice communications system (IVCS). Cost-cutting initiatives will be implemented. In addition, the Radar Set Controller Environment Simulator (RSCES) and Battle Force Tactical Trainer (BFTT) will be integrated into the Baseline 6 Combat System.

Plans called for addition of adjunct processors to reduce the load on the UYK-43s by absorbing programs for the BFTT and for identification (IFF) upgrades. Work on the adjunct processor began under the FY93 program. However, to absorb FY95 cuts, rehosting was delayed a year. A variant of the Baseline 5 Phase III computer program had to be developed so that equipment intended for DDG 79–81 could be tested ashore. Adjunct processor engineering development was delayed a year.

Baseline 6 was split into three phases in 1994, to absorb FY95 budget cuts. Phase I includes deletion of the towed array (SQQ-89[V]10) and of the vertical launcher loader crane. The SKR-4 missile telemetry system is eliminated. ORTS is upgraded to a

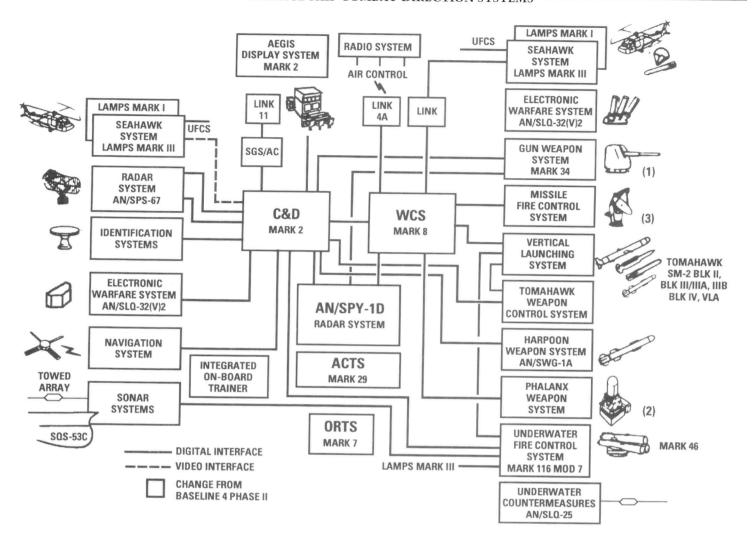

Baseline 5 Phase I is the current Aegis destroyer system. Shading indicates elements modified since Baseline 4 Phase II. (U.S. Navy)

TAC-3 computer. The Kingfisher mine-detection feature is added to the ship's SQS-53C. This version has full Combat DF capability. It introduces DSVL (Doppler sonar velocity log) and AOCD (Aegis operator-controlled device, replacing the earlier OL-267 computer data terminal, in this case emulated by the main computer). Due to the cuts described above, Baseline 6 Phase II had to be developed concurrent with Phase I.

Phase II (DDG 85–87, last ship in FY96) introduces the Radar Set Controller Environment Simulator (RSCES), integrates ASW into the BFTT, has ATWCS Phase II, and introduces an FCS upgrade (a stable mode oscillator, STAMO) and AOCD (native mode). This version also introduces a common data-link management system (CDLMS), which controls the gridlock system and C2P. This system was formerly known as TICA (Tactical Information Communications Analyser). Phase II introduces the Aegis LAN interconnect system (ALIS), which integrates the several existing LANs in the system.

Phase III (DDG 88–93, last ship in FY97) introduces SPY-1D(V) with ORTS mods in DDG 90. This radar is part of a response to a new threat assessment released in November 1989; engineering development began in FY92. The new threat was probably a fast low-flying missile; the corresponding redesign of SPY-1 (EDM-4B) is now under test.

Baseline 7 (begins with DDG 94; last ship FY00): this Baseline provides antitactical ballistic missile (SM-2 Block IVA) and CEC capabilities. ATBM improvements include a cueing sensor, to cue the SPY-1 system to a ballistic threat. Standard Missile Block IIIB will be fully integrated into this version. Tomahawk capability is to be upgraded to Block IV (TBIP). It is to have a distributed computer architecture employing a fiber-optic bus. It will also have ID Upgrade Phase II (CIFF and SLQ-20B) and an ASW upgrade (LAMPS Block II, Mk 50 lightweight torpedo with a periscope depth attack (PDA) feature.

Users: Japan (*Kongo* class), Spain (F100 class), United States (*Ticonderoga* and *Arleigh Burke* classes).

◆ CDS (ex-NTDS)/ACDS/C2P/JPTDS/JTDS and WDS

NTDS and successor systems are now termed CDS, combat-direction systems. Whereas NTDS software was primarily a U.S. Navy product, ACDS Block 0 was contracted to Unisys, Block 1 to Hughes Ground Systems. Aegis CDS is separate but has a parallel structure. Software is identified by Model: Model 4.0 is NTDS (using a CP-642 or UYK-7 computer and the UYA-4 display system). Model 4.1 is ACDS (Advanced CDS) Block 0 (NTDS software rewritten to run on a UYK-43 computer; also called restructured NTDS, or RNTDS). RNTDS (written at Dam Neck) is used only for NTU cruisers and *Kidd*-class destroyers. A modular version of Block 0 for carriers, which have one-bay UYK-43s and software written in CMS 2, is entirely different from RNTDS. Both versions employ the UYQ-21 display system. Block 0 entered service in FY87.

Models 5.0 and beyond are ACDS Block 1 and beyond. Block 1 Level 1 uses the UYK-43 computer with new software adapted to Link 16 (TADIL-J), which has more levels of identification than Block 0. A separate C&D processor (as introduced in Aegis),

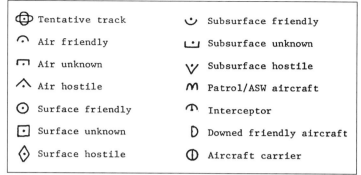

⊕ Tentative track	∪ Subsurface friendly
⌒ Air friendly	⊔ Subsurface unknown
⊓ Air unknown	∨ Subsurface hostile
⋀ Air hostile	⋔ Patrol/ASW aircraft
⊙ Surface friendly	⋒ Interceptor
⊡ Surface unknown	D Downed friendly aircraft
◇ Surface hostile	⨀ Aircraft carrier

Some standard NTDS symbols; this symbology is now standard throughout much of the West. The goal in symbology is to make the plot as vivid and as immediately meaningful as possible. NTDS seeks this end by using sharp symbols for enemy units and round (soft) ones for friendlies, and by using the upper part of the symbol for an air target, the lower part for a submarine, and the whole symbol (diamond, circle, or square) for a surface unit. Note also the "sea gull" symbol for an ASW airplane. These are warfighting symbols: there is nothing to represent a neutral. On the frigate *Stark*, the neutral Iraqi airplane that actually attacked the ship had to be classified as friendly, and that classification in turn made it impossible to engage automatically (the FCS could, however, track a dummy target following the same flight path). These are only a portion of the full NTDS repertoire. For example, the ACDS display (right) shows the standard sonobuoy symbol as well as the own-ship symbol. (*Shipboard Weapons Systems*, vol. 2 (USNA, n.d. [late 1970s].)

also a UYK-43, is added. The C&D processor applies decision-making (doctrinal) rules to the tactical picture in the first computer. The rules can be changed on board ship. The processor also contains intelligence data that can be used to enhance the tactical picture in the main UYK-43. Block 1 is intended to embody the Aegis Tactical Executive System (ATES), which runs on the C&D computer. Block 1 is also the first U.S. CDS to be designed for full integration with ESM data, included that collected by TFCC and POST (from the TADIXS B intelligence net). Development was ordered on 15 December 1988, and the Block 1 Decision Coordinating Paper was issued 22 August 1989. This version of CDS was intended for NTU ships (coding work for the CGN 38 and DDG 993 classes began in FY92).

The lead ACDS Block 1 ship is the carrier *Constellation* (CV 64), which previously had NTDS Model 4.0; the other active carriers will likely follow in the mid- to late 1990s. The LHDs (which already have UYK-43 computers) and the LHAs will probably also be fitted with Block 1, as will the two *Californias* and the *Kidds*. All of the other potential platforms, the oil-burning NTU cruisers and the four *Virginias*, have been or are being discarded.

The first ACDS Block 1 was delivered in December 1992 for an engineering test (with the accompanying carrier ASW Module Model 5.1) on board *Constellation* in the fall of 1993, and for demonstration tests between November 1993 and April 1994. Reportedly, results were impressive when the system ran, but computer capacity was barely adequate, and the system therefore often crashed. One conclusion was that the move toward much more powerful commercially based workstations (like those used by the French in the *Charles de Gaulle* system) was long overdue. The modified version planned for the new carrier *John C. Stennis* is to incorporate the Cooperative Engagement Capability (CEC).

An enhanced Block 1 Level 1 program was to have been delivered in June 1994. Coding of the CGN 38/DDG 993 program began in FY92, and due to delays it is not expected to begin operational evaluation until FY96.

Link processing is being removed to Hughes's separate C2P, a UYK-43 with a USQ-69 display terminal. That frees the main computer to quadruple the system's track capacity and effective surveillance range; it also increases the target-insertion rate. Because it is needed to support Link 16, C2P is required for ships

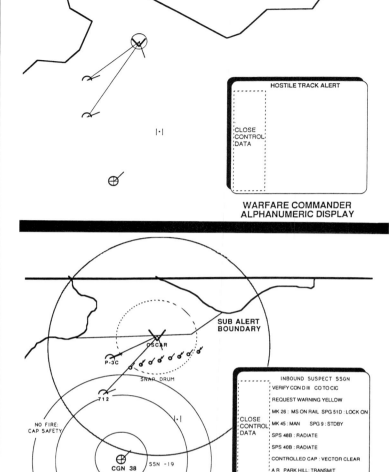

ACDS Block 0 and Block 1 pictures of the same tactical situation. Block 0 is equivalent to current NTDS; the diagram shows one hostile submarine (the "v") and two friendly aircraft (the semicircles), plus a ship (the circle) at the bottom. Interpretation is entirely the responsibility of the CIC personnel. Block 1 shows the effect of providing extensive online databases, displaying weapons capabilities and threats. (Hughes)

The combat information center (CIC) of the newly completed frigate *Curts* shows two standard OJ-194/UYA-4 consoles flanking the TAO (summary) console (OJ-197/UYA-4), with an SPA-25 radar repeater in the background. Not visible between the two status boards behind the consoles is a large backup vertical (manual) plot. The trackball of the console in the foreground has not yet been installed, but one is visible on the console on the right. (U.S. Navy)

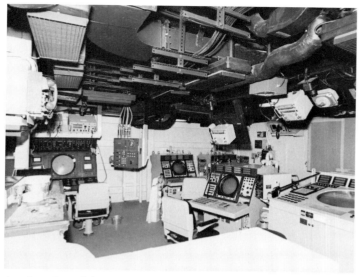

Another view of the standard frigate CIC (in this case aboard USS *Estocin*) shows the two-operator weapons-control console (WCC) to the left of the UYA-4 NTDS console. This picture was taken while the ship was fitting out in April 1980. (U.S. Navy)

not fitted with ACDS or its Aegis equivalent. The design of the C2P is complicated because Link 16 uses different (NATO) target categories than Link 11, yet the same processor must prepare information from both for insertion into the picture-keeping computer. C2P(V)0 supports ACDS Block 0 and Aegis Model 4; (V)1 supports ACDS Block 1 and Aegis Model 5. The C2P Operational Requirement was issued in December 1985, and the first UYK-43 computers intended for operational evaluation of the Version 0 system were acquired under the FY88 program. Funding cuts in FY88/89 delayed some tests from FY90 to FY91, others from FY91 to FY92. Version 0 was released to the Fleet (RTF) in FY92, to enter service in FY93 (but tests to verify corrections were not completed until FY96). It completed technical evaluation in April 1994. (V)1 was first tested in 1994, with development completed in FY96.

In Block 1, ASTABs complement the usual graphic displays, showing threat summary, task organization, and combat-system summary. All ASTABs can be displayed on either the dedicated ASTABs or on CRTs in the CDC, and the system operators can request ASTABs as desired. ASTABs can be defined as multipage electronic documents, one page being displayed at a time, but the overall computer system keeps the entire ASTAB up to date, to be called up as desired. There are 60 predefined formats (ownship and force data) plus 20 user-defined formats. All of this information can be pulled from the full ACDS database, including the track file and the intelligence data. For example, an operator might define an ASTAB listing ASW threats, giving for each threat platform its track number, its category (submarine, surface, air), its range, its ASW sensor, and its ASW weapon. Another page of the display (which could be called up as desired) might associate each threat with its lethal range. An ASTAB on force status might, for example, list the ships with the status of their ASW systems or their roles (e.g., picket, pouncer).

Compared to Block 0, Block 1 is said to offer eight times the track capacity and four times the range. Reportedly the real-time distributed software architecture of the system can be expanded to embrace 8 tightly coupled and 248 loosely coupled nodes; presumably the tightly coupled nodes correspond to the main and C&D computers. As installed on board the carrier *Constellation*, Block 1 provides two large-screen displays, 23 OJ-535 consoles, and 27 automatic status boards, plus several alphanumeric terminals. This is apparently considered Level 0. Level 1 is an upgrade that adds a TAC-3 NTCS-A computer coupled directly to the CDS (in the past, such computers have been kept separate).

The TAC-3 is used mainly to provide the NTCS-A global picture, but it also provides TDAs. Level 1 adds about 10% more software to the system, including automatic EW correlation. The TAC-3 is a two-way open gateway to NTCS-A.

Block 1 Level 2, now under development, unloads the picture-keeping UYK-43 by moving some graphics-generation functions out into intelligent consoles (the Advanced Display System, or ADS, UYQ-70). It is to be installed by refit on board the carrier *Eisenhower*, the LHAs, and the LHDs. The LHAs lack sufficient cooling in CIC, so the computer elements of the ADS must be moved down a deck, leaving dumb consoles in CIC. This version is to support CEC. It includes a geoserver loaded with map software.

Block 1 Level 3, now in the planning stage, eliminates the UYK-43 altogether; as conceived in mid-1995, it is a fully distributed system of ADS workstations, one of which carries the tactical picture. Aegis Baseline 6 corresponds to ACDS Block 1 Level 2; Aegis Baseline 7 corresponds to Level 3. Level 3 may be installed on *Spruance*-class destroyers; it is designed to be integrated with the ship's gun and underwater FCSs, LAMPS helicopter, and Harpoon. It will be the first version of ACDS designed for integration with SSDS.

As of mid-1995, Hughes was working privately to rehost Block 1 Level 1/2 from the UYK-43 to VME-backplane 68040/68060 commercial processors, to allow reuse of existing expensive software. Later Hughes switched to the TAC series.

Although Level 3 is physically fully distributed, it still has a single point of failure in the form of the dedicated picture-keeping workstation. As of 1995, Unisys (now Loral) was working on a fully distributed architecture, with the database completely or partly duplicated across the system. For example, the full tactical picture might not be required by each workstation, which might contain only those elements it needed; no single workstation might need the full picture.

NTDS is primarily a tactical picture-keeping system. It performs some TEWA, but the decision to engage is manual. Aegis added an automatic mode, supported by decision-making (doctrinal) rules embodied in software running on a second UYK-7 computer, the C&D processor. The rules can be changed on board ship. They are also used to suggest courses of action; Aegis was the first U.S. combat-information system to incorporate such decision aids. They are also used to control radar processing, for example, to reject targets in some selected speed ranges. The change, from information compilation (in NTDS) to combat direction, is reflected in a change from the old CIC designation to a new CDC (Combat Direction Center) designation for the central command/control space of a ship.

Aegis does not quite correspond to NTDS/WDS because it ties fire control much more tightly to the tactical picture-keeper; it is a CDS grown up out of a FCS. Thus the C&D element is not quite analogous to NTDS. However, like NTDS, it has an associated WDS (Mk 12).

The initial versions of NTDS were installed on board carriers and missile cruisers, using CP-642 computers. Initially, cruisers had two computers (a third was added to ships modified for SAMID); carriers had four (three in the prototype installation in *Oriskany*). Carriers with CP-642s later also received UYK-7s for auxiliary roles, such as controlling the ASW module (from an ASW point of view, the ASWM is the carrier's WDS). The carrier CP-642s were not replaced until ships underwent major refits (e.g., SLEPs) and new UYK-43s were installed. Thus CP-642s will remain on board a few nuclear carriers until their first major refits toward the end of the decade. The major upgrade to CP-642 installations was addition of an EMCU (enhanced memory core unit), providing enough memory (shared among the computers) that they could run all modules of the NTDS program simultaneously. Previously they had had to reconfigure the system dynamically, dropping modules so that others could be run.

The cruisers and the *Mahan* (DDG 37) classes retained CP-642 computers, typically with a capacity of 256 tracks (total of local and remote), unless they received ACDS (UYK-43) in major upgrades.

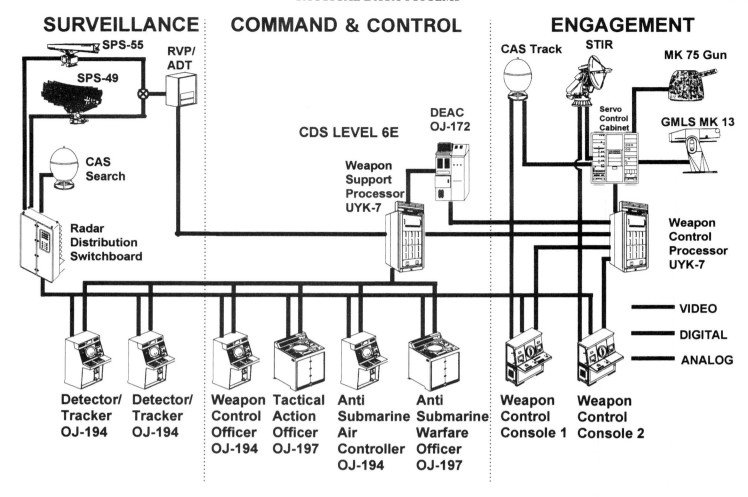

The combat system of the *Perry*-class frigate, initially designated JTDS (junior TDS), was designed about 1972 around a pair of UYK-7 computers, one for engagement (weapon-control processor) and one to maintain the tactical picture and carry out other CDS functions (the weapon-support processor). The names are somewhat deceptive; this was actually a small-ship version of NTDS rather than a simple weapons system. They were probably adopted because the ship was conceived as a minimum-cost project, and NTDS or some equivalent seemed rather extravagant. The arrangement is a classic star topology, with the weapon-support processor receiving digital radar data through the RVP/ADT at top left, and controlling six consoles via digital connections. All of the consoles also receive raw video from the search radars (SPS-49, SPS-55, and the search element of the STIR). In addition, the two weapon-control consoles receive analog signals from two elements of the Mk 92 system, the CAS tracker and the STIR. Their video is not available to the CDS consoles, although data can presumably be extracted via the link between the two UYK-7s. (Vitro)

This generation also included the *Mount Whitney*–class amphibious flagships (LCC), which have both CDSs and an Amphibious Support Information System (ASIS) running on a separate CP-642B. The main tactical system runs on four CP-642B with EMCU.

The UYK-7 computer was used in NTDS systems on board *Spruance*- (and, later, *Kidd*-) class destroyers and *Tarawa*-class amphibious ships. UYK-7 was installed on *Los Angeles*–class submarines specifically so that they could receive the tactical picture employed by the battle group with which they worked. These were all major fleet units, comparable to those fitted with first-generation systems. The *Kidd*-class system was unusual in that it had a separate WDS computer, initially a single-bay UYK-7 (the main computer was a four-bay UYK-7).

The *Tarawa* system is called ITAWDS (integrated tactical amphibious warfare data system), using a pair of UYK-7s, one for CDS and one for tactical information processing (TIPS) related to the assault proper. See TIPs in the Control/Surveillance section. Capabilities include both fighter and amphibious aircraft air control, since until the Marines are established ashore the

ship is the local air controller. It also monitors the tactical situation in the amphibious objective area.

A *Spruance* has a UYK-7 computer; as built it has one summary console (OJ-197) and nine one-man consoles (OJ-194). A second UYK-7 is responsible for ASW. However, ships with SQQ-89/Mk 116 have a UYK-43 in place of the second UYK-7; in effect it is an ASW WDS. A single UYK-43 in a modernized *Kidd*-class destroyer replaces a four-bay UYK-7.

With the advent of the UYK-7 computer, it became possible to extend the system down to missile destroyers and then to *Perry*-class frigates. To avoid resistance to placing a large-ship system aboard such minor units, their systems received different designations, JPTDS (Junior Participating Tactical Data System) for the original destroyer system and JTDS (Junior Tactical Data System, later WSS, for weapons-support system) for the *Perry* class. The key difference between the two was that JPTDS included Link 11 capacity; JTDS had provision for Link 11, but initially that was not installed, to save money.

JPTDS was developed specifically for the *Adams* class; it was, in effect, equivalent to SATIR and SENIT 2. The whole *Adams* class was to have been fitted, but only four ships received JPTDS (DDGs 9, 12, 15, and 21). DDG 15 survives in the Greek navy; none of her three sisters has a computer-driven CDS. JPTDS is the system aboard the Australian *Adams* class. The picture-keeper and the WDS (Mk 13) share a single UYK-7; the WDS designates targets to both missile and gun systems.

There are eight UYA-4 consoles: three for detection and tracking, one for surface/subsurface, two for display/decision, two for weapons assignment. There is also a 3D radar console. As initially installed, the JPTDS UYK-7 had only three of its 16 available 16k modules. Capacity as originally installed was 128 tracks, which might include the 64 of an FFG 7 plus another 64 received over Link 11. JPTDS installation included the digital upgrade to Tartar (Tartar-D). RAN missile destroyers have had their systems upgraded to 144 kwords of memory, but they are still limited to 128 tracks.

FFG 7 COMBAT SYSTEM MODERNIZATION

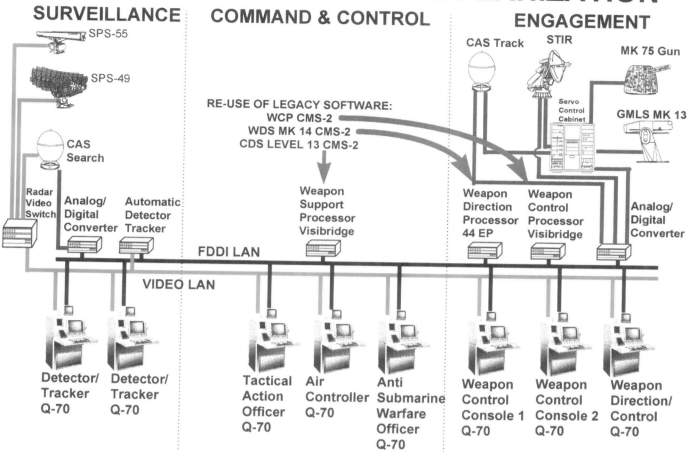

Vitro's proposed modernization of the *Perry*-class CDS shows the effects of COTS technology and of modern buses. The objective was to minimize cost and complexity, and to retain as much existing software as possible. VisiBridges are COTS boxes capable of emulating UYK-7s. 44EP is a single-board equivalent to a UYK-44. Vitro split the weapon-control element of the system in two to exploit WDS Mk 14 software it had written as part of the New Threat Upgrade program. In turn, it argued that providing NTU software to the frigate would make it easier to adapt the ship's combat system to the SM-2 missile, in a form of NTU. Such adaptation would considerably increase the frigate's firepower. Instead of leading search radar video through an RVP/ADT box, Vitro simply digitized it so that it could be sent along the system LAN. An automatic detector/tracker can pick video off the video bus, sending its output of target vectors onto the main system digital LAN (FDDI). The various consoles of the earlier system are all replaced by UYQ-70s. They are all interchangeable, offering the ship some insurance against system failure. In theory, the next step would be to abandon the VisiBridges and the 44EP in favor of a fully distributed system. To do that, however, would require considerable entirely new software; the emulation approach is attractive precisely because it requires little new software, and therefore little retesting. (Vitro)

In a *Perry* (FFG 7) -class frigate, the two UYK-7 computers are designated WCP (weapons-control processor, for the Mk 92 FCS) and WSP (weapons-support processor); the WSP is the picture-keeper, and the WCP is responsible for both fire control and the short-range air picture. There were originally six CDS consoles (two summary OJ-97 and four OJ-194) and two weapons-control consoles (WCCs); capacity in the original very limited version (single-bay UYK-7s) was 64 tracks. First- and second-flight ships were later updated with an optical sight system (a pair of Mk 24 target designators), nonintegrated SLQ-32(V)2, CIWS (Mk 15/1), RVP/ADT (i.e., automatic radar processing), and a rubber sonar dome. They also eventually got Link 11 instead of the original Link 14; presumably UYK-7 capacity was increased to accept external tracks.

Third-flight ships (FY79, from FFG 36 on) had LAMPS III instead of LAMPS I, an SQR-19 towed array, Link 11 instead of

Link 14, and integrated SLQ-32(V)2. To handle the much-expanded ASW capability, they added a third computer (the WAP, or Weapons Alternate Support Processor, another UYK-7) and a fifth OJ-194 console. To unload the UYK-7s, the consoles had the CIGARS/DDI modification, in which they generated symbols. Computer programs were revised. These ships had fully loaded UYK-7s, with 96-kword memories rather than the 16-kword memories of the original FFG 7s.

The fourth flight (FFG 50-60) had RVP/ADT "turn on," engageability, WAP/LAMPS enhancements, improved Link 11 capability, and further revised programs. The final ship in the class (FFG 61) has a single UYK0-43 replacing both the WSP and the WAP (the WCP is still a UYK-7) and UYQ-21 displays. The radars are SPS-49(V)5, Mk 92 Mod 6 (the CORT upgrade), and a modified SPS-55 with radar video converter; the radars are integrated by SYS-2(V)2. SWG-1A controls Harpoon missiles. This ship has the SQQ-89(V)2 sensor integration and display sharing (SIADS), which allows display sharing of the UYQ-21 display system between LAMPS III SQQ-28 Sonar Signal Processing Set (SSPS) and the SQR-19. Mk 92 Mod 6 employs two UYK-7s, the WCP (a UYK-7A) and a new CCP (converter control processor, a UYK-7B). The ship then has four computers in all, and she can operate with one or two computers if necessary, for example, one UYK-7 as WCP, one side of UYK-43 as WSP or WAP depending on mission.

The first CDS integration of SLQ-32 was in FFG 7s, in the FY89 Baseline. Later, the ultimate FFG 7, FFG 61, received an EW fire-control capability. The ship has a library of SSM seeker head emissions. If one is sensed, SLQ-32 automatically cues the FCS tracker, which is gated at the point, and automatically puts a missile on the rail, so the operator need only punch a button. This was the most sophisticated integration performed on an FFG 7. It was backfit to other units, presumably to all CORT units.

Ingraham (FFG-61), the unit with a major radar improvement (CORT) and with a UYK-43 computer, is now also designated

Baseline 8-E. This version forms the basis for the last two Spanish and all the Taiwanese ships, which incorporate non-U.S. equipment. The Australian *Perrys* presumably follow the Flight Two or Flight Three baselines; the first four Spanish ships presumably follow the Flight Three baseline. The last two Spanish ships have new Spanish-built (Sainsel-Ceselsea-Inisel) CONAM three-man consoles. They also have Spanish subsystems for torpedo launching, weapons indication, data conversion, IFF interrogation, and optical target designation. All the Spanish ships have the Meroka CIWS instead of Phalanx, and Nettunel instead of SLQ-32. At least the last two ships have GPS integrated into their navigation systems, and they have SINS.

The Royal Australian Navy is currently planning a progressive upgrade (PUP), to be carried out in stages while ships are in normal refit. In a separate program, UYK-43 computers are being installed to accommodate Australian-written software modules. Ships are also being fitted with SYS-2.

The U.S. Navy planned a weapon-system upgrade called CANDO for non-CORTS ships, but as of early 1996 it had not been implemented; money for 12 ships is in the FY97 or FY98 POM.

In April 1996 Vitro Labs announced its own proposed upgrade, substituting COTS for much existing JTDS hardware. The UYK-7s and the OJ-172 between them are replaced by three of VisiCom's VisiBridges, which can emulate the ships' UYK-7s and thus use existing CDS code. All six UYA-4 displays (four OJ-194, two OJ-197s) and the weapons-control consoles (one- and two-man, connected separately to the CAS and STIR trackers) will be replaced by eight single-operator UYQ-70s, which are much easier to maintain. Of the weapons-control replacements, one will be used for weapons direction/control, managing SM-1/2 engagements. One weapons-control operator will be eliminated (a reduction of three in the required crew). The current SYS-2 or RVP/ADT will be replaced by a DRS autotracker, which weighs about half as much. On the engagement side, Vitro hopes to use CMS-2 code it wrote for the DDG 993 WDS Mk 14 (New Threat Upgrade) system, running on a UYK-44 board (44EP) made by Loral. One advantage of shifting to this code is that the ship is then better prepared to fire SM-2 missiles, which may have to be adopted as stocks of SM-1s decline. Many foreign users may find SM-2 attractive in any case. The spider architecture of the existing system is replaced by an FDDI LAN. Finally, the upgrade would cut topweight by nearly 2 t (4225 lb) in a weight-critical ship, because the VisiBridge and the UYQ-70 weigh so much less than the devices currently installed.

Loral Unisys is offering a *Perry*-class upgrade with similar hardware (see the entry on Modular Improvement Packages).

NTDS was conceived in 1955 and its specifications were laid down in 1957. It was the world's first shipboard TDS based on programmable solid-state computers and using multiple computers in a distributed tactical data-processing system. It was also the first in the world to use automatic computer-to-computer data exchange, and the first naval implementation of an "expert" computer system in the form of a TEWA system. NTDS was the basis of the French SENIT, the German SATIR, the Italian SADOC, the Japanese OYQ, and the Spanish Tritan systems (the British and Dutch systems share a separate but parallel parentage).

The single NTDS computer time-shares several functions. In addition to picture-keeping and navigational calculations, it regularly cycles through the track files for threat evaluation and weapon assignment. Each unit maintains its own version of the force track file, updated via Link 11. Target data are transmitted in rectangular coordinates (the EW and NS axes lie in the ship's ground plane, tangent to the earth). Each ship is responsible for maintaining its earth position (longitude-latitude) with respect to an arbitrary DLRP. Each transmits its own position and the target position in its local ground plane. The nonspherical shape of the earth introduces errors in high latitudes, which may amount to as much as 1% at 63 North.

Navigation (gridlock) is perhaps the greatest problem of NTDS operation: assuring that all ships in an NTDS net use the same coordinates to identify the same points in space, that is, truly share a common grid. If the units do not, then the same target detected by two ships may be counted as two different targets, and thus assigned two (of a limited total number of) tracking and engagement channels. The gridlock problem has now, finally, apparently been solved, initially using Aegis hardware.

NTDS retained a separate FCS (initially, also a separate WDS) to provide a fall-back mode in the event the central computer fails. Similarly, Link 11 was designed so that it could degrade gracefully in the event of ship damage: any fleet unit could control the net.

NTDS was designed to use manually initiated rate-aided tracks, in which operators (detector/trackers) entered targets into the system and then confirmed that they were remaining on course. Later ADT became common.

An NTDS installation includes a summary console for the CIC supervisor and detector/tracker consoles (separate ones for air and surface/subsurface targets). The TAO, who fights the ship from CIC (under the general orders of the CO), does not operate a console but has access to one, to gain an overview of the tactical situation. A flagship will provide an additional summary for the embarked unit commander.

A ship controlling aircraft will often have separate consoles for air controller(s) and for intercept controller(s). Aircraft carriers have additional air-traffic-control consoles.

Systems with embedded WDSs add a console for the weapons-control officer (WCO), generally flanked by the FCS and EC consoles, to observe and manually control data flow between the computer and the fire-control launching systems. There is also a casualty weapons-direction panel (CWDP) in the missile-director control room, providing backup in the event that the NTDS computer fails. The CWDP can select missile mode (AA or surface), can designate from director to director, and can warm up and fire missiles.

The TAO sets target priorities (generally by exception rather than positive direction). The WCO designates assigned targets to the WDS embedded in the NTDS. It in turn indicates whether a target can be engaged and recommends an engagement sequence. The WCO actually selects weapons and fires them. He may also suggest maneuvers to unmask a ship's weapons.

In some cases targets may appear too quickly for this sequence to work in time. Both Aegis ships and *Perry*-class frigates were designed with the option of automatic engagement, the WCO having only a veto. That level of automation proved less than popular and has rarely, if ever, been implemented.

Typically, each air detector/tracker is assigned a specific sector. The number of consoles assigned to this role varies with the level of air activity. Low-altitude aircraft are the responsibility of the surface tracker. Friendly aircraft are automatically tracked by a beacon video processor (BVP) using their Mode II IFF responses. Usually there is at least one detector/tracker console per search radar. A special tracker (SPL-TK) is often present to provide high-precision data on a limited number of tracks for insertion into the associated WDS; the PPI is set on a four-mile-range scale.

The track supervisor monitors the system operators, assigning sectors to the detector/trackers. He helps correct confused track situations, trying to ensure that new tracks are not contacts already carried by other ships in the net, and is also responsible for gridlock. The track supervisor assists the ID operator and is responsible for the communication keyset.

Generally, the surface tracker/detector is also responsible for inserting sonar data, which are not entered automatically. This split between radar and sonar data reflects the AAW origin of the NTDS system.

Reportedly, NTDS suffers from limited track capacity, range, and vocabulary, the last limiting the system's ability to support online decision-making. Targets are described as friend/unknown/enemy, which leaves out considerable ambiguity. For example, in the case of the *Stark*, the track of the Iraqi aircraft that actually attacked the ship was initiated by an AWACS aircraft that identified Iraqis as friendly, and the ship carried the track with that identifier. It took an extra effort for the TAO aboard the ship to keep in mind that the airplane was actually not U.S., and not privy to U.S. tactical data (e.g., could attack by mistake). The ship's combat system was so arranged that she could not normally attack a target identified as friendly (although that software limitation could be overcome by clever operation).

Limited system vocabulary may also have limited the detail in which the surrounding geography could be presented, and that restriction may explain why the tactical picture in the *Vincennes* showed only a single line rather than an airliner corridor (the single line was the centerline of the corridor). One lesson of the *Vincennes* incident may be that, in combat, decisions are taken on the basis of what the display shows, and that limitations in display tend to be overlooked or ignored.

Weapons-direction systems (WDS) are outgrowths of post-World War II work on automatic and semiautomatic threat evaluation and weapon assignment (TEWA) systems; the TEWA was needed to decide, very rapidly, whether a given target could be or should be engaged, that is, to take into account the effective engagement capabilities of the weapons on board the ship. A ship's actual target-handling capacity depends on the capacity of her WDS, since directors are cued not directly from CIC, but rather from the tracks held by the WDS, which is fed directly from the NTDS picture-keeping computer. This limitation is entirely separate from the limitation imposed by the number of missile directors, that is, of fire-control channels. Once a particular fire-control channel has completed its engagement with a particular target, it obtains its next target not directly from NTDS but rather from the embedded WDS.

Surviving WDS versions are:

Mk 13 Pre-NTU system for Tartar (SM-1[MR]) ships with NTDS (GMFCS Mk 74 Mod 6): Mod 0 was in the *Virginia* and the *Kidd* class; Mod 2, the *Perry* class; Mod 3, modernized Australian *Adams*-class destroyers. Consoles: two OJ-194(V)3 PPIs, Mk 90 or 91 launch-system console, Mk 218 casualty weapons-director panel, and Mk 129 casualty battery-control unit. There is no launch-system console in the *Perry*-class version. WDS Mk 13 displays target engageability rather than the fire-control solutions displayed by the earlier WDS Mk 11. Computer-aided target scheduling by the Mk 152 missile computer makes for better capability against multiple targets. In the *Kidd* class, this WDS originally employed a single-bay UYK-7 computer with a memory sufficient for 10 tracks. In the *Adams* class, WDS Mk 13 was resident in the main UYK-7 computer. The original NTDS WDS, Mk 11, was apparently similarly embedded in the main computer system, albeit with attached CP-789 control formatter unit or units to reduce the load on the main computer.

Mk 14 System for NTU ships: This system is unique in being able to handle both (MR) and (ER) missiles, the latter now discarded. It incorporates two UYK-20A or -44 computers and two or three OJ-194(V)4 consoles to control one missile battery, including two trackers. Mod 4 is for missile cruisers. Mod 5 is for missile destroyers (*Kidd* class). Mk 14 superseded the Mk 11 in the *Virginia* class when they received NTU modernization. The system accepts tracks from the main CDS (capacity is 20 tracks in the old UYK-20 version), prioritizes them, and engages them in priority order.

The following CDS computers are in service:

CP-642B Carriers without ACDS, *Mount Whitney* class, some foreign ships

UYK-7 *Spruance* class; *Tarawa* class; and *Perry*-class frigates

UYK-43 CV/CVN (except CV 61, 64), CGN 36–41 (but CGN 38 still has UYK-7); DDG 993–996; and *Wasp* class.

The list does not include Aegis ships, for which the CDS is closely integrated with the weapons system.

MTDS is the analogous Marine Tactical Data System. Its roles include bringing in fire support to protect Marines in forward positions.

◆ **ISDS**

Improved Self-Defense System is the projected combination of ACDS and SSDS (see the Antiair Warfare section), for ships such as CVN 76 and LPD 17, which do not have long-range air-defense weapons, but which do have long-range air responsibility. Presumably the ACDS element would retain responsibility for the former, and an SSDS-like kernel would be merged into it. The installation of SSDS alongside the *Perry* and *Spruance*-class CDSs presumably provides relevant experience. It is not clear, however, to what extent ISDS is more than a transition of funds from the SSDS account to the wider world of CDSs.

◆ **CEC/FACT/FTEWA**

Cooperative Engagement Capability (formerly Battle-Group AAW Coordination) is a program to tie together all the ships of a battle group so that all can share all radar data for fire control. In contrast to early group combat-direction systems, CEC disseminates radar detections (discrete plots). Each ship combines all radar plots in the force, using her CEC processor (CEP). The radar data, tagged by the location of the originator and by the type of radar, are passed among the cooperating units (CUs) of the force by a highly directional data link, the data distribution system (DDS). Aircraft such as E-2s can also contribute radar data.

When a unit loses track, instead of simply coasting it (estimating its position from its past velocity), the track is continued with data from other units. Like NTDS, the system automatically assigns a single number to each track, even when each unit is tracking simultaneously. In some cases the net as a whole may track a target but the same target may not be acquired by a unit trying to engage, because of insufficient signal-to-noise ratio. Normally, in order to limit false alarms, radars require a target to exceed some threshold before declaring it real. However, if the target is already known to the net, the local unit knows that it is not a false alarm. It can therefore turn up its power and its sensitivity (localized sensitivity increase mode) in the area immediately around the target, to detect it in a single dwell or scan. This mode has been demonstrated.

A console on the selected net control unit (NCU) provides the net with a composite identification doctrine, which all the CEC units implement to jointly classify a target. Given such a doctrine, identification is based on data such as velocity and position relative to borders and airways in addition to direct IFF. This practice differs from that in NTDS, in which classification rather than doctrine is broadcast.

The object is to produce fused tracks so accurate that any ship in the force can fire weapons on their basis. CEC is the ultimate development of the Aegis philosophy, in which search data suffice for fire control. Fusing all weapons in a battle group also required the development of FTEWA, a force-wide version of threat evaluation and weapon assignment (TEWA). CEP is directly descended from RTLOS (remote track/launch on search), in which a missile is launched by a ship that is not yet emitting at all. The firing ship, then, can be (in effect) in ambush, since an oncoming airplane may well be unaware that it is within attack range. In the ultimate (1986) RTLOS experiment, an Aegis ship and an E-2C airplane controlled firing by an NTU ship.

It is now possible to reset a missile in flight so that it will respond to an illuminator on board another ship. If local interference fades sufficiently, the missile can then be reset to the illuminator of the ship that fired it. It seems likely that in future E-2s will provide illumination as well as connectivity and search radar support.

The CEP currently employs thirty 68040s on a bus; it will soon replace them with PowerPC chips. Each CPU performs at least one processing subfunction, for example, track filtering, track divergence/convergence testing, gridlock, sensor interface, cooperative engagement support, or DDS interface. The CEP receives data directly from a ship's sensors. The processor feeds a dedicated CEC support display system (CSD).

The net has a unique distributed architecture. When the operator on board the designated NCU enters the "net start" command, the DDS on that ship begins to search for other DDS by sweeping its array antenna and interrogating. Others sweep their arrays in similar fashion, locating other units, which may be beyond the NCU's horizon. A CU acquires a signal in omnidirectional mode, and announces its coordinates in the grid. Gridlock is achieved quickly after a few returns (to an accuracy of feet, since the DDS clearly has some radar characteristics). By the end of this phase, all units know where all the others are, and are communicating with units within their lines of sight. All exercise a common scheduling algorithm, sending bursts of data in parallel to different designated units at precise times with precise encrypted spread-spectrum sequences. Each unit tracks the others with which it communicates, so its CEP can begin gridlock alignment. All the DDS simultaneously switch to identical (individually generated) schedules, indicating which unit communicates with which in any multi-msec time frame (an embedded cesium clock synchronizes the system on a microsec scale). The net is automatically reconfigurable; the NCU operator is needed only to set the system state (on or off).

The DDS is a C-band pencil-beam system using an ITT active array. It transmits in bursts (packets), probably at a rate of several Mbit/sec. ECCM features include the narrowness of the beam itself, its high power, its redundant coding, error detection/correction coding, encryption, and the ability to frequency-hop. The link is described as several orders of magnitude more capable than other links, in capacity, cycle time, update rate, message error rate, jam resistance, and margin against propagation fading. The system on board any one ship originally used 11 processors (presumably 68020s), but later one 68020 and one 68040 were added.

The jam-resistant DDS is in a sense the next step beyond Link 11/16, and CEP is the step beyond CDS. It needs very high computing capacity to provide a combination of very precise gridlock (to allow full use of all sensors within a battle group) and actual fire control (including the decision as to which weapon is to engage a particular threat).

CEC is particularly attractive for littoral situations, in which individual ships may not be able to see targets. It also would seem to counter some forms of low-observable aircraft, which might appear only fleetingly to any particular radar (because they reflect signals strongly in only a few discrete directions, which become spikes in their reflection patterns), but which might leave an easily discernible track on the radars of the entire force. Too, CEC makes it possible for units (including batteries ashore) to cooperate more effectively in theater missile defense (TMD).

New kinds of cooperative engagements include:

Cued, in which firing ship uses local data to intercept at greater range, due to remote data

Aegis Engage on Remote (EOR), in which another SPY-1 or NTU FCS radar provides target tracking data to an Aegis C&D/WCS

NTU Engage on Composite (EOC), in which another SPS-48, SPG-51, or SPY-1 serves as tracking source

Remote VLS launch, with Aegis control ship providing initialization data, launch command, and in-flight control

Forward Pass, in which missile control is transferred to another ship either during midcourse or during transition from midcourse to terminal guidance

Work on CEC began in 1985; E-Systems received a contract for the data link in 1988. The system was not shown publicly until 1994. Johns Hopkins Applied Physics Laboratory (APL) did much of the system design.

To participate in a CEC system, a SPY-1B/C radar needs a new software program, as does a TAS Mk 23. An SPS-48 or -49 or SPG-51/FCS Mk 74 needs a special processor. New programs are also required for the Aegis C&D, WCS, and display elements, and for the ACDS of a carrier or NTU ship, the WDS of an NTU ship, and the FCS of such a ship. The existing SYS-2 must be replaced.

CEC was first demonstrated, using vans, off Newport News, aboard the Aegis cruisers *San Jacinto* (CG 56) and *Leyte Gulf*

(CG 55) in August 1990, including integration of Marine Corps ground assets. In September 1993 there were successful four-mode tests between *Kidd* and three CEC shore sites: the Aegis Combat Systems Center (ACSC), Wallops Island, and the Fleet Combat Direction Systems Support Activity (FCDISSA) Dam Neck.

The *Dwight D. Eisenhower* battle group (including the Aegis cruisers *Anzio* and *Cape St. George*, the NTU destroyer *Kidd*, and *Wasp*) tested CEC early in 1994. There was also an experimental ARPA radar on St. Thomas (Mountain Top, intended to simulate an E-2). Live rounds were fired at BQM-74E targets. This test demonstrated Aegis engagement on remote data, NTU engagement on composite data, and Sea Sparrow cued engagement.

Later in 1994 a Customs Service P-3B, which carries an APS-138 radar (as on an E-2), was modified by Lockheed Aeronautical Systems Company with a suite of prototype CEC hardware to demonstrate participation of an E-2C in the net. Initially the P-3B merely transmitted radar data, but from February 1995 its radar was brought into the net. Its system weighed 2200 lb, but the E-2C system was expected to weigh only about 500 lb.

In another test in the summer of 1994, the battle group tracked a Sergeant rocket fired from Wallops Island to an apogee of 580,000 ft (108 nm) and successfully transmitted the CEC picture to a Patriot battery ashore and to an air force control and reporting center (which would normally control tactical aircraft) via a commercial Inmarsat. Launch and predicted impact points were transmitted within seconds of launch. Secretary of Defense William S. Perry was so impressed that he ordered the program accelerated as much as technically possible, which meant beginning with FY96. This was the first time Washington officials had realized the connection between CEC and TMD.

In a February 1995 test, a rocket fired from Wallops Island was tracked and its launch point determined within 5 sec. That might have been soon enough to destroy a mobile launcher. The CEC program began work on a software patch to be used to transmit data to Patriot batteries via a Tactical Broadcast satellite. It seemed likely that launch points could be located to within $\frac{1}{4}$ nm, and the data passed quickly to AWACS or E-2C aircraft. This series (24–25 February 1995) included cued self-defense, in which an Aegis or NTU ship creates a remote track, and a CVN or LHD engages with Sea Sparrow. It also demonstrated Engagement on Remote/Composite Data. An Aegis ship was able to engage despite mainlobe standoff jamming of her SPY-1. She launched, midcourse-guided, and illuminated for the SM-2 Block III missile using remote data.

Also in 1995, CEC was very successfully tested in the Adriatic by the *Eisenhower* battle group.

One effect of CEC is that non-Aegis (even non-AAW) ships can become, in effect, spare magazines for Aegis ships, which can order launches and control the missiles in terminal engagements. That capability in turn is possible because SM-2 is fired into a preset basket and only intermittently command-guided.

It appears that LAMPS helicopters will also be brought into CEC, both as airborne relays and to network their usual surface targeting and ASW functions among the ships of a force. AWACS will probably also be brought into CEC.

Plans call for the integration of CEC into ships possessing only local defense weapons, mainly to provide cueing. Thus an LHA provided with ACDS Block 1 would have a combat-direction LAN. Elements on this LAN would include SSDS (with separate self-defense weapon and sensor correlation elements) and CEC. Thus the CEC picture would, in theory, be available to the ship's SSDS. Presumably much the same idea applies to a carrier.

The current shipboard system weighs 9393 lb, including four cabinets (high- and low-power amplifiers, processor, and CEP cabinet), the access and directive antennas, and data recorders. A lightweight common equipment set is being developed (its EDM is to be tested in 1997). The shipboard version is cut to a single cabinet and a single directive antenna (total 2353 lb). The corresponding airborne equipment (to be available in 1998, using an active aperture antenna) weighs 525 lb, and so meets the requirement for E-2C installation.

Critical technologies for the CEC are (a) MMIC (monolithic microwave integrated circuit) for the phased array, to cut system weight by 4000 lb (a prototype on the P-3 showed a world record 35% power-added efficiency); (b) ASICs to cut circuit cards by over 50%; and (c) new-generation microprocessors based on the PowerPC chip.

CEC was Phase III of an ongoing battle group AAW coordination (BGAAWC) program, Phase I of which sought to solve the problem of creating a common grid (gridlock) for a force; without good gridlock ships cannot use one another's data. By 1986 an SPS-48 detection data converter had been tested and deployed. A surface-gridlock system was installed on board the *Ticonderoga* class, solving a 20-yr-old problem. An airborne-gridlock system was under test on board an E-2C. Air gridlock was demonstrated in the *Vinson* battle group, and Aegis autogridlock technology was transferred to non-Aegis ships. BGAAWC Phase II concerned force-control items to place weapons on target, for example, improved gridlock using the GPS satellites and improved Aegis displays.

FACT, force AAW coordinating technology, is a related program which developed auto-identification techniques, silent gridlock, and FTEWA. FTEWA is described as a decision aid that predicts engagement effectiveness versus deployment options. It also provides a very high-resolution 3D track picture, in perspective, of a selected area; the targets are shaped to indicate their identification (using a planned precision-identification system). The FTEWA picture, developed by the Johns Hopkins Applied Physics Laboratory, is particularly attractive because it seems to promise the solution to the difficult tactical problem demonstrated when USS *Vincennes* shot down the Iranian Airbus. However, as in many other computer applications, it acts only on the information provided, and it enjoys no special imaging capability.

◆ DANCS

Lockheed Martin's Distributed Advanced Naval Combat System is Aegis for frigates, using the Aegis WCS. It exploits a new U.S. Navy willingness to export Aegis technology. As of early 1995, Spain was reportedly interested in DANCS for its F100-class AAW frigate, and DANCS had been offered to Australia for the FFG-7-class upgrade. On 6 December 1994 Germany formally selected DANCS as a fall-back in the event the Dutch active phased-array radar (APAR) was not ready in time for the new F124 class. DANCS would exploit the open distributed microprocessor-based architecture currently planned for later Aegis baselines.

◆ FFISTS

Frigate Integrated Shipboard Tactical System, a distributed combat system for *Knox*-class frigates using four DTC I computers, is in effect a poor man's NTDS. Like JOTS, this program was run by the Naval Ocean Systems Center (NOSC) at San Diego; it was conceived by a NOSC employee, Mike Pastore. One of the computers acts as a two-way Link 11 terminal and as the track supervisor. It can accept processed radar data from a SPA-25G radar console. A second computer is responsible for data fusion. A third is responsible for the sonars: it is the interface with the active (SQS-26) and passive (SQR-18) sonars, conducting performance prediction and noise monitoring. The fourth computer conducts TMA for the towed array (the software is called automatic TMA for tactical commanders, ATTAC). The four computers are linked by their access to a shared resource monitor (SRM), essentially a large hard disk, via Hewlett-Packard connectors (HP-IB links). The system can accept Link 14, intelligence, and OTCIXS messages, presumably via the data-fusion computer.

FFISTS appeared in the mid-1980s as a rapid-prototyping project; the first ship fitted with it was the USS *Harold E. Holt*. A total of nine were installed (on board FF 1078, 1079, 1084, 1085, 1089, 1090, 1095, and 1097). FFISTS was removed from most frigates when they were decommissioned, but the frigates of this group transferred to Taiwan (FF 1073, 1086, 1087) did not retain their FFISTS. As of late 1995 EDO was trying to sell FFISTS to Taiwan. Alternatives were Loral Librascope's Surface Ship Integrated Combat System and Unisys's (now Loral) combat-direction upgrade (using UYQ-70). The Egyptians had FFISTS retained in one *Knox*-class frigate they obtained, and had it reinstalled in the other.

A planned second-generation FFISTS, using DTC II computers, never materialized.

◆ COMDAC/ICES

The Unisys (Paramax) Command, Display, and Control and Integrated Cutter Electronics System for WMEC-270-class (*Bear* class) Coast Guard cutters, COMDAC is a two-seat bridge console system, each station of which has two CRTs (showing alphanumerics, graphics [synthetic video], radar/graphics, and closed-circuit TV [e.g., to observe a landing helicopter]). The computer is probably a UYK-44, as in the now-extinct HYCATS from which this system was derived. This system is being superseded by one based on JMCIS.

◆ LCAC Command/Surveillance System

Paramax integrates this system for the LCAC: navigation/collision avoidance, surface search radar, and voice communications; it displays heading, pitch, roll, speed, and drift angle. A prototype navigation data integrator provides a workstation to display radar and navigational data.

◆ RADDS (SPQ-12)

Radar Data Distribution System is a rudimentary CDS built out of SPA-25G consoles, probably broadly analogous to the British Kelvin-Hughes system. It is being developed on an evolutionary prototype basis by the Naval Surface Weapons Center at Dahlgren for Navsea 62X, for ships without computer TDSs. RADDS was conceived by Cardion (which devised SPA-25G) for test purposes. The production version is being developed by Frontier Engineering and Sechan Electronics (which now makes SPA-25G). RADDS has an interface to NTCS-A, and can designate targets to a Mk 92 FCS (as in some Coast Guard cutters) via a synchro output. It also has an interface with Link 11, either via the low-cost Link 11 Display System (LEDS) being developed by West Coast NRAD (NCOSS), or via the EDO Link 11 in Coast Guard cutters. As of 1994, the Link 11 interface was one-way (outgoing), but a two-way interface is now being developed. All ships lacking computer CDSs are to be fitted with RADDS as soon as their elderly radar displays are replaced by SPA-25Gs. RADDS provides navigation services, but is also used for tracking and air control.

Enhanced RADDS (ERADDS) employs multiple SPA-25Gs netted together and will use two-way Link 11. The PC-clone (USQ-69) used for Link 11 display has a touch panel for database queries, for example, for IFF.

Radar video is fed through a scan converter (CV-3989/SP) to a switchboard (SB-4229A). Own-ship analog data (heading, dead-reckoning, synchro antenna heading) goes to converters, which produce a 64-bit/sec RADDS data stream. Both video and digital stream go into a SPA-25G display, which acts like a tactical summary. It can take three video outputs, can view two of the three, and can maintain a track file database (TFDB: range, bearing, course, speed) for up to 64 target tracks plus fixed points (99 total).

The switchboard, which includes the RADDS controller, can also be connected to tactical computers and to IFF systems. Similarly, it can feed either SPA-25Gs or other display systems.

The associated LEDS employs software running on a PC-clone (USQ-69, using an 80386 processor) or, now, a TAC-3, which communicates with the MX-512 and KG-40 crypto units. It is on many ships, such as the flagship *Mount Whitney* and Atlantic Fleet TAGOS surveillance ships.

As a whole, RADDS can now accommodate up to 16 radar inputs and 16 display outputs. Upgrades include a touch-screen panel showing network status and a 19in CIC display. Planned future improvements include a GPS interface, collision avoidance system, integrated mapping, and BFTT (battle force tactical training) modules.

◆ SYQ-12

Unisys (Paramax) combat system for Egyptian route survey vessel and coastal minehunter, with associated shore-based mine-warfare data center. This system is also on board the U.S. MSOs stricken and sold to Taiwan.

◆ SYQ-13

Paramax combat system for the new *Cardinal* (MHC 51) -class minehunter. The system is tied together by a triple-redundant serial data bus, fed by three data-acquisition units (for the sonar and SLQ-48 mine neutralization vehicle). It is connected to a pair of consoles in the CIC, a single console in the pilot house (for ship control and for the SSQ-109 integrated machinery control system), and a pair of consoles in the central (machinery) control station.

SYQ-13 software is derived from that of SYQ-12.

SSQ-109 is derived from the machinery/ship control system of the Canadian frigates (*Halifax* class).

◆ H930/MCS/CDCS

The Modular Combat System is the only U.S.-produced distributed surface-ship combat system. It was developed by Honeywell and then sold (in 1988) to Hughes. Hughes has continued development and may also be working on a separate small-ship (fast-attack-boat) system. Hughes is currently marketing an advanced version, MCS 2000, based on the H930 concept but using much more powerful processors. Five versions are currently in service: H930 Mods 0, 1, 2, and 3, and MCS. The designation H930 refers to the system's origin as an extended version of the Kollmorgen Mk 93 FCS. The first version, Mod 0, was not particularly modular, but later ones were.

The fully modular system (MCS) is built up of nodes called data control units (DCUs), each with its own local (resource) processor (a UYK-19) and an I/O controller (IOC). Any DCU can perform any particular function, that is, it can be loaded with any system program. Each DCU can function independently because the associated IOC periodically moves device data into the resource processor and draws data from it for processing into messages for the other DCUs. Because the IOC can access the resource computer's memory without the latter's intervention, the resource computer can be programmed with little or no concern for overall system operation. Its program is truly modular; changes in the program have no effect on other parts of the system. This modularity is achieved without using any special language, such as ADA (which was developed after H930 had been completed). Honeywell (Hughes) argued that in a more tightly coupled system, an increasing fraction of the power of each of several linked computers is drained into coordination. In the H930 the limit on system power is bus capacity.

Software written for any application can be modified freely for another because such changes do not affect other portions of the system. For example, a standard ballistic program was written using a different set of coefficients for each gun. Such standardization greatly reduces the labor of programming, and it also makes programming errors much less likely. Moreover, changes to adapt to a new gun or a new type of ammunition require only revision of the table of coefficients. The tabular technique also makes it possible for operators to modify system operation relatively simply. For example, threat ranking can be modified by changing a table that weights various parameters describing a particular target. Such modification has no effect on the operation of other programs within the overall system, yet it can greatly change the way the ship reacts to a particular situation.

The system uses two redundant buses, each of which has a capacity of about 2.5 Mbit/sec. Typically, the global bus handles 20 messages/sec, and it is shielded from more than 100 messages/sec. That is practical because sensors that produce high raw-data rates filter their data through their own processors (e.g., ADT in the case of a radar).

Messages (variable length, up to 128 16-bit words) are transmitted in time slots. Each DCU is assigned a sequence number, which it applies to its bus messages. When an IOC reads a message passing through, it adds one to the sequence number, transmitting only when it reaches its own assigned number. This method would fail in the event an IOC failed, so each IOC is assigned a time-out period, during which it waits before transmitting in the event the bus is quiet. There is no system time standard. Instead, each DCU has its own clock, and each message includes the DCU's clock time, which is used to the clock of each DCU that receives it.

Although they are distributed systems, both Mod 1 and 2 (and possibly Mod 0) concentrate their DCUs in operator consoles, in effect in local networks (typically two function modules, such as radar and launcher, with a control module). Overheating was also a problem, since all five system computers were packaged in two consoles. In both systems, particular computers were tied to particular functions. The MCS (Taiwanese Wu-Jinn III program) is fully modular, partly because it had to adapt to a number of different ship configurations. In this case each DCU can, in theory, perform any system function.

Versions:

Mod 0 (1975): fast patrol boat version, with two consoles (one minicomputer each, for air and surface warfare but either can engage any target) and five microprocessors. The two main computers are mutually supportive, that is, they are not independent. Sensors: SPS-58 air-search radar, HC 75 surface-search radar, W-120 tracker, Mk 35 optical director (part of Mk 93 FCS). Weapons: 76mm gun, Emerlec-30 gun, Harpoon. *Users:* On board five South Korean PSMM Mk 5 patrol boats (operational November 1978).

Mod 1 (1976) used five UYK-19s in two operator consoles, connected by a bus, plus a command console. Each operator console in turn was connected to combat-system elements such as radars, guns, and missiles. There were also 23 microprocessors. Console 1 was fed by the ESM sensor, the Mk 35, and one of the two trackers; it was wired directly to the surface-to-surface missiles, to the 76mm gun, and to one each of the two 5in/38 and 40mm mounts. Console 2 was fed by the air/surface-search radar and the second tracker; it was wired to the other twin 5in/38 mount and the second 40mm mount. The effect of the system bus was to allow the consoles to exchange data. Sensors: SPS-10/58 (digital ATD in SPS-58), SPS-55 (TWS processor), two HR-76 trackers, Mk 35 optical director (with LLLTV camera and laser RF), and an ESM receiver. Weapons: two 5in/38 gun mounts, one 76mm gun, two 40mm guns, and SAM (Sea Chaparral) and

SYQ-13 on board a minehunter, with the two tactical display consoles in the foreground, and the X-Y plotter at right. The units in the background are sensor and ROV controls. Each console is built around a 12-slot VME bus carrying up to four processors (68020s with 68881 math coprocessors) and 4 to 24 Mbytes of memory, for processing speeds of up to 6 MIPS. The associated graphics generator (768 × 1024 or 1024 × 1024 or 1024 × 1280 pixels) can support two independent monitor drivers, with four graphics planes (expandable to eight) per driver, producing 16 colors and 50,000 vectors and 5,000 characters/sec. Software uses the VRTX operating system. (Unisys)

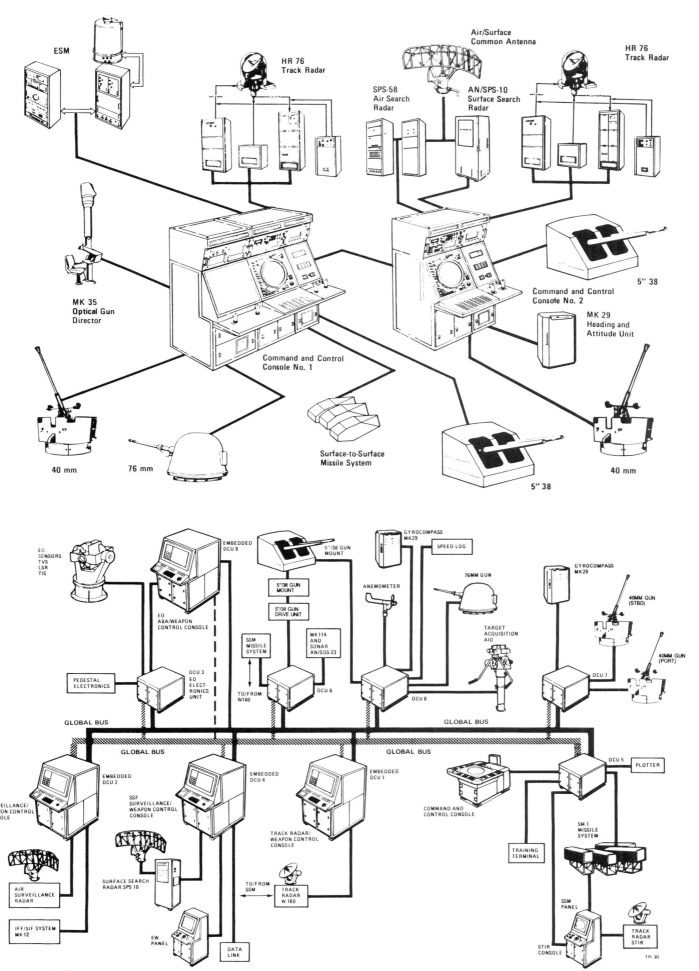

Two versions of the H930 system illustrated the transition from distributed to fully modular operation: Mod 1 at top, Mod 4 at bottom. (Hughes Ground Systems)

SSM (Hsiung Feng I) missiles. The Mod 1 system was designed so that it could be expanded to accommodate ASW weapons and sensors and so that it could accept a data link. This system is credited with a capacity for eight simultaneous surface/air tracks (it can engage three targets simultaneously). Given one target track, the computer typically takes 4 sec to evaluate a second report. If the second is more threatening, the computer takes 10–18 sec to slew onto that new target. Against a low-flying target, with the HR-76 director initially centered in a 60-deg sector, reaction time from the arrival of the antenna at the designated position (0.75–2 sec after SPS-58 detection) is 6–12.5 sec (10 sec average). Net reaction time may be 20 sec or more. This system was installed on board 13 ex-U.S. destroyers of the Taiwan navy, rebuilt under Weapon Improvement Program Phase I (*Wu-Jinn I*).

Mod 2 (November 1980) is Mod 1 adapted to a 50m patrol boat, with four rather than five UYK-19 in two consoles (and 19 microprocessors). Sensors: SPS-58, LN-66, one HR-76 tracker, Mk 35, ESM receiver. Weapons: one 76mm and one 40mm gun and Hsiung Feng SSMs.

Users: Two Taiwanese *Lung Chiang* (PSMM Mk 5) patrol boats.

Mod 3: One-console (two UYK-19, 11 microprocessors; three operators) land-based coast defense system. Sensors: one surface-search radar, one HR-76 tracker, one optical director. Weapon: Hsiung Feng I SSM. Five were delivered to Taiwan, beginning in March 1980.

MCS: Fully distributed version for Taiwanese Wu-Jinn III destroyers. There are four operator consoles (EO/weapons control, AAW/surveillance/weapons control, surface surveillance/weapons control, and track radar/weapons control), plus a horizontal command/control console and a computer-driven plotter. In some cases data are passed through the console into the global bus, but each console can execute any function. Thus, the air-search-radar data and the IFF data pass through the AAW console; EW, surface-search-radar, and data-link data pass through the surface console. Overall capacity: 24 tracks (including underwater), four simultaneously engaged (reaction time about 8 sec). Sensors: DA-08 air-search radar (with DA-05 antenna), SPS-10/58A, W-160 tracker, Signaal STIR tracker, a Honeywell-developed EO sensor, a data link, Chang Feng III ESM (derived from the Hughes SLQ-31), and a Krupp-Atlas DSQS-21 sonar. Weapons: a 76mm gun, two single 40mm L70 guns, ASROC ASW missiles, lightweight ASW torpedoes (shipboard and carried by an MD 500 helicopter), and SM-1 surface-to-air missiles. ASW weapons are controlled through a Mk 114 (analog) FCS, which was supplied when the ships were transferred by the U.S. Navy.

MCS was designed to accommodate upgrades. Honeywell (and then Hughes) tested a four-DCU system. The operating system as a whole was rewritten to accommodate ADA software (it was originally written in Algol), and one ADA DCU was incorporated into the test system. In addition, one of the four DCUs had its processor replaced by the processor of the more powerful ROLM 1666 (the new processor is designated ROLM 1822). The new processor is about five times faster than the existing unit and has 16 times the memory capacity. Yet it occupies a circuit board compatible with those of the earlier Mod 3 system and, thus, can be used to upgrade existing ships.

Elements of MCS are in service in Egypt and Taiwan. In Egyptian *Descubiertas* it is responsible for data links (YE and Z), for TWS capability, for Harpoon, and for EW integration. In the Taiwanese *Perry* class, MCS is responsible for SSM and 40mm gunfire control.

Users: Egypt (elements in *Descubiertas*), Taiwan (Wu-Jinn destroyers, *Lung Chiang* class).

ACS (Advanced Combat System) or MCS 2000 was offered to Taiwan for the abortive Flight 2 frigates, but it was not adopted. The destroyer MCS may be installed on board a new series of Taiwanese gunboats, as the destroyers are withdrawn from service.

In 1992 Hughes announced an open-architecture H930 combat direction and control system (CDCS) built around a dual 100 Mbit/sec FDDI network carrying a series of VME-based workstations. Each workstation is fed directly by one or more sensors, and all of the ship weapons are connected directly to the FDDI. In a published diagram, the workstations are ORTS (operational recording test, no sensor inputs), ASUWC (surface search radars), ASWC (sonars, via the sonar operator console), ASAC (ASW aircraft control: helicopter link), TAO/CO (IFF and air search radar), AAWC (laser warner and 3D radar), three tracker/weapons control consoles (bridge pointers and tracker/illuminator radars for two, a tracker/EO for the third), EW (EW and IRST), and TS/DL (tactical data link and external communications).

The two-screen workstations are based on the OJ-663 proposed to the U.S. Navy (and rejected in favor of UYQ-70), using 68040 processors (and some embedded 68030s) and the OJ-663 graphics engine, but with a new scan converter (for both radar and TV images). Software includes TDAs as well as the usual picture-keeping and engagement elements. Outline maps, intelligence databases, and digital imagery can also be stored and called up. Thus CDCS is somewhat analogous to later versions of ACDS/NTCS-A. Screens are all capable of displaying both alphanumeric and tactical data, the former in windows. Similarly, tactical pictures can be overlaid. For example, a standard PPI picture can be displayed together with a range-altitude picture below it.

Software is partitioned into standardized weapon, sensor, and command/control packages, each forming a largely independent subsystem. Sensor processors report only tracks, not individual contacts, responding to standardized command/control queries (the local processor interprets the query as it applies to that sensor). Data control is in effect distributed, and modules can be added or subtracted with little effect on each other.

◆ ITACS

EDO's Integrated Tactical Command System is an outgrowth of FFISTS. A typical system might consist of four DTC IIs in a LAN (Ethernet or fiber-optic network), feeding a large-screen display and other remote displays. The DTCs would be a track supervisor (connected to the ship's radar and her communications system [for data links]), a localization (TMA) console, an environmental/sonar console (connected to the sonars), and the ship's weapons coordinator console, connected to the weapons system. EDO clearly sees ITACS as an inexpensive way of modernizing ships either lacking computerized CDSs or with obsolete systems.

EDO suggests ITACS for a variety of platforms: the U.S. *Adams*, *Knox*, and *Hamilton* classes, which lack any computer combat systems (and the first two of which are being transferred to foreign navies); and the *Spruance* and *Perry* classes, which have combat systems but many of which have not yet been fitted with SQQ-89 (FFISTS is broadly equivalent to parts of SQQ-89).

◆ Cardion MCDS

Modular Combat Display System is a small-combatant CDS based on the video processors Cardion developed for the SPA-25G and SPA-50G radar consoles. It is, then, broadly analogous to RADDS (see above). In 1990, when it was announced, Cardion stated that it had been in production for a friendly navy for some time, as a subset of a larger CDS. Most likely it is made for Israel, as part of the *Eilat* system. As Racal's CANE and CTC demonstrate, the gap between an ADT radar console and a full CDS is narrow.

In MCDS, a 1553B bus carries sensor data to vertical operator consoles (19in color or 23in monochrome monitors, 1365 × 1024 pixels) and a horizontal three-man command console (23in monochrome monitor, 1024 × 1024 pixels). Each console contains a microprocessor (dual 68000-based units, with 32 kwords of 16-bit RAM and 32 kwords of 16-bit EPROM), a video processor (scan converter with three to five memory planes, for three to five sensor pictures simultaneously), and a graphics processor (three or four memory planes, i.e., separate pictures, with 8 or 16 colors/region). The system carries 256 programmable symbols. There are eight range settings (2.5–320 nm). Consoles can also incorporate separate applications processors, for example, a sonar signal processor.

Users: Israel (part of *Eilat* system), and Singapore (*Victory* class).

◆ Korean Naval Command System (KN-NTDS)

Litton's system, the contract for which was awarded in July 1989, uses Link 11 to connect three *Ulsan*-class frigates (one console each) to a shore headquarters (FCC, with seven consoles). The frigates in turn act as leaders for groups of smaller craft (but as yet there is no requirement for a ROLE, which would allow the smaller units to accept the frigate's tactical picture). The object of the system is to detect and intercept small coastal craft trying to penetrate South Korean coastal waters, particularly infiltrators and intelligence-gatherers from the North. The FCC is fed by five shore radars over two links (Link 11 and the HF ISDL, intersite data link). The FCC is also connected to the main air control center (MCRC, master control reporting center).

The system will also be installed on board the new KDX class.

The basis of the system, the TDC (tactical display console), is widely used by the U.S. Air Force and the National Guard in the antidrug war. It is a gateway for multiple data links (TADIL-A, TADIL-B, ATDL [a missile link from command to battery], Link 1), using packet-switching technology. The TDC is built around a VME bus carrying three single-board computers (SBC), each comprising a 68030, a math coprocessor, and 4 Mbytes of DRAM. One is the control processor; the other two are used for track control, link control, track position, and related functions. Function distribution is controlled by software, to keep any one SBC from being overloaded. The bus can also carry a separate global memory board, I/O boards (which can connect to modems through which the Links are received), and a graphic controller, whose output appears on a 19in color monitor (1280 × 1024 pixels, range scales 2–2048 nm). One of the SBCs can connect to floppy and hard disk drives. The console can carry up to 1024 tracks, bearing lines, EW strobes, and pointers, and it can drive a large-screen display. Litton offers the TDC in both portable and stand-alone form.

The TDC display incorporates a transparent touch panel (TTP). Such construction entirely eliminates the need for trackballs, joysticks, or light pens. Internally, the global memory and graphics controller feed into a VME bus, which in turn feeds the system-control and situation-control (data-filtering) processors and the interface- and link-control processors. The console is designed to grow to accept a 25in color monitor. The same Litton TDC was a TADIL-A (Link 11) receive-only terminal on board the battleship *Iowa*, where it also drove a large-screen display and two remote monitors. Similar consoles (OJ-656) were later installed on board LHD 1 and CG 20 and at U.S. naval shore stations. The first such console was delivered in 1990.

A closely related two-screen console is used in the SSQ-91 Combat Simulation Test System. It is very similar to the Korean system's tactical coordination console (TCC).

◆ Loral Surface Ship Integrated Combat Control System

Loral Librascope's modular system, based on its submarine CDSs, has been offered to Taiwan to upgrade *Knox*-class frigates. It competes with EDO's FFISTS 2. Loral sometimes describes its system as an upgraded Mk 114. A LAN carries the three basic elements: the combat-data manager (picture-keeping computer and, in effect, switchboard), one or more multifunction workstations (MWS), and a computer-driven command plot, which is presumably used for TMA calculations. All sensor data, including sonar data, are routed into the combat-data manager, and it is connected to all the surface weapons. The display/analysis side of the Mk 114 system (Mk 53 attack console) is replaced by a digital workstation, the MWS. The MWS provides the usual data for the weapon interface and signal converter (digital/analog) elements of the Mk 53, which directly controls the Asroc and surface torpedo tubes.

However, the workstation is much more. It receives data-link data (presumably including that from helicopters) directly, and

carries the system's tactical picture and its contact management system (CMS). It fuses all data, including ESM and radar, to construct a complete tactical picture, and it is used to generate weapons orders for all of the ship's weapons. The LAN architecture of the system makes it possible to supplement the main MWS with others, to support simultaneous engagements against, for example, air and underwater targets. The MWS can fuse data link, sonar (under-the-horizon), and ESM (OTH) data to support an OTH missile strike. MWS capabilities include a sonar performance estimator.

The workstation or stations provide capabilities such as automated TMA (e.g., maximum likelihood estimators [MLEs], Ekelund ranging, bearing/Doppler, and Speiss), TDAs (screen planning; maneuvering tools such as CPA calculation, torpedo danger areas, and limiting lines of approach); missile/strike planning for OTH-T (which might be based on sonar data); and navigational improvements. Plotting is automatic (the usual plotting team is reduced from six to two). The system bus can accommodate additional systems. The data manager automatically constructs a tactical picture including radar, ESM, and sonar data. The system includes a sonar performance predictor.

At a minimum, installation requires modification to the existing Mk 53 attack console, replacement of the existing DRT (by the new command plotter), and addition of the single-cabinet combat-data manager, plus installation of a new LAN.

◆ Raytheon ICS

Raytheon announced a new integrated combat system at the March 1991 U.S. Navy League show. The company hopes to use the CDS design and integration expertise built up during the NAAWS effort to develop and sell core systems of its own. Its work includes the track management and TEWA software required for combat direction, and a series of new consoles that can be adapted to an advanced bus to form a distributed and reconfigurable combat system. The question then will be which element, the core or the missile, is the limiting factor in overall system reaction time or defensive capability. At present the kinematics of the Sea Sparrow missile limit existing systems much more than their core architecture. The solution would be to use the tail-controlled version with a new motor. Once the missile is fixed, then it becomes more important to provide the new core.

ICS is a fully distributed combat system using a pair of buses (port and starboard) that communicate with sensors, weapons, and support systems via a series of system interface subsystems (SIUs). The command and display subsystem will have four to ten consoles, one to two plotters, and one to two hard-copy terminals. Processing will be done by a series of computers tied to the same bus, with two mass storage units and one to two tape units. The baseline system processor is a MIPS RISC machine running a POSIX-compliant operating system and incorporating a VME-type backplane. It can be upgraded to the next-generation Futurebus + backplane. Each multifunction display console carries one or two screens and a single keyboard; it is driven by a MIPS R2000 display processor. The displays are militarized versions of the Silicon Graphics (SCI) Personal IRIS workstations and, thus, are related to the CCS Mk 2 consoles that Raytheon has already developed for submarine use. The system bus is either Ethernet or the fiber-optic standard (FDDI) in its militarized form (Safenet II).

◆ Modular Improvement Packages

Unisys announced a variety of potential *Knox*-class upgrades (for export customers) in 1995. As transferred, the ships lack a computer-driven CDS. Unisys offered to install a pair of UYQ-70 workstations (ADS) on a dual-FDDI LAN. One would be for the track supervisor (TRK SUP), the other for the weapons coordinator (WCO). The usual detector/tracker consoles would be eliminated by using automatic radar detection and tracking. Unisys offered to consolidate search radars, weapons, and the EW system into groups reporting to LAN access units (LAUs), each of which would communicate with the CDS LAN. For example, in a proposed AAW upgrade, the surface and air search radars

(SPS-10/67/58 and SPS-40) would report to the radar LAU; the gun, a RAM launcher, a vertical Sea Sparrow launcher, the Mk 92 FCS ("egg" only), and the Harpoon system would all report to the weapons LAU. ASW functions would be separate, but would be connected to the combat-direction LAN. The SLQ-32 ESM system would report via an EW LAN.

As of the fall of 1995, no such package had been ordered, but (except for Turkey) navies operating the *Knox* class have not invested in any other improvement packages either.

Unisys has offered a related open-architecture combat system for the Australian *Perry*-class upgrade program. In this case a UYQ-70 replaces each existing UYA-4 combat-direction console. The workstations are connected to a dual-fiber-optic LAN, which in turn is connected to ship sensors (including the Mk 92 FCS) and to the picture-keeping computer (presumably the existing UYK-7) via LAUs. Additional wiring is minimized. The UYQ-70s can either emulate dumb UYA-4 terminals, or they can add substantial new capability; at the least, they will take over some of the graphics load currently carried by the UYK-7 central computer. This arrangement is not too different from that envisaged in ACDS Block 1 Level 2, although presumably the software would have to be quite different.

Loral Unisys is currently marketing a wholly distributed combat system as FaCS (Family of Command Systems). A typical system might use five consoles: two for surveillance/tracking, one for situation assessment/operations summary, one for system control/communications (link) control, and one for threat evaluation/engagement planning. All would be connected to a LAN, to which other ship elements (such as sensors and weapons) would be connected.

◆ Vision 2100M

Sperry Marine's command/control system is currently used on board the U.S. *Cyclone* (PC-1) class and is the core of the company's Naval Integrated Bridge System. Because the CDS is based on a voyage management system, the basic display is a chart showing own-ship position, which can be overlaid with windows (for detailed information) and with other ship tracks. The primary system components are the voyage management system (VMS) workstation, the target correlator/position filter module (TC/PFM), the TAO workstation, all in CIC; and the situation display workstation on the bridge. They are connected by an Ethernet/FDDI LAN.

The TAO workstation contains both the TAO computer and computers for situation display and for TC/PFM. The VMS workstation includes not only a VMS computer, but also a chaff launcher control panel and the electronics for the RASCAR navigational radar. All three workstations have 19in high-resolution color monitors with touchscreens, 1.44-Mbyte disk drives (plus a 1.2-Mbyte 5.25in drive in the TAO console and a CD-ROM in the VMS module), and paired hard disks (one for data logs, one for digitized charts, navlines, voyage plan data, and the operating system). All the computers use 80486 CPUs. In the Captain's Cabin is a 386 computer with a 14in color monitor, which can operate either independently or as a slave to the situation display workstation on the bridge.

The VMS workstation can be switched between mission-planning and radar-display modes. The TAO workstation can share situation-display video (and the situation display on the bridge can be switched to TAO video). For maintenance, the TAO monitor can be switched to the TC/PFM.

This is fundamentally a navigational system (VMS 1000 Voyage Management System) with a target correlator attached to it. The correlator integrates all sensor (RASCAR radar, FLIR, LLLTV) data into a single target list keyed to the electronic chart, which is the basis of the ship's tactical picture. This picture is also fed by a retractable sidescan sonar which is usable below 12 kt, for enhanced sounding and limited minehunting. Target threat level is set manually (as hostile, neutral, unknown, or friendly). The target correlator calculates CPA/TCPA and paths to intercept targets.

The primary C^2 display shows the chart and own-ship position, course and speed vector, and track history, based on the

operator's selected navigational sensor (the identity of which is displayed alongside). Similar choices apply to heading source, speed source, and set and drift source. The main display also shows wind sensor and engine-room data. The TC/PFM automatically integrates and weights sensor data to find its own best estimate of ship's position, heading, speed, set and drift, which is shown as a selection alongside the outputs of other sensors.

Windows on the basic chart include video (FLIR, sonar, or remote inputs such as those from a boarding party), radar/chart, navigation (with route plan and ARPA targets), precise anchoring, man overboard, and engineering (showing machinery data).

VMS supports waypoint navigation (up to 240 waypoints per voyage), calculating the usual steering parameters: heading-to-steer, cross-track errors, distance-to-go, and estimated time of arrival. It can be used to compare alternative voyage options. The VMS workstation is also used to digitize existing paper charts, which are stored on its hard disk.

The bus design of the system accommodates gateways to external data sources (such as OTH-T data) and to a future automated weapons system.

DISPLAYS

◆ CDS/NTDS Display Systems

The current standard Hughes UYA-4 is being superseded by the Hughes UYQ-21. UYQ-21 is also the standard display for several other systems. The follow-on system is the Advanced Display System, UYQ-70. RNTDS Emulation System (RNTDES) uses UYQ-21 hardware to emulate UYA-4, which is becoming more difficult to maintain. RNTDES was included in the FY93 program.

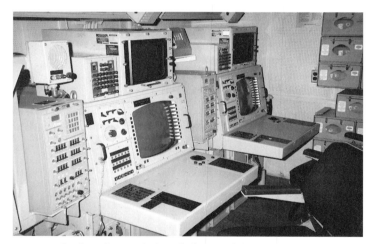

UYQ-21 displays (OJ-451) aboard the amphibious carrier *Kearsarge*. (E. Grove)

The CIC of the amphibious carrier *Kearsarge* shows, at left, an OJ-535 single-monitor console of the UYQ-21 system. Next to it is an OJ-451 console, with an auxiliary monitor atop it. At right is a JOTS console, with maps on its two screens. (E. Grove)

UYA-4 (designed about 1965) introduced integrated circuitry and a standardized console, OJ-194/UYA-4. Each has 18 variable-action buttons (VABs) but also six fixed-action buttons, so that each VAB can adopt up to 48 labels. OJ-194 has 45 operating modes. The system as a whole has 16 radio channels, compared to the 10 of the earlier SYA-4. Hughes announced an OJ-194B console—a color workstation upgrade to the standard dumb OJ-194A—in 1992. It is a simple field change to the earlier console, providing it with a VME bus (12–19 6U and two 9U slots), which can accommodate 68040 processors and an acoustic processor. As modified, it has a 19in color monitor (1280 × 1024 pixels, 60-Hz refresh rate). An electroluminescent panel (5 × 8 in, 640 × 400 pixels) can be added.

UYA-4 includes a large-screen (20in) horizontal summary console, originally OA-7981 and then OJ-195/197. OA-7981 has an internal memory (4k 30-bit words). OJ-195 has an improved display, and OJ-197 has 18 VABs (48 labels) and six fixed-function buttons in place of the action entry panel and rollerball of the earlier console.

The system also employs an OA-7980 height-finding console, with 3 × 5in CRTs (two for height, one for raid size estimation). One CRT shows targets within selectable bearing gates (3, 6, 11, 22 deg), the other targets within selectable range gates of 4, 16, 32, and 64 nm. Each can call up a track by number and can show either full altitude scale (100,000 ft) or low altitude (30,000 ft). The raid-count CRT has selectable range gates (4, 8, 16 nm), azimuth lines (7, 15, 31, 63 deg), and bearing gates (3, 6, 11, 22 deg). Multiple CRTs are needed because the associated radar operates in three dimensions, not the two of a single CRT.

With the CIGARS (console internal generation and refresh system) field change, OJ-194 can create 1000 separate graphic symbols and also has much better ability to generate circles. The 12in-dia CRT has a minimum range scale of 1 nm.

Pre-CIGARS consoles have no internal memory capacity. In their case the UYA-4 system includes a refresh memory unit (RMU), which actually produces the successive screen images at a refresh rate of 15/sec, for flicker-free presentation, via a central pulse amplifier/symbol generator (CPA/SG). All UYA-4s include the CPA, which has two input and two output channels. Each channel can drive 15 consoles. Thus, two computers can drive two groups of up to 15 consoles each, and they can switch between the two. Prior to the advent of the RMU, the central computer had to generate displays directly. The RMU was, then, the earliest attempt to unload a central-computer function onto peripherals.

UYA-4 also includes a radar azimuth converter, CV-2095/UYA-4, for each radar, converting analog range and bearing data to digital form suitable for display on the digitally controlled consoles; the converters also produce the range marks used by the consoles.

A version of the OJ-194 console with CIGARS serves as the display of the SPS-48 and -52C radars. The display is computer driven, and it provides the operator with descriptions, such as land clutter or jamming, automatically selecting the best possible fix.

A full NTDS/WDS installation incorporates two separate types of operator console, one with a single CRT for data input or data utilization, and one (with three smaller CRTs in parallel) for height/size display. The latter, OA-7890/UYA-4, is used to evaluate and supply target height and raid size; two CRTs are range-height indicators, and the third is a size-analysis indicator. The main CRTs are PPIs with a maximum range of 512 nm. In early versions of UYA-4, each is associated with a separate read-out console, carrying a square CRT and providing alphanumeric data on track number, IFF (SIF) code, track bearing and height, track range and speed, threat evaluation, interceptor data, and weapons recommendations. The OJ-194 console combines the two CRTs in one.

UYA-4 is becoming more difficult to maintain. In 1996 SurfLant reported that OJ-197 was one of its worst maintenance problems. OYQ-70s were substituted for three OJ-194s on board the frigate *Clark* in 1994. Corrective maintenance was reduced to a third (2 rather than 6 hr weekly) and preventative mainte-

nance was halved (1 rather than 2 hr weekly). Replacement parts were also far less expensive; a UYQ-70 power supply costs about $7000, compared to $20,000 for the comparable OJ-197 part, which now represents obsolete technology not available on the commercial market.

Hughes's UYQ-21 was derived from experimental (EXDM) vertical and horizontal consoles produced in 1974 and acoustic and TDS vertical consoles of 1976–78. The standard consoles entered production in 1982–83. The HDP-2000 liquid-crystal projector (for large-screen displays) appeared in 1978 and was first applied to a shipboard system in 1980–81 (it is now being adapted to civilian use for large-screen home television). The graphic terminal system appeared in 1983. The acoustic converter, digital TV generator, ASTABs, and digital scan converter all appeared in 1982–83. Hughes's proposed next-generation vertical display, OJ-663, appeared in 1991. The U.S. Navy bought the UYQ-70 workstation instead, but foreign navies may yet choose to upgrade their systems using it.

UYQ-21 is modular; as of 1986, 85% of all electronic card assemblies were used more than once. Operator control panels are standard across all consoles/terminals. Analog and digital interfaces are also standardized.

Consoles within the system are OJ-451/452, OJ-471, OJ-535, OJ-601, and OJ-663; see also the AVP (OJ-653), below. The system also includes the PT-525 liquid-crystal projector described below. UYQ-21 can display 256 unique shapes (64 alphanumerics [ROM], 128 tactical symbols [ROM], and 32 symbol modifiers [ROM], plus 32 computer-programmable symbols [RAM]). Symbols can appear in multiple sizes and intensities, and they can be made to blink to emphasize them. Lines are point to point, velocity vectors, and connected segments. The system can also generate circles, ellipses, and arcs in any size or orientation. All may be dashed, solid, or blinked.

UYQ-21 also includes ASTABs driven by a CAG (central alphanumeric generator) which produces 525-line video: it has 16 separate status display output channels and accepts eight external videos for selection on any output channel. It has programmable formats from 512 to 2048 characters. The image displayed can be remotely selected.

OJ-450 is the basic console. The tactical version, OJ-451, adds an auxiliary display (CRO). The acoustic version, OJ-452, adds a second graphic/sensor display. All use a microprocessor-based architecture for flexibility, growth, and adaptability to varied software environments. The main display is a 13 × 11in (1024 × 1024-pixel) stroke-written (cursive) CRT, which can show synthetic or raw (raster-format) video. It is self-refreshed (16k × 32-bit word memory), with internal text, symbol, vector, conic generators, adapts to vitually any sensor format. Spot size is 0.010 in. Contrast ratio in OJ-451 is 5:1 (3 bits/pixel). Range scale is in 13 binary steps from $\frac{1}{2}$ to 2048 miles or computer defined. It can emulate the OJ-194. OJ-452 has an acoustic display generator (ADG: CV-3550) for each screen; each ADG accommodates up to 2 Mbits of memory to refresh the display. The associated contrast ratio is 12:1 (4 bits/pixel). Dimensions: OJ-451: 56H × 29W × 40D (weight 700 lb, power 1.5 kW). OJ-452: 61H × 29W × 40D (900 lb); power 3.1 kW (400Hz).

OJ-451 is used in Aegis systems and in recent NTDS installations. There is also an OJ-451 bright bridge display with a radar scan converter and special CRT phosphor. The digital scan converter enhances radar video presentation. Among other ASW applications, OJ-452 is used in shipboard LAMPS installations.

The degree of centralization depends on the number of consoles. Up to eight OJ-451s can be fed directly by an NTDS computer and radar switchboard. For 8–15 consoles, the system typically adds a central data buffer (CDB) with software-controlled switch and data-distribution functions, which can accommodate up to six computers and 40 displays. Large systems generally have two CDBs, for redundancy.

OJ-535 is an alternative monitor, for systems employing digital-television (DTV) technology, which includes raster-scan radars. It can also emulate UYA-4 displays. The (V)1 and (V)2 versions are single-screen; (V)3 is two-screen. It is the high-resolution raster-scan (1280 × 1024 or 1024 × 1024 pixels,

OJ-535 displays on board the Aegis cruiser *Philippine Sea* at Kiel, June 1995. (H&L van Ginderen)

selectable on the front panel) display of the system, measuring 13 × 11 in (17in diagonal). Frame refresh rate is 30 Hz (2:1 interlaced) or 60 Hz (525 lines). Current consoles are monochrome, but three-color 19in units are replacing them. Up to 4000 characters can be displayed (Type I has the same symbology as OJ-451; Type II is fully programmable). Symbols can be in four sizes and in two intensity levels (solid and blinking). The console has five input channels, three for composite video and two for composite or noncomposite video. Dimensions: 20 (height) × 29 (width) × 44 (depth) (weight 200 lb).

A group of OJ-535s is fed by a DITEG (digital television generator) with six graphic channels, each 1024 × 1024 or 1280 × 1024; monochrome or RGB color, six 525-line tabular channels with EDIT, 2 × 1024 × 1024 monochrome LSD projector channels, and two hard-copy unit channels. There is also a single-drawer DITEG module, providing one 1280 × 1024 graphic channel and one 525-line tabular channel. Both include area fill with shading or color, and full UYQ-21 symbols/graphics/text.

OJ-535 is used in cruiser and carrier CDSs (non-Aegis). In a mixed installation, OJ-451s are used in positions requiring sensor data and OJ-535 in nonsensor positions.

The OJ-451/2 and -535 consoles are all equipped with keyboards, with trackballs, with a computer-controlled action entry panel (3 × 6 switches), with 20 variable function keys, and with a separate 6 × 7 array alongside the keyboard.

OJ-451 and OJ-535 exist both in single-screen versions and in versions with 12in CROs (CRT read-out: IP-1357) above the main screen. The CRO is a 525-line TV monitor (to show up to 2048 characters in a 64-character font or 525-line external closed-circuit television).

OJ-471 controls the large-screen display (LSD), the light for which is projected by a PT-525 liquid-crystal unit. It is a synthetic video unit (the LSD cannot show raw video). The controller has a 525-line alphanumeric display (2048 characters in 25 × 80 or 32 × 64 format) and an auxiliary 525-line composite video input; it can edit off-line. The console shows a small screen flanked by standard controls. In a typical command display system (e.g., on board an Aegis cruiser), the system computer drives a single six-drawer cabinet, which connects to ASTAB monitors, six OJ-535s, two PT-525s, and two hard-copy units.

OJ-601 is the group operations console, a horizontal table intended to replace the OJ-197 of earlier NTDS systems. The screen uses a 1000-line high-brightness projector (as in PT-525) with gray-scale shading, compatible with 1075-line composite video TV formats. OJ-601 can display radar images. Tactical images can be projected through and registered to nautical charts.

OJ-663 is a workstation intended to replace the OJ-450 series. It carries a touch pad, a keyboard, a trackball, and a 19in color monitor (1280 × 1024 pixels). This console uses X-windows software with real-time tactical extensions (e.g., it can show real-time radar video and NTDS synthetic video simultaneously).

In NTDS applications, UYA-4 radar and beacon video processors and the tactical-system computers (via a data converter, OL-191) feed a switchboard connected to the tactical display consoles (OJ-450/451).

In an acoustic display system, sonars feed acoustic-system computers, which feed an acoustic-data converter (OL-190) for display on OJ-452 consoles.

In the command display system (LSD), command-system computers and the OL-191 data converter feed a TV converter (OL-224), which feeds the group operations console (OJ-601), the AS-TAB monitors, and the terminals: graphics terminals (OJ-535), the large-screen projectors (PT-525), and LSD controllers (OJ-471).

Aegis ships and some others now have large-screen projection displays, PT-525/UYQ-21, as part of their UYQ-21 display systems. Aegis cruisers have four projection displays; Aegis destroyers (*Arleigh Burke* class) each have two. LSDs are also being installed on board carriers, as part of their TFCCs (two each), and on board some classes of NTDS ships. Current ones include two each on board the *Virginia-* and *California-*class nuclear cruisers; two each on board *Kidd-*class missile destroyers (for installation in FY97/98); and four each on board *Wasp-*class amphibious carriers (LHDs).

The PT-525 liquid-crystal projector is driven by a digital television-signal generator, CV-3582, which processes computer output. One generator drawer suffices for four channels, as in Aegis cruisers. The generator provides 1024 × 1024-pixel resolution. Projection can be vertical or horizontal; in a CIC, the projector is generally located behind the large display screen. The typical image size is 42 in sq. PT-525 is controlled by OJ-471 (see above).

◆ Advanced Video Processor (AVP) (OJ-653/UYQ-21) and UYQ-65 (AIDS)

Developed by Diagnostic/Retrieval Systems, AVP is an addition to a UYQ-21 display system. The AVP is built around a standard VME bus. The embedded host processor uses a 32-bit 68020 chip with a 68881 coprocessor; memory is 1 Mbyte of ROM/PROM (for program software), 32 kbytes of fast read/write memory, and 4 Mbytes of data memory. The separate graphics processor has 256 preset characters, plus 512 software-defined characters, with four sizes per font. The graphic acoustics processor has a throughput of 5 MFLOPS (expandable), with a pipelined architecture; it provides 110,000 10-pixel vectors/sec per screen. The associated image memory is 8M pixels, in 256 colors and 256 shades of gray (24-bit planes). Claimed MTBF is 3000 hrs (15min MTTR).

In May 1991 the Navy abandoned its opposition to the AVP, succumbing to congressional pressure. AVP and UYS-2 (EMSP) will be inserted into existing SQQ-89 systems; the program is tentatively designated AIDS (AVP Improved [later Advanced Integrated] Display System). There had been a question as to whether AVP could emulate existing UYQ-21-series stroker displays. A preliminary design review (PDR) should be completed in FY93. Because AIDS is an engineering change proposal (ECP), it does not require major Milestone reviews.

The resulting UYQ-65 workstation was shown at the 1995 Navy League exhibition. Intended for use in ASW, it is part of later versions of SQQ-89, and is compatible with UYQ-70 (ADS; see below). DRS describes it as the U.S. Navy's first totally COTS-based workstation compatible with modern environmental requirements, for example, in the *Arleigh Burke* class. The cabinet contains two 19in color screens (1280 × 1024 pixels), one atop the other, two VME backplanes (internal buses), and dual processors (SPARC-10 or HP-743 series). There is also an auxiliary flat plasma touchscreen display just above the keyboard (9.5in diagonal, 640 × 480 pixels). UYQ-65 can accommodate up to four hard drives (2.4 Gbyte), a 600-Mbyte CD-ROM drive, and a 4mm tape drive. The display software is commercial (X-Windows, MOTIF, and so on, with a POSIX-compliant Real-Time Operating System). Dimensions (excluding terminal shelf): 33 × 25.5 × 72 in.

◆ UYQ-37

Hughes's Plotter and Combat Summary Display (PACS) is used on board U.S. submarines. It is an expanded version of the OJ-601 console in the UYQ-21 system described above, using a liquid-crystal projector (1024 × 1368 pixels, 256 characters/symbols). It can display raw sensor video (it includes a radar scan converter), and it can function as a DRT (inputs are inertial navigational data, heading, speed, depth, and periscope and sonar data). The display (yellow on blue for normal viewing, or red for dark-adaptation) is 23 × 31 in (1024 × 1368 pixels); overall dimensions are 49 × 26 × 41 in (1100 lb).

◆ UYQ-70 (ADS)/SMART

The Unisys/DRS Advanced Display System is, in effect, the successor to UYQ-21, having defeated Hughes's alternative. It is an intelligent workstation. In ACDS Block 1 Level 2, it is used to unload the central processor by taking over some graphics processing. That hardly exploits its full capacity; in Level 3, the central computer (UYK-43) is to be eliminated, all processing moving to the UYQ-70s. UYQ-70 is also the display/workstation of SSDS. It can run in three modes: emulation (using existing software), native, or hybrid. Unisys (now Loral Unisys) sees it as a catalyst for the transition to open distributed COTS command systems. For the Navy, the key sales point was apparently that adopting UYQ-70 would make it possible to develop ACDS into a federated system, which could then evolve into a distributed system. The first fully distributed system (ACDS Block 1 Level 3) will probably be an LHA upgrade that is now under discussion. Other distributed systems will be those on board LPD 17 and CVN-76. All will use FDDI/Safenet LANs to connect their workstations.

At present (ACDS Block 1 Level 2), the operational modules remain in the central UYK-43 computer. UYQ-70 unloads it to the extent that it carries its own graphics and communications network software. In effect, it is the step beyond CIGARS, but that hardly exploits its computing power. The next step is clearly to move the operational modules into the UYQ-70s, which is ACDS Block 1 Level 3.

Unisys described UYQ-70 as the first full-scale implementation of open-system architecture for a shipboard CDS. It can emulate the standard NTDS displays (UYA-4 and UYQ-21), or it can operate in native or hybrid mode. In emulation mode, ADS legacy software is transposed to the ADS and resident ADS software emulates the user interface. Software need not therefore be reinvented. In hybrid mode, ADS is connected to a UYK-44 legacy system as well as to an FDDI network; for example, one X-Window operates in emulation mode, another in native mode.

ADS has a VME internal bus and can connect to the new standard FDDI and Safenet; each ADS can act as a tactical real-time server on a shipwide network. The cabinet contains a 100-MHz PA-RISC single-board processor with 64 Mbytes of RAM (expandable to 256 Mbytes) and a modular graphics subsystem (using a Barco CX4100 display generator) which can mix radar and video data digitally for 1024 × 1024- or 2048 × 2048-pixel graphics. The scan converter produces 1024 × 1024-pixel graphics while retaining eight scans of history; it has a graphics bus connecting it directly to the graphics subsystem. There is also a 30-Hz video frame grabber.

The Barco display generator can be integrated with both HP UNIX and HP RT (real-time) operating systems. In UYQ-70, it employs 8 or 12 memory planes for overlay graphics and 8 or 12 memory planes for underlay graphics, integrated with radar windows and video windows. Barco's video-screen buffer will allow the display of up to two live windows controlled by standard commercial X-Windows software, which is used in current command systems.

There are three configurations: stand-alone (main 19in screen plus separate 14in screen above), rack-mounted console (two 19in screens, one atop the other), or unattended equipment rack.

UYQ-70 can support a 21in pedestal-mount display or a 42in large-screen display. It uses HP-RT2 operating software for deterministic real-time applications and HP-UX for nonreal-time applications. It can now emulate OJ-194, -194A, -451, and -535; others are planned.

DRS has also shown an open-architecture SMART (Standardized Modular Architecture Real Time) workstation, presumably its concept of a UYQ-65/70 successor. SMART has a large color CRT (HDTV) above a smaller color CRT alongside a pair of flat-panel displays. Internally, the VME bus carries input/output, real-time data processor, graphics processor, image processor, digital signal processor, special-purpose, and bus bridge/repeater boards. A typical real-time processor on a single VME board would use a RISC chip operating at 66 SpecMarks with 8–64 Mbytes of onboard memory, a 64-kbyte memory cache, a 64-kbyte instruction cache, and five I/O ports. Graphics processors offer 640 × 480 to 2048 × 2048 pixel resolution, 4–24 display planes, and 0–8 overlay planes in one to eight VME modules. A typical image processor uses an image manager board (four types of processing, image memory, acquisition, and display functions), plus additional boards carrying one to three acquisition, display, and processing modules. A typical digital signal processor module contains one to four DSPs operating at 80–320 MFLOPS and 40–160 MIPS, with 16 Mbytes of DRAM and 32-bit DMA. Input/output options include NTDS (Mil-STD-1397), the 1553 bus, FDDI, SCSI II, and SAFENET. Bridge/repeater options include VME to VME, VME to Futurebus+, and VME to Eisa.

The UYQ-70 family of consoles. The console at center is the one most commonly associated with CDS. That at left can be used in an airplane. At right of center is the two-screen vertical configuration often used for sonar processing and in submarine combat systems. It is the version in the Loral Unisys proposal for the Egyptian submarine CDS. (Loral)

◆ USQ-64

USQ-64 is the special tactical intelligence terminal, using FLTSATCOM, which exchanges data among systems such as Outboard and Combat DF. A single net can carry up to 23 subscribers.

◆ ACWS/AMW/BSY-2 Console

Librascope's Advanced Color Work Station (ACWS) and Advanced Multifunction Workstation (AMW) were displayed at the U.S. Navy League show in April 1990. ACWS is the display of the Kollmorgen nonpenetrating periscope now under development. The two workstations are very similar; AMW is a growth version of ACWS. The periscope console has two CRTs and two image processors (forming two image channels for the two cameras of the periscope). The console includes image postprocessing. For example, the image produced by a FLIR in fog can be intensified using a pixel-by-pixel processor.

ACWS is available in both single- and dual-screen (vertically stacked) versions, in each case with 19in (1280 × 1024-pixel, refreshed at 60 Hz) CRTs. It is built around a 32-bit VME bus, which normally carries a display processor (a Motorola 68020), a display memory, and a graphics engine feeding the screen(s). The bus can also carry a hard or optical disk, an applications processor (another 68020, which can be supplemented by an array processor), and an MMI processor (a third 68020 handles input devices: keyboard, joystick, trackballs, electroluminescent touch screen, digitizing tablet, and audio inputs). The ACWS can digitize up to three separate analog video inputs, which enter via its graphics engine.

Each display/applications processor carries 4 Mbytes of memory and operates at 2 MIPS (100 kFLOPS).

The graphics engine uses a 68020 I/O processor, a 12-MIPS display list processor, and a 20-MFLOPS array processor; its image generator is a separate high-speed ASIC processor. It can calculate 1M (10 pixel) vectors/sec, 27M pixels/sec, 50,000 flat shaded polygons/sec, or 60,000 5 × 7 characters/sec. It can erase a full screen in 150 microsec, and it can support pan, zoom, and scroll functions on the screen at a rate of 24 frames/sec. There are two color-output (red-green-blue) channels, each of which can have up to 12 bit planes (for overlays) and each of which can be drawn using a 4096-color palette (i.e., 12 bits/pixel). The engine can accommodate an optional shading processor. Radar and sonar-sweep converters are available.

AMW is a growth version with an array processor, a real-time relational database manager, and an image processor (ACWS has only the image processor); the chassis can accommodate three processors. The array processor will provide sufficient capacity to display active sonar and radar data; to enhance active sonar, radar, and optronic data; and to generate 3D presentations of the acoustic environment (e.g., ray traces), minefields, navigational aids, and weapons trajectories. AMW is also somewhat more application- (or engineering-) oriented than ACWS.

Like ACWS, AMW is built around a VME bus with 34 slots. Typically, it accommodates relational processor(s) with associated 28-Mbyte RAM, plus array processor(s) with their associated RAM, plus 150 Mbytes of hard disks. The relational processor can store and sort its 28 Mbytes 1000 times faster than a 68020-based software system. The array processor operates at 25 MFLOPS, for parallel processing of sonar, radar, or optronic data. These are in addition to application processor(s), each with 4 Mbytes of RAM, and a graphics processor.

The graphics processor is much more powerful than that of the ACWS. It consists of up to six types of elements, each connected both to the VME bus and to a separate picture element bus: frame grabber(s), a display list processor, a display list memory, hardware vector generator(s), and bit-map (frame-refresh) memories/display output processors. The latter interact with the two 1280 × 1024-pixel (60 frames/sec) touch-interactive (using IR with the resolution of the monitor) color CRTs, which also connect with the applications processor. The optional frame grabbers convert standard composite video to 640 × 480-element (8-bit monochrome or 12-bit color) images for input to the display-refresh memories, which actually feed the monitors. Im-

ages are processed at 30 frames/sec. The bit maps have 4–16 planes/monitor, which can be overlaid with 4-bit plane/16 color transparent annotations.

CRT graphics capability is similar to that in the ACWS.

The operator panel provides fixed function keys, programmable keys, a typewriter keyboard, track marbles (trackballs), and a 512 × 256-element electroluminescent touch screen.

The BSY-2 submarine combat system uses a simplified version of ACWS with only a single graphics engine. However, the chassis allows for later growth.

◆ ATW

Tiburon Systems's Advanced Tactical Workstation incorporates a dedicated correlation "engine." It is used in several OTH-T systems, including Outlaw Hunter and its successor, OASIS. ATW uses the Navy-standard maneuvering target statistical tracker (MTST), combined with ELINT and attribute correlation, to associate reports with tracks and also to associate dissimilar tracks. The ATW software runs on a standard AT-compatible personal computer (such as a CP-1933/UYK) with a high-resolution color (VGA) monitor driven by an 80386 chip (with an 80387 coprocessor), with 4–16 Mbytes of RAM, a Video 7 VRAM graphics card (with 512 kbytes of RAM), a hard disk with at least 40 Mbytes of storage, and a Microsoft mouse or trackball. The current software is written in Turbo Pascal, and a translation into ADA is under evaluation. It is also being modified to work with the X-Windows graphics package used in JOTS and JOTS-related systems.

The ATW executive system controls five program packages: communications processing (data reception from OTH-Gold, TACELINT, Bullseye [HF/DF], ATARF [Automated Tracking and Reporting Format], ISAR), correlation processing, track-file management, tracker processing, and tactical-display processing. The correlation processor correlates received track numbers, unique attributes, ELINT data, hull-to-emitter data, and Tactical Information Broadcast files and associates tracks. The track-file manager updates, deletes, merges, disassociates, and reprocesses tracks, and conducts periodic track maintenance. The tracker processor updates track parameters, generates track solutions, and assesses whether the generated positions are in fact feasible (i.e., whether a ship of known capabilities can get from a past known position to a projected position in the time available). The display processor includes TDAs.

ATARF is a message format used with IUSS messages. The Tactical Information Broadcast is a U.S. Air Force intelligence broadcast associated with the RC-135 (Rivet Joint) program. OTH-Gold is the message format, formerly JINTACCS, used by a battle group's FOTC; it is a machine-readable format that gives a ship's name, location, and time. This is the format read by JOTS.

The major advantage claimed for ATW is that its database is flexible enough to handle a wide variety of data, from both onboard and external sensors. It can form multisource track files, support bearings-only tracking, and allow track merging and unmerging (when a track merge proves erroneous). It can also generate free-text TACNOTES to provide a distant commander with some feeling for the confidence in which track or location data are held. ATW supports both FOTC participant and nonparticipant modes of operation. ATW also logs incoming and outgoing messages.

ATW is both similar to and competitive with many aspects of JOTS. See also Outlaw Hunter/OASIS above.

The connection with Outlaw Hawk/Outlaw Shark is not coincidental: Jere Patterson, the founder and president of Tiburon, managed both programs while at Lockheed Missiles and Space Company (Tiburon, Spanish for "shark," recalls the earlier association).

ATW is currently being modified for the OASIS III program (AIP modification to the P-3C). Production began in October 1994. This workstation is also used by the Royal Navy, aboard carriers.

With 8 (preferably 16) Mbytes of RAM and 100 Mbytes of hard disk (500 preferred) and Windows 3.1 software, ATW can handle

10 reports/sec, respond to a query in 1 sec, and can handle 2000 tracks (variable) with 400 reports per track (variable).

A successor ATW II uses the ELINT correlator proven in operational trials of the ATW. ATW II is used in the Royal Navy FOCSLE command system. Compared to ATW, it uses a RISC processor (such as SPARC 10, DEC Alpha, or PowerPC) rather than the CISC of the earlier system. Memory capacity is 64 Mbytes of RAM and a 1.2-Gbyte hard disk. With X-Windows and ADA software, ATW II can do 5 reports/sec, answer a query in 5 sec, and handle 2000 tracks, with 400 reports/track.

The successor system is Rockwell's IDLS (see the Aircraft Systems section below). Tiburon is now part of Texas Instruments, which is a partner in IDLS.

♦ MRCS

UNISYS's Militarized Reconfigurable Console System is its VME-based intelligent console, presumably based in part on experience gained with the *Kanaris* project (see the Antisubmarine Warfare section). The console has 12 slots for 68020/68881-based processors (up to four on the bus) and can accommodate 4–24 Mbytes of RAM. Processing speeds can be up to 6 MIPS. The bus can also accommodate up to four 68020-based I/O processors and up to 12 interfaces. The embedded graphics generator supports two independent monitor drivers (four graphics planes per driver, expandable to eight) with 16 colors (expandable to 256). It can generate 50,000 vectors and 5000 characters/sec, and the hardware incorporates a cursor generator. Resolutions: 768 × 1024, 1024 × 1024, and 1024 × 1280. Dimensions (single monitor): 53 × 26 × 55 in, 725 lb.

♦ Multifunction Workstation

The Rockwell (Autonetics Marine Division) workstation, announced in 1990, is an offshoot of the OJ-564 console used in the SOSUS system. It is included here (rather than under ASW) because it seems to fit the same basic requirement as the Librascope ACWS. The French navy has ordered a half-height version and the associated cabinet. Like the other workstations described here, the Rockwell unit is built around a VME bus (backplane), which can accommodate standard cards for functions such as analog-to-digital conversion and video processing boards. The basic workstation contains a one-channel processor but can accommodate a beam-former.

Although the workstation has two monitors, it can display four video channels simultaneously by windowing; it accommodates two separate video buses, each of which can be fed by two video channels. The graphics engines are Sun Windows with enhanced throughput (a polygon can be filled at the rate of about 25M pixels/sec, and 200,000+ vectors/sec can be generated). The video channels can accommodate 256 colors and have a bandwidth of more than 100 MHz; they produce 60 frames/sec without interlacing. Displays are 16 or 19 in (diagonal) or 20 × 20 in, with resolution of 1280 × 1024, 2048 × 2048, or 2048 × 1536. They can be color or monochrome. Each monitor has 4, 8, or 24 memory planes.

A diagram of workstation architecture shows four main buses feeding the VME bus: a CPU bus, an array processor bus, and two video buses; the VME bus also carries RAM, an operator interface, and a controller with its own disk memory. The CPU (a 68020 with a 68881 coprocessor) carries 4 Mbytes of RAM, and the system can accommodate a 12-Mbyte RAM card. Available operator interfaces include a keyboard, a trackball, track marbles, a joystick, a stiff stick, a light pen, a mouse, hard and soft (programmable) function keys, and a flat touch panel. The console accepts up to 18 channels of RS-232 I/O, and it can accommodate a 344-Mbyte hard disk.

Dimensions: 75 × 22 × 48 in (fits a 24in hatch); weight is less than 500 lb.

Rockwell offers a related single-monitor acoustic processor. One application is a specialized torpedo alert processor (TAP), which is fed by existing acoustic sensors and which provides an audible alarm as well as a CRT display. TAS shares unique software and special hardware (acoustic display, spectrum analyzer, and beam-former) with other Rockwell acoustic processors.

♦ SPA-25, SPA-50, and Other Radar Displays

SPA-25 and SPA-50 are the standard U.S. raw-video radar repeaters, superseding the earlier SPA-4. The earliest version dates from the mid-1960s. The chief current version is SPA-25F, a horizontal or vertical 10in, digital, solid-state PPI. SPA-25G (see below) is a very different and much more capable replacement and, thus, merits separate treatment.

In SPA-25F displayed range is −300 nm, with $\frac{1}{4}, \frac{1}{2}$, 1, 2, 5, 10, 20, and 50nm range rings. The range strobe can be used to read off ranges within 0.03%. Resolution is 10 yd below 50 nm and 0.1 nm above 50 nm. LED readouts show bearing and range of strobed targets (range in nm and yd). The display can accept radar signals at 10–5000 pps, with widths of 0.3–25 microsec and a scan rate of up to 60 rpm. This display can function either as a conventional PPI or as a range-height indicator for 3D radars. SPA-25 can be connected to a dead-reckoning unit that offsets its sweep (so that the radar shows something approximating true rather than relative motion). MTBF is 4000 hr (MTTR 20 min).

SPA-25 is often used alongside SPA-50, which is generally similar except that its CRT is about twice as large (22in dia). SPA-25 accepts PRFs between 15 and 5000 pps. There is also a smaller-diameter PPI, SPA-18 (7in screen, range scale 2–30 nm, PRFs 57–3000).

SPA-25G has a raster-scan display, uses radar digital scan conversion, and incorporates a 5-Mbit digital memory. SPA-25G can function as an electronic plotter and, thus, can form the basis of a very simple TDS on board a ship without such a system (or as a system backup). See RADDS and the Cardion systems above.

The 17in rectangular screen shows both raw and processed video; the radar processor accepts 100–3600 pps, antenna rates of 0–60 rpm, and signals as short as 50 nanosec. Radar data are stored in digital form in three 1024 × 1024-bit memory planes (to provide a gray-scale level of eight shades, corresponding to 3 bits). The display itself is 1280 × 1024 pixels, the central 1024 × 1024 elements of which are dedicated to radar video (the rest are tabular). The CRT is raster scanned in 1125-line format (80 frames/sec, interlaced 2:1, i.e., a full 40 frames/sec). Resolution is 92 vertical lines/in.

Memory suffices to store, plot, and label 99 targets, 64 of which are target tracks. The system automatically calculates range, bearing, speed, and CPA and displays these data in a track-data-file block on the CRT; the data are also automatically made available to the data bus connected to the SPA-25G. Graphic images using up to 128 display lines can be created to show traffic lanes, harbors, marshaling areas, restricted zones, and so on. Because radar data are held in a digital memory, the display need not fade (decay time is adjustable between 250 msec to no decay). Range scales are $\frac{1}{4}$–250 nm or $\frac{1}{2}$–500 nm; range rings are set at $\frac{1}{8}, \frac{1}{4}, \frac{1}{2}$, 1, 2, 5, 10, 20, and 50 nm (with 0.25% accuracy).

There is a special air-intercept mode, in which the processor calculates an intercept solution and displays alternatives for near-collision intercept and forward-quarter intercept. Outputs can be synchro or digital.

The associated executive controller is a 68000 16-bit chip, assisted by 8-bit microprocessors. MTBF is 3000 hr (MTTR less than 30 min).

Both versions of SPA-25 are manufactured by ISC Cardion.

SPA-50G (made by Cardion) is intended to supplement SPA-25G. SPA-50G is intended as a tactical display, as a means of multisource data correlation and display, and as a real-time TDA. Because it incorporates considerable memory and computing power, it adds to the overall reliability of the CDS it serves. It can also be used for data-link access, and it can be connected to a shipboard data bus network. For example, it can perform an electronic mailbox function.

SPA-50G uses scan-conversion techniques (i.e., raster scan) to display data from several sensors as well as graphic overlays. The cabinet is tied together by a VME bus. It incorporates five microprocessors (a 68020 system processor, a 68020 application processor, a 6809 operator-control processor, a 6809 for 1553 bus control, and a bit-slice graphics generator) with over 7 Mbits of digital bit-mapped memory for graphics, to accommodate three radar memory planes (i.e., video from three radars simultaneously) and four graphics memory planes (typically a status and designator plane, an own-ship plane, a graphics plane, and a map plane, each of which can be switched in and out of the display). There is also a radar-video integrator. The display is 1280 × 1024 pixels, refreshed at 40 or 80 Hz.

System processor memory capacity is 64 kwords of PROM and 64 kwords of RAM (expandable to 126k and 256k, respectively). The application processor memory is up to 8 Mbytes of RAM and 512 bytes of PROM, with further expansion capability. The application processor board can accommodate a 68020 (16.67-MHz clock rate), a 68881 math coprocessor, 4 Mbytes of dual-port dynamic RAM, up to 512 kbytes of EPROM, and up to 32 kbytes of static RAM. The graphics generator board uses a 125-nanosec instruction cycle and a 16-kword display list buffer. It has two standard character sets, large and small. The system runs at 16 MHz.

Further internal circuit boards can be added to expand SPA-50G capability.

As in the case of SPA-25G, this is another example of a display merging with combat-system computers.

For other obsolescent displays, see the 1991/92 edition.

◆ UYQ-23

Motorola's smart interactive terminal is used for intelligence systems such as NIPS (SYQ-9) and BGPHES (SLQ-50). It fits a standard 19in rack; it incorporates a stroker display and can also display real-time or time-compressed video. The (V)3 and later versions have a split-screen display, and its keyboard includes a trackball. The (V)5 version has two trackballs. The (V)6 version has three split-screen displays. Internal memory varies with the version: 8k, 16k, 32k, or 128k 16-bit words. The digital interface is NTDS fast or RS-232C, depending on the version. The (V)1 version (8k memory) is part of OK-324/SYQ (NIPS terminal). (V)6 is part of OJ-557(V)/USQ-88(V) (TFCC).

◆ UYQ-31

Raytheon's standard multimission displays are used in many current systems. UYQ-31 is a modular device that can fit through a standard submarine (25in) hatchway when its keyboard shelf is removed. It is an intelligent programmable console that can be used either with a host computer or on a stand-alone basis, and it can also be backfitted to existing devices. The 15in raster-scan CRT (946 × 1136 pixels) has a 50-Hz refresh rate and is fed via a programmable display processor (16-bit RP-1610). Operator controls are a keyboard and a stiff stick. Versions include (V)1 for SLQ-32, (V)2 for SQS-56 (two 15in CRTs), (V)3 for BQQ-9 (17in CRTs), (V)4 for TWCS (as operator-interactive display terminal), and (V)5 for SQQ-32. UYQ-31 is also used with Sea Sparrow.

SUBMARINE COMBAT-DIRECTION SYSTEMS

Submarine CDSs differ from those of surface ships in that they generally deal with bearings-only and frequency data, which cannot in themselves directly provide the user with a full tactical picture. On the other hand, the function of the submarine system is the same as that in a surface ship: to maintain and process track information in support of command decisions. Because of the bearings-only character of much of the data, compiling a geographical plot is a much more complex proposition. Hence submarine CDSs typically carry only a fraction of the number of tracks carried by their surface-ship counterparts, using the same computers.

As in a surface ship, a submarine CDS automates functions originally performed manually. Automation in most pre-1945 submarines was limited to a very simple fire-control function, solving the ballistic triangle for their torpedoes. The torpedo had to be fired at (or steered into) the appropriate lead or lag angle to hit a ship. To do that, the submarine commander had to estimate target course, speed, and range. That was done by plotting, once the target was in sight. For example, a submerged submarine periodically raised her periscope to obtain a target bearing. The commander might estimate target speed (e.g., from the bow wave), course (inclination), and range (e.g., by stadimeter). That combination could be projected ahead to predict the next bearing. Corrections (the target bearing would probably be slightly off) could be fed back. The commander steered for an intercepting position, at which the submarine would be within range of the target. The plot indicated what relative courses and speeds would be at that time, and a relevant ballistic triangle was set up and solved, generally in analog fashion, that is, semiautomatically. Only one target could be handled at a time.

The plotting process prior to attacking, moreover, could be separated into construction of a tactical picture during a long-range approach to the vicinity of the target (which might be chosen on the basis of the plotted data) and a much shorter-range precision determination of the course, speed, and range of the chosen target. For example, in theory a submarine trying to slip into a convoy would need an overall tactical-picture plot, whereas the attack on a particular ship in the convoy would concentrate on a single target.

The next step, which the U.S. Navy took in the 1930s, was to automate the short-range target solution, using a mechanical computer (the torpedo data computer, TDC). The submarine still used manual plotting to obtain a long-range tactical picture, and that picture gave the initial input to the TDC. As it ran, the TDC projected ahead target position, hence expected bearing as seen from the submarine. These projections could be checked against observations, and the TDC parameters corrected accordingly. To reach a solution, the TDC generally had to have at least two range measurements, or a range and a target inclination (course angle relative to the submarine). Instruments such as stadimeters (later supplemented by range-only periscope radar) were devised to provide this data. As it projected ahead, the TDC automatically solved the torpedo triangle and set torpedo gyros.

This was a remarkable achievement, broadly equivalent to contemporary work on surface fire-control computing. Its most immediate drawback was that it could handle only one target at a time. Under some circumstances a submarine might be able to attack several targets in quick sequence. In the mid-1950s Signaal devised what amounted to a multiple TDC, the M8 submarine FCS. Parallel operation became possible when digital computers (in this case, hard-wired) drastically shrank the volume associated with the TDC. A submarine could now engage several targets simultaneously or in quick succession.

These systems still required accurate range input. M8 appeared at about the same time as a series of passive triangulation rangers. Thus it could use a radar ranger (against surface ships), a single-ping sonar ranger, or a fully passive ranger. It was still a relatively short-range system. Any long-range inputs had to come from the plotting table. Moreover, such systems are not yet full CDSs because they cannot provide much in the way of situational awareness. M8 and its contemporaries are described in the sonar section of the Antisubmarine Warfare chapter of this book.

The step beyond is a computer carrying what amounts to an underwater tactical picture. Typically it is formed passively. Modern digital sonars feed a series of automatic target followers (ATFs). Although in theory fully automatic TMA is possible (using Ekelund ranging, for example), in practice individuals periodically subject targets to computer-aided manual TMA (MATE, in the U.S. Navy). If a target does not maneuver, the TMA solution can be projected ahead, and in theory a series of such TMA solutions yields a tactical picture (the computer projects ahead the motion of each target). In practice, targets maneuver, so a single computer operator can probably evaluate about 10 targets before the first of them must be re-evaluated. In theory, then, the number of aided TMA stations in a submarine CDS determines the number of targets the submarine CDS can usefully handle.

As submarines operate closer to shore, such limitations become less and less acceptable. The only solution seems to be to depend more heavily on automation, which submarine officers dislike. One possibility is to merge multiple sensors. It seems likely that references to new and very powerful TMA algorithms generally mean mixing available passive sensor data. Another is to use simple forms of analysis to reject the great majority of detected targets as irrelevant, leaving the others to semi-automatic TMA.

The automated submarine CDS was originally attractive partly because it could accept a surface picture via data link, thus making it easier for a submarine to cooperate with surface forces. For example, the Royal Navy wanted a computer AIO (action information organization) in its first nuclear submarines mainly so that they could work effectively with surface consorts. That was also why the nuclear submarine sonar, Type 2001, was digital. This concept included what amounted to an acoustic data link (actually a teletype, Type 2010, working on the underwater telephone circuit, supplemented by the Type 2009 IFF). These devices presented no great problem because they would communicate almost vertically, along the reliable acoustic path (RAP). It was probably assumed that the submarine and surface units would be able to clarify the picture by correlating their sensor data. The AIO was so important that initially the Royal Navy did not even append an underwater FCS (it used an existing analog unit). By way of contrast, the U.S. digital submarine CDS grew out of an FCS.

In the U.S. case, UYK-7s were placed on board *Los Angeles*–class submarines partly in hopes that, provided with the Link 11 tactical picture, these units could cooperate effectively with surface ships. Ironically, in both the British and U.S. cases, CDS capability matured just as submariners realized that the last thing they wanted to do was operate close to surface ships and their aircraft.

Even so, NATO submarines are being fitted with receive-only Link 11. One reason why may be that its tactical picture amounts to a limited form of OTH-T support for Sub-Harpoon.

DENMARK

♦ TACTICS/ISAACS

Terma's Torpedo Attack Controller and Tactical Information Co-ordinator was designed for the Danish *Kobben* (*Tumleren*) and *Narhvalen*–class submarines. The associated Terma torpedo FCS has its own processor cabinet and can control four wire-guided torpedoes simultaneously. The main components are the data processing unit (DCU), the graphic display (GD), the system terminal, and the torpedo-guidance unit (TGU). The graphic display is a 20in-high color raster monitor, whose lower portion is used for alphanumeric data. The upper portion can show three alternative pictures: a general operational plot (GOP), which is a PPI-like picture including all tracks, ESM data, and maps in an area, and which can be ship- or geographically oriented; a contact

evaluation plot (CEP), a waterfall display oriented to passive sensors, carrying comprehensive operator comments; and an attack plot (ATP), which extracts data from the GOP and the CEP to produce a dynamic vector picture of the local attack situation, including predictions and recommendations for torpedo attacks against selected targets. The system terminal is the means of communication with the system; it consists of an alphanumeric keyboard, 60 dedicated function keys, and a rollerball.

The double-screen console, related to that in the *Flyvefisken* class, carries a pair of 20in portrait-shaped monitors (1024 × 1024, with 18 lines of 80 characters for menus/tell-backs, using 68020/68040 processors on a VME backplane, with 8-bit color planes) with a pair of keyboards and trackballs. Dimensions: 1230 mm (height) × 1460 mm (width) × 1000 mm (depth), 325 kg.

TACTICS can maintain up to 250 tracks (any of which may have been obtained by data link), with attack plots (ATP) for four weapons. It can provide bearing data on up to 10 targets. It can maintain contact evaluation plots (CEPs) for up to 40 targets and conduct simultaneous TMA on 10 of them (using operator inputs if required). It can handle 60 EW "rackets," eight periscope lines of bearing, and eight wire-guided torpedoes or 20 mines. The system can also handle Harpoon fire control and can be used for minelaying. It can maintain two digital charts (including color fill) and eight maps.

Options include Link 11 and connection to an Ethernet LAN.

TACTICS was originally designated Sub-TDS. Deliveries began in May 1989; the first submarine, *Tumleren*, was commissioned in October 1989. Installations were completed in 1991. ISAACS (Integrated Sonar and Arms Control System) is an export version marketed by Honeywell ELAC of Germany under a 1993 agreement.

FRANCE

♦ SAT/SADE/TITAC/SAD/SYTAC/SUBICS/SUBTICS

DCN's Système d'Armes Tactiques was the first French integrated submarine combat system, employing a digital tactical data–handling system (TIT) integrated with a DLA-series FCS, for the *Redoutable* (now *L'Inflexible*) -class SSBNs. It entered service in 1985. The corresponding *Rubis* (SSN) -class system was SADE. The system in the successor *Amethyste* (and rebuilt *Rubis*) class is the Thomson Sintra SUBICS, which is built around the TITAC tactical data-handling system (TDHS). SAD, presumably Système d'Armes Defensives, is part of the *Le Triomphant* combat system; the integrating tactical data-handling element is SYTAC. SUBTICS is the export tactical system for the new Pakistani *Agosta* 90B class.

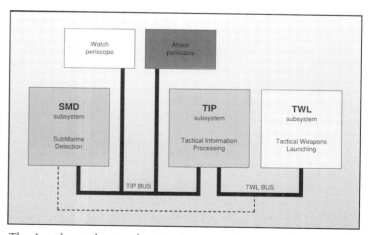

The TACTICS system on board a Danish submarine. (Terma)

The *Amethyste*-class combat system is subdivided into a detection element (SMD), a tactical information processor (TIP), and a weapons launching element (TWL). Earlier classes of submarines had the SMD and TWL (including FCS) elements, but lacked any computer to bridge the gap between the two. At long range, the tactical picture was formed by plotting sonar data; at shorter attack ranges, sonar data could be fed to the submarine's FCS. (DGA/DCN)

The torpedo FCS element of the *Amethyste* system shows its three screens. The console on the right, beyond the FCS screens, is one of the single-screen TIP units. (DGA/DCN)

Two of the three single-screen consoles of the *Amethyste* CDS are shown, flanked on the left by three single-screen FCS consoles (one is visible) and on the right by dual-screen sonar consoles (one is visible). These consoles are lined up along the starboard side of the navigation/combat information center; this view looks forward. The after bulkhead carries a radar console, and the two periscopes are on a raised platform along the centerline. As in U.S. submarines, the forward bulkhead carries the plane controls, in this case for one-man operation. The submarine normally operates in autopilot mode, using three separate computers that monitor each other. Controls at the steering station include engine-room order transmitters. Alongside the steering station is a diving safety board, which includes remote monitors of the nuclear fireroom and of the electric power plant (the submarine is turbo-electric). (DGA/DCN)

SAT employs nine 15M125X computers, most of them paired to provide a hot spare for every function. All are connected to a Digibus via three intelligent bus controllers. Two of them are used for CDS (SITAC, situation assessment, including torpedo FCS), two for ballistic missile targeting, two for ballistic missile launch control, two for maintenance, and one is a hot spare.

SUBICS has three elements: DSM (Detection Sous-Marine), TITAC (Traitement des Informations Tactiques), and LAT (Lancement des Armes Tactiques). They are linked by dual digital buses (a tactical information processing [TIP] bus for TITAC, one for LAT).

DSM is the submarine's Eledone sonar plus the other sensors. It produces track data that go to TITAC. The sonar element of DSM uses a CRT for the submarine's passive sonar and two double-screen consoles for intercept/ranging and active sonars; the

towed array has a separate console. Presumably radar and ESM consoles are also separate. Targets are identified by analysis of their radiated noise signatures, and also of their own sonar pulses (using a library look-up). The system can also use ESM and optronic-periscope data. Data from the different arrays are automatically correlated to form a single integrated picture, using data association and computer-aided data fusion. Reportedly this combination can track 20 targets automatically and three manually.

The TITAC computer, which is the 15M125X of the contemporary SENIT 6 system, feeds a plotter and a disk drive directly;

Operators are shown at a fully integrated submarine combat system, presumably a SUBICS II mock-up. The consoles are all standard two-screen Colibris. This photo shows the stages through which the tactical problem goes. The console at extreme left presumably shows sonar video. The next console appears to show a TMA or track association display. TMA is used to build up the PPI-type tactical picture on the next console, which is used for decision-making. The console at right is used for the actual attack, with weapon-status information at top and an engagement-planning display below it. Earlier in the tactical problem, more of the consoles might have been devoted to sonar video and hence to manual target detection. (Thomson Sintra)

through the bus it also feeds a pair of consoles with CRTs. All contacts are subject to automatic TMA, and manual TMA can be conducted simultaneously on four targets. As in other navies, standard practice is to refine a TMA solution manually before using it for fire control. LAT uses these outputs to control two torpedoes simultaneously.

SUBICS II (TSM 2295) is a next-generation bussed system employing the new Colibri multifunction display consoles, with their 68000-series microprocessors. As in SUBICS, sonar preprocessing (ADT) produces track data. In this system it filters the data by contact motion analysis (CMA). CMA is an initial filter: it rejects contacts outside a preset range of interest. These contact data are fed into the system bus, but the operators can also refer back to raw acoustic data (waterfalls, LOFAR) for sensor fusion. An operator associates different sensor data for track management (a process Thomson calls MSSE, multisensor situation elaboration). MSSE acts as a filter on the processed sensor data to form a clear tactical picture. For example, different sensors may see the same track at different times. System memory retains earlier track data. The ADT function is used to associate different lines representing the same track. These lines are automatically merged at the plot extractor level. Typically, the system may pick up about 270 tracks at sensor level, filtering them to 100 at MSSE level.

MSSE includes track classification and interactive TMA. The filtered tactical picture formed at the MSSE level is used for tactical planning. This stage, STAP, situation threat-assessment planning, provides TDAs to help in planning attack or escape (using Thomson Sintra's patented method based on kinematic constructions). STAP helps optimize weapons parameters, that is, hit probability. Because the system is digital and software-based, it can easily be adapted to a wide variety of weapons. It controls torpedoes, mines, and also the Sub-Exocet missile (Thomson Sintra makes a special point of the value of the towed array in extending submarine sensor range for missile engagement).

MSSE can handle 300 sensor tracks for 8 hr, or 100 for 24 hr, or 20 target tracks stored for the entire mission. STAP can plan for up to 20 targets, develop attack scenarios for 10, and compute hit probabilities for 10. The system can control four weapons simultaneously. On the operator level, system acknowledgment time is less than 0.1 sec, and picture access time is less than 1 sec. Localization accuracy is 1 deg in bearing, 5% in range, 5% in speed, and 1 deg in course (time to achieve these figures by TMA is not given). A hostile-weapon warning is given within 10 sec, and a snapshot can be fired in reply in 45 sec.

A large-screen command plot summarizes the system's tactical picture. Threat analysis includes torpedo alerts.

Because the system uses a single bus, console functions are not fixed. Typically SUBICS II uses four multifunction duty stations (five if fitted with a towed array) and five processing cabinets. In the patrol state, three would be manned: long-range sensor operator, short-range sensor operator, and sensor coordinator/tactical operator. When a potential threat is classified, four duty stations are automatically configured: two sensor operators, one tactical operator (situation evaluation), and one classification operator. The sensor coordinator is responsible for situation elaboration. Once tactical planning has been completed, the system is again reconfigured; the classification console becomes the weapons-control console. Attack reconfiguration time is 5 sec.

The system can accept data from 8 to 12 sensors, including radar and ESM. The acoustic sensors are a towed array, a PVDF flank array, a bow array (passive and intercept detection), distributed arrays for ranging, an obstacle- and mine-avoidance array, an intercept array, an active array, and a stern arc array. Presumably this amounts to DMUX 20 (see below).

The ADT and operator-initiated tracking/automatic target tracking (OIT/ATT) functions are in service on board French and Pakistani *Agosta*-class submarines and French *Amethyste*-class submarines, and they are part of the Australian *Collins*-class suite. MSSE and STAP are at sea on board French SSBNs. The Spanish *Agosta*-class is being modernized with a new command

system, presumably SUBICS. Work began with *Galerna* in 1993.

SUBICS is a digital sonar plus a TDHS module (CDS including an FCS). Thomson Sintra distinguishes the tactical data elements of the system as TSM 2072, a family of command/control systems that can replace existing ones. In this connection it describes TSM 2072 as the functional equivalent of M8/SINBADS in the Dutch *Zwaardvis* class, albeit far more capable. This version is programmed in ADA and C, using 68020 and 68040 processors and Colibri (French) or MOC (Dutch) consoles. The basic version is a tactical picture-keeper (using data from the sonar). It also provides threat assessment and some TDAs. The extended version adds track association algorithms (for acoustic and nonacoustic sensors), target localization (automated TMA), final classification, and engagement support (weapons and decoys). The associated digital FCS is programmed in ADA, using 68020 processors. Its export version can be integrated with SUBICS or can function as a stand-alone system.

At Bourget Naval in 1992 it was stated that SUBICS uses the same architecture, signal processing, and system functions as the Signaal SEWACO VIII on board Dutch submarines; however, it also uses French displays (the French manufacturer is an arm of Thomson-CSF, which bought Signaal). A future version will probably employ the Thomson-Signaal MOC (and dispense with some or all of the separate computers). See the entry on the TACTICOS combat-direction system for details of the MOC console.

SUBTICS (Submarine Tactical Integrated Combat System), the system planned for the three new Pakistani *Agosta*-class submarines, is a new open-architecture modular system closely related to SUBICS II but which employs elements developed for the *Le Triomphant*–class SSBNs. All sensors feed a dual-redundant bus through four processors: one (broad-band low-frequency) for active sonar and the cylindrical bow array, one (broad-band) for the ranging array (distributed array) and intercept array, one (narrow band) for the flank and towed arrays, and one for ESM, periscopes, and radar. The system controls weapons and tubes via a torpedo/missile control processor connected to the bus. Each of six twin-screen Colibri multifunction color consoles (using 68040 processors) is separately connected to the main system bus; there is no command LAN. Software is written in C. Major software modules are:

Classification/identification (audio and LOFAR/DEMON analysis, with interactive hypothesis generation)
Track management (automatic and interactive association and fusion, sorting of best representative acoustic tracks)
Contact motion analysis (automatic and interactive)
Situation elaboration modules: refinement of the tactical picture by associating and fusing acoustic and nonacoustic data, conducting interactive TMA, track management to select tracks of particular tactical interest among the 100 carried by the system
Command and decision modules: threat evaluation of localized and classified tracks, also attack and escape planning tools
Engagement and launching modules (based on DLA 4A and SSBN DLT software) to launch two wire-guided and two fire-and-forget weapons simultaneously

Remarkably, there will be *no* shore test facility. Thomson-CSF argues that the system is constructed out of tested modules, some of them downgraded *Le Triomphant* systems. Skeptics may argue that it is the interaction of the modules which has to be tested.

GERMANY

◆ ISUS-83/ISUS-90

The German ISUS-83 and -90 are integrated submarine combat systems. The manufacturer, STN Atlas, claims that ISUS-83 was among the very first to use multisensor TMA. ISUS stands for integrated-sensor underwater system; the German initials are SLW. ISUS-83 was developed as part of the Type 206A submarine modernization program, in which existing Type 206 submarines

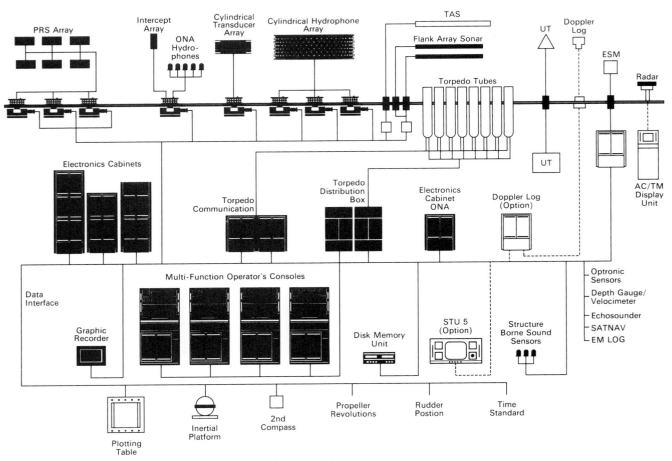

ISUS-83 showing the multifunction consoles (bottom). (STN Atlas)

had their analog sonars replaced by digital CSU 83s. At the same time the existing Signaal M8 FCS was replaced by a new computer-driven LEWA (Lageerarbeitungs und Waffeneinsatzanlage, i.e., position-keeper and weapons-control device). This combination of sonar and FCS was called ISUS-83. The new configuration, intended specifically to fit the limited space in the submarine, was adopted in April 1984. The German navy version uses four BM 802 consoles (each with two 15in color screens, the upper carrying alphanumeric tables and the lower providing graphics, e.g., a PPI): typically two for sonars, one for position-keeping (using a contact-evaluation plot and a waterfall)/FCS, and one for weapons control. The consoles are installed side by side on the starboard side of the submarine control room. The system can accommodate up to nine consoles, but all known installations have four. A separate STU 5 console, provided for training, can be the CO's console during combat.

Each sonar in the system can initiate a target track, the data then being supplemented by data from the other sonars. Each track is subject to automatic classification and TMA (for up to 24 targets) before being combined with periscope and ESM data in the TDHS. The TDHS in turn generates a combat-situation display. The system can handle up to three simultaneous engagements, either from a single console or from several consoles.

The color-coded raster-scan displays are interchangeable between the MFCCs. Design objectives include automatic interactive detection, tracking and analysis of all acoustic signals, automatic classification and contact-motion analysis, threat and combatability analysis, and optimized control and guidance of several types of weapons. The system provides panoramic passive detection (PPD) of targets, measurement of bearing and level of target noise over the whole horizon, complemented by ATT (automatic target tracking) information fed to the WCS. A hard copy of the ATT data is provided in the form of a time-bearing plot.

The multifunction consoles are the same as the standard German type now being used in the Type 123 frigate. All the

important processors have battery-buffered memory to guard against temporary loss of power.

The data transmission network has spider web architecture, which Atlas considers much faster than a conventional bus. To allow each console to shift between sonar analysis and other roles, acoustic data must be carried to all of them. For example, in search mode three consoles may all be used to analyze acoustic data.

ISUS-90 is the open-architecture submarine combat system incorporating the CSU 90 sonar. All operational software is written in ADA; the processors are all MPR 2300-Bs (ISUS-83 used the earlier EPR 1300M and EPR 2300M). In the new processor, an Atlas chip-set, RT 6400, replaces the earlier Motorola 68020. The processors are arranged in Cluster Frames (with VME backplanes) in standard cabinets. They are connected by an Ethernet (for digital data) and by a fiber-optic bus (for sensor, including sonar, video). A typical system employs five multifunction two-screen color consoles (three for sonars, two for tactical displays); there is also a separate contact evaluation plot (CEP). Typical interchangeable displays include one channel of the cylindrical passive array sonar with DEMON shown for comparison; a cylindrical sonar frequency-azimuth display with a sector LOFAR-gram; own-noise analysis, showing outputs of the six external and six internal (structure-borne) own noise detectors; TMA; a tactical display including a bathymetric chart; and a periscope optronic image.

Users:

ISUS-83: Germany (12 Type 206A), Korea (Type 209), Turkey (CSU 83/1 in new Type 209/1400 submarines), Venezuela (Type 209s refitted to 206A standard 1990–92).

ISUS-90: Israel (*Dolphin* class). The German Type 212 submarines use a version of the Norwegian MSI-90U system. The Italian submarines will probably duplicate the German ones, although they may have some Italian components in their CDS.

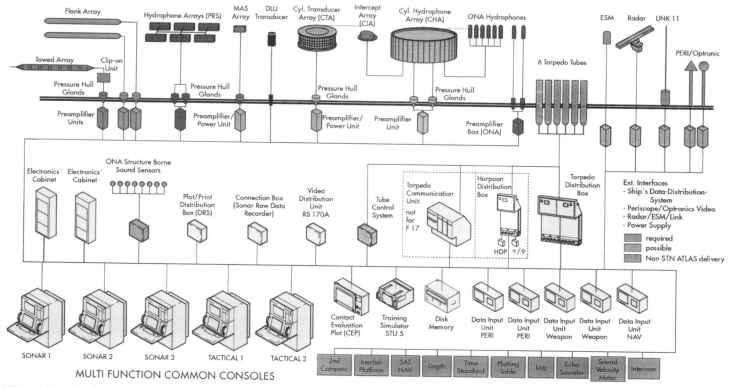

ISUS-90. Despite the designations shown, the five consoles at bottom left are completely interchangeable. (STN Atlas)

ITALY

♦ BSN-716 (SACTIS)

SMA's SACTIS is the standard current Italian navy submarine CDS, using a central computer (a Rolm MSE 14 with disk memory). At least in its original version, it did not transmit target data to the submarine FCS, which is separate. There are two operator positions, each with a large circular CRT and a small rectangular alphanumeric screen above it. Up to 30 targets can be displayed simultaneously. Individual track histories can be selected for presentation, with 10 available as filtered targets. There are four presentations: the general unfiltered situation; a tactical picture; a time-bearing display; and interactive TMA.

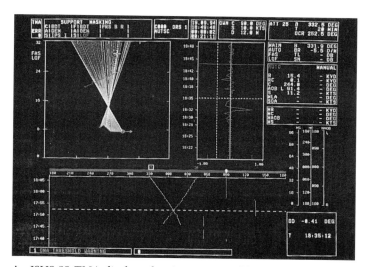

An ISUS-90 TMA display, showing a series of bearings and a possible solution (a straight-line strip plot) at left. The right-hand graph is equivalent to the U.S. dots; it shows bearing error vs. time (descending) for the selected solution. A perfect solution would show a straight vertical line. The graph is continuous because the target has been tracked continuously. At bottom is a waterfall plot of bearing vs. time for the two targets the system is tracking. The box at right gives parameters corresponding to the test solution (which is manual rather than automatic). (STN Atlas)

Sonar-ray paths can be displayed, and own and target's sonar performance calculated. The associated sensors are the IPD-70 sonar, Thetis ESM, and BPS-704 radar. The system performs navigational calculations, such as those required for barrier or screen penetration or evasion, target interception or collision course.

BSN-716(V)2 adds a third operator position and a direct connection to the submarine FCS. It also incorporates receive-only Link 11 and the Elettronica ELT/810 sonar performance predictor. Computer memory is expanded.

SMA was selected in 1981 to develop BSN-716; sea trials began in 1983. This system was retrofitted into the *Sauro* class, which previously had only the SISU-1 FCS. The more integrated BSN-716(V)2 equips the second and third batches of *Sauro*-class submarines, the first of which entered service in 1988. These systems are offered for export as SACTIS (Submarine Action Information System) 1 and 2.

NETHERLANDS

♦ SINBADS/GIPSY/Spectrum

Signaal's Submarine Integrated Battle and Data System is the successor to the M8 series. The original designation, M8/41, suggests that it began as an M8 in which the hard-wired computer was replaced by a fully programmable SMR-S optimized to process track data by Kalman filtering. The single operator can call up any one of three displays: a track display for target evaluation (TMA); a PPI for weapons control; and an alphanumeric display showing selected data. Alternatively, raw data from any particular sensor can be called up (a time-bearing [waterfall] display for passive sonar or ESM, or a PPI for active sonar or radar). SINBADS can track automatically after a firm contact has been established, based either on continuous bearing data or on range and bearing supplied intermittently by an active sonar. There is also a semiautomatic mode allowing comparison of information from various sources; this mode is capable of detecting target maneuvers and of determining the target's new parameters after a maneuver.

The console is the standard Signaal tactical and weapons-control console used in the WM20 series (M8 uses the M20-series console, with its smaller CRT). It has a 16in CRT, a 7in rectangular graphics display showing bearings-only data, a 7in rectangular display of alphanumerics, and an optional 15in tote (alphanumeric) display on top. A separate passive-sonar console is attached to the main console.

SINBADS can track up to five targets simultaneously.

Weapons-control functions are (a) weapon assignment/torpedo setting; (b) prediction for aiming; (c) firing preparation; and (d) torpedo wire-guidance/monitoring. Up to three torpedoes can be assigned simultaneously to different targets. Prediction includes continuous calculation of a torpedo's course (from assignment to end of run for guided torpedoes, or until firing for nonguided ones). The system automatically tests torpedoes before firing them. It handles digital and analog torpedoes (including wire-guided ones) for up to eight tubes. The system must be connected to amplifiers to preset analog torpedoes.

Users (systems exported 1975–85): Argentina (TR 1700 class), Chile (Type 1300), Greece (later Type 209s), Indonesia (Type 209s), Peru (later Type 209s, some replaced by SEPA Mk 3), and Turkey (initial customer, for the later Type 209s). SINBADS may have replaced M8/24 on board the Ecuadorian Type 209s. A plan to replace SINBADS in the Turkish submarines (in line with the new *Preveze* class) was deferred as too costly. The SINBAD systems of Indonesian Type 209s are being upgraded with new computer memories and hard disks in place of tape recorders. The first upgraded submarine returned to service in October 1995.

A much-improved SINBADS was announced in the mid-1980s; it became the core of the GIPSY/Spectrum systems described below. It might be imagined as a submarine equivalent to the minicombat system Signaal offered for surface ships, that is, a two-element system comprising a long-range picture-keeper plus a fire-control element (including short-range picture-keeper) equivalent to the earlier SINBADS. Sonar and other sensor data feed into a processing cabinet containing a pair of SMR-MU computers. It is connected to a pair of side-by-side one-man display and control consoles (DaCCs), each with its own 16in CRT and its own SMR-MU. The computers in the separate cabinet maintain the system track database. Presumably they form tracks out of target plots supplied by the sonars. Applications programs, such as those for TMA, are conducted in the DaCCs. There are also two weapon-electronics cabinets, each containing its own SMR-MU computer, for a total of six SMR-MUs. The weapon-cabinet computers perform ballistic calculations and control wire-guided torpedoes after launch. In effect, a single DaCC with its computer is equivalent to an M8.

The enormous jump in computer power represented by the late version of SINBADS was apparently needed to support a shift toward long-range bearings-only (all-passive) operation. It is not clear whether any of the installations listed above are of this type. However, this version directly led to the current Spectrum and GIPSY.

GIPSY, Geintegreerd Informatie en Presentie Systeem, was designed specifically for the *Walrus* class. It is SEWACO VIII, a federated combat system. The associated sonar is fully integrated into the system, controlled by standard consoles. Sonar processing adds another pair of unattended SMR-MUs to the two already in the processing cabinet. In all, GIPSY requires seven standard single-operator consoles, probably arranged along a data bus connected to the processor cabinet, so that they can operate interchangeably. Presumably two are typically used for sonar display (active and passive), one for contact evaluation (waterfall to determine which targets are most important), one for interactive TMA, one for target classification, one for command decision (to display the overall tactical plot or to solve navigational problems), and one for weapons control.

On midlife modernization the two *Zvaardvis*-class submarines were fitted with a scaled-down GIPSY, retaining the earlier M8/7 FCS. It employs a single central computer cabinet (CCC, containing one SMR-MU) and two DaCCs. As in a *Walrus*, sensor (medium-range sonar, a down-sized Eledone, and radar) data feed into the CCC, which forms the tactical picture. It in turn feeds targets into the FCS. Overall capability is described as a third of that of a *Walrus*. A possible upgrade, now that the submarines are for sale, would be to replace the M8/7-14 and the

passive sonar ranging unit (LAS-10) with two more DaCCs, one for the tactical plot and the other for FCS. The other two DaCCs would be used solely for sonar control.

Spectrum is the corresponding system developed for the two Dutch-built Taiwanese submarines, which have Dutch-developed SIASS sonars. As in the earlier systems, a processing cabinet contains a pair of SMR-MU picture-keeping computers. Apparently the sonar data computers are included in the associated SIASS system rather than in Spectrum. The system has sufficient signal-processing capability to conduct LOFAR analysis in each preformed beam (and sufficient memory to store the results). The data bus feeds three or four multifunction two-operator SIGHT consoles (each with a 19in color screen and a smaller alphanumeric processor), each containing a pair of SMR-MU computers. As in other systems in this series, two identical weapon-electronics cabinets each contain interfaces to control half the torpedo tubes (normally four each).

The active transducer and cylindrical receiving array feed into a common processor (with separate preprocessors for active and passive operation); the passive ranger and acoustic-intercept arrays share a common processor (with separate front-end preprocessors); and the nonacoustic sensors (ESM, radar, periscope, and navigational aids) share a common processor.

Spectrum can maintain 35 simultaneous tracks, and it can control four missiles (such as Harpoon) and four wire-guided torpedoes simultaneously. The classification library holds up to 300 signatures. The version sold to Taiwan did not include Harpoon or, reportedly, Mk 48 software.

An improved Spectrum II would have equipped follow-on Dutch export submarines. It would have used the standard processing and display components of the new *Karel Doorman*–class frigates. The display units have 1376×1024-pixel color raster screens and employ 68020-series microprocessors. They are connected by Ethernet data buses (10 Mbytes/sec), and data are recorded on two digital optical disks with a capacity of up to 250 Mbits each.

Users: GIPSY: Netherlands (*Walrus* class); Spectrum: Taiwan (*Hai Lung* class). A scaled-down GIPSY is in the two *Zwaardvis*, currently for sale.

NORWAY

◆ MSI-70U

Kongsberg's Multi-Sensor Interface for the *Kobben*-class submarines, MSI-70U was one of the first systems to employ Kalman filtering to assist in associating data from different sensors to form a fire-control solution. The associated computer is SM-3. Units being modernized are being fitted with the new MSI-90U and the Thorn-EMI D3 data-distribution system built around a 1553B bus.

Users: Norway (*Kobben* class).

◆ MSI-90U

Development of Kongsberg's automated submarine command/control system began in 1980, for new Norwegian and German submarines (*Ula* class and Type 212). The initial study was completed in 1982, and a Norwegian-German MoU signed in December 1982. The prototype multifunction display was completed in mid-1983. MSI-90U will form a common-core (federated) combat system, with each partner supplying its own sensors, and will communicate with the consoles via a new BUDOS data bus. The computer is KS900F. Because both navies expect to operate in target-rich environments, MSI-90U is designed to support multiple engagements in quick succession.

A full system consists of four multifunction operator consoles (each with its own computer), a computer rack (with three main computers), and a weapons-control unit (WCU) (with two to three weapons computers), all tied together by a BUDOS data bus (as in the NFT surface-ship systems). All of the computers are KS900s, and the BUDOS bus is provided with three multiplex terminals (MUX), each of which can connect with up to eight users. BUDOS itself can accommodate up to 15 MUXes, far be-

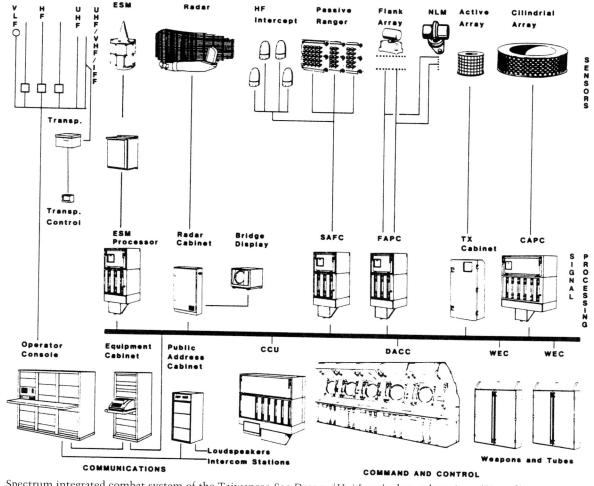

Spectrum integrated combat system of the Taiwanese *Sea Dragon* (*Hai Lung*) -class submarines. (Signaal)

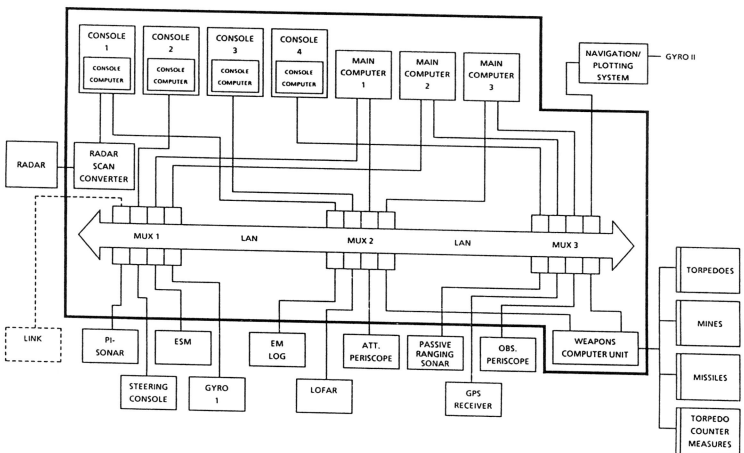

MSI-90U is a fully distributed submarine CDS. (Kongsberg)

yond the needs of the system. Each of the single-operator consoles has two high-resolution, color, raster-scan screens; the operator enters data via a programmable plasma touchscreen, a trackball, and a standard keyboard.

The console display shows:

Situation and Interaction Plot (SIP), the overall tactical situation

Four workplots, which can be viewed in sequence: TMA, Torpedo, Tactical, and Auxiliary

The display can show a digitized radar picture; radar data can be used for target range and bearing. Presumably, the system can easily accommodate a future optronic periscope since its raster-scanned screen has sufficient flexibility and resolution.

One console (the central command unit) is fed by the digital scan converter for the submarine's radar. It is near the steering console and the plotting table on the starboard side of the boat. The other (identical) consoles are arranged in a line on the port side, next to the sonar consoles.

The system as a whole can conduct simultaneous automatic and operator-interactive TMA on up to about 30 targets, can guide several torpedoes (the number depends on the design of the submarine) simultaneously, and can prepare and lay up to about 50 mines (registering positions, while also keeping track of up to 15 hostile mines being laid). Missile preparation and firing (one missile at a time) is an option. Torpedo-guidance modes are LOS, collision course, and manual.

The system carries classification databases for radar, sonar, and platform identification, both for IFF and to plan engagements. It also conducts geographical/oceanographic modeling, forming contour maps and predicting sonar performance. Sonar ranges are used for TMA, for threat evaluation, and for weapons control. MSI-90U provides threat evaluation as well as engagement analysis. The latter function shows whether a target is within torpedo range, computes firing positions (estimating hit probability), and automatically optimizes firing parameters.

Factory tests began in 1986, and the first unit, for the Norwegian submarine *Ula*, was delivered in April 1988.

NFT received a small start-up contract for the improved version (for the German Type 212 submarine) in third quarter 1993; the full-scale development contract was awarded in June 1994. The new version reflects experience with the *Ula* class and has improved MMI. The computers are being upgraded with 68040s, a new display processor, improved graphics, new Barco 14in monitors with better resistance to electromagnetic interference, a new programmable entry panel, enhanced RAM and Flash EPROM, and a new power supply. The new version retains the existing 4156 standard interface between processors, but a new dual redundant fiber-optic Ethernet LAN replaces the 4156 between MSI-90U and submarine sensors. About a third of the software is being rewritten or altered, much of it by a German software house, CAP-Debis.

Users: Germany (Type 212 submarine), Norway (*Ula* class).

RUSSIA

Work on "second captain" systems for submarines apparently began in the 1960s. The "Alfa" (Project 705) class has always been described by the Russians more as highly automated than as fast or deep-diving. This class was equipped with a computer information system called Akkord. "Charlie" (Project 670) -class submarines had combat-direction systems (Brest), possibly the first on board missile units. They were separate from the integrated navigational system (Sigma-670) and the missile and torpedo FCS (Tantal-670, Usta-670, and Ladoga-P-670). The first fully automated submarine CDS was probably aboard "Victor III"–class submarines. Presumably it was developed as part of the 1971–80 fleet plan that produced "Sierra" and "Akula," with "Victor III" an adaptation of some of the new systems to the current production submarine.

By the mid-1970s, the Russians were publicly describing a second captain system on board a missile submarine, in an article about the work of a computer specialist, who fed data into the ship's computer, *by means of which the CO communicated with the ship's weapon system.*

According to a recent Russian account, the first diesel submarine to have a computer CDS was the "Tango" (Project 641BUKI), the first of which was completed in 1973. It seems likely that a similar system was installed on board "Victor II" (Project 671RT) -class submarines; it may also have appeared on board late "Victor Is" (Project 671K). These systems were probably related to the introduction of the SS-N-15 (82-R, RPK-2 Viyoga system) missile, equivalent to the U.S. Subroc. Note that the U.S. Navy developed a computer-based CDS, the Mk 113 FCS, specifically to handle Subroc itself. Too, the Russians often stated that the sonar installed in "Victor"-class submarines was broadly equivalent to the BQQ-2 of the U.S. *Permit* class which had introduced Mk 113.

"Kilo" (Project 877) is a highly automated submarine designed around a central computer. The design requirement (TTZ, tactical-technical requirement) for this submarine was issued in 1974, and thus it apparently represents the generation after "Tango" and "Charlie." The computer receives sonar data and other sensor data and forms a tactical picture. It generates attack data and includes an automatic FCS element. It also provides decision-aid suggestions to the command for performing maneuvers and also for the use of weapons. In the FCS role the computer performs fire-control calculations and transmits torpedo settings; it also controls wire-guided torpedoes. It can maintain the submarine on an ordered course, and executes navigational calculations (such as computation of CPA). It also controls propulsion and diving. The effect of automation is that most submarine functions can be conducted from a single central panel. According to the designers, special attention was paid to human factors, all weapon and navigation control aids being concentrated in a single main control room without internal divisions. Note, however, that there is still a separate integrated navigational system, Andoga. The most common export version, Project 877EM, uses an MVU-110EM digital computer.

Project 877 apparently uses an analog sonar, since its target-tracking capacity is quite limited (two targets can be auto-tracked, and three targets can be manually tracked). The submarine clearly has a cylindrical scanning sonar in the bow. These figures suggest that the sonar incorporates three compensators (in effect, scale models of the sonar in each of which a single commutator moves the sonar beam). Manual tracking may mean three separate tracking CRTs, or else a single CRT using rail-aided tracking. Presumably some equivalent to the U.S. ball-tab is used to turn analog sonar data into digital data for the CDS.

The follow-on Project 636, which entered Russian service about 1990, apparently replaces the analog sonar with a digital equivalent. That may further reduce manning, since there is no longer any need for human trackers.

Published descriptions of the 877/636 design do not indicate how, or whether, the passive flank array (MG-53) is integrated into the ship's combat system. Nor is the distinction between Projects 636 and 877 entirely clear from published Russian accounts.

SOUTH AFRICA

◆ Orca

This Altech Defence Systems (UEC Projects) system replaces the current computer-based CDS of the South African *Daphne* class, using three processors. The main console has three elements: two sonar consoles flank a torpedo firing console, and to their right are two CDS (AIS, action information system) consoles.

The two right-hand interchangeable units form the AIO element (AIS) proper, assembling the tactical picture, conducting TMA, and developing fire-control solutions. System memory carries time-bearing information on up to 20 targets for up to 2 hr/target. The system conducts automatic TMA (ATMA) on 16 targets and computer-aided TMA (CATMA) on 6 targets. It also develops torpedo-firing solutions and allocates targets. Torpedo controls are housed above the AIS consoles, which have plasma touchscreens, QWERTY keyboards, and trackballs. The two

PROJECT 671RTMK COMMAND SYSTEM (SIMPLIFIED AND SANITIZED)

SECOND CAPTAIN LOCAL AREA NETWORK

COMMAND CONSOLE 1	COMMAND CONSOLE 2	COMMAND CONSOLE 3	COMMAND CONSOLE 4	DATALINK
CONSOLE COMPUTER	CONSOLE COMPUTER	CONSOLE COMPUTER	CONSOLE COMPUTER	SPECIAL DATALINK

NAVIGATION AND PLOTTING LOCAL AREA NETWORK

GYRO-1 · GYRO-2 · DATALINK · OMEGA/LORAN · GLONASS

STEERING CONSOLE · NAVIGATIONAL PLOT

RADIO-ELECTRONIC WARFARE LOCAL AREA NETWORK

SNOOP TRAY 2 "RADAR" · RADAR SCAN CONVERTER

DATALINK · OPERATOR CONSOLE · ESM THREAT LIBRARY

BRICK PULP ESM · CONSOLE COMPUTER

PARK LAMP DF

VIKING CENTRAL PROCESSING LOCAL AREA NETWORK

MAIN COMPUTER 1 · MAIN COMPUTER 2 · MAIN COMPUTER 3

MULTIPLEXER 1 — DATABUS — MULTIPLEXER 2 — DATABUS — MULTIPLEXER 3

SENSORS SUITE LOCAL AREA NETWORK

BARRACUDA LF A/P BOW SONAR · ACOUSTIC COUNTERMEASURES

OPERATOR CONSOLE 1 · OPERATOR CONSOLE 2 · OPERATOR CONSOLE 3

CONSOLE COMPUTER · CONSOLE COMPUTER · CONSOLE COMPUTER

AKULA FLANK ARRAYS · MULTIPLEXER 4 — DATABUS — MULTIPLEXER 5

CHANEL PASSIVE INTERCEPT · PERISCOPES

PASSIVE RANGING SONAR · WAKE SENSOR SYSTEM · PITHON TOWED ARRAY · FIRE CONTROL SONAR · UNDER-ICE NAV SONAR · MINE AVOIDING SONAR · UNDERWATER TELEPHONE

WEAPONS CONTROLS LOCAL AREA NETWORK

53cm TORPEDO TUBES · NUCLEAR RELEASE

65cm TORPEDO TUBES · 65CM TORPEDO TUBE CONTROL · TORPEDOES CONTROL · MISSILES CONTROL · ESCAPE & EVASION · MAIN COMPUTER 4

CONSOLE COMPUTER · CONSOLE COMPUTER · CONSOLE COMPUTER

The command system of a modernized "Victor III"–class submarine (Project 671RTMK) is built around a single data bus (broken up in this diagram to simplify arrangement). The special data link in the second captain LAN is to authorize the release of nuclear weapons (note the special nuclear release lock in the weapons-control section). The net computing power of the four command consoles in the second captain network exceeds that of the main computers. The Viking system is modeled on the Norwegian MSI-90U. Note that, as in the Krivak III, the surface-search radar is included in the ECM system because of its ESM role. Note, too, that there is a special data link associated with ESM, allowing units to pass data so as to triangulate targets. (Stuart Slade, DMS/Forecast International)

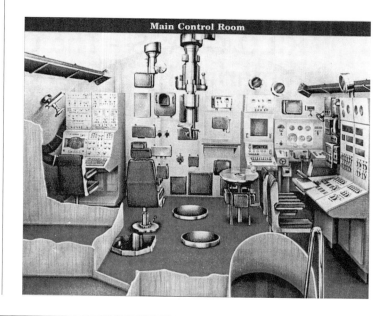

Main Control Room

The control room of a Project 877 or 636 ("Kilo") -class submarine, in a drawing published in an advertisement by the Rubin design bureau. The design of the submarine emphasized automation. None of the consoles in this drawing was labeled, but it seems likely that the panels on the extreme left are the FCS. To their right, the large rectangular screen is probably a second captain workstation, normally displaying a tactical summary. Next to it, to the right, is a one-man steering/control station. The two seats facing right are probably for machinery and ballast control. The seat on the left, with the extra headrest, is presumably for the CO. An enclosed space just abaft the FCS contains another pair of consoles with another single operator seat. They are probably the sonar consoles. (Rubin bureau via Dave Markov)

UEC's submarine combat and surveillance subsystem comprises (left to right) a sonar console, a torpedo firing console, a second sonar console, and the paired consoles of the action information system (AIS). The AIS performs computer-aided TMA (CATMA) or automatic TMA (ATMA) on multiple targets, and can control wire-guided torpedoes. This version of the submarine combat system is now being productionized; a prototype is on board the submarine *Emily Hobhouse*. The existing system, which entered service about 1985, uses the same arrangement of consoles. However, in this version the big screens (both sonar and AIS; larger ones for AIS) are circular. They have banks of special-purpose buttons instead of the plasma touch-screens of this version. The two sonar consoles have paper recorders on top instead of the smaller CRTs in the raster-scan version. (Altech)

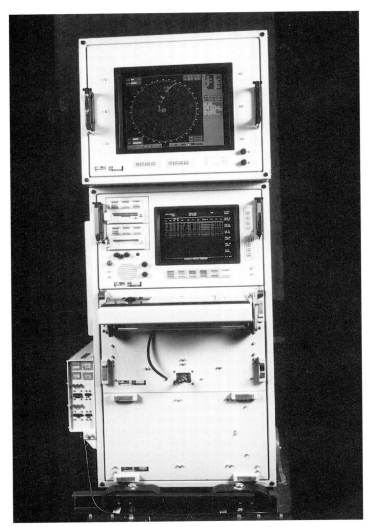

The EW and radar console of UEC's submarine combat system. Typically it is located across the submarine control room from the navigation subsystem, adjacent to the sonar signal processing cabinet. (Altech)

The navigation subsystem of UEC's submarine combat system. Typically it is located alongside (abaft) the sonar and action information consoles. (Altech)

large consoles are intended to display passive sonar data; they flank the active sonar console. The active sonar is also used for obstacle avoidance.

There are also separate consoles for surface sensors (radar, ESM), for communications, and for navigation. The surface search radar operates at 25 kW at 9.4 GHz and has variable pulse width and PRF. The ESM system operates at 2 to 18 GHz and offers three alarm levels. The navigation subsystem employs a 19in electronic chart for route planning, passage appraisal and track control, and sensor selection and monitoring. It maintains the officer of the watch log. Navigational data are fed automatically to the other elements of the system.

Each sonar console contains a pair of color CRTs, which can be used for waterfall displays for the passive tracking sonar (PTS) or the intercept sonar (IS) or the passive ranging sonar (PRS). Each of two PTS has five autotrackers; the IS has five autotrackers; and the PRS has two autotrackers, for a total of 17 autotrackers in the system. There is also a bottom bounce unit.

The torpedo firing cabinet in the torpedo room is unmanned.

This upgrade is designated DSCS-2; it follows a less radical modernization of the 1980s. It includes a new ESM system, new sonars, and a new sonar classifier including a library. The existing medium-range active sonar was improved. Both periscopes (ST3 and M41) were upgraded with fewer optical elements and larger exit pupils for better (reportedly doubled) light transmission. Both now have stadimeters, and the search periscope (M41) now has day and low-light video channels with recorders and an inboard display.

The prototype system is aboard the submarine *Emily Hobhouse*. The next will be *Maria van Riebeck*; the last will be *Johanna van der Merwe*.

SWEDEN

◆ 9SCS Mk 3 (SESUB)

CelsiusTech's CDS for the *Gotland* (A19) class is related to 9LV Mk 3. SESUB is the Royal Swedish Navy designation. It employs two computer consoles, one accommodating a pair of database (tactical-picture) computers, the other a pair of command and weapons control (CWC) computers, both on a dual copper Ethernet bus with three Terma-bult Type IID multifunction consoles, one of which has an upper display for the Manta ESM system (the others are all double-screen). Software includes a Kockums TMA module developed with the University of Lund. The CSU 90 sonar (bow cylinder, flank arrays, intercept sonar, and self-noise monitor) uses three consoles on a fiber-optic bus, the extra capacity being needed to handle digitized acoustic data.

In the control room, the one-man control panel is on the forward bulkhead to port, with the navigation console next to it. Just abaft the control station on the port side is the diving and safety console. Abaft it is one of the three CDS consoles (the one carrying the Manta read-out), and abaft that is the radio room. On the starboard side, fore to aft, are two CDS consoles, then a CSU 90 console, then plotter/recorder, then the other two CSU 90 consoles.

Sonar data processed at the CSU 90 consoles are fed directly into the CWC computer, which is directly connected to a torpedo interface unit, to ESM and radar, to a dual torpedo-tube control computer, and to a dual navigation computer.

◆ NEDPS/AI-FCS

Nacken Electronic Data-Processing System, manufactured by DataSAAB, was the first Swedish submarine computer FCS. It is the step beyond the Philips 9TCI210 system, which was presumably equivalent to the contemporary Signaal M8. AI-FCS (Action Information-FCS) was an export designation. The Royal Swedish Navy designation was IDPS-14, the *Nacken* (A14) Electronic Data Processing System. An IDPS-11 version was developed for retrofit into the *Sjoormen* (A11) class, and an IDPS-17 for the *Vastergotland* (A17) class. Requirements were formulated in 1966–67; they included passive fire control (by TMA, which the Swedes call target-factor calculation, or TFC) on several targets simultaneously. That capability clearly required a computer. The same computer could also be used for other shipboard tasks, such as machinery control and depth-keeping, and the system evolved from weapons and sensor control to overall submarine control. A simulator, ordered in 1970, was used in 1971–74 to test and develop the requisite software. The system is built around two Censor 932 64-kbyte computers. One maintains the tactical picture; the other is used for fire control. The two computers share a common mass memory and a common input channel for the submarine sensors (sonar, radar, periscope bearings). They feed a pair of interchangeable consoles with CRTs. Typically one shows a tactical plot (TP), the other a fire-control plot (FCP). Between them is mounted a torpedo status board (the torpedo fire-control display, or FCD), and there is also an alphanumeric display, the general communication unit (GCU), manned by the ship's electronics officer. The consoles are equipped with keyboards and trackballs.

Calculated target tracks are displayed on the TP, which replaces the conventional paper plot; it can also display the signal-to-noise ratios of various targets being tracked. The system can carry up to 50 targets, and it can automatically provide simultaneous TMA (for fire control) for up to 10 of them. Up to 12 torpedoes can be controlled simultaneously. The FCP normally shows relative motion (own-ship at center), but it can be centered on a torpedo.

The Mk 2 version uses one multifunction System 800 console with two side-by-side rectangular CRTs, each with its own display generator. Presumably each half of the console has its own Censor 932. Weapons-data boards are above the CRTs. These three boards also include alphanumeric displays, for example, of data links.

Added computing power increases system capacity, so that two more displays are added to those of the Mk 1 system: operational plot (OP) and contact-evaluation plot (CEP). The OP (in effect, a navigational plot) is used during transit to the patrol area. OP shows features such as own and enemy minefields, mission information, coastal radars (with their parameters), the route, and the operational area itself. The OP can show 50 internally generated points, 10 target channels for TMA, up to 240 plots received externally by data link, and 32 ESM emitters or emitter modes. CEP is used mainly when a contact can be detected only sporadically, or at very long range. Collected information is shown in time-bearing (waterfall) form, covering all 360 deg and up to 2 hr vertically. It replaces the earlier paper plot. Normally the TP is used as the submarine is preparing to attack; up to 10 targets can be analyzed simultaneously. In the TP, own-ship is at the center, and there are no navigational displays, although eight reference points can be used to show, for

example, the boundaries of the patrol area. Up to 50 internally generated plots can be shown, and also a list of which sensor is tracking which target. Typically one half-console is used as command station (showing CEP or OP or TP), and the other as fire-control station.

Users: Sweden (Mk 1 in *Nacken* class; Mk 2 in *Vastergotland* and modernized *Sjoormen* classes).

UNITED KINGDOM

◆ DCB/DCG/TIOS

The standard British automated submarine AIO/FCS was essentially a combination of the earlier DCA picture-keeper (which appeared in 1973, built around a single FM1600B) and a digital FCS to replace the earlier unintegrated TCSS Mk 9. The integrated digital FCS, built around a second FM1600B, was needed because TCSS Mk 9 was incompatible with the new sub-launched missile (ultimately Sub-Harpoon) in prospect for the mid-1970s. DCB entered service on board HMS *Superb* in 1976.

DCB maintains data on 20 or 24 targets, including two current ones (much as the contemporary U.S. Mk 113 maintained 20 targets and tracked two). Originally automated TMA was limited to CREM (cross-range error minimization), a British equivalent to MATE (using different graphics). Increased computer power later permitted the computer to conduct automatic TMA simultaneously with CREM (KATE, Kalman [Filter] Analysis and Track Evaluation). Type 2027 passive ranges can be incorporated.

DCB employs a three-position AIO console (Principal Sonar Officer flanked by two AIO operators) and a two-position FCS console. The central console has a large CRT showing a geographic (PPI-type) plot of all sonar contacts. Each of the other positions has two 12 in CRTs, one for graphics, the other for alphanumerics and for interaction with the system via a light pen. The graphic displays are LPD (target bearing, own ship at center), TBD (time/bearing display), TFD (time-frequency display), BFD (bearing-frequency display), and sound velocity profile. Once an acceptable TMA solution has been found, it is sent to the FCS position. The FCS graphic display is generally a PPI showing own and target position and weapon position, projected course, and enable point (with tellbacks in the case of a wire-guided torpedo). Weapon presets are displayed on the left-hand CRT. Two FCS consoles can manage two simultaneous engagements.

An automatic contact-evaluation plotter (ACEP) can be used for manual TMA, for example, of distant slow-moving targets, or to check the automatic solutions provided by the system. Typically the ACEP is placed on one side of the main AIO console, the FCS console on the other.

The usual command team of eight presumably comprises the five console operators, the ACEP operator, an ACEP plotter, and the PWO.

In September 1990 Ferranti was awarded a contract for F2420 computers to replace the FM1600Bs, parallel to the ADIMP upgrade of ADAWS. There is apparently no increase in track file storage, but presumably the improved computer made KATE possible. An associated Smiths Navigation and Plotting System (SNAPS, a tactical plotter) can keep track of up to 128 targets, their bearings provided by DCB (the AIO-assigned number is input via a keypad at the table). SNAPS provides a line-of-position (LOP) plot. There have also been considerable software improvements, reportedly five in 1988–91 alone. Gresham Lion updated DCB to fire Spearfish.

DCB was also upgraded through installation of a peripheral PDP-11/44 processor (with a CSPI Minimap MM11 array processor), the Gresham-CAP DCG, which added a mass memory of 128 kbytes specifically to store long runs of data. Speed is about 8 MFLOPS. DCG is intended to do automatic TMA (to improve the accuracy of the tactical picture) and to provide TDAs. It does oceanographic prediction. It is also used for simulation (for on-board training). The main DCG display is between the two DCB AIO consoles; there are also three remote monitors elsewhere in the control room. The operator interacts with the system via a light pen and a lightweight hand-held keypad. The Royal Navy let a contract to rehost DCG software to BAeSEMA, using Sun SPARCStations running UNIX software. Because this version of DCG uses the same processors as those in SMCS Releases 6 and 7, the software can ultimately be used in SMCS. The first hardware is to enter service in mid-1996, and five submarines are to be retrofitted.

Gresham Lion (later Dowty) was prime contractor for DCB. Gresham Lion and Ferranti later developed the commercial TIOS (Tactical Information Organization, Submarine) integrated submarine command/control/FCS for a consortium headed by Vickers. It also used Ferranti's FM1600B computer. TIOS-B and -C, which used the FM1600B, could handle one or two targets simultaneously, performing TMA on them. Track memory capacity was not given.

Users:

   DCB: United Kingdom (*Swiftsure, Trafalgar, Resolution* classes)

   TIOS: Brazil (TIOS-B, *Oberons*), Israel (TIOS-C, Vickers 540 class). TIOS-C was upgraded in 1983 to control Sub-Harpoon. It may be replaced by a Singer-Librascope system (see the U.S. section below).

◆ KAFS/DCC

KAFS was Ferranti's commercial version of the DCC, the CDS of the *Upholder* class, which is now for sale. It was also intended for the new *Vanguard*-class SSBNs, but the distributed DCM (see below) was bought instead. DCH was a KAFS derivative intended for British *Oberon*-class modernization (but all such submarines have now been discarded). Thus DCC and KAFS are the last British submarine CDSs to be built around central computers, analogous to the surface ship ADAWS and CACS. Dowty-CAP was subcontractor for consoles and fore-end hardware.

In DCC, two FM1600E computers drive three multifunction consoles, each of which can be used for either command/control (picture-keeping, TMA) or fire control. Each console contains two 12in circular cursive CRTs, with light pens for input. Compared to DCB, capacity has been increased to 35 tracks, but current tracking and engagement capability is still two targets.

KAFS (SSK AIO and FCS) uses a single Ferranti FM1600E computer (192k expandable to 256k) and a single two-operator console for both AIO and FCS functions, the computer fitting into the bottom of the console. Each position carries two CRTs, a tactical display on the left and a tote (alphanumerics) display on the right; only one pair is operated in the patrol condition. The displays are canted rather than upright so that the lengthy use of light pens will be less fatiguing. Interaction is via light pen and keyboard.

KAFS console, comprising AIO and FCS positions. Only one operator is normally needed (two at action stations). (Ferranti)

System memory suffices for 35 tracks (expandable to 50), two being tracked and engageable at any one time. The system can control up to four wire-guided torpedoes. KAFS was announced in 1981. It employed much of Ferranti's existing surface ship hardware: the prototype (1982) used a cannibalized WSA-420 surface-ship AIO/FCS console.

A compact version, COMKAFS, never sold. However, a COMKAFS Mk 2 derivative, Nautilus, was announced at BARNEE 1995. It uses a new open architecture. GEC Marconi Combat Systems Division used a proprietary software tool to semi-automatically translate Coral code used in DCH to ADA, directly translating about 80% of the programming. Translated software includes that used for data fusion, input/output, and TMA. The FCS software, some of it written in Fortran, was still being translated as of 1995. Software is now split into modules so the system can use a network client/server architecture, a central computer holding the track database. Ultimately the tactical database (track file) will be replicated across the system, eliminating any central computer. This software is also being considered for use by a surface ship towing an array.

Users: Brazil (KAFS: Type 1400 class; installation in *Oberons* to replace TIOS-B abandoned because of cost, 1989), United Kingdom (DCC: *Upholder* class, for sale). The Brazilian *Oberons* only had the earlier TCSS Mk 9.

◆ DCM (SMCS)

BAeSEMA's (formerly Gresham-CAP's) submarine multiscreen command system is to replace the existing DCB on board all future British submarines (SSN). It equips the new *Vanguard*-class strategic submarines. It uses a dual-redundant fiber-optic data bus (one of the first at sea) to connect four full-color multifunction consoles, a main tactical display, two sensor-input nodes, two common-service nodes, and two remote terminals. The multifunction consoles house 80386 computers (programmed mainly in ADA) used for general processing; the common-service nodes store bulk data and house Transputers (programmed in OCCAM) for such computation-intense high-speed applications as automatic TMA. Each common-service node contains eight processing cards, each carrying eight T800 Transputers, for a net throughput of 50 MFLOPS; SMCS was the first announced dedicated military application of the Transputer. In all, the system employs 11 computers using 80386 processors. It is tied together by a high-capacity (166 Mbits/sec) fiber-optic data bus. Each fiber-optic link is duplicated; when a failure occurs, the stream of data is automatically rerouted to the intact link (the system is called self-healing). SMCS required about 1 million lines of code; the later related SSCS required about 1.5 million.

The same consoles and computers are used both for information processing and for weapons control. All consoles are identical, and all are software-configured, for maximum redundancy and flexibility. For example, in one role all the consoles may be devoted to sonar data; at periscope depth one or more may display ESM data. In another role, one or more may function as fire-control or countermeasures consoles. The system is designed to process data not only from current sensors but also from future ones such as very long towed arrays (with many more elements than at present) and optronic periscopes.

Like the later SSCS for surface ships, SMCS uses Racal's multifunction consoles (MFCs), with 80386 applications processors, 68030 display processors, and a 60-Mbyte hard disk. Each console incorporates a graphics input tablet and a programmable keyboard. Unlike earlier British command systems developed by Ferranti, which used light pens, this system uses menu-driven, pull-down, touch-sensitive plasma panels. The panel on each MFC displays detailed numerical data in tabular form and controls the two monochrome alpha information panels above the main display.

Gresham-CAP claims that SMCS has more than 20 times the processing power of previous conventional submarine combat systems, at lower acquisition and ownership costs (and with better than 99.9% projected availability). This sort of improvement is probably a natural and virtually universal consequence of recent developments in computer hardware, paralleling well-known civilian experience.

Development of SMCS began with the award of a contract in December 1986 after a 3-yr competition. The first, for installation on board the lead Trident submarine, HMS *Vanguard*, was delivered to the Trident Tactical Weapon System Shore Development Facility (SDF) at VSEL Barrow, and completed its Part 1 Naval Weapon Harbour Trial in mid-1990 (the ship commissioned in 1992). The second SMCS was installed as a shore trainer at Faslane.

Release 3 software supported *Vanguard*'s successful torpedo trials (about January 1994). By mid-1994 the new SSBNs had initial Release 4A software, with Release 4B expected at the end of the year. Release 4A added oceanographic information and some on-board training; Release 4B provides the rest of the on-board training and adds resilience to that of 4A.

The first two SSNs fitted with SMCS are HMS *Sovereign* and *Trafalgar*, which ran trials in 1995. The initial Release 3 software provides the tactical picture and weapons functionality. It is part of the SSN Update Phase I refit, formerly Phase 1 and 2 of the *Swiftsure* and *Trafalgar*–class midlife update. Other elements are installation of the 2074 improved bow array, the 2046 towed array, the 2081 oceanographic sensor, and the 2082 intercept sonar. The first contract provides for Release 5 software to interface with the improved sonars installed at the same time; hardware modifications include introduction of some i486 to replace i386, and a 30% increase in available memory.

The remainder of the four-year program covers Releases 6 and 7, ordered in mid-July 1994 for delivery in 1998. They are part of Update II (formerly the Major or Final Phase). They are needed to process new types of data from the new Type 2076 sonar. Reportedly, Releases 6 and 7 were largely driven by the vast increase in data expected from the 2076 suite, which will be capable of autodetection and sonar fusion. According to one description, 2076 will construct a sonar "world picture," which will be displayed in the control room. That suggests large-scale TMA and a geoplot rather than the classic waterfalls. This view is consistent with another description, in which the greatly increased computing power is needed for selection and control of the information sent to the command system. The increased data load will require a new fiber-optic data bus (tactical weapon system highway). Releases 6/7 will presumably support the Tomahawk missiles that the Royal Navy is ordering.

A diagram of Release 6 and 7 functionality shows an oceanography element communicating with the tactical picture (charts), with the input subsystem (which communicates with sensors and provides sound speed profile), and with the weapons-management element (provides sea state and layer depth). The input subsystem feeds sensor data to the tactical picture-keeper, which in turn sends target location to the weapons-management element. A weapons tactical aids element (presumably a submarine equivalent of CCA) provides the tactical picture with tactical advice, and provides the weapons-management element with weapons-performance data. Operational aids provide compilation advice to the tactical picture-keeper.

New displays are being developed to present the command team with details of the sonar data processes conducted within the Sound Room (and, presumably, within the sonar computer system). One advantage claimed for SMCS is that although it will fuse sonar data, it can also maintain the original data so that it can be withdrawn from the fused picture if it is later considered incorrect. The Update II system will use X-Windows software (UNIX operating system) and new graphics-processing hardware using ruggedized RISC processors; a VME backplane replaces the current Multibus II. This degree of modification is possible because the system uses a Distributed Real-Time Applications Kernel (DRAKE), a BAeSEMA-funded development that ports the existing common infrastructure to UNIX and makes it possible to integrate software written in languages other than ADA, running in slower time.

This major expansion exploits the capacity inherent in the original system: the company's DRAKE ports the existing common infrastructure to UNIX and gives the ability to integrate software written in languages other than ADA which run in slower time.

Users: United Kingdom, to become standard submarine system; variants are: -V for *Vanguard* class (1993), -T for *Trafalgar* class, -U for *Upholder* class (canceled), and -S for *Swiftsure* (may be canceled). As of 1991, estimated total cost of 14 SMCS was £115M.

UNITED STATES

With the advent of very powerful TAC-series computers, the U.S. Navy's Undersea Warfare Advanced System Technology Office has developed a software library, SFMPL (submarine force mission-planning library) containing a wide variety of tactical aids, some vital to fire control. They include new TMA algorithms. Typically a submarine will have two TAC-series computers running SFMPL software, one for acoustics, one for combat control.

There is current interest in single-leg multisensor TMA solutions (an algorithm completed laboratory testing in FY94), in automated TMA, and in automated detection/automated classification (AD/AC). ARPA continues to sponsor development of more automated submarine combat systems (see below).

◆ Mk 113

Librascope's Mk 113 FCS was the first U.S. underwater FCS to transcend short-range fire control and thus to become a CDS. The only surviving version, Mod 9, is on the two *Lafayette*-class strategic submarines converted to support special operations. For details of earlier versions of Mk 113, see the 1991/92 edition. This version originally used an ASW Computer Program (ASWCP) sharing the geoballistic computer of the submarine with the Poseidon missile program, which enjoyed a higher priority: both could run simultaneously, but during missile operations the ASWCP was turned off. That could be done gradually, the missile program taking over 20% blocks of memory until at 60% ASWCP the program would run only half the time, and it could support only one module instead of the usual two (CHURN and MATE, TBP, or SIT). CHURN is automatic TMA; TBP is time-bearing picture; SIT is geographic situation (plot) based on a MATE solution.

In 1991 Librascope supplied new elements to the Mk 78 analyzer (in effect the system digital computer terminal) including UYK-44 computers (presumably to replace the geoballistic computers formerly used) and new CRTs, so track capacity is now probably considerably greater. The description which follows applies to Mod 9 as originally delivered, not to the modified version with a UYK-44 computer.

Mod 9 interposes a digital picture-keeper, the Mk 78 analyzer, between its analog sonar and its analog position-keeper and torpedo FCS. The sensors are the BQQ-2 passive array (BQR-7), the analog BQS-4 active sonar, and a stand-alone BQR-15 towed array. The analyzer has two 10-target memories, A and B, and it normally receives track data for one target in each at any one time. If more than two targets are involved, bearings can be manually input into the other track memories. The ATF is an analog device; its output is periodically sampled and then averaged to form a data point in memory (non-ATF bearings are also averages). Ranges can be associated with bearing data. Memory capacity limits the number of entries per source; after an hour old data points are dropped as new ones are entered. For the two targets in active memory, the computer itself estimates solutions (CHURN) while the human operator develops MATE solutions. MATE can handle up to 3 hr of data. Target limits are 72,000-yd range and 50-kt speed.

Computer memory retains strings of bearings from other targets for later recall and analysis. Once a target has been analyzed using MATE or some other TMA technique, the solution is retained in computer memory and projected ahead (position-kept).

The rest of the system corresponds exactly to earlier torpedo FCS/TDC systems. The Mk 75 attack director can be used independently to track a target and to obtain a solution on its dials; alternatively, it can be fed with the TMA solution developed at the Mk 78. Just like a World War II TDC, it includes both a position-keeping (PK) element and a torpedo ballistic computer, for torpedo setting. For a wire-guided torpedo, a separate torpedo director issues commands and the PK section dead-reckons torpedo position based on those commands. Torpedoes are actually set and fired from a separate Mk 50 attack control console alongside Mk 75.

The digital Mk 48 torpedo required a separate Mk 66 torpedo-control console (with analog-to-digital converter) and with its own tone generator. It (a) selects one of four groups of preset tactics; (b) individually presets the trajectory mode, antiselfhoming (ASH), pre-enable speed, search speed, search mode, acoustic mode, Doppler enable, ping interval, pitch angle, search depth, floor setting, ceiling setting or operational depth setting, and target mode parameters; (c) commands readback of functions set into the torpedo; (d) selects one of the two function memories in the console and the tone-signal generator; (e) selects the most desirable laminar distance for the torpedo; (f) commands changes after launch to search depth, pitch angle, pre-enable speed, search speed, acoustic mode, search mode, Doppler enable, and keylock parameters; (g) checks torpedo acceptance of presets; and (h) monitors continuity of guide wire after launch. All torpedo presets except gyro angle are set at this console (gyro angle is set by the attack director and monitored by the torpedo-control console). Run-to-enable is set at the director and received at the torpedo-control console for setting into the torpedo. The console has two memories, so it can preset two torpedoes.

Note that because the sonars were analog, the system had to accept an encumbrance in the form of analog-to-digital conversion of sonar data; and because the FCS itself was analog, solutions had to be translated into analog form and then back into digital form for Mk 48 control. In effect, Mk 117 (in the *Los Angeles* class) was Mk 113 Mod 9 with the converters eliminated, and with the digital computer responsible for the relatively simple fire-control steps conducted by the Mk 75 attack director.

◆ CCS Mk 1/ADAC/Mk 117

Combat Control System Mk 1 is the principal current U.S. submarine combat-direction system. It is essentially the Mk 117 FCS, developed for the *Los Angeles* class, modified to control Tomahawk missiles. Mk 117 was backfit into existing *Permit*- and *Sturgeon*-class submarines, most of which were later refitted with CCS Mk 1.

Mk 117 was the first U.S. all-digital submarine CDS, built around a two-bay UYK-7 computer with double-density memory. It is associated with the digital BQQ-5 sonar (the analog BQS-15 provides its data via an analog/digital converter). The decision to buy all-digital systems made the analog Subroc missile obsolete, although there was an attempt to retain it by modifying some Mk 117s.

Mk 117 was generally credited with about twice the target-handling capacity of Mk 113 (20 targets). This figure would seem to correspond to doubling the number of MATE stations. However, it has also been said that sensor tracker capability and man-machine interface (presumably MATE stations) limited Mk 117 performance to less than one-fifth of its theoretical track capacity. That suggests an ultimate capacity of about 200 to 250 tracks. Note that BSY-1 has been credited with 10 times the target capacity of Mk 117, presumably about 400 targets, but it has no more MATE stations than Mk 117. Probably most of the targets with which it is credited are surface tracks, which do not require MATE.

The Mk 117 system console consists of two weapons-control consoles (WCCs) Mk 81, one Mk 92 attack-control console (with a control panel), and a third Mk 81 WCC. The stroke-graphics WCCs are used for TMA (of single or multiple targets in multiple modes), for attack evaluation, and to review computer-recommended weapon presets. They can also display environmental data (sonar ray traces, for example). The standard CRT display is divided vertically into an auxiliary read-out area (alphanumerics), a tactical display area (used, for example, for MATE), and a lower control label area.

The Mk 92 console between the Mk 81s monitors the tubes

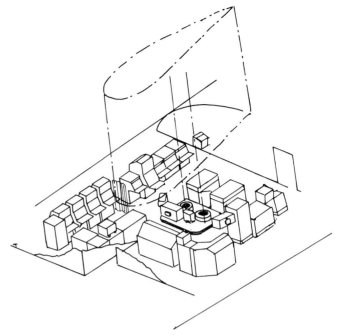

Sonar, control, and attack arrangements in an "Improved" *Los Angeles*–class submarine (SSN 719 or later). To port, note the integrated control/ballast console, as in the *Ohio* class. To starboard, the sonar room (with four two-screen ICDC displays) is forward of the attack center (BQQ-5C and later versions of the earlier BQQ-5 sonar have four ICDCs; earlier versions have three). This space also contains a performance-monitoring console and a raw video display. The consoles in the attack center are a Mk 92 attack-control console, next to a Tomahawk weapon-control console and three Mk 81 weapon-control consoles (for torpedoes and Harpoon missiles). Pre-Tomahawk ships, with the Mk 117 all-digital attack center (ADAC), had two Mk 81s next to a Mk 92, with another Mk 81 on the after side of it. Because all the Mk 81s are connected to the same digital computer (and because they have general-purpose raster-scan displays), they are interchangable. Typically, a pair of Mk 81s is manned by a pair of target trackers; the attack-control console, which actually fires weapons, is manned by the weapons systems officer. For example, one of the trackers may be responsible for a MATE TMA solution on the target, while the other watches a digital version of the classic pair of fire-control dials—showing submarine and target courses—to monitor the accuracy of the fire-control solution. Other Mk 81 display formats include multiple-target tracking, weapon-attack evaluation, and generation of computer-recommended weapon presets based on the weapon model, target solution, and environment. The big console next to the ship-control is for navigation. Other consoles in this space serve the surface-search radar and the EMS antennas; there is also a dead-reckoning tracer (DRT). Two bearing and range indicators (BRIs) hang above the periscope stand, the edge of which is shaded. The two periscopes have been omitted for clarity (their ceneterlines and wells are shown). Across from the sonar room are the CO's and XO's staterooms. Abaft the attack center is the radio/BCM room; abaft the control room is the navigational equipment space. (Author)

and the status of their contents, displaying the type of missile or torpedo in each. Its desktop contains the firing key and the tube selector. Presets are homing type (off, passive, active, or combination), stratum (below limit, no limit, and above limit), anticapture (set between 1 and 8), speed (low, low/medium to high, and high), and horizontal search pattern (circle left, straight, circle right, and automatic). The system also presets initial gyro angle, running depth, and enable run.

CCS Mk 1 adds Tomahawk capability, in the form of a fourth Mk 81 console (Mk 81 Mod 3) and new software running on a pair of additional computers (UYK-44s): one to process OTH-T data, the other to process weapon data. Typically the row of Mk 81s and the Mk 92 are on the starboard side of the attack center, with the Tomahawk Mk 81 Mod 3 on the forward bulkhead. The latter has a console data bus, a 32 bit × 32k display refresh/bulk memory, an alphanumeric keyboard, an edit capability for keyboard and list set functions, and a UYK-20 emulator for target correlation and processing. The console, therefore, has quicker responses, gains real-time access to expanded databases on board the submarine (which are needed for Tomahawk flight planning), gains internal refresh capability, and has a reserve for future growth.

Virtually all Mk 117s were converted into CCS Mk 1s.

CCS Mk 1 Mod 1 was approved for service use in July 1980. Mod 2 supports the submarine vertical-launching system. The associated sonar is BQQ-5C. Mod 3 is Mod 2 with Mk 48 ADCAP capability, for SSN 719-25 and 750. Mod 4 (on *Sturgeon*-class submarines) can control SLMM mobile mines.

Under the FY94 program, installation of NTCS-A (JMCIS) computers aboard CCS Mk 1 and BSY-1 submarines was certified. They provide battle-group interoperability and OTH correlation algorithm updates.

CCS Mk 2 is the replacement system.

◆ Mk 118

The Trident (*Ohio* class) all-digital defensive FCS is based on Mk 117 but is simplified because it controls fewer types of weapons, and also because it makes greater use of digital equipment. Later units of the class are receiving CCS Mk 2. Mk 118 controls Mk 48 torpedoes, 3in and 6in countermeasures, and MOSS (mobile submarine simulators) fired from catapults in torpedo tubes. The basic control consoles are the two SIDs (situation information display, OJ-326(V)3/UYK) in the submarine command/control center. They perform TMA analysis of the target and generate weapons orders. Each has a single CRT, and they flank the ACC Mk 92 Mod 1 (Mod 1 is similar to the Mod 0 of Mk 117 systems except that it can control countermeasures). The ACC in turn connects to the external countermeasures launchers and to the 3in countermeasure control and display unit.

Either of the two SID operators uses the ACC to select a weapon or countermeasure and fire it. This was the first time the SID console was used in an FCS; it expanded on the capabilities of the WCC Mk 81 of FCS Mk 113-10 and FCS Mk 117 to provide an operator-interactive digitally driven CRT display. One SID operator is present primarily for TMA. The other develops orders to preset and control Mk 48 torpedoes and countermeasures. Either may view the other's display; the functions

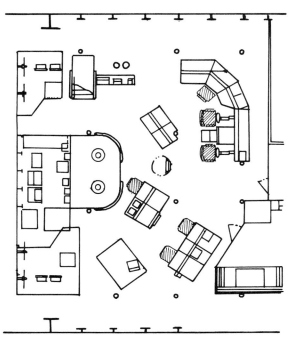

This plan view of the *Ohio*-class control space shows Mk 118 consoles. The two double circles are the periscopes on their raised platform. The console at top right is for ship control and ballasting. Forward and to starboard is the two-man defensive weapons system (DWS) console. Aft of it is the DRT table with a BRI above it. DWS is the main Mk 118 console, consisting of a pair of digital standard information displays (SIDs) flanking a Mk 92 attack console. The SIDs are used for TMA and then for weapon settings and control; the Mk 92 is used to select and launch weapons or countermeasures. Typically one operator performs TMA and the other sets weapons, but either operator can perform the entire sequence from TMA through attack. (Author)

of the two consoles are completely interchangeable, and either can perform full fire-control functions. The system uses the bearing/range indicator (BRI) Mk 116, similar to that in FCS 117, to remotely display target-position data for the submarine commander. The associated computer is a three-bay UYK-7 in the ship's computer complex (see below).

A Russian account of Mk 118, published in 1992, credits the system with the ability to track eight targets continuously, guiding two torpedoes at a time. This reported track capacity seems low compared to that of Mk 117 or even Mk 113.

At the other end of the system, in the torpedo room, the defensive weapon launch console (DWLC) consists of two TT control panels flanking an unmanned weapons-launch console (WLC) Mk 96-0. This arrangement is markedly different from (and simpler than) previous torpedo-room equipment. Mk 118 eliminates most switching and analog interfaces, with fewer types of weapons and use of digital equipment (it is almost totally a digital system). Mk 96 converts digital signals from the control-room consoles to analog for Mk 48 and MOSS and also replaces several other pieces of equipment, to greatly reduce cabling. The fire-control switchboard of earlier submarines is eliminated altogether. Rather than using a single firing circuit with tube-select switch, Mk 118 uses a separate circuit in each tube, with one control per tube in Mk 92. The weapons-select switch is eliminated because there are only two types, Mk 48 and MOSS. To switch a tube, the cable connecting the breech door with weapons-launch console Mk 96 is disconnected at the console and mated with a different console connector dedicated to the weapon involved. The result is only 45 cables in all, compared to over 200 in the *Lafayette*-class Mk 113-9. All countermeasure launching is controlled at the Mk 92 panel, which can remotely control 3in countermeasures.

Software is similar to that developed for Mk 113-10 and Mk 117. It processes data for multiple contacts, using various techniques for determining contact and target position and motion. Typically, it initially uses KAST for a rapid estimate of relative location; the operator refines the estimate on the SID console. The options include KAST edit, manual adaptive TMA evaluation (MATE), Ekelund ranging, and depression/elevation (angle) ranging. The SID software also provides analysis of the environment; it can show search and avoidance modes, that is, areas favoring disclosure of a target and areas providing greatest chance of avoiding counterdetection. The software also includes evasion tactics and a system-alert module.

According to the Russian article quoted above, the core of the *Ohio*-class combat-control system is a pair of UYK-7 computers (245 and 196 kbytes) provided with a hard disk drive (UYH-2) and with two data converters. Another UYK-7 controls the sonar, two more are used for missile control, and another is used for navigation. Upgraded ships of this type have two UYK-43s. Again, according to the Russian article, there are also at least eight UYK-20s (one [with a hot spare] for monitoring self-noise, at least one for navigation, and five for communications control). In an upgraded unit, there are four or five UYK-44s.

The main computers run the Mk 118 system. There is also an autopilot mode for submarine control, for example, to come to periscope depth. There is also a self-noise monitoring function, with data collected via a UYK-20 and 205 hydrophones, 13 outboard, 49 inboard, and 143 on rotating machinery. All are monitored through a UYK-20 computer feeding an OJ-326 console.

According to the Russian article, *Ohio*-class submarines carrying Trident II missiles have upgraded navigational systems with UYK-43 and UYK-44 computers rather than the original UYK-7 and UYK-20, with better sonar logs (BQN-33 rather than -31), and with a new gravitational navigation system (gravimeter for coarse navigation using gravitational anomaly charts and gradiometer for measuring the gravitational vector as a correction to SINS).

Ohio-class submarines currently use a pair of UYK-43s to run the sonar, the FCS, and the navigational system. There is also a UYK-20 in the sonar system, and two HP 9020s (DTC Is), probably for SIMAS and for TDAs. The self-monitoring UYK-20 remains. The radio room employs a pair of UYK-20s and a pair of

UYK-44s. Reportedly no UYK-7s remain on board *Ohio*-class submarines, even though not all units in the class are receiving the CCS Mk 2 upgrade.

Users: Ohio class (SSBN 727–33, 735–40); other units have CCS Mk 2 Mod 3. Units with Mk 118 are to have them upgraded using COTS elements, rather than replaced as previously planned.

◆ CCS Mk 2

Raytheon's Combat-Control System Mk 2 is the successor to CCS Mk 1 in *Los Angeles*–class submarines. Work on the core system began in 1988, and as of mid-1995 it had just completed its operational evaluation prior to production release. This system replaces the UYK-7 computer of the earlier system with a UYK-43, one of whose processors handles weapons data. A single UYK-44 (rather than the two of CCS Mk 1) remains, to maintain the OTH-T picture. It is supplemented by an ASPRO (CP-2037/UYK) for track correlation. This combination is 20 times faster than the CCS Mk 1 equivalent. The associated sonar is BQQ-5E, in which UYK-43 replaces the UYK-7 of earlier versions of BQQ-5. As in some recent surface-ship CDSs, the dumb terminals of the past are replaced by intelligent workstations that unload some functions from the central computer. It is therefore possible ultimately to eliminate the central computer altogether.

Like earlier combat systems, CCS Mk 2 uses a star architecture, with a central UYK-43B interfaced to four Mk 130s. System software is carried in the UYK-43B, with applications downloaded to individual workstations. The consoles can also connect to an Ethernet LAN, and they have VME backplanes. Each console carries its own shadow database (the main base is carried in the UYK-43). With the appearance of the workstations, the

A diagram of CCS Mk 2 Block 1 A/B shows how rapid insertion of commercial technology, in the form of TAC-3 processors, can transform a centralized CDS into a nearly distributed one. In this case most of the additional processors are to be used to support either missile control (ATWCS) or the naval command system (JMCIS). The UYK-43, which is far less capable than the TAC-3s, must be retained for mission-critical functions such as torpedo firing. (U.S. Navy)

UYK-43 is reduced largely to I/O tasks; it becomes the system bottleneck. The next stop is a fully distributed system on a LAN. CCS Mk 2 performs all the functions of BSY-2 and can use some of the same software. Raytheon points out that the CCS Mk 2 contract was awarded a year after BSY-2, and thus that it embodies later-generation hardware.

Normally the CCS Mk 2 UYK-43, like the UYK-7 of CCS Mk 1, works on the basis of sonar detections (ranges and bearings). It would be possible for the CCS to do limited processing of raw sonar data (using a special card), for example, for self-defense snapshots.

The current workstations operate in monochrome, but they have the hardware needed for color operation, and as of April 1992 an ECP for this conversion was in process. The hardware will also support a second independent CRT, a version Raytheon calls Mod (x). Additional cards will be needed, but the wiring is already in place (at present consoles use only five of the 17 available slots). Current CCS Mk 2 software is designated C4; the follow-on series is Programs D1, D2, D3, for enhanced weapons deployment capabilities and rapid software update procedures.

A new common-display console Mk 130 replaces the Mk 81 WCC and SID of earlier systems. It is a multifunction workstation based on the Raytheon SC-2000 series, which in turn is derived from the Silicon Graphics 4D/20 Personal IRIS Workstation. The workstation incorporates special-purpose processors to convert analog PPI data to raster-scan; to convert sonar data to LOFARgrams, waterfalls, and A-scans; and to superimpose synthetic data on raw video. The 19in color CRT has 1280 × 1024 pixels (24 bits/pixel, refreshed at 60 frames/sec). The screen can show as many as 16 simultaneous windows. The embedded 32-bit RISC computer, which uses a VME bus, has a throughput of 8 MIPS. An associated image memory generates alphanumerics, symbols, and graphics. The earlier consoles used cursive CRTs. Outputs include two NTDS channels (Type H). The operator controls are variable-action switches, a programmable flat panel (with switch overlay), a keyboard, a keypad, and four track marbles with entry switches and label readouts. Optional features are a second CPU, a graphics processor, and bulk memory.

A Mod 1 version is used for OTH-T. It is similar to Mod 0 but

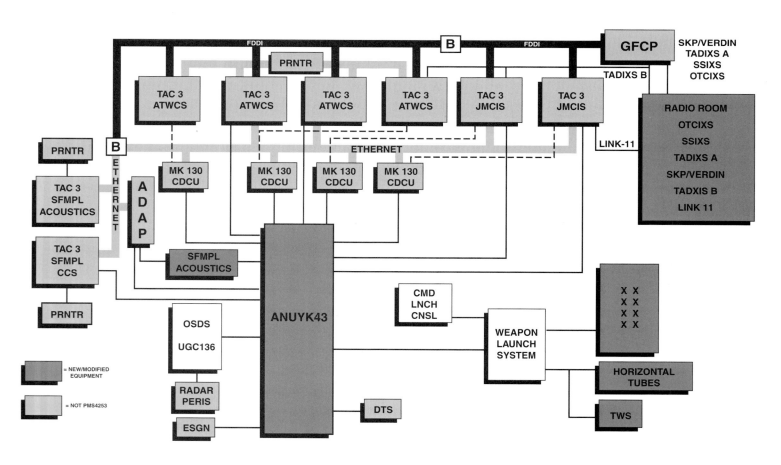

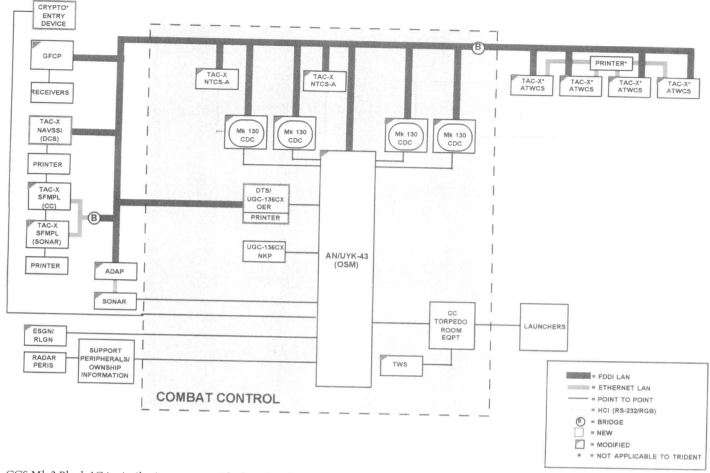

CCS Mk 2 Block 1C is similar in concept to Block 1A/B. The UYK-43 has been modified by the addition of an Open System Module (OSM) which contains COTS processors. (U.S. Navy).

Raytheon's CCS Mk 2 console. (Author)

adds two more NTDS channels (Type B). Mod 2, for Trident submarines, is similar to Mod 0 but has a 17in monochrome CRT, Type B NTDS channels, and no keypad or track marbles. Mod 3, also for Trident submarines, is similar to Mod 0 but has a 17in monochrome CRT, two additional NTDS channels (Type B), one trackball, eight multifunction switches, and no keypad or flat panel display.

Probably much more important is the modular software design, which permits Raytheon to offer versions of CCS Mk 2 for all four current U.S. submarine types (see below). One requirement is sufficient computing power to support a powerful emulation mode, so that the workstation can replace several current consoles without any impact on existing interfaces.

The existing weapons-launch console, weapons-data converter, and TT control panel (all located in the torpedo room) are retained (in BSY-1 they are replaced by a new weapons-launch-system console). These systems incorporate a new submarine random-access-data storage set, SubRASS (BYH-1), which replaces the earlier UYH-2. Submarines with vertical tubes but without BSY-1 have an additional set of Tomahawk control panels and interface consoles in a separate missile-control room (not required for Tomahawks loaded in standard torpedo tubes).

CCS Mk 2 is part of a more general program to merge submarine FCSs into more comprehensive combat-control suites combining sonar operation, TMA, tactical display, weapons control, navigation, and communications.

Versions:

Mod 0 is for *Los Angeles*–class submarines without vertical-launch tubes (SSNs 688–718). The former Mk 81 consoles are replaced by four common display consoles Mk 130 Mods 0/1, but the single attack console Mk 92 Mod 5 or 6 is retained. The associated sonar is BQQ-5E(V)3, and the system is compatible with an HP 9020 (DTC I tactical decision aid) computer.

Mod 1 is for *Los Angeles*–class submarines with vertical-launch tubes (SSNs 719–25 and 750).

Mod 2 is for later *Los Angeles*–class submarines with vertical-launch tubes (SSNs 751–79) and BSY-1 sonars. There is no attack console; instead there is a weapons-launch console (WLC) designated 2015–2020.

Mod 3 is the SSBN version, controlling only torpedoes and countermeasures (it replaces Mk 118). Since it does not control Tomahawk and Harpoon missiles, it lacks the UYK-44 of the other versions. It has four new common display consoles (Mk 130 Mod 0) but retains the single ACC (Mk 92 Mod 1) of the earlier system. The associated sonar is BQQ-5E(V)4.

CCS is subject to a combat-control system improvement program (CCSIP), which develops replacements for obsolescent equipment as well as new software. Thus the CCS Mk 1 C4.2 Revision 1 software underwent operational testing in November 1993. The current focus is on CCS Mk 2 Program D0, BSY-1 ECP (engineering change proposal) 134, and insertion of NTCS-A (JMCIS). CCS Mk 2 Program D0 provides a modular software architecture, introduces Tomahawk Block III and Harpoon Block IC capabilities, introduces Mk 48 ADCAP on Trident submarines, and replaces obsolete equipment. D0 Mod 0/1 completed developmental testing in August 1993. ECP 134 provides Tomahawk Blocks I and III capabilities to AN/BSY-1–equipped submarines. Integration of NTCS-A into CCS Mk 1 and BSY-1 (CCS Mk 2) began in FY93.

This program also supports installation of the new Common Ring Laser Gyro (design award 1994, tests scheduled for 1996, and a production award for early 1997).

CCS Mk 2 Program D0 Block 1 is a major hardware change to insert COTS technology (largely in the form of TAC-3 computers) into the system. Block 1 specifications were developed in FY93. This version was intended to integrate CCS Mk 2 into BSY-1, to provide a direct GPS interface, and to implement Tomahawk Block III Phase III (Tomahawk Strike Planning System) and ADCAP torpedo improvements. In fact the program was broken down into a series of sub-blocks.

Block 1A is to go to sea about May 1996, following a 1994 contract award. The UYK-43 is retained. The Mk 130 workstations remain but are modified. The system is modified to handle the ADCAP torpedo. The UYK-44, ASPRO, and the hard-disk Tomahawk data-transfer device (SubRASS) are eliminated because ATWCS is installed. An Ethernet LAN is installed, connected to eight TAC-3 computers to form a distributed system: two for NTCS-A (JMCIS), four for ATWCS (Tomahawk weapons control), and two for submarine force mission-planning library (SFMPL) (one acoustic, one for combat control). Unlike the original CCS Mk 2, this version provides a two-way SFMPL interface. The installation of NTCS-A is new. The Ethernet is also connected to the four Mk 130 consoles, which in turn are separately wired to the UYK-43. The UYK-43 is also wired directly to two ATWCS computers, for redundancy. The BSY-1 acoustic system is connected to both the UYK-43 (as before) and to the bus. This version uses an autonomous GPS receiver.

The NTCS-A (JMCIS) computer carries the master tactical database, receiving the targeting broadcasts (TADIXS B) directly from the radio room. ATWCS runs as a slave. For antiship engagements, ATWCS accepts OTH tracks. Because only the UYK-43 and the Mk 130s are Mil-Spec, they must be used for actual weapon firing. The UYK-43 continues to carry the track files (the tactical picture). However, all new functions are in the TACs, which accept rapid changes due to the open architecture of the system as a whole.

Block 1A was to have been installed in all attack submarines, but funds will limit it to one or two. A projected Block 1B added a fiber-optic FDDI connecting the ATWCS/JMCIS TAC-3s to each other and to the Ethernet, and also connecting them to a standard communications processor (GFCP) by means of which

both JMCIS and ATWCS computers would receive targeting broadcasts (Verdin, TADIXS A, SSIXS, OTCIXS). Block 1B was folded back into 1A.

The production version will be Block 1C, with a fiber-optic LAN (FDDI) and with COTS insertions in the Mk 130s to supplement the TAC-3s. They will have color/landscape displays. Software will be upgraded to handle Mk 48 ADCAP Block IV (if needed), as well as Harpoon 1G and Tomahawk Block IV (TBIP). JMCIS will be upgraded to use Link 16. SFMPL will be used for tactical control rather than simply for advice. The radio room will also be upgraded.

This version adds a ninth TAC-series computer, for NAVSSI (navigation sensor system: integrated GPS navigation), to the eight of Block 1A. The ATWCS machines share a local Ethernet, as do the two SFMPL machines (they are connected to the FDDI LAN only via their own local Ethernet, whereas the ATWCS computers are all connected directly to the main LAN). Wiring is simplified, in that the UYK-43 is connected directly to the LAN rather than to any particular TAC-series computer. The GFCP is connected directly to the FDDI LAN. This version also adds a ring-laser gyro to the electrostatically suspended gyro navigation system (ESGN) of the earlier system. This upgrade includes some Fleet Tactical Advisory Group (FTAG, Submarine DevRon 12) items.

As of 1994, a Block 1C design contract award was projected for early 1996, with operational testing in 1999. The design contract for the follow-on Block 2 was expected late in 1998.

Users: As of fall 1995, the only *Los Angeles*–class submarines with CCS Mk 2 were SSN 688, 690, 691, 710, 721, 723, and 724.

◆ BSY-1 (SubACS)

The Submarine Advanced Combat System replaces BQQ-5 and Mk 117/CCS Mk 1 in the last *Los Angeles*–class submarines. It appears to have been conceived as a submarine equivalent of the SQQ-89 on board newer ASW ships: a system that would automatically detect targets on a variety of arrays and meld these data (obtained in various frequency ranges) into a single usable tactical picture. One advantage of such detection would be the ability to range passively on a target detected simultaneously (in different frequency ranges) by several arrays, for example, by a towed and a flank array. As in SQQ-89, the minimum required for integration is that adjoining consoles be able to show the output of any array, for comparison and correlation. That, in turn, requires that sonar data be carried by a data bus available to each console.

Compared to BQQ-5, major sonar improvements are a digital transmitter (SADS, submarine active detection system) providing much greater beam agility and also more flexible waveforms (much as in SQS-53C). The arrays match those of BQQ-5, but the sphere uses new transducers (TR-217/218). BSY-1 also incor-

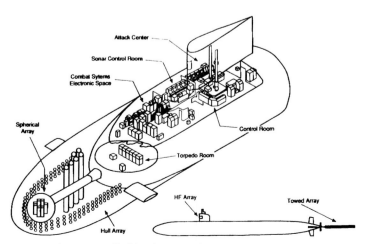

BSY-1 is shown installed (with CCS Mk 1) on an Improved *Los Angeles*-class submarine; the small drawing shows the HF array for mine avoidance and the towed array (not to scale, as the array would normally be far abaft the submarine). (U.S. Navy)

porates WAA (BQG-5) and the thin-line towed array. There are also a new common beam-former cabinet (CBC) and a modified plotter Mk 19 (Mod 20). The BSY-1 fire-control/picture-keeping functions are carried out by a modified CCS Mk 1, the main change being that several weapons-compartment elements are merged into a single weapons-launch system (WLS). Own-ship data collection is merged into an own-ship's data system (OSDS).

Early hopes for a fully distributed and fully integrated system (SubACS) using interchangeable consoles for sonar and for fire control were dashed. In May 1985 the program was split, IBM developing an interim BSY-1 (SubACS Basic) for the later *Los Angeles* class and GE developing BSY-2 for the *Seawolf* class.

As delivered, BSY-1 employed two UYK-7 computers: one for the sonar subsystem, one for the CCS Mk 1 element, plus the two UYK-44 of CCS Mk 1. Later, the UYK-7 of the sonar subsystem was replaced by a UYK-43; ultimately the CCS element will be upgraded to CCS Mk 2 standard, with another UYK-43. The sonar subsystem employed four control-display system consoles (CDSCs: the ICDCs introduced in BQQ-5), and the CCS element employed the usual four Mk 81 consoles (three Mod 3, one Mod 2), one command launch–control console (replacing Mk 92), and four weapons launch–control consoles (one for the vertical launcher). There are two signal conditioners (one for the bow sphere, one for the WAA and towed arrays). The system incorporates two graphic plotters (Mk 23 Mod 0), two computer plotters, and one Mk 19 Mod 20 plotter. There is also a console for acoustic support (presumably for the intercept receiver or

receivers). The signal processor was UYS-1 (Tri-ASP). Improvements over BQQ-5 include much better fault detection and a greatly reduced number of distinct types of logic card.

IBM describes BSY-1 as the first military application of distributed architecture on a large scale. There are five linear beam-formers, two digital (DIMUS) beam-formers, and six advanced signal processors (in the form of two Tri-ASPs). Overall, the system has 30 MCOPS in raw general-purpose computing power, supported by 60 Mbytes of online RAM storage and 400 Mbytes of disk storage. The computer power required for signal processing dwarfs general-purpose power: 120 MCOPS of signal processing, 800 MCOPS of linear beam-forming (for towed arrays, presumably), and two GCOPS (giga-COPS) of DIMUS beam-forming. All of this power requires about 4,519,000 lines of instruction code. Total weight is 32 tons, and total power requirement (aside from the transmitter) is 142 kW. The system occupies 117 units with 11.5 miles of wiring. Presumably, the enormous amount of wiring reflects the failure of the optical-fiber data bus originally planned.

The first BSY-1 was delivered in July 1987, for installation on board the attack submarine *San Juan* (SSN 751). A postcompletion upgrade, for the *San Juan* and the next four *Los Angeles*–class submarines, was installation of new UYK-43 computers, new software, active sonar improvements, under-ice capability, and new weapons capability (presumably the abortive Sea Lance). From SSN 756 on, submarines were completed with the full BSY-1 suite.

The BSY-1 Operational Requirement was issued on 17 April 1980. Unit cost is $43 million.

Users: United States (*Los Angeles* class [from SSN 751]).

♦ **BSY-2**

BSY-2 is the combat system (including an integrated sonar suite) of the new *Seawolf*-class submarine. The program was split from BSY-1 when the latter encountered severe problems in 1985–86.

The BSY-2 system layout. Note the separate large spherical array, MF active array, and LF bow array. The large spherical array is the receiver for the MF active array; the pair correspond to the earlier BQS-6 and -13. The LF bow array, which is wrapped around the large spherical array, corresponds to the earlier BQR-7 and to the hull array of BQQ-5. BQR-22 is a separate signal processor. BMFRs are beam-formers; RCVRs are receivers. Ps denote processors: AP for active, FP for Fourier (narrowband), WP for wide-band. ATs are active transmitters. (Lockheed Martin)

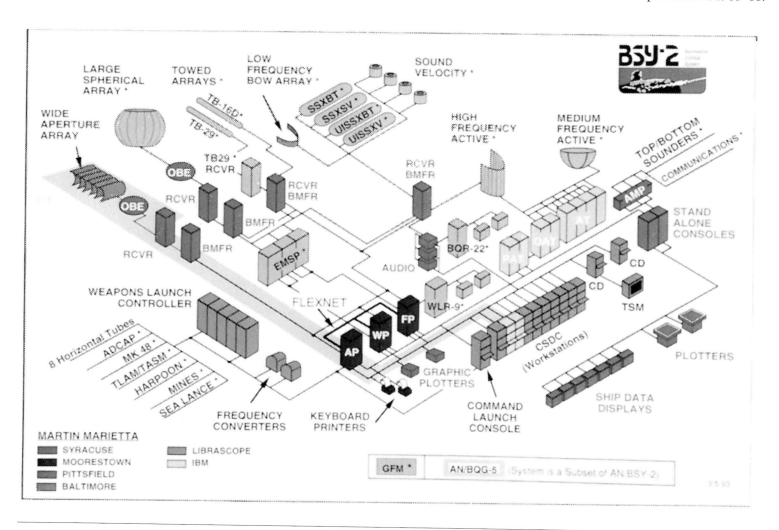

BSY-2 retains the original goal of largely distributed processing, with multipurpose consoles (MPCs), combat-system display consoles (CSDCs), a horizontal large-screen display (HLSD), a vertical large-screen display (VLSD), a horizontal plotter (HP), and a tactical-situation display (TACSIT). The prime contractor is Lockheed Martin (formerly Martin Marietta, which bought the naval divisions of the original prime contractor, General Electric). The prototype, delivered in December 1993 after a two-year integration test, cost about $280 million (FY93 dollars); the two others cost about $250 million each. Total program cost is probably about $7.4 billion. That was to have been amortized over 29 *Seawolf*-class submarines, but the program has been cut to three, and it is not clear to what extent the next CDS will resemble BSY-2. See below.

BSY-2 is the first U.S. fully integrated submarine combat system, all the sensors, data processors, consoles, and weapons controls riding the same high-capacity Flexnet bus. The consoles can, therefore, be switched among all the command/control tasks; there is also a separate geosit (geographical situation, i.e., PPI) console. BSY-2 is the first application of the EMSP (UYS-2) signal processor, which has been used in development work since 1989. Initially, the sixth unit was to have employed the SEM-E version of UYS-2, but later that was shifted to the third unit. BSY-2 incorporates 25 display surfaces (10 two-screen CSDCs, three command displays, two tactical-situation monitors), three beam-former cabinets, six EMSPs (UYS-2), and three data processors. It can fire eight weapons at a time and can control four wire-guided torpedoes simultaneously.

BSY-2 incorporates a unique application-specific beam-former chip (40,000 gates using VHSIC technology), which is presumably needed to exploit the great sensitivity of the big WAAs on the submarine's flanks. Another critical electronic item is the outboard electronics (OBE), a signal conditioner mounted externally to the hull. Because it reduces the data load into the internal signal processors, the OBE reduces the hull penetrations (and overall structural footprints) for the various submarine sensors. OBE is important not only for the new *Seawolf* but also for *Los Angeles*–class submarines (which are very space-limited) fitted with the new WAA.

The data bus is Flexnet, a packet-switched, fiber-optic bus with a capacity of 50 Mbit/sec (1000 messages/sec). All the system computers use militarized 68030 chips (often combined with 68882 math coprocessors on a single small board). BSY-2 uses about 200 68030 microprocessors. The system is broken down into four subgroups: acoustics, command/control, weapons, and display. The system is made highly redundant through the use of common hardware running different software. In the weapons section, each of the four processors has a designated backup. Each of the other groups has two or three spares. Thus, each cluster can shift to other processors within itself as not all are used simultaneously. If necessary, any function can be shifted to processors within another cluster (other functions are slowed or stopped). The loss of functions is preprioritized.

System software is written in six series (threads); the submarine can go to sea without the full set (but also without some capability). Total software includes 2979 kslocs (thousands of software lines of code) of unique software. Through 1990 there was some question as to whether all of this software could be written in ADA because of the paucity of ADA programmers. That situation raises the question of just how wise the shift to ADA has been. DoD had directed that this new standard language be used in all new mission-critical programs as a way of ensuring that software could be used in later, more powerful, computers without rewriting. For a time it appeared that only 5–15% of the system software would be written in ADA. However, of a total of about 3.6 million lines of code, 2.2 million were written in ADA. Ultimately, Martin Marietta tried to simplify development by breaking down the software into 113 "building blocks," none of which would require more than 75,000 lines of code (and the average size of which would be limited to about 30,000). Thread 3 (BQG-5) integration and testing was completed in September 1993, Threads 4 and 5 in 1994, and Thread 6 in 1995.

The standard console, CSDC, has two high-resolution, raster-scan color displays (it is the basis of the Librascope naval workstation series). It is the first high-resolution color monitor with magnetic compensation to have been shock-tested (September 1990). The software provides six tactical aids: automatic contact following/aided detection (ACF/AD), automatic contact correlation (between arrays), automatic aided contact classification, automatic TMA, recommended weapons presets, and operator alerts.

System design and development were conducted in 1985–88, followed by detail design work in 1988–90. By early 1991, the bulk of the critical items in BSY-2 had been tested, and the system was entering limited production. The WAA will also enter service in stand-alone form as BQG-5; the first such unit went to sea in 1993 on board a *Los Angeles*–class submarine. It uses the same beam-former hardware, software, and display as in the integrated BSY-2 system.

The major system sensors are an LF bow array inside the bow (LFBA), an active hemispherical array (AHA) below the LFBA (using a transmitter group, TG), an HF array (HFA) in the sail (for SADS/MIDAS), the WAA (BQG-5), a long thin-line (TB-29) towed array, and a shorter TB-16D array. The long thin array is associated with TARP, the towed array range processor. The same system processes all six arrays to form a coherent tactical picture. As in earlier integrated sonars, passive targets are detected primarily by automatic line integration (when the strength of a line exceeds a threshold, the target is detected and inserted into the system). BSY-2 differs from its predecessors in the number of lines and frequency ranges it can monitor simultaneously. All sonar output flows into array processors for signal conditioning and beam-forming. Outputs go into signal processors (UYS-2s) and also into the workstations/functional processors. The latter also receive processed signal data. The workstations are connected with the weapons-launch system by a Flexnet data bus, and they also feed into the combat system's display consoles. There is no central computer. The system as a whole comprises 61 enclosures, and it requires a total of 570 kW and a maximum of 157 gal/min of cooling water.

General Electric (now part of Lockheed Martin) is the prime contractor; the company received the BSY-2 FSD contract in March 1988. Librascope is responsible for multifunction displays, and Lockheed Martin makes the WAA.

The first unit was delivered in February 1995. Construction of a fourth BSY-2 was approved in August 1995 (it had previously been canceled).

◆ New Attack Submarine Network (BSY-3?)

A new attack submarine is planned to succeed *Seawolf* in production. The goal is to cut cost dramatically while maximizing flexibility, given the uncertainties of the post–Cold War world. Any such system must be distributed, but there are two very different possible approaches. One, adopted in BSY-2, integrates system elements despite the use of a data bus. The alternative would be more like a telephone system, which is an independent spine that can carry entirely independent entities obeying minimal interface requirements. The advantage of the telephone network solution is that modernization and alteration are relatively easy. There is no single monstrous software package. Indeed, individual entities can use more common software languages, such as UNIX, without any impact on each other. The only real requirement is that the spine have sufficient data capacity to carry the data from entity to entity. It seems likely that this latter solution will be adopted. All data, including raw acoustic data, will be transmitted along one or more buses in packet-switched form.

The prototype telephone-type network was built during 1995.

A recent unclassified sketch of the command system of the new attack submarine shows nine common color display consoles (CCDCs: two screens, one man each), five on the port side and four on the starboard side, with a large-screen horizontal console in the center of the space, and a corner console (command workstation). At the forward end of the space are the two ship-control stations, with flat-screen displays above them. Accounts of the design mention a large-screen vertical display for a tactical action officer, something that submarines have lacked in the past. The large horizontal console may be an alternative. As in BSY-2, sonar room and weapons-system functions have been merged in one space using a single type of console. There is one fewer multipurpose console. Accounts of the design mention a government-furnished Tactical Support Devices (TSD) subsystem providing tactical advice through TDAs including sonar performance predictors. TSD also provides torpedo presets and controls off-hull message traffic. It is presumably an outgrowth of the current modifications to CCS Mk 2, using TAC-series computers.

Current plans are to use a *Los Angeles*–type bow array (one sphere instead of the two in the *Seawolf* design), partly to hold down hull diameter to roughly that of the *Los Angeles*. There will also be a *Los Angeles*–type bow conformal array. A lightweight version of WAA (using fiber optics) is to be installed, reportedly largely because the towed array rapid ranger (TARPS) has not been successful. However, the submarine will have the pair of arrays (fat and thin) of the *Seawolf* class. There will also be ancillary arrays: acoustic emission sensors spread around the hull, a chin mine-detector array, an HF array (mine and ice detector) in the sail, and a separate acoustic communication dome aft. A long-range tactical acoustic communications system is to use the main bow array as its transducer. An unclassified sketch published in March 1995 also shows a row of lidar sensors along the top of the hull and in the sail, presumably to detect an enemy lidar.

As of early 1996, reported planned capacity of the network was nearly 25 Gbyte/sec. Signal processing capacity is to be 190 GOPS, to serve sonars producing data at the rate of about 30 Mbit/sec (sonar RAM data storage capacity is to be greater than 25 Gbytes). Overall computer capacity in the New Attack Submarine is to exceed 8000 MIPS.

Loral received the New Attack Submarine Network contract on 24 April 1996.

♦ ARPA Submarine CDS Projects

For some years ARPA has been trying to develop AI techniques as a way of reducing submarine attack center manning. As in a radar CDS, the hope is clearly to form a tactical picture more or less automatically, using that picture as input for semiautomated tactical decision-making. One argument in favor of this approach is that reaction speed is likely to be crucial in future short-range encounters. Originally the fear was clearly that, as the Soviets eliminated the U.S. acoustic advantage, U.S. submarines would have less and less warning of an encounter. After the end of the Cold War, much the same could be said of a surprise encounter with a quiet diesel submarine in shallow littoral waters, where sound conditions are poor.

The ARPA submarine technology initiative was authorized in 1988. In February 1990 GE (which later became part of Lockheed Martin) received a contract (completed 1993) to develop the Submarine Operational Automation System (SOAS). The work was ultimately conducted by the Martin-Marietta Advanced Technology Laboratory. SOAS was expected to use AI techniques to interpret and integrate sensor data, in effect using automatic TMA to form a tactical picture. The chosen approach was to form several hypothetical pictures corresponding to the received acoustic data, then choose among them. This type of comparison makes use of known negative information. It may also be able to recommend specific maneuvers to clarify the situation. The kind of computer logic that juggles several alternative hypotheses is also suited to planning with uncertainty, as in choosing the safest path to disengagement. SOAS should also be able to assess the acoustic consequences (flow and other self-noise) of particular maneuvers, and to integrate that assessment into its tactical advice. It was also expected to assist in emergency damage control.

SOAS included a redesign of the submarine attack center, which typically requires 28 personnel and four combat-control workstations. The SOAS attack center would use four large-screen displays: one for command situation assessment (the tac-

tical picture), one for command tactical planning, one for weapons status, and one for ship-systems status. Sensor information would flow into the situation display, from which a "world scene" would feed into the tactical planning display; the latter would also receive own-ship data. The command team would be reduced to seven: the CO, supervising a situation-assessment officer (SAO) and a tactical planning officer (TPO); a ship-control coordinator (SCC), a weapons-control coordinator (WCC), a damage-control coordinator (DCC), and an officer of the deck (OOD) supervising the SCC and DCC. The DCC would be responsible for signature management. There would also be a sonar supervisor, a radio-room officer, and an OTH-T operator.

It was hoped that a SOAS submarine would be able to use new kinds of tactics, classifying targets more accurately in about a third of the usual time, reacting in about a quarter of the usual time, and reducing tactical picture ambiguities and errors tenfold. More active signature management might cut maneuvering signatures by 90%.

SOAS used a distributed combat-planning system, with a case-based weapons utilization planner from Librascope (ARMOR, attack response mission-oriented reasoner) and an embryonic tactical planner from Advanced Decision Systems. Loral Librascope developed its SOAS work into SEPACS (Submarine Engagement Automated Planning and Control System), which employs case-based reasoning and decision-theory planning techniques.

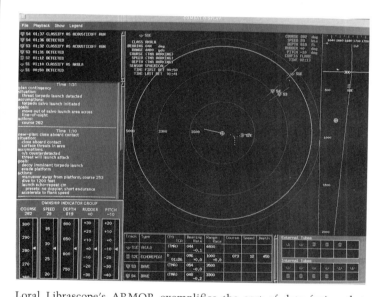

Loral Librascope's ARMOR exemplifies the sort of data fusion that ARPA has supported in recent years. ARMOR was designed to operate either autonomously, reacting to a tactical situation it sensed, or semiautomatically, prompting the operator. This typical combat display combines a geographical picture (center) with a depth display (at right). The latter includes a sound velocity profile, with the layer marked. The enemy contact, S1E, is shown off the range scale at upper left because the system has not yet reached a TMA solution. Similarly, it is not shown in the depth profile. S2E, which is shown, is an echo repeater. Both S3 and S4 are also being localized by TMA; bearing cuts are drawn through the three potential targets. In each case, the table below the PPI shows bearing, bearing rate, range, and range rate; presumably the ranges for the three targets are initial estimates. The table at lower right indicates available decoys. At right is shown the series of events leading to the current situation and recommendations made at 1:10 and at 1:31. The Akula was detected at 0:50 and classified as a nearby Akula at 1:10; the system assumed that the Akula would counterdetect and attack. To cover that possibility, it proposed that the submarine maneuver away while launching a decoy, S2E. Two new targets, S3 and S4, were detected at 1:12 and at 1:31. At 1:32 the system identified S3 as an incoming acoustic torpedo (the table suggests that it had already decided that the Akula had fired). It assumed that the Akula had launched a salvo, and suggested new action to evade the torpedoes, a run across the line of sound to them and the Akula. The submarine turned onto the suggested evasion course. It was still diving and accelerating in response to the earlier plan. This reasoning is shown to the left of the PPI. Such explanations are common in knowledge-based tactical advice systems, since the operator may well want to know just why the system is preferring its advice. (Loral Librascope)

Lucent (part of Bell Labs) is currently developing a submarine system under an ARPA Ship Systems Automation contract. As in SOAS, one goal is a drastic cut in manning, hopefully by a factor of 5 in combat-system operators. The first prototype of the Lucent system was a submarine sensor integrator (active, passive, transient), displays for which were shown at the 1996 Navy League exhibition. At that time Lucent was adding radar, IFF, and ESM. All sensor outputs are stored in a common database, which includes data on relationships among the sensors. The main display is the fused sensor tactical picture. However, the operator can also query the database to examine the outputs of the individual sensors. The Lucent project includes novel types of display, such as a synthetic 3D presentation of multiple sonar beam traces (to show both frequency and bearing over time), which the operator sees by using special glasses (as in a 3D movie).

The Lucent project suggests that ARPA is retreating from attempts to automate submarine operations toward attempts to automate the formation of the tactical picture itself.

◆ Kanaris System/USFCS/ENFCS

Unisys (now Loral Unisys) developed this new FCS for the Greek *Kanaris*-class submarines, in collaboration with the Hellenic Navy Research and Development Center (GETEN). The system consists of a main control console consisting of two side-by-side, color, multifunction tactical modular displays (TMDs), two sensor peripheral units (SPUs), and two operator-control units (CUs); plus a two-cabinet firing distribution unit. Each combination SPU/TMD/CU has a UYK-44(V) computer embedded in it, and a channel connects the two computers. The TMD displays the tactical situation as well as digitized radar and sonar video. The associated control unit contains a trackball as well as manual entry buttons, for example, for FCS data entry and also for the display of FCS status. There is also a 12 × 40-character plasma display/touch entry panel.

Sensor and other input data pass through junction boxes into the two SPUs, which feed the TMDs. Decisions made at the TMDs are fed to the firing and distibution unit, which incorporates actual fire-control calculation.

The SPU is essentially an analog-to-digital and discrete-to-digital converter, with 24 single-speed synchro input channels, two linear analog-to-digital input channels, two single-speed synchro output channels (with growth to six), eight discrete inputs (with growth to 24), and eight discrete outputs (with growth to 24). Data are provided to the UYK-44s of the TMDs via a 16-bit A-NEW bus. Radar data are provided directly to the TMDs.

Each TMD contains a 19in color CRT (1024 × 768 pixels), with eight memory planes for data prioritization; it is capable of displaying eight colors or intensities for radar video. The TMD incorporates a special high-speed sequencer and two pages of

The Loral Unisys USFCS is shown on board a Type 209 submarine, a configuration the company proposed for the new Egyptian submarine program to be financed by the United States. The tactical console is a version of UYQ-70. (Loral Unisys)

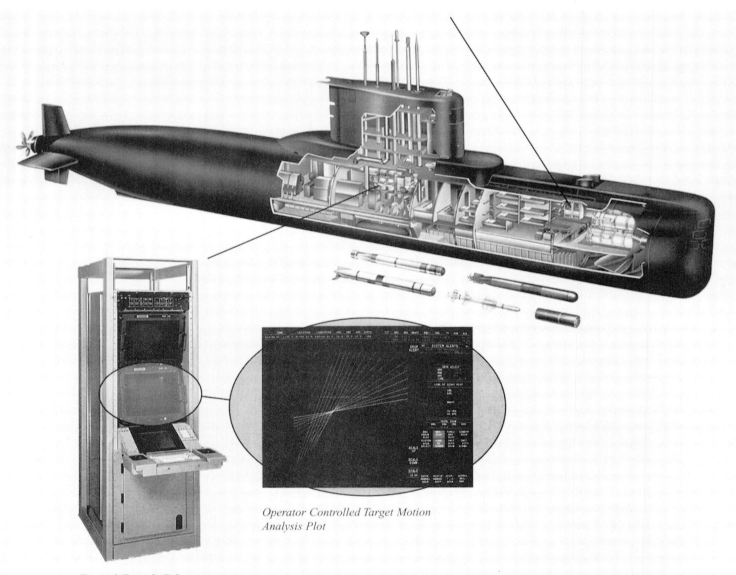

Operator Controlled Target Motion Analysis Plot

Tactical Console Subsystem

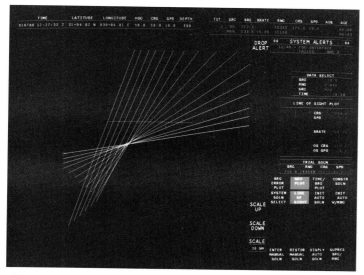

The TMA display of the Loral Unisys USFCS is shown. This strip (navigational) plot shows a series of bearing lines and a trial solution (a straight line crossing the bearing lines). Barely visible in the original plot is a series of vertical chops across the trial solution to indicate equal-time segments corresponding to the series of bearing cuts. They do not quite intersect the bearing lines, indicating that the solution is not quite correct. The operator has selected a navigational plot rather than a bearing-error plot (which would have corresponded to the U.S. display in which the dots must be arranged vertically). Other alternatives are a time/bearing plot (waterfall) and a manually inserted (constructed) solution. The LOS plot shown is associated with a bearing rate across the line of sight. Given an estimated target speed and course, bearing rate gives a range. (Loral Unisys)

graphics image memory for fast graphics. The value of the two pages is that the operator can rapidly flip between them. The TMD has separate display and graphics processors, the latter translating the former's tables into pixel data for actual display. The operator can interact with the computer by touching the screen (finger-on-glass, or FOG, operation). The associated version of UYK-44 has a 128k ROM and 256k of nonvolatile read/write memory (protected by battery backup); throughput is 800 KOPS.

The firing and distribution unit (FDU) selects, presets, and guides torpedoes; it also passes firing data to the two missile-data processors used to fire Harpoons.

The entire system is two-sided, for redundancy, and the FDU can operate as an independent FCS if the TMDs fail.

Basic system functions are divided into surveillance and tactical evaluation (including contact and track display, track correlation, identification, classification, prioritization, and targeting); motion analysis (including automatic tracking, interactive tracking using graphics, and tracking solution endorsement); navigation; engagement and guidance; maneuvering (threat and own-weapon avoidance); and attack evaluation (including simulated weapon runs and action recommendation). The system tests, presets, launches, and controls four weapons types, presumably three torpedoes and Harpoon. The system will be able to control six torpedoes simultaneously. The Greek navy has ordered five systems, one for training and four for submarines.

As of mid-1992, the Kanaris upgrades of the Greek Type 209/1100 submarines (*Glavkos, Nereus, Triton, Proteus*) were complete; work was about to begin on the slightly larger Type 209/1200s (*Amfitriti, Okeanos, Pontos, Posydon*). Kanaris can engage four targets simultaneously. The associated Sea Lion ESM is used to help engage OTH targets with Harpoon.

Unisys developed a modified version of *Kanaris* and sold it to Egypt as part of the "Romeo"-class modernization program funded by the United States. This version was called USFCS, the Unisys Submarine FCS, or ENFCS, the Egyptian Navy FCS; it may also briefly have been called PISCES, the Paramax International Submarine Combat System. USFCS employs a new modular multifunction console (MMC) using Motorola 68030/68040 processors and 68881/68882 math coprocessors with up

to 16 Mbytes of RAM and 2 Mbytes of EPROM. The console carries a 19in CRT (1280 × 1024 pixels). This system can track over 200 targets simultaneously. Typically one console is used to maintain the tactical picture (including manually initiated TMA); the other is for weapons control. The FDU in the torpedo room can control four weapons. One peculiarity of the "Romeo" upgrade was that it had to retain the capability to control Russian-supplied torpedoes with old-fashioned spindle inputs, while adding such Western weapons as NT-37 and Sub-Harpoon, which use standard NATO electrical interfaces.

Users: Egypt (modified form to modernize "Romeo" class, in service 1994), Greece (Type 209/1100s).

◆ Singer-Librascope SFCS Mk I/II/Rockwell ACS/SUBICS 900

The SFCS Mk I digital FCS is in service in the Australian, Canadian, and Indian navies. The manufacturer claims that Mk I was the first all-digital SFCS. Librascope described it as closest in technology to the U.S. Mk 118. In 1977 the U.S. Navy stated that SFCS Mk I had proven much less expensive than a comparable system purchased under standard DoD procurement rules. This is a central-computer system, built around a pair of UYK-20 computers with a star architecture (sensors all feed the command-display console, and the tactical picture is constructed and weapons controlled from the separate pair of fire-control consoles, which receive plots and track data from the command console). The UYK-20 track-keeper is supplemented by a Librascope CL 107MA mass memory (409 kwords). The pair of fire-control consoles uses a second UYK-20.

Design objectives were automation (reduction of operators from 10 to 3), integration (all sensors can be coordinated by one operator at the command console), improved availability, and adaptability to new weapons (torpedoes Mk 8, Mk 23, and Mk

Librascope's multifunction console for the Australian *Collins*-class submarine combat system. (Author)

48–3). Computers perform TMA and generate firing orders. The system can display 20 targets, refine four by manual-aided TMA, and engage two. The three manned positions are the command-display console in the control room (which must be manned continuously) and the two fire-control consoles, each with its own CRT. The latter are manned only in action and standby conditions. Normally, one of the fire-control consoles provides target motion analysis, the other controlling weapons and TT status. Input into these consoles is by both light pen and keyboard.

The command-display console contains a sensor-data converter (SDC) that accepts data from 15 sensors and has nine passive sonar-tracking channels that are presumably time-shared among as many as 20 targets in memory. The display itself is a 20×24in paper plotter. Sonar operators can designate sonar bearings by means of one of the three sonar-assignment units at each sonar console, or the operator may designate one of the nine sonar-data channels. Such designation causes the system to store all data from that channel (for the most recent 30 min) in the computer's memory. Any four of the nine channels may be designated threats and therefore subject to TMA. Typically a tactical analyst at the CRT of the separate fire-control console carries out threat assessment, normally at the right-hand console (with the left-hand console—which is functionally interchangeable—reserved for weapons control).

For TMA, passive sonar measurements are sampled every second and averaged over 20-sec intervals. The submarine can maneuver to improve TMA ranging, and both automatic and manual target solutions can be obtained. There is also an acoustic environment display (ray-path predictor).

Claimed MTBF is 400 hr (98% online availability).

Before the merger of Librascope into Singer, this system was called LFCS Mk I (Librascope submarine FCS Mk I). Development began after Librascope won a design competition in September 1974. The first system was delivered in mid-1978.

In February 1992 Loral Librascope received a contract to upgrade Canadian SFCS Mk Is, integrating the new Triton (Type 2051) sonar with the fire-control system and replacing the existing plotter with a plasma panel. Delivery was scheduled for December 1992.

Users: SFCS Mk I: Australia (*Oberon* class), Canada (*Oberon* class). SFCS Mk I+: India (Type 209 class). The other reported designations are Mod 0, the original Australian type; Mod 1, the Australian type upgraded to handle Mk 48 Mod 4 and Harpoon (which may have been upgraded with 68000-series chips); Mod 1I, for India (with SUT torpedoes); and Mod C, the upgraded Canadian version (which probably uses 68000-series chips in its displays). Mod C replaces the paper output of the command console with a plasma display, as in Mk II (see below).

Mk II is a developed SFCS Mk I with a bus architecture, ordered about 1985 by Israel to modernize *Gal*-class submarines. Three shipsets were manufactured, but the Israelis tried to cancel the program in 1987 as the system was nearing completion, reportedly for fear of jeopardizing the *Dolphin* program. Once those boats had been bought, modernization of the earlier units again became practical, so Mk II will probably enter service. The Rockwell ACS described below is a modified version of Mk II (Librascope considered it Mk III). Loral Librascope showed a new SUBICS 900 (see below) at the 1991 U.S. Navy League exhibition; it is in effect a simplified Mk III.

The pair of computers in the Mk I system survive as sensor-data converter/processor and weapons-data converter/processor (UYK-20s were replaced by Israeli computers). Both connect to the 5-MHz fiber-optic combat data bus, which carries three to eight multifunction combat-control consoles and a single command (summary) display. Each combat-control console has two separate screens: an upper plasma screen (17×8.5 in) with an IR touch overlay and a lower 19in raster-scan CRT (1280×1024 pixels, 45-Hz refresh rate) with a light pen. The display also includes a keyboard and a joystick. The summary display is identical with the plasma display of the combat-control console. Each console uses a 68000-series microprocessor programmed in Pascal.

Because all the control consoles share the same data stream (which includes data from all available sensors and from any data link to which the submarine can have access), individual operators can be assigned to concentrate either on particular targets or on overall surveillance. All sensor data are automatically entered into a combat database for processing and recording. For example, data can be selected for up to 25 simultaneous target-motion analyses.

Four targets can be engaged simultaneously with wire-guided torpedoes, and the system can also support submarine-launched missiles such as Sub-Harpoon.

All elements of the system are sized to fit through a standard 650mm hatch, so existing submarines can be upgraded with the system without having their hulls opened.

The Rockwell ACS for the Australian *Collins* class, developed by Rockwell Submarine Systems Australia, is based on SCCS Mk II (Librascope wanted it designated SCCS Mk III). In this system the pair of sensor data converters is replaced by a pair of system supervisory units (SSUs); there are also two weapon-data converters (in each case, for redundancy). The multifunction common consoles (MFCCs) were supplied by Singer-Librascope. In this case the system bus carries seven MFCCs and one command-plotting (CP) console. Consoles and separate computers are all built around 68000-series processors. The bus is a Rockwell fiber-optic Expanded-Service Ship-Data Multiplexing System (ESSDMS), derived from the new U.S. Navy USQ-82(V) multiplexing system.

Each MFCC contains two 19in touch-screen color CRTs. The CP, which is horizontal, has a 39in color CRT, for tactical analysis or for reproduction of one of the MFCC displays. There are also four supplementary plasma displays, two for supplementary alphanumeric data, such as weapons status, and two used as remote presetting, testing, and control panels for the port and starboard sets of torpedo tubes.

ACS is credited with automatically detecting 1000 targets, initiating tracks on 200, and automatically localizing (conducting automatic TMA on) 25. A recent brochure compares it with systems at sea, which can track only 8 to 12 targets, and which are limited to two to four octaves for analysis (the *Collins* system can handle 50). Its sonar produces over 1 Mbit/sec of sonar data, compared to about 100 kbit/sec for earlier systems; signal processing is over 1500 MOPS (each equivalent to one multiply and one add), compared to fewer than 500 for earlier ones; and its data-processing power is over 100 MIPS (38 CPUs), compared to less than 10 MIPS (two to five CPUs) in earlier systems. System memory exceeds 130 Mbytes (compared to less than 8 Mbytes in systems currently at sea). Perhaps most impressively, ACS/Scylla divides the area around itself into about 1 million resolution cells (beam/amplitude bin/band), compared with 64 in a typical existing system. These figures combine the capabilities of the French-supplied Scylla sonar with those of the ACS itself.

The *Collins* system is tied together by a fiber-optic bus with a capacity of 30 Mbit/sec. According to some recent press reports, fiber-optic network management, which was Rockwell's major contribution to the project, has been a problem. Problems were also reportedly encountered due to a requirement that all software be written in ADA, and that it reflect an object-oriented approach. Thus in April 1994 it was reported that software would amount to 2.5 to 3 million source lines of code (SLOC), compared with a 1991 estimate that about 600,000 would suffice (however, these comparisons may be misleading, since the low one may not have included the operating system and network management software). The object-oriented approach was adopted in hopes that it would make the system both more fault-tolerant and more adaptable to later upgrades. Software was to have been delivered in three major increments. According to recent press reports, software problems delayed the sea trials of HMAS *Collins* by about six months.

SUBICS 900 (Submarine Integrated Combat System), announced in 1991, in effect renames the pair of data converters of SCCS Mk II as data managers (combat-data manager and weapons-control manager). They are built around RISC processors comparable in performance to the Hewlett-Packard units in the U.S. Navy's UYQ-70. The system also employs some 68000-

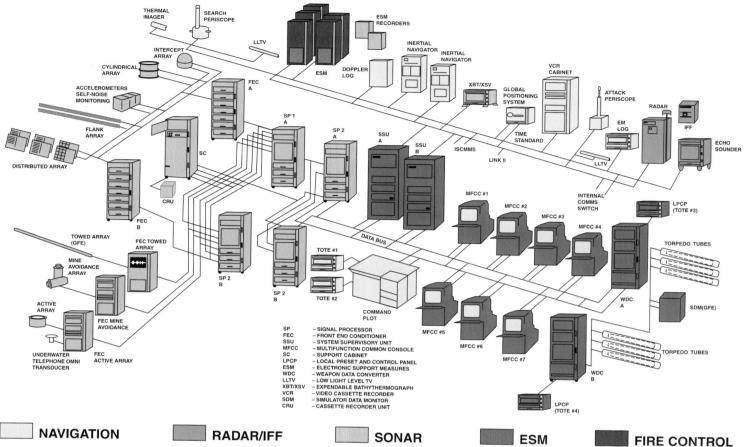

SP — SIGNAL PROCESSOR
FEC — FRONT END CONDITIONER
SSU — SYSTEM SUPERVISORY UNIT
MFCC — MULTIFUNCTION COMMON CONSOLE
SC — SUPPORT CABINET
LPCP — LOCAL PRESET AND CONTROL PANEL
ESM — ELECTRONIC SUPPORT MEASURES
WDC — WEAPON DATA CONVERTER
LLTV — LOW LIGHT LEVEL TV
XBT/XSV — EXPENDABLE BATHYTHERMOGRAPH
VCR — VIDEO CASSETTE RECORDER
SDM — SIMULATOR DATA MONITOR
CRU — CASSETTE RECORDER UNIT

NAVIGATION   **RADAR/IFF**   **SONAR**   **ESM**   **FIRE CONTROL**

Rockwell-Librascope CDS for the Australian *Collins* class. (Rockwell)

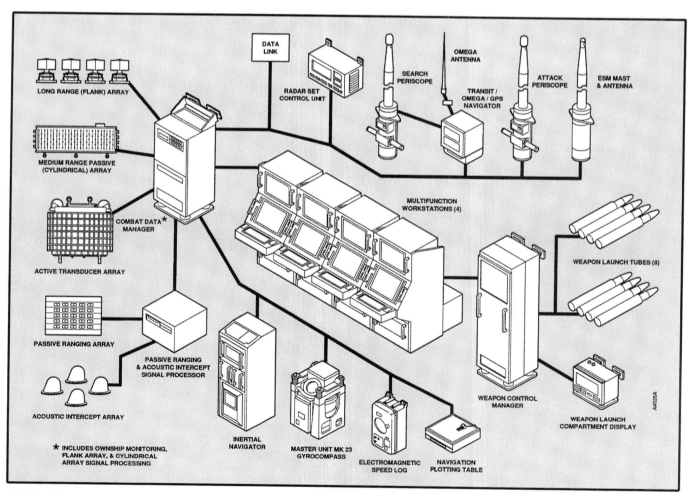

* INCLUDES OWNSHIP MONITORING, FLANK ARRAY, & CYLINDRICAL ARRAY SIGNAL PROCESSING

SUBICS-900 system. (Loral Librascope)

series chips and COTS graphics engines. The passive ranger and intercept sonars feed into the data manager via a separate passive processor. The workstations are those of the Australian system. Each incorporates a pair of 19in CRTs (1280 × 1024 pixels, 60-Hz refresh rate). As of mid-1992 Singer-Librascope (now a division of Loral) was proposing a four-workstation version (Type 901) for projected Egyptian submarines, to be built abroad using U.S. aid funds. This SUBICS configuration probably uses Atlas sonars (medium-range passive cylinder, long-range flank array, passive ranger, and active cylinder). The system can maintain 68 target tracks and can engage four targets simultaneously (three wire-guided torpedoes and a salvo of missiles [presumably Sub-Harpoons]). Ironically, in Egypt this system is competing against another Loral system (from a different division).

SUBICS 900 is closely allied to the Loral Integrated Surface Ship Combat System described separately above.

ISCWS is Raytheon's concept of a next-generation small-submarine CDS. It is a competitor for the Egyptian submarine contract. The two double-screen displays are intended to integrate all sonar data (from flank, narrow-band, and broad-band arrays). (Raytheon)

◆ Raytheon ISCWS

Raytheon's Submarine Signal Division is currently offering its Integrated Sonar, Command, and Weapon System (ISCWS) to equip the two diesel submarines planned for sale to Egypt under the U.S. aid program (the competitors are Loral Librascope with SUBICS 900 and Loral Unisys with USFCS). The core of the system is a central digital processing unit (DPU) in a single cabinet, with a VME backplane, using 68040 general-purpose processors and TMS320C50 signal processors. Standard modules process inputs from all combat-system sensors, and operational functions are implemented via software. In a typical installation, a submarine would have two two-screen sonar consoles on one side of the control room, with two single-screen CDS consoles against the after bulkhead. The system bus is an Ethernet. The CDS consoles would be standard types, such as UYQ-70s (they can also be a locally produced type). Raytheon expects to offer an SQS-56 variant as the transmitter (in the sail or in the bow above or below the passive cylinder). The company has developed its own hydrophone, suitable for both the bow cylinder and a flank array. Processing will be both narrow- and broad-band.

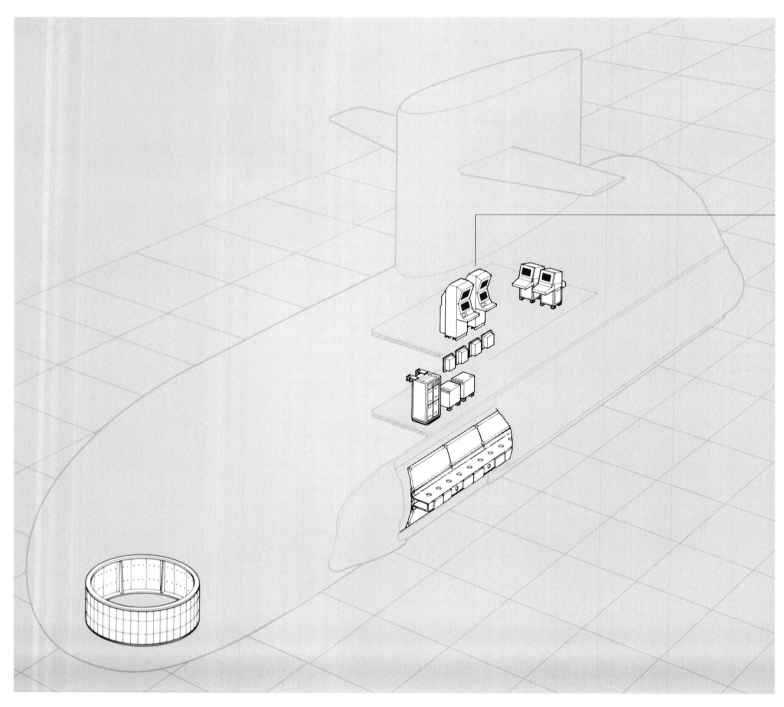

AIRCRAFT TACTICAL DATA SYSTEMS

Just as with ships, aircraft can benefit from the integration of their sensors to form a coherent tactical picture. Large patrol aircraft are analogous to ships, with separate sensors served by individual operators. The TDS forms a single coherent picture out of the various pieces of data available on board to different operators. The first example of such integration was probably the Airborne Tactical Data System (ATDS) of the Grumman E-2, which is analogous to NTDS. Another very early example was the Lockheed P-3C (A-NEW).

Single- or two-seat aircraft are integrated on a very different level, the pilot's HUD and raster-scan CRT. Originally the HUD merely projected the outputs of key instruments onto a glass in front of the pilot, so that the pilot could fly at low level without taking his eyes away from the windshield. In that form the first HUD appeared in the U.S. Navy Vigilante attack bomber, designed in 1955. In this aircraft the HUD was presumably associated with the digital navigational computer, which could transmit waypoint directions through the HUD.

Before HUDs, aircraft already had one indicator in the pilot's field of view, a gunsight or bombsight. One lesson of the Vietnam War was that a pilot also needed a simple computer to indicate whether a target was within the engageable envelope of his missile. Adding such a computer, inevitably with a display superimposed on the pilot's view, enormously improved the effectiveness of the Sidewinder missile.

Gun- and bombsights were naturally combined with the HUD via a weapons aiming computer (WAC) or bombing computer. Because it must display instrument readings, the HUD collects the instruments' outputs. They can therefore be passed on to a bomb-aiming computer. This computer in turn can continuously project onto the HUD an estimated bomb-impact point, the CCIP (continuously computed impact point). When the CCIP passes over the desired target, the pilot can release the bomb. One effect of the CCIP capability is to allow the pilot much greater freedom to maneuver near the target. This capability first appeared in the A-7E, which thereby achieved strikingly better accuracy than earlier versions of the same airplane. An added refinement was to designate the target, then have the bombing computer release bombs when the appropriate drop point was reached. Another refinement in the A-7E was that, because it was programmable, the bombing computer could easily be adapted to a wide range of different bomb ballistics. A more powerful computer, like that in the F/A-18, can function in multiple modes, for example for air-to-air combat as well as for bomb or missile fire control.

As in a ship, a central computer can compile a tactical picture, creating a TWS capability. The first airplane to enjoy this sort of advantage was the F-14, whose AWG-9 is actually a central tactical computer connected to a pulse-Doppler radar. Without such a computer, a pilot can scan for targets or track and engage a single target, but tracking requires that the radar be locked on. At the least, the lock-on is detectable by the potential target. These considerations probably also apply to surface targets. An airplane without any tactical computer would have to lock onto a surface target in order to perform fire-control calculations prior to launching a missile; the lock-on (which is detectable) would be clear evidence of hostile intent. In some cases the missile fire-control system may be a separate box capable of deducing target track from a series of radar observations input by the pilot.

Too, the central computer can accept inputs from an external system, such as the U.S. TAMPS described in the preceding section. They can include the desired flight path to the target area, which can be displayed on a digital map; they can also include switch settings, for example, for radio frequencies and weapon-release settings. The central computer can also accept data from a forward air controller, as in the current U.S. ATHS. The great significance of such computer-to-computer communication is that it grossly reduces the possibility of error, which is always present when information is relayed by voice or copied by hand (as in a conventional ready room). The U.S. Army hopes, for example, to solve most friendly-fire problems by adopting a digital

battlefield control system, which in turn includes computer-to-computer connections to close support aircraft.

Aircraft differ in the way in which different system elements are distributed. For example, the British Sea Harrier has a single computer controlling its HUD and providing weapons control. In some cases (as in the British Blue Vixen), the radar may incorporate a TWS computer, as in a surface ADT radar; in others, the track files are kept by the central mission computer.

The amount of data a pilot can process is inherently limited, and the computer can help by filtering (integrating) some of the relevant data, and also by combining them in more usable form. Even this filtered picture is often too complex. Modern HUDs connected to digital computers often have de-clutter switches by means of which the pilot can eliminate all but the most essential data, for example, for air-to-air combat. The pilot must still look almost directly ahead to see the HUD superimposed on the sky. That must be distracting during violent maneuvers, as in close air-to-air combat. The ultimate HUD displays its data, not on a fixed screen in the cockpit, but on the pilot's visor.

Pilot reactions still impose a time lag. The pilot sees a target and must move to react, for example, to fire a weapon. No matter how perfectly coordinated the pilot is, hand movement will lag behind head and eye movements. One solution is to place sensors in the cockpit to pick up the pilot's head movement. The Russian MiG-29 and Su-27 and the U.S. AH-64 ground-attack helicopter use a simple form of this system. The concept has a potential shipboard application: allowing quicker defensive reactions to lookout sightings, for example, of incoming aircraft or missiles.

It seems inevitable that the extent to which the central tactical system combines different sensor outputs will expand. Current aircraft generally still segregate ESM data from other tactical data; they are fitted with separate RWRs, for example. It seems likely that future tactical aircraft will have integrated EW suites (warning, identification, reaction).

Another likely future development is actual control by the aircraft central tactical computer. Many current aircraft use fly-by-wire systems, in which the pilot's commands are translated by a computer into appropriate control responses. Such systems incorporate autopilots, which may follow the flight plan in the central computer. However, generally the control circuit and the sensor circuit are entirely separate, just as on board a ship steering and engine orders are not controlled by the TDS. For an airplane, maneuver is intimately connected with air combat; the airplane itself is used to aim many of the weapons. Violent evasion triggered by ESM warnings is often necessary for survival. The next step, then, would seem to be to integrate existing fly-by-wire systems and existing computer-based air-combat systems. The pilot would still decide what to do, but the aircraft system would make many more of the implementing decisions. A current U.S. ARPA program, the Pilot's Associate, makes much of this promise. One justification for more computer control is that a pilot may be unable to control an airplane through the really violent maneuvers needed in future air combat. This sort of integration already exists, in a limited way, in terrain-avoiding or ground-following systems.

Central computers are associated with a shift toward aircraft digital data buses, now including bus connections to the weapons pylons and bomb bays. In the past, the wiring that actually communicated with bombs and other ordnance was analog: simple DC or AC voltages were sent to the pylons to set and release weapons. Each pylon needed its own wiring from the bomb controls in the cockpit. Because the messages sent along that wiring were quite simple, the system had to be adjusted specifically for each weapon the airplane carried. Setting errors would make for incorrect delivery, even for no delivery at all.

A bussed system (typically using a 1760 bus) is dramatically simpler, because all hard points receive a single broadcast (in effect) of arming information; coding tells each hard point how to set (and whether to release) its own weapon. Because the digital bus transmits relatively complex messages, it can handle complex weapons, such as those requiring GPS or inertial data before firing. Because the bus communicates in both directions, the central tactical system is automatically aware of which weapon is on which hard point, and it selects, presets, and fires. With the advent of the digital weapons bus comes a separate digital stores management computer, which may also function (as in the AV-8B) as a backup bomb-release system. For the moment, many current weapons are set by analog signals, so aircraft with weapons buses often have digital-to-analog converters at their hard points. As the older weapons disappear, aircraft weapon systems should become all-digital.

Unlike shipboard CDS, aircraft tactical systems often are not standardized, even though many of their hardware components are. Thus the entries below are often designated by aircraft rather than by system.

Helicopters are intermediate between the large multioperator aircraft and the tactical fighter or bomber. Typically, integration means that there are no longer any displays unique to any one sensor. Instead, the multifunction displays can be switched to any sensor, using an internal data bus.

Deletions: Hinpads/MSDHS (due to cancelation of the Canadian version of the EH-101 helicopter).

FRANCE

♦ Atlantique Nouvelle Génération

This version of the Atlantic maritime patrol airplane is analogous to the P-3C version of the Orion: a central tactical computer (in this case a 15M/125X with 512 kwords of storage) integrates the system. Design of the second-generation aircraft began in 1978, the prototype appearing in 1985. The first production airplane was handed over to the French navy in October 1988. At that time the Atlantique Nouvelle Génération was described as the most complex aircraft yet developed in France.

The tactical system incorporates two two-position TSM 8200 (DSAX 1) SADANG (Système Acoustique de l'Atlantique Nouvelle Génération) acoustic processors. The French system differs from that of the U.S. P-3s in that it is designed to be equally effective against surface and submarine targets. The TACCO and radar operator are therefore provided with two alternative stations. In the antiship role, the TACCO sits forward, near the ESM operator, and in the ASW role, aft, near the acoustics processors. Each of the two identical TACCO/radar-operator stations has a bicolor multipurpose display to show raw video and the tactical situation, plus an alphanumeric display, a display selection panel, programmed action keyboards, and a trackball. These stations include the FLIR display. There are also alphanumeric displays for the navigator/communications operator and for the acoustic operator. An automatic plotting station (the aircraft's position is marked by a point of light) at the navigator/communications station functions as a backup to the computer-driven tactical plot.

The basic combat-system crew (other than two pilots and a flight engineer) consists of the TACCO, the navigator/communications operator, the ESM-ECM-MAD operator, the radar operator, two acoustic operators, and a front observer; the airplane can carry two more observers as reliefs.

The normal load is 100 sonobuoys and four torpedoes or two Exocets, for an 8hr mission on station at low altitude 600 nm from base. The buoys are carried in four reloadable launchers, plus four 18-buoy launchers; there is internal storage for 30 buoys. There are four hard points under the wings (two 750 kg, two 1000 kg). The bomb bay carries either eight Mk 46 torpedoes, twelve depth charges, nine mines, two AM 39, or three Mk 46 and one AM 39.

The earlier Atlantic 1 is operated by Italy, Pakistan, and West Germany (Dutch Atlantics have been replaced by P-3Cs and French Atlantic Mk 1s have been retired). It lacks any integrating computer system. The sonobuoy processor is the U.S. AQA-5; the radar is DRAA-2B; the MAD is DHAX-1; and the standard ESM set is ARAR-10B. French aircraft were later equipped with a Sparton demultiplexer and display for DIFAR buoys, TD-1135/A. The Italian aircraft were upgraded by Dassault, with IGUANE radars, AQS-902 processors, and a U.S. TDS, probably ASN-150.

The West German aircraft were modernized by Dornier in 1979–83. New APS-134 radars and Loral EW-1017 ESM sets were installed. The old AQA-5(Mod) acoustic system was retained but improved using an eight-channel ESCO modification kit. A new Dornier sonobuoy launcher was added. No central tactical system was installed. After procurement of a replacement (the abortive U.S. P-7A) failed, a lifetime extension program was ordered. It began in 1996. The radar receives a new TWS capability, the ESM system receives a new display and processor, FLIR is added, and a GPS/INU replaces the earlier navigation system. Apparently a central tactical system, or at least a system integrating GPS with aircraft navigation, is being added.

♦ AMASCOS

Thomson-CSF's Airborne Maritime Situation Control System was announced early in 1993. AMASCOS-100 is a basic radar/navigation package for coastal surveillance, using a single operator. AMASCOS-200 (two operators) adds a FLIR (Thomson-TRT Clio) and a DR-3000A ESM system. AMASCOS-300 (three operators) adds a MAD (Crouzet Mk III) and a SADANG 1000 sonobuoy system (with a dipper, for helicopters). The radar is Ocean Master and the navigational system is the Sextant NADIR II (inertial/GPS). The system can support Link W and aircraft can use it to fire Exocet missiles and lightweight torpedoes. The first order, for Chile, was canceled because the required lightweight torpedo, Murene, could not be delivered on time (Murene had been superseded by the Franco-Italian Impact). The launch order was from Indonesia, for the CN-235.

Users:

Amascos-100/200: Indonesia (CN-235 maritime patrol aircraft).
Amascos-300: Pakistan (three Atlantic 1 as modernized, one Fokker F-27).

♦ Mirage F1

The initial versions, F1A and F1C, lacked HUDs and had separate navigational and bombing computers (Crouzet Type 115 and Type 31 or 32, respectively). F1E outwardly resembles F1C but has a digital central tactical system: a HUD (VE.120C), a Ginabus, an ESD M182 central computer, a Crouzet air data computer, and a SAGEM inertial navigation system. Apparently the computer does not confer multitarget air-tracking capability on the radar. The French air force reconnaissance version (F1CR) has the central digital computer introduced in the F1E, but it seems unlikely that other versions of the F1C were upgraded to match; the French air force later upgraded 57 F1Cs to F1CT (tactique) standard with digital computers. Users of the digital version are Ecuador (F1JA based on F1E), France (F1CR/F1CT upgraded to digital operation with M182-XR computer), Jordan (F1EJ), Iraq (F1EQ), Libya (F1ED), Morocco (F1EH), Qatar (F1EDA), and Spain (F1EE). Some Iraqi aircraft have Agave radars for antiship attack. The other aircraft have a multimode version of the Cyrano IV radar with provision for ground attack.

M182 used hybrid electronics (presumably meaning some chips and some discrete circuitry). The current M182-XR offers a threefold improvement in performance to 1 MIPS with 512 kwords of storage. It incorporates some VHSIC circuitry and a battery backed-up semiconductor RAM replaces the earlier core memory. This version is being installed in French air force Mirage F1s and presumably is available for export upgrades. Although details of M182 have not been published, presumably it was broadly equivalent to such ESD 16-bit computers (with 32-bit floating-point functions) as ESD 2084 and 3084. Each had 512 kwords of 16-bit memory. For 2084, single-precision addition time was 1.5 microsec, multiplication time was 6.75 microsec, and division time was 7.5 microsec. The 3084 cut these times to 0.65, 2.0, and 7.0 microsecs, respectively.

♦ Super Étendard

Remanufactured Étendard strike fighters were fitted with a Thomson-CSF VE-120 HUD fed by a Kearfott UAT 40 central tactical computer built under license by SAGEM. The computer receives both radar (Agave) and inertial-navigation (a Kearfott UNI 40, built under license by SAGEM) data. Functions include navigation to a point stored in memory; bomb delivery, including automatic or manual release; and direction to a missile-firing point in space.

This program dates from 1974–77. A further upgrade (48 aircraft: three prototypes plus 15 per year in 1993–95) is now underway, to extend airframe service life to 2005. The prototype began flight tests on 5 October 1990. Improvements include installation of a Super Anemone TWS radar (in place of the current Agave), a new inertial platform, a new wide-angle HUD (which can also display TV and FLIR images), the Sherloc RWR, extra stores attachment points, provision for night-vision goggles, a HOTAS control, and a new central computer (SAGEM UAT 90 in place of the earlier UAT 40).

As of 1996, France had a total of 54 Super Étendards, of which 32 were in first-line service. However, only two squadrons (flotillas), 12F and 17F (12 aircraft each), are used for attack; these aircraft were modified to carry ASMP missiles. There are also eight Étendard IVP photo aircraft (16F). The unmodernized Super Étendards are in a training squadron, 59S.

INTERNATIONAL

◆ EH-101

The mission-control system developed by GF-Sistemi Avionici of Italy employs two computers in a hot/standby configuration. Both the mission computer and the navigational computer are modular, employing the same building blocks; they are multiprocessors employing 80386s. The mission bus is a 1553B. The computer family was begun about 1979 for ECM, using an 8086 processor. The first EH-101 computer (for navigation) used 80286 chips, but the 80386 was adopted because the Royal Navy wanted more powerful software, hence higher processor performance. Only after this replacement did the planned software work properly. Attempts to export this approach to other platforms, such as maritime patrol aircraft, led to a series using RISC processors, initially the Intel 80960, which can replace an 80386. That in turn led to the navigational concept for the Aster missile (OTI, Organ de Traitement d'Information), which uses the 80960 with a math coprocessor (Aerospatiale Missile Division's 29050).

◆ Tornado

The Tornado weapon system is a slightly more elaborate and more automated equivalent to that of the U.S. A-6E. In its case terrain avoidance is automatic; the airplane was designed to fly at high speed at about 200 ft altitude. The Panavia Tornado was the first aircraft in the world designed for fly-by-wire, although the fly-by-wire F-16 flew first. The main sensor is the Texas Instruments TNR multimode radar feeding a 64kword Litef 16-bit (32-bit floating point, with 69 instructions) LR-1432 central computer (upgradable to 512 kwords), and there is a 1553B bus. No computer running speed was published, but core access time was 450 nsec for an 8/16-kword module and 350 nsec for a 32-kword module. Tornados were later upgraded with LR-1432Fs, which add one or more 68040s running ADA software. The main navigational sensors are an inertial platform and a Doppler radar. The main computer can store planned targets for preset attack (using dive or loft bombing, air-to-surface missiles, or guns). Bombs can be dropped on targets of opportunity, using a continuously computed impact line (CCIL) displayed on the HUD, or (in British aircraft only) designated by a laser (as was done by Buccaneers during the Gulf War).

All Tornado users (Germany, Italy, Saudi Arabia, and the United Kingdom) use at least some Tornados for maritime strikes. German and Italian aircraft are armed with Kormoran missiles. Saudi and British aircraft have Sea Eagle. Nine German naval Tornados are equipped to fire HARM.

A German midlife upgrade program envisages installation of a new central computer to support new weapons as well as a FLIR and embedded GPS. Italian aircraft (some of which have a secondary maritime strike role) will probably be upgraded in parallel to the German program.

ISRAEL

◆ Maritime Patrol Suite (MPS)

Elisra's new maritime patrol aircraft tactical system was announced at the 1995 Paris Air Show. It is intended specifically for installation aboard existing aircraft. A new central computer (the data gathering, processing, and display manager, or DGPDM) communicates with operator workstations via a 1553 bus and a video bus. It communicates with new sensor systems, such as a radar and IFF interrogator, via a similar pair of buses. The new systems may include ESM, TV/FLIR, MAD, INS/GPS, communication systems, and a sonobuoy system (which communicates only via a 1553 bus). The central computer can also be connected, via existing avionic buses, to existing systems, such as a data link, IFF transponder, VLF/Omega, and weapons. The company describes MPS as modular, suited to "managed and user-friendly" integration of mission and weapons systems. That suggests something broadly like Rockwell's IDLS (see below), a central data-gathering/tactical tracking box providing a tactical picture in the form of overlays from the various sensors. Presumably it also incorporates simple navigational decision aids (such as interception calculations needed for missile fire control). It manages displays and can control an air-to-air or air-to-surface data link. Elisra offers an extended version of MPS incorporating its IR missile warner (Passive Airborne Warning System, PAWS) and chaff/flare dispensers.

Elisra's system was probably ordered for the modernized Argentine S-2s and is likely planned for the Chilean P-3s; it is probably also the system used in the An-72P surveillance aircraft. In 1995 Elisra claimed that it was also being considered for a foreign helicopter. As of 1996, installation designs exist for the An-72, CASA CN-235, DHC-7/8, DASA Do-328, Embraer Brasilia 120, Fokker F-50, Grumman S-2, and Lockheed P-3.

ITALY

◆ MIDAHS/Mission Core System

GF-Sistemi Avionici S.r.l. (a Finmeccanica company, the old Alenia avionics division) displayed this generic mission data-handling system at the 1995 Paris Air Show. It is intended to support fixed- and rotary-wing maritime patrol aircraft. The 1553B bus can support up to two mission computer units (MCUs), three control display units (CDUs), three tactical display units (TDUs), and a mission data-entry unit. Each CDU is a VME enclosure carrying up to nine boards (up to three processor boards, each carrying a 68040 running at 25 MHz, 2 Mbyte of SRAM, and up to 8 Mbyte of EEPROM for mission software; plus the 1553B controller, three graphic controller boards, and special I/O interfaces). Sensor video is fed directly into the computer, which in turn connects to either or both of the TDUs and CDUs. Each TDU has a color LCD display (7.66 × 5.74 in). Typically the tactical operator console would display tactical navigation and summary data; the surface operator console would show FLIR, radar, TV, ESM, and MAD data; and an acoustic terminal would show data derived from the airplane's acoustic processing subsystem.

This system was selected for the new NH-90 helicopter, which will have separate mission and navigational computers, as in the EH-101 described above. The bussed system is open to alternative processors, and leads to the concept of a mission core system adaptable to a wide range of aircraft types and missions, somewhat analogous, say, to the 9LV Mk 3 ship/submarine/shore system. Modules for input/output and for symbol generation (raster or stroke) can be added as required. The system has been adopted for the AMX light strike fighter and is being developed for EFA. The core comprises the display, symbol generator, processor, data input, system capability, and programmable graphics.

MIDAHS may be used in the Italian navy's upgraded version of the Atlantic patrol airplane, and has been proposed for modernization of the Tracker. The Tracker will require a separate analog/digital converter for the existing avionics. Presumably the system would come with its own sensors from the same industrial group, for example, a Grifo radar, a Galileo FLIR, and Elettronica ESM.

RUSSIA

◆ Bear F (Tu-142)

Tu-142M (Bear F Mods 1 and beyond) is the closest Russian equivalent to the Orion or the Nimrod. It differs from these Western aircraft in that it has a pro-, as well as antisubmarine mission, to help Russian submarines evade Western barriers. It can therefore carry air-delivered submarine decoys, which appear not to have any Western analogs. The Russians also differed from their Western rivals in continuing to use explosive echo-ranging ("Julie") alongside conventional passive sonobuoys. Active buoys appear not to have been used very extensively.

The airplane's computer search/attack system, Korshun was apparently conceived in the late 1960s specifically to deal with quiet SSBNs. The earliest version, Mod 1, seems to have used only broad-band buoys. Reported requirements included the ability to detect submarines operating on the surface, snorkeling, or submerged to 500 m (about 1600 ft) at speeds of up to 50 kt, although only with the advent of the APR-2E rocket torpedo could such demands be met. Work on an improved version, presumably Korshun-M, began late in 1974. It was intended specifically to deal with quiet submarines, and presumably it introduced the LOFAR processor. The aircraft that first carried it was Bear F Mod 3. Like equivalent Western systems, Korshun was designed to provide both flight-control data and sensor and weapons-release cues. According to a Russian article published in 1994, an upgraded version of Korshun can find and track sub-

The command system of a Bear F Mod 4 maritime-patrol aircraft shows an organization similar to that of a ship or, for that mater, to a U.S. P-3C. The laser scanner is the Ametyst LIDAR to detect shallow submarines. (Stuart Slade, DMS/Forecast International)

marines submerged to 800 m (about 2600 ft) in Sea State 5, consuming only two-thirds as many sonobuoys. It is not clear whether this was the version in Bear F Mod 4.

The equivalent of the shipboard BIP is the "battle station" abaft the flight deck. At least Mod 3 has three ASW operator consoles (plus a TACCO); it is not clear that all consoles are sonobuoy positions. Mods may include changes in sonobuoy signal processors, Mod 1 having virtually none (it uses the old BM-series broad-band buoys). Clearly at least Mod 3 and Mod 4 use LOFAR (Type 75) buoys, but the quality of their signal processors may be quite different.

At least some aircraft may data-link with Il-38 Mays (the two are often seen together, except in the Mediterranean).

Mod 0 (first flown 1968) combined the May (see below) system (Berkut) with a Bear airframe with a redesigned wing. Only 15 were made, 5 of which were transferred to India. The other 10 were used for R&D, then reconditioned as Mod 3s.

Mod 1 (Tu-142M, 1974; design bureau designation Tu-142MK, for Korshun) introduced Korshun. This version of the airplane was identifiable by its numerous ram-air intakes and the absence of a chin radome. It has three sonobuoy terminals, a radar under its belly, ESM, and a MAD stinger. Each sensor reports electronically to a plotting table in the "battle area" aft of the cockpit. This area also contains a weapons-release terminal, the first such (in previous aircraft weapons were dropped manually by the pilot on command). The export version for India is Tu-142MK-E.

In Mod 2 (1980), the battle station was approximately doubled in size (the forward fuselage was lengthened 9 in), and the aircraft was provided with a fully equipped galley and bunk areas. ESM was more elaborate than in Mod 1, and there are more data links for operation with surface ships (in addition to Karas) and with submarines (a new feature). There are also transponders, and much-enhanced airborne track-keeping. This version had a very crude airborne "second captain" computer. This may have been the first version to use Type 75 LOFAR sonobuoys. Mod 2 was

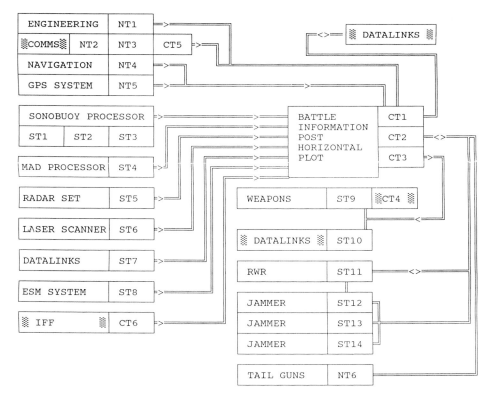

TUPOLEV TU-95 BEAR FOXTROT MOD.4
(simplified and sanitized)

NT = Normal terminals usually associated with aircraft functions
ST = Sensor terminals equipped with tracker balls
CT = Command terminals with tracker balls, touchpads and cardkey access
▨ = Command-encrypted system with cardkey access

an interim version, in effect a Mod 3 airframe without the full electronic suite. Mod 2 introduced self-defensive weapons (jammers and chaff). This was the first Tu-142M version. Work began in 1972, and the prototype flew on 4 November 1975.

All earlier aircraft were converted to Mod 3 (1982), which has enlarged weapon bays (27 and 14 m). It used a new Ladoga MAD (very similar to the U.S. ASQ-81) reporting to two stations rather than one (this was the first version with the MAD boom on top of the tail fin), and two ESM terminals. This version still had three sonobuoy terminals (perhaps for different types of buoys: broad-band, Julie, LOFAR) and one radar terminal. All reported to a "work area" in the battle station forward, which was now an airborne command center. There were 12 data links (air-air, air-surface, air-subsurface). This version required its own gas-turbine generator. It had a full second captain–type tactical computer, which processed ESM data directly. Its output was fed directly to the weapons-control station for weapons release, both for the airplane and for the other platforms it controlled. In a reversal of the earlier arrangement, a single Mod 3 could control several Kresta IIs. In this version and Mod 4, there is a self-defense "complex" with several terminals (for jammers and chaff). Mods 3 and 4 have full satellite communications capability.

Mod 3 apparently handles (or handled) several different sonobuoy types. A May 1986 photograph of a Bear F Mod 3 over the Pacific shows a mix of buoys in the bomb bay, all carried horizontally in racks. The forward bay carries large buoys in two vertical racks, probably nine per rack (i.e., one attack per rack). The middle section carries smaller buoys, each about half the length of the large ones. The after section carries torpedoes. The after bay also carries buoys (two large vertical racks). The larger buoys are probably the earlier broad-band type (BM series); the small ones are likely to be Type 75 LOFAR buoys. This particular airplane dropped nine large buoys, each retarded by a parachute, in three close groups of three; presumably each buoy of a group was set to place its hydrophone at a different depth. The group of three triplets would form a line barrier. As modernized to carry only Type 75 series buoys, Mod 3 carries 100 sonobuoys rather than the 70 of earlier versions.

Mod 4 (Tu-142MZ), the current version, uses a new sonobuoy system, Zarechye, and data bus. It has been heavily modified to use the new Ametyst LIDAR; the big box under its nose carries FLIRs, LLLTV, LIDAR, and a new radar altimeter. This version has a communications room separate from the battle station. However, the data links feed directly into the battle station. Reportedly Mod 4 carries 114 passive omni and 10 directional buoys (RGB-25 and RGB-16). Another report credits it with 100 Type 75 Series L (LOFAR-type) sonobuoys. This version reinstates the chin radome and carries a short-range navigational radar (thimble) on its nose. Fairings are revised. Mod 4 maximum weapons load is about 16,000 kg (up to 12 APR-2E torpedoes [which replace short 53cm torpedoes], four to eight nuclear depth bombs, as well as conventional bombs for ASW and ASMs, in a rotary launcher).

Tu-142MR (Bear J) is a communications relay version corresponding to the U.S. TACAMO, with a ventral pod for a trailing wire VLF antenna and a satellite antenna on the upper forward fuselage.

As many as 245 Tu-142s may have been built, about 55 remaining in Russian service (plus a few Bear Js) in 1995. India operates eight aircraft.

The projected maritime patrol version of the new Albatros (Be-44; NATO nickname "Mermaid") flying boat will probably have much the same ASW system as Bear F Mod 4.

Of earlier maritime patrol aircraft, Be-12 (Mail) has a Baku ASW system integrating sonobuoys (SPARU-55 receiver), MAD (APM-60 Orsha), and nose radar (PSRS-2 Initsiyativa 2B). In all, 132 were built 1963–72, of which about 90 remained in Russian and Ukrainian service prior to the beginning of conversions for fire-fighting (as Be-12P) in 1992 (as of 1995, 10 had been converted). This type is also used by Vietnam (12 transferred) and possibly by Syria. Be-12N is a modified version with a Nartsiss (narcissus) search/attack system; the name suggests an ELINT function.

May (Il-38) was originally designed for Indonesia, to be used in patrolling the archipelago against surface craft. Presumably it would have called in Badgers armed with antiship missiles. It therefore incorporated only a search radar (with onboard terminal), crude ESM, and a manual plotting table. When Sukarno fell, about 30 had been completed. These aircraft were diverted to the Soviet navy.

Some, equipped as intended for Indonesia, were sent abroad (e.g., to Socotra and Camranh Bay) for maritime patrol (surface surveillance). The Soviets preferred to use austerely equipped aircraft abroad to avoid compromising their ASW technology.

Other aircraft were modified for ASW, to work with Kara-class cruisers. They were equipped with radar, sonobuoys, transponders, MAD stingers, and ESM. Each sensor fed its own terminal, and there was a manual plot in the "battle area" abaft the cockpit. A data link to the Kara reported in the battle area. Each Kara could control four to six Mays via its second captain. The ASW system is Berkut.

In all, about 65 Il-38s were built, about 40 remaining in Russian and Ukrainian service in 1995. Versions: Il-38, Il-38M (second radome instead of forward bomb bay), Il-38P (suffix suggests ESM or jamming role). Typical loads: (a) search, 216 RGB-1 sonobuoys; (b) search/attack, 144 RGB-1 plus 10 RGB-2 plus 2 AT-1 torpedoes or 19 PLAB-250-120 depth bombs or 1 nuclear depth bomb; (c) mining, 8 AMD-2-500 mines.

◆ Ka-25/27

These helicopters process their sonobuoys on board. Ka-25 originally carried 12 broad-band buoys without a processor. It now carries three Type 75 Series S (LOFAR buoys). The search/attack system in Hormone A (Ka-25B) is Baykal, integrating an Initsi-yativa-2K radar, a dipping sonar (Oka-2) or a MAD (APM-60 Orsha), and sonobuoys. The larger Ka-27 carries 12 Type 75 Series S buoys. Presumably it was specially designed to accommodate the processor and the LOFAR buoys, which were back-fitted into the smaller Ka-25. On the newest ASW ships (Neustrashimyy, Udaloy, and Krivak III), Ka-27PL data are data-linked to the ship combat system, as in a LAMPS III.

The Ka-27PL CDS is called Osminog; the export version, for Ka-28, is Osminog-E. The dipping sonar is Ros. Unlike a Ka-25, a Ka-27 can carry both search equipment and weapons simultaneously. An improved Ka-27K (prototype only) has the Kamerton-1M search/attack system. Osminog detects and locates a submarine, and advises the crew on the weapon used to attack it by displaying the tactical situation on the systems navigation/tactical monitor.

◆ MiG-29 and Su-27 Weapons Control System (SVU)

These aircraft have full computer-driven central tactical systems integrating their radars with optronic sensors. A MiG-29 has an SVU-29 weapon system, comprising an N-019E Doppler radar, OEPNK-29E (S-31) opto-electronic fire-control and navigation system (employing a KOLS optical radar comprising an OEPS-23S IR sensor and an LD laser range-finder; the Su-27 equivalent is OLS-27), NSC-29 pilot helmet target designator, SEI display system (HUD and head-down display), SUO fire-control system, and a computer. The Su-27 system is similar. Both IRST and radar have automatic target detection/track modes. KOLS is optimized for dog-fighting, but OLS-27 is also effective for long-range missile combat. The Su-27 carries a mixture of long-range R-27 and short-range R-11 missiles. R-27 employs a mid-course uplink from the fighter; its seeker (semiactive radar or IR) is turned on only after it has been guided into a basket near the target. Thus if the fighter tracks its target entirely optically, it need turn on a radar illuminator only a short time before its semiactive radar missile arrives at the target. The fighter can track 10 targets simultaneously but it can lock on to only one at a time.

In an Su-27, "C2 cycle time," presumbly the data-link refresh rate, is 60 sec. Typical radar search range is 70 km and track range is 60 km (against a target like a MiG-21). The radar can scan +/−50 deg horizontally and +/−18 deg vertically. It can be set to scan over a much narrower sector (+/−15 or 20 deg) when the airplane is under ground control.

The weapons-system computer of the MiG-29 (and, presumably, that of the Su-27) apparently selects which weapon to fire based on sensor input. The system can automatically interrogate a target; it can be set either not to fire on a positive IFF reply, or else to disregard the reply. Thus standard practice is to operate with the trigger depressed, relying on IFF to protect friendly aircraft. The trigger and other weapons switches are widely separated and are probably difficult to press in quick succession. During the Gulf War, an Iraqi pilot apparently failed to set his system to avoid engaging friendly aircraft (or suffered an IFF failure), and therefore shot down his wingman. Apparently similar failures occasionally resulted in Russian losses during training.

The opto-electronic sensor system (which the Russians often call an optical radar) entered service in 1983. The visible element is a glass ball mounted forward of the cockpit, containing mirrors for the coaxial passive and active (laser ranger) elements. Later Su-27s and Su-33s have another pair of balls mounted in the lower fuselage sides abaft the wings. They may be for fuller coverage or for missile approach warning. A Russian pilot pointed out that they make it relatively easy for a pilot executing a ''cobra'' maneuver to fire an off-boresight missile at a target in their field of regard, then accelerate up and away from the target.

The mirror in the ball automatically scans, presenting its IR picture on the aircraft sensor displays (the HUD and the head-down display, both of which also show corresponding radar data). The displays also carry cross-hairs corresponding to the position of the pilot's helmet. Normally the IR scanning system cues the pilot, who designates targets. The cross-hairs can also be used to cue the aircraft radar, or the radar can cue the IR sensor and the pilot. The aircraft FCS (controlling gun and missiles) is slaved to the pilot's helmet. For close-in targets, the pilot is the primary tracking element of the system, keeping targets in sight for off-boresight shots. The IR element presumably tracks designated targets to measure rates for longer-range shots. The pilot can press a button to measure the range to a designated target.

In KOLS, the 8–12 micron IRST has two alternative scan sectors: +/−30 × +/−15 deg and +/−15 × +/−15 deg. They are scanned horizontally at about 17 scans/sec for the large field and 30 scans/sec for the small. Maximum automatic tracking rate is 30 deg/sec. Typical maximum search range is 15 km, maximum track range 15 km. The laser range-finder is effective between 200 m and 6.5 km, which makes it useful mainly for gun FCS. Accuracy is 50 m in range, 0.15 deg in elevation/bearing, and 10 m/sec in target speed.

Using his helmet, the pilot can designate targets within a +/−60 × +60/−14-deg sector. A small television camera behind the pilot tracks five IR-emitting diodes atop the helmet to indicate to the system the direction in which the pilot is looking. That moves cross-hairs across the pilot's display. The seekers of air-to-air missiles are also slaved to the helmet. A small optical sight in the pilot's field of view is combined with an emitting diode unit. The sight shows the pilot where the system thinks he is looking. Cueing lights on it indicate that a target has been detected by IR or radar or locked onto by a missile; they direct the pilot to that target. They also indicate when a missile has been launched.

The OLS-27 optical radar achieves better precision and in some modes its range is similar to that of the radar. OLS-27 apparently also connects the pilot's head sight more tightly with the rest of the weapon system: when the pilot's head moves, the IR sensor, laser range-finder, radar dish, and missile seekers can all move with it. The search scan sector has been widened to +/−60 × +/−37.5 deg, but the narrow-scan sector has shrunk to +/−10 × +/−2.5 deg. A target can be acquired at about 70% greater range. Compared to KOLS, accuracy in range does not change (the range-finder is the same), but angular accuracy improves to 0.08 deg. Maximum tracking rate is reduced to 25 deg/sec. OLS-27 weighs about twice as much as KOLS.

Reportedly, EO radar was originally developed in the 1970s because the Soviets lacked an effective radar look-down/shoot-down system to counter low-flying bombers and then cruise mis-siles. A Russian pilot reportedly explained the system as a whole as an attempt to avoid emissions in intercepting a target. Typically the radar operates in dormant mode. A clear-air target is acquired and tracked electro-optically; the radar is used only when it disappears into cloud.

◆ Mi-14 (Haze)/Kalmar

Like a Bear F, an Mi-14 has a weapons system built around a tactical computer (in effect, an airborne second captain). Each of four sensor consoles (fore to aft: MAD, radar, sonobuoys, dipper) preprocesses its data, feeding detection data into the computer (track supervisor, weapons-system overseer). The computer is on the port side forward, with the weapons-control computers (separate units for torpedoes and nuclear depth bombs) aft. Opposite it are the sensor terminals, all in a row, with the dipping sonar console roughly abeam the sonar winch. Some helicopters may also have an EO sensor console. As in a ship, the second captain processes ESM data directly. The second captain–type computer allocates targets, and transfers them to the weapons-control station. The helicopter carries 44 Type 75 Series S LOFAR buoys in 20 top-loaded drop tubes. Readouts are paper (presumably LOFARgrams) and CRTs. The helicopter data link connects it to a ship or to a shore station (when it operates inshore).

Kalmar is the weapon system of the Polish navy's Mi-14PW ASW helicopters. It may be a degraded export version of the Soviet system described above. In Polish service, the Mi-14PW replaced an ASW version of the Mi-4, the Mi-4M (the first Mi-14PWs arrived on 15 July 1981).

The navigator forward is the system operator, using head-down displays (i.e., using the second captain track-keeping and tactical computer). The system sensors are the APM-60 MAD, streamed at the end of a cable, and the OKA-2 dipping sonar. A 1990 description does not mention any sonobuoys. A modified ASW version, Mi-14PW-M, with improved equipment (not specified) was introduced in the mid-1980s. The associated weapons are bombs, depth charges, and torpedoes, carried on pylons and in special cassettes (sic). The IFF is Chrom Nikiel. The radar, in a chin radome, is designated 12-M.

Users (export version): Bulgaria, Cuba, Libya, North Korea, Poland, Romania, Syria, and Yugoslavia; they were operated by East Germany.

◆ Sea Dragon (Su-32FN)

In March 1996 Sukhoi advertised this general-purpose naval weapons system for its Su-32FN two-seat attack fighter. The system operator sits alongside the pilot, using a CRT display for surface search, surface attack, and ASW missions. To the extent that Sukhoi's claims are credible, this system exploits the flexibility inherent in general-purpose processors, including radar signal processors. Thus the nose radar is usable both for air strikes by missile and for Russian-style sonobuoy interrogation. The internal computer(s) can be used both for missile targeting and for sonobuoy processing. None of this is inherently implausible. For example, in the 1960s the U.S. Navy seriously considered using pods on A-6 Intruders to drop sonobuoys (which would have been processed on board the carrier, the A-6 also acting as airborne relay). The S-3 was designed to operate with a single sonobuoy processing console. One might imagine that a powerful mission computer could make up for the absence of a tactical coordinator.

The system employs dual central computers that manage the crew interface and coordinate crew workload. There are also Argon general-purpose computers and specially programmed signal and other applications processors. A diagram suggests a system bus connecting radar, control/display system, FLIR, ELINT system, MAD, digital on-board computer, and hydrolocator (sonobuoy processor).

Sukhoi claims that the coherent search radar outperforms APS-137 by 25 to 30% in periscope or snorkel detection, that it can detect a wake at 150 km, and that it can detect large surface ships (3000 sq m cross-section) at about 250 km range. The same radar is used to monitor sonobuoys. Sonobuoys include passive and active types, and the system can control explosive wave generators for explosive echo-ranging. A Western account refers to detection of *submarine* wakes at 150 km, but that seems unlikely. Other sensors are a FLIR/TV and a laser range-finder.

The airplane itself was displayed at Paris in 1995 and completed static tests that November. It carries defensive weapons on wingtips and on outer wing pylons, with two more hard points under each wing, one under each engine, and two tandem underbody hard points, for a total load of 8000 kg plus two or four air-to-air missiles. In the ASW role, a 72-buoy pod is carried on the centerline, with four homing torpedoes (two under each wing). In the strike role, the airplane can carry two Moskit (Kh-41) or three Kh-65SE or three Kh-59M or six Kh-31 or Chelomei Alpha missiles. It also has an internal GSh-301 cannon.

SOUTH AFRICA

◆ Pelican

UEC's TACCO system is intended to integrate an MPA's combat systems. As in the company's surface-ship and submarine systems, all functions are contained in a single workstation, in this case containing a 20in situation display and a 14in tabular display plus tape and hard disk drives. The console uses COTS processors and has up to 12 serial ports (RS232, RS422) for communication with aircraft systems; it can also accommodate an Ethernet interface. Existing aircraft subsystems communicate directly with the TACCO station in a star arrangement: the lookout (marking events), the navigation subsystem, the acoustic subsystem, the sonobuoy launcher, the communications subsystem, the ESM subsystem, the radar subsystem, the FLIR, and the aircraft airframe and power subsystem (including the autopilot). Pelican can handle more than 500 tracks in real-time. It can steer the airplane to fixed and moving waypoints, for example as part of a sonobuoy search or an attack. It can also operate a data link (for example, to surface units).

Pelican has an open architecture designed specifically for further growth. For example, it can accommodate a shipping information system and a digital chart system. Display of radar, TV, and FLIR video is optional.

Pelican is the central tactical system intended for the 7 to 12 C-47s that the South African air force plans to convert into TP-47 Dakota maritime patrol aircraft ("Dakletons"). South Africa already uses C-47s fitted with ASV.21 radars removed from the retired Shackletons, but they lack central tactical systems and, apparently, modern sonobuoy systems. Reutech Systems received the prime contract in September 1995. Aircraft will be fitted with a row of four consoles roughly above their wings, amidships: an acoustic station (for the acoustic subsystem, ASS), a radar station (for the radar subsystem, RSS), a tactical station (TACCO), and a communications subsystem console (CSS). UEC's ASS console can handle active or passive or bathymetric buoys. Using an Israeli EL/M-2022 radar, the RSS provides the system with plots and tracks. Radar data are also displayed in the cockpit. CSS handles HF, broad-band and marine band radios, and a data link. The same console controls the airplane's ESM DF array, receiver, and processor/display (which are provided by Sysdel). ESM parameters include frequency, pulse length, PRI, angle and time of arrival, and pulse jitter. If the operator decides that a particular "racket" (ESM contact) is of interest, the TSS designates it for automatic data collection (racket identification, signal parameters, and time and bearing). The CSS console also controls a Kentron FLIR mounted below the airplane's nose, in a stabilized turret. The turret can accommodate a color television camera and a laser range-finder. Elevation limits are $-95/+10$ deg. TSS includes the aircraft navigation subsystem, developed by Decca, and built around a GPS receiver. The crew comprises three on the flight deck, two observers, and four console operators.

An aerodynamic prototype is currently flying. A sketch recently published shows both a nose radome (with a FLIR turret beneath it) and a large belly dome, perhaps a sonobuoy launcher. Atop the airplane are two prominent new blade antennas (with others in the belly) and a prominent "wedding cake"–type ESM antenna just abaft the crew station, atop the fuselage.

Note that there is apparently no provision whatever for weapons: this maritime patrol aircraft is intended to work with surface ships or submarines, using its data link.

SWEDEN

Early in 1996, CelsiusTech and McDonnell-Douglas signed a teaming agreement to jointly pursue a bid for the New Zealand Project Sirius (P-3K upgrade) based on 9LV Mk 3 technology. The resulting system will be offered for other MPA projects.

The Swedish Space Corporation has developed a maritime surveillance version of the Casa-212 for the Portuguese air force, in conjunction with OGMA. The airplane carries a Telephonics nose radar and a pair of Ericsson SLAR pods as well as an EO turret (including a microwave thermal radiometer to sense sea surface temperature) in the belly. The system is tied together by a bus and a central computer. Internally, there are separate consoles for SLAR or IR/UV or microwave; for the nose radar; and there is an athwartships main console which is also the main radar control for the nose radar. Aft, there is a separate camera run by the auxiliary operator. A stand-alone computer on the equipment rack carries a boat database, allowing the aircrew to enter boat names, and thus to compare observations with known boat identities. Other operators of the Swedish Space Corporation system are India (on coast guard Do-228s) and Sweden (C-212s).

UNITED KINGDOM

In the spring of 1996 the British government was considering alternative bids for a Replacement Maritime Patrol Aircraft (RMPA): BAe/Boeing (Nimrod 2000), Lockheed Martin/GEC-Marconi/Hunting (Orion 2000), and Loral Europe/E-Systems/Marshall Aerospace (Valkyrie). Nimrod 2000 is a heavily rebuilt version of the existing Nimrod; Valkyrie is a rebuilt P-3A/B. Orion 2000 is a new-build airplane, which may also be offered to the U.S. Navy as a P-3 replacement. The RAF wants a minimum of 18 aircraft (maximum 25) to operate for another 25 years. Whichever bid is chosen is likely to have a considerable impact on the P-3 upgrade market.

Presumably the Nimrod 2000 tactical system would be the Boeing DPDS; Orion 2000 would use a GEC-Marconi system (probably ASN-990), and Valkyrie would use the Unisys data-distribution system bought by the RAAF.

The RAF specified internal arrangement in some detail, calling for a two-man cockpit (no flight engineer) and seven consoles: two acoustic consoles ("wet 1" and "wet 2") facing aft, two non-acoustic (radar and ESM, "dry 1" and "dry 2") facing forward, and three facing athwartships (TACCO flanked by sensor manager and navigation/comms operator). The airplane is to carry an additional crew member for ancillary (nonacoustic) tasks. As in the U.S. AIP program, there is a strong desire for antiship capability, including radar target identification (using ISAR or range profiling, as in Searchwater) and improved ESM with near-ELINT capability. All bidders are offering the Israeli EL/M-2022 radar with Searchwater 2000 as an option. The central tactical system must be able to grow to include the ability to fuse own-aircraft data with offboard data (as in OASIS). To accommodate future weapons, the data bus to weapons stowage is Mil-STD-1760B rather than 1553B.

ASW capability is also important; the RMPA is to carry more buoys (to search 10,000 sq nm for quieter submarines) and to be able to grow to handle new types, such as the GPS buoys now under test and others that may have functions remotely settable before launch. The aircraft will carry two rotary buoy launchers plus four fixed tubes for hand launch (including a large-diameter tube for Barra buoys), with stowage nearby. The new MAD may have some directional capability.

Other requirements are integral self-protection (towed decoy), satellite communications, and the ability to use Links 11 and 16.

A decision is due in September 1996.

◆ Central Tactical System

The Nimrod was the first maritime patrol aircraft to fly with a computer TDS, flying slightly earlier than the P-3C. Its system

Loral's bid for the Replacement Maritime Patrol Aircraft (RMPA), Valkyrie, was based on a reworked P-3A/B airframe, presumably using a version of the Unisys Loral tactical system supplied by E-Systems for the Australian P-3C upgrade. The RAF specification was tight enough that all three bidders had to choose much the same internal arrangement, which is clearly shown in this model. In this version the nose and forward top dome are for a Condor ESM system; the after dome is for satellite communications. The structure aft of the two after consoles is sonobuoy stowage; total capacity is probably 87 (in three 29-round cages) plus 20 in the rotary launchers. The four fixed sonobuoy launchers (one of large diameter, for Barra) are visible, but not the two 10-buoy rotary launchers, all loaded during flight. (Stuart Slade, DMS/Forecast International)

was built around a GEC 920B computer in the MR.1 version and a 920 ATC computer in the current MR.2 version. The computer complemented a digital sonobuoy processor, AQS-901 (which uses a pair of 920 ATC computers). MR.1 used an analog radar, ASV Mk 21, but MR.2 introduced a digital Searchwater radar (with an FM1600D computer). It also has a Loral ESM system, which has its own 920 ATC computer.

The operators all sit in a tactical station abaft the flight deck, with the three-man AQS-901 console (SENSO, supervisor, SENSO) facing the starboard side. Across from them are Searchwater radar equipment racks. The Searchwater operator sits athwartships facing forward, and at the other (forward) end of the racks the communications operator sits facing aft. This space is closed at its forward end by a diagonal bulkhead carrying the consoles for the tactical navigator (equivalent to the U.S. TACCO) and, next to the door, the routine navigator. Behind the TACCO seat is a seat for an air electronics officer. Forward of this diagonal bulkhead is a pair of visual observer stations. Aft of the main compartment is the ESM/MAD operator, facing forward.

The primary system display is a 24in circular CRT (summary plot) at the tactical navigator's station.

Sonobuoys are launched from a pair of six-barrel rotary launchers and from two single-barrel launchers. They are stowed in four or six "frames" aft, 18 A-size buoys per frame, for a total of 72 or 108.

Digital control probably simplified Falklands War modifications, which included provision for Sidewinder and Harpoon missiles.

♦ **RAMS/CTS**

The Racal Avionics-Management System provides a helicopter with a partial glass cockpit, the main displays being two alphanumeric screens (control display units, or CDUs). RAMS 4000, the military version, employs two processor interface units (PIUs) containing up to three microprocessors, a data-transfer device (DTD) to load initial data, and the two CDUs. The CDUs and PIUs are all connected to a dual 1553B bus, and the PIUs and DTD are also connected to a non-1553B internal aircraft equipment bus, for equipment not compatible with a 1553B. The Royal Navy uses a five-node version, which includes a 12in programmable color tactical situation display (TSD). Further CDUs and PIUs can be added to the basic system, which can accommodate more than one TSD. RAMS uses nonvolatile mass memory (presumably bubble memory).

The central processor is the Zilog Z80.

Users: Denmark (Lynx), Japan (MH-53E), United Kingdom (Lynx HAS .3 and later, as Central Tactical System [CTS], and probably EH-101).

♦ **Sea Harrier**

A single Smiths Industries 20-kword computer controls the HUD and serves partly as mission computer, converting radar video into synthetic video for the HUD. It does not provide any air-to-air TWS capability. A separate Ferranti weapons-control computer uses hand-inserted plugs carrying weapons ballistics data (for the 30mm cannon and freefall bombs). Attack modes are CCIP and manually depressed LOS (DSL). There is also a separate Ferranti FE541 digital inertial navigation/attack computer, whose display is a moving map with an aircraft symbol centered on it. Navigational corrections from other sources, such as TACAN, can be inserted manually. This computer carries the target position and planned waypoints; presumably it was required mainly for the nuclear delivery role of the Sea Harrier FRS.1.

Sea Harrier FA.2 has a more integrated combat system tied together by a dual 1553B bus. The main avionics change, however, was replacement of the earlier Blue Fox radar by the TWS Blue Vixen. The earlier analog displays are largely replaced by a pair of multifunction displays (one for the radar), leaving only a few heads-down instruments. There is still a separate RWR, but its information is passed into the bus and, thus, should be available on the multifunction displays driven by the central computer. When the display shows raw radar video, it will be driven directly by the radar. Otherwise, synthetic video will be taken from the bus via a control-and-interface unit that is directly linked to the HUD/WAC. For example, a display can show threat data, target priority, and navigational information.

FA.2 has an airborne IFF interrogator (Cossor IFF 3500) in addition to the usual transponder. It is scheduled to receive GPS in 1997 and JTIDS (Link 16) by 1999.

◆ TATTIX (ASN-902/903) and TMS

The GEC-Marconi TDS for maritime-patrol aircraft incorporates the company's AQS-902 acoustic processor (AQS-903 is the version without the processor). The data bus is an ARINC 429 or a 1553B. The tactical plot (625 lines, 50-Hz frame rate) can accommodate up to 256 data entries and can show up to 64 tracks, up to 16 operator-defined circles or areas, and up to 16 annotated vectors. Range scales are 8, 16, 32, 64, 128, 256, and 512 nm. The same display can be used for ESM/radar to show a sonobuoy field, for localization within a sonobuoy field, and as a sonobuoy tote. The display can be monochrome or color.

TMS (Tactical Mission System) seems to be an improved version of the same equipment, using the AQS-902B/C acoustic processor. It can employ the Super Searcher radar, TANS navigation system, and Hermes ESM. In the Indian Sea Kings it is connected to a French-supplied HS 12 dipping sonar. The microprocessors are 17 Z8000 and Z80 8-bit chips in two LRUs. Indian Sea Kings have two CRTs, each with its own keyboard.

Weights (for TATTIX) are as follows: tactical processing unit, 16.0 kg; tactical control unit, 4.5 kg; tactical display unit, 14.5 kg; cursor control device, 0.5 kg.

Users: Egypt (Sea King and special operations Commando helicopters), India (TMS in Sea King 42B helicopters), United Kingdom (TMS in modified Sea King helicopters). Other naval Sea King operators who may have TATTIX are Australia (HAS Mk 50), Germany (Mk 41), Pakistan (Mk 45), and Qatar (eight Mk 3 for antiship duties). TATTIX (ASN-903) is also on board some Fokker Enforcers. (Customers were Angola, Netherlands, Nigeria, Pakistan, Peru, Philippines, Spain, and Thailand. Angola and Peru no longer operate this aircraft).

UNITED STATES

The A-6E Intruder is being retired (the last aircraft should leave service by October 1997). For details of its CDS, see the 1991/92 edition.

◆ ASN-123/ASN-150

Teledyne Systems' ASN-123 was developed for LAMPS I (SH-2F) helicopters and then expanded for SH-3H Sea King helicopters and to the the EA-6B Prowler. ASN-123 is nominally a tactical navigation system, but in the helicopters it provides torpedo-attack solutions. In a helicopter, the main system display is in the cockpit, and the TACCO there has the main system-control panel. The SENSO manually enters MAD and radar data (up to 20 contacts) into the system; the TACCO enters ESM data. The system predicts sonobuoy and torpedo splash points, based on ballistics, using a manually entered aircraft altitude and manually entered or computed winds. Automatic inputs include the sonobuoy receiver (ARR-75, to indicate which channels are active) and the sonobuoy launcher (to indicate which buoys were dropped).

A Block Upgrade begun in 1983 provided the SH-2F version with more memory (128 kwords rather than 32 kwords), higher processing speed, and a shield to eliminate electromagnetic interference. An earlier program to update ASN-123s on board EA-6Bs was completed in 1986. ASN-123 production ended in 1991. The system survives on board SH-2Fs and EA-6Bs; U.S. Navy SH-3s are retiring in 1997.

ASN-150 (TDMS, tactical data management system) is an ASN-123 derivative for the SH-60F and for modernized LAMPS I (SH-2G) helicopters and has been exported both for H-60 helicopters and for fixed-wing aircraft. It uses dual CP-1820 computers (military versions of the Teledyne MECA 43) and is tied together by a dual-redundant 1553B bus. In the SH-60F, the dipping sonar processor handles the four sonobuoy channels. The associated acoustic processor in the SH-2G is UYS-503. The system is initialized before flight by inserting a data-loader cartridge (capacity 512 kbytes of RAM).

The export version of the system uses a tactical processor with 384 kwords of EEPROM program memory, 32 kwords of core, and 32 kwords of semiconductor RAM. The high-order language is JOVIAL J73/1. This version can carry one aircraft location, one datum, 30 sonobuoys, 30 DIFAR contacts, 15 range-only contacts, 30 DICASS contacts, 15 sonar contacts (entered through the data link), 15 target tracks, 15 surface ships, 30 radar tracks, 30 ESM contacts, 15 visual/manual contacts, 30 reference marks, 15 survivor locations (for search and rescue), 15 TACAN beacons, 30 fly-to points (fixed or moving), one intercept point, one weapons-release point, one snake-mode display, and one Harpoon launch envelope.

The ASN-150 tactical system of the SH-60F (S-70B-4) is the basis of two export versions of the SH-60: the Greek S-70B-6 and the Taiwanese S-70C(M)-1 (Thunderhawk). ASN-150 also equips the SAR version, the U.S. Navy HH-60H and the coast guard HH-60J (S-70B-5). The Australian version (S-70B-2) uses the *Collins* RAWS system, and the Spanish version is identical to the U.S. LAMPS III. The Greek version is equipped with an AQS-18 dipping sonar and with the Penguin missile adopted for LAMPS III Block I helicopters. The sonar is AQS-18(V)3, the radar is APS-143(V)3, and the ESM set is ALR-606(V)2. The helicopter is equipped with a sonobuoy launcher. Greece chose ASN-150 over the *Collins* RAWS system after evaluating each. Taiwan's version of the S-70, Thunderhawk, has the AQS-18(V) dipper with provision for sonobuoy processing, but the aircraft has only provision for a sonobuoy launcher. The radar is APS-128PC (APS-143), and the ESM set is ALR-606(V)2. ASN-150 has also been adopted for the Taiwanese upgrade of the S-2 Tracker (S-2T), and will be installed (probably with dipping sonars) on board the 12 SH-2H LAMPS I helicopters that Taiwan is now receiving. Like the Thunderhawk, the S-2Ts have ARR-84 sonobuoy receivers. The other systems are different: APS-504 radar, AQS-902F sonobuoy processor, AAS-40 FLIR, and ASQ-504 digital MAD. At least in the case of Taiwan, ASN-150 includes an RF data link (referred to only as ASN-150).

ASN-150(V) was originally specified for the Fokker Maritime Enforcer Mk 2, but it was superseded by a DASA system. It is not clear whether the Enforcers bought by Singapore have ASN-150. The original Enforcer (17 of which were sold) had a GEC-Marconi ASN-902 as an option.

◆ A-7E

The A-7E Corsair II was probably the first tactical aircraft to be integrated around a heads-up display (HUD). The pilot designates the target seen through the HUD, to whose reticle the APQ-126 radar is boresighted. Alternatively, the target can be designated on the radar display and the reticle slewed to it. A FLIR image projected onto the HUD can provide all-weather capability, since then the system can be used in what amounts to daylight mode. In any case, the APQ-126 radar measures target range and direction. The system senses own-airplane motion and measures winds (a major factor in bomb ballistics) by comparing Doppler/inertial velocities with measured air data. It provides steering and solution cues projected onto the HUD; a pull-up symbol warns the pilot that the plane has reached minimum safe pull-up distance. The system automatically releases weapons at the appropriate point, having continuously computed the release point as the pilot maneuvers. As delivered, the system carried ballistics for more than 100 weapons. The manufacturer, LTV, claimed that the system enjoyed twice the accuracy of its analog predecessors. Claimed accuracy: CEP for level bombing 150–200 ft, 8.1–9.6 mils for dive-toss delivery, 8.2–9.5 mils for strafing (rockets or 20mm fire).

Users: Greece, Portugal, Thailand. U.S. Navy A-7Es have all been retired, but many of those in foreign service are dedicated to naval strike roles.

◆ AH-1W Upgrade

For some years there has been strong interest in providing the Marines' AH-1W attack helicopter with a central tactical system, a review having shown that this aircraft imposed a particularly heavy combat management load on its crew. FY95 plans for such a program, which was won by a Unisys team, were killed off due to budget cuts. However, in the spring of 1996 plans were revived. Bell, which built the helicopter, will be prime contractor for an upgrade program, including a new rotor. A contract is expected in November 1997 (with major funding to follow in 1999). The new central system will provide "glass cockpits" for 180 AH-1Ws and 100 UH-1Ns. The first upgraded UH-1N is to be funded in 2002, the first AH-1W in 2003, and deliveries are to begin in 2005.

◆ A-NEW (P-3C)/AIP

The P-3C was one of the first two maritime-patrol aircraft to have a computerized TDS (the other is the Nimrod). The effect of the centralized computer was allow the TACCO to devote most of the time in the target area to tactical decisions, rather than to coordinating with the pilot and sensor operators (SENSOs). The system architecture is similar to that of NTDS: the SENSOs detect targets (in their case, using radar and AQA-7 sonobuoy processors), providing the elements of the tactical picture the TACCO builds up in the central computer (CP-901). The difference is that the TACCO and the computer generate the course the pilot has to fly to lay other buoys and then to attack.

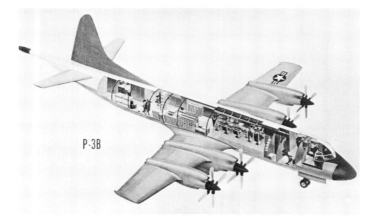

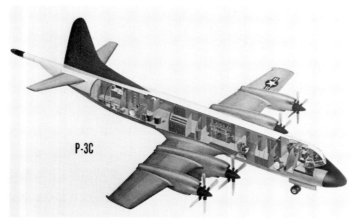

These drawings of the P-3B and -3C show one of the major effects of computerization. In the P-3B, all of the sensor operators are lined up facing one side of the airplane, so that the TACCO can look over their shoulders and integrate the data they produce. The airplane is far too narrow to allow for side-by-side seating facing forward or aft, which would be much more comfortable. In the P-3C, only the two acoustic operators face to the side, since only they use consoles too wide to be mounted athwartships, and the TACCO normally need not look over their shoulders, seeing what is needed on the TACCO display. In the P-3C, the TACCO seat is the one facing forward, on the right-hand side of the fuselage, just forward of the wing. (U.S. Navy)

The computer maintains a consistent tactical picture on board the airplane, using dual inertial navigators and a Doppler radar. Automated navigation eliminates errors due to low-altitude high-G maneuvers, and its accuracy helps an airplane chasing fast submarines. Automated navigation eliminates the lengthy and mechanical calculations needed to determine relative sonobuoy positions. Navigation also includes prediction of the splash points of all the stores the airplane drops, including sonobuoys and torpedoes. However, unlike the later S-3, A-NEW did not track sonobuoys drifting in the water, so the airplane had to overfly their positions periodically to verify them. The TACCO can use the computer to estimate the likely results of alternative tactics. Such estimates were impractical in noncomputerized systems because each entailed so much computation, particularly of navigational data.

The automated navigation system is combined with a flight director (which replaces the two-axis attitude indicator of the P-3B), providing the pilot with point-to-point steering commands calculated by the computer, such as for greater precision in dropping sonobuoys or in executing a MAD search.

All information in the airplane is centralized, so it can be recorded (for later playback and analysis) and also transmitted (via Link 11) either to a surface ship or to an airplane relieving the one on station. Playback is important because targets missed in flight may be detected after an airplane lands, to be prosecuted on a later flight. Parallel with A-NEW, specialized ground or shipboard centers (ASWOCs) were developed for real-time or playback analysis. Typically, they have computers and gram printers equivalent to those on the airplane.

A-NEW meant, literally, a new ASW weapons system. It was conceived in July 1960 at the Naval Air Development Center (NADC) at Johnsville, Pennsylvania (the contract for P-3A production was not let until that October). As the manufacturer of

An AQA-7 sensor station on board a P-3C shows both the CRT and the multichannel hard-copy recorder below it. The CRT is fed by a computer memory; operators can switch among buoys or the other bands. The hard-copy recorder, however, has no memory beyond what is on the paper, so it is very limited in the number of channels it can handle. (U.S. Navy)

the P-3C, Lockheed ultimately became system integrator (the company was displaced only with the advent of the Update IV version). The first Mod 1 version was flight-tested on board a P-3A early in 1964. It was reportedly so successful that the fleet tried hard to bring this interim version into production. The P-3C (Mod 3.2) was approved for production in August 1967, and the first production prototype flew on 18 September 1968, roughly contemporary with the Nimrod, which also has a computerized tactical system. The P-3C entered service in 1969. By 1965 work on a second generation (Mod 4 ground prototype), compact enough to fit on board a carrier airplane, was beginning, with first contracts awarded during FY66. Mod 5 was the airborne prototype. The result was the S-3A system described separately below.

In 1967 it was officially estimated that a P-3C would be 2 to 3 times as effective as a P-3B, essentially because of automation. Automation also brought complexity: it was said that the electronics part count in one P-3C equaled that in all 144 P-3Bs. However, reliability did not suffer badly because the new electronics was generally solid-state.

The TACCO is equivalent to a ship's TAO, supervising two acoustic sensor operators (SENSOs 1 and 2) and a nonacoustic operator (SENSO 3). Typically, a P-3C also carries two observers aft, plus a navigator-communicator and a flight-deck crew of three. Compared to a P-3A or -3B, there are two fewer acoustic operators. However, a P-3C can continuously monitor 16 sonobuoys, compared to eight for a P-3B or four for a P-3A, and the frequency spectrum covered is 10 times wider. These improvements all result from electronic rather than electromechanical data collection. A single operator can monitor one buoy or one narrow band visually while the system collects data from other buoys and other bands, then shift to those other data at will. Physically, the great change from past practice is to supplement the usual paper LOFAR recorders with CRTs.

The TACCO and SENSO 3 have ASA-70 summary tactical displays, whose 16in CRTs can show synthetic-video symbols, scan-converted raw radar video, and LLLTV (later FLIR) video. A second CRT shows alphanumerics, such as radio channels and remaining sonobuoys. The TACCO calls up information from the SENSOs and from the central computer via a trackball and keyboards.

The pilot and copilot have ASA-66 tactical data displays (with 7.5in CRTs) showing sonobuoy positions, fly-to points, aircraft position and track, and predicted submarine track and position. These data are also available to the TACCO. The pilot can enter visual contacts directly into the display (and then into the central computer).

Because buoys are selected through the computer (which is aware of the mix on board), the primary launchers on a P-3C are external: 48 unpressurized A-size preloaded chutes. They are supplemented by three reloadable A-size chutes (with 36 buoys stowed in launch containers) and one B-size chute. Earlier P-3s stowed all their buoys internally because they were manually selected: they used nine chutes (and the airplane had to be depressurized to launch buoys through them).

Aside from the new acoustic processors, the P-3C introduced the APS-115 radar for full 360-deg sea-surface coverage and an LLLTV instead of a searchlight. The 43rd production P-3C introduced the ASQ-81 MAD. There was also a new automated ESM suite.

The P-3C Update I program was begun before the first aircraft joined the fleet and entered service in 1974. Update I increased the computer's memory sevenfold (by adding a 384k auxiliary magnetic drum) and added an additional tactical display for acoustic sensor operators, acoustic processor improvements, a crash locator (beacon), and the Omega navigation system.

Update II doubled the capacity on the acoustic tape recorder (ATR) and added a sonobuoy reference system, the Harpoon antiship missile, and a FLIR to replace the earlier LLLTV. The sonobuoy reference system consists of antennas, located around the fuselage, that locate buoys by recording the phase differences in the signals received by adjacent antennas; the airplane no longer has to overfly buoys to locate them. This system was developed

for the S-3A Viking. Update II entered service in 1978 (the first such aircraft joined the training command in September 1977).

Update II.5 replaced some systems with more reliable equivalents (INS, Doppler, VHF, VOR/ILS, TACAN, ESM); it integrated aircraft-to-submarine acoustic communications (via buoy); it added a MAD compensation group adapter and a TACCO auxiliary IR display; it standardized wing pylons and improved fuel-tank venting.

Update III added an advanced sonobuoy receiver (the 99-channel ARR-78 in place of the 31-channel ARR-72), a single advanced signal processor (ASP: UYS-1), transparent logic units (XLUs), and an acoustic test signal generator (ATSG). An extra lower UHF antenna was added, plus environmental improvements (better cabin-air distribution, a heat-exchanger water spray system, and increased-capacity engine-driven compressors for air conditioning). In this version the airplane has three sensor stations (displays) plus a TACCO display. The airplane can monitor 16 different sonobuoy signals on 99 channels. The XLU designation refers to lighter-weight logic units that are functionally equivalent (i.e., transparent) to their bulkier predecessors, using integrated circuit technology. These logic units leave space for later installation of an AYK-14 computer.

Update III incorporates a new 99-channel sonobuoy reference system, ARS-5, replacing the ARS-3 of Update II. In contrast to the earlier reference system, it uses its own computer rather than the overall system computer (ASQ-114). The capacity of the embedded computer makes the reference system a more general-purpose VHF/DF, which can be extended for use in communications intelligence. The manufacturer, Cubic, offers the new version as a stand-alone sonobuoy reference system (SRS) with COMINT potential.

In Update III, a digital computer, Proteus (UYS-1, also called ASP), replaces the hard-wired AQA-7. It displays buoy data, either analog or digital, on two CRTs, each of which can show eight buoy channels. Each channel can be broken down into three narrow-band (vernier) windows. UYS-1 is heavier than its predecessor, and some reduction in airframe weight (such as by using lightweight floorboards) was needed to compensate. On the other hand, improvements in hardware made it possible to dispense with one of the two computers originally planned.

Perhaps the most important tactical difference between UYS-1 and AQA-7 is that UYS-1 provides no paper LOFARgrams, only a magnetic tape of buoy outputs. In the past, postmission analysis of grams, generally by eye, often disclosed submarines not detected by crews in flight (e.g., in cases in which a line varied slightly in frequency over time, and thus was obvious to the eye but not to a line integrator). The submarines moved slowly enough that a later flight, briefed to look at the appropriate frequency, could find them.

Continuing work on UYS-1 includes integration with passive tracking algorithms (PTA; see the entry on LAMPS above), broad-band capability, 32-channel half-bandwidth capability (channel expansion), 99-channel online capability, and provision for advanced buoys (using modular software).

In October 1992 Congress ordered the P-3C Update IV program terminated on the ground that deep-water ASW was becoming less important with the end of the Cold War. At that time only 28 update kits (109 were planned) were included in the 5-yr plan. The Navy then decided to bring all 247 existing P-3Cs up to Update III standard by 1999 (136 aircraft are already Update IIIs).

The AGM-65F Maverick missile was successfully fired from a P-3C in 1990. P-3Cs patroling the Adriatic from 1993 on carried Mavericks underwing, the first deployment of the missile on board this aircraft. Three control-display units are installed: in the copilot's station, the TACCO console, and SENSO 1 station. The P-3 on station in the Adriatic also has TRE, the intelligence data receiver. They also carry Mk 20 Rockeye bomblet dispensers.

The P-3C modernization program is a series of upgrades to system computer (CP-901) and ASP software. The current UYS-1 hardware/software configuration is integrated with PTAs (see the discussion under LAMPS); a 32-channel half-bandwidth capability (Channel Expansion—CHEX); constant resolution (CR) modes; broad-band, digital track (post-CHEX); and 99-channel online sonobuoy radio-frequency-monitor capability. This program also integrates advanced sonobuoys and detection algorithms, which are contained in the modular-software-design airborne air common acoustic processing (ACAP) package, into upgraded P-3C ASP and CP-901 tactical computers.

The critical design review for revised software to accommodate broad-band buoys (programs A4.8 for Tactical Mission Software and C4.8 for processing) was completed in April 1993. A similar review for ADAR (active receiver) software (A4.9/C4.9) is scheduled for June 1996.

Aircraft are being fitted with the new CP-2044 central processor as a replacement for CP-901. Through FY92, the Navy bought 69 CP-2044 from Unisys (now Loral Unisys). Plans announced in 1992 called for 73 P-3Cs to receive CP-2044s in FY93–95, and for 95 aircraft to receive new tactical displays (USQ-78A) in FY95–99.

GPS is another major upgrade, planned for all P-3C, for the four P-3 Special Projects aircraft (see the Electronic Warfare section under ARIES/EP-3), and for five VP-3 aircraft. The first eight aircraft were equipped by the end of 1994.

The FY94 program included a new AIP for 68 P-3Cs, an upgrade for improved surface-warfare capability based in large part on the Outlaw Hunter experience of the Gulf War. New equipment includes the Cluster Ranger stabilized long-range EO sensor (looking sideways out of an optically flat window), APS-137(V)5 ISAR radar, ALR-66B(V)3, an enhanced (larger-range) AAS-36 IRDS, and the Condor EP-2060 pulse analyser for target identification. Unisys (teamed with Texas Instruments) won the contract in 1994.

The OTH-T element of the aircraft is called OASIS III (see the Strike Warfare section for the original OASIS). Its workstation uses a new 19in color display. Using a new MATT (Multimission Advanced Tactical Terminal), the OASIS III aircraft can participate in the major OTH-T and TENCAP networks (OTCIXS, TADIXS B). It has dual TRE (to receive naval TENCAP data) as well as TRAP (TRE to receive the Air Force equivalent of TENCAP, e.g., from Rivet Joint EC-135s). DAMA will be installed to increase effective satellite communications capacity.

P-3C tactical communication capability is also being upgraded. Current aircraft have two ARC-161 HF radios (for voice, teletype, and Link 11), but it is impossible to operate both simultaneously in the transmit and receive modes, nor can the aircraft receive voice or teletype messages while operating on a Link 11 net. These limitations are being removed by installation of ARC-207 radios. The existing one VHF (ARC-101) and two UHF (ARC-143) radios were obsolete and suffered from crosstalk; they were replaced by ARC-182 (program completed 1993 for 134 P-3C, 11 P-3A/B) and ARC-187 (program completed 1993 for 163 P-3C) on a one-for-one basis.

These are all conventional radios. As of 1994, all P-3Cs were to be equipped with the jam-resistant Have Quick radio (ARC-210) in 1996–2000. There is an operational requirement for UHF FLTSATCOM capability.

In FY94 a Sustained Readiness Program (SRP), to extend airframe life by 8 yr (from 30 to 38 yr), was announced. The effect of the SRP is to put off any decision on a new maritime patrol aircraft in the wake of the P-7A and Update IV cancellations.

Eighteen aircraft are receiving a Counter Drug Update (CDU) Group A package: APG-66(V)3 nose radar (modified fighter radar), Cluster Ranger, and improved communications. Eight CDU Group B packages are being bought for cross-decking among these aircraft; presumably they include communications-intercept gear. These modifications are separate from those extended to four P-3s taken over by U.S. Customs, and called "slicks" because of their P-3A(CS) designation. Two are interceptors, one is a communications intelligence/relay platform, and one is a sensor R&D aircraft. Presumably the last was the one used to test CEC relay concepts. The interceptors have IRDS, a new APG-63 nose radar (from a fighter), an inertial navigation system, and new communications gear. They track drug-smuggling aircraft. Reportedly the test aircraft may be fitted with a variant of the SR-71's SAR radar.

P-3s operating abroad have been or are being modernized.

The 19 Australian P-3C Update II.5s are being modernized by E-Systems (AP-3C program). One driving concern was to reduce weight by at least 3500 lb so as to prolong airframe life to 2016. The RAAF had already bought an Israeli ESM system (ALR-2001 Odyssey) because the U.S. government rejected a request to release source code for the standard ALR-66. Similar considerations led to the choice of an ELTA radar. E-Systems proposed the CDC UYS-503 processor and a CDC data-management system, the latter because the Unisys CP-2044 had a single point of failure. Unisys then changed its architecture to a fully distributed system, and E-Systems adopted the result. It will employ 68060 chips with windowed displays for sensor and tactical data. The program, begun in 1995, is to be completed in 1997.

This success led E-Systems to develop a variety of updates for the P-3B, including a passenger/VIP/cargo version with a patented side door and an AEW version using the Swedish Erieye radar.

The Netherlands plans to upgrade its P-3Cs under a Capability Upgrade Program (CUP). Signaal will participate. As of 1995, E-Systems hoped to apply elements of the Australian upgrade. The U.S. government refuses to export the color raster-scan display used in AIP, so any Dutch system will probably use Signaal TACTICOS displays. As of early 1996, the Dutch had chosen the CP-2044 central computer and the UYS-503 acoustic processor for the upgrade. Dutch P-3Cs, which were delivered without IRDS, have already been fitted with AAQ-22 FLIRS originally bought for Lynx helicopters. In early 1996 the Netherlands had not yet chosen between ALR-66 and the Israeli ALR-2001 chosen by the Australians.

A Norwegian upgrade (Upgrade Improvement Program, UIP) was funded in February 1996. CP-2044s previously bought will now be installed. It seems likely that UIP will generally follow the U.S. AIP program.

There are also several candidates for upgrades.

Early in 1996 the United States approved a sale of six to eight P-3Bs to Argentina. Other aircraft are very likely to go to Colombia. Venezuela is reportedly interested, and possibly also Brazil.

Chile already has four P-3Bs and hopes ultimately for six. The upgrade is to be done in Israel. Probably it will entail installation of the Elisra MPA system and an Israeli radar, most likely EL/M-2022, plus ALR-2001. The Chilean version is likely to include an SP-100 station to communicate with the modernized surface units.

The Greek P-3Bs are being brought up to TACNAVMOD baseline status by Chrysler, but at least at present no further improvements are being made. As of 1996 Turkey had declined P-3Bs on the ground that they would have entailed too much effort.

Under the Rigel program, the Royal New Zealand Air Force modified its P-3s as P-3Ks. This Boeing program installed a central display and control system (see DPDS below), which was connected to everything except the acoustics and ESM systems, and added workstations based on AYK-14 computers. The combination of workstations and display system was the basis for the later Boeing UDACS system planned for the abortive P-3C Update IV. Rigel I also included new sensors (APS-116 radar and AAS-36 IRDS) and Omega navigation. Rigel was announced in 1980, the first aircraft being completed by Boeing in September 1983, and the remaining five locally between October 1983 and May 1984. Rigel II, planned for 1991 but shelved, would have provided a new acoustic processor (possibly AQS-903) with a second operator position and a data link; it would have cost $13.5–19M. New Zealand now plans a further upgrade, Project Sirius, to replace the 15-year-old Boeing system. It may include acoustic, ESM, and IFF upgrades, GPS, and provision for later installation of a data link. As of early 1996 competitors included a McDonnell-Douglas/CelsiusTech team. The current life-extension program (rewinging with P-3C wings) is Project Kestrel.

Spanish plans to modernize five ex-Norwegian P-3Bs (equipped with AQA-7s) and then two Deltic (i.e., AQA-5) P-3As to Update III standard have been dropped. This program called for installation of a new AQS-943 acoustic processor, a Searchwater II radar, ALR-66(V)3, a U.S. FLIR, a video-distribution bus, and color-display consoles. In February 1992 the program budget was cut in half. It seemed likely that modernization would be limited to off-the-shelf equipment, as in the upgrade of Portuguese P-3Ps by Lockheed and OGMA. The emphasis may be on improving the APS-80 radar for surface surveillance.

The Portuguese P-3Ps are ex-RAAF P-3Bs bought in 1985 and refurbished by Lockheed and OGMA; the first was delivered on 1 January 1988, and the last in 1989. They have digitally enhanced TACNAVMOD systems (with AYK-14 instead of the usual TACNAVMOD computer) with some Update II.5 avionics: IRDS (AAS-36) and improved radars (APS-134). As in the Spanish aircraft, the sonobuoy processors are AQA-7s. These aircraft have an improved ALR-66 ESM set using a unique belly-mounted directional antenna, for OTH-T for their Harpoon missiles. The ESM and IRDS are connected to a dedicated nonacoustic sensor station. The Portuguese air force is currently considering a variety of low-cost upgrades: ISAR for the radar, GPS, a new MAD, and improved ESM. Maverick capability may be added. Portugal is also considering buying a new threat warner linked to a decoy launcher and other defensive systems. An ELINT system may also be added.

The two Thai P-3Ts are TACNAVMOD P-3As with improved navigation and communication systems, better avionics and radar displays, and provision for an IRDS and for Harpoon. A third aircraft, designated UP-3T, is essentially a transport, but retains a single unique "SENTAC" (TACCO plus SENSO 3) station for limited surveillance capability. All three aircraft have commercial color weather radar in addition to their APS-80s. The first P-3T was rolled out on 6 February 1994.

The Iranian P-3Fs are a special case. They were P-3C airframes with P-3A/B equipment but without TACNAVMOD: AQA-5 sonobuoy processors (with AQA-1 to handle active buoys) and ALD-2 airborne direction-finders, but with P-3C buoy chutes. They probably lacked central computers. One was fitted to fire Harpoon, but it seems to have crashed.

See also TACNAVMOD (ASN-123) below.

◆ ATDS (E-2C)

The Airborne Tactical Data System, the airborne equivalent of NTDS, is carried on board E-2 aircraft. Its air-to-air link to fighters is Link 4 (now Link 4A). ATDS was conceived roughly simultaneously with NTDS; the specification was issued in November 1955. Grumman received a contract for the E-2 on 5 March 1957, and the first fully equipped airplane flew in April 1961.

In 1960 it was estimated that an E-2A (not yet in service) could maintain 250 tracks and control 30 interceptions (via automatic data link), compared to four to six tracks and two interceptions for the manual E-1B it was replacing. Newer versions have greater capacity. The crew consisted of one radar operator (instead of two), an air controller, and a CIC operator. Each has an APA-172 console, which currently carries a 12in monochrome main display unit (MDU), an upper main display (UMD), and a 5in auxiliary display unit (ADU, for alphanumerics). Targets are designated by light pen. The air-search radar automatically detects targets. The associated IFF system is OL-76.

The current system (picture-keeping) computer is a dual L-304, OL-77/ASQ (now with 128-kword capacity), supported by an ASPRO. A new computer has now been funded. Reportedly an E-2C can control three or four F-14s (i.e., in theory, up to 24 interceptions) via Link 4. Unlike other carrier aircraft, the F-14 has two-way ASW-27 communications and thus can exchange data with AEW aircraft. Reportedly an E-2C equipped with the current version of the L-304 computer can track over 600 targets and control over 40 airborne intercepts. The United States currently has a cooperative program with Egypt to develop a new E-2C Software Enhanced Display System, which should increase system display capacity from 250 to 1600 tracks. It includes design, coding, integration and testing of an Egyptian air force full capability L-304 computer program. The MoU was signed on 15 May 1991, and the program began with a February 1992 meeting.

Aircraft are described as Group 0, Group 1, and so on. Group 0 had the APS-138 radar with its low-sidelobe Randtron APA-171 antenna. Group 1 had APS-139, an ECCM upgrade, a surface-tracking module, and introduced the ASPRO processor, an enormous track-management upgrade.

The current configuration (Group 2) has more powerful engines (T56-A-427 [5250 HP] rather than T56-A-425 [4591 HP]); the new engine is also 13% more fuel-efficient), substantial improvements in radar (APS-145, with fully automatic overland ADT) and IFF range, improved navigation (GPS) and communications (JTIDS/Link 16), and enhanced tactical displays, which together add about 1500 lb (the current gross takeoff weight is 54,000 lb, compared to 48,000 lb for early E-2Cs). The main improvement is the APS-145 with digital processing; it divides the operational area into over 4000 cells, and can vary processing from cell to cell. All earlier E-2 radars were analog. Radar range is extended by 40%; radar volume nearly doubles, and number of targets that can be detected increases by a factor of 16. The use of three PRFs eliminates blind speeds and provides continuous ADT over land. These aircraft have a new APX-100 IFF with range commensurate with their radar range.

Group 2 aircraft have improved ASPRO processors that carry more than double the number of track files in Group 1 (which more than doubled the number in Group 0). New seven-color Loral COTS display units expand E-2C display capability by almost a factor of 10. They can show more than 2000 tracks on an 11 × 11in screen, rather than the 250-track limit of the current 10in Hazeltine unit. They can also overlay a map, and can carry three windows. Group 2 aircraft also have GPS. JTIDS has also been added. Deliveries began in December 1991. Production restarted in FY96 because it was found that 36 Group 0 aircraft could not be cost-effectively modernized to Group 2 standard. The first seven new aircraft were ordered late in 1994, the line having closed down that year; deliveries are to continue through 2004. The first new E-2C was delivered early in 1996, and the first series of 12 will be delivered through mid-1997. In addition, 18 Group 1 aircraft will be upgraded, with first kits ordered under the FY93 program (first deliveries in FY95).

These Group 2+ aircraft have a new mission computer, enhanced satellite capability (Mini-DAMA/MATT), and will have CEC capability. In September 1994 Raytheon Equipment Division was selected to provide a new mission computer (mission computer upgrade [MCU] program). It is Raytheon's Model 940, a ruggedized DEC 2100 Model A500MP, taking up less than half the space and less than a third the weight of the current L-304. This 64-bit computer offers five times the throughput of the L-304. Group 2+ aircraft are also to have adapted UYQ-70 displays. CEC capability will be provided by an active array under the fuselage, now being tested on a P-3B.

A further high priority is improved target identification. Other desired improvements are a tactical display in the cockpit, a glass cockpit, new ESM, and an IRST. APS-145 itself may be upgraded with a rotating phased array antenna.

Users: Egypt (Group 0 and 2), France (Group 2), Israel (Group 0), Japan (Groups 0 and 2; upgrades of Group 0 aircraft are to begin under the next Five-Year Plan), Singapore (Group 0), Taiwan (Group 2), United States (Groups 0, 1, and 2).

◆ AV-8B

Internally, the AV-8B differs sharply from the original AV-8A Harrier in that it has a central tactical system integrated by a 1553 bus and an AYK-14 computer (the British equivalent, the RAF's Harrier GR.7, has a British version of the AYK-14, ACCS 2000). This combination has made it relatively easy to add new equipment, most recently the APG-65 nose radar of the AV-8B Plus. The original AV-8A was relatively unsophisticated, with a HUD and WAC fed by the ASN-116 AHRS (airborne heading reference system). This combination limited the airplane to guns, Sidewinder missiles, and unguided bombs.

The AV-8B has a programmable multipurpose head-down display in addition to the HUD of the AV-8A. More important, both displays have access to all aircraft sensors via the 1553 bus. The original AV-8B mission suite included the ASB-19(V)2 or (V)3 bombing system in the nose, an ASN-130 inertial navigation system, and an ALR-67(V)2 radar warner. There was also provision for a podded jammer. This version introduced a stores management system and provision for Maverick missile delivery; it was also wired for nuclear weapons. The next step was to add night-attack capability (in the 167th and later aircraft), with the AAR-51 FLIR (by GEC-Marconi), a head-down display, a color moving map, and an improved HUD. The first night-attack aircraft was delivered 15 September 1989. The step beyond was the AV-8B Plus, with the APG-65 nose radar. The airplane can now employ AMRAAM, Sparrow, and Harpoon missiles. It retains its over-nose FLIR (in repackaged form). The prototype, the 205th AV-8B built, was first flown on 22 September 1992, and the first aircraft was delivered early in 1993. Plans currently call for the last 24 aircraft to be completed as AV-8B Plus (including three for Italy), to be followed by 73 early aircraft remanufactured as AV-8B Plus. These figures do not include most projected sales to Italy and Spain.

The AV-8B currently employs a Marine Corps mission-planning system, MOMS; it is scheduled to transition to TAMPS for commonality with other naval aircraft. ATHS capability is currently funded, and six prototypes are to have it in time for the Sea Dragon exercise in 1997. Production will begin in 1998. Link 16 (JTIDS) capability is wanted, but money is not available.

Unlike an F/A-18, an AV-8B is severely limited in space and weight, so it is impossible to install a second AYK-14; any increase in computing power has to come from a computer upgrade. That makes the AV-8B a particularly attractive candidate for open-system improvements such as AAYK-14 or VisiBridge.

The AYK-14 in this airplane has been upgraded as capabilities have been added. AV-8B originally had a version of the computer designated CP-1539A, using an XN-5 chassis. They were upgraded to CP-1984s, using the same chassis (i.e., the same backplane) with new cards to accommodate a software change. Night-attack aircraft received CP-1902s. The radar version has the XN-6 chassis (CP-2090). This last computer is to become standard on all versions (day, night, radar) as of January 1997. CP-2090 adds a third discrete serial I/O card to handle the APG-65 radar. Some of the CP-2090s are being produced out of parts from F/A-18s (which had their own computers upgraded) and from CP-1984s.

♦ **F-14**

The F-14 was the first U.S. naval fighter to have a full computer-controlled combat system. Like all earlier U.S. carrier fighters, the F-14A was designed for both air-to-air combat and bombing for close air support. Its weapon system incorporates a HUD, which is used both for air-to-air combat and for bomb aiming (as in an A-7E). The computer (made by CDC, and unique to this airplane) maintains a tactical picture, providing a TWS memory (for up to 24 targets) for the big pulse-Doppler radar, and merging its picture with that provided via Link 4A (the F-14A can transmit target data back via this link, but it cannot send this data to another F-14A). Previous aircraft had alternative search and single-target track modes. Thus, the F-14A and the F-4J introduced pulse-Doppler radars (AWG-9 and AWG-10) into U.S. naval air practice. However, because it lacked a central computer, the F-4J could not track multiple targets simultaneously. Both aircraft were also fitted for the new air-control digital link, Link 4. The F-4J could be cued to a single target (the commanding ship or airplane could send discrete commands, but not the target vector itself). The F-14A could receive data on up to eight targets simultaneously, which its central tactical system would integrate with its tactical picture (one consequence was that an E-2C could control many more F-4s than F-14s). In effect the F-14 system is analogous to the roughly contemporary Aegis: it is a tactical (situational-awareness) system grown out of a fire-control system.

The main system display is the tactical information display (TID) in the aft cockpit, with a detail data display (DDD) above it. The computer is located abaft this cockpit. The computer accepts raw sensor and avionics data, controls the sensors (radar and IR), maintains target track files, computes weapon launch zones and aircraft steering, presets and controls the air-to-air missiles, and processes ECCM data for the radar. It is also responsible for bombing ballistics, using target data obtained in the radar's ground-mapping and navigation mode.

The TID is limited to synthetic video, displaying the overall situation (targets from the airplane's own radar and from the data link) in PPI form, using standard symbology. Navigational and other data of interest can also be displayed. The picture may be ground- or airplane-stabilized. In the former case, it is a 360-deg picture, oriented north. In the latter case the airplane is shown at the bottom, headed up, with lines indicating the available engagement zone. The TID is also used to show television video, using the AXX-1 stabilized camera.

The DDD is the primary WCS sensor. Modes are radar, IR, and IFF. The display also shows target acquisition gates and computer-generated symbology. The pilot's HUD duplicates some DDD symbology.

As it happened, F-14 aerodynamics seemed to preclude bombing (bombs were reportedly sucked back up into the tunnel between the bottoms of the engines), and until the early 1990s F-14s operated only as air-to-air fighters. Some have suggested that the bombing problem was exaggerated at the time, since ground attack was not really an important mission.

As built, the F-14A was somewhat underpowered; plans called for a quick transition to a new engine in an F-14B. Funding was not available, and the great bulk of F-14s were completed as F-14As. Eventually a new engine (and ALR-67, to replace the analog ALR-45/50 ESM set) was provided in the upgraded F-14A+ (later redesignated F-14B). The -14B retained the ALQ-126B jammer of the -14A. In all, 38 F-14Bs were built as such and another 47 F-14As were rebuilt to -14B status (originally 32, but Congress added money for 15 more in 1992–93), for a total of 85.

F-14D combined the new engine with a new digital radar (APG-71) and a central digital system (incorporating a pair of AYK-14s easily adapted to new systems (JTIDS, IRST) and to new weapons. It has a weapons bus managed by an AYQ-15 computer. It adds a new defensive jammer, ALQ-165, integrated with ALR-67. With the end of the Cold War, F-14D production (and the remanufacture of F-14As as F-14Ds) was stopped in favor of concentration on the less-expensive F/A-18. The last of 37 new-build F-14Ds was completed in February 1995, and the last of 18 F-14Ds converted from -14As was delivered in May 1995. F-14D development was concurrent with much of the planned avionics and weapons work, so gaps had to be closed with a predeployment update (PDU) program, consisting mainly of new software. It offered a fighter-to-fighter data link (as on the F/A-18), improved radar ECCM, GPS navigation, and AMRAAM capability.

Work to revive the F-14's conventional bombing capability began about 1989. Tests showed that the aerodynamic problems had been exaggerated, and all aircraft had their four fuselage weapons stations modified so that they could carry bombs instead of Phoenix missiles. The result was called a "Bombcat." It became more important with the collapse of the A-12 and successor A/F-X programs, and with the 1993 decision to retire all A-6Es by 1999. Now the "Bombcat" provides some of the long-range punch previously associated with the A-6. A-6s are on average 15 years older than F-14s. OSD questioned the wisdom of leaving a 10-yr gap between A-6 retirement and availability of some successor. The first operational "Bombcats" were two squadrons (VF-14 and -32) deployed in October 1992 to the Eastern Mediterranean aboard USS *John F. Kennedy*. "Bombcat" capability becomes more important as carriers reduce to a single F-14 squadron. As of 1996, all F-14s will receive "Bombcat" modifications, and all will be wired to carry TARPS reconnaissance pods.

An upgrade program for F-14As and -14Bs was announced in 1991. Aircraft would have their elderly computers replaced by a hybrid, CP-2213, combining a computer emulator (a CP-1569 equivalent in two or three computer cards) and an AYK-14. They would also be fitted with a 1553 bus and with a 1760 weapons bus to handle smart bombs. They would receive programmable displays: PMDIG (programmable multiple display indicator group) and PTID (programmable tactical information display). Both the modified aircraft and the F-14Ds would be fitted with BOL chaff dispensers in weapons pylons. Initially 127 F-14As were included (for a program total of 212); that number later dropped to 113, for a total of 198 aircraft.

In 1993 the Navy proposed a $1.6-billion F-14 Block I Strike Program, to begin in FY94. A total of 210 F-14A/B/D would have been modified to drop laser-guided weapons, with supporting sensors and subsystems. Block I was a two-phase program. Phase 1 was the modification to the weapons rails. Phase 2 added a capability to carry laser-guided bombs (but no designator), cluster bombs (Rockeye, CBU-59, and Gator mines), and TALD decoys, as well as an IRST, ALR-67, and JTIDS. Evaluation was to have begun in June 1993. Phase 3, not yet funded, would have added a laser designator, precision weapons such as HARM and SLAM, more advanced smart weapons such as JDAMS and JSOW. A Loral FLIR/laser designator pod was to have been flight-tested later in 1993.

In fact, money was very tight. Block I was dropped as unaffordable. The Navy proposed instead an "F-14 Precision Strike" program, beginning in FY95, to provide 251 aircraft with the capability to deliver JDAMS bombs. Later 89 Lantirn laser targeting pods were bought as an inexpensive way to provide laser bomb capability. It turned out that a great deal could be done even without the planned program.

All aircraft are being modified for night attack by providing their crews with night-vision goggles while modifying cockpit lighting. The design used was developed by VF-11, which was the first F-14 squadron to drop bombs at night. Wiring modifications provide all aircraft with the ability to drop 500- and 1000-lb laser-guided bombs. Wiring has been added to accommodate the Lantirn FLIR/laser designator pod. In the F-14A, that requires an additional internal black box. In an F-14B or -14D, the mission computer accommodates the necessary software, and the new digital display shows the targeting FLIR image. All aircraft are receiving two-way Link 4C.

Meanwhile, the computer upgrade is continuing. As of April 1996, it has been restricted to F-14Bs; no F-14As are being modernized. The first production upgraded airplane was rolled out at NADEP Norfolk in January 1996. These aircraft retain their original AWG-9s, so in effect the new computer reduces the load on the former central computer. The new computer and the digital bus are needed both to handle new smart weapons and to receive data from the TAMPS mission-planning system. Integrated GPS is also needed, since TAMPS can preset target coordinates.

An F-14D has a pair of AYK-14s (APG-71 is just a radar, without an integral aircraft central tactical computer). It also has provision for Link 16, which an F-14B lacks. F-14Bs may eventually be fitted with MIDS (Link 16).

Separate programs were expected to add new digital flight-control systems (beginning FY96), install GPS (beginning FY95 in F-14D, FY97 in A/B upgrade aircraft), and add ARC-210 radios in FY98 and more robust mission recorders in FY99. Some of these features were delayed by a tight budget. Thus installation of digital flight-control systems was ordered only in 1996, following a series of accidents. Digital flight control is, in effect, digitized stability augmentation. It helps keep the pilot from making the wrong control inputs, and it also helps recovery from departures. It is very useful in air-to-air combat, and also in landing onto a carrier, in which case it damps control oscillations and helps keep the airplane on course by coordinating the motions of the control surfaces.

Earlier plans to install the ALE-50 towed decoy have been dropped. As of 1996, a decision had yet to be made concerning an ALR-45/50 replacement for F-14As; possibilities included ALR-67 and the digitized ALR-45/50 planned for the F-16.

As of April 1996, the active F-14 force comprised 199 F-14As, 80 F-14Bs, and 50 F-14Ds. As of May 1995, the planned year 2000 force had consisted of 118 F-14As, 82 F-14Bs, and 51 F-14Ds. Another 234 F-14As would be placed in storage or scrapped. For the present, jigs and tooling for F-14D conversions are being retained. Current (1996) plans call for retiring the F-14As in 2002 and the -14B/Ds in 2010.

Outside the United States, the only user of the F-14 is Iran, which received 80 F-14As in the 1970s. Few if any are probably still airworthy.

◆ F/A-18

The F/A-18 was the first fully digital airplane built for the U.S. Navy, with a pair of AYK-14 central computers (tactical and navigational), digital avionics (1553) and weapons (1760) buses, a "glass cockpit" (according to one account, it had the first of all truly modern cockpits), a full quad-redundant digital fly-by-wire system (using a special computer unique to the F/A-18), and a digital radar.

F/A-18A/B (-18B is the two-seat version) has three 1553B buses, one connecting the two computers and the other two connecting them to other avionics. This version uses an early AYK-14 computer with XN-5 chassis (CP-1539) and a capacity of 64 kwords (16-bit words). The stores management computer is the 16-kword AYQ-9.

F/A-18C/D is similar in configuration to -18A/B but has much greater capability due to an upgrade to five (later six) 1553 buses (upgraded to 1553B), a 1760 weapons bus, and the product-improved version of AYK-14 incorporating the XN-6 chassis, offering higher speed and twice the memory capacity of the original fighter's computer. This computer in turn is being replaced by a new one with a more capacious XN-8 chassis. The stores management set has been upgraded to 128k of memory, and now uses 8086 CPUs. Engine controls and fuel monitor have been digitized. This was the first version capable of firing AMRAAM (AIM-120; it can carry up to 10, two per wing pylon) and IIR Maverick missiles (up to four). It also has the ALR-67 ESM set (the five-prong antenna for which is visible on the gun bay door) and is wired for the ALQ-165 jammer. Later aircraft (FY88 and later; after the first 137 -18Cs and the first 31 -18Ds) are night-capable. In strike configuration they carry navigational IR pods (AAR-50) instead of ASQ-173 laser spot trackers (both versions carry AAS-38 attack FLIRs on their port nacelle stations). Beginning in 1993, AAR-50 was upgraded to incorporate a laser designator/ranger. These later aircraft also have a digital rather than projected analog moving map display. Marine night-attack F/A-18Ds have controls only in the forward cockpit, with two weapon-controller sidesticks in the after cockpit. There is also a special reconnaissance version of the F/A-18A, F/A-18A(R), with cameras and a laser line-scanner replacing the usual gun. F/A-18D(RC) is wired for an ATARS pod with a suitable data link. As of 1996, it seemed unlikely that ATARS would be used in any numbers, and the standard APG-73 radar was being modified to offer SAR capability.

The new F/A-18E/F has a much larger airframe with much the same avionics as -18C/D. It is presumably, however, a candidate for installation of AAYK-14 or of some alternative COTS upgrade.

The tactical computer is responsible for all sensor and weapon control and for the displays. The navigational computer keeps track of aircraft position, using the airplane's inertial and other systems. It calculates aircraft velocity. It also takes into account any flight plan fed into the fighter, for example, by the carrier's TAMPS system. The fly-by-wire system is separate, but it communicates with the two AYK-14s via a data bus, for example, to supply data for the displays.

Because all the controls send their messages through the same data bus, they do not need separate cables and so can be placed very close together, located for maximum pilot convenience. All are therefore above knee level, with the most vital controls, including those for sensors and weapons, clustered on throttle and stick (for HOTAS [hand-on-throttle-and-stick] operation). The consequence is that the pilot need never look down to change switch settings, hence can always keep his eyes on the scene outside.

As in other systems, the great advantage of the central computer is its adaptability, both to different aircraft missions and to changes in weaponry over the life of the airplane. Plans initially called for two parallel aircraft, the F-18 and the A-18, virtually identical in structure but with different weapons loads (two Sparrows on body hard points and two Sidewinders on wingtips for the fighter; the bomber would carry additional sensors on the body hardpoints, and bombs or missiles under its wings on four hard points). The bomber would have a moving map indicator in its cockpit, which the fighter did not need.

The effect of the mission computer is to provide both fighter and deep-strike capability in the same airplane, with absolutely the same hardware: hence the F/A-18 designation. For example, because the cockpit displays are general-purpose CRTs, they can show either a strip map or an air-to-air (or, for that matter, air-to-ground) radar picture. Because they are connected to a digital bus, the same hard points can be used for a wide variety of stores, including IR sensors.

As in the F-14, the central computer system also provides what amounts to TWS radar performance. That is not too important to an airplane firing Sparrows, since the radar must continuously illuminate the target. However, AMRAAM is a fire-and-forget missile, broadly analogous to Phoenix, though enjoying a shorter range. An F/A-18 armed with AMRAAMs can track multiple targets while conducting multiple engagements, just as an F-14 can, albeit at shorter range (advocates of the F/A-18/AMRAAM combination may argue that Phoenix is relatively ineffective at maximum range because it lacks end-game agility while coasting). The F/A-18A was credited with the ability to track 10 aircraft simultaneously, the central computer displaying the eight most important targets (on the theory that a pilot could not readily deal with more than eight).

The computers run a HUD and three general-purpose CRTs (head-down displays, HDDs): a master monitor display on the left (typically weapons status or FLIR imagery), a horizontal situation indicator in the middle (often used to show a moving map), and a multifunction display (typically of radar video) on the right. Originally the moving map was projected from film put aboard the airplane before flight time, but later -18C/Ds (see above) have a digital map system, hence have a fully flexible middle display. The main CRTs are interchangeable. Above the central display is the up-front control panel, with switches controlling the CNI (communications, navigation, IFF) system. Above each of the other main displays is a threat display. There is a separate ECM display on the right, under the multifunction display, among five back-up analog instruments.

As in the A-7E, an important element of the overall system is the ability to drop unguided bombs very accurately, the weapon system sensing aircraft motion and using preset bomb ballistics to determine the appropriate impact point. The U.S. Navy hoped that this improvement would make it unnecessary to invest heavily in guided bombs. The Navy's reasoning was that aircraft often could not return to a carrier with their full bomb loads on board. In many cases aircraft would have to jettison weapons. Unguided bombs are inexpensive, but guidance kits add considerably to the loss when bombs are jettisoned. Gulf War experience partly justified this view, in that F/A-18s proved capable of hitting Iraqi bridges, which are very small targets. However, it turned out that this accuracy was insufficient to drop the bridges, because pilots were unable to drop their weapons precisely on bridge supports. Laser-guided bombs were still vital.

The most widely advertised effect of the computer system is that the same airplane can easily switch between attack and air-to-air modes, as was demonstrated when two F/A-18s on a bombing mission during the Gulf War shot down a pair of Iraqi fighters, then reverted to bombing mode and completed their missions. Another consequence, less widely discussed, is that at flight time the airplane can automatically receive all its presets from a TAMPS computer system. In flight, the central computer can receive close-air-support tactical data in digital form from a hand-held terminal on the ground.

During the 1980s, there was intermittent interest in buying a two-seat F/A-18 to replace the aging A-6. At that time the decision was to forego this interim aircraft in favor of a new attack bomber incorporating stealth technology, the A-12, while modifying the A-6 to extend its useful lifetime. Then the A-12 program collapsed and the A-6F was abandoned as funding tightened. That left the F/A-18 as not merely the successor to the A-7

light bomber, but also, probably, to the long-range heavy A-6. F-14s are being modified as a stopgap, but in 1996 the only new naval fighter or attack airplane on the horizon is JSF, which may appear sometime in the next century. As naval finances tighten, pressure is growing to limit carrier air wings to a single combatant aircraft, the F/A-18. That this is even conceivable is due to the flexibility inherent in the airplane's computer-driven central tactical system.

Thus the same airplane can be effective both in short-range air combat and in medium-range fleet air defense (using AMRAAM, preferably in a next-generation longer-ranged version); it can also deliver the full variety of bombs, and it can easily carry a laser designator. It may well be modified to replace the EA-6B. In that role, much will be gained from the adaptability of the airplane's software-controlled nose radar and of its computer: it is striking that the proposed electronic warfare version of the F/A-18 is far closer to the fighter/attack version than the EA-6B is to the A-6. On the other hand, the airframe still lacks the sort of range associated with the A-6 and even the F-14. Acceptance of shorter effective range is generally justified in two ways. First, with the end of the Cold War, it is no longer necessary to strike from beyond the range of heavy land-based bombers (which only the Soviets ever operated in any numbers). Second, improved delivery accuracy makes it possible to achieve much the same results as with an A-6 with a much lighter load, so weight is left over for the fuel needed to fly a long distance.

Certainly the digital system of the F/A-18 offers drastic reductions in maintenance load and in fuel consumption compared to the F-14 or A-6.

Planned F/A-18C/D upgrades for FY97 include miniaturized GPS (to be installed in Lots 17–20 on the production line) and an IFF interrogator-transponder (aircraft previously had only transponders, hence could not interrogate potential targets). Planned FY99 upgrades include provision for JSOW, SLAM ER, JDAMS, and improved AMRAAM. Under the FY01 program these aircraft should receive AIM-9X and the associated Joint Helmet-Mounted Cueing System. Link 16 and a link to the army fire-support system (AFATDS) will be installed beginning about 2001, with computer upgrades.

◆ **LAMPS (SH-2 and SH-60B)**

The U.S. Light Airborne Multi-Purpose System is carried by a helicopter. LAMPS is conceived as a direct extension of a surface ship, rather than as a stand-alone device. It was conceived primarily as a means of acquiring and then attacking CZ contacts. A ship cannot fire a weapon directly at such contacts because the CZ is too broad. LAMPS was, therefore, conceived as the Light Airborne ASW Vehicle (LAAV); it gained the multipurpose designation because its tasks soon extended to assistance in OTH-T and ASMD. However, it is primarily an ASW sensor.

In the case of LAMPS I (the SH-2F Seasprite helicopter), which is intended to operate within 50 nm of a ship (for about 1 hr), the acquisition sensors—the sonobuoys—read out their data directly to the ship, which commands the helicopter into position to attack. The requirement for shipboard processing amounts to a limitation to LOS operation, that is, first CZ. A LAMPS I helicopter monitors four sonobuoys simultaneously (it carries a total of 15), using a single ARR-75 receiver. It also carries an LN-66 radar. The shipboard sonobuoy processor is SQS-54. LAMPS I is the redetection/prosecution sensor associated with the SQR-18A towed array.

LAMPS III (there was no LAMPS II), the SH-60B, carries its own sonobuoy processor (UYS-1) and thus can operate beyond the ship's LOS, out to the second and third CZ (nominal radius of action is beyond 100 nm, with 2-hr endurance). However, it, too, is intended primarily for direct operation from a ship's CIC, its sensors controlled by an acoustic-sensor operator (ASO) in the sonar room; a remote-radar operator (REMRO) in CIC (who receives the helicopter's radar output via data link, and who can directly control radar range and operating mode); an EW operator (EWO) in CIC; and the air-tactical control officer (ATACO). The helicopter carries a pilot; an airborne tactical officer (ATO), who takes over from the ATACO as directed (e.g., when the helicopter passes out of radio range); and a sensor operator (SO). The LOS data link is duplexed for voice and digital data, with low sidelobes for ECCM.

LAMPS III carries 25 buoys (although 12 would be used on a typical mission), two ARR-75 receivers, and an APS-124 radar. LAMPS III is the redetection/prosecution sensor associated with the SQR-19 towed array.

In each case, the usual final attack sensor is an ASQ-81(V)2 MAD, whose output is read out on board the helicopter. LAMPS I can also use active buoys for final attack data; it carries a paper range recorder sufficient for two SSQ-47 omnidirectional buoys or, presumably, one SSQ-62 DICASS. The LAMPS I sonobuoy chart recorder (RO-114) is controlled by an ASA-26B box. Range limitations at low chart speed (1 hr for recording) are 50 yd minimum and 15,000 maximum; at high chart speed (30 min), 50 and 7500 yd. In the SH-60B, the chart recorder, which is an attack aid, is replaced by a general-purpose UYS-1.

LAMPS III incorporates an acoustic target tracker (ATT) developed by IBM to automate the manual tracking process of the past. Past sonobuoy tracking was based on bearing fixes generated by pairs of buoys and on the tacit assumption that the submarine was not maneuvering. IBM's goal was to reduce localization time and the operator's localization workload by 50%, and also to provide a real-time solution even if the submarine maneuvered.

In the manual system, contacts are manually updated as the submarine runs through the buoy field (ideally, down a lane of buoys). The bearings are converted into fixes that then become a course and speed determined by least-squares fit. Because the LAMPS III system was automated, IBM could add Doppler information from the buoys, measuring a submarine's radial speed relative to them. The tracker maintains a real-time estimate of a target's position by filtering both frequency and bearing measurements from the buoys; there is no least-squares fit and, therefore, no need to assume straight-line motion. The algorithm begins with a crude estimate of submarine location based on bearings. Once that has been made, data are fed into parallel bearing and frequency trackers, which feed the target tracker.

Tests showed that the automated tracker could reach a consistent target-location solution very quickly, reaching attack criteria about twice as fast as the least-squares tracker and compensating automatically for the target's maneuvers. Often the least-squares tracker took as much as 10 min merely to come within 90 deg of the target's course, whereas the automated tracker could come within 15 deg in that time.

Ships were fitted with a "I/III Switch" that allows them to operate or to monitor either type of LAMPS helicopter, but note that LAMPS I is being retired.

As modified for operations in the Persian Gulf, LAMPS I helicopters were fitted with AAQ-16 FLIRs, ALQ-144 IR jammers, ALE-39 decoy dispensers, and door-mounted M60 machine guns.

Both LAMPS types are subject to upgrade programs. The current LAMPS I upgrade (SH-2G) provides an on-board sonobuoy processor (UYS-503), a secure ship-to-helicopter or helicopter-to-helicopter data link, a 99-channel sonobuoy receiver, and a 1553B bus. The current data link is AKT-22(V)7. The ASN-150 tactical system can display acoustic, radar, MAD, FLIR, or tactical (PPI) data. Because the helicopter is fitted with a data bus, sensors can be installed in modular fashion. For example, the bus can accommodate a FLIR. In trials, it has also supported a Cormorant dipping sonar and, reportedly, a classified British minehunting system tried out in the Persian Gulf. The current ESM system is ALR-66(V)3. The U.S. Navy is retiring its LAMPS I helicopters, but the upgrade is being applied to at least some aircraft exported for use on board *Knox*-class frigates.

The LAMPS III Block I upgrade (1987, beginning with Lot 9) includes provision for the Penguin missile and the Mk 50 torpedo, an ARR-84 99-channel sonobuoy receiver (to replace the current 31-channel ARR-75), the ARC-182 radio, and a five-channel GPS receiver. The helicopter will also be able to receive and display images from standoff land attack missiles (SLAM),

to guide them farther beyond the launching ship's horizon. A new 1553B bus supplements the existing 1553A.

Block I also adds provision for IR jammers, missile detectors, and door guns; helicopters have three stores stations. A fourth station is planned on the starboard side. The pylons are currently qualified to 1000 lb, but Sikorsky has proposed that LAMPS and SH-60F helicopters carry SLAMs (which require 1500-lb pylons). The UYS-1 acoustic processor is retained. The GPS receiver, sonobuoy receivers, and other new equipment require two additional dual 1553B buses. There is an engineering change proposal to add a FLIR, which could be used to identify surface contacts at night (the planned ISAR radar would have much the same purpose). Three different FLIRs were installed on LAMPS IIIs during Desert Storm: the Hughes AAQ-16 (Seahawk of HSL-48), the Texas Instruments AAQ-17 (HSL-42), and the GEC 30X Night Owl (HSL-46). These FLIRs were hung from the starboard weapons station, but they could be moved to the forward data-link antenna, which is little used. Block I ECP helicopters were fitted with the new AAS-44 FLIR.

Development of a Block II upgrade, now designated SH-60R, began in 1991 (the OR had been issued in May 1988). The Block II draft specification was written in FY90 and elaborated in FY91. IBM Federal Systems Division (now Loral) received a $242-million contract for engineering and manufacturing development in August 1993. Integration is to be completed in FY95, with tests and corrections of deficiencies through FY97. The schedule slipped two quarters in FY91 because of the delay in ALFS selection. FY91 funding was increased to add upgraded ESM to Block II. Block II includes the airborne LF sonar (ALFS, AQS-22), and an ISAR radar (APS-147). The UYS-2A processor will replace the current UYS-1. It can handle the dipper and eight buoys, or 16 buoys simultaneously. As in modified Block I helicopters, this one has the new AAS-44 FLIR, compatible with the Litton Darkstar laser designator used with the Hellfire missile. The new central tactical system employs a new AAYK-14 computer. This version uses a combination of 1553A and 1553B buses. The CDS (navigational system) will be able to receive instructions from TAMPS, which will be on every surface combatant by the time Block II enters service. The new radar can track several hundred targets simultaneously, and has fully digital processing for periscope detection. The new ESM set, based on the APR-50 of the B-2 bomber, is described as being an order of magnitude more precise than its predecessor in measuring target bearing, for OTH-T. ASQ-208 is to replace the ASQ-81 towed MAD. Block II will have a wide-band downlink capable of carrying FLIR, video, radar, and acoustic data simultaneously. A video downlink from an SH-60B was demonstrated in 1991. Block II will have a secure UHF burst tactical exchange link (the tactical data transfer, or TDT, system), to transfer data either to a ship or to a LAMPS I or LAMPS III helicopter relieving a helicopter on station. The new link will offer greater security, greater flexibility (helicopter-to-helicopter as well as helicopter-to-ship), and more bandwidth (to transmit ISAR images).

Block II is now SH-60R, the replacement for both SH-60B and the SH-60F inner-layer ASW helicopter operated by carriers. All SH-60B and many SH-60F are to be remanufactured.

SH-60B and -60F are being adapted to fire the Hellfire air-to-surface missile. This project is associated with a new Texas Instruments AAS-44 FLIR/laser designator (240 × 4-element focal plane array), being developed under a $3.8M subcontract with IBM. The FLIR is initially carried on the starboard bomb release, but is being relocated to a nose turret. The first Hellfire was launched from a LAMPS helicopter in March 1995. Production options under a $3.8M contract: 15 in 1994, 35 in 1995, 25 in 1996, 15 in 1997. A four-missile launcher can be fitted to the third stores position on the port side. Presumably the laser designator mentioned above would be used. Plans originally called for 90 aircraft (hence the series of options listed above), to be modified under the FY95–99 program, but most likely that will be cut to 45–50. As of 1995, plans called for Hellfire kits for 46 SH60B and 42 HH-60H. SH-60R will also have provision for a door machine gun (12.7mm FN M240).

Users:

　　LAMPS I ships: *Ticonderoga* (CG 47–48 only), *Kidd*, *Knox*, and some *Perry* class (Reserve ships). LAMPS I has been retired to the Reserves to save maintenance money. The first two *Ticonderogas* cannot easily be modified to operate the larger and heavier LAMPS III helicopter (they would be too top-heavy). LAMPS transfers: Egypt (5), Taiwan (12). Argentina has asked for eight SH-2F helicopters.

　　LAMPS III: Spain (S-70B-1), United States. The Japanese SH-60J (S-70B-3) has a Hitachi TDS, HLR-108 ESM and HQS-103 (AQS-18) dipping sonar. As of about April 1995, the U.S. Navy had 236 SH-60: 160 SH-60B (67 more planned) and 76 SH-60F (54 more planned). A total of 181 SH-60B and 18 SH-60F were to be converted to SH-60R beginning in 1997. Another 58 SH-60F were to be converted to combat SAR aircraft (HH-60H Jayhawks), to join the 18 already in service.

◆ JSF

The Joint Strike Fighter (formerly JAST) is to be built in three versions, for the U.S. Air Force, the U.S. Navy, and, in a STOVL variant, for the U.S. Marine Corps and for the Royal Navy. The hope is to cut costs sufficiently to reverse the decline in aircraft numbers; as many as 3000 JSFs may be built to replace aircraft such as the F-16 and F/A-18. Unfortunately, JSF is likely to fulfill radically different roles for its two main buyers, the Navy and the Air Force. For the Navy, it is the day-one penetrator, a relatively stealthy bomber that will open the way for the many F/A-18s. In effect, it will fill the role for which the A-12 was conceived. For the Air Force, however, JSF will be the inexpensive companion to the sophisticated F-22. The Marines demand a STOVL version to replace their AV-8B.

Since avionics now accounts for about 30% of aircraft cost, much depends on an attempt to cut avionics costs by adopting a new distributed architecture that can easily be tailored for the three planned variants. Existing aircraft use federated architectures, in the sense that each major subsystem (e.g., radar) has its own antenna and processors, feeding only highly processed data into the aircraft's central mission computer. As different RF functions (radar, ESM, CNI [communications/navigation/identification]) come to use much the same parts of the spectrum, it may be argued that these distinctions are more and more artificial. After all, all of the RF functions contribute to aircraft situational awareness (i.e., to forming an effective tactical picture). The hope in JSF is to cut costs by sharing resources: antennas, preprocessors (analog signal detection), digital signal processors. All signal processing is to be concentrated in a single common integrated processor (CIP), actually a series of standard modules. The system, then, is distributed electronically but not physically. Minimizing the number of antennas ("apertures") may also contribute significantly to the airplane's stealth. The CIP technique is being tried, for radar only, in the F-22. In JSF it is to embrace all RF signals. CIP preprocessing modules will, in effect, create an integrated sensor system (ISS); standard digital signal processors will form part of an integrated central processor (ICP), feeding into central mission computer elements which, like a shipboard CDS, will form an integrated tactical picture (for situational awareness). The main RF antenna will be an electronically scanned nose array offering near-simultaneous air-to-air and air-to-ground modes as well as high-gain ESM and wideband data links. Similarly, a situational-awareness (air-to-air) IRST and targeting FLIR will share apertures and processing electronics. The great advantage of the modular approach is that aircraft variants may be made more or less sophisticated by adding or subtracting ISS and ICP modules, with appropriate modular software changes. Of course, distribution often carries a massive software overhead in the form of the buffers between individual processors and the system bus, so much depends upon just how powerful those processors turn out to be.

Like a ship, JSF will depend heavily on external sources of data (which may be other JSFs or even be relayed via satellites) to form its tactical picture. Indeed, it is hoped that heavy reliance on externally provided data will help hold down the sophistication demanded of JSF itself, hence hold down its cost.

Contracts for a nose antenna demonstrator, MIRFS (multifunction integrated RF system) were awarded in 1996 to Hughes and Northrop Grumman (the former Westinghouse division). Hughes plans to base its radar on an earlier wide-band integrated-forebody technology demonstrator. The Northrop Grumman radar is based on its APG-76 and APG-77 (F-22 radar), and is to fly on a BAC 1-11 late in 1999.

As of mid-1996, the JSF program office hoped to achieve 90% avionics commonality between the different JSF variants, tailoring antennas as required, but retaining a common core and using software independent of system hardware, for less-expensive upgrades. An initial core architectecture has already been developed, implemented in a virtual avionics prototype (VAP) which permits tests to develop tradeoffs, for example, between different levels of SAR resolution. The modular approach yielded estimated avionics costs of $5.94M for $27.5M USAF version, $5.97M for USN (total $32.3M), and $6.13M for USMC (total $30.4M).

◆ S-3A/CP-140

The S-3A tactical system was conceived as a smaller version of that of the P-3C, with some of the reduction in size balanced by better automation and a faster computer (AYK-10). There are only three crew members, in addition to the pilot: the copilot, responsible for nonacoustic sensors (radar and MAD) and communications; the sensor (acoustics) operator; and the TACCO. Proposals for what became the S-3 were submitted in April 1968, and the airplane formally entered service in February 1974. The Canadian CP-140 uses much the same systems as the S-3A.

The key improvement in the S-3A, as compared to the P-3C, is more automated sonobuoy processing, so that two acoustic operators (in a P-3C) can be replaced by one, while the airplane retains the capacity to monitor 16 buoys simultaneously. Targets are detected primarily by automatic line integration (ALI), which is not quite the same as visual integration of a LOFAR-gram. In some cases such integration will not bring up a discontinuous or changing line that might be evident from visual examination. The signatures are automatically identified by comparison to those in a library. This technique is probably not altogether successful (mainly automatic detection has not generally been adopted in other ASW systems), but it is unavoidable in a small airplane. The computer memory retains a record of the rise of different buoy signals; in theory, the sensor operator can use these data to trace the movement of a submarine through a buoy field.

The other major electronic advance was the sonobuoy reference system (SRS, designated ARS-2), which locates them by passive interferometry, using 13-blade aerials distributed over the airplane's fuselage (i.e., by measuring phase differences between signals from the same buoy received at different aerials). Active buoys, which do not transmit continuously, are located by sending a modulated signal on their UHF command links and then measuring the same modulation as received on their VHF uplink. ARS-4 is a modified ARS-2 for the S-3B version of the Viking. The SRS was a major change from past practice, eliminating the requirement to overfly the buoys periodically, and permitting an airplane to remain at high altitude. A version of the S-3 SRS (ARS-3) was later incorporated into the Update II version of the P-3C. SRS made it possible for a single S-3 to monitor a large sonobuoy field from high altitude, without periodically overflying each buoy to be sure of its location (using an on-top indicator).

FLIR and radar video are sent directly to the tactical displays; the acoustic-data processor (OL-82) feeds directly into the TACCO and SENSO displays. ESM, sonobuoy, and MAD signals are fed into the AYK-10 computer and then into the displays. The computer (under TACCO control) normally controls sonobuoy dropping, although there is an alternative manual mode. Of the 60 sonobuoy chutes, one (chute P-2) is reserved for search and rescue.

The S-3 is subject to a weapons-system improvement program (WSIP). WSIP I was the conversion to the S-3B, with its APS-137 ISAR radar and provision for Harpoon missiles. The current WSIP II for the S-3B envisages installation of GPS (with a trial kit in 1996), an APS-137 upgrade for overland ground-tracking, and possibly CAINS II laser inertial navigation. The radar upgrade would be an alternative to a podded APG-76 for what would amount to a carrier-based JSTARS capability. There is also current interest in provision for Maverick, SLAM, and HARM missiles for ground attack. The WSIP program includes the U.S.-Canadian program for a new coprocessor memory unit (CPMU, formerly mass memory unit), which is required for a future open-architecture system. At the same time, existing Tactical Mission Program (TMP) CMS-2 code is being rewritten into ADA, a prerequisite for further system expansion. The FY93 program also included development of a systems engineering plan for ADAR (active sonobuoy receiver) hardware and software integration into the S-3.

One S-3B of VS-37 was converted into a prototype for Outlaw Viking. It began operating early in 1994, but as of early 1996 no money had been provided for any further conversions. Outlaw Viking adds a satellite link in a dorsal antenna and a new workstation integrated into the TACCO station (a 10in color LCD above the usual TACCO CRT, 14 VME cards including a GPS receiver, and a touch-screen for control).

There is also SEASTARS (Gray Wolf), an S-3B fitted with a podded APG-76 radar with GPS/INS interface. SAR imagery can be transmitted down to a carrier via a 240-kbps link (CHBDL) and it is also recorded on board the aircraft. The SEASTARS designation is a pun on the J-STARS designation of the E-8 aircraft which uses a SAR radar to detect moving vehicles on the ground. See the Strike Warfare section for further APG-76 details.

An S-3 upgrade program envisages installation of a new mission computer (AYK-23) in FY98, followed by ADA software in 2000. GPS is to be installed in 1997, and external communications are to be improved in 1998. A new Armament Control System is to be installed under the FY98 program. S-3s are to remain in service until 2015.

The Canadian CP-140 Aurora has a modified version of the S-3A suite. Compared to a P-3C, it has a larger multipurpose display (MPD). The tactical compartment contains three two-operator consoles, each with two MPDs and keysets to communicate with the AYK-502 (AYK-10) central computer. The acoustic processor is OL-5004, similar to the OL-82 of the S-3A but with added vernier displays and ambient sea-noise measurement.

Two contractors were selected in April 1995 to conduct a 12-month study of an upgrade for 18 CP-140s; the winner is to be

chosen in 1997, and the program completed by 2004. Improvements are to include an upgrade to the APS-116 radar with "searchlight SAR" mode, a 99-channel sonobuoy receiver and an upgraded or new processor, a new communications architecture to allow addition of new radios and SATCOM; GPS; and a new ESM suite, probably ALR-76.

◆ TACNAVMOD (ASN-124)

P-3B TACNAVMOD (ASN-124) is, in effect, a "poor man's P-3C," developed in the mid-1970s for remaining P-3As and -3Bs. The computer is the Lear-Sigler CP-1224, using the ASA-66 display console (-66A for the pilot, -66B for the TACCO). These aircraft are also fitted with AQA-7(V) sonobuoy processors. CP-1224 is a 16-bit computer with 103 instructions and a memory capacity of 64 kwords; it has 16 one-word registers, and can operate in single and double precision. It is connected to a dual 1553B bus and has a 16-MHz clock. There are eight input and eight output channels plus 32 input and 32 output discretes (switches or synchros). The later 1224B adds a 32-kword memory card to accommodate later software.

In U.S. service, TACNAVMOD aircraft were called Super-Bs. Block II aircraft added IRDS and Harpoon, and thus were called killer-Bs. These aircraft also received satellite communications gear and other communications gear allowing them to work with Update III P-3Cs.

TACNAVMOD applies to Greek P-3Bs (TACNAVMOD II), to Portuguese P-3Ps, to Spanish P-3Bs, and to Thai P-3Ts. It probably also applies to aircraft withdrawn from U.S. storage, such as those transferred to Chile and the P-3As that Australia plans to use as crew trainers. However, Iran did *not* receive TACNAVMOD in the P-3Fs acquired in the 1970s.

◆ DMS 2000/DDC 060

Loral Unisys's central tactical system is being installed in the modernized RAAF P-3Cs. DDC 060 replaces the central computer with a VME box containing six or seven computer cards (each carrying a 68060 CPU) and the usual input/output devices. DMS 2000 is the surrounding information-management system, which controls the displays and takes data from the sensors. The system is reconfigurable and highly redundant, since it can survive the failure of several processor cards. In effect it is distributed, even though the independent processors are all located together. The system bus is a 1553B.

◆ DPDS/MPAvionics

Boeing's Distributed Processing and Display System is intended for maritime patrol aircraft. It is closely related to ARGOSystems' MPAvionics suite (ARGO is a Boeing subsidiary). At present UDACS is being marketed for large aircraft (which in the spring of 1996 meant the British RMPA); MPAvionics is the corresponding small-aircraft system, installed in the Indonesian 737 and now marketed for the Indonesian-built CASA 235. DPDS is an outgrowth of the UDACS display system initially developed for the RNZAF P-3Ks and then adopted by the U.S. Navy for the abortive

This drawing shows Boeing's projected installation of UDACS (now DPDS) in the abortive P-3C Update IV. All four sensor-operator consoles are identical and are lined up together, with the TACCO console forward, facing forward. In this design, all sensor stations were interchangeable, using a distributed architecture with 68020 CPUs tied together by a 32-bit maxibus; burst mode throughput was 192 Mbps. (Boeing)

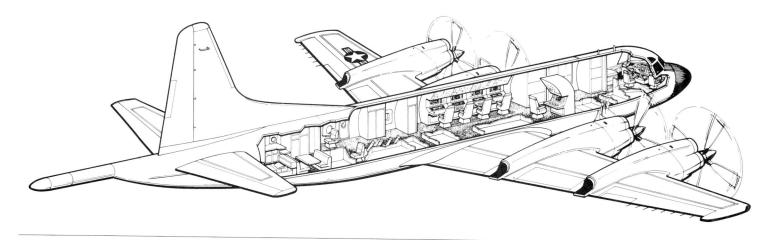

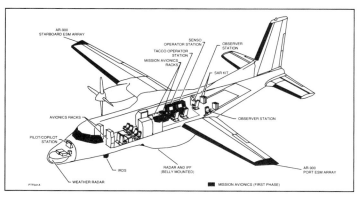

MPAvionics installed on a CN-235. (ARGOSystems)

P-3C Update IV. The Update IV version was fully distributed, without any central computer, using 68000-series chips.

DPDS consists of one or more operator workstations on a LAN, connected to an I/O processor (IOP), a unit containing multiple I/O cards and processors on a VME backplane. Processors are also connected directly to the LAN to which the workstations are connected. Current versions include several spare slots for expansion. Both workstation and IOP currently use a high-performance RISC processor running at over 160 MIPS; CPU cards also carry 8 to 128 Mbytes of memory. Sensor video is routed to the workstations via a separate video bus.

The IOP is connected to the workstations, to the aircraft sensors (radar, IFF, IRDS, ESM), and to the main aircraft subsystems (for example, communications, recording, navigation, ASW, and stores management).

The open-architecture DPDS console has a 19in color windowed raster-scan display (1280 × 1024 pixels), with a pair of plasma touch-screens below it and a conventional keyboard, trackball, and separate fast-action keys. The console also incorporates a pair of display processors (one with a hard disk), and an I/O processor. Consoles can be used both as sensor workstations and as general-purpose workstations (for example, for the TACCO and the navigator/communications officer), so console functions can be switched to suit different aircraft roles. A compatible version of the same workstation can be mounted in the cockpit. An Ethernet handles normal data traffic between the workstations, supplemented by a fiber-optic bus for quick system loads and rapid transfers of large blocks of data. A 1553B bus supports mission-sensor display and control. DFTDS uses a COTS operating system and ADA applications software.

MPAvionics is a small-airplane version of DPDS. It was initially developed for the updated Indonesian 737 surveillance aircraft and now offered as the preferred option for Indonesian-built CASA 235s. As of the spring of 1996 it had tentatively been adopted by Brunei, which had initially favored an alternative Racal system. The version in the Indonesian aircraft uses a Force SPARC 1E central processor running Boeing-built consoles with Barco Chromatics color displays and internal graphics engines. In this application the system has four consoles and a pilot's station. The sensors are a nose radar (APS-504(V)5), a FLIR (as in AAS-36), and a SLAMMR side-looking radar.

The Airtech (CASA/IPTN) CN-235MPA Persuader has a similar nose radar, a FLIR in an under-nose turret, and an ESM set; it can also accommodate a sonobuoy processor and MAD. Up to six underwing hard points can carry torpedoes or missiles. In this case the displays are monochrome. The central tactical system, built around a 1553B bus, is called a Tactical Integrator System (TIS). It employs one two-man console (TACCO plus SENSO) plus a separate computer cabinet; an additional one-man SENSO console is needed to handle an additional sensor (for example, sonobuoys/MAD in addition to radar/ESM). There is also an observer's station aft. The main displays are all windowed, with touch-panels beneath them plus quick-action keys.

As of 1995, the search radar alternatives for the CN-235MPA were APS-504(V)5, APS-134 (LW), Seapray 4000, and Ocean Master. Brunei reportedly chose APS-504. The ESM alternatives

were: Marconi Sky Guardian 300, AR-700, and ALR-85(V)1. The FLIR alternatives were GEC's TICM MRT-S (GEC) and Thomson-CSF's Chlio.

♦ **IDLS**

Rockwell's Interoperable Data Link System is actually a CDS picture-forming and -keeping (situational awareness) core, and it is being marketed as such. Developed jointly with Tiburon and with ACSI (Analysis Computer Systems, Inc.), it was announced in mid-1995. IDLS is housed in a $\frac{3}{4}$ ATR-sized VME-backplane chassis holding four microprocessors (486 or Pentium), 5 Gbytes of memory, and 18 expansion slots. It is designed to build up to two such chassis, with a total of 36 slots. The system's key virtue is its flexibility, due to its open architecture and the ability to package important devices, such as an embedded GPS receiver and data-link controllers, in single VME cards.

The two major elements are a tactical data processor (TDP) and a data-link processor (DLP). As in Tiburon's ATW, an inference engine, automatically performing correlation and attribute-matching to aid target definition and tracking, is a key component of the TDP, fusing own-sensor and external track data (it can accommodate a 5000-track database; Rockwell claims that IDLS can handle 5 to 10 times as many tracks as current systems). The TDP controls system displays, an image processor, a communications front-end processor and preprocessor, and the DLP. The DLP in turn can be modified to handle a wide variety of links by changing cards in the VME box (similarly, new sensors can be accommodated by adding interface cards). The system is compatible with OTH-T links such as OTCIXS and TADIXS B. It has sufficient computing power to handle video imagery.

In a typical application, IDLS would be connected directly to the aircraft navigational system (INU), to displays and keyboards, to aircraft sensors, to an aircraft tactical system (which might have its own connection to the navigational system and the sensors) and to data-link terminals. It would also be connected to the aircraft communication system bus, which would connect to various radio receivers. Links currently implemented are Link 11, Link 14, Link 16, Link Y, OTCIXS, and TADIXS B.

IDLS routes data to the aircraft tactical system and to the flight deck. Operating as a CDS core, the IDLS box can be connected directly to sensors and to mission processors. It contains sufficient memory to support high-resolution color displays, including digital maps for overlays. The box can include an embedded GPS receiver. The aircraft inertial unit can also be connected directly to IDLS, so that an accurate position on a digital map can be displayed, and track data can be shown in a precise manner, keyed to the maps. Similarly, way points can be input before or after takeoff, then displayed as the airplane flies. Selected tracks and track histories can be recalled for display, and unwanted ones can be filtered out.

Very precise mapping has important consequences. Most aircraft systems use manual rate-aiding for surface targets, for example, for TWS fire control against ships. IDLS is designed for completely automatic operation, on the ground that a human operator moving symbols is not as precise as a radar using GPS positioning and Kalman-filtered data. Sensor resolution is locked to map accuracy. The enormous memory and computing power make it possible for the system to present color maps, which are much easier to read than monochrome ones.

Great memory capacity makes it possible to load detailed historical data, so that the system can compare it with the current situation, for example, to find new or moved emitters. Vast memory also makes it possible to embed training techniques in the IDLS box, and even to eliminate all or most paper manuals. Training scenarios can be loaded and played out. Software functions can easily be tested.

IDLS is designed to be connected to a standard bus (Ethernet, 1553B or the equivalent fiber-optic 1773, RS 422, 232, or ARINC 429).

Users: Denmark (VIP Gulfstream IIIs, to provide Link 11 interoperability), Egypt (three special-operations helicopters; will probably be installed on board existing aircraft using ASN-902,

-903, and -123 central systems; also for six ships, presumably the Chinese-, Spanish-, and U.S.-built frigates, which need data-link capability; IDLS has an interface with EDO's FFISTS, which is installed on board the Egyptian *Knox*-class frigates), United States (as part of ATW, for the AIP version of the P-3C). There are two or three unnamed export customers. As of early 1996, Rockwell was offering IDLS to the UAE in a Fokker 50 as an alternative to ASN-150 in a CASA 235; presumably the Fokker collapse complicated matters. There was one other potential customer, and the Japanese were reportedly interested. IDLS is part of the U.S. link improvement program for aircraft such as the S-3, P-3, ES-3, and EP-3E. As of early 1996, Rockwell also planned to use IDLS to compete for Link 16/22, and hoped to demonstrate it in JWID-96, the Joint Warfare Information Distribution exercise, which is intended to promote seamless triservice multiplatform data exchange. In this context, IDLS serves both as a gateway, communicating over multiple links, and as a means of combining the pictures received over those links.

♦ **RAWS**

The *Collins* Role Adaptable Weapon System equips Australian S70B Seahawk helicopters. It was adapted from a TDS originally developed for U.S. Coast Guard HU-65As. RAWS is conceived as an independent system, like the S-3 Viking, rather than as an arm of the ship operating it, like LAMPS. The striking feature of RAWS is its icon-driven MMI (the operator moves a cursor using a joystick called a slew controller), which makes it unnecessary for the operator to look away from the display. This is much like that of using a mouse on a computer. As a result, a pilot, TACCO, and SENSO can fly a full ASW mission; the comparable

U.S. LAMPS III requires an additional four-man support cell aboard the operating ship. Large (8 × 8 in) raster-scan tactical displays serve the pilot and TACCO forward and the SENSO aft.

This is a distributed system; each tactical display is connected to a display control unit containing three 16-bit Rockwell proprietary microprocessors: one for system control, one for display, and one for I/O. Peak performance is 1.7 MIPS at a clock rate of 20 MHz. RAWS currently uses 70% of the installed memory and 50% of the ultimate maximum memory capacity. There is a current reserve of about 40% of processor throughput. The system is tied together by a dual-redundant 1553B bus, which has 22 terminals, three of which are reserved for future growth (ESM, FLIR, and a dipping sonar); the current system uses 46% of bus capacity. RAWS is initialized using a 32-kword data-loader cartridge. The acoustic processor is a UYS-503 sonobuoy processor (which can handle eight DIFAR buoys simultaneously). The sonobuoy receiver is the 99-channel ARR-84 used in the U.S. LAMPS III Block I upgrade. The helicopter carries 32 A-size sonobuoys (half in launchers) and two torpedoes or missiles.

The helicopter uses a unique data link. It can participate in a data link network (up to four PUs on a single frequency, usually one ship and up to three aircraft). There are 16 message types, within which are 24 link items.

As of 1994, the Royal Australian Navy planned a two-stage Seahawk upgrade: first a FLIR (probably a BAe Australia type that will feed the 1553B bus) and an ESM retrofit, then installation of a dipping sonar and provision of an antiship missile. For Gulf operations, the Australian Seahawks were fitted with AAR-47 missile detectors, ALE-47 flare/chaff dispensers, AAQ-16 FLIRs (not tied into the main dual 1553B data bus), and machine guns.

STRATEGIC STRIKE SYSTEMS

Deletions: M20 (France), SS-N-6, SS-N-17, SS-N-24, Polaris (to be retired with the last British *Resolution*-class submarine later in 1996), Poseidon C-3, Excalibur.

According to a leaked U.S. intelligence report (November 1995), India hopes to deploy a 300km SLBM by 2010.

CHINA (PRC)

◆ CSS-N-3 (Ju Lang 1, JL-1)

Dimensions: Approx. 1.5 × 10 m (60 in × 33 ft)
Weight: Approx. 14,000 kg (30,000 lb)
Warhead: 1 (reports vary on yield)
Range: Est. 2700–3600 km (1750–2300 nm)

The first submerged launch was carried out on 12 October 1982 by the single "Golf"-class trials submarine, at a range of 1600 km. The missile has two solid-propellant stages. Twelve missiles can be carried by Xia-class submarines; in 1988, two such submarines had been completed and two were under construction. Reportedly, this weapon was developed in part from the CSS-2 (DF-3) land-based ballistic missile, which has a range of 2700 km and which carries a single 1–3-MT warhead (and, in its newer version, three MRVs, 50–100 kT each). This missile was first fired by a Xia-class submarine during July 1988.

An improved CSS-NX-4 is currently under development; reportedly, this improved version carries a 2-MT warhead.

FRANCE

Submarine-launched ballistic missiles are ejected from their tubes by gas generators.

CSS-N-3 missiles. (*Ships of the World*)

The French submarine-launched ballistic missile M5 emerging from the water. (Armées d'aujourd'hui-SIRPA)

◆ **M4**

Dimensions: 1.93 × 11.05 m (76.0 in × 36.2 ft)
Weight: 35,000 kg (77,140 lb)
Warhead: Six 150-kT TN-70 (MIRVs)
Propulsion: Two-stage rocket with powered MIRV bus. First stage: Type 401(P10), 71,000-kg thrust; second stage: Type 402(P6), 30,000-kg thrust; third stage: Type 403, 7000-kg thrust. (156,500/66,100/15,400-lb thrust). Burn times: 65/75/45 sec.
Range: 4500 km (2900 nm)

M4 is the MIRV successor to M20. Almost twice as heavy as M20, M4 is designed to fit the launch tubes of existing French strategic submarines. Exploiting French research into small thermonuclear warheads, the French government decided to proceed with M4 in December 1974. Compared to M20, M4 is an all-new missile with new first- (401), second- (402), and third- (403) stage motors. The last powers the warhead-dispensing bus.

The M4 missile is launched by a powder charge; M4 can be fired at greater depths and in closer sequence than M20. The six TN-70 warheads are spread over a 150 × 350km (97 × 227nm) area.

M4 was first fired at sea on 10 March 1982 and became operational in 1985 on board the submarine L'Inflexible. M4 now arms all French strategic submarines except the new Le Triomphant (see below).

M4C is the upgrade variant, carrying TN-71 warheads. They are smaller and lighter than TN-70, but have the same yield. Through the end of 1993, 30 M4 (including six R&D missiles) and 78 M4C (including two R&D) were made. Estimated unit prices were $88.2M for M4 and $91.7M for M4C.

Delays in M5 development led to a new program for an interim weapon, M45, which entered service in 1996 on board the submarine Le Triomphant, the first of a new generation. M45 can carry a TN-71 warhead to a nominal range of 5000 km (3200 nm); however, an M45 carrying a single warhead reached 6000 km on 4 March 1986. M45 was then rethought to carry the TN-75 warhead (with penaids) planned for M5. A new TN-76 "stealth" warhead was developed for M5; it may also be carried by operational M45s.

◆ **M5/M51**

It is no longer clear that M5 will be developed. Instead, M51 (which will probably be a further evolution of M45) is to be developed for service sometime in the next century.

◆ **ASMP**

Dimensions: 0.30 m × 5.38 × 0.96 m over fins (11.8 × 211.8 × 37.8 in)
Weight: 840 kg (1851 lb)
Warhead: 300-kT
Propulsion: Integral rocket-ramjet; maximum speed Mach 3.5

Range: 80+ km at Mach 2, low altitude; 250+ km at Mach 3, high altitude (52 and 162 nm)

A medium-range nuclear standoff missile, ASMP (Air-Sol Moyenne Porte) is designed for use against both tactical and strategic targets. ASMP is carried by 24 (of a total of 55) Super Étendard carrier attack aircraft as well as by French land-based tactical (Mirage 2000N) and strategic (Mirage IVP) aircraft. In French official parlance the word "tactical" was changed to "prestrategic" before the ASMP went into service, to emphasize French reliance on deterrence through the threat of escalation. In the case of the Super Étendard, ASMP replaces a standard nuclear gravity bomb (the 60-kT AN-52, first deployed in 1977). This program began in March 1978 after a government decision to proceed with an aircraft-carried standoff weapon for attacking hardened targets. ASMP was, therefore, primarily a way of extending the usefulness of the French strategic air arm.

The carrier Foch was refitted in 1987–88 to carry ASMP in place of the earlier AN-52 bombs. However, her sister, the Clemenceau, is not being refitted because she is to be replaced by the new nuclear carrier Richelieu about 1996. It is reported that the French navy wanted a lower-yield version for antiship attack, but finances precluded development of two versions of the basic weapon.

The size of the missile was limited so that it could be carried by a Mirage 2000N. The missile design has some stealth features, including some radar-absorbing material. In addition, ASMP is hardened against EMP.

ASMP's aerodynamic design is unusual, having two prominent angled air intakes, whose fairings lead back to the after end, but no wings as such. At very high speeds, the intakes and fairings provide sufficient lift, and the only special aerodynamic surfaces are the four fins at the tail. The intake fairings carry such auxiliary equipment as the actuators for the fins. The air intakes are modeled on those of the Concorde airliner.

There are three alternative flight modes: high-altitude/terminal dive, low-altitude terrain following, or low-altitude with terminal pop-up for air burst (against naval targets). In the last case, the missile would attack from relatively short range (effective range is limited to about 60 km [39 nm] by the radar horizon of a low-flying attack aircraft). All three flight modes include preprogrammed evasive maneuvers.

The engine is probably the most interesting feature of the missile. The initial choice, a solid-fuel rocket, was rejected because it would have been much too heavy, resulting in an unacceptable 3- to 4-t missile. Instead, a solid-fuel booster is used to accelerate the missile to Mach 2, at which speed the main ramjet is efficient. The rocket burns out in about 5 sec, and about $\frac{1}{20}$ sec later the nozzle is ejected. The burnt-out booster becomes the combustion chamber, a "swirl type" developed since 1972. There can be no conventional flameholder (since all the volume of the chamber is occupied by the solid booster), so the flame is stabilized by the two jets of air from the air intakes, forming what amounts to a fluid flameholder. The fuel is conventional kero-

ASMP under the wing of a Super Étendard. (Aerospatiale)

sene rather than the denser Shelldyne used in U.S. cruise missiles (the former being much better known in France when ASMP was designed). However, a second-generation cruise missile will use denser fuel.

ASMP first flew on 23 June 1983 and was the first European missile to shift automatically from rocket to ramjet mode. The missile became operational on 1 May 1986 on board Mirage IVP bombers of the FAS (Forces Aériennes Strategiques). Total planned production is about 100 weapons.

ASMP will ultimately be replaced by ASLP (Air-Sol Longue Porte), carried by Rafales: range will be 1300 km, length 5.25 m, and speed will be Mach 3.0.

RUSSIA

The Russian ballistic-missile submarine force is being run down to only two types, Delta IV and Typhoon. As the Soviet Union collapsed, two more missile systems were in development, one (RSM-54M) for Delta IV–class submarines, and one (RSM-52M) for the Typhoon class (Project 941). It seems unlikely that any strategic Shaddocks (SS-N-3) survive. See the 1991/92 edition for details of missiles carried by earlier classes.

RSM designations were produced only for purposes of treaties; the internal designations are R-series rockets and D-series systems. Known system designations are D-1 (R-11FM, modified Scud, fired from Zulu-V class submarines and from early "Golf" and "Hotel" classes), D-2 (R-13/SS-N-4 missile), D-3 (R-15, unsuccessful alternative to D-2), D-4 (R-21/4K55/SS-N-5 missile), D-5 (R-27/4K10 Zyb/SS-N-6 missile), D-5K (4K18/SS-NX-13 antiship ballistic missile), D-6 (abortive solid-fuel rocket, 1960–61 project), D-7 (RT-15M, an unsuccessful solid-fuel missile), D-8 (1967 experimental two-stage liquid-fuel missile, possibly alternative to R-29), D-9(R-29/SS-N-8), D-11(R-31/RSM-45/SS-N-17), D-19 (SS-N-20). SS-N-18 and -23 are variants of D-9.

◆ SS-N-8 Sawfly (D-9 system, R-29/4K75 Vysota missile; RSM-40)

Dimensions: 1.8 × 13.0 m (6ft × 43 ft) without warhead
Weight: 33.3 t
Warhead: One RV (800 kT); throw weight 1100 kg
Propulsion: Two-stage liquid rocket
Range: Mod 1: 7800 km (4200 nm), Mod 2: 9100 km (4900 nm)
CEP: 1.6 km in Mod 2

This missile was developed by Makayev for Delta I and II submarines (Projects 667B and 667BD), using stellar-inertial guidance to achieve useful accuracy when fired from waters Soviet naval forces could expect to control. Reportedly, however, the stellar-inertial system was not always reliable, and initial reports of spectacular accuracy were exaggerated. This missile entered service in 1973. SS-N-8 Mod 2 is the D-9D system (R-29D, 4K75D). The follow-on was D-9U (R-29U). The full Delta I system is Murena; Delta II is Murena-M.

◆ SS-N-18 Stingray (D-9DU system, R-29DU/4K75DU Volna missile; RSM-50)

Dimensions: 1.8 × 14.1 m (6 × 46 ft) without warhead
Weight: 35.3 t
Warhead: Mod 1: 3 RV (200 kT), Mod 2: 1 RV (450 kT), Mod 3: 7 RV; throw weight 1650 kg
Propulsion: Two-stage liquid rocket
Range: Mod 1: 3500 nm (6480 km), Mod 2: 4300 nm (7360 km), Mod 3: 3500 nm (6480 km)
CEP: 1.4 km in Mods 1 and 2, but figures as low as 0.8 km have been reported

This was the first Soviet MIRVed submarine-launched missile. Mod 1 was introduced in 1977, Mods 2 and 3 in 1979. The system, including the Delta III submarine, is Kalmar. D-9R (R-29R) is SS-N-18 Mod 2 (1977). It was followed by D-9RL (R-29RL) of 1979, and by D-9K(R-29K) of 1982.

◆ SS-N-20 Sturgeon (R-39 Rif-M Missile/3M65/Treaty Designation RSM-52)

Dimensions: 2.4 × 16.0 m (without warheads)
Weight: 90 t at launch, including 6 t of components jettisoned after launch (first stage 52.8 t)

Warhead: Six to ten 100-kT MIRV (throw weight 2550 kg)
Propulsion: Solid-fuel (three stages)
Range: 8300 km
CEP: 500–900 m

SS-N-20 is carried by Typhoon-class submarines. The weapon system is D-19 Taifun (the Project 941 submarine was codenamed Akula by the Russians). It was first tested, unsuccessfully, in January 1980 (one source gives a 1979 date), but successful tests were reported in 1981, and four were launched by a submerged submarine in October 1982. The system was considered operational as of 1983. Design work probably began in 1972; in 1974 Leonid Brezhnev told then-President Ford that unless the United States abandoned its Trident program, Typhoon would go ahead. Reportedly, problems with this weapon delayed the Typhoon program, the submarine being ready well before the missile had become sufficiently reliable. Unlike the D-9 missile, which is floated to the surface before ignition, this missile is cold-launched and ignited in the air, like U.S. SLBMs. It can, therefore, be fired by a surfaced submarine (as has been demonstrated).

Although previously credited with six to nine RVs, SS-N-20 is counted with 10 under the START treaty rules. Guidance is all-inertial.

A new version of SS-N-20, R-39UTTKh (ss-N-28), with eight warheads, is being fitted to the first two Typhoon-class submarines, with further refits planned. The suffix indicates improved technical characteristics.

◆ SS-N-21

See the Strike Warfare section.

◆ SS-N-23 Skiff (R-29RM; Treaty Designation RSM-54)

Dimensions: 1.9 × 14.8 m (without warhead)
Weight: 40,300 kg
Warhead: See below (throw weight 2800 kg)
Propulsion: Liquid-fuel rockets (three stages)
Range: 8300 km
CEP: 500–900 m

SS-N-23, the first Soviet MIRVed submarine-launched missile, is carried by Delta IV–class submarines. It is similar in size to the earlier SS-N-18 but has greater throw weight and is more accurate. Flight tests began in June 1983, and the missile entered operational service about 1987; it was not yet in series production as late as March 1986. There were apparently early reliability problems.

For treaty purposes, SS-N-23 is now credited with 4 × 100-kT RVs, although as many as 10 have been reported in the past. A modified version of this missile probably completed sea testing in 1988.

Variants of the missile are Shtil-1, -1N, -2, -3A, and -3N. The associated weapon system is D-9RM; the combination of missile and Delta IV submarine is Delfin.

UNITED STATES

U.S. naval ballistic missiles are fired using gas generators; the missiles ignite when they reach the surface. They can, therefore, be fired by a surfaced submarine. However, reportedly, a Trident I (C-4) cannot be surface launched without some risk of damage to the firing submarine.

◆ Trident C-4 (UGM-96A)

Dimensions: 74 × 408 in
Weight: 70,000 lb
Warhead: Eight 100-kT Mk 4 MIRV
Propulsion: Solid-fuel rocket
Range: 4350 nm
CEP: 1500 ft

Trident I is Poseidon's successor, designed to fit existing tubes and to achieve 4000nm range without losing the accuracy of the predecessor. Its postboost vehicle (MIRV bus) incorporates a stellar sensor for positional corrections, thus achieving greater accuracy. This missile became operational in 1978. It is currently operational on board the first eight *Ohio*-class SSBNs, all earlier units having been retired or converted to other roles.

Trident C-4 (right) compared to Trident D-5 (left). Note the aerospikes. (Lockheed)

Compared to Poseidon, Trident I was conceived as a longer-range missile with about the same throw weight. Trident I achieves greater range partly by increasing its effective length, extending an aerospike at launch. The spike is credited with reducing frontal drag by 50%, adding 300 nm to the missile's range. The aerospike also made it possible to use a very blunt nose that could accommodate a third rocket stage together with the warheads. C-4 also benefits from advances in propellant chemistry, making fuller use of its fuel. Instead of blowing open ports (and thus neutralizing thrust) at a precalculated point in second-stage flight, it burns all its fuel and then calculates the appropriate third-stage trajectory. The new high-energy fuel is credited with about 40% of the range improvement, another 35% being credited to the use of improved chamber material (Kevlar), which allows increased propellant loading and higher operating pressures.

The missile is credited with a CEP of 500 yd (eight Mk 4 RVs with W76 100-kT warheads), and in 1982 it was stated that improvements in guidance optics could reduce CEP to 250 yd.

The FCS is Mk 98 Mod 0.

The guidance system, Mk 5, can function in all-inertial or stellar-inertial modes. Two proposed versions of C-4 were dropped because D-5 development was accelerated: C-4U, with improved guidance, and Long C-4 TFS (44 ft long, i.e., as long as D-5, with a terminal fix system for improved CEP). There was also a proposed "flat deck" version in which the third-stage motor was eliminated in favor of more RVs, reportedly up to 10 Mk 12A.

C-4 development was approved on 14 September 1971. Lockheed received the C-4 contract in 1974, and the first missile was launched in January 1977. Missile procurement ended in FY84.

◆ Trident II (D-5)

Dimensions: 83 × 528 in
Weight: 130,000 lb
Warhead: 8 to 12 Mk 5 RV (300–475-kT warheads) or 14 150-kT MIRV or 7 300-kT MARV; initially D-5 will use the Mk 12A RV of the Minuteman and MX land-based missiles (475-kT)

Propulsion: Three-stage solid-fuel rocket; burn time about 65 sec for each of two lower stages, and 40 sec for the third stage
Range: 6000 nm
CEP: 400 ft

The FCS on the submarine (Mk 98 Mod 1; Mod 2 in British submarines) matches that of Trident I but adds a gravity sensor and a new navigation sonar. The new Mk 6 guidance system, developed from the Mk 5 of the C-4 missile, reportedly uses GPS inputs. As a consequence, accuracy is at least as good as that for a land-based missile (400 ft, compared to 1500 ft for Trident I). The missile itself uses a new epoxy case for all three stages and a new high-energy propellant similar to that of the land-based MX. The Mk 5 vehicle/W87 combination was selected in October 1982. All missile tests up to September 1987 used eight warheads; in September 1987 a D-5 was tested with ten smaller warheads. However, in December 1987 President Reagan and Soviet General Secretary Mikhail Gorbachev agreed that for arms-control purposes the missile would be credited with no more than eight warheads. Alternative loads: 11–13 Mk 4 RVs or 6–9 Mk 5 RVs.

This program was accelerated in 1982 by Secretary of the Navy John Lehman, the object being to introduce the missile as early as possible so as to avoid the cost of refitting submarines completed to carry the earlier C-4. The planned introduction date of 1989 (on board the *Tennessee*) was 3 yr earlier than originally projected. At the same time, the planned number of D-5 submarines was increased to about 20. Full-scale engineering development of the D-5 (UGM-133A) missile began in October 1983, in parallel with its new W87 warhead (300–475-kT yield), the latter to deal with superhardened silos and similar targets, invulnerable to existing warheads. However, with the closing of the Rocky Flats warhead plant, production is limited, and some Trident IIs will have as few as four warheads. Some may also be armed with the much lower-yield weapons used on earlier missiles.

Eighteen *Ohio*-class submarines (SSBN 726–743) were built. SSBN 734 was the first to carry Trident II missiles. In February 1991 it was announced that the first eight submarines would not be rearmed with Trident II missiles. The post–Cold War strategic assessment supported a force of 14 Trident submarines. In October 1993 it was therefore proposed to decommission the first four submarines early, using operating funds to convert the remaining C-4 units to D-5 missiles. It was proposed that some missiles be downloaded to stay within the SALT treaty limits. Conversion of earlier boats to D-5 missiles was authorized in FY95. Congress has directed the Navy not to decommission any of the *Ohio* class, and some may be converted to other purposes, such as cruise-missile carriers or minelayers. Missile procurement: FY87, 21; FY88, 66; FY89, 66; FY90, 63; FY91, 52; FY92, 28; FY93, 21; FY94, 24; FY95, 18; FY96, 6; plan: FY97/99, 7 each (plus 5 for the Royal Navy); FY00, 12; FY01, 12. Unit cost in FY91 was $28.8M. About 1993 the U.S. Navy reported that Trident II had been developed two years ahead of schedule and 12% below estimated cost.

The missile first flew successfully from a submarine in August 1989. The effect of several early failures was to delay initial deployment from late 1989 to March 1990.

Britain chose Trident D-5 for the next-generation *Vanguard*-class strategic submarines. They will carry British warheads; but the missile bodies will be maintained by a U.S. facility, the Royal Navy turning missiles in for maintenance and drawing refurbished ones (which the British will then arm with their own warheads). Critics of the British Trident program have derided this practice as "rent a missile." The Anglo-American agreement was signed on 14–15 July 1980; 80 missiles will be acquired (16 per submarine plus enough spares to fill another submarine). Some British Tridents will have single low-yield warheads for the sub-strategic role, in which they will replace RAF WE177 bombs, which are to be withdrawn from service in 2007. Reportedly their yield is 15–20 kT.

◆ Tomahawk

See the Strike Warfare section.

STRIKE/ SURFACE WARFARE

The central distinction in classifying weapons, whether they are attacking fixed or moving targets, is between point-attack and area-attack weapons, that is, between small numbers of expensive but highly precise weapons and larger numbers of simpler (but less precise) ones that can be scattered over a target.

Some targets really cannot be considered points. For example, surely it is impractical to fire a separate long-range weapon at each of numerous troops dug in around a target area; however, area attacks on the troops may kill many of them and may so demoralize the rest as to make them ineffective. At present the area-attack approach is represented by bomblet-dispensing munitions such as the U.S. Rockeye and, presumably, also by fuel-air explosives.

Among weapons that are not inherently for area attack, it is common to distinguish among "dumb," "smart," and "brilliant" weapons. A "dumb" weapon is entirely unguided after release; all the intelligence in the system is concentrated in the launch vehicle. Conventional bombs and artillery shells are cases in point. A "smart" weapon attacks a target designated at launch time, homing on some element of the target's signature picked out in advance or on a signature, such as a laser spot, imposed by the launch vehicle or by some cooperating platform.

A "brilliant" weapon chooses its own target within a preset target area. In this sense an antiship missile is usually "brilliant," but the term normally applies to weapons attacking ground targets, which often have indistinct signatures. Effectiveness thus often requires some form of pattern recognition. The current near-term favorite technique for submunitions is to use mm-wave radar, either active (for imaging) or passive (as a form of IR) to form an image susceptible to processing. BAT uses the actual sound of the vehicle as a signature. Such techniques become affordable (if at all) with the advent of highly integrated chips; a single chip, relatively easy to make, could encompass all or nearly all of a submunition's guidance package.

It is tempting to imagine that the central issue is accuracy, that a very expensive weapon with a 10ft CEP solves all problems. Viewers of Gulf War film footage saw bombs hit their assigned aim points with extraordinary precision (later it was estimated that laser-guided weapons made about 60% hits, a remarkable figure by previous standards). In tactical operations, such accuracy may indeed be sufficient to destroy such obvious targets as tanks. The rub is that not all targets are easy to see.

The strategic air campaign against Iraq, from which so much was expected, failed not because the weapons failed but because there was insufficient intelligence: the Iraqi nuclear industry, for example, could not be wiped out because the targeters just did not know where it was (worse, they thought they knew). Such problems are likely to be almost universal in the Third World, where strategic intelligence is likely to be quite poor. Even when war against the old Soviet Union was contemplated, it helped enormously that the weapons involved were nuclear, and thus could make up for a lack of detailed information (and this about a country that had been almost the sole focus of intelligence efforts for nearly half a century).

RECONNAISSANCE SYSTEMS

Aircraft-Carried Sensors

UNITED STATES

PSTS, the Precision SIGINT Targeting System, is a joint service/Defense Department agency (presumably NSA) FY97 project to demonstrate target identification and location precisely and timely enough for correlation with other data to support air strikes and to provide strike damage assessment. PSTS can be seen as an outgrowth of earlier TENCAP projects (see the Surveillance and Control section). The published description of the program associates it with work on new signal processing and data-fusion algorithms and on specific emitter "fingerprinting."

◆ ATARS

The filmless advanced tactical air reconnaissance system, canceled in May 1993, has been revived for the Marines' F/A-18; 12

This F/A-18 engineering development aircraft has had its nose reshaped to accommodate ATARS sensors. (McDonnell-Douglas)

This TARPS pod is being prepared for installation on board an F-14; note the pod underwing on the aircraft in the background. (U.S. Navy)

pods manufactured for the Air Force before cancellation were transferred to the Marines to produce five usable ones. Tests with these pods proved sufficiently promising for the Navy to revive the program as lead service, replacing the Air Force. McDonnell-Douglas received a risk-reduction contract for this system in June 1994. As of 1996, plans call for 31 ATARS to be installed in two-seat Marine F/A-18Ds (in which the back-seater is the system operator) plus perhaps 40 more for single-seat Navy F/A-18Cs, to replace the current TARPS. The Marine version is to enter service in 1998 (production is to be complete by 2001). The Air Force, which had abandoned the program due to its high cost, may also adopt ATARS.

Because it is electronically recorded, ATARS imagery can be sent back to a surface terminal in real time, or it can be retained on board the airplane on magnetic tape, either for later edited replay from the air or for removal after the airplane lands. The pilot can view imagery on a cockpit display. The associated data link is CHBDL. A 32-bit computer, the reconnaissance management set (RMS), directs specified imagery to the right ground terminals. The sensors are daylight low-altitude EO (LAEO) and medium-altitude EO (MAEO), and a day/night IR line scanner; they feed a pair of digital tape recorders. Capacity suffices for images of 12 preplanned point, strip, or area targets and 20 targets of opportunity manually selected by the aircrew. Overall recording time is over 3 hr. The LAEO looks directly down or at a preset forward (oblique) angle, over a 140-deg FOV (side to side) angled within a 180-deg field of regard. Altitude limits are 200 to 3000 ft. In vertical mode it covers 1 nm from 1000 ft altitude; in 30-deg forward oblique mode it covers 2 nm. MAEO is designed to obtain high-resolution images from a 3–5nm standoff at a height of 2000 to 25,000 ft. Its 22-deg FOV is held on the target as the airplane maneuvers. The IR linescanner operates at 8–12 microns and at a height of 200 to 10,000 ft, with alternative 140- and 70-deg FOVs. The 70-deg FOV can be swung left or right oblique or held vertical. F/A-18s with ATARS will have their APG-73 radars modified to provide SAR data.

The reconnaissance version of the F/A-18C/D is to carry these sensors in its modified nose, replacing the 20mm cannon. It will retain all other F/A-18 capabilities. An additional sensor, Loral Fairchild's EO LOROP modified with IR capability (F-979-H), is being modified to be tested on an F/A-18 centerline station.

A review prior to full-rate production is scheduled for October 1997, with the production decision to follow in December 1998.

◆ TARPS

Tactical Air Reconnaissance Pods can be carried by F-14 and F/A-18 fighters. Currently, two F-14As in each carrier air wing are fitted to accept these pods, and three aircrew are trained to use TARPS. This system proved extremely effective during the Gulf War, when it was the main photo-reconnaissance asset

available to Central Command for anything close to real-time battle damage assessment.

The pod carries two cameras (Fairchild KA-99 low-altitude panoramic, with 9in focal length; and CAI KS-87B frame camera, with 12in focal length) and an IR line scanner (Honeywell AAD-5A, with both wide and narrow fields of view). Total weight is 1700 lb.

TARPS was developed by the Naval Air Development Center and is produced by the Naval Avionics Center. The pods are currently being overhauled (to be completed FY96), with a new KS-153 standoff camera and ASQ-197 sensor controllers for increased reliability. All F-14Ds and some -14As and -14Bs are wired for TARPS pods.

The Marines have not followed the same development path. Instead, they are developing an internal reconnaissance pallet for two-seat F/A-18D fighters, about one-third of which will be wired to accept the pallet. Installation of the pallet requires removal of the internal 20mm cannon of the F/A-18, and the pallet can accept any two of the three TARPS cameras.

◆ UPD-4/9

UPD-9 is a podded Goodyear SAR carried by Marine Corps F/A-18s, similar to the Air Force UPD-8. UPD-9 adds a data link so that the radar image can be received on the ground before the airplane returns. Data-link range is about 200–250 nm; radar range is about 50 nm. The pod, which can be carried by the F/A-18D, weighs less than 1500 lb and is cooled by ram air. At least some of the pods are repackaged UPD-4s (carried internally in RF-4s). The pods are about the same size as the standard 330-gallon centerline fuel tank and weigh about 1500 lb each.

◆ UGS

In September 1994 the U.S. Naval Command, Control, and Ocean Surveillance Center issued an RFP for a system of unattended ground sensors (UGS) to be distributed by cruise missile, to detect, classify, and identify time-critical targets (TCTs) as part of ARPA's War Breaker program. Targets would include mobile missiles, C² systems, tank battalions, and so on. Several UGS contracts were already underway. Each sensor would be precison air-dropped (within 5 m) and limited to 50–100m range. Raw sensor data would be converted into parameters such as vehicle weight, number of axles, wheel base, weight distribution, and engine and transmission type. Data would be transmitted to a deployable local processor for a mission planning and control system, where it would be fused with other sensor data. The program recalls Vietnam War attempts to seed the Ho Chi Minh Trail with sensors, including modified sonobuoys. At the time the Vietnamese found the sensors relatively easy to deceive; presumably, the current hope is that more sensitive ones would do far better.

UAVs (formerly RPVs)

Deletions: Frigate Bird (no sales), Helstar (Israel, canceled), Hunter/SR-UAV (U.S. version canceled January 1996; none placed in naval service), JSCAMPS (BQM-145, canceled November 1993).

GERMANY

◆ Seamos

In December 1995 the German Office of Defence Technology (BWB) awarded DASA a first-phase flight demonstration contract for Seamos, a UAV based on the old U.S. DASH (QH-50D) drone, the German contribution to the NATO PG 35 maritime UAV program. It combines DASH rotors and dynamic controls with DASA (formerly Dornier) avionics (including a new flight-control system), mission electronics (including a new data link), and system integration; and with a new Allison 250 C20 engine. It has an 80km (44nm) radius of action and can operate either autonomously or under remote control. Trials are to begin at the end of 1997 at a land test site at Meppen. Joint sea trials with Germany, France, Italy, the United Kingdom, and the United States are to be held in 2000. Seamos was first announced in 1989.

ISRAEL

◆ Pioneer

The U.S. Navy bought IAI's UAV to satisfy a requirement, stated in mid-1984, for a mini-UAV, for both the Marines and for naval gunfire support (spotting).

Pioneer was tested on board an LHA in June 1986 and became operational on board the battleship *Iowa* in December 1986 (installed June–December), carrying out reconnaissance over Central America. Pioneer was rocket-launched by the battleship and recovered in a net. In 1988 the program was limited to nine eight-vehicle systems (currently one at the DoD UAV Training Center, Fort Huachuca, Ariz., four in naval service, three for the Marines, and one for the Army; all are to transfer to the Navy by

Pioneer. (AAI)

FY98). The follow-on system is the Joint Tactical UAV (see below). The current U.S. contractor is Pioneer UAV Inc. of Hunt Valley, Maryland.

Pioneer is powered by a 26-HP Sachs gasoline engine, and the U.S. Navy wants to replace this engine with one running on JP-5, the standard (and considerably safer) Navy-wide gas-turbine fuel. The sensor is a television camera. Dimensions: span 5.15 m × 4.26 m length overall × 1 m height (16 ft 10.75 in × 13 ft 11.75 in × 3 ft 3.25 in); maximum payload 45 kg (99 lb); maximum takeoff weight 195 kg (430 lb). Maximum level speed is 48–70 kt (dash speed 100 kt); ceiling is 4575 m (15,000 ft), radius 100 nm, and endurance 6–9 hr. Fuel capacity is 11.1 U.S. gallons.

UNITED STATES

During the Gulf War, Pioneer UAVs flew from the battleships *Missouri* and *Wisconsin*, for a total of 151 sorties (520 flight hr). They were also in Army and Marine service. These small UAVs greatly exceeded expectations: they managed more than 125 flight hr per month per unit, whereas 60 had been expected prewar.

◆ UAV Master Plan

UAVs come under the new Defense Aerial Reconnaissance Office (DARO). As of the summer of 1994, the DARO UAV plan called for (a) a tactical UAV for the Army and Marines (see below), and (b) endurance UAVs: medium-altitude endurance (MAE, formerly Tier II) and high-altitude endurance (HAE, formerly Tier II Plus). HAE is managed by ARPA. MAE is to operate at an altitude of 25,000 ft for more than 24 hr, with a radius of about 500 nm. HAE is to have a similar endurance at about 70,000 ft, with a range of 6000 km. Some accounts of these UAVs suggest that they will ultimately be capable of accompanying a fleet on a sortie lasting many days. The program currently envisages a conventional/high-performance UAV (Tier II Plus) complemented by a low-observable/moderate-performance UAV (Tier III Minus). In mid-1995 Teledyne Ryan was selected to develop the Tier II + UAV. Lockheed Martin and Boeing have developed a Dark Star for Tier III-Minus. There may also be a black program for a Tier III low-observable UAV, but reportedly it would be too expensive to combine carrying capacity and stealth in a single high-performance UAV. See below for details. See the 1991/92 edition for details of earlier HALE projects.

Tier II Plus and Tier III Minus use a combination of SAR radar and EO and IR cameras. Hughes's X-band SAR (HISSAR) uses a mechanically scanned 4 × 1.2ft antenna. Westinghouse's Tier III Minus Ku-band radar is adapted from that developed for the abortive A-12.

Tier II Plus EO and IR cameras share a common stabilized aperture. Desired resolution equates to 6600 × 6600 pixels; no sensor that powerful exists. The EO sensor is a Kodak commercial 1024 × 1024 CCD; the IR camera uses the Hughes 640 × 480-element 3–5-micron common module FLIR sensor. The camera therefore scans across its FOV, moving the sensor array every 1/30 sec. Although the aircraft moves during the 5–10-sec process, it is possible to assemble the result into the desired high-resolution image. There are two operating modes, search and spot. In search mode, a 10km strip (20–200 km to the side) is scanned at 300 kt with 3ft resolution (EO maximum range is about 50 km). In spot mode, a 2 × 24km patch (at up to 200 km) is viewed with 1 ft resolution (2 ft for IR).

Tier III Minus avoids step-stare by using a Recon Optical linear array 12,064 × 32 pixels, using time-delay integration to reduce noise. Aircraft motion is canceled out by an on-chip compensation device. Even so, Recon Optical is working on a 5046 × 5046 CCD which would not have to scan at all.

The earlier medium-range UAV, JSCAMPS (BQM-145), has been dropped.

◆ Joint Tactical UAV

This program originally embraced three separate UAVs, a land-based type (won by the IAI/TRW Hunter in 1993), a shipboard

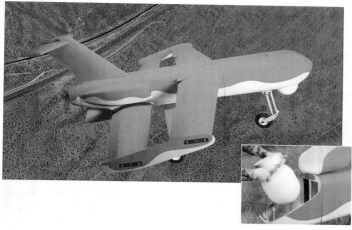

The Hellfox JTUAV air vehicle. (Alliant Techsystems)

variant (SR-UAV), and a maneuver variant (formerly CR-UAV) for Army brigades and battalions and Marine Corps regiments. Hunter was chosen for the Army and Navy, but it was canceled early in 1996. A JTUAV RFP was issued on 1 February 1996; industry responses were received 18 March. Target costs were $350,000 for the 33rd and $300,000 for the 100th aircraft, to include sensors. The planned range, originally 50 km, was increased to 200 km specifically to meet naval requirements, which include operation as a data-link relay ("poor man's satellite"). Thus, each unit of eight aircraft includes eight day/night sensor pods and four relay pods. Plans call for up to 61 systems (8 Navy, 11 Marine Corps, 38 Army; 4 for training). All twelve large-deck amphibious carriers are to be modified to use JTUAV. Alliant Techsystems won the competition in May 1996, receiving a $52.6M contract for six systems and eight attrition aircraft, to be delivered with full support by May 1998. The Hellfox tandem-wing air vehicle itself is built by Mission Technologies. It is to weigh about 350 lb, to carry a 50-lb payload, and to make 125 kt dash speed. Endurance is to be better than 4 hr (with a fuel reserve) and radius of operation greater than 200 km. Service ceiling is to be above 15,000 ft. Target location error is to be less than 100 m. JTUAV is to be able to take off and land within a 75 × 30 × 10m box. It is to be a roll-on/roll-off system for the amphibious carriers, and the system is to be transportable by a single C-130 or by two HMMWVs and a single trailer.

AIRBORNE SENSORS

Deletions: DRAA-2 (survives, if at all, only in two Pakistani Atlantic MPAs; the other two were fitted with Ocean Master and there is an option to fit this radar in the remaining pair), Vigil (not bought), Grifo (no naval version sold as of 1996), APQ-104 (French navy Crusaders are due to retire about 1996–97), APQ-173/183, APS-20. For details, see the 1991/92 edition.

AUSTRALIA

BAe Australia has developed a 3–5-micron FLIR based on the technology of AAMs. The company claims that this will be the first demonstration that such a FLIR can operate effectively at long range under humid conditions, as on the northern Australian coast. Flight trials began in 1993. The new FLIR is being bid for the Seahawk helicopter upgrade program.

CANADA

◆ APS-503

    Band: X (9.2–9.4 GHz)
    Beam: 4 × 5 deg
    Peak Power: 50 kW
    Gain: 30 dB
    Pulse Width: 0.5 microsec
    PRF: 400
    Scan Rate: 30 rpm
    Antenna Dimensions: 24 × 18 in
    Antenna Weight: Total weight 45 kg [100 lb]

APS-503 is the sea-search radar of Canadian Sea King (CH-124) helicopters and is manufactured by Eaton and by Litton of Canada. The antenna is stabilized in pitch and roll and can be tilted through 8 deg up or down. The display is a B-scope.

◆ APS-504/APS-140

    Band: X (8.9–9.4 GHz)
    Beam: 2.3 × 5 deg
    Peak Power: 100 kW
    Pulse Width: (a) 0.5 (b) 2.4 microsec
    PRF: 1600, 1200, 400, 200 pps (range scales 20, 50, 100, 250 nm)
    Scan Rate: 30 or 12 rpm (or 72 deg/sec sector scan)
    Antenna Dimensions: 112 × 33 cm (stabilized)
    Antenna Weight: Under 72 kg total

APS-504 is the maritime-surveillance radar developed from APS-503 by Eaton and by Litton of Canada. The (V)3 version incorporates a scan converter so that its video can be displayed on a standard 875-line high-resolution television, and so that it can be recorded by a standard television cassette recorder. It is stabilized in pitch and roll, and it can operate in variable-width sector-scan mode.

The basic version is (V)2; (V)3 has digital processing and a high-definition raster display. The (V)5 version is a pulse-compression radar with a TWT transmitter (8-kW peak power). Compression ratios are 210:1 and 500:1, for 200- and 30-nsec compressed pulse widths (there are also three noncompressed modes: short-range/navigation, weather, beacon). This radar is frequency-agile (in two patterns) over a 500-MHz band, 8.9 to 9.4 GHz (16 fixed frequencies). Typical detection ranges in Sea State 3: destroyer at 125 nm, patrol boat at 75 nm, snorkel or speed boat at 45 nm, periscope or outboard motor boat at 25 nm. A TWS version can acquire and display up to 20 contacts with range/bearing readouts. It is also possible to display ESM strobes on the radar screen. This version scans at 7.5 to 120 rpm (eight alternative speeds) and can scan a selected 30- to 120-deg sector. Range scales are 3 to 200 nm (seven ranges). The display uses 875-line video at a 30-Hz refresh rate. Typical maximum range is 370 km.

Note that the (V)2, (V)3, and so on are not formal AN designations. (V)3 is APS-141(V); (V)5 is APS-140(V).

Users: Angola (F27 MPA), Australia (GAF Searchmaster L), Brunei (CN-235: [V]5 version), China (Harbin Y-8), Egypt (navy Beech 1900), Iceland (coast guard Twin Otter), Indonesia (GAF Searchmaster L), Israel (Westwind Sea Scan, [V]2 version), Malaysia (CN-235), Netherlands (F27 MPA), Nigeria (Twin Otter and F27 MPA), Pakistan (F27 MPA: [V]3 version), Philippines (F27 MPA), Spain (F27 MPA), Taiwan (S-2T), Thailand (F27 MPA), and United States (Customs Service GAF Nomad, navy range safety Beech 1900).

◆ LN-66

See Shipboard Radars and Fire-Control Systems in the Antiaircraft Warfare section.

CHINA

Chinese bomb/nav radars equip two naval bombers: about 30 H-6 (unlicensed copies of the old Russian Tu-16 Badger, some of them modified to carry missiles as B-6Ds); and about 80 H-5s (unlicensed copies of the old Russian Il-28 Beagle).

The Russian Il-28 had a small PSBN-M-8 bomb/nav radar (NATO "Mushroom" series) forward of its bomb bay. The corresponding radar in a Tu-16 was probably similar. Chinese H-5 and H-6 bombers seem to resemble their Russian prototypes, so it is probably fair to conclude that their radars are directly descended from Russian prototypes (B-6D differs; it can be distinguished by its considerably larger radome). According to a recent Chinese account, in 1969 Type 241 was developed as a substitute for the old Russian radars. The successor Type 242 (1970) developed into Type 244 with better performance, reliability/maintainability, and a low-level autorelease function. The successor Type 245 (1985) is probably the B-6D radar; it introduced TWS capability.

FRANCE

◆ Agave

The multimode X-band (8.9–9.4 GHz) pulse-compression monopulse radar of the Super Étendard strike fighter is used to target Exocet antiship missiles, among other weapons. Pulse width is 40 microsec (compressed). Scan limits are 140 × 60 deg, and the radar can detect an airplane at 18–28 km or a patrol boat at 40–55 km. In the search mode, the radar scans over 140 deg horizontally. The position of the 6-deg horizontal bar is selectable through 60 deg up or down. Typically, vertical cover is limited to a single bar to reject low-altitude clutter; at higher elevation angles, two bars (12 deg) are used because the single narrow bar may miss a fast target. In the autotrack (monopulse) mode, the radar can transmit data either to a missile or to a HUD. Range gates can be set at 5–85 nm.

All controls (antenna elevation, bearing and range markers, lock-on for autotrack) are on a single hand grip. The antenna is an inverted Cassegrain. Total weight is 65 kg.

Agave entered service in 1978.

Users: Argentina (14 in Super Étendards), France (71 bought for Super Étendards, replaced by Anemone in updated aircraft; may later be installed in 40–50 AlphaJet M3 Marine trainers), India (eight Jaguar IM of No. 6 Squadron, equipped with Sea Eagle missiles; total 10 radars), Iraq (75 radars ordered for Mirage F1EQ-5 and F1EQ-6 with Exocet; some probably delivered to Pakistan and Peru after Iraq stopped paying for these radars), Pakistan (Mirage 5PA3 with Exocet missiles; 12 bought), Peru (reportedly in some Mirage 5P4s). Note that the Indian Jaguars have a locally developed central tactical system, DARIN (display attack and ranging inertial navigation), using a Sea Harrier–type HUD and a GEC-Ferranti COMED 2054 combined map and electronic display, as on F/A-18A/Bs. In these aircraft a raster-scan CRT replaces the usual PPI. In all, 170 Agave radars were made.

◆ AGRION 15/IGUANE/VARAN

Band: X (9.1 GHz)
Peak Power: 108 kW
Pulse Width: 0.25 or 1.5 microsec
PRF: 1200, 600, 300 pps
Scan Rate: 12, 24 rpm
Weight: 110 kg (total)

Data above apply to VARAN (TMV 118B).

These frequency-agile systems use pulse compression partly to reduce peak power, thus making them less detectable. In 1982 Thomson-CSF claimed that pulse compression made for an effective pulse width only a tenth that of magnetron radars, with 35 times the equivalent peak power, and that VARAN was 6–8 times lighter, 3–9 times more difficult to detect, and 6 times more discrete than any other pulse-compression radar on the market.

These radars use two pulse lengths, long (tenths of a microsec) for long-range detection of large targets and short (thousandths of a microsec) for small targets in a rough sea. The short pulse limits the size of the resolution cell, so that a target stands out against the surrounding sea clutter.

The basic unit is IGUANE. Work began in 1975, and IGUANE first flew in May 1981. For target classification by SAR the antenna is locked with its beam pointing sideways; a special unit (Anaconda) forms the image. The antennas used in the Alize and Atlantique are identical to those previously used for DRAA-2. Total weight is 75 kg in an Alize and about 130 kg in an Atlantique.

AGRION 15, which is used to target AS 15TT missiles, adds a monopulse tracking unit and a matched boresight-stabilized 1.3m cheese antenna. AGRION 15 has two scan speeds and a TWS mode. AGRION 15 includes a modem by which means it

An Atlantique Nouvelle Génération (Atlantique Mk 2) displays its IGUANE radar and its ESM systems in the wingtips. Any radar pushed out into the airstream creates drag, but that offset from the main airframe is the only way a single reflector can cover anything approaching 360 deg. Offset was the solution in aircraft such as Alize, the P-2, and the S-2. The alternative is to use two reflectors (as in the P-3) or to accept 180-deg scanning (as in the S-3, which has a nose radar). The bulge under the transparent nose contains a gyrostabilized high-reflection thermal imaging camera, Tango, with a switchable 6.45 × 4.30/2.15 × 1.43-deg FOV (the turret can turn 110 deg to either side of the airplane), and its elevation limits are +15/−45 deg. The output is a 625-line television signal, 50.5 frames/sec. (U.S. Naval Institute)

The Tango IR turret of the Atlantique-2 maritime-patrol aircraft, at the Paris Air Show, 1989. (Author)

can transmit nine target coordinates plus a reference point to a surface ship, updating at each antenna scan. Alternatively, the modem can be used to transmit target track data to each of two surface ships armed with long-range missiles (TWS on two tracks). Total radar weight is 188 kg.

VARAN is an IGUANE with a smaller antenna, for medium maritime-patrol aircraft to use for sea search and OTH-T.

Thomson-CSF, the manufacturer, credits all three radars with the ability to detect a lifeboat or a snorkel at 30 nm, a fast patrol boat at 60 nm, and a freighter at 120 nm.

The names of all three radars are acronyms: IGUANE is Instrument de Guet pour Avion Navale Embarqué; AGRION is Appareil de Guet de Recherche et d'Identification d'Objectif Navale; VARAN is Veille Aéroportée Anti-Navire.

Users: AGRION 15: Bahrein (on two Dauphin helicopters on FPB 62s), Iraq (6 Dauphin helicopters; may not have been delivered), Saudi Arabia (20 Dauphin helicopters), UAE (7 on Dauphin 2 helicopters). At least 85 in service or on order. This radar is probably produced under license in China for Zhi-9 helicopters.

IGUANE: France (27 modernized Alize, 26 on Atlantique Mk 2, 16 not in use), Italy (18 modernized Atlantic). Total 87 in service or on order. The Alize updates (1980–86) included a new Omega navigational system, ESM in the noses of the wing panniers, and new communications, to keep the airplanes in service through the 1990s. All surviving aircraft were further updated at Cuers in 1990 with a data link, improved decoys, and other modifications to keep them in service through the early years of the next century. They were also considered for use as AEW platforms, but were rejected in 1991 in favor of the E-2C.

VARAN: Brazil (12 on upgraded S-2E[T]), Chile (8 for Gardien 20 and Puma, to control Exocet), China (Zhi-9/Dauphin helicopters), France (5 Gardien surveillance aircraft, being replaced by Ocean Master). 25 in service or on order.

◆ Anemone

Anemone is ESD's replacement for Agave, for modernized French navy Super Étendards. It is a frequency-agile X-band radar using a wide-band monopulse flat slotted array antenna. Search and tracking processing are digital. The radar is described as having a special formation flight capability (presumably frequency diversity and perhaps adjustable sector scan). Anemone is primarily an air-to-surface radar but also has useful air-to-air performance. The cockpit display is normally a sector of a PPI, but it becomes a B-scan in expanded search mode. Range scales: 0–5, 0–15, 0–30, 0–60, 0–90, 80–200 nm. Air-to-surface (sea) functions: linear scan search within a 60- or 120-deg sector centered on the aircraft flight path; TWS mode within +/–60-deg cone, range bracket 3.5 to 200 nm; continuous tracking (CT) mode either on a target designated during search, or while in TWS mode (+/–60 deg, range 0.2 to 90 nm). Air-to-ground: Ground mapping (+/–30 or 60-deg azimuth, range scale 5, 15, 30, 60, or 90 nm) and ranging (limited to targets more than 5 deg below the horizon, maximum range 15 nm). The aircraft weapon system points the antenna in the ranging mode. Air-to-air: Modes are linear scan search with semiautomatic acquisition and continuous tracking (CT). Linear scan: Two bars, each +/–30 or 60 deg in azimuth. CT: Acquisition can be semiautomatic upon target designation in the search volume, or automatic in the HUD field of view, or automatic along a direction chosen by the aircraft system. Tracking is within a +/–60-deg cone, to a maximum range of 150 nm. Target radial velocity limits: –300 m/sec to +1500 m/sec. Weight 60 kg without radome.

Users: France (56 bought to update 50 Super Étendards). No exports. Unit cost is about $800,000.

◆ Cyrano

Thomson-CSF's Cyrano X-band 200 kW monopulse radar is standard in the Mirage series. Cyrano I was the radar of the original Mirage IIIC interceptor. Cyrano II was developed for the multifunction Mirage IIIE, which first flew in 1961. Cyrano IV, designed for the Mirage F1, has sufficient computer capacity to determine interception vectors and missile firing zones. It has a home-on-jam mode. For ground attack, it offers air-to-ground

Anemone as displayed at the 1995 Paris Air Show. The flat-plate antenna is a dummy, to conceal the pattern of slots that actually generates the radar beam. (Author)

ranging, ground mapping, terrain avoidance, and contour mapping modes. Cyrano IVM adds antiship capability (using Exocet missiles) in the form of TWS in a sea-search mode. This version also uses integrated circuit technology, for better maintainability and reliability. Cyrano IVM3 incorporates a digital fire-control computer.

Venezuela bought Cyrano IVM3 (sale announced April 1988) to upgrade Mirage 50 fighters so that they could deliver Exocet missiles. Cyrano IV is also installed in French and Spanish Mirage F1s, but in these cases it is not used for Exocet delivery.

◆ Ocean Master

Ocean Master uses RBE-2/RDY technology, including their programmable signal processors (for variable waveforms). It is now a joint venture between Thomson-CSF and Telefunken (part of DASA). The two-axis stabilized antenna can be 660 × 350 or 940 × 350 or 1800 × 300 mm (gain 30.5 to 33 dB, weight 15 or 27 kg). Tilt is selectable between +4/–29 deg, and scan rate is 6 to 30 rpm (automatically selected by mode; sector scan can be within 60 to 210 deg). The coherent X-band TWT pulse-compression transmitter has an average power of 0.1 or 0.4 kW (for Ocean Master 100 or 400). Peak power (for Ocean Master 100) is 6 kW. PRF is 300 Hz to 125 kHz. Pulses are described as having

The Thomson-CSF/DASA Ocean Master radar is shown with its two alternative antennas. (Thomson-CSF)

a high time-bandwidth product, that is, they can be relatively short but cover a wide bandwidth. The receiver can maintain automatic TWS on 32 targets. It reduces sea clutter by pulse-pulse and scan-scan integration, for example, to detect periscopes in sea clutter. Ocean Master can operate in ISAR mode, or it can produce a range profile of the target, using very short pulses (for 3m resolution). The 14in display has range scales from 7.5 to 240 nm, with a 5nm magnifier mode. In an optional version, video can switch between a FLIR and the radar. The scan-to-scan and pulse-to-pulse integration and digital-processing features have been tested on board an Atlantique 2 aircraft.

A "spotlight" SAR capability is under development.

Users: France (five for Gardien 50, replacing VARAN), Indonesia (three on Boeing 737-200, eight on Bo-105, eight for NC-212), Japan (selected 1996 for Shin-Meiwa US-1 for SAR), Pakistan (two on Atlantic MPAs [with options for two more], one on F27 MPA).

◆ **ORB-31 (Heracles I)**

    Band: X (9335–9415 MHz)
    Beam: (a) 4 × 7.5 (b) 3.2 × 6 (c) 4.8 × 7.5 deg
    Peak Power: 12 or 30 kW
    Gain: (a) 29.2 dB (b) 30.5 dB (c) 28 dB
    Pulse Width: (a) 0.2 (b) 0.5 (c) 4 microsec
    PRF: (a) 1600 (b) 800 (c) 400 pps
    Antenna Dimensions: (a) 608 × 308 mm (b) 728 × 368 mm (c) 460 × 308 mm
    Antenna Weight: (a) 1.1 (b) 1.3 (c) 0.8 kg (ORB 31D combines reflector [c] with 30-kW transmitters; ORB 31W combines reflector [a] with 30-kW transmitters)

The Omera-Segid helicopter sea-search radar was developed from a German Ekco weather radar, which was developed into ORB-3 and then into the ORB-31S2 of Alouette III helicopters and the ORB-31W of French navy Lynx helicopters; -31AS was for general ASW (for Alouette III helicopters), and -31D for Exocet targeting by Super Frelons. These radars all scan through 180 deg in bearing.

The ORB-31D and -31W versions use two transceivers, one for long range and another for short range and high resolution (and for clutter rejection). Range on a ship (1000 m²) is 80 km (ORB-31D) or 50 nm (ORB-31W), and total weight is 75 kg (ORB-31D) or 61 kg (ORB-31W).

Users: Argentina (5 navy Alouette III), Belgium (3 navy Alouette IIIB), China (16 Super Frelons with ORB-31D targeting radar; some may have ORB-32 instead; this helicopter is built under license as Zhi-8), France (Lynx helicopters; also Alouette III, being replaced), Iraq (16 Super Frelons with ORB-31D radar, carrying Exocets; at least one destroyed during Gulf War), Libya (12 navy Alouette IIIB), Mexico (3 navy Alouette III), Pakistan (2 Alouette III have radars for shipboard ASW use), Peru (2 Alouette III). Some of the Alouettes listed may not be equipped with ORB-31 radars.

◆ **ORB 32 (Heracles II)**

    Band: X (8500–9600 MHz or 9100–9500 MHz)
    Beam: 2.6–4.8 × 6.2–7.5 deg
    Peak Power: 80 kW
    Gain: 28.5–32 dB
    Pulse Width: 0.25 or 2.0 microsec
    PRF: 1200, 600, or 300 pps
    Antenna Dimensions: 46–85 × 30 or 36 cm
    Antenna Weight: Total weight 129 kg

The modular Omera radar for small maritime-patrol aircraft, developed from ORB 31, was announced in 1979. All versions use transmitters with the same peak power, PRFs, and pulse widths, but they can be fixed-frequency, tunable, coded jump, or frequency-agile. There are seven antennas, which can have front or rear illumination and can be one- or two-axis stabilized and can scan at 20 or 40 rpm (full or sector [60, 120, 180, or 240 deg] scanning). Range is 90 km on a 500m² target.

Users: Algeria (3 on Beech 200T), Brazil (6 AS 332F, with 9 more planned; the navy also operates 10 AS 332M transports), China (12 Super Frelons, others on Zhi-8s), France (97 on Nord 262 Fregate, Super Frelon, Dauphin/Panther, C-160 Transall), In-

donesia (26 on Cougar/Super Puma helicopters), Kuwait (16 bought for Cougar/Super Puma helicopters, 14 of which were destroyed), Portugal (10 on Pumas), Saudi Arabia (6 on SA 365/ SA 565SC Dauphins, probably others on AS 532 Cougars armed with Exocets; possibly also on 17 KV-107s), Sweden (19 on KV-107s, 10 on Cougar/Super Pumas; the Swedish designation is 9HCI 100 Hera), and UAE (2 on Cougar/Super Pumas). ORB-32ASD was developed (in cooperation with BEAB) specifically for the Royal Swedish Navy in the 1970s for ASW, to be carried by modernized KV-107 helicopters. It entered service in 1986. This radar is used both for periscope/snorkel detection and to target shipboard or land-based RBS-15 missiles. It can detect a snorkel at 25 m or a frigate at 100 nm in Sea State 5. A transponder allows two helicopters to coordinate their attacks. The 9HCI 200 version includes ASW fire control.

◆ **RBE-2**

The Thomson-CSF pulse-Doppler multimode radar of the new Rafale fighter uses an electronically scanned RBG antenna (which was first flight-tested in 1987). Due to the French budgetary crisis, this radar is unlikely to enter service before about 2002. It is also encountering developmental problems. Because the naval Rafale will enter service first, and because the navy's primary concern is fleet air defense, at least the first 16 radars produced will be limited to air-to-air operation, the ground-following and ground-to-air modes (planned for the second block of eight aircraft) having been deferred. As a consequence, the modernized Super Étendards will survive as naval strike aircraft. It was reported in June 1995 that work on air-to-ground capability was being deferred by 12–15 months. The desired combined capability would have provided the aircraft with time-shared modes, so that the radar could operate nearly simultaneously in air-to-air surveillance and terrain-following modes (for example, for low-level penetration). This capability will now be delayed until the first deliveries for the French air force, which may not occur until about 2005, due to recent budget cuts. Even work on individual air-to-ground modes such as targeting and terrain-following has been slower than expected. Terrain-following is apparently a particular problem.

The transmitter is a dual-peak power TWT and the signal processor operates at 1 MFLOPS. In the air-to-air role, the system automatically assesses threats, choosing the eight with highest priority and displaying their ranges and closing speeds. In the air-to-air TWS mode it is specifically intended to control IR-guided or active radar MICA missiles. In the alternative single target track mode, the radar controls semiactive missiles. Rafale is designed to incorporate a complementary optronic system, with a range beyond 30 nm (radar range is over 50 nm).

The RBG antenna uses a pair of tandem lenses (consisting of phase shifters) polarized at right angles, with a 90-deg polarizer between them, one steering the beam in azimuth and the other in elevation. Both are illuminated from behind by a flat-plate array.

The prototype RBE-2 was delivered in November 1992.

◆ **RDY/RDC**

RDY is a multimode X-band radar to replace the pure air-to-air radars (RDI, RDM) of Mirage 2000 fighters. RDY is designed to control both Exocet and Kormoran 2 missiles, the latter capability suggesting an attempt to sell it to Germany and Italy for Tornado upgrades. As in RBE-2, the key to multiple operation is a programmable signal processor. Waveforms include multiple-range gate high PRF, medium PRF, and low PRF with two alternative peak powers (one of them 120 kW), corresponding to different PRFs. The 655mm flat-plate antenna scans a 3.5-deg beam over a 60-deg cone. Maximum air-to-air range is 60 nm (20 nm in look-down mode). RDY can track eight targets while engaging four simultaneously with fire-and-forget missiles. Air-to-air modes are HUD search (in a conical volume), vertical search, and boresight aiming (for gunnery). Air-to-ground modes include real beam for low-level penetration, SAR, Doppler-sharpened beam, static target, and MTI. A special sea-strike mode (TWS or

RDY radar; the small dipoles are for IFF. (Thomson-CSF)

single-target tracking) uses a waveform adjusted to sea state, to minimize clutter. The entire system weighs 240 kg.

RDC, which has not yet sold, is a scaled-down RDY for Mirage F1s with single-purpose radars.

Users: France (37 for air force Mirage 2000Cs), Qatar (12 for Mirage 2005s assigned to antiship strike operations), Taiwan (60 for Mirage 2000s, presumably including antiship capability). As of the spring of 1996, Pakistan was negotiating for 50 Mirage 2000s equipped with RDY radars.

◆ Chlio

In March 1993 the French navy selected this Thomson-TRT FLIR, already in service on army helicopters, for the Alize.

ISRAEL

◆ EL/M-2022

This is a new Elta maritime surveillance radar for airplanes, helicopters, and UAVs derived from the EL/M-2035 fighter radar. Both use the same programmable signal processor. The antenna is a flat slotted plate. Features include Doppler beam sharpening, maritime (target) MTI (i.e., MTI for slow surface targets), and TWS for up to 100 targets. (V)1 is a lightweight, remote, digitally controlled radar (50 targets, small ships detected at 70 nm in Sea State 3, total weight 85 kg, 1.8 kW power); (V)3 is a long-range version capable of detecting periscopes, with a 100-target track memory. Claimed performance of A(V)3: in Sea State 3, 1-sq-m target detected at 30 nm, small ship at 80 nm. Modes: long-range surveillance, navigation and weather, AMTI, wide-area Doppler beam sharpening surveillance, and beacon interrogation. The system has expand and freeze functions, with sector and full-scan coverage. Total weight excluding the operator console is 100 kg.

Users: Australia (P-3C upgrade). In August 1995 Elisra won a $40M contract to upgrade Argentine S-2Es (radar and ESM), presumably using this radar. The program still depends upon whether Elisra can find a suitable funding package. EL/M-2022 has also been selected by South Africa for a projected upgrade of the C-47 maritime reconnaissance aircraft and the A(V)3 version was the baseline radar for the British RMPA program. The (V)3 version may be intended to displace APS-504 aboard Westwind maritime patrol aircraft. This was also the radar on the prototype An-72P coastal surveillance aircraft (with an EO FLIR and an Elisra ESM system), although it is not clear whether aircraft ordered by Russia will have the same radar.

◆ EL/M-2032/2035

Elta's X-band pulse-Doppler strike fighter radars have both air-to-air and air-to-surface capability. The series comprises three radars: EL/M-2031, -2032, and -2035, the main difference being progressively larger antennas. Air-to-air modes: look up/down, TWS, single target track, slewable ACM, HUD, boresight, and vertical scan. Air to surface: ranging, MTI, terrain avoidance, sea

search, SAR and real-beam mapping, Doppler beam sharpening, freeze. EL/M-2032 is credited with a look-up range of 35–55 nm (65–100 km) and a look-down range of 30–45 nm (55–85 km). Weight is 78–100 kg. Antenna size is 30–75 cm, depending on the airplane. Range can be measured between 150 and 15,000 m with an accuracy of 30 m or 0.5%. Targets are tracked by two-axis monopulse. The transmitter is a coherent TWT and the signal processor is programmable. TWS capacity is eight tracks, and Elta claims that the system has 40% spare computing power and 20% spare slots for functions such as NCTR.

EL/M-2035 was developed for the abortive Lavi fighter. Maximum range is 25 nm (46 km), and total weight is 138 kg. This radar reportedly has only air-to-air modes: look up/down, TWS, automatic lock-on, boresight.

Users:
EL/M-2032: Chile (16 on modernized F-5Es), India (22 ordered for Sea Harrier upgrade), Romania (120 ordered for MiG-21s). This is the radar of the Kfir 2000, offered to the Philippines.
EL/M-2035: China (J8-II "Finback" long-range interceptors), South Africa (Cheetah E upgrade). Reports of the size of the J8-II force vary. Recently China has announced a new version of this fighter, J8-IIM, employing the Russian Zhuk radar. According to one report, Zhuks are being provided by the Russians; the Chinese were license-producing EL/M-2035s.

ITALY

◆ APS-705/707/APQ-706

Band: X (dual frequency)
Beam: 2 × 7 deg (AB 212); 1.5 × 10 deg (SH-3D)
Peak Power: 25 kW (option: 75 kW)
Pulse Width: (a) 0.05 (b) 0.15 (c) 0.5 (d) 1.5 microsec
PRF: (a) 1600 (b) 1300 (c) 1300 (d) 650 pps
Scan Rate: 20 and 40 rpm
Antenna Dimensions: 1.2m aperture (AB 212) or 1.6m aperture (SH-3D)
Antenna Weight: Total system weight 87 kg

The SMA TWS radar (surface search, periscope detection, and tracking) employs two 25-kW transceivers (one antenna) for frequency diversity. The antenna is stabilized in LOS and can be tilted 20 deg up or down. There are both search and navigation modes (the latter including weather detection). Radar signals are digitally processed, and the resulting radar data are also handled digitally. Modes include TWS. The color raster-scan radar display can also show ESM, sonar, and data-link information.

APS-707 is a single-transmitter version of APS-705, produced in both low- (20 kW) and high- (90 kW) powered versions, the latter for fixed-wing aircraft. It is frequency-agile and has other

APS-707 antenna, designed to operate at a peak power of 90 kW. (SMA)

APS-707 installed on board an Argentine Electra airline converted for use in maritime patrol. The U.S.-built Orion (P-3) shares much the same airframe. (SMA)

APS-705 occupies the dorsal radome of this Italian Navy AB 212 helicopter. (S. Zaloga)

ECCM features. Like APS-705, it is a digital radar (automatic TWS is optional). Search modes: Search 1, for long-range; Search 2, for long range in clutter; Search 3, for small-target (such as periscope) detection at short/medium range in high sea clutter. A 1553B bus interface is optional, as is a color display and integration with LLLTV or a FLIR.

APQ-706 is a double-antenna radar (back to back) used to guide the Marte antiship missile. It uses two channels, one of fixed frequency and one with frequency agility, the latter to detect small high-speed targets. The fixed-frequency channel is used for navigation and periscope detection. The transmitter is the 75-kW frequency-agile unit available as an option in APS-705. The antenna is LOS stabilized.

Users: APS-705: Greece (14 AB 212ASW, of which 3 are used for ECM), Iran (20 AB 212ASW ordered 1974, probably no longer operational), Italy (all but first 12 of total 64 AB 212; at least 6 of total 36 SH-3), Spain (probably in all SH-3s and in AB 212s other than those used for jamming), Turkey (first 6 AB 212ASW, with CMA-708B/ASW computers and AQS-13 dipping sonars). A 1983 Iraqi order for 10 AB 212ASWs was canceled by the Gulf War. APS-705 probably equips export Italian-built SH-3Ds: 4 for Argentina, 9 for Brazil.

APS-707: Argentina (high-powered version in L-188 maritime patrol aircraft). By about 1992 the low-powered form of this radar was already on board AB 212s, probably in Peru (to support Otomat OTH-T). Some of the APS-705s listed above may be 707s.

APQ-706: Italy (at least 9 Sea Kings with Marte missiles), Venezuela (6 AB 212AS with Sea Killer missiles, on frigates). Peru is credited with Sea Killer missiles, which are presumably on board the 5 Sea King helicopters.

SMA also makes APS-717, a search/rescue and weather radar which can be used on maritime patrol aircraft. (V)1, with a flat circular-plate antenna in a thimble nose dome, is used on board HH-3F helicopters and G-222 aircraft. Modes are search and navigation, and digital processing is software-controlled. (V)2, for AB 412 helicopters, uses an antenna similar to that of APS-705/707. Maritime users: Finland (2 for coast guard) and Italy (24 for coast guard).

◆ APS-784

The SMA/FIAR X-band pulse-compression TWS radar for Italian EH-101 helicopters uses a TWT transmitter. An IFF antenna is mounted on the same pedestal as the main antenna. The radar incorporates a digital signal processor and a digital data processor (which seems to imply ADT operation).

The AEW version of the new EH-101 helicopter (four are being bought) uses APS-784E, a more powerful version with a larger antenna and new consoles.

SMA has offered a scaled-down version for the NATO NH.90 helicopter.

◆ Galiflir

Galiflir is either manually aimed, slaved to a radar (as in an AB 212), or caged (fixed relative to the aircraft axis) for navigation. In the helicopter, the screen shows the radar map with the IR image in a window. Galiflir can detect a destroyer at 39 nm and identify it at 15 nm. The 8–12-micron detector is an eight-element CMT SPRITE cooled by a split Stirling engine. FOV is 40×26.7 deg (nominal resolution 1.5 mrad) and the display operates to CCIR 625/50 standard, with 512 IR lines at a 25-Hz refresh rate. FoR is $-90/+45$ deg (turning 120 deg either way in azimuth), with an alignment accuracy of better than 10 deg and a slewing rate of 120 deg/sec. The FLIR platform weighs 18 kg and the electronic unit another 12 (controls weigh 2 kg more). Officine Galileo's new PACIS (Pilot and Close-In Surveillance) uses the same IR camera but with a less powerful telescope (magnifications $1 \times$ and $4 \times$, FOVs 40×26.7 and 10×6.6 deg) in a nonstabilized mounting (elevation limits $+45/-70$ deg).

Users: Italy (Atlantic MPA, AB 212), Portugal (CASA-212).

RUSSIA

See also Strike Complexes, described under Airborne Strike Fire-Control Systems, below.

◆ Big Bulge

This S-band surface-search radar is carried on Bear-D (Tu-95RTs) aircraft and (with a smaller antenna) on Hormone-A (Ka-25RTs) helicopters. There was also a version for the Badger (Tu-16RTs version). Reported PRFs for the Hormone version are 414–418 and 621–628 pps. The radar incorporates UHF video up- and downlinks. In the case of the Bear, Big Bulge is used mainly to obtain a picture of the OTH target for ships carrying long-range missiles (SS-N-3, -12, and in some cases -19). This radar video is downlinked to the firing ships. Big Bulge is reportedly descended from the U.S. S-band APS-20, widely used after World War II for both AEW and surface search.

Big Bulge radar under a Bear-D bomber, 1989. (U.S. Navy)

The radar/data-link system is called Uspekh, and this term (Uspekh-1A) may also identify the Big Bulge radar itself. Reportedly the Ka-25 version is Uspekh-2.

◆ Down Beat/Short Horn

The Blinder and Backfire missile-guidance radar appeared in 1959. Down Beat is associated with the AS-4 missile, and it is frequency-agile with variable PRF. Reported maximum range is 175 nm.

Down Beat nose radar on board a Badger. (U.S. Naval Institute)

Short Horn is an earlier Ka(J)-band (14–15 GHz) bombing radar on board Bear-Ds (chin radar, for sea search), Badger-Gs (AS-6 missiles), and Hormone-A helicopters. It is probably a smaller-antenna version of Down Beat. Short Horn is frequency-agile and has both circular and sector scan. Reported characteristics: pulse width (a) 1–1.8 (b) 0.5–1.4 (c) 0.4–1.3 (d) 0.01–0.9 microsec; PRF (a) 313–16 (b) 496–504 (c) 624–26 (d) 1249–53 pps.

Down Beat is probably PN-A. Short Horn is R-1 Rubin-1A (Rubin means "ruby"). The designation RPB-4 Initsiyativa has also been associated with this radar.

◆ Korshun

This big J-band belly radar equips Bear-F Mods 2/3. Presumably it is related to Berkut (Wet Eye), and is intended both for periscope detection and for sonobuoy interrogation. Korshun is also the name of the associated ASW weapons system (the Tupolev bureau called Bear-F Tu-142MK [K for Korshun]; the service designation is Tu-142M). This radar is also used by India (the Indian Bear-Fs were designated Tu-142MK-E). Bear-F Mod 4 is Tu-142MZ (Z for Zarecheye, the new ASW weapons system it carries). Both versions have similar radomes.

◆ Mushroom (RPB-2)

Formerly the standard Soviet bomb/nav radar, for example, on early Badgers and Bears (and on Tu-4s before them). A Chinese version made in the mid-1980s equips Chinese-made Badgers and Il-28 Beagles.

◆ Orion/Shtyk

The Su-24M attack radar is part of a PNS-24M Tigr-NS nav/attack system which employs a TsVM-10-058K Orbita central computer and a Relyef terrain-avoidance radar (which feeds an automatic flight-control system). The earlier PNS-24 is less sophisticated. Orion air-to-air range is 150 km (81 nm). The reconnaissance version (Su-24MR Fencer E) has a Shtyk (Bayonet) side-looking SAR radar with an MTI mode and a high-resolution (5 m) mapping mode. Its two flush-nose side antennas cover a swath 4–28 km from the aircraft, on either side, recording the radar image on film. Other sensors are film and TV cameras and an IR linescanner (Zima) which covers a strip whose width is 3.4 times the aircraft height above ground. There is also a laser line-scan pod. The reconnaissance system is BKR-1. Su-24 was not originally developed for naval service, but as of 1990, 99 were serving with naval aviation units (65 probably still remained five years later). It is not clear to what extent the Su-24 transfer was merely a way of avoiding treaty limits on the number of aircraft in ground force units, since transfers also included numerous MiG-23, Su-17, and Su-25 fighter-bombers. Remaining numbers, 1995: 50, 120, 50.

◆ Puff Ball (Yen)

The X-band navigation/attack radar on Badger-C, -D, -E, -F, and -J is used to target AS-6 missiles. PRFs are 410 and 620 pps. Maximum range is 175 nm.

◆ Slot Back (N019 Sapfir-29/Topaz/Rubin and N010 Zhuk)

Fazotron's Sapfir is the Doppler look-down/shoot-down radar of the MiG-29 and is related to the radar of the Su-27. It employs an inverse-Cassegrain antenna. The designator suggests that the radar was originally developed for MiG-29. Modes are look-up/look-down and TWS. There is no ground-mapping mode. Search range is 100 km (55 nm). Tracking range on a closing MiG-21-sized target is 70 km (38 nm); tracking range on an opening target is 35 km (19 nm). The radar can track 10 air targets, but lacks any air-to-ground mode. The associated attack system automatically selects the most important target for engagement. Search limits: 67 deg each side in azimuth, +60/−38 deg in elevation. N019E Rubin is the export version. N019M Topaz is a modified version with better ECCM and built-in test equipment; its export version is N019ME. It can track 10 targets and engage 2. This radar equips the MiG-29S. The MiG-29 system incorporating N019 is designated RPLK-29 (radiolokatsyonnyi pritselnyi kompleks, or radar attack system). It employs a Ts100.02-06 digital computer (the opto-electronic system, OEPNK-29, employs a Ts100.02-02 computer).

Zhuk (beetle: Sapfir-29M, N-010), announced at Paris in 1991, is a follow-on X-band multimode radar using a 68cm (26.8in) flat-plate antenna (gain 34.5 dB, possibly for a 70cm version), with peak power 5 kW (average 1 kW) and three receiver channels. Total weight is 240 kg. Like APG-65, Zhuk uses a digital signal processor to provide it with a variety of air-to-air and air-to-ground modes (including Doppler beam sharpening [ratio 120:1] and terrain avoidance). Detection ranges: air target (head-on/tail-on) 100/55 km (54/30 nm); ship target in Sea State 4–5 (cross-section 3000 sq m), 200 km. This radar tracks 12 targets while engaging 2 to 4 with active radar or IR weapons. The radar data processor is also used for airborne fire control. It equips the MiG-29M and probably the Su-27 and Su-34FN.

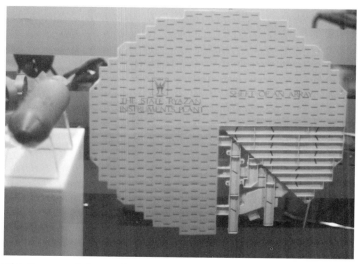

This Fazotron fighter-radar antenna is cut away to show the microwave plumbing behind the slotted array. Taken together, the horizontal waveguides steer the beam vertically. (Author)

The version for the Su-27 may also be designated Sapfir-27 and N001 Miech. Its RPLK-27 attack system uses a TsVM-80 digital computer. Search range against a closing target is 240 km (130 nm); tracking range is 170 km (92 nm). This system can track 10 targets and engage 2. The supporting EO attack system is OEPS-27, which uses a Ts-100 computer.

An improved Zhuk PH electronically scanned radar (for Su-30 and -35) can detect a closing target in velocity mode at 165 km (89 nm) and in range mode at 140 km (75 nm), and a receding target at 60 km (32 nm); it can track 24 targets, and can engage 6 to 8 of them. Coverage in azimuth and elevation is +/−60 deg. The alternative for these aircraft is NIIP's N-011, which can detect an air target at 400 km (216 nm) and a surface target at 200 km (108 nm); it also has ground mapping, terrain following, and terrain avoidance modes. Coverage is +/−85 deg. This radar can track 15 targets (including static ones, such as helicopters) while supporting 6 engagements. Su-35 has N-011 and a companion N-012 tail warning radar (range 3–4 km/1.6–2.2 nm).

Reportedly these radars reflect revelations of APG-65 technology. Zhuk was probably the first Soviet software-controlled radar, suited both to air-to-air combat and to ground attack (it measures aircraft ground velocity and provides both automatic terrain following and terrain avoidance.

◆ Wet Eye

The J-band surface-search radar of May, Haze (Mi-14), and Helix (Ka-27) ASW aircraft is associated with the BM-1 and, presumably, later sonobuoy systems.

Wet Eye radar as carried by an Il-39 May. (U.S. Naval Institute)

This radar may be a version of RBP-3. Installations include Initsiyativa-B on the Be-12 "Mail" ASW seaplane, Initsiyativa-2M on the Mi-14 ASW helicopter, and Initsiyativa-2K on the Ka-25 (Hormone A) ASW helicopter. The Wet Eye radar on Il-38 May is Berkut, which is also the designation of its ASW weapons system.

◆ AEW Radars

The current carrier AEW platform is the Ka-31 helicopter, originally designated Ka-29RLD (radio lokatsionnogo dozara), carrying a large foldable planar array under its belly (stowed flat against the belly when not in use). The system is said to detect fighters at 75 nm (also given as 100–150 km), and to carry 20 tracks. Surface vessels can be detected at up to 250 km. On-station time is 150 min at 11,500 ft. The radar was designed by the NNIIRT bureau. The helicopter first flew in 1988, and two were observed on board the carrier *Kuznetzov* early in 1992. A more conventional AEW aircraft, the twin-turboprop Yak-44E, was canceled.

SWEDEN

◆ PS-05/A

Ericsson's multirole I/J-band pulse-Doppler radar for the Gripen (JAS 39) fighter/attack aircraft uses a carbon-fiber planar array antenna. Air-to-air modes: search, TWS, short-range wide-angle scan, using high and medium PRFs. Air-to-surface: ground and sea search, ground mapping, missile fire control using low PRFs and pulse compressions. Peak power is 1 kW. This radar is part of the weapons system (DS80E, using a 32-bit SDS80 computer) used to deliver RBS 15F missiles (the AAMs are AMRAAM, AIM-9L, and RBS 73 [Skyflash, a Sparrow derivative]). Total radar weight is 156 kg. The follow-on PS-05/B version offers an enhanced processor, better ECCM, and NCTR capability. This radar has apparently been selected for the Indian Light Combat Aircraft (LCA), one version of which is to be flown from future Indian aircraft carriers (using ski-jumps).

◆ PS-37/A

Ericsson's X-band monopulse pulse-Doppler radar equips the AJ 37 attack version of the Viggen, which delivers RBS 15F antiship missiles. It employs a large-diameter Cassegrain antenna. The associated central computer is the SAAB CD 107, a license-built Singer-Kearfott SKC-2037. In modified form (PS-371/A) this radar equips the specialized coastal-reconnaissance version of the Viggen, SH37 (Spannings Havsovervakning), which also has a more capacious central computer, long-range camera, night reconnaissance pod, ECM pod, and self-defense missiles. The fighter version (JA 37) carries a specialized air-to-air radar, PS-46/A, which is probably related to PS-37/A but lacks its surface-attack modes, including a sea-search mode. A total of 75 early-production JA 37, SH 37, and AJ 37 are being converted into multirole AJS 37s with digital buses, new mission computers, new ECM pods, new terrain-following systems, and multirole radars. The computer can also be connected to the PLA computer mission planning system.

◆ SLAR

Ericsson's X-band (9.4-GHz) SLAR is used on board CASA-212 MPAs in Portugal and in Sweden. It employs a 3m underbody antenna pod and operates at 10 kW (1-kHz pulses, 0.5 × 33-deg beam). Up to 2000 range/bearing cells can be processed with 6-bit precision (system memory is 1.6 mbit). Medium or large ships can be detected at 100 km. Total system weight is 70 kg.

UNITED KINGDOM

◆ ASV 21

This old X-band surface-search radar survives on board South African C-47s used for maritime surveillance (it was taken from the Shackletons, now retired). Note that the Shackleton airframes have been retained pending possible installation of new engines. Characteristics: peak power 200 kW, pulse width/PRF 0.5 microsec/800 (scan 32 rpm) for 18- and 36nm scales; 1.0/400 (scan 16 rpm) on 72nm scale; 2.0/200 (scan 8 rpm) on 170nm scale. Slow scan (8 rpm) can be selected at all ranges. A sector scan (15–360 deg) can be oriented on any bearing. Nominal range: at 300 ft altitude, ASV 21 detects a small surface craft (less than 100 t) at 22 nm, a large one at 30 nm. At 2000 ft, nominal ranges are 38 and 63 nm.

◆ MAREC II/ARI 5955/Super-MAREC

Band: X(I)
Peak Power: 80 kW
Pulse Width: (a) 0.4 (b) 2.5 microsec
PRF: (a) 400 (b) 200

MEL's MAREC (Maritime-Reconnaissance) II has a maximum range of about 250 nm (maximum instrumented range is 219 nm). This and other MEL maritime radars are all associated with big horizontal plotting tables incorporating backlit radar displays. Super-MAREC substitutes a scan-converted color TV display similar to that in Super Searcher. It has three selectable pulse widths (including very short for bad sea clutter), uses a microprocessor signal processor, has this capability, and can guide Sea Skua missiles. The original MAREC did not sell.

MEL's first helicopter search radar, the progenitor of MAREC, was its Lightweight 15-kW X-band search radar, ARI 5955 (a version of the German Ekco AW 391), mounted on Sea Kings in a dorsal thimble. Pulse width is 0.5 microsec (PRF 400 pps). X-band was chosen because it gave better definition than S- or C-band and better weather penetration than Ka/Ku-band. This radar was introduced in 1968, and achieved a range of 50 nm. MAREC was an ARI 5955 development with higher peak power and antenna gain and dual pulse widths and PRFs.

Users: Algeria (8 F27-400 maritime patrol aircraft), Cameroons (3 Do 128), India (14 Super-MAREC and 13 MAREC II on Do 228 for Coast Guard, made under license by Hindustan Aeronautics).

ARI 5955: Australia (Sea King Mk 50/50A), Germany (Sea King Mk 41, with additional Seaspray radar in the nose), Egypt (Sea King Mk 47), India (Sea King Mk 41 and Mk 42A), Italy (possibly in 12 AB 212ASWs), Norway (Sea King Mk 43/43A for SAR), Qatar (Commando Mk 3/Sea King Mk 74), Pakistan (Sea King Mk 45), United Kingdom (Sea King AEW Mk 2, RAF HAR Mk 3/3A with 5995/2 radar). Royal Navy ASW Sea Kings use Sea Searcher/Super Searcher.

◆ Blue Fox/Blue Vixen

Ferranti's (now GEC-Marconi's) Blue Fox X-band monopulse Sea Harrier radar was optimized for mid-to-high-altitude air targets and for sea search/ground mapping. It lacks look-down air-to-air and air-to-air TWS capability. It does have a boresight range mode for targets acquired through the HUD. The flat roll-stabilized antenna array incorporates an IFF interrogator. The spin-tuned magnetron hops frequency on a pulse-to-pulse basis for clutter rejection (clutter characteristics vary with frequency) and glint reduction.

The replacement Blue Vixen, for the Sea Harrier FA.2, has a new pulse-Doppler transmitter (for look-down) and a radar data computer for air-to-air TWS, to support AMRAAM missile engagements. There is also a single target track mode. Two air-to-sea modes (both with TWS for Sea Eagle missile delivery) include one optimized for small target detection in high sea states. There are also air-to-surface ranging (for bombing), precision velocity update (for navigation), and beacon interrogation modes. Special covertness features are the ability to retain radar data after reception (transmit/freeze mode), single-sweep transmission (data update), spread-spectrum transmission, and sector search. Total weight is 141.5 kg.

Users: India (Sea Harrier), United Kingdom (Blue Fox in Sea Harrier FRS.1, Blue Vixen in FA.2).

◆ Sea Searcher/Super Searcher

Replacing the earlier ARI 5955, the MEL X-band search radar for Sea King helicopters is credited with twice the range. Sea Searcher is a TWS radar that can sector-scan. There are two alternative (selectable) pulse widths, for operation in various sea states. The antenna is enlarged: sizes from 107 to 610 mm in horizontal aperture (42–240 in) are available. Peak power is 85 kW, and scan rate is 30 rpm.

Super Searcher, announced in 1982, uses a 42 × 16in dish, or a 48 × 10in planar array, or a 30 × 10in planar array antenna, and has greater detection, tracking, and missile-guidance performance. All arrays are stabilized within 20 deg. A new color CRT replaces the earlier monochrome PPI. There are three selectable pulse lengths, including an ultrashort pulse for high definition in bad weather, and four alternate PRFs. Scanning is by sector or over the full 360 deg. The 14in raster-scan (625-line) CRT display has freeze frame and memory storage (and MTI). Range scales: 4, 8, 16, 32, 64, 128, 256 nm. This radar has TWS capability. Signal processing options are within-beam integration, scan-to-scan integration, pattern enhancement, and CFAR.

Users (Super Searcher): Australia (16 S-70B Seahawk), Brazil (10 EMB-111 patrol aircraft [as retrofits]), Greece (14 Super Searcher on HU-16 Albatross), India (20 Sea King Mk 42B), Norway (Sea King Mk 43B for SAR), Pakistan (1 Sea King Mk 45A), United Kingdom (82 Sea Searcher and Super Searchers on Sea King HAS 5 and 6, 11 on Dominie T.1).

◆ Seaspray/Blue Kestrel

Band: X
Antenna Dimensions: 27 in × 10 in (deep)
Antenna Weight: Total weight 65 kg

Data refer to Seaspray.

These GEC-Ferranti radars are now organized in a single series, announced August 1991: Seaspray 2000, Seaspray 3000, Seaspray 4000, Blue Kestrel 5000, and Blue Kestrel 6000. Seaspray 3000 is Seaspray Mk 3 on board Lynx helicopters; Blue Kestrel 5000 is the radar developed for the Royal Navy version of the EH-101 Merlin helicopter. Seaspray 2000 is a derated version for coastal patrol and fishery protection (EEZ enforcement). It is a 90-kW X-band magnetron radar with two pulse widths and four PRFs; maximum instrumented range is 100 nm. Seaspray 3000 (formerly Mk 3) uses a high-speed spin-tuned magnetron (PEAB type), with monopulse tracking in azimuth (to keep it turned toward the target it is illuminating for Sea Skua missiles). Seaspray 4000 is a pulse-compression version of Seaspray, using a TWT.

Blue Kestrel 5000 (formerly Blue Kestrel) is a pulse-compression radar for helicopters and medium maritime patrol aircraft, using a planar array antenna rather than the illuminated paraboloid of Seaspray. Blue Kestrel 6000, now in the development stage, combines Blue Kestrel 5000 with some technology from the Blue Vixen of the Sea Harrier FA 2 program. It is a pulse-Doppler radar for both air-to-air detection and for surface-target classification (using ISAR). It retains the Blue Kestrel 5000 antenna.

Super Searcher PC components. (MEL)

Seaspray Mk 3. (GEC Ferranti)

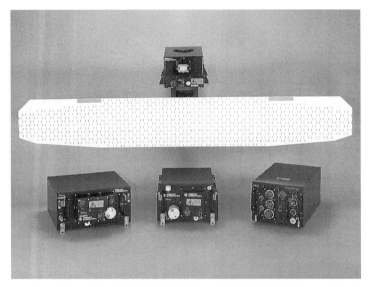

Blue Kestrel, for the Merlin helicopter. (GEC Ferranti)

Searchwater in its AEW form as carried by Sea King helicopters. (Westland)

Blue Kestrel scan rate is 12 or 24 rpm, and a small target can be detected at 25 nm. Blue Kestrel was first installed for tests (on board a Sea King) late in 1985, for flight trials in the spring of 1986. Development models were delivered by January 1989.

Seaspray originally used a Philips frequency-agile (spin-tuned magnetron) transmitter like that in Blue Fox. It was intended primarily to detect and track small fast craft, such as fast patrol boats, and can be used to guide Sea Skua missiles. It can also be used as a periscope detector. Tracking is monopulse. There are four selectable PRFs. Ferranti announced Seaspray Mks 2 and 3 in August 1982. Mk 2 had a new processor, and Mk 3 is a TWS version with a full 360-deg scan. Compared to Seaspray Mk 1, Mk 3 has full 360-deg coverage and TWS performance. The display is a television-type raster showing processed video, and the picture can be frozen if necessary.

Users: Seaspray Mk 1 (ARI 5979): Argentina (2 Lynx), Brazil (23 Lynx), Denmark (10 Lynx), Finland (Seaspray 2000 in Frontier Guard Do 228s), Germany (Lynx: total 34 including Mk 3), Netherlands (22 Lynx), Norway (6 Lynx), Pakistan, United Kingdom (76 Lynx, and Seaspray 2000 in two Vigilant aircraft of Scottish Fisheries Protection Agency). There is also one Seaspray 2000 in a "black" aircraft. The Finnish Seasprays are integrated with a GEC-Marconi FLIR turret.

Seaspray Mk 3: Brazil (Super Lynx), Finland (Seaspray 2000 in two Frontier Guard Do 228), Germany (Sea King Mk 41, replacing ARI 5955; also some Lynx), Korea (14 Super Lynx Mk 99, also boat version), Turkey (6 Mk 4 for last six AB 212 ASW), UK (1 Ministry of Agriculture F27-200). The 1994 Brazilian contract for Seaspray 3000 was a mixture of remanufactured Seaspray Mk 1 from five Lynx Mk 21 being upgraded and new-build Sea Spray 3000, for nine helicopters ordered in 1994.

Blue Kestrel: United Kingdom (Merlin helicopters).

◆ Searchwater (ARI 5980)

This X-band (8.6–10.0 GHz) pulse-compression ATD radar equips Nimrod Mk 2 maritime reconnaissance aircraft and, in modified form, Sea King AEW helicopters. Peak power is 65 kW (average is 500 W). Searchwater uses both a narrow beam and a short pulse to limit the patch of sea clutter surrounding a target. Pulse-to-pulse frequency agility helps eliminate sea returns, which are frequency-dependent. The radar integrates all pulses in any beamwidth during one scan and can also integrate from scan to scan. Searchwater is credited with a target-classification capability based on target size and aspect. The antenna is pitch- and roll-stabilized, with controllable tilt and automatic sector scan.

The operator has A-scope, B-scope, and raster-scanned PPI displays, the A-scope being used for range profiling for target iden-

tification. In 1985 Thorn-EMI was awarded a contract for a color display, with which synthetic video could be overlaid on raw video (in the monochrome version only synthetic video could be displayed). That was expected to improve anticollision performance, as well as detectability of targets.

Claimed performance: 28+ nm on a snorkel, 60+ nm on a fast-attack boat, and 130+ nm on a medium-sized ship.

Searchwater development began in 1972, initial tests following in 1973; the first production Nimrod 2 was delivered in August 1979.

The associated IFF is the Cossor Jubilee Guardsman.

Thorn-EMI's helicopter-borne early-warning version of Searchwater was developed in response to the experience of the Falklands War (a prewar proposal was rejected on the ground that the Royal Navy would always fight within range of ground-based AEW aircraft such as AWACS). The project was officially approved on 13 May 1982; the prototype Sea King AEW helicopters embarked on board HMS *Illustrious* on 2 August 1982. Production AEW helicopters became operational in 1986. British carriers now embark a flight of four AEW helicopters.

The AEW version substitutes a pencil beam with circular polarization for the fan beam of the patrol version. It has two alternative scan rates (faster to track faster-moving targets, slower for better detection at longer range) and four range scales (i.e., PRFs; pulse widths are adjusted to match range scales, presumably to maintain the same average power output). Alternative warning and search modes are optimized, respectively, for aircraft and ship detection. The antenna can also be tilted to scan for weather features. A separate A-scope is used to assist in target classification by range profiling.

Targets are manually detected (then rate-aided tracked) and designated. In the warning mode, the PPI brightens fast-moving targets. Any portion of the PPI can be displayed in expanded form on a B-scope (bearing vs. range) for more accurate positioning of the target designator, a feature presumably valuable if there are many targets close together. The associated computer maintains a track file and computes range and intercept vectors for fighters. A Sea King equipped with Searchwater controls fighters directly rather than handing target data down to a ship.

The system can track up to 16 air targets and can direct up to six simultaneous interceptions. There are two operator stations, side by side, with the tactical coordinator (in contact with the senior warfare officer on board the carrier) on the right. The tactical coordinator can track up to 40 surface targets, the helicopter providing OTH-T support for surface ships. The officer at the left-hand display is responsible for air targets. The system is being modified so that it can interchange data between the two displays so that fighters can be directed against designated surface targets. Work is also proceeding to increase computer capacity so that more air targets can be handled. The system currently lacks any air-to-surface data link. Reportedly, Searchwater also suffers from clutter when tracking low-flying air targets.

Searchwater is described as noncoherent, but its manufacturer claims that it can extract Doppler data from its pulse-compressed signals. That capability suggests that pulses are internally coded by phase rather than by frequency.

Searchwater 2000 was chosen for the Nimrod 2000 MPA replacement and is offered for the Sea King AEW upgrade. Searchwater 2, intended to provide Searchwater performance at about half the weight, was abandoned in the early 1990s because of its weight (600 kg), volume, and cost. Thorn-EMI then decided to develop a low-cost low-risk alternative, using a Texas Instruments transmitter and antenna and Array Systems Computing imaging software. The new radar retains and extends the range/amplitude profiling mode originally developed for Searchwater. As of early 1996, Racal-Thorn was claiming a fourfold improvement in MTBF over Searchwater itself. Total weight is 200 kg.

The Royal Navy is upgrading its 10 AEW 2A Sea Kings to AEW 7 standard in 1995–98 under an AEW mission systems upgrade (MSU) program. In the near term, helicopters will be fitted with a second Have Quick II radio (the single current one is used for fighter control). A new Mk XII IFF (APX-113 combined interrogator/transponder) with modes 1, 2, 3/A, C, and 4 integrated with Searchwater will replace the current Jubilee Guardsman, which lacks Mode 4. The new IFF will also be fitted to ASW Sea Kings and to Sea Harriers. The MSU program addresses more fundamental problems: the lack of any central tactical system in the helicopter (and a poor man-machine interface for the radar), poor subclutter visibility, and the total absence of any overland detection or tracking capability. MSU comprises a radar systems upgrade (RSU, envisaged as a new pulse-Doppler radar with a more powerful transmitter) integrated with related existing (Doppler, air data), near-term (IFF, video, enhanced communications), and new (JTIDS, ring-laser gyro, GPS) systems. The new central tactical system will use dual color displays. JTIDS is carried as a separate item, and the modified helicopter will have space and weight reserved for a future ESM system. The RSU is to begin in 1999.

As of May 1996 the radar contenders had been winnowed down to GEC-Marconi (upgraded Sea Vixen), Racal-Thorn (Searchwater 2000), and Lockheed Martin-Hughes (APG-63U).

Users: Spain (AEW Sea Kings), United Kingdom (AEW Sea Kings, Nimrods). Three Sea King HAS 5 are being converted to AEW aircraft, to provide a margin against attrition. This program was considered preferable to converting some of the new EH-101s to AEW aircraft. Spain selected Searchwater for her P-3 upgrades, but the order never went through. A reported Indian order for Searchwater for five AEW helicopters apparently was never fulfilled.

◆ ASR 360

> **Band:** X (9.1 GHz)
> **Beam:** 3×27 deg
> **Peak Power:** 25 kW
> **Gain:** 25 dB
> **Pulse Width:** 0.05, 0.25, and 1.0 microsec
> **PRF:** 825 pps minimum
> **Scan Rate:** 32 rpm
> **Antenna Dimensions:** 30in slotted waveguide

ASR 360 is Racal-Decca's standard surface-search marine radar, adapted for small maritime-patrol aircraft; it is also called ANR 360 (Navigator). ASR 360 was originally developed for the Royal Norwegian Navy in 1979 for periscope detection in fjords, to be flown on board a single- or twin-engined Cessna (the first installation was a Royal Norwegian Navy Cessna 337). A Norwegian Sea King version (to support OTH missile boat strikes) was proposed but apparently not bought.

Users: Norway, Oman (15 on Seavans [MPA versions of Skyvan]), United Kingdom (RN Jetstream navigation trainers).

◆ Modular FLIR/AAR-51

GEC Sensors' modular FLIR is used on the AV-8B (as AAR-51) and on the Hawk 100, Tornado, Harrier GR.7, and the British C-130. It operates at 8–12 microns, using eight parallel TEDs (CMT detectors) to produce 525-line video at a frame rate of 60 Hz. There is a 1553 bus interface. The sensor head weighs 18.6 kg, and the inboard electronics package weighs another 24 kg.

Cooling is closed-cycle; the FLIR takes 3.5 min to cool sufficiently at an outside temperature of 20 deg C.

◆ Sea Owl (PID)

GEC-Marconi's stabilized long-range FLIR for Royal Navy Lynx helicopters is also designated Passive Identification Device (PID). The stabilized FLIR uses standard TICM II modules, and the associated signal processor automatically searches for, detects, and tracks surface targets. The turret slews at up to 60 deg/sec, over 120 deg in azimuth; elevation limits are $+20/-30$ deg. Magnifications are $5\times$ and $30\times$ (FOVs 12×8 and 2×1.33 deg). The IR sensor uses eight parallel CMT SPRITE detectors (8–13 microns) and feeds a 625- or 525-line monitor. Turret weight is 66 kg. There are also a 17-kg signal processor and a 16-kg target tracker for automatic search, detection, and tracking of surface targets. The system is designed to connect to a 1553B bus.

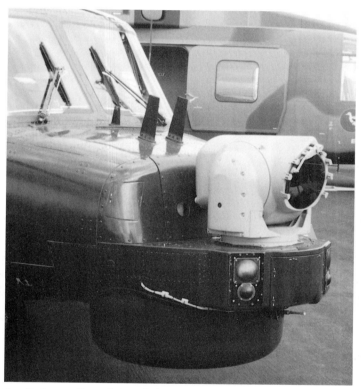

Sea Owl on a Lynx HAS.8 helicopter, Farnborough 1992, with Super Searcher radar below in a 360-deg radome. (Author)

UNITED STATES

The FY94/95 program began the modification of 68 P-3Cs for improved surface surveillance, presumably to Outlaw Hunter (OASIS: OTH-T Airborne Sensor Interface System) configuration under the ASUW Improvement Program (AIP). Desert Storm delayed Outlaw Viking (S-3) to FY92; no date for Outlaw Hawkeye has been set. The OTH-T aircraft program also includes Radiant Outlaw (see below), Outlaw Story Teller (EP-3E), and Outlaw Seahawk (SH-60); both of the latter were included in the FY93 program. Outlaw Prowler (EA-6B) was scheduled for FY94, but was not done, as the EA-6B was not provided with a new ISAR radar.

Radiant Outlaw is a laser radar that exploits the extreme frequency stability of the laser to sense the skin vibration of a target; hopefully that vibration (as transformed into a very small Doppler shift) yields an identifiable signature. This type of measurement may also yield data for battle damage assessment. In 1994 Radiant Outlaw was placed in a pod suitable for a P-3C, for airborne measurements. Reportedly an OpEval (Gatekeeper) in May–June 1995 on board both ships and aircraft revealed some problems, and there were also funding problems. The program seems to have stalled by early 1996.

Except for the F/A-18, the Navy's approach to obtaining night tactical capability has been a combination of night vision goggles and the appropriate cockpit lighting. This contrasts sharply with the Air Force approach, in which a wide-area (navigational) FLIR is used by the aircrew prior to attacking a target. Thus no navigational FLIRs are being bought for F-14s. Similarly, the AV-8B uses only a narrow-field (attack) FLIR, the GEC Modular FLIR. The Harrier night attack program, the precursor of the F-14 program, is described in greater detail in the 1991/92 edition.

◆ AAQ-13/14 LANTIRN

Lockheed Martin's Low-Altitude Navigation and Targeting for Night system, developed for the Air Force, has been adapted to F-14s to provide them with an off-the-shelf ability to deliver laser-guided bombs. The Air Force system comprises two pods: the AAQ-13 navigation pod, carrying a Ku-band terrain-following radar below and a wide-FOV FLIR; and the AAQ-14 targeting pod, which carries a narrow-FOV FLIR and a laser designator. The Navy is buying only AAQ-14. The targeting pod offers a wide-angle FOV (6 × 6 deg) for target detection. Once the target is spotted, the pilot switches to narrow FOV mode (1.7 × 1.7 deg) and engages a tracker. Once the tracker has locked on, the pilot can engage the laser, which functions either as a designator or as a ranger (to feed the aircraft FCS when the aircraft is dropping dumb bombs). FLIR aperture is large enough (8.1 in) to provide enough gain for long-range target detection. Pod dimensions are 15.0 × 98.5 in (540 lb).

The AAQ-14 LANTIRN targeting pod is now carried by F-14s. The upper window is for the laser ranger, the lower for the 8.1in aperture FLIR. The pod weighs 540 lb (15.0 × 98.5 in). (Author)

A total of 89 LANTIRN FLIR/laser designator pods were bought (the project was announced at the end of June 1995).

◆ AAQ-22 SAFIRE/AAQ-21 (System 2000)

FLIR Systems' Shipborne/Airborne Infrared Equipment turret-mounted FLIR and TV is designed to be interchangeable among ships, helicopters, and maritime patrol aircraft. The pitch- and yaw-stabilized turret can transmit data directly to a command system; the system can slew it and lock it onto a target, after which tracking is automatic. SAFIRE operates at 8–12 microns with 28- and 5-deg FOVs. It can be modified to incorporate a digital autotracker, and it can be roll-stabilized for ship use (the air version is three-axis stabilized).

FLIR Systems' AAQ-21 (FLIR 2000) is an earlier analog FLIR (hence less precise) with 28 × 15 and 7 × 3.75-deg (5 × 2.3-deg in the HP version) FOVs, and a resolution of 1.4/0.35 mrad. The G or HP version offers better accuracy and inertial tracking. The gymbal/FLIR head assembly is 486 × 411 × 336 mm. AAQ-21 also has a simpler stabilization system than AAQ-22. In all, over 600 have been sold worldwide.

FLIR Systems was formed in 1978, and by 1995 it had sold over 1200 FLIRs for 70 aircraft types in over 45 countries.

Users: AAQ-22: Denmark (*Thetis*-class frigates, Lynx helicopters [using the Ferranti radar display], S-61 search and rescue helicopters; total 28 sold, all interchangeable between ships and helicopters), Malaysia (four Beech 200 MPAs), Netherlands

FLIR Systems' System 2000HP (AAQ-21) extends under the nose of an Irish Air Corps CASA-235 maritime patrol airplane at the Paris Air Show, 1995. The airplane's APS-504 radar is in a belly radome further aft; the nose accommodates weather radar. (Author)

(P-3Cs and Lynx helicopters; in P-3s uses the retractor originally designed for the Texas Instruments AAS-36, which was not installed), Norway (for search and rescue, both ashore and on Sea Kings; total 17), Portugal (P-3Bs), United States (UH-1N helicopters for Marines, MH-60G for Air Force, Patrol Boat Mk III for U.S. Navy). It is also being offered as part of Marsh Aviation's S-2 maritime-patrol aircraft upgrade (an alternative is AAQ-21). SAFIRE may be on board Danish *Flyvefisken*-class corvettes.

AAQ-21: Belgium (FLIR 2000F in SAR Sea Kings Mk 48), Ireland (FLIR 2000HP in CN-235MPA), Morocco (FLIR 2000G in BN2T Defender), Norway (FLIR 2000F in SAR Sea King Mk 43Bs). The Irish Air Corps uses AAQ-21 Series 2000G on board its CASA-235s.

◆ AAR-50/AAQ-16 TINS

Hughes's AAR-50 is a thermal imaging navigation set for the F/A-18, derived from the earlier AAQ-16. With the AAS-38 described below, it forms the F/A-18 C/D night-attack package, replacing earlier ASQ-173. AAR-50 provides a pilot with an image (on the HUD) of the approaching terrain, in either black-is-hot or white-is-hot form (the latter looks something like a conventional television image). TINS has a fixed 20 × 20-deg FOV (and thus cannot be used for target-following), occupying a pod (10 × 78 in, 214 lb) on a stub pod adapter on the starboard side of the airplane. Hughes claims that MTBF is greater than 410 hr (MTTR is 17 min, using standard WRA components). As of 1993, about 125 AAR-50s had been delivered, at a unit price of about $700,000.

TINS (AAR-50) mounted on an F/A-18. (Hughes)

The earlier AAQ-16 is intended for both the U.S. V-22 Osprey and the Anglo-Italian EH-101; it was deployed to the Persian Gulf on board U.S. SH-2s (see below). AAQ-16 is a turret-mounted FLIR operating at 8–12 microns. It slews at 130 deg/sec, with azimuth limits of 210 deg and elevation limits of +85/−180 deg. It has two magnifications, 1× and 6× (corresponding fields of view are 30 × 40 and 5 × 6.67 deg). Video is 875, 625, or 525 lines at 50 or 60 Hz. The turret is controlled by a joystick. It weighs 54 lb and has a 12.95in dia (14.6 in deep). Hughes claims MTBF is 400 hr. The system incorporates an autotracker. It can use a conventional CRT or the FLIR image can be projected onto a helmet-mounted display. The current production version is AAQ-16B, introduced in 1989. An alternative hi-mag version (announced November 1991) would add a third FOV (1.9 × 2.5 deg, 16×) and a correlation autotracker with dual-mode option, increasing turret weight to 65 lb. AAQ-16D adds a laser designator (90 lb). All of these versions employ scanning optics.

Hughes is currently promoting AAQ-16( ), the version planned for the V-22. It employs a focal plane array (i.e., a staring array) of InSb elements to operate at 3–5 microns. Growth options include a video autotracker, third FOV, and eyesafe laser rangefinder. Turret weight of the improved version is 45 lb (12in dia × 14 in), and the options bring that to 57 lb; total system weight is 93 lb (100 lb with all options).

In 1988 AAQ-16s (in production for the Army and the Customs Service since 1985) were mounted on board LAMPS I helicopters operating in the Persian Gulf. On these aircraft the turret is in the nose, on the right-hand side, just forward of the radome. The AAQ-16 image can be downlinked to the ship operating the helicopter.

About 281 AAQ-16s had been made through June 1995.

◆ AAS-36

AAS-36 is the Texas Instruments IR detecting set (IRDS) for P-3 Orions. IRDS provides a thermal image of the target on a tele-vision set, and the detector is inertially stabilized against target motion. The passive tracker can be locked onto a target of interest. The set is carried in a small turret under the nose of the airplane. FLIR FOVs are 15 × 20 and 5 × 6.7 deg. Slew rate is 1 rad/sec (about 57 deg/sec), and azimuth limits are 200 deg. The turret is stabilized to within 0.125 mrad. It weighs 301 lb. MTBF is 300 hr (MTTR 30 min).

AAS-36 replaces the KA-74 camera originally installed on board P-3A and -3B aircraft. The first production contract was awarded in mid-1977. AAS-36 was initially installed only on board P-3C Update II aircraft, but was later extended to U.S. Navy -3As and -3Bs.

The AAS-36 IR receiver is incorporated in the AAQ-15 IR detecting-and-tracking set used on board Air Force HH-60 helicopters and C-130 gunships. In that application three simultaneous FOVs are presented, and there is an automatic video tracker.

◆ AAS-38 Nite Hawk

AAS-38 is the Texas Instruments/Ford Aerospace (now Loral) FLIR pod for F/A-18 Hornet fighter-bombers, used primarily for attack against land targets. Hughes was qualified as second source in 1994. AAS-38A includes a laser target designator/ranger using a Nd-YAG laser (Litton Target Designator/Ranger, LTD/R). This FLIR incorporates an automatic target tracker and automatic gain/level control for hands-off operation. It operates as an IRST, and can hand targets off to the air-to-air autotracker, scan slave on selected targets, and present the pilot with a display of scanned targets. The system as a whole employs ten weapons replaceable assemblies (WRAs); mean time to replace one is less than 12 min.

AAS-38 FLIR pod mounted on an F/A-18. (Hughes)

AAS-38B, the latest version, has a multifunction autotracker that can toggle between scene track and centroid track modes, for improved lock-on and maintenance of track during an air-to-ground attack. It also has improved air-to-air detection and tracking.

Loral is currently promoting a self-cooled (SC) version suited to aircraft without the internal cooling system of the F/A-18. Examples include the AV-8B, F-14 (on which the SC version was flight-tested), and F-16.

The pod is 13 × 72 in and weighs 347 lb (370 or 380 lb for AAS-38A). It is typically mounted on the lower left of the aircraft fuselage and provides the pilot with a 3 × 3-deg or 12 × 12-deg FOV. The pilot can move the LOS from −150 to +30 deg, with 540 deg of roll freedom in either direction. Targets can be tracked at 75 deg/sec. Loral claims an MTBF of 80 hr for the full FLIR/laser package (MTTR 15 min).

An AAS-36 turret under the nose of a P-3 Orion. (Naval Reserve Association)

AAS-38 was the first Navy FLIR designed for supersonic operation. It entered service in February 1985.

The AAS-38 design allowed for later installation of a laser. Flight tests of the laser designator/tracker/ranger (for laser-guided bomb delivery and buddy designation) were completed in February 1987 (tracking accuracy was better than 50 microrad in 5-G maneuvers) and it is incorporated in pods delivered from 1989 onward. The laser can perform some air-to-air radar functions when the airplane is operating in radar silence. Delivery of laser subsystems was completed in mid-1994: 215 targeting FLIRs and 435 F/A-18C/D are configured to accommodate the laser.

The manufacturer, Loral, claims that the AAS-38 can detect and track air targets at over 100 nm; up to 100 targets can be carried in its track file. The pilot slaves the system scan to a selected area of the sky, and the system provides synthetic video (i.e., automatically extracted targets) of that area. It then tracks the targets automatically. All of this is possible with the existing pod, with only a software change. Operation is entirely passive. Loral claims that the false-alarm rate approaches 4/hr.

Three major improvements are currently in production: pod boresight G-load compensation software; filtered inertial-to-sightline coordinate transformation (CSI) for better targeting accuracy; and air-to-air automatic tracking. A multifunction autotracker and an advanced air-to-air capability are under development. The multifunction autotracker automatically selects one of several possible air-to-air tracking methods (algorithms) to lock onto another airplane. The autotracker can conduct a search for an airborne target, automatically detecting it and locking on; alternatively, the autotracker can track several targets simultaneously (a FLIR equivalent of radar TWS performance).

During the Gulf War an AAS-38 pod was carried on the port stores station of one SH-60B LAMPS III helicopter of HSL-44. The pod's 875-line video was interlaced so that it could be displayed on the 525-line monitor on board the helicopter. This image could not be data-linked down to the ship. Six more production pods have the data-link capability, and the FLIR may be slaved to the helicopter's radar. The SH-60B cockpit could not be modified for night operations, so the crews were provided with hand-held, army-type, Texas Instruments TAS-6A FLIRS. Crews were also provided with Fujinon stabilized binoculars to identify distant surface contacts detected by the search radar. However, in the absence of a zoom-lens FLIR, such identification brings the helicopter well within the range of hand-held missiles, hence the importance of the FLIR pod.

◆ AAS-40 (Seehawk)

This lightweight Northrop FLIR was developed for the U.S. Coast Guard's HH-65 Dolphin helicopters but was not adopted; it has been included in the S-2 Tracker modernization project for Taiwan. Seehawk uses standard DoD FLIR components. The 39-kg turret-mounted FLIR has three magnifications, 1×, 2×, and 6× (corresponding FOVs are 30 × 40, 15 × 20, and 6.5 ×

AAS-40 is shown under the nose of a modernized Taiwanese S-2T Tracker. (Fu S. Mei)

5 deg). The turret slews at up to 180 deg/sec; azimuth limits are 190 deg, and elevation limits are +30/−105 deg.

◆ AAS-42 (IRSTS)

Lockheed Martin (formerly GE)'s F-14D IRST uses a nitrogen-cooled 1 × 256 (4 × 64 element modules) focal plane array operating at 8–12 microns, for maximum range against targets with reduced IR signatures, such as slow aircraft and cruise missiles. The FOV is 150 × 150 deg. The sensor head has a 9in dia and weighs 91 lb. The chin pod carrying the IRST also carries an AXX-1 television camera (see below).

Flight tests of a GE IRST began on board an Air Force F-15 in the summer of 1988 and continued on a modified F-14A. The first production IRSTs were delivered in 1992. They were first deployed in February 1994 on board the carrier *Vinson*.

This F-14D displays its twin nose sensor pod, with a stabilized television camera (AXX-1) on the left and an IRST (AAS-42) on the right. Mk 83 bombs are carried on the under-body stations otherwise used for Phoenix, with a pair of 267-gallon fuel tanks under the engines. Defensive armament consists of a pair of Sidewinders. (V. Vasquez, NAWC, 1994).

◆ AAS-44

Texas Instruments' second-generation FLIR will equip LAMPS III Block II (SH-60R) helicopters; a slightly modified version will equip U.S. Navy HH-60H. AAS-44 combines a FLIR with the Dark Star laser range-finder/designator (similar to that in the F-117) required to control Hellfire missiles. The sensor is a 240 × 4 FPA. There are three FOVs for navigation, search, and stand-off targeting. Image optimization will be either manual or by automatic local area processing (LAP), and there will be several types of automatic video tracking (e.g., both edge and centroid). The operator will be able to superimpose symbols on the display. AAS-44 will have multiple interfaces with the helicopter's 1553B data bus. Second-generation technology offers three times the performance of earlier (first-generation) FLIRs, 24× magnification, and an electronic doubler and quadrupler of the FLIR image. Real-time FLIR imagery will be sent to the mother ship via a modified LAMPS III data link. Unlike the earlier extemporized FLIR installation, AAS-44 will be installed in the helicopter's nose, where it commands an excellent view. FLIR components were delivered in FY95, with fleet introduction (on board SH-60Bs) in FY96.

◆ AAS-49 ("TIFLIR-49")

This Texas Instruments FLIR was displayed at Paris in 1995 on board a CASA-212 maritime patrol aircraft. It uses real-time local area processing (LAP) to reduce operator workload and improve image quality on a pixel basis. The alternative automatic gain-and-level techniques treat the image as a whole and bury much detail. The detector is a second-generation FPA and the image is stabilized electronically. Elevation limits are +40/−105 deg. FOVs are 22.5 × 30, 5 × 6.67, and 1.3 × 1.7 deg; the image can be zoomed electronically (ratios 2:1 and 4:1). The turret can slew at 3 rad/sec, with an angular resolution of less than 100 microrad (less than about 0.006 deg). The 12.75in-dia turret weighs 57 lb; the associated electronics weigh 43 lb.

♦ S-3 FLIRs (OR-89/AA and OR-263/AA) and AAQ-10

The Texas Instruments FLIRs installed in S-3s are integral elements of a larger weapons system. The first version, OR-89/AA, was also the first FLIR to be designed simultaneously with the overall airframe. The OR-89/AA is also installed on board many P-3Bs and Canadian CP-140 Auroras (as OR-5008/AA). Existing OR-89C/AAs are being upgraded to OR-263/AA configuration, incorporating DoD common modules. The OR-263 can be operated off-line as an independent FLIR. The FLIR is turret-mounted under the airplane, just abaft the cockpit. The FOV is 5 × 6.67 or 15 × 20 deg, with azimuth coverage of 200 deg in either direction and elevation coverage of 0 to −84 deg. Output is an 875-line television picture. About 1982 the specified MTBF, which had been demonstrated in service, was 345 hr. Turret diameter is 20.5 in. The first prototype OR-89 was delivered in March 1971.

The AAQ-10 (Pave Low III) of the HH-53 helicopter is a derivative. This device is also installed on board Israeli navy Westwind reconnaissance aircraft, in a special high-speed turret.

♦ APG-65/APG-73

Band: X
Beam: 3.3 × 3.3 deg
Peak Power: 4.5 kW
Pulse Compression: 13:1
Antenna Diameter: 26.625 in
Scan Rate: 60 deg/sec (100 deg/sec maximum)
Scan Limits: +/−70 deg azimuth × +/−60 deg elevation

The Hornet (F/A-18) multimode fire-control radar was developed by Hughes. Unit price in 1994 was about $1.2M. By that time, about 1328 APG-65 radars had been made.

The most important feature is a high-speed (7.2-MFLOP) software-programmable signal processor (PSP), which makes the radar flexible. Doppler-filter and range-gate configurations are defined by software, whereas in previous fighter radars these configurations were hard-wired. The 16-bit radar data processor has a 250-kword memory. The associated analog-to-digital processor operates at 1.3 MHz in the air-to-air mode and at 8 MHz in the air-to-ground mode.

The planar-array antenna uses direct electric drive rather than the hydraulic drive of earlier airborne radars. It incorporates a

APG-65 prototype, showing the microwave plumbing behind the flat slotted-array antenna. (Hughes)

guard horn to measure sidelobes in order to suppress them, a null-filling horn to reduce pattern nulls during Sparrow launches, and a flood horn to support visual Sparrow launches. A second antenna feed creates a wide fan beam for steep lookdowns. There is no IFF interrogator integral with the antenna (one is being introduced). The transmitter can vary pulse width and PRF. Sparrow missiles are controlled by pulse-Doppler (rather than continuous-wave) illumination (PDI).

Air-to-air modes: velocity search, range-while-scan, TWS (track 10 targets, display 8), single-target-track, raid-assessment (expanded coverage of a target to resolve a raid into individual aircraft), air-combat maneuvering, gun-director, narrow-beam vertical-scan, and boresight acquisition. In the latter, the radar searches the volume equivalent to the HUD view and locks onto the first target detected.

In velocity search, two values of PRF are used on adjacent scan bars, to avoid eclipsing (missing a target because it is at a blind speed). A spotlight option (in this and range-while-scan modes) moves the beam over a limited area at a high scan rate to aid in sorting targets within a raid.

Range-while-scan normally interleaves high and medium PRF waveforms (in adjacent scan bars), for, respectively, tail-on and head-on targets. Two values of high PRF are used in alternate high-PRF bars, to minimize eclipsing. Alternatively, high- or medium-PRF alone may be selected. The high-PRF mode uses FM to resolve range ambiguities: it consists of an unmodulated series of pulses, followed by steep FM, and then by moderate FM. Effective range is 2 to 160 nm. The medium-PRF mode uses phase-coded pulse compression.

For TWS, the pilot enters the search raster manually, or the radar automatically centers the scan to keep priority targets (chosen by the pilot) within the scanned volume.

Single-target tracking is by monopulse; the radar projects ahead target position if the target fades out of view during violent maneuvers. This mode employs a special high-PRF waveform for Sparrow guidance.

Air combat maneuvering modes are gun acquisition (GUNACQ), vertical scan acquisition (VACQ), boresight, and wide-angle acquisition (WACQ). In GUNACQ, the beam raster-scans over the same FOV as the HUD. In VACQ, the beam scans two vertical bars 2 deg apart. Both modes use short-pulse uncompressed medium-PRF waveforms. In boresight (range-only) mode, the beam is fixed. The radar uses a unique uncompressed medium-PRF waveform, achieving greater range because it spends so much time dwelling on the target. WACQ uses a long-pulse pulse-compressed medium-PRF waveform for maximum range. In each case, the radar automatically examines a range interval for a target, starting at minimum range and locking on automatically when a target is detected.

Gun director is a special precision tracking mode, using a medium-PRF waveform and coherent frequency agility to minimize target glint.

Air-to-surface modes: real-beam-ground-mapping (RBGM), Doppler beam-sharpening (sector or patch), synthetic-aperture, fixed-target-track, sea-surface-track, terrain-avoidance, precision-velocity-update, and air-to-surface-ranging. RBGM uses a low-PRF waveform, with pulse compression for 10nm and longer-range scales (range scales are 5, 10, 20, 40, 80, or 160 nm). Doppler beam sharpening achieves a 19:1 improvement in sector scan (for azimuth angles of more than 5 deg from the aircraft direction of motion) and a 67:1 improvement in patch mode. A 256 × 256 range element image is displayed.

Sea-surface search is used in high sea states. The waveform is frequency-agile, pulse-compressed low PRF. Scan widths are 20, 45, 90, and 120 deg, and range scales are 5, 10, 20, 40, and 80 nm. The pilot selects a target for fire control.

A boresighted air-to-ground ranging mode has a maximum range of 10 nm, using a coherent low-PRF waveform. The pilot can designate the target or can select a fixed antenna down angle. In an inverse ground angle mode, the radar reads out the angle to a target designated on a Doppler beam sharpened display.

There is also a position-velocity measurement mode.

The claimed MTBF is more than 100 hr. The entire system weighs 340 lb (exclusive of rack) and occupies less than 4.5 cu ft. Digital operation greatly reduces field adjustments; Hughes claims that built-in test equipment can detect 98% of all faults.

In early 1989 the Marines chose APG-65 for the Harrier II Plus (AV-8B upgrade) radar. Antenna diameter is reduced to about 22.8 in.

APG-73 is a modernized APG-65 for the F/A-18C/D and E/F aircraft by Hughes Radar Systems under a US/Canadian MoU, employing some parts of APG-71 (hardware is almost 60% common between the two). Work began in 1989, officially justified to some extent by reports that APG-65 had been compromised (reportedly before it even entered service) and therefore that it was vulnerable to some forms of ECM. Work began in 1989. Reported unit cost (1994) is $2.5M. This radar is currently in service.

APG-73 retains the transmitter and antenna of the APG-65 but replaces the receiver/exciter, signal-processor, and data processor of the earlier radar. The bandwidth, 3%, is wider than that of APG-65, for better ECCM. The two-channel monopulse receiver/exciter incorporates the digital-to-analog converter, so that all signal processing is digital. Compared to APG-65, faster analog-to-digital conversion reduces the size of the radar resolution cell, to about 100 ft in air-to-air mode.

The processor combines the signal processor (SP) and data processor (DP) roles. SP handles digital radar video. Roles include range gating, Doppler filtering, and automatic target detection. Words are 32 bits long. SP incorporates three processor elements (PEs), each running at 20 MCOPS, with 48 kwords of memory (they share a 1-Mword bulk memory). Access time is 100 or 300 nsec, and memory speed is 10 or 20 MHz. The processor has up to 256 instructions. High speed improves Doppler resolution, since FFT techniques can be used more effectively. Another 20 MCOPS can be added by filling a vacant card slot (the signal processors are assembled as a computer chassis with a backplane rather than as separate elements in the usual wire harness).

The two-processor DP controls SP and the rest of the radar. It uses MIL-STD-1750A architecture (i.e., 16-bit words) and is programmed in Jovial-73. The system clock runs at 6.6 MHz. Memory capacity of each processor is 1 Mword (access time 150 nsec, transfer rate 3.3 Mword/sec), altogether 8 times that of APG-65. Working (shared) memory is 256 kwords, with an access time of 450 nsec.

As delivered, APG-73 software uses only 60% of available hardware capacity. The preplanned product improvement plan for APG-73 envisages introduction of an all-weather real-time radar reconnaissance mode, which will make separate SLAR pods (currently used) unnecessary. The design also allows for later installation of an electronically scanned array antenna based on that of the APQ-181 of the B-2.

Users: Australia (F/A-18), Canada (F/A-18), Finland (F/A-18), Germany (upgraded F-4F), Italy (AV-8B Plus), Kuwait (F/A-18), Switzerland (F/A-18), Spain (F/A-18, AV-8B Plus), United States (F/A-18, AV-8B Plus, Coast Guard HU-25C drug interceptors; APG-73 in late production F/A-18C/D and in -18E/F).

◆ APG-66/APG-67/APG-68/W-160

Westinghouse's standard F-16A/B X-band pulse-Doppler digital radar, APG-66, was unique when it appeared in that all its separate elements (LRUs) were linked only by digital connections (except for the RF circuits and the system clock). Each had its own integral power supply. The radar scans over a 20-, 60-, or 120-deg sector; vertical scan is 1, 2, or 4 bars. Range scales are 10, 20, 40, and 80 nm. The transmitter is TWT-driven, and the antenna is a 740 × 480mm planar array. The radar has 16 available operating frequencies, any four of which the pilot can select. This radar incorporates not only a signal processor but also a digital computer (with 48 kwords of 16-bit ROM) which inserts symbols into its video output (for the HUD) and routes data to the airplane's FC computer. Westinghouse claimed that APG-66 was the first airborne radar to incorporate a programmable signal processor. It entered service in 1978.

There are 10 operating modes. Air-to-air modes are: look-down (range 20–30 nm), look-up (range 25–40 nm), and four air combat maneuvering (ACM) modes for automatic target acquisition in various dogfighting situations. Air-to-ground modes are ranging, real-beam ground map (and expanded real-beam map), and Doppler beam sharpening (64:1 improvement). There is also a dual sea-search mode. In SEA 1, frequency agility is used to cancel out sea clutter up to Sea State 4. In SEA 2, the radar uses a narrow Doppler notch to detect moving targets in higher sea states; this submode can also be used for MTI against ground targets. An upgraded version, APG-66(V), adds a TWS mode (10 targets, of which six can be engaged with AMRAAM missiles). MTBF is 140 hr; MTTR is 5 min. (V)2 is for the F-16A/B midlife upgrade; (V)3 is the version for Taiwan (it is Sparrow-capable).

In the cases of Norway and the United States (Air Force fighters based at Misawa, Japan), this radar in an F-16 is used to target Harpoon antiship missiles. Taiwan bought this radar for the strike version of the AT-3 trainer employing the Hsiung Feng II missile (20 AT-3Bs were bought); Norden may have adapted it to an antiship FCS. APG-66Z equips the New Zealand A-4K, a Skyhawk adapted to antiship attack. APG-66H equips the British Hawk 200 ground-attack aircraft, the Westinghouse Multi-Sensor Surveillance Aircraft (as APG-66SR), modernized Japanese F-4EJs (replacing APQ-120), and some U.S. naval training aircraft (APG-66T was installed in F-5J aggressor aircraft).

GE's APG-67 was a contemporary radar developed for the abortive F-20/F-5G export fighter program. It is functionally similar to APG-66. A locally built variant, incorporating some APG-66 components, equips the new Taiwanese Ching-Kuo fighter, which can carry three Hsiung Feng II missiles. It is designated GD-53 (Golden Dragon). Like APG-66, this is a computer-controlled X-band pulse-Doppler radar; it employs a pair of CPUs. One handles radar mode control and also communicates with the aircraft mission computer; the other is the radar data processor and symbol generator.

F-16C/D is equipped with the APG-68 with increased range (it adds a 160nm range scale), better resolution, and more operating modes. The antenna is slightly changed to 737 × 483 mm. The earlier single-mode (CW pulse) transmitter is replaced by a dual-mode unit, similar to that in the APG-67, which offers a pulse-compression mode (FM slide on pulse, at 9.7–9.9 GHz). Scan sectors are 2, 20, 50, 70, and 120 deg wide. APG-68 was based on APG-66; improvements were particularly required to support the AIM-120 (AMRAAM) missile. The major improvement was consolidation of all processing into a single 45-kg unit. The CPU runs at 1.6 MIPS with 96 kwords of high-speed RAM and 384 kwords of bulk memory. It works with an array processor (signal processing) capable of 192 MOPS. Clock speed is 8 MHz.

This radar can track 10 air targets while scanning, supporting eight AMRAAM engagements. The 22 operating modes include the following. Air-to-air modes: range-while-search, TWS, velocity search, medium-PRF look-up, look-down, raid cluster resolution (raid counting), situation awareness mode, auto-acquisition, ACM (multiple modes, as in APG-66). Air-to-ground modes: real-beam mapping (resolution improved eightfold over that of APG-66), medium resolution mapping, Doppler beam sharpening, scan freeze, ground target MTI/tracking, ground moving target rejection (fixed-target tracking), air-to-ground ranging. There is also a sea-search mode. MTBF increases to 150 hr, but the increased complexity of the radar is reflected in an MTTR of 30 min. APG-68 entered service in 1984. A version of this radar, APQ-164, equips the B-1B bomber.

W-160 is a Westinghouse private-venture shipboard FCS based on APG-66, presumably using the same transmitter and receiver. Peak power is 16 kW; there are eight pulse width/PRF choices between 1 microsec/14,200 pps and 10 microsec/1000 pps. The 42in reflector has an effective aperture of 36 in (gain 36 dB, 2.5-deg beam); range on a 1 sq m. target is 25 nm (instrumented range is 75 km). The monopulse tracker (accuracy better than 1 mrad, 15m) uses six (rather than the usual four) feeds for better ECCM. A 16-bit digital computer (16 kwords of RAM plus 48 kwords of UV EPROM) controls the antenna both for search and for tracking and is powerful enough to calculate gun ballistics, making the system self-contained. This radar also controls SM-1 missiles.

In addition to its six track modes (two surface, four air), W-160 has nine search modes (five surface search, including sea-skimmer detection, and four air search, at 15 rpm). At low elevation angles, the radar tracks off-boresight to avoid multipath problems. Claimed MTBF is 600 hr (MTTR is 30 min).

Users: APG-66: Argentina (as ARG-1, in 36 A-4s modified 1995), Belgium (F-16), Denmark (F-16), Egypt (F-16), Indonesia (F-16 and Hawk 200), Israel (F-16), Japan (F-4EJ), Malaysia (Hawk 208), Netherlands (F-16), New Zealand (A-4K), Norway (F-16), Oman (Hawk 203), Pakistan (F-16), Portugal (F-16), Saudi Arabia (Hawk 205), Singapore (F-16), Taiwan (AT-3 and F-16), Thailand (F-16), United States (F-16, six Coast Guard HU-25s, Customs Service Piper Cheyenne), Venezuela (F-16). As of spring 1996, the Westinghouse surveillance aircraft had not yet attracted any sales. The RNZAF A-4 system improvement program was Kaku (Hawk), using a small-antenna version of the radar. The program began early in 1985, and the contract was signed in 1986. These aircraft are optimized for shipping strikes using Maverick missiles. The upgrade included a Ferranti HUD/WAC, an ALR-66 ESM set, and an ALE-39 chaff dispenser. Other weapons used by these aircraft are GBU-16 laser-guided bombs and Canadian CRV-7 rockets.

APG-68 (all F-16s): Bahrein, Egypt, Greece, Israel, Singapore, South Korea, Turkey, United States.

W-160: Taiwan (Wu Jinn III destroyers, in MCS CDS).

◆ APG-76/Gray Wolf

Band: Ka (28 GHz)
Beam: 1.4 × 35–50 deg (FoR: 120 × 60 deg [+20/−40 deg])
Peak Power: Approx. 60 kW
Pulse Width: 4 alternatives, including 0.4, 1.25, and 3.0 microsec
Antenna Dimensions: 66 × 54 cm

Westinghouse Norden's Multi-Mode Radar System (MMRS) was originally developed for the Israeli Phantom 2000 program. It is a heavily modified derivative of the APQ-156 used on board A-6E attack aircraft. The first radars were shipped in 1991. This radar had both SAR and MTI capabilities against ground targets. It dealt with slow target speeds by using a powerful clutter-suppression interferometer (CSI), giving a clutter-free moving target image that can be overlaid by a simultaneous SAR image. That led to a 1993 U.S. Navy concept for a podded version, to be carried by an S-3. In 1995 the idea was tested in Project Gray Wolf. APG-76 was used as an OTH-T asset, using the radar's SAR and MTI capability. The APG-76 can also identify stationary and moving vehicles, providing some of the capability offered by JSTARS during the early stages of a conflict, before land-based surveillance aircraft would be available. Presumably any operational installation would include a down-link to a ship carrying radar operators.

This radar does simultaneous SAR and MTI. It has three high-resolution SAR modes (within +/−10 deg of the aircraft track) in baseline configuration, labeled by the area they cover (at 80nm range): SAR 5 (5 × 5 nm, 60ft resolution), SAR 2.5 (2.5 × 2.5 nm, 30ft resolution), SAR .8 (or SAR Spotlight), 0.8 × 0.8 nm, resolution 10 ft. In the Doppler beam sharpening mode the radar covers a 14 × 14nm patch at 60nm range with 180ft resolution. There is also a real beam mode (normal mode), and a high-resolution ground-mapping mode offering 1ft resolution at 35 nm. The radar was designed to produce an image at 40 nm, but the high power required to penetrate weather routinely gives images at 100 nm or more. The figures given above refer to patch sizes at a fixed range; the radar achieves, for example, a resolution of 1 ft at 30 nm. The antenna is roll-stabilized within +/−110 deg.

Norden's 1995 internal R&D program improved signal processing and changed waveforms to achieve 1m and 0.3m resolution. Images of this quality should be useful in implementing an automatic target recognition capability. Because this is a multichannel (multiple RF and IF channels) radar with multiple antenna ports with a unique architecture, it is being used to explore

and demonstrate 3D SAR and Interferometric MT Focusing for clear imagery of moving ground targets.

Gray Wolf was demonstrated very successfully on 19 January 1995: aircraft on a ramp could be seen and counted. In June, the House of Representatives voted to add $15M to Gray Wolf R&D funding.

Gray Wolf uses the S-3B cargo pod; an Air Force version, which will probably be adopted by all the services, uses a 600-gallon tank. The first S-3B version was delivered in October 1994. An Air Force equivalent, originally called Snake Eyes, was tested in the spring of 1995 under the auspices of the Air Force JAST program office.

◆ APQ-126

Band: Ku (seven selectable frequencies, 600-MHz band)
Beam: 2.5 × 18.4 deg (antenna tilts to cover 45 × +70/−30 deg)
Peak Power: 60 kW
Gain: 28.5 dB
Pulse Width: (a) 0.2 (b) 1 (c) 2 microsec
PRF: (a) 3600 (b) 720 (c) 360 pps
Scan Rate: 90, 120, 180 deg/sec (horizontal); 150 deg/sec (vertical)
Antenna Dimensions: 19.5 × 13 in
Antenna Weight: 45 lb (230 lb total)

Although the A-7E is no longer in U.S. service, this Texas Instruments radar survives on board aircraft in Greece, Portugal, and Thailand, many of which are intended primarily for maritime missions. Frequency agility (over a 30-MHz range at a switching rate of 100 Hz) is used to improve ranging accuracy and to achieve long-range target detection.

◆ APQ-156/APS-130/APS-146

APQ-156, Norden's Ku-band A-6E radar, survives on board most EA-6Bs as APQ-156C. APQ-156 has an interferometer (two rows of 32 horns each) to track a surface target in elevation, for what amounts to 3D location. The interferometer is also used for terrain avoidance. The main antenna produces a 1.4 × 35–50-deg beam and uses a 60-kW frequency-agile transmitter. Maximum instrumented range is 150 nm. Some aircraft have the simplified APS-146, which omits the interferometer but adds a weather-avoidance pencil beam. It replaces the reflector antenna of APQ-156 with a flat planar array. See the 1991/92 edition for further details.

◆ APS-80A/APS-115

Band: X
Beam: 2.4 × 3.6 deg (80A: 3.6-deg pencil beam, 18-deg csc² fan beam)
Peak Power: 143 kW
Gain: 34 dB (80A: 35 dB)
Pulse Width: (a) 2.5 (b) 0.5 microsec
PRF: (a) 400 (b) 1600 pps
Scan Rate: 6 or 12 rpm; sector scan 36 or 72 deg/sec (80A: 6 rpm/ 45-deg sector scan at 48 scan/min)
Antenna Dimensions: 42 in (80A: 42 × 24 in)
Antenna Weight: 84 lb (each); total system weight 523 lb

These Texas Instruments radars equip most P-3s. Each has nose and tail (under the MAD "stinger") antennas to provide full 360-deg coverage, but in APS-115 both are part of a single unit (otherwise a pair of APS-80As are integrated by a single PPI). Each antenna covers a 210-deg sector. APS-115 is an ATD radar introduced in the P-3C, to provide digital input to the airplane's digital combat system. Some users feel that, in the hands of an experienced operator, the analog APS-80 has a better chance of detecting a small target, such as a periscope, in sea clutter. Except as noted, data above apply to APS-115.

Users:

APS-80: Chile (P-3A), Greece (P-3B), Portugal (P-3P), Spain (P-3A/B), Thailand (P-3T).

APS-115: Australia (P-3C), Iran (P-3F), Japan (P-3C), Korea (P-3C), Netherlands (P-3C), Norway (P-3C), United States (P-3C).

◆ APS-88

Band: X (8.5–9.6 GHz)
Beam: 2.6 × 5.0 or 3.2 × 18.0 csc^2 deg (coverage: 40 × +10/−25 deg)
Peak Power: 45 kW
Gain: 33.5 dB
Pulse Width: (a) 0.35 (b) 0.8 (c) 4.5 microsec
PRF: (a) 2000 (b) 1025 (c) 200 pps
Scan Rate: 6 or 28 rpm; sector scan 36 deg/sec
Antenna Dimensions: 42 × 20 in
Antenna Weight: 61 lb (total 228 lb)

APS-88 is the periscope-detection and surface-search radar of S-2 Trackers.

Users: Peru (S-2E/G) and Uruguay (S-2A/G). Of other S-2 users, Argentina, Brazil, and Taiwan all announced modernization programs, although it is possible that this program will not be completed in Argentina. Thailand and Turkey have both retired their fleets (the Turkish aircraft are for sale). South Korea is retiring aircraft as P-3Cs are delivered.

◆ APS-116/134/137/506/SV/CP

Band: X (9.5–10.0 GHz)
Beam: 2.4 × 4.0 deg
Peak Power: 500 kW
Gain: 34 dB
Pulse Width (compressed): (i) .0025 (ii) 0.5 (iii) .012 (iv) .012 microsec (all pulses are transmitted at 0.5 microsec duration). (Compression ratio 250:1.)
PRF: (i) 2000 (ii) 400 (iii) 400 (iv) 400/2000 pps
Scan Rate: (i) 300 (ii) 6 (iii) 60 (iv) searchlight, for ISAR
Antenna Weight: Total system weight is 472 lb

These data apply to APS-137.

Manufactured by Texas Instruments, APS-116 is a coherent (MTI) high-resolution (short-pulse) radar. For periscope detection amid the clutter of rough water, or for high-altitude surveillance, this radar rejects clutter by using pulse compression and fast-scan processing. APS-116 has TWS capability but can also operate in a searchlight mode, tracking a single small target. Modes are (i) periscope and small-target detection, (ii) navigation and weather avoidance, (iii) long-range maritime surveillance, and (iv) ISAR imaging.

Performance in test: 26nm range on a snorkel (aircraft at 1500 ft), 33 nm on a FAC (from 5000 ft), 75 nm on a destroyer (8000–10,000 ft). These are maximum ranges in Sea State 3/4; mean ranges were shorter. For example, the average range on a snorkel was 15.5 nm. Minimum resolution is 1.5 ft.

APS-134 is the "international successor" to APS-116, incorporating the latter's less sensitive improvements and a fast-scan antenna. Modes are (i) periscope detection in clutter, with high resolution (1.5 ft): 2000 pps, 150 rpm, 32nm display, adjustable false-alarm rate; (ii) long-range search/navigation, with medium

A typical ISAR image. (Texas Instruments)

(250 ft) resolution: 500 pps, 6 rpm, 150nm scale; (iii) maritime surveillance, with high resolution (short pulses): 500 pps, 40 rpm, 150nm scale.

APS-134(+) has a better signal processor, a dual-channel digital scan converter, and can incorporate ESM features (presumably a shared-aperture ALR-66); it can track 32 surface targets in TWS mode.

In 1995 Texas Instruments announced an APS-134 (LW) family of radars, with two branches: the SV (Sea Vue: three box, high performance, upgradable, with optional ISAR/SAR feature) and CP (Coastal Patrol: two box, low cost, no export restrictions) series.

SV was initially developed for Japanese search-and-rescue aircraft (BAe-125-800 series) and for the Japanese next-generation ASW helicopter, HS(X). It is currently in production for the Japanese air self-defense force. Typical characteristics: 15-kW coherent TWT transmitter (50 kW optional); average power 250 W (500 W optional), linear FM or phase-coded waveform for pulse compression (or simple pulse operation). The stabilized antenna has a nominal gain of 34.5 dB and scans at 6, 60, or 120 rpm. Processing is digital, including multiple TWS. A patrol boat can be detected at 95 nm in Sea State 3, and a destroyer at the instrumented range limit (200 nm).

As advertised in 1995, the CP version uses a 100W average power coherent TWT transmitter using linear FM pulse compression and a 31-dB antenna (scan rates 6, 60, 120 rpm). In Sea State 3, a fishing vessel can be detected at 58 nm. Total weight is less than 50 kg. Signal processing modes lack the high resolution and multiple-target TWS features of the SV series. This system cannot be upgraded to ISAR/SAR performance.

APS-137(V) is a modified APS-116 incorporating ISAR, for the S-3B Viking. It will replace APS-115 on P-3Cs subject to AIP modernization. Current versions: (V)1 for S-3B, (V)2 for P-3C Update III, (V)3 planned for abortive P-3C Update IV (but may be procured to modernize P-3Cs), (V)4 offered to Coast Guard and for similar maritime surveillance. A modified APS-137, probably (V)3, tested in 1991, had upgraded signal processing circuits that doubled its resolution, from 6 to 3 ft. A new helicopter version lost out to Telephonics in the LAMPS III Block II competition.

APS-506 is the Canadian designation for APS-116. Unisys is modifying it to incorporate a "spotlight SAR" mode, that is, a form of SAR that can be pointed at a target, rather than the usual kind that forms an image of a swath parallel to the direction of flight (the radar has to scan, and considerable computer processing is required for the new mode). The modified radar will have three real-time imaging modes: range-Doppler profiling (ISAR), strip-map, and spotlight. The advanced development model is to be ready for installation late in 1996.

Users: APS-116: Canada (CP-140 and Arcturus as APS-506), United States (S-3A and EP-3).

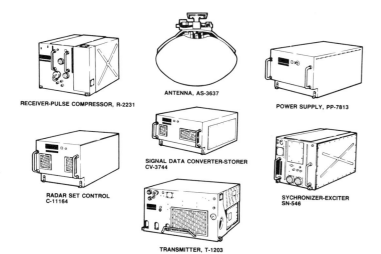

RECEIVER-PULSE COMPRESSOR, R-2231

ANTENNA, AS-3637

POWER SUPPLY, PP-7813

RADAR SET CONTROL C-11164

SIGNAL DATA CONVERTER-STORER CV-3744

SYCHRONIZER-EXCITER SN-546

TRANSMITTER, T-1203

APS-137(V)1. (Texas Instruments)

APS-134: Australia (Coastwatch service, on board civil DASH-8s), Germany (Atlantic as modernized), New Zealand (P-3K), Portugal (P-3P), Pakistan (P-3C), Singapore ([V]7 in Maritime Enforcer Mk 2), United States (Coast Guard HC-130H; six bought 1984); total 31 made through 1990. In the Australian aircraft, the radar and a FLIR/TV turret (Wescam 16DS Dual Sensor) feed the same mission console.

APS-137: Canada (EH-101), United States (S-3B, some P-3C [AIP], EP-3E CILOPs, Coast Guard HC-130H). Japan specified this radar for a planned P-3C upgrade, but as of mid-1995 no contract had yet been signed.

♦ APS-124

Band: X
Beam: 1.2 × 20 deg
Peak Power: 350 kW
Pulse Width: (a) 0.5 (b) 2 (c) 1 microsec
PRF: (a) 1885 (b) 940 (c) 470 (16-period staggered PRF) pps
Scan Rate: (a) 120 (for weather) (b) 6 (c) 12 rpm
Antenna Dimensions: 72 × 12in planar array
Antenna Weight: Total system weight is 208 lb

APS-124 is Texas Instruments' sea-search radar of the LAMPS III (SH-60) helicopter. Small targets are detected in the midst of sea clutter by sea-clutter decorrelation (fast scanning and scan-to-scan integration). With a low profile, the antenna can be slung under the helicopter, for full 360-deg coverage. The short-pulse rapid-scan mode is for weather. Estimated range on a 1m² target is 16 nm, compared to 20 nm for APS-115 or -116.

The antenna is AS-4035.

ANTENNA, AS-4035/APS-124

TRANSMITTER UNITS
T-1308/APS-124
C-9889/APS-124

SIGNAL DATA CONVERTER CV-3204/A

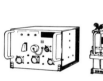

CONVERTER CONTROL C-9643/A

RECEIVER/SYNCHRONIZER
R-1979/APS-124

APS-124. (Texas Instruments)

Users: Japan (SH-60J), Spain (SH-60), United States (SH-60B/F).

♦ APS-127

Band: X
Beam: 5 × 6 deg
Peak Power: 200 kW
Pulse Width: (a) 2 (b) 0.5 microsec
PRF: (a) 400 (b) 1600 pps
Antenna Dimensions: 2 × 2.6 ft
Antenna Weight: Total weight 295 lb

APS-127 is Texas Instruments' surface-search radar for small maritime-patrol aircraft. Estimated range on a 1m² target is 18 nm. APS-127 is unusual in using a stabilized antenna. It integrates successive scans by using a direct-view storage-tube display for both plot and surveillance information.

Users: Denmark (Gulfstream III), United States (Coast Guard HU-25A).

♦ APS-128/APS-143 (formerly APS-128PC)/APS-147

Band: X (9375 MHz)
Beam: 2.4 × 9 deg
Peak Power: 100 kW
Gain: 32 dB
Pulse Width: (a) 2.4 (b) 0.5 microsec
PRF: (a) 400 (b) 1600 pps
Scan Rate: 15 or 60 rpm
Antenna Dimensions: 42 × 11 in

Eaton's (now Telephonics') sea-surveillance radars are for light aircraft, particularly for antismuggling and EEZ enforcement. Eaton had a subcontract with Litton for updated technology in APS-503 and -504. After its license ended, Eaton developed APS-128. APS-143 is a much-modified version; the latest in the series, APS-147, will equip LAMPS III Block II helicopters.

APS-143 installed in a Portuguese CASA-212 maritime reconnaissance airplane. (Author)

The flat-plate array antenna is compensated for pitch and roll up to 20 deg and can be tilted up to 15 deg up or down. The transmitter is frequency-agile (85-MHz peak-to-peak). Claimed MTBF is 442 hr in long-term use.

Unlike most radars, this one uses a television-type (raster-scan) display. The radar signal is converted into a digital signal before display, and the bright 8in (diagonal) tube can be shifted to display the outputs of other sensors, such as FLIRs. The display is bright enough to have signal-processing features, including target enhancement and scan-to-scan integration, so that target tracks can be generated. The radar is also fully integrated with inertial, Omega, or other navigational systems, and the display can be switched to other sensors, such as IR.

Claimed performance: 30nm range on a snorkel or a small fishing vessel (10 m²) in Sea State 3; 60 nm on a trawler (150 m²) in Sea State 5; 100 nm on a freighter (500 m²) in Sea State 5; 120 nm on a tanker (1000 m²) in Sea State 5.

APS-143 is a pulse-compression version (formerly APS-128PC) for small-target detection; the manufacturer claims that resolution is 5 times better than that of standard maritime radars. Frequency is selectable between 9.2 and 9.5 GHz in 20-MHz steps, and there is 100-MHz pulse-to-pulse frequency agility. Peak power is 8 kW minimum (10 kW nominal) but equivalent to 500 kW (50:1 compression ratio), for 5-microsec pulses (compressed to 0.1 microsec); there are also 17 microsec pulses (compression ratio 240:1). PRFs are 2000, 1500, 800, and 400 Hz. Claimed performance: Detects a 1m² target at 37 km in Sea State 3 from low altitude. Azimuth accuracy is 0.5 deg, and range resolution is 46 m. Total weight is 81.8 kg. The radar can be fitted for TWS and MTI and for missile guidance; it can interface with ESM or IFF. Maximum range is 370 km. The display is a digital raster-scan unit; memory is 512 × 512 × 3 pixels for video, and 512 × 512 × 1 for overlay graphics. Versions: (V)1 for Coast

Guard aerostats (shipboard balloons), (V)2 for U.S. Air Force for range surveillance and safety, (V)3 for naval helicopters (already selected for the Sikorsky S-70C[M]1 and for the NATO frigate helicopter, NH 90). Telephonics describes it as the lightest, least expensive pulse-compression radar of its type in existence. Total system weight (APS-143) is 180 lb.

Telephonics offers DTACS, the Digital Tactical System, an APS-128 plus added sensor capacity, with tactical-navigation and sensor-plot data displayed on the radar screen via microprocessor control. DTACS is installed on Puerto Rican police Beech 200T aircraft and has been offered as an S-2E or helicopter system.

APS-147 (multimode radar, or MMR), a follow-on to APS-143, was chosen in late 1993 for the LAMPS III Block II upgrade (SH-60R). It uses a modified APS-143 antenna pedestal but has a new transmitter, receiver, and signal processor. This is an ISAR radar with periscope detection capability (i.e., with improved clutter reduction). Telephonics is also developing an ISAR version of APS-143.

Telephonics describes APS-147 as an LPI radar, using a variety of waveforms and frequency agility to detect targets at medium to long ranges at a much lower peak power than that required by earlier radars. The signal processor is fully programmable, and the radar uses a multiple-waveform exciter. The design is described as flexible and modular, which presumably means that the radar is built around a local bus. Modes: target imaging (ISAR), small target (periscope) detection, long-range surveillance, weather detection and avoidance, all-weather navigation, short-range search and rescue, enhanced LPI search, and target designation.

Users: APS-128: Argentina (4 navy CASA-212 with APS-128D), Brazil (16 air force EMB-111), Chile (8 navy EMB-111: SAR-1 radar), Japan (22 Maritime Safety Agency Beech 200T with APS-128A/B, 2 Maritime Safety Agency Falcon Jet F-900s with APS-128D), Gabon (1 air force EMB-111 with SAR-1 radar), Indonesia (2 C-130MP with APS-128), Malaysia (7 C-130MP with APS-128B), Portugal (3 APS-128D for CASA-212s), Singapore (5 air force Skyvans with APS-128D; may have been retired), Spain (retrofit of 7 air force C-130 with APS-128D, 1 customs CASA-212 with APS-128D), United States (1 NASA Skyvan with APS-128E, 1 Puerto Rican police Beech 200T with APS-128D), Uruguay (1 navy Beech 200T with APS-128A), Venezuela (4 navy CASA-212 with APS-128D). SAR-1 (search and rescue version) had the frequency-agility feature deleted, to comply with export restrictions.

APS-143: Greece (8 S-70C with [V]3), Israel (6 Panthers with [V]3 on order), Japan (A[V]1 version for Maritime Safety Agency Saab 340Bs), Malaysia (5 air force Beech 200T with A[V]1), Taiwan (13 S-70C with [V]3), Thailand (6 navy S-70C with [V]3), United States (2 Air Force DASH-8s with [V]1 version, 11 Coast Guard aerostates with [V]2). In addition, there is a (V)2 on a commercial demonstrator aerostat operated by TCOM Limited Partnership.

APS-147: United States (naval SH-60R).

◆ APS-131/135/SLAMMR

These are Motorola X-band, side-looking, SAR radars. APS-131 and -135 are used by the U.S. Coast Guard to detect ships and boats as well as oil slicks. SLAMMR (side-looking airborne modular multimission radar) is a commercial version. APS-131 uses two 8ft slotted arrays mounted back to back in a stabilized pod carried under the belly of an HU-25A aircraft. There are four range settings: 13.5, 27, 54, and 108 nm. APS-131 has a peak power of 200 kW (0.2-microsec pulses, PRF 677 or 1477 pps) and produces a 1-deg beam. APS-135 is a similar radar carried by Coast Guard HC-130s. Its two 16ft antennas are mounted on the sides of the fuselage. The fan beam is 0.5 deg wide (csc² fan). In both cases, the output of the radar is a film image analogous to a strip map.

The 16ft SLAMMR antenna gives 0.5-deg resolution in azimuth. Peak power is 200 kW (generated by a magnetron; a 0.2-microsec pulse makes for 30m range resolution). Despite the noncoherent design, there is very good pulse-to-pulse stability

SLAMMR radar occupies the dorsal strake, aft, on this Indonesian Boeing 737. (Motorola)

for MTI; the optional MTI processor uses an FFT to detect targets simultaneously from 0 to 80 nm. Flying at 30,000 ft, SLAMMR can detect a 100m² target out to 100 nm (for maritime surveillance), depending on ocean conditions and aircraft speed and altitude. It can detect a 1m² target out to 35 nm. With the MTI processor, it can detect small targets moving at 5 mph at 50 nm and larger and faster targets at 80 nm. The single operator station uses either a dry film display or a color CRT. Current upgrades include a high-resolution digital recorder.

Users: Egypt (8ft SLAMMR in Beech 1900), Indonesia (16ft SLAMMR in Boeing 737-200 and C-130H), Saudi Arabia (C-130H), United States (7 HU-25B, 2 HC-130H); it is probably aboard several other C-130s in the Middle East. This is probably the SLAR on board Moroccan C-130s used for surveillance during the Polisario war. Probably 14 have been sold to foreign users. The Indonesian 737s have been rebuilt with MPAvionics suites and digital radar processors.

◆ APS-138/139/145

Band: UHF (400–450 MHz)
Beam: 7×20 deg
Peak Power: 1 MW
Gain: 21.5 dB
Pulse Width: 13 microsec (compressed to 0.2 microsec)
PRF: 300 pps
Scan Rate: 6 rpm
Antenna Dimensions: 2.5×24 ft (in rotodome)
Antenna Weight: 1700 lb

Lockheed Martin's standard U.S. naval airborne early-warning radar equips the Grumman E-2C Hawkeye. Although APS-138 and its relatives are primarily intended for air search, they have a very significant surface-search capability: aircraft equipped with these radars can control antiship attacks. Data given above are for APS-96, the defunct predecessor to the current series, to give some idea of overall characteristics. They are comparable to those of the SPS-40 UHF shipboard radar.

UHF frequency was chosen for maximum ability to detect small targets at long range (based partly on available transmitter power), much as it had been chosen for shipboard radars. Earlier S-band AEW radars suffered considerable transmission losses at long range. The radar uses pulse compression for high resolution and AMTI to overcome sea clutter.

The antenna is an array of two rows each of 8 yagis (one row of 12 in earlier versions) in a rotodome (a rotating radome) 24 ft in diameter and 2.5 ft deep. It uses monopulse processing to achieve narrow beam definition in the horizontal plane, dividing the antenna in half and comparing sum and difference signals, which are separately pulse-compressed. Two auxiliary antennas are used for sidelobe cancellation. The radar measures target altitude by measuring the time difference in reception of pulses reflected directly by the target and pulses that have reflected off the surface as well as the target (either coming or going or both). This technique is probably ineffective over land, which is not highly reflective.

APS-138, the earliest of the series still in service, has airborne ADT and a more stable (and reliable) 10-channel transmitter (introduced in APS-120) than earlier versions. It introduced the current antenna and a Loral array processor capable of maintaining

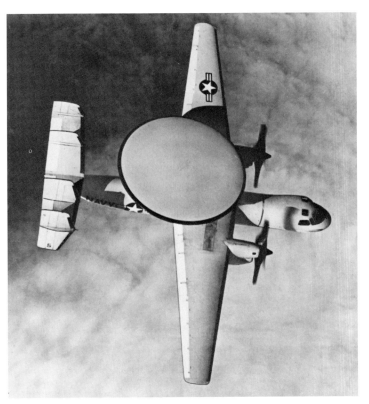

The Grumman Hawkeye carries an air-search radar comparable in size to that found on board a major surface ship. (Grumman)

600 track files (compared to 300 for its predecessor, APS-125). Maximum range is 250 nm, and APS-138 can reportedly track a cruise missile at a range of 150 nm. It was introduced in 1983, and all U.S. APS-125s were ordered upgraded to -138 standard. That probably also applies to export sets.

The overall effect of own-aircraft motion is approximated by a phase shift applied to the returning signal. Static targets (clutter) show no additional shift due to their own velocity. This type of processing, which improves the signal-to-clutter ratio by 55 dB, is possible because the radar transmitter is so stable. Surface clutter is worst at short ranges, the altitude of the airplane determining the point at which detection markedly improves. This point is at a range of about 170 nm for an E-2C at 23,000 ft over land.

After pulse compression, signals are digitized and passed through an FFT for Doppler processing. Because the radar's PRF is very low (to achieve long unambiguous range), the first blind speed is also very low (200 kt corresponds to the nominal PRF, 300 pps), so velocity is likely to be ambiguous. However, because the antenna rotates slowly, a target is painted many times while it is in the main beam (dwell period). The radar can estimate its velocity by observing the change of range during the dwell, to resolve velocity ambiguity.

There is still a problem. The radar finds it difficult to detect a target within 25 kt of a blind speed (notch); it functions best in the 130kt range around its optimum detection speeds. PRF is varied periodically to insure that targets do not fall into the 50kt-wide notches around the blind speeds.

APS-139, which entered service in 1989, is a further improvement with better ECCM and better surface-search performance. Reportedly it can maintain over 2400 tracks simultaneously. It was introduced in aircraft number 122 and fitted to 17 later aircraft.

APS-145 is a digital radar (all earlier ones were analog) of Group II aircraft. It is capable of fully automatic overland ADT. The operational area is divided into over 4000 cells (range interval × beamwidth), returns from each of which can be processed separately (adaptively) on the basis of the clutter and traffic in that cell; parameters are readjusted on each radar scan. PRF is

reduced to permit detections at ranges as great as 350 nm (effective range is 40% better than APS-138) and the scan rate is reduced from 6 to 5 rpm. Using three PRFs eliminates blind speeds and provides continuous overland ADT. Radar volume nearly doubles, and the number of targets that can be detected increases by a factor of 16. An enhanced high-speed processor increases track-file capacity by 400%, to over 20,000. A new main display unit expands E-2C display capability by almost a factor of 10. APS-145 has improved scan-to-scan correlation, automatic frequency evaluation and selection (to avoid jamming and EMI; automatically selects clearest operating frequency), continuous target identification using triple PRF to detect targets over land, sea, and beyond the horizon simultaneously.

APS-145 introduced automatic transmitter channel selection on the basis of monitoring, to avoid jamming (as well as to avoid some civilian signals: in Japan, for example, to avoid interference with taxi-radio signals). Channels are selected afresh on each scan (every 12 sec). A proposed 100-channel transmitter was rejected as unnecessary.

APS-145 entered service in 1990.

See also the description of the E-2C system in the Combat Direction System section.

Users: Egypt (E-2C: APS-138), France (E-2C: APS-145), Israel (E-2C: APS-138), Japan (APS-145), Singapore, Taiwan (E-2T: APS-138), United States (E-2C and Customs Service P-3: APS-138, -139, and -145). Japan was the first export customer to upgrade to APS-145. Radars are sometimes referred to as APS-125; it is not entirely clear how completely export radars were upgraded from -125 to -138.

◆ ASQ-173

The pod-mounted F/A-18 laser spot-tracker/strike camera (LST/SCAM) is manufactured by Martin Marietta. The stabilized LST occupies the forward end of the pod. The system picks up a target designated by a ground- or air-based laser, feeding digital target data into the F/A-18 FCS and indicating target position on the HUD. The target is acquired at maximum standoff range on the first pass, reducing aircraft vulnerability; and communication between the attack pilot and the forward air controller or ground-target designator is minimized. The 35mm strike camera at the after end of the pod is gimballed so that the target can be photographed while the attacking airplane maneuvers. Dimensions: 8 × 90 in, weight 155 lb, required MTBF at least 333 hr. This pod occupies the space on the starboard side of the F/A-18 body otherwise occupied by a Sparrow missile.

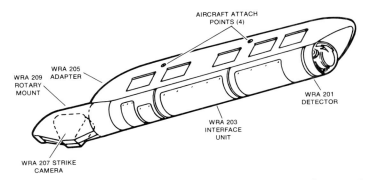

F/A-18 laser spot tracker/strike camera (LST/SCAM, or AN/ASQ-173). (Martin Marietta)

◆ AVX-1 (Cluster Ranger)

This near-IR (3–5-micron) imaging video camera is being adopted for P-3s to provide them with long-range standoff from surface targets they are observing. The system's telescope, mounted inside the airplane, looks out through a flat panel. The telescope feeds an IR camera whose output can be observed either directly or at a monitor. The combination of telescope and monitor allows the operator to zoom in the monitor while using the telescope to achieve long range. The image can also be transmitted via data link in real time. As of early 1995, two data links were competing: one (developed by Warminster) based on the Pioneer UAV link, the other based on a Photokinesis (San Antonio) link developed to transmit ground-intelligence images back to the United States via satellite (it was developed for the Drug Enforcement Administration).

Cluster Ranger was conceived as a trials device (codenamed Cast Eyes and Cast Glance) for the Pacific Missile Test Center, then was picked up by the Naval Air Development Center at Warminster, Pennsylvania. It was first installed on board a a Special Projects P-3. The prototype was borrowed by the fleet, used in Haiti, then in Caribbean counter-drugs operations, and also overland, in Bosnia.

Norway received one of the two prototypes about 1994. The U.S. Customs Service is getting Cluster Ranger, and others are reportedly interested.

◆ AWG-9/APG-71

Band: X
Beam: 2.3 deg
Peak Power: 10 kW (average: up to 7 kW in pulse-Doppler mode, up to 500 W in pulse mode)
Pulse Width: 0.4 and 50 microsec (pulse) 0.4, 1.3, 2.0, 2.7 microsec (pulse-Doppler)
Scan Rate: Horizontal: 80 deg/sec; vertical: 2 scans/sec
Antenna Dimensions: 36 in (gain 37.5 dB)

Data above date to the early 1970s. Current AWG-9 characteristics have probably been modified. The AWG-9 designation embraces not only the pulse-Doppler radar described here but also the airplane mission computer which provides an air-to-air TWS capability. The system as a whole tracks 24 targets and can engage six simultaneously with Phoenix missiles. See the F-14 entry in the Combat Direction Systems section.

The F-14 Tomcat's pulse-Doppler radar is built by Hughes. It weighs about 1300 lb, and volume is about 28 cu ft. The planar-array antenna has 12 (6 × 2) IFF dipoles on its face. AWG-9 uses raster-scan patterns consisting of a series of horizontal single beamwidth bars. They range from 8 bars and 65 deg (to either side of the airplane every 13 sec) down to 1 bar and 10 deg every quarter-second. Other azimuth limits are 20 and 40 deg; there are 1-, 2-, 4-, and 8-bar patterns. In an alternative vertical-scan lock-on (VSL) mode the radar sweeps a 4.8-deg-wide beam up and down a 40-deg vertical sector centered at +5 to +35 deg.

Pulse-Doppler modes: pulse-Doppler search (PDS, range rate and bearing only: detects a 5m² target at 115 nm); range-while-search (RWS, to 90 nm: range, range rate, and bearing); TWS (for Phoenix missiles: to 90 nm, forming a complete track file, and limited to 2 bars/40 deg or 4 bars/20 deg to achieve the required 2-sec data rate); pulse-Doppler single-target-track (PDSTT, including both velocity tracking and jam-angle tracking, JAT). Conventional pulse modes: pulse search (PS, out to 63 nm) and pulse single-target-track (PSTT, out to 49 nm). Mixed modes: vertical-scan lock-on and manual rapid lock-on, both to 5 nm, a range presumably determined by the spacing of the Doppler pulses. There are pulse-Doppler and pulse modes slaved to the television sensor (AXX-1). A planned lock-on centered on the pilot's LOS was presumably dropped when the Navy abandoned its helmet-mounted sight in the late 1970s.

In the F-14D, AWG-9 is replaced by APG-71. This radar retains the original transmitter and power supply, but incorporates some APG-70 (F-15C/D/E; replacement for APG-63) technology (signal processors are 86% common). APG-71 has a new broadband master radar oscillator. There is also a new receiver with a new high-speed analog-to-digital converter and better Doppler resolution.

Because most analog radar functions are replaced by digital equivalents, APG-71 has a programmable signal processor (for multimode operation). It improves overland performance and provides new ground-mapping and ground-attack modes. The usual separate head-on and tail-on target modes are replaced by a single new radar waveform developed for the APG-70: range-gated high PRF (200,000 pps), using a combination of range gates and Doppler filters (20,000 filters, 500 per range gate).

The radar also has a more flexible target-engagement zone, a new long-range raid-counting mode, a noncooperative identification capability, and programmable ECCM and clutter control.

Because the antenna is now digitally controlled, it is no longer constrained to fixed bar patterns, which might prevent it from detecting some targets widely separated vertically. Too, instead of sweeping all the way across a bar before shifting to the one below, the scan can be interrupted to update the track of a target before returning to the bar. In TWS mode (which requires that a target be painted every 2 sec), the antenna can be commanded to "steal" an occasional scan to look at other targets of interest.

The new signal processor has four units compared to three in the F-15 and operates at 40 MCOPS. The associated digital data processor operates at 3.2 MIPS.

APG-71 flight tests, on board a converted TA-3B, began in July 1987.

◆ TCS (AXX-1)

Northrop's television camera sight for the F-14A incorporates a stabilized long-range telescope in a chin pod. The 10× telescope can scan over a 30-deg FOV. It can scan independently or it can be slaved to the AWG-9 radar for target identification. Instantaneous FOV is selectable as either narrow (0.44 deg) or wide (1.42 deg); the black-and-white image is presented on the pilot's vertical display indicator and on the radar officer's tactical information display. This image is captured by a video recorder on board the fighter.

TCS was introduced to provide fighters with a means of positively identifying targets even at very long range, so that the planes could use their long-range AAMs effectively. Prior to the advent of the TCS, typical rules of engagement required the fighter virtually to fly alongside its target before firing. That handicap was unacceptable when enemy aircraft carried long-range AAMs.

Navy tests of a television sight unit began in 1977. Typical effective range was 9 nm, compared to 2 or 3 for the unaided eye; reportedly observers could even decide what sort of stores the observed aircraft were carrying. That was certainly the case for the TCS-equipped F-14s in the 1989 Libyan incident. The sight was tested at sea, on board the carriers Kennedy and Constellation, in the summer of 1978, proving particularly successful in reconnaissance. An airplane detecting a ship on radar could slave TVSU to the radar image and obtain a usable ship image at a range as great as 50 mi. Production (as TCS) began in 1981; TCS equips all F-14s.

◆ Helmet-Mounted Sight

Largely inspired by the Russian helmet sight, the U.S. Air Force and Navy are jointly developing their own Joint Helmet-Mounted Cueing System (JHMCS), which is to enter service about 2001 on board F-15C and F/A-18C fighters (plus F-14s if they have sufficient remaining service lifetime). This program follows a number of earlier failures. Perhaps the most prominent was a Navy/Marine Honeywell Visual Target Acquisition System (VTAS), about 500 of which were used on board F-4s in 1973–79. It used an IR tracker to determine head position, cueing a radar which in turn aligned the missile seeker. Alternatively, the missile could be cued directly. The radar or the missile seeker could also cue the pilot, using four lights (up/down, left/right) at the edges of the sight reticle (accuracy was 1–2 deg). VTAS was withdrawn partly because contemporary Sidewinders were too limited to exploit its capabilities, but partly also because it lacked feedback in the form of verification of the missile seeker aimpoint. For example, at large head angles it was never entirely clear whether the seeker had locked onto a false target, such as a warm cloud or even a wingman. On the other hand, simulations showed that VTAS doubled a pilot's kill ratio, and pilots liked it. VTAS lost much of its attraction as attention turned to longer-range AAMs.

In 1985 some MiG-29s visited Finland. All were clearly equipped with helmet sights. About that time the Air Force began a new helmet-mounted display program, Vista Sabre (which was succeeded in 1993 by Vista Sabre 2 and Vista Sabre Navy). Vista Sabre 2 is currently evaluating existing helmets in hopes of developing appropriate specifications for a next-generation affordable Visually Coupled Acquisition and Targeting System (VCATS). The program runs through August 1996 before transitioning to the VCATS acquisition program. It is complemented by the Air Force's First Shot Integrated Product Team, which studies integration with the projected next-generation dogfighting missile. Test engagements are flown by one F-14A (with a Kaiser Electronics helmet), two F-15Cs (Kaiser Electronics helmet), and one F-18C (Elbit DASH helmet). All carry captive missile seekers, Raytheon units in the F-15Cs and China Lake units in the Navy fighters.

The U.S. concept is to turn the helmet visor into a HUD. One advantage of such an approach is that the pilot always has access to key data, no matter which way he turns. Thus the helmet includes a small CRT projecting its symbology onto the faceplate, using characters bright enough to be visible in strong sunlight. At the same time, something in the cockpit must track the helmet, both as a way of inserting pilot heading into the airplane's weapon system and as a way of making sure that the HUD-like display coincides with the pilot's direction. As the pilot moves his head, the helmet shakes slightly, and a very sensitive helmet tracker may pick up too much head movement. Too, any tracker introduces a lag into the system as a whole. The combination of shake and lag introduces a pointing error. The new generation dogfighting AAMs have relatively narrow FOVs, mainly to exclude clutter and to avoid locking onto the wrong target as they are fired far off-boresight. One important question, then, is just how much error they can tolerate.

Under the VCATS program, McDonnell-Douglas received a contract in May 1994 for a producible prototype helmet to meet Vista Sabre 2 requirements. It uses the Kaiser display, a Smiths Industries graphics processor, a 3/4in CRT (rather than the usual 1/2in CRT), and a 240-Hz tracker (for a 4-msec delay in measurement; the current 60-Hz tracker imposes a 16-msec delay). The pilot's FOV is 20 deg, which is typical of HUDs and seems sufficient for dogfighting. The helmet can carry either a daytime visor or night-vision glasses. A special direct link to avionics should minimize delays, which currently amount to 50–100 msec for one-way bus transmission. Even so, total delay between a pilot's designation and action may be as great as a tenth of a second (100 msec). Pilots will sense that sort of delay, and will try to correct, with unhappy results (the Russians solved this problem by demanding less precision of their systems). The VCATS helmet should fly in an F-15C in August 1996.

VCATS is a step toward JHMCS, the contract for which is to be let about October 1996. Problems with the joint approach include the fact that the two services use different helmet shells and different avionics architectures. Likely competitors include Honeywell, possibly teamed with GEC-Marconi, Kaiser Electronics, Elbit, and Sextant Avionique. Elbit's DASH (Display and Sight Helmet) has been in Israeli service since 1986 and is being tested in Vista Sabre 2. The current third-generation version became operational in 1996. Elbit claims many international sales and a backlog of 500 helmets to equip 350 aircraft in six programs. Presumably sales include China. The company claims that pilots using its helmet enjoy a 3:1 advantage when firing standard Sidewinders (AIM-9M), but a 9:1 advantage when they (and their opponents) both have high off-boresight missiles such as AIM-9X.

◆ HISAR

Hughes's Integrated Synthetic Aperture Radar was announced in 1995. It is intended specifically for executive-class aircraft such as the Beech 1900. Modes are wide-area search, strip-map coverage with medium resolution (strip map), high-resolution imaging (spot), dedicated ocean reconnaissance (sea surveillance), and air-to-air. HISAR can image targets at very long range and offers MTI.

Wide area search is a side-looking scanning mode with MTI; it permits detection of both ships and surface wakes. The search sector covers more than 5600 sq km, and a scan is completed in less than 75 sec. It incorporates a selectable MTI, to alert the operator. Strip map is a conventional SAR mode, offering coverage of over 10,000 sq km/hr with MTI. Spot is spot SAR, offering high resolution in a limited area, for example, to estimate vehicle size. Sea surveillance is conventional scanning (300-deg sector) out to a range of 110 km; the radar scans a sector 74 km deep in 15 sec or a 150-deg sector on one side in 7.5 sec. The operator can switch from sea surveillance to spot or strip-map modes. The air-to-air mode is a two-bar 300-deg scan performed in 20 sec.

◆ RDR-1300/1400/1500/APN-215

Band: X (9305–9385 MHz; 9310 MHz beacon); RDR-1500: 9370–9380 MHz; 9305–9315 MHz beacon
Beam: 2.6 or 3.4 × 10.5 deg (in RDR-1500)
Peak Power: 10 kW
Pulse Width: (a) 0.5 (b) 2.35 microsec (RDR-1500: (a) 0.1)
PRF: (a) 800 (b) 200 pps (RDR-1400: (a) 740 (b) 240 pps)
Scan Rate: 12 or 36 looks/min (scan angle 120 or 40 deg)
Antenna Dimensions: 10, 12, or 18in flat plate (RDR-1500: 39 or 29 × 9 in)

These Bendix-FIAR radars have alternative sea-search and weather modes. They are widely used commercially. The antenna is stabilized in LOS to within 1 deg. Range accuracy is 1%, and minimum tracking range is 600 yd. Data are held digitally in the radar memory. Range marks for, respectively, the long/short range modes are 2.5/0.5, 5/1, 10/2, 20/4, 40/10, 80/20, 160/40, and 240/60 nm. RDR-1400C has a special sea-surveillance (clutter-rejection) mode. Maximum range: 185 nm with the 10in antenna, 240 nm with the 12in, and 322 nm with the 18in. RDR-1500 is a derivative radar with a high-resolution sea-search mode and a long-range weather-avoidance mode. Maximum range is 300 km (164 nm). The U.S. Army designation for RDR-1300 is APN-215.

Users:

RDR-1300: Israel (AS 365F Dauphin), Spain (500 Defender), Taiwan (500 Defender), United States (Coast Guard HH-60J; also in RU-38A as APN-215).

RDR-1400: Cyprus (Maritime Defender), India (6 Islanders modified for coastal MPA plus 12 Maritime Defenders and 6 Sea King Mk 42C), Indonesia (GAF Searchmaster B), Italy (utility Sea King), Mauritius (Maritime Defender), Pakistan (Maritime Defender), Papua New Guinea (GAF Searchmaster B), Philippines (Maritime Defender).

RDR-1500: Belgium (Sea King Mk 48 SAR), Brunei (probably, in Bo-105s), Ireland (AS 365F Dauphin helicopters, two of them on board the frigate *Eithne*), Israel (AS 365F Dauphin helicopters; may be RDR-1300), Italy (navy-operated P166 DL3EMs for environmental monitoring), Mexico (Bo-105 helicopters), Portugal (Lynx Mk 95), United States (Coast Guard HH-65A Dauphins).

Six TS-11Rs of the 7th Regiment of the Polish Naval Air Force carry Bendix King (Allied Signal) RDS-81 weather radars in their noses for surface ship detection (the display is in the rear cockpit). Unlike RDR-1300/1400/1500, this radar has no alternative sea-search mode (which may have made export easier). According to a recent Polish account, the radar was not entirely satisfactory in its new role, but finances prohibited anything better. RDS-81 has a peak power of 1 kW and a variable pulse width (depending on range) with a pulse rate of 115 to 126 pps, using a magnetron with a computer-controlled modulator. Beam width is 8 or 10 deg, depending on antenna diameter (12 or 10 in).

◆ TNR (TFR and GMR)

Texas Instruments' Ku-band pulse-compression Tornado Nose Radar equips German naval strike Tornado aircraft (the British nonnaval air-defense version uses a different radar). There is no official designation; TNR is commonly used.

Two separate elements share a common mounting, power supply, and computer/processor, the TFR (terrain-following radar) and the GMR (ground-mapping radar). The former is used for high-speed approach and escape, the latter for weapons control. TFR is limited to a terrain-following mode. GMR has mapping, air-to-surface ranging, air-to-air tracking, land/sea target lock-on, and beacon-homing modes. There is also a home-on-jam mode. The radar image is digitally scan-converted for HUD display. ECCM features include PRF jitter and frequency agility. The main GMR display is the combined display (CRT) in front of the rear seat; radar data can also be displayed on the pilot's HUD. GMR employs a conventional, stabilized dish antenna and operates at moderate PRF. It has a fairly narrow beam in both azimuth and elevation since it can be maneuvered in azimuth and in elevation for the air-to-surface ranging mode, the outputs from which are slant range, range rate, and pointing angles to the target.

The TFR antenna is a two-lobe, monopulse, phased array mounted below the GMR antenna; the central system computer integrates its output with other navigational sensor data. In straight flight it performs a two-bar box scan (8 deg in azimuth, $+10$ to -20 deg in elevation); when the airplane turns, those parameters open up, the scan being steered into the turn. At a high rate of turn, the scan becomes a figure-8 (total scan about 15 deg in azimuth, the antenna is steered as much as 7 deg into the turn). The antenna thus looks ahead into the direction the airplane is about to take. The associated computer lays down a "ski-toe" contour ahead of the airplane, the rise in the toe being set for a given level of pilot comfort (maximum push-over varied in -0.95-G increments for the hard ride, and -0.5-G in soft ride). The system climbs the airplane whenever a terrain feature is detected penetrating the set contour. TFR operates at high PRF.

TNR has a height-finding mode in which the angle to an identified surface target is measured as a datum.

The radar was built under license by Ferranti/GEC Avionics, AEG/Telefunken/Siemens, and FIAR. A Phase I improvement (1985) went into production in 1987; it provides the radar with a faster computer.

AIR FIRE-CONTROL SYSTEMS

See also the Aircraft Combat Systems described in the Command/Control section.

FRANCE

◆ AMASCOS

Thomson-CSF's Airborne Maritime Situation Control System is, in effect, a next-generation successor to TRES/TREW, using the newer Ocean Master radar and DR 3000, combined with a Sextant Avionique Nadir Mk II inertial navigation system. The simplest version, AMASCOS 100, for customs and coast guard aircraft, is limited to the radar and an altitude/heading reference system. AMASCOS 200, for medium aircraft with an antiship mission, has the full inertial reference system, as well as a FLIR (the TRT Clio) and DR 3000. AMASCOS 300 adds a sonobuoy processor (Sadang 1000), a MAD, a data link (Link W), and a dedicated tactical computer (in AMASCOS 100 and 200 the radar processor suffices for the tactical software). A helicopter version of AMASCOS 300 would use the Thomson Sintra HS 312 dipping sonar.

◆ Helos/Peace Bow

These programs provide light helicopters with a Thomson-CSF radar data link for OTH missile targeting. Eurocopter is apparently the system integrator, and the missile is Exocet MM 40. The radar used so far is the U.S.-made Allied Signal RDR-1500B.

Users: One Far Eastern customer (Peace Bow program: two Bo-105s), one South American customer (Helos program: four AS555 SN Fennecs; delivery due to begin August 1995). The South American customer may be Chile; Helos may make up for the collapse of the more ambitious French TREW program

for that country. The Asian customer is probably Brunei, but may be the Philippines.

◆ TRES/TREW

TRES combines VARAN with an ESM set, probably DR 3000A, as an Exocet targeting system, either for the airplane carrying it or for surface craft (via a data link). The first buyer was Chile, for two Exocet-firing Falcon 200 aircraft (1990). The new Super Pumas (which carry Exocets, and which fly from the "County" class) are similarly equipped. They are to be replaced by Eurocopter AS 532C Cougars, which will also carry Exocets. Chile also ordered a simpler system, TREW, VARAN plus a radar warner, for four SA.565 Panther helicopters, but the helicopter order was canceled due to late delivery. It may have been replaced by Helos, above. The Panthers would have carried Murene (later Impact) torpedoes in addition to their radars and data links.

RUSSIA

Large ASM/aircraft control systems are called "complexes" and are designated in a K series. Aircraft designations often show the K-series as a suffix, as in Tu-16K-10 for a Badger (Tu-16) equipped with K-10. The K-designator is *not* the missile designator (the missile usually has a Kh-number; occasionally it is mistakenly associated with the K-number). Presumably the complex includes not only the radar but also the associated computer and any data link.

Known operational complexes are:

K-22M: Kh-22 (AS-4) missile control system for Tu-22M (Backfire) and Tu-95K-22 (Bear) bombers, equipped with Down Beat radar. Note that the Bear version carrying AS-6 missiles, Tu-95M5, was a prototype only. The previously reported Tu-95K-26 designation seems to have been erroneous. According to CFE data, the latest Tu-22M2 or M3 version employs four sensors. Since it has only a single fire-control radar, this statement suggests the use of ESM, an electronic navigation system, and a data link. The bomber can engage two targets, and can detect them at 150–200 km. Angular accuracy was given as 0.3 (probably rad, not degrees). Fire-control cycle time is 300–600 sec (5–10 min). The earlier Tu-22M and Tu-22K "Blinder" used two sensors and were credited with the same accuracy and cycle time, but with a range of 100–150 km, implying that they had less powerful versions of the same radar as in Backfire. Each could handle one target at a time.

K-26: Multimissile type, adding KSR-5 (AS-6) capability to Badgers (Tu-16K-10-26 version; K-10 guided the KSR-2 [AS-2] missile). This is presumably closely related to K-22, as KSR-5 is apparently closely related to Kh-22. According to CFE data, the system can fire two missiles at one target. Range is 50–100 km (accuracy 300–400 m, angular accuracy 0.75 [probably rad]); fire-control cycle time is 300–600 sec. Versions of Tu-16 equipped with this system have one to three sensors.

UNITED STATES

◆ ARBS (AN/ASB-19)

Hughes's Angle Rate Bombing Set was developed for the Marine Corps, to improve the accuracy of visual bombing. Similar FCSs are part of many larger systems, such as the F/A-18, but ARBS was designed as a stand-alone complement to a relatively simple airplane (originally the A-4M, then the AV-8B). Spots designated by ground-based lasers are automatically acquired and tracked. The same sensor can track a designated optical target (if it has sufficient contrast and a sharp enough edge). Unlike radar- or laser-based bombing systems, this one is not fed with target range. It receives only the angle to the target and the rate of change of that angle, solving for range on the basis of airplane altitude and true air speed. As in other systems, the appropriate course is displayed on the HUD, and the computer releases bombs automatically.

Typical television acquisition range is 15 km (8.2 nm) for a 3m target with 10% contrast. A typical target-designation laser 1 km from a target can be detected at 15 km under similar conditions. The optics can slew to compensate for 450 deg of rolling motion, covering +10/−70 deg in elevation and 37 deg in azimuth. The system computer (CP-1278) is an IBM System/4 Pi SP-1, with 32k 16-bit words, operating at 440 KOPS. Total system weight is 59 kg (130 lb), and estimated cost, about 1987, was $210,000.

Testing began in the summer of 1976.

SURFACE MISSILE FIRE-CONTROL SYSTEMS

RUSSIA

♦ KLON

SS-N-2 FCS for "Osa"-class missile boats, using the Square Tie radar. The operator designates targets on the CRT using a *vilka* (fork, a pair of strobes) and a movable range marker, both controlled by joystick. Two consecutive detections suffice for rate-aided tracking to begin (typically the radar is turned off once the computer has calculated range and range rate; it is turned on only intermittently to check the accuracy of the tracker). The FCS is designed to accept intermittent data. It commands the missile to fly on autopilot until it is about 3.5 nm from the predicted target position, when the seeker is turned on (it then has just enough time to receive eight returned pulses from the target, then lock on).

♦ Korrell

SS-N-2D (P-20M system) FCS using the Plank Shave radar. In a Tarantul, a two-part command console is in a space abaft the bridge. Corrections are cranked into the left-hand panel. The right-hand side carries a Plank Shave CRT in a hood (range scales 1, 5, 25, 50, and 75 km) and a target indication receiver; the firing panel is below it. Deviations from standard conditions are cranked in, for example, temperature, wind speed, and direction. The console shows range to target, ship deviation from attack course (10- or 0.1-deg increments), seeker range setting (1.0- or 0.01km interval), free flight time (in intervals of 10 or 0.1 sec), and correction to attack course (intervals of 0.1 deg). The targeting method is also set on this console: (a) autonomous, using

The Korrell (P-20M) FCS computer on board the *Hiddensee*, showing its computing gears. (Author)

Korrell control console for the SS-N-2D (P-20M) missile system on board the "Tarantul"-class missile boat *Hiddensee*, in the boat's below-decks weapons-control space. On the panel above the two CRTs (just above the B-scan) is a switch used to choose between eight ESM frequencies. (Author)

Plank Shave and a calculated lead angle, (b) third-party targeting (target coordinates, speed, and course are manually entered), (c) without lead angle (used when target speed and course are unknown or the target is maneuvering violently and, presumably, against a fixed target), and (d) data link (remote control).

The Plank Shave radar console and the analog (geared) FCS computer are in a separate space below decks, near other ship FCS equipment. Given Plank Shave (Harpoon) data, Korrell computes missile course and flight time, based on target range and bearing, the desired range from the target at which the missile-guidance system is to be switched on, change of range and bearing as the target steers a presumably straight course, true wind direction and speed, and the average cruise speeds of the missile and the ship. The missile search sector setting is a function of range to target, given in a table. Missile speed depends on temperature (the average varies from 299 m/sec at −20 deg C to 316 m/sec at +10 deg C). Typically the missile is set to search within +/−5 deg (+/−15 deg when no lead angle is used). Set cruise height is 25 or 50 m (80 or 160 ft). The seeker turn-on point is set at 5, 10, or 15 cables (0.25, 0.5, or 0.75 nm) from the computed target position.

If Plank Shave or the computer fails, or if the ship is observing radar silence, the missile can be fired on the basis of data manually input from other radars (Bass Tilt or a navigational radar) or the optical viewer (periscope) in the roof of the bridge (in the "viewer" mode the missile is fired without any lead angle). When other radars are used, the ship's course is held manually. Free-flight range is set as the difference between estimated target range and seeker turn-on range. If the target range is estimated by eye, free-flight time is set as the shortest possible (3 to 4 km), so the seeker is turned on as early as possible.

The Plank Shave console below decks has a rectangular B-scan (20 deg × 20 cables [1 nm] centered on the expected target location) alongside a PPI, to indicate the range gates applied to the target. The radar can sector-scan within an 80-deg sector. Relative target speed limits are $+/-80$ kt; maximum computed target range is 80 nm (maximum solution range is 60 nm). Missile range is 55 nm (effective limits are 8 and 80 km [5 and 43 nm]).

To line up missile gyros, the ship must keep a steady (combat) course when preparing to fire missiles; the computer takes over the helm. The bridge unit can change heading within $+/-3$ deg. Missiles fly straight paths; they cannot dog-leg. Full missile warmup from cold condition (Readiness Level II) takes 400 sec (6.7 min). Missiles can be held fully warmed up for 30 min, and in a 200-sec mode for 8 hr (the last 60 sec is running up the gyro, altimeter, and rocket speed indicator).

UNITED STATES

◆ Harpoon Shipboard Command Launch Control System (SWG-1)

A Harpoon Shipboard Command Launch Control System

(HSCLCS) upgrade was introduced in 1986 as part of the Harpoon product improvement program (Block IC). SWG-1A(V) incorporates a display of the tactical situation showing the designated target as well as other friendly and neutral ships (background ships) near the target, derived from NTDS data. The terminal automatically generates missile flight plans with waypoints to optimize angles of approach for the highest probability of acquiring and hitting the target while avoiding being shot down. SWG-1A calculates time on target so that several missiles can be fired together to arrive together, saturating target defenses. It can also calculate from a designated time on target, so that weapons from its ship arrive with those from others. The operator can designate alternative flight paths and waypoints, and can alter the generated flight paths.

Other selections:

Missile waypoints to conceal the launch point, to fly around other ships or land masses, to avoid defenses, or to approach the target from several directions.

This SWG-1A display shows a planned missile attack on a target, track number 1234, using three missiles flying dog-legs. An ellipse of uncertainty surrounds the estimated target position; the targeter uses it to set missile seekers and also to avoid attacking the two nearby ships, track numbers 1232 and 1231. At top is a list of missile parameters, including presearch mode (sea-skimming flight), search pattern (RBL, range/bearing launch), attack mode (pop-up rather than sea-skimming), launch interval, and calculated time of flight (the system attempts to insure that all missiles approach the target simultaneously from different directions). (McDonnell-Douglas)

Radar-seeker search pattern expansion priority to improve target selectivity (e.g., biasing the search pattern to one side to avoid an unwanted target on the other side).

High-altitude flyout (to overfly friendly or neutral ships before descending to sea-skimming level).

Skim or pop-up terminal trajectory.

The display panel shows a synthetic-video PPI in its center. Target bearing, range, heading, and speed are displayed in the upper-left corner, with missile status along the top (attack number, cell number, FCS status, probability of acquiring the target, presearch skim flight [yes or no], search pattern, search priority, attack mode, plan status [e.g., approved], launch interval, and flight time). Buttons down the right-hand side of the panel allow adjustments to these parameters as well as setting for flyout range. The system can handle up to four missiles (port or starboard group) at one time. Buttons along the bottom set true target bearing in degrees, missile-enable range (kyds), and missile-destruct range (kyds); the panel also includes the missile enable and firing buttons.

Existing SWG-1s can be upgraded to SWG-1A standard.

◆ TWCS (SWG-2/3)/TEPEE

The Tomahawk Weapons Control System is the shipboard Tomahawk FCS, introduced in 1984. Designed primarily for antiship missiles, it incorporates OTH data-fusion to form a picture of the target array beyond the firing ship's horizon. Ships in a group armed with antiship Tomahawk form a network analogous to a Link 11 net. Each ship correlates offboard data independently. The ship selected as FOTC (force over-the-horizon track coordinator) acts as track manager.

SWG-2 is for ships with armored box launchers; SWG-3 is for ships with vertical launchers. TWCS comprises a Track Control Group (TCG) and a launch-control group (LCG), each built around a central computer (originally UYK-19, now UYK-64) and a pair of UYQ-31 displays (OIDTs, Operator Interactive Display Terminals). There are also four Rolm 1602Bs for launcher control and one for the OTCIXS link. The TCG maintains the OTH-T picture and is used to develop missile-engagement plans. One OIDT is used for track management, the other for engagement planning (in effect, for fire control). The LCG maintains a missile inventory (monitoring numbers and types), selects and programs missiles, and monitors launching.

For land attack, TWCS is used to insert the final phase of flight, to hit a selected target. This phase is a modification to an overland flight path generated by a TMPC ashore or by an APS on a command ship. Upgrades over the life of the system included more targeting flexibility, TDAs, and the ability to program the bomblet land-attack version (RGM-109D). ATWCS (see below) will merge TWCS and land-attack planning and control, using TAC-3 computers.

Tomahawk Engagement Planning and Exercise Evaluation (TEPEE) is the TDA software used to plan Tomahawk engagements. It can feed its data into a ship's NCCS-A system. Software includes time-of-flight corrections for Tomahawk land-attack missiles, planning for coordination of tactical air strikes with Tomahawk strikes, and scenario generation for training. TEPEE originally ran on a DTC I computer.

◆ Tomahawk Land Attack FCS: TMPS/TMPCU/APS/MDS

McDonnell-Douglas's Tomahawk Mission Planning System was developed in 1978 and is now deployed in nine TMPCs (Tomahawk Mission Planning Centers) worldwide. Planning for land-attack missions is complicated because the entire mission must be laid out in three dimensions, the missile being commanded to avoid both enemy air defenses and obstacles such as buildings and terrain (the missile has no forward-looking sensor, in the interest of preserving its stealth). The flight plan must also include the necessary altitude inputs to the missile's terrain-comparison guidance system. Data packages initially took several days to prepare, using VAX 11-780 computers. Once planned, missions must be viewable at the TMPC to test their appropriateness. In the nuclear case, an additional degree of ac-countability is needed, in the form of Tiburon's DTD Certification Processor (DCP).

Multiple flight plans are loaded onto 80-lb portable hard disks (DTDs, data transport devices) which are moved physically to C² nodes such as carriers and thence to Tomahawk shooters. Ships carry several DTDs. The DTD carries a data package (TCI, Tomahawk Command Information) for each mission. The TCI can be read into a Tiburon Tomahawk Mission Display System (TMDS) or used to prepare a mission folder.

The TMDS can electronically sort the missions available in a ship's DTDs to select a strike package (manual sorting would be impractical). It automatically retrieves and displays mission data (target, route, launch, TLAM route graphics) and can be used to plan combined aircraft and missile attacks. Strike package planning includes calculation of specific times on target. TacAir routes can be added manually and digital maps prepared showing TLAM and TacAir routes overlaid. MDS can also recall and display target images and the AAW threat against which the missiles are flying (which affects TacAir routing). The TMDS terminal automatically receives TCI updates, called mission folder updates, from the TMPC via its communications processor (the GFCP, receiving OTCIXS or TADIXS). If necessary, any TMDS can radio the updates to the shooters. The TMDS also receives and generates on-line Opnotes.

MDS currently runs on TAC-2 computers, and is being re-hosted to TAC-3 as part of the ATWCS described below.

Tomahawk mission flight plans admit only limited modification. For example, during the Gulf War it was necessary to hit Baghdad again and again, but there were only a few mission plans leading there from the ships offshore. Missiles therefore had to follow a very few tracks inland, although they could be commanded to hit a variety of targets once they arrived at Baghdad. That made their paths somewhat predictable, and after several flew over successfully, others were shot down because the earlier ones had alerted the Iraqis. Mission upgrades (end-point modifications) are typically transmitted directly to the shooters (the corresponding TCI upgrades go to the tactical commanders).

To overcome this limitation, the land-attack planning process is being moved to sea, initially on board selected flagships (as the Afloat Planning System, APS) and later as a system to be installed on board all Tomahawk shooters, ATWCS (see below). In each case, the key development was the availability of compact computers that could plan complex missions very quickly.

The two main TMPCs are located at the two Cruise Missile Support Activities (CMSAs) at Norfolk and at Camp Smith, Hawaii. Each is split into a TLAM Planning System (TPS), an imagery analysis section (for DSMAC images, using a DIWS), and a mission distribution center where DTDs are loaded. The TPS plans the route from the first preplanned waypoint to the target, using detailed maps (horizontal and vertical) and intelligence data. Planning is necessarily iterative, because choices made early in the mission may have unanticipated consequences later on. The mission planner calls for DSMAC scenes at points in the flight; the imagery analyst examines the area for suitable scenes. The analyst is also responsible for finding the precise geographical location of the aimpoint (the missile flies only to a selected point in space; it has no seeker).

TMPCU is an upgrade using faster computers for quicker mission generation. It uses a ruggedized Loral workstation first delivered in 1988. TMPCU came fully into service in 1994. Because it uses "national" imagery, it includes a special compartment information (SCI) isolation segment (SIS).

McDonnell-Douglas's APS is a parallel afloat system, including the Tomahawk Strike Coordination Module, which integrates Tomahawk, TacAir, and weapon planning. APS is built around a Silicon Graphics 240GX workstation (20–234 MIPS, 256 Mbytes of storage, 7.2 Gbytes on the internal hard disk). Unit cost is about $250,000. APS will be in NCCS-A spaces on board carriers. There are also containerized versions (rapid deployment suites, RDS) for theater commanders, housed in three air-transportable vans. Note that, unlike TMPC, APS cannot load DTDs. Instead, carrier helicopters will ferry mission tapes to shooters.

The first engineering development model was delivered in 1992 for the command ship *Mount Whitney*. The prototype passed its OpEval during FY93, software problems having delayed TMPCU and APS IOC from the planned date of January 1992 to April 1993. The first production installation was on board the carrier *Nimitz* (1995).

With the advent of ATWCS, APS capability will be on board all Tomahawk shooters, including submarines.

◆ ATWCS

The Advanced Tomahawk Weapons Control System will unify control of land- and sea-attack Tomahawks, using TAC-3 workstations and a fiber-optic LAN for internal interconnections. Beside planning Tomahawk strikes, ATWCS will plan Harpoon/SLAM strikes, and interface with future UAVs. ATWCS is, therefore, sometimes rendered Advanced *Tactical* Weapons Control System. It will provide all Tomahawk ships with Block IV capability. ATWCS is being introduced in two stages. Phase I replaces the TCG, where database management, communications, and shipboard mission planning are done. The existing UYK-19 computer of the SWG-2/3 system will be replaced by a TAC-3. The current OIDT (a UYQ-31) will be replaced by a TAC-3 with a color display of the type used in NTCS-A. This must be among the very first truly tactical (as opposed to nonmission-critical) applications of a TAC-series computer. Phase II replaces the launch-control group (LCG), which stores mission data and transfers them to the missile, which monitors missile health, and which connects to the launching system itself. Phase II is needed to handle Block IV missiles.

Upgrades of the APS element of ATWCS focus on development of a universal target database carrying the imagery needed for the missile's forward-looking imaging IR terminal sensor. Additions include an autorouter and an autovertical profile generator. The autorouter generates a mission's ground track, creating a flight path. It balances potential losses to ground fire against crashes. The vertical profile generator computes altitudes, flight speeds, and other parameters associated with the ground-path flight plan created by the router. Prior to Block 3, these were manual tasks. Another improvement is in how missions are conveyed for master strike planning, to cure the problems discovered in providing this data to the Air Force during Desert Storm.

Phase I was first installed for afloat tests in 1994; it is to enter service in 1996. Phase II should begin operational tests in 1996, and it should enter service in 1998, in time for Tomahawk Block IV.

MDS software is being rehosted on the TAC-3 as part of ATWCS, so that every ATWCS will also be able to function as an MDS.

MISSILES AND GUIDED BOMBS

Deletions: Martin Pescador (Argentina), Barracuda (Brazil), ANS (France), SS 11 (France, as Swedish RB 52), AS-2 (KSR-2), AS-5 (KSR-11) (both Russia), Rb 04E, RB 05A, Rb 08A (Sweden), Shrike

FOG-MPM at the 1995 Dubai show. (S. Zaloga)

(AGM-45), Skipper (AGM-123, now out of service), Standard ARM (AGM-78), SLAT/Harpoon II (US), Tacit Rainbow (AGM-136), TSSM/Senior Pennant (AGM-137, canceled), Have Slick. See the 1991/92 edition for details.

BRAZIL

◆ FOG-MPM

> **Dimensions:** 180 mm × 1.5 m
> **Performance:** Range 20 km

As of 1995, Avibras was proposing this small fiber-optic multipurpose missile (hence MPM) for the projected improved *Inhauma* class. It would be fired vertically from a launcher abaft the ship's uptakes. Because it is command-guided, the missile might also be effective against helicopters. FOG-MPM is already being made for the Brazilian army.

CHINA (PRC)

CATIC (FL and SY) and CPMIEC (HY) market similar missiles under different designations, presumably indicating different design bureaus; the manufacturer (the Nanchang Aircraft Factory) may be the same. However, FL-4 is described as a ship-launched version of HY-4.

Chinese missiles manufactured by CPMIEC on display at ASIANDEX, 1988. From the top they are M-1B, C-301, C-101, C-802, C-201, M-1, and HQ-61 (SAM). M-1 and M-1B are army artillery rockets fired from multiple launchers. -1B is heavier and achieves a greater range. (CPMIEC)

◆ HY-1

A reverse-engineered Styx, HY-1 was developed by the Nanchang Aircraft Factory as a coast-defense weapon. Work began about 1963. Small-scale production began in 1966, but the shock of booster ignition apparently caused three failures, that year and the next. Acceptance tests finally succeeded in May 1972, and the missile was certified in 1974.

Work on a shipboard version began in 1967. Unlike Styx/SY-1, which is fired from a launcher fixed to the deck of a ship or attack boat, HY-1 was intended for a trainable launcher; it would be fired across the deck. Such firing makes very different demands on the guidance system's gyros. Two simulation launches late in 1968 showed that it could be launched transversely from a moving ship, and two dummy missiles were successfully fired from a Chinese missile destroyer in September 1971. The same ship made the first successful live firings in September 1973 (four hits out of four shots). The missile was certified for production in January 1976. Batch production had already begun in 1975.

Initially the shipboard and coast-defense versions differed. However, a common version was developed, production beginning in 1978. HY-1 is carried on board Chinese Luda-class destroyers, and Jianghu-class frigates. It may have replaced SY-1 on board fast missile attack boats.

Work on a modified HY-1A began in 1983; the main changes were better ECCM, lower flight altitude, and longer range. Flight tests were conducted July–September 1985 (four hits out of four shots), and production began in October 1986 (deliveries began in 1987).

The HY designation stands for "Hai Ying," meaning "Sea Hawk."

Both this missile *and* HY-2 are described as Silkworm (CSS-N-2).

◆ Silkworm (HY-2, HY-4, FL-4, C-601, C-201)

	HY-2	HY-4	C-601
Diameter	—	0.76 m	—
	—	(29.9 in)	—
Length	7.36 m	7.36 m	7.38 m
	(290 in)	(290 in)	(291 in)
Span	2.75 m	—	2.4 m
	(108 in)	—	(95 in)
Weight	2998 kg	2000 kg[a]	2440 kg
	(6608 lb)	(4408/3834 lb)	(5378 lb)
Warhead	513 kg	500 kg	513 kg
	(1131 lb)	(1102 lb)	(1131 lb)
Speed	Mach 0.9	Mach 0.8–0.85	—
Range[b]	95 km	150 km	95–100 km
	(104 kyd)	(164 kyd)	(104–109 kyd)

[a]1740 kg, air-to-surface.
[b]Effective range 35–135 km (38–138 kyd).
Note: The NATO name for HY-2 is also given as CSSC-3 Seersucker.

Chinese HY-2 (Silkworm) coast-defense missiles. (U.S. Naval Institute)

The warhead of an HY-2 missile. The hollow of the shaped charge is clearly visible at left. (*Missiles* and *Spacecraft*, PRC)

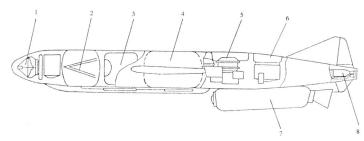

The arrangement of the HY-2 missile: (1) radar seeker, (2) fuel tank, (3) shaped-charge warhead, (4) oxidizer tank, (5) autopilot, (6) terminal homing electronics, (7) booster, (8) sustainer rocket motor. The related C-201W carries its terminal homing electronics in place of the oxidizer tank of HY-2; the turbojet takes up the after electronics compartment. (*Missiles* and *Spacecraft*, PRC)

C-201W, showing the turbojet air intake under its body. (CPMIEC)

C-601 under the wing of a PRC Badger (B-6D) bomber. (CPMIEC)

CPMIEC's HY-2 probably first appeared in the early 1980s. It is apparently exclusively a coast-defense missile. Its warhead is somewhat smaller than that of Styx, so it can carry more fuel for greater range. Like Styx, HY-2 uses a conscan seeker (HY-2A uses an IR seeker). HY-2 cruises at 100 m, but HY-2G (with a precision radar altimeter) flies at 30 or 50 m (98 or 164 ft). C-601 is a related air-launched missile with a monopulse seeker, carried by Chinese-built Badger (B-6) bombers (one or two per airplane). It is slightly more powerful than HY-2.

Reportedly, HY-2 is manufactured under license in North Korea, using Chinese- rather than Soviet-supplied technology and substantial Chinese content. It may also be made in Egypt and Iran. Reportedly, the Silkworms fired by Iran in the Persian Gulf (from April 1987 on) had been manufactured in North Korea; the PRC denied having provided them and announced that sales would be stopped.

Users: HY-1/HY-2: Bangladesh (Jianghu, Huangfeng, Houku classes), China (Luda class, Jianghu class, Huangfeng and Houkou classes), Egypt (Jianghu and Houkou classes, also coast-defense version; first recipient of FL-1 and HY-2, 1984–85), Iran (coast-defense version: three navy and one Pasdaran brigades, about 12 batteries, at least 140 HY-2/4), Iraq (coast-defense version), North Korea (Huangfeng class and coast-defense version), Pakistan (Houkou, Huangfeng classes). This missile may also have been exported to Albania and to Zaire (for coast defense). Some reported users may have SY-1, HY-1, or FL-1, all of which have much the same airframe. Iran received its first HY-2 missiles in the summer of 1986 and they were first test-fired successfully in February 1987, by which time 20 were on board, with 20 more to follow (some may have come from North Korea). Sales continued in 1988–89, at times in the face of U.S. protests.

C-601: China, Iran, Iraq (for B-6 bombers). Reportedly this missile was adapted for launching from B-5 (Il-28 Beagle bombers produced by China without a license), for use both by China and by North Korea. An adapted B-5 carries a single missile under its belly, whereas a B-6 carries two underwing. As of 1995, the Chinese naval air arm was credited with 30 B-6 (only some of which were missile carriers) and with 80 B-5; North Korea was credited with a total of 82 air force B-5s. It is not clear whether any B-6s survive in Iranian or Iraqi service.

The status of the turbojet derivatives of HY-1/2 (HY-4, FL-4, C-201) is unclear. All have belly air intakes. HY/FL-4 uses a con-scan seeker; the modified air-launched C-201W probably uses monopulse. All of these missiles cruise at 200m altitude and attack at 70 m (230 ft), diving steeply into their targets. Maximum C-201W range is 200 km (effective range 135 km). Takeoff weight is 1950 kg (warhead 500 kg, fuel 200 kg).

FL-1 (Fei Lung, meaning Flying Dragon: NATO CSS-NX-1 Mod 2 Scrubbrush), is similar to SY-1, with a new monopulse seeker (probably derived from that of C-801) operating at a higher frequency than that of HY-2. It cruises at 30 m (98 ft), using a radar altimeter. Its status is unclear.

FL-2 (NATO CSS-NX-5 Sabbot: 54 cm × 6 m, span 1.705 m, 1300 kg without booster) uses a Styx-like airframe with a new solid-fuel (propergol) engine. Warhead weight is 365 kg. Shown at Paris in 1987, it appears not to have entered service. FL-7 apparently uses a stretched (6.6 m, 1800 kg) version of the FL-2 airframe with a liquid-fuel rocket engine. Claimed maximum speed is Mach 1.4; range is 32 km. CATIC described FL-7 as an alternative to C-801, and the success of the latter suggests that FL-7 was never placed in production. A 1988 report that Iran had bought 100 FL-7s was presumably an erroneous version of the reported sale of C-801s. The Chinese account of C-801 development suggests that FL-7 was the original failed supersonic project.

◆ C-101/C-301 (HY-3) (NATO CSS-X-6 Sawhorse)

Dimensions: 54 cm × 6.5 m
Warhead: Shaped charge (over 300 kg)
Weight: 1850 kg
Propulsion: Two ramjets (and two solid-fuel boosters)
Speed: Supersonic (Mach 2.0)
Range: 50 km (27 nm)

CPMIEC's C-101, which resembles the British Bloodhound SAM in configuration, was announced in 1985. Flight altitude is 50 m. Length is sometimes listed as 7.2 m (283 in) and range as 70–80 km. It is not clear whether this surface-fired (ship or truck) missile is in service. This missile can also be fired from aircraft.

C-101 antiship missile, showing ramjets and boosters. (CPMIEC)

Comparative models of C-301 (*left*) and C-101 (*right*) at the 1995 Paris Air Show give some indication of relative size. (Author)

C-301 (HY-3) is a heavier and longer-range version of C-101, launched using four boosters. It is intended for coast defense (it is too large for either shipboard or air use). Dimensions: 76 cm × 9.85m; span 2.24 m; weight 4600 kg (warhead 512 kg). One brochure distinguishes between the 9.85m Stage I missile and the 9.46m Stage II missile. Range is 140 or 180 km, speed Mach 2.0, and cruise altitude 100–300 or 6000 m. This missile was first displayed at ASIANDEX 1988 in Beijing (November 1988). As in the case of C-101, its service status is uncertain.

Both missiles attain a speed of about Mach 2, running into the target at a preset altitude of 7–50 m. A photograph displayed at the Paris Air Show in 1989 shows a missile hitting at a height of about 3 m (10 ft). Both use active radar guidance, and each can be preset to execute a single terminal maneuver to evade close-in defenses.

◆ SY-1

SY-1 ("Strive Upstream:" NATO CSSN-1 Scrubbrush) is a licensed copy of the Soviet P-15 Styx missile (HY-1 is a reverse-engineered version). The license was received in 1959, successful certification tests following in November 1966. Missiles were made by the Nanchang Aircraft Factory. SY-1 was criticized for its conscan (on receive) seeker and its height-keeping barometer (which made it impossible to fly at low altitude). SY-1A has a monopulse seeker and a radio altimeter. Development was ordered in 1974, but 1977–80 certification tests failed, and the missile was not certified for service until December 1983. A modification in which the missile descends to very low altitude near its target was successfully tested in 1980. SY-1 presumably armed Chinese-built versions of the Russian "Osa"- and "Komar"-class missile boats. It is not clear to what extent it has been replaced by HY-2.

In its coast-defense role, SY-1 has been seen on the chassis of a T-63 amphibious tank.

◆ C-801 (SY-2 or HY-5)/C-802

Dimensions: 0.36 × 5.814 m; span 1.18 m (14.2 × 228.9 × 46.5 in)
Weight: 815 kg (1794 lb)
Warhead: 165 kg, semiarmor-piercing (364 lb)
Propulsion: Boost-sustain rocket (two motors)
Speed: Mach 0.9
Range: 8–40 km ship to ship; 10–50 km air to ship (8700–44,000 yd/10,900–55,000 yd). A 1995 movie showed a range of 42 km.

Data apply to C-801.

CPMIEC's C-801 (SY-2; NATO CSS-NX-4 Sardine) resembles Exocet and may be a reverse-engineered derivative of that missile. The current solid-fuel design replaced a liquid-fuel supersonic design begun in 1970 and badly delayed by the Cultural Revolution (it was canceled in 1976). The Chinese date crucial work on this missile to 1986, about when they gained access to a range of French naval technology (including the TAVITAC combat system). C-801 climbs after launch, then descends to a cruise altitude of 20 or 30 m; it attacks at 5 or 7 m. This missile has a monopulse active seeker.

C-801 antiship missile, with booster. (CPMIEC)

C-802. (CPMIEC)

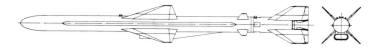

C-802, showing its underbody air intake. (CPMIEC)

The self-forging fragment warhead of C-802, taken from the manufacturer's film, shown at the 1995 Paris Air Show. The shallow depressions are, in effect, shaped charges. Similar warheads equip the German Kormoran and the Taiwanese Hsiung Feng II. (Author)

C-802 (NATO CSS-NX-8 Saccade), a turbojet derivative, was first shown at ASIANDEX in the fall of 1988; a 1995 movie appeared to show production in quantity. Unlike C-801, it has a self-forging fragment warhead similar to that of the Taiwanese Hsiung Feng II. Speed is Mach 0.8–0.9, maximum range is

120 km (65.6 nm), and minimum range is 15 km (8.2 nm). Dimensions: 360 mm × 6.392 m (14.2 × 252 in); weight is 715 kg (1576 lb). An air-launched version, C-802K, is being developed.

Reported unit price of C-801 (1990) was $780,000. It was reported in mid-1990 that some PRC Luda-class destroyers would be rearmed with quadruple C-801 launchers in place of their current FL-2s.

Users: C-801: China (one converted Wuhan-class submarine, Luhu, Jianghu III, Jiangwei classes), Iran (new Houkou-class missile boats and coast defenses at Straits of Hormuz; reported rearming Combattante II class), Thailand (Jianghu class). Reportedly C-801 has been sold to other Middle Eastern countries, but none has been specified. The Iranian sale was reported as early as 1987. The missiles may have been 100 C-802s (reported 1995). As of mid-1995 Thailand had reportedly received only a single C-801 (which was test-fired); the box launchers on the frigates may be empty.

FRANCE

◆ ANL

ANL (anti-navire legre) is a projected Aerospatiale-MBB aircraft- and helicopter-launched antiship missile: 200 kg (50-kg warhead), with solid-fuel ramjet propulsion (for speed greater than Mach 2) and 30km range. Guidance will be mid-course inertial and terminal active radar.

This weapon began with a German navy requirement for a missile for helicopters, combat aircraft, maritime-patrol aircraft, and even ships operating in narrow waters. However, ANL would also fill a potential French requirement for an AS 15TT replacement. MBB will probably collaborate with Aerospatiale on this project.

◆ ANNG/ANF

Anti-Navire Nouvelle Generation, announced at Bourget Navale in November 1994, is, in effect, successor to the abortive ANS. The French navy designation is ANF (Anti-Navire Futur). It is to fit existing MM 40 canisters, within the price of an MM 40. Aerospatiale expects to develop air and submarine versions, as in Exocet. Later versions may attack ground targets or use antiradar seekers. Like Exocet Block II, ANNG is to be programmable to fly offset attack axes to saturate defenses. ANNG is based on the strategic ASMP missile, but with revised air intakes (above and below the body, rather than at the sides) for better evasive maneuvering at sea-skimming altitudes. It is to use the 180-kg unitary warhead developed for ANS and the ADAC Mk 2 seeker of Exocet Block II. Speed should exceed Mach 2.0, and range is 180 km. Aerospatiale claims that the high-impact velocity doubles the effect of the warhead. Dimensions are 35 cm × 5.78 m, span 1.10 m, weight about 920 kg.

An ANNG model compared with existing French antiship missiles, at the 1995 Paris Air Show. The missile at top is AS 30L; at bottom is AS 15TT. (S. Zaloga)

ANNG was conceived to meet a Franco-German requirement for a 150km missile with good ability to penetrate terminal defenses. Its advent also removed pressure to spend considerable sums to make ANS operational, since as of 1996 ANNG is little more than a wooden mockup, hence entails only limited expenditures. The French goverment approved development at the end of 1994, apparently partly to compensate Aerospatiale for the award of the APTGD contract to Matra. Full-scale development is scheduled for 1998–2005.

◆ APTGD/SCALP

Matra's Armament de Precision Tirée à Grand Distance is derived from the company's Apache Franco-German air-to-surface bomblet-dispensing missile. SCALP is the name of the Apache derivative; APTGD was the military system name. The missile is stealthy (with a contoured body and radar-absorbing airframe), and intended to fly at low altitude with a range of over 400 km. Guidance would be inertial with mm-wave-radar updates, using satellite-derived mapping data, with an IR seeker turned on when the missile came within 2 km of the target. The French government has explicitly rejected GPS guidance on the ground that GPS cannot be controlled by France, and thus might not be available in a crisis. At present APTGD is an air-launched weapon intended for precision conventional strikes, but reportedly the French navy plans to buy a sea-launched variant (using vertical tubes) for its next-generation nuclear attack submarine. It may also be used on board surface ships. APTGD would then be, in effect, a French Tomahawk. Matra was selected over Aerospatiale for this project in December 1994. APTGD should enter service about 2002 with the French air force.

An Apache version, Storm Shadow (the RAF CASOM) at the 1995 Paris Air Show, next to a British Tornado strike bomber. The missile's angular lines are a form of faceting, to reflect radar signals away from their transmitters. (Author)

The submarine-launched version, using two boosters, was in the early study phase as of mid-1995.

The November 1995 French defense budget cuts included a moratorium on further spending on Apache during 1996. Work underway will be completed, but no decision on further phases (such, presumably, as APTGD) will be made during 1996. Apache itself first flew, in secret, about September 1994, from a Mirage 2000N fighter flying at 2600 ft; its Microturbo TRI 60-30 engine took it 140 km in 8 min. The missile used a combination of GPS and inertial guidance. Apache may ultimately be carried on board naval Rafale fighters. It is 630 × 480 × 5100 mm long (span 2.53 m) and weighs 1230 kg. The middle 2.2 m of length carries a 770-kg bomblet payload of MIFF antitank or MUSA GP or MUSPA area-denial mines or KRISS or Samanta antirunway bomblets (up to 10 Samanta). Guidance is TERCOM/inertial, with a mm-wave terminal seeker (which can also be used for midcourse corrections). Powered by a Microturbo TRI 60-30 turbojet, Apache cruises at 150 m and attacks at 50m altitude; range is settable at 50 or 150 km. MBB and Matra began studies for this

weapon in 1983, with initial flight tests in 1986. MBB then left the program in favor of the abortive U.S.-sponsored MSOW, Aerospatiale taking its place. Full-scale development was authorized by the French government in September 1989. In June 1992 Germany selected the antirunway version of Apache to arm Tornados (about 360 missiles are needed). The French requirement is for about 200 missiles. Unit cost of this version is about $4.25M. Unit cost of the more sophisticated SCALP may be as high as $14M (for a 200-missile production run).

The French 1992–2002 program includes 100 antirunway versions (to be delivered 1999–2002) and 100 area interdiction versions (to be ordered 1998 for delivery to begin 2002). A version, Sky Shadow, won the British CASOM contest in July 1996.

◆ ARMAT/MARTEL (AS 37)

Dimensions: 40 cm × 4.15 m (span 120 cm) (15.8 × 163.4 × 47.2 in)
Weight: 550 kg (1213 lb)
Warhead: 160 kg (353 lb)
Propulsion: Solid-fuel rocket
Speed: Mach 0.9 (supersonic in a dive)
Range: 40–120 km (43,700–131,200 yd)

This antiradar missile, carried by the Atlantique maritime-patrol aircraft, replaces AS 37 MARTEL (and uses much the same airframe). ARMAT has a new seeker and a much higher-impulse motor. This missile has been used by the Iraqi air force in the Gulf War (reportedly in 1984). ARMAT will be replaced by the lighter-weight ARF (ex-STAR).

ARMAT antiradar missiles carried by a French air force Mirage 2000 (the smaller weapons are Magic 2s). (Matra)

A few of the antiradar versions of the earlier MARTEL (Missile Anti-Radar Television) may survive in French service. See the 1991/92 edition for details.

For some years Matra has been working on a lightweight ramjet missile called ARF (Anti-Radar Futur), which was conceived as a strike support weapon for carrier aircraft. It appears to have evolved into the Franco-German ARAMIS, which is currently only a German project (see below). Matra distinguishes ARF from MARS, an evolved ARMAT it is developing for the French air force.

Users: Egypt, Kuwait, Iraq, France. About 1640 have been made; ARMAT entered service in 1984 (development began 1980). Estimated unit cost is $260,000.

◆ AS 15TT/MM 15TT

Dimensions: 18.4 cm × 2.16 m (53cm wing span) (7.2 × 85.0 × 21 in)
Weight: 96 kg (211.6 lb)
Warhead: 29.7 kg (65.5 lb)
Propulsion: Rocket (boost-sustain; burn time 45.2 sec)
Speed: 280 m/sec (919 ft/sec)
Range: 15+ km (8+ nm) (minimum 3 km)

Aerospatiale's AS 15TT ("tous temps," all-weather) is a radar command-guided follow-on to the wire-guided SS 12/AS 12 described below. Its impact-fuzed warhead is derived from that of the AS 12. The guidance radar, AGRION 15, tracks a transponder on the missile. It commands the missile in azimuth (the missile maintains a preset low altitude, below 50 m, using its radio altimeter). At a short distance from the target (as measured by AGRION 15), the missile is commanded to begin a shallow terminal dive, to hit even low-freeboard targets.

A trial installation of MM 15 on board a Trinity Marine patrol boat ordered by the Mexican navy, 1995 (the missiles were removed before the boat was delivered). (Aerospatiale)

AS 15TT, as carried by a Dauphin 2 helicopter, with AGRION 15 radar. (Aerospatiale)

MM 15 is a patrol-boat or coast-defense version of AS 15TT. Reports (at the 1995 Paris Air Show) of a sale to Oman, to arm three new P-400-class patrol boats, were apparently premature.

Reported unit price (1992) is $295,000.

During the war against Iraq, the Royal Saudi Navy reported firing AS 15TTs from its Dauphin helicopters against five Iraqi patrol boats.

Users: Bahrein (20, for Dauphin helicopters on board the FPB 62s), Chile (Dauphins), Iraq (60 purchased 1989, probably not delivered), Israel (Dauphins), Saudi Arabia (Dauphin 2 helicopters flying from *Al Madinah*–class frigates and shore bases: initial order for 221 missiles completed 1988; total 254), UAE (new order 1994 to equip seven Panther helicopters). The develop-

ment program was financed as part of the Saudi program; first deliveries were in March 1985. By 1990, 284 missiles had been made, probably excluding test rounds. A total of 306 missiles had been made as of 1992, probably including a few that the Saudis had ordered to make up for the 15 fired during the Gulf War. AS 15TT is *not* a standard French navy weapon (the optically guided AS 12 is still used; only about 32 missiles were bought for the French navy, for trials).

♦ **AS 30/AS 30L**

> **Dimensions:** 34.2 cm × 3.65 m; 1.0m span (13.5 × 143.7 × 39.4 in)
> **Weight:** 520 kg (1146 lb)
> **Warhead:** 240 kg (529 lb)
> **Propulsion:** Solid-fuel rocket (boost-sustain)
> **Speed:** 450 m/sec on sustainer, after 2-sec boost (1476 ft/sec)
> **Range:** 10 km; flight time to impact approx. 21 sec; minimum range about 3 km (10,900/3,300 yd)

Data apply to the AS 30L laser-guided version of the basic weapon. The original AS 30 (semiautomatic-command LOS guidance) was begun in 1958 and was delivered in 1964–70. It met a French requirement for a 10km range missile with a 10m CEP. AS 30 was produced in 1963–70. Work on the laser-guided version began in 1974, the ATLIS designator running its trials in 1977. The laser-guided missile first flew on 4 April 1980; it was first delivered June 1984. Only in 1995 was AS-30L integrated with French navy Super Étendards (it has long been in French air force service).

An AS 30L is fired; the laser illumination pod is outboard on the same wing. (Aerospatiale)

Production: Reportedly more AS 30Ls have been manufactured for export than for French service. A total of 5109 AS 30, 30 IIR, and 30L have been made, including 3870 AS 30. Estimated unit cost of AS-30L is $600,000.

Users (with numbers delivered through 1990):

AS 30: France (827), Germany (about 1200), India (about 50), Iraq (70), Peru (about 50), South Africa (1072), Switzerland (about 285), United Kingdom; some may also have been delivered to Israel.

AS 30L: Egypt (30), France (235), Iraq (about 240, out of 586 ordered), Jordan (10; may have canceled order when Mirage 2000 order was canceled). Deliveries to Iraq were suspended due to nonpayment; Iraq wanted to set up its own production line. Iraq reportedly used this missile during the Iran-Iraq War. French air force Jaguars fired 57 AS 30Ls during the Gulf War, claiming 95% hits. As it turned out, too few missiles had been brought to the Gulf, and French aircraft had to be rewired to deliver U.S. Paveways. After the war, the French government bought 55 missiles as replacements. In 1995, it bought about 15 more (for a total of $8.9M), presumably to make up for expected use in the former Yugoslavia.

◆ Exocet (MM 38/40, AM 39, SM 39)

	VERSIONS			
	MM 38	AM 39	SM 39	MM 40
Diameter	34.8 cm (13.7 in) all versions			
Length	520 cm (205 in)	469 cm (185 in)	580 cm (228 in)	580 cm (228 in)
Span	100 cm (39.4 in)	110 cm (43.3 in)	113.5 cm (44.7 in)	113.5 cm (44.7 in)
Weight[a]	750 kg (1653 lb)	655 kg (1444 lb)	666 kg (1468 lb)	855 kg (1884 lb)
Warhead[b]	165 kg (364 lb) all versions			
Speed	Mach 0.93 all versions			
Range	42 km (46 kyd)[c]	50–70 km (55–77 kyd)	50 km (55 kyd)	65 km (71 kyd)

[a]1345 kg (2964 lb) with capsule.
[b]Hexolite blast-fragmentation with a delayed impact fuze for SAP action. Explosive weight 132 lb.
[c]Minimum range 4440 yd.

Perhaps the best-known Western ship-launched antiship missile, the Aerospatiale Exocet sank the British destroyer *Sheffield* and the container ship *Atlantic Conveyor* in the Falklands. Exocet has also been used by Iraq in the Gulf War, severely damaging the U.S. frigate *Stark* and hitting numerous tankers. Exocet exists in ship-launched (MM 38 and MM 40), air-launched (AM 39), and submarine-launched (SM 39) versions, all of them fueled by a solid rocket, and all sea-skimmers with active-radar homing. ANNG is the projected replacement.

Exocet MM 38, the original version. (U.S. Naval Institute)

The OR was to disable the target, the designers arguing that to guarantee sinking they would have to provide so heavy a weapon as to preclude carrying it on board anything but a large ship. They also argued that even a relatively small (700–800-kg) missile penetrating a ship at Mach 0.9 or more while carrying a 160-kg warhead would have a devastating effect on a large ship. Some have compared this missile to a 13.5in semiarmor-piercing (i.e., battleship) shell. In practice, when Exocets have failed to explode after impact, their unexpended solid fuel, which contains its own oxidizer, has started major fires. This incendiary effect seems to have been entirely unexpected. A substantial number of duds were reported during both the Falklands War (for example, the *Sheffield* succumbed to the effects of the rocket-fuel fire, the warhead never exploding) and the Gulf War; but this problem has apparently been cured.

MM 38 range was relatively short (40 km, 44 kyds), corresponding to a small ship's radar or ESM horizon. MM 40 has a greater range (70 km) corresponding to the greater range of a radar on board a shipboard light helicopter. The helicopter links its data to the launch ship; the missile still operates on a fire-and-forget basis. The air-launched AM 39 has a range of 50–70 km, depending on platform speed.

Rocket propulsion makes for shorter range than a turbojet, but the designers claim that makes it unnecessary to boost an Exocet to anything like the initial altitude of a turbojet missile such as a Harpoon (which might provide a radar target, hence warning, at much greater range). The surface-launched version is fired from a fixed launcher (elevated to 12 deg), and the 2-sec boost brings the missile to a maximum altitude of 30–70 m (98–229 ft). The missile then cruises at 9–15 m (30–49 ft) in altitude. At a distance of 12–15 km (13–16 kyd) from the predicted target position, the missile descends to attack altitude (normally 8 m [26 ft], but as low as 2.5 m [8.2 ft] in a calm sea). The seeker is turned on at this point, and altitude is maintained by radar altimeter.

System reaction time is about 60 sec (time required to warm up the seeker radar's magnetron). Prefiring information is target range and bearing, own-ship heading, own-ship speed, and vertical reference, plus manual inputs for seeker angle search, seeker turn-on range, terminal altitude, and proximity function selection (impact or pseudoproximity). There is no proximity fuze as such, but the radar altimeter can be set to burst the missile as it passes over a target. The pseudoproximity fuze works through the seeker, which calculates a "should-hit" time from the range, and detonates the weapon about 0.015 sec after it should have hit. The pseudoproximity fuze can be activated by the chaff, causing the missile to explode after entering a chaff cloud, instead of seeking a real target after passing through the cloud. Missiles can also be set to begin a target-search routine after passing through a chaff cloud without detonating and without detecting an object above the sea's surface. Aerospatiale now offers a Super ADAC seeker (with better ECCM) for backfit.

In a 1994 Malaysian exercise, of two overage Exocets (MM 38) fired by the FAC *Handalan* and *Pendekar*, one hit a target at 40km range; the other failed to acquire it. Both were several years over rated shelf life.

AM 39 has modified control surfaces so that it can be carried at supersonic speeds, and it has a light-steel rather than an alloy motor casing. The motor provides more thrust for greater range. The SM 39 version is launched via a buoyant capsule (fired from the tube by a gas generator and powered underwater by a solid-fuel motor, which boosts the missile clear of the water). This version uses a waterproofed MM 40 digital computerized seeker. The capsule is powered so that it can break the surface some distance from the launching submarine, reducing the risk of detection for the submarine. Boosting from underwater also reduces the maximum altitude the missile reaches (50 m rather than the reported 600 m of Sub-Harpoon) and, thus, its detectability.

Exocet AM 39 carried by a Mirage 50 fighter. (Aerospatiale)

MM 40 is carried in a more compact canister (possible because the wings fold; total weight is 1150 rather than the 1750 kg of MM 38, and typically two MM40s can be carried for every MM 38). MM 40 is particularly suited for coast defense because this version can take a gyro angle as great as 90 deg (MM 38 can turn only 30 deg).

Exocet was first announced in October 1968, with an order from the French navy. AM 39 was first tested in 1972. SM 39 was announced in 1979 and first fired by the submarine *Agosta* in mid-1981. It became operational in 1985 on board the submarine *Saphir*. Series production of MM 40 began in January 1981. The 1000th Exocet was delivered in October 1980. First reports of combat use in the Persian Gulf were in 1984.

Estimated unit costs as of 1986 (export price in parentheses): MM 38, $350,000 ($450,000); AM 39, $525,000 ($650,000); SM 39, $850,000; MM 40, $490,000 ($600,000).

Production: Total deliveries as of 1986 (total orders in parentheses): MM 38, 1262 (1575); AM 39, 714 (809); SM 39, 24 (62); MM 40, 399 (470). Orders in 1986 amounted to two MM 38; three AM 39; 11 SM 39; and 31 MM 40.

An improved fuze (for better ECCM) is being marketed for MM 38 upgrades. MM 40 Block II is an upgrade revealed at the 1991 Paris Air Show; it had been a French black program. RCS has been reduced partly by the use of RAM at the wing roots and partly by modifying the radome. The missile corkscrews to evade terminal defenses. It can also dog-leg, changing direction by up to 90 deg. This version can fly a self-adapting sea-skimming profile in sea states up to 7, and it has better ECCM. The range, about 70 km, is not affected. The missile can select targets (i.e., it has some form of target identifier on board). A new FCS, ITL/ITS 70, allows multiple targets to be engaged, fires salvoes against more than one target, and fires a converging salvo on one target. Compared to earlier Exocet FCSs, it reduces operator workload. Block II was sold to five customers in 1992: Malaysia (corvettes), Oman (corvettes), Qatar (coast defense), Philippines (new 57m patrol boats planned for construction in Spain), and Saudi Arabia (coast defense). A sale to Cyprus (for coast defense) was announced at Defendory in October 1994. This missile arms the second and later units of the French *La Fayette* class. Tests of a parallel AM 39 Block 2, which has been fired from a Super Étendard, were completed early in 1993.

Users: Shipboard versions: Argentina (MM 40: MEKO 360 and 140, MM 38 in A69; total 212, including 38 for A69s), Bahrein (MM40 [est. 26] in FPB 62, TNC 45), Belgium (MM 38 in *Wielingen* class [est. 8]), Brazil (MM 40 in *Inhauma, Niteroi* classes [reportedly bought 10 MM 38 and 8 launchers, then 12 more; more than 25 MM 40]), Brunei (MM 38 in *Waspada* class [est. 16 missiles]), Cameroon (MM 40 in P48S class [9 missiles]), Chile (MM 38 in Counties [except *Latorre*], *Leanders* [*Condell, Lynch*], and *Almirante Williams* class [total 16]), Colombia (MM 38 in FS-1500 class [24]), Ecuador (MM 40 [est. 30] in *Wadi M'ragh* class, MM 38 [est. 12] in *Quito* class), France (MM 40 in *Cassard, La Fayette, Floreal* classes and *Aconit*; MM 38 in *Georges Leygues, Tourville, Suffren, Cdt. Riviere* classes and *Dupperre*; two MM 38 or four MM 40 in A69 class [total 154 MM 38, est. 72 MM 40]), Germany (MM 38 [350] in F123 and S143/143A/143B/148 classes), Greece (MM 38 [56] in Combattante II and in four of ten Combattante IIIN), Indonesia (MM 38 [26] in *Hajar Dewantara* and *Fatahilah*, PSK Mk 6 classes), Korea (MM 38 in "Wildcat" class), Kuwait (MM 40 in surviving FPB 57 and TNC 45 [bought 45; had to buy some replacements during the Gulf War]), Malaysia (MM 38 [est. 62] in FS-1500, Spica-M, and Combattante II 4AL classes; MM40 Block II in new corvettes), Morocco (MM 38 [20] in *Lazaga* class; also bought four MM 40), Nigeria (MM 38 in Combattante IIIB class), Oman (MM 40 in "Province" class, Block II in new corvettes [10 MM 38, est. 38 MM 40]), Peru (MM 38 [17] in PR 72 class), Philippines (Block II in new *Cormoran* class, being built by Bazan), Qatar (MM 40 [est. 44, more on order] in Combattante III class, Block II for coast defense), Thailand (MM 38 [12] in *Ratcharit* class), Tunisia (MM 40 [est. 27] in Combattante III class), UAE (MM 40 [32] in FPB 38, TNC 45, more for new Type 62s), United Kingdom (MM 38 [300] in Type 22 Batch 1/2). Another 172 MM 38 and at least 121 MM 40 are not accounted for, but may be for coast defense.

Coast defense: Cyprus, Qatar (MM 40 Block II: four batteries on Berliet 6 × 6 trucks), Saudi Arabia (MM 40 Block II), Thailand (10 batteries of MM 40 ordered 1986), United Kingdom (MM 38, at Gibraltar; system is called Excalibur, uses Type 1006 radar). Reportedly the unit at Gibraltar has been withdrawn.

Submarine version: France (strategic and attack submarines, operational 1985; 79 bought through 1989), Pakistan (*Agosta* 90B class, on order; probably for earlier *Agostas* as well).

Airborne version (AM 39): Argentina (30 for Super Étendard and two L-188 patrol aircraft), Brazil (Super Pumas), Chile (Super Pumas on "County" class), France (70 for Super Étendard, Atlantique Mk 2), Iraq (est. 770 ordered, 250 delivered through 1982), Indonesia (from Super Pumas), Pakistan (six Sea Kings, Atlantics [28 missiles]), Peru (Super Pumas from cruiser), Qatar (two of eight SH-3D can carry AM 39; it can also be carried by 12 air force Mirage F1 EDA and by two F-1 DDA; est. 12 missiles), Saudi Arabia (Super Pumas), UAE (Super Pumas), Venezuela (for air force Mirage V fighters, now being equipped). This missile may also have been bought by Kuwait and by Oman. Oman may have Exocets on board air force Super Puma helicopters.

China (PRC) reportedly obtained some of these missiles in April 1985 via a third party, possibly using Exocet as a basis for its own C-801 missile, and there have been reports of Brazilian production under license.

♦ Laser-Guided Bombs

For some years the standard laser-guided bomb (LGB) was Matra's BGL (Bombe à Guidage Laser), made in 250-, 400-, and 1000-kg sizes. The seeker, similar to that in the AS 30L missile, is made by Thomson-CSF. Development began in 1978. Standoff range is 2–8 km. BGL 400 (470 kg overall, 3.4 m long, maximum fin span 1.43 m), first tested in 1985, is specifically described as having an antiship capability. BGL 1000 (Arcole), which entered production in 1986 (about 100 were made, specifically for Mirage 2000 strike fighters), has a dual-charge warhead to penetrate heavy structures. The last to be developed was BGL 250. Maximum flight time is 40 sec at Mach 0.9, for a maximum range of 7–8 km; minimum altitude is 50 m, and claimed accuracy is 3 m. Of 1700 BGLs made, 75% were exported (probable customers were Egypt, Greece, India, Iraq, Peru, Taiwan, and the UAE). In 1994 the French government asked for tenders for a replacement, largely to meet the requirements of the Bosnian operation. Proposals included a follow-on BGL (Arcole) and a version of the Israeli Griffin (marketed by SAMP). The U.S. Paveway was chosen and a contract for 500 Paveway II (Mk 82 version) awarded in May 1995, for delivery through 1997. Contract options may bring the total to 1500. These weapons equip Mirage F1 and Super Étendard fighter-bombers.

Matra's BGL 400, with Apache at left and ARMAT at right. (Author)

BGL was used in combat for the first time in Yugoslavia on 21 November 1994, when four Jaguars each dropped one on Udbina airfield in Croatia as part of a NATO strike. Each Jaguar pilot designated the target for his own bomb. In addition, six of the lighter 400-kg version were used in Yugoslavia.

♦ Modular Propelled Bomb/Excalibur

This is a new project to develop a low-cost short-range powered bomb or ASM for standoff attacks (to avoid shoulder-fired weapons) against tanks and small structures that do not warrant the expenditure of more expensive weapons. The warhead will be a standard 250- or 1000-kg bomb or bomblets. Guidance will be GPS or low-cost inertial, as in the U.S. JDAMS project. The goal is to achieve a 20km range with accuracy 30 to 40% better than that of a gravity bomb at a lower cost than that of current LGBs. It would be somewhat less accurate than an LGB.

Excalibur, as displayed at the Paris Air Show, 1993. (S. Zaloga)

Matra's version of the French modular guided bomb (Armament Air-Sol Modulaire), broadly comparable to the U.S. JSOW, at the 1995 Paris Air Show. (Author)

SAMP's Excalibur (MP 22), development of which began in 1992, is probably intended to meet this requirement. It carries a standard 250-kg bomb and is powered by a slow-burning (15-sec) low-thrust rocket motor. Target coordinates are entered by the attacking airplane 10 msec before launch, and estimated CEP at 10km range is 30 m (100 ft). Dimensions are 273 mm × 2.25 m (tail span is 546 mm). Aerospatiale exhibited its version of the modular bomb, AASM (Armament Air-Sol Modulaire) at the 1995 Paris Air Show. Dimensions: 30 × 300 cm, span 58 cm. Range would be about 15 km (8 nm). As of 1996, it was not certain that this weapon would be powered. Matra is developing a competing weapon.

As of 1995 this weapon was in the project definition stage. Development is to begin sometime after 1998, with kits produced for French Rafale fighters some time after 2000. Probably about 5000 bomb kits are required.

◆ SS 12M/AS 12

> **Dimensions:** 7.1 × 73.7 × 25.6 in
> **Weight:** 165 lb
> **Warhead:** 62.5 lb. Several types, including OP3C, an SAP with a bulbous shape to aid fragmentation (actuates about 6 ft after penetration), containing about 13 lb of TNT/RDX mixture.
> **Range:** 6580 yd (670-yd minimum)
> **Speed:** 580 ft/sec (flight time 34 sec maximum)

Data are for SS 12M.

SS 12M is a naval version of a widely used army wire-guided missile; it was first demonstrated in 1966 and was first sold to Libya. The launcher fires up to eight prepackaged missiles in succession, all the missiles occupying forward-facing fixed racks. The attack boat, therefore, has to turn toward the target at the moment of firing. The missile aimer occupies a turret with a

SS 12M missiles on board the French patrol boat *La Combattante*, on the side of the turreted launcher amidships (the much larger launcher aft carries flares). These missiles are no longer carried by French patrol craft, but survive in small numbers in some other navies. (U.S. Naval Institute)

gyrostabilized APX.260 sight. The operator uses a joystick to guide the missiles in flight, this optical control limiting their use to visible targets. This system is extremely difficult to use from a moving ship or boat.

Users: Gabon (*Général Nazaire Boulingui*), Greece (*Kelefstis Stamou* class), and Tunisia (P 48–class patrol boats). The French *Trident*-class patrol boats originally carried SS 12Ms and reportedly they can be remounted.

AS 12 is an air-launched version, carried by Alouette III, AB 212/204, Gazelle, Lynx, and Wasp helicopters. One AS 12 is equivalent to one Mk 44/46 torpedo. Not all such aircraft are necessarily so equipped. A Lynx can accommodate four AS 12s, a lighter helicopter two.

Users: Brazil, Chile (10 Alouette III), Egypt (24 SA 342L Gazelles, of which nine are used for naval support), France (Lynx helicopters [four missiles each]), Greece (four Alouette III), Libya (12 Alouette III), Spain (AB 212 helicopters). Other buyers, which may well use the missile from shipboard helicopters, are Argentina (Alouette III, 500 Defender), India (Alouette III [Chepak] on *Leanders*), Iran (AB 212), the Netherlands (Lynx), Nigeria (Lynx on *Aradu*), Saudi Arabia, and the UAE (Alouette III on FPB 62). Other buyers were: Brunei, Gabon, Germany, Iraq, Italy (two on an AB 212, four on a Sea King; presumably all or most Italian naval helicopters now carry Marte), Ivory Coast, Kuwait, Madagascar, Norway, Qatar, Tunisia, the United Kingdom (which replaced AS 12 with Sea Skua), and Venezuela. Unit cost was $76,000 in 1987. AS 12 was cleared for carriage on board Atlantic and Alize fixed-wing aircraft and also on board Gazelle, Lynx, AB 212, Wessex, and Wasp helicopters.

GERMANY

◆ ARAMIS

This was initially a Franco-German ARM project; the French had to withdraw due to severe budget cuts. ARAMIS (Anti-Radar Missile) is a technology demonstrator for a possible HARM replacement, using a dual-mode (passive IR/RF) seeker and ramjet power. A full-scale mockup of the missile was exhibited at the 1996 Berlin air show. Initial development of a Sprint dual-mode seeker for the ARAMIS program was completed in 1993. It can either switch to IIR (8–12 microns, 64 × 64-element array) if the target radar shuts down, or it can fuse data from the two elements. Dimensions are 200 mm × 4 m; fin span is less than 700 mm, and the missile weighs about 220 kg. A Tornado can carry four ARAMIS missiles.

◆ Kormoran (AS 34)

> **Dimensions:** 34.4 cm × 4.4 m; 100cm span (13.6 × 173.2; 39.4 in)
> **Weight:** 600 kg (1320 lb)
> **Warhead:** 160 kg; 55-kg HE (353/121 lb)
> **Propulsion:** Boost-sustain rocket
> **Speed:** Mach 0.9
> **Range:** 30+ km (33,000+ yd)

Kormoran was designed specifically to be launched by a low-flying aircraft, popping up briefly to fire. It uses an active terminal seeker with mid-course inertial guidance. Firing modes are radar lock-on (by the missile, independently), radar acquisition (locked on by the aircraft radar), and visual. The delayed-action warhead carries 16 shallow shaped charges (called P-charges, or projectile charges), each of which forms a self-forging fragment that can penetrate 70–90 mm of steel. The P-charges are spread over the surface of the warhead, firing radially.

Kormoran was developed by MBB and Nord (now Aerospatiale) beginning with a 1962 MBB study; it first flew in 1967 and was approved for service use in 1974. The first production rounds were delivered in December 1977.

Kormoran 2 is a remanufactured Kormoran 1 with a digital bus carrying a new Thomson-CSF solid-state digital seeker (with better target selection and better ECM) and a new digital autopilot/computer. It has an improved 220-lb warhead and a new four-nozzle motor offering increased range (55+ km). It is designed to fly optimized paths after multiple launches by aircraft with digital bus connections to their hard points. This version

A Kormoran missile is shown on board a German navy Tornado, with a Sidewinder outboard. (Messerschmitt-Bolkow-Blohm GmBH).

weighs 630 kg and flies at Mach 0.95. The development contract was let in 1983, and the missile was declared operational in January 1991.

In 1987 estimated unit cost was $450,000 for Kormoran 1 and $575,000 for Kormoran 2.

Users: Germany (350 for Tornado strike aircraft: used by 156 Squadron in secondary antiship role), Italy (60 for Tornado strike aircraft). About 180 Kormoran 2 are on order; but it is also reported that the German requirement is for 262 missiles. Kormoran 2 entered service in 1996.

INDIA

Hindustan Aeronautics Ltd. is reportedly developing a Mach 4 ASM for air force and navy use, with a 100km (109,000-yd) range and a 35-kg (77-lb) payload. The missile is to be launchable from 30,000 ft altitude.

◆ Koral

HAL's antiship missile is to replace Russian-supplied weapons on board the new Project 16 destroyer; the X-band targeting radar is Aparna. Drawings of Aparna suggest that it is actually a derivative of the Russian Garpun (NATO Plank Shave) associated with SS-N-2 in "Tarantul"-class fast-attack boats. Note that Koral is the designation of the missile FCS in these boats.

INTERNATIONAL

◆ Polypheme

Euromissile's fiber-optic missile is now planned as the secondary armament of the German Type 130 corvette (the primary weapon will be ANNG or some equivalent). Because the man-in-the-loop guidance system is inherently flexible, Polypheme has also been proposed as a submarine AA weapon, to counter helicopters and slow maritime patrol aircraft. As of the spring of 1996, a contract for installation on board German Type 212 submarines was expected, and the U.S. Navy was reportedly inter-

Polypheme on display at Bourget Euronavale, 1994. (Author)

ested in this application (for which the U.S. Army FOG-M was an alternative). Like other fiber-optic weapons, Polypheme is also planned for a variety of land applications.

The missile carries a video or IR camera, whose digitized imagery is sent back down the fiber-optic cable to the control installation, which displays the image and also has image-processing software to help the operator choose a target and also to autotrack as the missile approaches the target. Alternatively, the software in the control station can choose a target. That can require considerable image processing, but the great advantage of the fiber-optic missile is that it need carry no processing electronics. The initial version uses an IR camera.

The powerplant is a small turbojet. The missile is launched at a shallow angle (7 to 20 deg), and flies at an altitude of 15 to 300 m. Dimensions: 165 cm × 1.6 m (span 0.8 m), weight 43 kg (3-kg warhead). An antitank version is 2m long (53 kg) with a tandem shaped-charge warhead. An antiship version would have a mixed charge (shaped and fragmentation).

Aerospatiale and MBB began work on fiber-optically guided missiles in the early 1980s, initially using modified Mamba antitank missiles. The Polypheme program began in 1986 as a demonstration that a missile could be guided over a 7km range, with guidance orders traveling up the fiber and stabilized images coming back from the missile, and finally with control by a ground-based autotracker (using the imagery) to track and attack a ground target. SS-12M missiles equipped with a stabilized CCD camera were used for the ensuing trials, culminating in four final full-scale shots in 1987–88. Meanwhile, static tests showed that fibers could be used for ranges beyond 60 km. These successes led to an exploratory development program, which began in 1991. DASA was responsible for the missile, Aerospatiale for the control installation (comprising an Alcatel optical element, DASA tracking/guidance and control, and Aerospatiale FCS and optical processor). Italy joined the program after a series of test shots in 1995.

A submarine-launched AA version was prominently advertised about 1989, then apparently superseded by surface-launched alternatives. Polypheme-SM would have weighed 43 kg (with a 3-kg fragmentation warhead) and would have been powered by a boost-sustain rocket motor capable of two flight speeds: 150 m/sec for target search and 250 m/sec for attack. The missile would have been launched, at depths as great as 300 m (1000 ft), in a 62-kg pressurized capsule, which would emerge from the water about 1 km from the submarine.

If target range and bearing were fairly well defined (for example, by the sound of helicopter blades or sonar pings), the missile could search a 3km wide swath as it flew. If target position was far less well defined, for example by the splash of sonobuoys entering the water, the missile could fly an ascending search spiral with a radius of 1 km.

ISRAEL

◆ Delilah/STAR-1

TAAS-Israel Industries Ltd's expendable GPS-guided turbojet UAV is used as an antiradar missile (Delilah-AR or STAR-1) and will form the basis for a long-range cruise missile being developed for an unspecified Asian customer, perhaps China (which has shown intense interest in a GPS-guided weapon to use against political targets in Taiwan). Ships can fire Delilah from a box launcher. Thus far Delilah has apparently been carried by F-4, F-16, and F/A-18 aircraft, and it has been fired from a four- or eight-round ground launcher. Dimensions: 33 × 270.8 cm; wing span 115 cm; fin span 82 cm (13 × 106.6 in; 45.3 in; 32.3 in). Total weight is 182 kg (400 lb), of which 22 kg (50 lb) is fuel (fuel weight can be traded off against payload). The powerplant is a 165-lb thrust Noel Penny NPT 151-4 turbojet. Warhead: 54 kg (120 lb). Delilah can cruise from sea level to 28,000 ft, at Mach 0.3 to Mach 0.7; range is up to 400 km, and positioning accuracy is better than 91 m. Instantaneous turn capability is 5G. Delilah-AR has a loiter mode reminiscent of the abortive U.S. Tacit Rainbow (AGM-132): the missile keeps enemy radars shut down by cruising overhead with its seeker activated. The computer associated with the 2–18-GHz seeker permits multiple discrimination, so that the missile can choose the most important of an array of radiating targets. Unit cost is probably about $120,000. Delilah development began in the mid-1980s as a follow-on to the Samson/TALD decoy series; the Delilah decoy entered service with the Israeli Defense Force about 1989. The Delilah brochure emphasizes its value as a decoy, but a much-enlarged version, suited to the British CASOM stand-off missile requirement, was shown at Paris in 1995.

◆ **Gabriel**

Versions

	I	II
Diameter	32.5 cm	35 cm
	(12.8 in)	(13.8 in)
Length	3.35 m	3.35 m
	(132 in)	(132 in)
Span	1.385 m	1.385 m
	(54.5 in)	(54.5 in)
Weight	400 kg[a]	500 kg
	(882 lb)	(1102 lb)
Warhead	180 kg[b]	180 kg
	(397 lb)	(397 lb)
Boost Thrust (lb thrust/duration)	3600/3	3600/3
Sustain (duration)	100 sec	200 sec
Speed	Mach 0.65	Mach 0.65 M
Range	20+ km[c]	36–40 km
	(22+ kyd)	(39–44 kyd)
Attack Altitude	4.5–6 m	2.5 m
	(14.9–19.7 ft)	(8.2 ft)

[a]Gabriel I in launcher/container: 600 kg (1322 lb).
[b]Explosive weight: 154 lb, with delayed-action fuze.
[c]Minimum range for Gabriel I: 5500 yd.

Gabriel was developed by IAI in 1964–68 (first successfully tested 1965) as a direct counter to the Styx missiles supplied to the Arab states. It entered service in 1972, proving successful during the October 1973 Mideast war. Although having a much shorter range than Styx, Gabriel could lock onto a smaller target (i.e., a missile boat) and apparently could be fired much more easily. Gabriel evolved from an earlier Rafael command-guided SSM, Luz, and retains some of its features. Luz was controlled by joystick, the operator following its tail flare. Tests about 1962 showed that this system was impractical on shipboard, partly because the smoke of the rocket motor soon obscured the flare. The missile's designer, Ori Even-Tov, moved to IAI specifically to develop Gabriel as a day-night system with autonomous guidance. Because Luz had no space in its nose for a radar dish, he had to settle for terminal semiactive guidance using antennas on either side of the missile, each covering a sector 5 or 6 deg wide. Presumably this is a very simple form of lobing, the missile trying to maintain a course for which returns in both antennas are equal.

The two-man OG.R7/2 director is slaved to an RTN-10X or EL/M-2221 conscan radar, which tracks the target. One operator launches the missile, then uses a joystick to gather it into the guidance beam by commanding it into the center of a circle etched on stabilized binoculars. He may continue to track the missile's tail flare to check its response to guidance commands (which the missile receives via a dielectric antenna on its dorsal fin). The other tracks the target as a backup to the radar. The missile is a beam-rider. When it gets close enough to the target, it is commanded to shift to semiactive radar homing. If the target jams, the missile seeker can be turned off and the missile will attempt to ride the beam all the way into the target. This system is probably related to that of the Italian Sea Killer; much of the Gabriel electronics were developed in Italy. However, Sea Killer lacks Gabriel's terminal seeker.

The original version of the system, which used an OG.R7 optical sight to track the missile, probably survives on board the Thai *Prabrarapak* class.

OG 20 is better adapted to the command backup mode, in which one operator tracks the flare in the missile tail, the other the target; it has an open sight for initial target acquisition. Presumably the director is stabilized (the Israelis initially abandoned pure joystick guidance mainly because their boats rolled and pitched too badly). OG 20 is on board Israeli missile boats (including those for Chile and South Africa) and also on board boats converted to fire Gabriel for Ecuador and Kenya.

Gabriel I climbs to about 100 m (328 ft) after launch, then at an estimated range (from the target) of 7.5 km (8200 yd), descends slowly to 20 m (66 ft). The missile can then be command-guided in azimuth. At a range of 1.2 km (1300 yd) from the target, Gabriel I descends to 3 m (9.8 ft), using either radio-command or semiactive-radar guidance. Later versions rise to only about 35 m (115 ft), and cruise at 17–20 m (56–66 ft).

Gabriel II (1972) has an upgraded sustainer (higher-thrust grain) and a larger warhead in much the same airframe as Gabriel I. The seeker may provide some antiradar capability and a home-on-jam mode.

Gabriel I was widely exported after its successes in the 1973 Mideast war, in characteristic sealed shipping/launching containers with a shelf life reported as 2 yr. By the time production had ended in 1992, probably about 600 had been made. The South African Skorpioen (100 made) is a licensed Gabriel II copy. However, the Taiwanese Hsiung Feng I (probably 350 made) is an unlicensed copy. The production figures given here are based on known installations. However, considerably higher estimates of Gabriel production, up to 1982 missiles, have appeared. For example, if in fact Iran received 200 missiles in 1987, then the production figure is probably closer to 1000 than to 600. It is also possible that the missile is used for coast defense. Estimated unit cost (1987) was $400,000.

Two further versions, the active-homing Gabriel III and the longer-range active-homing Gabriel IV, never entered service. Gabriel III was canceled when Israel bought Harpoon, and Gabriel IV seems to have been canceled about 1993. The latter's name has been reserved for a future weapon.

Users: Argentina (provision for Gabriel II in four Israeli-supplied Daburs), Chile (*Sa'ar* 2/4), Ecuador (*Manta* class [Gabriel II]), Israel, Kenya (37.5m and 32m boats, bought 1979: Gabriel II), Singapore (FPB 45 class, provision for two each on 12 "Swifts"), South Africa (*Sa'ar* 3), Taiwan (bought 1978), Thailand (*Prabrarapak* class). This missile was reportedly bought by Brazil and by Colombia, but no appropriate platforms have ever been identified; it may have been intended only for tests. Iran reportedly received 200 in 1987; Malaysia also reportedly received some missiles. If, as seems likely, Gabriel guidance is much like that of Sea Killer, the Iranian Gabriels may have been intended to arm the Iranian Vosper frigates.

ITALY

◆ **Marte/Sea Killer**

Dimensions: 31.6 cm dia × 4.84 m, including 1.09m booster (12.5 × 191/43 in); span 98.4 cm (38.7 in)
Weight: 345 kg (760 lb)
Warhead: 70 kg (154-lb) Tritolital blast SAP with impact fuze
Propulsion: Boost: 1.7-sec burn, to 250 m/sec (820 ft/sec); sustain: 75-sec burn
Speed: 300 m/sec (984 ft/sec)
Range: 20–25 km (22–27 kyd; minimum range 6 kyd)

Data are for Marte Mk 2.

OTO-Melara's missile is Sea Killer and the helicopter system is Marte; at present the name Marte is applied to the air-

Gabriel in flight. The two dipoles visible below the missile are presumably part of the radar altimeter.

Marte Mk 2 at the Paris Air Show, 1989. (Author)

Otomat, at the 1995 Dubai Air Show. (S. Zaloga)

launched missile as well. The Mk 2 missile can also be carried by a fixed-wing airplane, in which case it needs no booster (and is, therefore, 84 kg lighter). As of 1993, production of Marte Mk 1 was 472; of Marte Mk 2, 204 (including test missiles). Mk 2 production is probably continuing. Marte Mk 2 unit price is probably about $472,000.

Sea Killer Mk 1 (Nettuno) is extinct. The ship-launched Sea Killer Mk 2 (Vulcano), used only by Iran (160 were bought) in recent years, is probably no longer operable. In all, 367 Sea Killer missiles had been made. During the Iran-Iraq War, this missile hit at least six ships (total 280,975 GRT) during the period beginning in October 1986 and ending in February 1987; two warheads failed to explode. See the 1991/92 edition for details.

In the Marte Mk 1 system, a Sea King helicopter with SMA APQ-706 radar carries two Sea Killer Mk 2 missiles. The missile is a beam-rider flying at a set altitude (3.4–5 m) above the sea.

Marte Mk 2 has a larger-diameter nose containing an Otomat active terminal seeker (it still presumably rides a beam toward the target). Reports indicate that the warhead is no heavier than that of Marte Mk 1. The airframe and booster aft of the nose section duplicate those of Marte Mk 1.

The first Marte Mk 1 was delivered to the Italian navy in 1977. Marte Mk 2 was announced in mid-1983. It entered Italian navy service in 1987.

Users (with estimated quantities): Iran (160), Italy (450 Mk 1, 180 Mk 2), Venezuela (100 Mk 1, for AB 212 helicopters). This missile may also have been exported to Peru (Mk 1 for AB 212 helicopters). Marte can now be fired by a modified MB 339; a Marte 2A was test-fired this way on 17 June 1992. The airplane was fitted with a new inertial platform, Doppler velocity sensor, and with navigation/attack computers to program missiles. Target data appeared on the pilot's HUD. Since the MB 339 lacks a radar, targeting data must come from a third party. The modified aircraft is designated MB 339AM; it carries the same systems as the new MB 339C bought by the RNZAF. This version has not yet been sold.

◆ Otomat

Dimensions: 46 cm × 4.46 m; 1.35m span (18.1 × 189.8 × 49.1 in)
Weight: 770 kg at launch; 660 kg in flight (1697/1455 lb)
Warhead: 210-kg (463-lb) Herotol blast (132-lb explosive)
Propulsion: Turbomeca Arbizon III turbojet and two solid-fuel boosters
Speed: Mach 0.9
Range: Mk 1: 6–60 km; Mk 2L: 100–180 km (6.6–66 kyd/109–97 kyd). Minimum range for Mk 1 is 6600 yd; maximum effective range is 64 kyd; maximum flight range is 88 kyd.

Otomat is a collaborative French-Italian project (OTO-Melara and Matra); missiles are manufactured in both countries. Otomat uses inertial mid-course guidance and an X-band active terminal seeker. The launcher is fixed at an elevation of 12 or 18 deg. Mk 2 (Otomat Compact) has folding wings and can therefore be stowed in a smaller (elliptical) container: two fit in the same space as one cylindrical Mk 1 container (1.36m dia). This development corresponds to the shift from Exocet MM 38 to MM 40.

The missile can turn as much as 200 deg after launch. The rocket booster carries it to an altitude of 80 m (262 ft). The missile switches on its seeker at an expected range of about 12 km (13.1 kyd). Mk 1 climbs to 175 m (574 ft) at a range of 4 km (4400 yd) from the target then, at 2km (2200-yd) range, dives at 7 deg. That dive increases the chance of penetrating deep into a target ship but exposes the missile to hostile fire for an estimated 12 sec. Otomat Mk 2 is, therefore, designed to sea-skim throughout the run-in to the target.

Mk 1 receives its launch data (true target bearing, own-ship heading, time of flight, and vertical reference) from the launch ship. Warm-up time is 30 sec (gyro spin-up time). All Mk 1s use a three-axis Thomson-CSF Col Vert terminal seeker that scans in elevation and to 20 deg to either side of the missile. Italian-made Mk 2s have an Italian-made SMA ST-2 single-axis active seeker.

Otomat Mk 1 is a fire-and-forget weapon; Mk 2 accepts mid-course updates and so can exploit its greater range. There are two quite different systems, the French ERATO and the Italian TESEO.

In ERATO (Extended Range Targeting of Otomat), mid-course corrections are transmitted directly by the launching ship. The missile must, therefore, climb to 900 m (2952 ft) altitude to remain within range of the shipboard data link. The ship tracks the helicopter, which in turn detects and tracks the target. The missile descends to 20 m (66 ft) cruise altitude after receiving final instructions by ship data link, at a maximum range of about 80–100 km (the ship's radar horizon for the helicopter). A final pop-up maneuver is possible. Maximum total range is 166 km. The helicopter need not fly near the missile's flight path, and the system as a whole can engage several targets simultaneously (up to 16 missiles at six targets with six simultaneous mid-course updates). This flexibility makes it possible for the missiles to approach one target from several different directions more or less simultaneously. ERATO is used only by the Saudi *Al Madinah*–class frigates.

In the Italian TESEO system, the helicopter orders the turn toward the target, so the missile is initially directed toward the helicopter. Thus, the missile flies at low altitude all the way to the target, not needing to be high enough to receive mid-course guidance from a ship. However, because the missile must fly directly to the helicopter, the system as a whole cannot engage more than one target (or a few targets very close together) at a time. Moreover, the effect of the system is to increase flight time, as the missile must follow an angled path. For example, a missile fired by a Venezuelan *Lupo*-class frigate hit a target 131.5 km (144 kyd) away, but that engagement entailed a flight leg of 85.8 km (93.8 kyd) to the helicopter, and another of 51.9 km (56.8 kyd) to the target. Typical mid-course guidance platforms are AB 212 and Sea King helicopters.

OTO-Melara and Engins Matra conceived Otomat as a private venture and began studies in 1967 and development in 1969. The first successful guided flight was in February 1972. Mk 1 entered service in 1976 (first successful flight February 1972). Mk 2 development began in May 1973 (first test January 1974). In mid-1979 the Italian navy began to outfit AB 212 and Sea King helicopters to provide mid-course guidance (tested December 1979). The French Clio system was demonstrated to the Royal Saudi Navy on 25 April 1985.

A projected higher-speed version, Otomach, was dropped in 1992 because Matra Defense argued that speed was no longer a guarantee of penetration. An ASW version was announced in October 1986: MILAS (see the Antisubmarine Warfare section). A 1989 Matra proposal for an air-launched Otomat seems to be proceeding to development. The Italian navy's Harriers are the most likely initial platform.

Matra is now marketing Otomat Mk 3, which is based on MILAS. The current analog circuitry is replaced by digital alternatives, including a data bus connecting the seeker to a more powerful onboard computer. The computer might be fed with target data, so that the missile could attack a selected point on the target. It is also possible that the missile could use some form of ISAR to recognize a selected target from an array of ships. Improved guidance (e.g., for obstacle avoidance and selectable trajectory) makes somewhat longer range useful: the missile carries slightly more fuel, to extend range from the 160 km of Otomat 2 to 180 km (97 nm). The shipboard FCS would enable three missiles to approach a single target simultaneously from three directions, and they could combine sea-skimming with pop-up/dive terminal maneuvers. There is probably a time-on-target feature. No basic change in operating procedure (i.e., mid-course update) is planned. Reportedly the computer improves ECCM, and makes a (presumably programmed) terminal evasive maneuver possible. Because the missile is fully digital, and because it shares the same computer as MILAS, the same digital FCS may be able to handle both interchangeably. Presumably existing missiles can be remanufactured to Mk 3 standard. Otomat Mk 3 will probably be ready in 1996. As of mid-1995, there was French navy official interest, since a standard MILAS (ASW) canister can also carry Otomat Mk 3.

OTO-Breda is advertising a stealthy alternative (apparently also a codevelopment with Matra), which it calls TESEO Mk 3. This weapon meets an Italian navy requirement for a TESEO (Otomat) 2 replacement. The project was announced at the 1993 Paris Air Show, and a model was displayed for the first time at Bourget Euronaval in October 1994. At least some of the low-observable technology comes from Matra's Apache ASM. The turbojet missile cruises at high subsonic speed and approaches its target at transonic speed. Mid-course guidance is inertial, with terminal radar and IR seekers. RAM is used in the blended airframe (with faired shark nose, for the paired seekers) and mid-body cruciform wings extending from four air intakes; it also has cruciform rear fins, with two boosters aft. Maximum range is to exceed 300 km, almost twice that of Otomat 2.

In March 1996 it was reported that the U.S. Navy was considering joint development of a next-generation missile, Ulisee, based on TESEO 3 technology (a decision was expected in the fall of 1996). A joint OR was drafted after an MoU was signed in November 1995. Ulisee would enter service about 2003–2005. In U.S. service it might be a SLAM-ER successor, and might be carried aboard naval aircraft. The Italian version would equip both ships and aircraft, including the future MPA and the Tornado; it might also equip AV-8Bs, Eurofighters, and the AMX. The air-launched variant would have a range of over 300 km (160 nm), the ship-launched variant 250 km. It would cruise at Mach 0.88 and be boosted to Mach 0.95 for its attack. Total weight

would be 700 to 800 kg. Ulisee would presumably be one alternative to the Harpoon 2000 described below.

By late 1994, 1008 missiles had been made or were on order. As of 1990, a French missile cost $523,900; an Italian missile cost $514,800.

Users: Egypt (October and Ramadan classes), Iran (status not known), Iraq (*Wadi M'ragh* class, now for sale), Italy (Mk 2 in *Garibaldi, Animoso, Audace, Maestrale, Lupo, Sparviero* classes), Kenya (Mk 1 in "Province" class), Malaysia (ex-Iraqi *Wadi M'ragh* class), Nigeria (Mk 1 in *Aradu* and FPB 57 class), Peru (Mk 2 in *Alm Grau* [planned but not fitted] and *Lupo* class), Saudi Arabia (Mk 2 ERATO in *Al Madinah* class), and Venezuela (Mk 2 in *Lupos* and Mk 1 in three of six *Constitucion* class).

Coast defense: Egypt (30 missiles) and Saudi Arabia (155 missiles) use Otomat, mounted on a 6 × 6 Berliet chassis. Kenya may also operate this weapon. The associated radar is a truck-mounted SPQ-3. The launcher carries two missiles, and there is a reload vehicle with a hoist.

JAPAN

GCS-1 is Mitsubishi's strap-on IIR antiship guidance system for 225-kg (Mod 1) and 340-kg (Mod 2) bombs. The seeker is related to that of the Japanese hand-held SAM. Overall dimensions: 150 mm × 0.75 m (seeker end only). Flight tests (for initial use by F-1 fighters) began in mid-1988. This weapon is now operational.

◆ ASM-1/SSM-1/ASM-2

> **Dimensions:** 35 cm × 3.95 m; 120cm span (13.8 × 156.8; 47 in)
> **Weight:** 610 kg (1344 lb)
> **Warhead:** 250 kg (550 lb)
> **Propulsion:** Solid-fuel rocket
> **Speed:** Mach 0.9
> **Range:** 50 km (54,680 yd)

Data are for ASM-1. SSM-1 is 5 m long with a 116cm span (197 × 45.7 in) and weighs 661 kg (1457 lb) with a 225-kg warhead. The powerplant is a Mitsubishi TJM-2 turbojet with two boosters; range is 150 km (164 kyds).

Mitsubishi began work on the ASM-1 (Type 80) air-launched antiship missile in 1973. It was tested in 1977–79, entered production in 1980, and entered service in 1982, carried in pairs by F-1 fighters (with J/ASQ-1 FCS). This missile is similar in concept to Harpoon, with strapdown inertial mid-course and terminal radar guidance. Estimated unit cost is $1.2M. ASM-1C (Type 91) is a derivative (via the surface-launched turbojet SSM-1) for P-3C Orions, developed in conjunction with their Japanese manufacturer, Kawasaki.

ASM-2 (Type 93) is a derivative of ASM-1C with a Fujitsu IIR seeker instead of an active radar seeker. It is to be the primary antiship weapon of the new F-2 (F-16 derivative) fighter (four per aircraft). Tested against a moving target in May 1992, it entered production in 1994. This version may incorporate a ferrite-based RAM in its wing roots to reduce radar cross-section.

ASM-1. (*Ships of the World*)

SSM-1. (*Sea Power*)

TESEO Mk 3, the projected stealthy follow-on to Otomat, as displayed in scale model form by OTO-Breda at the 1994 Bourget Navale show. (Author)

SSM-1 (Type 88) is a turbojet coast-defense version, mounted on a six-tube truck. Proposed in 1981, its prototype was completed in 1983. Plans call for a total of 54 trucks in three groups, each about 60 mi from the coast.

SSM-1B (Type 90) is intended to replace Harpoon in Japanese service; it currently arms the new missile hydrofoils. Low-rate production began in 1992 (FY90 budget).

A new long-range antiship missile that entered development in 1988 will presumably be designated SSM-2. It will probably use the Fujitsu IIR seeker of ASM-2. Japan may plan to develop a follow-on supersonic ramjet missile, based on technology demonstrators already flown.

Production: 240 ASM-1; 160 ASM-1C through 1993 (plus 30 each funded for 1994 and 1995); planned total of 384 SSM-1 (of which 150 had been bought through 1993).

When SSM-1 was originally proposed, unit cost was to have been $385,000 (FY78 dollars), based on a purchase of 150 missiles. The purchase was increased to 250 missiles, but a later unit-price estimate was $697,000 (FY87 dollars); the prototypes cost $728,000 each (FY87). Unit cost in 1991 dollars is $915,000.

NORWAY

A new missile (NSM, Nytt Sjomalsmissil) is under development to arm the new Norwegian frigate and fast-attack boats and modernized coast defenses. The program was approved by the Norwegian parliament in the fall of 1994. NSM will probably later be used (in a longer-range version) for coast defense. In 1988 NFT (which is as of 1995 again called Kongsberg) began a program for a new missile, possibly to be called Penguin Mk 4, with a ramjet powerplant and two external boosters, for more range (perhaps about 50 nm), composite construction, and a new computer. Reportedly the missile will have an IIR seeker (developed by Kongsberg and NDRE) and a low-observable subsonic airframe. Payload will be similar to that of a Penguin. Officially NSM is said to be an entirely new weapon, rather than a Penguin derivative. A future upgrade may provide submunitions for land attack, a better IIR seeker, and better ECM resistance. NFT received a concept definition study contract in 1991.

As of about April 1996, NSM was expected to enter service about 2000–2001, initially on board the next-generation Norwegian fast-attack boat. However, in mid-May it was reported that no full-scale development contract had yet been awarded, and that the new attack boat would be armed with an existing missile, probably Harpoon or Exocet.

◆ Penguin (AGM-119)

Dimensions: 28cm × 2.95m × 1.42m span (11in × 118in × 55.5in span); Mk 2 length 2.96 m (117 in); Mk 3: 28cm × 3.20m × 2.00m span (11in × 10ft 5in × 3ft 3in)
Weight: Mk 1: 330 kg; Mk 2: 340 kg; Mk 3: 350 kg, 400 kg with launcher (Mk 1: 741 lb; Mk 2: 749 lb; Mk 3: 771/882 lb). Mk 3 weight has also been given officially as 820 lb with a 265-lb warhead.
Warhead: 250-lb SAP (Bullpup Mk 19)
Propulsion: Solid rocket
Speed: Mach 0.7 (Mk 2 and Mk 3: Mach 0.8)
Range: Mk 1: 20 km; Mk 2: 27 km; Mk 3: 40 + km (22/29.5/44 kyd). Minimum range is 2750 yd in the Mk 1 version.

Penguin was the first IR guided antiship missile (indeed, the first modern NATO antiship missile). It is boosted to an altitude of 80 m, cruising at 66 ft; the IR seeker is activated at a preset range. The designers chose IR homing because the prospective users, the Norwegian and Swedish navies, operate in areas of strong radar clutter, dealing with fjords and the Stockholm archipelago, respectively. IR homing also provides a target with less warning than an active-radar seeker, although requiring the missile to fly at a greater altitude. Prior to launch, the missile is provided with target bearing, target relative speed perpendicular to the line of fire, range to IR-seeker activation, and gyroplatform compensation data. Maximum flight time (Mk 1) is about 85 sec. Total reaction time, from the off condition to firing, is about 2 min but can be cut to 7 sec if seeker cooling is maintained.

The altimeter is a pulsed laser.

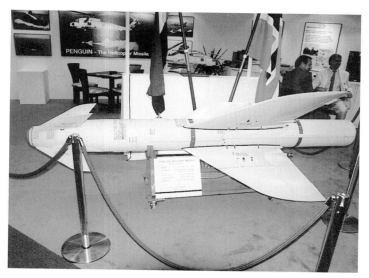

Penguin on display at Dubai, 1995. (S. Zaloga)

The warhead is a U.S. Bullpup Mk 19 with a U.S. Mk 312-2 contact fuze (delay changed from 8 to 10 msec, to allow some penetration of the target). The missile is biased to hit the target near the waterline. Total explosive weight is 103 lb.

Mk 1 is carried in the fiberglass shipping container (43.3 × 43.3 × 122 in, 396 lb) from which the missile is launched.

Mk 2 is a longer-range (for indirect attacks) ship-launched version using a new launcher. Mod 3 was developed jointly with the Royal Swedish Navy. It was also sold to Turkey, and may be the variant used by Greece. The U.S. Navy adopted Mk 2 Mod 7, a helicopter-launched version with folding wings, for LAMPS III helicopters. Despite its designation, Mod 7 is a development of the Mk 3 described below.

Mk 3 (AGM-119) is an air-to-surface version that flies a preselected search pattern. The missile can be launched at altitudes of 150–30,000 ft and at speeds of up to Mach 1.2. The pilot can launch Mk 3 at up to 50 deg off boresight. There are four trajectory options: altitude hold "on" (missile flies either at maximum cruise altitude or at launch altitude, whichever is lower, up to the waypoint); altitude hold "off" (missile descends to preset mid-course altitude); mid-course altitude high (about 300 ft); and mid-course altitude low (sea-skimming). The pilot also selects the search pattern (wide, normal, asymmetrical) before launch. Mk 3 was designed for the Norwegian F-16 force. It incorporates a new digital-control system compatible with the F-16 weapons-control system. It has a new high-resolution seeker capable of discriminating target temperature (for ECCM), a strapdown inertial mid-course guidance system, and a radar (rather than laser) altimeter. It also has a new single-chamber rocket motor and smaller wings (so that it can be accommodated underwing). Kongsberg has tried to market Mk 3 as a coast-defense weapon.

Penguin was developed in 1962–70 by the Norwegian Ministry of Defense and Kongsberg Vapenfabrikk, with some U.S. Navy financing (which is why Penguin uses a Bullpup warhead, and why the U.S. Navy has certain rights to the missile; it has been evaluated several times in the United States). Test flights were completed in 1971, and Penguin entered service in 1972.

As of 1988, estimated unit cost was $220,000 for Mk 1 or Mk 2, or $500,000–$550,000 for Mk 2 Mod 7 or Mk 3.

Users: Greece (last six Combattante III class [80 Mk 2 missiles, 20 more planned] and S-70B Seahawk helicopter), Norway (*Oslo, Hauk, Snogg, Storm* classes [225 Mk 1, 175 Mk 2] and F-16 fighters [120 Mk 3]; not yet adopted for coast defense), Spain (reportedly bought in 1988 as a war reserve for *Lazaga* and *Barcelo* classes, of which the former are gone and the latter, which did not carry the missiles in peacetime, have been transferred to the coast guard), Sweden (*Hugin* class [195 Mk 2]), Turkey (*Kartal* class [65 Mk 2]; has expressed interest in Mk 3 for F-16s), and United States (LAMPS III helicopters, as AGM-119B [106 missiles]). U.S. purchases: plan (1985) was 192 missiles; actual purchases were 24 in FY90, 40 in FY91, 42 in FY92/93. Became operational aboard USS *Conolly* May 1994. Only 28 helicopters have been modified to carry Penguin.

RUSSIA

Many naval missiles have alternative nuclear warheads, as noted below. In response to President Bush's initiative, President Yeltsin declared that tactical nuclear weapons would be withdrawn from CIS warships. Many may also have chemical warheads; certainly chemical weapons are very common in CIS land forces. No detailed information on naval chemical weapons has been published.

There are two main ASM design bureaus, Zvezda, which is responsible for most short-range tactical missiles, and Raduga (the Berezhniak OKB), which is responsible for long-range missiles and for many short- and medium-range ship-to-ship missiles (beginning with Styx). NPO Maschinostroyeniya (originally the Chelomei OKB) is responsible for long-range ship-to-ship missiles; Chelomei and Berezhniak probably competed for medium-range projects (SS-N-9, for example), and the same canister may have been used by several different missiles.

Recently a third organization, Novator (the Lyulev OKB), has offered the Alpha antiship missile. Novator developed SS-N-15/16 and SS-N-21.

At the 1995 Moscow Air Show Raduga stated that it was working on a next-generation stealthy hypersonic air-to-surface cruise missile, based on a GELA (hypersonic experimental-flight) test vehicle, which had flown "recently." It was launched from a Tu-95 Bear. A ram intake in the nose terminates in a flat section rather than in the usual cone, and wings and tail can be folded. Raduga stated that it was negotiating with the Chinese to export low-observable missile technology.

Many air-launched missiles have an additional *Izdeliye* (item, or type) designator. Izdeliye numbers are given below as Type numbers.

◆ AS-4 Kitchen (Kh-22)

> **Dimensions:** 0.92 × 11.65m; span 3.0 m
> **Weight:** 5635–5770 kg
> **Warhead:** 900 kg HE or nuclear
> **Propulsion:** Liquid-fuel rocket
> **Speed:** 3000–3600 km/hr
> **Range:** 340nm high-altitude flight profile; 250–270 km high-low

Raduga's Kh-22 was apparently designed specifically for the Tu-22K Blinder bomber, itself intended as the successor to the Badger, hence its designation. Developed under a 17 June 1958 Council of Ministers decree, Kh-22 entered service in 1967 aboard Blinders (Tu-22K). In naval service it is carried by Backfire (Tu-22M2 and -22M3) bombers. The air force strategic version was carried by Blinders (Tu-22K) and Bears (Tu-95K-22). The associated radar is Down Beat, and the FCS is K-22.

Kh-22 is normally launched at an altitude of 10–14 km (33,000 to 46,000 ft) climbing to a cruise altitude of 22.5 km (about 75,000 ft). Effective range depends on launch speed and altitude: 400 km for 950 km/hr at 10 km, 550 km for 1720 km/hr at 14km

AS-4 under a Tu-22M (Backfire) at Zhukovskiy, 1995. (S. Zaloga)

altitude. The target is designated by the launching aircraft. The missile uses an autopilot for mid-course guidance plus a J-band terminal seeker. The terminal seeker is activated about 80 nm from the expected target position, and the missile begins a 3-deg terminal dive when the seeker registers an appropriate depression angle. Minimum range is 70 nm; the missile is ineffective if it cannot distinguish its target in the 10 nm from seeker turn-on to minimum range. Time of flight from a typical operational range of 150 nm is 9.4 min. A launching airplane cannot detect targets at the extreme ranges quoted above, so these figures presumably refer to the all-autopilot nuclear version.

The combination of very high-altitude flight and a steep terminal dive made AS-4 a very difficult target; it inspired such U.S. efforts to extend defensive missile range as SM-2 Block II and SM-2 Block IV. The nuclear version presented particular problems, as it was feared that any interception during the terminal dive would leave the tumbling warhead intact.

Versions are Kh-22N (nuclear, with autopilot guidance), -22M (conventional warhead and active radar seeker, antiship), and -22MP (antiradar). The antiradar version was first reported in 1981.

◆ AS-6 Kingfish (KSR-5/Type D-5)

> **Dimensions:** 0.92 × 10.60 m; span 2.60 m
> **Weight:** 3950 kg
> **Warhead:** 700-kg (1540-lb) conventional or 350-kT nuclear
> **Propulsion:** Liquid-fuel rocket
> **Speed:** Mach 2.5–3.5 (at 60,000 ft) (also given as 3200 km/hr)
> **Range:** 350nm high-altitude profile; 160nm low-altitude (also given as 240 km)

AS-6 is in effect a smaller version of AS-4 for Badger bombers, embodying similar technology, and with a similar flight profile. Production of the antiship version (Type D-5) began in 1966; Kingfish was first reported about 1972.

AS-6 carried by a Badger bomber. Note the absence of a big targeting radome; this missile is probably an inertially guided land-attack version. (U.S. Navy)

The associated radars are Rubin (in a Tu-16K-26) or YeN (in a Tu-16K10-26), and the FCS is K-26.

Versions: KSR-5 (antiship), KSR-5N (nuclear), KSR-5P (antiradar, in service 1972), KSR-5NM (target).

◆ AS-7 Kerry (Grom, Kh-23/66)

> **Dimensions:** 275 × 3525 mm; span 785 mm (10.8 × 139; 30.9 in). Length of Kh-23M is given as 2491 mm, and span as 811 mm.
> **Weight:** 287 kg at launch, 222 kg at burnout (633/489 lb)
> **Warhead:** 111 kg (245 lb)
> **Propulsion:** Solid-fuel rocket
> **Speed:** 600–750 m/sec (1165–1456 kt)
> **Range:** 2–10 km (2200–10,900 yd)

Zvezda's Kh-23, introduced in the late 1970s, is a standard tactical missile roughly equivalent to the U.S. Bullpup. It is manufactured under license by Rumania, under the designation A921; the data above and the notes below apply to this version as displayed at Baghdad in 1989. The former Yugoslavia (probably Serbia) also manufactures a version of AS-7.

The missile is manually guided to LOS (via a radio command link), three radio correction points being provided in its flight pattern. In the version shown at Baghdad, it had an HE antitank warhead with an impact fuze. Kh-23 was considered unsatisfactory, in that the pilot had to view the target and missile images continuously, as well as the sight screen; moreover, pilots tended to mis-estimate the range to the target. Hence the development of Kh-25 (see below).

AS-7 can be launched at 80–5000 m (750–16,400 ft) altitude. Minimum launching altitude at a diving speed of 600–1000 km/ hr (330–550 kt) is 3–5 km (10,000–16,400 ft). Maximum G-load at launch is 4.6.

The first version of the missile, introduced in the late 1960s, was the shorter-range (2–6 nm) Kh-66. The order for a Bullpup equivalent initially went to the Vympel OKB (OKB-134), which was responsible for air-to-air weapons. When that bureau failed to meet the requirement that the guidance system fit existing fighters, the air force (early in 1966) accepted an alternative proposal by Zvezda, a small OKB working with the factory making the R-5 (AA-1) and R-8 (AA-3) AAMs. Zvezda proposed to use existing air-to-air components; it had already experimented, in the 1950s and early 1960s, with AA-1 (RS-2US/K-51) missiles fired at ground targets by MiG-19PMs. The designation Kh-66 (Type 66) was adopted because of the year the proposal was accepted, 1966; the key requirement was that the warhead weigh 100 kg. The existing K-8 missile was adopted, but its nozzle was split to provide space for the antenna of the beam-riding guidance system of the earlier K-51/RS-2US. Using this system, the missile could easily be fired by any fighter adapted to the earlier air-to-air weapon. Tests began in September 1966, and the missile was officially accepted in 1968.

Kh-23 (the number indicating that it was intended for the MiG-23) had higher-energy fuel and a new Delta-R1M guidance system (radio command) in its tail. The first ten were tested early in 1968, but it turned out that the smoke from the tracking flare interfered with the radio command receiver, which had to be moved to a tail extension. The aircraft element of the system could be carried either internally (Delta N or NM) or in a pod (Delta NG or NG2). The missile was type-certified as Kh-23M (Type 68) in 1974. Kh-23M platforms: Su-17M3, Su-20, Su-22, Su-22M3 and -22M4 export strike aircraft.

Note that some AS-7s have dielectric nose cones, which are not consistent with command guidance.

Users: Bulgaria, CIS, India, Iraq, Poland, Rumania (as A921), former Yugoslavia (probably Serbia).

The AS-10 family (Kh-25) evolved from AS-7.

◆ AS-9 Kyle (Kh-28/Type 93 or D-8)

Dimensions: 43 cm × 5.97 m; span 1.93 m
Weight: 720 kg
Warhead: 160 kg
Propulsion: Two-stage liquid-fuel rocket
Speed: Mach 3.0
Range: 80–95 km (44–52 nm) (also given as 120 km)

Raduga's defense suppression (antiradar) missile, carried by Badger, Backfire, Fencer, and Fitter-C and -D, was introduced in the mid-1970s. It is a scaled-down AS-6, originally designed for (but never carried by) the Yak-28 (hence the designation). Platforms: Su-7B/17/24, Tu-22M Backfire. The missile is programmed before launch by a radar receiver ("Filin" [Eagle Owl] on an Su-24 or podded "Metel" [Blizzard] on an Su-7B or -17 or a Tu-22M). Although no longer in Russian service, Kh-28 probably survives abroad, particularly in former Warsaw Pact air arms.

AS-9 was supplied to the Iraqis during the Gulf War. An Iraqi version displayed at Baghdad in 1989 was designated Nissan-28 and was reported to have three different seeker heads, for three different bands (for ground and naval radars).

Reportedly this missile is unpopular because it must be fueled just before flight; few tactical air bases are properly equipped for it. Hence the development of its solid-fuel successor, Kh-58 (AS-11), which also has a more flexible homing head.

AS-9 antiradar missile. Note the strong family resemblance to the much larger AS-4 and AS-6. This example was displayed in Baghdad in 1989. The missile in the background is Nissan-28, apparently a Soviet-supplied AA-7 mocked up to simulate an antiship weapon.

◆ AS-10 Karen (Kh-25)/AS-12 Kegler (Kh-25MR)

Dimensions: 275 mm × 3.83 m (10.8 × 150.8 in); span 0.82 m (32.3 in)
Weight: 320 kg (706 lb)
Warhead: 140 kg (308.7 lb)
Propulsion: Solid-fuel rocket
Speed: Mach 1.0
Range: See below.

Data apply to Kh-25MR.

Zvezda's Kh-25 (Type 71) is a command-guided solid-fuel missile intended to replace Kh-23 (AS-7). The initial version, Kh-25, used semiactive laser guidance in the Kh-23 airframe. Since no tail receiver was needed, it was replaced by an additional 24 kg of explosive (the nose carried 113 kg). The laser designator was Prozhektor-1. Tests began in 1973 on board an Su-17M, and the missile was officially accepted in 1974 as part of the Su-17KMG system. Zvezda's next step was an antiradar version, Kh-27PS (Type 72), which used two radar antennas tuned to the frequencies of the Hawk and Nike Hercules radars. To extend range, Kh-27PS had a two-pulse engine. It also had an autopilot allowing it to pop up near the target, so that it could attack at a 20–30-deg angle. The associated targeting set was Vyuga (Snowstorm), and the missile armed Su-17Rs and MiG-27s. It was accepted into service about 1975–77.

Kh-25 at the 1995 Paris Air Show. (Author)

Kh-25M is a more versatile second-generation modular (hence the M) version: Kh-25MDUL, Kh-25MK (export), Kh-25MP (antiradar, Type 711), Kh-25MR (radio command as in Kh-23, with Delta in tail, Type 714), Kh-25ML (laser-guided, Type 713). Effective range depends on the guidance technique: 8 km for radio command, 10 km for laser guidance, 40 km for antiradar. Kh-25MP is 4.353 m long (89.6-kg warhead, 320 kg overall); Kh-25ML is 4.255 m long (89.6-kg warhead, 300 kg overall). An EO (television-guided) version, Kh-25MTP, was shown at the 1992 Moscow Air Show (length 4.04 m, weight 300 kg, warhead 90 kg, launch range 2–20 km, altitude 100–10,000 m, maximum flight speed 800 m/sec). There is also a similar IIR version. The antiradar version (Kh-25MP) is 4.355 m long (310 kg, 90 kg warhead); launch range is 2.5–60 km (altitude 100 to 15,000 m), and maximum speed is 900 km/sec. The seeker is described as a "unified antiradar seeker type A, A' and A"." There may also be a KhA-25 version.

Kh-25MP/AS-12 is a lightweight self-protection ARM, for tactical aircraft such as the MiG-23, MiG-27, and Su-17. It entered service about 1978. The frequency band is preselected. The longer-range Kh-27PS (range 60 rather than 10 km) is used by the Su-24 and Tu-22M.

These missiles are comparable to the U.S. Maverick.

◆ AS-11 Kilter (Kh-58/Type 112, D-7)

Dimensions: 38 cm × 4.8 m; span 1.45 m (15 × 189; 57 in)
Weight: 640 kg (1411 lb)
Warhead: 160 kg (353 lb)
Propulsion: Solid-fuel rocket
Speed: Mach 3.6
Range: 120 km (27 nm)

Raduga's Kh-58 is a large solid-fuel antiradar missile for defense-suppression aircraft, hence broadly comparable to HARM; it replaced AS-9/Kh-28, initially on Su-24Ms. The onboard targeting set is Fantazmagoria (Su-24M) or Vyuga. Reportedly 80% of missiles hit within 20 m of the target. The original Kh-58, developed for the Su-24 (T-58 prototype, hence the Kh-58 designation), had an active radar seeker; Kh-58U is the antiradar version. Data above refer to the Kh-58U version carried by the Su-17M3 (Kh-58 is carried by Su-17R). This missile entered service about 1978; it is carried by the Su-17M3/M4/R, Su-24M, and MiG-25BM Foxbat F. Presumably it can also be carried by the large carrier-based fighters. Reports of a nuclear version have not been confirmed.

A version specifically intended to deal with Patriot and similar systems was announced at the 1992 Moscow Air Show. It is 5 m long (650 kg, span 1.17 m), with a minimum launch range of 10 km (maximum 160 km) and a maximum speed of Mach 3.6; the missile carries a B-band passive seeker. No warhead weight was given.

An antiship version with similar dimensions was announced at the 1992 Moscow Air Show; it carries a 150–200-kg SAP warhead and uses inertial guidance plus a mm-wave active terminal seeker. Maximum flight altitude is 30 km, and maximum flight speed is Mach 4. Range against a cruiser is 60–70 km, against a larger ship ("supership") 150–180 km.

A Kh-58E (AS-11) missile at the Moscow Air Show, 1993. (S. Zaloga)

◆ AS-13 Kingbolt (Kh-59 Ovod/Type D-9) and AS-18 Kazoo (Kh-59M Ovod-M)

Dimensions: 425 mm × 5.85 m; span 1.35 m (16.7 × 230 in; 53 in)
Weight: 875 kg (1929 lb)
Warhead: 250 kg (551 lb)
Propulsion: Solid-fuel rocket with a solid-fuel booster in the tail
Range: 32 nm

Zvezda's EO guided missile (its seeker probably related to that of the Kh-29T/AS-14) is carried only by the Su-24M Fencer. Kh-59 was first publicly shown at Dubai in 1991. The missile is similar in concept to Maverick, the launching airplane using an APK-9 data-link pod to lock the missile on after launch. Data above apply to this version.

The Ovod-M (Kh-59M, AS-18) EO-guided missile, at the 1993 Moscow Air Show. (S. Zaloga)

Kh-59M is a longer-range turbofan version (the engine drops down from the fuselage after launch) roughly equivalent to the old U.S. Condor, with twice the warhead weight. Ovod-M was first seen as an antiship missile at the 1992 Moscow Air Show. A shipboard version may be the missile planned for the sole "Nanuchka IV" (which carries a framework for some type of container). Guidance is inertial plus EO or active radar (in the shipboard version). Dimensions (air-launched): 38 × 510 cm (15 × 201 in) with 126cm wingspan; weight 850 kg with a 315-kg HE or 280-kg bomblet warhead. The shipboard version weighs 1000 kg and is 530 cm long. Maximum range is 200 km (109 nm), and cruising speed is 285 m/sec (561 kt).

◆ AS-14 Kedge (Kh-29)

Dimensions: 38 cm × 3.875 m; span 1.0 m (15 × 153 in; 39.4 in)
Weight: 657 kg (1449 lb)
Warhead: 317 kg (699 lb)
Propulsion: Solid-fuel rocket
Range: 8 km (8700 yd)

Data are for Kh-29L (Type 63). Range is 2–10 km (launch altitude 0.2–5 km). Kh-29T has the same dimensions (overall weight 688 kg, same warhead; wing and fin span also given as 0.97 and 1.1 m; launch altitude 0.2–10 km, range 3–12 or 4–30 km, depending on launch altitude). Kh-29MP: 250-kg warhead, range 12 km. The industrial designation 9M721 has also been reported.

This family of rocket ASMs was developed by the Molniya OKB, which otherwise specialized in air-to-air weapons. Developed specifically for the MiG-27, Su-17, and Su-24, it is intended for use against hard targets; almost half the missile's weight is its warhead. It can be used against shipping. There are four fixed rear fins, four fixed canards, and four movable canards controlled by the modular guidance unit. There are two basic series, Kh-29 and the improved Kh-29M. There are four sub-versions: Kh-29D (IIR), Kh-29L/29ML (laser; same seeker as in Kh-25ML), Kh-29MP (passive radar homing, i.e., antiradar), and Kh-29T/Type 64 (TV, i.e., EO). Kh-29ML is carried by Su-17M, -24M, -25; Kh-29T by MiG-27D/K/M and Su-17M4, -24M, -25. Kh-25MP is car-

AS-14 on display at the 1995 Moscow Air Show. (S. Zaloga)

ried only by Su-17M4. NATO designations: Kedge-A (laser-guided), Kedge-B (EO).

Aerodynamic range is variously reported as 30 or even 40 km (44,000 yd), and the disparity with effective range given here suggests that the missile can be used in an alternative ground-designated mode, the airplane dropping it beyond defensive range. In Iraqi service, a Mirage F1EQ-5 carried two underwing and used a French Thomson-CSF ATLIS laser designator pod in place of the Soviet equipment. ATLIS was developed for the 10-km AS-30L and can guide AS-14 out to a range of 12–15 km, compared to the normal range of 6–8 km.

AS-14 entered service about 1980. It is carried by the Fencer-D (Su-24), Fitter (Su-20/22), Flogger (MiG-23/27), and Frogfoot (Su-25).

◆ **AS-15 Kent (Kh-65; strategic version Kh-55/RKV-500)**

Dimensions: 51.4 × 310 cm
Weight: 1250 kg
Warhead: 410-kg warhead
Powerplant: Turbojet
Range: 500–600 km
Speed: Mach 0.48–0.77

Although conceived as a strategic missile (Kh-55), the air-launched equivalent of SS-N-21, a tactical version of this Raduga missile (Kh-65) was announced at the 1992 Moscow Air Show. There are both land-attack and antiship versions. AS-15 uses a form of TERCOM navigation, plus the Russian equivalent of GPS. Accuracy is given as 18–26m CEP with cluster or penetrating warhead. Cruise altitude is 40–110 m.

Kh-55 was flight-tested in 1978 and entered service on board Tu-95s in 1984.

The Kh-65SE antiship air-launched cruise missile at the 1993 Moscow Air Show. (S. Zaloga)

Versions: Kh-55 (Type 120, RKV-500/AS-15A), Kh-55OK (Type 124), Kh-55SM (Type 125, RKV-500B/AS-15B). Kh-65 was initially credited with a range of 600 km (Kh-55: 2500 km, Kh-55SM: 3000 km), but that was scaled back to remove it from the strategic category under the SALT 2 treaty. The range quoted in 1993 was 280 km when launched at low altitude and 280 km at high altitude.

This missile has been sold to China.

◆ **AS-16 Kickback (Kh-15S)**

Dimensions: 45.5 × 478 cm (17.9 × 188 in), fin circle diameter 92 cm (36.2 in)
Weight: 1200 kg (2646 lb)
Warhead: 150 kg (331 lb)
Propulsion: Solid-fuel rocket
Speed: Mach 5
Range: See below.

This is a conventional antiship version of the standard Russian air-launched short-range strategic (defense suppression) missile, their equivalent of the U.S. SRAM. The primary version is the antiradar Kh-15P (Type 115). The antiship version, variously designated Kh-15A and Kh-15S, is launched into a ballistic trajectory (climb before descent), and its aim point is corrected by its mm-wave active radar seeker. Maximum flight speed is Mach 5, using a solid-fuel rocket motor. Range depends on the target: up to 60 km for a fast-attack boat, up to 100 km for a destroyer, up to 150 km (82 nm) for a cruiser. The missile can be carried underwing or in a rotary launcher (on a Backfire or Blackjack; capacity 12 missiles). The antiship export version is Kh-15SE.

A Kh-15S aeroballistic antiship missile at the 1993 Moscow Air Show. (S. Zaloga)

The status of Kh-15S is unclear. A missile displayed in Moscow was cut away to show electronics, but it appeared not to have any radome, hence was presumably a mock-up. Some of the Kh-15S brochures appear to indicate that the weapon is a project, financing for which is being sought abroad.

◆ **AS-17 Krypton (Kh-31/Type 77)/MA-31**

Dimensions: 375 mm × 4.9 m; span 1.15 m (14.8 × 193 in; 45.3 in)
Weight: 600 kg (1323 lb)
Warhead: 100 kg (221 lb)
Propulsion: Rocket-ramjet
Speed: Nearly Mach 4.5
Range: 70 km (Kh-31P 110 km)

Zvezda's missile was first displayed (in antiradar form: Kh-31P/Type 77P) at Dubai in 1991. This weapon was first launched in 1982. Kh-31 uses mixed rocket-ramjet propulsion as in the land-based SA-6 (boost rocket in the tail and four ramjets wrapped around the body). A solid-fuel rocket in the tail boosts the missile to Mach 1.8, after which the burnt-out rocket becomes the ramjet combustion chamber (as in the French ASMP). It is carried by the Su-17M4 and Su-24M.

A dedicated antiship active radar version, Kh-31A, was developed from Kh-31P; it was first seen at Minsk in 1991. It is 5.232 m long and weighs 650 kg, with a 90-kg warhead. It is

The first MA-31 (Kh-31) flight article, as delivered to McDonnell-Douglas, 1996. (McDonnell-Douglas)

Raduga's GELA hypersonic test vehicle, shown here at the 1995 Moscow Air Show, may indicate the shape of next-generation Russian ASMs. GELA is similar to one of a series of wind-tunnel models exhibited at the 1993 air show, in which it succeeded a Moskit-like form. This design was marked "1980–1985;" the Moskit form was "1973–1978." It seems to have been designed for flight between Mach 2.0 and Mach 4.5. (S. Zaloga)

launched 5–70 km from the target, at an altitude of 50 to 15,000 m; maximum flight speed is 1000 m/sec (it hits the target at up to 350 m/sec). This version, comparable with the Franco-German ANS, is the first supersonic antiship missile to arm tactical aircraft. No surface-launched version was announced.

An air-to-air passive/active version, intended specifically to destroy AWACS and similar aircraft, was announced at the 1992 Moscow Air Show. It is 5.232 m long and weighs 600 kg (90-kg warhead); launch height is 100–1500 m, and maximum range is about 200 km. Maximum flight speed is 1000 m/sec (1968 kt). Presumably the active homing feature counteracts any attempt by the AWACS to avoid the missile by turning off its own radar.

On 12 May 1995 the U.S. Navy awarded a contract to McDonnell-Douglas for a flight demonstration of the Russian MA-31 (Kh-31) aerial target for its supersonic target (SST) program.

McDonnell-Douglas may market a ship-launched missile version (in which Zvezda is not interested) using a passive seeker and a new booster. The missile would grow in length by about 1.5 ft, and maximum speed would be about Mach 2.1.

◆ Kh-101

Raduga's stealthy long-range subsonic cruise missile began flight tests in the fall of 1995 on board a modified Tu-95, which had a large pylon fitted under its port wing. Reportedly the missile carries a 400-kg unitary penetrating warhead and employs EO/IR guidance to achieve a CEP of about 20 m. It is said to be 7.4 m long and to weigh 2200–2400 kg. It can be carried by a Tu-95 (8 missiles), a Tu-160 (12 missiles), or a Tu-22M3 (4 missiles). Kh-101 reportedly replaces an earlier abortive Kh-90. The conventional version of Kh-55/65, also designated Kh-SD (medium range), may have been conceived as an interim weapon.

This missile may replace an earlier program for a universal (air-, ground-, and submarine-launched) weapon, Chelomei's 3M25 Meteorit (AS-19/SS-N-24). Work on Meteorit began under a 9 December 1976 decree. This containerized weapon was first launched on 20 May 1980. Although a test vehicle achieved a range of 50 km on 16 December 1981, a series of 22 launches (through the end of 1984) were all failures, and the project was canceled at the end of 1984. This cancellation was not known in the West, and it was generally believed that the program was stopped about 1990 for budgetary reasons. It is possible that a naval missile, possibly called P-750 Grom, was a tactical derivative and that "Oscar II"-class submarines were lengthened (compared to "Oscar I") specifically to accommodate it, as a replacement for their P-700 (SS-N-19) antiship missiles. The air-launched version weighed 6380 kg (12,650 kg with boosters), was 12.8 m long, and had a rated range of 500 km at a speed of 3000 km/hr and a flight altitude of 22–24 km.

The NATO AS-19 designation has now been assigned to Kh-41, the air-launched version of Moskit/3M80, not yet flown; AS-20 is the air-launched version of Kh-35 (SS-NX-25).

◆ Guided Bombs

There are also guided bombs (KAB, for korrektiruyemaya aviatsionnaya bomba, correctible aircraft bombs): 500-kg (KAB-500) and 1500-kg (KAB-1500) bombs. It is not certain whether these versions are in naval service. At least in their 500-kg versions, both types may have rocket tails. The laser seeker (L suffix) looks not unlike that of a Paveway; the EO seeker (Kr suffix) is the full diameter of the bomb body. Details: KAB-500Kr E/O bomb: 350 × 3050 mm (tail span 850 mm; 560 kg, including 380-kg warhead; 200 kg of explosive); dropped at 0.5 to 5.0 km altitude, speed 550–1100 km/hr (300–600 kt), accuracy 4–7 m. This weapon uses a correlation seeker; the target is acquired before launch, after which the bomb homes autonomously. There is also a KAB-500Kr-U training version (85 kg, 350 × 1830 mm) which includes the correlation seeker. It is not actually dropped.

A Russian KAB-1500L laser-guided bomb shown at the 1995 Moscow Air Show. (S. Zaloga)

A KAB-500KR guided bomb at the 1993 Moscow Air Show. (S. Zaloga)

KAB-500L laser bomb: 400 × 3050 mm (534 kg, including 195 kg of explosive); KAB-1500L-Pr laser bomb: 580 × 4600 mm (tail span 850 mm folded, 1300 mm unfolded; weight 1500 kg including 1100-kg warhead). KAB-1500L-Pr is dropped at an altitude of 1 to 5 km (3300 to 16,500 ft) at 550 to 1100 km/hr (300–600 kt); accuracy is 7–10 m (23–33 ft). The bomb penetrates 2 m of reinforced concrete or 10–20 m of soil. A very similar KAB-1500L-F carries a blast (rather than SAP) warhead (1560 kg, including 1180-kg warhead). There is also a KAB-1500Kr EO (television correlation) bomb. The 1991 CFE documents listed two further 1500-kg versions, KAB-1500Ya and KAB-1500TK.

Soviet work on laser-guided bombs began in 1972; production began in 1975. Note that there are no podded designators; aircraft generally use nose designators with limited traverse. Thus they cannot overfly the target while the bomb is in flight (as in U.S. systems); one airplane designates for the others. Systems include Kaira-27 in MiG-27K, Klen-54 in Su-22M3/M4 Fitter, Kaira-24 on Su-24M, and Klen-PS on Su-25. The bombs can also be used with other (e.g., French) pods.

♦ Surface-Launched Missiles

Reference has been made to a previously unknown Bolid system (3M15 missile; the system may be designated 3K15) associated with a projected (abortive) submarine, Project 881.

♦ SS-C-2 Salish (S-2 Sopka)

Dimensions: 115 cm × 7.9 m; span 4.9 m (45.3 in × 25.9 ft; span 16.1 ft)
Weight: 3100 kg (6800 lb)
Warhead: 600 kg (can be increased to 1000 kg)
Propulsion: RD-500K turbojet
Speed: 510 kt
Range: 55 nm (13.5 nm for coast defense)

The earliest Soviet antiship missile survives only in its exported coast-defense version (the air-launched AS-1 version is extinct). In the early 1970s these weapons were replaced, in Soviet service, by SS-C-3 (the coast-defense version of the SS-N-2).

The missile uses a combination of beam-riding mid-course guidance (using the rearward-pointing antenna) and semiactive terminal guidance. The beam-riding guidance technique limits effective range to about 25 km. Exports began in the early 1960s. Reportedly, SS-C-2 is still in the inventories of Bulgaria, Cuba (50 launchers supplied 1962, probably no longer operational), Poland, Rumania, and North Korea. This weapon was reportedly withdrawn from Egyptian service.

There was also an army version.

SS-C-2 on its launch rail, on display in Moscow, 1995. (S. Zaloga)

♦ SS-N-2 Styx (and SS-C-3) (P-15/20/21/22)

Dimensions: 75 cm × 6.55 m; span 2.75 m (30 in × 21.3 ft; 9 ft) (P-20: 31in dia, length 6.5 m)
Weight: 2125 kg (SS-N-2A); 2500 kg (P-20)
Warhead: 480 kg (1050 lb); 500 kg (P-20)
Propulsion: Liquid-fuel rocket (solid booster)
Speed: Mach 0.9 (666 mph)
Range: 25 nm (effective to 16 nm); SS-N-2C: 45 nm

An SS-N-2 missile being checked before loading. (Sovfoto)

SS-N-2 was the first Soviet sea-based antiship missile to enter large-scale service. Intended to replace the torpedoes of small FAC, SS-N-2 is a radar- or IR-homing fire-and-forget weapon. Even in its later versions, it is relatively simple, capable of flying only a straight course and limited in most cases in minimum altitude by its barometric altimeter (it cannot sea-skim). Launchers are invariably fixed in train because before launch the missile must run up its gyros to maintain course in flight. Thus the launching ship must run a steady course for several minutes before firing. Berezhniak (whose OKB became the Raduga organization) was the developer.

Work on this P-15 missile (NATO SS-N-2A), intended specifically for small combatants, began in 1955. Missiles are 4K40 and 4K40T; the launcher is 4S30. The rocket powerplant was chosen to permit very rapid launch, on the theory that an attacking boat would not be able to remain within attack range for very long. There was no nuclear warhead, because the range was so short (initially 25 km/13 nm) that it was expected that the blast would damage the launch platform. Although the operational missile is fire-and-forget, a former Soviet naval missile test officer claims that, at least at first, there was a mid-course guidance phase while the missile flew at 400 m, before it turned on its active seeker.

The large shaped-charge warhead is carried just abaft the fuel tank (forward of the oxidizer tank). In theory, then, the effect of a hit is to blast a hole deep into the target while filling it with burning fuel.

Some major limitations in the original SS-N-2 were the minimum range of 5 nm (the homing and arming mechanisms are not activated until the missile has flown that far) and the inability to seek out the preferred target among a group of ships. Nor can targets be attacked from seaward within 4 nm of the shore, because of radar clutter. At least in its original form, SS-N-2 cannot be fired if the air temperature is below 4 deg F or above 101 deg F.

P-15 was first tested in October 1957, the first operational "Komars" appearing in 1959, and the first "Osas" in 1960. P-15 was formally accepted for service by the Soviet navy in 1960.

P-15 was the first modern antiship missile used in combat, sinking the Israeli destroyer *Eilat* in October 1967. It was also used successfully by the Indian navy against Pakistan in 1970–71, by the Chinese navy in the Paracels in 1974, and by the Iraqi navy against Iran from 1980 on. However, boats armed with this weapon were badly beaten in the October 1973 Mideast war, reportedly partly because of the considerable time required to line up gyros before firing.

Although the Soviets considered SS-N-2 strictly an antiship missile, the Indian navy very successfully used this missile against shore installations, such as refineries (which are strong radar reflectors) during the 1971 Indo-Pakistani War.

The Square Tie targeting radar can detect a destroyer under favorable conditions at up to 22 nm (theoretical range of the radar is 48 nm), and fast patrol boats can be detected at about 10 nm. The operator manually sets a range gate around the target, and missile firing data are computed for target ranges of 3 to 15 nm. At greater ranges, the impact point has to be calculated manually on a maneuvering board, which significantly reduces hit probability. The missile platform has to be turned into the direction of the impact point, and in theory the number of missiles launched varies with the target: seven to eight for a cruiser, four for a destroyer. Hit probability against fast missile boats is lower due to their limited radar cross-section, and the doctrine is to fire two to four. The missile is launched at 15 deg to the vertical, then climbs at 45 deg to an altitude of about 450 ft. The seeker, operating at one of six preset frequencies, is switched on 6 nm from the estimated impact point. It seeks the strongest echo and (at least in early versions) cannot distinguish fixed from moving targets. The terminal maneuver is a dive.

Early Soviet estimates were that it would take two hits to sink a destroyer (roughly consistent with the later *Eilat* attack) and that 12 shots (three boats) were needed to assure this level of damage. The six boats of a brigade were needed to insure that three would reach the target. Missile installation and arming initially took 15 hr, but was later reduced to 12; by 1962 an "Osa" could be outfitted with four missiles in 4 to 6 hr.

Maximum range was 25 nm, but effective range was 16 nm. The missile's altitude could be preset at 100, 150, 200, 250, or 300 m (the missile used a barometric altimeter).

From 1961 on Berezhniak developed an improved P-15U (Termit-U system, 40K40U missile; KT-67B, KT-67ER launchers; NATO SS-N-2B), with folding wings (so that it could be fired from a canister, rather than from a bulkier hangar) and with improved guidance. Carried by modified "Osas" (Projects 205U, 205ER), it entered service in 1965.

P-20 (P-20 missile, KT-97BE launcher) was the corresponding export weapon, for "Nanuchkas" and "Kashins."

Termit-M (P-15M) was the next modified version, using the P-15M (NATO SS-N-2C) missile, with an auxiliary IR seeker to supplement its radar seeker. The missile may also have been called Rubezh. It probably originated in a 1961 project for a 50–70-km patrol-boat missile. P-15M is 4K40M (later redesignated 3M40M). The corresponding launchers are KT-138 and KT-97B. With a radio (rather than barometric) altimeter P-15M could cruise at 25 or 50 m rather than at the 100–400 m of the earlier weapon.

Range increased to 80 km, at which distance the launching boat would not be endangered by a nuclear explosion. Termit-M therefore had a nuclear version with a 15-kT warhead.

This missile is considerably longer than P-15/P-15U (6.55 rather than 5.8 m). It was carried on board modified destroyers ("Kildin" and Mod "Kashin" classes) and aboard small combatants (Projects 205M [modified "Osa"], 206MP ["Matka"], and 1241.1 ["Tarantul 2"]). P-15M was different enough from P-15 that NATO originally assigned it a new designation, SS-N-11.

The P-15M system was modified to use a pair of new missiles, P-21 and P-22 (production designation 4K51, later 3M51); their NATO designation is SS-N-2D. It retained its Klon FCS, using the Square Tie acquisition radar. Termit-R is probably the replacement system using the Korrell FCS (with Plank Shave target acquisition radar; Korrell may also have incorporated a data-link command mode). P-21 has a radar seeker; P-22 has an IR seeker. This version has a Doppler radar altimeter to reduce missile drift in altitude; it also uses a different fuel to increase range (to about 55 nm). The designation P-20K may also be associated with these systems (for a missile with the new altimeter, perhaps a reworked P-20).

A "Tarantul" typically carries three radar and one IR missile. The Russians estimated that three hits would destroy a light cruiser, one to two hits would destroy a destroyer or frigate. Assuming that the missile itself is 95% mechanically reliable, the hit probability depending on the radar target, the Russians estimated that one missile boat carrying four weapons could destroy one missile destroyer or missile frigate; one or two missile patrol boats, landing ships or unprotected minelayers; or two to three unescorted transports. The IR version, which homes on the target's IR plume, has to be launched more than 30 deg from the

direction of the sun and is ineffective in visibility less than 100 m (i.e., thick fog and drizzle or snow).

The export equivalent of Termit-M (P-15M) is P-20M. It appeared on board export "Tarantuls" (Project 1241E), "Kashins" (Project 61ME), and "Konis" (Project 1159TR). Versions of P-15/P-20 were widely exported, and also made under license in India and Iraq.

P-27 is a new (ca. 1990) version with a new higher-frequency (V-band) seeker and possibly with a data link back to the launching platform. Its seeker and data link may be those associated with the P-270 (3M80) missile. Some "Tarantuls" carry this weapon. Styx is to be replaced in Russian service by Kh-35. Production (at that time, for export) ended about 1990.

See also the Chinese version above.

Users: Algeria (3 "Nanuchka" [2C], 9 "Osa II" [2B], 2 "Osa I" [2A]), Angola (2 "Osa II"), Bulgaria (3 "Osa II" [2B], 3 "Osa I" [2A]), Cuba (13 "Osa II", 5 "Osa I"), Ethiopia (4 "Osa II" [2B]), Finland (4 "Osa II" [2B]; reportedly now discarded due to safety problems with nitric acid oxidizer), India (5 "Kashin" [2C], *Delhi* class, 3 *Godavari* class [2C], *Trishul*, 12 *Khukri* class [2D], 24 "Tarantul" class [2D], 3 "Nanuchka" class [2C], 8 "Osa II" class [2B]), North Korea (1 "Soho" class [2A], 2 "Najin" class, 4 "Soju" class, 8 "So Hung" class, 16 "Osa I", 8 "Komar"), Libya (3 "Nanuchka" [2C], 4 Type 400 [2C], 12 "Osa II"), Poland (1 "Kashin", 4 "Tarantul" [2D], 8 "Osa I" [2A]), Romania (1 *Muntenia* [2C], 6 "Osa I"), Russia (2 Mod "Kashin" [2C], 19 "Tarantul I" [2D], 2 "Tarantul I" [2D], 16 "Matka" [2D], 25 or fewer "Osa II" [2B/C], 28 or fewer "Osa I" [2A]), Somalia (2 "Osa II"), Syria (8 "Osa II" [2B], 6 "Osa I" [2A]), Vietnam (8 "Osa II"), Yugoslavia (2 *Kotor* [2C], 2 "Koni" [2C], 1 Type 400 *Kobra*, 6 *Rade Koncar* [2B], 10 "Osa I").

The coast-defense version, SS-C-3 (Rubezh system), was developed in the late 1970s to replace the much larger SS-C-1 (coast-defense version of SS-N-3). Meanwhile the Chinese were using essentially the same Styx missile for coast defense. However, the standard Soviet transporter carries two Styxes and a Plank Shave fire-control radar, plus a control cabin, whereas the standard Chinese launcher is a single rail. Thus, each launcher truck is, in effect, an independent fire unit, even though doctrine calls for several such units to attack most warships. Effective engagement range is limited by the performance of the truck-mounted Plank Shave, which can probably detect a target at about 35 km (38,000 yd) at maximum elevation.

Exports of this coast-defense missile began in 1983–84, initially to East Germany and then to Yugoslavia, followed by Soviet clients in the Middle East. As in the case of SS-C-2, the standard organization is a three-battery battalion, each battery consisting of six launchers.

Styx coast-defense version users: Algeria (4 batteries), Bulgaria (1 battalion with 6 launchers), India, Libya (2 batteries at Tobruk; others at Benghazi, and Al Danya), North Korea (2 regiments, total 12–15 batteries at 6 sites; figure includes HY-2 batteries), Poland (3 battalions, 50 missiles; may be erroneous listing for SS-C-2), Rumania (1 brigade), Russia (and other CIS states), Syria (1 missile brigade, 12 missiles, possibly including SS-C-1), Yemen (on Perim Island), and former Yugoslavia (Serbia and Croatia). Cuba may operate a coastal version of this missile (one report claims at least 2 launchers). North Korea has locally made HY-2s. Note that each launcher carries a pair of missiles, often IR plus radar-homing.

P-25 (4K70) was an abortive solid-fuel Chelomei alternative to P-15, developed under an August 1960 decree and placed in limited production in 1961–62.

Iraq claimed to manufacture the SS-C-3 version of Styx under the designations Faw-70, -150, and -200. The numbers probably indicate the maximum range in km, Faw-70 being a locally built SSC-3, and Faw-150 and -200 having enlarged fuel tanks. All were advertised for export at the Baghdad exhibition in 1989.

Early in 1995 Iran was reported developing a cruise missile based on P-15. Work was reportedly being done by Defense Industries Organization, Military Industries Organization, Shahid Hemat Industrial Group (SHIG), and Shahid Bagheri Industrial Group (SBIG). A parallel report refers to a Silkworm derivative, which would be very similar. It is initially to be used for coast defense.

◆ SS-N-3 Shaddock (and SS-C-1) (P-5/6/35)

Dimensions: 0.96 × 11.85 m; span 3.2 m
Weight: 4600/5400 kg
Warhead: 900 kg
Propulsion: Liquid-fuel rocket
Speed: 1250 km/hr
Range: 500 km

This Chelomei missile probably survives only in its coast-defense version, S-35 (NATO SS-C-1). The autopilot-guided nuclear version (with some initial course correction by the launching submarine) was P-5 (4K95). P-5D (4K95D) had a Doppler rather than a barometric altimeter, for higher altitude, and could detect drift due to wind, for better accuracy. The radar-seeker follow-on was P-6 (4K48). A land-attack version, P-7 (4K77), was designed to hit assigned, rather than preplanned, targets; it proved insufficiently accurate and never entered service. P-35 was the radar-seeker version for submarines and surface ships, with a modified (nearly bifurcated) air intake. Work on the initial coastal version, using the P-35 (S-35) missile, began in 1960, and this Redut system was accepted for service on 11 August 1966. An upgraded version, Utes, was first fired 1971 and was accepted 28 April 1973. Work on the next version, 3M44 Progress, began in 1974. It incorporated a new on-board navigational system and a more automated FCS. This version was accepted for service in 1982. For further details, see the 1991/92 edition and the 1994 update. P-35/S-35 may have incorporated elements of an abortive P-40 missile, which was to have armed several warships of the 1956–60 program. This weapon evolved into SS-N-12 and SS-N-19. Data above refer to the original unguided coastal version, S-5. Angola may have been the first export customer, in 1987; this missile was also probably exported to Syria.

A P-5 (Shaddock) missile on display at the Moscow military museum, 1995. P-6 was very similar but had a nose radar. P-35, the ultimate version, is similar but has a nearly bifurcated air intake and, apparently, a flat-array radar seeker instead of the reflector dish of the earlier version. This missile beat out its competitor, Beriev's P-10, largely because of Chelomei's key innovation, folding wings which allowed stowage in a much smaller container. (S. Zaloga)

It now appears that SS-N-7 was Chelomei's P-70 Ametyst (4K66), in appearance a scaled-down SS-N-3 (3700 kg, 7 m long, compared to 4300 kg [5100 kg with booster]) and a length of 11.85m for P-5 (5300 kg with booster and 10.2 m for P-6). Speed was comparable, 1160 km/hr versus 1250 km/hr for P-5 or P-6. Cruising altitude was about 60 m, rather than 400–800 m for P-5 and 100–7000 m for P-6. Range was 40–60 km. Missiles were fired at an angle of 15 deg from a depth of 30m. The warhead was either nuclear or 1000 kg of HE. P-70 was designed specifically for "Papa" (Project 661) and "Charlie I" (Project 670A) submarines; it was tested on board a modified "Whiskey" (Project 613A).

Reports of a modified Styx (P-20L) on board "Charlie I"–class submarines have not been confirmed.

◆ SS-N-9 Siren (Malakhit: P-120/4K85)

Dimensions: 2.1 × 8.8 m (forebody diameter 0.78 m, aft body depth abaft jet intake, 0.87 m), span 2.1 m (planform similar to that of SS-N-2)
Weight: About 3200 kg
Warhead: 1000 kg

Propulsion: Solid-fuel rocket
Speed: 1100 km/hr (cruise altitude about 60 m)
Range: 110–150 km

Carried on board "Nanuchka"-class missile boats and "Charlie II"–class nuclear attack submarines, Chelomei's SS-N-9 is a longer-range equivalent of SS-N-2. Like SS-N-2, it is limited in minimum altitude because it uses a barometric altimeter. Work began under a 28 February 1963 decree (the same date as Bazalt) calling for a universal (submarine/surface ship) missile. The proposal design was approved in September 1963 and the sketch design in February 1964. The first missiles were completed in 1968, and the first test shot (without seeker) was on 25 September 1968. The test program was completed with shots from a converted "Charlie I"–class submarine in December 1974. The decree to arm "Charlie II"–class submarines (Project 670M) with this missile was issued on 21 November 1977. A further project for a 12-missile submarine (Project 686) was canceled. Missiles could be launched from a submarine at 50 m depth (compared to 30m for Ametyst), and range was 50% greater than that of Ametyst. The missile used a new guidance package including a new autopilot and a new seeker (reportedly radar/IR). As with Styx, the submarine must run a steady course and depth while preparing to fire and while firing.

Chelomei's solid-fuel Ametyst (P-70) missile was fired by "Charlie I" (Project 670A)-class submarines and by the sole "Papa"-class submarine. Some submarines may have carried modified Styx missiles instead. This Ametyst was displayed at Moscow in 1993. P-120 Malakhit was the successor. (S. Zaloga)

The standard triple surface-ship tube is designated KT-84. An export Malakhit-E version may later have been sold to India for the new *Delhi* (Project 15) class. On a "Nanuchka," P-120 is associated with the Band Stand and Fish Bowl or Light Bulb radomes. Apparently Band Stand contains a radar that tracks the outgoing missile; the other radomes contain the data link that receives the missile's radar picture and sends back instructions. The system, then, is a smaller equivalent of that which guides missiles such as SS-N-3 and -12 aboard larger ships.

Note that "Nanuchkas" produced for Soviet client-states are armed instead with SS-N-2C. That circumstance may reflect the security of the downlink or of the inertial guidance required for long-range flight before the active seeker is switched on.

There may be a nuclear version (200 kT), as at extreme range the missile is far enough away not to damage the firing platform.

SS-N-22 is the successor weapon. Raduga's SS-N-14 was probably based on a failed alternative to P-120.

◆ SS-N-12 Sandbox (Bazalt: P-500/4K80)

Dimensions: 1.6 (forebody 0.78) × 11.7 m; span 3.2 m
Weight: 4800 kg
Warhead: 2200-lb HE or nuclear
Propulsion: Jet (KR-17-300)
Speed: About 3000 km/hr (altitude 50–5000 m)
Range: 550 nm

Work on this missile began under a 28 February 1963 decree, apparently to produce a higher-speed P-6 (SS-N-3) successor with a larger warhead and greater range. It also had better guidance, allowing it to choose one target within a formation. The new special engine was probably a hybrid turbojet-ramjet. Flight profile is high-low, the missile detecting its target while at high altitude, then switching off its radar and diving under the target's

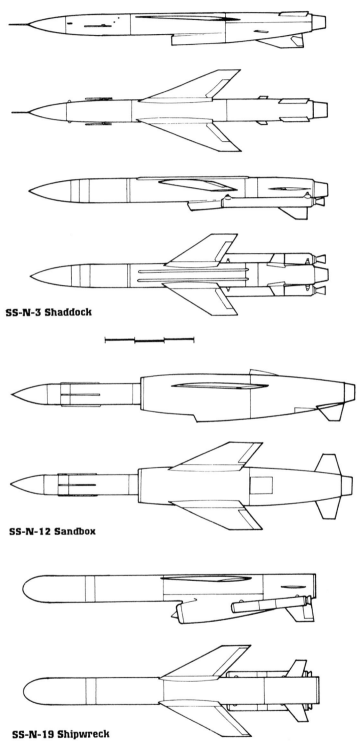

SS-N-3 Shaddock

SS-N-12 Sandbox

SS-N-19 Shipwreck

Russian long-range ship- and submarine-launched missiles designed by the Chelomei OKB. The top drawing shows the autopilot-guided version of Shaddock, P-5; below it is the early submarine version, P-6. P-35, the ultimate version, has a modified air intake. SS-N-12 (P-500) may have replaced a failed Lavochkin hypersonic missile, P-40, which would have equipped the Project 63 nuclear-powered missile cruiser planned for the abortive 1956–65 program. P-40 is described as capable of hitting moving targets at a range of 400 km without using terminal guidance, which implies both a large nuclear warhead and very high speed (to reach the target before the circle of uncertainty grew too large). Presumably the failure of P-40 led to reassignment of the project to Chelomei, hence the development of P-500. Early versions of P-500 apparently had the ramjet air intake extending much further forward. (S. Zaloga)

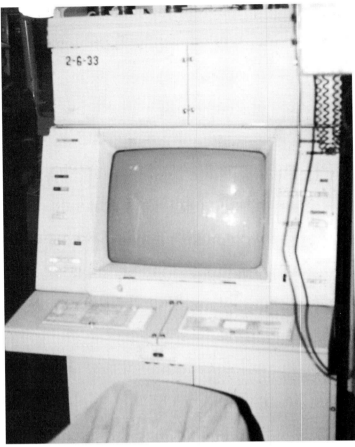

SS-N-12 control console in the BIP of the *Marshal Ustinov*. Standard practice seems to be to place such consoles only on the bridge and in BIP, never in a weapons-control space. (Author)

radar horizon. It then flies at low altitude, switching its radar back on only when it approaches the predicted target position. The sketch design was completed in December 1963, and flight trials began in October 1969. Bazalt was accepted into service in 1975 as a P-6 replacement for "Echo II" (Project 675) -class submarines; there was also an abortive Project 688 to carry 12–16 missiles of this type. In 1977 this missile was selected for the new aircraft carrier *Kiev*. It survives on board *Slava*-class cruisers. This missile is associated with an Argon shipboard command system. This missile may be an elaboration of an earlier project, begun as early as 1956, for a high-speed "universal" long-range weapon for both surface and submerged launch.

Targeting support is provided by a radar-equipped airplane or helicopter or by the Kasatka satellite system, which became operational (for both Bazalt and its successor, Granit) in 1978.

◆ SS-N-19 Shipwreck (Granit: P-700, 3M45)

Dimensions: 0.96 × 10.2 m; span 3.2 m
Weight: About 10,000 lb
Propulsion: Turbojet
Range: 300 nm

To date, the Chelomei OKB's Granit is the ultimate development of the SS-N-3 concept. It reportedly began as an attempt to circumvent the airframe problems of Bazalt by modifying the SS-N-3 airframe. Work formally began in 1969, using a high-speed turbojet (KR-93). Flight trials began in November 1975, and the missile was accepted into service on 12 March 1983. The shipboard launcher is SM-233. SS-N-19 is so fast (and probably has so good a search pattern) that it needs no mid-course guidance. An "Oscar"-class missile submarine can, therefore, fire the missile submerged, on the basis of information provided by a satellite via the Punch Bowl (Kasatka) downlink antenna. This weapon is also carried by *Kirov*-class missile cruisers and by *Kuznetsov*-class carriers. In their case the missile can be tracked and controlled via the ship's main air-search radar. Like its predecessors, SS-N-19 has a video data link back to the firing ship (not used in the "Oscar"-class version).

There are two alternative seekers, active and passive (ARM) radar; the ARM version is said to be intended specifically to attack Aegis ships. Presumably the ARM version gets its target signature from the Rum Tub OTH-T ESM system with which most SS-N-19-armed surface ships are equipped.

Warheads: Nuclear (200 or 350 kT), 1000-kg unitary shaped-charge high explosive, and bomblet (primarily for antiship attack, but also usable against land targets: 750 × 1 kg, a mix of incendiary, AP, HE, which can be varied to meet requirements).

◆ **SS-N-22 Sunburn (P-80 Zubr/3M82, P-100, and P-270 Moskit/3M80/Kh-41)**

Apparently a TTZ for a supersonic P-120 successor and a new ship to carry it (Project 956, *Sovremennyy*) was approved in 1969. Both Chelomei and Berezhniak seem to have developed weapons. Since both fit the same container (KT-190 launcher), and since neither was seen until the fall of the Soviet Union, it was assumed they were a single weapon, SS-N-22 Sunburn. However, a missile portrayed in a Chelomei poster exhibited at Moscow in 1992 was clearly associated with the *Sovremennyy* class, a submarine, and a coast-defense launcher (but *not* a fast-attack boat), whereas Raduga's 3M80 Moskit has also been publicly associated with the *Sovremennyy* class (and with the "Tarantul"-class fast-attack boat); it cannot possibly fit a submarine torpedo tube. A coast-defense version of 3M80 is under development, but SS-N-22 was reportedly sold to Iran (for coast defense) some years ago. This report may be no more than a misunderstanding. Iran may have bought SS-N-2.

To further complicate matters, although 3M80 has clearly been in service for some years, in 1993 Raduga was soliciting funds to develop a ship-launched version of Kh-41, which is generally supposed to be an air-launched derivative of the ship-launched 3M80. An article about 3M80 credited the system to the Altair NPO (which adapts SAMs to naval requirements), but the missile itself has been advertised as a Raduga product; the 1993 Raduga solicitation may refer to a new FCS for Kh-41.

Chelomei's version of SS-N-22 is shown on a wall poster at the 1993 Moscow Air Show. A similar poster at the previous Paris Air Show included a recognizable *Sovremennyy*-class destroyer. This missile was marketed at the 1994 FIDAE show in Chile as Yazma. It was also apparently the missile shown in Chelomei's Bastion coast-defense system. No photograph of this missile appears to have been published, so its existence has not been confirmed. (S. Zaloga)

The missile in the Chelomei poster appeared to be a pure rocket, similar in outline to the much smaller U.S. Sparrow. No such missile has been seen publicly, but there is evidence that it exists, and it is described below. This missile was apparently advertised as Yashma in Chile at FIDAE 1994.

It appears that the first 14 *Sovremennyys* and the two prototype "Tarantul"-class missile boats were armed with Chelomei's rocket-powered P-80, incorporating a SAR tell-back link. Reportedly a folding-fin submarine-launched version of P-80 has entered service as P-100 (it is fired from 65cm torpedo tubes); it may also be fired out of the torpedo catapults of the frigates of the *Neustrashimmyy* class. P-100 may be called Moskit-M, and it is associated with a KT-152M launcher. P-80 dimensions: 0.52 × 9.4m (fin span 1.8 m); the *Sovremmennyy* canister is 1.85 × 9.6 m. The 1992 Chelomei OKB poster gave range as 130 km (70 nm). The warhead is a 250-kg shaped charge. At FIDAE 94 Yashma maximum range was given as 300 km; launcher weight was given as 3000 kg, and container dimensions were given as 750 × 9000 mm. These figures suggest something rather larger than the missile shown in the 1992 poster. Drawings showed the missile on a *Sovremennyy*-class destroyer (fired either vertically or obliquely), on a ground mobile launcher in a towed configuration (tracked cab and trailer), and on a submarine (surface or submerged launch, vertical or oblique).

The missile seeker can operate in SAR mode (the SAR image is constructed on board the launching ship, via the data link). As it approaches the preset target area, SS-N-22 snakes, to pass (hence examine) each available target in turn. In each case, it transmits back the video needed to form a target image. The shipboard FCS will have formed its own image of the preferred target, presumably using the radar in its helicopter. The missile image and the target image are automatically compared. If they match, the missile is ordered to attack. If not, the missile retains the target as an alternate, and goes on to examine the next. If it passes out of the target area without finding the appropriate target, it automatically turns 180 deg and attacks the last target seen.

There is also an unbriefed mode in which the missile sends back target video, and the operator on board ship decides whether to attack. Presumably the missile can also be used in fire-and-forget mode.

Chelomei has displayed posters of a "Bastion" coast-defense system employing truck-mounted rockets (eight trucks, three

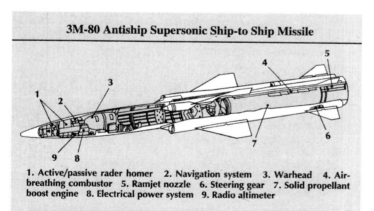

3M-80 Antiship Supersonic Ship-to Ship Missile

1. Active/passive rader homer 2. Navigation system 3. Warhead 4. Air-breathing combustor 5. Ramjet nozzle 6. Steering gear 7. Solid propellant boost engine 8. Electrical power system 9. Radio altimeter

Basic Specifications			
Firing range	90 km	Propulsion system: cruise ramjet engine with built-in solid propellant booster	
Cruising altitude	7-20 m	Probability of the missile guidance on any target when firing upon typical ship formations, radio countermeasures being considered:	
After-launch turn	+60° -60°		
Warhead weight	300 kg	for convoy and landing ship	0.94
Launch weight	3,950 kg	for ship strength groups	0.99
Flight speed	2,800 km/h	for missile boat units	0.99
Overall dimensions:		Warhead effectiveness (the number of missiles needed for combat capability loss):	
length	9,385 mm	of destroyer	1.2
diameter with folded wing and fin	1,300 mm	of transport ships with total displacement to 20,000 tons	1.5
		Continuous storage time in a launcher in combat-ready position	1.5

The missile can operate in all environmental conditions, and it is resistant to nuclear weapon destruction effects.

This sketch is based on one released at the Abu Dhabi military show in 1993. (Bill Clipson).

per truck) apparently identical to Yashma, with 300km range (other sketches show Bastion using the Yakhont missile described below).

Later destroyers, later "Tarantuls," the "Sivuch"-type surface-effect boat, and the WIGs (Ekranoplans) all have Berezhniak's (Raduga's) rocket-ramjet P-270 Moskit (3M80), which has a simpler data-link. P-270 (3M-80) dimensions: 130 cm (with wings folded) × 938.5 cm, wing span 2.1 m, weight 3950 kg with a 300-kg (150-kg HE) warhead, speed 2800 km/hr (1510 kt), range 90 km (as in SS-N-2C), flight altitude 7–20 m, capable of a 60-deg turn after launch. Maximum range has also been given as 120 km. Through the last 5 to 7 km of flight toward the target, the missile maneuvers evasively at 15 g. The characteristics suggest that this was the intended successor to Raduga's Styx. Raduga claims that 1.2 missiles suffice for a mission kill of a destroyer, or 1.5 for a transport. The seeker can be switched to an ARM mode. A cruise speed of 3600 km/hr has also been claimed for this missile.

According to one report, there are two different versions of this missile, 3M80 (90–120 km) and 3M80E (160 km).

The associated version of Band Stand is the 1–4-GHz Monolit. Later *Sovremennyy*-class destroyers, beginning with *Bespokynyy*, apparently carry longer missile tubes (about 2 m longer than those of earlier units), presumably holding a modified version of this weapon. These ships are a modified version (Project 956A) of the basic *Sovremennyy* (Project 956). Their missile may be 3M80E or P-100.

Kh-41 is an air-launched version of 3M80. Although it was first shown at Minsk in 1992, as of the fall of 1995 it had not yet been flown. An Su-24 or -27 can carry one underbody; presumably a Backfire can carry two underwing. The seeker was described as radar active-passive plus inertial midcourse. Launch interval is 5 sec. Dimensions: 76 × 974.5 cm (29.9 × 383.7 in), weight 4500 kg (9923 lb). The SAP warhead weighs 320 kg (706 lb). Speed is Mach 3.0 at high altitude and Mach 2.1 at low altitude (5 to 15 m). The missile can fly its entire course at low altitude (range 150 km) or it can fly 250 km including a 50 km low-altitude run-in. A drawing in the missile's brochure shows one airplane observing the target from high altitude and data linking to another, below the radar horizon, which fires at low altitude. Launch velocity is 200–470 m/sec (393–925 kt). The NATO designation is AS-20.

The export version of 3M80, 3M80E, omits the tell-back data link.

As in the case of SS-N-9, the outgoing SS-N-22 missile (of either type) is tracked by the radar in the Band Stand radome. Light Bulb is the antenna of the associated data-link system to the missile. The video-link receiver (for the associated aircraft) is Bell Strike. The fire-control radar (in Band Stand) associated with Moskit is Mustang. Monolit may be the radar associated with P-80.

3M80 has been exported to China. In 1994, the United States apparently considered bidding for the entire inventory of SS-N-22s (841 missiles). When negotiations stalled, the Russians stated that they were placing the missile on the open market. The discussion apparently concerned Moskit, and it was not clear whether missiles were still in production.

◆ SS-NX-25 (Uran: Kh-25/3M24)

Dimensions: 42 × 440 cm (93cm fin span [diagonal]); air-launched versions are 375 cm long
Weight: 600 kg (1320 lb); air-launched version 480 kg (1060 lb)
Warhead: 145 kg (320 lb)
Propulsion: Turbojet (intake under body)
Speed: 300 m/sec
Range: 5–130 km (air-launched version)

Zvezda's Kh-35 (Type 78) was conceived in 1972 as an equivalent to the U.S. Harpoon antiship missile. The current air-launched version is Kh-35U, the suffix typically indicating an upgrade. There seems to have been a parallel project to develop an equivalent to Tomahawk (it became SS-N-21). The system is designated 3K24. The air-launched program may have begun only in 1983; the air version of the missile may be designated

The air-launched version of Kh-35 (SS-N-25), "Harpoonski." (S. Zaloga)

3M60. Kh-39 may be a version adapted to attacking ground targets.

Initially the East German Zeiss organization was expected to develop an EO seeker for Kh-35. Well before the collapse of the Soviet Union, financial problems had aborted his plan, and the missile ended up with either a radar or an IIR seeker. Unlike the missiles described above, this one was developed by the OKB responsible for tactical air-to-surface weapons, Zvezda. The plan for an optical seeker suggests that in at least some versions there is a downlink, allowing the operator to select an aim point.

According to a drawing distributed at the 1992 Moscow Air Show, an air-launched IIR version is 375 cm long (480 kg), with a range of 5–130 km, launch altitude 200–5000 m, and flight altitude 5–10 m (speed 300 m/sec). Fin span (diagonal) is 93 cm. There is also an active radar version with similar characteristics.

Kh-35 has been shown in both ship- and air-launched versions and for coast defense. There is a helicopter version. An encapsulated submarine version has been discussed, but apparently was never built, and by 1995 was no longer on offer. A coast-defense system developed by the Granit central research institute, using the Kh-35 missile, is called Bal (Whale). It employs the Plank Shave (Garpun) radar and the 8 × 8 vehicles of the Barrikady 130mm coast-defense gun system, each truck carrying eight missiles. This system may have the NATO designation SS-C-6. It is not in Russian service, but has been offered for export. The air-launched version is carried in a four-round launcher on board Tu-142s (one under each wing) and on board Ka-27 helicopters (two per helicopter). Zvezda also offers an IC-35 training version.

Kh-35 is now being mounted on board modernized "Krivak"-class frigates. A triple Kh-35 launcher can replace a single SS-N-2 on board an "Osa," and a sextuple launcher can replace the usual triple SS-N-9 launcher on board a "Nanuchka." Some boats may have been refitted. A "Tarantul" can carry four quadruple launchers. The total weight of the 12 missiles is considerably less than that of the weapons it replaces. Ships under refit have been observed with new radome-enclosed radars, perhaps Positive (Cross Round). In that case some of the weight saved is probably going into a Kortik (CADS-1) defensive weapon (at least one "Tarantul," R-71, has been fitted with CADS-1). The canister (without the missile, it turns out) was first seen in 1988 on board the East German attack boat *Sassnitz*. The missile itself was tested on board a "Matka"-class attack boat. As of spring 1995 Kh-35 was described as being in the final flight test stage.

SS-N-25 configuration is similar to that of Harpoon (it was advertised partly as a "Harpoon"-like target for training and testing). A leaflet released in 1992 indicated that 1993 was "technical project deadline of any carrier armed [with] this missile," implying that new ships and aircraft may carry it.

◆ Alpha (Biryuza P-10 system, 3M54 missile)

Chelomei exhibited sketches of this Mach 3 turbojet missile at the 1993 Moscow Air Show, and a photograph of a model has appeared. The missile seems to have been intended for a modified *Sovremennyy* (Project 956U) with vertical launch tubes; the brochure also showed it being fired from an airplane, from a missile boat, and from a triple coast-defense launcher (on a truck). In mid-1995, the bureau complained that no funds were available for this weapon. If funds are released the missile can be flown by the end of the decade. Approximate dimensions: 0.6 × 9.2 m (wing span 1.5 m). The ship-launched version weighs 2500 kg, the aircraft version 1600 kg; the warhead weighs 300 kg. The missile flies at 10–20 m altitude to a range of 300 km.

Yakhont, as sketched by the Chelomei bureau, in a 1995 Moscow Air Show wall poster. Terminal attack speed is probably Mach 3.5. The canister in which the folded-up version of the missile lies is 68 cm in diameter. The missile can be fired by both submarines and surface ships. (S. Zaloga)

A full-scale mock-up of Chelomei's Alpha SSM and ASM, displayed at the 1995 Moscow Air Show. The missile's delta wings, which protrude just forward of the ventral air intake, are only barely visible. (S. Zaloga)

Chelomei's Alpha in sketch form, as shown at the 1995 Moscow Air Show. Other illustrations in the same poster (not reproduced here) show the missile's potential platforms: an Su-27, a submarine, a coast-defense truck (whited out by glare), and a surface warship; and also that the missile is usable against both ships and land targets. (S. Zaloga)

◆ SS-N-26 (P-800 Yakhont/3M55; Oniks/3K55 System, SM-312 launcher)

Drawings of Chelomei's supersonic (Mach 2–2.5) ramjet missile were first shown in 1993. It broadly resembles the old U.S. Talos, with a conical nose body and a cylindrical ramjet body abaft that. Yakhont seems to be intended to arm the modified "Nanuchka" (Project 1234.2), *Neustrashimmyy* (Project 1154), and modified *Sovremennyy* with conventional or vertical launch tubes (Project 956M and 956U). The associated radar is probably Monolit, which is also the radar used by P-80. Approximate dimensions: 0.6 × 8.4 m (wing span 1.4 m). Range is 300 km, which suggests that Yakhont was conceived as an alternative to Alpha.

Yakhont seems to have been conceived as a single missile to replace SS-N-9, -12, -19, and -22, to cut the number of separate types. Bastion (P-900) may be the associated coast-defense system, and P-1000 Vulkan (see below) may be the submarine version. As of mid-1995, the design/production bureau, Mashinostroyeniye, complained that no funds were available for Yakhont.

Development was continuing with internal funding. An article published in 1995 implies that both Alpha and Yakhont began as parallel programs in the early 1990s. Yakhont can be launched from a ship or submarine, and Alpha from an airplane (but an early Alpha brochure shows it launched from ship and submarine).

Mashinostroyeniye stated in 1995 that Yakhont is designed to be launched from a 600mm launch tube, to replace a system (unnamed) currently fielded in this canister. In fact canisters measured in Moscow (and associated with either Alpha or Yakhont) were 68 cm rather than 60 cm in diameter. The earlier missile would appear to be the folding-wing submarine-launched version of P-80 Zubr described above under SS-N-22, and the unwillingness to identify the missile suggests that it has never been publicly described (which would explain why only 3M80 is ever associated with SS-N-22).

According to a Russian account, Oniks replaced SS-N-9 (Malakhit) on board one "Charlie II" (Project 670M) -class submarine, B-452. According to another account, the sketch design for this missile was approved in 1983, Oniks being an internal design bureau name. As of September 1995 no decision had been made as to service use. This account also associates Bastion with Yakhont/Oniks.

◆ SS-N-27 (Novator Alpha/3M51) and SS-N-21 (S-10/3M10 missile, 3K10 Granat system)

Dimensions: 51 cm × 8.09 m (canister: 65 cm × 8.39 m) (span approx 300 cm) (20.1 × 318.5/25.6 × 330.3 in)
Weight: 1700 kg (2440 kg with canister) (3747/5378 lb)
Propulsion: Turbojet with rocket booster
Speed: Mach 0.7
Range: 1600 nm

Data apply to Novator's SS-N-21 strategic missile (Granat), which is broadly comparable to the U.S. Tomahawk. Granat was conceived in the late 1970s, roughly in parallel with Kh-35, and carried on board "Akula" (Project 971) and "Yankee Notch" (Project 667AT) -class submarines. A land-based equivalent, RK-55, was discarded under the SALT Treaty. SS-N-21 follows a low-altitude (approx. 190–200 m altitude [600–650 ft]) flight path. In 1992, the Russians stated that they had 240 SS-N-21 at sea.

The designers, NPO Novator, apparently developed their Alpha (not to be confused with the Chelomei Alpha described above) as a conventional equivalent. Although described as a coast-defense weapon, this Alpha has torpedo-tube lugs; indeed, its tail is essentially identical to that of Granat. Alpha was first shown at Abu Dhabi in 1993. It flies 200 km at subsonic speed (220–240 m/sec, about 440–470 kt). When it approaches to within 20 km of the expected target position, its warhead sheds the main body of the missile, accelerating to supersonic speed (700 m/sec, about 1380 kt) to penetrate terminal defenses.

Novator's Alpha coast-defense missile at the 1993 Moscow Air Show. The hump forward indicates the warhead section, which separates for its high-speed terminal run. (S. Zaloga)

◆ P-1000 Vulkan (3M70)

This Chelomei missile, never described in the West, was conceived as a replacement for SS-N-12. Development was formally ordered on 15 May 1979, the missile first flew in July 1982 (from a submarine, on 22 December 1983), and it was accepted for service on 18 December 1987. Vulkan was installed between 1987 and 1993 on three "Echo"-class submarines (Project 675MKV: K-1, K-22, and K-35) which had previously been modernized with Bazalt (P-500, SS-N-12) missiles replacing their original P-5s and P-6s. Work on two more units scheduled for this conversion, K-10 and K-34, was stopped due to lack of money, and the submarines were discarded instead. K-22, the last of the class, was decommissioned in 1995 (K-1 was stricken after a 1989 reactor accident, and K-35 was stricken in 1993). A list of equipment on board these submarines suggests that P-1000 used much the same FCS (Argon-KV FCS and Argument radar) as P-500.

SOUTH AFRICA

◆ Skorpioen

See Gabriel (Israel).

SWEDEN

Rb 12 is the Swedish designation for the Norwegian Penguin Mk 2 (see above). The U.S. Hellfire is designated RBS 17. Rb 04E and Rb 05 have been replaced by RBS 15. Surviving rounds are used for training. See the 1991/92 edition for details.

◆ RBS 15

> **Dimensions:** 50 cm × 4.35 m; span 85 cm folded/1.4 m spread (19.7 × 171 × 33.5/55.1 in)
> **Weight:** 598 kg (780 with boosters) (1318/1719 lb)
> **Warhead:** Estimated 250-kg (551-lb) semi–armor piercing (a modified, heavier warhead is under development)
> **Propulsion:** Microturbo TRI 60-1-077 (370-kg thrust) with rocket boosters
> **Speed:** Mach 0.9 (to Mach 0.7 by 3-sec booster burn)
> **Range:** 70 km (77 kyd); 150 km for air-launched version

RBS 15 is a fire-and-forget weapon with an active-radar (frequency-agile) seeker. Flight parameters, such as the search pattern, are automatically selectable by the FCS. The mid-course inertial system can be updated by data link. PEAB claims that frequency agility in the seeker reduces glint by a factor of 2 to 4 and increases target-detection range by more than 50%. Frequency agility is also said to eliminate target fading during lock-on, to reduce sea clutter, and to obviate any requirement to allocate different frequencies to the different missiles of a salvo. The seeker is designed to provide home-on-jam as an option, and the missile can also be modified to maneuver evasively (using memory tracking to remain locked on).

RBS 15F under the wing of a Viggen fighter. (SAAB)

The seeker is designated 9GR400; it is built around the same type of PEAB spin-tuned X- or Ku-band magnetron used in the 9LV200 FCS. Typical pulse width is 0.2–1.0 microsec, with a jittered PRF of 1000–4000, a peak power of 65–100 kW, and search limits of 30 deg either side in azimuth and 15 deg up or down in elevation.

Reportedly the RBS 15 airframe is derived from that of the earlier Rb 04E air-launched missile; the use of components of the earlier weapon drastically cut development time. It evolved out of Rb 04 Turbo (a development of the earlier Rb 04E), which itself replaced an earlier rocket-powered SAAB-Scania Mach 0.8 missile designed to replace Rb 08A; this project was canceled in 1977. Reportedly, too, the missile was developed at the urgent recommendation of the Swedish Aircraft Industry Committee to maintain missile design and production capability. The Swedish defense forces disagreed (presumably on grounds of cost) but were overruled: RBS 15 was chosen instead of the U.S. Harpoon or the French Exocet.

The development contract was let to SAAB in June 1979, and the design was frozen in mid-1980. The first live firing was in July 1981. Initial Swedish navy deliveries were completed in 1985.

RBS 15 is the ship-launched version; RBS 15K (sometimes called RBS 15CD) is used for coast defense; and RBS 15F is carried by Swedish air force Viggen fighters. A projected submarine-launched version was rejected by the Royal Swedish Navy on the grounds that long-range wire-guided torpedoes were preferable.

The RBS 15K coast-defense version became operational with Swedish forces in 1993. There are two platoons per battery, each with a radar, control center, and two firing trucks (four missiles per truck). Missiles can be launched from up to 30 km inland.

In 1991 SAAB received a contract to develop an upgraded version, TSA (Tungt Styrt Attackvapen, or Precision Guided Attack Weapon), for JAS 37 and 39 fighters attacking point targets in coastal waters. This program is also called ASOM, the Autonomous Stand-Off Missile. The ASOM project included TERNA (terrain navigation) and automatic target recognition (using IIR or television or imaging radar). An RBS 15 upgrade was chosen instead of a proposed German version of a stand-off dispenser weapon (DWS). This program apparently did not proceed, but the Swedish government placed a contract to develop a more modest Mk 2 upgrade in 1993. It applies to ship-launched (RBS 15M) and coast-defense (RBS 15K) missiles; the air-launched RBS 15F will have to wait until later in the decade. The production contract was awarded about May 1994. Mk 2 incorporated a new, more compact guidance system, to increase fuel capacity.

RBS 15AMIK was probably a related project, proposed for the British CASOM air-launched standoff missile project. AMIK means automatic target recognition and tracking. It would have employed a stabilized, slewable platform with selectable search width and 7-deg search height, carrying an 8–12-micron IIR terminal seeker.

A new Mk 3 program was revealed at IMDEX in March 1995. Mk 3 is the new baseline version. It is apparently a digital version of the missile, with an internal bus. That reconfiguration makes later changes much easier, since the different elements of the missile are buffered from each other. As currently envisaged, Mk 3 uses a new digital autopilot (for better maneuverability) and a new seeker with better target discrimination and better ECCM. The new tactical computer offers more flexible targeting and flight planning, reattack and other tactical options (dog-legs, for example), and more varied terminal maneuvers. The missile is now tail-controlled for maneuvers at up to 8G. The combination of more tankage and denser fuel (JP-10) extends range from the current 70 km to 150 km (80 nm). This version is to have a new wave-adaptive altimeter (for lower-altitude flight, down to 2 m). Associated with Mk 3 is a new Missile Engagement Planning System (MEPS), using a standard workstation running an industry-standard graphical user interface, with embedded decision-making software. It allows off-line scenario simulation and tactical training. This is in addition to the dog-leg capability always inherent in the missile. The new miniaturized components add space for fuel, boosting range to a possible 200 km. Conversions should begin in 1996, and missiles will enter service in 1998. By that time Mk 3 will be available for export. The Mk 2 designation now apparently refers to an existing RBS 15 upgraded to near–Mk 3 standard. This version has the denser fuel, improved guidance, and is compatible with the new shipboard FCS. It may be designated RBS 15M.

In Mk 3, minor aerodynamic changes increase maneuverability and reduce RCS (there is some recontouring around the nose and intakes). Mk 3 will be fired from a new lightweight low-RCS launch canister. Presumably Mk 3 is planned for the next-generation Swedish fast-attack boat now in the concept stage.

As of the end of 1993, estimated unit cost was $525,000. Production (including orders) was variously estimated as 616 in all and 210 for Sweden and 185 for export (through 1994).

Users: Croatia (*King Petar Kresimir IV* class), Finland (15M: *Helsinki* class, ordered March 1983 and in service 7 June 1984; and coast defense, first delivered April 1988; this version is RBS 15F [Finnish designation MTO-85]), Sweden (*Stockholm*, *Goteborg* classes, coast defense, and JAS 37 fighters [15F version]), Yugoslavia (coast defense [to replace SS-C-3], possibly also *Kobra*-class missile boats). Croatia seized 50 to 100 RBS 15K intended for coast defense, placing some aboard the missile boats listed above. Some systems are probably in Serbian hands.

TAIWAN (ROC)

A stealthy Hsiung Feng III is under development.

◆ Hsiung Feng I

Hsiung Feng I is an unlicensed copy of the Israeli Gabriel developed by CSIST (the Chung Shan Institute of Science and Technology); the name originally meant "Male Bee," but was changed to "Proud [or Brave] Wind") in 1980/81 in line with a general redesignation of new Taiwanese (ROC) systems with "Wind" names. Reportedly, the developers experienced problems with the rocket motor and with the copied guidance system. The warhead is a 70-kg blast-fragmentation type. This missile is used both on board ship and in coastal batteries. Hsiung Feng may not be a true sea-skimmer, since at least some films show it flying well above the sea and then diving steeply into its target.

Hsiung Feng I was developed in parallel with Gabriel II. Where Gabriel II packs a more powerful motor into much the same space, Hsiung Feng I was lengthened to provide greater range with the same propellant. It encountered propulsion problems (motor cracks) and aerodynamic heating just abaft the cruciform wings. A new propellant had to be bought, and the modified missile became Hsiung Feng IA. Hsiung Feng I/IA probably entered service about 1977, Taiwan having bought only three Gabriel systems (designated Hsi An, i.e., Angel, for *Sumner*-class destroyers).

A Hsiung Feng I missile on parade in Taiwan. (Fu S. Mei)

Hsiung Feng uses a radar tracker (as in Gabriel) but only a single optical director, to gather the missile into the director beam. In a *Hai Ou*–class fast-attack boat, the system sensors are the search radar (UPS-60), a periscope, and a tracker radar (SPG-24, now sometimes SPG-21A with a very different antenna). The consoles are side by side in that order below decks. The tracker is assigned to a target picked up by the search radar. The periscope tracks the flare in the missile's tail, to gather it into the guidance beam. It may continue to track the missile (as feedback) as the missile flies to the target. The operator in the center sees not a TV picture, but an oscilloscope trace; it is probably a correlogram of the tracker and the periscope (EO). As the missile approaches the target, the oscilloscope trace becomes narrower and steeper. The Wu-Jinn I destroyer *Dang Yang* uses an optical director similar to the OG.R7/2 of Israeli missile boats. Other destroyers apparently use periscopes and masthead R76 radars in radomes.

The land-based version of Hsiung Feng I is deployed in a triple towed trailer. There are both land- and air-launched versions, the latter for use by AT-3 attack trainers and presumably the new Ching-Kuo fighter.

Reported unit cost is about $500,000. Reported total Hsiung Feng production (presumably of both Hsiung Feng I and II missiles) was 642 as of the end of 1993.

◆ Hsiung Feng II

Hsiung Feng II resembles the U.S. Harpoon (or, for that matter, Otomat) but is powered by a French Microturbo 078 engine (other versions of which power Otomat and RBS 15) burning JP-5. This engine has a somewhat greater diameter than the U.S.

Hsiung Feng II missiles on parade in Taiwan. The fairing above the nose carries the IR sensor. (Fu S. Mei)

A recent photo shows the current IR sensor configuration. (Fu S. Mei)

engine (but develops 10% more thrust). Maximum range is said to be "considerably further than Harpoon" (also given as 160 km). Missile diameter is 5 cm greater than that of Harpoon, and length is about the same, so if both have about the same length (50%) devoted to fuel, Hsiung Feng II has about 30% more fuel volume. Taiwan bought a few Otomats before developing this missile, so the design may well have been influenced by that of Otomat. Reported warhead weight is about that of Harpoon, about 500 lb (Hsiung Feng I uses a 220-lb/100-kg warhead). Published photographs show that the Hsiung Feng II warhead uses self-forging fragments (about 20 in all), in effect shallow shaped-charge depressions spaced around its outside.

The missile appears to approach its target at very low altitude (5–7 m), using an active-radar seeker. Reports indicate that the missile can accept mid-course guidance data, for example, from a helicopter. The data link involved is probably similar to that of Otomat/TESEO. Unlike Harpoon, Hsiung Feng II incorporates an IR sensor, officially described as Automatic Target Recognition Image Tracking Module Mk 2, carried in a fairing above the main (radar) seeker. Presumably, the combination of radar and IR will defeat the relatively simple countermeasures currently employed on board PRC ships.

The dual seeker is almost certainly a local development. A recent Hsiung Feng II shows a new IR seeker radome shape, like that of Mistral. Both the radar and the IR seeker are turned on simultaneously as the missile reaches the predicted target area. Each has a programmed set of predicted target returns; the guidance computer compares the inputs from both. If either deviates from the allowed range, it is assumed to be jammed, and homing shifts to the unjammed sensor. The radar uses a planar-array antenna, that is, monopulse rather than conscan. Radar ECCM features include resistance to range-gate pull-off, reportedly due to reprogrammable software.

Film of test launches, shown in February 1988, appears to show a modernized *Fletcher*-class destroyer (Wu-Jinn I or Weapons Improvement Mk I) launch platform. Reportedly, the Taiwan navy will employ Hsiung Feng I and II side by side, as the Israeli navy employs Gabriel and Harpoon.

Development began in 1983. Hsiung Feng II entered production for coast-defense service in 1991. Missiles are forward-deployed to Tung-yin Island off the Chinese coast, to supplement or replace an existing Hsiung Feng I battery. This missile is also carried on board the new *Perry*-class frigates (2 × 4-rnd box launchers), and an official model shows it on board a Wu-Jinn I destroyer. The surface-launched version entered service in 1992. An air-launched version (for the AT-3 and the new Ching-Kuo fighter) entered service in 1993. Reportedly, a submarine-launched version is under development.

UNITED KINGDOM

On 24 June 1992, the Royal Navy announced that it was seeking proposals for a long-range antiship missile, the Surface-to-Surface Guided Weapon (Naval Staff Target 7021) to arm the Future Frigate. Reportedly required range is 150–300 km (82–164 nm),

and the missile will have to attack corvettes and frigates up to 4000 t, as well as FAC. As of May 1996 the main contenders were Harpoon Block 1G and ANNG.

The Royal Navy is also reportedly interested in a stand-off missile to attack point targets ashore. McDonnell-Douglas is offering SLAM, which can be fired from a Harpoon canister.

In 1995 the Royal Navy bought Tomahawk for submarines. Reportedly 65 missiles were purchased, against a planned total of 180.

In July 1996, the Royal Air Force chose the BAe/Matra Storm Shadow (an Apache derivative) as its next-generation land attack stand-off missile, CASOM. Although the Royal Navy is not involved in this program, it seems likely that Sea Harriers or the follow-on JAST will be required to carry CASOM missiles.

Finally, note that Iran adapted the Tigercat (land-based equivalent of the Seacat SAM) as a short-range antiship missile for PBI ("Swift") -type coastal patrol craft. Horizontal range is 6 km (3.2 nm). Presumably these are retired Iranian air force weapons; the air force had 15 Tigercat launchers. See the antiaircraft section for details of Seacat.

◆ ALARM

Dimensions: Approx. 23 cm × 4.24 m; span 73 cm (9 × 166.9 × 28.8 in)
Weight: About 200 kg (441 lb)

BAe's ALARM (Air-Launched Antiradar Missile) was developed for the RAF, but will probably also be carried by Royal Navy Sea Harrier fighters. Unlike earlier antiradar missiles, ALARM can loiter above a radar, forcing its operator to shut down. The missile is fired in an up-and-over trajectory, diving toward the target emitter. If the emitter radar shuts down, the missile deploys a parachute from which it hangs over the target area, deterring an enemy operator from turning the set back on. Seeker logic prevents multiple attacks on a single target if ALARMs are ripple fired in the corridor-suppression mode. The simpler universal mode involves a higher altitude launch for greater range.

ALARM antiradar missiles intended for tactical trials were used tactically (and successfully) in the Gulf War instead (January 1991). In all, 121 were fired on 52 sorties.

Users: Saudi Arabia (sold 1991), United Kingdom.

ALARM compared to two BAe air-to-air missiles at the 1995 Paris Air Show: S225X, a possible alternative to AMRAAM, and ASRAAM (top). (Author)

◆ Sea Eagle (P3T)

Dimensions: 40 cm × 4.14 m; span 1.2 m (15.8 × 163 × 47.3 in)
Weight: 600 kg (1325 lb)
Warhead: Approx. 230 kg, aluminized RDX-TNT (about 500 lb)
Propulsion: Microturbo/Toulouse TRI-60-1-607 turbojet engine
Speed: Mach 0.85 (cruise)
Range: 110+ km (120,000 yd)

BAe Dynamics' Sea Eagle was developed to replace both the television-guided AJ 168 and the antiradar AS 37 versions of Martel. Sea Eagle is essentially a Martel with a turbojet and a new seeker; it was originally called Cruise Martel. The development contract was announced in August 1979, and the missile was first fired in 1981.

Sea Eagle uses inertial mid-course and active terminal radar guidance. It can select a preferred target from among a target array (e.g., a task force or convoy), using target-signature data

A Sea Eagle missile, with a French cluster bomb (Belouga) in the foreground. (Author)

stored in the missile's computer before flight. Reportedly, the seeker head is capable of homing on jam or homing on a specific radar emitter.

The missile is designed to hit a target at or just below the waterline. The front face of the warhead is dished to ensure penetration at shallow grazing angles, recalling dished faces fitted to World War II air-dropped depth charges so that they would not skid on hitting the water. This warhead was developed at RARDE (Royal Armaments Research and Development Establishment) for the abortive Under-Sea Guided Weapon development of Martel.

Estimated unit cost in 1992 was $750,000. About 860 Sea Eagles had been made or were on order as of 1994.

Users: India (carried by six Jaguars, Sea Harriers, and Sea King helicopters), Saudi Arabia (on Tornadoes, ordered 1985), United Kingdom (Sea Harrier and Tornado). A reported sale to Chile for use on board CASA A-36 light strike aircraft did not go through.

◆ Sea Skua (CL 834)

Dimensions: 25 cm × 2.5 m; 0.72 m span (9.8 × 98.5 × 28.5 in)
Weight: 145 kg (325 lb)
Warhead: 35 kg (9-kg RDX) (77/19 lb)
Propulsion: Boost-sustain solid-propellant rocket (boost burn time 2 sec)
Speed: Mach 0.8
Range: 15 km (16,400 yd)

Sea Skua is a helicopter-launched antiship missile, conceived primarily as a counter to fast missile-armed patrol boats. The range was chosen so that Sea Skua could be fired from outside the lethal envelope of a Soviet SA-N-4 AA missile (located, e.g., on board a "Nanuchka").

Sea Skuas carried by a Lynx helicopter, 1984. (Westland)

Guidance is by semiactive radar, typically using a Seaspray. The flight path is preset, with a choice of four approach altitudes (choice based on sea state and type of target). Approach height is maintained by a radar altimeter. Typically, a Lynx shipboard helicopter carries two or four Sea Skuas. Missile weight was fixed by the requirement that three missiles and their associated equipment (but not the Seaspray radar) weigh no more than 580 kg. Frigates' space constraints limited the length of the stowage frame to 2.65 m, and wings and fins had to be detachable. The intended target set the type of warhead (30-kg SAP, for penetration).

Project definition for Sea Skua began in April 1972. The first airborne firing of a fully guided round came in November 1979. As of 1993, at least 1088 missiles (not including test rounds) had been made. Unit cost was about $316,600 (FY95).

Sea Skua was used very successfully against Iraqi (many of them ex-Kuwaiti) fast-attack boats during the Gulf War. These missiles had been modified to fly at lower altitudes so as to attack low-freeboard targets; too, the delay in the fuze was reduced. In one series of attacks, helicopters from two British ships sank at least four Iraqi boats and damaged another 12.

A ship-launched (SL) version employing a 4-rnd launcher was demonstrated in 1988. Late in 1994 it was reported that South Korea had bought this version for a patrol boat. There is also a truck-mounted coast-defense version, for which Bahrein was the lead customer.

Users: Australia (four on a rack on each side of the S-70 helicopter), Bahrein (shore-based), Brazil (Lynx helicopters: about 40 missiles), Germany (156 for Sea King helicopters, ordered May 1984), South Korea (about 126 for Lynx helicopters, shore batteries, and patrol boats), Turkey (about 120 for 10 AB 212 helicopters), United Kingdom (Lynx helicopters: 350 missiles). There is at least one customer in Africa (possibly Kenya). A version for the Indian Do 228 was developed, but the requirement lapsed when the aircraft were bought for the Indian coast guard (the planned naval purchase was deferred). The German purchase comprised 140 warshot missiles, four telemetry missiles, and 12 missiles for training. As of May 1996, a purchase of the patrol-boat version by Kuwait seemed imminent.

UNITED STATES

Although they received the greatest publicity, guided bombs and stand-off missiles accounted for only 7.4% of the total of 88,500 tons of weaponry used against Iraq. Most of the precision-guided weapons were laser-guided bombs (LGBs): more than 2500 GBU-10 (Mk 84 bomb), more than 4500 GBU-12 (Mk 82 bomb), more than 200 GBU-16 (Mk 83 bomb, mainly by naval aircraft), almost 2000 GBU-24/27 (including 1600 penetrators using BLU-109 bombs). In addition, the Royal Air Force dropped 1000 LGBs. A few EO bombs were also used, such as the GBU-15s dropped on the oil terminal pumping the great oil slick into the Gulf.

It turned out that unguided bombs made little impact against dug-in Iraqi armor, whereas enemy tanks could quite easily be destroyed one by one by laser-guided 500-lb (Mk 82) bombs. This was such a surprise that stocks of the light LGB kits ran short. There was also some unhappiness that Walleye, Mk 83, and Mk 84 could not penetrate bunkers and were ineffective against bridges. I-2000 was quite effective in these roles, and its LGB version, GBU-24, is now being bought by the Navy.

For the Navy alone, LGBs dropped prior to the ground campaign amounted to 22.6% of all Mk 84s, but to only about 2.5% of lighter bombs; they amounted to about 10% of cluster bombs (Rockeyes and APAMs). Navy and Marine Corps expenditures of short-range guided weapons were as follows: Walleye, 130; Skipper, 5; SLAM, 7; HARM, 900; Shrike, 25; Hellfire, 159; Mk 84 LGB, 260 (including 202 Navy); Mk 83 LGB, 205; Mk 82 LGB, 420 (including 216 Navy); Maverick, 40; and laser-guided cluster bombs, at least 550 (this figure does not include the Marines' expenditures). A total of 611 LGB kits were used for bombs other than the Mk 80 series, presumably including cluster bombs and reportedly including a few British-supplied 1000-pounders.

The Navy portion of the Desert Storm weapon replacement

package included 290 Tomahawk, 2033 HARM, 8 SLAM, 6000 Mk 83 bombs, and 800 Mk 83 LGB kits.

Because weapons must be suited to close air support, U.S. Navy policy favors keeping a man-in-the-loop in any tactical munition. Thus, LGBs are favored because they can be aimed at targets designated by lasers on the ground. EO weapons such as Walleye and SLAM are designed to use data links, and thus can be reaimed or even aborted after launch. However, when dropped on a moving ship, the aim point of an EO bomb can easily slide into the dark area between ship and wake, and then slide away from the ship. It seems unlikely that the Air Force's EO bombs will be used by the Navy, even if Walleye stocks run down.

Budget cuts have made it more difficult to maintain large carrier air wings. In 1994, the Navy reported that the optimum wing would include 60 strike aircraft (36 F/A-18, 14 F-14), but that it could maintain only 50 per ship, and that therefore it had to maintain a total of 251 F-14s. This was part of the rationale for the F-14 strike modification.

In recent years, the U.S. program for advanced strike warfare R&D (6.2/6.3 program) has included work on a solid fuel-air explosive warhead (completed FY90), on an integrated fiber-optic gyro on a chip (tested FY91, completed FY92), on a passive IR/active RF neural-net ship classifier and aim point selector (begun FY91, tested FY93), on a modular reconfigurable missile computer (demonstrated FY92), and on a reduced-signature (i.e., low-smoke) solid rocket fuel. Work on near-real-time mission planning for long-range precision strike cruise weapons began in FY92.

ONR is currently working on a standoff warhead that can be reconfigured in flight (e.g., to attack hard or multiple targets) under a Mission Responsive Ordnance (MRO) program. An RFP issued in mid-1995 asked for responses through 30 September 1995. Components are to be tested during FY96/97, followed by section-level feasibility tests in FY98/99. See the antiaircraft section (under guns) for missiles currently under test for naval fire support.

Early in 1995, it was reported that the United States had six ongoing black missile-related programs, none of them for an all-up missile (the last such missile had apparently been the abortive TSSAM). Instead, the programs reportedly concentrated on sensors, guidance, and warhead technology:

- Guidance alternatives to GPS, given fears that relatively simple broad-band jammers in a target zone can preclude precise missile navigation (opinion differs as to the practicality of jamming GPS, however).
- Automatic target recognition (ATR), in the expectation that partial ATR will be possible within 5 or 6 yr, and full ATR within a decade. Presumably ATR means recognition of any of a wide range of complex ground targets with limited contrast, near similar nontargets.
- New means of long-range precision guidance/sensing, to give CEPs in the 1–3ft range.
- Carbon-fiber warheads, to short out an enemy's electrical equipment. An officially denied report claimed that Tomahawks armed with carbon-fiber warheads knocked out the Iraqi electrical grid early in the Gulf War. This damage mechanism has been investigated many times, sometimes under the rubric of nonlethal weaponry. According to the unofficial report cited above, the Tomahawks carried spools of carbon-fiber wire, presumably chopped up the way bulk chaff launchers cut chaff as it is dispensed. It has also been reported that a classified Air Force program is developing a carbon-fiber payload for the new Wind-Corrected Munitions Dispenser (WCMD). It carries very short fibers, which are dispersed by a gas generator or explosion; the fibers can float in the air if there is no wind. It seems unlikely that carrier-based aircraft will deliver such payloads, since they would be extremely destructive if accidentally triggered on a flight deck. Much the same might apply to a ship-launched Tomahawk; but a submarine might fire fiber-bearing Tomahawks with impunity.
- High-power microwave (HPM) warheads, that is, nonnu-

clear means of creating EMP. Again, HPM concepts have a long history. It is not altogether clear whether an enemy's vulnerability to HPM can be estimated in advance, or whether HPM damage can be assessed after a strike. However, the threat of HPM is quite daunting.

- Continued work on low-observable missile airframes, which would not increase an airplane's radar signature if they were carried externally.

◆ JASSM

The Joint Air-Surface Strike Missile (JASSM) is to replace the canceled TSSAM (AGM-137). A version of some existing missile may well be chosen. This missile, with an autonomous seeker, is to be carried by F/A-18s as well as by a variety of Air Force aircraft. Initially maximum unit cost was set at $1M, and range was reported as 60 to 350 nm. Then the program was recast to show 2400 Phase I missiles ($600,000 each, range probably 100 nm) plus a P^{3}I Phase II. That made it easier for the Navy to provide a man-in-the-loop in Phase I. By way of comparison, TSSAM range was about 160 nm. Plans call for a first buy of 50 in FY99, followed by 100 in FY00, then 200, 400, 400, and 350 in FY01–04. As of the fall of 1995, a formal request for proposals was expected in January 1996. Likely bidders include Raytheon/Grumman Northrop (a low-cost TSSAM derivative to carry a 1000-lb warhead, using GPS/inertial mid-course guidance and IIR terminal guidance), Lockheed Martin (a previously classified weapon developed by the "Skunk Works"), McDonnell-Douglas (AGM-84H SLAM-ER), Rockwell (turbofan-powered AGM-130 derivative), and Texas Instruments (JSOW derivative with a unitary warhead, turbofan power, and terminal seeker). TSSAM would have weighed about 2000 lb (100in span × 168 in long), with turbofan power; the Navy variant alone would have had man-in-the-loop guidance. JSSAM may merge with the generally similar British CASOM program.

In August 1995 the Senate Armed Services Committee criticized the planned JASSM program as too rushed, and demanded that as a minimum SLAM-ER, AGM-130, and AGM-142 (the Israeli Popeye, in Air Force service as Have Nap) be considered as alternatives. The two final JASSM competitors are McDonnell-Douglas (using some JDAM and SLAM-ER components in a new stealthy airframe developed under the Have Slick program and offering either a single warhead or two warheads for strikes not requiring a CEP better than 40 ft) and Lockheed Martin (using a stealthy missile derived from a black program, but resembling a JSOW with wings mounted below rather than above its body). Both alternatives use IIR seekers and GPS mid-course guidance. Both contractors received 24-month program-definition contracts in June 1996, only 9½ months after the JASSM requirement was validated.

◆ JDAMS (GBU-29/30)

The Joint Direct-Attack Munition Program merges the earlier Navy advanced bomb family (ABF) program with an Air Force short-range adverse-weather guided bomb (direct attack munitions) program. In the process, the emphasis has shifted from direct replacement of existing iron bombs for mass use to a form of inertial/GPS guidance so inexpensive that unguided bombs may no longer be considered worthwhile.

The Air Force is lead service for the first phase of JDAMS, which provides inertial/GPS guidance for Mk 83, Mk 84, and BLU-109 as well as for a new guided (wind-corrected) munitions (bomblet) dispenser (WCMD). The modified bombs are GBU-29 (1000 lb) and GBU-30 (2000 lb). CEP targets are 30 m for inertial and 13 m for GPS (100 ft for WCMD). The weapon can be targeted from the aircraft bus, for example, by using a LANTIRN pod to generate target coordinates using its laser. The unit cost target was $40,000. In October 1995 McDonnell-Douglas won the bomb portion of the program. Its configuration uses strakes down the side of the bomb. Loral is responsible for the mission computer, Honeywell for the inertial-measurement unit, and Rockwell-Collins for the GPS receiver.

Plans currently call for low-rate production in FY98, followed by full-rate production beginning in FY99, ultimately of 62,000

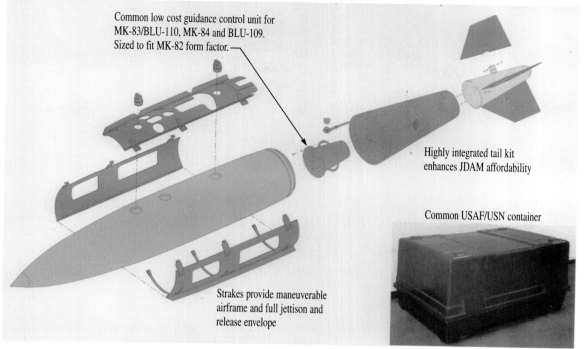

Common low cost guidance control unit for MK-83/BLU-110, MK-84 and BLU-109. Sized to fit MK-82 form factor.

Highly integrated tail kit enhances JDAM affordability

Common USAF/USN container

Strakes provide maneuverable airframe and full jettison and release envelope

McDonnell-Douglas' winning JDAMS design. (McDonnell-Douglas)

bombs (initially 4900) for the Air Force and 12,000 bombs (initially 3100) for the Navy. Total estimated Navy program cost is $1.191 billion, including RDT&E. There is some hope that unit bomb cost can ultimately be cut to $25,000 or less, in which case it may be possible to buy 100,000 or even 150,000 kits, and eliminate unguided bombs altogether. JDAMs is likely to be in service on board F/A-18s by mid-1999.

The JDAMS kit is likely to be far too heavy for the 500-lb Mk 82, which the Marines like to use for close air support (its limited size limits damage to Marines from near misses). The Navy is therefore developing a new 500-lb close air support all-up round with a hi-lo tail. A JDAMS kit is to be developed for it.

The next phase of the program develops the Air Force–managed Joint Programmable Fuze or Multifunction Joint Service Fuze. Motorola received the fuze contract in 1993; it offers multiple arm times, instantaneous and short and long delay, hard-target survivability, programmability, and increased shelf life.

The final phase of the program is product improvement (JDAMS PIP), in which a new sensor provides the bomb with a 3m-or-better CEP in any weather. This sensor would supplement inertial or GPS guidance. There has been some speculation that a seeker required only to operate very close to the target could be extremely inexpensive. The two current alternatives are SAR (Hammerhead) and real-beam mm-wave seeker (Orca). Raytheon won the SAR demonstration contract in the fall of 1995. Concept analysis began in FY94 and will continue through FY98. Procurement will not begin until after JDAMS has achieved full-rate production; the Air Force expects to buy 5000 PIP bombs in FY04.

◆ Cheap Shot (Fasthawk)

This is an FY97 advanced technology demonstration (ATD), following on a $14.9M investment in FY96. The objective is to develop a very inexpensive ($180,000) Mach 3+ precision weapon with a range of 700 nm, to carry a 700-lb warhead like that of Tomahawk. The ATD is based on the perception that manufacturing costs can be cut drastically by using an axisymmetric body without wings, made of rolled steel or aluminum, controlled by thrust vector using a simple joint in front of the propulsor to cut cooling costs, component stress, actuator loads, and erosion/corrosion. Much of the hardware would be taken off the shelf: the GPS/inertial guidance unit, the Mk 82 warhead, an existing universal joint with linear actuators, and an existing

fuel-management system. As of the spring of 1995, a design review was planned for May 1997, with flight tests in FY99. Cheap Shot would become Tomahawk Block V and also a future supersonic target. (See the addendum.)

A table of data prepared for potential manufacturers showed two versions: Cheap Shot, carrying 500 lb to 1000 nm at 4000 ft/sec, and Cheap Shot 2, carrying 700 lb to 700 nm at the same speed. This table showed a unit cost of $1.2M for Tomahawk, and over $400,000 for ATACMS.

◆ JSOW (AGM-154) (formerly AIWS)

Dimensions: 13.26 (wide) × 17.4 (high) × 160.0 in; wing span 106.0 in; tail span (horizontal) 16.5 in, (vertical) 21.0 in
Weight: 1065 lb (maximum 1500 lb in P^3I version)
Warhead: BLU-97 or BLU-108 bomblets
Propulsion: Unpowered; glide range 15 nm if launched at low altitude, 40 nm if at high altitude; over 120 nm if powered

Joint Stand-Off Weapon is to replace laser-guided weapons such as Paveway, Skipper, and Maverick. These three subject the launching airplane to too great a threat; JSOW will be fire-and-forget. As the Navy's AIWS (advanced interdiction weapon system), this missile was one of two new air-weapon starts of the

Texas Instruments' winning JSOW competitor, in model form (as AIWS, before being renamed JSOW), at the 1991 Navy League show. The pointed nose contour is intended to improve stealthiness. (Author)

JSOW
CONFIGURATIONS

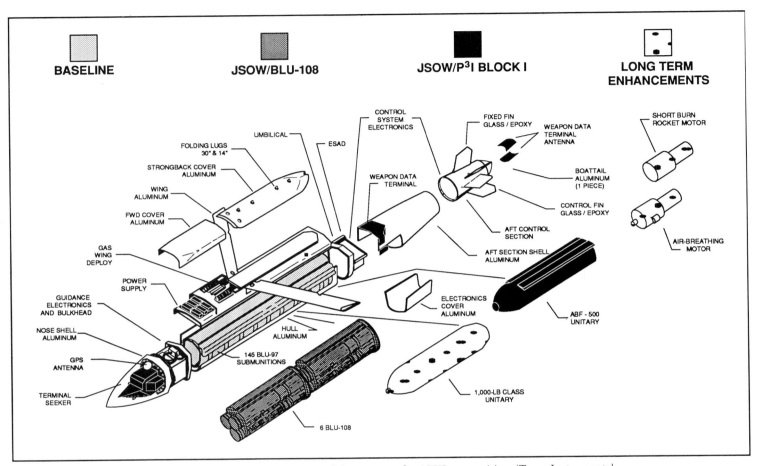

Alternative configurations for JSOW, Texas Instruments' successful entrant in the AIWS competition. (Texas Instruments)

JSOW makes its first live flight, dropped by an F/A-18C at China Lake in December 1994. (Texas Instruments)

FY87 program; the other was SLAM. Texas Instruments won the competition in December 1991. The Navy's AIWS was then joined with the Air Force stand-off weapons program under the title JSOW, joint stand-off weapon. Presumably the Navy had to accept that the Air Force's stealthy TSSAM would supersede its own companion requirement for a long-range successor to SLAM (ASWS). TSSAM was later canceled due to excessive cost, leaving the field to an enhanced SLAM.

JSOW was conceived as a low-cost weapon with a range of somewhat over 5 nm and with a maximum weight of 2250 lb, to carry three alternative warheads: 1000- or 2000-lb unitary warheads or a cluster of bomblets. Characteristics were developed at a May 1986 conference at NSWC. Much affected by lessons learned both in Lebanon and in the Libyan raid, the conferees wanted a low-altitude standoff range greater than that possible with Walleye, Skipper, and LGBs; the launch itself should not reveal the aircraft's location; the weapon should be difficult to detect en route to its target; it should make multiple kills per pass; and the aircrew should be provided with "last-frame assurance" that the intended target had been neutralized or destroyed, so that subsequent attackers could avoid wasting weapons on it.

The key requirement was for LOAL, so that a pilot would not have to pop up within AA range to acquire the target. The usual solution, a data link, was rejected because a pilot using one would have to loiter too close to the target. Instead, the missile guides itself toward a point specified by the pilot, during a brief pop-up at a safe distance. "Last-frame assurance" required a combination of some kind of imaging sensor and a data link, but that link would be needed for only a short time, just before the missile hit. The link could, therefore, be simpler than that used in earlier missiles.

Quiet launch required aerodynamic performance superior to that of existing weapons (a lift-to-drag ratio as high as 13:1), so that even when launched at low altitude the missile could coast for a time before its motor ignited (if power was required at all). Multiple kills per pass required a cluster munition. The missile could provide CEPs, at 5nm range, of 5–7 ft. Long range suggested GPS-aided inertial guidance. The system could be either completely prebriefed or the missile could fly to a target located by the airplane.

Studies soon showed that within a $50,000 ceiling (rather than the $70,000 to $120,000 initially estimated) imposed by then–Secretary of the Navy John Lehman the weapon could not have a terminal seeker, data link, or propulsion. Characteristics were, therefore, revised; the weapon would achieve a minimum operationally acceptable standoff range, using a low-cost inertial guidance system (estimated guidance costs were $14,000–$21,000), a cluster payload, and capacity for future growth to meet the initial requirements.

The missile's weight was reportedly set by the limit for an AV-8B landing vertically with one on board. Missiles are normally launched at Mach 0.6 to 0.95, at 200 to 40,000 ft, for a nominal range of 15 to 40 nm. JSOW can be launched well more than 90 deg off-bore, turning at 1.3 g after launch.

The formal OR was issued in March 1988.

The baseline design was changed to incorporate a GPS receiver for better accuracy. Preplanned product improvement (P3I) is to provide terminal guidance (an IIR seeker), data links, a unitary warhead, and to make the weapon suitable for attacking an expanded target set. The P3I version will probably cost 2 to 3 times as much as the baseline (which was to cost $50K in FY85 dollars, or $58.6K in FY90 dollars).

Versions:

AGM-154A: Baseline, carrying 145 BLU-97/B Combined Effects Munition bomblets. Low-rate initial production is to begin in FY97.

AGM-154B: Air Force version, carrying six BLU-108 Sensor Fuzed Munition bomblets, each of which carries six Skeet submunitions. Low-rate initial production is to begin in mid-1998, with up to 150 missiles.

AGM-154C: P3I version with unitary warhead (BLU-111, an insensitive-munitions version of Mk 82), an IIR seeker (with Texas Instruments FPA, derived from that of the canceled TSSAM), and data link for use with AWW-13 pod. Texas Instruments received an Engineering and Manufacturing Development (EMD) contract for the unitary warhead version in October 1995, calling for delivery of 22 missiles beginning in 1998, with an option for 50 more in low-rate initial production, to be exercised in the year 2000 for delivery in 2002.

Further improvements under study as of 1996 include use of the Lockheed Martin Advanced Penetrator (800 lb) planned for TSSAM (I-800; total weight would be about 1500 lb), a LADAR or mm-wave seeker, and a powerplant. A powered version offered for the British CASOM used the I-800 warhead.

To demonstrate the required CASOM capability, Texas Instruments built a version of JSOW powered by a Williams International WJ-24-8 engine, typically used to power target drones. The test vehicle flew successfully on 29 September 1995.

Estimated production requirements as of 1993: total 17,000; Navy: 300 in FY97, 387 in FY98, 550 in FY99, 16,563 to complete. Air Force: total 5,000; begin with 40 in FY98, then 135 in FY99, 4825 to complete. However, as of 1995 the estimated requirement was 6200 BLU-108 rounds and 7800 unitary-warhead rounds. In early 1995 Navy plans called for the first 126 in FY97.

◆ Bullpup (AGM-12)

Dimensions: 18 × 163 in; span 48 in
Weight: 1785 lb
Warhead: 970 lb (370 lb HE) SAP (Mk 40)
Propulsion: Storable liquid-fuel rocket
Speed: Mach 1.8
Range: 10 nm

Data are for Bullpup B (AGM-12C), typical of most versions.

Bullpup is radio-command guided into its target, the operator visually tracking a flare in the missile's tail. Bullpup A entered fleet service in 1959. Bullpup B and later versions carried the

Bullpups carried by a P-3B Orion, 1970. Although superseded in U.S. service, this missile survives elsewhere. (U.S. Navy)

heavier warhead listed above. Huge numbers were built, both in the United States and in Europe, and they were carried by ASW aircraft (such as the P-3) as a means of dealing with surfaced submarines (e.g., providing mid-course guidance to missiles) and with small warships. The Bullpup B warhead is incorporated in the Tomahawk missile and the Bullpup A warhead in the Norwegian Penguin.

Users: Argentina (A-4Q Skyhawks), Israel (AGM-12B version), Taiwan (probably on S-2Ts), Norway (AGM-12C version on P-3Cs), Turkey (may be gone with retirement of S-2s).

◆ Guided Bombs (GBU Series/Paveway)

GBUs fall into two categories, EO homers and Paveway series laser-guided bombs (LGBs). The U.S. Navy limits itself to the latter. Pre–Gulf War naval procurement of laser bomb kits was very limited partly because aircraft returning to a carrier still with bombs on board must often jettison them; better to drop inexpensive dumb bombs than laser-guidance kits. Too, about 1987 it was argued that LGBs expose the designating aircraft to AAW fire. Hence the intense interest in an excellent bomb FCS on the F/A-18. Wartime experience showed that even this system was still inadequate, hence the push to buy more LGBs.

Paveway (LLLGB, low-level LGB) is a generic seeker/wing combination applicable to Mk 80 series bombs, made by Texas Instruments. Paveway I was the original version. Most current bombs are Paveway IIs. They and the earlier Paveway I use "bang-bang" guidance, in which control surfaces are always deflected all the way, leading the bomb along a relatively inefficient wobbly path. A microprocessor, as in Paveway III, is needed

GBU-24/B (top, using Mk 84 bomb; total weight 2315 lb, length 173 in) and GBU-24A/B (bottom, using BLU-109 bomb; total weight 2350 lb, length 170 in). Both use the BSU-84/B airfoil group and WGU-12/B or -39/B guidance. (Texas Instruments)

for a smoother and longer flight, using smaller control-surface deflections. Paveway III, intended for low-level delivery, uses a mid-course autopilot and a very sensitive seeker. All Paveway-series bombs use a NdYAG laser operating at 1.064 microns (as in the U.S. Pave Knife or Pave Tack). The standard NATO laser designator operates at this wavelength using a 10–20-pps code.

Paveway entered service in December 1968. Paveway I development began in May 1969, and the weapon entered service in December 1970. The Paveway II engineering prototype was ordered in December 1974, and the weapon entered production in 1977 (FY76 program).

Paveway I uses a four-quadrant silicon detector array, which drives the four control fins to keep the bomb pointed at the target laser spot. The kits fitted to the U.S. Mk 82, 83, and 84 bombs are designated KMU-388, 421, and 351. Paveway I has been exported to 17 countries; the United Kingdom uses it with 1000-lb bombs (designated Mk 13 or Mk 17). Pave Storm was Paveway I applied to an SUU-54B cluster bomb. Paveway I lacked standoff range and had limited performance in mist and fog. Early bombs were controlled entirely by their forward fins. Versions still in service are GBU-10/B (Mk 84 bomb), GBU-12/B (Mk 82 bomb), and the 1000-lb LGB (Mk 83 bomb). It is not clear whether the 1000-lb LGB is identical to GBU-16A/B. GBU-10 and -12 each have a short-wing and a long-wing (A suffix, as in GBU-10A/B) version.

Paveway II has upgraded electronics and flip-out wings, and is less expensive (it uses some plastic parts). The Paveway II bombs are GBU-10E/B (Mk 84), GBU-12D/B (Mk 82), and GBU-16B/B (Mk 83). Earlier versions of GBU-10 and -12 (GBU-10B/B, -10C/B, and -10D/B, and GBU-12B/B and -12C/B) may also still exist. Britain uses a version applied to its Mk 13/18 1000-lb bomb family, with KMU-351E guidance kits.

Paveway III, which began full-scale engineering development in 1980, has a rocket booster. It incorporates microprocessor control, a digital autopilot, and flip-out wings; and it can be delivered in a dive, from level flight, or by toss-bombing. The seeker has an enlarged field of view and greater sensitivity for laser acquisition in poor (e.g., European) weather.

Paveway III's standoff range is probably about 3–5 nm, compared to 1–3 nm for Paveway II. It can therefore be delivered below the flight envelopes of most SAMs and outside AA-gun range. Texas Instruments claims that the bomb automatically compensates for varying release conditions, so that the pilot has merely to place the target in the middle of the HUD, minimizing exposure to enemy fire. The mid-course guidance allows for considerable offset from the airplane's flight path, and the bomb is designed for steep terminal trajectory. Inertial control is required for mid-course guidance, the bomb homing on a laser spot only at the end of the trajectory. Guidance is by four short wings attached to the seeker on the nose of the bomb; four big wings at the tail make for a 5:1 glide ratio to the target.

Versions: GBU-24 (Mk 84 and BLU-109 penetrator), GBU-27 (BLU-109 penetrator for F-117), GBU-28 deep penetrator (for F-111s).

Following the Gulf War came crash naval procurement of LGBs: 1250 GBU-24 (probably all conversions of the BLU-109 2000-lb hard-target bomb; this kit can also be used for a Mk 84) and 860 laser-guided versions of the Mk 83 bomb; at the same time 5000 Skippers were ordered converted into LGBs by 1995 (this work was ongoing as of late 1995). The Navy had not previously deployed GBU-24.

Unit prices: FY81, $8372; FY83, $17,643; FY85, $30,139; FY86 (Air Force) $40,262, (Navy) $33,972. In FY90, GBU-10C (Paveway II Mk 84) cost $22,000; GBU-24 (Paveway III Mk 84) cost $65,000. The EO (IIR) GBU-15(V)2/B cost $300,000.

Naval procurement: FY84, 350; FY85, 2752; FY86, 2109; FY87, 243; FY88, 222; FY89, FY90, and FY91, none; FY92, 850; FY93, none; FY94, 412; FY95, about 600. FY92–95 procurement was all GBU-24s.

These bombs have been exported very widely. Paveway I is used by 17 countries, Paveway II by 32. Paveway III was bought in 1994 by the United Kingdom (using a Royal Ordnance BROACH penetrating warhead) and by the Netherlands.

◆ HARM (AGM-88)

Dimensions: 10in × 13ft 7in × 44in wingspan
Weight: 798 lb
Warhead: 146 lb
Range: Depends on launch speed/altitude
Propulsion: Dual-thrust rocket motor (Mach 2 +)

The High-Speed Anti-Radar Missile is the current standard U.S. antiradar missile. Performance objectives were a broad frequency range, increased sensitivity, countermeasures resistance, and a smokeless motor (for low detectability). HARM is important both as a strike-protection weapon and as an antiship weapon; HARMs can be launched as precursors of an antiship-missile attack, forcing an enemy to turn off defensive radars before the heavier (and slower) Harpoons or Tomahawks arrive.

A HARM (AGM-88A) missile. (U.S. Navy)

The missile can be fired in prebriefed, self-protection, or target-of-opportunity modes. In the prebriefed mode, the missile can acquire the target after it is launched (the missile seeks out an expected signature); it can attack from very long range. Alternatively, an attacking aircraft can fire HARM automatically on the basis of information processed by its RWR. Finally, HARM can be fired at targets of opportunity, using the missile itself as the radar-search receiver, the weapon being fired manually.

The guidance system incorporates a strapdown inertial system; HARM (like its predecessor, Standard ARM) can continue to fly toward a threat radar even after the radar has shut down.

Normally, the missile is programmed with target range, bearing, and frequency before being fired. Given a preset range, the missile seeker can be set to activate 7–10 nm from the expected target position, to avoid distraction by other emitters resembling the target. Current HARMs must be fired within 15 deg of the direction of the target. Missile range is generally described as greater than 25 nm. In 1974, when HARM was first being developed, the desired maximum range was given as 100 nm. In 1988 it was reported that maximum range is 80 nm. Missiles are usually fired at 35–55 nm to ensure that their seekers acquire the targets.

HARM originated in the Navy's Tactical Air Armament Study of 1969. Texas Instruments was selected on 24 May 1974. The Air Force joined the program in 1975. Full-scale production was approved on 20 April 1983. HARM was first deployed on board the carrier *Kitty Hawk* (carried by A-7s) on 13 January 1984 and first saw combat during the April 1986 Libyan raids, when 40 HARMs, some of which had been on hand for up to 3 yr, very successfully destroyed Libyan radars. HARM was used extensively by F/A-18s and EA-6Bs (which fired 148) during the Gulf War.

AGM-88B has a programmable memory (using EPROM, electrically programmable and erasable memory chips) so that the missile can easily be adapted to changing threats, even in the air. The new warhead contains thousands of $\frac{3}{16}$in tungsten-alloy cubes, 3 times the density of the replaced steel cubes. This warhead can now do substantial structural damage to a radar station, not merely to the radar antenna proper, cutting through half-inch mild steel or quarter-inch armor. The current flyaway cost, about $200,000, is less than one-fifth the price of the original FY81 missiles, and MTBF greatly exceeds the original requirement of 200 hr.

The next version, AGM-88C, has a new seeker to deal with

more sophisticated radars. A single antenna replaces the two previously used to cover the missile's wide spectrum (0.5–20 GHz), and the new signal processor is several times more powerful than its predecessor. Even so, more than half of the new missile's plug-in boards are identical to earlier ones. Development of this Block IV missile was completed in 1989, and it entered service early in 1990. (Block II was a software change to AGM-88B.)

Missiles produced from FY90 on have a more lethal warhead, to enable the missile to damage a ship's bridge as well as destroy its radar (the steel cubes now used will be replaced with high-density tungsten that can penetrate 0.5in armor).

Earlier missiles are being upgraded to AGM-88C standard.

A new terminal sensor is being developed under the ERASE (Electromagnetic Radiation Source Elimination) program to meet a Marine Corps requirement to deal with shut-down radars. The missile flies a best-guess inertial path to within terminal sensor range. An RFP for this Advanced ARM Guidance Demonstration (AAGD) was released in July 1994.

The current MTBF is 300 hr, compared to 125 specified. HARM is now so reliable that the airplane carrying it can use its seeker for electronic intelligence, its guidance system detecting emissions from shipboard radars and identifying the ships based on their signature.

HARM platforms vary widely in capability. An F/A-18 pilot will generally respond only to a preprogrammed threat. The pilot can manually reprogram the missile; but without a sophisticated threat receiver such as the ALQ-99 of the EA-6B, the pilot cannot expect to detect an unexpected threat. Until the mid-1980s, however, installation of HARM on board EA-6Bs was resisted, partly for fear that the missile might home on the airplane's active jammers. Installation became necessary when the Navy experimented with all-Grumman (F-14, A-6, and EA-6B) air wings, since the new air wings did not include the usual HARM platforms, the A-7 and the F/A-18. It turned out that the missile could not home on the host airplane because its seeker was not turned on until well clear.

Using its ALQ-99, the EA-6B can detect, locate, and verify a threat, reprogramming its missile to suit. The Block 86 (ICAP-2) upgrade to the EA-6B removes the requirement that the aircraft point at the target and also adds a range-unknown firing mode. The first improvement is important for the EA-6B because otherwise it must interrupt jamming to fly toward the target before firing. Block 86 also allows the EA-6B to reprogram HARM in flight for threats not included in its preset threat library.

As of 1990, the requirement was for about 15,500 missiles (7672 for the U.S. Navy and 7821 for the U.S. Air Force, down from 8054 and 9006 as stated in 1985). U.S. Navy procurement: FY83, 160; FY84, 381; FY85, 813; FY86, 904; FY87, 766 (total 1078 for both services, against a request for 1177); FY88, 766; FY89, 1307; FY90, 1162; FY91, 2261 (including Gulf War supplement); FY92, 749. As of 1987, unit cost was about $285,000; in 1991 it was $281,000. The 1000th missile was delivered on 26 August 1986, and the 5000th missile was delivered in September 1988.

Foreign users: Australia (planned for F-111Cs, for late 1990s), Germany (announced 1985, for Tornadoes; 1000 ordered 1987), Italy (September 1991), Japan (announced January 1987), Spain (for EF-18s), South Korea, and Turkey (contract June 1993).

◆ Harpoon (AGM-84/RGM-84/UGM-84) and SLAM (AGM-84E)

Dimensions: 13.5 × 182.2 in (151.5 in long for air launch) (SLAM is 177 in long)
Weight: 1145 lb (air launch), 1439 lb (ASROC launcher), 1500 lb (SAM launcher), 1503 lb (capsule/canister launcher), 1385 lb (SLAM version)
Warhead: 488.5-lb HE (blast; semi–armor piercing)
Propulsion: J402-CA-400 Turbojet (cruise) (600-lb thrust) with solid-fuel booster (12,000-lb thrust for 2.9 sec) for ship or submarine launch
Fuel: 100 lb
Speed: Mach 0.85
Range: 75–80 nm surface-launched, 120 nm air-launched

Harpoon is fired from the ASROC launcher of USS *Knox* (FF-1052). (U.S. Navy)

Harpoon is probably the most widely deployed of all modern Western antiship missiles. By April 1992, more than 5800 had been delivered, including 2400 for export. Originally developed for air-to-surface use by P-3s, Harpoon also exists in surface- and submarine-launched versions, the latter employing a buoyant capsule for launch. The object was to develop a weapon that could be carried on board virtually all naval platforms. That requirement in turn limited Harpoon's dimensions to approximately those of the Standard Missile (surface-to-air) so that Harpoon could be fired from the usual surface-ship launchers. Even so, most Harpoons on board surface ships are carried in canisters that, incidentally, can only be replaced in harbor.

Harpoon was conceived in 1965 by NAVAIR as a longer-range (25 nm) follow-on to Bullpup, to be used against surfaced submarines (i.e., a harpoon to kill whales). That mission was later expanded to include antiship attack (e.g., attacks against Soviet-built missile boats), and the missile was being considered for ship mounting even before the *Eilat* incident of 1967 publicized the potential of antiship missiles. The project began formally in 1968. McDonnell-Douglas was chosen as prime contractor in June 1971, flying the first missile on 17 October 1972. The requirement for long (over 50 nm) range was imposed after McDonnell-Douglas was chosen, a small turbojet being substituted for the rocket envisaged in early studies. Production began in 1975, and Harpoon entered service in 1977. Overall, demonstrated flight reliability has been about 93% in 374 launches (100% since 1982).

All versions use a Texas Instruments active Ku-band frequency-agile radar seeker (fire-and-forget) with strapdown-inertial mid-course guidance. The autopilot employs an IBM 4PiSP-0A computer. The missile is normally fired to a preset point at which it turns on its radar, but it can also turn on its radar soon after takeoff (bearing-rider mode). Block 1B and later versions can fly dog-leg paths to the target area; their radars can be switched on intermittently. The missile can approach its target either at a shallow angle or via a pop-up.

The warhead is intended to explode after penetrating, to destroy at least a single compartment. Reportedly, five hits should disable a *Kiev*, four a missile cruiser (such as a "Kara"), two a frigate, and one a missile boat ("Nanuchka" or smaller). Most warships carry eight missiles in two clusters of four canisters each.

Block IB incorporated an improved guidance package, for the Royal Navy, which wanted a sea-skimming terminal phase for submarine-launched Harpoons. Deliveries to the U.S. Navy began in June 1982.

Block IC (AGM/RGM/UGM-84D) shows increased range (by adopting JP-10 instead of JP-6 fuel) and selectable terminal trajectory as well as improved ECCM. It can also fly several dog-legs to the target (way-pointing), concealing the position of the firing ship. A ship equipped with the improved Harpoon FCS, SWG-1A, can use way-pointing to arrange for several Harpoons to arrive simultaneously from different directions. Earlier versions can be upgraded to 1C standard at a unit cost of about $20,000.

McDonnell-Douglas received a contract to develop Block 1D (AGM/RGM-84F) in September 1989. The U.S. Navy first flew it on 4 September 1991, and production (modification of 1Cs) was approved in 1992, deliveries beginning in 1993 (the FY91 budget request included 124 Block 1Ds). The missile is lengthened to 174.9 in (compared to 151.5 in for 1C) to accommodate 70 lb more fuel, which doubles aerodynamic range, reportedly about 130 nm (compared to over 67 nm for 1C and over 50 nm for 1B). That extra endurance allows it to reattack a target not acquired on the first pass by flying a cloverleaf-shaped search pattern. Weight (air/sea) increases to 1400/1750 from 1224/1520 lb. The missile's wings have been moved forward to maintain the same angle of attack as in Block 1C. The guidance system has been modified for maximum commonality with SLAM, the software includes a unique target identification program, and the mid-course guidance section has been modified. The seeker is modified so that the missile hits lower on the target. Reportedly Block 1D incorporates more RAM in its structure for better stealth. Block 1D is too long to be fired from a submarine.

Blocks 1E and 1F are SLAMs (see below).

Block 1G is a Block 1C missile with Block 1D (reattack) guidance, but not lengthened, hence suitable for submarine use. This version also flies lower than Block 1C and has better ECCM. A total of 2000 missiles are being upgraded to this RGM-84G/UGM-84G version.

McDonnell-Douglas has made several attempts to develop a next-stage missile. McDonnell-Douglas announced a proposed Harpoon 2000 at the 1996 Navy League show. A navy Request for Information for a Harpoon follow-on was issued in the spring of 1996. McDonnell-Douglas proposes to use a SLAM signal processor; the existing seeker would be modified for better ECCM and also for target discrimination, presumably on the basis of radar fingerprinting. A GPS receiver would supplement the current strapdown inertial unit. Potential improvements include a data link, a new seeker, and vertical launch capability. The current mode (Quick Reaction) would be supplemented by Autonomous and Target Update/Selection modes. In the Autonomous mode, the missile would be guided by GPS/INS to the target area, where it would select the appropriate target from among several ships. In the Target Update/Selection mode, the missile would receive midcourse target updates, and might receive real-time seeker maps on which the operator would select the target itself. McDonnell-Douglas estimates that the combination of more precise mid-course guidance and better seeker signal processing (to overcome land clutter) should make for a five- to tenfold reduction in the allowable distance between the target and neutral shipping or land. The company claims that, given a FY98 go-ahead for engineering and manufacturing development, Harpoon 2000 could be in service in FY02.

The standard stand-alone shipboard launcher is a quartet of Mk 140 lightweight (17,472 lb loaded) or Mk 141 shock-hardened (27,126 lb) canisters, ships typically carrying two sets. The canisters cannot be reloaded at sea, and typically they are replaced rather than reloaded in port. Missiles are fired at a fixed elevation of 35 deg. There is no current vertically launched version, although some years ago effort in that direction was reported; the new cruisers and destroyers equipped with VLSs carry canisters. Harpoon can also be fired from the standard Mk 11/13 and Mk 26 Tartar/Standard launcher and from the standard ASROC "pepperbox," as well as from standard submarine torpedo tubes. Some export customers use truck-mounted Harpoon as a coast-defense weapon.

Combat use: Gulf of Sidra (March 1986: three engagements, five fired, three ships sunk), Persian Gulf (April 1988: two engagements, four fired, two ships sunk), Desert Storm (one engagement, one fired, one ship sunk [by Royal Saudi Navy]). Seven SLAM were fired.

The 1988 U.S. inventory goal was 4023; the 5000th missile was delivered 2 December 1988, more than 5400 having been ordered (40% for export). The 1000th Sub-Harpoon was delivered

SLAM at the 1995 Navy League show. The visible difference from Harpoon is the EO nose. (Author)

about August 1993. At the end of FY91 the U.S. goal was 3698 missiles. FY88 unit price was $1.27M, up from $773,500 in FY86. Recent U.S. procurement: FY83, 221; FY84, 315; FY85, 354; FY86, 395; FY87, 96; FY88, 124; FY89, 119; FY90, 190; FY91, 167 (end of production for the U.S. Navy). FY92 production contracts: 133 SLAM, 122 Harpoon for foreign customers. FY93: 90 SLAM for the U.S. Navy, 103 Harpoon for export.

SLAM (AGM-84E) is a modified Harpoon for long-range (120 nm) precision ground attack, using a Maverick IIR seeker and a Walleye II data link (off the shelf components selected for quick development). It is lengthened to 175.2 in (compared to 151.7 in for Harpoon 1C) and weight increases to 1364 lb (compared to 1224 for Harpoon 1C). The missile flies a complex path toward the target under inertial guidance, arriving within 16 m of its predicted position. For the last 60 sec of flight, it is controlled via its data link (using an AWW-13 pod on the guiding airplane). SLAM was adopted in 1988 as the interim U.S. precision-attack missile (in preference to the Air Force AGM-130), pending availability of the stealthy TSSAM (AGM-137); when that program was canceled in February 1995, SLAM became more important. A contract for 14 SLAMs was awarded on 1 February 1988; the first production missile was delivered on 3 November 1988.

Like Tomahawk, SLAM follows a complex flight path to its land target. It therefore requires a similar mission-planning process, for which no provision had really been made. Thus preproduction missiles, such as those fired during the Gulf War, each required 2 hr of planning, plus 30 min for typing into a prelaunch computer, 5 min to load data into a prelaunch data loader, and 5 min to load data into the missile itself. The prelaunch loader can accommodate up to 64 missions (in groups of four, corresponding to F/A-18 or A-6E capacity). ATWCS will combine Tomahawk and SLAM targeting (automating the latter) and will make for much faster operation.

The use of off-the-shelf components adds length and weight and reduces missile performance (for example, it must cruise in an inefficient nose-up attitude). The production version, which may be SLAM-ER (see below), will probably use more compact components to add fuel space. New SLAM guidance software introduced in 1992 allows launch at twice the previously specified altitude.

SLAM-ER (Extended Response), AGM-84H, is a new version proposed by McDonnell-Douglas in April 1992, work on which was funded under the FY94 program. Tomahawk pop-out wings (swept, in its case) increase range (by 50 to 100%) and maneuverability. A new penetrating cylindrical titanium-cased warhead with a tapered front end (as in Tomahawk Block III) doubles penetration. More compact guidance electronics (mission computer, inertial measurement, GPS receiver, and air data computer are all integrated into a single Guidance Navigation Unit [GNU] with improved performance) leave room for more fuel or a longer warhead. Memory can now be upgraded at relatively low-level maintenance sites. A multichannel GPS set is installed. An improved data link increases standoff control range 50% and is also more resistant to jamming. Improved software makes it easier for aircrew to direct the missile onto the aim point, and mission planning is now integrated with ATWCS and TAMPS. Special software makes it easier to switch targets just before launch to deal with pop-up targets. The missile is also made more survivable: it can follow terrain better, and its IIR seeker is hardened against laser countermeasures. The dome covering the seeker is also better protected against rain damage. A new search-while-track capability enables the operator to search for a better (e.g., more distinct) aim point without breaking lock on an existing one. Length is 172.0 in, slightly shorter than SLAM; wing span is 95.6 in.

SLAM-ER at the 1995 Navy League show, with its Tomahawk-type wings spread. The nose is slab-sided, rather than round as in SLAM. (Author)

SLAM was conceived as an air weapon, but it was successfully fired by the cruiser *Lake Champlain* (using a Harpoon booster) on 26 June 1990, using a LAMPS III helicopter for guidance. In 1995 ship-launched SLAM was included in the Naval Surface Fire Support demonstration program, with two launches (guided by an F/A-18 and by a LAMPS III helicopter). McDonnell-Douglas calls this version Sea-SLAM, and is also trying to excite interest in a VLS version (provision for which would apply to Harpoon).

Combat use: Early in the Gulf War a pair of preproduction SLAMs launched by an A-6E from the *Kennedy* (and guided by an A-7E) hit a hydroelectric power plant; the second missile flew through the hole made by the first. Some later shots were less successful, probably because guidance was by old AWW-9 Walleye pods rather than the more reliable new AWW-13, which was not yet available.

SLAM procurement: FY87, 14 (R&D); FY88, 26; FY89, 72; FY90, 125; FY91, 167; FY92, 110; FY93, 90; FY94, 75 (plus 6 for Reserves); FY95, 58 plus 17 R&D missiles (total 75); FY96, 75. In all, 604 had been delivered as of July 1994, and 737 (not counting FY96 missiles) had been delivered or were on order as April 1996. Current unit cost is $827K. Early in 1995 the Navy let a contract to develop kits to modify SLAMs into SLAM ER. The missile is to be approved for limited-rate production in 1997, and for full production in 1999. Plans (April 1996) called for 23 missiles in FY97, 23 in FY98, and 81 in FY99.

Grand SLAM is a SLAM-ER derivative offered to the UK (RAF) for its CASOM requirement.

Users: Australia (P-3C, Sub-Harpoon, destroyers, frigates), Brazil (18 ordered FY90, reportedly Sub-Harpoons), Canada (CP-140s, destroyers; submarines fitted to fire Sub-Harpoon but none bought), Denmark (*Nils Juels*, *Willemoes*, *Flyvefisken* classes; coast batteries became operational September 1994), Egypt (Sub-Harpoon in rebuilt submarines, also *Descubierta* class), Greece (Sub-Harpoon in modernized submarines [16 UGM-84 bought] and in frigates and new P 100 class; Osprey 55s fitted for but not with it; reported 84 bought as of 1991), Germany (Type 122 and refitted *Adams* class), Indonesia (*van Speijk* class), Iran (Combattante class, all nine missiles delivered probably expended), Israel (Sub-Harpoon [four each in *Gal* and *Dolphin* class, reported in external tubes in latter], missile boats, aircraft [100 AGM-84A]), Italy (Sub-Harpoon on at least two *Sauro* class), Japan (P-3C, Sub-Harpoon [two to four on each of 14 submarines], missile destroyers, frigates), Korea (*Sumner*- and *Gearing*-class destroyers [quadruple launchers], two *Ulsan*-class frigates [two twin launchers each], five PSMM Mk 5 attack boats [two quadruple launchers each], three coast batteries bought 1987; is currently interested in the air-launched version; reportedly had bought 172 as of 1991; this included 52 bought in 1988, 28 AGM-84), Kuwait (F/A-18s), Netherlands (destroyers and frigates; plan to arm P-3Cs dropped; submarines can fire Sub-Harpoon, but none were bought), New Zealand (may have been bought for P-3K), Pakistan (Sub-Harpoon ordered but not delivered; 44 surface missiles bought; on destroyer *Shahjahan* and probably on Type 21s), Portugal (MEKO 200 class), Saudi Arabia (PCG and PGG classes [108 RGM-84A]), Singapore (*Victory* and FPB 45 class), Spain (F/A-18, *Perry*, *Descubierta*, *Baleares* classes, and four coast-defense batteries; 55 bought before 1985, 25 ordered 1985 for delivery 1987–90), Thailand (PFMM Mk 16 class), Turkey (MEKO frigates [for which 40 were offered 1990], some destroyers, FPB 57 class; Sub-Harpoon to be in new Type 209/1400 submarines [85 as of 1991]), United Kingdom (Nimrods, Sub-Harpoon, Type 22 Batch III and Type 23 frigates), United States (P-3C, F/A-18, F-16, A-6E, S-3B aircraft, Sub-Harpoon, cruisers, destroyers, frigates), Venezuela (*Constitucion* class; 18 bought 1989). The U.S. Air Force modified 30 B-52Gs to fire 85 of the 222 air-launched missiles originally ordered by Iran (few of which were delivered), but these bombers were retired in 1993–94. The Air Force is now modifying about half the 94 B-52Hs to restore this and other nonnuclear capabilities. Air Force F-16s based at Misawa in Japan can carry Harpoon, but it is not clear whether they are normally provided with this weapon. Harpoon has been withdrawn from *Hamilton*-class Coast Guard cutters fitted to fire it. During the Cold War, Norwegian P-3s were provided with Harpoons under a "black" program; they were returned in 1989.

The Danish missiles came from scrapped frigates. They are organized into two coastal batteries, each of two trucks (four Harpoon each) plus a control center. Their Terma C3 system is linked to the overall C3 system for the Baltic. McDonnell-Douglas has a contract to upgrade all Danish Harpoon control systems to SWG-1A(V) standard, to be compatible with Block 1C (-84C) missiles.

♦ **Hellfire (RBS 17; AGM-114)**

Dimensions: 7 × 64 in; span 14.25 in
Weight: 108.5 lb for AGM-114F (compared to 99.6-lb for AGM-114B)
Warhead: 14.8-lb shaped charge
Propulsion: Solid-fuel rocket
Speed: Mach 1.3
Range: 4.3 nm

This laser-guided missile is the primary armament of Marine Corps AH-1W Sea Cobras and will arm upgraded LAMPS helicopters (SH-60R); it is also used abroad for coast defense and as a patrol-boat weapon. Hellfire I uses an analog autopilot and a minimum-smoke motor. It can be locked on either before or after launch, fired in ripple mode (one launcher, several designators) or in rapid-fire mode (one every 8 sec, a single designator shifting targets as missiles hit). AGM-114B is the Navy/Marine Corps version, with a safing/arming device to protect against electro-

Hellfire (RBS 17) in its coast-defense version. The missile weighs 48 kg (with its container, 71 kg). (Bofors)

magnetic interference. AGM-114C was an abortive experimental version with a tandem warhead, to defeat reactive armor. AGM-114D/E (E for the Navy, with the safing/arming device) were abortive experimental versions with a digital autopilot.

The Army placed AGM-114 (with a tandem warhead) into production, but the Navy did not buy the equivalent AGM-114G version. This version adds length and weight.

Both services are to buy the improved Hellfire II (AGM-114K) or HOMS (Hellfire Optimized Missile System); it will arm the SH-60Rs (they may use AGM-114B as interim armament). This version, work on which began in 1989, has a digital autopilot, which keeps the missile on course if it temporarily loses sight of the laser spot (for example, in cloud). The autopilot offers more maneuvering power and a steeper dive. Because it is programmable, it is adaptable to a high-speed airplane. Hellfire II accommodates the new tandem warhead within the original Hellfire length and weight. An improved seeker introduced in 1991 is hardened against signal loss due to dust, smoke, or haze, or to laser countermeasures. This version uses an electronic safing/arming device, which incorporates protection against electromagnetic interference. The Army's Longbow version (AGM-114L), which is not used by the Navy, has a mm-wave radar seeker.

The Swedish RBS-17 (Swedish Shore Defense System, SSDS) uses a special blast-fragmentation warhead. An air-to-air anti-helicopter version was tested in July 1990. New fire-and-forget passive seekers are under development.

During the Gulf War, this missile was used to destroy the Iraqi border radar stations, as well as numerous Iraqi vehicles and fixed installations (in all, 2876 were fired, mostly by the Army).

Hellfire is made by Rockwell and by Lockheed Martin (AGM-114K version).

Each SH-60B or SH-60R helicopter will be able to carry a 4-rnd launcher on the third stores station on its port side, which is also used for the Penguin missile. This program responded to Gulf War experience: the Navy had to rely on Army or British helicopters to attack Iraqi fast-attack boats. The first Navy H-60 Hellfire shots were fired on 2 November 1994, using a Marine Corps MULE laser designator to hit a seaborne target at a range of about 3.5 km. In all, 56 SH-60B Block I kits (down from a planned 90; one report has 56 helicopters fitted to take Hellfire, but only 46 kits on order, so they must be cross-decked) are to be made under the FY96 and later programs, for introduction in FY98; all SH-60Rs are to be Hellfire-capable. The laser designator is a modified Dark Star, the type used in the F-117 fighter, integrated with the new AAS-44(V) FLIR. This modification is part of an Enhanced Weaponization Kit, which also includes replace-

ment of the current M60 machine gun by a 7.62mm M240. The FLIR is repositioned to the helicopter's nose, providing much better video. The laser is not limited to Hellfire; it can designate for other laser-guided weapons, including shells fired from ships.

Hellfire II was part of the abortive SWPS program, but in March 1994 the Navy formally eliminated it from the draft RFP, asking only that tenders leave 700 lb plus space for a future SSM, to be determined. Then SWPS died, at least for a time.

Hellfire entered service in January 1985.

As of February 1992, the unit price of Hellfire was $50,500. U.S. Navy/Marine Corps procurement: FY84, 219; FY85, 438; FY86, 1304; FY87, none; FY88, 1393; FY89, 1000; FY90, 1098; FY91, 1198; FY92, none; FY93, 1000 (upgraded version); FY94, 1931.

Users (naval): Israel (*Dvora*-class patrol boats), Norway (coast defense ordered 1996 via Bofors), Sweden (RBS 17, on coast and on board patrol boats), Taiwan (on board helicopters which can be carried on shipboard, also possibly from shipboard Chaparral launchers), United States (LAMPS III Block Upgrade helicopters). Swedish RBS 17s replace old French SS 11s (25 battalions instead of the old 32; missiles are tripod-mounted both ashore and on board Stridsbat 90 assault boats. The missile has a new Bofors downward-pointing blast-fragmentation warhead and a modified autopilot. The designator is El-Op's PAL (portable advanced laser). The first missiles were delivered in 1989. Norway uses the same systems, buying them from Bofors under a 1996 contract. They replace old German 105mm guns covering minefields and are used both ashore and on board Swedish-built combat boats.

U.S. Marine Corps AH-1W Sea Cobras also carry TOW (BGM-71) missiles, which might be effective against small patrol boats.

◆ Maverick (AGM-65)

Dimensions: 12 in × 98 in × 28.5 in (span)
Weight: 635 lb
Warhead: 300 lb
Propulsion: Thiokol TX-481 dual-thrust solid-fuel rocket
Speed: Supersonic
Range: About 14 nm

Data are for the AGM-65F Navy IIR version.

The Hughes Maverick is now the standard U.S. short-range tactical standoff missile; JSOW is the planned successor. Reported average CEP is less than 4 ft. This missile has been very widely exported, combat use including South Vietnam, the Iran-Iraq War (by Iran), and the Gulf War. During the Gulf War, Air Force A-10s often used the seeker of the IIR version as a FLIR, with mixed results. More than 5100 Mavericks were fired during the Gulf War. Claimed results: 80 to 90% success rate for TV and IR versions, 60% for laser-guided versions.

Development began in 1965, the prime contractor (Hughes) being selected in 1968. The missile first flew in 1969; it entered service with the Air Force in January 1973. The IIR version was first successfully fired on 18 November 1975.

Versions are: AGM-65A, the original television-guided missile (over 30,000 made); -65B, the extended-range television version with scene magnification; -65C, a laser-guided version (-65E produced instead); -65D, the Air Force IIR version, with a 125-lb warhead (60,697 made); -65E, the Marine Corps laser-guided version with a 300-lb blast/penetrating warhead and a reduced-smoke motor; -65F, the Navy IIR version with the -65E warhead and motor, for day/night attack against ship or shore targets; and -65G, the Air Force IIR version with the 300-lb warhead. The A- and B-versions weigh 462 lb; the D-version, 485 lb; and the E-version, 645 lb.

AGM-65F Mavericks under the wing of an A-6. (Grumman Aerospace)

Unit cost: AGM-65A/B, $50,000 in FY80 dollars (production ended May 1978); AGM-65D, $124,000 in FY85, $119,700 in FY86, $88,343 with competition in FY88; AGM-65E, $140,000 in FY84. Recent Navy procurement (IIR/laser): FY84, –/185; FY85, –/600; FY86, 195/1500; FY87, 248/–; FY88, 425/1300; FY89, 731/–; FY90, 560; FY91, 36. The FY87 suspension of laser Maverick production was to allow incorporation of a new fuze. Air Force purchases also ended in FY91, with 5855 missiles. In mid-1993 the AGM-65G production line was reopened to build export missiles: 274 for Turkey, 80 for Egypt, and 250 to be held by the Defense Security Assistance Fund against future sales.

Maverick was test-fired by a P-3, and P-3Cs operating over the Adriatic currently carry it. Maverick has also been launched by an S-3.

Hughes's proposed helicopter-launched Longhorn version apparently lost out to Hellfire in the competition to equip LAMPS helicopters.

Users: Denmark, Egypt, Germany, Greece, Iran, Italy, Israel, Jordan, Korea, Kuwait, Malaysia (50 for Hornets), Morocco, New Zealand, Pakistan, Portugal, Saudi Arabia, Singapore, Spain, Sweden, Switzerland, Taiwan, Thailand, Turkey, United States, Yugoslavia.

◆ Sea Ray

Dimensions: 8 × 118 in
Weight: 400 lb
Warhead: 150-lb fragmentation
Propulsion: Mk 78 solid-fuel rocket motor
Speed: Subsonic
Range: Ca. 7 km (7700 yd)

Texas Instruments announced in 1985 that it was developing this missile for an unnamed foreign customer, most likely South Korea. The missile can be fired from shipboard, from a helicopter, or from an airplane. Sea Ray uses the Paveway III laser and guidance unit and the Shrike Mk 78 motor. The missile flies a ballistic path until the laser designator is switched on, about 10 sec before expected impact. Texas Instruments stated that during sea trials on board the customer's ships, a round hit the target at 7km range within 9 in of the nominal aim point.

Development began in 1981, and Sea Ray entered service, probably in South Korea, in 1987. Sea Ray was also the name of an abortive fiber-optic guided-naval-missile program.

◆ Standard Missile

See Antiaircraft Warfare section.

◆ Sidearm (AGM-122A)

Dimensions: 5 × 113 in; span 24.8 in
Weight: 195 lb
Warhead: 10-lb blast-fragmentation
Propulsion: Single-stage rocket
Speed: Mach 2.3
Range: About 18,000 yd (high-altitude delivery)

Sidearm is a low-cost self-protection antiradar missile, to be carried by Marine Corps helicopters and Harriers. A converted AIM-9C (semiactive radar-homing version of Sidewinder), Sidearm was developed by the Naval Weapons Center (China Lake), which modified the original narrow-band passive seeker to broader-band purely passive operation and also modified the original target detection device for air-to-ground operation. The

original rocket motor and wings were retained, but the canard fins were modified. Sidearm executes a programmed pitch-up shortly after launch, so that the missile can be carried by a very low-flying airplane.

Procurement: FY86, 885; FY87, 256; FY88, 276; none in FY89 (although continued production had been requested). The last missile was delivered in 1990. On 25 April 1988 a Sidearm successfully attacked an armored vehicle.

◆ SLAM (AGM-84E/H)

See Harpoon.

◆ Tomahawk (BGM-109)/Air Hawk

Dimensions: 20.9 × 252 in (submarine launch capsule diameter: 21 in [Teflon-covered stainless steel] for missiles fired from torpedo tubes, 23.5 in [fiberglass-graphite] for those fired from VLS)
Weight: 2650 lb (without booster)
Warhead: Various (see below)
Propulsion: F-107-WR-400 turbojet sustainer
Range: 250 nm for TASM, 675 nm for the conventional land-attack weapon, 472 nm for the land-attack submunition weapon, and 1350 nm for nuclear version

Tomahawk is now the standard U.S. ship-launched strike weapon for use against land and sea targets. It is likely to form the basis for a variety of new weapons, and it may also appear in air-launched form, as a replacement for the abortive TSSAM. As an antiship weapon, Tomahawk was responsible for the development of U.S. OTH-T techniques, culminating in the Copernicus and JOTS/NTCS-A systems. Land-attack Tomahawk has induced a similar revolution in distributing satellite and other intelligence images of targets deep inland.

As of 1995, U.S. submarines no longer carried antiship Tomahawks. Harpoon provided standoff antiship capability. Since Harpoon occupies roughly the same space on board as a Tomahawk, this suggests that antiship Tomahawks were needed for conversion into land-attack missiles. Tomahawk will return to the antiship role with the advent of Block IV (see below). All antiship Tomahawks have been withdrawn for conversion to land-attack versions. The strategic version, TLAM-N, was withdrawn from surface ships under a Presidential Order of 27 September 1991. At that time about 100 were at sea and another 267 were in storage; all can be restored to ships within 24–36 hr.

Tomahawk was conceived as a strategic weapon not covered by existing arms-control treaties and, therefore, as an initiative the United States could take to counter growing Soviet strategic forces. In this sense its main revolutionary effect was to frustrate existing Soviet attempts to track and thus to neutralize U.S. naval strike forces, since Tomahawk could be very widely distributed. The initial DoD cruise-missile studies were ordered in 1973, and it is reported that then–Secretary of State Henry Kis-

Sidearm carried by an attack helicopter. (U.S. Navy)

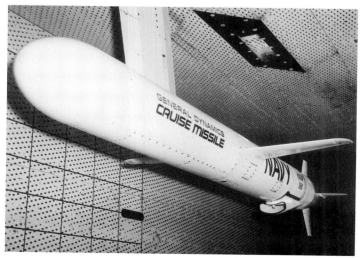

This early Tomahawk flight vehicle clearly shows the missile's configuration, with its air intake extended. (General Dynamics)

singer favored the weapon as a bargaining chip in SALT II negotiations. Tomahawk then acquired a life of its own, and critics of arms procurement have cited cruise missiles as examples of how a bargaining chip can become a permanent fixture of military forces. The Carter administration resisted deploying this strategic cruise missile for fear that it would breach the observability requirement built into the SALT II treaty. Late in 1980, however, the decision to deploy the tactical version of Tomahawk opened the way to deployment of the strategic version.

General Dynamics won a fly-off against LTV's ZBGM-110; more recently, McDonnell-Douglas has been selected as a second source, for competitive annual bidding. The first guided Tomahawk flight was in December 1976.

Tomahawk Block I comprised two versions, the nuclear land-attack TLAM-N (BGM-109A) and the antiship TASM (BGM-109B). BGM-109A employs a combination of TERCOM (terrain-comparison) and inertial guidance (TAINS, TERCOM-aided Inertial Navigation System) and an LC 4516A computer with two 16-kbyte core memories (which is not hardened against EMP). BGM-109B employs the Harpoon seeker (DSQ-28) and computer (IBM 4Pi) and the Bullpup B 1000-lb warhead. Both use the Williams 600-lb-thrust F107-WR-400. The related land-based BGM-109G was scrapped under the INF Treaty.

Surface ships carry Tomahawk in the Mk 41 vertical launcher and, in a few cases, in four-missile armored box launchers. Submarines carry Tomahawk either in torpedo tubes or in special vertical tubes. The supporting weapons system is Mk 36/37 (submarine/surface-ship vertical launcher); the shipboard FCS is SWG-2/3. Reportedly, the chief limitation in Tomahawk land-attack operation is the cumbersome mission planning, including the difficulty of estimating the missile's time of arrival over a target. See the APS (Afloat Planning System) entry.

The effective range of the antiship version is limited by the need to search for the target at the end of what may be a lengthy flight. The effect of the ship-tracking (and projection) algorithms is to minimize this dangerous search period. Antiship Tomahawks can discriminate among groups of ships by detecting their characteristic radar emissions, using preprogrammed Passive Identification/Passive Direction Finding (PI/DF) equipment; the four flush-mounted antennas feed a microwave receiver. An Improved Sea-Skimming Variant (ISSV) was operationally tested in December 1985 through May 1986.

Block II is a conventional land-attack missile, TLAM-C (BGM-109C): the unitary warhead Block IIA (approved for production FY86) and the bomblet-dispensing Block IIB (sometimes called TLAM-D or BGM-109D, operational FY88). In these versions, TAINS is supplemented by DSMAC (Digital Scene-Matching Correlation), in which the scene viewed optically (using a strobe for night vision) is compared to an on-board digital map, for better accuracy near the target. This is still not a terminal sensor of any kind: these missiles fly to assigned points in space rather than to imaged targets. This version has a more powerful computer, an LC 4516C hardened against EMP, with two 32-kbyte core memories and 128 kbytes of semiconductor RAM.

Block IIA has a preselectable terminal maneuver (straight run or pop-up) and can have over-water waypoints. Block IIB carries 24 bomblet packages (six each in two, seven each in 22; all are BLU-97/B combined-effect bomblets) which it can drop on several separate targets.

Block III is an extended-range version using GPS to supplement TAINS, and with an improved DSMAC 2A which uses a wider range of imagery and as many as 50% more scenes for a final fix; it is also expected to be less sensitive to seasonal and day/night variations in landscape. McDonnell-Douglas received the Block III contract in 1988. The new computer in this version probably has twice the memory of its predecessor. The new insensitive-munitions unitary warhead (WDU-36B) has been cut to 750 lb to increase fuel capacity 50% (range increases from 700 to 1000 nm); it has a programmable-delay fuze for better penetration. A new F107-WR-402 engine offers 10% more thrust (660 lb; 20% more in hot weather) and 3% better fuel economy. It solves a Desert Storm problem: missiles might be unable to negotiate hilly country on hot days. The engine is also reliable

enough to double recertification time to 6 yr. A new Mk 111 booster permits submarine-launched weapons to carry the same fuel load as current surface-launched missiles. All the Block III modifications are made when missiles arrive for maintenance every 3 or 4 yr. Desert Storm supplemental funds accelerated Block III into service.

Block III first flew on 13 February 1991, and entered service in 1993–94 together with the Block III version of the Tomahawk WCS, TMPCU, and APS. It was first used in combat in September 1995, when 13 missiles attacked Serbian SAM positions in Bosnia, in support of NATO air strikes. Block IIIA will incorporate some planned Tomahawk IV systems, notably the inertial guidance system.

A Precision Strike Tomahawk initiative responds to the Clinton administration's desire to keep missiles that miss their urban targets from inflicting unnecessary damage. It was ordered after three missiles of the 22 launched against Iraq in June 1993 missed the intelligence compound altogether (16 hit targets, three hit inside, three hit in a residential area outside). The idea is to upgrade planning software so mission planners can define flight paths that reduce the chance that strays will hit civilians, and will also help reduce potential errors at mission planning time. Each missile will monitor its course accuracy and systems status while in flight, to determine whether it is likely to reach a target and whether it is likely to strike its intended aim point. If the target is large and the estimated system error is relatively small (large enough to miss the aim point, but small enough still to place the missile inside the target area), the software might redirect the missile to an alternative aim point within the target. If the expected error is too large, the software might divert the missile to a preplanned uninhabited place, then fly the missile harmlessly into the ground. This project was planned for completion in FY96, with modified missiles available about mid-1996.

Hughes's Block IV (the Tomahawk Base Line Improvement Program, or TBIP) is conceived as a single weapon, the Tomahawk Multi-Mode Missile (TMMM) usable against land or sea targets. The key is an imaging seeker: the stored image can be either a shore target or a ship. TBIP will be the first land-attack version with a seeker. GPS will now guide the missile to a point at which the target should be within the seeker's field of view. The seeker will be either a FLIR or a mm-wave radar. Early estimates are that using a seeker will at least halve the usual miss distance. Autonomous terminal guidance would allow it to decide to attack a specific target in the target area, for example, an airplane whose position was not definitely known when the missile was launched. The combination of seeker and GPS should drastically reduce mission planning time (the goal is 1 hr), making missiles far more responsive to changes in the tactical situation, for example, to cueing by JSTARS aircraft. There is considerable interest in using the SLAM AWW-13 data link, which has a range of several hundred miles. It might provide information on how well the missile was carrying out its mission (so that multiple weapons would not have to be fired at the same target), and it might also be used to switch targets en route (if the seeker were provided with multiple images). Ultimately the link might provide video, for aim-point adjustment. SAR or LADAR (active IIR at about 10 microns) may be substituted for the currently planned FLIR. TBIP will also have antijam GPS (Block III has GPS, but not the antijam version).

Two versions of TBIP are planned: TMMM, with the Block III WDU-36B warhead, and a hard-target penetrator, THTP, with a warhead probably similar to that of SLAM-ER.

Some features of Tomahawk Block IV were tested during a spring 1994 flight from USS *Merrill*. A Block III missile was fitted with a special camera, which transmitted real-time imagery to ground stations in California, Nevada, and Washington, D.C., via a Hughes commercial satellite. On the basis of camera video, the missile dropped two-thirds of its submunitions on one target, then flew on to bomb another before entering a terminal dive.

The single-missile concept is attractive because Tomahawk has split into so many variants, some not even distinguished by Block or letter suffix: three TLAM variants, two baselines (Block

II and III), differing fuel loads, two engines, various warhead payloads, surface VLS and ABL, and subsurface TTL (torpedo tube-launched) and CLS (canister launching system). Too, the urgent demand for land-attack missiles has squeezed ship-attack Tomahawks out of operational service. The single-variant missile would restore a ship-attack capability.

In May 1996 the Navy decided to delay Block IV in order to buy more Block III missiles, and perhaps also to revive the remanufacture program (see procurement, below). On 13 May Hughes was issued a 90-day stop-work order. A more modest Block IVA will incorporate the antijam GPS receiver and a satellite link, but the new warhead and the IIR sensor will not enter service until 2004 (Block IV had been scheduled for service in FY00). There was some hope that money saved in this way will pay for 100 more missiles in FY98 and perhaps for 200 in each of FY99 and FY00.

As used in the Gulf War, Tomahawk was reportedly extremely successful, 51 of the first 52 fired hitting their targets. Hits included several within Baghdad, including one that clipped a television tower in half. Reportedly, about 100 Tomahawks were fired as precursors to the manned air strike on the first night of the war. In all, 291 Tomahawks were fired during the war with Iraq. It was reported in April 1991 that Tomahawk hit 80% of fixed Iraqi targets. Overall, about 85% of all Tomahawks reportedly hit and damaged their targets (95% launched successfully). Tomahawks were used against Baghdad, particularly when the weather was too bad to permit manned attacks with visually guided bombs. Often the Tomahawk attacks were timed so that the missiles would impact about 1 hr before a satellite passed over the target and assessed the damage.

It was reported that at the outbreak of war on 16 January 1991 the total inventory of land-attack conventional Tomahawks was about 900 BGM-109Cs and 100 BGM-109Ds (bomblet version). By mid-February missiles had been fired by both of the battleships in the area (*Missouri* and *Wisconsin*), by 11 other surface ships, and by at least two attack submarines. They were launched from the the Persian Gulf, the Red Sea, and the Mediterranean.

For submarines, 60 TLAM-C were converted on very short notice (by McDonnell-Douglas) to a maximum fuel configuration, so that they could reach their targets.

Targeting limitations became evident in the Gulf War. Due to lack of TERCOM maps, no missions at all could be flown before 13 August, and the 17 January 1991 attack could not have been executed before December/January. TERCOM map requirements did not begin to level off until about October, and DSMAC image requirements actually rose more steeply after mid-December. Missions required always exceeded resources.

Tomahawk continued to be fired in the Gulf after the end of the Gulf War. On 17 January 1993 a total of 45 missiles were fired at a nuclear facility at Zaafaraniyah, destroying 13 of 16 buildings. Missiles came from destroyers and cruisers in both the Gulf and the Red Sea. Iraq claimed that eight missiles had been shot down, and one damaged missile hit a hotel in Baghdad. Similarly, in June 1993, 22 missiles were fired at an Iraqi secret-police headquarters, destroying it, in retaliation for the Iraqi plot to kill ex–President George Bush.

In 1995 Hughes displayed a new employment concept, TSTAR (Tomahawk Stops the Advancing Regiments), which had been proposed by the Navy cruise-missile program office. It is an antiarmor version of Block IV carrying guided bomblets: 6 BLU-108 sensor-fuzed weapons (SFW) or 14 Brilliant Anti-Tank Munitions (BAT) or 9 Wide Area Munitions (WAM). The data link would be Link 16.

Procurement: FY83, 51; FY84, 124; FY85, 180; FY86, 249; FY87, 324; FY88, 475; FY89, 510; FY90, 400; FY91, 678 (including Gulf War Supplemental); FY92, 176; FY93, 402; FY94, 216; FY95, 274; FY96, 107; plans: FY97, 120; FY98, 100; none thereafter. Through August 1991, 2207 missiles had been delivered. Numerous missiles were to have been remanufactured to Block III standard. However, in November 1992 it was announced that new Block III missiles would be bought in FY93/98; remanufacture would be limited to Block IV, beginning in FY98. That

would save 48% in the unit lifetime of each missile. Planned inventory, as of 1991: 2698 in 1993, 2981 in 1994, 3147 in 1995, 3449 in 1996, 3700 in 1997. As of February 1992 unit cost was $2.02M.

In July 1995 the Royal Navy announced that it would buy Tomahawks to equip its nuclear-attack submarines. Cost, as reported in mid-1995, was $288M, and the missiles are to enter service in 1998. Presumably these missiles would be used largely to destroy enemy air defenses and thus as a force multiplier for the small number of Sea Harrier and Harrier strike aircraft on board British carriers. More recently the Royal Australian Navy has shown interest in Tomahawk to arm its new *Collins*-class submarines.

Hughes unsuccessfully prepared a modified version, Air Hawk or J-Hawk, for both JSSAM and the British CASOM.

◆ Walleye (AGM-62)

Dimensions: 18 × 159 in; span 51 in
Weight: 2340 lb
Warhead: 2000 lb
Speed: Glide bomb
Range: Maximum 20 nm (minimum 1 nm)

Martin-Marietta's EO bomb entered production in 1966; many were used in Vietnam, and a few in the Gulf. In July 1994 it was reported that the Navy wanted to dispose of surviving Walleyes, but no formal decision was taken, and they remain in the inventory, presumably as a war reserve.

Walleye. Note the television nose (covered until flight) and the windmill generator at the tail. (U.S. Navy)

UNGUIDED BOMBS AND AIR-LAUNCHED ROCKETS

All U.S. and British naval nuclear bombs and nuclear depth bombs have been withdrawn from service.

FRANCE

◆ Bombs

A Super Étendard carries 6 × 250-kg or 4 × 400-kg free-fall or retarded bombs. Typical dimensions are 273 × 2253 mm (10.75 × 88.7 in) or 324 × 2121 mm (12.75 × 83.5 in) for 250 kg, and 403 × 2195 mm (15.9 × 86.4 in) for 400 kg. Nuclear gravity bombs have been retired in favor of the ASMP missile.

Durandal/CBU-15 is not used by any navy (and not by any French air arm). The standard French runway-buster is the Brandt bomblet.

◆ Dispenser

The Super Étendard can carry an Alkan 530 bomblet dispenser carrying two blocks, each with 20 74mm (2.9in) Thomson-Brandt grenades or cartridges in tubes facing sideways. Each cartridge is 74 × 214 mm (2.9 × 8.4 in) and weighs 2 kg (4.4 lb); each grenade is 70 × 190 mm (2.76 × 7.5 in) and weighs 1.6 kg (3.5 lb). Cartridges carry chaff and IR flares. Grenades are parachute-retarded antiarmor bomblets, which can penetrate 200 mm of armor.

The standard droppable bomblet dispenser is Matra's Belouga (366 × 3300 mm, tail span 550 mm, 305 kg), which carries 151 bomblets (each 66 mm dia, 1.3 kg). Minimum attack height is 60 m at a maximum of 550 kt, producing either a high-density short carpet (over 5000 sq m) or a low-density long carpet (over 10,000 sq m). Belouga is primarily an air force weapon, but Matra claims that it will be carried by naval Rafales. Of 4150 made, 70% were exported. This weapon can be carried by a Mirage F1.

♦ Rockets

Super Étendards carry Matra 155 pods (18 68mm [2.68in] rockets). This pod can also be carried by British Sea Harriers. First-generation rockets have unitary warheads (shaped-charge, blast-fragmentation, or chaff); second-generation ones have multidart warheads (antiarmor or illumination). Typical rocket dimensions are 68 × 910 mm (2.68 × 35.8 in), 5 or 6.2 kg (11 or 13.7 lb) for first generation; 68 × 1380 mm (2.68 × 54.3 in), 8.3 kg (18.3 lb) for second generation. Range is 1000–4000 m (1095–4375 yd).

RUSSIA

♦ Bombs

Naval aircraft carry gravity bombs as well as missiles. For example, naval Badgers dropped bombs in Afghanistan.

Russian bombs on display at the 1995 Paris Air Show: ODAB-500PM in the foreground, OFAB-500U in the middle, and RBK 500U PTAB bomblet dispenser in the background. (S. Zaloga)

An MBD3-U9-68 tandem triple-ejector rack under a Tu-22M Backfire bomber carrying 500-kg high-drag bombs, 1995. An empty rack can be seen in the background. This particular aircraft also had an AS-4 on an underwing pylon outboard of the empty triple-ejector rack. (S. Zaloga)

Published designations consist of a prefix indicating the bomb type and then the weight in kilograms. In each case the suffix AB means *aviatsionnaya bomba*. Standard types include:

High Drag (general purpose, FAB Series): FAB-8, -10, -15, -20, -25, -50, -110, -500, and -1000. Example: FAB-500M-54, 474 kg (201 kg HE), 450 × 1500mm.

Low-Drag (general purpose, FAB Series): FAB-100, -250, -500, -750, -1000. Examples: FAB-500M-62, 497 kg, 400 × 2430 mm; FAB-500 ShN (with pronounced boat-tail), 513 kg (221 kg explo-

sive), 450 × 2188 mm; FAB-500TS, 500 kg (108 kg explosive), 400 × 1500 mm (delayed action, to dig a 7.6m crater).

Thick-cased (to attack concrete): FAB-250TS and FAB-500TS.

Heat-resistant (to be carried by MiG-25 at very high speed): FAB-500T.

Until recently, the major modern HE bombs were: FAB-250M-54 (i.e., 1954 type), FAB-250M-62 (i.e., 1962 type), FAB-500M-54 and -62, FAB-1500M-54, FAB-3000M-54, FAB-5000M-54, and FAB-9000M-54. The largest weapons could be carried only by Tu-16s and Tu-95s.

Some modern 500-kg bombs have braking fins and programmable fuzes (for burst height), for dropping from low (150 m) and very low (50 m) altitude: FAB-500Sh and FAB-500ShN, respectively. FAB-500ShR splits into two warheads as it falls from low altitude.

Braking fin kits analogous to the U.S. Snakeye can be added to 100-, 250-, and 500-kg bombs of older designs. In some cases rockets are added to attack concrete (as in FAB-250RU-TD, the RU indicating the rocket booster). A published photograph shows a low-drag bomb being retarded by the Soviet equivalent of the U.S. ballute.

"F" means *fugasnaya*, "demolition" (HE).

Fuel-air: ODAB-500P, -500PM. "ODAB" means *ob'emno-detoniyushchaya* ("area detonation"); these bombs are considered nearly 3 times as effective as HE bombs of similar size. This prefix may also have been used for thin-case demolition bombs (ODAB-100, 250, 750, 1100).

Low-drag blast-fragmentation: OFAB-100M/MW, 100-120, -250-270, -250Sh, -250ShN. Examples: OFAB-100-120, 120 kg, 273 × 1060 mm; OFAB-250-270, 266 kg, 320 × 1420 mm. "OFAB" means *oskolochno-fugasnaya*, "fragmentation/HE." Some have telescopic fuzes that detonate the bomb when it is still 1.5 m off the ground, for greater fragmentation effect.

Concrete penetrators: BetAB-250 and -500. Example: BetAB-500ShP, which has both a parachute and a rocket booster, to achieve the best attack angle: 424 kg, 325 × 2805 mm, penetrates 550 mm. There is also an M62 penetration bomb (500 kg; also exists in a 250-kg version). "Bet" means *betonoboynaya*, "concrete-piercing."

Napalm (low-drag): PLAB-250, -500. PLAB-150L is a reported designation for a 150-liter napalm bomb.

Incendiary (low-drag): ZAB-100, -250, -500, -750, -1000; there is also a ZAP-200 incendiary container weapon. "Z" means *zashigatelnaya*, "incendiary." Incendiary canister bombs are ZB-250ShM, -360, -500, -500Sh, and -500ShM.

Cluster bombs (single-purpose): RBK-180, -250, -500; there is also an RAB-120 carrying fragmentation bomblets. "RBK" means *razovaya bombovaya kasseta*, "single-use bomb cassette." RBK-250-275 AO-1SCh is 325 × 2119 mm, 275 kg, carrying 150 AO-1SCh bomblets (each 49 × 156 mm, 1.2 kg), effective over a 4800-sq-m area. Alternatively it may carry 60 A0-2.5RT antipersonnel bomblets (90 × 150 mm, 2.5 kg, each about as effective as a single 81mm mortar round) or 30 PTAB-2.5 antitank bomblets (68 × 362 mm, 2.8 kg with 0.45-kg warhead). There are also PTAB-1.5, -2, -5, and 5/1 antitank bomblets. RBK-500 AO 2.5RT (500 × 2500 mm, 504 kg) carries 108 bomblets, effective over a 6400-sq-m area. RBK-500 ShOAB-0.5 (450 × 1500 mm, 334 kg) carries 565 bomblets, effective over a 300 × 400m area. RBK-100 AO-25-33 carries three connected AO-25-33 bombs, which can be dropped together. There are also fragmentation bomblets (RAP-2.5, -3.5, -16) and incendiary bomblets (ZAB-2.5, 91 × 135 mm, 2.7 kg with 1.72-kg warhead). RRAB (no weight given) contains incendiary bomblets. AK-2 is a dispenser for 240 1-kg chemical bomblets (mustard and Lewisite). DPT-150 is a reported cluster-bomb designation (54 PTAB-1.5, 44 RAP-2.5, or 34 RAP-3.5).

Dispensers: PKPE-1 contains 29 70mm tubes, each containing two or three submunitions, launched laterally by a small charge;

the submunitions are either blast-fragmentation grenades or shaped charges (similar to the RPG-7 warhead). A helicopter or ground-attack airplane typically carries two, firing to each side. UPAE-1500 (listed in 1991 CFE documents) may be an analogous aircraft dispenser.

KMGU: Konteyner malogabaritnykh gruzov universalnyi, a "small universal cargo container"; that is, a multipurpose cluster-bomb carrier. Cassettes of eight bomblets each are arranged in container units, closed from below by pneumatically operated doors. When the bomb fires, the bomblets are scattered, as in the U.S. Rockeye. KMGU-2 (also sometimes called KMGU-500) is 460 mm (wide) × 545 mm (high) × 3700 mm and weighs 525 kg (170 kg without bomblets); it can be dropped from 30–1500 m at 700–1200 km/hr.

Chemical weapons: The Russians displayed high-drag bombs of World War II vintage and presumably developed modern low-drag equivalents. VAP-200 is a container bomb; VAP-1000 (BATT) is a dispenser (700 liters of hydrogen cyanide for low-altitude spraying). Examples of unitary bombs: KhAB-100-90P (Sarin), KhAB-250-150SM-46 (mixture of yperite and lewisite), KhAB-500-280S-M46 (thickened mixture of yperite and lewisite); and KhAB-500 (180 kg of phosgene). VAP is probably a general-dispenser designation, and newer weapons include an NOV-AB series of bombs containing nonpersistent toxic agents and an SOV-AB series containing persistent toxic agents.

◆ Nuclear Weapons

There are at least 14 types of tactical nuclear weapons, probably designated in an RN series. Most tactical aircraft are reportedly armed with relatively low-yield bombs (1–10-kT range); the higher-yield weapons (200 kT or more) are reportedly reserved to strategic bombers. Known bomb designations: RN-24 (10 kT, for Su-24), RN-28 (1 kT, for Su-24), RN-30 (strategic), RN-32 (strategic), RN-40 (strategic), RN-42 (strategic, 200 kT). Known bomb industrial designators, all for 1-kT weapons for Su-24: 6U57, 8U49, 8U63. There are also what seem to be Type (Izdeliye) designations: 244N (5-kT bomb for Su-24), 269A (20/40/60 kT warhead for Scud missile), 407N (bomb for Il-28D, obsolete). Some land-based missile warheads have AA designators, for example, AA-22 and AA-38 (3/10/20 kT for FROG-7 rocket), AA-52 (5/10/20/200 kT for FROG-7), AA-60 (similar yields for SS-21), and AA-75 (500 kT for SS-23). No designations of naval depth bombs are known, nor are these lists likely to be very complete. The data above also conflict with reports that at the end of the Cold War the standard weapon was a 1000-kg bomb with a 350-kT yield; a 700-kg bomb with a 250-kT yield was being introduced. Two older reported designations are TN-1200 and TN-1800.

◆ Rockets

Rockets are designated in an S-series. The generation of the 1950s comprised S-3, S-5, S-16, S-21, and S-24, of which S-5 and S-24 survive. The follow-on generation of the 1980s included S-8, S-13, and S-25.

S-5 (ARS-57): Introduced in 1955 to attack air and unarmored ground targets. S-5M was an improved version with an impact/time fuze. Variants: S-5K (KARS-57) with HEAT warhead, S-5P carrying chaff (three packets, time-released in sequence), S-5O illumination (15-sec burn, rate of descent 20 m/sec), S-5MO with prefragmented warhead (based on S-5M1, an improved S-5M), S-5KO with shaped-charge/fragmentation warhead (penetrates 150 mm), S-5KP/S-5KPB with piezoelectric fuze for quicker ignition (penetrates 250 mm), S-5I with IR decoy, S-5S with flechettes. S-5M1/K1/P1/O1 are improved versions of S-5M/K/P/O. Typical burnout speed is 620 m/sec (2034 ft/sec). S-5KO: 55 × 1006 mm, 4.5 kg with 0.263-kg warhead, range 1.8 km. S-5 is typically fired from a 16-tube UB-16 or from a 32-tube UB-32 introduced in the 1970s.

S-8: 80mm rockets with fold-out fins, prefragmentation/shaped-charge warheads, and instant-action piezoelectric fuzes. S-8A penetrates 300 mm of armor. Other versions: S-8B (68mm sub-caliber warhead, 400mm armor penetration); S-8D with fuel-air explosive; S-8M can be fitted with an inertial fuze which is more effective at low-impact angles; S-8O flare; S-8OF with fragmentation/HE warhead; S-8P chaff. Sometimes S-8A and -8B are lumped together as S-8KO: 80 × 1445 mm, 11.65 kg (3.6-kg warhead), range 2.0 km, penetrates 420 mm of armor. There may also be V-8 and V-8M, probably chemical rockets. These rockets are fired from 20-tube launchers on airplanes and helicopters.

S-13: 122mm folding-fin rocket with 90mm subcaliber warhead, intended to penetrate 1 m of concrete covered by 3 m of earth, or to destroy runways. It creates 1500–1800 fragments upon exploding. S-13T has a two-stage subcaliber warhead, to penetrate 1 m of concrete covered by 6 m of earth. Dimensions: 122 × 2892 mm, 67 kg (31.8-kg warhead), range 2.5 kg. S-13OF is a fragmentation/HE weapon with a buffer that explodes it before it hits the target: 68 kg, 32.2-kg warhead, 1800 fragments. S-13 is fired from a 5-rnd launcher, four of which are typically carried by a fighter-bomber.

S-24: 240mm rockets, which appeared 1960; specially developed for the Su-7B. Typically a fighter-bomber carries four (Su-24) or six (Su-17). S-24B is typical: 240 × 2330 mm, 235 kg (123-kg warhead, 4000 fragments), range 2.0 km. S-24B has four fixed fins, like those of the old U.S. 5in HVAR.

S-25: 260mm rockets with enlarged warheads. S-25O carries a 420mm fragmentation warhead (5500 fragments). S-25OF has a 340mm warhead (length is 3310 mm): 480 kg (190-kg warhead, attacks 1820-sq-m area), range 3.0 km. S-25OFM uses a remotely set electromechanical impact/delay fuze. Other versions: S-25M, S-25MD. Unlike the smaller S-24, which is launched like a conventional ASM, S-25 is carried in a single-shot O-25 pod. It has flip-out fins.

S-25L is a laser-guided version, operational since 1979, which uses the guidance system of the Kh-25ML missile (AS-12). Guidance more than doubles the rocket's effective range (from 3 to 7 km) and greatly improves accuracy (CEP is 5–6 m at 7 km, compared to 20–30 m at 3 km). S-25LD is an improved version (range 10 km) introduced in 1985. It was the version displayed at Moscow in 1992. Platforms: Su-17 (2 missiles), MiG-27 (2), Su-27 (4), Su-24 (6), Su-25 (8).

UNITED KINGDOM

◆ Bombs

The standard Sea Harrier load is three British Mk 13/18 or U.S. Mk 83 1000-lb bombs. During the Falklands War, Sea Harriers also delivered U.S.-supplied Paveway LGBs, reportedly using hand-held laser target-designators. Mk 13/18 is considerably fatter than the U.S. low-drag bombs but has a fairing for streamlining; like the Mk 80 series, it can be fitted with a parachute retarder.

◆ Carrier Bomb Light Stores

Sea Harriers carry BL 755 bomblet dispensers (419 × 2451 mm [16.5 × 96.5 in], 277 kg [611 lb] loaded), which carry 21 shaped-charge/fragmentation bomblets in each of seven compartments.

◆ Rockets

The standard Royal Navy rocket pod carries 19 2in rockets; Sea Harriers also carry the French Matra 155 pod and the U.S. LAU-69/A (2.75in FFAR).

UNITED STATES

For details of chemical bombs, see the 1991/92 edition.

◆ Low-Drag Bombs/Snakeye/Ballute (Mk 80 series)/ BLU-110/111

The Mk 80 series are the primary U.S. Navy bombs, developed in the late 1940s at the suggestion of Douglas Aircraft. All have the same aerodynamic shape (aspect ratio 8.5), the Mark number indicating the weight: Mk 81, 250 lb (9 × 76.1 in); Mk 82, 500 lb (10.8 × 90.9 in); Mk 83, 1000 lb (14 × 110.9 in); and Mk 84,

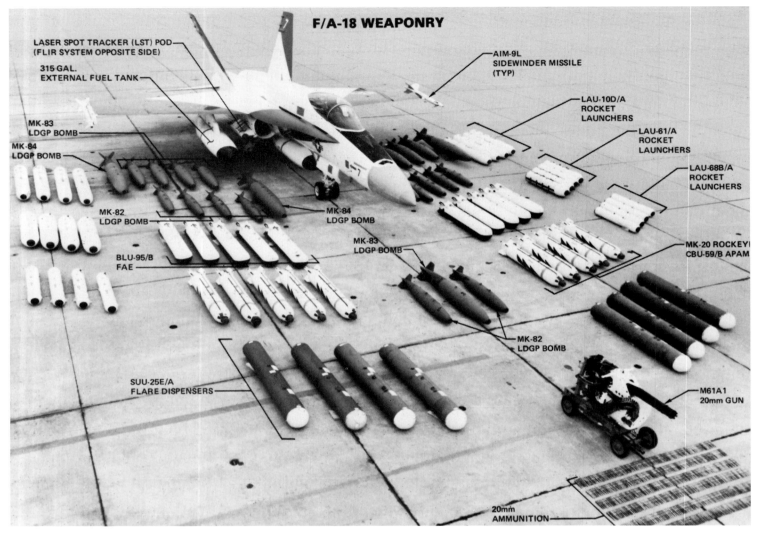

F/A-18 WEAPONRY

LASER SPOT TRACKER (LST) POD
(FLIR SYSTEM OPPOSITE SIDE)

315 GAL.
EXTERNAL FUEL TANK

MK-83
LDGP BOMB

MK-84
LDGP BOMB

MK-82
LDGP BOMB

BLU-95/B
FAE

SUU-25E/A
FLARE DISPENSERS

AIM-9L
SIDEWINDER MISSILE
(TYP)

LAU-10D/A
ROCKET
LAUNCHERS

LAU-61/A
ROCKET
LAUNCHERS

LAU-68B/A
ROCKET
LAUNCHERS

MK-84
LDGP BOMB

MK-83
LDGP BOMB

MK-20 ROCKEYE
CBU-59/B APAM

MK-82
LDGP BOMB

M61A1
20mm GUN

20mm
AMMUNITION

An F/A-18 can carry all the standard U.S. unguided weapons, which are shown here. LDGPs are low-drag (i.e., streamlined or "slick") general-purpose bombs. FAE is fuel-air explosive. (McDonnell-Douglas)

An AV-8B Harrier II drops Snakeye (Mk 82) retarded bombs. Note the fins opening. (McDonnell-Douglas)

2000 lb (18 × 154 in). Ninety percent of Navy bombs dropped in Vietnam were Mk 82s, with Mk 83s accounting for most of the rest. Mk 81 is no longer used. Mk 83 is the only bomb body currently in production for the Navy and Marines (it is not used by the Air Force). These weapons, or bombs of similar form, are very widely produced abroad.

The two main developments have been retarders and anti-cook-off casings. Retarders make low-level delivery practical (so the bombs will not explode directly under the airplane). The major current retarder is a set of four pop-out fins (Snakeye); but they are not always reliable. Snakeyes were originally designated in an SE series, as in Mk 82SE, with Mk 15 fins. Later retarded bombs were designated in an R series, as in Mk 82R with BSU-

86 fins. Goodyear developed an alternative, the inflatable Ballute (BSU-49 for Mk 82, BSU-50 for Mk 84) or air inflatable retard (AIR: BSU-86 for Mk 82, BSU-85 for Mk 83). BSU-33 is the standard conical tail for Mk 82, to make it spin as it falls.

Anticook-off bomb casings reduce the risk inherent in flight-deck fires. A conventional Mk 82 in a fuel fire will cook off in about 4 min. A coated Mk 82 will last 9 min and will then burn rather than explode, so that it can be tossed off the flight deck. BLU-110 and BLU-111 are insensitive-munitions (PBXN-109) versions of Mk 83 and Mk 82, respectively.

Mk 82 can be launched at 600 kt; the ballute version can be launched at up to 700 kt. Lethal antipersonnel radius for Mk 81/82/84, in ft: against standing personnel, 38/52/72 ft; against prone personnel, 27/33/55 ft; against personnel in foxholes, 9/12/23 ft.

Unit prices without fuzes (FY90): $498 for Mk 82 ($1100 for ballute version), $1871 for Mk 84 ($2874 for ballute version).

Several attempts to produce Mk 80 follow-ons (most recently ABF, the advanced bomb family) have proven fruitless. Instead, effort has gone into guidance devices, including inertially aided guidance.

◆ Hard-Target Penetrator

In mid-1992, Lockheed was selected over Rockwell for a 52-month technology demonstrator program for a hard-target penetrating bomb. It is developing a 1400-kg (2980-lb) rocket-boosted bomb small enough to be carried by an F/A-18 (and internally by B-2 and F-117, externally by F-16). Rocket boost allows the weapon to be dropped from lower altitude than the gravity-driven GBU-28 used at the end of the Gulf War.

BLU-109 (also known as I-2000) is a special 2000-lb hard-target penetrator, capable of passing through 6 ft of concrete. In current U.S. naval service, it is used only as the warhead of the GBU-24 LGB. This weapon is made by Lockheed. FY90 unit price was $12,640.

♦ **Napalm**

The current standard weapon is BLU-27 (750 lb, filled with 100 gal of Napalm-B).

♦ **2.75 in Folding-Fin Rockets (FFAR)/ARS**

These rockets, used mainly by Marine attack helicopters, are carried in 7-rocket (LAU-68 and -131 and Army M260) or 19-rocket (LAU-60, -61, -69, -91, and -130 and Army M261) pods. The Mk 4 (high-speed launch: 750-lb thrust for 1.2–1.4 sec, burnout speed 2300 ft/sec) and Mk 40 (low-speed launch, spin-stabilized by the rocket exhaust) motors are being replaced by the low-smoke Mk 66 WAFAR of the Hydra 70 family. Mk 66 adds about 40% in range, and weighs 13.6 lb compared to 11.4 lb for the earlier type. It provides 1300 lb of thrust, for a burnout speed of 3300 ft/sec. Accuracy is considerably improved by the higher spin speed of the motor, 600 rpm in the launcher and then 2100 rpm in flight. The Navy version, Mod 2, has a HERO filter. BEI is the sole producer of Hydra 70 (70 for the caliber, 2.75in or 70mm).

Improvements increased warhead weight from 6 lb to 10 lb by the mid-1960s, at which time range was 550–6500 yd (3750 yd effective). Standard production warheads: M151 (10-lb HE, white phosphorous, or fragmentation, equivalent to an 81mm mortar round), M156 (10-lb chemical), M229 (17-lb HE, white phosphorous, or fragmentation), M255 (585 or 2500 flechettes), M261 (multipurpose submunition, with nine shaped-charge bomblets), M264 (smoke), M267 (practice version of M261), and M274 (practice version of M151).

Lockheed's ARS (advanced rocket system) is the Navy program for an insensitive-munitions 2.75in rocket to replace Hydra 70 as well as the 5in Zuni. The new motor is to drive a rocket with a 10-lb warhead to a burnout speed of at least 1000 m/sec (3280 ft/sec) with a minimum effective range of 10,000 m (15,000 m in loft mode). Required missions match those of earlier rockets, including an ability to attack coastal shipping (penetrating 1 in of steel at 4 km, with a delayed-action fuze and incendiary effect) and antiarmor (penetrate 3 in of armor). Warheads will be interchangeable, and the fuze will be remotely settable (presumably via a 1553 bus) in flight. There will be two alternative launchers. ARS will first be carried by the AH-1W Cobra, then by the AV-8B and the F/A-18. ARS was first announced in 1989, to provide rockets by FY95, but there has been some slippage. The RFP was issued in May 1991, and Lockheed Missiles and Space/BEI won in July 1992. Unit cost is not to exceed $452 for 271,888 rockets over 10 yr. Release for full-rate production is expected in 1997. As an indication of the numbers involved, in June 1990 the Marines were 200,000 rockets (24%) below wartime inventory requirement.

The Army withdrew from the program in 1994, the Navy becoming lead service but guaranteeing that Army features would be retained. However, it seems unlikely that the Army, which needs huge numbers of rockets, will gladly pay the extra unit price for the insensitive munitions the Navy and Marines want.

♦ **Rockeye/Gator/Cluster Bombs**

Rockeye is an unguided bomblet-dispenser. Unlike most such dispensers, Rockeye is dropped by the airplane carrying it, so the airplane need not fly directly over its target. This weapon was developed by China Lake and was widely used during and after Vietnam. It was reported in 1988 that 40,000 of the 120,000 Rockeye II in U.S. service would be modernized. Their filling was to have been replaced by insensitive explosives, and the bomblet casings would be preframented. This program was awarded to the Tactical Systems Division of ISC Technologies (now Ferranti International Signal).

In 1993 Ferranti International and Thomson Brandt announced that Rockeye was being adapted to carry French BAP

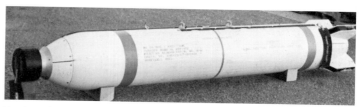

Rockeye (Cluster Bomb Mk 20 Mod 1). (U.S. Navy)

100 and BAT 120 runway-breaking munitions (four weapons per dispenser); tests began in 1994.

The basic Rockeye concept is well known, and many similar weapons are used by other forces.

Cluster bombs in naval service:

Rockeye II: Mk 20 bomb/Mk 7 dispenser (13.2 × 92 in, 94.5 in including fuze cover) carrying 247 Mk 118 shaped-charge AP bomblets; total weight 490 lb. Four fins pop out of the rear end of the casing (span 17.2 in closed, 34 in open). Minimum release altitude in level flight is 250 ft, or 100 ft in a toss delivery. The typical bomblet pattern from 500 ft forms a 30,000-sq-ft oval. The Mk 339 fuze is set before takeoff; it requires that the bomb be released at a specific speed and altitude for optimum dispersion.

CBU-55: Low-speed FAE weapon: three 100-lb BLU-73s, each 13.75 × 21 in (total bomb dimensions are 13.75 × 78.75 in). Each bomblet weighs 100 lb, including 72 lb of ethylene oxide; CBU-55 weighs 460 lb (500 lb nominal) and has a retarding drogue chute. CBU-55A has an external hardback, strengthening it so it can be carried by high-performance aircraft such as AV-8Bs.

CBU-59: Mk 7 Mod 3 dispenser, carrying 717 BLU-77 APAM bomblets.

CBU-72: FAE bomb, a modified CBU-55 with a Rockeye-type Mk 339 fuze. In this case the bomblets burst at an altitude of 30 ft, each creating a cloud 60 ft in dia and 8 ft thick, producing 300 psi overpressure when it explodes.

CBU-78: Mk 7 dispenser carrying 26 BLU-91 and 38 BLU-92 bomblets. Dimensions: 13 × 85 in (490 lb). This is the U.S. Navy version of the Gator air-delivered land-mine system. The dispenser is a modified Rockeye.

Bomblets:

BLU-73: 100-lb FAE bomb; see CBU-55 above.

BLU-77: 1.02-lb antitank fragmentation bomblet, intended to discriminate between hard and soft targets, and also with a secondary antipersonnel function (in which case the shaped-charge warhead bounces the bomblet up into the air to burst).

BLU-91: "Gator" antitank minelet, 5.75 × 5.0 × 2.6 in (4.3 lb). Microelectronics in the minelet magnetically detect a vehicle and discriminate against unarmored vehicles. An upward-pointing shaped charge (Misznay-Schardin explosive) destroys the vehicle's belly armor.

BLU-92: "Gator" antipersonnel minelet using tripwires. Dimensions match those of BLU-91, but weight is 3.7 lb. This minelet is intended to discourage attempts to clear BLU-91 minefields.

BLU-97: 3.4-lb submunition of Tomahawk and the CBU-87 Combined Effects Munition; dimensions are 2.5 × 6.6 in (10.2 in length with tail extended). The bomblet contains a shaped charge at one end, a fragmenting shell (which disperses when the charge explodes), and an incendiary element.

BLU-106: 43-lb (4 × 53.5 in) boosted kinetic-energy penetrator (BKEP) to be carried by Tomahawk cruise missiles (28 bomblets in two bays), by the SUU-54 dispenser (AGM-130 missile), and by the SUU-64 dispenser in the Direct Airfield Attack Combined Munition. The warhead is 6.5 lb of HE, and the rocket driving the bomblet into its target is fired when its nose dips below 65 deg below the horizon.

BLU-108: Sensor-fuzed weapon (SFW), containing four Skeet warheads with IR sensors. The weapon spins to search a cone on the ground. When the sensor is activated, it fires a shallow shaped-charge (self-forging fragment) warhead, which forms an armor-penetrating dart moving at about 2750 m/sec. This weapon arms the Air Force version of JSOW.

BAT: Northrop Grumman's Brilliant Anti-Tank munition uses acoustic sensors on four wingtips to detect armored vehicle concentrations; the sensors' large footprint compensates for delivery errors and location uncertainty (due to vehicle motion). The nose carries an IR terminal sensor, and the tandem warhead is designed to defeat known armor. BAT can be carried by standard bomblet dispensers (4 BATs), by Tomahawk (14), by SLAM (6), and by ATACMS (13). Low-rate production is to begin in 1997. Improved BAT (the P³I version) will have a multimode seeker (IR and mm-wave as well as acoustic) allowing it to attack static as well as moving vehicles. It will also incorporate automatic target recognition (ATR) designed to distinguish between armored and soft vehicles; a dual-effect warhead will use a penetrator against the former and fragmentation against the latter.

WAM: The wide-area munition incorporates a self-contained antivehicle sensor. When a vehicle approaches, it launches a Skeet warhead to attack it from above. As of mid-1995, WAM was in engineering/manufacturing development.

Damocles: This new Textron submunition was reported as being in the final stage of development in 1994. It combines a mm-wave/IR seeker with a fast processor and a steerable parachute. The sensors scan by allowing the bomblet to spin as it falls, so that a total area of about a square km is visible from about 500 m altitude. The warhead is an explosively formed penetrator (EFP).

◆ Zuni

The 5in FFAR replaces earlier finned rockets. It is typically carried in a 4-rnd pod (LAU-10) with their warheads protruding. The old Mk 16 motor has been superseded by a low-smoke Mk 71 WAFAR analogous to the Mk 66 of the 2.75in rocket. Warheads: Mk 24 (GP), Mk 32 (antitank/antipersonnel), Mk 33 (flare), Mk 34 (smoke and incendiary versions), Mk 63 (HE fragmentation), as well as practice rounds. A typical assembled rocket is 110 in long, weighs 107 lb, and reaches 2370 ft/sec (about 1400 kt).

AIRCRAFT GUNS

Both the British ADEN and the French DEFA 551/552 are direct descendants of the wartime German Mauser MG/MK213C, the first modern revolver cannon. It was conceived to meet a 1942 Luftwaffe requirement for a "million point" cannon (1000 rnd/min at 1000 m/sec). No conventional reciprocating breech could, it seemed, act quickly enough because it had to wait through a cycle of recoil, cartridge ejection, reloading, and chambering between firings. That cycle was prolonged because it involves a considerable mass (the higher the muzzle velocity, the heavier) moving back and forth, accelerating and stopping.

The solution was a five-chamber revolver feed, in which cartridges moved through different steps as the revolver breech rotated. Two positions are for loading (in stages), one (at 12 o'clock) is the firing position, one is for ejection, and one is empty for safety. Some later guns eliminate the safety position. Each time the gun fires, the chamber in which firing occurs moves away and a loaded and prepared chamber comes into line with the barrel. Since the cylinder revolves, there is no start-and-stop motion. Moreover, since the cylinder ejection position is not in line with the breech, cartridges can be punched directly out the back of the gun, making for a simpler design that can be fed from either side.

In fact the high-velocity 20mm round was rejected in favor of 30mm lower-velocity (550 m/sec) ammunition (the revolver chamber and barrel were replaced; a lower-energy cartridge was adopted so that the length of the chamber did not have to be changed). At the end of the war there were only five firing prototypes and ten assembled guns.

After 1945 members of the Mauser team went to France (where work on the DEFA 541/551/552 series began in 1948), to Switzerland (where work on the Oerlikon 302RK began in 1947, leading to the 304RK), to the United Kingdom (where production of the ADEN cannon, essentially an MK213C converted to English dimensions, began in 1949), and to the United States (where work began on 60-caliber revolving cannon in 1947, leading eventually to the 20mm M39, which was adapted into a surface weapon by Taiwan). The ADEN round was based on that of the German gun, but with a lighter projectile (0.240 kg vice 0.330) for increased muzzle velocity (2640–2690 ft/sec vs. 1815 ft/sec). Note that Oerlikon did manage the "million point" gun in conventional reciprocating-breech form in its postwar 204GK/KAA.

The current French DEFA 791 is a second-generation seven-chamber revolver cannon. Mauser's BK 27, used on Tornado, is its first revolver since 1945.

The Russians experimented with revolver aircraft cannon, but with little success; their first revolver weapon was the shipboard AK-230, which is also produced under license in China. Later the lightweight GSh-301 revolver cannon was developed.

A Gatling gun might be considered an extension of the revolver idea in which each chamber of the revolver is furnished with its own barrel. The advantage is simplicity. Since no gas seal need be made between chamber and barrel, more of the total gas energy can be used for firing. However, the greater inertia of the Gatling limits the rate at which it can be run up to full firing rate, and the motion of the barrels introduces some inaccuracy (the barrel moves sideways while the bullet travels down it).

FRANCE

◆ DEFA 552A

> **Caliber:** 30mm/47
> **Muzzle Velocity:** 815 m/sec (2674 ft/sec)
> **Rate of Fire:** 1250 rnd/min
> **Ammunition Supply:** 125 rnd/gun
> **Weight:** 81 kg (179 lb)

This gas-operated revolver cannon arms the Super Étendard strike fighter (two carried). Rated barrel lifetime is 5000 rnd. The ammunition is the same as that of the British ADEN 30mm cannon. The gun is gas operated.

◆ M791

This new 30mm gas-operated seven-round revolver cannon arms the new Rafale fighter. Rafale firings began in mid-1992. Muzzle velocity is 1025 m/sec. Burst rate can be varied (2500, 1500, or 300–600 rnd/min), and the gun can feed from left or right. It has low recoil. Muzzle velocity is increased from the 810 m/sec of DEFA 552/553 to 1025 m/sec (3380 ft/sec). Total length is 2400 mm.

GERMANY

◆ Mauser BK 27

> **Caliber:** 27mm/62.96
> **Muzzle Velocity:** 1025 m/sec (3363 ft/sec)
> **Rate of Fire:** 1700 or 1000 rnd/sec (other rates selectable)
> **Ammunition Supply:** 180 rnd/gun (Tornado)
> **Weight:** 100 kg (202.5 lb)

This gas-operated revolver cannon arms Tornado strike fighters, German Alpha Jets, and the Swedish JAS 39 Gripen. Ammunition can be fed from either side. The high rate of fire is intended for air-to-air use, the lower rate for air-to-ground firing. The weapon is unusual in that, although the Tornado program was multinational, it did not use an existing standardized NATO round. It seems likely that the caliber was chosen specifically to achieve a very high muzzle velocity within the weight available.

See also the MIDAS/Drakon CIWS.

RUSSIA

◆ GSh-301 (9A4071)

The carrier-based Su-27 and MiG-29 are armed with GSh-301, a single-barrel recoil-operated and electrically fired 30mm gun introduced in 1980. The projectile weighs 0.388 kg (a full round weighs 0.832 kg). Muzzle velocity is 860 m/sec, and rate of fire is 1500–1800 rnd/min. At 50 kg, GSh-301 is claimed to be the lightest existing aircraft cannon. Reported time between overhaul (TBO) is only 2000 rounds.

◆ NR-30

This recoil/gas-operated weapon, introduced in 1955, reportedly arms the Su-24MR. Gas is used to limit recoil and to return the gun to the firing position. The barrel does not recoil as far as the breech. Reloading is by compressed air. The projectile weighs 0.41 kg (the full round is 0.84 kg), muzzle velocity is 780 m/sec, and rate of fire is 850 rnd/min.

◆ GSh-6-23 (9A620)

This Gatling gun was designed specifically for the Su-24. It is carried both in the belly (with 500 rnd) and in a three-gun SPPU-6 pod, in which each gun can depress through 45 deg, and carries 400 rnd of ammunition. Rate of fire is 6000–8000 rnd/min. The improved GSh-6-23M (9A768) achieves 8000–10,000 rnd/min. The projectile weighs 0.2 kg (the full round is 0.34 kg), and muzzle velocity is 700 m/sec.

◆ NR-23/AM-23

Twin-turreted gas-operated NR-23s and AM-23s arm land-based naval bombers. Some aircraft also carry fixed forward-firing weapons with longer barrels; the data below apply to the short-barreled version. NR-23 was introduced in 1949. Many bombers (such as later Badgers) are armed with the improved AM-23 (1953). The Badger is typically armed with seven cannons: a long weapon in the nose (PU-88 mount, with 100 rnd), a twin remote-controlled dorsal turret (DT-V7, 500 rnd, elevation limits +90/−3 deg), a twin remote-controlled ventral turret (DT-N7S, 700 rnd, 95-deg traverse either way, elevation limits +2/−90 deg), and a twin tail turret (DK-7, 1000 rnd, 70-deg traverse either way, elevation limits +60/−40 deg). The overall FCS, which is based on the old U.S. system developed for the B-29, is designated PVB-53C. The tail turret employs a PRS-1 (Argon) radar. The 23mm projectile weighs 0.2 kg (the full round weighs 0.34 kg); muzzle velocity is 690 m/sec, and the rate of fire is 850 rnd/min. The gun weighs 39 kg (AM-23 weighs 43 kg, and achieves 1300 rnd/min).

UNITED KINGDOM

◆ ADEN Mk 5 Cannon

Caliber: 30mm/47.8
Muzzle Velocity: 790 m/sec (2590 ft/sec)
Rate of Fire: 1200–1400 rnd/min
Ammunition Supply: 150 rnd/gun
Weight: 87 kg (192 lb) (projectile approx. 1.1 lb)

Carried by Sea Harrier and AV-8A/8C fighters in a detachable two-gun pallet, the ADEN (Armament Design Establishment, manufactured at Enfield) is a gas-operated revolver cannon broadly comparable to the French DEFA 552. Work began in September 1945. The gun was first flight-tested in a Beaufighter in August 1951, and the low-velocity (LV, 603 m/sec) ammunition was approved for service in 1953. By that time, however, work was already proceeding on a high-velocity (HV, 712 m/sec) alternative, which was approved for service use (superseding the LV) in 1955. Mk 4 was the main production version. Mk 5, which arms the Sea Harrier, is a modernized Mk 4 with an increased rate of fire (1500–1700 rnd/sec).

UNITED STATES

◆ M61A1/M197

Caliber: 20mm/62
Muzzle Velocity: 3400 ft/sec
Rate of Fire: 4000 or 6000 rnd/min
Ammunition Supply: 570 rnd
Weight: Total 841 lb (gun 252 lb, feed system 270 lb, ammunition 319 lb)

Data apply to the gun as mounted in the F/A-18.

General Electric's 20mm Gatling gun is mounted in the A-7E bomber and the F-14 and F/A-18 fighters. This gun is also the basis of the Phalanx close-in defensive weapon (see the Antiaircraft Warfare section). Current rated barrel life is 20,000 rnd.

M197, which arms the Marines' AH-1W Sea Cobra helicopter, is a three-barrel version (weight 145 lb, ammunition supply 750 rnd) with a selectable rate of fire (750 or 1500 rnd/min). JMSDF ships carry this weapon on a pedestal mount.

The 30mm GAU-8/A, used in both the A-10 ground-attack airplane and the Goalkeeper CIWS, is an enlarged version.

◆ GAU-12/U Equalizer

Caliber: 25mm
Muzzle Velocity: 3500 ft/sec (HEI, TP; 3400 ft/sec AP)
Rate of Fire: 3600 rnd/min
Ammunition Supply: 300 rnd
Weight: Total 900 lb empty, 1230 lb loaded (280-lb gun)

General Electric's 25mm five-barrel Gatling gun was developed specially for the AV-8B Harrier II attack fighter. This gun incorporates GAU-8/A (30mm) technology. The gun is in the left-hand pod and the ammunition on the right. The rounds are moved along a fixed track by a continuous-loop driving chain. The gun takes 0.4 sec to reach its firing rate. Rated barrel life is 15,000 rnd (20,000 rnd MTBF), and dispersion is 1.4 mil.

COAST-DEFENSE GUNS AND ROCKETS

BRAZIL

In 1995 Avibras advertised a coast-defense system using its Astros II (artillery saturation rocket system) unguided rocket, which carries bomblets. Reportedly two Astros II batteries were delivered to the Brazilian armed forces and a third in 1996, two of them for coast defense. Each battery includes six 4-rnd launchers and six ammunition supply vehicles. The associated Giraffe radar can acquire naval targets at ranges up to 90 km (55 nm). Astros rockets were used by Iraq, Qatar, and Saudi Arabia during the Iran-Iraq and Gulf Wars.

Astros was first delivered in 1983. Rockets use wraparound fins for stability and air brakes to drop them at the intended ranges. There are four different rockets: SS-30 (32-rnd launcher, 127 mm × 3.9 m, 68 kg, range 9–30 km), SS-40 (16-rnd launcher, 180 mm × 4.2 m, 152 kg, range 15–35 km), SS-60 (4-rnd launcher, 300 mm × 5.6 m, 595 kg, range 20–60 km), and a 90km rocket. SS-40, -60, and the long-range rocket all carry bomblet warheads (there are eight different warheads altogether, including an antiarmor/antipersonnel version that can penetrate 220 mm of steel).

FINLAND

◆ 130mm

This locally produced (VAMMAS, ex-Tampella) 130mm/52 gun, in a turret emplacement, replaces older 152mm guns. It entered service in the mid-1980s. Range is 24 km; it can fire 6 rnd/min and is remotely aimed (with manual backup). Training rate is 200 mrad/sec (approx. 0.11 deg/sec). Elevation limits: +50/−5 deg. Ammunition is of the separate type (12-kg shell, 33-kg cartridge, the latter power-loaded). The normal crew is nine, but the gun can be handled by three in an emergency. The turret weighs 16 t. The standard light coastal weapon is a 100mm gun derived from that of the Soviet T-55 tank, and there are also towed Soviet-supplied K54 130mm guns. Finland also still uses some 152mm guns in splinter shields, as well as 254mm (presumably Bofors) weapons.

There are six readiness forts, nine manned training forts, about 30 guarded forts, and 11 training units, all organized in five military districts. These numbers may be somewhat deceptive, in that many of the forts are probably quite small. The annual intake, in 1989, was 2300 conscripts, with about 3000 reservists being given refresher training that year. The organization consists of a mobile battalion in Vasa and two fixed battalions. Coastal artillery is administered by the army.

The FCS is RAVAL, a Finnish acronym meaning coastal-artillery automatic-surveillance fire-computing system; it is probably a BEAB system (see the entry for Sweden). Each computer serves up to 16 guns, taking into account local conditions as well as the position of that gun. The system can control fixed and mobile guns as well as missiles. There are two sets of software, one for surveillance and one for fire control. Each center contains three consoles and, thus, can engage three targets simultaneously. The system as a whole uses radar, laser range-finders, and optical range-finders.

GERMANY

♦ 150mm

Denmark, Norway, and Portugal use 150mm guns, presumably of German manufacture. During World War II the Germans used a 150mm/40 for coast defense, firing a 40-kg (88-lb) shell at 800 m/sec (2625 ft/sec) to a maximum range of 14,300 m (15,640 yd). This weapon presumably survived postwar.

Denmark retains coast-defense turrets taken from World War II German battleships. This twin 150mm mount from the battleship *Gneisenau*, emplaced in 1952, is one of two at Stevenfort (four single 150mm guns are at Langeland Fort, built in 1952 with guns taken from a German battery at Fynshoved on the island of Fyn in Denmark; two more guns are emplaced nearby as a practice battery). The guns are 15cm SK C/28s in a Dreh L: C/34 mount, with 150mm face armor, 75mm roof armor, and 50mm sides and back; gun range is given as 22.3 km (about 24,400 yd). Both forts were reduced to reserve status in 1983, but a mobilization crew trains at each every year (firing live ammunition). These two forts are probably the only ones remaining active. Until recently, there were six others. Middelgrundsfort (12 × 170 mm, 4 × 105 mm AA), Flakfort (6 × 210 mm, 4 × 150 mm AA), Dragorfort (4 × 150 mm, 4 × 105 mm AA), Kongelundsfort (4 × 150 mm), Bagsbofort (4 × 150 mm, 4 × 105 mm AA), and Hornback battery (4 × 120 mm). All the forts were originally protected against air attack by 40mm guns, but these weapons were declared obsolete in 1983 and scrapped. (C. B. Robbins)

Denmark built two forts after World War II, Stevenfort and Langland Fort, at the entrances to the Sound. Each is armed with two twin 15cm SKC/28 guns from the battleship *Gniesenau*. They remain active, manned mainly by reservists. There are also six single SKL/45s manufactured specifically for coast defense. Both types fire 45.3-kg (99.8-lb) shells to a range of 23,500 m (25,700 yd). Denmark also has a few ex-U.S. 3in/50 naval guns in coastal mountings.

♦ 127mm

Norway uses a 127mm coast-defense gun, presumably an ex-German 127mm/45 destroyer weapon firing a 28-kg (61.7-lb) shell at 830 m/sec (2723 ft/sec), to a maximum range of 17,400 m (19,030 yd).

♦ 105mm

Now in Norwegian service, this gun is presumably the standard German 105mm/65 AA gun, firing a 15-kg (33.3-lb) shell at 900 m/sec (2953 ft/sec) to a maximum range of 17,700 m (19,360 yd).

♦ 88mm

Possibly Albania and the former Yugoslavia still use the old German 88mm/56 gun in coast defenses, in fixed emplacements. It fires a 44-kg (97-lb) HE shell at a muzzle velocity of 820 m/sec (2690 ft/sec), to a maximum range of 14,860 m (16,250 yd).

NORWAY

In 1994 the Norwegian coast-defense artillery comprised: nine batteries of modern 75mm or 120mm guns, to be retained beyond 2000 (the 120mm program was terminated in 1994); 14 batteries of older 150mm and 105mm guns, all to be discarded by 2000 (replaced by 12 batteries of Hellfires); seven batteries of 127mm guns, some of which may be retained; eight controllable minefields, six of which are to be retained and modernized; and five torpedo batteries, all of which are to be retained. Medium-range missiles may replace some of the surviving guns, but at present plans to install Penguin are apparently in abeyance. The close-in air defense of the batteries is by 20mm and 12.7mm automatic guns and by RBS 70 light AA missiles.

Project Ida is Kongsberg's modernization of four Norwegian coastal torpedo batteries and five controlled minefields and associated FCS, to be completed by the end of December 1997; it also adds a new torpedo battery and minefields at Namsen Fjord and a new minefield in the Tromso area. The first installation is Herdla Fort guarding the approaches to Bergen. Total cost is NKr 700M (£62M). Ida employs new EO sensors and radars (Terma radars, Simrad EO sensors) and adds an integrated communications system including digital telephone exchanges. Equipment includes the KN9000 weapons-control console and KS900 computer of other recent Norwegian projects, such as the MSI series CDS. A new seabed sonar may later be added.

The current torpedoes are old T-1s, the last type built by the Horten Torpedo Factory (to German plans, for G-7a), modernized after World War II with wire guidance. Similar weapons were carried by the *Kobben*-class submarines and by Norwegian motor torpedo boats. Some fortresses may also be armed with old British Mk 8s. These weapons are being replaced by Tp 613s, beginning about 1995. Modernization includes replacing the current above-water torpedo tubes with protected ramps sloping down at a 20-deg angle, the weapons emerging underwater.

Bottom and moored mines are controlled from a fortified underground control room; Ida also includes a new independent (uncontrolled) rising mine. The mine control panel receives regular status reports from the minefield and from individual mines, and also has an alarm function to indicate faults.

Studies began early in 1987, and Kongsberg was chosen in July 1990. Specifications were upgraded following the Gulf War, in light of successful attacks by coalition forces on hardened Iraqi positions using penetrating weapons. Norwegian authorities reconsidered housing the shore-based elements in ex-German bunkers; they decided instead to house the torpedo magazines and associated command/control in containers suspended from heavy cabling to attenuate shock, buried over 15 m underground.

Kongsberg has developed a coast-defense turret for the 20mm Rh 202 or the 25mm Mauser E; Norway ordered it in January 1986 for AA protection of coast defenses. The turret weighs about 1 t; elevation limits are +50/−10 deg.

A current requirement for a new 155mm gun has not been filled.

PORTUGAL

According to a recent report, coastal artillery amounts to six 9.2in guns, six 6in guns, fifteen 150mm guns, and recoil-less rifles (128 × 106 mm, 112 × 90 mm). Presumably the 6in guns are ex-British, the 150mm guns ex-German.

RUSSIA

Work on mobile 100, 130, and 180mm mobile coast-defense guns began at the end of World War II, the theory being that they could advance with Soviet forces to protect their flanks. Extemporized batteries had done that during the advance along the Baltic in 1944–45, helping to stop shelling by German warships.

Khrushchev terminated this program by a 4 February 1956 directive, by which time 100mm and 130mm weapons were already in service and a 152mm gun had been tested (and rejected because it was not sufficiently superior to the 130mm gun).

◆ **Bereg**

At Abu Dhabi in 1993 the Russians exhibited this mobile 130mm gun system ("complex"), produced by NPO Barrikady. The gun system is in three 8 × 8 vehicles: an A-222 gun, a command vehicle, and a generator vehicle. The system can handle targets moving at up to 200 kt and at ranges up to 20 km; it can destroy a target (probability 0.8) in 1–2 min and can control two guns. The radar autotracks four targets (acquisition range is 35 km). An associated optronic system covers a 270-deg sector. The control vehicle can be up to 1000 m from the guns. The gun fires up to 10 rnd/min and the vehicle carries 40 rnd. Elevation limits are +50/−5 deg. Ammunition and ballistics are identical to those of the naval AK-130.

Design work on this system began in December 1976, and tests began in January 1987, with government tests of a battery of four following between 3 November 1992 and 30 May 1993. The battery was then seized by Ukraine.

◆ **305mm**

The Soviets used both their new 305mm/56 and their old (dreadnought-type) 305mm/52 for coast defenses during World War II and planned to emplace 12 batteries of the new guns and 8 batteries of the older ones (four four-gun in the Baltic, two four-gun in the Black Sea, and two five-gun in the Far East). Many of these weapons must have been destroyed, but some reportedly survive in active service, perhaps in the Northern Fleet. The 305mm/56, which was designed for the abortive battle cruisers, fired a 480-kg (1058-lb) shell to 43,900 m (48,000 yd), probably at about 850 m/sec (2789 ft/sec). The older 305mm/52 fired a 470.9-kg (1038-lb) AP shell at 762 m/sec (2500 ft/sec) to a maximum range of 24,620 m (26,925 yd). In at least one case, 305/52s were emplaced postwar in a triple turret taken from a scrapped battleship.

◆ **152mm**

These guns, of the type formerly mounted in the *Sverdlov* class, are in Soviet, Bulgarian, Romanian, and possibly Finnish service; they were also used by East Germany. Some were mounted in Soviet coast-defense batteries during World War II. In coastal service the 152mm fired a 55-kg (121-lb) AP shell to 29,000 m (31,700 yd), probably at a muzzle velocity of about 885 m/sec (2900 ft/sec).

◆ **130mm SM-4-1**

This gun has been very widely adopted; reported export users are Angola, Bulgaria, Egypt, North Korea, Poland, Romania, South Yemen, Syria, and Yugoslavia. The Israelis captured some when they took Sharm el Sheikh in 1967. In addition, earlier Soviet-type 130mm guns arm Chinese (PRC), Cuban, and Finnish coast defenses. Performance approximates that of the 130mm/58 naval gun, probably with a maximum range of about 29,500 m. The ammunition is also the same. Maximum elevation is 45 deg. The APHE shell weighs 33.6 kg and is fired at a velocity of 1050 m/sec. Rate of fire is 5 rnd/min. The gun is mounted on a four-wheel carriage (with removable axles) with a nearly vertical shield. The associated radar is ZALP-B (Long Bow). Design work began in May 1944, using a mounting similar to that of the 100mm KSM-65 described below. Four prototype mounts were tested between 23 December 1950 and 19 February 1951 near Riga. In all, 140 mounts were made in 1952–56.

Soviet client-states first adopted 130mm coastal guns in the early 1960s, at a time when the U.S. Navy was eliminating its heavy shipboard guns. The remaining 5in guns were outranged by the new 130s, and the abortive U.S. lightweight 8in gun program was begun as a counter to this new Soviet-bloc capability.

◆ **100mm KSM-65**

Work on this weapon began in 1944. The prototype was ready in May 1946, and in 1948 a battery passed official tests at the "Red Fort" on the Gulf of Finland. It used the HE fragmentation ammunition of the BS-3 field gun and the proximity-fuzed shell, HE, and practice shell of the B-34 naval gun. The first four weapons (with gun carriages) were completed in September 1951, and in all 112 KSM-65s were made in 1953–56. They were used by China (PRC) and the Soviet Union. Reports of 100mm guns in Bulgarian service probably refer to this weapon.

◆ **Other Russian Guns**

122mm guns are in Cuban, Finnish, North Korean, and possibly Yugoslav service. Finland uses T-55 (100mm) turrets embedded in concrete and controlled from a blockhouse. Maximum range is about 15 km. Finally, the 85mm gun is in Yugoslav service, and also (presumably copied) in Chinese (PRC).

SPAIN

According to a recent report, the Spanish coast artillery inventory is 7 Vickers 15in/45, 16 Vickers 12in/50, and 117 Vickers 6in/50. These figures differ somewhat from those given in the United Kingdom section, and may reflect additions from the batteries of discarded warships. The recent report does not mention the 8in/50 listed in the United Kingdom section.

SWEDEN

CelsiusTech is developing STARKA (Sea Front System 2000), a fixed/mobile coast-artillery (KA) system, for Norway and Sweden. The 155mm guns will be able to fire from a variety of preregistered positions, instead of from fixed sites as now. STARKA is to be procured in 1997–98.

CelsiusTech makes the electronic elements of Swedish coast defense, some of which have been supplied abroad:

Kondor (9KR 400) is the coastal-surveillance radar, based on the 9GR 600 X-band fast-tuned magnetron and the 9GA 205 antenna. It uses two of the same operator displays as STINA (see the Surveillance and Control section) and can be fixed or mobile. This is an ADT radar. This radar can be supplemented by a helicopter-borne 9HCI 200 standoff surveillance radar.

Kaskad is the local (battalion-level) command center, using a 23in color PPI and communicating with Kastell, Kardinal, or Karat battery-level control systems.

Kastell (9KA400)/*Kardinal* (9KA500) is the coastal TWS fire-control radar, capable of engaging three targets simultaneously. It operates in X- or in Ku-band. 9KA500 is the mobile version. See the 9GR series in the radar part of the Antiaircraft Warfare section for electronic details. Kastell/Kardinal can include optronic sensors.

Karat (9KM 400) is an integrated missile-launch and combat-control system, carried on a truck and including an X-band radar and optional optronic sensors. A typical battery might consist of two launch vehicles carrying Penguin Mk 2 missiles.

Kolibri (9KA 50)/*Kobra* (9KA 100) are optronic gun fire-control sensors using paired binoculars and a laser. An image intensifier (starlight scope) and an FLIR are optional. Azimuth and laser range are fed directly into a fire-control computer. Kolibri is a lightweight version for amphibious assault units. Kobra has a higher-powered laser range-finder and a computer-controlled azimuth servo for extra accuracy (presumably in rate-aided target tracking).

Klara (9KM 100) is a missile-firing analysis and launch-control system, displaying a tactical situation as seen at higher-echelon levels so that long-range missiles can be fired without relying on local sensors. It can also be used to integrate data from coastal-surveillance radars, naval vessels, and helicopters. In its brochure for these systems, PEAB mentions RBS 15 as a specific case of a long-range defensive missile that need not be based near the coast, that is, near both its search sensors and enemy threats.

BEAB manufactures a combined automatic gunsight and ballistic computer, MARIA, for its mobile coastal guns (listed below). MARIA automatically compensates as the gun digs into the ground after each round.

◆ Bofors 254mm Gun

This prewar weapon may survive in Finnish service; the gun was originally built for two Finnish coast-defense ships. This 10in/45 fires a 225-kg (496-lb) shell at 850 m/sec (2790 ft/sec) to a maximum range of 30,300 m (33,140 yd). Sweden still uses 152mm and 210mm coast-defense guns, presumably prewar Bofors naval weapons.

◆ Bofors 155mm L39 (CD77)

This mobile gun, developed specially for export, uses many Karin (see below) components. Total weight is 12 t, and elevation limits are +70/−3 deg. Rate of fire is 10 rnd/min. Muzzle velocity (range): 827 m/sec (HEER rnd: 41.65 kg, 30,000 m or HE rnd: 42.6 kg, 24,000 m) or 700 m/sec (HCER rnd: 53 kg, 30,000 m). The HCER is probably the gun bought by Finland.

◆ Bofors ERSTA 120mm/62

This fixed coast-defense gun, developed about 1970, had by 1987 replaced about half the Swedish heavy coast-defense weapons, the remainder dating from the 1950s. Maximum elevation is 50 deg (limits +50/−3 deg), to achieve maximum range. Rate of fire is 25 rnd/min (200 rnd in 20 min). The gun barrel is water-cooled. Total weight: 70.5 t plus 103.5 t of concrete. Muzzle velocity (projectile weight, range): 880 m/sec (HE: 24.6 kg, 24,000 m; HCER: 26 kg, 34,000 m). The shells are similar to those fired by the Karin gun (see below), but the cartridges are larger.

This weapon is used by the Swedish navy and in 1980 was ordered by Norway (first delivered 1987; original order for 12 reduced to eight in 1989). Norway has installed these guns in three new fortifications, at Andfiord (in service 1989), Vestfiord (1990), and Trondheimfjord (1991).

◆ Bofors Karin 120mm L55 (CD80)

This mobile gun was first delivered in 1978 and has many elements in common with ERSTA. Karin has the same carriage as the FH77 155mm field gun.

Typically, there are four guns/battery, and they can be towed by road at 70 km/hr. When the guns are emplaced, their arc of fire is 60 deg. Each gun has its own computer. Elevation limits: +50/−3 deg. Rate of fire: 15 rnd/min. Muzzle velocity (range):

A modern coast-defense weapon. The ERSTA 120mm gun as emplaced in Norway. (*Ships of the World*)

790 m/sec (HE: 24.6 kg, 21,000 m) or 830 m/sec (HCER: 26 kg, 30,000 m).

◆ Bofors 75mm L60

This turreted gun, actually a 76mm/62, was developed about 1960 for the Swedish navy and exported to Norway and, probably, other customers. Elevation has been limited to 20 deg (limits are +20/−5 deg) to minimize the opening in the turret (range is limited to 11,400–16,000 m). Rate of fire is 25 rnd/min. Muzzle velocity is 870 m/sec (range 12,000 m) for the 5.52-kg HE rnd, and 890 m/sec for the HCER rnd (6.4 kg, 16,000 m). Total weight is 17.5 tons.

Sweden also uses a mobile form of this gun, on a four-wheel towed carriage. It has a total of 12 mobile and 53 fixed coast-defense batteries (including missile units).

UNITED KINGDOM

◆ 15in/45

Vickers Model 1926 is still in service in Spain. The AP shell weighs 859.65 kg (1895 lb), and the HE shell 801.84 kg (1767 lb); muzzle velocity is 2500 ft/sec (AP shell), and range is 35,100 m (38,400 yd). Guns are mounted singly, in armored gun houses. There are 12 or 16 mounts in Groupos of four (two batteries per Groupo). Probably seven are still operational. The associated FCS is the Swedish 9KA 410 built in Spain.

Spain will keep the 15in gun in service until it is replaced by a coastal missile, probably Harpoon, in the late 1990s.

◆ 12in/50

Spain retains 14 Vickers 12in/50 guns, some of them originally built for its dreadnoughts, some specially built. The gun fires an 850-lb AP shell at 3010 ft/sec.

◆ 9.2in

This gun is in Portuguese and Turkish service. When Britain and Canada gave up their coast defenses in 1956, they transferred their weapons to the NATO Southern Tier nations, primarily Portugal and Turkey. Guns were supplied in batteries of three: two to Turkey, one to Portugal (for the Azores, to protect the airfield). The batteries came from Canada (two from the East Coast, one from the West). These weapons were also supplied to Ireland (they may have been the old British guns originally emplaced there) and remained in service until the mid-1980s. The standard 9.2in/47 fired a 380-lb HE shell at 2700 ft/sec, to a maximum range of 36,700 yd.

◆ 8in

Spain retains 24 British-supplied 8in coast-defense guns. It is alone in using this caliber. These weapons are probably Vickers 8in/50 cruiser guns similar to those in the former Spanish heavy cruisers; the guns fire a 256-lb AP shell at 2725 ft/sec to a maximum range of 29,200 yd.

◆ 6in/50

Vickers 6in/50 guns, installed in 1915–25, remain in Spanish service, in both single and twin mounts; up to 113 may be operational. Maximum range is 21,600 m. There have been proposals to replace the gun tube with that of the Spanish 155mm/39 howitzer, which fires standard NATO rounds. The 155mm coast-defense gun would have a range of 22,500–24,000 m (30,000 m with enhanced-range ammunition) and fire 2 rnd/min (4 rnd/min in a burst).

Brazil and Paraguay use a 6in Vickers Mk V. Portugal also uses 6in guns, presumably also of Vickers type.

UNITED STATES

◆ 12in/45

At least four 12in Mk V Mod 9 guns were transferred to Brazil about 1945–46. They may still be in service. These U.S. Navy guns were transferred to the Army after the Washington Treaty scrappings in 1923–24. Others were obtained in 1941–42. These were among the most modern Army coastal guns at the time, and work on a new gun carriage began early in World War II, at Watertown Arsenal. The prototype (T 1) was completed only in 1945, and the pilot Brazilian gun shipped in 1945. This was the culmination of negotiations with Brazil begun about 1938. The gun was in an open mount, and elevation/depression limits were +47/−8 deg. It fired an 870-lb shell with 310 lb of powder, and muzzle velocity was 2700 ft/sec, for a maximum range of 30,000 yd.

When the U.S. coast defenses were disbanded in 1948–49, some 6in guns were retained for possible transfer to Norway, Portugal, and Turkey, but they were never shipped abroad. The only other heavy U.S. guns transferred abroad were about eight 8in to Canada in 1940–41, and 7in guns to the Netherlands East Indies at about the same time. None of these weapons survive.

◆ 155mm

The United States supplied Chile with 16 155mm coast-defense guns in 1942; they are still active, equipped with a locally developed FCS using small commercial microcomputers. The guns are World War I–type GPFs of French design but probably of U.S. manufacture (reported designations mix French and U.S. nomenclature). The GPF gun was 38 calibers long and fired a 95-lb shell at 735 m/sec (2411 ft/sec) to a range of 18,600 m (20,300 yd). Similar guns were supplied to several other Latin American countries, including Peru and Venezuela (to protect oil fields), but the Chilean weapons are probably the only ones still in service (there is a slight chance that the Peruvian guns are still active). Brazil and Trinidad received other weapons, probably ex-naval 6in guns. Aruba probably had Dutch guns.

Chile still uses old U.S. 155mm GPF guns, supplied during World War II, for coast defense. They were intended to protect the copper-exporting ports of Antofagasta, Barquito Island, San Antonio, and Tocopilla, but have presumably been moved since. This particular gun was an M1917A1, made in France but modified with a U.S. breech and firing mechanism. This weapon was photographed in Iquique, Chile, in June 1992. (Dr. R. S. Scheina)

◆ 5in/38 and Lesser Weapons

Taiwan uses ex-destroyer 5in/38 single-mount Mk 30 enclosed gun houses with EO target-acquisition sensors on their roofs. They are emplaced on Quemoy, Matsu, and Penghu. Also on Quemoy are ex-U.S. 240mm and 8in gun-howitzers, typically used to duel with artillery batteries ashore in China. There are also 90mm AA guns assigned to deal with landing craft (and no longer equipped with AA FCSs). On some other islands there are ex-U.S. 6pdr (57mm) antitank guns in bunkers. There are also numerous recoil-less rifles. Standard 105mm and 155mm Army guns are also used (105s may have been replaced with 155s).

YUGOSLAVIA

As of 1991, Yugoslavia was marketing a coast artillery FCS, capable of engaging two targets simultaneously. It can handle six types of shell, 12 types of propelling charge, and five types of fuze. The computer provides nonvolatile storage for 100 target

locations, 30 fixed (registration) points, 10 forward observer locations, 10 reference points, and 10 no-fire zones. The system provides fire-control solutions within 15 sec of target detection. The system computer is a dual processor using 8086/8087 CPUs with an 80 × 40-character LCD. System sensors are radars, laser range-finders, and forward observers (two of which have dedicated channels; the other eight share a single channel). System accuracy: range 0.03%, bearing 0.03 mils, fuze setting 0.03% time of flight.

An M/87 coast-defense gun consists of a 100mm tank gun on the carriage of a 122mm D-30J howitzer. The gun can fire 15 rnd/min (36 rnd sustained in 4 min). Elevation limits are +45/−5 deg. Shell weights: 27.1 and 30.2-kg HE, 30.5-kg AP.

Before the collapse of Yugoslavia, coast defenses amounted to 25 installations (gun and missile); guns included 45 D-44, 55 German 88mm, 75 × 122mm M-37, 85 × 130mm, and 85 × 152mm D-20 gun-howitzers.

BOMBARDMENT ROCKETS

Deletion: Italian 81mm rocket launcher (no known sales).

ITALY

◆ Breda 105mm Multiple Launcher

See the 105mm Breda launcher in the Electronic Warfare section.

RUSSIA

◆ BM 14/17 and BM 14/18

BM 14/17 is a 17-barrel 140mm (5.5in) army-type rocket that entered service in 1954. The 70-lb rocket has a maximum range of 4.8 nm. The designation has been applied by NATO.

BM 14/18 is a 140mm rocket launcher specially designed for naval service, on board all *Polnocny*-class amphibious ships. This launcher fires the same rocket as BM 14/17.

Maximum elevation of the manually reloaded BM 14/18 is about 50 deg. Reloading takes about 4–5 min. Rockets are ripple fired at 1-sec intervals. Speed is about 400 m/sec (1310 ft/sec), and maximum range is about 10,000 yd.

The 17-rocket launcher is a lighter-weight version for river patrol boats such as the *Shmel* class; extra rockets are stowed in two crates abaft the launcher.

◆ BM 21/BM 11/Damba/APRN

This 40-barrel 122mm rocket launcher (101 lb, range 8 nm) is found on board some amphibious ships. It is automatically reloaded: the launcher carries two clusters of 20 tubes, empty sets

Soviet 122mm barrage rocket launcher, showing its two 20-rocket clusters.

being discarded and replaced from below. The rockets carry a 19.2-kg fragmentation warhead. The 40-barrel version arms the Rumanian "Brutar"-class river monitors and Russian amphibious ships.

A 40-rocket BM 21 became the standard Soviet army rocket launcher in the mid-1960s. The naval system is two half-launchers carried on a specially designed mounting. The rockets are 2.8 m long and weigh about 140 lb each; range is about 23,000 yd. Three Egyptian "Shershens" were armed with this weapon.

Shmel-class monitors can carry an eight-barreled 122mm launcher. The Pomornik-class LCAC carries 2 × 22-tube 122mm rocket launchers. They retract into its side walls and reload below decks.

BM 11 is a North Korean version of BM 21, developed in the mid-1970s.

Users: Iran (Chaho and Hengam classes), North Korea (Chaho class).

At Defendory in October 1992 the Russians displayed a truck-mounted 40-rocket version of BM 21 as a coast-defense weapon ("anti-diversion coast system 'Damba'"), protecting the entrances of naval bases and "also provid[ing] protection of sea frontier against diversion forces such as extra small submarines and submarine wreckers [presumably saboteurs] within the firing range from 300 to 5000 m." All 40 rockets can be ripple-fired in 20 sec. The launcher weighs 13.8 t. Shelf life is 1 yr.

China announced a 40-rnd 122mm rocket at the 1989 Paris Air Show (66.6 kg, 18.4 kg warhead, range 40 km). It is probably an unlicensed copy of BM 21. In the fall of 1994 Aerostar SA of Bucau, Rumania announced its own 40-barrel APRN, which is probably a BM 21 copy. This weapon may already be in use for Rumanian coast defense, deployed in two-launcher pits spaced at 8–10km intervals along the Rumanian coast. Quoted range is 5 to 20.5 km.

UNITED STATES

◆ ATACMS (MGM-140)

The Army Tactical Missile System, made by Loral Vought, is likely to be adopted as the standard U.S. Navy shore bombardment missile. It is inertially guided and carries submunitions. Unlike most ballistic missiles, it follows a shaped (porpoising) trajectory, which makes it difficult either to predict its target based on its initial flight path or to deduce the firing position from its end trajectory. Thus it can be fired as much as 30 deg off-axis. As it descends, it is steered by fins. The combination of steering and trajectory-shaping reduces accuracy somewhat, compared with a pure-ballistic weapon. Development began in 1983 (as JTACMS; the Air Force left the program in 1985), and the first missile was flight-tested on 26 April 1988. The first production missiles were delivered in June 1990. A total of 32 ATACMS (out of 105 in theater) were fired during the Gulf War, mainly against fixed missile sites. In one case, however, the missiles destroyed a convoy of 200 unarmored vehicles attempting to cross a bridge about 54 nm from the launcher. The Gulf War supplemental request included 32 replacement ATACMS.

Dimensions: 23.96 in × 13 ft, fin span about 55 in, weight (Block I), 3687 lb. Warhead weight is about 1000 lb. Power is provided by a 40,000-lb thrust Atlantic Research rocket engine.

Range is 81 nm with an M74 warhead containing 950 M42 APAM (antipersonnel/antimateriel) bomblets. CEP at 135 km range is 225 m. The dispersion pattern is variable. Block IA halves the number of bomblets to double the range to 300 km (160 nm). It is in the engineering manufacturing development (EMD) stage. The Block II follow-on warhead, now in the continued development phase, carries 13 BAT guided submunitions to a range of 140 km, dispersing 10 in an outer ring and 3 in an inner ring. It is intended to attack moving armor. Block IIA will carry six Improved BATs to 300 km. In addition, a deep penetrating warhead has been developed in a cooperative program with the Navy. It separates as the missile approaches the target and has its own terminal guidance.

Procurement (for the U.S. Army): 1015 (plus 51 development missiles) through 1993; FY94, 265 (plus 3 for Navy tests); FY95, 185 plus 30 Block II development missiles. The Army requirement increased from about 1600 to 2465 when the service withdrew from the abortive TSSAM (AGM-137) program. Unit cost fell from $1.07M in FY89 to $541,000 in FY92; in FY95 it was $783,000.

The first ATACMS firing at sea was on 12 February 1995 from a self-propelled M270 launcher on the deck of USS *Mount Vernon* (LSD-39); a Block IA was fired over a range of 75 nm, dispersing nonexplosive bomblets around a target on San Clemente Island. ATACMS will probably be test-fired from a vertical launcher during 1997. Because of its diameter, ATACMS would have to occupy a new thin-wall (0.5 in) canister.

Interest in adapting the Army's MLRS to the naval fire-support role seems to have evaporated.

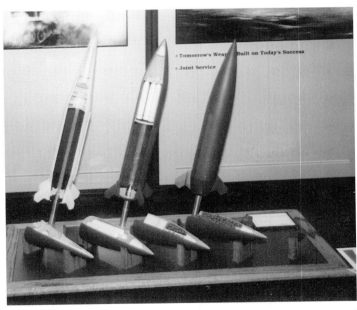

Models of ATACMS at the 1996 Navy League Show display a variety of warheads: a unitary hard-target penetrator at left, BAT submissiles in the center, bomblets (the small spheres) in models on the table. (Stuart Slade, DMS/Forecast International)

ANTIAIRCRAFT WARFARE

SHIPBOARD RADARS AND FIRE-CONTROL SYSTEMS

Deletions: SAR-8 (Canada, not adopted), Volcan/Narval/VIGY 50 (France, no sales), OFLA-M (German: never entered service), DS-35 (Israel: now reported abandoned after 1978–80 tests), OPS-1/2 (Japanese, extinct), DA-04 (extinct), LW-04 (extinct), MR-05 (no buyers reported), VI-01 (only on board Argentine carrier *25 de Mayo*; unlikely ever to return to service), Neptune (Russian, extinct with disposal of last Riga-class frigate), Sun Visor (Russian, extinct with disposal of last Don-class tender), Wasp Head/Sphaera (Russian, extinct with disposal of last Don-class tender), Eagle (Swedish, dropped from Trinity as too complex), Type 982 (last ship with this radar, *Umar Farooq*, had the below-decks electronics removed on transfer to Bangladesh), Lookout (British: no buyers), Marconi 400 Series/Sea Cobra (British, no sales), SNW-10 (British: only survivor is on board the Egyptian *El Fatah*, now apparently being converted to a museum ship), Mk 13 radar/Mk 38 FCS (U.S., extinct with striking of *Iowa* class, may be restored if ships are resurrected [two were restored to the Navy List], but not for several years), Mk 26/Mk 52 FCS (U.S., probably extinct), Mk 115 MFCS (U.S., extinct), Kollmorgen Model 975 (no sales), TASD (program seems defunct), SMATCALS (abandoned due to end of Cold War). For details, see the 1991/92 edition.

BULGARIA

Several microwave radars have been announced in recent years. Presumably they are used primarily for coast defense, since no warships of Bulgarian design have as yet been built. Some radars may be Russian designs built under license.

Kintex of Sofia advertises a coastal or shipboard radar using a slotted array to produce a 0.7 × 15-deg beam (90-kW peak power with 0.15-, 0.3-, and 1.2-microsec pulses). Range performance: destroyer, 55 km; guided missile boat, 40–59 km; fishing boat, 10–12 km; fixed-wing aircraft, 35–45 km; periscope, 12–18 km; sea buoy, 15–20 km; mine splashdown, 20–25 km; floating mine, 8–10 km. Resolution: 30 m in range, 0.7 deg in bearing. The coastal version is mounted on a ZIL-131 truck, a second truck housing the associated communications center.

The next-generation system is probably an Electron Company X-band frequency-agile pulse-compression TWS radar with a peak power of 25 kW, which can automatically track 40–50 targets and designate 20 of them for engagement (presumably by artillery or by coastal missiles). There are both fixed and mobile versions. The antenna can be either a reflector or a slotted waveguide (for shorter-range surveillance).

Kaliakra is a mobile (truck-mounted) radar to detect surface targets and low fliers. It can detect a surface target at 40 km (resolution 50–100 m) and a fighter aircraft at 80–90 km (resolution 70 m in range, 0.8 deg in bearing). Accuracy is 50–80 m in range and 0.3–0.4 deg in bearing.

At least in shape, the antenna resembles that of the Russian Don Kay.

CANADA

SPG-501 is the TWT-driven version of the Signaal STIR, in the TRUMP class. SPG-502 is the Signaal LIROD, in the TRUMP class. SPG-503 is the magnetron-driven version of the Signaal STIR, in the "City" class. In the "City" class, ADT is provided by a UYK-507 interfacing with both the SPS-49 and the Sea Giraffe.

FIRE-CONTROL SYSTEMS

◆ SPG-515/MK 69

Mk 69 Mod NC6 or Mod 2, a Canadian-developed solid-state digital version of the U.S. GUNAR, employs the Norden X-band solid-state SPG-515 conscan radar (250 kW, 40in enclosed dish, 2.6-deg beam, 39-dB gain, 0.25-microsec pulses at 1000 pps). The new FCS is said to offer a 40% improvement in accuracy against moving incoming targets. Additions include an angle-error indicator and a digital range computer. Limits probably match those of the U.S. system: maximum lead angle 30 deg, maximum target speed 1250 kt. GUNAR was conceived as an on-mount derivative of Mk 56, but the Canadian ships have aloft directors carrying their radars. Typical manning: two in the director, two below decks.

The Canadian destroyer *Annapolis* shows her SPG-515 FCS radar, on the director above her bridge. The big air-search antenna above it is for her SPS-503 radar; above that is her SPS-10D. (G. Till, 1989)

User: Canada (*Annapolis, Gatineau, Terra Nova*).

RADARS

SPS-502 (Cardion version of SPS-10) and SPS-503 survive in the elderly frigate *Nipigon* (and in *Gatineau* and *Terra Nova*, which are to be stricken soon). Marconi's S-band SPS-503, a modified Marconi S1821, is a stealthy pulse-compressed air-search set operating at a peak power of 20 kW (average 800 W) with 54 microsec pulses compressed on reception in a ratio of 207.7:1. It uses an AWS-4 antenna (beam 1.5 × csc^2 to 40 deg). PRF is 739 pps. Note that this radar was *not* adopted for the two major current classes, the TRUMPs and the "City" class. See the 1991/92 edition for further details of these radars.

◆ **LN-66 (CMR-85/90, SPS-59, TPS-66)**

Band: X (9375 MHz)
Beam: 2.5 × 22 deg
Peak Power: 75 kW
Gain: 30 dB
Pulse Width: 1.0 or 0.1 microsec
PRF: 500 or 2000 pps
Scan Rate: 22 rpm
Antenna Dimensions: 36 in
Antenna Weight: Total weight 22.9 kg

Data above refer to LN-66 HP, the search radar of the U.S. LAMPS I helicopter. Alternative antennas: 5 ft (1.6 × 19-deg

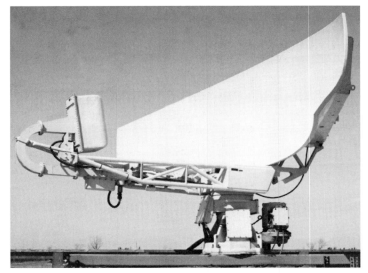

SPS-503 radar antenna at the Canadian Marconi plant, Kanata, Ontario. (Canadian Marconi)

LN-66 occupies the small radome halfway up the mast of the USS *Barnstable County*, 1986. The masthead antenna is SPS-10, and the "washtub" in the foreground is the OE-82 SATCOMM dish. (S. Terzibaschitsch)

beam, 29 dB, scan 24 rpm) and 8 ft (0.88 × 19-deg beam, 31-dB gain). Canadian Marconi offers a 90-kW replacement for the 75-kW transmitter.

This surface-search radar, built by Canadian Marconi, has been very widely exported, both in its shipboard version and in a related helicopter version (on board U.S. LAMPS I helicopters).

A related radar is used for submarine navigation (U.S. *Ohio*-class submarines), on board U.S. LCAC landing craft, and also on board U.S. small combatants such as the SEALs' Seafox. In the 75-kW version described above, range discrimination is 18.3 m. Range scales are 1, 2, 3, 12, 24, 48, and 72 nm.

TPS-66 is a dual-display version used in the U.S. Navy AN/TSQ-108 Radar/Sonar Surveillance Center.

LN-66 SP (CMR-85) is a 6-kW version for submarines and small craft using either a 3ft radome antenna or a 4ft detachable slotted waveguide (1.9 × 26-deg beam, gain 28 dB). Pulse widths are 0.5 and 0.12 microsec (PRFs 1200 and 3000 pps). Minimum detection range is 25 yd, and range scales are 0.5–32 nm.

The basic 10-kW version is designated SPS-59 in U.S. Army (but not Navy) service. Canadian Marconi now offers a 12-kW version, CMR-90: 0.5 microsec/1250 pps or 0.06 microsec/2500 pps. CMR-91 is an alternative 25-kW version with variable pulse width (in 0.05 microsec steps), typically 0.1 microsec/3000 pps, 0.3 microsec/1000 pps, and 1 microsec/900 pps.

Users: Brazil (*Garcia* class), Colombia (*Asheville* class), Greece (*Adams* and *Knox* classes), Malta (Swift type), Mexico (FRAM destroyers), Philippines (PBS and Swift III patrol craft), Saudi Arabia (LCU 1646 class), Senegal (Interceptor class), Spain (*Paul Revere* class), Taiwan (*Knox* class), United States (SH-2F LAMPS I helicopters, some *Spruance* class, some *Knox* class, LCUs, *Iwo Jima* class [except LPH 9], LPD 2, LPD 4 class, LSD 36 class, LST 1171 class, LKA 113 class [except 113], Seafox class, destroyer tenders, ammunition ships, *Mars* class, oilers, *Simon Lake* class, *Hunley* class, *Fulton* class).

CHILE

◆ MM-4/SNG-21

This system, developed by ASMAR (which upgraded the existing Marconi SNG-20 radar; the new radar was designated SNG-21) and the Catholic University of Chile (Valparaiso), was the first domestically produced electronic FCS in Latin America. It entered service in 1989 on board the *Almirante Williams* class. The program began about 1985. The new system takes up about a quarter of the space of its predecessor. The processor is an 8-bit Zilog Z-80 programmed in Macro-Assembler language. A master computer (using a Z-80) controls a master (target) tracker (using Kalman-filtered radar data) and a master (ballistic) predictor to control both 4in and 40mm guns. All target designation, weapon allocation, and computing elements are housed in a single IC Mk 2 console, which has a plasma-screen display. The project was called Maule-Metuc. The -4 may refer to the replacement of the original Signaal M4/1CH FCS.

The X-band (9.2 GHz) SNG-21 radar uses a 1.15m monopulse

The Chilean-developed gun FCS (and two of the 4.4in guns it controls) on board the destroyer *Almirante Williams* in 1992. Although this ship has been retired, a modified version of this system is being developed to replace the British MRS 3 in *Leander* and "County"-class ships in Chilean service. (Dr. R. S. Scheina)

antenna. It can detect targets at 19 nm and track them at 13.5 nm.

A new version of this system is now being developed to replace the MRS 3 FCS of the "County"- and *Leanders*-class ships in Chilean service.

CHINA (PRC)

China Shipbuilding Trading Company (CSSC) has published characteristics of missile boats (Types M47 and EM9) equipped with SR47 search and TR47 fire-control radars, otherwise not described. According to a recent Chinese account, from the mid-1960s to the mid-1970s over 10 naval radars were developed, including at least one monopulse FCS set. Sets listed below amount to four search radars (including two for surface search) and four FCS radars; the statement suggests that there is also at least one submarine search set, and perhaps a range-only periscope set. The Type numbers listed below suggest a classification by frequency range: 300 may be high S-band, 500 may be metric-wave, and 700 may be X-band. Similar numbers are apparently applied to radars for the other Chinese services: 100-series for ground-surveillance sets, 200-series for aircraft radars, some 300-series for battlefield surveillance and fire control (which extend into shipboard radars), 800-series for ground FCS. There are, of course, exceptions to these rules.

"Jiangwei" (and the latest Jianghu) -class frigates and Thai *Naresuan*-class frigates have a new short-range air-search/target indication radar, Type 360 (also designated SR-60 and S-3), presumably a successor to Eye Shield. Its open-work antenna has squared-off ends.

The large air-search antenna on the "Luda"-class prototype *Harbin* resembles (but does not quite match) the antennas of both Thomson-CSF air-traffic-control radars and of the Chinese JY-9 low-altitude air-search set. The latter is a two-beam S-band set (1.5 × 40-deg csc² beam, scan rate 6/12 rpm, peak power 200 kW, pulsewidth 20 microsec, 790 pps). Free-space range (2m² target) is 150 km. Accuracy (resolution) is 80 (120–40) m and 0.3 (1.3) deg. The land-based system, which is made by ECRIEE (East China Institute of Electronic Engineering), can automatically handle 200 plots and maintain 72 tracks. ECCM features include pulse-to-pulse frequency agility over a wide bandwidth, MTI, and automatic spectral processing. MTBF is better than 900 hr. The Chinese designation for the naval radar is Hai Ying ("God Eye").

SEARCH RADARS

◆ Bean Sticks/Pea Sticks/Type 515(?)

The names Bean Sticks and Pea Sticks indicate alternative antennas for the same P-band early-warning radar. Bean Sticks consists of four bays, each with eight yagis. Pea Sticks uses a simpler antenna comprising four much longer yagis with X-shaped supports. This may be the Type 515 air warning radar.

Users: China ("Luda" class [Bean Sticks or Pea Sticks], "Jiangwei" [Pea Sticks], *Zhoushan* [Jianghu III class with Pea Sticks], *Dandong* [Jianghu II class with Pea Sticks]). Other Jianghu-class frigates may have Pea Sticks radars.

◆ Eye Shield (Type 354, MX-902)

Band: C
Beam: 1.2 × 5 deg
Peak Power: 500 kW
Pulse Width: 2 microsec
PRF: 400 or 800 pps
Scan Rate: 4–10 rpm

This low-altitude air-search radar is used for target acquisition on board Jianghu-class frigates. The antenna is roll- and pitch-stabilized. Claimed range on a 10m² target is over 50 nm, accuracy is 5 m in range and 5 mrad in bearing, and resolution is 300 m in range and 1.3 deg in bearing. The system can track four targets and can direct fire on two of them. The antenna is a long, slim paraboloid, similar in overall shape to the Russian Slim Net, except that the Chinese antenna is of solid rather than lattice construction.

The new Luhu-class destroyer *Harbin* displays her Hai Ying air-search radar. The small antenna atop her mainmast is probably for helicopter control. (*Ships of the World*)

The new missile destroyer *Harbin* (lead ship of the Luhu class) shows the big antenna of her Hai Ying (God Eye) air-search radar, aft. The solid mast forward of this radar carries a small search antenna. The forward air-search (target-indication) radar is the French Sea Tiger. The surface-search antenna below it probably belongs to Type 756 (Fin Curve). The topmast above it carries the DESM array associated with the Rapids ESM system; halfway down the lattice mast are the corresponding scimitar jammer antennas. The two big radomes at the base of the mast are for SATCOMM antennas. Forward of and below the mast are a CTM missile director for the Crotale Naval missiles and an FCS radar, reportedly Type 347G. This radar may be similar to the Italian RTN-30X. The gun mount forward appears to be a new type of twin 100mm. (*Ships of the World*)

The "Jiangwei"-class frigate *Huinan* displays her Type 360 short-range air-search/target-indication radar. The dish below is Fog Lamp, controlling HQ-61 missiles fired from the sextuple launcher forward. The small paired radomes at the base of the mast probably cover directional jammers; Jug Pair directional ESM radomes are visible halfway up the mast, below the platform for the Type 756 navigational radar. Omnis seem to be mounted on the yardarm visible above the Type 360 radar. (Singapore MOD via *Ships of the World*)

This Luda-class destroyer carries a Bean Sticks long-range air-search radar (4 × 4 array of yagis) just forward of her after tunnel. The foremast radar is an Eye Shield (MX-902) short-range (target-indication) air-search set. The forward end of the platform carries a surface-search radar. The secondary battery consists of twin 37mm and 25mm machine cannon, and she carries two triple missile launchers. (U.S. Naval Institute)

This Luda-class destroyer carries a Pea Sticks long-range air-search radar. (U.S. Naval Institute)

A Chinese "Jianghu"-class frigate shows an Eye Shield radar at her masthead, with a Type 756 navigational radar (the slotted waveguide) and Square Tie (missile fire control) below it. The 100mm guns are the Chinese version of the old Russian B-34. (U.S. Naval Institute)

The Chinese export designation for Eye Shield is MX-902.
Users: Bangladesh (Jianghu class), China (Luda, Jianghu, Dajiang classes and Dakin-type training ship), Egypt (Jianghu class), Thailand (Jianghu class).

◆ **ESR-1/Type 347(?)**

Band: S
Beam: 2 × 10 deg (dual-beam pattern)
Gain: 33.5 dB
Scan Rate: 30 rpm
Antenna Weight: 350 kg (770 lb)

This low-altitude air-search radar was displayed at the ASIAN-DEX exhibition in Beijing in the fall of 1988. The antenna is roll-stabilized, and the 31cm (12in) PPI is arranged for plot extraction by rollerball. The scope can also display synthetic video, and the radar can extract moving targets. The MTI improvement factor is 22 dB. The manufacturer, the China Shipbuilding Trading Company, claims that ESR-1 can detect a 0.1m² sea-skimming missile (flying at a height of 8 m) at a range greater than 12 km (about 13,000 yd).

The data above are taken from the manufacturer's brochure. No power or pulse data were given.

This may be the Type 347 target acquisition radar for twin 57mm guns in Luhu-class (Type EF5) destroyers.

◆ Fin Curve

This surface search radar, superseded by Type 756, is a copy of the Decca 707.

User: China (Luda [some], Jiangnan, LSM, Yanbing, Dajiang, Fuqing classes).

◆ Rice Screen (Sea Eagle)/Type 381

Band: C (described as upper end of G-band)
Beam: 2.7 × 1.4 deg
Peak Power: 150 kW
Pulse Width: (a) 40 (b) 20 microsec (compressed to 1 microsec)
PRF: (a) 370 (b) 730 (average power 2.2 kW) pps
Scan Rate: 5 rpm

This planar-array 3D pulse-compression radar entered service in the mid-1980s and was publicly displayed (with the data given above and below) at the ASIANDEX 1988 exhibition in Beijing. Rice Screen is marketed for export by the Nanjing Marine Institute.

Rice Screen (*top*), Type 756, and Fog Lamp (*bottom*) on a Jiangdong-class frigate. (U.S. Naval Institute)

There are two types, with larger and smaller antennas. The data above refer to a large antenna, much taller than it is wide. A smaller type is reportedly 2.3 × 3.0 m, which would not quite correspond to the beam figures above. However, the beam figures come from the claimed resolution performance, and the resolution in azimuth may be degraded somewhat as the beam sweeps up while the radar turns. The radar antenna shows a prominent fin on one side, presumably carrying a serpentine (fre-

quency-scanning) waveguide. Phase shifters are presumably used to allow the radar to sweep in frequency (both for pulse compression and for frequency agility) without sweeping its beam up and down.

This radar can track 10 targets simultaneously, using what the manufacturer calls an extraction PPI operating semiautomatically. Probably the operator designates the targets to the associated computer. Two or more entries of the same target (on subsequent scans) provide the computer with a track. The operator then monitors later detections of the same target to see whether it remains on a constant course and speed. The target's altitude may be as high as 25,000 m (82,000 ft). There are two operating modes: low angle (up to 7.2 deg in elevation) to a maximum tracking range of 180 km (197,000 yd), and high angle (to 28.8 deg) out to a maximum range of 120 km (131,000 yd).

The transmitter is a TWT CFA chain, and reception is coherent, with an MTI improvement factor of 30 dB. Accuracy is 100 m in range and 0.8 deg in azimuth and elevation. Resolution is 200 m in range. Operation is over a wide band (10% of frequency), with adaptive frequency selection on a pulse-to-pulse basis.

This radar is eventually to be mounted on board all "Luda"-class destroyers, to direct shore-based fighters in support of naval forces at sea.

This radar is probably Type 381, developed by Shanghai Laboratory Equipment Factory, Northwest Telecommunications Institute, No. 724 Institute of the 7th Academy, and Shanghai No. 4 Radio Factory. There is also an improved Type 381A using a broad-band high-power forward-wave amplifier.

User: China ("Luda" hulls 108, 110, and 132 and Jiangdong class).

◆ Type 756

Band: (a and b) X (c) S
Beam: (a) 1.3 × 20 deg (b) 0.8 × 18 deg (c) 2 × 22 deg
Peak Power: 50 kW
Gain: (a) 30 dB (b) 32 dB (c) 27 dB
Pulse Width: (a) 0.08 microsec (b) 0.5 microsec (c) 1 microsec
PRF: (a) 2000 (b) 1000 (c) 500 pps
Scan Rate: 18–22 rpm
Antenna Dimensions: (a) 2 m (b) 3 m (c) 3.8 m

This navigational radar supersedes Fin Curve; it uses a slotted-waveguide antenna. Range scales are 0.5, 1.5, and 3 nm with short pulse; 6, 12, and 24 nm with 0.5-microsec pulse; and 48 and 96 nm with long pulse. The complete system uses both X- and S-band antennas for all-weather performance. Minimum range is about 30 m (mast height 15 m), and range discrimination is 25 m. Accuracy is 1% of range or 0.02 nm (whichever is greater) and 1 deg.

Users: Bangladesh (Jianghu, *Huchuan* classes), China ("Luda" [some have Fin Curve], Jianghu, Jiangdong, *Huchuan*, T-43, ex-U.S. LST classes, Dadie-class AGI, Dakin-class training ship), Egypt (Jianghu class), Rumania (*Huchuan* class).

FIRE-CONTROL SYSTEMS

The early generation of FCS radars also included Type 342, which may be Fog Lamp.

◆ Type 331

Chinese version of the Soviet Square Tie SSM missile-control radar.

Users: Bangladesh (Jianghu, Huangfeng, Hoku classes), China ("Luda," Jianghu, Huangfeng ["Osa"], Homa, Houku classes), Egypt (Jianghu and Houku classes), Pakistan (Huangfeng, Houku classes), Thailand (Jianghu class).

◆ Type 341 (Rice Lamp)

X(I)-band radar for 37mm and 57mm fire control, also designated MW-5 for land service. The radar is used for target cueing, typically for four twin mounts, the guns being aimed manually.

Users: China (Luda [57mm in some ships], Jianghu, Jiangwei class), Thailand (Jianghu class).

(Top to bottom) Rice Lamp, Fog Lamp, and a twin HQ 61 missile launcher on a Jiangdong-class frigate. (U.S. Naval Institute)

◆ Type 343 (Wok Wan)

Chinese version of the Soviet Sun Visor radar, for main battery fire control. Wok Wan is the associated Chinese version of the extinct Russian Sphaera FCS. Sphaera was a stabilized director with a reported maximum tracking range of 81,000 yd; maximum AA target speed is reportedly 950 kt. Sun Visor (Yakor-2M), which appeared in 1953, was an X-band (9.3–9.44 GHz) radar (0.8-deg beam, 0.2 microsec pulses/2500 or 3500 pps, 40 scans/sec).

Wok Wan (on the 100mm director) is shown aboard the Chinese "Jiang-wei"-class frigate *Anqing*, 1992. The fat tubes apparently accommodate HQ-61 AAW missiles. (*Ships of the World*)

Users: China (Luda, Jiangwei, Jianghu III, Jiangdong classes), Thailand (Jianghu class).

◆ EFR-1

The China Shipbuilding Trading Company displayed this new naval radar FCS at the ASIANDEX exhibition at Beijing in No-

vember 1988. EFR-1 is a radar FCS externally similar to the French Castor series (i.e., with a Cassegrain antenna), with a television camera and a laser alongside the radar. EFR-1 was described as operating in X-band, with MTI processing, and was credited with the ability to acquire targets with cross-sections of less than 2 m^2 at ranges beyond 30 km (and small sea-skimming missiles at 13 km).

EFR-1 is being offered as a feature of several new warship designs being offered for export; presumably this system is planned for a new generation of Chinese warships.

◆ Fog Lamp/Type 342(?)

This radar is the H/I-band SAM fire control for the HY-61 missile, in the Jiangdong class. Other ships are fitted with canister-launched HQ-61, and presumably also with this radar (the Jiangdongs have rail-type launchers). This may be Type 342.

◆ Type 702/MW-5

Land- (and possibly sea-) based 57mm X-band fire-control radar, derived from the Soviet Fire Can conscan radar (ultimately derived from the U.S. SCR 584). This radar is used to control coastal batteries.

◆ Round Ball

FC radar for 30mm guns, superseding Bass Tilt.

A Chinese-built "Osa"-class (Huangfeng class) missile boat shows the big radome of her Round Ball fire-control radar, aft. This radar is also on board Haijui-class patrol boats. (*Ships of the World*)

User: China (Haijui class, some Huangfeng ["Osa II"], Dakin training ship).

◆ Twin Eyes

Chinese-designed optical director for 100mm guns, in Jianghu IV, Jianghu I/II, and "Jiangnan" classes. This system was exported to Bangladesh and Egypt for Jianghu-class frigates.

◆ Type 88C

This FCS was announced at the 1991 Paris Air Show. Like other current Chinese weapons-control systems, it is built around a digital-computer console, in this case designated ZKJ-3. A published system diagram shows inputs from a radar (via a PPI bootstrap routine, presumably digital processing of digitized radar data rather than true ATD), a TV tracker, and a laser rangefinder, as well as a log and gyro. There is a backup optical director (JM 833). The system can control both guns and PL-9 missiles. Reportedly this system equips the Chinese "Houjian" (Type 520T) demonstrator FAC and the Thai Jianghu III (*Chao Praya*) -class frigates.

COASTAL RADARS

Details of four types of coastal radars have been published. Type 404A is an X-band set with a solid elliptical antenna similar in shape to that of Eye Shield. Claimed accuracy (resolution): 100 (200) m, 0.35 (0.8) deg. The second type is an otherwise undesignated X-band coastal tracking radar, using a 200-kW transmitter (pulse width 0.2 microsec), and a 1 × 2-deg beam antenna.

An Egyptian Jianghu-class frigate shows a Twin Eyes optical director atop her bridge. Radars on the mast, top to bottom, are Eye Shield (Type 354), a Type 756 navigational radar, a Square Tie (Type 331) missile target-designator radar, and a Decca navigational radar. (U.S. Naval Institute)

Claimed range on a 7500t target is 60 nm; accuracy (resolution) is 30 (60) m and 1.5 (20) mils. The third type is the Eagle coastal radar, a mobile (truck-mounted) X-band radar. A published photograph suggests that the radar proper is radome-mounted, with a large co-located IFF antenna (which itself resembles a radar antenna but has far too thin a mesh to work at X-band). Claimed range is 50 km on a 1000–2000t ship, and accuracy is 15 m in range and 0.09 deg in bearing.

In addition, at the Paris Air Show in 1989, CEIEC (China National Electronics Import and Export Corporation) announced a new JY-9 low-altitude search radar, which could also be used for coastal defense. It operates in S-band, using a dual-beam low-sidelobe antenna (4.2 × 7.5 m, for a 1.3 × 40-deg beam; the upper and lower beams cross at 4 deg of elevation). The transmitter is pulse-to-pulse frequency-agile and coherent, for Doppler MTI, and the radar automatically detects and tracks targets. The antenna can be erected on a lattice mast for better low-altitude coverage. The radar can be set up or dismantled by four operators in 20 min.

DENMARK

The domestic radar manufacturer is Terma Elektronik AS. CWS-1 (Plessey AWS-1 with a different antenna) was replaced by AWS-6 in 1985–87, and is now extinct. CWS-2 (AWS-2 with a different antenna) survives on board the *Falster*-class minelayers and in the one ship of this class built for Turkey. The NWS series are surface-search radars. NWS-1 (*Soloven* class) is a Decca slotted-waveguide radar. NWS-3 (*Willemoes* class) is Terma 20T48, a Decca 1629 built under license. NWS-4 and -5 are submarine radars, presumably Calypso (French) antennas with Terma electronics. NWS-6 is Skanter-Mil X; -10 is Skanter-Mil S. The Royal Swedish Navy designation for the Terma navigational radar in the *Goteborg* and *Stockholm* classes is PN-612 (it is Skanter 009 in older units).

◆ Terma GCA Radar

Band: X (9.0–9.2 GHz)
Peak Power: 80 kW
Pulse Width: 0.18 microsec (0.02 microsec)
PRF: 3500 pps

This radar has been adopted (in navalized form) for the Brazilian carrier *Minas Gerais*. The data above refer to the land-based version. The radar uses two separate antennas for elevation and azimuth, as in the U.S. SPN-35 and the Italian SPN-720. Both outputs are displayed together on a 16in CRT (elevation above, azimuth below, both in expanded form: 8× elevation, 3× azi-

muth). The range scales are 10 and 15 nm (range markers at 1nm intervals). Electronic cursors on the elevation display show glide path and maximum permissible downward deviation (safety cursor). Typically, the elevation display shows alignment lines at 6, 3, and 1 deg, and the azimuth display shows similar lines at 15, 5, 0, and −5 deg. These data apply to a GCA-radar modernization program offered by Terma for any of a range of standard GCA radars. The beam characteristics are probably similar to those of the U.S. SPN-35.

◆ Terma Skanter Mil Radars (NWS-1/2; Skanter 009)

Band: X (9 GHz) or S (3 GHz)
Beam: 1 deg (horizontal beamwidth) at X-band (2 deg for S-band version)
Peak Power: 20 kW
Pulse Width: (a) 0.06 (b) 0.6 microsec
PRF: (a) 4400 (b) 2200 pps
Gain: Greater than 30 dB (X) or 28.5 dB (S-band)
Scan Rate: 24 or 48 rpm (60-Hz power; 20 or 40 rpm using 50-Hz power supply)
Antenna Dimensions: 2.1 m (X-band), 4 m (S-band)

These are standard slotted-waveguide surface search and navigational radars for the Danish and Swedish navies. The data above refer to a radar whose development was completed in 1972. Both X- and S-band versions use magnetrons, and radars in both bands can feed a common display. All displays are bright (daylight) raster scans; they can show tactical system symbology and can operate with automatic tracking.

Users (Skanter 009): Brazil (Skanter Mil in *Minas Gerais*, other Terma radars for patrol and service craft), Denmark (*Nils Juels, Thetis, Hvidbjornen, Stanflex 300* classes), Sweden (PN-612 in *Goteborg* and *Stockholm* classes; 009 in *Hugin, Spica II, Skanor, Carlskrona, Alvsborg, Landsort, Arko, Gassten, Gilloga, Orion* classes; Terma TM-610 in *Dalero* class).

FRANCE

All French shipboard naval radars are products of Thomson-CSF. TRS numbers in parentheses are the commercial designations, where they apply. Many directors are produced by CSEE.

The French carrier *Clemenceau*, 1972, shows typical radars (*top to bottom*): TACAN, IFF Mk 10, DRBV 22, DRBV 20 (large-ship version), DRBI 10 (both fore and aft of the funnel). (G. Arra)

RADARS

◆ DRBI 10

Band: S
Beam: 2 × 2 deg
Peak Power: 1000–2000 kW
Gain: 37 dB
Pulse Width: 4 microsec
PRF: 500 pps
Scan Rate: 4 rpm (vertically: 800 scans/min)
Antenna Dimensions: 3.4 × 3.4 m

Like the extinct U.S. SPS-8 and -30, this height-finder uses a high-speed (Robinson) scanner to move its beam vertically. Work on this radar began in 1958, and each carrier was fitted with two sets. A mobile land-based radar, Picador (TRS 2200), was developed from it (the prototype appeared in 1968). Data above are taken from the published details of Picador. Range on a fighter is said to be 100–140 nm.
User: France (*Clemenceau* class, *Ile d'Oléron*).

DRBI 23 occupies the big radome of the French frigate *Suffren*. The two 100mm guns are controlled by the DRBC 32A forward of the bridge, and the navigational radar is DRBN 32. The small radar on the foremast just above the big radome is DRBV 50. (Dr. R. S. Scheina)

◆ DRBI 23

DRBI 23 uses a large L-band radome-enclosed pulse-Doppler inverse-Cassegrain antenna. It uses stacked beams for monopulse height finding. The peak power of several megawatts is generated by a carcinotron fed through six amplifier stages. Plots are automatically extracted (ATD) for use by the ship's SENIT combat system.
User: France (*Suffren* class).

◆ DRBJ 11

Band: S
Scan Rate: 15 rpm
Antenna Dimensions: diameter 3 m (dish)

The Thomson-CSF electronically scanned radar uses a circular planar antenna covered by 1000–1500 phase shifters, which steer the beam in elevation (over a 60-deg angle) and in bearing. The antenna itself is inclined at a 15-deg angle and rotates inside a radome. DRBJ 11 scans electronically in both elevation and bearing to detect and confirm a target on a single scan, then begins tracking on the second scan. That is, once a target has been detected, the beam skips back to redetect it before the array has fully turned away. Surveillance range is about 100 nm.
Development began in 1982; the current version is DRBJ 11B (DRBJ 11 suffered from incurable ECCM problems).
User: France (*Charles de Gaulle* and *Cassard* class).

The French frigate *Jean Bart* displays the radome of her DRBJ 11B radar aft (just forward of the two SPG-51 missile guidance radars). (B. Prezelin via *Ships of the World*)

◆ DRBN 32

Decca RM 1226 navigational radar (see the British section, below) is being superseded by Decca 1229.

◆ DRBR 51

DRBR 51 is the Masurca missile's C-band monopulse guidance radar, roughly equivalent to the U.S. SPG-55. As in the U.S. case, the 7cm beam-riding channel is no longer used. The main antenna tracks the target (with CWI for semiactive guidance), and smaller antennas generate gathering and reference beams. The two tracking channels are designated "blue" and "yellow."
User: France (*Suffren* class).

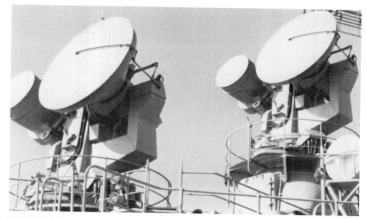

DRBR 51 directors for the French Masurca missile. (*Ships of the World*)

◆ DRBV 15 (Sea Tiger: TRS 3001)

Band: S
Beam: 1.65 × 8 deg csc^2 (to 45 deg)
Peak Power: 60 kW (1 kW average)
Gain: 29.5 dB
Pulse Width: (a) 5.5 (b) 12 microsec (compressed to 0.5) (In a later version, this radar produces two types of burst, each consisting of a 0.5-microsec pulse and then a chirp, either 7.5 or 15.5 microsec long, compressed to 0.5 microsec in either case.)
PRF: (a) 2200 (b) 1100 pps
Scan Rate: 12 or 24 rpm (also given as 15 or 30 rpm)
Antenna Dimensions: 4.54 m
Antenna Weight: 675 kg

Sea Tiger is a combined air/surface and antisea-skimmer search radar (maximum range 170 km to 55 deg elevation) for medium and larger ships, its design emphasizing a low false-alarm rate to permit automatic tracking. It was originally the search radar associated with frigate versions of Vega, in effect a larger equivalent of Triton.

DRBV 15C. (Thomson-CSF)

DRBV 15 on board the frigate *Latouche-Treville*. The open frames at the masthead are part of a Telegon HF/DF; below them are UHF/DF dipoles. The ship's monopulse ESM arrays are on the platform below these DF arrays, partly hidden by the radar antenna. (DCN photo by Jean Biaugeaud)

The chief antijam and anticlutter measures are coherent transmission/reception (which allows Doppler filtering of clutter), true frequency agility (either pulse-to-pulse on the non-Doppler channel, or randomly in short bursts of 10 pulses on the Doppler channel), and use of two pulses at two different frequencies. The radar uses pulse compression and detects automatically using CFAR; and DRBV 15 can provide digital data to a weapons system. Doppler processing is by four- or eight-point FFT.

There are two operating modes, each using two pulses: one long pulse with compression followed by one short pulse for short-range surveillance, at a different frequency. PRF can be jittered ("wobbulated").

Free-space range on a $2m^2$ target (Swerling 3 case) is 110 km; on a $0.1m^2$ nonfluctuating target (probability of detection 0.9), 40 km. Actual performance depends upon the degree of surface clutter. Clutter-rejection ratios: 45 dB versus ground clutter, 40 dB versus rain and sea clutter.

DRBV 15C (Sea Tiger Mk 2) has a roll-stabilized planar-array antenna (30 dB, 1.65-deg beam) with reduced sidelobes and better gain at high elevation (to detect steep divers). Free-space range is 100 km on a fighter and 50 km on a missile. The short-range 2D battlefield radar, TRS 2630, uses a very similar antenna technology. The new antenna can be coupled to an existing Sea Tiger transmitter/receiver assembly. However, Sea Tiger Mk 2 also employs a new two-stage (TWT and CFA) coherent transmitter/receiver. The two stages allow it to operate at two power levels, depending on whether a voltage is applied to the CFA. There are two channels: air (long pulse and pulse compression) and surface (short noncompressed pulse). The transmitter is frequency-agile (pulse to pulse or burst to burst). There are four receiving modes: normal surveillance (60 nm instrumented range, 15 rpm, FFT4), long-range surveillance (90 nm, 15 rpm, MTI), antimissile surveillance (30 nm, 30 rpm, FFT4), and antimissile surveillance in bad weather (30 nm, 15 rpm, FFT8). Here FFT4 and -8 refer to the use of four or eight FFT Doppler filters. By rejecting signals in five out of eight Doppler filters, the radar can filter out moving clutter (sea returns). The receiver improvement factor is 40 dB against sea and rain clutter. Air tracks are automatically initiated (ADT); they are also automatically associated with IFF returns. The system can carry up to 128 tracks.

Users:

Sea Tiger: Colombia (FS 1500 class), Saudi Arabia (*Al Madinah* class).

DRBV 15: France (*Cassard* class, last three *Georges Leygues* class [DRBV 15A], *Duquesne* [will replace DRBV 50 in *Suffren*], *Aconit*).

DRBV 15C (Sea Tiger Mk 2): France (*Charles de Gaulle* [first order, November 1989], *La Fayette* class, experimental ship *Monge*), Saudi Arabia (*La Fayette* class), Taiwan (*La Fayette* class).

◆ MARS (DRBV 21A; TRS 3015)

This 2D L-band radar is related to the solid-state DRBV 26C and to Astral. MARS uses a solid-state transmitter and employs digital pulse compression. It employs a two-module transmitter (DRBV 26C has 16 modules), with a total of 32 (rather than 256) power elements. Instrumented ranges are 110 km for the air channel and 80 km for the optional surface channel. The MTI improvement factor is 45 dB for fixed echoes. The radar cabinet is fitted for (but not necessarily with) an extraction/tracking (ADT) unit to automate its operation. The 600-kg antenna (a modified version of that of DRBV 22) has a gain of 26 dB and scans at 12 rpm. The receiver is that of DRBV 15C.

This radar was announced in the fall of 1990. It is now being offered with the MR-05 antenna under the designation MARS 05; in the *Floreals* it will have the reconditioned DRBV 22 antenna. In this form it should be able to detect aircraft at 60 nm, and the optional automatic tracker can accommodate up to 100 tracks. This radar has sometimes been referred to as DRBV 24.

User: France (*Floreal* class, *Foudre* [on next refit], one installed at a Pacific naval base).

◆ DRBV 22/23 (Jupiter: THD 1077)

Band: L
Beam: 2.5 × 50 deg (3.5 × 16 deg csc²)
Peak Power: 2000 kW (600 kW)
Gain: (26 dB)
Pulse Width: 2.5 microsec (1.3 or 4 microsec)
PRF: 450 pps (600 or 200 pps)
Scan Rate: 7.5 and 15 rpm (6 or 12 rpm)
Antenna Dimensions: 24.6 × 9.9 ft (5.18 × 2.13 m)

Jupiter (now extinct) was the export version of DRBV 23; its characteristics are listed above (DRBV 22 data in parentheses). DRBV 22 resembled the U.S. SPS-6B externally; DRBV 22C introduced a new elliptical stabilized antenna, which in turn was combined with a new and much more powerful transmitter in DRBV 23. Development of this set began in 1961; its maximum range is about 160 nm. DRBV 22's range is about 70 nm.

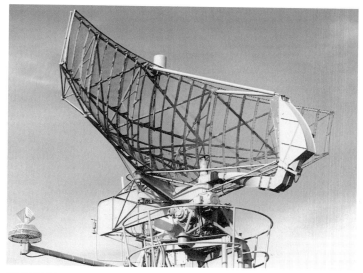

DRBV 22A on *Aconit*, 1993. DRBV 21A (MARS) uses the same antenna. (Stuart Slade, DMS/Forecast International)

Users:

DRBV 22A: France (*Aconit*), Portugal (*Commandante Rivière* class), Uruguay (*Commandante Rivière* class)
DRBV 22C: France (trials ship *Ile D'Oléron*)
DRBV 22D: France (*Jeanne d'Arc*)
DRBV 22E: France (experimental ship *Rance*)
DRBV 23B: France (*Clemenceau* class)

◆ DRBV 26 (Jupiter II: TRS 3010)/DRBV 26C (Jupiter IIS)/ DRBV 26D (Jupiter 08)

Band: L (23 cm)
Beam: 2.5 × 8.3 csc^2 (to 50 deg)
Peak Power: 2 MW (average 2 kW)
Gain: 29 dB
Pulse Width: 2.5 microsec
PRF: 450 pps (fixed or staggered)
Scan Rate: 7.5 or 15 rpm
Antenna Dimensions: 7.535 × 3.05 m
Antenna Weight: 1000 kg approx (total 1450 kg)

Work on an improved Jupiter, DRBV 26, began in 1972, for the new generation of missile ships. Range is said to be 150+ nm (on a 10m^2 target). Protection against false alarms and clutter includes a low-sidelobe antenna, filters for protection against signals from nearby ships (high-frequency bands as well as the same band), multiple reception channels with wide dynamic-range receivers and anticlutter circuits, MTI for air surveillance, and a CFAR antijam receiver. The main improvement over Jupiter I may have been in reliability. Resolution is 400 m and 2 deg.

Jupiter IIS (DRBV 26C or TRS 3011) has a pulse-compression transmitter (130 microsec, compressed to 0.8) and is frequency-agile on a burst-to-burst or pulse-to-pulse basis. The tube transmitter of Jupiter II is replaced by a solid-state transmitter consisting of 16 modules in parallel. Claimed reliability: MTBF for each module is 6060 hr, and for the entire transmitter, excluding the modules, 2180 hr. MTTR is 15 min for the transmitter (excluding modules) and 4.5 min/module; modules can be replaced while transmitting. Thomson-CSF claims that the new transmitter makes for a service life 6 times that of any earlier radar, and better than 99% availability. Operating voltages in the trans-

DRBV 26C (Jupiter IIS). (Thomson-CSF)

mitter are only 50 volts since no single transmitter need be particularly powerful. Transmission frequency is very stable because of the use of a frequency synthesizer, making it possible to use more sophisticated types of signal processing, such as Doppler filtering (using FFTs). Air tracks are automatically initiated and followed; surface targets are automatically tracked after manual acquisition. The radar can track up to 64 targets automatically, handing over their coordinates to the associated CDS. A 2m^2 fighter can be detected at 215 km (which can be increased to 250 km by adding an additional transmitter module to the 16). Instrumented ranges: 350 km at normal power, 200 km at reduced power (backup mode, at which level no cooling is required), 60 km in optional surface-channel mode. The MTI improvement factor is 45 dB for fixed echoes. In this version the antenna weighs 1630 kg.

Growth possibilities for DRBV 26 include provision of a three-beam antenna (for "2½D" search capability) and an increase in transmitter power by a factor of 2 or 4.

DRBV 26D or Jupiter 08 (Jupiter electronics and the LW-08 antenna) was announced in 1993. This is the version sold to Taiwan for *La Fayette*–class frigates. It has two (vice one) transmitters in parallel to double its average power, and a track data processor dedicated to multisensor tracking.

Users:

DRBV 26A: France (*Tourville* class, first four *Georges Leygues*, and *Cassard*)
DRBV 26C: China ("Luda" hulls 17 and 18), France (*Jean Bart*)
DRBV 26D: France (*Charles de Gaulle*), Taiwan (*La Fayette*–class frigates)

DRBV 27 (Astral, TRS 3505) was de-selected as the FAMS long-range radar at the end of 1996, but it may ultimately be installed on board the *Charles de Gaulle*. See the 1991/92 edition for details.

◆ DRBV 50

Band: C (5350 to 5750 MHz)
Beam: 1.3 × 20 deg (csc^2 20 to 70 deg)
Peak Power: 250 kW
Gain: 28 dB
Pulse Width: (a) 1.25 microsec (b) 0.25 microsec
PRF: (a) 750 (b) 2000–4000 (manually adjusted) pps

This low-flier/surface-search (and helicopter control) radar was developed in the late 1950s, specifically for the *Commandante Rivière* class. It was intended to provide solid cover (of 1m² targets) out to 10 nm, between −7 and +70 deg elevation, for cover up to 10,000 ft (the antenna is tilted up at 3 deg). The unstabilized antenna scans at high speed. The antenna design is unusual. It consists of a pair of superimposed cheeses, with a dielectric lens across the aperture to form the csc² beam. Unlike contemporary British "cheeses," this one is not blocked by the feed. Instead, energy reaching the back of the bottom cheese is coupled to the upper, unblocked cheese by a long slot parallel to the back of the antenna. The antenna radiates from its upper portion.

DRBV 50 was relatively unsuccessful, and in French service has largely been superseded by DRBV 52.

Users: France (carriers, *Jeanne d'Arc, Suffren, Rhin, Ile D'Oléron*), Portugal (*Commandante Rivière* class).

◆ DRBV 51/Triton II MTI (TRS 3035)

Band: C (5.5–5.8 GHz)
Peak Power: 200 kW
Pulse Width: (a) 0.6 (b) 1.7 microsec (DRBV 51A and 51B) (c) 0.6 microsec (DRBV 51C)
PRF: (a) 1045–1090, 1165–1190, 1215–1245, 1280–1305, 1383–1393, 1500–1600, 1808–1830, 1960–2020, 2085–2145 pps (b) 349–360, 420–440, 500–510, 540–580, 590–615, 675–715 pps (c) 1013 pps staggered (for MTI)
Scan Rate: 24 rpm (DRBV 51A and 51B); 30 rpm (DRBV 51C)

Data apply to DRBV 51A. Triton II MTI has a 2 × 22-deg beam (antenna 2.3 × 1.4 m, including pedestal; gain 28 dB); peak power is 250 kW. Pulse widths are (a) 0.5 and (b) 1.0 microsec, and the staggered PRFs for MTI are around 1820 pps. The adjustable PRFs are (a) 1000–2000 and (b) 333–666 pps. Scan rate is 12 or 24 rpm.

The corvette *d'Estienne d'Orves* shows a DRBV 51A main search radar and a DRBC 32E fire-control radar atop her superstructure. The two light-colored circles in the after superstructure cover two torpedo-firing catapults. The small slotted waveguide immediately above the bridge is DRBN 32. (U.S. Naval Institute)

Triton II MTI is a combination air- and surface-search radar intended as the primary search and target indicator for small ships, and as the target indicator for ships equipped with a long-range air-search radar such as Jupiter (DRBV 26). Detection range on a 2m² air target is over 30 km.

The main features are a lightweight low-sidelobe antenna; a tunable-frequency (and adjustable-PRF) transmitter; an antijam (STC, CFAR) receiver; and a linear digital MTI, useful at ranges of up to 56 km, for clutter rejection. The MTI uses a three-memory filter with a minimum blind speed of 340 m/sec (0.5-microsec pulses). The CFAR channel uses 1.5-microsec pulses. Clutter-rejection ratio: ground, 30 dB; sea (3 m/sec), 25 dB.

DRBV 51A, a low-altitude air-search and Exocet target-designation radar, is a Triton with a higher-gain slotted-waveguide antenna (for longer range). DRBV 51B and 51C are secondary air-search versions with conventional antennas.

DRBV 51 (*top*) and DRBV 26 (*below*) search radars on board the destroyer *Duguay-Trouin*. (L. van Ginderen)

Users:

Triton II MTI: Libya (Combattante IIG), Greece (Combattante III), Nigeria (Combattante IIIG).
DRBV 51: Argentina (A69 class [51A]), France (A69 class [51A], *Georges Leygues* class [first four ships: 51C], *Tourville* class [51B], *Ouragan* class [51A]).

◆ DRUA-33 (Calypso)

Band: X
Beam: 3 × 8.5 deg
Peak Power: 70 kW
Gain: Less than 29 dB
Pulse Width: (a) 0.15 (b) 0.5 microsec
PRF: (a) 1500–3000 (b) 500–1000 pps
Scan Rate: 12 or 24 rpm
Antenna Dimensions: 1 m × 48 cm
Antenna Weight: 60 kg (total weight 450 kg)

Data are for Calypso III. Calypso II (THD 1030) introduced the magnetron and antenna used in Calypso III (TRS 3100), which adds a precise range measurement facility. Calypso III was developed in conjunction with the German IKL design organization, for Type 209 submarines, with a special nonpenetrating mast, and was adopted by three navies. Calypso IV (TRS 3110) uses the same antenna and console as Calypso III, but with a navigational radar klystron (25 kW) transmitter, to simulate a merchant ship radar (1 microsec and 50 nsec pulses for long and short ranges). This is presumably the version incorporating Terma electronics (Thomson-CSF does not produce a navigational radar of its own). Operating modes for all versions: continuous transmission, sector scan (10 to 180 deg; quick scan over 10 deg), manual scan, short-time transmission (0.1 or 1 sec only), and silence/receive only (dummy load). Range on a 10m² ASW airplane at 8000 ft: Calypso II, 16 nm; Calypso III, 18 nm; Calypso IV, 20 km (10.9 nm).

Masts of the French submarine *Sirene*, February 1995, include one at right carrying a Calypso antenna. (H&L van Ginderen)

Users:

Calypso: Argentina (Type 209/1200), Brazil (Calypso III in Type 209/1400 Mod 3), Chile (Type 209/1400), Colombia (Type 209/1200), Denmark (Type 205 and Type 207, with Terma electronics), Ecuador (Type 209/1300), Greece (Type 209/1100 and /1200), Indonesia (Type 209/1300), Korea (Calypso IV in Type 209/1200), Norway (modernized Type 207s, probably with Terma electronics), Peru (Type 209/1200), Sweden (version with Terma electronics), Turkey (Type 209/1200; probably later Calypso in Type 209/1400), Venezuela (Type 209/1300). Three navies bought Calypso III. Calypso may have been sold to China along with other submarine systems, for the Han and Xia classes.

DRUA-33: France (all submarines; DRUA 33C in *Agosta* class), Spain (*Agosta* and possibly *Daphne* classes). The earlier DRUA-31 survives in Pakistani, Portuguese, and possibly Spanish *Daphne*-class submarines.

◆ Arabel

Arabel is the multifunction X-band radar for Aster missile control (FAAMS system). The planar antenna is inclined at 30 deg inside a radome, rotating at 60 rpm. The beam is 2 deg wide and

Arabel radar. (Direction de Constructions Navales)

can scan up to 75 deg in elevation. The transmitter can hop frequencies over 10% of its frequency range. Thus, the radar is a much shorter-range, higher data-rate expression of much the same technology as is used in DRBJ 11. Production antennas will use a lens antenna (Radant) to steer the beam, reducing the overall number of phase shifters from several thousand to about 100, and drastically reducing both cost and energy consumption.

The first development contract was announced in April 1988, with completion of a naval prototype scheduled for the early 1990s, to meet the SAAM schedule (service entry 1999). SAAM is a short-range system, and Arabel is designed to match, with a stated range of about 50 km against $0.5m^2$ missiles and 100 km against larger targets. Later figures were: 70 km (37.7 nm) against an airplane and 20 km (10.7 nm) against a missile. The associated computer is to be able to conduct simultaneous monopulse tracking of 50 targets, and to direct 16 simultaneous engagements.

At the 1992 Bourget Naval exhibition, two distinct versions of Arabel were shown, one for target acquisition and one for fire control. The first production Arabel fire-control radar began land tests in December 1993 (prototype tests were conducted in 1989–90). Sea tests on board *Ile d'Oléron* began late in 1995. As of mid-1995, the first production radar (which had already been completed) was scheduled for delivery (for the carrier *Charles de Gaulle*) in June 1996.

Arabel stands for Antenne Radar Balayage Electronique.

Users: France (carrier *Charles de Gaulle*, Project Horizon air defense ships), Saudi Arabia (Sawari 2 *La Fayette*–class frigates). British Project Horizon ships, with longer-range missiles (PAAMS system), will use the Anglo-Italian EMPAR radar instead of Arabel.

◆ Triton/Neptune (TRS 3030/3035, THD 1040)/Triton G (TRS 3050, DRBV 52)

Band: C (5.3 cm)
Beam: 2×22 deg
Peak Power: 250 kW (200 kW in early units)
Gain: 38 dB
Pulse Width: 0.2, 0.5, or 0.7 microsec
PRF: Variable over a wide range
Scan Rate: 12 or 24 rpm
Antenna Dimensions: 2.5×0.4 m
Antenna Weight: 170 kg (350 kg if stabilized)

This combined air/surface-surveillance and target indication radar, for small- and medium-sized ships, was developed as part of the Vega system. Triton can shift both frequency and PRF as a counter-countermeasure. The antenna is not stabilized. Triton can detect a $2m^2$ air target at 30–45 km. Accuracy in range is 30 m. Work began in 1967, and the prototype appeared in 1968.

TRS 3035 adds an MTI filter channel to the basic Triton for air search, and a clutter-suppression channel (with extended dynamic range) for surface search.

Triton G is a pulse-compressed (8-kW peak power, pulse width 6.5/12 microsec compressed to 0.5 microsec; an uncompressed 0.5-microsec pulse can be included in the burst for close-range surveillance) ADT (32 tracks) version. Air (not surface) tracks are automatically initiated. This radar uses the Sea Tiger (DRBV 15) signal processor and a coherent TWT transmitter with MTI processing. Antenna gain is reduced to 27 dB (antenna width is 2.3 m, weight 180 kg), but clutter processing improvement is 40 dB. Scan rate is increased to 40 rpm. A $2m^2$ target can be detected at over 19 km. The lowest blind speed is 800 m/sec. The French navy considered adopting this radar as DRBV 52.

Users:

Triton: Ecuador (*Quito* class), Greece (Combattante IIIN class and Combattante II class), Libya (Combattante II class), Malaysia (Combattante II 4AL class), and Peru (PR-72–560 class).

Triton G: Germany (S148 class).

Neptune: Chile (*Reshev* class), South Africa ("Minister" class). Neptune is almost certainly an alternative name for Tritons sold to Israel, as it shares the same THD number. Israeli radars of this type have probably been replaced by EL/M-2207/2208.

◆ **Triton S (TRS 3033)**

Band: S
Beam: 3 × 22 deg
Peak Power: 10 kW (average 250 W)
Gain: 25 dB
Pulse Width: 2.7 microsec (Doppler channel); 0.17 microsec as pulse-compressed; compression ratio of 10
PRF: 5380 pps (Doppler channel); pulse compression: fractions of 5380 pps
Scan Rate: 24 rpm
Antenna Dimensions: 3 m wide
Antenna Weight: 215 kg

Triton S is a pulse-Doppler development of the basic Triton. It uses a crystal-controlled TWT and produces three frequencies for air search and six frequencies for surface search. Air-search frequency can be shifted on a scan-to-scan basis. Surface-search frequency can be shifted on a pulse-to-pulse basis.

A Nigerian Combattante IIIB–class fast-attack boat shows a Triton S radar at her masthead, with a Castor II director; at the right, at the foot of the mast, is a Panda optical director. (U.S. Naval Institute)

Triton S is effective against sea-skimmers by virtue of its very high clutter-cancellation ratio (50 dB) and its high data rate (2.5 sec). Like several other recent Thomson-CSF radars, Triton S uses a coherent transmitter for Doppler processing (16-point FFT), both to get target speed and to reject clutter. Using pulse compression on the non-Doppler channel, the radar is also frequency-agile on a scan-to-scan basis. The lowest blind speed is Mach 1.

Performance of the pulse-Doppler channel: $1m^2$ (Swerling III case) at 26 km; $10m^2$ target (Swerling III) at 44 km.

Users: Nigeria (Combattante IIIB), Qatar (Combattante IIIM) and Tunisia (Combattante IIIT class).

◆ **MRR/ASCORE**

Band: C
Beam: 1.75 deg (azimuth). See below.
Scan Rate: 10 or 30 rpm

The Thomson-CSF Multi-Role Radar is intended as a Triton/DRBV-51 replacement, and can replace Sea Tiger in a larger ship.

It is the radar element of the Vega successor small-ship combat system (Signaal TACTICOS). There are two operating modes, surveillance (mainly to detect medium- and low-altitude targets, primarily for peacetime) and self-defense (all elevations fully covered with a high data rate, primarily for missile defense). Each mode is further divided into fine- and bad-weather modes. In the normal surveillance mode, the instrumented range is 70 km. The maximum altitude is about 25 km (about 80,000 ft). The vertical beamwidth, then, is probably about 20 deg. In the self-defense mode (presumably using the higher of the two scan rates given above), the main low beam (instrumented out to 60 km) is supplemented by two higher-elevation beams, instrumented out to 40 km (high) and 50 km (medium); the maximum elevation is 70 deg. The intermediate beam probably extends from about 20 deg to about 30 deg. The radar searches with a synthesized fan beam, tracking with a pencil beam (like Astral).

The MRR radar antenna. (Thomson-CSF photo by Kervizic Christian)

The designers preferred a pencil beam to monopulse height-finding (beam-forming on reception only, as in Smart) on the theory that the pencil could change at each elevation. The envelope changes at each elevation, so the waveform can be adjusted for each signature and elevation angle. The alternative is to use a common waveform (Doppler pulse rate, for example) at all elevations simultaneously. The designers also argue that, although a fan beam provides more hits on each target, each hit has less power. An agile pencil beam can spend more time in any one chosen direction, pouring on more energy. In particular, it is easier to concentrate on low elevations. Adaptive processing can cut the sidelobes.

The surface-channel instrumented range is 40 km. The air channel uses long compressed pulses, the surface channel short pulses. Pulses can be transmitted in bursts. The coherent transmitter uses a TWT. In some modes the air-channel signals are Doppler processed (on a burst-to-burst basis) for better low-altitude performance in clutter. MRR is an ADT radar (surface tracks are manually initiated) programmed in ADA. It has a capacity of 128 tracks. Signals are horizontally polarized, and the antenna is roll- and pitch-stabilized.

The RAC alert and coordination radar is a ground-based equivalent.

ASCORE (Air/Surface Coastal Radar Equipment) is a simplified MRR with a 2D antenna.

Users: Kuwait (PBR-37BRL class), Oman (Project Muheet corvettes), Qatar (new 56m patrol boats).

◆ TRS 3405/3410/SCORE/SURICATE

Band: X
Beam: 0.24 × 25 deg (inverted csc² to −25 deg)
Peak Power: 200 kW
Pulse Width: 0.05 microsec
PRF: 1080–570 pps

TRS 3405 is a fixed coastal radar, which may be mounted atop a tower for vessel traffic control; antenna gain is 44 dB (scan rate 5 or 10 rpm). TRS 3410 is the mobile version with a foldable 4.8m antenna (gain 42 dB, beam 0.55 × 3 deg, scan rate 11 rpm). Both have TWS processors. Sea clutter is reduced by frequency diversity, an adaptive detection threshold, short pulses, and a very narrow beam (to avoid illuminating low clouds). The signal can switch from linear to circular polarization. Each radar has two transmitters/receivers for reliability, and both can operate simultaneously in a frequency-diversity mode.

A mobile SCORE radar. (Thomson-CSF)

A typical fixed coastal installation for a TRS 3400-series radar. The adjacent tower carries microwave communications links. (Thomson-CSF)

SCORE (Surveillance Coastal Radar Equipment) combines the TRS 3410 antenna with an IGUANE pulse-compression (hence stealthy) transmitter. Performance: the 10m² mast of a fast patrol boat can be detected at 45nm using a radar 300 m above sea level; a low-flying fighter (2.5m²) can be detected at 93 km. This radar can also be equipped with a 2m antenna, with range reduced by about a third. SCORE is used as an Exocet FCS radar.

SURICATE (TRS 3445) is a follow-on ADT radar (400 tracks) using a 32-bit computer; it uses the TRS 3405/3410 antennas. It is optimized for small-target detection, using a TWT transmitter (with pulse-to-pulse frequency agility) and digital video pulse compression (20-nsec compressed pulse). Using a 4.40m antenna (gain 40 dB), it has a 0.6 × 4-deg (downwards 30 deg csc²) beam. A 4.80m antenna (42 dB) produces a 0.55 × 27-deg beam; a 10m antenna (44 dB) produces a 0.27 × 2.5-deg (25 deg csc²). Its extremely small cell (0.6 deg × 3 m) makes for particularly good rejection of atmospheric clutter. Performance with 4.4m (10m) antenna: 10m² target detected at 104 (165) km, 2.5m² target at 74 (117) km. Instrumented range is 180 nm.

Users:

> TRS 3405/3410: France (3405 in CROSS system), Iraq (3410 for Silkworm control), and others. CROSS is Centres Regionaux Operationnels de Sauvetage et Surveillance.
> SCORE: Cyprus (first sale, 1991) and at least five others. They probably include the other coast defense customers for Exocet Block II, Qatar and Saudi Arabia.

The first SURICATE buyer (1996) was Estonia. Thomson-CSF claims that its coastal radars are used in the Channel, in the Gulf, in the Indian Ocean, in the Mediterranean, and elsewhere.

OPTRONIC SYSTEMS

◆ DIBV 10 (Vampir)/VIGY 105 (DIBC-2A)/VIGY 200

SAT's Vampir (Veille Air-Mer Panoramique Infra-Rouge), announced in 1980, was developed to meet a NATO IRST requirement for low- and medium-altitude surveillance. More than fifteen years later it is still the only shipboard IRST in service, at least in any Western navy. The sensor head weighs 450 kg and scans at 60 rpm. Total weight is 450 kg. It operates at both 3–5 and 8–14 microns, but only one at a time, with a 25-deg FOV. Maximum elevation is 25 deg. Target designation accuracy can be 1 mrad, and an incoming antiship missile can be detected at about 10 km. The display is divided into three horizontal strips: two for the two IR bands and one for processed video. In 1980 it

The three versions of Vampir: The original version at top, on a *Cassard*-class AAW frigate; Vampir MB at left, and Vampir ML (for corvettes and FAC) at right. (SAT)

was reported that Vampir had detected a small helicopter at 8 nm, and in 1988 it was reported that Vampir had detected an Exocet's heat plume beyond the horizon. The first Vampir was delivered to the French navy in 1989.

Vampir ML 11 was announced in 1988 as a lighter (80 kg) and less expensive ($\frac{1}{3}$ to $\frac{1}{2}$ the price) version for corvettes and FAC, operating in only one IR band at twice the scan rate, with wider elevation limits (+60/−10 deg) but a narrower FOV (6 deg). Range in good weather should be about 15 km. The operator presets ML 11 in elevation. Once it acquires a target, it changes elevation angle as required on a scan-to-scan basis to keep the target within a tracking window. Up to 50 targets can be tracked. It takes about 20 min to change bands. ML 21 would be a version with two heads for the two bands.

SAT's Vampir MB (Modular Bispectrale) is a new version to meet a 1992 RFP. It employs a SAGEM turret and 4 SOFRADIR 228 × 4 IRCCD FPAs. FOV is 5 deg in elevation (limits +45/−20 deg), and the turret trains at 90 rpm. The system can carry 100 tracks. Total weight is 150 kg. Typical ranges: supersonic missile, 14–27 km; subsonic missile, 9–16 km; fighter, 10–18 km; helicopter, 7–10 km. Track accuracy is 1.5 mrad. The display shows six strips, three for each IR band, with a bearing strip below each. Vampir MB was first delivered late in 1994.

SAT offers a TWS fusion system, PARIS (Passive and Active Radar IR System) to merge data from Vampir MB, radar, and IFF.

SAGEM's VIGY 105 FCS, announced 1992, is essentially Vampir (a SAGEM turret with SAT algorithms) with SAGEM algorithms. It carries an 8–12-micron FLIR (FOVs 1.6 × 2.4 and 4 × 6 deg), an eye-safe (1.54 microns at 20 Hz) laser range-finder, and a CCD TV (0.5–0.9 microns at 50-Hz frame rate, FOVs 3.75 × 5 and 1.5 × 2 deg). Elevation limits are +65/−25 deg in the current ALIS version, in which the line of sight is stabilized to within 100 microrad. Because of its Vampir ancestry, VIGY 105 has both a search mode (with automatic target acquisition within less than 1 sec) and a tracking mode; it can typically detect an airplane beyond 15 km. Total weight is 115 kg.

SAGEM is now marketing an export version of VIGY 105 which would add an IRST capability. It would incorporate the new IRIS imager, which uses a 288 × 4 element 8–10-micron IR detector (625 lines at 50 Hz) with FOVs of 5 × 6.67 and 1.8 × 4 deg. There is reportedly also a 3–5-micron version.

CSEE's (now CS Defence's) alternative, Narval, attracted no buyers.

Users:

Vampir (DIBV 10): France (two on *Georges Leygues* for trials)
Vampir ML 11 (DIBV 10A): France (two on *Cassard* class, three on *Tourville* class, probably one ashore)
Vampir MB (DIBV 10B): France (*Charles de Gaulle*, *Georges Leygues*, and *La Fayette*–class frigates; total six ordered as of 1995; planned for Project Horizon class), Oman (83m corvettes), Qatar (56m boats), Saudi Arabia (*La Fayette* class), Taiwan (*La Fayette* class). Current production unit price is $1M.
VIGY 105: France (ALIS version in OP3A system: contract for 22, first delivery February 1995; total of 25 VIGY 105 bought as of 1996 for *Charles de Gaulle*, *Georges Leygues* class, *Foudre*, *Ouragan*, and as reserve for cross-decking). The first unit was delivered December 1994 for land tests and installed March 1995 on board an LSD.
VIGY 200: United States (for tests by ONR and NSWC under the Horizon IR Surveillance System [HISS] program, shipped early 1995). This is an IRST version of VIGY 105.

Note that in the *Georges Leygues* class, *La Touche-Treville* and *Primaguet* received neither Vampir nor VIGY 105.

◆ Murene/DALAS

SAT's navalized version of the SAT/TRT Système Modulaire Thermal (SMT), the French common 8–12-micron module, complements the company's CTX series of thermal imagers. FOVs: 1.9 × 2.8 and 5.7 × 8.6 deg, with 500 pixels/line (510 lines), corresponding, respectively, to 0.1- and 0.3-mrad resolution. Scan is serial-parallel, and frame shape is 3 × 2. Frame rate is

25 Hz. Weight is approx 50 kg. An optional subscanning module increases range by about 20% by reducing FOV. Applications: TTAc, TTAd, SADRAL, and TOTEM directors, NAJIR EO sight, DALAS (Dispositif Aide a l'appontage Laser) EO carrier-landing system on board all French carriers.

◆ Pirana (DIBC 1A)

SAT's passive two-color tracker (4–5 and 8–12 microns used in parallel) is used in the CTM FCS. FOV is about 17 mrad for acquisition (optical aperture 170 mm), and Pirana can detect sea-skimming missiles at about 10 km. The detector is a nitrogen-cooled FPA. Total weight is 50 kg. The current Pirana III is installed in stand-alone form on board the frigates *Cassard*, *Duquesne*, and *Jean Bart*. In these ships it is cued by the Vampir IRST.

◆ VIGY 10

SAT's optronic surveillance system (FLIR plus image-intensified TV) is intended for coast guards. In 1994 it ran successful sea trials on board *Mette-Mols*, a ferry of the Danish Mols Linien Cie, showing what SAT described as excellent performance in bad weather. Danish naval representatives were present.

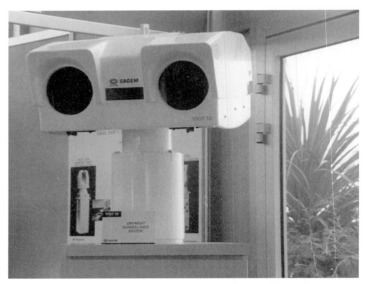

VIGY 10 on display at UDT 95. (Stuart Slade, DMS/Forecast International)

◆ VISION

This CSEE periscope is under development. Fitted with a computer, it can function as an optical FCS. The head is stabilized, with a 30- or 7.5-deg FOV (2× or 8×) and with a TV camera (for autotracking) in the optical path. Elevation limits are +70/−25 deg. Head and periscope weigh about 125 kg, and total system weight is about 300 kg.

FIRE-CONTROL SYSTEMS

CTA and CTD, the two major systems, are related to the Vega/TAVITAC CDSs and are therefore described above in the Command and Surveillance section.

Gun (artillery) directors (telepointeurs) are divided into primary units (TTA, originally TT Type A) and secondary remote units (TRA). Originally the DRBC 32 FCS radar was always mounted on a quadraxially stabilized director carrying a stereo range-finder, designated TT type A (TTAb was installed on board the frigate *Aconit*); approximate weight is 11 t. The director (telepointeur) was initially to have had a crew of three, but that was reduced to two (pointer and observer/range-finder), at least in the case of the *Aconit*. Presumably, earlier versions had pointer, trainer, and range-finder operator. In this type of director, two of the axes are used to stabilize the platform of the director, and the other two point it at the target. Elevation limits:

+80/−2 deg. A new lightweight unmanned biaxially stabilized radar-only TTAc director was developed for the *Tourville* class, based on the Masurca director. It is used with DRBC 32D and 32E, and with some 32Cs. CTM (multisensor) uses the lightweight TTAd.
Users:

CTA/TTAb director: *Suffren* class (being replaced by CTM), *Jeanne d'Arc*, also *Commandante Rivière*–class frigates in Portugal and Uruguay.
CTD/TTAc director: *Tourville* class, *Aconit*, using one of the two 1230 computers in the ship's SENIT CDS for ballistic calculations.
CTM/TTAd director: *Georges Leygues* (D644–646), *Cassard*, and *La Fayette* classes.

◆ DRBC 32/DRBC 31

DRBC 32 is an X-band monopulse pulse-compression radar designed specifically to control the 100mm automatic gun. Its beam is 1.5 deg wide. DRBC 32C has a peak power of 80 kW (4-microsec pulse) and can track a 0.1m² target at 15 km. Targets are automatically acquired, and all processing is digital (the FCS in the A69 corvettes employs a hybrid analog-digital computer).

DRBC 32 radar/optical director on board the carrier *Clemenceau*. (L. van Ginderen)

DRBC 32D on *Aconit*, 1993. (Stuart Slade, DMS/Forecast International)

The DRBC 32A and 32B versions both employ Cassegrain antennas; the others all use lightweight dishes with offset feeds. This series was begun in 1961.
Users:

DRBC 32A: France (*Suffren* class [being replaced by DRBC 33], *Jeanne d'Arc* [100mm guns], *Clemenceau* [replaced by 32C in *Foch*], Uruguay (*Commandante Rivière* class).

DRBC 32B: France (*Aconit* [100mm guns]).
DRBC 32C: France (*Foch*, *Commandante Rivière* class, and some A69 class), Uruguay (*Commandante Rivière* class).
DRBC 32D: France (*Tourville*, *Georges Leygues* classes [the three last ships of the latter class have DRBC 33 instead]).
DRBC 32E: Argentina (A69 class), France (A69 class).

An earlier DRBC 31 (presumably the nonpulse-compressed monopulse predecessor to DRBC 32) survives on board the Portuguese *Commandante Rivière* class (DRBC 31D version).

◆ Castor I/Castor II/DRBC 33/CTM

Band: X
Beam: 2.45 × 2.3 deg
Peak Power: 30 kW (average 120 W)
Gain: 36 dB
Pulse Width: 0.5 microsec
PRF: 4000 to 8000 pps
Antenna Dimensions: 1.053 m dia, working circle 1.6 m
Antenna Weight: Total director weight 620 kg

Data are for Castor IIC (TRS 3204).

The monopulse pulse-Doppler Castor I (TRS 3200) was conceived to replace the Pollux conscan FC radar (to track fluctuating targets more accurately) in the Vega system. These radars can control gunfire by displaying both target and shell splashes (in TWS mode), and they can be used for search, scanning the horizon at constant elevation. They can also passively track a jammer, using range information from an associated search radar.

Castor IIC. (Thomson-CSF)

Castor I uses a magnetron transmitter (peak power 175 kW, pulse width 0.4 microsec, PRF 4000–8000 pps, stepped variation). The dish antenna (gain 37 dB, 2.3-deg beam) is stabilized. Maximum acquisition and tracking range is about 30 km.

Castor II (TRS 3201), which is more widely used, substitutes a Cassegrain antenna for the dish of Castor I (and Pollux). Castor IIB (TRS 3203) introduced a new 30-kW coherent TWT transmitter (3600 or 7200 pps) with single-knob tuning over a 700-MHz band. MTI processing uses a three-memory filter. Sea-clutter rejection ratio is 30 dB.

Castor IIC (TRS 3204) has computer control for its 30-kW TWT, which transmits in 1.5-msec bursts at fixed frequency and PRF; it can also hop frequencies on a pulse-to-pulse basis (frequency range is 700 MHz). The first blind speed is 1000 m/sec. This radar can acquire an antiship missile (0.1m²) at 15 km and a fighter at 25 km; tracking range is 500 m to 27 km. Sea-clutter rejection ratio is 35 dB. Elevation limits are +85/−25 deg. Maximum train/elevation speeds are 1/1.5 rad/sec.

DRBC 33A is the French navy version of Castor IIC.

The associated TV/IR camera (TRAKIR) has a 35 × 27-mrad FOV and places tracking gates (2.2 × 1.7 or 4.4 × 3.4 mrad) around a target.

Castor IIJ was an abortive J-band (Ku-band) follow-on system for the Satan CIWS.

CTM (Conduite de Tir Multisensor) combines Castor IIJ with a separate IR camera (Pirana) and with a TV tracker. It replaces the earlier CTA and CTD (see above), and is the FCS for Crotale NG (and also for guns). The director has its own stabilizing gyro. Total height above deck is 2.422 m. As in Castor IIB, Castor IIJ uses a TWT transmitter and a Cassegrain antenna (gain 43 dB, beam 1.5 × 0.67 deg). It can acquire an antiship missile at 18 km and a fighter at 30 km (tracking range 350 m to 30 km). Elevation limits are +85/−25 deg. Unlike the earlier versions, this one uses pulse compression (7.5 microsec pulses) as well as pulse-Doppler processing (first blind speed 1000 m/sec). With 90-deg slewing angle and 5-deg vertical search, CTM acquires an air target in 2.8 sec; it acquires a target identified as a sea-skimmer in 1.75 sec (presumably avoiding the elevation search).

CTM. This director controls Crotale missiles on board the Chinese destroyers armed with them. (P. Pinault via Thomson-SDC)

The Pirana FLIR has two FOVs (2.7 × 1.8 and 8.1 × 5.4 deg) and can detect targets at up to 15 km; it uses split-Stirling cooling. The daylight CCD camera has a 2.4 × 1.8-deg FOV.

This system employs a pair of 15M05E (extended) computers running software written in LTR, and is controlled from a single below-decks console. A special low-altitude tracking algorithm overcomes multipath problems. In 1987 tests, CTM tracked a target flying at 7 m at 300 kt with a standard deviation of 0.3 mrad (about 30 cm) at 1000m range.

Users:

Castor I: Greece (Combattante II and IIIN classes).
Castor II: Germany (S148 class), Peru (PR-72–560 class).
Castor IIB: Colombia (FS 1500–class frigates), Libya (Combattante IIG), Nigeria (Combattante IIIG), Qatar (Combattante IIIM), Saudi Arabia (*Al Madinah* class, being modernized to IIC standard in current refits), Tunisia (Combattante IIIT).
Castor IIC: Taiwan (*La Fayette* class).
DRBC 33: *Cassard* class, last three *Georges Leygues* class.
CTM: France (*Suffren* and *La Fayette* class), Germany (replacement for Castor II on S148-class FAC), Oman (new corvettes), Qatar (new corvettes), Saudi Arabia (*La Fayette* class), Taiwan (*La Fayette* class), UAE (new FAC). This may be the version of Castor supplied to China for "Luda" hulls 17 and 18.

◆ Pollux (THD 1280, TRS 3220)

Band: X
Beam: 2 deg
Peak Power: 200 kW (90 W average)

Gain: 30 dB
Pulse Width: 0.3 microsec
PRF: 1500 pps
Antenna Dimensions: 1.1 m dia
Antenna Weight: 450 kg

A Thomson-CSF export conical-scan fire-control radar, Pollux was the tracker of the original Thomson-CSF Vega WCS. Because a sequence of several pulses is needed to define a target's angular position, a fast or fluctuating target can confuse such a system. Later Vegas use the monopulse Castor II instead. Conscan was also unattractive because of its vulnerability to ECM, and Pollux was not accurate enough to control 100mm guns.

Pollux can acquire and track a 2m^2 aircraft at 16 nm. Accuracy is 1 mrad in bearing and 20 m in range. Tracking accuracy is 0.5 mrad and 20 m in range at 18 km (2m^2 air target).

The Ecuadorian missile boat *Quito* has a Triton air/surface-search radar on her mast (with an ESM array above it), and a Pollux fire-control radar. The mast platform just aft of the Pollux dish carries a Decca 1229, barely visible because its antenna is end-on to the camera. (U.S. Naval Institute)

Users: Ecuador (*Quito* and *Manta* classes), Malaysia (Combattante II 4AL class), Portugal (*Baptiste de Andrade* class) and Qatar (Combattante III class).

◆ Lynx/PAON/Panda/NAJA/NAJIR

CSEE's Lynx pedestal-mounted target optical sight is used in the Radop FCS described below, and forms the basis for a series of optronic directors. The binocular sight (FOVs 9 and 5 deg, corresponding to 2.5× and 8×) views the target via an LOS-stabilized mirror, which is slewed onto the target bearing and is then scanned in elevation (+65/−25 deg, maximum rate 1 rad/sec) to acquire the target. Sychros transmit the target elevation to the FCS. PAON is Lynx equipped with an image intensifier for night operation.

Panda (CSEE Model 71) is an optical FCS (with an on-board ballistic computer), essentially a Lynx power-driven in bearing. Search rates are about 30 deg/sec in elevation, 60 deg/sec in bearing. Once the target has been acquired, the operator measures its angular velocity by tracking. Total weight is less than 330 kg. Panda Mk 2 (about 500 kg, including 260 kg for the remote-control console) adds an LLLTV. Elevation limits are +70/−25 deg; train and elevation rates are 60 deg/sec. Panda is used in one version of Radop.

NAJA (CSEE Model 74) adds a laser ranger (1.06 micron, 5 MW, 20 pps).

NAJIR (announced 1982, first shown 1994) adds a FLIR to the director's optical, TV, and laser channels; its image can be observed either through the binoculars or on the below-decks console. The Panda/NAJA analog computer is replaced by a digital unit (68000-series CPU), and the director can autotrack. Eleva-

Panda on board the Belgian frigate *Wandelaar*, 1994. The curved windshield atop the face of the director is only barely visible. (Stuart Slade, DMS/Forecast International)

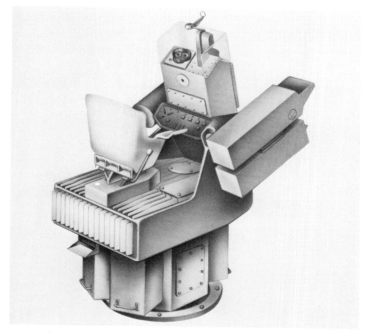

NAJIR director, with IR camera and laser range-finder alongside. (Compagnie de Signaux et d'Enterprises Électriques)

tion limits are +70/−20 deg (train and elevation rates 90 and 60 deg/sec). Weight is 560 kg.

NAJIR Mk 2, announced in 1994, is entirely remotely operated. It can control two guns of different calibers and uses a standard Calisto console. The sensors are a SAT Murene 8–12-micron FLIR, a Radamec HK 202 TV camera (see the Radamec entry below), and a CILAS THS 304 eye-safe laser ranger. The LOS-stabilized mounting is that used in the Sagaie decoy launcher. The follow-on system now under development is NAJIR 2000.

Users (other than with Radop):

Lynx: Bahrein (Lurssen 38m class), Finland, France (*Cassard* class), India (*Vikram*-class coast guard cutters), Kuwait (TNC 45–class fast-attack boats), Morocco (*Lt. Col. Errhamani*), Oman (*Nasr Al Bahr*), and Saudi Arabia (modified *Durance* class).

Panda: Bahrein (Mk 2 on FPB 62 and TNC 45 classes), Belgium (*Wielingen* class), Congo (Mk 2 in *Pirana* class),

France (*Georges Leygues*), Germany (*Tiger* class), Greece (Combattante IIIN class, Mk 2 in *Jason* class), Libya (Combattante II class), Mauritania (FPB 36 class), Morocco (PR 72 type, *Lazaga* class), Nigeria (Mk 2 in Combattante IIIB class), Peru (PR 72–560 type), Portugal (*Baptiste de Andrade* class), Qatar (Mk 2 in Combattante III class), and Spain (*Descubierta* class). By 1976 more than 150 sets had been ordered. Many of those listed above were probably replaced by NAJA.

NAJA: Algeria (*Kalaat Beni Hammed*–class landing ships), Argentina (*Granville*; other A69s have Panda Mk 2), Cameroon (*Bakassi*), China (Jianghu IV, to control 100mm guns), Gabon (*Gen Ba Oumar*), Malaysia (*Jerong* class, *Sri Indera Sakti*–class support ships), Mexico (*Uribe* class), Morocco (*Lazaga* class), Saudi Arabia (*Al Madinah* class, modified *Durance* class), Senegal (PR 72M class), Tunisia (Combattante III class), Turkey (*Girne*), Uruguay (*Vigilante*).

NAJIR: France (*Cassard* and *Floreal* classes), Kuwait (Mk 2 in PBR-37BRL class), Pakistan (Mk 2 selected for Type 21 upgrade), Taiwan (*La Fayette* class), United Kingdom (as DMAC); presumably will be on board the Saudi *La Fayette* class. This FCS was specified for the Combattante IV offered to Kuwait, but not ordered at the time of writing.

◆ SAS 90/TDS 90

SAGEM's low-cost, lightweight, optronic, AA FCS and sighting system for FAC was shown at Bourget Naval 1990 (October 1990). It is intended for both ground (fixed and mobile) and naval applications. The gyro it incorporates (to measure target motion) can also be used to stabilize a naval gun mount. The target range is measured passively, apparently by comparing the target motion with the assumed target speed. SAS 90 consists of a sight-display assembly (color LCD matrix projecting a generated image overlaid on the optical image and the measuring/stabilizing gyro); an automatic tracking and range-finding CCD camera (the picture is directly digitized for easier image processing); an electronics unit (which tracks and ranges based on the CCD camera image, which generates the LCD images and conducts lead-angle computations and firing calculations; it also transmits sight data outside the system); a monocular optical sight for ground firing (5× magnification and etched reticle); and an optional FLIR. The direct-view sight has a 30 × 30-deg FOV. The target direction is measured by gyro or potentiometer. The telescopic sight has a 150-mrad FOV. The CCD camera has two FOVs (50 × 40 mrad or 80 × 100 mrad) with a resolution of 500 pts/line. The overall fire-control accuracy is 2 mrad. An optional IR camera operates at 8–12 microns, with two FOVs; it has an effective detection range, in average weather, of 5000 m (5500 yd).

The TDS 90 optronic target designator combines the British MSI-Defence TDS with a SAGEM SAS 90 reflex sight. It can accommodate an ALIS IR camera. TDS 90 transmits target

SAGEM DMAe target designation sight, on board *Aconit*, 1993. (Stuart Slade, DMS/Forecast International)

parameters to the ship's CDS, but can also be used as a secondary or backup FCS. Deliveries began in November 1994, initially for the *La Fayette*–class frigates. The director weighs 82 kg; elevation limits are +65/–20 deg. Target designation accuracy is 3 mrad.

◆ OP3A/SARA/Cuirasse

OP3A (Amelioration Autodefense Anti-Missile, or improved antimissile self-defense) was developed to meet a 1992 French requirement. SARA (Système d'Autodefense Rapprochee Antiaerien) is DCNI's export designation. Cuirasse is a broadly comparable commercial system described below.

OP3A is built around SENIT 8.01 command/control hardware (one Hewlett-Packard computer and Calisto workstations on the bridge and below decks) and IR sensors and weapons: a Vampir IRST, two VIGY 105 FCSs, and Mistral missiles fired from Sadral launchers. The system also controls a pair of 30mm Mauser guns in single Breda launchers, to counter surface and slow air targets. It also has an EW element comprising a Dassault jammer and the Dagaie decoy launcher.

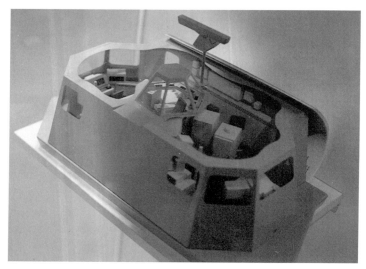

A model of an OP3A bridge-top installation, showing the cupola for the AAW officer, at Bourget Naval 1994. (Author)

Part of the interior of the OP3A cupola, showing two Calisto consoles. The one in the background controls Sadral. (DGA)

The prototype OP3A installation, in the cupola above the bridge of *Jean de Vienne*. Note the Sadral launcher just abaft the cupola, below the fire-control radar. (A. Preston)

The command/control element is STIDAV (Système de Traitement de l'Information de la Defense a Vue). The close-in air defense officer stands under a cupola, providing an overhead view; the system display is a PPI showing radar tracks and optronic and ESM bearing indicators, sources of data being identified by color. The screen also shows weapon arcs of fire. In effect the officer performs tactical fusion, designating targets to the missile and light gun systems. The officer has two trackballs and fast-action buttons. Behind and below the self-defense officer are five consoles: one for an assistant responsible for electronic warfare, two for Sadral operators, and two for 30mm-gun operators. The consoles are all connected by a LAN. They use specially bright screens with large symbols, so the operators can look out as well as at the screen. Targets are detected at 10 km, identified and correlated with the SENIT CDS at 5 km, and targets are designated less than 3 sec after detection.

The system is modular, partly because the command/control element employs a bus architecture. The full suit goes aboard the carrier *Charles de Gaulle* and the F70-class ASW frigates of the power projection naval force (FAN, the Force Aero-Navale) at Toulon. The carrier *Foch* receives two VIGY 105s and two Sadrals. The ASW frigates at Brest and *La Motte Picquet* are limited to the ECM element of the new system. The major amphibious ships (*Foudre, Ouragan, Orage*) also each receive a pair of VIGY 105 and 30mm guns. *La Fayette*–class frigates receive laser range-finders for their 100mm guns.

CSEE delivered the prototype system in November 1993; ultimately it will be installed on board the carrier *Charles de Gaulle*. The prototype installation will be on board *Montcalm* during her December 1994–November 1996 refit.

Cuirasse is a privately developed close-in system offered by a consortium including Lacroix, Matra, and SAT, incorporating Vampir ML 11, Dagaie Mk 2, and Sadral.

◆ Radop

This small-ship FCS was a joint CSEE/Racal/Decca product. It combined an S- or X-band surface-search radar (initially Racal-Decca Series 12), a CSEE optical/optronic director, an artillery-supervision unit, and a CANE central tactical console (CTC). Any version could be extended by integration with a plotting table, radio-electronic navigation system, and/or an air-search radar. The first two extensions were in line with Racal's CANE series of command/control systems. Different versions of Radop were distinguished mainly by the type of CSEE optical or optronic device they incorporated:

Radop 10, for craft under 100 tons, controlling up to two guns, used Lynx and, typically, an X-band radar. *User:* Bahrein (FPB 38 boats).

Radop 20, controlling up to two guns, used Panda Mk 2 and a CTC vertical console with, typically, an S-band radar. *Users:* Argentina (A69 corvette *Granville*), Congo (*Pirana*), Libya (PS700), and Morocco (PR 72).

Radop 30, for craft over 100 t, used a NAJA director and a dual-frequency radar, a CTC console, a remote-control console, and a ballistics calculator. The remote control was an integral tracker and processor. Operators: Algeria (Brooke-Marine-type landing ships), Argentina (A69-class corvettes other than *Granville*), Malaysia (*Sri Indera Sakti* class), Saudi Arabia (*Durance*-class replenishment ships), Senegal (PR 72M class), Turkey (*Girne*), and Uruguay (*Vigilance* class)

Radop 40, for craft over 200 t, was intended to use the Totem fully automatic director (see the 1991/92 edition for details) or at least NAJIR, but the only example installed (on board the Cameroon P48S-class patrol boat) used NAJA. This version used a CANE console and could control several guns.

The Radop series was first announced at Asian Defense Expo 80, although the first example appeared on board the Turkish *Girne* in 1976. Twenty-five systems were delivered before production ended in 1984.

GERMANY

◆ KAE 7600/8600/9600

	X	S
Band:	X	S
Beam:	0.9×21	1.7×20 deg
Peak Power:	25	30 kW
PRF: (both)	2000 (to 1.5 nm)/1000 (to 12 nm)/500 (above 12 nm) pps	
Scan Rate:	23 rpm	23 rpm
Antenna:	8 ft	14 ft

Each of these raster-scan navigational radars is available in both X- and S-band form. Targets are acquired manually and then tracked automatically: 10 for 7600, 20 for 8600, 40 for 9600. The two latter radars can also automatically acquire targets (at up to 200 kt) in operator-set guard zones. The radar automatically provides navigational data such as CPA and TCPA. Atlas 7600 uses a 16in display, but 8600 and 9600 use 24in memory-backed screens. Atlas 9600M offers four times the resolution of its predecessors. It (and probably 8600) can interface with target indication or air-search radars, and can feed into a CDS. Maximum instrumented range (in 8600) is 72 nm.

By mid-1995, Atlas had sold over 10,000 of these radars, including some used in its VTS 9730 vessel traffic-control system. Atlas 8600 was adopted for the Australian/New Zealand ANZAC frigates.

◆ TRS-N

TRS-N is an X-band surface-search radar installed from 1963 onward on board German *Thetis*-class corvettes and minecraft to replace the Kelvin-Hughes 14/9. It had a parabolic-reflector antenna (which was tilted slightly downwards) and presumably used a magnetron transmitter. Presumably it was used when greater definition and precision were needed; most German warships continued to show the slotted-waveguide antenna of the earlier Kelvin-Hughes radar. The first ship fitted with TRS-N was the last of the *Thetis*-class corvettes, *Theseus*, completed in 1963. This radar survives on board ships of this type transferred to Greece. On board most German minecraft, TRS-N has been replaced by TRS-C.

Users: Germany (the sole surviving German unit with this radar is probably the MCM diving support ship *Stier*), Greece (*Thetis* class).

◆ TRS-C/TRML-CS

TRS-C, DASA's C-band high-definition naval surface-search radar, in effect the successor to TRS-N, is derived from TRM-L, the German Roland missile target–acquisition radar. It uses either the land-based radar's TWT or a magnetron, and was first ordered early in 1989. TRM-L uses phase-coded pulse compression and Doppler processing. It can change its PRF and frequency on a burst-to-burst basis, using separate adaptive detection thresholds for each Doppler channel (to defeat clutter, chaff, and noise jamming). Presumably the German navy considered TRS-N a test case for the digital technology involved. It uses what appears to be a large slotted-waveguide antenna. Scan rate (for TRM-L) is 15 or 30 rpm. TRML-CS is a coastal surveillance radar derived from TRM-L, hence analogous to TRS-C.

Two German Troika control craft, *Dueren* (foreground) and *Wolfsburg*, display their TRS-C antennas. The masthead antenna is presumably for Troika control. (H. Vanhoefen)

Users: Germany (Type 351 minesweeping-drone control ships). Type 394 inshore minesweepers, which are credited with this radar, appear to have SPS-64 instead.

◆ TRS-3D and TRS-L

DASA's C-band 3D radar is derived from the land-based TRM-S, which uses phase-coding so that it can combine pulse compression and Doppler processing. The TWT transmitter has a solid-state driver under software control. Phase coding, pulse length, PRF, polarization, and frequency can therefore all be altered on a burst-to-burst basis, and frequency can be varied pseudo-randomly.

The TRS-3D/16 antenna, with integral IFF interrogator below it. (DASA)

The flat passive-array antenna (0.4 × 1.2 m, less than 370 kg; antenna plus platform are 2.7 × 2.32 m, 820 kg) is tipped back and its stabilized mounting can accommodate a 7ft X-band navigational antenna below the main antenna. The antenna shapes the beam only in the vertical. In the TRS-3D/16 version, it comprises 16 vertical rows, each of 46 radiators. The radar has sidelobe blanking and coherent sidelobe cancellation.

The radar has separate air and surface channels (plot extractors), each with its own jam detector, and autojammer avoidance circuits automatically select the least-jammed frequency. It automatically classifies helicopters and provides alerts for pop-up targets. ADT capacity is 300 air and sea targets.

Because the array forms the beam under software control and the transmitter is software-controlled, the radar can operate in several different modes. It generally produces a single pencil beam. The short-range mode employs seven elevation-beam positions (between about 20 and 70 deg), the long-range mode two beam positions at lower angles (between about 0 and 15 deg, each about 7.5 deg wide). There is also a surveillance mode (against aircraft) with seven beam positions (at varying energies) between 0 and about 45 deg. These modes can be interleaved as the antenna turns. A sea-skimmer can be detected at 15 to 20 km (PD 0.8). In free space a fighter at 10 deg can be detected at 60 to 75 km (PD 0.5), but only out to about 40 km at higher elevations.

1. Self-defense, using a 2-sec scan (30 rpm), combining long- and short-range scans and providing high elevation cover; a sea-skimmer can be detected at 42 km at the 10-deg point;
2. Self-defense/clutter, using an adaptive waveform and 3.5-sec scan (17 rpm);
3. Surveillance: 92km instrumented range, 17km altitude cover, 6-sec scan (10 rpm), useful in up to medium clutter;
4. Long-range: 180 km for ducting conditions, 6-sec scan (10 rpm). A fighter can be detected at 110 km.

Users: Denmark (TRS-3D/16 in last six Stanflex 300 corvettes, with option for first seven; selected for *Nils Juels*–class modernization), Germany (TRS-3D/32 in Type 122 frigate upgrade, re-

placing DA-08; chosen 1996 in preference to SMART-S). TRS-3D/32 uses 32 rather than 16 vertical rows of radiators and has a separate, rather than integral, IFF antenna. Reportedly the Germans chose this radar because SMART-S showed an excessive false-alarm rate and also because it was more expensive. The first radar is to be delivered to a land test site some time in 1996, with the first refit following in the second quarter of 1997, and the program being complete in 1999. A new track management system is being added to merge TRS-3D and WM25 data. As of 1996, DASA was trying to sell this radar for the future German Corvette Type 130 program.

TRS-L is a planned D-band active-array follow-on to TRS-3D with an ATD capacity of 400 targets. TRS-18L (18 vertical linear arrays) is expected to detect a 2m² target at 300 km. It is being offered for the German Type 124 AAW frigate. Presumably it will be derived from MAREX, DASA's C-band Marine Array Experimental Radar, which began development in 1991 and sea trials in 1994. A total of 32 broadband Tx/Rx elements (30 W each) feed a 32-column stripline antenna (as in TRS-3D/32). As in TRS-3D, the beam is steered in one plane by a computer driving phase shifters. There are 16 parallel receivers; the returns are stored digitally for off-line analysis. MAREX uses GaAs MMICs developed by DASA. Instrumented range is 60 km. The project was intended partly to demonstrate adaptive nulling (as in the British Mesar/Sampson) for ECCM against both sidelobe and main-lobe jammers.

◆ KR-75

This AEG-Telefunken X-band coastal radar was first installed in 1977, and by mid-1982 at least nine had been sold. Peak power is 60 kW (average power is 0.07 kW, and PRF is 4800 pps), and the beam is 0.35 deg wide, scanning at 18 rpm. A typical aircraft is detected at 13.5 nm.

INDIA

Bharat Electronics was largely established by Signaal, which is why it manufactures Signaal products under license.

◆ Aparna

This surveillance and SSM control radar (Active and Passive Radar for Navigation and Attack) is probably derived from the Russian Harpoon (Plank Shave). It has two transmitter-receiver channels (main and navigational); with each it can scan at two speeds. Channel I (high power, long pulse, with fixed PRF with or without wobbulation, with the magnetron tunable over the frequency band) is used for missile targeting, automatically tracking a target (there are 20 TWS channels) and feeding coordinates and motion parameters to an FCS. ECCM features include staggered PRF and a CW noise protection circuit. Channel II (navigational) uses fixed PRF and frequency (low power, narrow pulse). There is also a passive mode in which the radar can determine a jammer bearing. There is also a SROP (Ship Remote Observation Post) mode, in which target coordinates are transmitted by radio to other attacking ships, which determine the SROP coordinates.

Claimed ranges (Channels I/II): light cruiser at 40–45/30–40 km; missile boat 25–30/20–25 km. Channel II minimum range is 50 to 70 m; bearing resolution is better than 1.3 deg, and range resolution is 50–70m. The display is a 14- or 19in diagonal raster-scan CRT with 1/5/25/50/75nm scales. MTBF is 8 hr on Channel I, 16 hr on Channel II.

The high-gain parabolic antenna is 2.5m wide.

As of early June 1996, 18–25 Aparna radars were on order. These radars equip Indian *Khukri*-class missile boats (eight of which are built or building, with four more planned). Presumably they are also intended for the *Delhi* and Type 16A classes, serving as target designation radars for their SSMs. Note that Bharat is now marketing Aparna as a surface-duct radar.

◆ Indra

This is a version of the Thomson-CSF Tiger; it exists in naval (Indra 1) and land (Indra 2) versions. Indra 1 will probably be the

SAM target-acquisition and missile-detection radar of the new Type 15 (*Delhi*-class) destroyer.

According to the Indian annual Defence Ministry report for 1988/89, an indigenously developed naval surveillance radar has been installed at INS *Dronacharya*, Cochin, to detect very fast sea-skimmers. Presumably, it is the prototype for a shipboard radar, and almost certainly it is a Bharat Electronics product. It may well be Indra 1.

♦ RAWL-2/PLN 517

RAWL-2 is a derivative of LW-08. It will probably be the air search radar of the new Type 15 (*Delhi* class) destroyer. As of May 1991, nine Dutch-supplied LW-08 were in Indian service, and Bharat Electronics expected to manufacture 20 more, at about $8M each.

This is probably the radar currently marketed as PLN 517. Unlike LW-08, it does not employ pulse compression (peak power is 1 MW/750/500 kW for 2 microsec/500 pps or 4 microsec/250 pps pulses). There are 10 spot frequencies (6 in LW-08). A $1m^2$ target can be detected at 75 to 100 nm. The beam is 2.2 deg wide (as in LW-08) and range resolution is 300 m with the short pulse and 600 m with the long pulse. The antenna is 7.55 × 4.82 m (1325 kg).

♦ RAWS/PFN 513

RAWS is a version of the Signaal DA-05. RAWS-3 is a pulse-compression radar with variable pulse width, described as similar to RAWS. It is probably the radar currently marketed as PFN 513.

PFN 513 appears to be a derivative of DA-08 with slightly different pulse characteristics. It emits a long chirped compressed pulse (67 microsec, 500 pps, peak power less than 100 kW) for long range, followed by a short pulse for short range, using a separate receiver for each. There are also short-pulse modes: 35 microsec/1000 pps and 9 microsec/4000 pps. The antenna tilts 2.5 deg. Beam 1.55 × 5.3 deg (but more likely this is a csc² beam), gain 31 dB (antenna 3 × 1.6 m, 675 kg), scan rate 13.5/27 rpm. The raster-scan display has a resolution of 1280 × 1024 pixels (range scales 2/4/8/16/32/64/128 nm). Claimed range on a $2m^2$ target is at least 70 nm. Processing includes MTI (improvement 30 dB on static clutter).

♦ Rani/Rashmi/Type 1245/PIN 515

These surface-search or navigational radars are derivatives of the Signaal ZW-06; each uses a 24in raster display. Rani uses a 6ft slotted array (1.4 × 22-deg beam, gain 26 dB, scan rate 22 rpm with 50-Hz power or 27 rpm with 60-Hz power); Rashmi uses a parabolic antenna (0.9 × 19-deg beam, gain 31 dB, scan rate 20 rpm at 50 Hz, 24 rpm at 60 Hz; antenna 2650 mm wide). Both operate at X-band (peak power, 45 kW in long-pulse mode, 35 kW in short-pulse mode; pulses 0.1 microsec/4000 pps or 0.8 microsec/1000 pps; range discrimination, 20 m; maximum range, 20 nm on a small vessel and 12 nm on a helicopter). These are ARPA radars with 1024 × 1024-pixel raster-scan displays.

Rani is probably the Type 1245 radar fitted to the new corvette *Khukri*. It is probably the radar now being marketed as PIN 515.

♦ Shikari

This Contraves Seaguard TMX-Ka tracker module, made under license, will form part of the FCS of the new *Delhi*-class (Type 15) destroyer, for which Contraves is largely responsible. Like Seaguard, this system employs three trackers (in this case Shikaris) on a data bus. Early plans called for the ship to have one tracker for each of the port and starboard 30mm batteries (two mounts each) and a third for the OTO-Melara 76mm gun and the 6-rnd Trishul missile launcher, all with NTDS-type links to a central computer system (the Indian-built IPN-10, which is now standard in that navy). Contraves convinced the designers to opt for a bus so that directors can shift between weapons. Trishul's range is about 20 km. The requirement was to acquire at 20 km and fire and intercept at 14 km. The Indians rejected a Contraves suggestion that C-band would be better than S-band against sea-skimmers (they specifically rejected AWS-6).

Bharat also manufactures the Signaal Flycatcher land FCS radar. It is being used for initial tests of the Trishul missile planned for the *Delhi* class.

ISRAEL

RADARS

♦ Barak FCS Radar

The Elta X/Ka-band, pulse-Doppler, target-tracking and missile-guidance radar of the Barak point-defense missile system is coherent in both bands. The typical ship installation employs two such radars (port and starboard) for 360-deg coverage. The topside antenna weight is 700 kg, with 3 m² of deck space required internally for the radar and FCS. Missile elevation limits are +85/−25 deg. Published references to one radar handling two targets simultaneously suggest that this system time-shares its receiver/transmitter between two topside dishes.

This radar may be related to the X-band pulse-Doppler EL/M-2021 developed for the F-16 and the cancelled Lavi (peak power 3 kW, average power 200 W, bandwidth 500 MHz, with a digital processor).

Users: Israel (*Nirit*, *Lahav* class [*Sa'ar 5*]), Singapore (*Victory* class).

♦ EL/M-2207/2208

Band: S	X
3.1–3.3 GHz tunable	9.345–9.405 GHz fixed
Beam: 3 × 10 deg	1 × 5 deg
Peak Power: 425 kW	25 kW
(425 W avg)	
Gain: 28 dB	34 dB
Pulse Width: (i) 1.4 microsec	0.25 microsec
(ii) 0.4 microsec	
PRF: (i) 500–750 pps	1000–1500 pps
(ii) 1000–1500 pps	
Scan Rate: 12 or 24 rpm	
Antenna Dimensions: 2.4 × 1 m	
Antenna Weight: 270 kg (245 kg S-band only, 200 kg X-band only)	

Elta's air- and surface-search radar, part of the EL/M-2200 series of shore and naval radars, was developed to replace the French Neptune/Triton on board *Sa'ar*-class missile boats. Elta claims that the antenna design is such as to require only 66% of the reflector area of a more conventional radar. Radar volume and weight were reduced by exploiting IAI's experience with airborne radars. Dual frequency provides both air- and surface-search capability in a single unit: S-band (with digital MTI) gives better range against air targets; X-band is better for avoiding multipath at short range (the Italian RAN-11 L/X exemplifies much the same idea). Air tracks are automatically initiated (ATD); surface tracks are manually initiated but autotracked (TWS mode).

Antenna elevation angle can be remotely controlled, and the radar incorporates a sidelobe blanking antenna.

An Israeli missile boat of the *Reshef* class, equipped with an Elta air-search radar (either EL/M-2207 or -2208; both use the same antenna) and probably with an EL/M-2221 gunfire-control radar. The gun is an OTO-Melara 76mm. Two single-barrel long-range chaff launchers are visible alongside the superstructure, under the bridge windows. Two box launchers (24 barrels each) for short-range chaff are visible, canted outboard, abaft and below the bridge. (U.S. Naval Institute)

All radars in the series use the same basic transceiver unit. EL/M-2208 adds an X-band transceiver to the S-band EL/M-2207; the two are externally indistinguishable. Both transmitters (and the L-band IFF) share the same antenna, for reduced total weight. The designers chose a csc^2 beam (rather than helical scanning, as in the Signaal "egg") for S-band air search, to minimize delay in detecting an air target. Range is 30 nm against a 2m^2 air target; surface targets can be detected out to the horizon. Resolution is better than 75 m for the short pulse, better than 230 m for the long pulse. The PRF can be staggered to avoid MTI blind speeds, and pulse width and PRF variation can also reduce clutter (such as chaff).

The S-band beam is vertically polarized to reduce multipath (lobing) effects; alternatively it can be circularly polarized to reduce weather clutter (circular polarization improves the signal-to-clutter ratio by 10 to 20 dB but reduces the target's radar cross-section). The operator changes S-band polarization from vertical to circular by inserting a mechanical polarizer in front of the feeder connecting the radar transmitter to the mast waveguide.

The designers selected a pencil beam for surface search in X-band (for high gain, to detect small targets); it had to be stabilized. However, full antenna stabilization would have been too heavy, so only the reflector is stabilized. The X-band beam is horizontally polarized to reduce the effects of sea clutter. IAI accepted limited peak power in X-band (for surface search) on the ground that the signal-to-clutter ratio is not a function of transmitted power. In narrow waters, moreover, echoes of excessive power may be received too easily through its sidelobes, introducing ghosts and false targets. Resolution in X-band is 1 deg in azimuth and 50 m in range.

The TWT X-band transmitter is frequency-agile (for ECCM as well as to reduce STA problems, to eliminate target fading, and to decorrelate sea and rain clutter). Surface search is usually by pulse-compression, but for short-range detection short noncompressed pulses are interlaced between the compressed pulses. The operator can vary both pulse width and PRF, and can synchronize PRF with the S-band transmitter (not necessarily in a 1:1 ratio). The system incorporates an adaptive (rather than manual) STC (sensitivity time control) to keep the threshold for displayed signals just above the sea clutter, taking into account the clutter's range and bearing. In at least some versions, the radar is not automatically frequency-agile but instead can be tuned rapidly by hand knob, to use frequency-band diversity.

In L-band (IFF), the beam is 7 × 20 deg (gain 17 dB).

Compared to the Neptune originally carried aboard Israeli missile boats, this radar can better distinguish small seaborne targets near shore clutter.

The version in *Eilat* (*Sa'ar 5* class) adds a 3D (multibeam array) back-to-back with the original 2D antenna; total weight is about 550 kg, compared to 220 kg for the 2D version. Both use the same high-power coherent transmitter.

Users: Chile (*Sa'ar* boats), Israel (*Sa'ar* boats), South Africa (*Sa'ar 4* class), Taiwan (Wu-Jinn II destroyers). As of 1980, well over 50 EL/M-2200 series radars were reported delivered or on order, many of them for export to unspecified customers. The installations listed here add up to 4 Chilean, 22 Israeli, 12 South African, and 4 Taiwanese, a total of 42. The difference is presumably shore-based radars. All the radars listed above are probably the dual-frequency version, since both the *Sa'ars* and the Taiwanese destroyers lack dedicated surface-search radars.

◆ EL/M-2216

> **Band:** S (3.1–3.3 GHz, with 2.7–2.9 GHz optional)
> **Beam:** 1.4 × 5 deg
> **Peak Power:** 425 kW
> **Pulse Width:** 0.95 or 0.4 microsec (latter only in 2216)
> **PRF:** Fixed one of four or four staggered (900–1050 pps) plus short-pulse mode (1360 pps) in 2216 only
> **Scan Rate:** 12.5/6 rpm

This coastal-surveillance radar is the EL/M-2215 ATC radar with a different antenna (AT-102); data above (including antenna data) are for EL/M-2215 (AT-103 single-beam antenna). EL/M-2216 is a high-resolution dual-band (X- and S-band) system with

a fast-scanning X-band component, for surface search (including small-target detection) and optional low-flier search. The -2215 radar has dual MTI, and the first blind speed is Mach 3. In addition to the single-beam antenna, -2216 has an optional dual-beam (high-low) type, AT-104. The same radar is also sold in a mobile version, EL/M-2220. It was developed from the earlier EL/M-2205.

EL/M-2216 can detect ships at a range of 20 nm.

◆ EL/M-2221

Elta's X-band fire-control radar for guns and Gabriel missiles was originally a license-built version of the Italian RTN-10X, the first radar fitted to the *Sa'ar* class (1972). Like that radar, this one has an autonomous search mode (although it usually acquires targets designated by a search radar). This radar is probably the unit typically described as RTN-10X in boats equipped with Gabriel.

EL/M-2221. (IAI/Elta)

A variant of this radar, EL/M-2221-GM STGR, is used to control Barak. It can also control Gabriel missiles and a 76mm gun. In the Barak control mode, it captures one or two Barak missiles upon launch, then guides them by CLOS techniques. The same radar can be used for AA gunnery control or for surface search, as a backup to a conventional search radar.

Users: Chile (*Sa'ar* boats), Ecuador (*Manta* class), Israel (missile boats), Kenya (*Mamba* and 32m class), South Africa (*Sa'ar* class), Singapore (*Victory* class) and Taiwan (destroyers).

◆ EL/M-2226

Elta's third-generation X-band Advanced Coastal Surveillance Radar (ACSR) scans its 1.5 × 2.6-deg beam at 300 rpm. Elta claims that at this high data rate traces (such as shadowing) of nonreflecting targets can be detected by analysis of what might otherwise be dismissed as clutter. As a consequence, it claims that this radar can detect rubber boats at 20 km in Sea State 3. Range resolution is 1 m; this radar can image larger ships for identification.

◆ EL/M-2228 (AMDR and SGRS)

Elta's Automatic Missile Detection Radar designates targets for the Barak missile. It can also function as a conventional short-range air-search radar. There are two versions, EL/M-2228S and -2228X.

EL/M-2228S, showing its back-to-back 2D and 3D antennas. (IAI/Elta)

EL/M-2228S has two back-to-back antennas, a conventional 2D reflector and a 3D array giving coverage up to 70 deg. Scan rate is 12 or 24 rpm, and the antenna is stabilized against 20-deg roll and pitch. A drawing suggests that the 3D array forms five simultaneous beams, the 2D reflector concentrating its power at lower elevation. Vertical width of the elevation beams is probably about 12 deg. This pulse-Doppler radar (PRF over 10 kHz, velocity coverage Mach 0.3–3.0; targets below Mach 0.2 are rejected) has an instrumented range of 100 km. It is expected to detect a fighter at 70 km, and a missile at 20 km (with a false alarm rate less than one per day). It can maintain over 100 ADT tracks. Threats are automatically evaluated and ranked; target azimuth and speed are extracted by a 64-kword programmable microprocessor. The display may be a 16in PPI, a raster-scan CRT, or an alphanumeric display (CRT). The full 3D high power configuration (TWT and cross-field amplifier) requires two electronics racks (1600 kg below decks); above-decks weight is 550 kg.

An alternative earlier 2D configuration (csc² beam) can have either low (TWT, one cabinet below decks, 500 kg) or high (TWT plus cross-field amplifier, two cabinets below decks, 1500 kg) power. Above-deck weight is 237 kg. The low-power version could track 20 targets and had an instrumented range of over 30 km. It could detect a 0.1m² target at 10 nm and a sea-skimming missile at 16 nm.

EL/M-2228X is a related 2D X-band coherent pulse-Doppler surveillance and gunnery radar, also with 100-track capacity (in-

cluding splashes for gun FCS). The csc² beam extends up to 30 deg in elevation. Instrumented range is 100 km (a fighter is detected at 50 km, a surface target at 10). Splash measurement is accurate to within 2.5 mrad and 10 m. As in the S-band version, above-decks weight is 237 kg (the same 2D antenna can be used for both S- and X-bands, as in EL/M-2208), the scan rate is 12 or 24 rpm, and the antenna is stabilized against 20 deg in pitch or roll. Below-decks weight is 460 kg.

Users: Israel (*Nirit*, *Lahav* class [*Sa'ar* 5]). This radar may also be planned for the Singaporean *Victory* class, which now has Sea Giraffe.

OPTRONICS

El-Op is working on a new IRST using its MSIS turret and elevation assemblies and a new three-axis stabilization system. Reportedly it uses a 3–5-micron FPA, and an 8–12-micron detector may later be added. Work began in 1990, and new signal-processing algorithms are now (1996–98) being developed; the IRST may be marketed about 2000. It is now known that DS-35 was abandoned after tests in 1978–80.

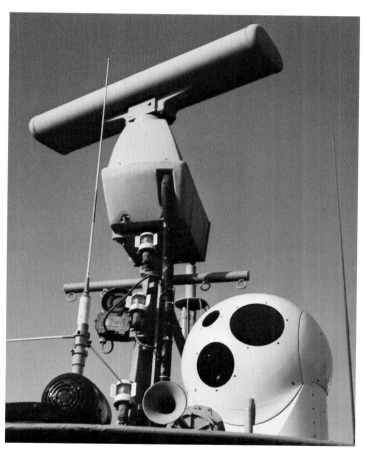

MSIS turret on board a patrol boat. (El-Op)

◆ **Eagle Eye**

IAI's new optronic air-defense system (for 30–40mm guns) uses a laser and an optical tracker; it can be cued by a radar, such as EL/M-2106HE (UPS-3). Eagle Eye can control up to six weapons simultaneously. Typical radar range is 20 km; laser range is 7 km, and TV identification range is 6.4 km. Track accuracy is given as 5 m.

◆ **MKD 600**

Tadiran's gyrostabilized daylight TV camera is suitable for use on board ships and helicopters. It uses a 40/400mm focal-length zoom lens (FOV 15.7 down to 1.57 deg), and can use a 60/600mm lens. Acquisition range on a tank is 29 km, and the vehicle can

EL/M-2228X. (IAI/Elta)

be identified at 3 km. As of mid-1989, MKD 600 had been exported to two countries, and a publicity photograph showed it on board the hydrofoil *Shimrit*.

The earlier MKD 400 is used on board the Pioneer UAV.

◆ MSIS

El-Op's Multisensor Stabilized Integrated System carries three sensors (FLIR, television, and laser) in a four-axis stabilized (550 mm, 60 kg) spherical turret. The associated command/display unit incorporates a video tracker and can control guns of up to 76mm caliber. The laser ranger has a minimum range of 300 m. Angular coverage is +85/−15 deg, and maximum slew rate is 60 deg/sec. LOS stabilization is within 20 microrad. FOVs are 25.7 × 9.2, 7.4 × 5.5, and 2.1 × 1.57 deg. El-Op claims that the FLIR can detect a missile boat (4 × 6m target, presumably head on) at 17,000 m and recognize it at 8200 m; the FLIR detects an aircraft (2.5 × 4m target) at 16,000 m and recognizes it at 5900; and it detects a dinghy (1.5 × 1 m) at 6500 m and recognizes it at 2100 m. Corresponding figures for the daylight TV camera are: missile boat, 12,000/6500 m; aircraft, 9000/5000 m; and dinghy, 6500/3500 m.

Total system weight is 100 kg (220 lb).

Ultimately MSIS is to equip all Israeli ships, including the *Sa'ar 5s*. One was installed on USS *Halyburton* during the Gulf War. As of 1993, 50 were on order or delivered.

User: Israel (*Eilat* class, "Sa'ar 4.5," and Dabur and Super Dvora patrol boats; ordered for the latter in 1988), possibly also Sri Lanka (Super Dvora); may also be on Dvoras in Sri Lankan and Israeli service. There was at least one other export customer.

◆ Sea-Eye

Rafael announced this modular stabilized pedestal-mounted FLIR in 1992; it has two FOVs: 1.7 × 1.25 and 4.5 × 3.5. It can scan at 20 deg/sec over 180 deg in bearing and 56 deg in elevation.

ITALY

RADARS

Selenia uses the prefixes RAN (Radar Avvistamento Navale, or naval search radar), RAT (Radar Avvistamento Terrestre), and RTN (Radar Tiro Navale, or naval fire-control radar) for its radars. The letter in the suffix indicates the frequency range (e.g., RAN-10S operates in S-band).

Many ships have a BX-732 commercial navigational radar: *Pietro de Cristofaro* class, *Albatros* class, *Adjutant*-class patrol boats and minesweepers, *Agile*-class minesweepers, the former netlayer *Alicudi*. The two-letter designation would normally indicate an element of a larger system.

As of spring 1992, Alenia was beginning a family of S-band coast-defense radars based on its ARGOS-73.

◆ BPS-704

See 3RM Series below.

◆ SPN-703

See 3RM Series below.

◆ SPN-720

This combined carrier-landing radar was initially supplied to Argentina for the carrier *25 de Mayo*, and then to the Italian navy for the carrier *Giuseppe Garibaldi*. SPN-720 links the SPS-702 search radar with a new tracker. This radar, developed by SMA, was announced in 1984. The radar covers the 150–270-deg sector abaft the ship, and the glide path is adjustable between 2 and 21 deg. Search range is about 15 nm; approach-control range is about 8 nm. Aircraft can be detected at altitudes up to 2000 m (about 6600 ft). This radar is shown as installed on board the *25 de Mayo*.

◆ SPN-728

SMA's X-band surface-search ATD radar uses a high-gain double-curvature antenna with csc² vertical cover; SPN-728 can be used

SPN-720 carrier-controlled approach radar. Search range is about 15 nm; approach-control range is about 8 nm. Aircraft can be detected at altitudes up to 2000 m (about 6600 ft). (SMA)

SPN-728 antenna, for navigation and surface search. This medium-power X-band radar is supplied with several alternative roll- and pitch-stabilized antennas. There are four alternative pulse widths, and the display is a raster rather than a rotating scan, partly so that the radar can use low-cost television-type monitors as repeaters. Targets are automatically detected. (SMA)

for helicopter control. This medium-power X-band radar is supplied with several alternative roll- and pitch-stabilized antennas. There are four alternative pulse widths, and the display is raster-scanned, partly so that the radar can use low-cost TV-type monitors as repeaters.

User: Italy ([V]1 in *Giuseppe Garibaldi*, [V]2 in *Minerva* class, [V]3 in *Lerici* and *Gaeta* classes; [V]3 has slotted-array antenna, [V]1 has a wider reflector than [V]2; this radar apparently supersedes SPS-702/SPQ-2).

◆ SPN-748/751

Gem Elettronica's X-band navigational radar for large ships uses a 10in CRT. It can be fitted with a digital scan converter.

User (SPN-748 except as noted): Italy (*Audace* class, *Amerigo Vespucci* [with two antennas], *San Marco* class [main radar], *Cassiopea* class [main radar], *Zara* class [customs service], SPN-748 and -751).

◆ SPN-749

Gem Elettronica's X-band (9345–9405 MHz, peak power 20 kW) navigation radar for the carrier *Giuseppe Garibaldi* consists of a master antenna at the bow and a slave antenna at the stern, for 360-deg coverage that does not interfere with the flight deck.

SPN-749 on the carrier *Giuseppe Garibaldi*, 1991, with the dish of RTN-30X to the right. (Author)

◆ SPN-753(V)

Gem Elettronica's raster-display ARPA navigation radar was announced in 1989. Up to 50 targets, including fast (600kt) aircraft, are autotracked. They can be auto-acquired, or up to 20 can be manually acquired. Each tracked target is assigned a two-digit tag, and data for each target can be read out: bearing and range, course and speed, CPA, theoretical CPA, latitude, and longitude. The display also shows alert and failure signals. The display can be either a ship-centered or off-centered PPI. The color display (1280 × 1024 pixels, 4 bits per pixel) can show video maps (including those drawn by the operator) and alphanumerics as well as raw video. There is a data window (alphanumerics) to the right of the radar image. The system can carry up to 200 target-identification symbols, as well as a selectable alert zone. The radar image can be zoomed, and it can also be frozen. Because SPN-753 interfaces with navigational systems such as GPS and Loran, own and target positions can be associated with their latitude and longitude. Both 19in and 26in displays are available.

The commercial equivalent appears to be GEMANT 2(V)1, which uses 6-, 7.5-, and 9ft antennas and has alternative 10-, 25-, and 50-kW transmitters.

SPN-753 can feed Gem's SSN-752 automatic tactical table.

Gem also manufactures an SPN-751 navigational radar, apparently the last of its line not to incorporate a digital scan converter (the company makes a scan converter for SPN-748 and -751).

◆ SPQ-2/SPQ-701/SPS-702/SPQ-3/CORA/CONDO-R

Band: X
Beam: Approx. 0.6 deg wide
Peak Power: 180 kW
Pulse Width: (a) 0.15 (b) 1.5 microsec
PRF: (a) 2500–3000 (b) 450–550 pps
Scan Rate: Fast rotation (40 rpm) available as option
Antenna Dimensions: Approx. 3 m wide

Data are for SPQ-2. SPQ-2D uses alternating 1.0- and 0.15-microsec pulses at a peak power of 60 kW, scanning at 15–20 rpm.

SMA's SPQ/SPS-701/702 operates in two modes, tactical (180 kW, 8450–9220 MHz, frequency-agile, with 0.3-, 1.0-, and 1.6-microsec pulses) and navigational (50 kW, fixed frequency between 9440 and 9500 MHz, 1.1-microsec pulses). PRFs: navigational, 1000 or 1028 pps; tactical, 593–594, 622–623, 837–839, 934–936, 1000–1004, 1036–1038, 1968–1984, 2034–2052. These radars scan at about 15 rpm.

This radar alternates long and short pulses for both medium-range air- and surface-search and precise short-range navigational coverage. SPQ-2 is sometimes used for target designation. Options include fast antenna rotation (up to 40 rpm) and a transponder. Both stabilized and nonstabilized versions exist. This radar should not be confused with the U.S. SPQ-2, an obsolete

SPS-702 (the solid antenna) is shown on the carrier *Giuseppe Garibaldi*, 1991. The big open-mesh antenna below it is RAN-3L; the fire-control radar in the foreground is RTN-30X. The antenna at bottom left belongs to RAN-10S. (Author)

SPS-702 is the solid antenna halfway up the mast of the Italian frigate *Zeffiro*, shown here in 1995. The short antenna below (sharing the roll-stabilized mounting with the larger solid reflector) is the associated IFF interrogator (a navigational radar antenna occupies a similar position in SPQ-701). The fire-control radar below is RTN-30X. In the background is the U.S. assault carrier *Nassau*. (Author)

(and extinct) missile-control set for the Regulus surface-attack missile.

SPQ-701 and SPS-702 are developments of SPQ-2. The SPQ-701 antenna is a parabolic reflector with a narrow vertical dimension, for surface- and air-target detection. SPS-702 uses a broader antenna with a high-elevation component above the main reflector.

SPQ-3 is a related shore Otomat target-acquisition radar, using back-to-back S- and X-band reflectors fed by S-band horns above X-band slotted arrays. Both elements are frequency-agile, and PRF is variable. Data can be transmitted in either analog or digital (ATD) form. SPQ-3B has a special minewatching feature, detecting the splashes of mines dropped by air into coastal waters or harbors.

SMA's CORA OTH-T radar, presumably for Otomat, is designed specifically to exploit ducting; its dish automatically moves in elevation to achieve maximum range. The CORA kit installed on an existing radar (presumably SPQ-2) combines a slightly modified circular dish antenna with a transmitter modification (presumably producing longer or more energetic pulses at a lower PRF). CORA was installed about 1991 atop the bridges

A *Lupo*-class frigate displays the radome of her CORA radar, above her bridge.

of at least two *Lupo*-class frigates, *Orsa* and *Sagittario*. The designation means "duct radar" in Italian (*condotto* means "duct"). CONDO-R is a land-based (coastal) equivalent, presumably related to SPQ-3.

The CORA dish antenna is probably related to that of SMA's TPS-755 coastal air/surface surveillance and tracking radar, but the feed is very different. CORA uses a waveguide pointed toward the dish. TPS-755 uses a horn in the dish pointed at a secondary reflector above the dish, apparently carrying a drive motor for conscan operation.

Users:

SPQ-2: Italy (-2F in *Lupo* class, -2B in *Pietro de Cristofaro* class, -2 in *Albatros* class) and Venezuela (SPQ-2D in *Constitucion* class).
SPQ-701: Italy (*Sparviero* class).
SPS-702: Italy (*Vittorio Veneto, Maestrale* class).

◆ **SPS-768**

See RAN-3L below.

◆ **SPS-774**

See RAN-10S below.

◆ **MM/SPY-790 (EMPAR)**

Band: C (5.6 cm) (frequency-agile over 10% of frequency)
Beam: 2.6 deg (scan angles 45 deg in azimuth, +95/−25 deg in elevation)
Peak Power: 120 kW (10–12% duty cycle) (digital pulse compression)
Scan Rate: 60 rpm (for horizon search); uses phase-phase shifting to scan volume search beam at 7.5 rpm (data rate 8 sec)
Antenna Dimensions: 1.5 m²
Weight: 2500 kg above decks, 6000 kg below

The Alenia-Marconi EMPAR (the European Multi-Purpose Array Radar) is to be used in the Italian variant of the Franco-Italian FAAMS missile system, for target search, acquisition, and tracking. The French equivalent is Arabel. EMPAR employs a square array of 2160-pin diode 4-bit phase shifters, tilted back at an

angle of 30 deg. The beam is steered by phase scanning in both elevation (+/−60 deg) and azimuth (+/−45 deg), while the antenna itself turns; it is also electronically stabilized. The rotating array was chosen for its simplicity and relatively low cost. Elevation-only scanning (as in, say, SPS-48) was rejected because that would have made for too low a data rate. By scanning horizontally, the radar can vary its effective data rate on a mode-by-mode basis, with slow scanning for longer range and faster scanning for higher data rates closer in. Scanning in two directions also makes it possible for the radar to track targets by monopulse techniques, since adjacent beams can rapidly be formed.

The radar is managed by an Alenia MARA-series computer programmed in ADA (its tasks include translation from rotating coordinates fixed in the radar to coordinates fixed in the ship). A separate three-cabinet signal processor uses Texas Instruments C40-series processors. It can be reconfigured in real time,

EMPAR on its test stand. (Alenia)

to vary waveform and also to vary the length of the DFT and FFT Doppler filters.

The transmitter is a software-controlled driven TWT. The radar can operate at low or medium PRF and can automatically choose optimum frequency. Pulses are digitally compressed and Doppler-processed. C-band was chosen to avoid interference with existing X-band radars. The original back-to-back design (intended to double data rate) was dropped to halve the number of phase shifters. Alenia dropped plans to use an active array because the promised mass production of C-band modules failed to materialize and because of problems of heat dissipation and phase-matching between modules. The entire array is liquid-cooled, through a water rotating joint.

According to a 1987 account, the radar is required to detect medium-altitude targets at 50–100 km and low-fliers at 20 km, and to be able to track a target over the zenith (over a 120-deg elevation angle). EMPAR is designed to detect a 0.1m^2 target at 50 km, a 2m^2 target at 100 km, and a large aircraft (10 m^2) at 180 km. It is to be able to handle about 300 long-range targets and to track 50 of them well enough for missile engagement (the current maximum missile control load is 24). Estimated tracking accuracy is 3–5 mrad.

Operating modes:

- Volumetric search (VOS), at short (SRS) or medium range (MRS), in each case in elevation as well as in bearing. Data rate is 8 sec (7.5 rpm) and each scan consists of a mixture of horizontal and vertical searches, together amounting to 3191 beam dwells. On each rotation, the radar scans once in each MRS and SRS direction, conducts four scans in each horizontal direction, updates each HPT target eight times (effective data rate 1 sec), updates each LPT target once or twice, and conducts eight uplinks to missiles under radar control.
- Long-range search (LRS).
- High-priority tracking (HPT): 1-sec data rate (60 rpm), 36 tracks.
- Low-priority tracking (LPT): 4- or 8-sec data rate (12.5 or 7.5 rpm), up to 264 tracks, but with lower-quality information than in HPT.

Fully loaded, the radar spends 75% of its time seeking new targets, 20% tracking ones already detected, and 5% uplinking.

Alenia (then called Selenia) began work on multifunction radars as early as 1965. EMPAR was the Italian choice for the radar of the abortive NATO frigate and its NAAWS system; it was then offered for FAAMS. The development contract was awarded in 1986 and a prototype was installed on board the test frigate *Carabinieri* in mid-1995.

◆ RAN-3L (MM/SPS-768)

Band: L
Beam: 2.15×9 deg plus csc^2
Peak Power: 135 kW
Gain: 30 dB
Pulse Width: 78.4 (compressed to 1.6) microsec
Scan Rate: 6 rpm
Antenna Dimensions: 7.56×3.65 m (24.9×11.8 ft)

Alenia developed this large-ship air-search radar to meet a May 1966 Italian navy specification for an SPS-12/40 replacement. The transmitter offers scan-to-scan frequency agility (for ECCM). By phase-coding pulses within each burst (equivalent to the chirp of a frequency-coded pulse-compression radar) Alenia was able to combine pulse compression (for high effective power) with pulse-Doppler processing (for MTI and clutter rejection). One limitation on this technique is that the length of each burst cannot exceed about 10% of the interval between bursts, to avoid excessive dead time (which would make for excessive minimum range). Filter criteria are shifted as the transmitter frequency changes on each scan. Rated maximum range is 150 nm (100+ nm on a fighter). Accuracy is 0.4 deg and 70 m. Maximum range can be increased to 160 nm by using dual-frequency diversity (to overcome the STAE problem). The antenna is designated G12.

RAN-3L (SPS-768). (Selenia)

Alenia received the development contract in 1968, and operational tests were completed in November 1975. RAN-3L was considered too heavy for frigates (such as the *Lupo* class), so a smaller RAN-10S was designed, using much the same technology. Some of this technology is also incorporated in Alenia's RAN-11L, which is intended for small warships and patrol craft.
Users: Garibaldi, Vittorio Veneto, Mimbelli, Audace classes.

◆ RAN-10S (MM/SPS-774)/Pluto

Band: S
Beam: 1.5×17 deg (coverage to 60-deg elevation)
Peak Power: 140 kW
Gain: 28 dB
Burst Width: 20.8 (compressed to 0.4) microsec
PRF: About 900 pps
Scan Rate: 15 or 30 rpm
Antenna Dimensions: 4.3×0.7 m (14.1×2.3 ft)

This radar, announced in 1980, is in effect a frigate equivalent to RAN-3L. It also serves as the target-acquisition radar of the Dardo CIWS. Like the larger radar, it uses phase-coded bursts of pulses and a frequency-agile transmitter. Each burst consists of four pulses.

The Pluto coast-defense radar probably uses the same transmitter (de-rated to 135 kW), receiver, and processor, with a larger antenna (beam 1.5×4-deg super csc^2, tilt between $+5/-2$ deg, scan rate 12 or 15 rpm). IFF is integrated into the antenna, using a secondary feed in the main horn. The associated mobile reporting station (MARS-402) can handle 40 tracks, initiated automatically or manually, and can display 50 synthetic plots. Typically there are two console positions. Accuracy: 40m, 0.35 deg.

RAN-10S. (Selenia)

The new solid antenna for RAN-10S. (Alenia)

Maximum unambiguous range is 90 nm; effective range about 40 nm on a fighter. A sea-skimming missile (cross-section 0.1 m² at 3m altitude) can be detected outside 10 km (about 11 kyds, 5.5 nm). Range accuracy is 20 m, and angular accuracy is 0.35 deg.

The roll-stabilized antenna is designated G10. A new stabilized SMA-7104 antenna was exhibited at Genoa in June 1986

Pluto coastal-surveillance radar. (Selenia)

(beam 1.5 × 15 deg, gain 28 dB, scan rate 15/30 rpm, and weight 960 kg).

Users: Ecuador (*Wadi M'ragh* class), Italy (*Mimbelli, Audace, Maestrale, Lupo, Minerva* classes), Libya (*Dat Assawari*), Peru (*Lupo*), Venezuela (*Lupo*). The *Minervas* have new solid OA-7104 antennas rather than the usual mesh type.

◆ RAN-11 L/X and -12 L/X

Band: L and X (combined antenna)
Beam: (L) 6.6 × 16 deg, (X) 1.1 × 6 plus csc² deg
Peak Power: (L) 0.3 kW, (X) 135 and 180 kW
Gain: (L) 22 dB, (X) 35 dB
Pulse Width: (L) 20 microsec (compressed to 2.9), (X) 1.5 and 0.15 microsec
PRF: (X) 450–550 pps
Scan Rate: 15 or 30 rpm
Antenna Dimensions: 8 ft wide

Selenia/SMA's small-ship (hydrofoil) search radar operates simultaneously in L- and X-bands, using the X-band transmitter of the SPQ-2 and a new pulse-Doppler L-band transmitter. The latter uses pulse compression. The antenna is cut horizontally, the upper portion reflecting in L- but not in X-band. Range accuracy is 160 m in L-band and 45 m in X-band; angular accuracy is 1.5 deg in L-band and 0.2 deg in X-band.

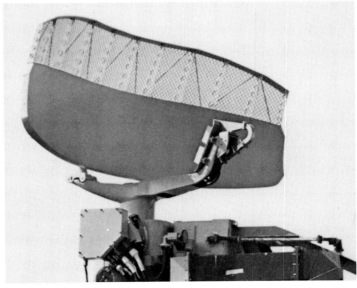

RAN-11 L/X. (Selenia)

A RAN-20S stabilized planar-array antenna. (Alenia)

RAN-12 L/X is the -11 with a higher-power (1.1 kW) L-band transmitter. Effective X-band range against a low flier is 20+ nm. At medium altitude, range (L-band) is 12+ nm for RAN-11, and 14+ nm for RAN-12. These figures are shorter than X-band ranges because the pulse-Doppler L-band transmitter necessarily operates at a higher PRF.

Development of this system began in 1969.

Users:

RAN-11 L/X: Italy (*Mimbelli* and *Audace* classes and ex-Iraqi *Lupo* class), Peru (*Lupo* class), Spain (*Principe de Asturias*), Venezuela (*Lupo* class)

RAN-12 L/X: Iraq (*Wadi M'ragh* class, now for sale), Malaysia (ex-Iraqi *Wadi M'ragh* class), Spain (*Perry*, *Baleares* classes)

◆ RAN-20S

This is a new Alenia solid-state radar with a planar-array or reflector antenna. RAN-20S is 2D, with an antenna swing diameter of 4.5 m. Elevation coverage is over 65 deg. Range on a fighter is over 150 nm. Accuracy is 0.3 deg and 20 m. Scan rate is 6 and 12 rpm. This rdar has a solid-state transmitter with a peak power of 20 kW.

Users: RAN-20S has been ordered for the Brazilian *Niteroi*-class modernization program.

◆ RAN-30X

Alenia's small-ship air/surface search radar, announced about 1987, was derived from the phase-coded pulse-compression RTN-30X FCS radar and can share that radar's transmitter/receiver. It can also be integrated with an RAN-12L radar. There is also a three-beam 3D antenna, using three separate feeds (the uppermost tiltable by remote control), to produce stacked beams. Operating modes are long-range/15-rpm scan rate and medium-range/30-rpm scan. A fighter can be detected beyond 20 nm. Accuracy: 25 m, 0.4 deg.

Users: Spain (for upgrade of RAN-12X Meroka target-acquisition radars). This upgrade may also have been applied to other export RAN-12L/X radars (for Iraqi ships, some of which have now been sold to Malaysia, and for the Libyan *Dat Assawari*, now defunct) and posssibly for Italy (for the RAN-11L/X); the manufacturer claims several RAN-12L/X upgrades. No exports of the stand-alone version are known.

◆ Argos 73

Alenia's S (E)-band coastal radar employs a solid-state signal generator (for high MTBF) rather than the tubes of the company's earlier coastal radars. Like the company's naval search radars, it uses phase-coding (with Doppler processing within each burst of pulses) for frequency-agile pulse compression. The parabolic-reflector antenna scans at 10 rpm, creating a csc^2 beam. A fighter can be detected at over 64 nm. This set won a 1991 NATO coastal radar competition.

◆ RTN-10X (SPG-73)/RTN-20X (SPG-74) (Orion)/RTN-25X

Band: X
Peak Power: 200 kW
Pulse Width: 0.5 microsec
PRF: 2000 pps
Antenna Dimensions: 1.4 m dia

RAN-20S reflector version. (Alenia)

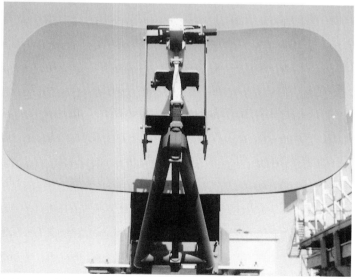

RAN-30X. (Alenia)

RTN-10X trackers of an NA-21 FCS. (Selenia)

RTN-10X is a conical-scan set employing the same X-band transmitter as RAN-11 L/X. It was designed for one-person operation and particularly for integration into the Albatros FCS. Orion can scan in three modes: automatic blind-fire, operator-assisted blind-fire, and area. In the first mode the radar searches around a designated point, then locks on and tracks without further assistance. In the second, less accurate data are available, and the tracker searches a larger area. If the radar fails to lock onto a target, the operator can steer the radar to the target position shown on the display. Area search is a horizon or sector search at low elevation, or near a passive ESM bearing. A TV camera is bore-sighted to the radar for use under heavy jamming. Targets can be acquired out to 35 km. The 10/XP version in the Italian *Lupo* class is frequency-agile.

Development of RTN-10X began in 1970, and series production began in 1972. This radar was first installed on board Israeli *Sa'ar*-class missile boats (1972), then on board the Italian destroyer *Ardito*. Orion was redesigned from 1974 on for coherent operation using TWTs and then with digital technology.

Users (RTN-10X): Brazil (*Inhauma* and *Niteroi* classes), Chile (*Sa'ar 2/4*), China (two on each "Luda III," Jianghu III/IV, "Jiang-wei"-class frigates), Denmark (*Nils Juels* class), Ecuador (*Wadi M'ragh* and *Manta* classes), Israel (missile boats), Italy (*Vittorio Veneto*, *Lupo*, and *Sparviero* classes, *San Giorgio*, *Stromboli*, *Quarto*), Kenya (32m class), Malaysia (ex-Iraqi *Wadi M'ragh* class), Pakistan (as Type 912, being retained on board ex-British Type 21 frigates), Peru (*Lupo* class), Philippines (projected *Cormoran* class), South Africa (*Sa'ar 4* class), Venezuela (*Lupo*, *Almirante Clemente*, *Constitucion* classes). Greece bought RTN-10X for several FRAM destroyers, now discarded; these radars and their associated FCSs will probably be installed on board "Osprey"-type OPVs.

RTN-20X was the first monopulse version of the series, optimized for low-altitude tracking, initially for the Dardo CIWS in the *Maestrale* class. RTN-20X is a digital coherent monopulse radar (TWT transmitter tube) with special ECCM features (antinodding and anticlutter). Image effects (because of reflections off the water) are reduced by comparing received signals in sequence, to select the direct-path signal. The antenna is a 1.2m-dia inverse-Cassegrain with twist polarization (beamwidth 2.2 deg, gain 37 dB). There are two different (selectable) pulse widths, and the radar hops frequencies on a pulse-to-pulse or burst-to-burst basis. Signal processing includes coherent MTI. RTN-20X acquires its targets at 2–6 nm. This radar can acquire and track a target (e.g., an antiship missile) fired by a target being tracked. Typical tracking accuracy on a frigate is 2 min of arc and 3 m; on an airplane (2 m^2), 1.5 min of arc and 3 m.

Development began in 1973.

Users: China (one each on "Luda III," Jianghu III/IV, "Jiang-wei"-class frigates), Ecuador (*Wadi M'ragh* class), Greece (76mm fire control on FRAM I *Gearings*), Italy (*Garibaldi*, *Vittorio Veneto*, *Maestrale*, *Lupo*, *Minerva*, *Cassiopea* classes), Peru (*Lupo* class), Venezuela (*Lupo* class).

RTN-25X is a higher-powered version of RTN-20X, part of the NA-25 FCS, which is an element of the new generation of distributed combat systems. The two operating modes are long pulse (coded waveform) and short pulse (single pulse). The fire-control radar of the new Myriad system (which is also called Myriad) uses 25X components (monopulse, coherent [TWT], pulse Doppler) but operates in X- or K-band, depending on which TWT is fitted.

An RTN-25K Myriad FCS radar was displayed at Bourget Naval in October 1994.

♦ RTN-30X (SPG-76)

This automatic-target-acquisition and monopulse tracker is the basis of the NA-30 FCS; it replaces RTN-10X in the Albatros missile FCS. Unlike the earlier radar, it incorporates CWI (no second transmitter is required). It is the most powerful tracker of the series, with twice the power of RTN-10X. Range on low-level targets (such as sea-skimming missiles) in clutter is up to 8 nm. Features include MTI, frequency agility, a coded waveform (i.e., pulse compression), and jam alarm. As in the earlier Orions, there is special antinodding (i.e., antimultipath) signal processing. Peak power is 12 kW (6.5 microsec pulse compressed to 0.5 microsec plus 0.5 microsec single pulse). Range on an airplane is over 45 km.

RTN-30X tracking radar of the NA-30 system. Note the two coaxial optronic sensors. The new RTN-25X is apparently externally indistinguishable from this radar. (Alenia)

Users: Brazil (bought for *Niteroi* upgrade), Italy (*Garibaldi*, *Mimbelli*, *Audace*, *Maestrale*, *Etna* classes), Peru (*Lupo* class).

♦ 3RM Series (BPS-704, SPN-703, etc.)

Band: X
Beam: 0.8–2.0 deg × 26 deg (shaped to 40 deg) (SPN-703: 1.2 × 25 deg; BPS-704: 2.2 × 11 deg)
Peak Power: (a) 7 (b) 20 kW
Gain: BPS-704: at least 27 dB
Pulse Width: (a) 0.05 (b) 0.15 (c) 0.5 (d) 1.5 microsec
PRF: (a) 6000 (b) 3000 (c) 1500 (d) 750 pps (SPN-703: 5200, 2600, 1300, 650, respectively)
Scan Rate: 25 rpm

SMA's surface-search radars have limited air-search capability. All use slotted-waveguide antennas, beamwidths depending upon dimensions. Two transmitters are available, as noted above (the numbers after the 3RM indicate the radar's transmitter power).

Users:

3RM20: Algeria (Mangusta-class patrol boats), Germany (*Bremen* class and S143/S143A/S148 classes), Italy (*Cassiopea* class, 105ft class, *Meattini* class, *Gabriele* class), Peru (*Lupo* class), Venezuela (*Lupo* class).

The Italian submarine *Sauro* displays her BPS-704 radar antenna. The other two antennas are part of her Thetis ESM system. (*Ships of the World*)

3RM20 SMG (BPS-704): Argentina (TR 1700 class), Italy (*Sauro, Toti* classes).

3RM20-B (SPN-703): Iraq (*Wadi M'ragh*, now for sale), Italy (*Animoso, Lupo, Lerici, Agile* [minehunters]), Nigeria (probably in *Lerici* class). Components of this radar are also used in the MM/APS-705 and -707 and in the MM/APQ-706 (see airborne radars).

♦ BX-132/164 (or 732/764)

These GEM Elettronica X-band solid-state navigational radars are aboard many Italian warships. They use 4- or 6ft slotted-waveguide antennas (beam 1.6 or 1.3 × 22 deg) scanning at 22 rpm; peak power is 10 kW, for a maximum instrumented range of 32 or 64 nm (BX-132 vs BX-164).

Users: Pietro de Cristofaro class, *Albatros* class, *Adjutant*-class patrol boats and minesweepers, *Agile*-class minesweepers, the former netlayer *Alicudi*, and inshore customs craft. The two-letter designation would normally indicate an element of a larger system. These radars are sometimes called BX-732, and it is not clear which designation is correct. Many customs craft (in effect small coast guard cutters) are equipped with GEM BX-3072 (*Corrubia* and CNL 39 classes) and SC-1400 (*Corrubia* class) radars.

GEM Elettronica also makes a variety of commercial navigational radars, some of which may correspond to the naval types listed above. SC-1005-RD is a very small X-band radar (4 kW, using a 55cm antenna with a 4 × 24-deg beam) using a 10in display. SC-1510/1525 is a 10/25-kW digital raster-scan X-band radar using a 4-, 6-, or 7.5ft antenna (beams 1.6 × 22, 1.3 × 23, 1.1 × 23 deg) and a 15in display. Range scales are 0.25 to 96 nm.

♦ HSS-1

SMA's X-band harbor-surveillance radar employs a parabolic narrow-beam reflector. HSS-1 employs frequency and polariza-

tion decorrelation to distinguish targets in high-density shipping lanes within highly reflective land areas, such as estuaries. The radar is semimobile.

♦ RAT-10S/8S and RAT-33S/M

Alenia's S(E)-band 450-kW coast-defense radars have pulse rates of, respectively, 500 and 1000 pps. RAT-10S scans its 0.8-deg beam, generated by a tunable magnetron, at 6 rpm. Instrumented range is 150 nm; vertical beamwidth is about 3 deg. Processing includes anticlutter to detect and track surface units. Development began in 1965, and this radar was adopted by several countries, and also as a NATO standard. There is also a transportable RAT-8S.

RAT-33 S/M coastal-surveillance radar. (Selenia)

RAT-33S/M is a combined air/surface ATD surveillance radar with a dual-beam antenna (swing circle 5.5 m) which scans its 15-deg beam at 15 rpm. Signal processing includes Doppler filtering (to eliminate clutter) and an azimuth correlator (to eliminate targets behaving unphysically). The radar automatically adjusts to different clutter environments (distinguishing, for example, between clear areas and ground or sea clutter).

OPTRONIC SYSTEMS

♦ Medusa

Alenia/Elsag's Mk 3 version carries day (0.5 in CCD) and low light-level (intensified CCD) TV cameras; the stabilized pedestal can also carry a 3–5-micron (FPA, FOVs 1.9 × 1.9 or 7.9 × 7.9 deg) or 8–12-micron (8 SPRITE elements, FOVs 2.5 × 1.67 or 6.7 × 4.4 deg) FLIR. A laser ranger (1.54 micron, instrumented range 20 km) can be added. The below-decks console carries a single screen and a joystick. Elevation limits are +85/−40 deg (train/elevation speeds are both 2 rad/sec). Mk 3/I, which is currently being marketed, carries both TV and FLIR (and the laser) and has a double-screen console, so both images can be viewed simultaneously. It has more modern electronics, and is designed both to control two guns and to feed a ship combat-system data bus. Sensor and platform characteristics match those of Mk 3.

Medusa Mk 3 (TV/FLIR version) was bought for the Italian customs service; it is on board the *Corrubia* and CNL 39 classes as FCS for their 30mm guns. It is probably also on board the Thai marine police boat *Srinakarin*. The earlier manned unstabilized single-sensor target-designation version (with below-decks console with 7in monitor) appears not to have sold.

Medusa Mk 3 on board a Customs (Guardia di Finanza) boat, probably of the *Corrubia* class. The two GEM Elettronica radars above are BX-3072A and SC-1400. (Alenia)

An OG 30 optronic director is shown forward of and below the accompanying RTN-30X director (which carries a camera) of the NA-30 FCS aboard the Italian frigate *Zeffiro*, 1995. Forward of and below the directors is the cylindrical radome of a jammer. (Author)

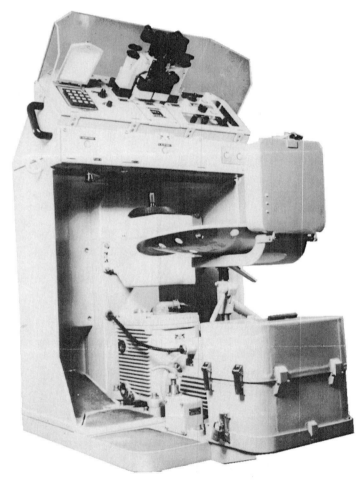

OG.R7. (Officine Galileo)

◆ NA-18

See Fire-Control Systems below.

◆ OG 30

Officine Galileo's optronic director, part of the NA-30 FCS (hence the name), was introduced in 1980 in the *Maestrale* class. OG 30A carries a laser range-finder (P0700, 1.06 microns, 20–25 MW, 15 bursts/sec, range 400 m to 15 km) and IIR (Galileo 8–14-micron camera, 3 × 6-deg FOV, 200 lines/frame, 25 frames/sec) and TV (P4651, 1.8 × 2.4-deg FOV, 700 lines to CCIR standard) cameras on a stabilized platform. The cameras can operate in either surveillance or tracking mode. The assembly elevates at up to 2.2 rad/sec (about 126 deg/sec; limits −2.5/+85 deg) and trains at up to 1.5 rad/sec (about 86 deg/sec). Typical ranges: air target, 16 km; sea-skimmer, 6 km. OG 30B is a simpler version (thermal imager only) mounted on an NA 30 director in the Dardo-E system.

> Users:
>
> OG-30A: Italy (*Maestrale* class [backup director for NA-30, atop the bridge])
> OG-30B: Brazil (*Niteroi* upgrade), Italy (part of Dardo-E in *Audace*, *Mimbelli*, and *Minerva* classes and in *Garibaldi*)

◆ OG.R7/OG 20

Officine Galileo's OG.R7 one-man director is probably the standard secondary FCS of Combattante-type FAC; it may also be aboard most Italian- and Spanish-built warships and their derivatives. The two-man OG.R7/2 version (sometimes erroneously called OG 20) is standard on board Israeli missile boats (including those for Chile and South Africa) and on board Ecuadorian and Kenyan boats converted to fire Gabriel. As of 1988, about 250 had been made.

OG.R7 combines a pair of stabilized LOS: an open sight for target acquisition, and a binocular telescope (2.3× and 7×, corresponding to 30- and 10-deg FOVs) for tracking. A joystick is used to initiate and control target tracking and for gunfire control. Maximum rates of train (elevation) are 100 (60) deg/sec; maximum lead angle (in train) is 25 deg (20 deg in elevation). Crossing range limits: 100–2000 m; target speed limits: 60–350 m/sec.

A Kenyan missile boat displays her Gabriel system, including the two-man OG.R7/2 director and the target-tracking radar. (Royal Navy)

The Israeli Gabriel system originally used OG.R7 (this version survives in the Thai *Prabrarapak* class) but then switched to the two-telescope OG.R7/2, in which one operator holds the target, the other the flare in the tail of the missile. This director is also used for 76mm fire control on board Israeli missile boats.

OG.R7/2A is a more elaborate two-axis stabilized version with an external image intensifier and a digital FCS computer. The sight is moved electrohydraulically in bearing and by servo in elevation. Typical total weight is 550 kg. The current version is OG.R7/3.

Users: Brazil (*Niteroi* class), Ecuador (*Wadi M'ragh* class), Egypt (*Descubierta* class), Germany (Type 143 missile boats, Type 331 and 351 minehunters [as modernized], Type 394 in-shore sweepers, probably many others), Greece (*Kelefstis Stamou* class and ex-German *Thetis* class), Iran (*Saam* class, as adjunct to Sea Hunter 4), Italy (*Lupo* and *Maestrale* classes, probably also *Alpino* class), Morocco (*Descubierta* class), Peru (*Lupo* class), Thailand (*Makut Rajakumarn, Prabrarapak* class), Venezuela (*Lupo* class and modernized *Almirante Clemente* class). Germany was the main, and probably the first, customer, buying the system about 1970. The Italian navy was the other major customer (ca. 1978). Ships with Signaal FCS bought prior to the advent of LIOD probably were fitted with OG.R7 as a backup (the French Panda series was the main alternative). The early Israeli missile boats probably had OG.R7 as an interim director until OG.R7/2 was ready. When integrated with an NA-series FCS, this unit is probably designated CO3. Most OG.R7s use analog computers, but late ones, probably including those ordered by Italy, have digital computers.

◆ VTG 120/N and VTG 240/N

Officine Galileo announced these naval 8–14-micron FLIRs at Mostra Navale 1989; VTG 120/N is based on the army's VTG 120. Both use 60-element parallel-scanned arrays of CMT detectors. VTG 120/N is a pedestal-mounted target designation sight carrying a miniature CRT in its eyepiece; VTG 240/N is intended for integration into an optronic or radar/optronic FCS. These FLIRs have two magnifications, $4\times$ and $12\times$ (corresponding FOVs are 6.9×3.45 and 2.3×1.15 deg). Output in each case is a 240-line IR image that can be fed into a tracker or converted to 625-line TV format for display. Resolution is 0.16 mrad.

FIRE-CONTROL SYSTEMS

◆ Albatros

Albatros is the Aspide missile FCS, often (but not always) associated with RTN-10X (which was originally designed specifically for Albatros). It adds a CW channel (RTN-12X Sirio) to an existing radar tracker. In some installations two radar channels share the same antenna: the radar can track CW illumination reflected from the target or it can track conventionally. Total reaction time, from target designation to missile launch, is 8 sec. Mk 1

(tested 1973) controls the Sea Sparrow (RIM-7H) missile; it is the version in the Egyptian, Moroccan, and Spanish *Descubiertas*. Mk 2 controls Aspide.

Versions: Mod 3 (NA-10 FCS), Mod 5 (NA-21 FCS), Mod 7 (NA-30 FCS), and Mod 9 (Signaal WM25 FCS). Mods 3 and 5 employ RTN-10X radar.

Users: Argentina (MEKO 360 class), Ecuador (*Wadi M'ragh* class), Egypt (*Descubierta*), Iraq (*Wadi M'ragh* class, for sale), Italy (*Garibaldi* and *Animoso, Maestrale, Minerva* classes and ex-Iraqi *Lupos*), Malaysia (ex-Iraqi *Wadi M'ragh* class), Morocco (*Descubierta*), Nigeria (MEKO 360), Peru (*Lupo* class), Spain (*Descubierta*), Thailand (PFMM Mk 16 class), Venezuela (*Lupo* class). The Argentine, Egyptian, Moroccan, Nigerian, Spanish, and Thai ships have WM25 FCSs with Mod 9.

◆ Dardo

Selenia-Elsag's close-in weapons-control system combines a dedicated low-flier search (target acquisition) radar (RAN-10S) with a new tracker (RTN-20X). The weapon is a Breda twin 40mm/70. As in NA-10, search radar video is processed directly by the Dardo system to automatically detect and track air targets, evaluating the threats they represent and selecting those to engage. The system can also accept target designation by a pair of optical sights. The system's Orion RTN-20X was developed specifically for the CIWS role; it carries a television camera. The television monitors the engagement and can control the gun in a jamming environment. Any target within a preset range can be engaged automatically. The system shifts automatically to deal with a sequence of targets. The console is similar to that used in NA-10; presumably Dardo is in effect the CIWS version of the NA-10 series. This system employs an 18-bit computer and can track 10 targets (using plots from the search radar) while engaging one.

Dardo is designed to engage targets between 900 and 3000 m. Its effectiveness derives from its very low dispersion, 2.5 mrad for the system as a whole (based on about 1 mrad for the 40mm gun).

This system was first used on board *Lupo*-class frigates (the first of which was delivered in 1976). In July 1980 the frigate *Sagittario* used Dardo and the associated twin 40mm to engage a series of six Rushton aerial targets (19 cm dia, 2.8 m long) towed at high speed to simulate sea-skimmers. Four were shot down by the initial bursts, and two more were considered sufficiently damaged to count as kills at a range greater than 1000 m.

Users: China (Luhu, modified "Luda" and "Jiangwei" classes), Ecuador (*Wadi M'ragh* class), Iraq (*Wadi M'ragh* class, for sale), Italy (*Maestrale, Lupo*), Malaysia (ex-Iraqi *Wadi M'ragh* class), Peru (*Lupo*), Venezuela (*Lupo*). Dardo is made under license in China (PRC).

◆ NA-10/NA-9

Elsag's NA-10 introduced a new RTN-10X conscan radar (suitable for CW injection) in place of the Orion 250 of the earlier transistorized NA-9. It was miniaturized and added a closed-circuit television coaxial with the tracking radar. Initially it was a dual-ballistics analog system (like NA-9), but production versions are digital, presumably with a fixed-program computer. The large-ship production version is associated with the IPN-10/SADOC digital CDS. It entered service aboard *Lupo*-class frigates from 1977 on (RTN-10X itself had been bought by the Israeli navy, associated with the Gabriel missile system, about 1971). Albatros employs this system with a separate FCS computer and CWI for missile guidance. Like the contemporary French Vega and the Signaal "egg," the Mod 0 large-ship version of the system has an associated target-acquisition radar, in this case RAN-10S. It also has a pair of periscopic optical target designators behind windows in a cab under the radar dish. Using a single radar tracker, NA-10 can engage two targets, one tracked by RTN-10X, the other optically (with range taken from RAN-10S video). The main console houses the ballistic computer (open- or closed-loop) plus a programming section (for autonomous search) and two radar displays (round and A-scan) below a large TV monitor. This version can control three guns of two different calibers.

The Italian frigate *Lupo* shows the characteristic windowed cab of an NA-10 FCS atop her bridge, with an RTN-10X radar mounted on it. The cab contains the system's optical trackers. The later NA-30 system on the *Maestrales* has no such cab. (Italian Navy via *Ships of the World*)

Mod 1, for smaller ships, lacks the dedicated target-acquisition radar and the target designators of Mod 0 and uses a lighter mount for its RTN-10X (which carries a TV camera but lacks the CWI of the heavier version). The computer and other unmanned equipment is relegated to a separate cabinet. This version can control two guns of one caliber. Mod 2 is a modified large-ship version, probably using a programmable digital computer. Mod 3 is a modified version equivalent to Mod 2.

Users: Italy (*Maestrale*, *Lupo*, *Cassiopea*, *Sparviero* [Mod 3], *San Giorgio*, *Stromboli* classes), Peru (*Lupo* [Mod 0] class), Taiwan (*Lung Chiang*), Venezuela (*Lupo* [Mod 0], *Almirante Clemente*, and *Constitucion* [Mod 1] classes).

The earlier fully analog NA-9 (using the RTN-10X radar) survives on board the Italian cruiser *Vittorio Veneto*. It uses a pair of LOS-stabilized optical sights for pointing, and can handle one or two sets of ballistics. A missile version (to control Seacat) was developed for Argentina, for the cruiser *Belgrano*.

◆ NA-18 (Pegaso)/NA-21/NA-30

These modular FCSs use versions of the Elsag ESA 24 24-bit (bit-slice) multiprocessing general-purpose computers whose firmware includes trigonometric functions. The computer uses a combination of ROM, semiconductor memory, and tape memory. It has a 250-nanosec memory-access time (clock rate 4 MHz). It can handle two independent sets of ballistics (for guns of two calibers) in parallel. All versions of the system use common console elements and a data bus.

NA-18 is optronic only (it can use the ship's search radar for target acquisition). It can control a SCLAR rocket launcher, and it uses the simplest version of the computer. Work on NA-18 began about 1975, and it entered service in Indonesia (aboard *Mandau* and *Rencong*) in 1979. Elevation limits are +84/−22 deg, and train (elevation) rates are 2.2 (1.5) rad/sec. The more compact NA-18L, designed for the Italian *Minerva* class, entered service in 1987. Train rate is reduced to 1.8 rad/sec. The director carries an 8–12-micron IR camera (4 × 2.6 and 2 × 1.3-deg FOVs), a TV camera, and a laser range-finder (18-MW NdYAG). NA-18L can be limited to the TV camera only.

Users: Bangladesh (-18B on *Megna* class), Indonesia ("Dagger" class), Italy (*Minerva*, *Zara* classes), Mexico (*Aguila* class), Thailand (PSMM Mk 5 class), Venezuela (*Capana* class). The version on board *Zara* may be modified; it is described as Pegaso-F, with CSDA-10 directors.

NA-21 (announced 1980) is a digital equivalent of ANTI-10, in effect a more sophisticated version of NA-18 using the RTN-10X radar. It controls three guns of two different calibers plus the Aspide missile; it can also designate targets to a surface-to-surface missile. The periscopes of NA-10 are replaced by simple target-designation sights. The system automatically acquires

Pegaso (NA-18L) is shown on board an Italian *Minerva*-class corvette. The second photo shows its new-type console. If a second sensor is fitted, the large screen is moved up into the upper portion of the console, a small screen being placed below it. Alternatively, a large upper screen can display synthetic video corresponding to the video on the lower screen. (Alenia)

targets from the associated search radar (whose video is fed directly into it rather than into the ship's CDS) and from the RTN-10X in search mode. NA-21 in turn feeds its synthetic video into the ship's CDS.

There is no NA-16 (previously listed).

Users: Ecuador (modified *Wadi M'ragh* class), Greece ("Hellenic 56" class, "Osprey 55" class), Iraq (modified *Wadi M'ragh* class, now for sale), Italy (*Artigliere* class), Malaysia (ex-Iraqi *Wadi M'ragh* class), and Philippines (projected *Cormoran* class).

NA-30 is the most powerful member of the NA-18/21/30 family, using the Orion RTN-30X radar plus EO sensors. In NA 30A (*Maestrale*) the radar director carries IR and TV cameras but it is supplemented by an OG 30A optronic director. NA 30B (*Garibaldi* and destroyers) has only the radar/optronic director. The computer can handle three guns of two different calibers with one fuze-setting computation, or one gun plus the Aspide missile.

The main (supervising) console carries two monitors: a 19in raster-scan CRT to show radar PPI (search radar or fire-control radar, the operator choosing between them) or B-scan; and a 15in

NA-21 console, with the characteristic combination of A-scan (left) and PPI (right), and a television monitor above. NA-10 uses a similar console, but in some versions with massive side elements that probably contain the system stabilizer element. The later NA-25 replaces this specialized console with a standard MAGICS one- or two-screen console. (Alenia)

raster-scan CRT for TV or IR images with superimposed alphanumerics (e.g., CIC orders, FCS and weapons status, and alarm messages). The operator has a variable-function keyboard, a numeric keypad, a trackball, a joystick, and a range handwheel. Pedals are for gunfire control and to initiate radar tracks. NA-30A uses two consoles, one for radar and missile control and the other for the EO director. Because each console accommodates a computer, NA-30A can control four different weapons.

NA-30E (Dardo E, or Extended) is a successor to Dardo based on NA-30B and a dedicated search radar (RAN-10S, for automatic target acquisition), first used in the carrier *Garibaldi*; it can control two weapons (e.g., twin 40mm, 5in/54, or Aspide).

Users: Brazil (bought for *Niteroi* upgrade), Italy (*Garibaldi* [Dardo E], *Mimbelli* [Dardo E], *Animoso* [Dardo E], *Maestrale* [NA-30A], *Minerva* [Dardo E]).

◆ NA-25/28

These modular next-generation Selenia-Elsag FCSs use the new standard MARA 286 computer (instead of the earlier 24-bit machine) and MAGICS consoles (incorporating two high-resolution color monitors). NA-25 uses the Orion RTN-25X radar, supple-

mented by an IR camera and a laser range-finder (a television tracker is optional). The system can be set for programmed autonomous search (360 deg or by sectors). It uses two MARA computers, one for tracking and one for ballistics. NA-28 is the MARA-series successor to the optronic NA-18.

JAPAN

RADARS

◆ OPS-9

Fujitsu's X (I/J)-band surface-search radar, with a very long slotted-waveguide antenna, is a version of the British Type 978 high-definition surface-search set used by MCM craft; it was presumably bought as part of the same package that produced ZQS-2 (Type 193). OPS-9 equips the MCM craft and some miscellaneous auxiliaries. Versions are OPS-9B and -9C. The original OPS-9 had two separate displays, one for true and one for relative position. Both are combined in OPS-9B and are transistorized.

OPS-9D. (*Ships of the World*)

Users: Japan (*Utone, Hatsushima* [some], *Takami, Atsumi* [LST], *Kasado, Akashi, Kurihama* [9B], *Muroto, Fushimi* classes).

◆ OPS-10/19/22/29

Fujitsu's X-band (9–9.8 GHz) navigational radars have slotted-waveguide antennas. OPS-19 is used in conjunction with OPS-28; effective range may be 100–150 km (which suggests a ducting mode). OPS-22 is a J-band, high-sensitivity radar with high data-processing capability. Used on icebreakers, it is designed for great resolution.

Users:

OPS-10: Target service craft ASU 81–83
OPS-19: *Kongo, Kurama, Yubari, Ishikari* classes, target service craft ASU 85
OPS-22: *Haruna* class, icebreaker *Shirase*
OPS-29: PB-type patrol boats, target service craft ASU 84

◆ OPS-11

OPS-11 (B-band: 400–450 MHz), produced by Mitsubishi Electric (MELCO), is the first Japanese-designed air-search radar. The antenna is an 8 × 4 array of yagi antennas. Previous Japanese dependence on U.S. radar technology suggests that OPS-11 may be related to SPS-40, with a radically different antenna (it has also been reported that OPS-11 was developed when the United States refused to supply SPS-40 technology to Japan). Reports that OPS-11 is a UHF long-range pulse-compression radar would corroborate that relationship. OPS-11B is a retrofit with an improved amplifier. OPS-11C incorporates MTI. These radars have much greater range than the 3D sets with which they are used. The array on top is an IFF. Effective range is reportedly 350–450 km.

Users: Japan (*Haruna* [11C], *Hatakaze* [11C], *Tachikaze* [11B], *Tayutsuki* [11B], *Yamagumo, Minegumo* classes).

OPS-11 on board a *Takatsuki*-class destroyer, with OPS-17 surface-search radar above, and GFCS-1 atop the bridge. The big radomes are part of a jamming system called OLT-3; the small ones are probably DF radomes (NOLR-6). (Author)

◆ OPS-12

This planar-array S-band air-search radar is probably similar in operation to SPS-52. OPS-12 lacks a serpentine feed running up one edge, but an extension visible on the right side of the main antenna may contain the feed. This arrangement might make for a more symmetric array, easier to stabilize.

The antenna of NEC's land-based NPG-880 is similar in appearance to that of OPS-12. NPG-880 is a frequency-scanning (serpentine feed) radar employing ferrite phase shifters between the serpentine feed and the radiating elements themselves. That arrangement makes it possible to use chirped (pulse-compressed) pulses at fixed elevation angles, the ferrites canceling out the effect of frequency change within each chirp. The U.S. SPS-48E employs similar techniques. NPG-880 employs a TWT/CFA transmitter.

Users: Japan (*Shirane* class).

◆ OPS-14

Mitsubishi Electric's L-band air-search radar equips destroyers of the FY67 and later programs (FY73 and later ships have OPS-14B, with MTI). Some ships of this period have OPS-11 instead.

Peak power: 500 kW (400 kW in -14B); the beam is 5 deg × 30 deg csc². In OPS-14C, the magnetron is replaced by a klystron, for coherent (pulse-compressed) operation.

Users: Japan (*Asagiri* [14C], *Hatsuyuki* [14B], *Abukuma* [14C], *Chikugo*, *Souya* [MMC], *Hayase* [MMC], *Miura* [LST] classes).

◆ OPS-16/17/18/35/36/37

Band: C (5450–5825 MHz)
Beam: 2 × 20 deg
Peak Power: 150–200 kW
Pulse Width: 0.3 or 1.4 microsec
PRF: 604–667 pps
Scan Rate: 15 rpm

Data apply to OPS-18, built by Nihon Musen.

Japan Radio Company's surface-search radars superficially resemble the U.S. SPS-5/10, with their openwork antennas. They are all descended from the now-extinct OPS-3, which was based on the C-band SPS-5B. Its frequency had to be shifted down from 6 to 5 GHz to avoid interference with Japanese television; the modified set was OPS-37. OPS-16/17, developed in the 1960s, is a second-generation series with a different frequency and improved ECCM; these radars are broadly equivalent to SPS-10. OPS-16D is a solid-state version of OPS-16C with a different PRF. OPS-17 (which is now being replaced by OPS-28) uses medium PRF. The frequency-agile OPS-18, the next stage (1970s and 1980s), apparently has a version equivalent to the U.S. SPS-58/65, with a pulse-Doppler channel for better low-flier detection and tracking (OPS-18–1 is the target-designation set for Sea Sparrow aboard the *Hatsuyuki* class). OPS-18 is often equipped

OPS-16 on board a frigate. (*Ships of the World*)

The new Japanese destroyer *Asagiri* shows both the OPS-14C air-search radar (forward) and the new FCS 2-12E missile (Sea Sparrow) fire-control radar (aft, under the big radome). The small surface-search radar on the platform atop the foremast is OPS-28, and the radomes on the main mast are part of an EW suite consisting of an OLR-9C passive system, an OLR-6C, and an OLT-3 jammer, plus SRBOC launchers. The gun director atop the bridge is FCS 2-21A. (*Sea Power*)

with IFF interrogators. An ARPA radar capable of displaying 10 targets simultaneously, OPS-18B is replacing OPS-9 aboard minesweepers.

OPS-18–1 is similar but more sensitive. In the *Hatsuyuki* class, it is probably the target-acquisition set for Sea Sparrow, and thus most likely incorporates a Japanese equivalent to SPS-65. OPS-18B is superseding OPS-9 on board minesweepers.

No platforms for OPS-35/36/37 have been identified.

Users:

OPS-16: *Chikugo, Isuzu, Souya* (16C), *Hayase* (16C), *Miura, Sagami, Kurobe, Tsugaru* classes, *Azuma*
OPS-17: *Amatsukaze, Takatsuki, Yamagumo, Minegumo* classes
OPS-18: *Hatsuyuki* (18–1), *Towada* (AOR: 18–1), *Awashima* (18B), *Hatsushima* (some, with 18B rather than 9), *Futami, Shirase*

◆ OPS-24

OPS-24 is a D-band, 3D, long-pulse (pulse-compression) radar using active array elements and is produced by Mitsubishi Electric (MELCO). It uses a hybrid layout, in which a single Tx/Rx module feeds small groups of antenna elements. Heat is dissipated in a pair of heat exchangers flanking the array, and the IFF array is carried below the main array. Coverage is from the zenith to below the horizon. This is the first active array radar to enter service. It may be related to the higher-frequency (C-band, in conventional nomenclature, i.e., 5 cm) FCS-3.

OPS-24 replaces OPS-14 on board the *Hamagiri* and on board later *Asagiri*-class destroyers.

◆ OPS-28

Japan Radio Company's L-band (1.2–2 MHz) pulse-Doppler radar is analogous to the U.S. TAS Mk 23. The slotted-array antenna is stabilized (roll up to 15 deg, pitch up to 7 deg) and has a high scan rate (to acquire horizon targets). The transmitter is a TWT with a CFA (crossed-field amplifier). The current version, OPS-28C, is the functional successor to OPS-17, replacing it in the *Tachikaze*-class destroyer *Sawakaze*. OPS-28 is also replacing OPS-18.

Users: Japan (*Shirane, Haruna, Kongo, Asagiri, Hatakaze, Hatsuyuki, Yubari* [DE—main search set]).

The new destroyer *Murasame* shows her OPS-24 radar. Above it is the radome of the SH-60J link. The small director atop the bridge is FCS 2-31, which controls both her gun and her Sea Sparrow missiles. The box on the platform abeam the foremast is for an NOLQ-3 ESM set. (*Ships of the World*)

The foremast of the destroyer *Setogiri* shows her OPS-24 3D active array radar (D). Other antennas shown are the ORN-6C TACAN (A), the SH-60J data relay antenna (C, comparable to the U.S. SQQ-89 relay), and the OPS-28(D) radar. (*Ships of the World*)

◆ ZPS-4/6

Submarine search radars (X-band: 8–9 GHz); ZPS-4 uses a horizontal cylindrical radome like the old U.S. BPS-1.

The Japanese submarine *Makishio* shows a ZPS-4 radar. (*Ships of the World*)

Users:

ZPS-4: *Uzushio* class
ZPS-6: *Yushio* and 2400t class (new)

◆ Furuno Radars

These commercial navigational radars are used by the U.S. Navy; they do not appear to be used by the Japanese Maritime Self-Defense Force. For details, see the U.S. entries below.

The foremast of the helicopter destroyer *Shirane* shows an OPS-28 radar (B). Other antennas shown are the ORN-6C TACAN (A), the NOLQ-1 ESM radomes (C), and the OPS-12 3D search radar (D). (*Ships of the World*)

FIRE-CONTROL SYSTEMS

◆ GFCS Model 1 (GFCS-1; Type 72)

FCS-1 (Type 72) is comparable in performance to the U.S. Mk 57 and Mk 63; in some ships it replaced Mk 63. It can, then, deal with subsonic aircraft at medium range, setting fuzes and com-

Type 72 (GFCS-1) radar directors, each with its optical element next to it, in a partial gun tub. (*Ships of the World*)

puting lead angles. Some versions use a single ballistic computer to handle both 3- and 5in guns; Model 1A controls 5in guns, Model 1B, 3in. There are two above-decks elements, an unmanned director carrying a radar and a TV camera, and a manned director. Targets are designated from remote PPIs fed by a ship's search radars. Data for ballistic calculations are taken from either the manned or the unmanned director, the computer supplying rates against which observed data can be checked. An unusual feature of the system is the use of Contraves-type bellows stabilizers (as in Sea Hunter) at both directors.

Users: Japan (*Shirane, Haruna, Tachikaze, Yamagumo* [DDK 120, 121 only], *Minegumo* [DDK 117, 118 only], *Chikugo, Souya, Miura* [LST] classes).

◆ GFCS Model 2 (GFCS-2)

FCS 2 (Type 79 FCS) is a digital replacement for the analog Type 72. It has limited ECCM features. The dome protecting FCS 2–12 covers separate search and track antennas, as in the Signaal WM 20 series "egg." During search, all radar energy goes to the search antenna. Once a target has been detected, 40% of the total

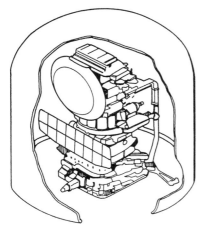

The Japanese FCS 2-12. (*Ships of the World*)

FCS 2-21A, used to control 76mm guns. (*Ships of the World*)

energy goes to the tracking antenna. A 1m² target can be detected at a range of 30 km and at an altitude of 10–15 km. A 0.5m² target can be detected at 10 km. FCS 2–12 is a combined gun and missile (Sea Sparrow) FCS which replaces the WM 25 "egg" used initially to control Sea Sparrow. FCS 2–23 is an upgraded version with better CW injection for missile guidance. It is an MTI set using a TWT transmitter for frequency agility. FCS 2–21, on an open pedestal, controls guns only. FCS 2–22 is an upgraded version capable of tracking up to 100-deg rather than 82-deg elevation.

The full FCS 2–12/2–23 uses a pair of UYK-20 computers, one for air targets (to control Sea Sparrow and the 76mm gun), the other for surface targets (FCS-2 Low, to control the 76mm gun). Presumably less capable versions use a single UYK-20. In the new destroyer *Murasame*, FCS 2–31, a dish similar to 2–21A, controls both a 76mm gun and Sea Sparrow missiles.

All versions are manufactured by Mitsubishi Electric.

Users:

> FCS 2–12/2–23: *Haruna, Asagiri* (2–12E), *Hatsuyuki, Takatsuki* (2–12B), *Minegumo* (DDK 118 only; prototype of system, for 76mm GFCS)
>
> FCS 2–21/2–22: *Asagiri* (2–21A), *Hatakaze* (2–21C), *Hatsuyuki, Amatsukaze, Abukuma* (2–21A), *Yubari, Ishikari, Kurobe* (2–21A)

◆ FCS-3

FCS-3 uses a C-band (5cm) TWS phased array. It is a sort of mini-Aegis system, guiding a SAM version of the new XAAM-4 Sparrow replacement. The trials ship *Asuka* has fixed arrays (as of 1995, one of the four was a dummy, its array having been retained ashore for tests). Directors are slaved to the array via its computer. A rotating version is in the new *Takao* (4400 t) class (two per ship, each capable of guiding 16 Sea Sparrow missiles). This ship is equipped with Mk 41 VLS forward (29 cells) and aft (61 cells). The forward cells are to be filled with quad-packed Sea Sparrows and, reportedly, a vertically launched version of the Japanese SSM-1 antiship missile. The after cells are to be filled with SM-2 Block IV missiles controlled mainly by accompanying *Kongo*-class ships using a Japanese-developed form of cooperative engagement (CEC). The 4200t experimental ship (ASE) *Asuka* is reportedly intended specifically to test the FCS 3/CEC system. Progress has been slower than expected; the fixed-face FCS probably will not be ready until 1997. This system is credited with controlling missiles against 10 targets simultaneously.

NETHERLANDS

The first Signaal all-solid-state L-band transmitter (D-SSTX) was delivered in the spring of 1992. Power transistors consist of seven chips in parallel, each of which has up to 216 parallel transistors; each such device produces 300-kW peak power. The basic module (PA-Module) is a 4:1 cascade: one drives four, each of which drives four transmitters, for a total of 4 kW. Up to 32 PA-Modules can be combined, for a total of about 100 kW produced by 512 final output transistors. The entire array is microprocessor-controlled. A peak power of 100 kW is quite acceptable for a pulse-compressed radar using long pulses. D-SSTX will be used in the SMART-L radar.

RADARS

◆ DA-01/02

Band: S (2.9–3.1 GHz)
Beam: 1.5 × csc² (DA-02 1.7 deg)
Peak Power: 400 kW
Gain: 32 dB
Pulse Width: (a) 1.3 (b) 0.5 microsec
PRF: (a) 500 (b) 1000 pps
Scan Rate: 6–60 rpm
Antenna Dimensions: 15.3 ft wide
Antenna Weight: 4400 lb

One of four FCS-3 active arrays is shown on the foremast of the experimental ship *Asuka*, with an OPS-14 air-search radar above it. Unlike Aegis, FCS-3 uses no illuminators, because the AAM-4 missile the ship fires has an active seeker. Note the Aegis-type AIMS IFF antenna at the masthead. (*Ships of the World*)

DA-01 was the first postwar Dutch target-designation (DA) radar, introduced in 1954 on board Dutch destroyers. The commercial (Signaal) designation was SGR-105. Claimed performance included detection of a 2m² target at 50 nm and at 35,000 ft. DA-02, a larger-ship set, has a broader-beam (1.7-deg) antenna and greater power (500 kW, 40 nm at 30,000 ft). There was no DA-03, and DA-04 is extinct.

Users:

DA-01: Germany (*Rhein* class), Turkey (*Rhein* class)
DA-02: Peru (*Aguirre*)

◆ DA-05

Band: S (six preset frequencies between 2900 and 3100 MHz)
Beam: 1.5 × 8 deg (csc² cover up to 40 deg)
Peak Power: 1200 kW
Gain: 32.2 dB
Pulse Width: (a) 1.3 (b) 2.6 microsec
PRF: (a) 1000 (b) 500 pps
Scan Rate: 10 or 20 rpm
Antenna Dimensions: 4.87 × 2.75 m (about 16 × 9 ft)
Antenna Weight: 725 kg

DA-05 was the first of a new series of DA radars, analogous to LW-04, using elliptical antennas and more powerful magnetrons. Like LW-04, DA-05 has digital MTI. Claimed performance includes detection of a 2m² target at 72–84 nm and about 60,000 ft; minimum range is 1000 m. This radar can discriminate targets 1.5 deg apart in azimuth and 200–400 m apart in range. DA-05/M is a land-based mobile version, and both DA-06 and -07 are land-based.

DA-05. (Signaal)

DA-series antenna on board a Dutch frigate, 1978. The British UA-8/9 ESM antenna is on the pole mast above. (U.S. Naval Institute)

Many DA-05 installations (like those in Taiwan) now have DA-08 below-decks electronics.

Users: Argentina (DA-05/2: MEKO 140 class), Belgium (*Wielingen* class), Egypt (*Descubierta* class: DA-05/2), Finland (*Pohjanmaa*), India (*Vikrant* and two *Talwar*-class frigates), Indonesia (*Fatahillah* and *van Speijk* classes: DA-05/2), Ireland (*Eithne*), Korea (eight *Ulsan*-class frigates), Malaysia (two *Musyatari*-class patrol vessels), Morocco (*Descubierta*: DA-05/2), Netherlands (new LPD *Rotterdam*), Spain (*Descubierta* class: DA-05/2), Thailand (*Makut Rajakumarn*, two *Tapi* class [replaced SPS-6C], two *Rattanakosin* class). Television footage shot in 1995 showed DA-05 in place of the SPS-37 series air-search radars on at least one Korean destroyer.

◆ DA-08

Band: S
Beam: 1.5 × csc² to 40 deg
Peak Power: 145 kW (5.1 kW average)
Gain: 33 dB
Pulse Width: (a) 35 (b) 69 microsec
PRF: (a) 1000 (b) 500 pps
Scan Rate: 10 or 20 rpm (selectable)
Antenna Dimensions: 4.4 × 3.9 m; depth 6.5 m
Antenna Weight: 2500 kg

This coherent pulse-compression radar is derived from, and is analogous to, the larger LW-08. Claimed range on a 2m² target is 78–92 nm. Minimum range is 0.8 nm. The antenna is stabilized. Each pulse consists of a 1-microsec nonmodulated pulse and a 34- or 68-microsec frequency-swept (pulse-compression) pulse. Compressed pulse length is 0.6 microsec. There are six fixed crystal-set frequencies plus a jumping frequency. Resolution: 1.5 deg in azimuth, 120 m in range. A modified version of this radar scans at 15 rpm and has a PRF of 2400 pps; instead of the digital MTI of the basic radar, it uses an FFT for MTI. DA-08/1 is the single-feed version; DA-08/2 has a dual feed, and twice the power. Suffixes: LS indicates hydraulic stabilization, S indicates electromechanical stabilization.

DA-08. (Signaal)

Users: Argentina (*25 de Mayo*, four MEKO 360 class), Canada (TRUMP upgrade program for four "Tribal" class), Germany (eight *Bremen* class), Greece (four MEKO frigates), Korea (probably in KDX class), Malaysia (two FS 1500 frigates and two new corvettes), Pakistan (replaces Type 992 in Type 21s), Peru (cruiser *Almirante Grau*), Portugal (three MEKO frigates), Netherlands (two DA-08/2 on *van Heemskerck* class [to be replaced by SMART]), Taiwan (seven Wu-Jinn III destroyers: DA-08 with DA-05 antenna), Turkey (*Koln* and MEKO-class frigates). DA-08 also equipped the German *Hamburg*-class destroyers, now discarded.

◆ LW-02/03

Band: L (1220–1350 MHz)
Beam: 2.2 × csc² (ratio 1:10) deg
Peak Power: 500 kW
Gain: 31 dB
Pulse Width: (a) 2 (b) 5 microsec
PRF: (a) 500 (b) 250 pps
Scan Rate: 1–10 rpm (in some, 3/6 rpm)
Antenna Dimensions: 7.8 × 4.25 m (25.6 × 13.9 ft)
Antenna Weight: 2100 lb

Data are for LW-02, the first postwar Dutch destroyer radar; it was exported to Australia, Colombia, Sweden, and West Germany under the commercial designation SGR-114/12. Claimed performance included detection of aircraft at 100 nm and 59,000 ft. The similar LW-03 scans at 5 or 10 rpm. The much larger LW-01 is apparently extinct (Argentina decided to replace the radars on the carrier *25 de Mayo*).

LW-03 is the larger (lower) of the two air-search radars visible in this photograph of the Dutch frigate *Tjerk Hiddes*, now the Indonesian *Ahmad Yani*; the upper radar is DA-05/2. The fire-control radar is M 45. The mast above DA-05 shows the characteristic flanges (between slots for different bands) of the UA-8/9 ESM system, and the mast is topped by the "birdcage" of the FH-5 HF/DF. The ship at left has similar radars. (Author)

Users:

LW-02: Australia ("River" class), Malaysia (*Rahmat*), Peru (cruiser *Aguirre*)
LW-03: Indonesia (*van Speijk* class)

◆ LW-08

Band: L (six preset frequencies between 1250 and 1350 MHz)
Beam: 2.2 × csc² to 40 deg
Peak Power: 150 kW pulse compressed; average power 5.2 kW
Gain: 30 dB
Pulse Width: (a) 35 (b) 69 microsec
PRF: (a) 1000 (b) 500 pps

Scan Rate: 7.5 or 15 rpm
Antenna Dimensions: 8.8 × 7.525 m
Antenna Weight: Total 5000 kg (antenna 1500 kg)

The pulse-compression waveform includes a 1-microsec pulse for short-range resolution, and then a long "chirp" for long-range performance. The high average power (5.2 kW) corresponds to 5100 kW applied to 1-microsec pulses; that power gives some idea of range performance (a range of 145 nm at 85,000 ft is claimed for a 2m² target). The short initial pulse is used for surface warning. Any of six preselected frequencies can be used, and there is provision for pulse-to-pulse frequency jumping through the entire band. Resolution is 2.2 deg in azimuth, 300 ft in range. Pulse-compressed pulses are equivalent to 0.6-microsec pulses. LW-08 can handle target speeds up to Mach 5 (which must be the first blind speed), and up to 64 tracks. The MTI improvement factor is 35 dB. Minimum range is 2 km. The antenna is stabilized.

LW-08 on board a *van Heemskerck*–class missile frigate. This version has a double feed; there is also a single-feed version. (Signaal)

As installed in the two *van Heemskercks*, LW-08 has a double transmitter with double feed, to form a high-angle beam as well as the usual fan beam (to detect high divers). The whole radar is tilted back slightly to reduce sea clutter. This radar autotracks but does *not* autodetect (SMART autodetects).

LW-08 was first used on board the Dutch "standard" frigate *Kortenaer*. The British Type 1022 marries an LW-08 transmitter to a Marconi narrow-beam (squintless) antenna.

Users: Argentina (*25 de Mayo* carrier), Australia (eight AN-ZAC frigates), Canada ("Tribal"-class update), Germany (four Type 123 frigates), Greece (five *Elli* and four MEKO classes), India (*Vikrant*, five *Nilgiri*- and three *Godavari*-class frigates), Netherlands (two *van Heemskerck*, seven *Kortenaer*, and eight *Doorman* classes), *New Zealand* (two *Canterbury*, two ANZAC-class frigates), Peru (*Almirante Grau* cruiser), Thailand (two *Naresuan* class), United Kingdom (in modified form, as Type 1022). In addition, 14 LW-08 were sold for civilian air traffic control as LAR 2s.

◆ LW-09

LW-09 is LW-08 with D-SSTX solid-state transmitters. A PA module, comprising 16 parallel transmitter elements, produces a peak power of 4 kW; ganging 32 such transmitters produces 100 kW. The first D-SSTX upgrade unit was delivered to the Royal Netherlands Navy in October 1992. A radar using this transmitter will be the British Type 1022 successor.

◆ SPS-01

Band: S
Beam: (Search) 1.5 × 2 to 30 deg; (track) 1.5 × 1.5 deg (approx, depends on elevation)
Peak Power: 750 kW
Gain: About 39 dB
Pulse Width: 40 microsec
PRF: 460 and 540 pps, staggered
Scan Rate: 20 rpm

SPS-01 is the big multifunction radar of the Dutch missile destroyers *Tromp* and *de Ruyter*. It combines a broad-beam search radar with a high-data-rate radar for tracking multiple targets. Five antennas rotate together: two back-to-back paraboloids (with feed horns moving to generate any of five alternative beams, plus a sixth, fixed, low-angle beam); two back-to-back frequency-scanned arrays at right angles to the paraboloids; and an IFF mounted below one of the two paraboloids. The low-angle search beam operates continuously to provide short-range warning (40 scans/min using the back-to-back antennas). The other five search beams are used in sequence (one by one during subsequent rotations), so that for each the effective data rate is 8 scans/min. This scheme is used not for height finding, but rather to give solid vertical coverage. The search beam's dimensions vary with elevation, the vertical beamwidth being 2 deg at an elevation of 2.5 deg, but 30 deg at an elevation of 21 deg. Targets are automatically detected, and their 2D (range and bearing) positions fed into the central computer, which instructs the two frequency-scanned radars to find the contacts in three dimensions for tracking. Each of the two frequency-scanned arrays is slanted to the vertical, the combination of the two oppositely slanted arrays making for full 3D operation. The net data rate is 40 scans/min, because of the back-to-back operation.

SPS-01 occupies the large radome of the Dutch destroyer *Tromp*. The small radome forward of the bridge is for a Signaal WM 25 and two SPG-51s aft control the Standard Missile. The two slotted-waveguide surface-search radars are Decca 1226s. (U.S. Naval Institute)

The entire radar is fed by a single time-shared power source. Discussions with the Royal Netherlands Navy began in 1958, and a first working model was completed in February 1964. The two operational radars were completed in 1969. SPS-01 was originally known as MTTR, the Multi-Target Tracking Radar, and for a time (as "Broomstick") was a joint project with the Royal Navy.

◆ ZW-01/3 (SGR-103)

Band: X (8.5–9.6 GHz)
Beam: 1.0 × 3.5 deg
Peak Power: 180 kW
Gain: 39 dB
Pulse Width: (a) 0.1 (b) 0.3 microsec
PRF: (a) 2000 (b) 1000 pps
Scan Rate: 7.5 or 15 rpm
Antenna Dimensions: Width 2.56 m
Antenna Weight: 300 kg

ZW-01 appeared in 1954 and was widely used in the Dutch and German navies. ZW-03 is an improved version; ZW-04 was for minesweepers. These radars are described as surface and low-altitude air-search sets. The search antenna is stabilized on the horizon.

Typical performance: a jet fighter (1–3 m²) can be detected at up to 30 nm, and a bomber (10–40 m²) at up to 48 nm. Small vessels can be detected at about 18 nm, and periscopes at 4.5 nm. Minimum range is 50 m.

Users: Argentina (carrier *25 de Mayo*), Eritrea (ZW-04 in *Wildervank*-class ex-minesweeper MS 41), Germany (*Rhein*-class tenders), Peru (ZW-03 in cruiser *Aguirre*), Turkey (*Koln* and *Rhein* classes).

◆ ZW-06/07

Band: X (9.325–9.475 GHz)
Beam: 0.9 × 19 deg
Peak Power: 60 kW
Gain: 32 dB
Pulse Width: (a) 0.06 (b) 0.6 microsec
PRF: (a) 4000 (b) 2000 pps
Scan Rate: 24 rpm
Antenna Dimensions: 2.9 × 1.2 m (about 9.5 × 3.9 ft)
Antenna Weight: 130 kg (287 lb)

For ZW-06, range on a 10m² target is about 14 nm, and an airplane at 20,000 ft can be detected at that range. The very short pulse was adopted for high resolution. The air coverage is necessary for helicopter control in ASW. The transmitter is coherent, for clutter and jamming rejection.

ZW-06 surface-search radar. (Signaal)

ZW-07 surface-search radar for submarines. (Signaal)

Users: Brazil (*Niteroi* class), Egypt (*Descubierta* class), Greece (*Kortenaer* class), India (*Godavari*, *Nilgiri*, and *Trishul* classes), Korea (*Ulsan* class), Morocco (*Descubierta* and *Lazaga* classes), Netherlands (*Kortenaer* and *van Heemskerck* classes), Singapore (*Victory* class), Spain (*Descubierta* class), Thailand (*Makut Rajakumarn*, two *Rattanakosin*, three *Chonburi* classes).

ZW-07 is a submarine version of ZW-06, with a peak power of 50 or 60 kW (pulse width 1 microsec, PRF 1200 pps). There are also a short-pulse mode (0.1 microsec, 35 kW, 2400 pps) and a single-pulse mode (0.22 microsec, 100 kW, can be 2500 pps). Gain is 28 dB; dimensions of the half-cheese antenna are 1.0 × 0.250 m. The beam is 2.4 × 16 deg. Performance: range on a 10m² target is about 16 nm (at 25,000 ft). In the single-pulse

mode a ship (50 m²) can be detected at 13.5 km, and a 10m² target at 9 km.

Users: Netherlands (*Walrus* class), Taiwan (*Hai Lung* class).

◆ LIROD-8 GFCS4

See LIOD under Optronic Systems below.

◆ SMART/SMART-S/SMART-L/MW-08

Band: S
Beam: 2 deg horizontal; each beam is about 9 deg wide
Peak Power: 150 kW
Gain: 23-dB transmitter; 31.5-dB receiver
Pulse Width: 0.6 microsec compressed
PRF: 3800 pps
Scan Rate: 27 rpm
Antenna Dimensions: 4.8 m × 2.05 m
Antenna Weight: 1200 kg (plus 385-kg drive)

SMART is the Signaal 3D radar designed particularly to deal with antiship missiles, with radar cross-sections as small as 0.1 m², and with speeds as high as Mach 3. It covers all threats from sea-skimmers up to divers approaching at a 60-deg angle. SMART can automatically detect and track (ADT) up to 160 air and 40 surface targets at medium and long range. Signaal chose S-band as the best balance among range, clutter rejection, and

SMART. (Signaal)

MW-08 on board the new Portuguese frigate *Vasco da Gama* in 1990. (Signaal)

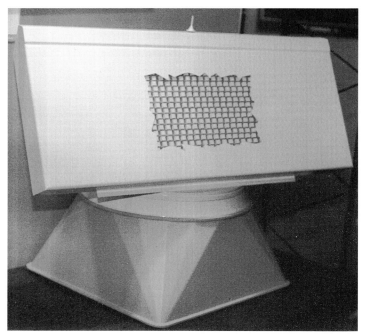

Signaal displayed this model of SMART-L at the 1995 Navy League show. (Author)

overall dimensions (for frigate installation). Detection probability is maximized by transmitting a single fat beam; the receiving beams are stacked so that the radar can distinguish targets at different elevations. This type of operation is equivalent to that of an ODT scanning sonar, using preformed receiving beams.

Inside the antenna are a single transmitting horn and a linear array of 16 strip-line receiving antennas. Received signals are preprocessed within the antenna itself: the output of the 16 receivers is fed into a digital beam-former producing 12 independent elevation beams. The antenna rotates in bearing. In effect this operation is monopulse height finding by a novel form of stacked beams. The 12 beams cover the entire hemisphere (from 0 to 90 deg of elevation). The combination of narrow beams (in bearing and elevation) and a high data rate makes it possible to designate targets directly to directors. Sidelobes are very small.

The transmitter is a TWT for pulse-to-pulse coherence and, therefore, MTI. MTI analysis (by FFT) is applied only to areas affected by weather or sea clutter, to reduce the overall processing load. PRF is optimized to avoid STA problems. The radar is arranged to react automatically to jamming by changing PRF, and the radar can vary PRF or frequency by burst. Target range and speed are compared on a burst-to-burst and scan-to-scan basis to avoid false targets (which can be discerned by their unnatural behavior).

Transmission modes are fixed frequency, frequency agility over scan, and burst-to-burst frequency jump.

The antenna is stabilized against roll and pitch.

With the advent of SMART-L, this radar is now called SMART-S. This radar is being adapted for land use as Vanguard.

Users: Germany (Type 123 frigate), Netherlands (*van Heemskerck* [replaces DA-08] and *Karel Doorman* classes). The Canadian TRUMPs will ultimately be fitted with a 3D radar, probably SMART-S, in place of their DA-08s.

An L-band derivative of SMART is being developed as SMART-L under a 24 July 1991 RNLN development/delivery contract; trials began in September 1995. It combines LW-08 and SMART performance in a single radar, to improve ship reaction time and sensitivity. The concept, based on NAAWS requirements, outlived that program. The 8.2m (6200 kg) electronically stabilized antenna scans at 12 rpm. Horizontal beamwidth is 2.2 deg. Maximum elevation (using 16 stacked, slightly overlapping, 60-deg receive beams, 14 of them above the horizon) is 70 deg. To burn through jamming, the vertical transmit beamwidth can

be reduced to 8 deg. Pulse-Doppler processing is applied to each beam. Thus SMART-L provides range, bearing, elevation, and target velocity on each scan. The receiver incorporates 32 parallel amplifiers. Signaal claims that it can detect a low-observable target at 55 km, and a conventional target beyond 100 km. Maximum instrumented range is 400 km. The ADT track file can carry up to 1000 aircraft, 40 surface targets, and 32 jammers simultaneously. This radar incorporates the new LW-09 solid-state transmitter.

The front-end processor uses Texas Instruments C-40 digital signal processors plus ASICs. The back-end processor uses SunSPARC boards.

SMART-L is being integrated with an X-band FMCW (Scout) radar for surface surveillance. This radar will have a 1.4-deg beam and power levels of 1000, 100, 10, and 1 mW (milliwatts).

The first SMART-L is to be delivered in mid-1996.

Users (SMART-L): Netherlands (planned: *Karel Doorman*, *Heemskerck*, four *Kortenaer* class). SMART-L replaces both SMART *and* LW-08. This radar will also presumably equip the Dutch-German next-generation air-defense ship (German F124 class).

MW-08 (which might be thought of as SMART-C) is a SMART development in G- (formerly C-) band for short- and medium-range cover, up to 70-deg elevation. MW-08 can automatically detect and track up to 20 air and 10 surface targets, and it can control gunfire against two surface targets. The array is reduced to eight strip-lines (hence the reduced elevation coverage). Each of six pencil beams is 2×12 deg, and peak power is 50 kW (pulses are compressed to 0.6 microsec). The antenna is 2.488×1.160 m (weight 430 kg plus 90-kg drive). Maximum free-space range (single scan, 80% probability of detection) on a $0.1m^2$ target is 17 km (45 km for SMART); on a $1m^2$ target, 27 km (65 km). The radar can handle target speeds of up to Mach 4 (Mach 5 for SMART).

Signaal announced a 22 July 1991 contract for three Greek navy coastal radars based on MW-08. One replaces an existing radar. The other two will be new, with a microwave link. All will be linked both to the existing NATO South Flank infrastructure and to the Hellenic Navy General Staff Headquarters. These radars are shelterized for quick relocation.

Users: Greece (MEKO frigates and coast defense), Portugal (MEKO frigates).

◆ Scout

Scout is the Signaal equivalent of the Swedish BEAB Pilot; Signaal and BEAB are no longer associated companies, so each has its own version. Scout was first shown at Bourget Naval in October 1990 (Signaal is now associated with Thomson-CSF). The X-band Scout has an output (equivalent to the average power of a conventional radar) of 1 W (in later versions this has been reduced to 0.001 W). The current 1.8m antenna (1.4×22-deg beam, gain 30 dB) scans at 24 rpm; and weighs 75 kg (the associated processor weighs 21 kg). Frequency sweep (corresponding to pulse width) is 50, 25, 12.5, 6.25, 3.125, and 1.5625 MHz; sweep repetition frequency (SRF, corresponding to PRF) is 1000 Hz. The processor has 512 range-cells. A $1m^2$ target can be detected at about 5.5 nm, a $100m^2$ target (a large craft) at 15.6 nm. Scout is expected to detect a corvette at the horizon and a 15ft wooden or GRP boat at 8 nm. An alternative 1.2m antenna produces a 2.1×22-deg beam (gain 29 dB). The ESM counterdetection range (free-space, using a -60-dBm receiver) is estimated as 1.5 km, that is, well within Scout's own detection range. Range scales are 0.75, 1.5, 3, 6, 12, and 24 nm. Signaal claims that Scout is equivalent to a conventional 20-kW radar.

Signaal feels that, compared to Pilot, Scout has gone much further in using FFTs (the key to other Signaal radar performance) for signal processing. The sale price has also been reduced very sharply (according to Signaal, by a factor of 5 or 6), the limiting factor now being the Kelvin-Hughes (Type 1007) display. Using the display, Scout enjoys all 1007 facilities (i.e., TWS for surface fire control).

Signaal now offers Scout B and Scout D, which incorporate conventional pulsed 25-kW transmitter/receivers. Operating

Scout, the Signaal stealthy radar. (Signaal)

The Variant antenna, positioned on a wedge stabilization platform. The Scout (LPI radar) element is behind the wide flat bar under the main antenna. (Signaal)

with them, a ship can avoid giving away the LPI character of the radar. Scout now also has a conventional-looking antenna. As of mid-1996, projects for a D-band surface-search version, a submarine version, and a maritime patrol version had proved fruitless.

Scout is offered in a mobile coast-defense version, capable of detecting a fast patrol boat at 15 nm. This version was sold to Egypt. Signaal markets a coast-defense version of Scout as Squire.

As marketed in the U.S. by MSSC (Magnavox-Signaal), Scout uses the Sperry Marine RASCAR (raster-scan collison-avoidance radar) 2500C display (105 kg, 750 × 1300 × 750 mm), with touchscreen controls. There is also an extremely compact Mini Display (2 kg, 305 × 450 × 155 mm) using an LCD and touchscreen controls.

Users: Belgium (*Wielingen*-class upgrade), Egypt (30 for coast defense: MSSC version), Germany (Type 123 frigates, possibly also on Type 212 submarines), Netherlands (*van Heemskerck* and *Karel Doorman*–class frigates, new LPD *Rotterdam* and new AOR *Amsterdam*), United Kingdom (two for harbor surveillance, at least six on submarines, possibly some on surface combatants); also at least two Far Eastern navies, probably Korea and Singapore. Indonesia is reportedly installing Scout on board all PB 57–type fast-attack boats.

◆ Variant

This 2D dual-frequency (C[G]- and X[I]-bands, frequencies an octave apart) pulse-compression digital ADT radar for small combatants was proposed about 1991 and was first sold in 1994. It includes an integral Scout LPI radar, which can be used alone. The stabilized double pillbox antenna scans at 27 rpm; C-band beamwidth is 1.8 × 16 (X-band: 1.2 × 11 deg). The TWT transmitter has a peak power of 2 kW; average PRF is 6000 pps (7500 in X-band), with pulse widths between 1 and 16 microsec. Instrumented ranges are 60 km for air targets and 70 km (i.e., surface-ducted) for surface targets. Reportedly a typical air target is detected at 30 km in C-band or at 28 km in X-band. Typical track accuracy is 0.25 deg/25 m. The aloft stabilized antenna weighs 263 kg; below-decks electronics adds another 375 kg. Air tracks are all automatically initiated. Surface tracks are manually initiated (automatic over predefined zones) but are automatically maintained. Pulses are digitally compressed and then subjected to pulse-Doppler (FFT) processing.

Users: Indonesia (four ordered 1994 for delivery 1996 for new PB 57–class fast-attack boats with Tacticos CDS); one ordered for unnamed customer.

◆ APAR/ARTIST

Signaal's next-generation X(I)-band fire-control radar, an active phased-array radar (APAR), is intended for the Dutch-German AAW ship. The sponsors are Canada, Germany, and the Netherlands. The project definition MoU was signed 20 July 1993; Signaal's team includes Daimler-Benz Aerospace of Germany, Northern Telecom of Canada, Thomson Systems Canada, and Lockheed Systems Canada. Northern Telecom is particularly interested in active transmit/receive arrays for civilian microwave communication, and claims that it has cut the cost of a single module to $500. Each array employs 3200 modules (quad-packed Ga-As MMIC Tx/Rx elements). The radar uses four fixed planar arrays, with one waveform generator per array, plus two additional waveform generators to provide missile guidance uplinks and illumination in terminal phase. The feed controls only the waveform; the array (consisting of programmable clusters of transceivers) controls the beam pattern. Bandwidth is 20–30% centered around 10 GHz. Signaal expects to generate four beams per face for 16 simultaneous engagements (with 30 missiles in the air). Pulses are emitted in bursts with frequency and PRF fixed only within each dwell period of multiple bursts; variation in both parameters varies the clutter content of the burst. Elevation coverage will be 70 deg. Each pencil beam produced by any one face will be able to scan +/−60 deg in bearing, so the faces will produce overlapping beams. Each array has its own digital processing unit (DPU) to deal with clutter and plot extraction using a DASA-built signal processing unit (SPU, containing Texas Instruments C40-series DSPs, which are also used in SMART-L) which it programs; the SPU does FFT, pulse compression, and Doppler filtering of the raw signal. Instrumented range will be 150 km. The system will be able to handle over 250 tracks. The radar will also perform horizon search out to 75 km. Signaal claims that APAR will have a wide bandwidth (20–30%) centered on about 10 GHz. Frequency flexibility will make it easier to classify targets based on their detailed structure.

In effect APAR is conceived as a STIR replacement for midlife upgrades. It may be used to control the new ESS (Evolved Sea Sparrow) missile. As of 1995, APAR was scheduled to enter

An APAR array. (Signaal)

A model of the German Type 124 frigate, displayed at Bourget Naval 1994, shows relatively small APAR arrays at the masthead, forward. The radar aft is SMART-L. An ESM array crowns the foremast. Note the Harpoon canister launchers amidships. In 1996 the Trilateral Frigate consortium announced that it would pay for development of a vertically launched Harpoon, to be fired from an enlarged (48- rather than 40-cell vertical launcher, to accommodate 32 SM-2, 32 quad-packed ESSMS, and 8 Harpoon). (Author)

service about 2002. A land-based test site for the new frigate combat system is to enter service in 1998, followed by a year of sea trials with a single-face APAR.

ARTIST (Advanced Radar Techniques for Improved Surveil-lance) is the associated software program, conceived for the defunct NAAWS program (the contract was signed on 1 November 1991). It uses software beam-steering, hence the name (it paints the beams across the sky). ARTIST includes ACTOR (Advanced Classification Techniques for Object Recognition, for anti-stealth techniques), MUSICIAN (Multi-Sensor Integration Concept in an All-Supported Network), PIANIST (Program for Investigation of Adaptive Nulling and Improved Super-Resolution), and PAINTER (Parallel Architectures for Integrated Thresholding and [Plot] Extraction [i.e., ADT] in Radar). ARTIST was completed in 1995.

Users: Canada (planned for AAW upgrade of four "City"-class frigates about 2002–2004, to replace the TRUMP class), Germany (Type 124 class; also for *Bremen*-class midlife upgrade), Netherlands (new LCF frigate, upgraded *van Heemskerck* class, upgraded *Kortenaer* and *Karel Doorman* classes). The upgraded *Bremen, Kortenaer,* and *Karel Doorman* classes will be limited to the ESSM missile; the others will have SM-2 and ESSM. The new AAW system is LAMS-NL; its long-range sensor is SMART-L and its IRST is Sirius. In May 1996 the UAE asked to join the LAMS-NL group; it took out options to buy up to six LCF frigates.

◆ **STIR/STING**

Band: X and K
Beam: 1.4 deg (0.3 deg K-band)
Peak Power: 220 kW (20 kW K-band)
Pulse Width: 0.29 (0.14) microsec
PRF: 1800 or 3600 (7200) pps
Antenna Dimensions: 1.8 m dia
Antenna Weight: Total weight 1700 kg

Data apply to STIR 180 magnetron.

The Signaal Tracking and Illuminating Radar is essentially the 1.8m Cassegrain monopulse tracker of the WM 20 series, removed from the "egg" and provided with a magnetron transmitter as STIR 180 magnetron (it can now also be fitted with a TWT). Instrumented range is 60 km; total weight is 1800 kg. STIR 240 combines a larger (2.4 m) antenna with a coherent TWT transmitter (for pulse compression) developed for Goalkeeper (peak power 100 kW, pulse width 0.3 microsec, PRF 3200 to 6400 pps). Instrumented range is 180 km; a $1m^2$ target can be acquired at 140+ km. This version was conceived for missile control in the *van Heemskerck* class.

By the end of 1986, over 50 STIRs were operational, with over 30 more on order. The 100th STIR was ordered in 1988.

Both versions of STIR with ZW-06 (*below*) and DA-08 (*above*) on board the missile frigate *Jacob van Heemskerck*. (Signaal)

Users: Argentina (MEKO 360 class), Canada (TRUMPs and "City" class; the TRUMPs use TWTs with the 1.8m antenna because the larger one would add too much topweight), Germany (*Bremen*, *Brandenburg* classes), Greece (*Kortenaers*, eight on MEKO 200s), Korea (36 ordered for KDX destroyers 1991), NATO (two for the firing range on Crete), Netherlands (*Heemskercks*, 12 *Kortenaers*, 16 on *Karel Doormans*), Nigeria (*Aradu*), Peru (one on *Almirante Grau*), Portugal (three *Vasco da Gamas*), Taiwan (14 on *Gearings*, 6 on *La Fayette*–class missile frigates [these are *not* U.S. STIRs]), Thailand (four Type 25T frigates being built in China, probably four on the two LPDs now planned), and Turkey (ordered for *Yavuz* class 1982, then four more ordered December 1989, probably for a project to fit *Gearings* to fire Sea Sparrow). The Turkish *Gearing* project was dropped and the radars were refurbished for use in the Turkish Track IIB program. Previous reports that the Taiwanese *Perry*-class frigates have this STIR rather than the very different U.S. Navy STIR are apparently incorrect. The Dutch *Karel Doorman* and the German *Brandenburg* classes have a Signaal multiweapon control system (MWCS) controlling both Sea Sparrow missiles and 76mm guns. It comprises two STIR 180 and a central control panel with two STIR control consoles in CIC. Track data are passed to the MWCS by the ship's CDS.

Announced in 1987, STING is a lightweight small-ship version of STIR (1.2m Cassegrain antenna, 810-kg director) with hydraulic rather than electric drive, for higher slewing and elevating speeds. The X- and Ka-band signals are processed by a single unit, which also handles the missile gathering beam in some versions. Beam data: X-band (2.0 deg, peak power 200 kW, PRF 3–6 kHz); Ka-band (0.6-deg beam, 40 kW, PRF 6–12 kHz). As in STIR 240, the power tubes are TWTs. Instrumented ranges: 72 km in X-band, 17 km in K-band. Compared to STIR, STING has a better EO package (full vs. only TV). Versions: BS (basic), CW (adds CWI), EO (adds IR camera, laser, and TV tracker), SW (Sea Wolf: adds command link, gyro, gathering unit for missiles).

Users: Oman (Vosper-Thornycroft corvettes), Qatar (new fast-attack boats), Turkey (*Yildiz*-class attack boats).

◆ Signaal Coastal Radar

This slotted-waveguide radar is in service in the Netherlands, Belgium, France, Germany, and Saudi Arabia. Characteristics: X-band (8850–9150 MHz); beam 0.25, 0.4, or 0.5 deg × inverted csc^2; pulse width 0.050 or 0.200 microsec; PRF, respectively, maximum of 4000 and 2000 pps; peak power 40 kW.

◆ Reporter

Signaal's TWS coast-defense radar was announced in 1980. It can track up to eight targets automatically or four manually. The prototype was completed in 1979, using parts from the existing Flycatcher (Goalkeeper) radar.

◆ SCORADS

Signaal's C(G)-band surface and low-altitude air-search radar can track up to 100 surface and 200 air targets simultaneously; maximum instrumented range is 67 nm.

OPTRONIC SYSTEMS

◆ LIOD/LIROD-8/LIOS

LIOD is an unmanned optronic director carrying a television camera or IR sensor and a laser range-finder, controlling two dual-purpose guns (with identical ballistics). LIOD can operate either autonomously or in conjunction with a larger FCS. The daylight TV camera has a 3–30-deg FOV (automatically selected lens filters, CCIR standard: 625 lines, 25 frames/sec, 2:1 interlace). The basic LIOD director weighs 335 kg, has a swept diameter of 1500 mm, and a maximum height of 1370 mm. LIOD includes an integral control unit for target acquisition and data processing, and a below-decks control console.

Extended LIOD carries a laser range-finder (beam 1.2 to 1.5 mrad, range 200–32,766 m, solid-state Neodymium-YAG laser, wavelength 1.06 micron, 20-nsec pulse length, PRF 10 Hz), an IR camera (long focal length system, germanium lens, 3-deg

LIROD (*foreground*) and a WM 20–series "egg." (Signaal)

A LIOD optronic director carrying a daylight television, FLIR, and laser range-finder. (Signaal)

FOV, CCIR picture as above), and laser tracker (divergency 1.5 and 6 mrad, transmitter identical to laser RF but pulse rate 25 Hz). The extended version includes a target designation sight: a manned, fast reaction, pedestal type carrying a telescoping sighthead with 7 × 50 binocular and coarse sight, and a 7in TV monitor for presentation of TV picture and alphanumeric data. It trains +/− 170 deg and elevates +65/−15 deg. Swept diameter is 900 mm and maximum height is 2237 mm; weight is 110 kg. Total weight of the Extended LIOD director is 450 kg, swept radius is 1500 mm, and height is 1450 mm.

The current Mk 2 version of LIOD carries both daylight TV and an 8–12-micron thermal imager and a laser ranger. The standard gated contrast centroid tracker can be supplemented by a correlation tracker which can acquire a target when the director is slewed to an indicated bearing (a human operator must lock on the centroid tracker). Signaal claims that LIOD Mk 2 can track a large surface ship at 20 km and a fighter at 10 km, both in clear weather.

Signaal recently introduced a new lightweight servo-driven pedestal, initially to support its Passive Observation System. The same pedestal is used for a LIOD-successor Compact EO FCS (laser ranger plus TV or IR) and for a Compact*plus* EO FCS (TV *and* IR channels). In each case the complete FCS comprises the EO pedestal plus a below-decks console and FCS processor. The lightweight servo pedestal can also be used to support an EO surveillance device, LIOS (Lightweight Optronic Sensor), carrying the same sensors as LIOD Mk 2, but with total director weight 125 rather than 225 kg.

LIROD is a smaller version of LIOD in which a Ka-band tracking radar replaces the IR sensor. In LIROD-8, the radar is the Ka-band (35 GHz/8mm, beam 1 deg from a 0.6m dish) monopulse tracker set used in Goalkeeper. Peak power is 20 kW (pulse width 0.14 microsec, PRF 14,400 pps). The director does carry a television camera, and LIROD-8 can be used as a tracking channel for a WM20-series FCS. Extended LIROD adds a laser range-finder (or laser tracker) and an IR camera.

Range on fast aerial targets is about 11,000 yd in good weather. Estimated reaction time from target designation to open-fire is 5.5 sec. The director can slew at 120 deg/sec and can elevate at 80 deg/sec (limits − 25 to +85 deg).

A LIROD Mk 2 now in production introduces a new TWT transmitter for better range performance. The antenna is changed to a vertical ellipsoid for better low-elevation performance (beam 1.5 × 0.55 deg, dimensions 0.4 × 1 m). Pulse width is 0.4/16 microsec, PRF greater than 6 kHz. Better signal processor technology offers better tracker ECCM. The television camera is upgraded to Signaal's new lightweight CCD camera Mk 3 (FOV 2 to 22 deg).

Users:

    LIOD: Ghana (PB 57 and FPB 45 classes), Indonesia (PB 57–class ASW version, Mk 2 ordered 1994 for *Van Speijk* class and for new series of PB 57s), Ireland (*Eithne*), Korea (HDC 1150–class frigates), Malaysia (FS 1500–class frigates), Nigeria (Vosper-Thornycroft Mk 9 frigates), and Turkey (FPB 57 class).

    LIROD: Argentina (MEKO 360 and 140 frigates), Australia ("River"-class frigates), Canada (LIROD-8 in "Tribal" class), Greece ("Osprey 55" type), Korea (*Ulsan* and *Donghae* classes), Indonesia (*Fatahillah* and former Dutch *Van Speijk* classes; LIROD-8 in new series of PB 57s), Kenya ("Province"-class missile boats), Mexico (*Cormoran* class), Thailand (*Ratanakosin*-class and *Chonburi*-class FAC [LIROD-8]).

◆ IRSCAN/Sirius

Signaal's IRSCAN 8–12-micron IR scanner employs a rotating (78 rpm) stabilized turret carrying a window elevating up to 14 deg. The 1024 detector elements are in a staggered line array, using CMT and CMOS readout technology. The head weighs 100 kg. An incoming airplane can be detected at 15 km, and a missile at 12 km; target designation accuracy is better than 1 mrad. The system can carry over 500 tracks, and provides automatic alerts on 32 classified as threatening, with a false alarm rate of less than 1/hr.

Sirius is a follow-on dual-band device for the M-class and the new Dutch-German air-defense ship. A draft requirement for this long-range IRSCAN (LR-IRSCAN) was issued in mid-1993, and an initial contract signed 22 December 1993. In October 1994 Signaal and Spar Aerospace of Canada (which had developed SAR-8) signed an MoU for joint development, and a Sirius development/preproduction contract was signed by the Dutch navy on 23 December 1994. The program is to take 4 yr, the prototype to be shipped for testing after 3 yr.

As currently conceived, Sirius resembles IRSCAN with a second window (3–5 microns) emerging from its other side. Elevation coverage will be reduced to 3 deg, and scan rate to 53 rpm. The detectors are the same 1024-element staggered-line arrays as in IRSCAN. The enlarged turret is to weigh 150 kg, with a below-decks weight of 660 kg (compared to 515 kg for IRSCAN).

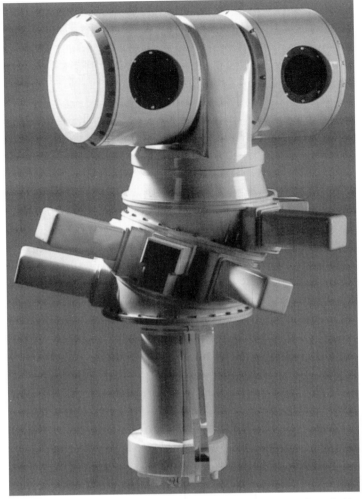

Sirius shows its two separate apertures. IRSCAN uses, in effect, half a Sirius head. (Signaal)

Unlike IRSCAN, Sirius is to provide data directly to the ship's CDS (both digital data to the data bus and video to the video bus). Sirius will process both bands separately, providing three outputs: each band separately, or a combined output. The two processors use different detection criteria.

Users:

    IRSCAN: Netherlands (tested on *Zuiderkruis*, also on new AOR and LPD, under a February 1993 contract), Qatar (*Barzan* class). All are to be used to cue Goalkeeper, but IRSCAN can also be used on a stand-alone basis.

    Sirius: Planned for Canadian, Dutch, and German AAW frigates, as part of LAMS-NL system.

FIRE-CONTROL SYSTEMS

Signaal does not distinguish between fire-control radars and the associated fire-control systems.

◆ M1/M2/M4

Few of these elderly systems survive. M1 (6in FCS) and M2 (57mm FCS) use an open-dish circular antenna and operate at S-band (about 8 cm: 400 kW, pulse width 0.5 microsec, 1000 pps). The X-band M4 (40mm FCS) uses a distinctive cut paraboloid (pulse width is also 0.5 microsec; 1600 pps).

Users: M1/M2: Peru (cruiser *Aguirre*); M4: Turkey (some, not all, ex-German *Koln*-class frigates; supplanted in many or all cases by M45; possibly in some *Rhein*-class tenders). The other Peruvian ex-Dutch cruiser, *Almirante Grau*, appears to lack the old 6in FCS with its optical range-finder; her WM25 probably controls 6in fire.

◆ M40 Series

Band: X
Peak Power: 180 kW

These radar directors succeeded the M1 through M4; they use roll- and pitch-stabilized enclosed-dish antennas with conical scan for air-target tracking and elliptical scan for surface targets. Because the stabilizer is in the director, no axis conversion is needed (as it would be from a below-decks stable element), and overall weight is reduced. There is no optical range-finder, the director operator acquiring and following the target using a pair of binoculars on an aiming bar. Total director weight is 1250 kg; working circle diameter is 2.8 m.

An M45 director on board the German training ship *Deutschland*, now discarded. A similar radar, without a manned cab, was mounted above the ship's bridge. (R. Cheung)

The radar transmitter is almost certainly the same one originally used in the M20/WM20 series described below, and computing limits match those of the other system (maximum target air speed 900 yd/sec, maximum surface target speed 34 yd/sec, maximum target range 32,000 yd). The two main versions are M44 (Sea Cat missile control) and M45 (medium- and light-caliber guns). Each has an associated optical sight, but FOVs differ depending on application: 12 deg (magnification 4×) for M44, 8 deg (magnification 6×) for M45. Displays are A- and B-scopes. The associated solid-state digital computer of M45 is hard-wired for particular ballistics (for two or three different weapons, depending on how extensive the range tables are, i.e., on how much memory they consume). Computer functions: tracking of an air target, tracking of a surface target, AA fire, surface fire, and shore bombardment, in the last two cases with star-shell fire. In the case of M44, the gunfire functions are replaced by firing bracket computation and launcher control.

M44 gathers the Sea Cat missile by means of a flight controller on the aiming bar. Guidance is generally visual, but the director can guide the missile by radar, using a second range gate and an F-scope.

Users:

M44: India (*Leander*-class frigates), Indonesia (former *Van Speijk*–class frigates), and Turkey (former German *Koln*-class frigates).

M45: Australia ("River"-class frigates), India (*Leander*-class frigates), Indonesia (former *Van Speijk*–class frigates), and Turkey (*Koln*-class frigates and *Rhein*-class tenders).

◆ WM20/M20 Series

Band: X
Beam: 1.5 × 7.0 deg (search antenna); 1.5 × 4.7 deg (later search antenna); 2.4 deg (track antenna)
Peak Power: 180–200 kW
Gain: 33.5 dB (small search antenna)
Pulse Width: (a) 0.22 (b) 0.45 microsec
PRF: (a) 3600 (b) 1800 pps
Scan Rate: 60 rpm

Radar data are for the system as originally developed. This digital FCS is broadly comparable to the nearly contemporary French Vega and Italian NA-10 series, except that in its case the search and air tracking antennas are co-located on a stabilized platform in a characteristic egg-shaped radome, sharing a single transmitter (which shifts some of its power to the tracker once an air target is acquired) and a single source of dry air. Co-location eliminates parallax corrections. Using a single transmitter eliminates problems of switching range scales between search and tracking modes. Co-location does make for a relatively heavy system, which cannot be mounted very high in a small ship. The success of the WM series is reflected in the U.S. decision to adopt a modified version as Mk 92 (see the U.S. section below) and in the Japanese decision essentially to copy this system as FCS 2–21.

WM25 "egg" on board the Spanish frigate *Descubierta*, 1991. Visible forward of the mast is the ship's ZW-06 search radar antenna. (A. Raven)

The air tracker uses a monopulse Cassegrain antenna mounted above the cut-paraboloid search antenna. The latter scans either in fixed elevation or helically. Surface tracking is by TWS using the search antenna (scan rate 60 rpm). The pulse-Doppler radar was presumably that used in the M44/45, with a short-pulse mode added primarily for navigation. Polarization is circular. During the early 1970s Signaal introduced a new 1-MW CFA transmitter.

Performance of the original version: $2m^2$ target detected at 30.5 kyd (and at up to 25,000 ft) and tracked at 29 kyd. First blind speed for air targets 720 yd/sec (approx 430 kt; originally 900 yd/sec, 540 kt); maximum surface target speed 100 kt (60 kt for a search radar in helical mode). Originally maximum allowable projectile time of flight was 64 sec (depending on ballistic tables), a figure probably determined by the cycle of ballistic calculations and correction. Claimed reaction time, from detection to opening fire, was 6 sec.

In 1973 Signaal claimed that the cumulative effect of improvements had been nearly to double effective range to about 25 nm on a $1m^2$ target: 50% from the new transmitter, 20% from an enlarged search antenna (see below), and 20% from a new tunnel-diode amplifier.

The original M series of the mid-1960s had a fixed-program digital computer; the WM series substituted an SMR-S (in WM20; later versions have SMR-S1) programmable digital computer. With a tactical table attached, a WM-series system becomes a "minicombat system"; with multiple consoles it becomes Signaal's Compact Combat System. See the CDS section for details. All versions have a standard radar tracker console and a standard weapons-control console carrying a 16in PPI (raw video plus alphanumerics) and A- and B-scopes and an alphanumeric display (16 lines of data, 32 characters each).

STIR (see above) is essentially a stand-alone WM20-series tracker.

Upgrades have been offered both by Signaal and by Bofors.

A 1979 Signaal-proposed upgrade substituted a 150-kW TWT (as in some STIRs) for the magnetron radar transmitter with separate search and tracking signals and added ADT. This coherent radar would detect a 1m^2 target at 60 km and track it at 50 km. Search mode: 12.4 microsec (compressed to 0.2) at 2000 pps or 6.2/0.2 microsec at 4000 pps or 0.2 microsec (uncompressed) at 2000/4000 pps. Track mode: 0.6 microsec at 12,000 pps. Up to 20 targets can be automatically detected and tracked. Signaal offered a reduction in reaction time (3–5 sec) and gun-aiming accuracy of better than 0.8 mrad.

A later digital ATD upgrade applied to the German WM27s (Type 143 fast-attack craft) substituted a solid-state coaxial magnetron for the Varian coaxial magnetron which replaced the original Philips spin-tuned magnetron (which offered great frequency diversity, but limited stability and a relatively short lifetime). The new magnetron is far more stable (at one of six crystal-controlled frequencies) and also far more reliable. A squintless slotted-array antenna (vertical beamwidth 30 deg, tilted up at 15 deg) is added to the back of the existing 4.7-deg antenna, to add instantaneous elevation coverage. The operator can feed radiation to either search antenna. Two outward-facing horns are mounted on the antenna platform, for sidelobe suppression.

The modified radar uses a digital version of PRF jitter to eliminate STAE pulses. New software greatly reduces multipath effects at low angles; it also improves ballistics and prediction calculations. The existing pseudo-random PRF-stagger program is replaced by a step-stagger program that divides the PRF range (3200–4000 pps) into 10/11 steps, causing STAE pulses to appear in different range bins.

The preamplifiers, MTI plus linear amplifiers, cross correlator, test generator, and filter are all replaced.

The 5-yr German program was completed late in 1992.

The alternative Bofors upgrade replaces 1300 circuit boards with 13, cuts reaction time to 5–6 sec, and improves range and bearing discrimination by 15%.

Recent reported upgrades (all by Signaal) are: Belgium (*Weilingen* class, WM25, with improved ECCM and better data processing, including solid-state memory for the SMR computer); Egypt (WM25 for *Descubierta* class, similar to the Belgian upgrade, reported early 1996); and Korea (pilot WM28 upgrade contract signed January 1996). As of early 1996, Malaysia was reportedly close to a decision on a WM22 upgrade.

About 1970 Signaal developed a larger search antenna (for greater gain, to achieve about 20 km greater range) with a larger vertical dimension (hence a narrower beam in the vertical). To accommodate it, the standard egg-shaped radome was enlarged, the portion below the joint being given a short straight section so that the egg seemed elliptical (dia 2.39 m, height 3.26 m, 780 kg) rather than spherical. The new search antenna entered service in 1973 and is exemplified by the U.S. Mk 92 system. In each case, the search antenna can scan either horizontally or helically, rising by one vertical beamwidth every second (i.e., every 360-deg scan) to reach its maximum height in 4.5 sec. That maximum is 25.5 deg in the case of the 7-deg antenna, and 21.1 deg for the 4.7-deg antenna.

Versions and users:

M20: Germany (*Zobel*-class torpedo boats, transferred to Type 343 MCM ships). This version originally had one air, one surface gun, and two torpedo channels (it could track one air and three surface targets).

M22: Finland (*Turunmaa* class), Indonesia (PB 57–class patrol boats), Malaysia (frigate *Rahmat*), and Sweden (*Alvsborg*-class minelayers). This version was intended for use with a long-range air search radar, to track one air target (two guns) and one surface target.

WM22: Argentina (Lurssen TNC 45–class FACs; WM22/41 in MEKO 140 class, with WM28), Australia ("River"-class frigates), Indonesia (four *Andau* FAC), Malaysia (FS 1500–class frigates), Philippines (planned for Australian-financed patrol boats, letter of intent issued 1992; this might be the minicombat system; later reported in the *Cormoran* class to be built by Bazan), and Thailand (frigate *Makut Rajakumarn*; WM22/61 in *Chonburi*-class patrol boats, WM22/61 in PF 103 class as modernized). Removed from Canadian "Tribal" class when they were rebuilt. Programmable version of M22.

WM24: Nigeria (*Erin'mi*-class frigates). One air and one surface channel plus an ASW control element (unique in the WM-series). The Nigerian ships are now inoperable and this system may be removed if they are refitted.

WM25: Argentina (MEKO 360H2–class frigates), Belgium (*Wielingen*-class frigates), Egypt (WM25/41 in *Descubierta* class), Germany (*Bremen*-class frigates), Greece (ex-Dutch *Kortenaer*-class and "Osprey 55"-class missile corvettes), Japan (two *Shirane* class), South Korea (*Ulsan*-class frigates), Morocco (/41 version in *Descubierta*, FCS version in four *Lazaga*-class attack boats), Netherlands (*Tromp*-class destroyers and *Kortenaer*-class frigates), Nigeria (MEKO 360H frigate), Peru (cruisers), Spain (WM25/41 in *Descubierta*-class frigates; some may have WM22/41), Thailand (WM25/41 in *Ratanakosin*-class corvettes, *Ratcharit*-class missile boats), and Turkey (MEKO 200–class frigates). WM25/41 is the minicombat system version. This version provides CWI for SAM control, plus two gun channels; it can simultaneously track one air and two surface targets (one of which may be on shore).

WM26: Norway (*Storm*-class fast-attack boats), Singapore (110ft Type B fast-attack boats). This version, the only one in the series without the egg radome, omits the air tracker; it controls two single-purpose guns.

WM27: Germany (S143/143A/143B-class fast-attack boats). This version has one SAM channel, one air-gun channel, one surface-gun channel, and two torpedo channels.

WM28: Argentina (MEKO 140 A16-class corvettes), Bangladesh (*Megna*-class fishery-protection patrol boats), Indonesia (WM28/61 in *Hajar Dewantara* training frigate, WM28/61 in *Fatahillah*-class frigates, and PSK Mk 5–class patrol boats; WM28 in new "Dagger"-class patrol boats), Iran (Combattante II–class attack boats), South Korea (WM28 in *Ulsan* class, WM28/61 in *Donghae* class, WM28/41 in *Po Kang* class, and WM 28 in HDC 1150–class frigates), Nigeria (WM28/41 in FPB 57–class fast-attack boats), Singapore (FPB 45–class fast-attack boats), Thailand (*Prabrarapak*-class patrol boats), and Turkey (WM28/41 in *Dogan*-class fast-attack boats). This version has one SAM channel and two gun channels (air and surface); it is license-built in the United States as Mk 92.

POLAND

◆ N-25 (NUR-25)/NUR-27XA

The air-search radar of the sole Polish AGI (*Tur*) is now offered for export (the manufacturer is RAWAR). N-25 is a pulse-compressed radar (using a TWT/CFA transmitter) with pulse-to-pulse frequency diversity, digital MTI, and automatic detection and tracking. It can also discriminate between targets in different altitude zones. ECCM features include a jammer strobe. The antenna is roll- and pitch-stabilized. Range is 100 km (55 nm) with height coverage up to 4 km (13,000 ft); range on a low-level airplane or surface ship is 30 km (16.4 nm).

The N-27 (NUR-27) surface search radar equips the *Orkan* (Project 660) class (ex-German *Sassnitz* class) patrol boats. It uses a slotted-waveguide antenna.

N-25 and N-27 are part of a series that includes the NUR-21 (N-21) mobile radar and the NUR-23 (N-23) static radar, both of which use parabolic antennas. NUR-22 is a mobile radar using a 16-bit microprocessor.

◆ RN-231, SRN-744, and SRN-7453

Standard navigational radars, used only by Poland, they are part of a larger series, comprising a first generation of tube radars (RLM-6 [1958–61] and RN-231 [1962–71], both 80 kW; ranges, respectively, 1.5–48 and 0.8–48 nm); a second generation of transistor radars (TRN-300 [1970–76], 9 kW, 0.25–24 nm; TRN-400 [1974–80], 25 kW, 0.50–48 nm; TRN-500 [1972–75], 25 kW, 0.75–60 nm); a third generation of integrated-circuit radars (SRN-200 [1977], 3 kW, 0.50–32 nm; SRN-300 [1976–82], 3 kW, 0.25–24 nm; SRN-600 [1974–83], 25 kW, 0.50–60 nm); and a fourth generation of radars employing large-scale integration (SRN-400, 25 kW, 0.3–48 nm; SRN-700, 25 kW, 0.25–60 nm; and SRN-800, 25 kW, 0.30–72 nm). In these designations, RN means Radar Nawigacyjny; TRN means Tranzystorowy RN; SRN means Scalony (solid-state, i.e., integrated-circuit) RN; and there are also SRRs, Scalony Radar Rzeczny (solid-state search radar). Except for RLM-6, all of these radars use slotted-waveguide antennas. SRN-745XS (SRN-7453 Nogat) operates in both X- and S-bands.

Users:

RN-231: *Obluze, Krogulec*, T-43, *Wodnik* classes, auxiliaries
SRN-744: *Kaszub* and *Project 151A* class
SRN-7453: Kashin and *Lublin* classes

RUSSIA

Where real designations are known, they are given in parentheses; names are mostly NATO nicknames (Niyada and Kivach are the exceptions).

SEARCH RADARS

The back-to-back arrangement is widely used (see Cross Sword, Head Net C, Strut Pair, Top Pair, Top Steer); presumably, both antennas typically share a common waveguide feed running up the mast between them. This arrangement reduces structural interference with radar emissions and increases the net data rate of the radar. In the case of a 2D/3D combination, the back-to-back arrangement probably greatly simplifies designation of a target from radar to radar, since there is no parallax error, and also economizes on the mechanical stabilizers the Russians seem to favor.

Salyut NPO of Moscow is responsible for 3D search radars such as Fregat (Flat Plate and derivatives) and Podberezovik (Flat Screen) and for the standard radar track combiner, Poima; Salyut also presumably produced Top Sail and its derivatives.

◆ Ball End (Ryf)

Band: S (2950–3020 MHz)
Beam: 7 deg
Peak Power: 150 kW
Pulse Width: 1 microsec
PRF: 427 pps
Scan Rate: 6 rpm

One of a series of four surface-search and FCS radars (the others are extinct) developed under the 1946/48 3-yr radar plan; tested on board the cruiser *Molotov* in 1948, Ryf could detect a cruiser at 20–22 nm, a destroyer at 14–16 nm, and a periscope (height 1.5 m) at 1.0–1.5 nm. Accuracy on PPI is 15 m on 1nm scale. Ball End was first seen in 1950.

Users: Albania (T-43 class), Syria (T-43 class).

◆ Big Net (MR-500 Echo or Kliver)

Band: L (about 850 MHz)
Peak Power: 1.5 MW
Beam: 5 deg
Pulse Width: 3.5 or 2.0 microsec
PRF: 250 or 550 pps
Scan Rate: 6.7–8.6 rpm
Antenna Dimensions: 25 ft wide

The large 2D air-search radar entered service about 1957. About a decade after its introduction it was succeeded, in effect, by the 3D Top Sail. This radar operates on one of four fixed frequencies. Minimum range is 0.5 nm. Detection ranges on air-

A Big Net air-search radar on board the "Kashin"-class destroyer *Strogiy* at Massawa, 1972. (Royal Navy)

craft: Il-28 or MiG-17 at 500 m altitude, 270 km; Yak-25 at 13 km altitude, 300 km.

Users: India ("Kashin" class), Poland ("Kashin" class), Russia ("Kashin" class).

◆ Cheese Cake

Surface-search radar, in a flat circular radome, atop the bridge of at least some Matka-class missile boats. It is analogous to the Kivach-3 of a "Tarantul."

◆ Cross Round (MR-352 Positive)

This new radome-enclosed air- and surface-search radar is reportedly the search element of the Cross Swords fire-control set. The new radar may have a secondary surface fire-control role (in TWS mode), as the "Pomorniks" lack any specialized fire-control radar for their 30mm guns (although one was photographed with Drum Tilt in place of its big radome). In the new frigate *Neustrashimyy*, a single Cross Round (atop the hangar between the two CADS-N-1) functions both as the helicopter landing radar *and* as the target acquisition radar of the two CADS-N-1s. Instrumented range is 128 km; elevation coverage is 40 deg; weight is 3.5 t. An account of the new Indian corvette *Khukri* calls this radar Positive E (probably E for export) and credits it

The prototype Pomornik-type surface effect assault craft displays the big radome of her Cross Round radar. Forward of it is the flat radome of a Curl Stone-B navigational radar. The object visible beneath the Curl Stone is an EO director for the craft's 122mm rockets, a modified Squeeze Box (Kondensor) without a weather cover. (MOD Bonn via *Ships of the World*)

with a range of 70–75 nm; it is said to be effective against low fliers. Radome diameter is about 3 m.

Users: India (*Khukri*), Russia (*Neustrashimyy, Parchim II, Pomornik* classes).

◆ Curl Stone-A (Ekran)

This is the enclosed surface-search/navigational radar on the *Dergach* surface-effect missile corvette.

◆ Don Series

Band: X (9375 MHz)
Beam: 1.1 × 20 deg
Peak Power: 80 kW
Pulse Width: (a) 1 (b) 0.5 microsec
PRF: (a) 800 (b) 1600 pps
Scan Rate: 12 or 15 rpm

This series includes Don-2 and Don Kay (Volga). There was also a Donets-2, with a slotted waveguide (68.7 × 4.8 in, 1.4 × 20-deg beam, seen in 1960 on board a trawler). The data here are for Don itself. Most large ships carry three such radars; the typical combination of Don Kay and two Don-2 has been superseded by three Palm Fronds. Multiple navigational radars are usually explained as insurance against the failure of one set, but the use of larger radars as data links (Plank Shave and Strut Curve at least) suggests that two of the three nominal navigational antennas could be used for narrow-beam ship-to-ship communication while the centerline antenna was used for navigation.

A Koni-class corvette shows a Don-2 radar just above her yardarm. The air-search radar above is Strut Curve; the fire-control radar forward of the mast is Hawk Screech, and Drum Tilt is partially obscured aft. (U.S. Naval Institute)

Users: Algeria (Koni), Bulgaria (Koni), Cuba (Koni), Egypt (Yurka class), Eritrea (Petya class), India ("Kashin," "Nanuchka," Petya, Natya, Polnocny, Ugra, T-58 classes), Libya (Koni, "Nanuchka," Natya classes), Poland ("Kashin"), Romania (Poti, *Democratia* classes), Russia (Kara [one Palm Frond or Don-2, two Don Kay], "Kashin" [two Don Kay], Krivak III [Don Kay plus Palm Frond], Krivak I/II [Don Kay or Palm Frond], Grisha, Petya, Mirka, Pauk, Poti, *Ivan Susanin* [patrol icebreaker], Sorum [armed tug], Babochka, Alesha, Natya I/II, Yurka, Vanya, *Ivan Rogov* [others in class have Palm Frond], Ropucha [two radars, some with Palm Frond or Spin Trough], Ugra [one to three radars], Don [one to two radars], Amga, Lama, *Vitse Adm Fomin*, Andizhan, MP-6, Melitopol, Amur, Oskol, Dnepr, Tomba, *El'brus*, Nepa, Prut, mod. T-58 [rescue ship version], *Berezina* [one Don-2, two Don Kay], *Boris Chilikin* [two Don Kay], Dubna [two Don Kay], Altay [two Don Kay], *Olekhma*, Uda [two radars],

Don Kay surface-search radar is visible below and forward of the Head Lights C missile-guidance director on board the "Kresta II"–class cruiser *Vasily Chapaev*. The small radomes visible just abaft the missile director (one pointed up, one down) are the Bell Slam and Bell Tap associated with the Side Globes ECM system. The larger radome on the centerline is Bell Clout. (*Sea Power*)

Kazbek [two radars], oilers, water tankers, transports, lesser auxiliaries, AGIs), Serbia (Koni class), Vietnam (Petya class), Yemen (Ropucha class).

◆ Head Net C (MR-310U Angora-M)

This small-ship S-band radar is a development of a set roughly contemporary with Slim Net. Head Net A, now extinct, used a single antenna, about 22.5 × 5 ft, to produce a fan beam somewhat less than 1 deg wide. Head Net C, the only surviving version, has two Head Net A antennas back to back, presumably sharing a common feed, one of them canted at 30 deg to the horizontal. The two fan beams are, therefore, canted, and the relative apparent positions of the same target in the two beams measure its height (vee-beam height-finding). The operator finds the target with the conventional antenna, marks it, and sets range gates on the second beam to measure altitude. This vee-beam system was invented during World War II, and a U.S. vee-beam set, CPS-6, provided to the Soviets under Lend-Lease, was copied postwar. This simple system is not as satisfactory as a true 3D radar. Peak power is 1.5 MW. This radar operates on four fixed frequencies. Minimum range is 0.5 nm. The instrumented range is 180 km; the elevation limit is 55 deg. Scan rate is 6–12 rpm; total weight is 10 t. Typical performance: destroyer detected at 22 nm, patrol ship at 16 nm, submarine at 9.5 nm, aircraft at 1 km altitude at 85 km, at 10 km altitude 140 km. Head Net C entered service in 1963.

Head Net C was superseded by Top Plate in later designs.

Users: India ("Kashin" class), Poland ("Kashin" class), Russia (Kara, "Kashin," Krivak, *Ivan Rogov* [Top Plate in *Moskalenko*], *Smolnyy, Artika* classes).

◆ Kivach 3

Kivach 3 is a current navigational radar. It is often connected to ESM equipment, for fine ESM cuts (as in a Krivak III).

Users: India ("Tarantul" class), Poland ("Tarantul" class), Russia (Krivak III, "Tarantul" classes).

◆ Mius

X-band surface-search radar.

User: Algeria ("Nanuchka").

Head Net C air-search radar on board the "Kashin"-class destroyer *Strogiy* at Massawa, 1972. The object at the base of the radar pedestal is a Watch Dog ESM antenna. (Royal Navy)

◆ Nyada (MR-212)/MR-201

X-band surface-search radar. Maximum detection range on a large destroyer is 16 nm; accuracy is 0.8 deg and 40 m. Resolution is 1.2 deg and 25 m. Total weight is 0.8–2.1 t.

Users: Russia (*Neustrashimyy* [with two Palm Frond], Grisha V, some "Nanuchka," Gorya, *Aleksandr Brykin*, Vishnaya-class AGIs).

◆ Palm Frond (MR-320 Topaz)

This surface-search/low-flier radar is the current standard, replacing Don 2 and Don Kay from the Krivak class on. In accord

A Palm Frond antenna is visible in front of the Strut Pair air-search radar on board the *Udaloy*-class destroyer *Admiral Vinogradov*. The back side of another Palm Frond is visible at left, and Kite Screech is in the foreground (*right*). (S. Zaloga)

with previous policy on surface-search radars, the usual complement is three sets (Krivaks have only one, plus a Don Kay in Krivak II; all Krivaks have two navigational radars). The version on an *Udaloy*, MR-320M Podkat, is apparently the target-acquisition radar for her SA-N-9 missile system.

◆ Peel Cone (Positiv)

This air/surface-search radar supersedes Strut Curve on ASW corvettes. On Pauk- and Stenka-class boats it supersedes Pot Drum.

Users: India (Pauk class), Russia (Svetlak, Pauk, Muravey, Babochka, Stenka [some] classes).

Peel Cone. (Royal Navy)

◆ Peel Pair (Dubrava)

X-band surface-search radar of the late 1960s, only on board Russian "Nanuchkas." It looks like a pair of Don-2 antennas (somewhat differently shaped) mounted back to back. This radar is not mounted on board export "Nanuchkas," which use Don 2 or Mius instead.

User: Russia ("Nanuchka" class).

A Peel Pair radar on board a "Nanuchka III," 1989. The large vertical cylinder is the Stump Spar radio antenna. Note the difference between the two antennas of the pair. The forward-facing antenna seems identical to that of Don Kay; the aft-facing one is similar to Palm Frond.

◆ Plank Shave (Garpun)

This missile-targeting radar is the successor to Square Tie. Its antenna is about the size of that of Don 2 and is marked by its large stabilizing vane and its overhead feed.

There are three operating modes: radar (which can be at a fixed bearing), targeting ESM (with discrete frequency settings), and directional data-link receiver. Radar scan modes: 360 deg, sector scan, and directional. Presumably the fixed-bearing radar mode is used to find the range to a target indicated by an ESM cut.

The name means Harpoon.

Plank Shave radar on board the "Tarantul"-class missile boat *Hiddensee*. (Author)

Users: India (*Khukri*, "Tarantul" classes), Libya (Koni class), Poland ("Tarantul" class), Russia ("Tarantul," Matka classes).

◆ Pot Head (Reya)/Pot Drum (MR-102 Balkan)

Band: X (9275–9460 MHz)
Beam: Approx. 3 deg
Peak Power: 100 kW
Pulse Width: 0.25–1.0 microsec
PRF: 1600–1650, 3200–3300 pps
Scan Rate: Circular at 2.5–4 or 5–6 rpm; sector at 7–8

Standard radar in many patrol craft, Pot Head superseded Skin Head from about 1960 on. Pot Drum, which is externally very similar, entered service in 1958. It appears that Pot Drum had a peak power of 150 kW and a pulse width of 0.5–1.0 microsec, whereas Pot Head, which would have needed more resolution (e.g., for periscope detection), had a shorter pulse width (one source gives 0.3–0.5 microsec). These radars were succeeded by Peel Cone in recent patrol craft.

Users:

Pot Drum: Angola (Shershen class), Bulgaria (Shershen class), Cambodia (Stenka, Turya classes), Congo (Shershen class), Cuba (Stenka, Turya classes), Egypt (Shershen class), Eritrea (Turya class), Guinea-Bissau (Bogomol class), North Korea (Shershen class), Rumania (Shanghai II and Epitrop classes), Seychelles (Turya class), Russia (Stenka [or Peel Cone], Turya classes), Vietnam (Shershen, Turya classes), Yugoslavia (Shershen class).

A Turya-class hydrofoil torpedo boat shows a Pot Drum radar forward (with Square Tie IFF interrogator below it) and Drum Tilt aft. Some units have a new Peel Cone radar with a large reflector instead. The guns are twin 30mm (AK 230). (U.S. Navy)

Pot Head: Albania (Shanghai II class), Cape Verde Islands (Shershen class), China (Haijui, Hainan, Shanghai II [or Skin Head], 25m classes), Congo (Shanghai II class), Eritrea (Mol class), North Korea (Najin, Taechong, Shanghai II, S.O. 1 [or Don-2], P-6/Sinpo [or Skin Head], Nampo classes), Sierra Leone (Shanghai II class), Somalia (Mol class), Tanzania (Shanghai II class), Vietnam (S.O. 1 class), Zaire (Shanghai II class).

◆ Skin Head (Zarnitsa)

Band: S (3000 MHz)
Beam: 17 deg
Peak Power: 80 kW
Pulse Width: 1 microsec
PRF: 400 pps
Antenna Dimensions: Radome: 0.8 × 1 m

This patrol craft surface-search radar was reportedly derived from the U.S. S.O. series. Skin Head was developed in 1946–48 and tested in the Black Sea in April–June 1948. Test results: destroyer detected at 7.5 nm; torpedo boat at 3.4 nm; aircraft at 100–300 m altitude detected at 9–17 nm. This radar was manufactured in China during the 1960s and remains in service aboard Chinese-built small combatants.

Skin Head radar on a Soviet torpedo boat preserved as a memorial. Although the memorial is for World War II, the P-4–class boat and its equipment (including the twin 14.5mm machine gun aft) are postwar. (U.S. Navy)

Users: Albania (Huchuan class), China (P-4 and P-6 classes), Guinea-Bissau (Shantou class), North Korea (Najin, Chodo classes), Tanzania (Huchuan class), Vietnam (Shanghai II class).

◆ Sky Watch (Mars-Passat)

The carrier *Admiral Gorshkov*, the fourth of the *Kiev* class, emerged in mid-1988 with a new flat-sided four-faced array radar on her superstructure; the same radar also appeared on the newer carrier *Kuznetzov*. It replaces the Top Pair of earlier ships of the *Kiev* class and presumably operates at a similar frequency to achieve a similar range performance. Top Steer is retained as a

Sky Watch electronically scanned arrays on the island of the Russian carrier *Kuznetzov*. Above the arrays are Big Gall SATCOMM antennas and the big cylindrical Cake Stand, a Russian equivalent of TACAN. The back-to-back antenna above Cake Stand is Top Plate. (SOVFOTO)

backup. It is possible that the internal space required for the radar (and, presumably, for those maintaining it) precluded the installation of any long-range SAM system; whereas the other ships of the *Kiev* class all had SA-N-3, *Admiral Gorshkov* is limited to the SA-N-9 point-defense system. This radar has apparently been entirely unsuccessful. Development funding was reportedly cut about 1990. The superstructure of the second full-deck carrier, the incomplete *Varyag*, was apparently adapted instead to a conventional mechanically scanned radar.

◆ Slim Net (Fut-N)

Band: S (2840 MHz)
Beam: (est.) 1 × 3 deg
Pulse Width: 1–1.5 microsec
PRF: 420–425 pps
Antenna Dimensions: 5.5 × 1.8 m

This early (ca. 1957) S-band radar can be used for both air and surface search, varying rotation rate (data rate) for the two functions (slow for surface targets, fast for air targets). Developed in 1948–55, it was tested in the Baltic in 1955, detecting aircraft at a range of up to 150 km. A modified version is built in China as MX-902 (Eye Shield).

Users: India (Petya II and Ugra classes), Indonesia (Don class), North Korea (Najin class).

◆ Snoop Head (Bukhta)

This X-band submarine search radar has an ESM radome (Bald Head) on the same mast, above it. The reflector is slotted. This radar appeared in the late 1970s on board Alfa- and Oscar I–class submarines. In the case of Alfa, it was described as a combat illumination radar, which suggests that it was used to guide missiles.

Slim Net on board a Mirka II–class corvette. (MOD Bonn)

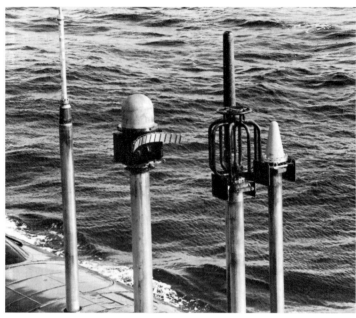

Antennas on board a Typhoon-class strategic submarine (*left to right*): Pert Spring, HF communications, Park Lamp, Shot Gun, and Snoop Pair/Rim Hat.

Masts of an "Oscar"-class missile submarine (*left to right*): HF communications, Snoop Head/Bald Head (radar/ESM), Shot Gun (VHF/UHF communications), Park Lamp (VLF/LF receiver), and Pert Spring (satellite navigation).

◆ **Snoop Plate (Flag)/Snoop Slab (Burya)**

Band: X (around 9370 MHz)
Peak Power: 80 kW
Pulse Width: 1–2 microsec
PRF: 1618 pps
Scan Rate: 10 or 20 rpm (but rotation can be manual or sector scan, and minimum rate is 4 rpm)

The first Soviet postwar submarine search radar was seen in 1953; Snoop Plate was standard through early Foxtrot-class boats. Many components duplicate those of Neptune, Don, and Post Lamp. Range scales are 2, 5, 10, and 40 nm, but maximum range is about 10 nm in practice. Snoop Plate was replaced by Snoop Slab (Burya) in Romeo- and Foxtrot-class and later submarines.

Users: Albania (Whiskey class), Algeria (Romeo class), China (Wuhan, Ming, Romeo classes), Bulgaria (Romeo class), North Korea (Romeo class), Syria (Romeo class). Romeos for Soviet service had Burya radars. Foxtrots in Russian service were refitted with Snoop Tray (Albatros).

◆ **Snoop Tray 1 (Albatros)/Snoop Tray 2 (MRK-50 Tobol)/Snoop Pair (Tobol)**

The X-band Snoop Tray submarine surface-search radar was introduced in 1962. It has a nearly flat and almost rectangular reflector, tipped over at an angle of about 25 deg. This radar succeeded Snoop Slab in production (initially on board Tango, "Golf," November, Hotel, "Echo" classes). Snoop Tray 1 appeared in the early 1960s. Snoop Tray 2 appeared in the mid 1970s. At least in Victor III, this radar is closely associated with ESM; it is presumably used mainly for high-precision DF cuts for targeting. Submarines have a two-way data link allowing them to share ESM information for cross-bearings. The export Kilo version of Tobol is MRK-50E; it feeds the submarine combat system. The associated IFF is MRP-25EM. The "K" in the designator indicates a "complex," that is, something more than a simple radar.

Snoop Pair is apparently a further development of Snoop Tray 2, using back-to-back antennas for increased data rate. The two feeds appear to be somewhat different, so it may be a dual-beam (not vee-beam) set. The solid reflectors resemble that of Snoop Slab (albeit fed from above rather than from below, as in other Soviet radars; this type of feed is probably necessary because the waveguide runs up the mast between the reflectors). The associated ESM antenna, Rim Hat, includes a ring of intercept an-

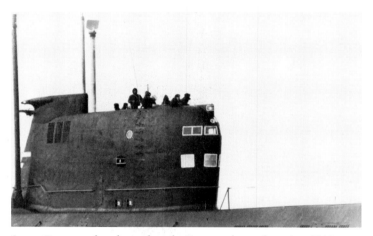

Snoop Tray search radar on board a Foxtrot-class submarine, 1982.

tennas (presumably for monopulse DF) around the base of the radar. Snoop Pair is the current standard nuclear submarine radar, appearing in the early 1980s on board Typhoon-, Sierra-, Akula-, and "Oscar II"–class submarines.

Users (Snoop Tray): Algeria (Kilo class), Cuba (Foxtrot class), India (Kilo, Foxtrot classes), Iran (Kilo class), Libya (Foxtrot class), Poland (Kilo, Foxtrot classes), Romania (Kilo class), Russia (see below). Russian versions: Snoop Tray 1: "Charlie-," Kilo-, some Tango-, "Victor I-," Lima-, and Bravo-class submarines. Snoop Tray 2: Delta I/II/III/IV–, some "Charlie II," "Victor II/III," some Tango, Kilo, India, and Yankee Notch–class submarines.

◆ **Spin Trough (Vyaga)**

The X-band slotted-waveguide surface-search radar is the successor to Don 2. This is the helicopter-landing radar in a Krivak III.

Users: Angola (Yevgenya class), Benin (Zhuk class), Bulgaria (Poti, Zhuk, Sonya, Yevgenya, Polnocny, Vydra classes), Cape Verde Islands (Zhuk class), Congo (Zhuk class), Cuba (Sonya, Yevgenya, Polnocny, Zhuk classes), Egypt (Toplivo 2 and Oktenskiy classes), Eritrea (Zhuk class), Guinea-Bissau (Poluchat I class), India (Pauk, Yevgenya classes), Libya (Polnocny class), Mozambique (Zhuk, Yevgenya classes), Nicaragua (Zhuk, Yevgenya classes), Russia (Krivak [or Don 2], Mayak, T-58 picket, Zhuk, Sonya, Zhenya, Yevgenya, Alligator [or Don-2], Polnocny, Vydra, *Smolnyy* classes), Seychelles (Zhuk class), Somalia (Poluchat I class), Syria (Natya, Zhuk, Yevgenya, Polnacny classes), Vietnam (Sonya, Yevgenya, Zhuk classes), Yemen (Zhuk, Yevgenya, Polnocny classes).

◆ Square Tie (Rangout)/Type 331

This X-band surface-search/targeting radar for SS-N-2 missiles is now being superseded by Plank Shave. Square Tie is enclosed in the Band Stand radomes of export "Nanuchka"-class missile corvettes, which are equipped with SS-N-2C rather than SS-N-9 missiles. The associated FCS is Klon.

The PRC designation for this radar is Type 331.

Strut Pair radar on board the *Udaloy*-class destroyer *Admiral Vinogradov* at Norfolk, July 1990. (S. Zaloga)

Square Tie search and missile-targeting radars at the mastheads of Chinese "Osa"-type missile boats (*center and left*). (U.S. Naval Institute)

Users: Algeria ("Nanuchka," "Osa" classes), Angola ("Osa" class), Bulgaria ("Osa" class), Cuba ("Osa" class), Egypt ("Osa" class), Eritrea ("Osa" class), India ("Nanuchka," "Osa" classes), Libya ("Nanuchka," "Osa" classes), North Korea (Soho, "Soju," "So Hung," "Osa", "Komar" classes), Poland ("Osa" class), Rumania ("Osa" class), Somalia ("Osa" class), Syria ("Osa" class), Vietnam ("Osa" class), Yemen ("Osa" class), Yugoslavia ("Osa" class).

◆ Strut Curve (MR-302 Rubba or Fut-B)/Strut Pair (MR-302M)

This S-band small-ship air-search radar, contemporary with the Head Net series, is installed on Petya- and Mirka-class frigates and Poti- and Grisha-class corvettes. Strut Curve reportedly operates at the high end of the S-band and is unusual in lacking a balancing vane behind its reflector. That lack might indicate that the antenna was not stabilized, the vanes on other Soviet antennas being used to reduce the load on the stabilizer. Note the evident connection with Slim Net, Fut-N.

Like Plank Shave, Strut Curve can act as a data-link receiver, in this case to accept commands for concerted ASW action (presumably using the RBU-6000 launcher). Presumably it supersedes the combination of Slim Net and a dedicated data-link receiver, perhaps Fig Jar.

Strut Pair is two Strut Curve antennas arranged back to back (for high data rate), using pulse compression. It is not associated with any data link. There are two versions. Strut Pair I appeared in the mid-1970s. Strut Pair II, with improved air-search capability, appeared in the early 1980s.

Users:

Strut Curve: Algeria (Koni class), Azerbaijan (Petya), Bulgaria (Koni, Poti classes), Cuba (Koni class), Eritrea (Petya II class), Indonesia (Parchim class), Libya (Koni class), Rumania (*Mutenia*, Tetal, Poti, Cosar, Croitor classes), Russia (Grisha I/II/III, Poti, *Ivan Susanin*, T-58 picket, Ropucha, Ugra, Lama [or Slim Net] classes), Syria (Petya class), Vietnam (Petya class), Yugoslavia (*Kotor*, Koni classes).

Strut Pair: Russia (*Gorshkov*, some *Udaloys*, some Grisha-Vs [later ones have Half Plate], *Marshal Nedelin*).

◆ Top Plate (MR-700 Fregat)/Half Plate (MR-760 Fregat-MA)/ Plate Steer (Fregat-MR)/Top Steer (Fregat)

These S-band 3D radars are higher-frequency equivalents to Top Sail/Flat Plate. As in Top Sail, the first-generation frequency-scanning antenna was a semicylindrical reflector fed by a waveguide twisted around a pipe running up along its focus (in Top

Strut Curve air-search radar on board an East German Koni-class frigate, 1978. (U.S. Naval Institute)

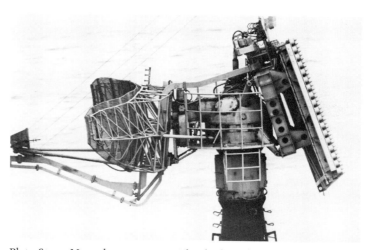

Plate Steer. Note the two waveguides feeding the antenna at left; the larger (lower frequency) of the two extends back up to the IFF array at right and is presumably used for IFF by both antennas. The characteristic serpentine feed of a frequency-scanning radar is visible on the outer edge of the right-hand antenna. Note that the array is not vertical.

Top Plate in a *Udaloy*. Note the back-to-back IFF interrogators atop the two planar arrays.

Top Steer aboard the *Sovremennyy*-class destroyer *Otlichnyy*. Note the waveguide cross-connecting the two antennas, and the narrower waveguide (presumably for IFF) leading into the feed of the 2D element of the radar.

Steer). This antenna was backed by a 2D antenna similar to that in Strut Pair. The next step (Plate Steer, Fregat-MR) was to replace the cylindrical reflector by a planar array, canted to the horizontal, fed by a flat serpentine running up one edge. In Top Plate, the 2D antenna is replaced by a second planar array; both arrays are canted. Half Plate is a single planar array.

The effect of canting would be to run the beam diagonally across the sky as the radar elevated. If the beam is relatively narrow, and the time between pulse trains of different frequencies relatively long, such operation might compensate for the rotation of the antenna. The advantage of such a design would be that the radar could dwell longer at each elevation angle, achieving a better probability of detection. Back-to-back construction might make for a better net data rate, the shorter antenna producing a somewhat broader beam (in elevation) inter-

Plate Steer on board the *Admiral Gorshkov*. Compared to the cylindrical reflector in Top Steer, the flat planar array in Plate Steer should have far lower sidelobes, which should improve its performance and also better protect it from jamming.

mediate between the fan beam of a 2D radar and the pencil beam of a true 3D radar.

Half Plate (Fregat-MA) is a single face of the Top Plate radar.

Fregat-MA (Half Plate) data given at Abu Dhabi, 1993: S(E)-band planar array with less than 30-dB sidelobes; 30 kW peak power (i.e., pulse-compressed), with a 4-sec data rate. 55-deg max elevation. Detects a 7m^2 target above 5000 m at 130 km (70 nm), a 500m^2 ship at 30 km; min range is 3 km. Total weight 7.5 t (2.2t antenna).

MR-1000 is a related radar.

The version of Top Plate on *Udeloys* and the *Kuznetzov* is MR-710 (instrumented range 300 km; elevation 70 deg; scan rate, 6–12 rpm; total weight 17 t). MR-750 is a similar radar (300 km, 55 deg, 6–12 rpm, 16 t). MR-755 is a version of Half Plate for Krivak-class frigates (150 km, 55 deg, 15 rpm, 6.5 t).

Users: Russia (*Kuznetzov, Kirovs, Slavas*, on eight *Udaloy*-class, five *Sovremennyy*-class destroyers [Top Steer in first unit, Plate Steer in *Osmotritel'nyy* and *Bezuprechnyy*], Krivak IIIs [after the first two], SSV-33, later *Artika* class). Half Plate: Russia (Half Plate A: *Aleksandr Brykin*; Half Plate B: later Grisha Vs, superseding Strut Pair)

◆ Top Sail (MR-600 Voskhod)/Top Pair (MR-800 Flag)

The large frequency-scanning 3D radar introduced in 1967 in the *Moskva* is the main search radar in all ships armed with SA-N-3 missiles. Top Sail probably operates at about the same frequency as Big Net, that is, about 850 MHz, which is well below that used by the roughly analogous U.S. systems of a decade earlier (SPS-39/52 series). The typical U.S. flat serpentine waveguide is replaced by a waveguide twisted around a vertical pole in front of the reflector; very clear photographs show the twists, which are required to provide the greater length needed to operate at a longer wavelength. Presumably there are radiating slots on the pole where it faces the reflector. Antenna dimensions are about 6.1 × 7.5 m.

The Russian name, Voskhod (Dawn), seems particularly appropriate to a radar whose beam rises (like the sun).

Top Pair consists of Top Sail and Big Net antennas arranged back to back. Presumably that arrangement makes for better long-range coverage; the U.S. Navy has found that frequency-scanning radars do not dwell on any particular part of the sky long enough to provide the sort of detection probability achievable with a fan-beam (2D) radar. Instrumented range is 500 km; elevation limit is 55 deg; scan rate is 3–12 rpm. Top Pair first appeared in the *Kirov* and *Slava*. The usual associated shorter-range radar is Top Steer.

Top Pair radar on board the missile cruiser *Marshal Ustinov*, Norfolk, 1989. Note the interrogator (IFF) atop the array. (S. Zaloga)

Users (all Russian): Top Sail: Kara class. Top Pair: *Kirov* and *Slava* classes.

◆ Flat Screen (Podberezovik)

This planar-array antenna replaced Top Sail aboard the Kara-class missile cruiser *Kerch* during an April 1988–February 1989 refit. Presumably it is analogous to the flat-array antennas that replaced the original cylindrical array in the U.S. SPS-39, the predecessor to the current SPS-52 (which uses the flat array). The serpentine feed characteristic of frequency scanning is quite visible on the right-hand side of the array, which is about 6×7 m and is tilted back at about 5 deg. This may be the Podberezovik-E radar described at Abu Dhabi in 1993: peak power 110 kW, maximum elevation 30 deg, 5-sec data rate (12 rpm); it detects a $7m^2$ target at 1500 m altitude at 300 km (162 nm). A $500m^2$ ship can be tracked at 30 km. Minimum range is 5 km. Total weight is 13 tons (antenna 3.0 tons). The low peak power suggests pulse compression. Although only a single example has been seen, in 1996 the manufacturer, Salyut, claimed that there were several versions, including two with solid-state transmitters.

A recent Salyut article mentions 3D frequency-scanning radars (possibly Podberezovik) using several beams simultaneously, presumably like SPS-48. A reference to intrapulse modulation suggests that Salyut's current radars use pulse compression. Other features include multichannel adaptive MTI and the ability to shift frequency, number, duration, and parameters of intrapulse modulation for ECCM.

FIRE-CONTROL RADARS

The first postwar generation of Soviet naval radars included separate target-indication sets (which rapidly scanned a narrow beam across their antennas, to give high resolution, while they rotated) and dedicated range-only FCS radars. The first modern

Flat Screen on board the Russian cruiser *Kerch*, early 1989. The radar in the foreground is the Head Lights set used to control the ship's SS-N-3 missiles. The small flat array projected out from the uptakes is an IFF interrogator (Square Head). Although the ship retains her original series of ESM/ECM radomes, Rum Tub has been added (array visible just behind Square Head). (Eric Grove)

FCS radars, Hawk Screech and Owl Screech, embodied a horizontal or diagonal rapidly scanning feed; the radar itself scanned the horizon. These radars operate in TWS mode: the console measures the movement (in range and bearing) of a designated target, transmitting the rates to an FCS computer. The operator monitors rate-aided tracking. In theory such a radar can track several slow-moving targets simultaneously. The external mark of TWS operation is the cylindrical radar feed, housing a spinner.

The next generation (Drum Tilt, Bass Tilt) added a dedicated tracker, initially in the form of a tilting plate that the operator kept centered on the target. Like their predecessors, these radars scan the horizon until their operators designate targets for precision tracking (TWS/rate-aided tracking suffices for surface targets). In the next generation, Kite Screech, the scanning and tracking mechanisms are moved into the radar enclosure. Missile-guidance radars use the same TWS technology, although they may have a rough equivalent of monopulse in the form of SWC (scan with compensation).

The SS-N-3/12 guidance radars, Binom (Scoop Pair) for surface ships and Argument (Front Door/Front Piece) for "Echo II"- and Juliett-class submarines, are now extinct.

◆ Band Stand

This radome covers a radar that tracks an outgoing antiship missile so that it can be controlled by data link. Identical radomes cover a variety of systems. "Nanuchkas" have Titanit, to control SS-N-9 (Malakhit, P-120). *Sovremennyys* have either Monolit (P-80) or Mustang (3M80).

A "Tarantul II" missile corvette shows her Band Stand missile tracker radome atop her bridge. Above it are a Bass Tilt FCS radar and, at the masthead, a Light Bulb missile data-link antenna. The small slotted-waveguide antenna atop the bridge serves a Kivach-3 navigational radar. (*Ships of the World*)

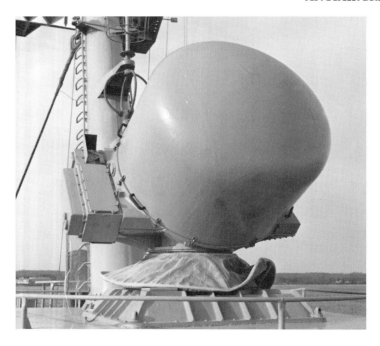

◆ Bass Tilt (MR-105 Turel, MR-123 Vympel)

These radars operate in C-band. MR-105 controls a single gun. MR-123 controls two guns. The X(H/I)-band MR-123 controls AK-230, AK-630 (or -630M), and AK-176 guns; one system can control two guns. Alongside the radar antenna are a TV camera and a laser ranger. The radome resembles that of Drum Tilt but the radar operates very differently. The MR-123 system on board an export "Tarantul" uses a 200 kW pulse-Doppler radar (200 kW, pulse width 0.5 microsec, PRF 1800 or 3600) with a first blind speed of 700 m/sec (about 1400 kt). The 3-deg beam rises 3.6 deg after each search scan of the radar; maximum elevation is 18 to 36 deg. The initial display is a PPI. Once the operator sees a target blip, rotation is stopped, the radar switches to monopulse tracking by switching feeds behind its flat-plate antenna. Target data are displayed on the system control panel. The associated TV monitors track precision. The system is then switched to auto-engage mode.

The later X(I)-band MR-123–2 (250 kW, 1.8-deg beam) scans at 15 rpm, the beam rising helically at 5 Hz. Instrumented range is 45 km (30 km with MTI). Maximum elevation is 85 deg. As in earlier versions, tracking is monopulse (accuracy 1 mrad, 5 m). MR-123–2 controls AK-176M and AK-630M1–2 guns.

Associated gun FCS: AK-230-MR-123, AK-630-MR-123, AK-630M1-2-MR-123-02, AK-176-MR-123/76 (30mm and 76mm), AK-176-MR-123-02/76 (AK-176M and AK-630M1-2).

Users: Bulgaria ("Tarantul"), Guinea-Bissau (Bogomol class), India (*Khukri*, "Tarantul," Pauk classes), Poland ("Tarantul" class), Rumania ("Tarantul" class), Russia (*Gorshkov, Kirov*, Slava, Kara, *Udaloy, Sovremennyy*, Mod "Kashin," Krivak III, Parchim II, Grisha III/V, Dergach, "Tarantul," "Nanuchka III," Svetlak, Pauk, Babochka, Matka, Muravey, Pomornik, *Aleksandr Brykin*, Berezhina, SSV-33 classes).

The Bass Tilt radar on board the "Tarantul"-class fast-attack boat *Hiddensee*. In search mode, the flat plate antenna directs the 3-deg beam. After each scan, it tips up by 3.6 deg; the maximum elevation can be set at 18–36 deg. Once a target has been designated, the monopulse cluster alongside the tilting plate locks on for precision tracking. In a later version, the tilting plate may elevate continuously so that the radar scans helically. Maximum target speed is 800 m/sec. An associated MTI can eliminate static targets. Antenna gain is about 30 dB; peak power is 200 kW. Pulse width is about 0.5 microsec. (PRF is 1800 or 3600.)

Vympel (Bass Tilt) GFCS consoles in the below-decks weapons-control space of the "Tarantul"-class missile boat *Hiddensee*, showing the television (*top*) and radar screens. The device at right is the ballistic computer, with separate dials showing the bearings of the 76mm and 30mm guns. The guns are fired from the main console, which has bearing repeaters for the two 30mm guns (to the right of the radar scope); below them are dials showing how many rounds remain. A switch selects long or short bursts. (Author)

◆ Cross Sword

Serving as the missile guidance for SA-N-9, which is the successor to SA-N-4, the Ku/X-band Cross Sword, like the Ku/C-band Pop Group, incorporates its own search antenna. In this case, however, there are no separate target and missile-tracking antennas, only a single flat face with a prominent illuminator. The antenna is not dished in any way and, therefore, cannot be a passive reflector for the feed. Nor is there sufficient depth for the flat plate to be merely a weather cover. Most probably the flat plate is an active reflector, in the sense that different elements change the phase of the incoming signal (from the feed) in different ways, so as to form one or more beams. Such a solution would square with the fact that Cross Sword is roughly contemporary with the phased-array Top Dome, and also that Cross Sword has apparently encountered serious manufacturing problems (a simple monopulse would not present any great difficulty). Presumably, the prominent pimple centered on the Top Dome radome is an analogous feed.

A Cross Sword director on board a *Udaloy*, 1989. (Royal Navy)

Such radars are quite different from Western phased arrays, in which the phase shifter is interposed directly between transmitter/receiver and antenna element. Presumably, they are simpler to wire and need not pass quite the same amount of power as in such Western radars as SPY-1.

The surveillance element employs two paraboloids arranged back to back for a high data rate. They differ in configuration (particularly at their edges), and each appears to be made in two layers. In other cases, this type of construction is used with two beams of different polarization, one layer reflecting only in one polarization. Such an arrangement might provide two beams at slightly different angles, so the radar could not only acquire a target but also determine its position more precisely (similarly, the two-beam radar might provide initial altitude information). The high data rate (compared to the one-antenna Pop Group) may have been chosen in response to a new requirement to protect ships against very small antiship missiles appearing suddenly at the horizon at a relatively short range. The double surveillance radar incorporates its own IFF interrogators, carried above the search antennas.

Cross Sword has two smaller antennas above its main antenna, aligned with its main axis. One is probably a missile-command transmitter. The other might well be a phased-array missile-beacon tracker. There are also EO devices at the lower corners of the main antenna.

In the case of Cross Sword/SA-N-9, the initial installation was on board *Udaloy*-class destroyers, which have eight vertical launchers but one or two directors. Since the missiles are all vertically launched, either director should be able to control all of them. An analogy can be made with the design of the *Kirov*, in which all the missiles are forward but there is a second director aft. Past Soviet practice has been to associate two launchers or launcher arms with each target channel, so one would assume that Cross Sword can handle four targets with a total of eight missiles. The presence of two directors on the same ship would not be too significant since each has only a limited effective arc (whereas each missile, like a Western vertically launched weapon, can presumably cover all 360 deg).

This radar may be MR-350.

Users (all Russian): *Kuznetzov, Gorshkov, Udaloy* classes).

◆ Drum Tilt (MR-104 Rys)

This radar operates in X(H/I)-band; it controls twin 30mm (AK-230) guns. Drum Tilt was the first of a new generation of drum-shaped fire-control antennas (1961). The housing is tipped up permanently at an angle of about 25 deg, and approximate dimensions are 1.5 m in diameter and 1.7 m in length. This radar is fully stabilized. Like the earlier Hawk Screech, it is almost certainly designed for TWS operation, the feed rather than the antenna as a whole scanning a limited volume of space. The fixed radome elevation would seem to imply that the antenna itself is fixed in elevation. TWS operation presumably suits Drum Tilt to more conventional search operation (it is the primary search radar in Natya- and Yurka-class minesweepers). Reported acquisition range on an aerial target is 41,000 m (about 45,000 yd), and maximum tracking range is 22,800 m (about 25,000 yd). Reportedly, at least the early radars of this type required skilled operators because the radar tended to lose targets after it locked on. The initial version could track only a single target.

Drum Tilt radar on board an East German Koni-class frigate. (U.S. Naval Institute)

Associated gun FCS: AK-230-MR-104, controlling AK-230 guns.

Users: Algeria (Koni, "Osa," Polnocny classes), Angola ("Osa," Shershen, Polnocny classes), Bulgaria (Koni, "Osa," Shershen, Polnocny classes), Cambodia (Stenka class), Cuba (Koni, "Osa," Polnocny classes), Egypt ("Osa," Polnocny classes), Eritrea ("Osa," Mol, Polnocny classes), Finland ("Osa" class), India ("Kashin" class, *Godavari* class, *Trishul*, "Osa," Natya, Polnocny classes), Korea (North) ("Osa," Shershen classes), Libya (Koni, "Osa," Natya, Polnocny classes), Poland ("Osa," Mod Obluze, Polnocny classes), Romania (*Muntenia*, Tetal, "Osa," Epitrop, Cosar classes), Russia ("Osa," Stenka, *Gorya*, Natya I, Yurka classes), Somalia ("Osa," Mol classes), Syria (Natya, "Osa" classes), Vietnam (Shershen, Yurka classes), Yemen ("Osa," Polnocny classes), Yugoslavia (*Kotor*, Koni, "Osa" classes).

◆ Eye Bowl (Sprut)

S-band tracker (two antennas per installation, one scanning horizontally and one vertically) for the SS-N-14 ASW missile, which is command-guided. Eye Bowl is, in effect, the missile-tracking element of Head Lights. Ships with Head Lights SAM guidance radars use those sets to track and guide their SS-N-14s.

Eye Bowl (SS-N-14) control antennas are shown above the bridge of the Krivak-class frigate *Komsomolets Litvii* at Kiel, June 1990. Below them is a Pop Group director (with a Don Kay antenna below it); above them are Palm Frond and Head Net C, with a Salt Pot IFF interrogator above the Head Net radar. (H. van Ginderen)

Eye Bowl on board the *Udaloy*-class missile destroyer *Admiral Vinogradov*. (S. Zaloga)

Users: Russia (*Udaloy* and Krivak I/II classes).

◆ Front Dome (Orekh)

The C-band missile guidance tracker-illuminator for SA-N-7 resembles the Bass Tilt gunfire-control radar but is larger. In the *Sovremennyy* class, three such radars are associated with each SA-N-7 launcher. Like the Cross Sword FCS radar, this one apparently uses a passive phased-array reflector illuminated from the front.

A Front Dome missile-guidance radar on board the destroyer *Otlichnyy*, at Norfolk, 1989. The optronic device next to the guidance radar is unique to the *Sovremennyy* class and is paired near the SA-N-7 launchers; presumably, it is an EO part of the SA-N-7 system. (S. Zaloga)

◆ Front Door (Argument)

The tracker/command antenna for SS-N-12 antiship missiles survives only on board the *Slava* class and *Admiral Gorshkov*. It is a slightly cylindrical antenna, taller than it is wide, which can scan in bearing. Surface-ship versions were initially designated Trap Door; they do not fold (but the version in the *Kiev* class folds down at one end, hence the name). The submarine antenna was ultimately designated Front Door A, and Trap Door became Front Door C. As an indication of size, the antenna in the bows of the *Admiral Gorshkov* is covered by a 3×5m door. The associated FCS is Argon.

Front Door/Front Piece on board a *Slava*-class cruiser, with what appears to be a surface-search antenna mounted directly atop it. This small antenna is presumably used to acquire the beacon signal from the missile. The larger surface-search radars are Palm Fronds.

◆ Hawk Screech (Yakor')

Band: X (9.2–9.5 GHz)
Beam: 0.6 deg
Peak Power: 150 kW
Pulse Width: 0.6 microsec
PRF: Approx. 1250 pps
Scan Rate: 30–31 cycles/sec linear scan (narrow sector)
Antenna Dimensions: Approx. 1.7 m dia

Hawk Screech is the X-band fire control for 45mm, 57mm, and 76.2mm dual-purpose guns (1954); it always has an optical backup. This fully stabilized radar, conceived in 1949, introduced TWS techniques to Soviet radar technology. Presumably the scan across the antenna was considered quick enough to capture the motion of an air target. Maximum range is probably about 6500 yd and 18,000 ft (altitude).

Hawk Screech radar on board an East German Koni-class frigate. (U.S. Naval Institute)

Users: Algeria (Koni class), Azerbaijan (Petya), Bulgaria (Koni class), Cuba (Koni class), Eritrea (Petya II class), India (Petya II class), Libya (Koni class), Romania (*Muntenia*), Russia (Petya, Mirka, Don, Amga [alternative to Muff Cob] classes), Serbia (Koni class), Syria (Petya class).

◆ Head Lights (4R60 Grom)

The X-, C-, and S-band missile-control radar for SA-N-3 consists of two large (4m) and two small (1.8m) tracking dishes and a small dish for the command uplink. The large dishes track the target, the small dishes the missile. Like Peel Group, this is a TWS radar; one of each pair of dishes is scanned vertically, the other horizontally. Previous suggestions that Head Lights is a monopulse radar are entirely incorrect. There are several versions. Head Lights B added SS-N-14 control. All *Kievs* had Head Lights C, which presumably has additional power to control a longer-range version of SA-N-3. Head Lights C appeared in the Kara class. The early Kresta IIs had Head Lights B forward and Head Lights A aft, but later ones had Head Lights B fore and aft.

Head Lights. The circular shape of the feed on the left indicates a vertical scan rather than a monopulse cluster. The barely visible but apparently cylindrical feed of the other antenna appears to be horizontal. That would suggest that, like Peel Group, this director scans separately in elevation and in train (using the far-side antenna for that). In that case it continues the TWS technology of the earlier systems, each pair of antennas (large and small) constituting a single TWS unit.

The name means Thunder.
User (Russia only): Kara class.

◆ Hot Flash

The CADS-N-1 radar array consists of a pair of vertical orange peels, which can train as well as elevate. There is no on-mount acquisition radar, but in *Neustrashimyy* Cross Dome is probably used for that purpose. The radar is used for gunfire control; the associated missile is guided by the EO backup.

Hot Flash radar on a CADS-N-1 (Kortik) mounting on board the frigate *Neustrashimy*, June 1995. The usual missiles are not being carried. (H&L van Ginderen)

Users: Russia (*Kuznetzov, Nakhimov, Petr Velikiy, Admiral Chabanenko, Neustrashimyy* class; modernized Krivak class; may appear in many other combatants as they are modernized).

◆ Kite Screech (MR-114 Lev, MR-145 Drakon, MR-184)

The fire-control radar for 100mm and new 130mm dual-purpose guns is similar in appearance to Hawk Screech but larger. This radar has a characteristic V-shaped strut supporting a feed, most likely monopulse, operating at two frequencies (X-band search, Ka-band tracking); presumably each is fed through its own side of the V-feed. Kite Screech appeared about 1975. Kite Screech A (MR-114: mid-1970s) controls Krivak-class 100mm (AK-100) guns. MR-145 is the successor on board, for example, the *Udaloy* class. MR-114 may also be known as Yakhond-M. Kite Screech B (MR-184: early 1980s) controls 130mm (AK-130) guns.

Kite Screech B radar director for 130mm guns, on board the destroyer *Otlichnyy* at Norfolk, 1989. The hole is for a television camera. The radar abaft the director is Palm Frond. (S. Zaloga)

The MR-145 mounting carries an autotracking TV camera and a laser range-finder; the FCS is digital. The X(I)-band search beam is 1 deg wide (300 kW peak power); the K-band tracker beam is 0.25 deg wide (25 kW). Instrumented range is 75 km, and maximum elevation is 75 deg. Accuracy: 0.5 mrad, 5 m. Weight: 8 t. The system tracks its own shells for correction, and can direct two guns (e.g., two AK-100 on an *Udaloy*) simultaneously.

Associated gun FCS: AK-100-MR-114, AK-100-MR-145, AK-100-MR-184.

Users (Russia only): *Gorshkov, Kirov, Slava, Udaloy, Sovremennyy,* Krivak II/III classes.

◆ Muff Cob (MR-103 Bars)

Controlling 57mm twin automatic guns, Muff Cob operates in C(G/H)-band and has an attached TV camera. This system first appeared about 1962. Although Muff Cob has a barrel-shaped radome similar to that of Drum Tilt, it elevates; therefore, the entire antenna presumably tracks its target in both elevation and azimuth.

Muff Cob 57mm gunfire-control radar director on board the Indian frigate *Ganga*. In Indian service this director is designated MR-103. (*Ships of the World*)

The name means Wildcat. The associated gun FCS is AK-725-MR-103.

Users: Algeria ("Nanuchka II" class), Bulgaria (Poti class), Cambodia (Turya class), Cuba (Turya class), Eritrea (Turya class), India (*Godavari* class, "Nanuchka" class), Indonesia (Parchim class), Libya ("Nanuchka" class), Romania (Poti, Cosar classes), Russia (Grisha I/II, T-58 picket, Turya, Ugra, Amga [alternative to Hawk Screech], *Berezina* classes), Vietnam (Turya class), Yemen (Ropucha class).

Owl Screech, showing the characteristically canted cylindrical feed and the opening in the antenna for an EO camera.

◆ Owl Screech (MR-105 Turel' or Fut-B)

This C-band fire control for AK-726 76.2mm DP guns (about 1961) is an improved Hawk Screech. The cylindrical (rotating) feed is tilted at 45 deg to the horizontal so that its beam scans in both elevation and azimuth. The reflector's diameter is about 2.3 m. Peak power is reportedly 250 kW. There is no associated backup director/target designator. There may be an improved MR-140 version.

This radar may also be known as Yakhond. The associated gun FCS is AK-726-MR-105.

Users: India ("Kashin"), Poland ("Kashin"), Russia (*Kiev,* Kara, "Kashin," Krivak I, *Ivan Susanin, Smolnyy* classes).

◆ Peel Group (4R90 Yatagan)

This missile-control radar for SA-N-1 consists of a command dish plus two groups of antennas: one to track the target, the other to track the two missiles normally fired in a salvo. Each group consists of two parabolic reflectors, one vertical and one horizontal; hence the name (they resemble pieces of orange peel). The feeds are almost certainly organ-pipe scanners, rotating rapidly to form beams scanning in height and elevation, like the beams of the old U.S. SPS-8 and SPS-30 series. Presumably, the command dish sends the missiles signals for vertical and horizontal course correction. The target is tracked in S-band, the missile in X-band. The director also carries a TV camera for use under heavy jamming. Maximum range is about 30–40 nm.

Although unknown in contemporary Western missile-control systems, Peel Group's TWS operation was typical of contemporary Soviet missile-guidance radars. Compared to a single con-scan tracker, a TWS tracker requires much less in the way of accurate radar-antenna movement, as the antenna need not track the target (except to keep the target within the antenna

Peel Group missile (SA-N-1) fire-control radar directors on board the "Kashin"-class destroyer *Strogiy* at Massawa, 1972, showing the characteristic pairs of large and small horizontal and vertical antennas, for target and missile tracking. (Royal Navy)

field of view). TWS tracking is, however, relatively difficult to automate. In the Soviet case there are probably separate elevation and azimuth operators who match the observed target motion with rate-aided trackers, applying corrections as required. Such operation would seem to imply poor performance against a radically maneuvering target. TWS fire control also carries the disadvantage that the radar spreads most of its energy outside the target and thus should be easier to jam (and should enjoy shorter effective range) than a radar continuously pointed at a target.

In theory, a single pair of TWS antennas could track both target and missiles (as in the land-based equivalent to Peel Group, Low Blow), but Soviet naval practice has been to provide separate missile and target trackers. In theory, at least in this case, that should permit the use of more energy-efficient missile trajectories (the missiles need not fly near the targets), as well as up-and-over surface-attack trajectories.

Users: India ("Kashin" class), Poland ("Kashin" class), Russia ("Kashin" class).

◆ Poima (MRO-560)

Salyut NPO's Poima is the standard shipboard ADT processor, accepting plots from up to two radars, combining data to form tracks, and providing that data to a ship's CDS and WCS. Track data processing is described as adaptive, with identification by source information. Poima also reports the status of a ship's radars, ESM systems, and target designation systems back to the CDS and other consumers. Poima is modular, with three displays (each with its own memory): primary situation, tracking, and target distribution. The export version (5t) carries 20 target tracks.

MRO-560 is probably the version in the *Sovremennyy* class. MRO-550 is probably the version in larger ships.

There is also a Russian equivalent of Western automatic radar plotting aids (ARPA), MR-226, which can automatically track 20 targets, with errors of 3 deg in course and 1.5 kt in speed. (Data are presented on a PPI.)

◆ Pop Group ("Osa"-2M, MPZ-301, 4P33)

The missile-guidance radar for SA-N-4 incorporates its own acquisition radar, atop the cab, with target and missile trackers in front (flat plate antennas). Presumably the acquisition radar is co-located with the trackers to reduce handover delays; in this sense Pop Group is analogous to the Signaal M20 series and to the U.S. Mk 92.

Although the missile launcher has two arms, there are only a single missile-tracker antenna and a single target-tracker antenna. Dual operation would still be possible using polarization diversity, two signals sharing a common antenna. That sharing might be the reason for the flat plate some distance ahead of the antenna proper.

A Pop Group missile director on board the cruiser *Marshal Ustinov* at Norfolk, 1989. (S. Zaloga)

The analogous land system (Land Roll) has one large and two small antennas plus a surveillance/acquisition antenna similar in appearance to that of Pop Group. In the land system, the search antenna operates at 6–8 GHz (slightly below Western C-band wavelength), with stacked feeds (probably for frequency diversity, possibly for integral IFF). Reportedly, the big target tracker is a frequency-hopping monopulse antenna operating at 14.2–14.8 GHz (slightly above X-band as used in the West); reported maximum range is 25 km (effective range 20 km). The target tracker is almost certainly an inverse Cassegrain. The smaller antenna is a higher-frequency replica of the larger.

In the case of the land-based system, the two missile trackers can operate at different frequencies, to track two separate missiles engaging the same target.

At least in a Krivak, the radar is called Korund ("Osa" is the full system).

Users: Algeria ("Nanuchka," Koni), Bulgaria (Koni), Cuba (Koni), India ("Nanuchka"), Libya (Koni class), Russia (*Kiev, Kirov, Slava*, Kara, Krivak, Grisha V, "Nanuchka" classes), Serbia (Kotor, Koni classes).

◆ Top Dome (Volna)

The X-band missile-guidance radar for SA-N-6 uses a 4m-dia radome fixed in elevation but trainable. Three smaller radomes are mounted on the face of the mounting pedestal, and there is also a much smaller hemispheric radome below. The smaller radome may be the link transceiver for the track-via-missile system. The main tracking radar almost certainly operates in X-band, in analogy to the land-based Flap Lid engagement radar.

Top Dome missile-guidance radar on board the Soviet *Slava*-class missile cruiser *Marshal Ustinov* at Norfolk, 1989. (S. Zaloga)

Each Top Dome is associated with six vertical launchers; on the basis of two missiles per target, presumably Top Dome can simultaneously control three intercepts against three targets. Since there is no separate target or missile tracker, the system must time-share between the target- and missile-tracking functions. Because Top Dome does not elevate, it must scan electronically (as, indeed, the land-based SA-10 fire-control radar does).

In the past, it has been Soviet practice to assign one launcher per director per target. However, it is possible that the Soviets consider the array of six SA-N-6 launchers as a single entity, and that doctrine now calls for more than two missiles per engagement.

Top Dome missile-guidance radar on board the Soviet *Slava*-class missile cruiser *Marshal Ustinov* at Norfolk, 1989. (D. Steigman and S. Zaloga)

Users (Russia only): *Kirov* and *Slava* classes and *Azov* (test ship).

IFF

As in the Western navies, the Russians developed interrogator-transponder IFF systems. There is no evidence of any attempt to integrate IFF for a ship; each air-search radar has its own interrogator. Transponder feeds are integrated into the feeds of most of the standard microwave radars, but it appears that the big frequency-scanning types require separate interrogators. Sky Watch has small flat panels near its main panels; they are presumably interrogators. The other large-radar interrogators are Long Head (a long array of dipoles, e.g., atop Top Plate) and Tooth Brush (square enclosure atop Top Sail and Top Steer and their relatives). Small combatants generally have Square Head (a 2.0 × 1.5m reflector carrying an array of vertical dipoles). Square Head dipole dimensions correspond to a wavelength of 50 cm (600 MHz). In an "Osa"-class missile boat there are two Square Heads, one for the Square Tie surface-search radar and one for the Drum Tilt gunfire-control radar. It is not clear whether different interrogators correspond to different IFF systems. Square Head(s) and a High Pole A or B transponder are part of a system designated Nikhrom-2. The other current transponder is Salt Pot (there are A and B versions), generally in larger ships. A few older large ships (*Moskva*- and *Kynda*-class cruisers) have an earlier transponder, Hour Glass. Presumably, it is part of an older IFF system now being discontinued (some ships have both it and Salt Pot).

A 60P-series system currently advertised employs 670P shipboard transponder and 673P shipboard interrogator. The airborne equivalents are 620P and 623P; the ground equivalents are 65P and 64P/673P. Beside the usual IFF functions, the system includes position location (including that of emergency signals), a further interrogation mode ("who is guiding," for surface ships), and a ground-to-air fighter interception data link. Modes are: nonspoofproof general identification (I), spoofproof general identification using a random binary code (II), selective identification (III: 84 codes, IV: 100,000 codes); emergency (reply to interrogator), and alarm (no interrogator). The system operates at 20 and 45 cm; the manufacturer describes it as interoperable with the earlier Kremniy 2 IFF system. For interrogation, the system uses pulse-time coding; responses use pulse frequency-time coding. Mode III interrogation uses two pulses at any of six positions (12 codes); the reply uses a single pulse in any of seven positions (the combination yields the 84 codes). The Mode IV reply uses a 5-decade 4-bit binary code. The signal PRF is about 488.28 pps.

OPTRONIC SYSTEMS

♦ **Kolonka**

Kolonka is a simple optical director, used as a secondary control channel, and to control light automatic guns, such as AK 230s, which lack any on-board controls. Kolonka carries a very simple sight with speed rings; it is not a lead-computing sight like the old U.S. Mk 14 used in the Mk 51 and 63 FCSs. The operator has a pair of pistol grips, triggers on both of which must be depressed to fire. Lights on his side of the director show which guns he controls, and also whether he is in control.

Kolonka, the standard Russian optical backup director, is shown on board the missile destroyer *Bezuderzhannyy*. That it has no computing function whatever is obvious from its use of a simple ring sight. (Author)

♦ **Squeeze Box (Kondensor)**

In *Sovremennyy*-class destroyers and in amphibious ships with bombardment rockets, Squeeze Box probably combines IR TV with a laser range-finder. The version in a *Sovremennyy* is Kondensor-218. An "uncovered" version is carried by Pomornik-class ACVs. Squeeze Box is a fire-control device, not a remote-vision device like Tee Plinth or Tin Man.

Squeeze Box on board a *Sovremennyy*-class destroyer. This EO device is associated with 130mm-gun fire control. It contains a laser, presumably for range-finding. Reports that the same device was used to blind or dazzle pilots temporarily (like the British LDS) suggest that it can operate continuously, which in turn would be useful primarily to guide shells. (S. Zaloga)

♦ **Tee Plinth**

This television sensor was installed in the 1960s and 1970s and is now replaced in newer ships by Tin Man. Tee Plinth supplements the large optical periscopes that modern Soviet warships (from the Kynda class on) carry either atop or abeam their bridges. Both Tee Plinth and these periscopes presumably serve the below-decks command center/secondary bridge (BIP). Tee Plinth and its successor (Tin Man) are trainable. The Russians also use small fixed television cameras (Tilt Pot).

Users (Russia only): *Slava, Kara,* mod. "Kashin" classes; *Soobrazitelny* was probably test ship.

♦ **Tin Man**

Successor to Tee Plinth, Tin Man probably incorporates a laser range-finder, in newer ships.

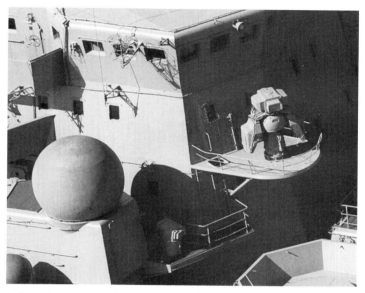

A Tin Man optronic device on board the cruiser *Kirov*. The nearby radome is a Big Ball for satellite communications. (*Sea Power*)

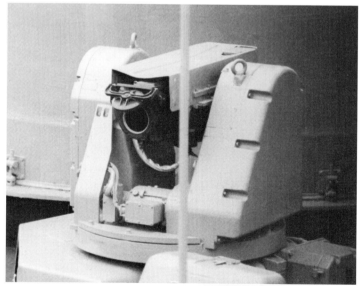

One of these EO devices is located approximately above each 30mm Gatling gun on board a *Sovremennyy*-class destroyer (and also close to each Front Dome SA-N-7 guidance radar, which lacks any EO element). It probably incorporates a television tracker (this one was photographed when the destroyer *Bezuderzhannyy* was anchored in New York), but it may also incorporate a laser dazzler. Its NATO nickname is unknown.

Users (Russia only): *Gorshkov* and *Kirov* class.

FIRE-CONTROL SYSTEMS

Later radar FCSs (e.g., Bass Tilt, Hawk Screech) are designated by the associated radar. Wasp Head was an early postwar optical/radar director.

♦ **Rakurs (SP-521)**

This optronic FCS, outwardly similar to NAJIR, was announced in 1995. Incorporating a laser range-finder, it was developed by the Ametist Design Bureau in coordination with the LOMO joint stock company of St. Petersburg. The operator has a ring sight and two optical windows; FOVs are 30 deg ($2\times$) and 7.5 deg ($8\times$). Rakurs can accept designation data from other shipboard sensors, or the operator can acquire the target independently. The below-decks computer can switch it to rate-aided tracking if the target is temporarily obscured or if the range-finder is turned off. Elevation limits are $-25/+85$ deg; maximum slew/elevation rate 60 deg/sec. Rakurs can control one or two gun mounts, such as AK-176 and AK-630. Weights: 750 kg total, of which 425 kg is below decks. The system bus is a 1-MHz single wire.

SOUTH AFRICA

♦ **HESIS**

This new helmet sight was announced in 1992. In the new South African coastal patrol craft, it directly controls a 20mm gun (carrying a gunner) and it indirectly controls a slaved twin 107mm rocket launcher on the cabin roof. The sight, powered by a 9V battery in the helmet, presents the gunner with a red dot (generated by an LED) focused at infinity in front of his eye. The gunner sees the dot on a half-silvered mirror, so he can see the target with the same eye. Hence the sight requires no calibration to adjust to different gunners' eyes. The system's angular error detector is coupled to the gunner's helmet and to a reference point behind him; it is a flexible coupling between two flat connector plates. The plate on the helmet back is at 90 deg to the LOS; the plate on the mount is rigid to weapon line of fire. The angular deviation is fed directly to the traverse and elevation servo drives. A joystick can input the lead angle and trajectory corrections. The coupling has 6 deg of freedom, allowing the gunner completely free head movement within a considerable envelope. The system has alternative search and attack modes. In search mode, it is de-tuned, so that it follows the gunner's head with a time lag. It does not respond to his quick searching movements. The firing circuit is disabled. In the attack mode, the gun immediately follows the gunner's head. The joystick, firing button, mode selection, and power switches are on a bar suspended from the mounting. The gunner rests his right arm on this bar and thus has all the controls immediately to hand.

♦ **Triton**

M-Tek's day/night EO tracker is part of the proposed Kingfisher coastal-patrol system and has been fitted to the fast-attack boat *Jan Smuts* for trials. It was conceived as a follow-on option for the current fast-attack boat upgrade program. The sensors are an Eloptro 8–12-micron FLIR, an M-Tek 2/8 deg FOV TV (light-level range 2 to 200,000 lux), and a laser with a firing rate of 12.5 Hz. The basic version omits the FLIR, and uses a monochrome display. All versions employ a horizontal cylindrical body (with ports on the side) with elevation limits of $-20/+85$ deg, which can slew at up to 2 rad/sec using direct-coupled motors, and which can position its LOS to within 0.3 mrad. The head weighs 150 kg, and is 90 cm high. A fighter can be acquired at over 15 km, and range to 10 km is accurate to within 5 m. Below-decks electronics, in a VME cabinet (with COTS cards for digital control and video imaging), include a fiber-optic gyro to stabilize system LOS, as well as the usual TV autotracker. The console carries a color monitor (for target selection using crosshairs, and also for overlays of other data), as well as three raw video monitors (one per sensor) and a video recorder. Two multifunction hand controllers are used for all inputs and for manual track control. Triton is intended to provide target position and velocity data to a gun or missile system. The three-sensor version costs $600,000.

SPAIN

◆ DORNA

Direccion de tiro Optronica y Raddrica, a joint venture by Inisel and FABA (Fabrica Artilleria de Bazan), is based on Inisel's Felis Mk 3 land optronic system. Its 27-GHz radar tracker, FLIR, laser ranger, and high-definition TV camera are all mounted in a Meroka-sized turret. Inisel is responsible for software (written in ADA); the processors are 68020s. FABA contributes its experience in distributed architecture, system integration, and precision digital servos. Work began in 1986; the prototype was completed in 1993 and announced in 1994. DORNA is to be installed on board the new F100-class frigates, and probably will be backfitted to the *Baleares* and *Perry* classes. Estimated development cost is Pt2492M.

SWEDEN

The primary electronics manufacturers are Ericsson and Bofors (BEAB). BEAB was formerly PEAB (Philips), formed in 1975 by combining three companies of the large Philips industrial electronics group. Philips also owned Signaal and MEL, and Signaal and PEAB had a noncompetition agreement. However, in 1989 Philips decided to sell off its defense arms. It sold PEAB to Bofors (hence the renaming, to BEAB), and it sold majority control of Signaal to Thomson-CSF, ending the noncompetition agreement. MEL was sold to Thorn-EMI.

Most of the Philips (now BEAB) radars are based on a tunable (i.e., frequency-agile) magnetron developed in 1955. This device was intended primarily to solve the problem of echo fluctuation (due to small phase differences from different parts of the target, so that reflections from different parts of the target interfere with each other) and glint (apparent movement of the target echo center, even beyond the physical area of the target). Both phenomena vary with signal frequency and thus can be avoided if the radar rapidly changes frequency. The PEAB (BEAB) magnetrons change resonant frequency by spinning a tuner coupled magnetically to an external motor. These magnetrons entered production in the mid-1960s; Ferranti used a license-built version in the Seaspray helicopter radar.

RADARS

◆ HARD

Ericcson's X-band 3D pulse-Doppler ADT radar may be adopted as an on-mount FCS radar for the new Bofors 40mm L70 Mk 3. HARD was adopted by the Swedish army as the PS-91 vehicle-mounted (land-based) radar to support light self-propelled guns or short-range missiles. Peak power is 65 kW (average is 8 W). HARD uses phase-coded pulse compression (on bursts of pulses) combined with Doppler processing, and is frequency-agile on both a burst-to-burst and a pulse-to-pulse basis. Non-Doppler MTI processing is used to distinguish slow-moving targets (such as helicopters) with high-Doppler elements (rotor blades). A hovering helicopter can be detected at 8–10 km (5–6 mi) and an aircraft at 16–20 km (10–12 mi); instrumented range is 20 km. Horizon scans (for helicopter detection) are interleaved with full 3D scans, presumably using stacked beams for monopulse height-finding (scan rate is 40 rpm). Accuracy: range within 50 m, elevation within 1 deg, bearing within 0.5 deg. The antenna and transceiver weigh 60 kg and the signal processor weighs another 50 kg. HARD trials began in 1984. The Swedish army production order was placed in May 1989. Deliveries began in 1992.

◆ Pilot

Pilot was the original Philips stealthy radar; Signaal developed its own Scout (see above) when the company split up its defense arm. CelsiusTech is now marketing Pilot Mk 2. The Royal Swedish Navy ordered four of these radars for its *Goteborg* class and 16 more to equip its new YSB and YSM-2000 surface ships. No other sales have been reported.

◆ Sea Giraffe 50/50HC/75F/150HC (PS-75)/DCR and BEAB C/X-Band Radar

Band: C (5.4–5.9 GHz)
Beam: 2.1 deg (50), 1.8 deg in larger versions; csc^2 for beams
Peak Power: 15 kW (50 and 50HC); 60 kW (150HC)
Gain: 29 dB (50); 30 dB (50HC and 150HC)
Pulse Width: 3.2 and 6.4 microsec, compressed to 0.3 microsec in surface-search mode. There is also a short pulse (0.2 microsec) for fire control.
PRF: 1000–7000 (depends on mode)
Scan Rate: 30 or 60 rpm
Antenna Dimensions: 2.3 × 0.7 m (50); 2.4 × 0.8 m (50HC and 150HC); 2.4 × 1.8 m (150HC)
Antenna Weight: 250 kg (50); 700 kg (150HC)

Sea Giraffe, developed by Ericsson beginning in 1980, is a family of multipurpose (air- and surface-search, fire-control) naval radars derived from the land-based Giraffe (PS-70) air-defense radar and first tested on board a fast-attack boat in 1981–82. The main difference from Giraffe is greatly improved range resolution (through pulse compression). It uses two different fully stabilized antennas (one for Sea Giraffe 50 and one for 50HC and 150HC) and two transmitters (15 kW and 60 kW). Both transmitters are fully coherent so that MTI can be used for clutter rejection (50–55-dB ratio). Instrumented ranges are 25, 50, and 100 km.

The Sea Giraffe 150HC four-beam antenna chosen for the Canadian "City"-class frigates. (Ericsson)

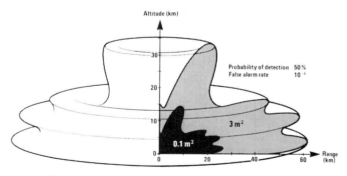

Sea Giraffe 150HC coverage. (Ericsson)

Sea Giraffe 50 uses a single-beam antenna (there is also a 50LW using a slotted waveguide). In the designations, HC (high coverage) denotes a high-elevation stabilized antenna to detect missiles diving at angles of 60–80 deg. Thus, Sea Giraffe 50HC uses a three-beam antenna. Sea Giraffe 150HC has three or four beams (covering 0–70 deg in elevation). All antennas have integrated IFF via their feeds.

The 9LV Mk 3 C/X-band radar uses both the Sea Giraffe 150 C-band transmitter and a parallel X-band transmitter (presumably using the standard 9LV magnetron). Although antenna dimensions are given as 2.4 × 1.0 m (scan rates 30/60 rpm, weight 100 kg plus 350-kg platform), this antenna is probably that of Sea Giraffe 150HC. Both radars use BEAB displays. The antenna produces three C(G)-band beams: low (34-dB gain, 1.9 × 5 deg), high (30.5 dB, 1.9 × 9 deg), and extra high (26.5 dB, 1.9 × 3.5 deg). The separate X-(I-)band beam is 1.1 × 3.7 deg (37 dB). It can be fed by a PILOT LPI radar, although the radars sold thus far use conventional X-band systems.

Waveform, PRF, and pulse width can all be varied. The transmitter tube is a TWT. All versions are frequency-agile both in MTI (pulse-Doppler) and non-MTI modes. For air search, the radar operates in pulse-Doppler mode to reject clutter (C-band was chosen as the lowest frequency at which sea clutter could effectively be rejected: the longer the wavelength, the higher the clutter speed at which MTI begins to lose efficacy). For surface search, the radar transmits chirps that are pulse-compressed on reception for better range resolution. The operator can shift among four frequencies to avoid spot jamming. There is also a combined mode in which every two air-search scans are followed by a surface-search scan. Air targets are automatically detected and tracked; surface targets are manually detected and then autotracked. Finally, there is a narrow-pulse fire-control mode, in which the radar scans a narrow area around the target (splashes can be spotted with an accuracy of 1 deg and 20 m).

Sea Giraffe 50 and 50HC were indeed for FAC. For compactness, all the radar units are mounted in a single cabinet. Maximum range against a 0.1m² target (single scan, 50% probability of detection) is about 18–19 km; a 4m² target at low altitude can be detected at about 40 km by version 50 (45 km by 50HC). Accuracy is 0.3 deg in azimuth and 25 m in range; resolution is 1.7 deg in azimuth and 45 m in range.

Sea Giraffe 150HC was intended for larger attack craft, corvettes, and frigates. Maximum range against a 0.1m² sea-skimmer is about 27 km; against a 4m² airplane, about 63 km (Sea Giraffe 100 and 150 appear not to have sold).

Coastal Giraffe 75F is a new version, with an instrumented range of 75 km. The radar should be able to detect a 3m² target, flying at about 2000 m, at a range of about 100 km; a 0.1m² target flying at about 1000 m should be detectable at about 43 km.

The Ericsson-Marconi 3D radar (formerly ELSA) is now designated Sea Giraffe 150 3D or Sea Giraffe DCR. It can directly replace the current 150HC, an additional processing unit being added to the signal/data cabinet below decks. This radar scans in elevation (it rotates to scan in bearing), by phase shifting (by about 30 ferrites). Marconi is responsible for the antenna and beam-steering computer. The carbon-fiber antenna is electronically stabilized so that it weighs about one-third as much as a conventional 2D stabilized antenna. A sketch released by Marconi in 1989 showed 10 beams, providing solid coverage out to 60km range and up to a height of 20 km, the lower beams reaching greater ranges (i.e., provided with more energetic pulses). The drawing suggested a maximum elevation angle of about 85 deg, each beam being about 6 deg wide. This radar will scan at 30 rpm.

This project became Sea Giraffe DCR, for the new Swedish missile corvettes (YSM-2000 class). It is to retract when not in use. The antenna housing itself is a narrow-band pass material (using conducting patterns printed on its surface) which reduces the probability that an enemy radar can detect it, while remaining transparent to DCR emissions. Both the transmit and receive beams will be steerable, with several stacked receive beams per transmit beam. Beams will also be steerable in azimuth. Sea Giraffe DCR should be released for export in 1996.

Users: Australia (150HC in ANZAC class), Bahrein (50HC in *Al Muharaq* class, 50 in TNC 45 class), Canada (150HC in "City"-class frigates), Finland (150HC in *Rauma* class), Kuwait (Giraffe 50 on *Al Sanbouk,* 50HC on *Istiqlal*), Malaysia (150HC in new corvettes), New Zealand (150HC in ANZAC-class frigates), Singapore (150HC in *Victory* class), Sweden (50HC in *Stockholm, Norkopping, Carlskrona* classes; originally ordered for modernized *Spica II,* on trials September 1982; 150HC C/X version in *Goteborg* class), UAE (50HC in 62m corvettes, 50 in *Mubarraz* and TNC 45 classes). Canada and Singapore use a larger 150HC antenna, with four rather than three beams. The Australian, Finnish, New Zealand, and Swedish *Goteborg* class all use the C/X dual-band system, which may use a different antenna. Singapore uses Giraffe 100 for shore-based surveillance of the Singapore Straits. They are located at Bedok, Pedra Blanca, Raffles Lighthouse, St. John's Island, and Sultan Shoal lighthouse.

♦ 9GR600 (9LV Search Radar) and 9KR400/9KA500

Band: X (8700–9500 MHz, with 400–450 MHz bandwidth)
Beam: 1.1 × 7
Peak Power: 200 kW
Gain: 35.5 (38) dB
Pulse Width: (a) 1 microsec (b) 0.25 microsec
PRF: (a) 1000 (b) 3000 pps
Scan Rate: Up to 60 rpm
Antenna Dimensions: 2.1 × 0.3 m
Antenna Weight: 260 kg including turntable

Data refer to the radar with the 9GA209 antenna used in the 9LV200 FCS. This stabilized antenna can scan helically, elevating its beam to cover up to 40 deg vertically (20 deg vertically as used in the 9LV200 Mk 2 system). Elevation and scan are independent, so the operator can trade off coverage against data rate. The tunable-magnetron transmitter tunes at 1 kHz/sec.

The high scan rate was adopted for TWS operation (16 surface targets). A target is typically detected at 9 km and designated within 5 sec (at about 7.5 km).

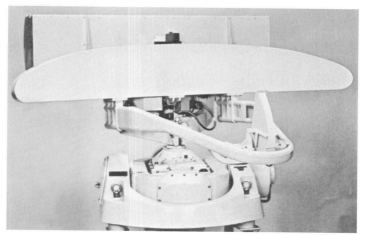

The 9LV search radar. (PEAB)

The same radar is the main sensor of the TORCI torpedo FCS (see the ASW section), using a stabilized 9GA202 antenna (2.1 × 0.56 m, beam 1.1 × 4 deg, gain 37 dB, weight 135 kg). An optional spiral-scanning feature (up to 20 deg elevation) adds 25 kg to the antenna weight. It seems unlikely that the analogous Subfar submarine torpedo FCS radar (9GA300 antenna) survives. Nor does it seem likely that the enlarged 9GA218 antenna, which added an L-band feed, was ever placed in service. For details, see the 1991/92 edition.

The standard Swedish fixed coast defense FCS, 9KA400 (Kastell), uses the 9KR400 Mareld radar, which is the same transmitter connected to a 9GA205 antenna (4.5 × 0.625 m, 0.6 × 4.5-deg beam, gain 40 dB, weight 225 kg, scan rate 40 rpm). This system also employs the same digital computer as in 9LV200 Mk 2. Mareld entered service in 1965, and a digital version became operational late in 1976. Sweden and at least four other countries (including Norway and Spain) ordered at least 70 Kastells, and Inisel produces the 9KA410 version under license. Mareld is the main sensor of the Swedish 9CSI600 STINA naval command system. It may be used by Yugoslavia for coastal surveillance.

9KA500 (Kardinal), the mobile version of 9KA400 Mk 3, uses a lightweight 2.3 × 0.55m antenna. With the transmitter described above, it produces a 1.2 × 4-deg beam (gain 36 dB). Substituting a 65-kW K-band transmitter (probably that of the 9LV200 tracker described below) narrows the beam to the dimensions of the shore-based X-band set, 0.7 × 2.2 deg (gain 42 dB). In each case, the horn-fed reflector scans at two speeds (ratio 1:2) in the 6–60-rpm range. In Swedish service, 9KA400 is designated ARTE 727; two equip each m/80 coastal battery.

◆ 9LV200 Tracker

> **Band:** Ku (bandwidth 670 MHz)
> **Beam:** 1.3 deg
> **Peak Power:** 65 kW
> **Gain:** 40 dB
> **Pulse Width:** 0.2 microsec
> **PRF:** About 2000 pps
> **Antenna Dimensions:** diameter 1 m

Data apply to the Mk 1/Mk 2 tracker. A TV, an IR camera, and a laser RF are typically mounted alongside the stabilized monopulse Cassegrain antenna, whose hydraulic drive can slew it at 85 deg/sec. Frequency can be shifted randomly on a pulse-to-pulse basis. Processing is pulse-Doppler/MTI. This tracker won the 1968 Swedish competition for a new FCS partly because its new type of motor and bearing promised very high tracking accuracy. The manufacturer estimates that multipath would begin to degrade tracking on a typical 0.1m² sea-skimmer (2–3 m altitude, speed about 650 kt) at about 6-km range, after which the system would have to switch to IR tracking. Typically the target symbol would be positioned on the IR display at about 4.8 km, with IR lock-on achieved at about 4.3 km.

The 9LV Mk 2 tracker. (PEAB)

The 9LV200 Mk 3 tracker (9GR400) employs a new Ku-band helix TWT wideband transmitter (peak power 1.5 kW, bandwidth more than 10%, with more than 100 frequencies) to replace the earlier spin-tuned magnetron. Radar waveform is automatically chosen; pulses are compressed in the receiver to 0.2 microsec (there are multiple pulse widths and PRFs). The new antenna has the same beamwidth but slightly increased gain

(41 dB); it has a new low-sidelobe feed. Receiver noise is reduced from 11 to 10 dB. Modes: pulse-Doppler, MTI, frequency-agile, fixed frequency.

EO units: TV (FOV 42 × 31 mrad), 8–12-micron IR camera (FOV 52 × 35 or 157 × 105 mrad), laser RF (NdYAG, 1.06 microns, peak power 4 MW, PRF 10 kHz). The TV/IR tracker follows either a centroid or an edge, with an accuracy of better than 0.15 mrad.

The 9LV Mk 3 tracker in the ANZAC frigates has X-band CWI added to Ku-band tracker; this version was intended also for the Danish *Nils Juels* class, to accommodate NATO Sea Sparrow. It uses an X-band Cassegrain with frequency-selective subreflector in front of the existing dish, so it passes Ku-band signals.

COAST DEFENSE

◆ 9KA100

BEAB's EO coastal-artillery FCS consists of a sighting unit (Kobra) and a ballistic computer. Kobra incorporates a laser range-finder, and the pedestal can carry an LLLTV or an IR imager. This device is used to supplement the heavier 9KA400 and 9KA500 and also, as a stand-alone unit, to modernize older fixed or mobile coastal-defense batteries. At least 20 have been ordered, for use in Sweden and abroad.

OPTRONIC SYSTEMS

◆ TVT-300/EOS-400/EOS-450/EOS-500

Saab's series of gyrostabilized optronic directors is based on the manned TVT-300 (TV camera tracker). The pedestal carries a TV camera on one side and a monitor on the other, the above-decks operator acquiring the target. Once the target is in view, the below-decks operator places contrast-tracking gates around it by joystick. Alternatively, the director can be slewed to a radar-indicated bearing. Elevation limits are +85/−30 deg; train/elevation rates are 40 deg/sec. The director weighs 115 kg; below-decks units are the 25-kg tracker and the 20-kg control unit, including the TV screen.

TVT-300, a television sight. (Saab)

EOS-400 (announced 1979, but redesigned and remarketed in 1983) eliminates the above-decks monitor altogether in favor of a laser ranger (plus an optional FLIR). Slew and elevation rates increase to 150 deg/sec; director weight increases to 220 kg (plus 450 kg below decks). This system can control up to two weapons, using ballistics in its associated microcomputer. The digital correlation tracker can deal with contrasts as poor as 5%. The below-decks operator can manually track by joystick, or the system can autotrack; it also has a memory mode in which it projects ahead the position of a target temporarily obscured, for

EOS-400. (Saab)

The 9LV100 optronic director, carrying an IR camera and gyro (*left*), a laser range-finder (*upper right*), and a television camera (*lower right*). The most basic version of the director lacks the IR camera. (PEAB)

example, by trees. There is an optional surface surveillance mode.

Reaction time: locks on in 1–2 sec, calculates gun data for an approaching low flier in 3 sec; maximum slew time (180 deg) is 3 sec. In 23-km visibility, a target occupying 1% of the full picture frame (contrast 60%) can be tracked out to 23 km with accuracy 0.4 mrad.

Sensors: TV (300mm focal length, FOV 40 × 30 mrad); laser (NdYAG, PRF 10 Hz, maximum range 20 km; range accuracy 4 m for ranges less than 5 km, 5 m beyond).

An updated version, intended to control the Bofors Trinity/3P weapon, was adopted for the Brazilian *Niteroi* upgrade. It carries new sensors: a Saab CCD TV camera, a GEC V3800 FLIR, and a new eye-safe laser RF. New clutter-reduction software takes it close to the IRST class, since it can now automatically detect and acquire targets. The digital tracker has been replaced. The system has a new color display, for quicker target acquisition by its operator. This version can handle several engagements (by different guns) simultaneously.

A new EOS-450, announced at the DSA 96 show, is based on the upgraded version of EOS-400, and can handle more simultaneous engagements.

EOS-500, which predates EOS-450, is a more sophisticated version of EOS-400. It accepts target designation. On coming onto the designated bearing, the operator scans vertically (by joystick) to acquire the target, manually tracking it until it comes within a gate and the system begins to autotrack.

Users:

TVT-300: Brazil (training ship *Brazil*), Norway (*Oslo, Hauk, Storm, Vidar* classes); and possibly Singapore (110ft Type B class)

EOS-400: Brazil (*Inhauma* class [planned], upgraded version chosen in *Niteroi* modernization), Finland (*Turunmaa* and *Helsinki* classes)

EOS-500: Sweden (coast defense)

FIRE-CONTROL SYSTEMS

LV indicates antiair warfare (luftvarn).

◆ 9LV100 Series

BEAB's (formerly PEAB's) small patrol boat EO FCS uses the same sensors as Saab's TVT-300; it can also accommodate a Philips 8–13-micron USFA IR camera. It is based on the Swedish army's KALLE 40mm/70 FCS. On board ships, the cueing sensor

is an unstabilized S-band navigational radar. In KALLE land tests, average reaction time was about 5 sec, and a 40mm/70 was able to place 80% of 300 rnd within lethal radius (5.5 m) of a target at 2–3 km.

This system was announced in 1977 and thus was developed after 9LV200.

Users: Bahrein (FPB 38), Finland (*Pohjanmaa*), Sweden (*Stockholm, Landsort*).

◆ 9LV200 Series

The 9LV200 FCS was designed to meet a 1968 Royal Swedish Navy requirement to replace (and hence is broadly equivalent to) Signaal's M22 installed on board the Swedish *Spica* class; it was selected in 1969. It combines an X-band target acquisition/ surface TWS radar with a separate Ku-band air tracker (see above for separate radar details).

The 9LV200 Mk 3 director, with television, laser, and IR camera (*left*). (PEAB)

The Danish missile boat *Bille* is equipped with a 9LV200 FCS, including the 9GA208 search antenna (on the masthead platform). The slotted waveguide is designated NWS-2 in the Danish navy. (L. van Ginderen)

Mk 1 employs a fixed-program digital computer like that of the Signaal M-series "eggs." Mk 2 substitutes a programmable P800 digital computer. The associated torpedo FCS for Mk 1/2 is TORCI (see the ASW section for details). Mk 2.5 introduced a new high-level RTL 2 software language. Mk 3 (called 9LV Mk 3 rather than 9LV200 Mk 3) introduces new sensors (a C-band pulse-compression search radar and a new tracker) and unifies FCS and CDS in a distributed architecture (see the CDS section for details). One effect of distribution is to provide separate (multiple, if desired) air and surface (gun control) channels.

Unlike the Signaal minicombat system, Mk 1 or Mk 2 is normally connected to a separate EPLO CDS (a typical fast-attack boat has both a three-operator EPLO console and individual 9LV200 consoles, each with a 12in CRT, for AA and antisurface gun control and, if necessary, torpedo control).

In Mk 1/2, the main displays are a 12in PPI and a north-stabilized relative-motion 12in display in the main control space, a 16in true-motion PPI for surface targets, and a TV screen (for the optical sensor mounted alongside the tracker dish). Air targets are designated from the 12in PPI. Surface targets are designated from the PPI to a B-scope (for rate-aided tracking) or to the main search radar's TWS memory. The system can, therefore, track and engage one surface and one air target simultaneously. The fall of shot against a surface target can be observed on either the B-scope or the television (in this case using the tracker's A-scope to detect misses in range). As track quality (against a low-altitude target) degrades due to multipath, the system operator manually shifts to the IR sensor mounted alongside the radar tracker dish.

PEAB also marketed a larger-ship equivalent to Mk 2, 9LV400, but the only installation was on board the Swedish training ship *Carlskrona*, which has two CICs, one duplicating that of a *Hugin* and the other that of a *Stockholm*. An ASW version of 9LV400 was planned for the *Goteborg* class, but instead they have the distributed 9LV450, a form of 9LV200 Mk 3. The 9LV450 series designation was also applied to the Mk 3 system for the ANZAC frigates.

Users:

Mk 1: Denmark (*Nils Juels* class [RAKEL 203], *Willemoes* class [RAKEL 203]), Malaysia (*Spica-M* class: 9LV212), Norway (9LV218 in *Nordkapp* class), Sweden (*Norkopping* class [ARTE 722]), Yugoslavia (early units of the *Rade Koncar* class [9LV202]). ARTE means Artilleriedling. RAKEL means Radar Kanoneldledning.

Mk 2: Bahrein (*Ahmad al Fateh* class [9LV223]), Croatia (*King Petar Kresimir IV* class [9LV249]), Finland (*Pohjanmaa*, *Helsinki* class [9LV225]), Iraq (*Ibn Khaldum*), Kuwait (FPB 57 and TNC 45 [9LV228]), Norway (*Oslo* class), Oman (*Nasr el Bahr*), Sweden (*Stockholm* class [ARTE 726E], *Hugin* class [ARTE 726], *Alvsborg* class), UAE (FPB 65 class, *Baniyas* class), Yugoslavia (9LV249 in later units of *Rade Koncar* class). Introduced 1977.

Mk 2.5: Versions include 9LV230 (Malaysian *Musytari*).

Mk 3: Australia (ANZAC class [as 9LV453]), Denmark (StanFlex 300), Finland (*Helsinki II* class), New Zealand (ANZAC class [as 9LV453]), Oman (9LV207 EO system ordered March 1995 for Project Mawj [Super P400] patrol boats), Sweden (*Goteborg* class [part of 9LV450]). Development began late in 1980 and was completed in 1985, the first production contract (for the *Goteborg* class) following in December 1985.

◆ 9LV300 Series

This WCS for 250–400t vessels, manufactured by PEAB, consists of 9LV200 plus 9LV100. This system can handle two air targets simultaneously; its search radar operates in TWS mode to control antiship missiles.

Users: Bahrein (FPB 44 class [9LV331]), Oman ("Province" class [9LV307], but not in *Dhofar*), Sweden (*Stockholm* [as ARTE 726E]).

SWITZERLAND

◆ Denezy/M-46/CGS-1

The four Danish *Falster*-class minelayers, completed in the 1960s, use this Contraves FCS to control their 3in/50 guns (the Turkish *Falster* uses U.S. Mk 63s with SPG-34 radars). An additional system was installed at the Danish naval training base. This project, the first full Contraves naval system, was code-named Denezy within Contraves, and the designations M-46 and CGS-1 have been published; they are presumably Royal Danish Navy designations. The system consists of X-band conscan trackers, with unique six-axis stabilization, and a below-decks analog predictor, using the Contraves computing capacitor. The

An M-46 FCS radar is shown (*left*) on board the Danish minelayer *Moen*, March 1990. Note the bellows covering its stabilized base. The slotted waveguide is a Danish NWS-2. The radomes on the yardarm at the same level probably covered the spinner antennas of a WLR-1, since removed. (L. van Ginderen).

trackers are probably those used later in Sea Hunter. This system competed with the contemporary Signaal M40 series. Previous Contraves naval work, from the early 1950s on, had been at the subsystem level for the French, German, Japanese, and U.S. navies.

◆ Sea Hunter 4

Contraves and Contraves Italiana developed this FCS in the mid-1960s; it was first installed on board the modernized Iranian destroyer *Damavand* in 1967. Like the roughly contemporary Signaal M-series egg, with which it unsuccessfully competed, it combined an earlier tracker (M-46, see above) with a co-located search antenna (TWS against surface targets) sharing a common radar transmitter (X-band, 180 kW, randomly variable PRF about 2000 pps, pulse widths 0.5 and 0.27 microsec [the tracker operates only at 0.27 microsec]). In the surviving installation, on board Iranian frigates, only the upper of the two trackers carries the search antenna. The lower tracker is used to track targets for the Sea Killer antiship missile (the system includes a separate small masthead dish transmitting the beam-riding guidance signal of the Sea Killer missile). The suffix "4" refers to four-axis stabilization (roll, pitch, bearing, elevation).

The conscan tracker uses a 100cm paraboloid (2.2-deg beam, total 4.4-deg cover when tracking by conscan); the search antenna is a 2m slotted waveguide feeding a cylindrical hog-trough antenna (1×30-deg csc^2 beam, scan rate 20–50 rpm [continuously variable]). Note that the tracker is not, as is sometimes

Sea Hunter 4 on board an Iranian Vosper-Thornycroft frigate, with a separate search antenna. Both tracker mounts carry Sea Killer command antennas. (Contraves)

reported, the Selenia RTN-10X; it is Contraves' own design. A $3m^2$ target can be acquired at 45 km (Swerling Case I) and tracked at 40 km.

As in M-46 (and the land-based Super Fledermaus), the analog ballistic computer uses Contraves' computing capacitor. It is shared by two system consoles, one for air targets (using the main tracker), the other for surface targets (using the search radar in TWS mode). An additional console, connected to the lower tracker, is used for Sea Killer control; it also contains a television and joystick for optical command guidance. This channel could also control Sea Cat AA missiles (which have now been replaced by 23mm guns). Because this console lacks a separate ballistic computer, it cannot be used as an alternative channel to control guns.

User: Iran (*Saam*-class frigates).

◆ Seaguard/Sea Hawk/LSEOS

Contraves' modular digital FCS is, in effect, the company's successor to Sea Hunter. Development began late in 1977 and the system was announced at the beginning of 1980; all modules had been tested in prototype form by mid-1982. Sea Hawk (and now LSEOS) is the purely optronic equivalent. Each module contains its own Contraves proprietary 16-bit bit-slice CORA computer, its processor comparable to a 68000 series chip. A proprietary Contraves bus ties together a target-acquisition radar (the Siemens-Plessey Dolphin/AWS-6: see separate entry, as the SRM search module), a three-axis stabilized tracker (TM module, see below), weapon modules, and a common support module (CSM). Each tracker has its own control console. The CSM connects the system to its target-acquisition radar and to the host ship's CDS. As a stand-alone system, Seaguard has its own command console (CCM), with a 24in CRT, for threat-evaluation/weapon assignment. Each weapon has its own weapons-control module, carrying its ballistics. A separate surface engagement console (SEC), controlling the 5in gun and Sea Sparrow missiles, is used on board Turkish MEKO Track IIA frigates. The bus architecture is designed so that, like the Swedish 9LV Mk 3, it can be expanded into a WCS/CDS (Cosys).

This combination can control Contraves' quadruple 25mm gun (Sea Zenith 25), but in the Indian *Delhi* class it will control Russian guns, and in the Saudi *Sandown* class it controls an Emerlec 30 gun. The modular structure of the system allows it to use alternative target designation radars and trackers.

The alternative Contraves trackers are:

TMK (Ku-band Siemens-Albis radar [1.23m dish, 0.9-deg beam, 85 kW, 0.08 microsec pulses], elevation limits $+120/-30$ deg from an axis canted to the horizon, track rate 172 deg/sec in

The main external elements of the Seaguard system, on display at RNEE, 1989; the Dolphin acquisition radar, the radar director, and the four-barrel 25mm gun, capable of pointing up to the zenith and very agile. (Author)

Contraves's LSEOS Mk III lightweight director, at the 1993 Navy League Show. (Author)

three axes [train, cant angle to the horizon, and antenna elevation relative to the cant angle], 1350 kg above/1350 kg below decks).

TMK/EO: TMK combined with an 8–11.5 micron FLIR (FOV 3 ×2 deg, with a centroid tracker) and a laser RF (1.06 microns, 13-nanosec pulses, 25 pps).

TMX (X-band, 1.315m dish, 31-mrad beam, 2 or 4 kW, 0.4–4-microsec pulses, tracking range 0.3–45/70 km, 1200 kg above/ 1300 kg below decks).

TMX/KA-CW (1.4m dish; X-band TWT radar [1.7-deg beam, 25 kW, 0.3/1.65 microsec compressed/uncompressed pulses, tracking range 0.3–70 km] and Ka-band TWT radar [0.5-deg beam, 75 kW, 0.13/3.7-microsec pulses, tracking range 0.3–20 km], sharing a common antenna). Weight: 1440 kg above/1390 kg below decks. The CW suffix indicates CW injection for semiactive missile guidance. A related TMX/TV-CW replaces the Ka-band radar with a TV.

TMEO/Sea Hawk (7.5–11-micron FLIR [FOVs 20 × 15 or 2.7 × 2.0 deg; resolution 0.11 mrad] or TV [FOVs 31 × 23 or 3.1 × 2.3 deg] plus laser RF [1.57 microns, 1–3 pps]; elevation limits +80/ −20 deg, train/elevation rates 74.5 deg/sec; weights 230 kg above/490 kg below decks). The biaxially stabilized pedestal can also carry a W-band radar.

Sea Hawk Mk II, announced in 1990, uses Contraves Pittsburgh EO components (zoom TV, diagonal FOVs 26 to 2.6 deg; 8–12-micron FLIR [FOVs 12 × 8 and 3.16 × 2.1 deg], and NdYAG laser [1-mrad beam, 10 pps, range limits 280–20,500 m]). Elevation limits are +80/−30 deg; train/elevation rates are 1.3 rad/ sec (2.6 rad/sec available). The pedestal weighs 310 kg (total 990 kg) and requires 1.5 m of swing clearance. It and the below-decks components (weapons-control module and weapons-control console) are connected by a 1553 bus. Mk IIA is a modified version replacing the CORA CPU with a 68030. This was an unsuccessful competitor for the *Arleigh Burke*–class EO FCS.

LSEOS Mk III, a Sea Hawk Mk II successor announced by Contraves Pittsburgh in 1993; total weight is reduced to about 450 kg (180 kg above decks). Like Mk IIA, this version uses a 68030 microprocessor and an updated architecture.

See below (under guns) for details of the Sea Zenith gun associated with Seaguard.

Users: India (trackers for *Trishul* system in *Delhi* class), Saudi Arabia (*Sandown* class [Sea Hawk II optronic director]), Turkey (MEKO I and IIB [TMK/EO] and IIA [TMX/TV-CW plus TMK/

EO] frigates), United States (a version of Sea Hawk II without ballistics, for surveillance in an unnamed program). In the Turkish Track IIA frigates, TMX/TV-EO replaces a Signaal WM 25, but the IIB ships revert to STIR 1.8 for the surface and Sea Sparrow engagement role. Seaguard trackers are made in China for the PRC army and, presumably, for the navy. The unnamed customer for whom a missile tracker is being developed is probably India. As of mid-1996, Mk III had been produced in prototype form and tested at Dahlgren. Mk IIA and Mk III are currently on offer.

TAIWAN (ROC)

Taiwan makes the SPG-24 fire-control radar, which is used on board fast patrol boats armed with Hsiung Feng I missiles. Reportedly, the U.S. contractor for the SPG-24 program was ABA. The main developmental problem was conversion of the radar from analog to digital processing. CS/SPG-24 has replaced HR-76 in some coastal-defense units.

The SPG-24 radar on board a Taiwanese (GRC) *Hai Ou*–class missile boat. The slotted waveguide above is UPS-60. There is a periscope in the foreground. (Fu S. Mei)

Taiwan also manufactures a UPS-60 navigational radar using a small X-band slotted-waveguide antenna. The initial batch, to equip missile-firing boats, was 57 radars, and more have been ordered. UPS-600 is a larger (and presumably lower-frequency) surface-search set, possibly derived from the U.S. SPS-64. At least 15 SPS-64s have been bought for coastal surveillance. UPS-60(X)C is employed with mobile coastal-defense units.

UNITED KINGDOM

RADARS

◆ **Type 262/GWS 21**

This X-band (30 kW, 20/200 microsec pulses at 1500 pps, 5-deg beam) conscan radar feeds an angular-rate FCS comparable to the U.S. Mk 63. A target is typically acquired at 7 kyd and tracked at 5 kyd. The sole surviving application is the GWS 21 Sea Cat missile FCS, the radar tracking the incoming target while the operator controls the outgoing missile with a joystick.

◆ **Type 275/FPS 5**

This S-band conscan radar (two 4ft dishes, 6-deg beam, 400 kW, 0.25/0.5/0.75 microsec at 500 pps) equips the British Mk 6 director. A target is acquired at 36 kyd and tracked at 30 kyd. The associated FPS 5 FCS (Flyplane Predictor System) can handle range limits of 500–15,000 yd, and shell time of flight of up to 30 sec. Target speeds can be up to 700 kt (70 kt for surface targets). The tracker can handle rates of train and elevation up to 10 deg/sec; the predictor can generate 45 deg/sec in bearing and 25 deg/sec in elevation.

Users: Bangladesh (*Leopard* class).

◆ **Type 277/278**

These S-band nodding height-finders use an 8ft spherical paraboloid antenna (ANU) with clipped sides (4.5 × 2.2-deg beam). Type 278 (500–750 kW, 0.5 or 2 microsec/500 pps) is controlled by a ship's CDS computer. A bomber at 1000 ft can be detected at, respectively, 40 and 60 nm; at 20,000 ft, ranges are 55 and 70 nm.

Users: Chile ("County" class).

Type 901 radar. The gathering beam is on the other side. (R. Cheung)

The Chilean Type 901s have been modernized with solid-state components, reportedly with foreign (probably U.S.) assistance. This program is associated with the Sea Slug upgrade described below.

◆ **Type 903/904/MRS 3/GWS 22**

Band: X (8.5–9.05 or 9.05–9.6 GHz)
Beam: 2 deg
PRF: 3000 pps
Pulse Width: 0.1 microsec

This X-band conscan fire-control radar, used in the MRS 3 system, was based on the U.S. Mk 35 (which is described below). Data given here apply to the Mod 1 version, as used in MRS 3. Scanning was spiral (to acquire targets) or conical (for tracking). Minimum range was 32.8 yd, and maximum lock-on range was 29,500 yd. Range accuracy was 10 yd, and targets could be resolved within 1 deg or 25 yd. Typical preset range rates in the MRS 3 system were 180 yd/sec (closing) in AA mode, or 22 yd/sec in the surface-fire mode. The director could turn 100 deg/sec when being run in to a designated target.

Type 278 radar, on board a "County"-class missile destroyer (second series). (R. Cheung)

◆ **Type 901**

Band: X (9–10 GHz)
Beam: 0.9 deg
Peak Power: 750 kW
Gain: 24 dB
Pulse Width: 0.2 or 0.3 microsec
PRF: 1840 pps
Scan: Conical, 2 deg at 30 scans/sec
Antenna Diameter: 9 ft

Data above apply to the earliest version of Type 901, which had a maximum range of 60,000 yd. The associated gathering beam was 7.4 deg wide, scanning over a cone 18.8 deg wide, at a peak power of 250 kW (0.1-microsec pulses).

The missile-guidance radar for the Sea Slug system survives in the Chilean navy. The antenna is stabilized in roll and pitch. It scans conically or in a rosette pattern, and it also generates a secondary (transmitted only) missile-guidance beam. The associated computer coordinates the beams. A third (gathering) beam is generated by a small horn on the right-hand side of the nacelle (the gathering radar was originally designated Type 902).

A single radar can guide two missiles along the same beam, using pulse coding (the radar tracks the missiles by transponder).

MRS 3 director, HMS *Diamond*, resembles the U.S. Mk 56. The radar is Type 903. (A. Raven)

Type 903's development began about 1946, and the radar entered service in 1958. Type 904 is a modified version for Sea Cat missile control, as part of the GWS 22 system.

The associated MRS 3, which became the standard British postwar FCS, was adapted from the U.S. Mk 56. An electromechanical predictor (like that developed for Flyplane, FPS 5) was substituted for the U.S. mechanical linkage of Mk 56. That carried a space and weight penalty, but it also made for easier changes in ballistic. The predictor is most effective between 3000 and 5000 yd. Work began in 1948, and MRS 3 entered service in 1958. A Mod 3 update program began in 1962, and about half of all MRS 3 were updated with solid-state electronics in 1974–78. GWS 22 is MRS 3 adapted for Sea Cat blind-fire control. It entered service in 1962. The follow-on GWS 24 is the WSA-4 system (using the RTN-10X radar) on the Brazilian *Niteroi* class (the British version is becoming extinct as the Pakistan navy modernizes its Type 21 frigates).

Users: Chile ("County" class and *Leander* class), Ecuador (904/GWS 22 in *Leanders*), India (*Nilgiri*), Indonesia ("Tribal" class), New Zealand (*Waikato*), and Pakistan (*Leander* class). *Leanders* (other than Ecuador) have both 903/MRS 3 *and* 904/GWS 22.

◆ Type 909

Type 909 is the tracking and illuminating radar for the Sea Dart missile system; in destroyers it is also used for 4.5in gunfire control. Each ship has two radars. Type 909 is normally radome-enclosed but may be seen uncovered when ships are undergoing alignment trials. It is relatively heavy and, reportedly, unreliable. Some Type 909 radars are being replaced by Type 909I with a more reliable transmitter. Dish diameter is 2.4 m.

A Type 909 radome, HMS *Glasgow*. The ship in the background is HMS *Cumberland*. (Author)

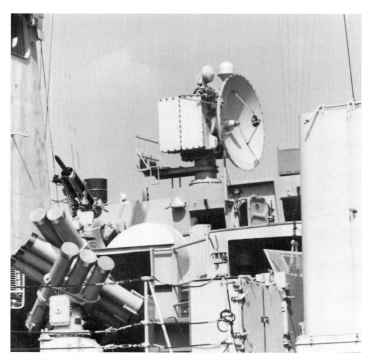

Type 909 with the radome removed. (R. Cheung)

Type 910 Sea Wolf control radar on board HMS *Brazen*, 1984. (R. Cheung)

Users: Argentina (Type 42 destroyers), United Kingdom (*Invincible*-class carriers and Type 42 destroyers).

◆ Type 910/Type 911

Sea Wolf directors track both target and missile, transmitting command signals to minimize the angle between their paths. In the original Type 910, the target tracker was an X-band pulse-Doppler radar (1.6m dish, beam about 1.5 deg) flanked by a pair of 80cm dishes, one tracking the missile and the other carrying command links (probably both in Ku-band). Between the main antenna and the two dishes is a transmitting horn with a monopulse cluster, to gather the missile for initial guidance. The missile is tracked using signals from antennas in two of its wings (the other two receive commands).

The director also carries a TV differential tracker, using a flare in the missile's tail, and (as modernized) a manually controlled IR tracker.

Type 911 is a lighter-weight alternative derived from the Marconi ST805SW. The X-band pulse-Doppler tracker on its left side uses a twist-Cassegrain, narrow-beam reflector with a monopulse feed. The two right-hand Ku-band antennas are replaced by a single dish (an offset folded Cassegrain reflector with a steerable sub-reflector). It tracks the missile and transmits commands (which are emitted by a drum-shaped device behind it). The cluster-gathering antenna is retained. No EO tracker is fitted, as it would have required additional operators. Weight: 1725 kg above/2155 kg below decks.

Type 911 Sea Wolf control radar on board HMS *Cumberland*, 1990. (Author)

Type 911 may be superseded by ST1805SW (see below).
Users:

Type 910: Brazil (Type 22 Batch I frigates), United Kingdom (Type 22 Batch II frigates *Boxer* and *Beaver*)
Type 911(1): GWS 25 Mod 3 in Type 22 Batch II frigates (HMS *Brave* and later) and Type 22 Batch III frigates
Type 911(2): Vertically launched Sea Wolf in Type 23 frigates

◆ **Type 965/966**

Band: P (about 1.4 m)
Beam: 12 × 40 deg
Peak Power: 450 kW
Gain: 20 dB
Pulse Width: (a) 3.8 (b) 10 microsec
PRF: (a) 400 (b) 200 pps
Scan Rate: 8 or 10 rpm (depending on whether the power supply is 50 or 60 cycle)
Antenna Dimensions: 26 ft × 8 ft 11 in (or 16 ft 9 in) × 6 ft 1 in
Antenna Weight: 2425 or 5480 lb

Type 965 was the standard British long-range air-search radar of the 1960s, adopted in place of the roughly contemporary U.S. SPS-6, partly because U.S. trials showed that its UHF frequency would be more effective than L-band in detecting fast jet aircraft. The disadvantage was (and is) too broad a beam for precision. There are two alternative "bedstead" antennas (in effect, squintless horn arrays), AKE(1) and AKE(2), the latter in effect two AKE(1)s superimposed. Each of the 8 or 16 array elements is shaped as a reflector horn surrounding a loop dipole.

Type 965 radar (AKE-1 antenna, seen from behind). The "candlesticks" on the yardarms are UHF radio antennas, in this case either receiving or transmitting (the double candlestick carries both antennas). (Author)

Type 965 was adopted as a frigate radar in 1955, and the "double bedstead" followed as a radar picket or missile destroyer set in 1957. The latter offers much more nearly gapless vertical coverage; Type 965 coverage breaks into three widely separated lobes.

Reportedly, this radar performed poorly in the Falklands because, without MTI, it was unable to detect Argentine aircraft approaching from overland. A modified version with crude MTI, 965M, has been reported. Type 966, which may be a private designation, is Type 965 with a modernized transmitter/receiver (but with the same antenna), which Marconi advertised in the mid-1980s.

Type 965 was superseded in British service by Type 1022.

Users: Argentina (Type 42s), Bangladesh (*Leopard* class), Chile ("County" class and *Leanders*), Ecuador (*Leanders*), India (*Viraat*), Indonesia ("Tribal" class), Pakistan (*Leanders*). This set is extinct in the Royal Navy. The Type 42s and the "County" class have the "double-beadstead" AKE(2) antenna.

◆ **Type 967/968**

Type 967
Band: L (1260–1360 MHz)
Beam: 4.6 × 68.6 deg (est.)
Peak Power: 50–60 kW
Pulse Width: 6 microsec
PRF: 7320 staggered

Back-to-back Type 967/968 radars at the masthead of the British Type 22 frigate HMS *Cumberland*, 1990. The antenna halfway down the mast is a Type 1007 surface-search set. The flat oblong visible near the base of the mast is used to calibrate the ship's forward Sea Wolf director. The array of directional antennas surrounding the mast beneath the 967/968 platform serves the UAA-1 ESM system; several small radomes on yards are omnidirectional antennas (for IFM) for the same system. Near the base of the mast is a DS-30B gun. (Author)

Type 968
Band: S (2950–3040 MHz)
Beam: 2 × 30 deg
Peak Power: 3 MW
Gain: 30 dB
Pulse Width: 2 microsec
PRF: 750 pps
Scan Rate: 30 rpm (max)
Antenna Dimensions: 4 × 1 m

Marconi's Sea Wolf search-and-acquisition radar consists of two units arranged back to back that designate to the Type 910 target tracker. Type 967 is an L-band pulse-Doppler automatic-detection air-search radar; Type 968 is an S-band radar for low air cover and surface search. Type 968 is basically a repackaged 992; 967 is similar in principle to SPS-58/65. The Type 967 antenna contains the Type 1010 IFF interrogator. Signals from both radars are fed into a common Ferranti FM1600B computer, which evaluates targets, decides to engage, and feeds target coordinates into the tracker. All Type 967 have now been made frequency-agile, as Type 967M.

The antenna is fully stabilized.

In the new "Duke"-class frigates (Type 23), the more compact 996 was selected over 967/968.

Users: Brazil (Type 22 frigates), United Kingdom (Type 22 frigates).

♦ Type 975

Band: X
Beam: 1.2 × 25 deg
Peak Power: 50 kW
Pulse Width: 0.17 or 0.32 microsec
PRF: 1100 pps
Scan Rate: 20–24 rpm
Antenna Dimensions: 6 or 10 ft

Kelvin-Hughes's surface-search and seaward-defense radar, a modified 14/12, was replaced in British service by Type 1006. Minimum range is less than 35 yd. Range discrimination is 35 or 70 yd, depending on pulse width.

Users: Australia (*Adams* class and *Derwent*), Bangladesh (*Leopard* class and *Umar Farooq*), Chile ("County" and *Leander* classes), India (*Nilgiri*), Indonesia ("Tribal" class), Malaysia (*Hang Tuah*), New Zealand (*Waikato*). Type 14/9 (commercial equivalent): Germany (*Adams* class, Type 331, *Rhein* class, Type 701 replenishment ships, Type 760 ammunition ships, Type 740 AGI *Holnis*, Type 720/722 tugs, KW 15–class air-sea rescue craft, *Neustadt*-class patrol boats), Greece (*Thetis* class [ex-German] and AGI *Hermis* [may have 14/7]), Malta (Yugoslav Type 131 class), Mauretania (*Neustadt* class), Mexico (*Fletcher*, ex-U.S. APDs, ex-minesweepers), Portugal (*San Roque* and *Albatroz* classes), Saudi Arabia (probably Type 141 class), Turkey (*Koln*, Type 141, *Rhein*, and *Angeln* classes and AGI *Yunus* [may have 14/7]), Yugoslavia (Type 131 coastal patrol craft).

♦ Type 978

Band: X
Beam: 1.2 × 21 deg
Peak Power: 40 kW
Pulse Width: (a) 0.2 (b) 1.0 microsec
PRF: (a) 1000 (b) 500 pps
Scan Rate: 24 rpm

Obsolescent and being replaced, Type 978 was designed by Decca as a Royal Navy high-definition surface-warning radar. It uses a double cheese antenna (outfit ATZ), whose upper half transmits and lower half receives.

Users: Australia ("Ton" class), India ("Ham"-class minesweepers), Indonesia ("Tribal"-class frigates), Malaysia (*Hang Tuah*), and South Africa ("Ton"-class minesweepers). The Japanese OPS-9 is a version of this radar, with a very different antenna.

♦ Type 992

Band: S
Beam: 1.4 × 32 deg
Peak Power: 2 MW
Gain: 30 dB
Pulse Width: 2.0 microsec

PRF: 750 pps (833 pps in 992P)
Scan Rate: 15 rpm
Antenna Dimensions: 6.4 m
Antenna Weight: 640 kg

Data are for 992Q.

Marconi's target-indication radar is the last of a long series. The original Type 992 had a cheese antenna; 992M introduced a new transmitter (gaining about 30% in range), and 992P introduced the current slotted-waveguide antenna (gaining another 30% in range). All surviving versions use this antenna. It is not clear whether Argentine and Chilean ships have 992R or the improved 992Q. The sole remaining British set is probably the 3-MW solid-state 992R. It may incorporate an MTI kit offered about 1981. The successor radar in British service is Type 996.

Type 992 can be synchronized with other radars (probably mainly 278) in pulse and in rotation, for quick target designation. Scan rate was originally 45 rpm for target indication, 15 rpm for search (to get more paints on a target). Effective range on an air target is probably 80 or 90 nm.

Type 992 on board HMS *Ark Royal*, 1990, with the UAA-1 DF array below it. The four small radomes on the ends of the short yards below the antenna platform are the omnidirectional antennas of UAA-1, for IFM. The "candlesticks" on the longer yards are UHF radio antennas. (Author)

Users: Argentina (Type 42 class), Chile ("County" class, *Zentano, Baquedano*), United Kingdom (destroyer *Birmingham*).

♦ Type 993

The short-range Type 993 S-band target indicator or search radar (550–750 kW, 0.5- or 2-microsec pulses/400–500 pps) uses a quarter-cheese antenna (outfit AKD, beam 2 × 30 deg, scan rate 24 rpm). In this design the feed horn does not obscure the main radar beam, so that the beam is better defined, even over a broad tuning band. A bomber flying at 20,000 ft can be detected at 35 nm, and a carrier at 30 nm; minimum range is 160 or 640 yd, depending on pulse width.

Users: Bangladesh (*Leopard* class), India (*Nilgiri*), New Zealand (*Waikato*).

♦ Type 996/AWS-9

Band: 2850–3100 MHz
Peak Power: 60–80 kW
Pulse Width: 1.8–2.2, 20 microsec
PRF: 700–800 pps
Scan Rate: 14 rpm

Data are unofficial estimates.

Siemens-Plessey's Type 996 is now the standard British target indication radar; AWS-9 is the export version. Reportedly based on AWS-5, it won a 1983 design contest and entered service in

The radar has three different modes (it replaces both 992 and 967/968):

> Normal, combined long-range surveillance for air-picture compilation and target indication for Sea Wolf missiles (maximum tracking range on a fighter is over 115 km);
> Missile mode (optimized against sea-skimmers);
> Long-range mode (power is concentrated in long pulses in the bottom beam, and an MPA can be tracked beyond 150 km).

The three antennas visible on top of the main 996 antenna serve a Doppler DF used to localize jammers (see the Electronic Warfare section in the introduction). The measured bearing appears as a strobe on a special double parallel index plot (DPIP) in the ship's CIC; information from other 996s received via data link can be displayed to obtain cross-bearings.

AWS-9 is the commercial version (without the Doppler DF). Weight: 1090-kg masthead, 2700 kg below decks. The AWS-9 (2D) version for Norway has been described as a 2.5-D radar, since it provides limited elevation data using a few stacked beams. It employs coherent Doppler processing followed by automatic target detection and tracking. The latter process uses two different hypotheses (presumably air and surface) to correlate targets on a scan-to-scan basis and thus to construct tracks. There are two color consoles (one for the picture compiler, one for the ship's gunnery officer) using the software of the Odin CDS air-picture subsystem, and the new radar picture is also displayed on the CO console in CIC (which can also show the Link 11 and MSI-3100 CDS pictures). This subsystem will be linked directly to the ship's Sea Sparrow missile and her LLLTV and optical sight; there will also be links to the IFF and to the chaff launcher. An Ethernet will link AWS-9 to Link 11, and new interfaces will connect Link 11 with MSI-3100. Factory acceptance tests of the first radar were due in May 1996, with installation in the summer of 1996 and sea trials in December 1996, with the last unit installed and on trials in September 1997.

Total program cost of 37 Type 996 radars was £144M, or about £3.6M each (about $9M each).

Users: Norway (AWS-9[2D] for *Oslo*-class upgrade, replacing MPD-45), Turkey (AWS-9 in Track II frigates; first export sale), United Kingdom (*Invincible* [996/1], Type 23 [996/2], and Type 42 [996/1] classes). Planned installation in the British *Fort Victoria*–class AOR was canceled when the planned Sea Wolf installation was deleted.

◆ **Type 1006/Type 1007**

Band: X (9445 MHz)
Beam: (a) 1×18 deg (b) 0.75×18 deg
Peak Power: 25 kW
Gain: (a) 31 dB (b) 34 dB
Pulse Width: (a) 0.08 or 0.25 (b) 0.75 microsec
PRF: (a) 1600 (b) 800 pps
Scan Rate: 24 rpm
Antenna Dimensions: (a) 2.4 m (b) 3.1 m

Data apply to Type 1006.

Kelvin-Hughes's Model 19/9A was developed for the Royal Navy beginning in 1969 as a solid-state replacement for Type 975, using a slotted-waveguide antenna (Outfit AZJ or AZK) rather than the earlier cheese. There is also a submarine version. Production began in 1971. The PPI can display helicopter transponder data, for ASW. Range scales: 0.5, 0.75, 1.5, 3, 6, 12, 24, 48, 64 nm.

Versions: 1006 (1) for submarines (9650 MHz, 10-rpm scan); 1006 (2) and (3) for major surface units and OPVs (9445 MHz, 25-rpm scan); 1006 (4) for MCM craft (9425 MHz).

The successor radar, Type 1007 (1600+ Red Pac), was developed from 1971 on and adopted by the Royal Navy in 1984 (production began in 1986). It has very similar characteristics (with the minor exceptions that it operates at 9410 MHz, the larger antenna has a gain of 33 rather than 34 dB, the medium and long pulse widths are 0.3 and 0.8 microsec, the longest pulse width can be transmitted at 400 as well as 800 pps, and scan rate is 26 rpm; maximum instrumented range is 96 nm). Probably the vital

Type 994 radar on board the British frigate *Penelope*, 1988. The slotted waveguide is for Type 1006. (A. Raven)

1988. Like SMART, it apparently uses frequency scanning to form beams on reception for height-finding. The transmitter is a TWT. Based on the characteristics of Plessey's earlier AR-320, Type 996 probably emits trains of bursts at different frequencies, the subpulses within each burst being phase-coded for pulse compression. There are two alternative frequency-management modes, and MTI processing (three- or four-pulse cancellation) is used to reject rain and land clutter (which proved so embarrassing in the Falklands). IFF Type 1010(5) is mounted with the 996 antenna.

Type 996. (Plessey)

The German submarine U22 displays the antenna of her Type 1006 radar. (Gyssels Gilbert)

A Type 1007 radar atop the pilothouse of the Saudi minehunter *Al Jawf*, at Portsmouth in 1994. (Author)

difference is that this is a modern autotracking radar (ARPA type) that can display track history and guard zones. It can operate in sector-scan mode. There is a dual-array version for use with a helicopter transponder and Outfit RBB. Kelvin-Hughes offers an alternative 25-kW transmitter.

Users: Type 1006: Australia (*Fremantle* class, *Oberon* class, *Rushcutter* class), Brazil (*Oberon* class, Type 22), Canada (*Oberon* class), Chile (*Oberon* class, *Ministro Zenteno*), Ecuador (*Leander* class), Ireland (*Peacock* class), Netherlands (*Walrus* class [designated ZW-07; these boats may have 1007]), Pakistan (*Leander* class), South Africa (*Protea, Kimberley*), United King-

dom (*Invincible*-class, submarines, Type 42, Type 22, *Peacock* class, "Castle" class, "Island" class, *Kingfisher* class, "Hunt" class, *Herald*).

Type 1007: Australia (new helicopter ship), Canada ("City" class), Germany (Type 206/206A submarines, replacing Calypso), Ireland (*Peacock* class), Jordan ("Hawk" class), Malaysia (new corvettes), Netherlands (new AOR), Norway (*Ula* class and coast defenses), Oman (new missile boats), Qatar (new missile boats), Portugal (MEKO frigates, *Cacine* class), Saudi Arabia (*Sandown* class), Singapore (*Victory* class), Spain (new AOR), Turkey (new FPBs), and the United Kingdom (standard navigational radar, in Type 23, *Sandown, Sir Galahad, Fort Victoria, Argus* classes). This radar is also used by Bangladesh, Germany, and Indonesia; in some cases it may be used for coastal surveillance. Of the 18 navies using Type 1007 radars, 13 have the CTD tactical display either in service or on order; the exceptions are Oman, Qatar, Saudi Arabia, Turkey, and the United Kingdom.

◆ Type 1008

The Royal Navy issued a requirement for this new commercial-based S-band surface-search radar in March 1994. Racal won in mid-1995 with its Bridgemaster ARPA radar. Modifications probably include a pulse-blanking connection to Royal Navy ESM sets.

◆ Type 1010/1011

Type 1010 is a Cossor IFF interrogator (Mk X system). It can be mounted either independently or on the antenna of a radar, such as Type 965. A typical Cossor interrogator antenna, CS.381, is 3.35 m long. Type 1011 is the corresponding transponder; Types 1010/1011 supersede the earlier Type 944/954 combination.

◆ Type 1013

Type 1013, carried by British minecraft, is a lightweight, nonmagnetic IFF Mk X transponder, the Royal Navy version of the Cossor IFF 2720 airborne set.

◆ Type 1022

Type 1022 is described as a STIR, a combined surveillance and target-indication radar, to replace both 965 and 992Q. 1022 combines a new Marconi antenna with a Dutch LW-08 L-band radar transceiver. It was first installed on board the carrier *Invincible* in 1979.

The Marconi antenna is probably Outfit AZV, with a squintless feed (an array of 40 feed horns) and a single-curvature reflector. Beamwidth is 2.3 deg (the vertical beam is csc^2). The feed is derived from that of the land-based S625 radar, although the reflector is different. The antenna scans at 6–8 rpm, and Type 1022 is credited with a range of 225 nm (compared to 230 for Type 965).

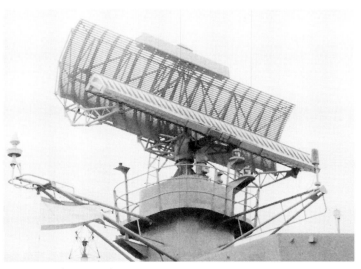

Type 1022. (A. Raven)

Late in 1990 it was reported that the Royal Navy was experiencing sidelobe problems with its Type 1022 radar and that a get-well program was underway.

During the Gulf War, HMS *Gloucester* reported routinely detecting F-117As at ranges of 40–80 nm, and sometimes as far as away as 120 nm. Conditions were very humid but also quite calm. It would appear that detections were made by reflection off the sea surface.

Users: United Kingdom (carriers and Type 42 destroyers).

♦ SAMPSON/MESAR

SAMPSON (formerly TRISAR) is the Siemens-Plessey S-band active phased-array radar planned for the British Project Horizon air defense ships now in the design stage. SAMPSON may also replace Type 996 radars aboard other British warships, such as Type 23 frigates. It is a development of the earlier DRA/Plessey MESAR. Estimated unit price (1994) was $15M.

MESAR. (Plessey Siemens)

The 6t masthead antenna is a box (rotating at 30 rpm) with two faces, each carrying 2560 GaAs transceivers (Rx/Tx modules) in quadpacks (one controller for four Rx/Tx). Peak power is 25 kW. X-band uplinks for missile guidance can be located between the main faces of the array. A zenith-search array can be placed atop the box.

The masthead array is cooled by air, which travels down the mast to a heat exchanger deep in the ship (to avoid producing a hotspot detectable by an IR sensor). The modules take low-voltage ship service power, and are controlled by signals transmitted by fiber optics (via a 12-Gbit/sec rotating optical joint). Because the beam shape can be controlled so delicately, Siemens-Plessey claims that SAMPSON can defeat jammers by steering its beam nulls over them, without losing much detection capability.

Like EMPAR, SAMPSON promises alternative long-range (low PRF) and horizon search (high PRF) modes, in each case with the variable dwell time permitted by electronic beam steering. Too,

Siemens-Plessey claims that by using two arrays it can combine a high data rate with an increased number of pulses hitting a target (which can be further increased by beam steering onto a particular target), hence with better resistance to clutter and ECM. As a measure of performance, before the merger with Siemens, Plessey claimed that a pigeon (0.008m²) could be detected at 105 km in clear conditions. Too, the very wide bandwidth and special monopulse algorithms should improve angular accuracy, especially well off broadside, where phased-array antennas often encounter problems.

Pulses are digitally compressed on reception and adaptively processed (the current processor is a parallel unit using Intel 860s). The radar requires six below-decks cabinets: two radar control units (for the transmitted beams), two pre-processors, and two 16-channel adaptive beamformers (for the receive beams). Each array has four independent channels, each with its own integrated radiating element, 6-bit phase and amplitude controller, and ASIC chip (which determines the settings demanded of individual modules by the system management computer to insure transmission at the required elevation, bearing, and frequency).

SAMPSON uses 50% of the software developed for the single-face MESAR. As an indication of expected SAMPSON performance, MESAR used a 1060-element array (2 W per module, about 2 kW peak power) to form a 3.1-deg transmission beam and a 3.4-deg receiving beam. It operated over 20% of S-band, using pulse compression with a duty ratio of up to 25% (compression ratio 256:1, pulse lengths 0.1 microsec to 1 msec long). It rejected clutter using coherent and noncoherent MTI and pulse-Doppler processing, tracking targets by two-channel monopulse.

The underlying MESAR program began in 1977, and the contract with Plessey was signed in 1982. Tests of a four-faced version at Freugh, Scotland, beginning in January 1994 were financed by the U.S. SDIO (ballistic missile defense organization).

The first SAMPSON prototype should be completed in 1999. Royal Navy trials on board the test barge *Longbow* are expected in 2000–2001.

♦ AWS-1/AWS-2

Band: S (2880 and 3020 MHz)
Beam: 1.5 × 40 deg
Peak Power: 750 kW
Gain: 32 dB
Pulse Width: (a) 0.35 (b) 1.5 microsec
PRF: (a) 1000 (b) 400 pps
Scan Rate: 10–12 or 20 rpm
Antenna Dimensions: 16 ft × 6 ft 6 in
Antenna Weight: 576 lb

The Ghanaian corvette *Kromantse* uses AWS-1 as her air-search radar. The small slotted waveguide serves a Type 978 navigational set. This ship and her sister are armed with single 4in and 40mm guns and with Squid. (U.S. Naval Institute)

The prototype of Plessey's AWS-1 appeared in 1960. AWS-2 (developed 1965–1970) is a more sophisticated radar using the same antenna (in some cases in stabilized form). In its simplest form it offers frequency diversity in the form of two alternative transceivers. Plessey claimed that it was the first shipboard radar to have a digital MTI processor. Claimed range on a "small aircraft" is 60 nm.

Users: Brazil (*Niteroi* class), Denmark (*Falster* class, as CWS-2, with a different antenna), Iran (Vosper Mk 5 frigates), Malaysia (*Hang Tuah*), Nigeria (*Erin'mi* class), Peru (*Daring* class), Turkey (*Falster* class, as CWS-2, with a different antenna), Venezuela (*Almirante Clemente* class).

◆ AWS-4/Type 994

Band: S
Beam: 1.9 × 30 deg
Pulse Width: (a) 1 (b) 0.3 microsec
PRF: (a) 680 (b) 1360 pps
Scan Rate: (a) 10 (b) 20 rpm
Antenna Dimensions: 3.8 × 0.8 m
Antenna Weight: 990 lb (unstabilized version) or 2640 lb (stabilized version)

AWS-4 is a further development of the AWS-1 series with a new antenna, a wide-band tunable magnetron transmitter, and pulse compression; it was intended to match AWS-2 at half the weight. There are two receivers, one matched to plot-extractor requirements and one with various ECCM fixes. The radar can also be fitted with two parallel transmitters, for frequency diversity. Claimed detection range is 80–110 km on a 4m² helicopter, using the long pulse (maximum range). Using the short pulse for best resolution, AWS-4 can detect the same target at 85 km (height 9000 rather than 12,000 m).

The Kenyan missile boat *Nyayo* shows her AWS-4 radar. She has a LIROD EO director on her bridge. The spherical radome covers a Cygnus jammer (the DF array of her Cutlass ESM set is wrapped around the mast above it). (W. Sartori via *Ships of the World*)

Combined with the Type 993 antenna (see above), this radar forms Type 994.

Users: Brazil (four *Inhauma* class), Chile (two Type 994 on ex-British *Leanders*), Ecuador (two Type 994 on ex-*Leanders*), Kenya (two "Province" class), New Zealand (four Type 994 on *Leanders*), Norway (*Nordkapp* class), Oman (one on *Dhofar* class), Pakistan (two Type 994 on ex-British *Leanders*), Thailand (three *Khamronsin* class), United Kingdom (as Type 994 on *Fearless*-class LPDs, *Dumbarton Oaks* OPV, *Argus*, "Castle"-class OPVs). In the Kenyan ships, the Otomat mid-course guidance antenna is mounted back-to-back with the main AWS-4 antenna. *Argus* and the "Castles" have the AWS-4 antenna.

◆ AWS-5

Band: S
Beam: High beam is 1.5 × 30 deg, directed upward at 45 deg; low beam is 40 deg wide in elevation, directed upward at 5 deg. AWS-5B antenna: 1.5 × 32 deg (azimuth squint less than 1 deg over the operating range).

Peak Power: 58 kW (mean power 1.3 kW)
Pulse Width: (a) 0.4 (b) 20 microsec compressed to 0.4 microsec (typically transmitted in sequence)
PRF: 1100 pps
Scan Rate: 15 or 30 rpm
Antenna Weight: 2640 lb

Transmitter data are estimated from those of the Watchman ground radar (see below).

AWS-5 at the foremasthead of the Danish frigate *Peter Tordenskjold* with a NATO Sea Sparrow fire-control radar (Mk 91) aft. The two slotted waveguides are probably Decca TM 1229s (Skanter 009). (L. van Ginderen)

Developed in 1972–75, Plessey's AWS-5 combines a modified AWS-4 antenna with a new TWT transmitter offering programmable frequency agility and digital MTI (due to its coherence). Like AWS-4, this is a pulse-compression radar. Processing features include skew correction for fast targets (correction of the error in bearing due to the motion of the antenna between transmission and reception). Instrumented range is 240 km. This radar has an ADT capacity of 250 tracks. It operates in two modes, target indication for a point defense system, and surveillance (medium- or long-range).

The antenna is essentially that of AWS-4 topped by a squintless linear array canted back to provide cover above 60-deg elevation. The high beam is normally clutter-free because it does not touch the sea.

AWS-5 has the same transmitter as the Watchman coast-defense radar. AWS-5C is a land-based version using a low-beam horn and reflector (range over 60 nm, elevation up to 40 deg). AWS-5D is a two-speed shipboard version of -5C, with two-speed scanning.

Several improved versions have not sold; the original AWS-5 became AWS-5 (MP), for medium power. See the 1991/92 edition for details.

With the low beam, a 4m² target can be detected at about 85 nm and 50,000 ft; a 0.1m² target (such as an antiship missile) at about 40 nm and 25,000 ft.

Users: Denmark (three *Nils Juels* class), Nigeria (*Aradu* [5D]).

◆ AWS-6 (Dolphin)/Guardsman/Coastguard

Band: C
Beam: Beamwidth 1.5 deg (see below)
Peak Power: 49 kW
Gain: 29/26 dB (low/high beams)
Pulse Width: 0.1 and 4.3 microsec; option 10-microsec pulse (for 30-rpm scan)
Scan Rate: 30 or 60 rpm
Antenna Dimensions: 2.6 m wide (102 in)
Antenna Weight: 520 kg, including mounting (1150 lb)

Data refer to Dolphin, the version of AWS-6 used in the Contraves Seaguard system (see separate entry above).

AWS-6 is a C-band equivalent to AWS-5, combining a dual-beam antenna with a TWT transmitter, pulse compression, and ATD. It is intended for target indication, using its narrow beam.

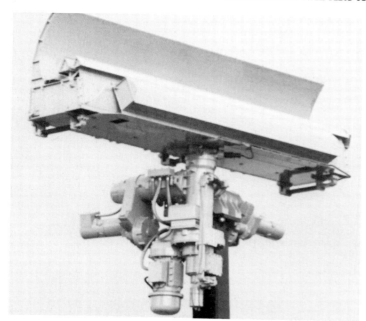

AWS-6 (Dolphin). (Plessey)

Plessey, the manufacturer, attributed its commercial success to its better-than-expected ability to track missiles.

The short (uncompressed) pulse listed above is for navigation and splash-spotting.

The main reflector (covering angles between 0 and 20 deg, with csc^2 shaping up to 40 deg) is center-fed by a squintless linear array, as in Type 1022; a second linear array forms the high beam (up to 70 deg). The entire antenna is roll- and pitch-stabilized. Weight is 520 kg above/1340 kg below decks.

In missile defense mode, the radar scans at 30 rpm. If a missile is detected, it switches to 60 rpm to provide an adequate data rate. Instrumented ranges at 30 rpm are 30/70/200 km (20/30/35 km at 60 rpm). Low fliers can be detected out to 35 km, diving missiles (at 70 deg) to 20 km, and medium- and long-range instrumented air surveillance ranges are 70 and 200/240 km. For gunfire control, splashes can be spotted out to 20 km. There are two extended-surveillance modes using the 30/15 rpm dual-rotation rate version of the radar.

A larger-antenna single-beam version, Danfish (in a radome), was supplied for Danish fishery-protection vessels.

In 1989, suffixes were applied to versions of AWS-6: A for the dual-beam version, B for a single-beam version. AWS-6D is a 3D stacked-beam (on receive) version announced in 1991, and -6E is a simplified two-beam version (with height-finding capability) announced in 1993. Neither has, apparently, as yet been sold.

Existing versions are AWS-6A/100, AWS-6B/200 (scan rate 15/30 rpm, instrumented ranges 60/120/240 km; uses 6A antenna but lacks the high-beam array at the bottom in front), and AWS-6B/300 (scan rate 30/15 or 20/10 rpm, instrumented ranges 60/120/240 km).

Guardsman or Coastguard is a medium-range air search and coast-defense radar derived from AWS-6. It can be carried on an elevating mast (height 12 or 18 m). Beam width is 1.5 deg (2.5 × 1.1 m); peak power is 60 kW (pulse lengths 20/10 microsec compressed to 0.4 microsec, PRFs 2200/1100 respectively). Scan rate is 6/12 or 12/24 rpm. Blind speed is 2000 kt. The radar is agile among 32 frequencies. Instrumented range is 100 km (200 km optional); minimum range is 1.5 km. Resolution (accuracy): 120 (75) m, 1.5 (0.3) deg. There is also a version using the Dolphin antenna, scanning at 15/30/60 rpm. Guardsman-C (1993) adds a third beam for limited height-finding. Guardsman-S combines the S-band Watchman radar electronics with the Guardsman transportable cabin and mast. In this case the mast is 10 m high (15 m optional), compared to 9.5 m in the standard Guardsman.

Users: Denmark (*Thetis* [AWS-6B/300], StanFlex 300 [AWS-6A/100, replaced in later units by TRS-3D], classes and *Besky-*

terren [AWS-6B/300]), Greece (planned for "Osprey 55" class, probably will not be fitted), Oman ("Province" class [AWS-6B/200], except *Dhofar*, which has AWS-4), Pakistan (two coast-guard coast defense radars), Turkey (MEKO frigates of *Yavuz* and *Barbaros* classes [AWS-6A/100]).

◆ Racal (formerly Decca) Navigational Radars

In most cases, the first digit or two (9, 12, 16, 24, 26) indicates CRT diameter; the last two digits indicate the series and (in some cases) the size of the antenna (4, 6, or 9 ft); in the 1290 and 1690 series the antenna size is a suffix, as in 1690/9. Operating at X-band, the 6ft antenna produces a 1.2 × 23-deg beam (gain 30 dB); the 9ft antenna produces a 0.8 × 23-deg beam (gain 32 dB). Later there was an S-band alternative (12ft antenna, two 30-deg beams, 30-kW peak power with the same pulse characteristics). The 900 series of the early 1970s (914A, 916, 926, 929) introduced solid-state microelectronics. The 1220 series (late 1970s) uses pulse compression (pulse widths are 0.05, 0.25, and 1.0 microsec; PRFs are 1300, 1300, and 650 pps, respectively, and peak power is 25 kW). The next series (1290/1690) added provision for ATD. The step beyond was to introduce rectangular raster-scan displays (819 lines, 64 Hz monochrome, 30 Hz color) using digital scan conversion, in 2490/2690 (in these the CRT is measured diagonally). In these sets synthetic video can be superimposed on raw radar video. 2490 uses a monochrome PPI; 2690 uses color. Both can be switched between relative and true motion. 2459 is a dual-frequency set (see below).

Prefixes indicate signal processing: AC for anticollision (i.e., true motion), RM for relative motion, TM for true motion (some ships combine the two), ARPA for automatic plot extraction (ATD) introduced in 1290/1690. The suffix C indicates clear-scan, a form of clutter suppression. Thus TM1226C is a true-motion radar with a 12in clearscan CRT and a 6ft (72in) antenna.

The 1290/1690 series introduced a bright (daylight) PPI and automatic plotting (ARPA). The system can carry up to 20 target tracks, acquiring targets at 0.5 to 20 nm, tracking at 0.5 to 20 nm. Targets are continuously tracked after they are acquired and have appeared on five out of ten consecutive scans; they are extracted by limited-area analysis (a fixed window), the gain within the window being set according to expected target size and the local measured noise level. The track table is assembled in true motion form. Up to nine markers can be positioned to monitor the bearing of a potential threat vessel. The markers are all short

Two Decca TM 1226C radar antennas are visible on board this British "River"-class minesweeper, seen at Portsmouth in 1994. (Author)

constant-bearing lines pointing back to own-ship: an echo that remains on the marker is closing at constant bearing and is on a collision course. The system also easily measures CPA.

Color is used to denote echo characteristics, for example, orange for targets, black for tracks, white for ancillary data, and red for a guard zone.

2459 F/I mounts a 9ft X(I)-band antenna atop a 12ft S(F)-band antenna tipped up at an elevation of 15 deg for limited air search (alternatively the S-band antenna can scan the horizon). The naval transceivers have adjustable PRF so that they can mimic commercial radars.

The Spanish offshore patrol vessel *Serviola* shows her 2459 F/I dual-band radar. (G. Arra via *Ships of the World*)

The BT360/500 series are successors to the 1220-series, smaller-screen equivalents to the 2490/2690 described above. The two-digit number indicates the screen size in cm (36 cm, 14 in, corresponding to a 9in-dia PPI; or 50 cm, 20 in, corresponding to a 12in-dia PPI); the final digit indicates the antenna (1, 2, 3 for 4, 6, or 9 ft). ARPA capacity is 10 tracks.

These radars are extremely widely used on board warships, partly because they are also widely used commercially; a warship operating her Decca radar produces a merchant-ship signal. Decca 2459 is probably the only one of the series conceived for naval use.

At RNEE 1991 Racal displayed a new Kevlar radar for its standard X-band navigational radars. It is much cleaner than the usual slotted waveguide (it has no squint angle), and it offers reduced magnetic signature. Gain is more than 30 dB, beam is 1.2 × 20 deg, and the scan rate is either 28 or 0–60 rpm. It was adopted by Norway for some units of the *Oslo* and *Hauk* classes and for the new MCM craft.

The prototype of Racal's Kevlar reflector antenna (6ft open parabolic scanner) is shown on board the Norwegian fast-attack boat *Tjeld*, 1991. Similar antennas were bought for the *Oslo* class and for the new MCM craft. The slotted array below the reflector serves a second TM 1226. The object forward of the antennas is the Penguin missile director, enclosing a TVT-300 tracker and a laser ranger. Sometime after this photograph was taken the masthead comms antenna was replaced by a Matilda ESM antenna. (Racal)

Users (of 2459): Indonesia (PB 57 class), Netherlands (*Poolster*), Portugal (this is probably the radar that replaced the old MLA-1B in the *Joao Coutinho* class), Spain (*Milano* class).

◆ Marconi HF Radar

Marconi is advertising a shipboard version of its land-based surface-wave HF radar (see the Surveillance section for details of the land version). The principle was tested by ARE (now DRA) on both a fleet auxiliary (which used the ship's radio antennas with new signal processors) and on board a frigate (with receiving loops over the side). In the latter case, the entire length of the frigate became the antenna aperture. In 1989, Marconi estimated that by using a single whip transmitting antenna and eight receivers on each side of the ship a frigate could detect a low-flying fighter at 120 km in Sea State 4 (at 3–12 MHz, with a mean power of 500 W). Accuracy would be 2 km and 5 deg.

◆ Marconi ST802

Band: X (bandwidth about 900 MHz)
Beam: 2.4 deg
Peak Power: 150 kW (100 kW at PRF 4400) (200 kW optional)
Gain: 36.5 dB
Pulse Width: (a) 0.33 microsec (b) 0.67 microsec
PRF: (a) 4400 (MTI) (b) 3000 (non-MTI) pps
Antenna Dimensions: Aperture 1 m (1.4 m in ST858)
Antenna Weight: Director weight 550 kg; double-bay cabinet 690 kg; weapons-control console 450 kg

Developed in conjunction with Ericsson, Marconi's ST802 monopulse tracker shares a common transmitter (Ericsson's tunable magnetron, as in the 9LV search radar) and digital MTI processor with the S810/811 surveillance radar (see below). MTI is by a double canceller using shift register storage, the PRF being staggered around 4400 pps to eliminate blind speeds (instrumented range is 10 or 20 km). ST802 is associated with the S810/820 search radar and with the Sapphire FCS (see separate entry below). The stabilized antenna is a twist-Cassegrain with a separate splash-spotting channel and a TV camera mounted alongside. ST802 can search (at 20 rpm) to acquire targets, stepping up helically by a full beam width (2.4 deg) under computer control to perform low, medium, and high scans. It can detect an airplane at 10,000 ft at 20 km. Once a target can be acquired, a button shifts the radar to tracking mode.

An Egyptian *6 October*–class missile boat (with her Otomat racks empty) shows an S810 search radar (in the big radome) and an ST802 fire-control radar (atop the superstructure). (L. van Ginderen)

Users: Egypt (*October* class), Kenya (*Nyayo* class).

◆ Marconi S810/S811

Band: X (8.6–9.5 GHz)
Beam: 2.2 × 25 deg (S810P: 2.2 × 4.7 deg; S810: 1.5 × 25-deg beam with alternative 1.8m antenna)
Peak Power: 180 kW (MTI: 135 kW)
Gain: 29.5 dB (S810P: 33.5 dB)

Pulse Width: 0.67 or 0.33 microsec
PRF: 1500 (4400 for MTI) pps
Scan Rate: 24 rpm (S810P: 40 rpm)
Antenna Dimensions: 1.2 m wide (radome dia 1.7 m; 2.3 m with 1.8m antenna)
Antenna Weight: 250 kg at masthead (plus 695-kg transmit/receiver)

These radars were announced about 1974.

The antenna is mounted inside a radome. There is an alternative antenna in a 1.8m radome (1.5-deg beam, masthead weight not including radome 300 kg rather than 180 kg).

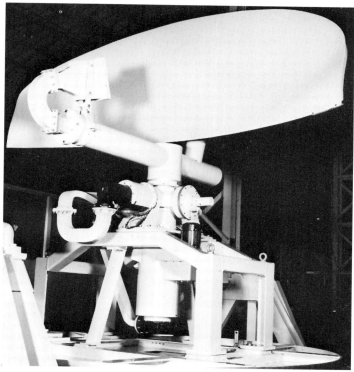

Marconi S810, without its radome. (Marconi)

S811 is a version without provision for MTI.

Estimated ranges against a 5m^2 airplane: 28 km at 2000 m altitude (1.2m antenna), 20+ km at 6000 m; with a 1.8m antenna, 32 km at 3000 m and 25+ km at 8000 m. S810P (for better low-altitude coverage) will detect a 0.1m^2 target at 15 km.

Users: Algeria (*Kalaat Beni Hammed*–class LSTs [version not given, probably S811]), Egypt (S810 in *October*-class FAC).

◆ Marconi ST1802

Band: X (8.9–9.5 GHz)
Beam: 2.4 deg
Peak Power: 50 kW (average 150 W)
Gain: 37 dB
Pulse Width: 0.67, 0.3 (for surface gunnery), or 1.0 microsec (long-range, 3000 pps)
PRF: 3000 (non-MTI); 4400 (MTI) pps
Antenna Dimensions: Aperture 1 m
Antenna Weight: 550 kg (director weight)

In analogy to ST802/S810, ST1802 shares a TWT transmitter with the S1800 series of search radars. Data above are for the abortive 1802AS (Aspide control) version. As in ST802, the stabilized antenna is a twist-Cassegrain with a TV camera alongside. MTI processing is pulse-Doppler.

Maximum tracking range is 40 km (24 km if MTI is used), and maximum slewing rates are 120 deg/sec in train and 50 deg/sec in elevation (limits +85/−30 deg). Continuous elevation rate (for target acquisition from a 2D search radar) is 20 deg/sec. Above-decks weight is 550 kg, plus a total of 1200 kg below decks (including a 650-kg transceiver and processor).

ST1802 fire-control radar, with optronic backup. (Marconi)

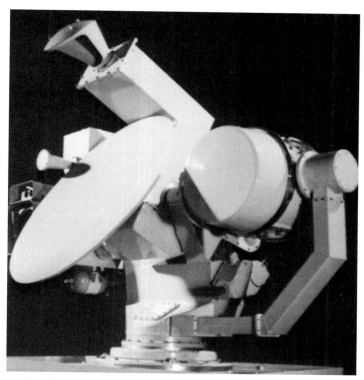

ST1802SW. (Marconi)

ST1802SW is Marconi's commercial Sea Wolf director radar incorporating the TV missile tracker of the Javelin system and the S805SW command link. At 1900 kg, it is about half the weight of the 805SW that became the Royal Navy's Type 911. The tracker uses a gregorian offset feed and is mechanically counterbalanced (for quick tracking) by an optronics head. The separate 30-kW (18 W mean) J-band missile-command transmitter, in a drum-shaped radome, is on the antenna's left side. Acquisition range is 32 km against a 3m^2 target, and 13 km on a 0.1m^2 target. Instrumented range in surface mode is 24 km (e.g., can acquire a patrol vessel with masthead height of 10.7 m). In search mode, the antenna trains (elevates) at 20 (30) deg/sec. Slew and elevation speed to a designated target is 120 deg/sec. For Sea Wolf control, the director tracks at 11 deg/sec.

The associated V3800 thermal imager has a 3 × 2-deg FOV.

A very similar ST1803, announced in 1991, seems not to have attracted any sales. It is offered both in single-band (X-band) and in dual-band (X- and Ku-band) versions, both employing a single 1m twist-Cassegrain antenna (the Ku-band element enjoys a

47-dB gain and produces a 1-deg beam). Elevation limits are +85/−20 deg.

Users: Egypt (ST1802 in *Ramadan* class), Korea (Samsung-built version in *Ulsan* and *Donghae* classes), Malaysia (ST1802SW in *Lekiu*-class corvettes, controlling Sea Wolf). ST1802SW will probably form the basis for a future British lightweight Sea Wolf director, superseding Type 911. No Type number has been assigned.

◆ Marconi S1810/S1830/S1834

Band: 3 cm (X-band: 8.6–9.5 GHz)
Beam: $1.1 \times \csc^2$ 5–30 deg
Peak Power: 50 kW
Gain: 36 dB (midband)
Pulse Width: (a) 2 microsec compressed to 0.1 microsec (chirp); (b) 1 microsec for air search; (c) 0.2 microsec for surface search
PRF: (a) 2000 (b and c) 4000 pps
Scan Rate: 24 rpm
Antenna Dimensions: 2.44×0.84 or 1.2×0.42 m
Antenna Weight: 640 or 250 kg

Data apply to S1810.

The Egyptian patrol boat *El Yarmouk* shows a Marconi S810 radar in a radome on her foremast and a Cygnus jammer in the smaller radome on her mainmast. At her foremasthead she carries Cutlass and Matilda ESM, and she also carries two Protean chaff mortars. (L. van Ginderen)

Announced in 1978, S1810 is the TWT equivalent of S810, just as ST1802 is the TWT equivalent of ST802. Signal processing includes digital MTI. Beside the standard antenna described above, there is also a more compact antenna, about the size of that of S810 (1.2m in a 1.7m radome). Both are housed in spherical radomes. This radar can also be used for coastal surveillance. Typical detection ranges: aircraft at 45 km, small surface craft at 30 km.

Users: Egypt (*Ramadan* class [compact version]), South Korea (two Korean *Ulsan*-class frigates and some of the *Donghae* and *Pohang* classes; total 25 systems bought, so some may be retrofitted).

S1830, announced September 1993, combines a new modular solid-state transmitter (2.8–3.1 GHz, 18-microsec pulse compressed on reception to 0.4 microsec) with the S1810 signal processor with digital MTI. Instrumented range is 200 km, and ADT capacity is 300 tracks. None had sold as of mid-1996, S1830 having been proposed unsuccessfully for both the *Oslo*-class upgrade and the Pakistani Type 21 frigate upgrade. S1834 is a stacked-beam version of S1830, using an enlarged 12-beam version of the S1812 planar-array antenna (44 stacked boards rather than the 24 of S1812) scanning at 10 or 20 rpm. Maximum range is 187 km using 5 beams, or 120 km using 12.

◆ S1812 (Marconi 3D Radar)

This radar may be the Ericsson-Marconi product formerly called ELSA (see the Swedish section above). According to Marconi, this radar uses C-band frequency-agile (over 500 MHz) versions of the S1810 transmitter, receiver, and signal processor: 50 kW,

2-microsec pulse compressed on reception. The 130-kg antenna (an array of 24 horizontal linear feeds [boards], in elements of four each, using phase-shifters) is stabilized mechanically or electronically. Vertical coverage is either five-beam (25 deg) or eight-beam (57 deg). Modes: long range (scan at 15 rpm), instrumented range 66 km (detects a $2m^2$ target at 49 km); short (30 rpm), 33 km (38-km detection with Pd 0.8); anti-seaskimmer (30 rpm), 33-km range (detect $0.1m^2$ target 5 m above sea at 13 km with Pd 0.8). There is also an I(X)-band version.

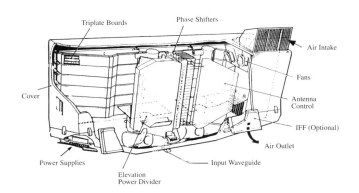

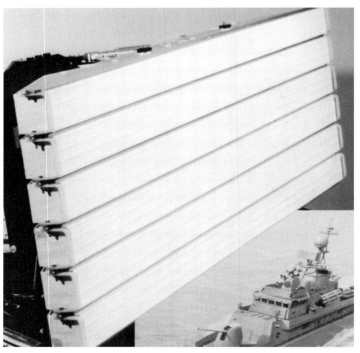

The antenna for Marconi's S1812 small-ship 3D radar, front and back. Note the elaborate cooling arrangements. (Marconi Radar Systems)

◆ Smartello (S1850L)

This radar was chosen in July 1995 for the new Project Horizon frigate. After the French Astral was rejected at the end of 1994, the alternatives considered were SMART-L, the new Alenia RAN-32L, and a navalized version of Marconi's Martello land-based long-range air-defense radar. Smartello was the compromise choice, combining the SMART stripline antenna with Martello below-decks elements. GEC-Marconi is prime contractor; Signaal (part of Thomson-CSF) is principal subcontractor.

Like SMART-L, Martello is a long-range L(D)-band 3D radar producing a single fan beam with heightfinding by beamforming on reception. Each horizontal array element has its own receiver; beams are formed at the IF stage. The original version, S713, used 60 elements and scanned at 6 rpm. Peak power was 3 MW. S723 uses a modular solid-state transmitter (peak power 132 kW, average 5 kW) and a new antenna (wider but with about 40 horizontal elements). It produces either six or eight beams, depending on the version, each beam being processed separately. The next version, S743, provides both a broad-band solid-state transmitter and a pulse-compression receiver for each horizontal element, again forming eight beams on reception only. The receiver employs Doppler processing to eliminate clutter. The signal processor incorporates transputers in its 80 computing nodes. S753 is a more transportable version.

◆ Sentinel

Marconi's coast-surveillance radar is for surface and low air cover out to 30 km against a 5m² target. It uses an S1810 antenna and a standard marine radar transceiver, probably that of the Type 1007 radar. Peak power is 25 kW (90 kW optional), and the antenna scans at 20 rpm. Pulse widths: 0.08, 0.3, 0.8 microsec (PRFs 1600, 800, 400 pps, respectively). The 2.44 × 0.84m antenna produces a csc² beam over 5–30 deg in elevation.

◆ Watchman/Guardsman

Watchman and Guardsman are Siemens-Plessey coast-defense radars. Watchman has been selected by the British Ministry of Defence, and Guardsman has been exported. The S-band Watchman can detect a 1m² target at 148 km (30 km at low altitude), and it can track over 100 targets simultaneously. The Watchman's transmitter is a high-powered TWT using pulse compression. Characteristics of the air-search version: peak power 58 kW; pulse pattern 0.4-microsec short pulse followed by 20-microsec long pulse (compressed to 0.4 microsec); average power 1.3 kW (implying a PRF of about 1100 pps; there is also an 840-pps mode); scan rate 12 or 15 rpm. Range on a 1m² target is 100 or 110 nm. The air-search version uses a dual-beam antenna similar in form to early AWS-series naval radars. There are also a transportable air-search version and a coastal version with special signal processing for surface and low-flying targets.

Watchman was first ordered, for the RAF, in June 1983 (33 fixed and 6 transportable units); the first was handed over in September 1986.

Users: Bahrein (1), China (1), Dubai (1), Finland (7), Ghana (1), Oman (1), Pakistan (2), Portugal (2), Spain (1), Switzerland (3), United Kingdom (39 for Ministry of Defence; 13 civilian), and United States (1). It is not clear whether any of these radars is being used for coastal surveillance. As of December 1992, a total of 77 Watchman radars had been produced.

RADAR INTEGRATION

◆ British Radar Plot Extractors

Radar plot extractors are, in U.S. parlance, radar-video converters. Royal Navy radar automatic track extractors (RATEs) are equivalent to the U.S. ADT. The first experimental British RATE system was developed by Thorn-EMI and ARE Portsdown in the late 1970s; that experiment led, in turn, to three production systems: LFA (for Type 965), LFB (for Type 1022), and LFC (for Types 1006/1007). LFD will serve Type 996. These RATEs will appear on board ships now under construction and will also be retrofitted to ships already in service. At least in the case of LFC, the system combines radar plots with information from the radar transponder (Outfit RRB) used to track the ship's ASW helicopter. Typical capacity is 500 tracks.

ADIMP, the ADAWS improvement program, includes a Thorn-EMI radar track combiner (RTC) system comparable in theory to the U.S. SYS series. Previously, ADAWS had selected the radar providing the best track information, rejecting all the rest. It creates a Recognized Air and Surface Picture (RASP) for the CDS. In a ship so equipped, each radar's radar track extractor (ATD) feeds track data into the ship combat-system bus. The RTC maintains over 1000 tracks, with a maximum update rate of over 150 tracks/sec. RTC differs from the U.S. SYS series: it operates on tracks, rather than individual radar plots. RTC weights the individual radars' track data according to their measured statistics, correlating and merging them. It also projects ahead tracks during fades lasting up to a minute.

OPTRONIC SYSTEMS

◆ ADAD/ARISE/HHTI/NTIS/TIGS

Thorn-EMI has developed a version of the army ADAD as an IRST for air surveillance for DRA (formerly ARE). This ARISE (ARE Reconfigurable IR Scanner Equipment) is intended to help ARE (now DRA maritime branch) specify an optimum IRST. ADAD is a single-band air-defense alerting device (8–13 microns) used to cue hand-held AA missiles such as Javelin. It saw British army service in the Gulf War, and was formally accepted into service in July 1993. ADAD units have been transferred to the Royal Navy for ships supporting the UN in Bosnia.

ARISE meets a naval requirement, formulated about 1987, for a dual-band threat warner. The near band (3–5 microns) is considered preferable in very humid weather and is used to detect missile and aircraft exhaust plumes. The far band (8–13 microns) is used to detect aircraft and helicopters by their skin friction. The threat warner includes a processor that classifies targets, prioritizes them, and indicates their azimuth to operators, automatically pointing the sight and autotracking in azimuth and elevation with less than 1-mrad error.

A single set of optics is used for both IR colors: the two lines of elements are mounted side by side, scanning vertically while the mirror spins. ARISE can sector-scan or continuously scan at 60 Hz. The total FoR is 10 × 240 deg, and the 10-deg zero line is steerable within +/−7 deg.

After 1993–94 trials, ARISE was returned to the manufacturer for modification. It is to be integrated with the SAMPSON radar to provide a radar/EO system for the new AAW frigate (CNGF).

Thorn-EMI's Naval Thermal Imaging System/Thermal Imaging Gun Sight is an application of the company's Thermal Imaging Common Module Class 1 direct-view night-observation device. The 8–13-micron CdHgTe array (cooled to 80K) is scanned across a scene in series-parallel mode; outputs are displayed on a scanned red LED array or fed into a television. There are 2 FOVs (NTIS 1: 4.3 × 2.8 and 11.1 × 7.4 deg; NTIS 2: 3.3 × 2.2 and 8.1 × 5.4 deg). Weights: director and imager 100 kg, compressor (for cooling) 115 kg, console 130 kg. Total travel in azimuth is 190 deg; elevation limits are +65/−35 deg. Maximum slewing speed (bearing) is 120 deg/sec.

The much smaller TIGS weighs only 5 kg. TIGS FOV: 20 × 6.6 deg with 2× magnification, 8 × 3.4 deg with 5× magnification. A hand-held version (HHTI) of TIGS uses hybridized modules to reduce weight.

Users: Bangladesh (probably aboard ex-HMS *Jersey*, which happened to be the first unit to carry it), France (Mistral sight), United Kingdom (TIGS/HHTI as gunsight and for general surveillance, NTIS in "Island" class [in service 1976]), United States (special forces, air base perimeter patrols). Some Far Eastern navies use HHTI for river patrol, to spot people on river banks.

◆ DAS

Defence Equipment and Systems (Laurence Scott) director aiming sight is an LOS-stabilized unit carrying a pair of binoculars, with provision for two other sensors (e.g., FLIR, TV, and laser range-finder) alongside the seated operator. The operator can control the training and elevating servos by joystick, or they can be slaved to the associated FCS. Outputs are target bearing, elevation, and range (if a range-finder is fitted).

Maximum balanced sensor load is 150 kg, and total weight is 650 kg. Elevation limits are +70/−20 deg, and train (elevation) rates are 90 (100) deg/sec; corresponding acceleration rates are 245 (400) deg/sec². Training slew time over 180 deg (rest to rest) is less than 3.5 sec; over 60-deg elevation (rest to rest) is less than 1.5 sec. Overall height is 1.82 m, the binocular axis is 1.735 m above deck, and the swept radius is 0.64 m. Below-decks weight is 182 kg.

DAS replaces the earlier Lookout Aiming Sight in Type 42 destroyers; the first two were in HMS *Birmingham*. It is also in the Egyptian *Ramadan* class.

DAS aboard HMS *Birmingham*, 1991, with a SCOT satellite antenna radome on the level above it. (A. Raven)

Canvas-covered DEC dazzler-laser on board HMS *Edinburgh* in 1992. (R. Cheung)

◆ Laser Dazzle System (LDS, Outfit DEC)

ARE's laser gun is intended to disable EO surveillance and tracking equipment and also to dazzle, and thus to drive off, approaching pilots. Typically, two are mounted on tripods abaft the bridge of a frigate. At least the early version was portable and could be cross-decked. More recent units appear to be power-trained (on board HMS *Gloucester* in June 1991 they were marked "may train without warning"). LDS was first tested on board HMS *Euryalus* in the Irish Sea in 1981, and several ships (reportedly including the two carriers and the frigates *Brilliant*, *Broadsword*, and *Argonaut*) carried it during the Falklands War. It may have caused the loss of several Argentine aircraft, including one whose pilot reported that intense glare had driven him away from an attack on HMS *Argonaut*. LDS has also been fitted to (and reportedly used by) British frigates on the Armilla Patrol in the Persian Gulf. The existence of LDS was not reported until January 1990 because of British security restrictions. The advent of LDS may be associated with the shift, in the Sea Wolf system, from a combined radar/EO to a fully radar-controlled director. LDS was apparently inspired by experience of the optical hazards of laser rangers and target designators; work began about 1978.

The original version, manually aimed using a pair of binoculars atop the laser barrel, was DEC(1). DEC(2), the current version, is power-operated, remotely controlled by a ship's radar, probably by Type 1007. Originally it was on board Sea Wolf ships, and then on board all major combatants, DEC(1) being relegated to mine warfare ships, amphibious ships, and major underway replenishment ships. Presumably DEC(1) operates only in the visual spectrum (0.4–0.7-micron wavelengths). Reported effective range is 1600 m. By 1990, DEC was reported on board all British warships operating on Gulf patrol. DEC(3), the

new version (which entered service in 1993), adds a secondary near-IR wavelength (0.7–1.4 microns) specifically to defeat protective lens coatings and antilaser goggles. Reported effective range is 5 km. DEC(3) also has a variable modulation rate.

There are three operating modes: versus aircraft, versus EO weapons, and versus boats. In the first, the laser is aimed at the sea in front of an approaching airplane, throwing up a wall of laser light that the airplane's optical sight can concentrate into the pilot's eyes. The plastic canopy fluoresces and turns opaque. The glowing canopy disorients the pilot. The other modes blind the weapon or the boat crew directly.

DEC is manufactured by Irwin Desman Ltd. Estimated unit cost is $0.25 to $0.5M, and by mid-1994 up to 200 of various versions had apparently been made. Some may have been manufactured for the British army, for tanks and other fighting vehicles.

Reported Royal Navy installations include three on each carrier and *Fearless*-class amphibious ship, two each on board destroyers, frigates, MCM craft, and underway replenishment ships. Some may have been supplied to other NATO navies, including the U.S. Navy, for tests.

Possibly because of the existence of DEC, the official British Institute of Aviation Medicine developed antilaser goggles for pilots, using reflecting filters.

◆ Hydra (MEOSS)/Vistar 1M 405

Pilkington's Hydra was originally announced as Thorn-EMI's lightweight Marine Electro-Optical Surveillance System in 1991. It is McLennan Marine's system incorporating a McLennan Marine LLLTV (FOV 16 × 12 deg) and a Thorn-EMI (now Pilkington) FLIR, LITE. The same system was formerly marketed as GEC-Marconi's Vistar 1M 405 (announced 1987), carrying a GEC-Marconi FLIR. The two-axis stabilized sensor head, which is joystick-controlled, can slew at up to 30 deg/sec over a total azimuth of 340 deg; the helmsman has an override control which can slew the head 20 deg to either side of his heading. The sensor head can also be slaved to an electronic line of bearing generated by a radar. Elevation limits are +/−30 deg. The head weighs 50 kg. The Vistar version uses a Marconi 8–12-micron CdHgTe FLIR (FOVs 9.6 × 5.6/4.0 × 2.3 deg for magnifications of 2× and 5×) imager. The below-decks CRT can show both images in split-screen mode. The FLIR can detect a 20m boat at about 7.5 km and a man in the water at about 1.5 km. The wider-angle LLLTV is used for observation and navigation. The console can show either an image from one sensor or a split screen of images from both. The U.S. version of Vistar is now being upgraded; a prototype carries the same Pilkington HDTI FLIR as in Phalanx Block 1B. Pilkington now offers HDTI and LITE as alternatives.

Users: Norway (selected for *Nordkapp*-class upgrade), United Kingdom (Brooke Marine 26 and 33m patrol boats of the Customs Service), United States (Vistar 1M 405 in *Cyclone* class).

Hydra (MEOSS) uses the small EO box above the bridge of this British *Protector*-class customs and excise patrol boat, 1994. (Author)

◆ OFD

Defence Equipment and Systems (formerly Laurence Scott) Optical Fire Director is the director of the Royal Navy GSA 7 (Sea Archer) system. The operator stands on a ring around the base of the director, observing the target through a pair of Type CF 42 7×50 binoculars, and controlling the director using a two-axis joystick. In the alternative remote-training mode, the OFD is manually controlled in elevation only. There is also a full remote-control mode, the operator presumably acting to check the tracking of the remote sensor. Like the same manufacturer's DAS (described above), OFD can carry 150 kg of EO sensors (the Royal Navy leaves the sensors on the separate Sea Archer pedestal).

Total weight is 485 kg, and overall height is 1.95 m (binoculars are 1.858 m above deck); swept radius is 0.795 m. Elevation limits are +70/−20 deg, and train (elevation) rate is 96 (67) deg/sec; corresponding accelerations are 120 deg/sec^2 for both train and elevation. Tracking accuracy is better than 1.5 mrad, and MTBF is greater than 1100 hr.

Users: Algeria (Brooke Marine 37.5m class), Brunei, Egypt, Hong Kong (ASI 315 class), Kenya (*Mamba*), Nigeria (*Obuma*), Oman ("Province" class and 37.5m class, with Sea Archer; formerly also on board *Al Munassir*), United Kingdom (OPVs).

◆ Radamec Series 1000/2000

These are EO surveillance units and FCSs, the function depending on below-decks electronics. Series 1000 is built on a light-weight dual-axis stabilized HK 409–010 pedestal; Series 2000 is built on the heavier HK 409–029. The standard sensors are a Radamec daylight TV camera (HK 202–002) and a GEC V3800 (since 1992, V3900) thermal imager (see separate entry below). The Radamec camera has a 16–160mm zoom lens (FOVs 21 × 16 to 2.1 × 1.6 deg), a CCD sensor (604 × 576 elements, image resolution 450 lines horizontally and 420 lines vertically, scan rate 625 lines at 25 frames/sec or 525 lines at 30 frames/sec). The alternative LLLTV is HK 203–001, also with a 16–160mm zoom lens (FOVs 48 × 36 to 4.8 × 3.6 deg), which can tolerate levels of light from full sunlight to starlight. CCD size and resolution match those of the daylight camera.

Series 1000 is generally used for surveillance, but it can incorporate a lead computer for 30mm and 40mm guns. Typical weight (above decks) is 150 kg (height 0.5 m) and swept radius is 1.2 m. During the IDEX 1995 exhibition at Abu Dhabi, HMS *Liverpool* displayed a new 1000N with an additional video auto-tracker for high-speed targets and a twin-screen operator's console on the bridge. The ship retained the RNEOSS (System 2100) standard on board British warships in the Gulf, on either bridge wing. Series 1000 is sometimes called the optical fire director (OFD).

Radamec Series 1000 EO director. (Radamec)

Series 2000 is LOS-stabilized and joystick-controlled; it can also autoscan for surveillance. It generally includes an integral gun predictor (ballistics in ROM). Series 2100, the simplest, is a surveillance device that can be slewed to a target detected by radar. Series 2200/2300 is a gun FCS with a laser RF. In System 2200, the operator standing at the director views the outputs of the EO sensors through a hood and controls the director via two joysticks. Series 2300 substitutes a below-decks console for the hooded monitor. Series 2400 adds a Radamec IDT 2000 "intelligent" digital video autotracker and shore bombardment modes: direct fire, indirect fire (at map grid references), and beacon track.

IDT 2000 (HK 250–001) switches automatically between centroid and correlation tracking. It is carried on a VME bus-compatible extended double Eurocard (and expected to be available shortly on an IBM PC/AT-compatible circuit board). The video signal is digitized at 10 MHz, giving 512 × 512-pixel resolution. The board carries dual 128 × 128 × 8-bit (the latter for shades of gray) high-speed image memories, which can be reconfigured as 512 × 512 × 1-bit memories to cover the full FOV. Alternatively, the image may be digitized at 5 or 2.5 MHz, so that a larger (but less distinct) image may be stored. The board also carries a 256 × 256 × 4-bit overlay memory to store graphics and text. Six "areas of interest" in the image can be captured and/or processed independently. Some frequently used image-processing functions are realized directly in hardware, and the board is provided with a 20-MHz 32-bit processor and 64 kbytes of program and data memory. Outputs are Video 1 (raw video with superimposed graphics) and Video 2 (digitally enhanced video without graphics); target position and size output; servo tracking outputs; and target and scene data output to a master control processor in a multisensor application.

Radamec announced Series 2500 and Series 2600 in 1995. Series 2500 is essentially an improved Series 2400 with its sensors in a streamlined egg roughly equivalent to that of Sea Archer 30; options are 3–5- and 8–12-micron FLIRs, TV, and an eye-safe high-PRF laser RF. As in Series 2400, the below-decks console has two screens (for two imaging sensors) and a joystick; a touch-screen is used for control. Software includes a multimode auto-tracker. The system can operate in TWS mode (five targets). Radamec states that this system employs several new or improved tracking and processing techniques. A fast airplane can be detected beyond 18 km.

The version for Australia uses a BAe Australia 3–5-micron FLIR (640 × 486 PtSi FPA), which is said to offer three times the range of an 8–12-micron FLIR in hot/humid conditions. It also carries an eye-safe laser ranger.

Series 2600 carries a Siemens frequency-agile J(Ka)-band radar tracker (with MTI) instead of the laser RF. Radamec and Siemens describe Series 2600 as the first fully integrated radar/EO system; its management processor automatically decides its mode of operation, taking into account target parameters, environmental conditions, and EMCON state.

Note that Radamec calls its stabilized platforms directors, although many of them carry other payloads, such as jammers or radar antennas.

Users: Australia (Series 1000N in *Huon*-class minehunters, Series 2400 in ANZAC frigates, Series 2500 in *Perry* class [contract for three with option for three more announced fall 1995]; reports of 2100 in the *Adams* and *Perry* classes seem to have been premature), Brazil (2100 on Type 22s), Denmark (two on frigate *Beskytterren*), Finland (two 2400 on *Hameenmaa*, 2100 on two *Kiisla* coast guard OPVs), Hong Kong (2100 on six Pacific Forum–type patrol craft), India (2400 in four *Samar* OPVs), Jordan (2300, a simple gun-pointer, in "Hawk" class), Korea (2400, a full FCS, in *Ulsan*, *Pohang*, and *Donghae* classes and in "Sea Wolf"–class Maritime Police Patrol boats), Malaysia (2400 in two *Lekiu*-class frigates), Spain (two 2100 on *Principe de Asturias*), United Kingdom (2100, a full FCS, designated RNEOSS, in Type 42 destroyers, Type 22 Batch 2, "Castle"-class OPVs). Other reported users (probably of pedestals, not of EO systems) are Belgium, Chile, Egypt, Italy, New Zealand, Norway, Paki-stan, Singapore, and Sweden. Bharat Electronics has a license to make Series 2400, presumably for the coast guard craft listed above.

♦ TDS

Target Designation Sight, manufactured by Defence Equipment and Systems Ltd. (formerly Laurence Scott), is the standard Royal Navy target designator, comparable in function to the U.S. Mk 24. It is also in service with nine other navies. The head, to which a standard pair of binoculars is fitted, is counterbalanced for easy tracking in elevation, and height can be adjusted to suit the operator; an illuminated bearing scale atop the pedestal allows the operator to align the sight with a given target bearing. The target-designation switch is in the right-hand grip. The pedestal (less binocular) can be extended from 1.52 to 2.03 m in height, and swept radius is 0.3 m; total weight is 77 kg. Training limits are 170 deg, and elevation limits are +85/−15 deg. Transmission accuracy is 30 minutes of arc.

The Laurence Scott LASS (Look-Out Aimer Stabilized Sight) has been made for the Royal Navy since about 1964.

♦ V3800/V3900

GEC Sensors thermal imager is widely used, for example in Radamec directors, in Seaguard, and in upgraded Saab EOS-400s. Based on the 8–13-micron UK Thermal Imaging Common Module (TICM II), it has a zoom lens (FOVs 2 × 3- to 8 × 12-deg). Its SPRITE detector uses eight parallel CMTs. Pupil diameter is 10 mm. The image is produced at 625 or 525 lines at 50 Hz. The scanner head weighs 9.5 kg.

V3900 is a successor, also using the SPRITE detector, with a closed-cycle Stirling refrigerator and digital remote control. It was ordered for the Radamec systems on board the Malaysian frigates and the Hong Kong patrol craft (see Radamec entry above).

FIRE-CONTROL SYSTEMS

♦ Sea Archer 1 (GSA 7)/Sapphire/Sea Archer 30 (GSA 8)

Sea Archer is a Sperry (UK) optronic FCS using a modified Laurence Scott OFD and a Sperry 1412A computer (16 kwords, recalculating gun orders 64 times/sec, providing new output 512 times/sec) carrying two sets of ballistics. Development began in 1974 based on an EO (television) tracker developed for the land-based Rapier missile system.

Sea Archer 1A (Royal Navy GSA [gun system automation] 7) adds below-decks controls. Mod 1 uses a heavier Mk 5 OFD, which is stiffened against vibration and offers better tracking accuracy. Mod 2 can control two different guns simultaneously rather than alternatively. Unit price for the Thai Mod 2s, ordered 1986–88, was about $2.23M.

Mod 1 can carry three sensors. British GSA 7s, which originally had only televisions and laser rangers, had V3800 FLIRs added in 1986. The Thai version bought in 1986 carries a dual-FOV LLLTV (12/3 deg), a V3807 FLIR (in the LST only), and laser ranger.

These versions are manned and LOS-stabilized. The associated target indication system slews the director onto the target, the operator searching only in elevation, then manually tracking to measure bearing rate. Once the target has been acquired, the operator fires the laser to determine its range.

Sea Archer 2 was abortive, the limits of the 1412A computer having been reached.

Marconi's Sapphire is an ST802 or ST1802 FCS radar (with coaxial TV camera) combined with a Sea Archer computer (predictor) and a one-operator console. Evaluated for the Royal Navy in 1975, it was announced in 1976; the ST1802 version was announced in 1985 (but, apparently, it had already been supplied to Egypt for the *Ramadan* class in 1981). Special features include an air target coasting mode (rate-aided tracking if a target is temporarily lost in clutter) and fuze computation for star-shell and chaff. Maximum surface target speed is 60 kt. If a target drops below 1.5 deg above the horizon, the system automatically switches to tracking by TV, to overcome multipath.

The DES Target Designation Sight, on display at RNEE, 1989. The bulbous object is a handhold (the target side of the designator is visible). (DES)

Sea Archer 30s atop the bridge of the British frigate HMS *Cumberland*, with a Sea Wolf director between them. (G. Arra, 1989)

The Omani fast-attack boat *Dhofar* shows a Sea Archer optronic director above her bridge. The radar is AWS-4. Barricade chaff launchers are visible on the bridge abaft the pilot house. The large tubes visible aft are Exocet launchers. (Sultan of Oman's Navy)

Sea Archer 3 became Sea Archer 30 (adopted 1985 as Royal Navy GSA 8/GPEOD [general purpose EO director], the first Royal Navy entirely autonomous digital FCS). The dual British designation reflects a decision to buy a single unit instead of the projected combination of an EO FCS and a surveillance device.

It explains the combination of a very large object lens (240mm, 3-deg FOV at maximum zoom) with a 20-power telescope. The distinctive spherical hood was chosen to minimize both wind resistance and RCS.

Unlike Mk 1, Sea Archer 30 is unmanned and it autotracks. Its single-VME board computer employs a Zilog Z8000 series CPU (the 21-slot box can accommodate up to five CPU cards). The director (swept radius 448 mm) carries a CCD daylight TV, an 8–12-micron SPRITE FLIR (with integral Stirling refrigerator), and a laser ranger (1.06 microns, 10 MW, 10.5 pps). Elevation limits are $+75/-35$ deg; training and elevation rates are both 90 deg/sec. Both TV and FLIR have zoom lenses ($3.6\times-20\times$, FOVs 16.7×11.1 to 3×2 deg). Claimed maximum range is over 20 km, and IR resolution at 10 km is less than 1 m. Designed MTBF is 175 hr. Below-decks weights: console 230 kg, predictor 110 kg, power supply 45 kg.

Automatic tracking modes are: edge, centroid, and correlation. Centroid is automatically selected for air targets and correlation for surface targets (i.e., for targets in strong clutter), but the operator can override these choices. The tracking gate around the target automatically adapts to target size, to exclude decoys. The point of aim can be moved manually while the system auto-tracks, for example while tracking a crossing air target. In correlation mode, the system automatically coasts at the last known angular rate if the target is lost in clutter. There is also an optional auto-acquisition mode.

The predictor has two separate filtering/prediction channels, so in theory it can control two guns firing at two different targets simultaneously. In theory, however, Sea Archer 30 can handle up to six surface targets.

Users:

GSA 7 (Sea Archer 1): Brunei (*Waspada* class), Ireland (*Peacock* class), Oman (*Dhofar* [Mk 2 version], 37.5m-class patrol boats and *Al Munassir*), Thailand (*Khamronsin* class [Mod 2], T93 class [Mod 1], and PS 700–class LSTs), United Kingdom (*Peacock* and "Island" classes). Planned for the Royal Thai Navy *Naresuan*-class frigates and carrier *Chakkrinareubet* and probably on two projected LSDs and three projected LSTs.

Sapphire: Egypt (*October*, *Ramadan* classes), Kenya (*Nyayo* class).

GSA 8 (Sea Archer 30): United Kingdom (Type 23 [GSA 8B] and Type 22 Batch 3 [GSA 8A] classes).

UNITED STATES

Since the end of the Cold War, U.S. naval interest has turned to littoral operations, where ships may not be able to help defend each other and where the main threat may be relatively short-range pop-up missiles, some of them supersonic. The current responses are mainly much better integration of shipboard weapons and sensors (SSDS) aboard non-Aegis ships and better integration within the fleet (CEC; see the CDS section). There is also considerable interest in countering future low-observable (stealthy) missiles; reportedly the Navy leads a "black" counter-low observables (CLO) office, possibly partly under the code name Link Iron (a "black" element of the ship self-defense program).

Two new types of shipboard radar under development, HF surface-wave (see below) and ultra-wide-band (UWB), both offer some CLO capability, HF because it is not confused by details of target shape, and UWB because a target is unlikely to be equally stealthy over a very broad frequency range. UWB typically employs extremely short (picosecond) pulses that are inherently very broad-band. It offers an ability to penetrate earth and other obstructions. Work on a UWB phased-array design (a space-fed 8×8 array) for quick-reaction ship self-defense began in FY95, with field tests scheduled in FY96/97.

There is also reported interest in a rapidly variable, highly adaptive antenna, which might be able to work over a very wide range of frequencies, achieving small effective beamwidths despite its limited size (and hence its limited RCS). This may be work reported as the development of superresolution radars. It is also possible that the rapidly variable antenna would be used to reinforce (hence make more detectable) the regular variation characteristic of radar reflections from some types of low-observable aircraft, though that seems more likely to be a function of radar signal processing.

Work has also been proceeding on radar waveforms, which might be less vulnerable to attacks by enemy antiradar missiles. Tri-service tests of these waveforms began in FY95. It is not clear to what extent this work coincides with work on LPI radars (field tests of which, for surface search, began in FY95).

Some conceptual work is proceeding on a future multifunction radar (design and concept development were completed in FY95).

Another major theme of the past few years has been electro-optics, which offers more or less fully passive target detection and tracking. In FY93, for example, work on three-dimensional algorithms to distinguish air targets in clutter was completed. That year's program included work on a means of compensating for nonuniformities in a focal plane array, a means of cutting the cost and weight of IR sensors and seekers. A French VIGY 200 was bought as a test bed for IRST research, the U.S. Navy installing its own two-color system. The FY96 program included a joint Army-Navy program to develop a real-time signal processor and algorithm for a multicolor IRST, as well as joint U.S./UK sea trials of the multicolor IRST on board a British frigate. This work was to culminate in an operational system comprising an IRST and a thermal imaging sensor system (TISS), comprising, in effect, a TWS EO FCS. The IR program suffered very considerable delays, and to date (mid-1996) only the TISS has been bought. There is apparently some question as to whether the IRST element is worthwhile, given false target problems due to, for example, clouds and haze.

The Gulf War popularized a new U.S. naval mission: theater missile defense (TMD). That would certainly be applicable to Marines operating on foreign shores, but it may also be important to allies threatened by future Sadaam Husseins. The marine-protection mission entails relatively short-range area air defense; the missiles will generally be intercepted within the atmosphere. Allied support, particularly from the sea, requires longer-range interception, probably often outside the atmosphere. The Navy signed an MoU with the Strategic Defense Initiative Organization (SDIO) in October 1991. LEAPs (Lightweight Exoatmospheric Projectiles) were tested atop SM-2 missiles in 1994–95. Although the tests were not completely successful, the Navy has argued that they proved out the concept, and current U.S. plans for ballistic missile defense include modified SM-2 missiles fired from Aegis ships. See below for details.

RADARS

◆ HF Surface-Wave Radar

The Navy is conducting a $2\frac{1}{2}$-year advanced technology demonstration (ATD) program to prove this technology to detect low-altitude missiles beyond a ship's horizon. Lockheed Sanders (with SWRI, which makes the HF/DF used in Classic Outboard) won the contract to develop a prototype radar on 27 January 1996. After a demonstration at Point Mugu, the radar will be tested on board an LSD. The transmitting antennas are meandering-wave units (to limit size) mounted on either side near the bridge. The receivers are deck-edge or superstructure side units similar to those used in Classic Outboard and in the Spartan HF/DF system.

This radar uses inherently stealthy FMCW waveforms with a 50% duty cycle, with co-located transmission and reception antennas. The ATD apparently required sea-skimmer detection at 37 km (cross-section 0.1 m²) and aircraft detection at 74 km.

◆ BPS-12/14 and SS-2

Band: X
Beam: 2.6 × 16 deg
Peak Power: 110 kW
Gain: 29 dB
Pulse Width: 0.5 microsec

PRF: 600 pps
Scan Rate: 0–8 rpm
Antenna Dimensions: 3 × 0.75 ft
Antenna Weight: 300 lb (total weight 2050 lb)

Data apply to BPS-14.

These submarine surface-search radars all produce much the same signals. SS-2, the wartime standard, was the prototype for the series. Reliable range on a destroyer is 12 nm; range limits are 400 and 80,000 yd. Bearing accuracy is 0.25 deg. These radars have an integral periscope range-only attack radar (which replaces the earlier ST): beam is 30 × 10 deg. In BPS-14 the antenna drive has been moved inside the submarine.

Users:

BPS-12: Turkey (*Tang* class)
BPS-14: United States (*Narwhal,* some *Sturgeons*)
SS-2: Peru (*Dos de Mayo* class), Taiwan (Guppy II class), Turkey (Guppy III, Guppy IIA classes)

◆ BPS-15/16

Band: X
Beam: 3 × 13 deg
Peak Power: 35 kW
Gain: 29 dB
Pulse Width: (a) 0.1 (b) 0.5 microsec
PRF: (a) 1500 (b) 750 pps
Scan Rate: Up to 9.5 rpm
Antenna Dimensions: Aperture 40 in
Antenna Weight: 168 lb

Data apply to BPS-15. Sperry's surface-search/navigational radar uses a horn-array antenna. Minimum range is 25 yd, and range resolution is 30 yd in the short-pulse and 100 yd in the long-pulse modes.

BPS-15 radar, USS *Hawkbill.* (*Ships of the World*)

BPS-16 has a 50-kW frequency-agile (8–12 GHz) transmitter with the same pulse characteristics as BPS-15. Sperry won this contract in 1987 after protesting its initial award to Norden.

Users: BPS-15: United States (*Ohio, Los Angeles, La Fayette, Permit/Sturgeon* classes). BPS-16 is being bought for the *Seawolf* class, for the last three *Ohios,* and for backfit into other *Ohios,* but it is not yet planned for new *Los Angeles*–class submarines.

◆ SPS-5 and SPS-53/60

Band: Xb (6400 MHz); C (5450–5825 MHz) in SPS-5C and -5D
Beam: 1.75 × 15 deg (csc² to 22 deg)
Peak Power: 350 kW
Gain: 29 dB
Pulse Width: 0.5 microsec
PRF: 680 pps

Scan Rate: 17 rpm
Antenna Dimensions: 101 × 52.5 (including pedestal) × 101 (depth) in
Antenna Weight: 205 lb including pedestal

Raytheon's small-ship surface-search radar was first delivered in 1952. Data above are for SPS-5C, introduced about 1960, which shifted from Xb- to C-band.

Sperry's SPS-53 is a later, roughly equivalent, high-resolution X-band navigational radar (in some ships it replaced SPS-5); the solid-state version was SPS-60. It could use either a 5ft or an 8ft slotted-waveguide antenna (beams, respectively, were 1 × 20 or 1.6 × 20 deg). Peak power is 40 kW (0.5 microsec/750 pps or 0.1 microsec/1500 pps). Except for the *Ashevilles*, ships apparently generally had these radars replaced with commercial sets when exported. In the U.S. Navy, the replacement is SPS-64 or -69, and few SPS-53/60 probably survive.

Users:

SPS-5: Colombia (*Dealey* class), Greece (*Cabildo* class), Mexico (some *Auk*-class ex-minesweepers), Taiwan (*Cabildo*-class LSD). The Brazilian carrier *Minas Gerais* may retain the very similar SPS-4.

SPS-53: Greece (*Asheville* class), Turkey (*Asheville* class), United States (some *Spruance* class, *Edenton* class).

◆ SPS-6/12

Band: L (1250–1350 MHz)
Beam: 3.5 × 30 deg (SPS-12: 3 × 30 deg)
Peak Power: 500 kW
Gain: 27 dB (SPS-12: 25 dB)
Pulse Width: (a) 4 microsec (b) 1 microsec
PRF: (a) 150 (b) 600 pps (SPS-12: [a] 300 pps)
Scan Rate: 2.5–15 rpm
Antenna Dimensions: 204 × 95 7/8 in (SPS-12: 205 × 92 in)
Antenna Weight: 924 lb (including pedestal) (SPS-12: 990 lb)

These data apply to the SPS-6C version commonly installed on board destroyers and frigates of the 1950s and early 1960s. This radar could detect large high-altitude aircraft at 70–140 nm and fighters at 60–80 nm. SPS-6D omitted the integral IFF of SPS-6C, and -6E had a better receiver. Some sets may have had a peak power of 750 kW. The antenna was designed with a beam broad in its vertical dimension to reliably detect high-altitude jets.

SPS-12 and SPS-10 radars on the foremast of the Canadian destroyer *Fraser*, 1989. (G. Till)

SPS-12 was, in effect, an improved SPS-6. Although peak power did not increase, long pulses could be emitted at a higher rate, for twice the average power of the earlier radar.

Users:

SPS-6: Colombia (*Dealey* class), Greece (*Cabildo* class), Indonesia (*Claud Jones* class), Iran (PF 103 class), Thailand (two *Tapi* class; may have been replaced by DA-08).

SPS-12: Taiwan (command ship *Kao Hsiung*).

◆ SPS-10/SPS-67

Band: C (5450–5825 MHz)
Beam: 1.5 × 16 deg
Peak Power: 500 kW
Gain: 30 dB
Pulse Width: (a) 0.25 (b) 1.3 microsec
PRF: 625–650 pps
Scan Rate: 15 rpm
Antenna Dimensions: 126 in × 76 in (with pedestal)
Antenna Weight: 442 lb including pedestal

Data are for SPS-10B (AS-936 antenna).

SPS-10 was the standard U.S. surface-search radar; it has been superseded, to a limited extent, by SPS-55 and is being replaced by SPS-67, which is essentially a solid-state version. The latest version is SPS-10G.

SPS-10 had a 285-kW transmitter; -10B introduced the current 500-kW type. SPS-10E introduced a new antenna (1.9 × 16-deg beam, 17 rpm), and -10F a new PRF (625–660 pps). The two pulse widths make for resolutions of, respectively, 41 and 213 yd. During trials in 1956 SPS-10 showed that it could detect a continu-

Although SPS-6 is virtually extinct in the U.S. Navy, many survive abroad. This photograph was taken in 1950, but current installations use the same antenna, typically at the masthead. (U.S. Navy)

Chien Yang is fitted with an H930 modular combat system. She is fitted with a Signaal air-search radar, SPS-10/SPS-58, for surface and low-altitude air search, and a Signaal STIR fire-control radar, which also provides illumination for her SM-1 SAMs. The masthead radome is a TACAN. (Fu S. Mei)

The new SPS-67(V)2/(V)3 antenna. (Northrop Grumman, formerly Westinghouse Norden)

ously exposed snorkel in Sea State 2 at an average of 9630 yd (maximum reliable range 12,100 yd) and could track a periscope (with 6 ft exposed) in Sea State 1 at 16,000 yd. Maximum reliable tracking range on a 3ft attack periscope in Sea State 1 was 10,100 yd. These trials showed that the radar could reliably detect a submarine attack periscope intermittently exposed during an attack in Sea State 2 and below.

The associated IFF is integrated with the basic radar, and the IFF beam is 6 × 22 deg.

Some versions of this radar used the AS-1161 lightweight antenna, identical with the AS-1002 of SPS-5C. SPS-10 and -10A used AS-615; later versions use AS-936, which is essentially the same antenna with a 440-V three-phase drive instead of the earlier 110-V single-phase drive. AS-936B adds an extension to the bottom of the antenna and "blinders" on the sides of the feed horn, to reduce sidelobes and minor interference with other ship antennas.

Deliveries began in October 1953.

Norden's (now Grumman Northrop's) solid-state SPS-67 is intended to replace SPS-10 on a one-for-one basis, using the same antenna. The magnetron is the same as that of the SPS-55. SPS-67 is the first U.S. Navy radar built of standard electronic modules (SEMs) for commonality with future radars. Designed MTBF

is 600 hr (1000 hr exceeded), and designed MTTR is 29 min, the short repair time being achieved partly by means of built-in test equipment. By way of comparison, SPS-10 was credited with an MTBF of 150 hr (which was the best of any U.S. naval radar in 1976), but MTTR was 5–6 hr because it had no automatic fault-finding equipment.

A new harbor-navigation mode (using a 0.1-microsec pulse) allows clutter-free detection of targets (buoys and small craft) at shorter range than is common with SPS-10. Tests have shown that buoys and small obstructions can be detected at 75 yd. The width of the long pulse was reduced to 1.0 microsec. Peak power was cut to 280 kW, and instrumented range is 56 nm.

SPS-67 currently exists in three versions. (V)1 is the original type, essentially duplicating SPS-10 with more modern technology. (V)2 and (V)3 replace the original SPS-10 antenna with a nuclear-survivable (and much more reliable and maintainable) two-speed (15/30 rpm) linear-array antenna with integrated IFF. (V)2 should perform much better under conditions of extreme roll and pitch (e.g., in northern waters), and bearing accuracy is improved. (V)3, for the *Arleigh Burke* class, has a 2- or 4-sec data rate, coherent on-receive clutter lock DMTI (better than 24-dB improvement factor), ATD, TWS, and a direct interface to fire-control, command-and-decision, and SYS systems. The new antenna has a 1.5 × 31-deg beam (12-deg elevation in the earlier version). There is a new high-scan-rate mode (scan rate 15 or 30 rpm, rather than 15 rpm). Track file size in (V)3 is 128 (expandable).

Users: Argentina (*Cabo san Antonio*), Australia (*Adams* class [67]), Brazil (*Garcia* class), Canada (*Annapolis, Restigouche* classes [as SPS-502]), Germany (*Adams* class), Greece (*Adams, FRAM destroyers, Terrebonne Parish* classes), Indonesia (*Claud Jones* class), Iran (FRAM destroyers), South Korea (FRAM destroyers), Mexico (FRAM destroyers), Pakistan (FRAM destroyers), Spain (*Baleares, Paul Revere* classes), Taiwan (some destroyers [many with SPS-58], *Kao Hsiung* command ship), Turkey (destroyers, *Derya*), United States (carriers [67], *California* class [67], *Arleigh Burke* [67], *Knox* [10 or 67], *Blue Ridge* [10/65], *Wasp* [67], *Tarawa* [10F], *Iwo Jima, Austin, Raleigh, Harpers Ferry* [67], *Whidbey Island* [67], *Anchorage, Thomaston, Newport, Charleston, Samuel Gompers, Kilauea, Nitro, Suribachi, Mars, Coronado, La Salle, Cimmaron* [only AO 180, 186; others are SPS-55], *Ashtabula, Supply* [67(V)1], *Sacramento, Wichita, Spear, Simon Lake, Hunley* classes).

SPS-29 antenna, USS *Intrepid*. (A. Raven)

Radars are shown (as in August 1995) aboard USS *America*, now decommissioned. The white radomes are for SATCOMM. Below the upper white radomes are the dark radomes of the carrier's WLR-1 ESM system, with a WSC-3 communications dish at right on this level. Below is SPS-10, partly obscured. Below it is TAS Mk 23, on a platform projecting forward of the mast, and SPN-43 (partly obscured) to the left of the mast. The big antenna below TAS Mk 23 is for SPS-49. Forward of it is a small navigational-radar antenna. (Author)

◆ SPS-29/37

Band: P (215–225 MHz)
Beam: 19 × 25.5 deg
Peak Power: 750 kW
Gain: 18 dB
Pulse Width: 10 microsec
PRF: 300 pps
Scan Rate: 7.5 or 15 rpm
Antenna Dimensions: 210 × 102 in (140 with pedestal)
Antenna Weight: 1275 lb including pedestal (below-decks weight is 8700 lb)

The mattress antenna, AS-943, consists of 28 folded dipoles spaced a half wavelength apart vertically and horizontally, and about a quarter wavelength in front of a flat reflector. SPS-29 was first delivered in 1958; in all, 89 were made. SPS-37 has the same antenna but uses pulse compression. Peak power is 180 kW; pulse width is 200 microsec (compressed to 6), and PRF is 230–250 pps.

Users:

SPS-29: Greece (*Gearing*-class destroyers), Iran (*Sumner* class), South Korea (*Gearing* and *Sumner* classes), Mexico (*Gearing*-class destroyer *Netzahualcoyotl*), Taiwan (*Gearing* and *Sumner* classes), Turkey (*Gearing* class). Television footage shot in 1995 showed at least one Korean destroyer with DA-05 in place of SPS-29.

SPS-37: Taiwan (*Fu Yang*).

◆ SPS-39/42/52

Band: S (2910–3090 MHz)
Beam: 1.1 × 2.25 deg
Peak Power: 1000 kW
Gain: 39.5 dB (37 dB in SPA-64)
Pulse Width: (a) 2.5 (b) 4.6 (c) 10 microsec
PRF: (a) 1220–2000 (b) 488–2000 (c) 329–1050 pps
Scan Rate: (a) 15 (b) 6 (c) 6 rpm (SPS-39A: 5, 7.5, or 15 rpm)
Antenna Dimensions: 165 × 167 in (including pedestal)
Antenna Weight: 3200 lb (including pedestal)

Data apply to SPS-52 with SPA-72 antenna.

Hughes's SPS-39, the first operational U.S. 3D frequency-scanning radar, was first delivered in January 1960. Work on the improved SPS-52, essentially a digitally controlled version, began about 1963. All remaining examples have the flat planar-array antenna introduced in SPS-52. In the late 1980s, U.S. plans called for replacing all surviving SPS-39s with SPS-52s, but most of the ships so equipped were soon scrapped. SPS-52 production ended in 1989, partly because Hughes hoped to substitute a 3D version of TAS Mk 23 (which proved abortive).

The current SPA-72 antenna is a stack of 60 linear arrays (98 slots each) tilted back at 25 deg, with a serpentine delay line (for frequency scanning in elevation) running up one side.

SPS-39 has two modes: (a) high data rate (quick detection and rapid update of a nearby target), instrumented range 60 nm, scan at 15 rpm; and (b) high-angle (moderate range and data rate), instrumented range 160 nm, scan at 10 rpm. SPS-52 introduced a long-range mode (high-energy pulse), 245 (240 in SPS-52) nm, scan at 7.5 rpm. SPS-52B added an MTI/clutter rejection mode (scan at 7.5 rpm). In the high-data-rate and high-angle modes the beam elevates all the way up to 42 deg (41.6 deg in SPS-52B); for long range the beam elevates to 13 deg (there is also a 4.5-deg mode for very long range).

These radars have klystron transmitters. Although SPS-39, now extinct, had fixed pulse rates for the short and medium pulses (1850 and 925, respectively), existing radars have the variable PRFs given above.

The original SPS-52 computer was a Hughes H3118, but SPS-52B has a UYK-15, and -52C has a UYK-20. Besides beam control and stabilization, the UYK-20 provides target processing and the interface with SYS-1. A video extractor and control group

An SPS-52C antenna, on board USS *Tattnall* (DDG 19), the first ship so fitted. The bar above is an IFF interrogator. (Hughes)

SPS-40, with SPS-10 below it. (W. Donko, 1987)

(VECG) stores up to nine consecutive detections of the same object, computes their centroid in three dimensions, and passes the result to SYS-1, limiting its workload.

Reliability: as reported in 1979, SPS-52C MTBF was 216 hr, compared to the required 170 hr (and compared to a reported maximum of 67.4 hr for SPS-39 at that time).

Below-decks weights: SPS-52, 15,500; -52B, 15,934; -52C, 14,040 lb.

Users:

SPS-39: Greece (*Adams* class)

SPS-52 (all -52C except as noted): Australia (*Adams* class), Germany (*Adams* class), Italy (*Vittorio Veneto* [-52B], *Animoso, Audace* classes), Japan (*Hatakaze* and *Tachikaze* [52B] classes), Spain (*Principe de Asturias, Baleares* class [52B]), United States (*Tarawa* class, *Wasp*). The Spanish -52B is reportedly midway between -52B and -52C, with a Spanish-developed radar-integration system. The Japanese -52C has a locally developed antenna (elements embedded in plastic rather than covered by a thin plastic sheet) and special features.

◆ **SPS-40**

Band: UHF (400–450 MHz band) (10 channels)
Beam: 10 × 19 deg
Peak Power: 125–225 kW (pulse compressed)
Gain: 21 dB
Pulse Width: 60-microsec (compressed to 1.0 [0.6 in some versions]) and 3-microsec mode
PRF: 278 or 300 pps (jittered)
Scan Rate: 7.5 or 15 rpm (6 rpm in SPS-40 and -40A)
Antenna Dimensions: 216.0 × 116.8 × 111.0 (deep) in
Antenna Weight: 1425 lb, including pedestal (1728 lb for SPS-40B and later versions) (3200 lb below decks; 3400 lb for SPS-40A; 3474 lb for later versions)

Data apply to SPS-40B.

SPS-40 is, in effect, a shipboard equivalent to the radar of the E-2C. It operates at about the lowest frequency at which reasonable target definition is possible. Low frequency makes not only for a broad beam but also for big sidelobes (27 dB horizontal, 10 dB vertical). The current manufacturer is Northrop Grumman (formerly Norden).

SPS-40A introduced the broad-band transmitter (for pulse compression) and an improved solid-state receiver. SPS-40B added a low-flier detection mode (the short pulse: LFDM), ATD, DMTI, and a new IFF (AIMS, to control friendly ASW aircraft). SPS-40C and -40D are -40A modified to or above -40B standard, with additional reliability improvements. The transmitter is a tetrode tube. MTBF is 252 hr (MTTR is 45 min).

Westinghouse's (now Northrop Grumman's) SPS-40E incorporates a new SSTx solid-state transmitter intended for 90% probability of maintenance-free operation for 90 days, with no more than 11% loss of range due to module failure. The SSTx automatically shuts down in the event of damage to antenna or waveguide, then powers up to the level allowed by the other components.

A new Doppler processor provides quick track establishment; clutter improvement factor is 66 dB, compared to 54 dB without Doppler processing. The current ADT version can carry 511 tracks.

Users: Australia (*Adams* class [40C]), Brazil (*Garcia* class), Egypt (*Knox* class), Germany (*Adams* class), Greece (*Adams* and *Knox* classes), Japan (*Azuma*), Taiwan (*Knox* class), Thailand (*Knox* class), Turkey (*Berk* and *Knox* classes), United States (*California, Spruance* class [except DD 997], *Tarawa* [40B], *Iwo Jima, Austin, Raleigh, Anchorage, Sacramento* [AOE 1, 2 only]) classes and *Hamilton*-class coast guard cutters).

◆ **SPS-48**

Band: S (2900–3100 MHz)
Beam: 1.5 × 1.6 deg
Peak Power: 2.4 MW
Gain: 38.5 dB
Pulse Width: 3 microsec (per beam: 27 total); or 9-microsec single pulse
PRF: 1250–2000 pps
Scan Rate: 7.5 or 15 rpm
Antenna Dimensions: 194 × 228 in (including pedestal)
Antenna Weight: 4495 lb (including pedestal) (below-deck weights: -48, 18,211 lb; -48A, 19,651 lb; -48C, 20,548 lb); SPS-48E: 5684 lb above-decks (24,018 lb below-decks).

Data refer to SPS-48C, the ADT version with the original antenna (which survives in very small numbers). The principal version is SPS-48E, which is associated with NTU. Compared to -48C, it doubles effective radiated power by reducing sidelobes 10 dB and by increasing peak power to 2.4 MW. Its antenna has 95 rather than 76 linear arrays. Receiver sensitivity is increased. All SPS-48Es now have four-stage solid-state transmitters (SSTx), the final two stages being a 600-kW driver and then a 2400-kW output. A lightweight SPS-48E antenna (3200 vice 6600 lb) was tested late in 1995.

Development of this radar began in 1959, and the prototype was tested in 1965.

SPS-48 on board the USS *Enterprise*, 1990. (A. Chiffolo)

ITT-Gilfillan's frequency-scanning SPS-48 was intended to overcome the major flaw in SPS-39/52, that its single elevating beam did not dwell long enough in any given direction. The solution was, in effect, to stack nine beams. Each train of nine pulses (at different frequencies) contributes a pulse to each group of beams, which covers a 5-deg elevation angle. In effect each of the nine beams (beam groups) scans in elevation from pulse train to pulse train. Maximum elevation is 65 deg (45 deg in earlier versions). Instrumented range is 220 nm. Current tracking accuracy is 0.2 deg (against a requirement for 0.6 deg). MTBF is now over 500 hr (190 was specified).

Power modes are high, medium, and low. The main operating modes are EAC (equal angle coverage; energy is concentrated at low angle); MEM, maximum energy management (high power in the four lowest angle beams and medium power in the four highest angle beams); AEM (adaptive energy management, to adapt to a priority track gate or surveillance priority gate around a target generated by SYS-2; power level is adjusted to the target RCS and the jamming environment); and Low-E (low elevation, giving priority to the lower five beam groups, covering 0–28 deg; the radar transmits a Doppler waveform at 2778 pps). The radar can also transmit over a single steerable beam group, or it can concentrate power in a single beam (2 deg wide) to burn through jamming, using a chirped pulse (27 microsec compressed to 3 on reception). In this last mode, ferrite phase shifters cancel out the elevation shifts that would otherwise be caused by the changes in frequency within the chirp.

Low-E was first demonstrated on board USS *Kidd* in 1990, and then installed on board 12 NTU ships between November 1990 and November 1991. Its high pulse rate increases average power; a 1m^2 target can be detected against sea clutter at 17 nm. Low-E proved quite effective during the Gulf War, and it was further improved in 1993, after operational tests.

The success of Low-E presumably led to a February 1995 contract to ITT-Gilfillan for a pulse-Doppler upgrade (PDU) of SPS-48 analogous to the SPS-49 MPU described below, to improve detection of small targets such as sea-skimming missiles against sea clutter as well as land clutter amplified by ducting. A new PDU processor is added (partly to select waveforms automatically), and the first and second transmitter stages are replaced by a single-stage 60-kW Ultra Stable Transmitter; as a result, phase and amplitude stability are improved by 20 dB. The modified radar can detect a 0.1m^2 target flying at Mach 3 overland at 30 ft altitude (PD 0.95), compared to an earlier ability to detect a 0.3m^2 target (at Mach 0.95, PD 0.5) over water (Sea State 3) at a similar altitude. Detection range would fall from 16 to 15 nm and from 18 to 17 nm with a 50ft duct.

ITT is currently marketing a lightweight SPS-48F without the final 2.4-MW transmitter stage and with a smaller antenna (71 elements, composite construction, 3.96 × 3.65 vice 5.48 × 5.18 m, 1125 kg rather than 2970 kg, below-decks weight 6750 rather than 9900 kg). This set would detect a 1m^2 target at 90 rather than 125 nm and a 5m^2 target at 150 rather than 220 nm. Embedded microprocessors would replace the UYK-20 and SYS-2 associated with SPS-48E. MTBF would increase from 650 to 950 hr. As of mid-1996, no export sales had been achieved (although SPS-48F is short-listed for several current projects), and ITT-Gilfillan hoped that this radar would replace surviving U.S. SPS-52s.

By August 1992, 39 SPS-48E had been delivered, with six more on order (three ordered January 1992, presumably for new LHDs). Accelerated retirement of NTU cruisers has probably released sufficient SPS-48s to equip the major amphibious ships without new production.

Users: United States (carriers, *California*, *Virginia*, *Kidd* classes, *Wasp* class [except *Wasp*], *Blue Ridge* class). SPS-48 has been chosen for the projected LPD-17 class.

◆ SPS-49/SPS-100

Band: L (850–942 MHz)
Beam: 3.4 × csc^2 to 30 deg
Peak Power: 360 kW (13 kW average)
Gain: 28.5 dB
Pulse Width: 125 microsec, compressed (ratio 83:1); there is also a 2-microsec pulse for short ranges
PRF: 280 pps for long range, 800 or 1000 pps for short range
Scan Rate: 6 or 12 rpm
Antenna Dimensions: 288 × 171 in (including pedestal)
Weight: 3165 above/14,004 below decks (lb)

Data describe the (V)5 version.

Raytheon's SPS-49 is the best current U.S. 2D air-search radar. It was initially bought in quantity to equip *Perry*-class frigates. The antenna is mechanically stabilized in LOS. Work on a proposed solid-state transmitter was abandoned because the existing klystron has a service life of 5000 hr, and because development costs would have raised the price of the transmitter to about that of the radar itself.

Versions of SPS-49:

(V)3 is the Canadian version, with ADT (SHINPADS requires track rather than plot data).

(V)4 is the frigate version (an upgraded [V]2) with a radar video processor but without the coherent sidelobe canceler (CSLC) of other versions. These radars are being upgraded to (V)5 standard. This version uses a radar video processor based on UYK-20.

(V)5 is the current version for carriers, pre-Aegis cruisers, destroyers, and modernized frigates, an upgraded (V)1 or (V)4. This version, which is required for SYS-2/TMS, adds a video processor (for ATD, which was absent in [V]1) and incorporates a digital signal processor that requires its own cooling. Peak power is increased from 280 to 360 kW. Pulse characteristics (those above are for an earlier version) probably do not change, since the new average power is proportional to the old. This version uses pulse-Doppler processing (albeit with a very low first blind speed) to eliminate fixed and low-speed clutter. In a special antichaff mode, PRF is increased to increase the first blind speed. The beam can be elevated (up-spotted) to help reject main-lobe jamming.

(V)7 is the Aegis cruiser version with ADT (255 tracks: like SHINPADS, Aegis needs track rather than plot data), using the

Aegis system's cooling system. The first three *Ticonderogas* originally had (V)6, which had only ATD.

A(V)1 and *A(V)2* are new versions with medium PRF upgrade (PMU), providing a pulse-Doppler mode to detect small low-altitude targets in sea clutter. Detection range is more than doubled. PRF reportedly rises to about 3500, reducing unambiguous range to about 20 nm. The increased number of pulses/sec increased the volume of video to the point where the radar now needs four FDDI cables. The first production contract for -49A(V)1 (plus a contract for nine modification kits) was let in December 1994.

Raytheon is working on several new versions:

A private-venture (IR&D) planar array was tested on board the cruiser *Leyte* Gulf. The new antenna is lighter, offers lower sidelobes (by beam-forming), and forms vertical beams (on reception) for height-finding. Raytheon envisages two versions: (a) producing beams sequentially for surveillance (i.e., moving a single beam vertically) to track targets up to 70 deg; (b) producing multiple beams (probably three), processing them simultaneously, at a cost in range.

Raytheon's proposed planar-array antenna for SPS-49, at the 1995 Navy League show. (Author)

SPS-49(VSR), the volume search radar, is Raytheon's active-array version of SPS-49.

SPS-49LW, lightweight, is a version with a small antenna.

SPS-100 (Raytheon's designation) is a new export version with a lightweight antenna (5182 × 3302 mm, gain 27.8 dB, scan 15 rpm, 766 kg above/2886 kg below decks) and solid-state transmitter (based on that of the ASR-23SS air-traffic-control radar: 47 kW peak power, 1.2 kW average) for small foreign ships (1000 t and above) such as corvettes. Estimated free-space range to detect a 1m² target is 137 km. This ADT radar would have an instrumented range of 100 km against small targets, or 200 km if only large ones were expected. The smaller antenna would produce a 3.3-deg × csc² to 30-deg beam, concentrating more energy at high angles, hence making the radar more difficult to overfly. Raytheon claims that SPS-100 is the lightest available L-band radar.

Users: SPS-49: Australia (*Perry* class), Canada ("City" class), Korea (chosen for KDX class), Spain (*Perry* class), Taiwan (*Perry* class), United States (carriers, *Virginia* class [except CGN 38, 39],

Ticonderoga class, *Kidd, Perry, Wasp, Whidbey Island, Harpers Ferry,* LPD-17 classes, *Stalwart* [T-AGOS 1]).

♦ **SPS-55/Seahawk**

> **Band:** X (9.05–10.00 GHz)
> **Beam:** 1.5 × 20 deg
> **Peak Power:** 130 kW
> **Gain:** 31 dB
> **Pulse Width:** (a) 0.12 (b) 1.0 microsec
> **PRF:** (a) 2250 (b) 750 pps
> **Scan Rate:** 16 rpm
> **Antenna Dimensions:** 80 × 28 in (including pedestal)
> **Antenna Weight:** 195 lb including pedestal

SPS-55 is the X-band successor to the C-band SPS-10; the frequency was chosen to avoid interference with C-band missile trackers. The antenna consists of two slotted waveguides arranged back to back, the operator choosing either circular or horizontal polarization. The former helps to overcome rain clutter, as the raindrops tend to reverse the circular polarization of the waves they reflect, and the radar can reject signals of opposite polarization. More complex targets do not reverse polarization in so systematic a way; and their echoes are, therefore, not entirely rejected (although some target echo is lost). Each antenna consists of an array of 80 narrow slots skewed in angle (with alternating skew angles for squintless feed). Minimum range (short-pulse mode) is 50 yd; it is 300 yd in the long-pulse mode. Resolution: 75 and 650 ft, respectively. Reliability: 500hr MTBF was required, 1200hr demonstrated.

SPS-55 antenna, showing its back-to-back construction. (Cardion)

SPS-55 was developed by Raytheon but produced by Cardion; the first contract was let in June 1971.

Cardion currently advertises a solid-state derivative of SPS-55, SPS-55(M) Seahawk, with an integral IFF antenna mounted directly over its slotted-waveguide array. The receiver is improved (sensitivity is increased by 5 dB) and a new radar scan-converter is provided. The system can support a plot extractor/tracker (i.e., ADT) with a capacity of over 200 tracks. The company also offers a conventional high-gain reflector version (7.5 × 1 m, gain 46.5 dB, 0.3 × 1.8 deg, azimuth sidelobe level −27 dB within 5 deg, −34 dB between 5 and 10 deg, −40 dB outside 10 deg).

Users: Australia (*Perry* class), Israel (*Lahav* class), Saudi Arabia (PCG, PGG, and MSC 322 classes), Spain (*Principe de Asturias, Perry* class), Taiwan (*Perry* class), United States (*Ticonderoga, Arleigh Burke, Spruance, Kidd, Perry* classes).

♦ **SPS-58/65**

> **Band:** L (1215–1365 MHz)
> **Beam:** 4 × 18 deg
> **Peak Power:** 12 kW
> **Gain:** 26 dB
> **Pulse Width:** 5 microsec (SPS-65: 7 microsec)
> **PRF:** 2290 or 3050 pps (SPS-58A: 2285 or 3048 pps; SPS-65: 2315 or 3064 pps)
> **Scan Rate:** 15 or 19 rpm
> **Antenna Dimensions:** 234 × 120 in
> **Antenna Weight:** 1200 lb (2100 lb below decks)

Westinghouse's L-band pulse-Doppler radar was developed at high priority as part of the new antiship missile defense system (BPDMS) developed from 1967 on. It was derived from the same German Siemens mobile pulse-Doppler radar (MPDR-45) which was used as a target designator (for NATO Sea Sparrow) in the Norwegian *Oslo* class. SPS-58 (with a three-stage klystron transmitter) was a stand-alone system; SPS-65 (with ATD and a solid-state transmitter driver) could feed into a ship's CDS. Both shared the SPS-10 antenna (Taiwan uses a stand-alone version of SPS-58, data for the antenna of which is given above). The version using the SPS-10 antenna has a 6 × 16-deg beam (gain 23 dB) and scans at 15 rpm. Instrumented range of the Taiwanese version is 125 nm (minimum 1 nm); a 1m² target can be detected at 66.4 nm. The radar automatically detects any target flying faster than an 80-kt MTI threshold.

A Taiwanese *Lung Chiang*–class missile boat shows her stand-alone SPS-58 antenna, 1996. The surface search radar is UPS-60, which is made in Taiwan. The optical director visible forward of the lattice mast is Kollmorgen's Mk 35. The masthead radome covers the antenna of the R76 FCS used to control the ship's Hsiung Feng I missiles and her OTO-Melara 76mm gun. (Fu S. Mei)

Users: Taiwan (SPS-58A [using SPS-10 antenna] in all destroyers; stand-alone version in *Lung Chiang* class), United States (SPS-65 in *Iwo Jima* class; all in carriers replaced by TAS Mk 23).

♦ **SPS-64**

Band: X (9345–9405 MHz) or S (3025–3075 MHz)
Beam: Four alternative X-band slotted-waveguide antennas: (a) 1.9 × 22 deg (b) 1.25 × 22 deg (c) 0.9 × 22 deg (d) 0.7 × 22 deg; S-band slotted-waveguide antenna: (e) 2 × 25 deg
Peak Power: Three alternative transmitters: (a) 20-kW fixed or tunable X-band, (b) 50-kW X-band, (c) 60-kW S-band
Gain: 28 dB
Pulse Width: (a) 0.06 (b) 0.5 (c) 1.0 microsec
PRF: (a) 3600 (b) 1800 (c) 900 pps
Scan Rate: 33 rpm
Antenna Dimensions: (a) 4 ft X-band only (b) 6 ft (c) 9 ft (d) 12 ft (e) 6 ft
Antenna Weight: (b) 140 lb (d) 332 lb

Raytheon's family of navigational radars for the Army, Navy, and Coast Guard employs (a) a high-powered S-band radar to detect surface targets out to 20 or 30 nm (AS-3195 antenna, RT-1241A transmitter-receiver); (b) a high-resolution X-band navigational radar (6-, 9-, or 12ft antenna); (c) an interswitch unit that can connect any indicator/receiver/transmitter combination (so that the 12ft antenna can be used for X- or S-band, for example); (d) a RAYCAS V CIC indicator; (e) a RAYPATH indicator; (f) an ESM interface; and (g) a fire-control interface. The RAYCAS V 16in PPI is used in the (V)6 and (V)10 versions below. It can track up to 20 targets within 40 nm automatically, with direct readouts of target range/bearing and course/speed. Target true or relative vectors can be displayed. Intercept course/speed are automatically calculated. Up to 20 ground-stabilized true marks can be used to mark datum or reference points, plus up to 16 ground-stabilized navigational line segments (e.g., boundaries, fairways, danger zones). As an option, up to 1500 geographic data points can be stored. RAYPATH (12in PPI, in the [V]11 version) automatically tracks up to 20 targets within 20 nm; automatically displays target CPA, course/speed, and bow crossing distance; provides automatic warning when a target violates the operator's

CPA threshold; displays target true or relative vectors; and has true-motion and trial maneuver (to analyze proposed evasive action) modes. Fire-control data can be transmitted to these indicators, and they in turn can transmit data to a ship's FCS. A synchronization mode slaves X-band navigational radar transmission to the fire-control radar to avoid mutual interference. The ESM interface (AM-6933) provides blanking pulse outlets for the X- and S-band radars, to avoid self-detection.

SPS-64 on board the Coast Guard cutter *Bear*. The "egg" atop the bridge is a Mk 92 FCS for the 76mm/62 gun forward. Also visible is the box containing an SLQ-32 ESM system, on a platform just aft of the bridge windows. The flat object atop the mast is a TACAN aircraft beacon. (U.S. Naval Institute)

Versions (with Raytheon commercial designations in parentheses, where applicable):

(V)1 for the Coast Guard, with 6ft X-band antenna (20-kW X-band transmitter) (RM 1220 6X), is the radar in *Reliance*- and *Diver*-class cutters, and in patrol boats.

(V)2 for the Coast Guard, with 6ft X-band antenna (two 20-kW X-band transmitter-receivers and three displays) (RM 1220 6X, RM 1620).

(V)3 for the Coast Guard, with two 6ft X-band antennas (two 20-kW transmitter-receivers) (RM 1220 6X, RM 1220 6X RM16).

(V)4 for the Coast Guard, with one 6ft X-band antenna and one 12ft S-band antenna (20-kW X-band and 60-kW S-band) (RM 1220 6X, RM 1660 12S RM16).

(V)5 for the Army, with one 6ft X-band antenna (20-kW X-band transmitter) (TM 1620 6X).

(V)6 for the Coast Guard, with one 6ft X-band and one 12ft S-band antenna (50-kW X-band and 60-kW S-band transmitters and two displays) (RM 1250 6X, RAYCAS 1660 12S), is the radar in *Hamilton*- and *Bear*-class cutters.

(V)7 for the Coast Guard, with one 6ft X-band antenna (20-kW X-band transmitter) (RM 1225 6X).

(V)8 for the Coast Guard, with one 6ft X-band antenna (20-kW X-band transmitter) (RM 1025 6X).

(V)9 for the U.S. Navy, with one 6ft X-band antenna (20-kW X-band transmitter) (RM 1220 6X).

(V)10 for the Coast Guard, with two 6ft X-band antennas (two 20-kW X-band transmitters and three displays).

(V)11 for the Coast Guard, with one 6ft X-band antenna (20-kW X-band transmitter) (RAYPATH 1225 6X).

(V)12 for the Army, a 10-kW X-band set (1210 4X).

(V)13 for the Army, a 10-kW X-band set (1010 E 4X).

(V)14 for the Army, a 10-kW X-band set using a radome (1010 E D).

(V)15 for the U.S. Navy, with one 6ft X-band antenna (50-kW transmitter) (RM 1650 6X, RAYCAS V).

(V)16 for the Army, with one 6ft X-band antenna (50-kW transmitter) (RAYPATH 1650 6X).

(V)17 for the Army, with one 12ft S-band antenna (60-kW transmitter) (RAYPATH 1650 12S).

(V)18 for the U.S. Navy, with one 9ft X-band antenna (50-kW transmitter) (RAYCAS 1650 9X NWU-51).

Users: Bahamas (Cape class), Costa Rica (Cape class), Dominican Republic (*Mella, Cohoes,* and *Admirable* classes), Germany (Type 332, 343 MCM ships), Korea (HDC 800 class, *Donghae* class, HDC 1150 class), Mexico (*Aquila* and Cape classes), Micronesia (Cape class), Panama (Point class), Philippines (*Cormoran* class, 77ft class, amphibious ships), Saudi Arabia (77ft class), Spain (*Perry* class), Thailand (new Type 25T frigates), United States ([V]9 in carriers, in CGN 36/38 class, *Ticonderoga* class, *Arleigh Burke* class, *Kidd* class, some *Spruance* class, some *Knox* class, "Osprey" class, *Cyclone* class [PBCs], some *Avenger* class, older MCM craft, *Blue Ridge* class, LHAs, LHDs, LSD 41/49 class, AOEs, AORs, *Edenton* class, YP 676 class, [V]6 in *Hamilton* and *Bear* classes, *Reliance, Diver, Polar Star, Mackinaw,* "Island" [Coast Guard], "Point" [Coast Guard] classes, Coast Guard buoy tenders, Coast Guard tugs; also in many Army craft, including [V]2 in LSVs and LSCU 2000 class), Uruguay (Cape class).

◆ SPS-69 and SPS-71

Raytheon's R21X/R41X (SPS-69) and R20X/R40X are solid-state X-band replacements for the earlier SPS-66/Pathfinder 1900. R20/21X use 7in displays; R40/41X use 10in displays. SPS-69 uses a slotted-waveguide antenna; SPS-71, standardized in 1993, uses a radome. Peak power is 4 kW. Pulse characteristics: 0.08 microsec/2250 pps, 0.25 microsec/1500 pps, 0.5 microsec/750 pps. Beam: 4 × 25 deg. The cylindrical radome is 620 mm in diameter and weighs 9.5 kg.

These radars, which are widely used on board small boats, are being purchased by the Navy and Coast Guard under the Radar B program (Radar A is a Mil-Spec set such as SPS-55 or -67); in mid-1990 the U.S. Coast Guard signed a 3-yr contract for 758 R41X radars to replace existing SPS-66s and -66As (Pathfinder 3100s). Radar B is a navigational set with true-bearing capability.

The SPS-70 designation has not, apparently, been assigned.

◆ SPS-72

Sperry Marine's RASCAR (Raster-scan Collision Avoidance Radar) S- or X-band navigational radar was given this designation in 1993. The console can incorporate an ARPA automatic tracker, or the radar can operate as an indicator only. Range scales are 0.25 to 96 nm. The X-band transmitter operates at 25 kW, the S-band at 30 kW. Antennas: 7- and 9ft X-band, 14ft S-band.

◆ SPS-73? (Furuno radars)/HSSR 2200

In April 1996, as agent for Furuno, Hughes announced that the Furuno navigational radar was being standardized for U.S. Navy use. No SPS number had as yet been assigned (unless SPS-70 was being held for this radar). These X-band digital raster-scan radars were already in widespread U.S. Navy service. Carriers use the 3-kW Furuno 904. Some Coast Guard cutters have 5-kW 1510s. The Hughes-Furuno set is 8050D, which is similar to 1510. Furuno 1510 has three alternative slotted-array antennas (4, 6.5, 8 ft; beams 1.8 × 25, 1.23 × 25, and 0.95 × 20 deg), and some versions have 10- and 25-kW transmitters. Pulse data: 0.08 mi-

crosec/2100; 0.3 microsec/2100 pps; 0.6 microsec/1200; 1.2 microsec/600 or 500 pps. Furuno 805D has a 3ft 5in antenna (beam 2.4 × 25 deg); pulses are 0.08 microsec/2500 pps and 0.5 microsec/840 pps.

Hughes integrates the Furuno radar (including receiver/transmitter) with its own processor and own-ship sensor data ports to form the HSSR 2200 system. It has 16 data ports, and track capacity is 200. Potential upgrades include integration with an electronic chart information system.

◆ SPY-1/FARS

Band: S (3100–3500 MHz) (sustained coherent bandwidth 10 MHz, instantaneous 40 MHz)
Beam: 1.7 × 1.7 deg
Peak Power: 4–6 MW (average power 58 kW)
Gain: 42 dB
Pulse Width: 51, 25.4, 12.7, and 6.4 microsec (pulse-compression ratio 128:1)
PRF: Variable
Scan Rate: Horizon 1 scan/min, above horizon, 12 scans/min
Antenna Dimensions: 12ft hexagon

Lockheed Martin's (formerly RCA's) phased-array radar is the core of the Aegis system. Development began in 1965, sea tests beginning in 1974. SPY-1A, the first production version, uses four octagonal arrays (on two separate deckhouses), each containing 140 modules (each containing up to 32 radiating elements and phase shifters; some are not filled, so the total is 4096 radiators and 4352 receivers, plus 128 auxiliary elements). Modules are paired to form transmitting and receiving subarrays. The subarrays are grouped to form 32 transmitting and 68 receiving arrays. The transmitting arrays are driven by eight transmitters (32 CFAs, each producing 132 kW peak power). The beam is controlled by UYK-7 computers. Each beam can update target positions several times per second; over 200 contacts can be tracked simultaneously, using a monopulse technique (using sum, azimuth, and elevation difference, and sidelobe-blanking channels). Required power input is more than four times that of SPS-48E. Volume-scan instrumented range is reportedly 175 nm; horizon-search instrumented range (to detect sea-skimmers) is reportedly 45 nm.

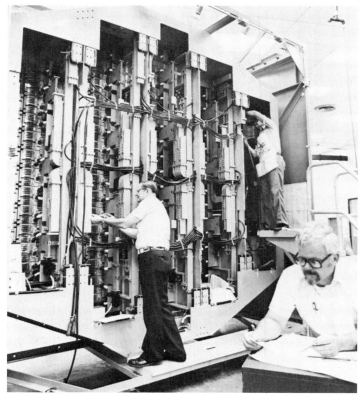

Microwave "plumbing" in the back of an SPY-1 panel. (U.S. Naval Institute)

Two SPG-62 illuminators are visible above the after face of the SPY-1 radar on board the USS *Ticonderoga*, 1983. The large circular structure is the IFF associated with the Aegis system; above it are the TACAN (the flat radome at the masthead) and the LAMPS data link. (DoD)

SPY-1B (first on *Princeton*, CG-59) has an upgraded transmitter capable of supporting twice the duty cycle (at the same peak power), to provide longer pulses or to provide more energy at higher elevation angles to counter steep divers. The antenna has lighter phase-shifters (7900 vs. 12,000 lb per face) and about 15-dB lower sidelobes. Each face consists of 4350 radiators and two sidelobe-blanking antennas, but more compact wiring made it possible to reduce subarray size from 64 to 2 elements to eliminate grating lobes, sharpening beams. Using 7- rather than 4-bit phase shifters made for smoother beam motion. VLSI electronics reduces the number of electronic cabinets from 11 to 5 (weight from 14,700 to 10,800 lb). The total number of separate digital modules falls from 3806 to 1606. At the same time, signal-processor performance improved. It uses a total of 11 16-bit microprocessors. Lockheed Martin is currently planning an upgrade in which one module replaces all eleven microprocessors while tripling performance, greatly improving tracking of fast targets.

A SPY-1A Upgrade, responding to lessons learned when *Ticonderoga* operated off Lebanon, is intermediate between -1A and -1B. It turned out that the radar would pick up and track nontargets such as swarms of insects. Also, high mountains ashore created numerous false alarms; it was difficult to distinguish threats until they emerged from the land, which could take too long. A series of five ORDALTs was proposed, but instead the system was redesigned over a period of about 10 yr, about 10% of the software (about 30,000 lines) being rewritten. The problem was that sensitivity had to be turned down uniformly to keep the radar from detecting too many false targets. The solution was to allow the operator to change the sensitivity profile of the radar, for example, periodically to reduce attenuation so as to detect small incoming targets. The operator could also distinguish between threat and nonthreat sectors, setting parameters for each to respond to a changing environment. That made for more efficient allocation of resources and reduced clutter loading, making it easier to discern a real target against land or sea clutter. The upgrade was installed on board *Ticonderoga* during her regular 1993 overhaul.

SPY-1D is a destroyer version of -1B, with all antennas in a single deckhouse, controlled by a UYK-43 computer, and with UYQ-21 rather than UYA-4 displays (late-production SPY-1Bs have these improvements). Its antenna is used for the missile

uplink of the Aegis system (-1A has a separate uplink transmitter and antenna).

SPY-1D(V) is a modernized version for DDG 82 and later ships (Baseline 7). It is being developed for greater effectiveness against sea-skimmers in clutter due either to jamming or to nearby land. The changes are in the transmitter, signal processor, and radar-control computer program. The land prototype of the modified radar is EDM-4B (engineering development model 4B). Tests began late in 1994. ECM tests were conducted during FY95. Production may begin as early as 1997/98.

SPY-1F (FARS, frigate array radar system) is a proposed lightweight version of -1D, using arrays a quarter the size and two-rather than four-channel processing. It was adopted for the abortive Taiwanese Flight 2 frigate program (which, as of 1996, seems destined for revival in a larger hull). It was proposed for the Australian frigate upgrade. Although none of the finalists in the competition included Lockheed Martin on its team, the RAN apparently demanded that each provide SPY-1F as an option. This radar is also being considered as a fallback in the event that the Canadian-Dutch-German APAR program encounters excessive delays.

Beginning in 1994, Lockheed Martin displayed a series of proposed active-array versions of SPY-1, which it was developing on a private-venture basis, to use 6ft (LHD), 7½ft (frigate), 9ft (carrier), and 12ft (destroyer or cruiser backfit) arrays. At the 1995 Navy League exhibition, the company showed a sketch of an FFG 7 refitted with an active array; presumably that was the version proposed to Australia. Apparently the total weight of the active-array version will be roughly the same as the current weight, but more of it will be concentrated in the antenna, leaving more space below decks (but contributing to topweight problems).

See also the Aegis system under CDS and the SM-2 missile entry below.

Users: Japan (-1D in *Kongo* class), Spain (F100 class [-1D]), United States (*Ticonderoga* [-1A in CG 47–58, -1B in CG 59–73]; -1D in *Arleigh Burke* class).

◆ **TPS-44/Type 5544 SeaAirSearch**

This land-based L-band (1.25–1.35 GHz) Cardion radar has been navalized as the air-search radar of the new Israeli *Lahav* (*Sa'ar 5*) class. Characteristics: beam 4.9 × 9.6 deg (csc² to 20 deg), using a 4.4 × 2.5m antenna (gain 26 dB, scan rate 8/16 rpm; the antenna is stabilized so that the 3-dB point of the beam is always within 2 deg of the horizon [maximum pitch and roll 7.5 and 15 deg, period at least 5 sec]). Peak power 1 MW (pulse width 1.4 microsec/800 pps; 2.4 microsec/400 pps; 4-pulse stagger). Resolution is 6 deg/6.5 deg at 8 rpm (narrow/wide pulses) and 6.5/7 deg at 16 rpm. Range resolution is 700 m in narrow- and 1400 m in wide-pulse mode. Track accuracy is 1.5 nm against surface targets and 1.6 nm against nonmaneuvering air targets. Track capacity is 200 tracks/scan (decreasing to 100 at maximum pitch and roll). Maximum tracking velocity is Mach 2. Antenna weight is 700 kg (swing radius 2.2 m); below-decks equipment weighs 930 kg.

The naval version replaces the MTI and video integrator of the land-based radar with digital plot extractor (ADT) functions and adds ship's motion compensation. The radar can detect fighters at 10,000 ft at over 50 nm, and larger aircraft at 10,000 ft at over 75 nm. Unambiguous range is 80/160 nm (depending on pulse rate).

In the Israeli ships, TPS-44 has a plot extractor/tracker (ADT) feeding a Cardion CDS. The processor is 68000-based; the trackkeeper is provided by Elta. The *Lahav* surface-search radar is SPS-55.

Cardion is now marketing the TPS-44/SPS-55 combination as the Type 5544 SeaAirSearch radar suite, with one or more Cardion CRD5544 color displays, and a capacity of up to 200 tracks per radar. Each radar feeds a plot extractor, and the outputs of both are sent to a single tactical display console or consoles. The first 5544 was shipped in mid-1994.

SeaAirSearch RADAR SUITE

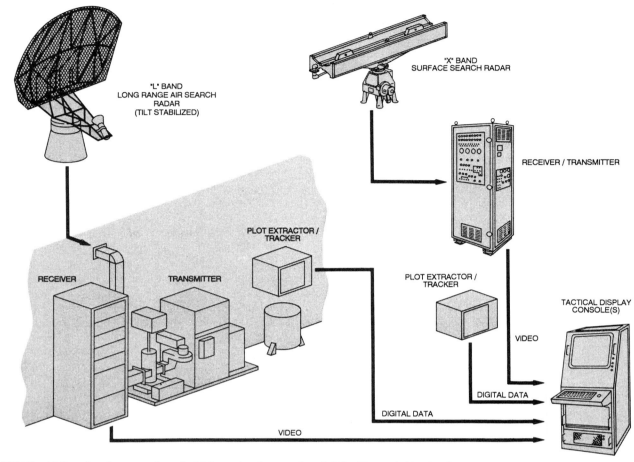

Cardion's 5544 SeaAirSearch radar, a version of which equips the new Israeli *Eilat* (*Sa'ar V*). (Cardion)

◆ **UPS-3**

> **Band:** S
> **Beam:** 8 × 17 deg
> **Peak Power:** 230 W
> **Gain:** 22 dB
> **Scan Rate:** 60 or 90 deg/sec
> **Antenna Weight:** 56 lb (plus 45.2-lb pedestal and 25-lb quadrupod)

This lightweight radar, by Lear Astronics, was developed to alert Stinger operators assigned to provide forward-area air defense for the U.S. Army's Light Divisions. UPS-3 is included here because it has been supplied to the Navy to support Stinger missile operators on board ships. UPS-3 is designated TDAR (Tactical Defense Alert Radar) and can be set up by two people in less than 10 min. Maximum range is 20 km, and maximum target altitude 10,000 ft. Solid-state electronics makes for very high reliability (MTBF is 2180 hr). The antenna is a slotted waveguide. The LED display identifies a target as either a fixed or rotary-wing aircraft, presumably on the basis of an MTI.

This radar was based on the Israeli EL/M-2106 point-defense alert radar.

◆ **Pathfinder 1500/SPS-66**

This Raytheon commercial radar was very widely installed on board U.S. warships during and after the Vietnam War, supplementing standard naval surface-search sets for navigational purposes. At the time Pathfinder was also an extremely popular civilian radar, and its use may have been intended to confuse some hostile ESM operators.

Typical characteristics (1500B): X-band, 7 kW, pulse width 0.14 microsec, PRF 750 or 1500 pps, 48in slotted waveguide, 2 × 20-deg beam.

Raytheon also produced a radome-enclosed 1900, which was installed on board many lesser craft. Typical characteristics: X-band, peak power 5 kW, pulse width 0.16 microsec, PRF 2000 pps, scan rate 20 rpm, reflector 33 in wide, beam 3 × 27 deg.

The military designation, SPS-66, is only rarely used.

◆ **Danish Coastal Radar (Orion)**

> **Band:** S (3.1–3.5 GHz)
> **Beam:** 1.6 × 4.0 deg (csc^2 from 2 to 20 deg)
> **Peak Power:** 107 kW
> **Gain:** 34.7 dB
> **Pulse Width:** 9.3 microsec
> **PRF:** 1000 pps or staggered (949.7, 1000.4, 1136.1 pps)
> **Scan Rate:** 10 rpm
> **Antenna Dimensions:** 8 × 16 ft

ISC Cardion developed this unattended-site gap-filler radar for Denmark under a 1980 NATO contract. It searches for low fliers and surface targets; its beam can be tilted by remote control. The transmitter is a TWT, and the waveform is coded (in 31 segments) for pulse compression (ratio 31:1). The transmitter can operate at a fixed frequency, or in burst or frequency-agile modes; a different mode can be selected for any of four quadrant sectors. Processing includes digital MTI, and ADT can be added; and the radar can distinguish air from surface targets. Instrumented range is 120 km (minimum range is 2 km). Accuracy (resolution): 0.24 (2.36) deg in azimuth, 15 (90) m in range. Targets are automatically detected; the system can carry 400 tracks. The first MTI blind speed is 933 kt. A jamming strobe can be located within 2 deg. The antenna carries an integral L-band IFF horn (gain 26 dB in L-band, vertical beamwidth 10.3 deg). Rated MTBF is 3700 hr (MTTR is 36 min). As of 1988, six were in service and two more were on order.

Cardion coastal radar. (ISC Cardion)

Falcon coastal radar. (ITT)

Users: Denmark, Norway (bought 1991), Turkey.

◆ Falcon

Falcon is ITT-Gilfillan's C-band pulse-compression (two alternative compression ratios) coastal-surveillance ADT radar. Development began in 1981, and by 1988 nearly 50 copies were on order (or had been delivered) for five countries. Each resolution cell is individually processed, to improve performance in rain or against sea clutter. Polarization can be circular or horizontal, to limit rain clutter, and Doppler processing limits the effect of sea clutter. The antenna produces two beams, one 4 deg above the other. Falcon is frequency-agile over a 500-MHz band (48 channels). When Doppler processing is being used, the radar hops in four-pulse bursts. Radar characteristics: beam $1.25 \times \csc^2$ to 25 deg; peak power 60 kW (average 1.5 kW); instrumented range 100 or 160 km (corresponding to PRFs of 1500 and 9375 pps, respectively). Accuracy (resolution) is 20 (85) m, 0.2 (2.4) deg. Scan rate is 6 or 12 rpm. The system can maintain 100 target tracks simultaneously. Two systems were delivered by the end of 1990, probably one in Latin America and one in Asia.

FIRE-CONTROL RADARS

◆ Mk 25/Mk 37 FCS

Band: X
Beam: 1.6 deg
Peak Power: 250 kW
Gain: 39 dB
Pulse Width: 0.25 microsec
PRF: 1320 pps
Antenna Dimensions: 60in dia
Antenna Weight: 625 lb

Mk 25, the dish antenna radar associated with the World War II Mk 37 GFCS, employs spiral scanning (over a 12-deg cone) to acquire the target and conical scanning (over a 2.6-deg cone) to remain on target. Accuracy in bearing is 0.1 deg. For spotting, it has a 10-deg FOV. Angular resolution is 1.3 deg, and range ac-

curacy is 15 yd 0.1% of range. Maximum tracking range is 100,000 yd. The antenna, but not the feed system, was also used in the later SPG-53. Tests were completed in 1947; over 400 of these radars were built.

The Pakistan navy destroyer *Taimur* shows the director of her Mk 37 FCS (with Mk 25 radar on top) and the twin 5in/38 gun it controls. The big air-search radar is SPS-40. (*Ships of the World*).

The associated Mk 37 linear-rate (i.e., relatively long-range) system was the standard U.S. dual-purpose FCS of World War II. The aloft director carries a 15ft stereo unit, and the below-decks computer is the electromechanical Mk 1 (Mk 37 was the first U.S. FCS to employ a below-decks computer separate from the aloft director). Typical operating limits (Mod 62): 30-deg lead angle, 450 yd/sec (810 kt) range rate. Maximum computed range was about 20,000 yd. Elevation limits: +110/−25 deg. Total weight was 40,150 lb including the below-decks computer.

Users: Iran (*Sumner* class), Mexico (*Gearing*, *Fletcher* classes), Pakistan (*Gearing* class), South Korea (*Sumner*, *Gearing* classes), Turkey (*Gearing* class). Note: Some Taiwanese ships retain Mk 37 without the Mk 25 radar (H930 electro-optics has been substituted). The Mexican *Fletcher* reportedly retains her wartime Mk 12/22 radar combination, almost certainly no longer operable.

◆ SPG-34/Mk 34/SPG-50/FCS Mk 63 and SPG-52/Mk 70 FCS

Band: X (8740–9168 MHz)
Beam: 2.5 deg
Peak Power: 50 kW
Gain: 36 dB
Pulse Width: 0.3 microsec
PRF: 1800/180 pps
Scan: Conical (3.9 deg total coverage at 29 Hz)
Antenna Dimensions: 40in dia

SPG-34 is the conscan radar of the World War II Mk 57 and Mk 63 FCSs; it appeared in 1953 as a revised version of the wartime Mk 34 (a repackaged Mod 17), with a larger antenna (40 vs. 30 in) and better facilities for target designation and acquisition. Targets are acquired using a 12.6-deg spiral scan (at 2 Hz). Range resolution is 200 yd (accuracy is 15 yd 0.1% of range). Maximum displayed range is 60 kyd. Maximum range rate is 843 yd/sec (approximately 1500 kt).

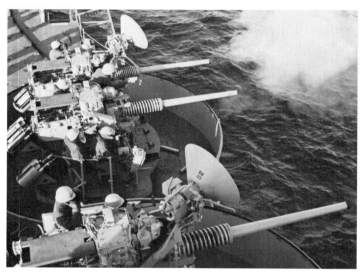

Twin 3in/50 mounts, with the dishes of SPG-34 radars atop them. The associated Mk 63 directors were mounted separately. (U.S. Navy)

SPG-50 superseded SPG-34 in Mk 63s installed after about 1956. It operates at a slightly higher frequency (8600–9600 MHz) and with a slightly shorter pulse (0.25 microsec) at a slightly higher pulse rate (2000/200 pps). Total conical scan coverage for tracking is 4.1 deg, and targets are acquired by spiral scan over 12.6 deg. In contrast to SPG-34, SPG-50 has automatic range designation and range tracking; range and range rate are generated in the radar and sent directly to the gunsight. Typically, the ranging mechanism is controlled by a ship's target-designation system, but bearing and elevation data are inserted manually either by the director or the radar operator. Maximum range is 34,500 yd; minimum is 300 yd. SPG-50 has many components in common with SPG-53.

Mk 63 is a version of the World War II short-range FCS (Mk 51, see below) with a tracking radar on the gun mount. Operating limits: maximum lead angle 20 deg, maximum computing range 7000 yd (minimum 800 yd), range rate +350 kt, −800 kt. The above-decks director pedestal (carrying a Mk 29 sight) weighs 1300 lb (total weight is about 3900–5400 lb).

Mk 70 is an alternative to Mk 63 using a Ku-band (16.3–16.5 GHz) SPG-52 range-only radar (which, like SPG-50, passed range data automatically to the lead-computing gunsight). Max-

imum target speed is 650 kt. Peak power is 50 kW (5-deg beam, 0.5-microsec pulses, 1500 pps; instrumented range 10,000 yd).

Users: Colombia (*Boyaca*), Greece (*Asheville*, *Terrebonne Parish* classes), Iran (PF 103 class), Japan (DDK 116/117, *Hatase*, *Katori*), South Korea (PSMM Mk 5 [PGM 352–355, with Standard ARM missiles]), Spain (*Paul Revere*, *Terrebonne Parish* classes), Turkey (*Berk*, *Asheville*, *Terrebonne Parish* classes). SPG-52/Mk 70: Indonesia (*Claud Jones* class).

◆ SPG-35/Mk 56 FCS

Band: X (8.5–9.6 GHz)
Beam: 2 deg
Peak Power: 50 kW
Gain: 37.5 dB
Pulse Width: 0.1–0.15 microsec
PRF: 3000 pps
Scan: Conical (3 deg)
Antenna Dimensions: 48in dia

SPG-35 is the radar of the Mk 56 FCS. Accuracy is 20 yd 2.5% of range. Resolution is 35 yd and 1.5 deg. Limits: tracking 100 deg/sec in train, 35 deg/sec in elevation. Maximum tracking range is 30,000 yd. In acquisition mode, the radar spiral scans over a 12-deg cone.

Mk 56 gunfire-control system, in this case controlling 5in/38 guns on board a U.S. *Essex*-class carrier, now discarded. (U.S. Naval Institute)

This standard U.S. postwar 3in/50 blind-fire director also incorporated 5in ballistics. It was the first U.S. blind-fire director without an optical range-finder. Unlike Mk 37, Mk 56 is a relative rate, that is, a medium-range, system. The overall fire-control problem is approximated by concentrating on the motion of the target relative to the firing ship at any given moment; the faster the target, the less the effect of omitting the motion (other than roll and pitch) of the firing ship. A firing solution is generated within 2 sec of beginning to track a target. Operating limits: lead angle 30 deg, range rate 260 yd/sec (470 kt). Maximum computing range is 15,000 yd. Elevation limits: +82/−23 deg. Total weight: 17,000–26,000 lb, with a 51in (radius) working circle. Above-decks weight is 9809 lb.

Users: Brazil (*Garcia* class), Japan (*Minegumo*), Turkey (*Carpenter* class).

◆ SPG-51/Mk 74 FCS

Band: C (track) X (illuminate)
Beam: 1.6 deg (track), 0.9 deg (illuminate) with 80-deg ancillary
Peak Power: 81 kW (track), 5 kW (illuminate)
Gain: 39.5 dB (track), 45 dB (illuminate)
Pulse Width: 2.1–3.2 microsec (track)
PRF: 4.1 kHz (surface mode), 9.5–16.7 kHz (air mode)
Antenna Dimensions: 92in dia

Data apply to SPG-51D (AS-2234 antenna).

Raytheon's radar guides SM-1 missiles. Its C-band pulse-Doppler cosro tracker and X-band illuminator (CWI) share a common structure but use separate feeds and reflector surfaces (the horizontally polarized X-band wire-grid reflector is embedded in dielectric material on the C-band reflector face). Like an air-to-air radar, the tracker uses multiple PRFs to resolve the usual Doppler range ambiguities. The radar uses a narrow speed gate to reject clutter. An ancillary antenna provides the missile with a rear reference signal. Tracking range is 200,000 yd.

SPG-51 Standard MR directors, USS *Mississippi*, June 1988. (S. Terzibaschitsch)

SPG-51 is the only U.S. Navy Doppler FCS radar. Transmitted frequencies are such that the operator can actually hear the Doppler signature of a target; an experienced operator can use this signature to distinguish targets by type and number.

SPG-51C, the oldest version still in service, made full use of solid-state components and was designed to feed a digital FCS. It introduced automatic acquisition and tracking. It introduced two new modes, horizon search (to detect low fliers) and surface acquisition/track (to deal with FAC). In the former mode, elevation is fixed and the range and speed gates are set to detect, acquire, and engage targets at Mach 1.2 or less without the delays inherent in the usual designation-and-acquisition process. In the latter mode, the antenna is held at 0-deg elevation and PRF is set so that unambiguous range reaches out to the horizon. A special B-scope is used for both modes. Peak power is 30 kW, and antenna (AS-2649) diameter is 91 in.

SPG-51D, the latest operational version, was introduced with the Tartar-D (digital Tartar) FCS. It introduced a new off-mount, frequency-agile, pulse-tracking transmitter (which could change frequency up to 4 times/sec) with more than a fivefold increase in power over its predecessors; a new free-rotating, dual-frequency rotary joint; and a new antenna system with a fivefold increase in gain. SPG-51D employs a new pulse-shaping technique that makes for a cleaner spectrum and thus for less interference with other radars. The associated Tartar-D system projects ahead-target motion on a straight-line basis, allowing the radar to minimize tracking bandwidth (and, therefore, tracking noise). The resulting range estimate is used when jamming denies range data (but provides angle data).

The associated missile FCS is Mk 74, using a two-axis stabilized Mk 73 director (carrying the radar and a Mk 5 LLLTV camera; elevation limits +83/−30 deg) and a computer (originally Mk 118, one per radar). The computer aids the tracking radar in acquiring a target and projects the target's position ahead for rate-aided tracking. It generates orders for the Tartar launcher (and, at least in the case of an *Adams*-class destroyer, can simultaneously generate orders for two 5in/54 mounts). It also generates Tartar missile orders and the display data for target evaluation in the WDE. The associated WDS is Mk 4 (Mk 11 or Mk 13 when it is integrated with NTDS).

Most SM-1 ships also have a Mk 68 gun FCS. The two systems interconnect through the WDS, providing a back-up tracking mode: Mk 68 can track targets and slave the SPG-51s. The Spanish *Baleares* class, with only a single SPG-51, has a second Mk 118–2 computer associated with the Mk 68 GFCS to provide a second missile-control channel. This computer accepts target position and rate functions from the Mk 47–12 computer of the GFCS.

The most important development in this series was Tartar-D (digital Tartar, using SPG-51D: Mk 74 Mods 4 and 5). Its extended tracking range more nearly matched the extended range capability of the SM-1(MR), compared to the earlier Tartar.

Capabilities of the original Mk 74 system (Tartar missile, predecessor of SM-1[MR]): acquisition range, 120 kyd (on an F6F airplane); reliable tracking range, 20 kyd; minimum range, 500 yd; range rates, 50–1320 kt; angle rate, up to 120 deg/sec. About 1975 the FCS was credited with a tracking range of 2 to 200 kyd.

Versions:

Mod 6: Digital update for DDG 2–24, with SPG-51C and a Mk 152 computer. The Spanish *Baleares* class was upgraded to this standard, and it applies to three of the Greek *Adams* class.

Mod 8: Similar to Mod 6 but WDS Mk 4 is upgraded to Mk 13 Mod 1/JPTDS (Junior Participating Tactical Data System). The WDS Mk 13 computer is integrated with the Mk 152 Mod 1 computer (1971). This is the FY71 upgrade for four *Adams*-class DDGs (DDG 9, 12, 15, and 21). The radar is SPG-51C. This is the version in the Australian *Adams* class. It is installed in the Greek *Themistoklis* (the others have Mod 6).

Mod 11: Tartar-D for the *Adams* class, with SPG-51D and a Mk 152 computer. This is probably the version in the Italian *Mimbelli* class.

Mod 13: Derived from Mod 8, for modernized *Adams*-class destroyers (DDG 19, 20, 22, with SPG-51C radar and LLLTV Mk 5, for SM-1 missiles). It was designed to work with WDS Mk 13. This is the version in the Italian *Audace* class and in the Japanese *Hatakaze* and *Tachikaze* classes. It is probably also the version in the German version of the *Adams* class. The German ships have Mk 86 FCS, providing an additional missile-control channel via the SPG-60 tracker.

Mod 15: NTU Baseline, with SPG-51D and CWAT (CW acquisition and tracking). Total weight: 44,835 lb. In U.S. *Kidd*, *California*, and *Virginia* classes.

Users:

SPG-51C: Australia (*Adams* class), Germany (*Adams* class), Greece (*Adams* class), Italy (*Audace* class), Japan (*Hatakaze*, *Tachikaze* classes), Netherlands (*Tromp* class), Spain (*Baleares* class)

SPG-51D: Italy (*Mimbelli* class), United States (*Virginia*, *California*, and *Kidd* classes)

The Dutch *Tromp* class probably lacks any Mk 74 system.

◆ SPG-53/Mk 68 FCS

Band: X
Beam: 1.6 deg (spiral scan for acquisition; conscan for tracking)
Peak Power: 250 kW
Gain: 39 dB
Pulse Width: 0.25 microsec
PRF: 1000 pps
Antenna Dimensions: 60in dia
Antenna Weight: 163 lb (antenna only); total 5000 lb

Data apply to SPG-53A.

Western Electric's SPG-53 is the direct successor to Mk 25, just as its FCS, Mk 68, is the postwar successor to Mk 37, intended to handle faster targets using a better computer (the analog electronic/electromechanical Mk 47) to provide faster, smoother solutions. In Mk 68, the radar is supplemented by an 11ft stereo range-finder. The successor system is Mk 86, with SPQ-9 and SPG-60 radars.

Mk 68 director, with its SPG-53 radar (USS *Pharris*). (U.S. Navy)

During the early 1970s SPG-53As were fitted with RSPE (radar signal processing equipment), a form of ATD: while spiral-scanning, the radar automatically detects targets and gates them in range (within 4 msec). RSPE automatically generates the error signals required to center the beam on the target so that conscan tracking can begin. RSPE also added antijam features. SPG-53A instrumented range is 120 kyd. Resolution is 80 yd and 1.3 deg. Tracking limits are 50 deg/sec in train and 30 deg/sec in elevation.

SPG-53C is a CWI version for the Spanish *Baleares* class, the CW signal provided by a version of the SPG-51C illuminator and (as in -51C) reflected off the vertical wires of a secondary reflector mounted on the main radar reflector. Gain is 38 dB for the main antenna and 41.6 dB for the secondary reflector; diameter is 64 in.

SPG-53F is a monopulse version of -53A, to improve capability against sea-skimmers and to provide quicker reaction. It also has simulated ECM input for training. It is not clear to what extent the conversion program was carried out. Ten *Adams*-class destroyers were modernized with the digital Mod 19 version of the Mk 68 system, with a Mk 160 digital computer, and with SPG-53F radar. It is not clear whether any of the modernized units survive, or whether the Australian *Adams* class received the new FCS.

For the associated Mk 68 FCS, maximum lead angle is 50 deg, maximum range rate is 1125 yd/sec (2025 kt), and computing range is about 18,000 yd. Elevation limits are +85/−20 deg. Above-decks weight is 15,300 lb (working-circle radius 80 in). Total installed weight: 26,600–28,000 lb. Mod 13 (FF 1078 and beyond) has provision for firing rocket-assisted (RAP) shells.

Users:

SPG-53A: Australia (*Adams* class), Egypt (*Knox* class), Greece (*Adams* and *Knox* classes), Taiwan (*Knox* class), Thailand (*Knox* class), Turkey (*Knox* class), United States (*Knox* class, in reserve).
SPG-53C: Spain (*Baleares* class).
SPG-53F: See above.

◆ SPG-55/Mk 76 FCS

Band: C (track) and X (CWI)
Beam: 1.6 deg (C); 0.8 deg (X); 72-deg auxiliary beam (X)
Peak Power: 1 MW (C); 5 kW (CWI)
Gain: 39 dB (C); 47 dB (X-band)
Pulse Width: 26 and 1.5 microsec
PRF: 203–225 pps
Antenna Dimensions: 175 × 218 in (total); dish 96 in
Antenna Weight: 12,970 lb (total radar assembly)

SPG-55 controls SM-1(ER) missiles as part of the Mk 76 FCS. SPG-55C is the only surviving version, on board the Italian *Vittorio Veneto*. Pulse width and PRF above refer to operation in C-band target acquisition-and-tracking mode.

A pair of SPG-55 fire-control radars, with Harpoon canisters visible in the foreground. (U.S. Navy)

Mk 76 can control missiles out to 80 kyd and at altitudes of 50,000–80,000 ft against Mach 2.5 targets, which the radar can track out to 120 nm. Maximum angle rates: 120 deg/sec (60 deg/sec in elevation). In 1975 total system reaction time was given as 60 sec, including target-data processing, threat evaluation, launcher loading, and weapons assignment. The launcher (Mk 10) took 45 sec to fire its first salvo and 30 sec between later salvos.

◆ SPG-60/Mk 86 FCS

Band: X
Beam: 1.2 × 1.2 deg
Peak Power: 5.5 kW
Gain: 41.5 dB
Pulse Width: 0.27, 1, or 6 microsec
PRF: 25,000–35,000 pps
Antenna Dimensions: 160in dia
Antenna Weight: 4015 lb total

Lockheed Electronics' SPG-60 is the stabilized pulse-Doppler monopulse tracker (and CWI illuminator) of the Mk 86 FCS. As in the contemporary Signaal egg, the French Vega, and the Swedish 9LV, targets are acquired (and surface targets tracked) by an associated TWS radar, in this case SPQ-9 (see separate entry). Range ambiguities are resolved by computer-controlled variation of pulse width and PRF. Instrumented range is 100 kyd (a 1m² target can be detected at 85 kyd); the first blind speed is Mach 3. Range granularity is 5 yd. Elevation limits are +85/−30 deg. The associated LLLTV, which looks through the SPG-60 dish, has a zoom lens for a 2.1 to 21-deg FOV (output at 729 lines). CWI: 5 kW injected, sufficient for an SM-1 to engage a 1m² target at 20 kyd. Under the FY90 program a CWI was added to provide a second Sea Sparrow control channel for *Spruance*-class destroyers and large amphibious ships. The FY90 program included a product-improvement program (implemented in FY92) to make this radar more effective against sea-skimmers. Specified MTBF was 300 hr.

The two radars of the Mk 86 GFCS on board the USS *Mississippi*, June 1988; radome-enclosed SPQ-9A above, SPG-60 below. The hole in the SPG-60 antenna is for the television tracker. (S. Terzibaschitsch)

SPQ-9 and SPG-60 are linked through the Mk 86 system computer. It can also accept targets from a target-data transmitter (TDT) or from NTDS or ITAWDS or the Mk 74 missile FCS. The system began in 1961 as a surface FCS to support amphibious operations; it had to be able to track four targets and to engage two, to be compatible with the variety of guns in the fleet (3in to 8in) and to interface with NTDS. Hence the decision to use a general-purpose (programmable) digital computer. About 1967 requirements for AA fire control and CWI (for missile control) were added, requiring a separate monopulse air tracker (SPG-60). Because surface fire and AA fire used separate antennas, Mk 86 could track five targets (four surface, one air) and engage two targets (surface and air or two surface) simultaneously (it has two separate gun-control consoles). It used a Univac 1219 (Mk 152) computer (32k 18-bit words, with 16 I/O channels). Computing range was 131 kyd, maximum angular rate (air targets) was 12 deg/sec, maximum range rate (air) was Mach 3, required MTBF was 416 hr, and required MTTR was less than 18 min. In this form Mk 86 could communicate directly with NTDS and with the Tartar (now Standard Missile) system without special buffers. The upgrade to the UYK-7 computer increased tracking capacity to 120 targets.

There are two consoles: one for the control officer (COC) and a weapon (or gun) control console (WCC or GCC). The associated CDS designates targets directly to the system computer, and it sends target engagement orders to the control officer console. It in turn assigns targets to the WCC or GCC, whose operator ac-

quires and engages the target. The COC is a standard NTDS-type console with a single large circular CRT; the WCC carries a pair of smaller rectangular CRTs (B-scan, TV, and alphanumeric data). The system uses one WCC/GCC per gun it controls.

The FY88 program included an emergency improvement (HSMT, high-speed maneuvering target) to the Mk 86 system to engage fast, radically maneuvering surface targets (such as Boghammers), which were then being encountered by the Middle East force. Work on HSMT was completed in FY91. Under the FY90 and FY91 programs, a more efficient computer-memory usage program for Mk 86 was developed. Under the FY91 program, the Mk 86 Video Processor Mk 2 was improved to provide false-alarm filtering, adaptable video thresholds, a capability to track 10 or more targets, and also full-range low-altitude detection/acquisition (LAD/A) coverage against small targets. An EO capability was developed and integrated into the system. Under the FY92 program, target filtering and detection in Video Processor Mk 2 Mod 3 were further improved.

Existing versions:

Mod 3 (*Spruance* and *California* classes) uses the Mk 152 computer and has two remote optical sights. Most *Spruances* retain this version. Two ships, *Briscoe* and *Hayler*, have the upgraded Mod 10 with UYK-7 computer.

Mod 4 (*Tarawa* class) uses a pair of Mk 152 computers and has three remote optical sights. It is being upgraded with UYK-7 and WCC rather than GCC as Mod 11.

Mod 5 was developed for the *Virginia* and *Kidd* classes; it uses a UYK-7 computer. This version adds CWI to control missiles. Total weight is 14,200 lb. All NTU ships were probably refitted with Mod 12, which is compatible with WDS Mk 14 of the NTU system. It also has better MMI. Conversion of Mk 86 Mod 5 systems to the UYK-43 computer began in FY88.

Mod 8 was the version for modernized *Adams*-class destroyers; the program was canceled after the first three (now stricken) had been modified. Mk 86 did replace the earlier Mk 68 system on board the West German *Adams*-class destroyers. A similar program planned for the Australian ships of this type was canceled. The computer is UYK-7. WCCs replace the GCCs of the earlier versions. Total weight is 14,750 lb.

Mod 9 is the version for Aegis ships. It has no SPG-60 radar, using Aegis data for gunfire control against air targets. The computer is UYK-7 (being upgraded to UYK-43), and total weight is 10,000 lb. This version has WCCs rather than GCCs.

Users: Mk 86: Germany (*Adams* class), United States (*Spruance*, *Kidd*, *California*, *Ticonderoga*, *Virginia*, *Tarawa*, *Wasp* classes). The *Ticonderoga* version has no SPG-60.

◆ SPG-62/FCS Mk 99

Band: X
Average Power: 10 kW
Antenna Dimensions: 90in dia

SPG-62 is the illuminator associated with the SPY-1 (Aegis) radar and its Mk 99 MFCS. The associated director is Mk 82. Unlike SPG-51, which SPG-62 resembles, it does not track its targets. The Aegis system points the illuminator at targets detected and tracked by the main radar, during the last few seconds of missile flight, to provide terminal guidance for the SM-2 missile.

By 1994, there was considerable interest in Mk 99 upgrades to deal with tactical or theater ballistic missiles. At the 1994 Navy League show Raytheon displayed a Mk 99 STAMO (low-noise front-end local oscillator) which would enable Mk 99 to control both SM-2 Block IV and ESSM. The company proposed that SPG-62 be turned back into a radar, primarily for ballistic missile discrimination at lower altitudes. This system would also help in horizon search due to its low noise.

The following year Raytheon showed a trainable dual-FOV phased-array X-band tracker based on ground-based radar ballistic missile defense technology. On its DDG 51 model, the new tracker was mounted just forward of a pair of slaved SPG-62s. Its outer section would be used for ballistic missile defense, offering a 45 × 45-deg FOV for very long range. The inner core would provide 120-deg coverage at shorter range. It could also be used to illuminate targets for AA work. The entire tracker would use 12,000 Tx/Rx modules. As of 1995, this concept was at the viewgraph stage, attracting considerable attention.

◆ SPQ-9/SPQ-9B

Band: X
Beam: 1.35 × 3 deg
Peak Power: 1.2 kW
Gain: 37 dB
Pulse Width: 0.3–16 microsec
PRF: 3000 pps
Scan Rate: 60 rpm
Antenna Dimensions: 80.5 × 30 in (radome 120 × 96 in)
Antenna Weight: 1185 lb (including radome)

SPQ-9 is the TWS surface-search and target-acquisition radar of GFCS Mk 86; it can also acquire and track low-flying aircraft (at altitudes up to about 2000 ft). A proposed air-search variant was never used. SPQ-9 is a digital radar with DMTI. The antenna is stabilized against roll and pitch. The operator can choose among five operating frequency ranges, using pulse-to-pulse frequency agility for ECCM. SPQ-9 uses pulse compression, having been one of the earliest applications of optical pulse compression (16.4 microsec compressed to 0.12 sec, also given as 167:1 ratio). Maximum instrumented range is 40,000 yd (PD 0.90 for a 1m² target at 30,000 yd). Minimum range is 150 yd. Range resolution is less than 50 yd and range accuracy is 10 yd +/−0.025% of range. One source gives a peak power of 3 kW. In 1967 MTBF was given as 784 hr.

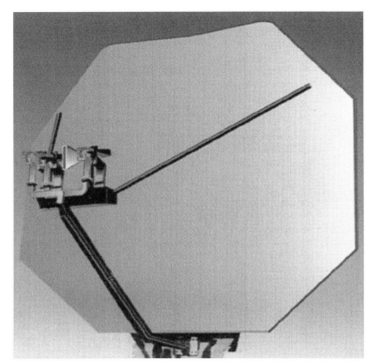

The SPQ-9B antenna. (Northrop Grumman)

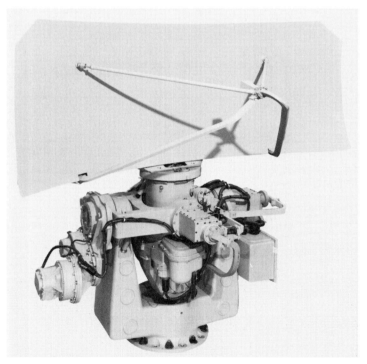

SPQ-9 radar without its radome. (Lockheed Electronics)

In November 1989 Lockheed Electronics delivered the first of a series of ORDALT kits developed under a 1985 contract, providing a DMTI and a low-noise front end (LNFE) for the SPQ-9A radar. The LNFE is built around a solid-state low-noise amplifier; it should reduce the minimum radar cross-section of a target to a quarter of the present value. Test and evaluation were completed under the FY90 program. The FY90 program included further improvements to SPQ-9A so that it can detect small radar targets more effectively, in response to requests by the Middle East force. Presumably, the LNFE was intended primarily to deal

with air targets; the new program concerns small attack boats such as Boghammers.

SPQ-9B is a new radar using a modified SPQ-9 antenna, intended specifically to detect incoming low-flying antiship missiles. It will be part of some SSDS packages. SPQ-9B was developed by NRL, beginning in 1990, and Norden (which was taken over by Westinghouse) received the production development contract in 1994. The original transmitter was replaced by a modified APG-68 X-band pulse-Doppler unit (as in an F-16 fighter, producing about 35,000 pulses/sec, for an unambiguous range of about 2 nm). Peak power is now 18 kW, and pulse width is 0.1 to 8.0 microsec. Antenna height is increased (to narrow the beam in the vertical direction, to reduce sea clutter; beam width is now 1 × 1 deg) and it is provided with two more feeds, at 12-deg intervals from the primary feed. Scan rate is halved, to 30 rpm (2-sec data rate), which still suffices for surface gunnery.

When a target is detected at the primary feed, an electronic switch energizes the other two in sequence, so that during a single scan the radar detects the target three times, each time measuring its speed and its range. In fact there is sufficient time for two coherent dwells (bursts at a fixed frequency and PRF) within each beamwidth, or a total of six looks per scan. The normal Doppler range ambiguity is resolved because PRF varies from dwell to dwell. Thus a single scan, rather than the usual three, suffices to establish a firm track.

An extremely stable exciter and an efficient analog-digital converter combine to provide excellent DMTI for additional clutter reduction, which Westinghouse claims is the best of any existing naval radar. DMTI alone is responsible for a 90-dB improvement factor, 20 or 30 dB better than anything else currently available, with another 20 or 30 dB possible.

Each burst of Doppler pulses includes a single fixed-width pulse used for surface mode. The surface mode uses every fourth or fifth such pulse to establish a useful unambiguous range. The developers discovered that the 60 rpm (1-sec data rate) of SPQ-9 was not needed for surface targets; 30 rpm provided sufficient time for the air mode to detect on one scan.

Compared to SPQ-9, -9B uses a slightly modified antenna pedestal, a slightly enlarged radome, and completely new below-decks elements. However, the operator interface for surface gunnery has remained unchanged. Existing SPQ-9s may be modified to -9B by ORDALT. These radars will probably enter service about 1997–98. They benefit considerably from recent efforts to relax military specifications, and also from the use of surplus air force transmitters.

◆ VPS-2/Sharpshooter

Band: X (9200–9250 MHz; six crystal-controlled frequencies)
Beam: 4 deg
Peak Power: 1.4 kW (average 10 W)

Lockheed Electronics's on-mount digital-radar FCS for 20–40mm guns, announced in 1974, is incorporated in the Spanish Meroka CIWS. It embodies some Mk 86 FCS technology. The monopulse radar tracker is derived from the VPS-2 range-only pulse-Doppler radar of the Army Vulcan air-defense gun (it is *not* the radar of the U.S. Phalanx system). Compared to VPS-2, the Sharpshooter radar has much-improved clutter rejection. The radar is slaved to a stabilized optical sight with zoom magnification, which the gunner uses to acquire the target and to monitor tracking (the sight then being slaved to the radar). Maximum target lock-on range is 7000 m, and accuracy is 1.5 mrad and 30 ft in range. Maximum radial target speed is Mach 1.8. The director's angular rate in both axes is 2 rad/sec. Elevation limits: +90/−25 deg. Total weight is 1323 lb.

◆ TAS Mk 23/Mk 91 FCS (SWY-1)/Mk 95 radar

Band: L
Beam: 3.3 × 75 deg
Peak Power: 200 kW
Gain: 21 dB
PRF: See below
Scan Rate: 15 or 30 rpm
Antenna Dimensions: 231 × 129 in (including pedestal); aperture is 14 × 2 ft
Antenna Weight: 1950 lb topside; 10,000 lb total

Hughes's Target Acquisition System is part of the U.S. version of the NATO Sea Sparrow system (Mk 91 FCS; SWY-1 system); the associated tracker/illuminator is Mk 95. TAS is broadly equivalent to the British 967/968 of the Sea Wolf system. Engineering development was ordered in 1971, production of 100 systems was ordered in April 1978, and TAS Mk 23 became operational in October 1980.

The roll-stabilized antenna consists of 26 flared feed horns (plus one for sidelobe blanking and one for sidelobe cancellation); topside weight is 2000 lb (plus 8000 lb below decks). The antenna's broad vertical fan beam was chosen to detect both steep divers and sea-skimmers (most of the beam's energy is transmitted at low angles). Doppler processing was chosen to overcome sea clutter. This ADT radar uses a ramped FM (chirped) waveform. There are two main operating modes, normal (point defense, 20nm scale, 2-sec data rate, PRF about 4000 pps, first blind speed about 1900 kt) and medium-range (4-sec data rate, PRF about 900 pps). In both cases echoes are pulse-compressed and subject to DMTI processing; in normal mode they are also Doppler-processed and range-gated. Range-gating makes it possible for an operator to concentrate on targets without accidentally tracking nearby friendly aircraft or surface ships (the operator chooses a controlled-reaction zone). Target detection can be semiautomatic, so the operator can reject friendly or neutral targets.

The system computer was originally UYK-20, which could maintain 54 target tracks (20 words each, total memory 60 kwords). UYK-44 (512 kwords) was introduced into production systems in 1984. The associated reaction time, typically 60–80 sec, can be as little as 30 sec; in 1994 Hughes offered VHSIC components to cut reaction time 35%. The operator console is a standard UYA-4 or UYQ-21.

Unit price (FY93) was $9.5M.

Hughes developed a 3D version, ITAS, but was unable to attract funding, although the issue was regularly revisited. See the 1991/92 edition for details. ITAS is sometimes called Mk 23M.

NATO Sea Sparrow itself is an automatic modular system capable of accepting other target-acquisition radars (see below) but always using the same Mk 95 X-band tracker-illuminator (2-kW average CW power, 100 × 96 in, 3315-lb antenna) on a Mk 78

director. The U.S. version, SWY-1, includes the TAS Mk 23 radar. In this version the UYK-20 or UYK-44 associated with the TAS acts as tactical picture-keeper, transmitting data to a Norwegian-built (Kongsberg, for a time known as NFT) Mk 157 FCS computer. Mk 157 is responsible for TEWA and for engagement. The FCS part of the system is controlled from a Mk 86 firing officer's console linked to a Mk 83 radar console for each Mk 95 radar. Mk 83 displays both radar data and the image from the LLLTV on the director.

The Mk 95 radar uses separate transmit and receive antennas, both 39in in diameter; the transmitter is a parabolic dish, the receiver a twist-Cassegrain reflector. There is also a wide-beam missile reference antenna (to support proportional navigation). The Mk 95 CW signal is modulated so that the radar can track in range as well as in angle. If the target fades during tracking, the system coasts in range, bearing, and elevation until the target reappears. The system computer continuously calculates Sparrow time of flight to the target, alerting the operator (or beginning automatic engagement) if the target is engageable. Shortly before the target comes within range the launcher is automatically assigned to the appropriate radar director and aimed at the predicted intercept point. In automatic mode, a salvo is fired when the target becomes engageable. In semiautomatic mode, the operator issues a firing command. Typically the U.S. Navy operates its Sea Sparrows in semiautomatic mode. European navies tend to use the automatic mode. This distinction reflects a difference in operating conditions. Except in wartime, when they would face submarine-launched missiles anywhere at sea, U.S. ships probably would not face air attack unless they approached hostile shores. European warships are almost always within range of potentially hostile air or missile attack.

The Mk 78 director also carries a Mk 6 LLLTV camera (2.4 × 2.4-deg and 10 × 10-deg FOVs). The entire director weighs 1.56 t.

The NATO Sea Sparrow program began with a U.S. proposal to the NATO Naval Armaments Group in the winter of 1966–67; it became more urgent after the sinking of the Israeli destroyer *Eilat* (the first combat casualty caused by a surface-to-surface guided missile) in 1967. Later that year a NATO Project Group prepared an MoU; it was signed by Denmark, Italy, Norway, and the United States. Belgium and the Netherlands joined the consortium in 1970, West Germany in 1977, Canada and Greece in 1982, and Spain in 1992. Raytheon was awarded the prime contract in September 1969. A production contract followed in August 1973. The other development firms were Terma Electroniks of Denmark (microwave receiver), Selenia (now Alenia) of Italy (firing officer's console/display module), and NFT of Norway (director controller, director pedestal, and computer). The system was first tested on board the frigate *Downes*, a second model going on board the Norwegian frigate *Bergen*; and all evaluation was completed by the end of April 1973. The first production systems were delivered in 1975.

U.S. Sea Sparrow systems are being rebuilt with LANs (for console, director, and launcher) rather than the current point-to-point wiring, so they can be integrated with SSDS/QRCC. This program also replaces the current console with a UYQ-70. Other current improvements (ORDALTs) add a CCD/Night Sensor Assembly, upgrade the transmitter, and modify the software (for compatibility with SSDS, among other things). The stand-alone system evaluator and trainer (SEAT) is being removed because, once Sea Sparrow is linked to SSDS, it will be able to share the new system's battle force tactical trainer (BFTT).

Users: TAS Mk 23: United States (*Spruance* class, carriers, *Tarawa*, LHDs, AOEs, AORs [planned for whole class, only on board AOR 5 and 6]). On board *Tarawa* TAS Mk 23 acquires targets for a RAM system. The original *Spruance*-class version was Mod 1, with UYK-20 computer and OJ-451(V)9/UYQ-21 display. The contemporary stand-alone version, for the AOE/AOR, was Mod 2, with a UYK-20 computer and OJ-194(V)3/UYA-4 console. Mods 5 and 6 are corresponding versions with UYK-44 computers, introduced in 1984 and scheduled for fleetwide service by FY90. Newer corresponding versions are Mods 7 and 8, which presumably equip the later carriers and the new AOEs.

Mk 91/Mk 95 Sea Sparrow system: Belgium (*Wielingen* class), Canada ("City" class), Denmark (*Nils Juels* class), Germany (F123 and *Bremen* class), Greece (*Kortenaer* and MEKO 200 classes), Italy (*Lupo* class), Japan (*Shirane, Haruna, Asagiri, Hatsuyuki* classes), Netherlands (*Tromp, Karel Doorman, Kortenaer* classes), Norway (*Oslo* class), Portugal (MEKO 200), Turkey (MEKO 200), United States (carriers, LHD, *Spruance* class, AOE, AOR). Mod 0 is the single version, Mod 1 the dual version as used by the Danish, Italian, Norwegian, and U.S. navies. Upgrades are Mods 2 and 3, respectively. The Italian version (in the original *Lupo* class) is unique in that it controls the Aspide missile (but these ships were armed with RIM-7H, and are being adapted to fire RIM-7M). The Belgian, Dutch, German, and Japanese navies use a special "Netherlands" configuration in which Sea Sparrow is controlled by the tracker of the WM25 FCS (with a Raytheon CWI). Later Japanese ships substitute FCS 2–21 for WM25. VLS Sea Sparrow (for Canada, Germany, Greece, Netherlands, Portugal, and Turkey) is generally controlled by the Dutch STIR radar FCS. Note that different navies use different target-acquisition radars.

◆ Mk 92

Mk 92 is a U.S. version (produced by Sperry, later Unisys and now Loral Unisys) of the Dutch Signaal WM28 FCS. Like WM28, its egg-shaped radome (the combined antenna system [CAS], UD 401) contains a TWS acquisition radar (eight tracking channels, two for engagement) and a tracker (diameter is 96 in and topside weight is 6300 lb). The search antenna of the CAS scans at 60 rpm. It provides a measure of height-finding, by spiraling the beam up in three revolutions (four beamwidths), then down again in half a revolution, for interlaced coverage. This system can track and engage two surface targets and one air target.

In the Mod 2 version in the *Perry* class, the egg is supplemented by a STIR (separate target illumination radar, with 100in UD 417 antenna) monopulse tracker-illuminator, which provides a second surface engagement channel. Both egg and STIR are driven by the same type of X-band radar transmitter (Mk 91–0) and both use the same type of CWI transmitter, T-1085B,

STIR on board the USS *Rodney M. Davis*, 1987. (F. Jentsch)

the type used in SPG-51D. The two antennas operate independently, linked through the system computer. As in WM28, the egg uses one radar transmitter/receiver for either its search or its track element. Because of its greater diameter (hence greater gain), the STIR can track targets at greater ranges than the tracker of the egg.

Radar video from the egg goes to a weapons-control console Mk 106–1, which is the system control center. It carries the system tactical display (PPI) and two track displays (A- and B-scopes). Targets are designated from the PPI, which can also display other ship radar data. The A-scope shows an acquisition gate around the designated target. Once it is being tracked, the A-scope displays engagement limits so that the operator can gauge when to engage. The time-shared B-scope indicates designation or track error by the position of the target blip relative to the scope's center. Maximum instrumented range on the PPI is 128 nm (on the A-scope, 64 nm).

In the *Perry*-class version (Mod 2), STIR radar video goes to a separate Mk 107–1 console. It is similar to Mk 106 except that surface track-and-search controls have been eliminated; it carries displays for detection, acquisition, and tracking of air targets by the STIR, as well as controls for target assignment, target selection, and weapons utilization. Both of the air channels (2 and 3) are controlled from the Mk 107 (in this version, Mk 106 controls channels 1, 4, and 5).

A system bus connects the consoles with a UYK-7 weapons-control processor and its OJ-172 console, and with an OJ-194(V)3/UYA-4 PPI (weapons-control officer) console (not in the CAS-only versions of the system).

The Phase I near-term get-well program included provision for the SM-1 Block 6 missile. The test ship was the *Stephen W. Groves* (1983).

Phase II (Mk 92 Mod 6) adds a new coherent receive/transmit (CORT) transceiver to counter heavy jamming, clutter, and STA

The antenna inside the Mk 92 Combined Antenna System (CAS). (Sperry)

clutter (i.e., targets just beyond instrumented range that are so large that their STAEs swamp echoes from small nearby targets). The STIR tracker is modified to provide a horizon-search capability. The prototype (with IADT) was installed on board the last *Perry*-class frigate (*Ingraham*, FFG 61), and CORT is being installed on a total of 12 U.S. and 9 foreign ships. The upgrade includes replacement of the separate picture-keeping and fire-control computers (UYK-7s) by a single UYK-43. A second UYK-43B is added to act as converter control processor. The U.S. upgrade includes installation of SQQ-89 (full-spectrum towed-array processing).

Unisys claimed in March 1991 that Mod 6 (CORT) offers the following improvements over Mod 2: twice the transmitter power; twice the instrumented range (search and track); 100:1 improvement in clutter rejection; coherent cancellation of second/third-time-around clutter; an order of magnitude reduction in the minimum radar cross-section the system can handle; improved capability to handle target velocities; better ECCM; twice the MTBF; half the MTTR. Unisys (now part of Loral/Lockheed Martin) has also offered a simplified Mod 6 (for small combatants) without the STIR.

Mod 6 first fired an SM-1 Block VIB missile in September 1992, the missile entering service in FY94. Work on a Mod 2 version followed. Under the FY95 program, a Mod 6 track processing improvement for better clutter rejection and ECCM was developed.

A more modest upgrade, CANDO (COTS Affordable Near-term Deficiency-Correcting Ordalt), is to be applied to 10 ships, to improve performance against small low-fliers in multiple-interval clutter (MIC). Raw Mk 92 Mod 2 video is passed through a high-speed CANDO processor before being displayed. An automatic target track (which the ships' RVPs do not produce) is displayed on WCCs. CANDO ships receive the MPU to their SPS-49 radars. This program also produced a solution to the multiple interval clutter (MIC), that is, land-clutter, problems encountered by Mk92 Mod 6. Hughes produces the ORDALT kits. Development testing (data collection) began aboard USS *Copeland* (FFG 25) in December 1992. *Stark* tested a preliminary version in March 1994. The CANDO engineering development model (EDM) was tested on board *Copeland* at sea on 15 and 16 August 1994. However, as of April 1996 CANDO had not been installed on board any ships.

A proposed phased-array radar upgrade was never carried out.

Work on a midlife upgrade to Mk 92s aboard *Perry*-class frigates began in FY92. These ships may fire SM-2 Block IIIB missiles. Tactical improvements include Guard Gate, Priority Engage (and improved automatic engagement scheduler), and Sector Scan. Technical improvements include heavy-duty-rate transmission for the combined antenna (the egg) and reduction of high-failure-rate items. Under the FY93 program, EO improvements to the STIR began, and work also began on improvements to CWI to deal with low fliers. However, as of April 1996 no funding for any such upgrade was available. See the CDS section for some possible future upgrades.

Weights: Mod 1, 1905/5637 lb; Mod 2, 6318/15,848 lb; Mod 5, total about 7835 lb; Mod 6, total about 24,000 lb.

Users: Australia (*Perry* class [Mod 2]), Saudi Arabia (PCC and PCG classes [Mod 5]), Spain (*Perry* class [Mod 2]; CORT [Mod 6] in last two ships), Taiwan (*Perry* class, with CORT [Mod 6]), United States (*Perry*-class frigates [Mod 2; Mod 6 in CORT ships: FFG 36, 47, 48, 50–55, 57, and 59], *Hamilton*- and *Bear*-class coast guard cutters [Mod 1]). Mod 1 is CAS only; Mod 2 adds STIR; Mod 5 is an improved Mod 1 with more U.S. content.

◆ R76/HR76

Band: X (12 preselected frequencies over 800 MHz)
Beam: 2.7 deg
Peak Power: 250 kW
Gain: 32 dB
Pulse Width: 0.25, 0.5, or 1 microsec
PRF: 1000–3000 pps
Antenna Dimensions: 1 m
Antenna Weight: 205 kg (1200 kg total; 360 kg including TV)

RCA's small-ship FCS uses a gyrostabilized monopulse radar tracker (with a coaxial EO contrast tracker) derived from satellite trackers and a distributed architecture (16-bit microprocessors on a bus with a 100-Hz frame rate). The system uses two types of microcomputers, an RCA control processor (RCP) and a Rolm 1664. A typical installation includes as many as eight microcomputers: one for track radar, one for the search console, one for the tracking console, one for gunfire control (ballistics), one for plot extraction, one for the ship interface (to other sensors and weapons), one for bus control, and one to control EAROM (electronically alterable ROM, in which constants such as magazine temperature are manually entered). Each microcomputer is housed in a 64-card chassis, typically with 16 microprocessor cards (each with its own ROM). For example, one processor is used for mode control, another for target range, another for target angle, and so on. RCA argued that this dual level of distribution made modification easy, and also easily accommodated additional functions (with their own microcomputers).

A separate EO director carries a tracker with a laser rangefinder and a remote-control zoom lens (with an FOV variable from 30 to 1.5 deg). Acquisition range on a 1m² target is 40 km (43,700 yd), and accuracy at 20 km is 10 m in range and 1 mrad in bearing/elevation. Search-scan period is 4 sec (15 rpm), and reaction time from designation to tracking averages 3.5 sec. To track a target less than half a beamwidth above the horizon, the antenna is held at a fixed elevation, and the target is tracked off-axis.

Users: New Zealand (R76C5 in *Leander*-class frigates, installation beginning February 1985), Taiwan (HR-76 in Wu-Jinn I class destroyers, *Lung Chiang* class, and probably coastal defenses using H930 CDS).

◆ W-120/W-160/W-1200

Westinghouse's private-venture W-120 shipboard fire-control radar is based on the APQ-120 of the F-4J. Typically a 4000-yd acquisition window is placed around the designated range. The radar acquires a target in 20 msec after designation. If automatic track is lost, the radar attempts to reacquire the target. There is also a low-flier mode. Peak power is 165 kW (pulse widths 0.4 and 2.0 microsec, PRFs 1000 and 500 pps). Westinghouse claims that W-120 can detect a 1m² target at 30 nm and that angular accuracy is better than 2 mrad. The antenna is a radome-

The W-160 "golf ball" on board the Taiwanese destroyer *Chien Yang*, a *Gearing* subject to WS-III modernization. The box at the base of the mainmast is one of two Chang Feng III (Hughes MEWS) arrays; note the launchers atop the deckhouse, forward of the array. The radome at the top of the mainmast, not entirely visible here, is probably the Argos 680. The boxes hold SM-1 missiles. (Fu S. Mei)

enclosed 32in paraboloid (gain 34.5 dB) that can elevate/depress to +90/−30 deg. Beamwidth is 2.8 deg. Search patterns are 10-deg azimuth × 30-deg elevation scan; 10 × 15-deg scan; spotlight or fixed beam position. Reliability: 300hr MTBF. The antenna/pedestal assembly weighs 860 lb, and the display/controls 100 lb.

W-160, announced in 1982, is a follow-on based on the APG-66 fighter radar; see the Strike Warfare section (under APG-66) for details.

W-1200 was a series of Westinghouse modular FCSs developed to compete with H930 Mod 1; the tracker was W-120. Other elements were an optical director, an LN-66HP radar, a UYK-19 computer, and a Westinghouse UPA-62 display. W-1200 could control 35- and 40mm guns.

Users:

W-120: Korea (*Paek Ku* class)
W-160: Taiwan (Wu-Jinn III destroyers, in MCS CDS)
W-1200: Korea (*Paek Ku* class)

Radar Integration

◆ New Threat Upgrade (NTU)

NTU is an AAW upgrade for U.S. missile cruisers and *Kidd*-class destroyers, often characterized as the "poor man's Aegis." As in Aegis, the SM-2 missile, with its commandable autopilot, replaces the earlier SM-1, so the ship need not illuminate a target throughout the missile's flight. However, because the ship's search radars are not as precise as SPY-1, NTU still needs illuminators capable of acquiring and tracking the target. Each illuminator must, therefore, spend more time per target, so overall firepower cannot quite match that of an Aegis ship. NTU was applied to numerous SM(ER) ships, which were stricken and scrapped after the end of the Cold War. It survives aboard a few ships armed with SM-2(MR) missiles. One reason for the abandonment of the expensive NTU(ER) system was that the naval environment had changed drastically.

Had the Cold War turned hot, the U.S. Navy would have faced large-scale air attacks launched from a great range. The problem would have been to deal with saturation at long range. Launch rate would not have been as important as the ability to handle multiple targets per ship. In the post–Cold War world, it is far more likely that ships will be suddenly attacked at relatively short range, so reaction time is much more important. The two-stage ER missile could not be launched very quickly (it had to be manually finned just before being rammed onto the launcher). The single-stage MR missile needs no such preparation.

In the NTU system, the ship tracks the target only, transmitting the target's position to the missile. The missile computes the trajectory required to hit the target. In contrast, Aegis, which has a more precise tracking radar, tracks both missile and target, commanding the missile into position. Existing air-search radars are replaced by SPS-48E and SPS-49(V)2, and a new SYS-2 IADT feeds NTDS, which in turn feeds a new WDS Mk 14. NTU uses CW acquisition and tracking (CWAT) to improve performance against high-altitude, supersonic, steeply diving missiles.

The first SM-2(MR) NTU ship was *Scott* (DDG 995).

◆ SSDS/QRCC

SSDS (Ship Self-Defense System), the current U.S. Navy program for relatively close-range shipboard air defense, was mandated by Congress after the attack on the *Stark*. The SSDS Mission Need Statement (MNS) was submitted in August 1991. SSDS builds on an earlier Quick-Reaction Combat Capability (QRCC) program developed by the former U.S. NAAWS (NATO AAW System) project office. These programs exploited the work that several U.S. NAAWS competitors did on weapons-system-oriented CDSs ("cores"). Like the Aegis CDS, these cores were intended as WDSs, grown up to handle further CDS tasks. As it happened, the rules of the NAAWS competition required the companies to develop Aegis-like cores without the associated radars.

The idea was to develop an all-U.S. system mainly from existing components, linking existing autonomous hard- and soft-kill devices for greater effectiveness. RAIDS (see below) became SSDS Mk 0. It is merely an advisory device. The next step is to integrate it directly into shipboard sensor and weapons systems. This development was based on a long-standing General Dynamics proposal to use the Phalanx search radar to trigger RAM missile firing. The computer that coordinates the two and passes Phalanx radar data through to the RAM mount can also accept SLQ-32 data and can in theory accept inputs from an IR search-and-track system. The computer can set and change jammer frequency and fire chaff. SSDS Mk 1 is the combination of RAM, Phalanx, and available sensors.

SSDS Mk 1 is for *Perry*-class frigates with CORT, for the LHD 1, LSD 41, LSD 49, and LPD 17 classes. The pre-prototype was installed in USS *Whidbey Island* (LSD 41) in March–April 1993 for summer 1993 tests that were successfully completed on 5 June 1993. The fiber-optic LAN is Safenet FDDI. System elements were: two Phalanx (used partly to provide a radar sensor), RAM (with its own UYK-44 computer), SPS-49, SLQ-32 with a chaff launcher, the prototype SAR-8 IRST, and a pair of UYQ-70s (sensor supervisor and weapon supervisor workstations). A systems review (December 1993) determined the configuration for the baseline, intended for AOE 6 and to be tested on the ex-destroyer *Decatur* in 1997. Hardware and software requirements for the new operational computer program (OCP), which integrates sensor data and manages tracks for threat evaluation and assignment choices among multiple weapons, were set by NSWC Dahlgren and APL in 1993–94.

The successful test series began with a 450kt drone, system track on which was established by SLQ-32 and SPS-49. Both CIWS radars contributed track data before a RAM shot down the drone. Then an A-4 towed a target at 300 kt. SPS-49 initially detected it, CIWS provided a continuous track, then CIWS destroyed the target. This test verified the system's ability to maintain a composite track. SLQ-32 was not involved because the target was a nonemitter. Finally, a BQM-34S drone at 450 kt and a towed target appeared. SPS-49 provided initial tracks, then all sensors contributed track data. CIWS destroyed the target, RAM the BQM-34S. This demonstrated an ability to engage multiple targets simultaneously and automatically.

SSDS Mk 2 (medium-term) replaces the current NATO Sea Sparrow system, using the Evolved Sea Sparrow Missile (ESSM). It is being tested on board the rebuilt remotely controlled destroyer *Decatur*. A distributed system on this ship links a TAS(I), SLQ-32, NATO Sea Sparrow, RAM, and Phalanx. Mk 2 is intended for integration with a ship's CDS. In effect it adds Sea Sparrow to Mk 1. This version is for the *Nimitz*, *Spruance*, *Wasp* (LHD 1), and AOE 6 classes, and is to enter service in FY98.

Mk 3 (far term) will, in theory, be integrated with cooperative engagement concept (CEC) and with the new combat-direction system (ACDS). This version will use a new multifunction radar (MFR), the next-generation ECM system (AIEWS), and a new missile (either ESSM or an SDIO-derived weapon).

About a third of the SSDS budget goes to a black program, Link Iron. It probably seeks counters to stealthy (low-observable) attackers.

Ship AAW systems are being upgraded under the QRCC program, which includes SSDS installation. For example, in the prototype *Ashland* (LSD 48, completed in 1992), the new sensors are SPS-49A(V)1 (the MPU upgrade, to be completed in September 1996) and SPS-67(V)1. The ship's RADDS is being upgraded so that these sensors can feed her new SSDS Mk 1–0 system (completed late June 1996). The upgrade also feeds own-ship data into RADDS and hence into SSDS (via a modified IC switchboard and the usual analog readouts, such as the ship's electromagnetic log). Hard-kill systems are RAM (installed August 1996) and an upgraded Phalanx Block 1A. The ESM system has been upgraded from SLQ-32(V)1 to A(V)1 and a Mk 36 Mod 12 decoy launcher installed. Finally, the ship was fitted with a Battle Force Tactical Trainer (BFTT) in June 1996, to provide training inputs to her SSDS operators. As installed on the ship, the three-operator SSDS console has five screens plus a pair of large-scale display screens. In effect it and RADDS provide the ship with an AAW CDS.

As of mid-1996, plans called for deploying SSDS on board the LHD 41 class beginning in FY97, on board LHD 1s beginning in the last quarter of FY98, in the LHA 1 class in the last quarter of FY99, and in existing carriers at about the same time. New carriers and LPD 17s are to be built with SSDS installed. Note that SSDS is apparently no longer planned for destroyers and frigates.

◆ RAIDS (SYQ-17)/ASDCS

Rapid Anti-Ship Missile Integrated Defense System is a near-term project begun by NSWC early in FY88 (and made a formal acquisition program in FY89) in response to fleet requests (i.e., presumably in response to experience in the Persian Gulf, including the *Stark* incident). The *Stark* seems to have suffered from excessive false alarms, which reduced alertness when the attack actually developed. Nor was an unusual signal, which turned out to be that of an Agave attack radar, properly interpreted. Reactions were too slow, and there was no useful guide to the sort of integrated maneuver and chaff-launching reaction that was needed. Appropriate maneuvers depend on too many variables to be extemporized. RAIDS, then, was conceived as a better way of using all the information already available aboard ship, from both passive and active sensors, and using both hard- and soft-kill defenses. Although ESM and ECM have always been associated with U.S. CDSs, these systems rely overwhelmingly on active sensors and are designed mainly to support hard-kill systems. Software, written in commercial languages such as "C," was developed on 386-based laboratory computers (operational systems use 486 chips).

RAIDS ran *Spruance*-class operational trials in January–March 1993.

RAIDS connects three elements: the sensors (including ESM) providing the ASMD picture, the sensors used primarily to determine whether soft kill succeeds, and the display/analysis element, which uses a rule-based software "tactical engine." All are linked by a data bus (an Ethernet LAN). The ASMD sensors are NTDS (CDS) itself (i.e., the main search radars and off-board data provided via Link 11), SLQ-32/ULQ-16, and the radars of the two Phalanx guns. The main soft-kill evaluation sensors are the Mk 86 FCS radars and the Mk 23 TAS. Presumably, the latter are used because they are needed to initiate the alternative hard-kill measures. All of the sensors are connected to the system via RAIDS interface units (RIUs) incorporating 486 chips. CDS and SLQ-32/ULQ-16 share a common RIU via a T-bar switch; Mk 86 and Mk 23 share a common RIU. The two Phalanx each have their own RIU. The system uses a total of eight 32-bit CPUs on a LAN.

TAS Mk 23 antenna. (Hughes)

The main computing element, a track manager, is intended to minimize false alarms by associating radar tracks formed in the ship's CDS with particular emitters, using both range/range rate in CDS and emitter character to decide which tracks merit reaction. If a missile seeker is not detected, RAIDS guesses the most likely platform and provides a synthetic missile track with estimated impact time. Threats are ranked according to which is likely to hit first. The ship's officers can insert the weights they consider appropriate (depending, e.g., on where the ship is operating). SLQ-32 can be preset to report radars of particular interest.

The main RAIDS displays are located next to the SWC (surface-warfare coordinator)/TAO console in CIC (a UYQ-70 for the TAO), next to the SLQ-32 console in CIC (a UYQ-70 for the EW supervisor), and near the centerline pelorus on the bridge (i.e., convenient to the OOD ordering evasive maneuvers). Each display uses a color CRT showing a threat evaluation (in PPI form), recommended actions, and a timeline showing just how urgent those actions are.

Maneuver recommendations are based on factors such as wind, chaff-cloud size and development time, ship cross-section (on a given bearing), and sensor and weapon blind arcs.

The FY92 program included two EDM, three trainer, and nine operational RAIDS. However, the operational units were eliminated pending tests of the EDMs. RAIDS completed OpEval in July 1993; approval for production (MS III) was granted in August 1993. RAIDS has now been installed on board *Spruance*-class destroyers and is planned for *Perry*-class frigates without CORT.

A Phase 2, including automated reactions, both by countermeasures and by ASMD weapons, became SSDS Block 1 (see above).

ASDCS (Advanced Self-Defense Combat System), a Dahlgren ATD using Loral Librascope automated planning and Engineering Research Associates situation-assessment techniques, is a RAIDS follow-on. It is intended to replace the reactive rule-based planning of RAIDS with pro-active planning; its Tactical Response Planner (TRIP) constantly plans an optimum route to an objective while minimizing exposure to known or projected threats. It manages ship's sensors, looking for data that will allow the TAO to anticipate and potentially avoid problems. Elements of ASDCS were inserted into the SSDS program in FY96.

◆ SWY Series

These are new designations for integrated radar/weapon systems. SWY-1 is the NATO Sea Sparrow system, including the target-acquisition radar, TAS Mk 23. It has been in service since 1980. SWY-2 is TAS Mk 23 plus RAM, for the LHAs; it entered service in 1993. SWY-3 is the probable designation for the combination of TAS Mk 23, Sea Sparrow, and RAM on LHD 5 and later units.

◆ RVP/SIDS

Radar-video processors provide radars with an ADT capability. One such system, the Hughes CV-2834/UYA-4(V), was developed for *Adams*-class destroyers. SIDS (sensor-interface data system) is an enhanced version, incorporating a UYK-20, aboard non-SYS *Perry*-class frigates; it is also part of the TAS Mk 23 radar. RVP/SIDS processes video from one radar at a time (the later SYS-1 fuses data from all the ship's radars). Trials of RVP on board HMAS *Perth* were so successful that the RAN specified it for its *Perry*-class frigates. However, it later adopted SYS-1 for its *Adams* class.

Initially (1974–75) air tracks were manually initiated and then automatically tracked; there was no surface-tracking mode. The RAN asked for fully automatic tracking, the CV-2834 program being modified for ATD (with manual override). By 1981 the Australians operated in automatic mode 90% of the time, finding excellent target resolution at long range, and (because the system does not lose alertness as its operator tires) a sevenfold improvement in probability of detection for a given opportunity. In the *Perth* system, ADT data are checked by a tracking program to see whether they correspond to realistic target motion, and those that are evaluated as real are retained in a target track file.

In a U.S. *Perry*, SIDS feeds track data from SPS-49 or -55 to the shipboard command/control system as would a manual operator.

♦ SYS-1/2/3 and TMS

The integrated automatic detection-and-tracking (IADT) system is intended to integrate the disparate radars on board a ship into a single system. ATD contacts (plots) from all the ship's radars are correlated to form tracks, the computer tracking the apparent centroid of the array of plots associated with each target. The resulting track data are supplied to the ship's CDS. Compared to RVP/SIDS, IADT can maintain track on a much more violently maneuvering target, partly because the system's effective data rate is far higher (different radars paint the target much more frequently than a single radar can). The system's developer, Grumman Northrop (Norden division), argues that the U.S. IADT is superior to many foreign track combiners because, unlike them, it always uses the outputs of all the ship's radars, exploiting their different characteristics. In the late 1970s it was claimed that SYS-1 more than halved a ship's reaction time.

SYS-1, which was conceived for *Adams*-class missile destroyers (with CDS), was developed under a 1977 contract from Johns Hopkins Applied Physics Laboratory, which has been responsible for many U.S. Navy AAW programs. SYS-2 was developed for NTU ships; it entered service in 1987. SYS-3 uses 68020 processors rather than standard Navy computers. TMS (track management system) is a COTS successor (68040 chips) designed to fuse radar, IFF, ESM, and EO data, using an adaptive video processor (AVP) hosted in a 63-slot VME chassis. It can handle up to 1500 track updates/sec. The developers claim that by using multiple hypothesis synthesis/resolution techniques, they can form tracks with a very low false track rate.

SYS-1/2 employ two standard computers (UYK-20 in SYS-1, UYK-44 in SYS-2): Computer A accepts radar detection data; Computer B carries the merged picture and provides it to the ship CDS (and directly to the WDS in SYS-2). The system employs a pair of standard OJ-194(V)3/UYA-4 consoles, whose operators include the radar-control (RC) and detector-tracker-monitor (DTM) operators. Track symbols and vectors are shown on the PPI together with a track history display (THD), a time-compressed display of about 1 min of history for tracks requested by the operator. There is also a digital display of track data, radar environment parameters, and program status. SYS-2 has a special quick-reaction mode in which track data are passed directly to the WDS.

The U.S. Navy has bought a version of TMS using PowerPC 604 processors as SYS-2 Field Change 2. The German navy bought TMS(68040) as SYS-1 Field Change 1, installations beginning in mid-1996.

Users:

SYS-1: Australia ([V]3 in *Adams* class), Germany ([V]1 in *Adams* class; was in 4 U.S. JPDTS ships), Greece ([V]1 in *Themistoklis*), Italy ([V]2 in *Audace* and *Mimbelli* classes and one other ship).

SYS-2: Taiwan ([V]2 in *Perry* class), United States ([V]2 in *Kidd* and *California* classes and in *Perry* class, [V]3 in *Wasp*, [V]4 in *Kitty Hawk*, [V]5 in later *Wasp* class [LHD 2 and beyond], [V]6 in LHDs modified with SSDS).

SYS-3: Israel (*Eilat* class).

TMS: Australia (probably in *Perry* class as upgraded), Canada (January 1996 demonstration contract for installation in TRUMP ships), Germany (*Adams* class and *Bremen* class as upgraded with TRS-3D radar), New Zealand (*Wellington* [installed May 1995] and *Canterbury*, to feed Nautis system; first customer), United States (aircraft carriers, *California*, *Kidd*, *Perry*, *Wasp* classes).

AIR-TRAFFIC-CONTROL RADARS

♦ SPN-35

Band: X (9000–9160 MHz)
Beam: (e) 3 × 1.15 (scans in 10- or 35-deg sectors) (a) 1.1 × 3.5 (tilted −1 to +25 deg)

Peak Power: 175 kW
Gain: (e) 34 dB (a) 36.5 dB
Pulse Width: 0.2 or 0.8 microsec
PRF: 1200 pps
Antenna Dimensions: (e) 30 × 152 in (a) 78 × 159 in
Antenna Weight: 3500 lb (total for radar, including radome)

First evaluated at sea in 1963, ITT-Gilfillan's SPN-35 was designed to enable its operator to direct a pilot along a predetermined glide path to a point a mile from a ship, after which the pilot could land visually. Enclosed in a radome, it employs separate antennas to measure the elevation (AS-1669) and azimuth (AS-1292) of an incoming airplane. In the list above, these antennas are distinguished as (e) and (a), respectively.

The successor is likely to be SPN-47, a shipboard version of the Marines' TPN-30 MRAALS (marine remote-area approach and landing system).

SPN-35 (in the radome) on board the Spanish carrier *Principe de Asturias*, 1989. (S. Terzibaschitsch)

Users: Spain (*Principe de Asturias*), United States (amphibious carriers). This radar was removed from all U.S. CV/CVN.

♦ SPN-43

Band: S (3590–3700 MHz)
Beam: 1.5 × 45 deg
Peak Power: 850 kW
Gain: 32 dB
Pulse Width: 0.6 or 0.25 microsec
PRF: 1125 pps
Scan Rate: 15 rpm
Antenna Dimensions: 120 × 150 in
Antenna Weight: 3400 lb (including pedestal)

ITT-Gilfillan's SPN-43 is the marshal or air-search component of the carrier-controlled landing system. It can also function as a secondary or backup air-search radar. Maximum range in clear weather is 50 nm (35 nm in rain), and minimum range 250 yd. The antenna can be tilted from 2.5 to 6.0 deg.

Users: United States (all CV/CVN).

SPN-43 is shown on board the amphibious carrier *Wasp,* August 1995. The radar on the right is SPS-67; above both is the back of a TAS Mk 23. Below SPN-43 is the flat antenna of an SPS-52C. (Author)

◆ SPN-42/SPN-46

SPN-42 is a dual-channel automatic-aircraft-landing system, each channel of which can handle one airplane at a time. Each channel employs a Ka-band conscan dish (AS-1347/SPN-42) with a smaller X-band beacon receiver (AS-2407/SPN-42) rigidly mounted to it. The main 0.57-deg beam scans at 6000 rpm. The track of the incoming airplane is transmitted to the ship's CDS, which computes course corrections and transmits them via Link 4A. There are three alternative operating modes: automatic (commands are sent directly to the autopilot of the airplane); semiautomatic (the pilot follows a pointer in the cockpit); and manual (talk-down).

Textron's SPN-46 replaces SPN-42, using the same antennas but taking over the computing function using a standard AYK-14 computers on a 1553B bus. The Ka-band tracker operates at 50 kW (pulse width 0.2 microsec, PRF 2000 pps); the system has a 10nm operating range and monitors a 4nm approach-control zone (55 × 30 deg). Scan rate is 12 scans/sec (25 × 1-deg box 1200 ft deep in range). This radar experiences acquisition problems in rain, and a moving-target detection (MTD) capability is being developed (the engineering development contract was awarded in FY93). Ultimately such radars may largely be eliminated in favor of a link transmitting an airplane's GPS position to the ship. Ashore, GPS is already superseding Tacan for point-to-point navigation along air lanes. Work on the naval version of the GPS link (SABER; see IFF) began in FY94.

The first two SPN-46s were authorized in FY86; OpEval followed in FY90. A next-generation lower-observable system died after the end of the Cold War.

Textron is currently promoting an amphibious ship (LHD/LHA) version, using an X-band (9.0–9.5 GHz) low-PRF pulse-Doppler waveform (peak power 100 kW, pulse width 0.25 microsec, PRF 2–5 kHz), searching automatically through a 15 × 2-deg basket, out to a range of 3000 ft at 15 scans/min. It would use a 4ft parabolic antenna (monopulse Cassegrain fed). Minimum range would be 150 ft, with a range resolution of 2 ft, as in SPN-46. The system computer would be AYK-14 plus VME-based SMJ320C40 processors. The system would control an approach zone 8 nm deep.

SPN-42 on board the carrier *John F. Kennedy.* (S. Terzibaschitsch)

OPTRONIC SYSTEMS

◆ Mk 51 FCS

Mk 51, essentially a remote lead-computing gunsight, was the most successful World War II lightweight director. Gyros in the director measure the angular speed of the target as the operator tracks it optically; range is not measured (the operator estimates it, based on the observed size of the target). The director computes the amount by which the gunner must lead the target, based on its estimated course and on gun ballistics. Typical limitations: target speed (component across the LOS) 350 kt, lead angle 25 deg. Mk 51 is almost always associated with the twin or quadruple 40mm/60 gun. Ballistics: 40mm/60, 3in/50, 5in/38. Typical weight: 710 lb (above decks). Mk 63 (see separate entry above) is a radar-equipped version. The main modern equivalents are the French Lynx/Panda/NAJIR series and the Italian OG.R7. Many navies also use gun-mounted lead-computing gunsights.

Users: Argentina (modified *De Soto County*–class LST), Brazil (*De Soto County*–class LST), Greece (minelayers: all Mod 2), Iran (PF 103 class: Mod 2), Japan (*Chikugo, Miura, Atsumi* classes), Mexico (*Cuitlahuac,* APDs, former minesweepers), Philippines (*Cannon, Auk,* PCE/AM, LST classes), Portugal (*Joao Coutinho* class), Taiwan (LSTs), Thailand (LSTs, LSMs), Turkey (*Bayraktar-* and *Mordogan*-class minelayers). Some other ships, particularly LSTs, may retain Mk 51 directors.

◆ Mk 24 Target Designation Transmitter/WDS Mk 11

Mk 24 is the standard U.S. Navy optical target designator, transmitting target elevation and bearing to a ship's combat system. It consists of a pair of counterbalanced binoculars atop a pedes-

The optics of a Mk 51 director on board a Japanese ship. (*Ships of the World*)

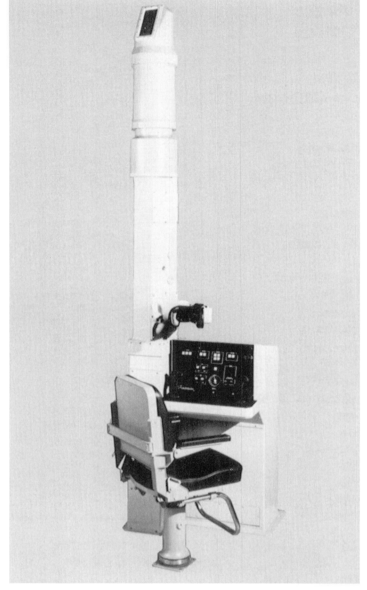

The periscope director and the console of Kollmorgen's Coastal Protection System. (Kollmorgen)

tal. Elevation limits: +90/−20 deg. The transmitter proper weighs 210 lb and is 70 in high, with a swept radius of 12 in. A below-decks control unit (Mk 79) adds another 95 lb. When combined with a data transmitter, Mk 24 is part of WDS Mk 11, incorporating four (Mod 2 or 3) or two (Mod 4) Mk 24s.

◆ Coastal Protection System/Model 985/Mk 35/H930 Optronic Sensor/Mk 93 FCS

Kollmorgen combined its Model 985 periscopic director with a 20mm Gatling gun (whose mount could also carry dual Stinger missiles) into its Coastal Protection System. Director elevation limits are +70/−25 deg; slew rate is 80 deg/sec, and tracking accuracy is 1.0 mrad. FOVs (magnifications) are 30 (2×) and 7.5 (8×) deg. The GE gun could elevate to +50/−10 deg (train limits were +/−110 deg). It could slew at 80 deg/sec with a tracking accuracy of 2.0 mrad. The system could also be combined with Kollmorgen's Model 445 Optronic Director or with the GCS-362 Gun Control System. The director could be provided with an LLLTV or FLIR. The sight itself is reportedly Mk 35 Mod L3. The system has been called HSV-20NCS, but Kollmorgen does not use that designation.

Model 985 is a slightly lighter and less expensive version of the Mk 35 Director, a periscope system designed by Kollmorgen for the U.S. post-Vietnam small-combatant program of the early 1970s, for FCS Mk 93 (EX-93). Mk 35 has been incorporated in the Korean *Paek Ku* class and in H930 Mods 0, 1, and 2. The periscope carries day/night stabilized optics plus a television. The operator can estimate range by stadimeter (i.e., by an angular measurement of a known distance on the target), or the director can track in bearing while radar is used for ranging. Although Mk 35 is primarily driven by the operator's joystick, it can autotrack using the television camera. Elevation FOV limits are +80 and −30 deg; FOVs are 8 deg (5.2×) and 32 deg (1.3×). The director can slew at 80 deg/sec (e.g., when accepting designation from another source). Resolution is 0.2 m at 3000 m, or 0.9 m at 15,000 m in daylight; corresponding night figures (clear with quarter moon) are 1.5 and 7.5 m.

Honeywell's Mk 93 (EX-93), designed for the abortive CPIC export coastal boat, is associated with the Mk 35 director and with the Emerlec-30 gun; it appeared aboard many of the units listed below. The associated radar is a Litton LN-66HP, the system computer offering two-target TWS operation. The optical director adds two more target tracks. Maximum target crossing speeds: 100 kt for a surface target (minimum range 500 yd), 350 kt for an air target (minimum range 500 yd, minimum altitude 300 ft). Ballistics could be provided for 20mm through 76mm calibers. EX-93 was the progenitor of the Honeywell/Hughes H930 series (hence the latter's name).

Users: Honduras (*Guardian*, 105ft and 85ft classes), Korea (Mk 35–0 in PSMM Mk 5 class [PGM 356–361], possibly also Sea Dolphin–class patrol boats), Saudi Arabia (Jetfoil tender to royal yacht), Taiwan (Model 985 in 50 Hai Ou–type missile boats, to control Hsiung Feng I missiles, and Mk 35 in Wu-Jinn destroyers), Thailand (HYUSCAT 18). Kollmorgen made 22 Mk 35 Mod 0 and Mod 1H in 1970–74, and 70 Model 985 Mod T and Mod H in 1976–88.

◆ Director Mk 46

Kollmorgen's EO director was developed for the *Arleigh Burke* class. It feeds data into the Mk 34 gun weapon system (GWS), whose only other sensor is the ship's SPY-1D radar. The associated computer is Mk 160 GCS (gun computer system).

Unlike earlier Kollmorgen directors, this is a stabilized pedestal flanked by two sensors (daylight imaging TI/CCD television and a MICROFLIR). There is no laser. Elevation limits are +80/−20 deg, and slew and elevation rates are 90 deg/sec (accuracy 1 mrad). The rotating head weighs 260 lb (about 30 × 28 in). Daylight FOVs are 2.0 × 1.5 deg (16×) and 5.0 × 3.75

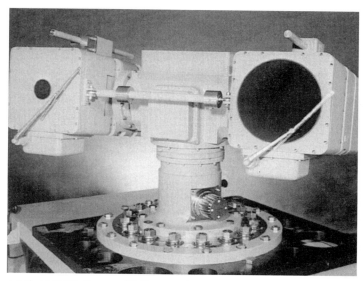

A Mk 46-0 EO director. (Kollmorgen)

deg (6.4×). The sensor is an 1134 × 486-element CCD; it should detect small surface craft at 20 km and air targets at 8 km. The MICROFLIR has 3.0 × 2.25 and 1.0 × 0.75-deg FOVs; it should detect surface targets at 16 km and air targets at 10 km. Its detector is a nine-element SPRITE array scanned both horizontally and vertically (it is a hybrid-serial FLIR). The display is a 1000-line 14in CRT; it tracks by correlation, centroid, or selectable edge, or it can coast (rate-aided track) if a target disappears behind some obstruction. Mod 0 is in the *Burke* class. Mod 1, developed 1995, is proposed for the *Ticonderoga* class, incorporating a laser ranger as standard, interfaced with the Mk 86 FCS. A Mod 2 has been proposed for the *Perry* class. The development contract was awarded in June 1990. Unit cost, initially about $3M, will probably fall to about $1.5M for later production.

♦ TISS (Thermal Imaging Sensor System) EX-8 Mod 0/IRST

McDonnell-Douglas won the TISS competition in October 1995 with a 115-lb ball director carrying a dual FOV 512 × 484-element InSb Amber Engineering FLIR (3–5 microns), a Videospection dual-FOV CCD TV camera, and a Hughes eye-safe laser ranger. Patented McDonnell-Douglas stabilization technology holds jitter to less than 15 microrad. McDonnell-Douglas claims that the 3–5-micron band chosen is the only one offering sufficient range in hot humid environments such as the Gulf. It claims that a device operating at the alternative 8–12-micron band could have met the TISS requirement at temperatures below about 90°F, but that inherent internal noise would have kept it below the TISS objective at all temperatures. Reported detection ranges: P-3 at about 55 kyd, tanker at about 45 kyd, small fast boat at 30 kyd, periscope at 11 kyd.

The CDU (control and display unit) in CIC uses COTS technology. It holds track data, accepting cues from the ship CDS and passing TISS tracks to the CDS. The contract calls for delivery of a prototype in mid-1996, with an option to buy a first lot of 24 systems for delivery in 1997. As many as 120 may ultimately be bought, initially for Aegis cruisers and destroyers.

This TISS was probably developed from Nighthawk, an ATD optronic FCS developed by McDonnell-Douglas and Rockwell for SPAWAR as Radiant Mist. Displayed in 1994, it was described as the first truly integrated optronic FCS, fusing the output of its sensors (long- and short-wave IR in one aperture, mm-wave in another, visible-range in a third, and a laser ranger in a fourth). Nighthawk was about the same size as MMS but slightly heavier (400–500 lb).

An RFP for a nondevelopmental TISS issued 28 November 1994 was suspended in January 1995 because funding was not in place and because the OR document had not yet been signed out. It was reactivated in May 1995. Planned procurement (as of June 1996): five in FY96 (for delivery FY97), eight in FY98, eight in

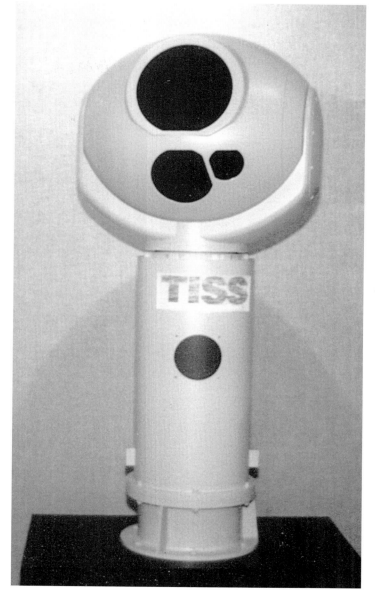

TISS on display at the 1996 Navy League Show (Stuart Slade, DMS/Forecast International)

FY99, three in FY00. TISS is to be permanently installed on board CG 47–class cruisers and cross-decked aboard other classes.

TISS is intended as part of a larger EO system in which it would be cued by an IRST, the RFP for which was also issued in November 1994, suspended and then revived. Like TISS, it is to be a low-risk system, in this case a single-band (3–5 micron) imager upgradeable to both bands. Other preplanned growth options may be a laser ranger, true dual-band operation (simultaneously processing both bands), dual-midwave operation (using two tones within one band), or installation of a large staring array which might spend increased dwell time in any one direction, ratcheting around the horizon rather than scanning continuously. Scan rate would probably be 60 rpm. Compared to foreign systems, IRST would have a larger aperture, for better signal reception. Because it is to be mounted 100 ft above water, the IRST must weigh less than 500 lb. Because no money was available in 1996, the program was restructured. As of mid-1996, plans called for a first demonstration in FY00, with final qualification in FY02. Potential installations: CG 47, DDG 51, LPD 17, CV/CVN, AOE 6, LSD 41, LHD/LHA, DDG 993, DD 963. Lockheed Martin (with Hughes as subcontractor) won this program in the fall of 1996.

NWC Dahlgren is testing a technology-demonstration Horizon IR Sensor (HISS), a French VIGY 200 stabilized turret carrying Hughes Santa Barbara 8–12-micron and Hughes El Segundo 3–5-micron (480 × 4 element) arrays, with a signal processor based on a Loral ASPRO-VME. The first was delivered in March 1995, the second in April 1995.

◆ CWDD (AN/KAS-1)

Texas Instruments' Chemical-Warning Directional Detector is a modified Army TAS-6, mounted on a ship's railing or TDT pedestal. CWDD is a binocular direct-view FLIR that can also be used for intelligence collection and gunlaying. Production began in 1982.

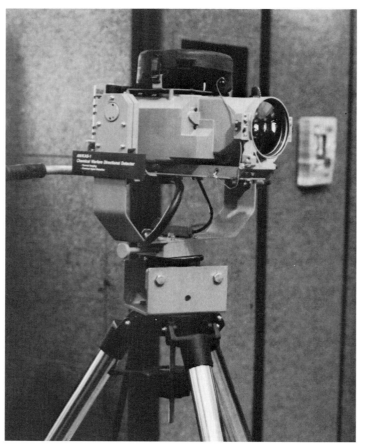

The Brunswick KAS-1 laser, chemical-warfare directional detector (CWDD) uses a common-module, 60-element FLIR (with two FOVs). It is the U.S. Navy's current standard standoff nerve-gas detector. A comparison of images in the filter's three bands is used for gas detection; the FLIR can also be used for night surveillance, navigation, and search and rescue. FOVs are 3.4 × 6.8 (resolution 0.40 mrad) and 1.1 × 2.2 (resolution 0.13 mrad). Minimum resolvable temperature is 0.3 deg at 3 cycles/mrad, 6 lines/m at 1 km. The sensor weighs 28 lb (plus 18 for the power control unit). (Author)

◆ SDV-1

Contraves' optical surveillance system (Model 066) equips *Bear*-class coast guard cutters. One stabilized platform carries an LLLTV surveillance camera; the other carries a slaved army-type 50 million candlepower searchlight. Targets detected by the LLLTV are spotlighted by the slaved light. Each of the two stabilized pedestals is 49 in high, including the sensor. This program began in 1978 and was completed in 1988; 15 units were supplied (13 for installation, 2 for support). Note that Model 066–3 is the EO element of the Hughes H930 in the Taiwan navy, and that Model 066–2/T is the LSEOS Mk II/IIA of Saudi *Sandown*-class minehunters.

The U.S. branch of Contraves is actively engaged in developing self-contained FCS for small weapons. The first, for the Army, was a prototype Small Arms Common Module FCS (SACMFCS) which is mounted atop machine guns such as Mk 19. A target is acquired via the device's LLLTV; range is found by coaxial

AN/SDV-1 searchlight (left) and LLLTV camera (right, pointing aft) on board the Coast Guard cutter *Campbell*, 1991. (A. Raven)

laser. The small device computes wind correction and ballistics. The next stage, BSTING (Ballistic Sight Technology Improving Night/Day Gunnery), was adapted for a moving platform. It was demonstrated on board a Mk V Special Forces craft in September 1995. Finally, OICW (Objective Individual Crew Served Weapon) is a rifle-sized development. All of these programs were financed by the U.S. Army, but they have potential SEAL and Marine Corps applications.

◆ Mast-Mounted Sight (MMS)

Developed for OH-58D helicopters, McDonnell-Douglas's Mast-Mounted Sight was was fitted to *Perry*-class frigates operating in the Gulf in 1989, primarily to detect floating mines. Human lookouts had missed mines in the heat, dust, and humidity. Re-

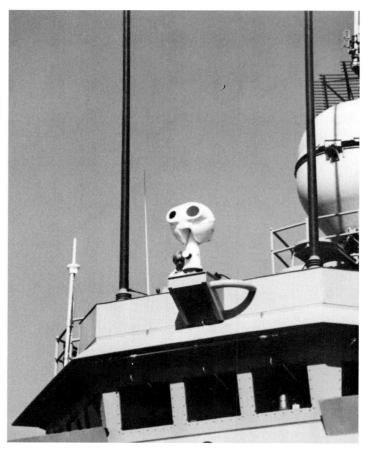

The mast-mounted sight on board a *Perry*-class frigate. (McDonnell-Douglas)

portedly, MMS was also quite useful against FAC and low-flying aircraft. Controlled by an operator in CIC, the spherical MMS turret uses a special "soft" mounting on a bridge pedestal on the centerline. One of two other displays is on the bridge. The turret carries an 8–12-micron 6in aperture 2-FOV FLIR (120-element common module HgCdTe detector, 275-line resolution) and a 2-FOV LLLTV (4in aperture, 0.65–0.9 microns, 700-line resolution) camera (the Army version also carries a ranging/designating laser). The outputs of both imagers are converted digitally to an 875-line format. FLIR FOVs are 9.6 and 2.8 deg (3× and 10.35×); TV FOVs are 8 and 2 deg. In Army tests, the criterion to detect a target was to get two lines on it; recognition took 12 lines. Tracking is digital. Turret slew rate is 60 deg/sec; bearing limits are 190 deg and elevation limits are 30 deg. Total turret weight is 73 kg (161 lb).

TISS has apparently superseded further U.S. purchases of MMS.

Users: Australia (*Adelaide* and *Sydney*) and United States (10 bought, rotated among ships, mainly on frigates).

♦ **Sea Tiger/Sea Dragon**

Texas Instruments' optronic FCS was tested by the South Korean navy in 1985. A derivative, Sea Dragon, was sold in the Far East, probably to the Korean navy. The stabilized cylindrical body, on trunnions, carries a laser range-finder/designator next to a day television camera, above a larger-diameter thermal imager (as used in Night Chaparral). The automatic video tracker can use either the television or the IR image. The one-operator console is below decks. Sea Tiger was originally designed to control guns and SSMs, but it can also control SAMs, since it can elevate to 70 deg. Frigates can be acquired and tracked at up to 14 km. The pedestal-mounted director weighs 270 kg and has a working circle (radius) of 60 cm.

Sea Tiger was intended for use with the Sea Ray laser-guided SSM.

TARGET DESIGNATION SYSTEMS (TDS) AND WEAPON DESIGNATION EQUIPMENT (WDE)

These are, in effect, analog buffers between the search radar picture in CIC and the ship's FCS. They replaced designation by sound-powered phone (the talker in CIC relaying coordinates to the director, which searched around them to acquire the target). Electrical designation eliminated both the dead time and the errors involved in such a procedure. These systems also, in effect, maintained a memory of important targets from which the FCS could select the next to engage. These systems were superseded by electronic CDS.

TDS Mk 5 probably survives aboard FRAM destroyers in the Korean, Mexican, and Turkish navies. It employs a horizontal PPI repeater (actually a television) with four joysticks (supervisor and three designators). Each joystick moves a designating hook (semicircle) on the screen. Repeat-back hooks show the directors' positions. A designator manually tracks a target until the appropriate director picks it up. Maximum displayed range is 30 nm (60 kyd). Although this analog system does not impose any target velocity limit, clearly very fast targets cannot be manually tracked for designation.

WDEs were the equivalents for missile ships. The surviving type is Mk 1 (WDS Mk 4), designed for Tartar ships, and probably on board the Greek *Adams* class (the Spanish *Baleares* class probably lost its Mk 1 systems when the Tritan CDS was installed). All other surviving missile ships of U.S. design have computer CDS, hence do not need an analog WDE.

This is a more sophisticated system, with six rate-aided tracking channels: a single designator can juggle multiple targets. The system employs a pair of Mk 37–0 target selection and tracking consoles connected with the missile system computer. Each displays raw search radar video. The operator inputs a target into a tracking channel by means of a pantograph, in effect measuring its speed and course on subsequent radar scans. Once the target has been entered, the missile computer repeats back its projected position as synthetic video, which the operator compares to the continuing search radar presentation. Each operator is respon-

sible for three targets, but each console can display all six. Targets are selected for engagement on an additional director-assignment console (Mk 47), whose PPI shows all six targets (with a velocity vector for one of them) as well as ship track and missile-system blind zones. A second monitor shows target speed, height, time interval for missile-director assignment (assignments resulting in earliest and latest intercepts), and remaining busy time for fire-control channels currently assigned. When a target is assigned, the system computer slews the two directors and causes them to search to acquire it. A fourth console, for weapons assignment (Mk 48), controls the launcher. Its operator makes the final evaluation of the blind zones and of the range, altitude, and seeker-angle limitations of the missiles. The Mk 48 operator actually fires.

IFF

In 1991 the U.S. Navy was made the lead service for a new U.S. IFF program, Combat Aircraft Identification (CAI) or All-Service Combat Identification (ASCID), to replace the canceled Mk XV. A COEA was conducted in FY95, and advanced concept demonstrations began in FY95. ASCIET (All-Services Combat Identification Evaluation Team) began work in FY96. The first ASCIET exercise was conducted on 4–15 September 1995 at Gulfport, Mississippi, using Mk XII, a SINCGARS/EPLARS-based Situational Awareness Data Link, CEC, JTIDS, SABER, and COBRA (a communications system). One problem is that the Navy favors noncooperative forms of IFF, whereas the Air Force favors cooperative systems, requiring positive identification of friendly aircraft. During the Gulf War the Air Force enforced just such positive rules to successfully avoid blue-on-blue attacks. The Navy counter would be that positive identification is far too cumbersome for a rapidly changing situation, particularly when missiles are involved, and that (in effect) it is more important to avoid losing ships than to avoid blue-on-blue aircraft losses. Too, as the Navy moves into littoral operations, combat identification concerns will likely include ground-vehicle identification; much of the impetus for the Army's digital battlefield was its unhappy experience of attacks by friendly aircraft during the Gulf War. The Army has also developed its own form of IFF, the TRW/Magnavox BCIS (battlefield combat identification system), which by mid-1995 had passed through the EMD stage. Like Mk XII, it is an interrogator-transponder system, but it works at 38 GHz (the interrogator is boresighted to the tank's laser range-finder; the gunner sees a red circle in the sight). In trials early in 1995, BCIS worked at a range of 10.2 km, almost twice the Army's required 5.5 km. Production may begin in 1997, if BCIS performs well enough in a February 1997 digital battlefield exercise. Note, however, that BCIS may not be adopted throughout NATO; European laser and 95-GHz systems are currently in development. Meanwhile, separate efforts (possibly including a podded BCIS) are being directed at improving air-to-ground IFF. BCIS may ultimately include a separate L-band ground-to-air element, using the same processor as the Ka-band element.

A recent NRL experiment using an ultra-high-resolution radar suggests some NCTR possibilities. Inserting seven very wide-band (200 MHz) pulses into a conventional radar's waveform and then compressing them on reception, NRL achieved a resolution of 1 m. It turned out that each type of aircraft showed a characteristic scattering profile: a large jet showed numerous individual scatterers of roughly constant size for each pulse, but a P-3 showed large fluctuations at its propellers. Targets could be classified as "small jet," "small prop," "helicopter," and "missile" with about 90% accuracy.

Ongoing work on specific emitter fingerprinting may also be useful for NCTR, particularly if next-generation ESM systems are fully integrated with CDSs. However, it is by no means clear that mass-produced civilian and military aircraft radars are as amenable to fingerprinting as the big naval radars analyzed in the past, which were almost hand-made. A trend toward solid-state software-controlled transmitters, whose elements are easy to change, may also make this technique less effective. A variation (albeit probably short-range) on this concept is to focus

ESM on the inadvertent emissions of an airplane's avionics. The Army is currently funding a Magnavox VSX-2 system for this purpose.

The standard tri-service aircraft transponder is Allied Signal's APX-100, which equips over 12,000 platforms. During Desert Storm, the lack of a naval aircraft interrogator created considerable problems. The Navy plans to buy about 500 Hazeltine APX-111 CITs (combined interrogator-transponders) for an F/A-18C/D upgrade program. This device was designed in the 1980s; Kuwait (40 F/A-18s) was the first customer. The U.S. Navy EMD contract was announced in January 1995. APX-113, for the F-16, is a derivative (Hazeltine currently has contracts for 300 for NATO, 150 for Taiwan, and 40 for Greece).

Several airborne NCTR efforts are underway: jet-engine modulation (JEM) measurement is being integrated into the F-14D and F/A-18, and PNCTR (passive NCTR) is being developed for the F/A-18. There is also a Positive Friendly Cooperative Aircraft Identification program for the F/A-18, to support coalition warfare. PHID (Positive Hostile Identification) is programmed for the F-14A and is a far-term possibility for the F/A-18.

Major programs:

The current Mk XII single-radar shipboard interrogators are UPX-23 and -27 (with an improved Mode 4 decoding capability). The standard SPS-48 interrogator antennas are AS-1065, AS-1688 (integral with antenna), AS-2188, and AS-3430. All but AS-1688 are also used by other major air search sets. Beamwidths: 9×45 deg for AS-1688, 7×48 deg for AS-2188, and 7.5×50 deg for AS-3430. Alone of the major rotating air-search radars, SPS-40 has an interrogator feed integral with its feed horn. Mk XII is being upgraded with new digital hardware. As of 1995, it seemed likely that Mk XII would be modified with a new waveform, possibly incorporating spread-spectrum Modes 7 and 8 (as a sort of low-budget Mk XV). The result, which could still use some Mk XII equipment, might be called Mk XVI or Mk XVII. As of mid-1996, Hazeltine hoped to sell its TPX-56 (already bought by the Army) to the Navy as a UPX-27 replacement, at half the size and a quarter of the price.

The Aegis IFF system, UPX-29, employs UPX-24/25 and the AIMS electronically scanned interrogator antenna. It codes transponder replies and positions (which it determines), providing digital data to up to 22 consoles, using six independent passive decoding channels (corresponding to different radars aboard one ship: in theory it can handle up to four radars). The presence of IFF interrogator antennas on the SPS-49 antennas of Aegis cruisers suggests that AIMS is usually associated only with SPY-1. UPX-24 (beacon video processor) provides triggering pulses to the receiver/transmitter, provides antenna steering signals, and processes replies for the ship's CDS. UPX-25 generates and transmits the interrogating pulses and sorts the replies. The associated Lockheed AIMS interrogator (AS-3134/UPX antenna) consists of 64 electronically scanned elements, in a 12.5ft ring, 16

in high. The interrogator can operate in continuous, sector-scan, or jump-scan modes, shifting from beam to beam in 50 microsec. Beamwidth is 7×44 deg in any of 1024 directors (a signal can be localized more accurately than the beamwidth alone might indicate). UPX-26 and -28 are the corresponding transponders.

UPX-30 is Allied Signal's CIFF (Central IFF), which merges interrogator functions for all of a ship's radars. Begun in the mid-1980s, CIFF was merged with AUTO-ID in 1989. Its VME chassis accommodates 680x0 microprocessors whose memories embody force doctrine (as in the Aegis C&D processor). Transponder tracks (up to 1000) are smoothed by Kalman filtering and associated with ACDS or SSDS tracks. CIFF synchronizes one or two interrogators with up to six radars (dual stabilized interrogators, about 15 ft apart, can overcome fading due to multipath). CIFF can interface with dual SARTIS (UPX-34) and to shipboard LANs such as FDDI and Ethernet. It has dual-channel IFF control (UPX-27, etc.) and can control/process SLQ-20A data. Mode 4 processing is speeded, with a higher probability of detection in denser EW environments, and antispoofing safeguards. SIF performance is improved, with easier use of time-changing codes and better processing of interleaved and overlapped replies. Displays: UYA-4, UYQ-21, SPA-25, and the RADDS console. Pre-production prototypes now under evaluation are called CIFF-SD (CIFF for ship defense); production units should become available about 2000.

AUTO-ID, developed by Johns Hopkins Applied Physics Lab (APL), adds position and kinematic data to normal IFF responses in order to filter out nontargets using an embedded doctrine. Development was apparently inspired by the *Vincennes* incident. For example, AUTO-ID would have rejected the Airbus as a target because it would have received the radar data showing that it was climbing. AUTO-ID can also be fed with commercial airway and air schedule data, for example. It is being adapted to process surface targets as part of SSDS. In the initial test on *Whidbey Island,* AUTO-ID functions are being assigned to SSDS processors and displays. Later the ID algorithm will take electronic emissions, IR, and noncooperative identification data into account.

UPX-34, Condor's SARTIS (Shipboard Advanced Radar Target Identification System), identifies air targets by measuring blade rate, using modulation of the echo (jet-engine modulation [JEM] technique). This system is being installed on board Aegis cruisers. A SARTIS-like technique is being provided to SSDS ships (as NCTR-SD), using the Mk 95 Sea Sparrow illuminator. It was under test as of May 1995. As of that time, SARTIS was the leading Navy NCTR project.

NATO Sea Sparrow launchers and Mk 91 illuminators (radar Mk 95) on board the carrier USS *Ranger,* July 1986. An EO tracker is located between the two radomes of the radar illuminator-tracker. (Hughes)

AIMS Aegis system interrogator with SPS-49 antenna in the foreground, USS *Hue City,* summer 1995. (Stuart Slade, DMS/Forecast International)

SABER (Situational Awareness with Beacon and Reply), using GPS-derived position and platform data sent via UHF and FLTSATCOM OTH links. SABER is particularly attractive because it uses existing systems and thus is very inexpensive (as of mid-1995, about $5000 per beacon). Each subscriber to a SABER net reports GPS-derived position every 2 min, timed by the GPS clock (this cycle time suffices for 500 reports on a UHF satellite channel 25 kHz wide or for 2000 reports over one of eight simultaneous WSC-3 UHF LOS nets). A TAC-3 computer with JMCIS software can display up to 200 simultaneous SABER tracks, associating each reporter with an identification. A SABER terminal operator can query any other SABER terminal by "name" or can poll groups by identification code or GPS parameters. For example, the operator on a carrier can obtain the ship's own position within 2 min, or he can mix categories to locate all aircraft of a particular squadron above a particular altitude but within a particular range of a given base. Given this degree of situational awareness, SABER supports a "Don't Shoot Me" (DSM) net. Shooters transmit the location (or line of bearing) of the target to be engaged. Any SABER beacon monitoring the DSM net and finding itself matching the "shoot" parameters immediately transmits its GPS and platform data to the shooter; less than 2 sec after its own transmission, the shooter sees the location and identification of all friendly platforms in the kill zone. The SABER beacon was developed by SWRI, which has also produced a miniaturized version, SILO (signal intercept from low orbit: Radiant Snow), which is designed to function less frequently. Work began after a 1993 Secretary of the Navy wargame established combat ID as a top naval priority. SABER performed well in the September 1995 ASCIET exercise; the platforms employed were 2 Aegis cruisers, 13 vehicles, 2 Blackhawks, 1 AV-8B, and a C-130 acting as communications center.

SLQ-20B, for DDGs, provides both cooperative and noncooperative identification by conventional IFF and IFF spoofing. The preliminary design review for the SLQ-20 Upgrade processor was conducted in FY94, followed by a concept design review in FY94/95, with production planned for FY97.

SURFACE-TO-AIR MISSILES

Deletions: Marine ADATS (Canada, no sales), VSRAD (international program, dropped when Italy dropped out), Crossbow (U.S. program, canceled).

CHINA (PRC)

♦ LY-60N

Dimensions: 203 mm (forward)/208 mm (aft) × 3.89 m; wing span 680 mm
Weight: 220 kg
Propulsion: Solid-fuel rocket
Performance: Maximum speed Mach 3; intercept range 1–18 km

This semiactive missile, apparently derived from the Italian Aspide, was announced in 1995. There is also a ground version. The associated FCS, at least in its ground version, can process 40 targets, track 12, and control up to three illuminators. System reaction time is 9 sec.

An LY-60 missile. (CPMIEC)

Maximum maneuverability is 35 g. Target performance can be up to 600 m/sec at an altitude of 30 to 12,000 m, with maximum maneuverability of 7 g. Maximum elevation angle is 70 deg.

♦ RF-61/SD-1

Dimensions: 28.6 cm × 3.99 m; span 1.166 m (11.3 × 157 × 45.9 in)
Weight: 320 kg (705 lb)
Warhead: Continuous rod
Propulsion: Single-stage rocket (boost-glide)

Speed: Mach 3
Range: 10 km against a low-flying target; maximum altitude is 8 km; maximum range at that altitude, about 5.5 km (10,900; 8700; 6000 yd)

RF-61, the ship-launched version of the ground-launched HQ-61, is a CPMIEC ship-launched short-range SAM. Guidance is semiactive, using a tracker-illuminator (Fog Lamp) and a rear reference beam for proportional navigation. The requirement for a medium/low-altitude missile was levied in August 1965. The Chinese already had three high-altitude programs, HQ (Hongqi, i.e., Red Flag) -1, -2, and -3 (intended to intercept the SR-71). HQ-1 and -2 were versions of the Soviet SA-2 (S-75), the latter initially intended to deal with intruding U-2s. The new missile was initially designated HQ-41 (presumably the "1" indicated a departure from the previous generation) and then HQ-61 to indicate the new technology of the 1960s. The shipboard version of the missile was assigned to Shanghai No. 2 Bureau of Machinery and Electronics in 1967, and design work was completed in 1970. A vertical-loading launcher was planned. The missile was tested at sea in December 1976, apparently with only partial success. Design-certification test firings were not conducted until December 1986, when seven targets were shot down.

HQ-61. (U.S. Naval Institute)

In September 1990 CPMIEC distributed brochures describing a new version of this missile, designated SD-1. However, the photograph illustrating the missile had previously been printed with the earlier HQ-61 and RF-61 designations. The ground-launched version (HQ-61A) is now designated SD-1A.

The missile's configuration broadly matches that of the U.S. Sparrow, although RF-61 is a much larger weapon. The current launcher, in "Jiangwei"-class frigates, carries six single-missile canisters (loaded separately). The two Jiangdong-class frigates, which carried an earlier twin-rail launcher, have been scrapped. It is possible that the canister launcher can also be used for CY-1 ASW rockets. Reportedly the second Luhu-class destroyer will fire this missile from vertical launch tubes.

Users: China (six "Jiangwei"-class frigates).

♦ FM-80/KS-1

CPMIEC announced a new low-altitude missile, FM-80, at Farnborough in 1990. It is probably derived from Crotale. KS-1, which is probably the same missile, was shown at FIDAE (in Chile) in 1992. Although only the land version was displayed, there is also a naval version, perhaps intended to supersede RF-61. Dimensions: 40 cm × 5.6 m (900 kg); performance: maximum speed 1200 m/sec (2360 kt, about Mach 3.6), altitude limits 500 to 25,000 m (1600 to 80,000 ft), range 7 to 42 km (3 to 23 nm). Maximum target speed is 750 m/sec (1480 kt) and maximum target maneuverability is 4–5 g.

This may be the low/ultra-low-altitude truck-mounted missile designated HQ-7, whose development was ordered in June 1979. This system was first tested in August 1985.

The PRC bought two Crotale systems and about 86 missiles from France in 1989. One is mounted aft on board the "Luda"-class destroyer *Kaifeng* (109); another is mounted forward on board the new Luhu-class destroyer *Zhanjiang*. Some reports suggest that further ships of both classes will be so armed, in which case there have been either further sales or local production, perhaps of KS-1.

◆ **QW-1 Vanguard**

Dimensions: Length 1532 mm in tube
Weight: 16.5 kg (including tube and gripstock)
Propulsion: Booster plus dual-thrust motor
Performance: Maximum slant range 5000 m, altitude limits 30 to 4000 m

CPMIEC's new man-portable missile was announced in 1994; a twin naval mount was announced that fall at Defendory. At about the same time, a brochure for a proposed M43 fast-attack boat showed an eight-tube launcher, with four canisters each side of a traversable turret. The operator in the turret is seated, with an eye-level optical sight. Vanguard is described as a great improvement on HN-5 (SA-7 development), with all-aspect capability. By way of comparison with the above figures, HN-5B offered a slant range of 4400 m, and a maximum altitude of 2500 m. Maximum engageable target velocity was 260 m/sec tail-on or 150 m/sec head-on. System weight was 16 kg (missile dimensions 72 × 1440 mm).

◆ **Naval Combat System Type 88C (PRC)/PL-9**

This gun-missile air-defense system, for destroyers and smaller craft, was first shown at the 1991 Paris Air Show. The weapons are the H/PJ 76A gun (a twin Soviet-type 37mm in a turret externally similar to that of the Breda Compact Forty), the Type 69 twin 30mm gun, and a quadruple ground-launched version of the PL-9 (Python derivative) AAM. The system is said to be compatible with the Oerlikon 35mm gun and with the 122mm rocket launcher. The system can also control chaff launchers. Targets are acquired by a search radar (probably based on the French Sea Tiger), then tracked by a stabilized EO director (carrying both search and tracking TV cameras, a FLIR, and a laser ranger; its console has two screens). Target data are fed into a digital computer. A JM233 computing gunsight (similar in appearance to the French NAJIR) is available as a backup; it can control two or three guns against a low flier, and is intended as a last-ditch control station.
PL-9 is an all-aspect AAM made by the China National Aero-Technology Import and Export Corp (CATIC). Dimensions: 157 × 2900 mm (wing span 641 mm, fin span 856 mm including air-driven gyros); launch weight is 115 kg. Maximum altitude is 21 km; maximum range is 15 km (minimum 500 m). The missile can maneuver at more than 35 g. The cooled IR seeker has a 3-deg FOV; the dead zone around the sun is 15 deg wide. The missile can be fired well off boresight.

◆ **CSSC Gun-Missile System/PL-8**

Another combined gun-missile system was shown at Defense Asia (March 1991) by CSSC (China Shipbuilding Corporation). It combined a twin 37mm power mount (Type 715I) with two PL-8H missiles, plus FCS and tracking radar. The missile was described as all-aspect IR, probably 120 kg with 11-kg warhead, range 4.5 km. This was the first appearance of PL-8 (PL-7 and -9 had previously been seen). The mount is unmanned (centrally controlled); missiles are launched only when the target is within their envelope.

FRANCE

◆ **Crotale Naval (R.440/R.460)/Crotale NG (VT-1)/Chun Ma**

Dimensions: 15 cm × 2.89 m; span 54 cm (5.9 × 113.7 × 21.3 in)
Weight: 80 kg (176 lb)
Warhead: 15 kg (33 lb) directed blast (forward-directed)
Propulsion: Boost-glide rocket (SNPE Lens III motor; burn time 2.3 sec)
Speed: Mach 2.3 (800 m/sec; 2624 ft/sec): acceleration time 2.3 sec; missile is subsonic at 13 km (20 sec after firing)

Range: 8.5–13 km (6.5 km vs. a sea-skimmer; 700 m minimum). Effective range is 10+ km against an airplane and 13+ km against a helicopter. Altitude: 150–12,000 ft (9300–14,200 yd; minimum 765 yd): see below for antisea-skimmer modification.

Thomson-CSF's standard French command-guided point-defense system for high-value warships employs the Matra R.440N missile described above. The next-generation Crotale NG uses a new LTV VT-1 (see below). The typical installation is an 8-rnd launcher and 16 manual reloads. Reload time for the entire launcher is about 5 min. Typical response time (from reception of designation signal) is 4.5 sec. The land version fires the larger R.460 missile, which has a dual-thrust engine and can reach Mach 2.5. The naval version has larger-diameter tubes, to keep the missile's fins from striking the sides of the tubes when launching in rough weather; it also has lighter caps.

Crotale Naval launcher with co-located fire-control radar. The IR tracker is to the left of the radar dish. (Thomson-CSF)

Development of the basic land missile, Crotale, was largely (85%) financed by South Africa, beginning in 1964. Development of the naval version began in 1972, the French navy ordering 10 systems (for major surface ships) in May 1974 (the carriers were fitted with Crotale in 1986/87). Trials were completed in October 1979, and series production began in January 1980.
The missile is tracked by a monopulse Doppler radar (range 20,000 m) via a fin transponder, having been gathered by an IR tracker (FOV 5 deg); commands are transmitted by a Ku-band uplink. Multipath, which originally limited the tracker to targets flying above 50 m, has largely been cured for ranges of 3000 m or less. An earlier cure was IR tracking (SEID, Système d'Ecartométrie Infra-Rouge Différentielle, the entire system being EDIR, Ecartométrie Différentielle Infra-Rouge). SEID is effective down to 4 m and out to 8500 m, depending on weather. Missiles guided this way must be fired offset from the target, so that their own IR signature does not blank out the target's.
The IR gatherer can be used to launch a second missile while the first is in flight. Thomson-CSF claims that, using this "anticipation" mode, Crotale can kill five targets in quick succession, before they pass within its minimum engagement range.
The successor system, Crotale NG, uses a new multisensor CTM director (see above) and a new VT-1 missile, developed in the United States by LTV, in a 12-rnd (2.6 t) launcher. Unlike Crotale, this system combines all sensor data in a single computer, rather than choosing radar or IR. The system computer selects the 8 most threatening targets out of 20 it processes (it also selects the optimum modes of target tracking and of missile guidance). The operator validates the system's choice and then

fires. The trackers define a window containing target and missile as well as false targets already detected. Each target is surrounded by a measuring window, within which measurements made by different sensors are correlated. All data are sent to a 2D filter.

Work on Crotale NG began in 1985 in response to the U.S. Army FAADS-LOS-L-H program (ADATS won), and LTV received the Thomson-CSF contract for VT-1 in 1986; production began in 1989, the first deliveries (for Finland) following in 1991. The 2.4m VT-1 missile weighs 75 kg and accelerates to Mach 3.6 (1250 m/sec) in 3 sec, after which it coasts. At 8 km (10 sec after launch) speed is 600 m/sec (1180 kt). Thomson-CSF claims that VT-1 is the fastest current short-range defensive missile. At 8-km range the missile retains enough kinetic energy to maneuver at 35 Gs (compared to 20 Gs for Crotale). Maximum range is 11 km at an altitude of 6000 m. The 13-kg blast-fragmentation warhead has a lethal radius of 8 m. Typically the system locks on after 2 sec and fires after 8 sec.

A recent estimate of VT-1 deliveries shows 280 for France and 106 for Saudi Arabia.

Users:

Crotale: China (*Harbin* [112] and *Kaifeng* [109]), France (*Clemenceau*, *Georges Leygues*, *Tourville* classes), Saudi Arabia (*Al Madinah* class), UAE (FPB 62 class).

Crotale NG: France (*La Fayette* class), Oman (new corvettes); probably also in *La Fayette* derivatives for Saudi Arabia and possibly for Taiwan. Note that no procurement of this missile is included in the 1997–2002 French defense plan.

The VT-1 missile of the Crotale NG system in 1990. (Author)

The new Luhu-class destroyer *Harbin*, at Vladivostok in mid-1996, displays her Crotale Modulaire mount. Behind it is a reload box, which swings up to mate to the rear of the missile mount, in much the way Aspide reloads work. The object outboard of the bridge wing is reportedly a television tracker for the twin 37mm guns. (*Ships of the World*)

Most missiles are for land use. As of 1994, about 4620 R.440, 4088 R.460, 451 Cactus, and about 1000 VT-1 had been made or ordered. Crotale missiles are made under license in Greece and possibly in Egypt; KS-1 (see China, above) may be a Chinese derivative of R.440/460. Chun Ma (Pegasus) is a Korean derivative developed by Thomson-CSF for Daewoo (as of 1996, it had yet to attract Korean official interest). As of 1993, R.460 unit price was about $135,900, and VT-1 unit price was variously estimated as $341,000 and $520,000.

♦ **Masurca**

Dimensions: 406 mm × 5408 mm; span 1277 mm; booster length 3222 mm and tail span 1500 mm. The missile penetrates 114 mm into the booster, so total length is 8516 mm. (16 × 212.9 × 50.2 in; 126.9 × 59.0 in; total length 335.2 in)
Weight: 840 kg; booster 1858 kg (1850/4095 lb)
Warhead: 120 kg (264 lb)
Propulsion: Booster (burn time 4.5 sec) plus sustainer (burn time 30 sec); booster thrust about 35 t, sustainer thrust 2300 kg (5070-lb thrust)
Speed: 900 m/sec max (2952 ft/sec), about 1800 kt
Range: 40,000 m; kinematic range 62,000 m (43,700/67,800 yd)

Masurca is an area-defense weapon broadly comparable to the U.S. Terrier/SM-1(ER). The configuration is similar, but the French missile is larger and heavier. Only the semiactive Mk 2 Mod 3 remains in service, guided by a DRBC 51 tracker-illuminator. The design requirement was to intercept two 1 m² targets at altitudes of up to 18,000 m and at ranges of 35,000–40,000 m.

Like SM-1(ER), Masurca is stowed horizontally, on a revolving drum; the long booster fins are hand-fitted before firing. The rate of fire is one two-missile salvo every 30 sec. The launcher carries a total of 46 missiles (18 per drum plus 10 missiles in reserve, broken down with missile and booster separate). Total system weight: 111.5 t for fire control, 31.5 t for the launcher itself,

202.0 t for the loading system, and 105.0 t of missiles, 450 metric t in all.

The remaining systems, on board the two *Suffren*-class destroyers, were modernized 1983–85 to maintain the system until the end of its scheduled life in 1998–2000.

♦ **Mistral (Sadral and Simbad Systems)**

Dimensions: 90 cm × 1.81 m (3.5 × 71.3 in)
Weight: 17 kg (37.5 lb)
Warhead: 3 kg (1800 tungsten balls) (6.6 lb)
Propulsion: Boost-sustain rocket (The booster burns only inside the launch tube, accelerating the missile to 40 m/sec [131 ft/sec], and the sustainer [burn time 2.5 sec] ignites 15 m away; the motor is based on that of the Super 530 AAM.)
Speed: Mach 2.6 maximum; average speed 600 m/sec
Range: 6 km against aircraft; 4 km against helicopters; 6 sec to 4000 m. Minimum range: 500 m (6600/4400 yd; minimum 550 yd)

Matra's Mistral short-range missile is now the French navy's main close-in antiair weapon; it meets the SATCP (surface-air, à très courte portée) requirement. It is widely used on land.

Matra describes Mistral as the first shoulder-fired Mach-2.5 defensive missile. It uses an all-aspect two-color (2–4 and 3–5 micron) cooled IR seeker (by SAT) and laser proximity and impact fuzes. The multielement seeker has a narrow FOV (to reject decoys and interference) but it can tilt +/−38 deg. The manufacturer claims that Mistral can attack helicopters with reduced IR signatures. Unlike many previous IR-guided missiles, Mistral employs proportional (rather than pursuit) navigation, using a gyro as a reference. One effect of such guidance is to reject flares ejected from the rear of a target. On the launcher, the missile runs up its seeker and gyro in 2 sec; total reaction time is 5 sec.

Sadral (Système d'auto-défense Raprochée Anti-aérien Légère) is a close-in 6-rnd defensive system, using Mistral. The stabilized fully automated rapid-reload launcher carries a TV camera and FLIR, images from both of which appear on a below-decks console. CSEE makes the director, which is integral with the mount. The missile is locked onto the target before firing, presumably to limit the amount of background visible to the seeker, thus

Masurca on board the cruiser *Colbert*. (ECP Armées)

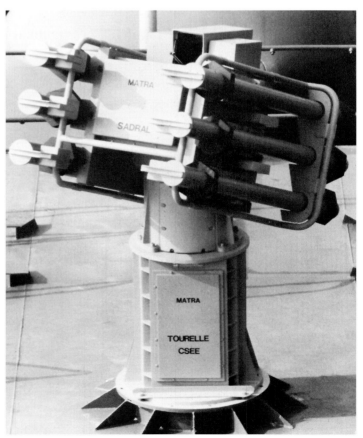

Sadral six-missile launcher for Mistral. (Matra)

Simbad two-missile shipboard launcher for Mistral. (Matra)

improving the effective signal-to-noise ratio. An audio signal indicates that the missile has locked on before it is launched. The loaded launcher weighs 1080 kg; the console weighs another 280. Sadral arms the French frigates *Cassard* and *Jean Bart*. In November 1992 it was announced that Mistral would eventually arm *all* French surface combatants.

The lightweight 2-rnd launcher, Simbad (Système integré de Mistral bimunition pour l'auto-défense), is a modified 20mm pedestal mount (a configuration that in itself explains the function of this and analogous weapons) carrying a simple optical sight.

This program began with feasibility studies in 1978, Matra being selected as prime contractor in August 1980. The naval version was announced in October 1980, and tests began early in 1985. Tests of the basic Mistral missile were completed in March 1988, with firings against low-flying CT20 drones. One firing resulted in a head-on hit at 5 km. Deliveries of Mistral began in June 1988. Simbad sea trials began in 1989.

Both Finland and Norway are developing their own missile mounts. The Finnish navy is to use a converted Soviet-type, 25mm, unstabilized, hydraulically operated, locally controlled mounting (which receives only target-designation data from the ship's CDS). The two guns are replaced by six Mistral tubes arranged in an arch above the FLIR and TV camera. Total weight is about 1500 kg.

Estimated unit price (FY92) is $46,950 ($33,000 for the launcher). About 10,900 missiles (7990 for export) had been made or were on order as of the end of 1994. The first missiles were delivered in 1988.

Users (naval): Brazil (Simbad in carrier *Minas Gerais*), Brunei, Cyprus (Simbad bought 1991), Finland (12 Sadral bought 1989 for Helsinki classes and minelayers), France (*Charles de Gaulle*, *Cassard*, *Floreal*, LSD classes; some in SARA system), Indonesia (Simbad), Kuwait (37BRL class), Norway (*Storm, Snogg* classes, ordered September 1990; options for *Hauk* class, MCM craft: six-tube Sadral for FACs, two-tube Simbad for MCMVs), Qatar (new light frigates), Singapore (Simbad in place of 40mm aft in FPB 45 class), Spain (man-portable version for army and navy, 1991), Thailand (Sadral and man-portable version), UAE (Sadral in FPB 62, FPB 38 classes). Mistral is included in a model of the new Combattante IV offered to Kuwait. As of early 1994, the French navy had purchased ten Sadral launchers for the carriers *de Gaulle* and *Foch* and for the destroyers *Georges Leygues, Du-*

pleix, Montcalm, and *Jeanne de Vienne.* In addition, ten manually controlled Simbad launchers were ordered to form a pool, to equip ships as required, including *Floreal*-class frigates and the landing ships *Foudre, Ouragan,* and *Orage.*

Buyers of the land-based version include Belgium, Cyprus, Finland, France, Kenya, Korea (South), Norway, Philippines, Saudi Arabia, and Spain. During the Gulf War, Matra began a crash program to adapt Mistral for helicopter air-to-air combat. The resulting ATAM systems were first delivered late 1994 to the French ALAT (light army aviation corps). According to the 1997–2002 program (as announced in July 1996), the last French naval deliveries of Mistral will be 40 missiles in 2001 (the army receives 630 in 1997–2002).

◆ Sylver

DCN's Système de Lancemjet Vertical was designed for the Aster 15 and 30 missiles, but the French navy required that it also be able to fire the U.S.-supplied Standard Missile. It can also accommodate Sea Sparrow. As of October 1992, it had made more than 26 full-scale launches. Each 8-rnd module (12.5 t) is fitted with two rows of 22in missile cells surrounding the uptake for exhaust gas. A lightweight version has unarmored doors and lacks the automatic pumping device for the plenum chamber, the launcher power supply, and the electronic launcher management bay. Reportedly the launcher is still too heavy; in mid-1996 the nocturnal Project Horizon battery had to be cut from 64 to 48 missiles.

INDIA

◆ Akash

This is the medium-range ramjet SAM of the second stage of the 10-yr Integrated Guided Missile Development Program begun in June 1983. It is to replace Soviet-supplied SA-3 and -6. With the low-altitude Trishul, it will arm future Indian naval vessels. Approximate dimensions are 40.1 cm × 7.5 m (600 kg); performance goals are Mach 3.0, 30 km range (16.4 nm), and 22 km (72,000 ft) maximum altitude. It is to be guided semiactively (with active terminal guidance) by a phased-array radar, which can support simultaneous engagement of several targets. A photograph of a model shows three missiles on a tracked launcher, similar to that used for SA-6. Unit cost goal is $300,000 to $500,000. Akash and Trishul have both encountered serious delays.

◆ Trishul

This quick-reaction low-level missile, developed under the same program as Akash, has been described as an Indian version of the Sea Wolf concept. Mockups show an airframe very similar to the Russian SA-N-4 Gecko (9M33). Trishul uses a dual-thrust motor and has a range of 9 km (minimum 500 m). The lethal radius of its prefragmented warhead is 20 m (65 ft). The FCS radar is Shikari. Trishul first flew in September 1985, and by September 1991 19 out of a planned 36 test flights had been made. In August 1992 Trishul shot down its first target, a drone. However, as of mid-1996 this missile still was not in production. Trishul is expected to arm both the *Delhi*-class destroyer and the Indian Type 16–class frigate. Stated unit cost is $80,000.

INTERNATIONAL

◆ FSAF (formerly FAAMS)/SAAM/PAAMS/Aster

Dimensions: 18 cm × 2.6 m (7.1 × 102.4 in); booster 36 cm × 1.6 m (14 × 63.0 in); span 36 cm
Weight: 100 kg (220 lb); booster 198 kg (440 lb)
Warhead: 15 kg focused fragment (22–33 lb)
Propulsion: Rocket
Speed: Average speed 800 m/sec for Aster 15 (peak speed 1000 m/sec); 950 m/sec for Aster 45 (peak speed 1400 m/sec)
Range: 5–15 km (see below)

Data are for Aster 15.

FSAF is the Family of Surface-to-Air Defense Systems (formerly FAAMS, the Family of Anti-Air Missile Systems) being developed by the French-led Eurosams consortium (France, Italy,

Aster 30 at the 1995 Paris Air Show. (Author)

and the United Kingdom) for both naval and ground use. In two versions, FSAF is to equip Project Horizon frigates built in Britain, France, and Italy. SAAM (Système de defense surface-air antimissile) is an alternative system designation. PAAMS (Principal Anti-Air Missile System) is the British variant; it is also known as LAMS (Local Area Missile System) and SDMS (Support Defence Missile System). The overall weapons system is also called Syrinx (Système Rapide Interarmes base d'Engins et Fonctionnant en Bande X). Aster is the two-stage missile, developed by Aerospatiale.

FSAF/FAAMS is an antisaturation system developed in competition with the abortive NAAWS. Unlike NAAWS, which shared the Aegis philosophy of integration of CDS and weapon system, FSAF is conceived as a stand-alone weapon system which can be connected to a separate CDS. Alternatively, it can function independently (like any WDS, it has inherent short-range CDS-like functions). In mid-1996 the Project Horizon group reportedly discovered that there was no agreed interface between PAAMS and their as-yet undesigned CDS. Presumably SAAM is already integrated with the SENIT system aboard the carrier Charles de Gaulle.

The potential targets are Mach-2.5 (15-g) sea-skimmers, diving antiradar missiles, and fighter aircraft. The French and Italian version is intended for close-in defense at about 10 km against supersonic and maneuvering missiles, or 15–17 km against high-altitude aircraft and subsonic missiles. The corresponding version of the system, SAAM, uses the Aster 15 missile.

The Royal Navy wants something closer to area defense, which demands not only range but also higher acceleration, to get out to the attacker more quickly. Indeed, the British argued that the maximum range offered, 30 km (Aster 30), was insufficient. The missile had to be modified to offer 30 km range against antiship missiles (reportedly 70 km against aircraft). It is still not altogether clear whether the planned FCS will meet LAMS requirements. As of 1996, the Aster 30 booster was 2.2 m long, weighing 350 kg. Missile speed was given as Mach 3.5.

The FCS core uses paired MARA computers (in MAGICS workstations) in 16-Mbyte-shared/16 Mbytes local memory/three processors configuration on an Alenia MHIDAS bus. They are connected by data bus to the Sylva vertical launchers (with a total of 64 missiles). As in Aegis, the tight connection between FCS and target acquisition radars is expected make for a very short reaction time, estimated at 4 sec (initial detection to first firing), compared to 15–20 sec for many existing systems. The FCS is called either EGES (Ensembles de Gestion et Exploitation Système) or AGIS (Assieme per Gestione e Impiego del Sistema). The long-range radar is Smartello (see above). Alternative target acquisition radars are the French Arabel, the British SAMPSON, and the Italian EMPAR.

Like Aegis, FSAF overcomes saturation by tracking both target and rising missile, exerting control via a digital uplink to missile autopilots; it can control up to 16 missiles simultaneously against 10 targets. Unlike Aegis, its missiles use active radar seekers (the same AD4A as in MICA; it is argued that at short range there is insufficient time to illuminate), so there is no need for terminal guidance by the FCS.

Missile terminal weight is minimized by separating the small guided "dart" from its booster. Because the dart is so light it can be extremely maneuverable (up to 50 Gs); it can, therefore, get within the very limited lethal range (2 m) of its small warhead. Light weight of course also minimizes ship impact. The dart uses a combination of aerodynamic and reaction (rockets firing perpendicular to its axis) control. The latter, "PIF-PAF," offers high maneuverability even at low angles of attack.

At present the only difference between versions of the missile is the booster, the size of which determines missile range. They are: Aster 15/SAAM, the French and Italian point defense weapon, Aster 30/SAMP-T (army [T for terrestre] version, MP for moyen portée, medium range), Aster 30/LAMS, Aster 45/SAMP-N (naval medium range), and Aster 60, which is being proposed as an antitactical ballistic missile. The Aster 45 booster is optimized for range; the LAMS/Aster 30 booster is optimized for rapid acceleration to deal with fast incoming missiles.

The French government issued an RFP for a collaborative European missile in 1980/81. Aster was selected over the Matra SAMAT early in 1986. The first missile test, which demonstrated PIF-PAF maneuvering, was at the French CEL test range, 17 June 1987. At that time the estimated unit price of an Aster was $400,000–$700,000. In October 1988 the French and Italian defense ministers agreed that their nations would collaborate on FAAMS/FSAF. In December 1989 the British officially chose FAAMS as their next-generation naval air-defense system. Spain entered the consortium, but dropped out in April 1992. A French-Italian MoU for low-rate production of the naval version of Aster 15 was signed 12 June 1995, with ratification scheduled for October. However, a trilateral (French/Italian/British) agreement was delayed in September 1995 because the system was judged too costly.

Aster 30 made its first fully controlled flight (using the uplink but no seeker) in August 1995, making a simulated interception of a target aircraft at 46,000 ft (14 km) at a range of 30 km (16 nm). Firings from Ile d'Oléron are to begin after the vertical launcher is delivered in November 1996. However, overall the system has suffered badly from delays. As of mid-1996, no all-up guided flight (using a seeker) had yet been made. The first launch using a seeker is now scheduled for 1997. Only then will integration with the EMPAR and SAMPSON radars be testable.

The Project Horizon version has encountered a variety of problems. The VLS is apparently heavier than expected, so missile capacity has dropped from 64 to 48. The combat-system design is running at least 18 months late, partly because it has proven impossible to define a PAAMS system that meets national requirements. Without a missile-system definition, the combat management system (CMS) cannot be designed, since interfaces between it and the missile system have not been set. Since the Joint Project Office has no control over PAAMS, a special interface working group had to be set up. Thus, although feasibility studies were completed early in 1992, new contracts were let in 1993, and only now are specifications being refined to the point at which an RFP (ITT) can be released for the project definition phase, the phase 1 contract for which is to be awarded by the end of 1996. It is to be completed by the end of 1998, leading to a contract for full-scale development in 1999. The radars are also subject to delay. No FSD contract has been let for SAMPSON due to PAAMS delays (it is due in 1997, two years late). Too, as of mid-1996 no development contract for the Smartello acquisition radar had been let. It seems unlikely that any detailed design MoU will be signed before 1998.

Aster 15 is now (mid-1996) expected to enter production about 1998. It will enter French navy service on board the carrier Charles de Gaulle. The French 1997–2002 program provides for delivery of 60 PAAMS missiles in 2002 and 40 SAAM (Aster 15) missiles in 2000–2001. At the same time the French army is to order 2 SAMP-T systems and 50 missiles in 2002 for delivery beginning in 2006. Reportedly the French share of the Project Horizon frigate program is to be halved (two ships are to be ordered in 1998 and in 2002), as is the Italian share (three rather than six ships); the British may stand firm at 12, in which case they may be less inclined to invest heavily in what they see as basically a French system. The other likely candidate to carry naval Aster is the *La Fayette*–class frigate (for France and Saudi Arabia; the French program has just been cut from six to five ships, the last three to be delivered in 1997, 1999, and 2002).

◆ RAM (RIM-116A)

See RAM under United States, below.

ISRAEL

◆ Barak I

Dimensions: 170 mm × 2.175 m; span 0.68 m (6.7 × 85.6 × 26.8 in)
Weight: 98 kg (216 lb)
Warhead: 22 kg (48.5 lb)
Propulsion: Triple-thrust rocket
Speed: 580 m/sec (1900 ft/sec) (average speed 400–500 m/sec)
Range: 0.5–10 km (550–10,900 yd)

Israel Aircraft Industries' point-defense missile for small FAC is designed to achieve very short reaction time (time to maximum range less than 30 sec). Barak is vertically launched, and guidance is by automatic command to LOS. There is also a backup optical command-to-LOS tracker using a laser range-finder. Engagement is fully automatic (with operator veto). Fuzing is EM or IR (the Israeli navy chose EM).

Barak. (IAI)

Control immediately after launch is by thrust vanes (which flip the missile over in 0.6 sec, at 25 Gs, i.e., 10 rad/sec), which are jettisoned once the missile has accelerated sufficiently for aerodynamic control. Total angular coverage is from −25 to +85 deg (and 360 deg in bearing). The missile maneuvers at 45 Gs. In 1987 Barak was successfully tested against a TOW missile representing a low-cross-section sea-skimmer.

The rocket motor has three thrust levels, presumably low initial boost (to avoid damaging the launching ship), then high-energy boost, then sustain. The weapon uses a special Rafael adaptive proximity fuze with an integrated altimeter to control the sensitivity of the downward part of the fuze envelope.

The weapon is carried in eight-missile cells, and one control system can accommodate up to 32 missiles. Each vertical launch unit can be split into pairs of two to eight missiles, either in above- or below-deck launchers. The radar and fire control weigh 1300 kg, and one eight-cell unit weighs 1700 kg. Canister size: 2550 × 376 × 300 mm (100.4 × 14.8 × 11.8 in). Barak was conceived for the *Reshef* class, which has a total armament weight of 40 t. IAI claims that 32 cells can replace a 76mm gun. The new *Eilat* class has two 32-cell groups and three EL/M-2221 fire-control radars, which can also control the 76mm gun (and, presumably, the Gabriel missile).

Barak was announced at the June 1981 Paris Air Show, development having begun in 1979 for planned deployment in 1986. Development was reportedly accelerated because of the experience of the Falklands War. This semiactive version employed a stabilized trainable 8-rnd launcher carrying a tracker-illuminator derived from the EL/M-2021 airborne set (using an inverse-Cassegrain antenna). The trainable launcher proved far too heavy

(it would have accounted for 25% of the weight available for armament in a *Reshef*-class fast-attack boat). The system was rethought. The new Barak I, announced in 1983, is command-guided, fired from a vertical launcher. IAI claims that the missile airframe is unchanged, apart from modifications to suit it to vertical launch. Tests began in 1985. Barak I was accepted for Israeli service in mid-1992 after a series of successful tests between August 1991 and May 1992, culminating in a low-altitude shot on 1 May 1992. Estimated unit price (FY92) is $341,000.

A land-based version of this missile, Adams, is credited with a limited ATBM capability, presumably against short-range tactical weapons (such as the FROGs that the Soviets supplied to many client states).

Users: Chile (modernized "County" class, initially in *Blanco Encalada*, with two groups of 16 launchers each, and two radars), Israel (*Nirit* and *Eilat* class [2 × 32-cell groups, three EL/M-2221 FCS radars]), Singapore (*Victory* class). South Africa was probably involved in the program, but Barak is unlikely to be fitted to any South African corvettes that may be built. In 1991 it was announced that there were two Asian customers, presumably Singapore and Taiwan. Taiwan may have bought Barak as part of a technology-transfer package. Thailand may also be a prospective customer. Colombia has also been a reported customer, for the *Padilla* class.

ITALY

◆ Aspide

Dimensions: 20.3 cm × 3.7 m × 80 cm (100 cm in the air-to-air version) (8 in × 12 ft 2 in × 2 ft 7.5 in/3 ft 3.4 in)
Weight: 200 kg (485 lb)
Warhead: 35 kg (77.2 lb)
Propulsion: Single-stage solid-fuel rocket
Speed: Mach 4.0 (AAM role)
Range: 15+ km (16,400 yd); max altitude 5 km (16,400 ft); can engage a target at a cross range of up to 8 km (8600 yd)

Aspide is an Italian-designed alternative to the Sparrow and Sea Sparrow. The associated shipboard FCS is Albatros. The airframe is derived from that of AIM/RIM-7H, but the internal systems are new, including an X-band monopulse seeker for snap-up/snap-down firing and for better countermeasures and clutter resistance. The missile enjoys better endurance than Sparrow, using closed-loop rather than open-loop hydraulics. It also has a new SNIA motor with higher thrust and specific impulse, for greater velocity and range. There is a home-on-jam guidance mode.

Sixteen-missile automatic loader for Aspide. (Alenia)

Four-cell Aspide launcher for corvettes. The Orion tracker-illuminator is visible above the launcher. (Selenia)

Aspide 2000 at the 1995 Paris Air Show. (Author)

Aspide is carried in both four- and eight-cell launchers, the latter duplicating the NATO Sea Sparrow Mk 29 launcher (one missile can be substituted for the other simply by changing some circuit boards and programming, even at sea). The Aspide eight-cell launcher can have an automatic reload magazine carrying up to 16 missiles in 4-rnd trays. The magazine pivots up for reloading; each missile is rammed into its launcher cell (which contains a loading rail) by a loading arm. In the 4000-kg four-cell launcher, each removable cell is both launcher and container. There is no autoloader for the four or eight reloads. Elevation limits: +50/+10 deg (+80/−5 for the eight-cell launcher). Working circle diameter is 4774 mm (5628 mm for the eight-cell launcher).

Development of the air-to-air version began in 1969, with trials in 1974–75. Albatros was developed in parallel (initially using the Sea Sparrow missile), with sea tests in 1973. The first Albatros/Aspide system was exported to Peru in October 1978. The first Italian navy firing of the Aspide missile was in July 1979. By 1993 over 4474 Aspide missiles (including air- and ground-launched [Spada/Skyguard] versions) had been made or were on order, including test missiles. Unit cost in FY94 was about $195,000.

In 1995 Alenia announced a new surface-to-air version, Aspide 2000, with a new rocket motor offering 30–40% more range and speed, with better ECCM and an improved uplink. It was chosen for the Brazilian *Niteroi*-class upgrade. Earlier work on an active-seeker version, Idra, has been abandoned.

Users (naval SAM version): Argentina (MEKO 360 class), Brazil (*Niteroi* upgrade), Ecuador (*Wadi M'ragh* class), Italy (*Garibaldi* and *Animoso, Maestrale, Lupo,* and *Minerva* classes), Malaysia (ex-Iraqi *Wadi M'ragh* class), Morocco (*Lt. Col. Errhamani*), Nigeria (MEKO 360), Peru (*Lupo* class), Thailand (PFMM Mk 16 class), Venezuela (*Lupo* class). The *Wadi M'ragh* class has a quadruple launcher. The *Garibaldi, Animoso, Maestrale,* and the MEKO 360s have the autoloader version. The Iraqi *Lupos* (now bought by Italy) had no reloads, and that probably applies to the Italian, Peruvian, and Venezuelan *Lupos* as well, since the launcher is atop their hangars. The Italian *Minervas* have space and weight reserved for a reload facility, but it is not currently installed. The Spanish and Egyptian *Descubiertas* apparently carry Sea Sparrow rather than their original Aspides (for which Spain has a production license). The Chinese LY-60N is an unlicensed copy of Aspide (China bought several hundred missiles).

NORWAY

◆ Norwegian Automatic Short-Range Air-Defense System

NFT has developed this system primarily for small combatants, such as the projected new fast-attack boat. This system uses a combined autotracker/launcher (three Mistral launch tubes on either side of the director) controlled by a KMT-340 console. The launcher maneuvers on three axes, with a maximum elevation of 120 deg. It carries a Ku-band tracking radar and EO trackers. The KMT-340 console is a reduced version of the new MSI-340 CDS planned for the new Norwegian fast-attack boat.

POLAND

◆ Wrobel 2MR (ZU-23–2MR or Wrobel II)

This combined gun-missile system (equivalent to the land-based ZUR-23–2S), designed by the Naval Research and Developmental Center for Mechanical Engineering, Tarnow, consists of a twin ZU-23-2 23/87mm gun with a pair of 72mm Strela 2M (SA-7 series) missile launchers on top. Elevation limits are −10/+90 deg for the gun and +20/+60 deg for the missile tube. The mounting weighs 2.5 t. The powered mounting carries the gunner and a 200-rnd ammunition box for each gun. It can be equipped with a GP-02MR lead-computing sight. Reported unit price is $230,000 ($50,000 for the gun-only version).

Poland made the ZU-23-2 naval gun mounting between 1975 and 1990; the Wrobel 2MR is based on the Polish army's combination 23mm and SA-7 weapon. The Wrobel 2MR first appeared on board the new minelayer/transport *Gniezno*; a total of 25 had been ordered or completed by the beginning of 1993. Known installations: corvette *Kaszub*, "Notec"-class MCM craft (but without the missiles), *Lublin*-class minelayer/landing ships, *Wodnik*-class training ships.

The Polish Wrobel 2MR combination gun-missile turret. (Author)

RUSSIA

The main SAM design bureau is Fakel, originally the Grushin OKB which branched off from Lavochkin. At Paris in 1995 Fakel showed several new technologies: the use of lateral thrusters for precision control (developed 1988–93), directed missile warheads and adaptive warheads (e.g., selectable between wide and narrow circular blast and a directed blast), and a double-cut (two-pulse) motor, to increase effective range 1.5- to 2-fold.

◆ Volna (NATO SA-N-1 Goa)

Dimensions: 45 cm × 5.885 m; span 1.2 m; booster diameter 55 cm and span (folding fins) 2.3 m (18 × 232 × 47 in; 21.6/90.6 in)
Weight: 923 kg; warhead: 60 kg (132 lb)
Propulsion: Separate booster (burn time 3 sec) and sustainer (19 sec); boost-glide flight
Speed: Maximum 600 m/sec
Range: 15 km, minimum 4 km; altitude limits 100 m to 10 km

Data are for V-600.

A navalized version of Lavochkin's land-based SA-3, SA-N-1 was the first Soviet naval SAM to enter widespread service. The system is M-1, the missile is V-600 (4K90), the launchers are ZiF-101 and -102, the command system is Yatagan (Peel Group director) and the radar director is Parus. The improved version of the system, M-1M, uses the V-601 or RZ-61 (industrial designation 4K91) missile (NATO SA-N-1B): 379/552 × 5948 mm, 980 kg (72 kg warhead), range limits 4–22 km, altitude limits 100 m–14 km, maximum speed about 730 m/sec. Later versions may have reached a range of 31.5 km. Improved versions developed in the 1970s were Volna-P and Volna-N (V-601M missile).

An SA-N-1 missile on its dual launcher. (TASS from SOVFOTO)

The missile is command-guided, with one double Peel Group director per twin-armed launcher. The director can engage only one target at a time; doctrine is presumably to fire two weapons per target. The system presumably operates as command to LOS, measuring the error between the LOS to the missile and to the target, and sending correction signals. SA-N-3, -4, and -9 probably operate similarly.

Like most other Russian naval SAMs, this was derived from a land system. Development was ordered on 17 August 1956; the prototype system appeared on board the destroyer *Bravyy* in 1959. Initially limited to air targets, it was developed into a general-purpose weapon with ship-to-ship capability (in 1973 it was credited with a range of 3–9 nm in this role).

Magazine capacity (ZiF-101) is 16 in two vertical cylinders.
Users: India (Kashin class), Poland (Kashin class), Russia (Kashin class).

◆ Shtorm M-11 (NATO SA-N-3 Goblet)

Dimensions: 60 cm × 6.1 m; span 1.4 m (23.6 × 240 × 55.1 in)
Weight: 1844 kg (120-kg warhead)
Propulsion: Boost-sustain rocket motor

Speed: 800 m/sec (1580 kt)
Range: 30,000 m (16 nm); (improved version, in *Kiev*, 55 km/29 nm) (altitude 100 m–25 km)

Grushin's command-guided M-11 is unique among Russian naval SAMs in having no army equivalent; reports that it is related to the semiactive SA-6 were wrong. The missile is V-611 (4K60), and the command system is Grom (4R60, NATO Head Lights radar: one director per twin launcher). An improved Shtorm-M system uses 4K65 missiles (NATO SA-N-3A) and Grom-M (4R60M). M-11 replaced an unsuccessful M-3 system (M-2 was the naval version of SA-N-2); the number suggests that it was derived from Grushin's M-1 (SA-N-1). Development was ordered on 25 July 1959.

A pair of SA-N-3 missiles are shown on their rails on board a Soviet Kara-class missile cruiser, with their Head Lights fire-control radar visible between them. The large tubes are for SS-N-14 ASW missiles.

The missile has shallow delta wings, perhaps intended to lengthen its surface-to-surface range, for something approaching dual-purpose use (in 1973 surface-to-surface range was quoted as 2 to 20 nm).
Users: Russia (Kara class: B-187A launcher, 36 missiles each); all other ships carrying this missile have been discarded.

◆ Osa-M (NATO SA-N-4)

Dimensions: 21 cm × 3.158 m; span 64 cm (8.2 × 126 × 25.2 in)
Weight: 126 kg; warhead: 14.25 kg
Propulsion: Boost-sustain rocket (burn times 2 and 15 sec)
Speed: 800 m/sec
Range: 1–7 km (3.9 nm); 14.8 km (8 nm) in Osa-2M version; altitude limits 60 m to 7 km (22,800 ft)

SA-N-4 is a naval equivalent of the land-mobile SA-8 (Gecko). Apparently the naval version entered service first. Development of both versions was ordered on 27 October 1960. The system is RZ-13, with a 4K33 missile, a 4S33 (ZiF-122) launcher, and a 4R33 "Baza" (NATO Pop Group) control system. The improved version (1973: NATO SA-N-4B) is Osa-M2 (4K33M, 9M33M3, and 9M33M5 missiles). A further development, Osa-MA (tested 1979) reduced minimum altitude to 25 m; Osa-MA-2 (1980s) reduced it further to 5 m. This point-defense missile corresponds roughly to Sea Sparrow.

Missiles are housed nose-down in the protective silo. The twin-arm ZiF-122 launcher is normally housed; it emerges before firing and retracts to pick up reloads. Missile capacity per

SA-N-4 missiles on their twin launcher. (J. Cislah)

A standard quadruple SA-N-5 mounting. Many Russian submarines carry single SA-N-5 tubes.

standard 4.2m-dia silo is 20, on four revolving drums, each carrying 5 rnd. The nose-down position reduces the distance missiles must be lifted into firing position and may be required for fuzing before firing. This arrangement would also simplify protection against a cook-off, since all that would be required would be to open the door to vent. Reportedly the 20-rnd magazine leaks.

SA-N-4 is command-guided and can be used against surface targets. In 1973 it was credited with a surface-to-surface range of 1.5–4 nm. Reportedly, this capability is often exercised.

The successor system is Kinshal (NATO SA-N-9 Gauntlet).

Users: Algeria (Koni, "Nanuchka" classes), Bulgaria (Koni class), Cuba (Koni class), India (*Godavari*, "Nanuchka" classes), Libya (Koni, "Nanuchka" classes), Russia (*Kirov*, Kara, Krivak, Grisha, "Nanuchka," Sarancha, *Ivan Rogov*, *Berezina* classes), Yugoslavia (*Kotor* and Koni classes).

◆ Strela 2/3 (SA-N-5 Grail/SA-N-8) MGP-86

Dimensions: 72 mm × 1.41 m
Weight: 9.8 kg
Warhead: 1.15 kg (370 g RDX/AP)
Propulsion: Boost-sustain rocket
Speed: 430 m/sec
Range: 2.2 km; altitude limits 50–1600 m

Data are for Strela-2M.

Strela-2 (9M32 missile, 9P43 launcher) is NATO SA-N-5, the naval version of the SA-7 Grail hand-launched IR-guided missile. Strela-2M (System 9K32M) uses the 9M32M missile and the 9P58 single-tube launcher. Strela-3 (SA-N-8 Gremlin, 9K34 system) uses the 9M36 missile and, often, the MTU-4S launcher. It is the naval version of SA-14, successor to SA-7. Strela-3M is a modified version using the 9M36M missile. MTU-4S is presumably the Russian designation of the East German–designed 4-rnd FASTA-4M launcher. Another reported designation, FAM-14, may be a corruption of SAM-14.

Strela-3 reportedly introduces a more sensitive IR detector but still lacks full forward-aspect capability and, thus, does not quite compare with the U.S. Stinger. It entered service about 1980. The follow-on SA-16 Gimlet (9M313 Igla-1 [Needle]) can attack an approaching target and is probably also in naval service. Compared to Strela-2M, Strela-3 is slightly longer and heavier (1.42 m, 10.3 kg) and offers higher speed (470 m/sec) for longer range (2.7 km) and higher maximum altitude (3000 m vs. a helicopter, 1000 m against a jet, which Strela-2M cannot attack). Igla (9M39) is a larger missile (72.2 mm dia, 10.6 kg). The Igla-1EH IR seeker has a 40-deg FOV, compared to the 5 deg of earlier equivalents, and maximum range is 5000 m (5500 yd). Targets can be engaged at altitudes of 10–3500 m (33–11,500 ft), and maximum target speed is 360 m/sec (700 kt); average missile speed is 570 m/sec (1100 kt). Reaction time is 5 sec. Maximum effective range is 3.0 and maximum missile velocity is 680 m/sec. Activation time is 13 sec (presumably to ready the missile to fire), and reaction time from target detection to firing is 4.5 sec. Claimed probabilities of engagement against an F-4 are 0.33 head-on/0.48 tail-

SA-N-8 launcher (*upper center*) on board the intelligence-gathering ship SSV-33. It is one of three on board (two are aft). Immediately abaft it are a Kolonka remote visual sight and a pair of Tin Man remote optronic devices; forward is a 76mm gun. The launcher presumably reloads automatically from below. (*Sea Power*)

on; against an F-15, 0.11/0.32. The generation beyond is Igla-M (9M39M, NATO SA-X-18 Grouse).

SA-N-5 is widely distributed on board Russian and client-state patrol and amphibious craft, much as the U.S. 20mm gun once appeared wherever space was available. Many submarines reportedly carry one or more in the sail, for self-defense when surfaced. For example, "Echo II" (Project 675) submarines modernized in the 1980s to fire a new Vulkan antiship missile were also fitted with two or three fixed mounts, each carrying six Strela-3M. Kilo-class submarines probably have platforms for missile operators.

SA-N-10 is a quadruple-powered launcher (probably 9P516) for Igla-1, reloaded vertically through a single hatch in its base. The two launcher arms elevate separately, so that each can line up with the reloader. This system seems comparable to the French Sadral/Mistral. Missile range is 3 km (1.6 nm); targets between 32 and 11,500 ft, at speeds up to 680 m/sec (1300 kt), can be engaged. SA-N-10 is on board at least later Kilo- and Typhoon-class submarines and the AGI *Ural* (SSV-33). The submarines may have single (9P519) rather than quadruple launchers.

SA-7 is produced in China as HN-5; HN means Hong Nu, or Red Cherry. The current HN-5A is an improved HN-5 with a more powerful warhead and a better seeker, the latter for greater detection range and better discrimination against clutter. Slant range is 0.8–4.4 km. This missile is carried on board FAC and small auxiliaries.

MGP-86 is an Igla launcher developed by the Centro de Fabricacion de Armas (CEFAR), part of the SIMA shipbuilding group, for the Peruvian navy (MGP means Marina de Guerra del Peru) to fire 9M39 missiles bought from Nicaragua in 1994. It is being refitted to *Lupo*-class frigates and to PR 72–class corvettes; a single mounting has been seen on the stern of a frigate abaft her flight deck.

Users:

FASTA-4M launcher: Guinea-Bissau (possibly in Bogomol), India ("Tarantul" and Natya classes), Russia (Pauk, "Tarantul," Natya classes), Libya (Natya class), Poland ("Tarantul" class).

Single missiles: Algeria (Kilo class), Cuba ("Osa" and Turya classes), Egypt ("Osa" class), India (Kilo class), Poland (Kilo class), Romania (Kilo class), Russia (some "Osa"-class, minecraft, landing ships, auxiliaries), Peru (*Lupo*, PR-72 classes), Yemen (Polnocny class).

SA-N-10 (Russia only): *Urals*, Typhoon- (eight missiles), and Kilo-class submarines (eight single missiles).

◆ **Fort S-300F/Ryf System (SA-N-6 Grumble)**

Dimensions: 45 cm × 7.25 m
Weight: 1500 kg (3300 lb); warhead: 133 kg (283 lb)
Propulsion: Solid-fuel rocket
Speed: Mach 6
Range: 90 km; max altitude 30.4 km, min altitude 25 m; maximum target speed 1300 m/sec

Data are for the 5V55 missile. SA-N-6 is a naval version of the land-based SA-10 area-defense missile. S-300 was conceived in 1969 as a family of three closely related systems, one for strategic air defense (S-300P), one for tactical air defense (S-300V), and one for the navy (S-300F for "flotskiy," fleet), to deal with a new generation of high-speed threats, presumably including the new U.S. SRAM short-range ballistic standoff bomber missile. In naval service, SA-N-6 supersedes the SA-N-3 area-defense missile and provides (in theory) the ability to counter much faster threats and, probably, pop-up threats (thanks to the vertical launcher). The land-based system was developed by the Grushin design bureau; tests began in 1972. The naval test ship, the cruiser *Azov*, appeared in 1977.

Fort is the Russian naval version; Ryf is the down-rated export version. The system uses the 3M41 missile, 3S41 launcher, and 3R41 Volna command system. There is also an S-300M Fort-M, probably using the 48N6 missile. Guidance is by track-via-missile (as in Patriot). The advantages are optimum flight path (command) plus good terminal accuracy and the ability to time-share

An SA-N-6 launcher on board the cruiser *Marshal Ustinov*. In contrast to Western vertical launchers, only one missile can be launched at a time (only one section opens); the triple circular plates over other missile positions are apparently blow-out plates. (S. Zaloga)

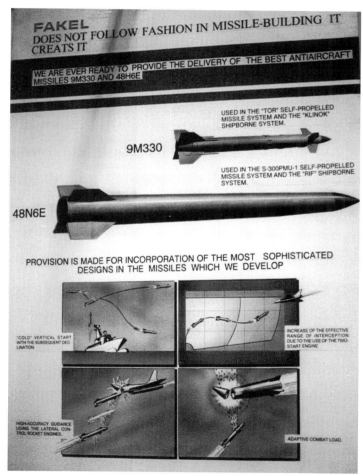

Fakel's poster at the 1995 Paris Air Show compares the SA-N-9 (*above*) and SA-N-6 (*below*) missiles; it also shows some of the design bureau's new concepts. (Author)

guidance, so that one director can handle multiple targets. Missiles are carried in revolver-type 8-rnd vertical launchers, one every 4–5 sec. They are loaded in their canisters, and are considered good for 10 yr before overhaul. The missiles ignite only after they clear the ship's deck, at an altitude of about 20 m. Each Top Dome guidance radar can handle six targets simultaneously, controlling 12 missiles, within an arc of about 120 deg. Due to this angular limitation, Fort cannot be considered a true anti-saturation system like Aegis.

Maximum slant range against targets at 2000 m (6600 ft) and higher altitudes is 90 km (49 nm), against low-altitude targets (altitudes 25m [80 ft] and less), 25 km (13.7 nm). Maximum speed at interception is 4200 km/h (2296 kt).

Four versions of the equivalent land-based system were developed: S-300P, S-300PT, S-300PM/PMU, and S-300PM-1/PMU-1; in this case U means simplified. The -300PMU and -300F missiles are of the 5V55 family; the longer-range weapon of -300PM-1 and -300PMU-1 is 48N6 (48N6E for export). This missile became operational aboard warships in the early 1990s. It is 7.5 m long and has a maximum range of 150 km and maximum altitude of 25 km; maximum speed is 1700 m/sec and maximum target speed is 2800 m/sec. The warhead weighs 143 kg. This much more energetic missile fits the same canister as 5V55.

Users: Russia (*Kirov* class [B-203 launcher], *Slava* class [B-204 launcher]).

◆ Uragan M-22/Shtil (NATO SA-N-7 Gadfly)

> **Dimensions:** 40 cm × 5.55 m; span 86 cm
> **Weight:** 690 kg
> **Warhead:** 70 kg (154 lb)
> **Propulsion:** Solid rocket
> **Speed:** Mach 3
> **Range:** 30 km; min 3 km (3300–33,000 yd); altitude limits 100–46,000 ft; missiles maneuver at up to 20 g

Uragan is the Russian navy version; Shtil is the export version. Uragan uses the 9M38 (formerly 3M90) missile, the 3S90 launcher, and the 3R90 Orekh control system (NATO Front Dome illuminators). This is the naval version of the land-based Bukh (SA-11) missile, which was derived from the semiactive SA-6; it is the first Russian naval semiactive missile. Shtil (as well as the land-based SA-11) is apparently a simple homing-all-the-way system comparable to the U.S. SM-1(MR), but Uragan apparently is more like the New Threat Upgrade system which controls SM-2 (MR). The missile has a commandable autopilot. Commands are sent up after burnout, to avoid interference from the motor plume. This practice makes it possible to engage more targets simultaneously, and it also reduces a target's evasion time, to the degree that illumination provides warning. Some recent Russian long-range AAMs are also guided in this manner.

Sovremennyy-class destroyers are arranged so that two Front Domes are located on each side of each launcher, with two more on the sides of the ship near the forward launcher. An EO device, presumably a backup associated with the system, is located on each side near a Front Dome near each launcher. At least two Front Domes, therefore, bear on each heading (three on the broadside). This pairing would seem to correspond to the previous Soviet practice of providing two missiles per target (on two

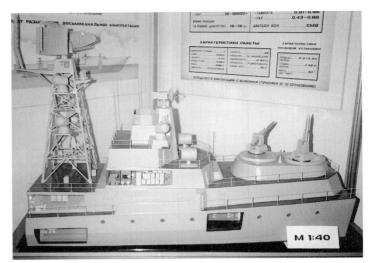

A model of the M-22 (SA-N-7) system, shown at Moscow in 1992. (S. Zaloga)

launcher arms of a slow-firing launcher). However, the two launchers must share one Front Dome when they engage targets approaching from directions near the broadside. Presumably, the Soviets could not adopt the typical U.S. solution, to place the illuminators on the centerline, because these ships are extremely limited in centerline space. The trials ship, *Provornyy*, has eight Front Domes, giving her a pair on each quarter. Presumably, *Sovremennyy* is too short to allow for this arrangement (the after position equivalent to one of the two forward Front Dome positions is occupied by the Light Bulb data-link antenna).

Maximum range for a crossing target is 18 km for an aircraft, 6 km for an ASM. Altitude limits are: 15–15,000 m for an aircraft, 10–10,000 m for an ASM. Maximum target speed is 420–830 m/sec for an aircraft, 330–830 m/sec for an ASM (depending on altitude). Ranges (closing target) are 3.5–25 km for aircraft above 1000 m, 3.5–18 km for aircraft below 1000 m, and 3.5–12 km for ASMs. Claimed two-shot kill probability is 0.81–0.96 for aircraft and 0.43–0.86 for ASMs. Maximum FCS radar elevation angle is 70 deg.

As displayed in Moscow in 1992, this system is available in 1-, 2-, 3-, and 4-launcher (24 missiles per launcher) versions with 2, 4, 6, 8, 10, or 12 firing channels (guidance antennas). The launcher fires a missile every 12 sec. The missile magazine has an area of 5.2 m and a depth of 7.42 m; weight (empty) is 30 t. The antennas of the six-channel version weigh a total of 7.1 t; total system weight (without missiles) is 96 t, with a tactical crew of 19. Total electrical load is 320 kW.

The land-based SA-11 appeared about 1979; the naval test installation (on board the destroyer *Provornyy*) appearing in 1981.

The follow-on system is Yezh, the naval equivalent of SA-17.

Users: China (reported purchaser of *Sovremennyy* class) and Russia (*Sovremennyy* class).

◆ Kinzhal/Klinok (NATO SA-N-9)

> **Dimensions:** 23 cm × 2.28 m; span 75 cm
> **Weight:** 159–165 kg (363 lb)
> **Warhead:** 14.5 kg (32 lb)
> **Propulsion:** Boost-sustain rocket
> **Speed:** Mach 3 (maximum speed 850 m/sec)
> **Range:** 12 km (6.6 nm); minimum 1.5 km; altitude limits 10 m and 6000 m

This is Fakel's vertically launched successor to SA-N-4. Kinzhal is the Russian navy version, Klinok the export version. The single-stage (dual-thrust) missile is 9M330 or 3M95; the launcher is 3S95, and the control system (using the Cross Sword radar director) is 3R95. Missiles are carried in 8-rnd groups feeding vertical launchers; they may be stacked vertically, for a total of 16 per group. Each SA-N-9 vertical launcher loads a missile into the central position and pops it up from there using a catapult. The missile uses a gas generator in its nose to turn toward

The ground-launched version of the SA-N-7 missile at the 1992 Moscow Air Show. (S. Zaloga)

Four SA-N-9 revolver launchers on board a *Udaloy*-class destroyer. Presumably, they are loaded via the large centerline hatch. The shrouded objects farther forward are twin chaff launchers. (*Sea Power*)

The 3M330 (SA-N-9) missile, on display in Moscow in 1992. (S. Zaloga)

its target before igniting its engine. Turnover lasts about 1 sec. Each director can guide up to eight missiles against four targets in a 60 × 60-deg sector. Response time is 8 to 24 sec, and a missile can be fired every 3 sec (20/min). Target maximum speed is 700 m/sec (acceleration 300 m/sec²). Targets at 3.5 km altitude (11,480 ft) are detected at 45 km (49,200 yd).

Systems can accommodate 3 to 8 launchers. Without ammunition, the system weighs 41 t, and it requires 13 personnel. The system employs four types of console: a one-man console carrying a rectangular CRT and a pair of small alphanumeric screens (as well as a keyboard and trackball), corresponding to a fire channel; a monitoring console; a large-CRT weapons-control console (presumably for target assignment, showing the target-acquisition radar picture); and a smaller console carrying a CRT and a large alphanumeric screen. The latter (which is set apart from the other consoles) is probably the interface with the ship's second captain.

SA-N-9 first appeared in the destroyer *Udaloy*. Reportedly, it is a naval version of the land-based SA-15 (Tor), which superseded SA-8 in Soviet ground forces. Data above describe SA-15. Tor is credited to the Antey design/production bureau.

In 1996 Fakel announced that it was working on a new active-radar missile, 3M96, intended to replace the command-guided 3M95 (SA-N-9). It has also been offered as an AAM, and was probably developed as such for the new (and probably abortive) Mikoyan I 42. A photograph suggests that 3M96 uses much the same airframe as 3M95.

◆ **Kortik/Kashtan (NATO SA-N-11 Grison)/CADS-N-1**

Dimensions: 76/152 mm × 2500 mm (container: 225 × 170 × 2562 mm, 57 kg)
Weight: 43.6 kg; warhead 9 kg
Speed: Mach 2.6 (maximum 910 m/sec, average 600 m/sec)
Range: 8 km (4.5 nm); minimum 2.5 km; altitude limits 15 m to 3500 m (about 11,300 ft)

This is the missile component of the CADS-1 gun-missile system. Kortik ("Dirk") is the Russian navy version; Kashtan ("Chestnut Tree") is the export version. The missiles are 3M87 and 3M88 (the corresponding land-based SA-19 is the 9M311 missile) using the 3S87 launcher and the 3R87 control system incorporating the 3P87 (NATO "Hot Flash") radar. Missiles are command-guided on the basis of either an EO tracker or a mm-wave radar; the system apparently automatically chooses the sensor. The optronic system uses television to track the target and near-IR to track the outgoing missile. The missile tracker has two channels, one capturing and tracking the missile (actually its exhaust) after it is fired, the other operating after the booster has been dropped, tracking a pulsed IR source on the missile. Electro-optics can guide the missile to within 1 m of a target, whereas radar precision is 2 or 3 m. The designer claims that processing of both sets of sensors is integrated. The radars also apparently form a closed-loop FCS for the gun element of CADS-N-1. The mounting carries eight tube-launchers (auto-reloaded from a 48-rnd magazine below the mount) and a pair of 30mm Gatling guns. 9M311 is a two-stage rocket with a larger-diameter booster. Maximum target speed is 500 m/sec. The missile has a lethal radius of 5 m.

SA-N-11, the missile of the CADS-N-1 gun-missile system, on a poster at the Moscow Air Show. (S. Zaloga)

A brochure claims that the system can engage up to 6 targets/min. The system consists of a command module and a combat module (i.e., the mounting proper); total weight is 13,500 kg. Swept radius of the turret is 2760 mm, and maximum height is 2250 mm. One command module can control up to six combat modules (i.e., presumably can engage up to 36 targets/min). CADS-1 was first seen on board the cruiser *Admiral Lazarev*. The Russian army's equivalent Tunguska (256) tracked system uses long single-barreled revolver cannon. A competing gun-missile system, Palash, was built in prototype form at Tula but apparently lost out to Kortika/Kashtan.

Users (Russia only): *Kuznetzov, Admiral Lazarev, Neustrashimyy*; gun-only version offered as replacement for paired AK-630s. On at least one "Tarantul" (PN952).

◆ **Yezh (NATO SA-N-12)**

This is the naval equivalent to the land-based SA-17. The land version fires the 9M38M2 missile (SA-11 is the 9M38 missile).

Photographs of SA-N-7 on its launcher show the missile in a somewhat awkward position; the launcher may have been designed to accommodate the larger SA-N-12 equivalent. The target-acquisition radar is Podberezovik (probably Cross Round).

◆ Trebuzets

This developmental self-defense system was announced by Altair in 1993. The fire-control sensor is a scanning J-band radar with a planar-array antenna, rotating at 60 rpm in search mode and at 360 rpm in tracking mode (which is clearly actually short-range TWS mode). Up to 16 targets can be tracked simultaneously. The gyrostabilized (i.e., aimed) launcher carries a pair of 5-rnd modules, which can be reloaded from a below-decks carousel carrying six modules. Each 220mm × 1.7m unguided rocket weighs 60 kg and carries a 25-kg warhead. Four targets can be engaged simultaneously at up to 1 nm range, with a reaction time of 2 sec. Total weight is 10 t (5 t above deck). Presumably each unguided "rocket shell" bursts to form a lethal cloud through which the target is expected to fly.

SOUTH AFRICA

◆ SAHV/LRAAM

Dimensions: 180 mm × 3.36 m; wing span 0.4 m
Weight: 130 kg
Warhead: 20 kg (prefragmented)
Propulsion: Solid-fuel rocket (boost-sustain)
Performance: Speed Mach 2.3–3.0; range about 2–12 km; maneuverability 40 G. Altitude limits 100 ft to well over 20,000 ft. Reaches 8km range in under 14 sec. Elevation limit is 60 deg.

Data refer to the SAHV-IR version.

Kentron's missile is intended for the future South African corvette (Barak is unlikely to be bought). Work began in 1987, initially as a Crotale replacement. The 180mm airframe diameter was chosen at that time, and the program was pursued largely to develop advanced technology. SAHV-3 uses the Crotale command-to-LOS guidance system and tail control. SAHV-IR uses the same airframe, but adds a new two-color mechanically scanned IR seeker (with up to 90-deg off-boresight angle) developed for the Darter AAM. As of 1995, Kentron was marketing it with Oerlikon, offering it in box launchers on a modified AA gun mount with Skyguard FCS. The next step, displayed at Paris in 1995, is LRAAM, a ramjet with an IIR seeker (156 kg, range over 30 km). The step beyond might be an active pulse-Doppler radar seeker.

Kentron's ramjet LRAAM at the 1995 Paris Air Show, with the winged SAHV-IR in the background. (Author)

All versions retain the Crotale command link. SAHV has a digital autopilot with strapdown-inertial mid-course guidance, hence can be guided into an acquisition "basket." Command update can make for a more energy-efficient (or low-drag) flight profile. Missiles can be fired in LOAL mode, guided by autopilot while searching with the seeker, then locking on as soon as the seeker acquires a target. Alternatively, for a close-range target, the missile can be locked on before it is fired. The missile has thrust-vector control (using vanes in the nozzle) usable both at launch and in the end-game.

As of mid-1995, Kentron was working with a foreign naval customer pursuing a modernization program. SAHV would be launched from a ramp rather than vertically, using a box launcher added to the existing system. It may enter service about the year 2000.

SWEDEN

◆ Baltic/Bolide

The new corvettes will probably be armed with Baltic, the naval version of a new Mach 3 laser-guided Bofors missile, Bolide, announced in 1995. It will combine an EO tracker with an 8-rnd launcher (estimated weight 1 t). Intercept range would be up to 10 km, and maximum altitude 7 km. The combined shaped-charge/prefrag warhead will have a programmable proximity fuze. The missile will be carried in a sealed box container/launcher.

◆ RBS 70 (Rayrider)

Dimensions: 10.6 cm × 1.32 m; span 32 cm (4.2 × 52.0 × 12.6 in)
Weight: 15 kg (33 lb) (system weight 250 kg [551 lb])
Warhead: 1 kg prefragmented (with tungsten pellets) using impact and laser proximity fuzes (2.2 lb)
Propulsion: Boost-sustain rocket (booster burns only in launch tube; sustainer ignites at a safe distance)
Speed: Mach 1.0+ (average speed 340 m/sec)
Range: 5000 m (5500 yd); 7000 m in the Mk 2 version. Height coverage is 3000 m (9480 ft).

Rayrider is the naval version of the Bofors laser-guided infantry weapon. Bofors claims that it is unjammable because it receives its information from the launcher, not the target. Laser beam-riding automatically confers forward-aspect capability. Because the laser transmitter/tracker is gyrostabilized for use on light trucks it is easily adaptable to a moving ship. The standard installation is a single missile-launcher tube on a pedestal, which also carries the operator's seat. Reaction time is 4–5 sec.

RBS 70 Missile Mk 2. (Bofors)

The current RBS 70+ (Mk 2) version, fully interchangeable with Mk 1, entered production during the winter of 1988–89. Its digital guidance takes up less volume than the earlier analog electronics, leaving space for a 50% larger warhead (shaped charge plus fragmentation pellets), and a larger sustainer. Bofors describes Mk 2 as armor-piercing and, therefore, capable of dealing with armored missiles and aircraft such as helicopters. In August 1988 tests, a Mk 2 destroyed a sea-skimmer approaching at an altitude of 5 m (about 16 ft) at a range of 1800 m.

A more elaborate quadruple remote-controlled version, developed by Bofors and Signaal, attracted no naval customers. See the 1991/92 edition for details.

Work on the basic missile began in 1967, and Bofors received a development contract in 1969 and a production contract in June 1975. In 1988 the estimated cost per missile was $90,000–$100,000. The Iranians used RBS 70 extensively during the Iran-Iraq War and reportedly shot down about 45 aircraft with it.

Users: Finland (*Helsinki II* class) and Sweden (*Landsort* class); Australian army missiles were carried during the Gulf War by the Australian support ships. A new stabilized mounting is being developed.

UNITED KINGDOM

♦ ILDS

In mid-1994 the UK Ministry of Defence asked for expressions of interest in a new Inner Layer Defence System (ILDS) for the new Anglo-French Project Horizon frigate. The system was to be nondevelopmental; it entails somewhat less stringent requirements than the abortive VSRAAD (very short range AA defence). Incoming missiles must be killed at 1–2 km range. Current proposals include missiles (BAe's naval version of ASRAAM, Sadral/Mistral, Crotale NG, SR2000/Seastreak, and Starstreak), guns (Oerlikon's MPG-35 Millenium with AHEAD ammunition, Myriad/Barrage, Goalkeeper, and the 76mm Compact gun with programmable ammunition), and mixed systems (MSI's Sigma D30 with Seastreak or Mistral missiles). RAM and Bofors' Trinity may also have been proposed.

BAe's IR-guided ASRAAM (advanced short-range AAM) would be distributed around the ship in fixed canisters, and the missiles fired into parabolic trajectories, acquiring their targets as they looked down at the sea. The 16.6 cm × 2.9 m (87 kg) missile uses a Hughes imaging IR seeker (128 × 128-pixel staring array) and has a 90-deg off-boresight capability, which BAe hopes to translate into fire-and-forget capability. Average speed is 800 m/sec, somewhat more than Mach 2. Unit cost, as estimated in 1994, was £200,000.

As of mid-1996, no choice had yet been made.

♦ Javelin/Starstreak/Blowpipe

Dimensions: 3 × 54.7 in (fin span 10.8 in)
Weight: 28 lb
Warhead: 6 lb (1.3 lb HE)
Propulsion: Boost-sustain rocket
Speed: Mach 1 (Starstreak: Mach 4; average 950 m/sec)
Range: 5000 yd vs. jet aircraft, 6000 vs. helicopter; minimum range about 500 yd; effective altitudes 30–10,000 ft

Data above apply to Javelin. Starstreak is heavier (about 30 lb, with a 7-lb warhead, 127 mm × 1397 mm in 274mm tube) and much faster. The older Blowpipe is about the same size, but has a shorter range and a shaped-charge rather than blast-fragmentation warhead.

Short Brothers' hand-held missiles are comparable in role to the U.S. Stinger, the French Mistral, and the Russian SA-N-5/8, but they are command guided, for better performance against an oncoming target. Javelin is semiautomatic, the operator keeping the target in the aiming sight while the system automatically tracks four IR flares on the outgoing missile and issues radio guidance commands, which are received by four whisker antennas. In practice operators sometimes track the flares rather than the target.

The successor missile, Starstreak, differs in that its warhead comprises three separate laser-guided warheads (darts), each

This model of a naval Starstreak (Seastreak) mounting was displayed by Short Brothers at RNEE in 1989. (Author)

about 2 × 45 cm (1 kg HE). After it has burned out, the main motor drops away, leaving a clear LOS between the aiming unit and the command receivers in the rear of the three unpowered darts. The guidance unit contains a pair of laser diodes, which scan horizontally and vertically to establish the matrix in which the darts position themselves.

The version of Starstreak proposed for ILDS would use a 6-rnd launcher on a Radamec 2400 carrying EO elements (TV, FLIR, laser ranger) and the missile guidance package, at a total weight of 750 kg. Seastreak is also an option for MSI's SIGMA mount (see below under MSI guns).

Users (naval):

Javelin: Canada, Oman (in a 3-rnd launcher on the royal yacht), United Kingdom (minesweepers in Persian Gulf; RFAs in the Gulf in 1991 each had a battery [8 missiles] of Royal Artillery Javelins for self-defense). First bought by the Royal Navy in 1984. Unit price in 1988 was $12,000. British army Javelins have been upgraded with Starstreak laser-optical guidance as Starburst (two laser receiver pods in the tail of the missile transmit very short range radio commands to the whisker antennas; the tracking flares are eliminated).

Starstreak: No naval sales yet (1996).

Blowpipe: Argentina, Chile, United Kingdom (war reserve); was carried by Canadian warships in the Gulf, 1990. Blowpipe was sold to at least 14 countries, about 36,500 having been made (one clip-on aiming unit for every 5–10 rnd). Unit price in 1988 was $8000.

♦ Sea Cat (GWS 20, 21, 22, 24)

Dimensions: 7.5 × 58.3 in; span 25.6 in
Weight: 138 lb
Warhead: 45 lb (38 lb HE) in Mod 1; Mod 0 is a 31-lb continuous-rod warhead (5 lb HE); both mods have both impact and IR proximity fuzes
Propulsion: Boost-glide
Speed: Mach 0.6 (average at the end of boost)
Range: 5000 yd, minimum 1500 yd; max altitude 3300 ft

Short Brothers' subsonic command-guided Sea Cat, the first naval point-defense missile (flown in 1960), was conceived to replace the twin 40mm gun. Tigercat is a land-based equivalent. The 6600-lb launcher carries four missiles. In the most common surviving version, GWS 22 (first ordered 1972), a slaved television tracks the outgoing missile while the system's Type 904 radar tracks the target. Some missiles, particularly in British service, were modified from 1977 on with a special altimeter to attack low-flying missiles. Sea Cat has also been used as a target. In all, 5724 were made; unit price (FY89 terms) was $134,000.

Sea Dart. (*Sea Power*)

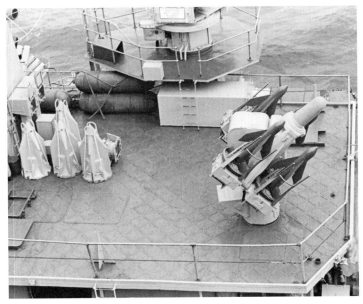

A quadruple Sea Cat launcher on board the British frigate *Argonaut*, 1975. (U.S. Navy)

Users: Brazil (GWS 24 in *Niteroi* class, with RTN-10X radar), Chile (GWS 22 in *Leander* class and unmodified "County" class), Ecuador (GWS 22 in *Leanders*), India (version with Signaal M45 radar in *Leanders* except *Nilgiri*, which has GWS 22), Indonesia (version with M45 radar in *Van Speijk* class, GWS 21 in "Tribals"), Pakistan (GWS 22 in *Leander* class), United Kingdom (GWS 22 in *Fearless* class). All other users have retired this missile. Note that Iran uses Tigercat as a surface-to-surface weapon.

◆ **Sea Dart (GWS 30; CF 299)**

Dimensions: 16.5 × 172 in, including booster; span 36 in
Weight: 1200 lb
Warhead: 50 lb HE/continuous rod
Propulsion: Ramjet with rocket boost
Speed: Mach 2.5–3.0
Range: 40 nm (altitude 100–60,000 ft)

Sea Dart is the standard British area-defense missile, a semiactively homing ramjet. Like the defunct U.S. Talos, it uses four interferometer aerials (polyrods) for guidance rather than a dish. They provide monopulse tracking; the missile has a reference antenna pointing back and flies a proportional-navigation path. The associated tracker-illuminator is Type 909. The ADIMP upgrade adds a commandable autopilot, as in the U.S. SM-2. Space became available when the original six circuit boards were replaced by one board. Effective missile range against high-altitude targets is doubled (probably to about 80 nm); it is also possible to fire missiles before their targets have been acquired, and to shift targets once a missile is in flight. This capability (and the success of efforts to make the missile effective against low fliers) was demonstrated in HMS *Gloucester*'s spectacular performance against a Silkworm (with an "over the shoulder" shot) in the Gulf in 1991, screening USS *Wisconsin*. Of two missiles fired 50 sec after the ship had detected radiation from the Iraqi targeting radar, one hit the Silkworm and the other passed through the wreckage.

Like its predecessor, Sea Slug, Sea Dart was designed to have a considerable surface-to-surface capability.

There have been two major guidance upgrades (1983–86 and 1989–91 [ADIMP plus motor improvement]); a new blast warhead (GMk 39A1) was delivered beginning in 1987, and work is proceeding on a new IR fuze. Early in 1996 BAe won a contract, running through 1999, to refurbish existing Sea Dart missiles. The missile is likely to remain in Royal Navy service through 2020.

Unlike their U.S. or Russian counterparts, missiles are stowed vertically below the waterline and loaded in two stages: first by chain hoist to an intermediate position where they are warmed up and finned, and then by hydraulic ram onto the launcher. Reportedly HMS *Invincible* fired six missiles in 2 min on one occasion (one two-missile salvo every 40 sec).

Development began in 1962; production was announced in November 1967. The 500th missile was fired by HMS *Bristol* in November 1986. Sea Dart is credited with having shot down seven Argentine aircraft in the Falklands. Limited reliability apparently caused the Chinese to abandon plans to use this missile to modernize their "Luda"-class destroyers.

Users: Argentina (Type 42 destroyers [22 missiles]), United Kingdom (*Invincible*-class carriers [36 missiles], Type 42 destroyers [20 or 22 missiles in all variants]). Estimated production was about 2000 missiles (unit price $252,000 [FY89]).

◆ **Sea Slug Mk 2 (GWS 1)**

Dimensions: 16.1 in × 20 ft (19 ft 8 in for Mk 1); span 56.6 in
Weight: Approx. 4400 lb total (1980 lb without boosters)
Warhead: Approx. 200 lb
Propulsion: Strap-on boosters with sustainer rocket
Speed: Mach 1.8
Range: 24.3 nm, max altitude 65,000 ft

This elderly beam-rider survives only in Chile, which bought up all spares along with the "County"-class missile destroyers. Reportedly these missiles then received new boost-sustain motors (i.e., no longer need wrap-around boosters) and guidance systems. However, they probably still lack any means of terminal guidance. Because the missile guidance beam is separate from the target-tracking beam, the missile can be commanded to fly up and then dive toward a ship or a low flier, out to 40,000-yd range.

Missiles are stowed horizontally, with four strap-on boosters. "County"-class magazine capacity is 39: about 18 ready-service rounds, with about 20 more forward requiring winging and finning (narrow unfinned missiles could be stowed more densely than ready-use rounds).

Work on Mk 2 began in 1957, and tests were completed in 1965. However, the system was apparently never certified for British service, partly because missiles tended to break up as they shed their boosters one by one by aerodynamic forces (this

A pair of Sea Slugs lie in their distinctive lattice-work launcher on board a "County"-class missile destroyer. Only the four boosters wrapped around the head of each missile are visible here. (Author)

problem seems to have been solved about 1972, by which time the successor Sea Dart program was well underway).

Users: Chile (*Prat* and *Latorre*).

♦ **Sea Wolf (GWS 25, 26)**

Dimensions: 18 cm × 2 m; span 56 cm (7.1 × 75 × 22 in)
Weight: 82 kg (180 lb)
Warhead: Approx. 14 kg (31 lb) (also reported as 9 kg)
Propulsion: Boost-glide; burn time 2–3 sec
Speed: Mach 2 (average speed 550 m/sec)
Range: Approx. 5 km (5500 yd)

BAe's command-guided Sea Wolf is the standard British point defense weapon. The associated acquisition radars are Types 967/968 and 996; the trackers are Types 910 and 911 and Marconi's ST1802SW. Ships carry two trackers (two independent guidance channels, operating at different frequencies), which can also direct gunfire. Operation is automatic (subject to operator veto), the system ranking and engaging threats in turn. The system computer is FM1600B in GWS 25 Mod 0 (early Type 22s), FM1600E in Mod 3 (Type 22 from HMS *Brave* onwards, with Type 911 trackers), and F2420 (with a Ferranti LAN) in GWS 26 (Type 23 frigates). In a Type 22, each 6-missile launcher is backed

up by 12 ready-use missiles. A Batch I ship carries another ready-use load (total 48 missiles); Batch II and III ships have paired magazines (total 60 missiles). Type 23s have 32 vertical launchers, without reloads (they can be reloaded at sea, but probably only in calm weather). The vertical launcher uses a finned booster (with thrust-vector control), which may add 50% to missile range (maximum about 7.5 km).

Sea Wolf was conceived as a supersonic follow-on to Sea Cat; the initial production contract was let in July 1968, the first missile being fired in 1973. This missile was considered extremely successful during the Falklands War, and was credited with five kills.

BAe has a midlife upgrade contract for Sea Wolf.

Users: Brazil (Type 22 Batch I frigates [GWS 25]), Malaysia (*Lekiu* class), United Kingdom (Type 22 [GWS 25] and Type 23 [GWS 26] frigates). Plans for installation on board carriers, Type 42 destroyers, and AORs were all abandoned. The Royal Navy bought 950 VL Sea Wolf missiles through March 1995, at a unit cost of £300,000 for the first and second batches.

UNITED STATES

The February 1991 budget (FY92/93) included initial work on a magnetohydrodynamic (MHD) warhead. Such a weapon would presumably generate an intense electromagnetic pulse, to burn out the circuits on board an attacking weapon. The FY95 program began overwater tests against representative seekers. Another new concept is to use a water-activated munition to produce a water barrier, into which a missile may fly (doctrine already calls for medium-caliber guns to fire into the water to create splashes, but the new munition offers a wider barrier which lasts longer). Full-scale multicharge tests were conducted under the FY94 program. Moderate interest in high-energy lasers continues.

For defensive missiles, work is proceeding on reactive-case warheads (to make better use of limited payload weights). A dual-mission advanced missile airframe (with jet-reaction controls) is a FY96 advanced technology demonstrator. A semiactive fuze (presumably actuated by guidance illumination rather than by the missile) is a FY96 new start.

♦ **Aegis**

See SM-2 below.

♦ **ESSMS**

Evolved Sea Sparrow Missile System is to be the Sea Sparrow successor. Missile wings will be folded so that they can be quad-packed in a single vertical launcher cell, releasing launcher slots for other weapons. Aboard Aegis ships, ESSMS and SM-2 will share the same Aegis FCS, including uplinks; the advent of ESSMS will justify elimination of Phalanx CIWS from later ships

Sea Wolf being loaded. (British Ministry of Defence)

Hughes's winning proposal for Evolved Sea Sparrow, in model form at the 1995 Navy League show. (Author)

of the *Arleigh Burke* class. In June 1995 the U.S. Navy announced that Hughes would be prime contractor, to conduct a 54-month development program at a cost of $154M. Raytheon protested. Rather than risk restarting the competition (and thus delaying the program, while upsetting the international partners), Hughes agreed to a partnership with Raytheon in ESSMS development.

ESSMS is a tail-controlled missile (for 50G maneuverability, to engage a 4G missile). Virtually eliminating the wings makes it possible to neck-out a new all-boost motor (10 in dia), for 2 to 4 times the energy of the earlier Sparrows. Early motor burnout will reduce missile smoke and clear the FOVs of shipboard EO sensors. ESSMS will also have a new autopilot. This combination offers Mach 3 speed and twice the range of RIM-7M. Other expected advantages will be quicker reaction, the ability to time-share a single illuminator (which will be able to control three missiles simultaneously), and an insensitive-munition warhead. The initial version may be RIM-7PTC, an upgraded RIM-7P with the new motor and autopilot. A later version might get the dual-mode (radar/IR) seeker based on that of the abortive interim RIM-7R, developed under MHIP (major homing improvement program). The existing reprogrammable computer is adaptable to multimode guidance (semiactive mid-course, IR terminal, and antiradar homing).

As of 1995, it seemed likely that ultimately the U.S. Navy would buy about 2000 missiles, another 1000 going to allies.

ESSMS is the missile of the later SSDS systems. Since coastal (littoral) warfare is likely to involve relatively short-range engagements, it may become extremely important to the U.S. Navy, particularly since quad-packing makes it possible to retain numbers of missiles while vacating launch cells for shore bombardment weapons.

Dimensions: 8/10 in × 144 in, weight 620 lb.

◆ Tactical Aegis LEAP

The upper-tier companion to SM-2 Block IVA is Tactical Aegis LEAP, which adds a third-stage dual-pulse motor (Advanced Solid Axial Stage, ASAS) and a homing vehicle to an SM-2 airframe retaining its Mk 72 booster and Mk 104 motor. The missile's wings are shortened and its inertial reference unit replaced by a GPS-aided inertial unit (GAINS, the first use of GPS in a Standard Missile). The Lightweight Exoatmospheric Projectile (LEAP) kinetic (energy) kill vehicle (KKV) is intended to destroy theater ballistic missiles. Its sensor is a FLIR. For example, Hughes claims that its 7–9-micron 128 × 128-element HgCdTe FPA (using a 200-MIPS processor) can detect an approaching missile at 300 km. The third stage (ASAS plus LEAP) would separate from the missile at 187,500 ft. The missile remains under uplinked control up to about 300,000 ft, when the third stage pitches over toward the threat and ejects its nose cone to expose the KKV sensor. Its motor continues to burn for about 16 sec. After the KKV inertial system is aligned at about 400,000 ft, it ejects from the third stage. It then acquires and begins to track

the target, seeking a direct hit at about 410,000 ft. At kill LEAP velocity would be about 2.7 km/sec.

Late in 1995 Hughes and Rockwell, the two competitors, began negotiation to form a joint LEAP program; an agreement (with Hughes as prime contractor) was expected in mid-1996. Hughes's FTV-1 (September 1992) was the first controlled exoatmospheric flight of an SM-series missile. Rockwell's FTV-2 (September 1994) was the first ejection of a lightweight kill vehicle from a tactical missile. FTV-3/4 were intended to intercept actual missiles, which would have flown about 430 km, at a range of 173 km from the launch ship (the cruiser *R.K. Turner*). Neither test was entirely successful. However, Hughes's FTV-3 achieved 38 of 42 objectives. Its ASAS stage separated, ignited, and guided; its new LWIR sensor acquired the target at twice the expected range, the KKV tracked and guided below its rated minimum operating altitude, and it operated 4 times longer than the expected mission lifetime. The GPS receiver acquired early and maintained lock. Guidance was effective throughout the flight. Rockwell's FTV-4 made 39 of 43 objectives. It guided to within 170 m of target (1500 m required), acquired the target prior to ejecting the KKV, operated effectively throughout the flyout, and placed its third stage well within the engagement basket. Both test vehicles used liquid fuel; an operational KKV would probably have a solid-fuel engine.

The next step is a more autonomous vehicle, which can increase the effective range of the system. For example, a SPY-1 cannot see an object at 25 km altitude beyond about 345 km. Even if a target is picked up at long range, it can drop below the radar's horizon well before it can be intercepted. A more autonomous vehicle can deal with a target re-entering the atmosphere. At that time the target is likely to break up (naturally or by design) and the warhead may be able to maneuver on its way down. The KKV must, therefore, be able to distinguish the warhead from numerous other closely spaced objects, which may well include decoys and jammers. It must therefore form a target object map (TOM); plans call for a combination of active (LADAR or mmw radar) and passive (two-color IR) sensors, the data from which will be fused on board. In theory such data fusion can also defeat missile-borne ECM. BMDO is developing the necessary hardware and software under a Discriminating Interceptor Technology Program (DITP); a companion Advanced Sensor Technology Program (ASTP) is for a planned airborne detector/tracker, which would cue the SPY-1 radar and feed updated data into the ascending interceptor missile. The interceptor may dump its processed sensor data down to the ship, which may fuse it with other data for uplinking.

As of 1995, technology requirements were:

Passive detection: Acquire a 0.16m² target at up to 800 km at 240°K (cold) or at up to 1200 km at 300°K (hot); current 128 × 128-element HgCdTe arrays acquire targets at 300–500 km (BMDO wants 256 × 256). FOV 1–2 deg (IFOV less than 50 microrad, angular track accuracy less than 25 microrad—about 3:1 subpixel tracking accuracy). Tracking time is less than 30 sec (less than 10 sec for TBMs) for initial discrimination and handoff to the LADAR or mmw radar. BMDO plans to use single multicolor FPAs to avoid problems of spatial alignment and temporal registration.

Active detection: Acquisition range 250–400 km for 0.003m² (discrimination prior to choice of target), FOV 1–2 deg, beam 40–50 microrad, angular track accuracy better than 20 microrad, range discrimination less than 0.2 m, Doppler resolution less than 0.02 m/sec, tracking time less than 10 sec (time to go for target selection). The radar is to be able to deal with more than 10 objects in FOV, and to detect target features down to less than 20 cm. Total passive/active seeker weight should be less than 15 kg.

The fusion processor is to discriminate between target and clutter on the basis of factors such as shape, 3D track (velocity and deceleration due to apparent atmospheric drag compared to apparent target area), and IR radiance at a given range versus temperature based on two-color comparison.

LEAP vehicle in an SM-2 upper stage, as displayed by SMCo., the joint Raytheon-Hughes Standard Missile manufacturer, at the 1996 Navy League show. The object in the background is an SM-2 Block IV booster. (Stuart Slade, DMS/Forecast International)

◆ RAM (RIM-116A)

Dimensions: 5 × 111 in; span 17.25 in
Weight: 162 lb
Warhead: 5 lb
Propulsion: Solid-fuel rocket
Speed: Mach 2.0+ (average speed 650 m/sec)
Range: 5 nm

The Rolling Airframe Missile (RAM) point-defense weapon was developed as a joint U.S. (Hughes [ex-General Dynamics])–West German (RAM GmBH)–Danish (Per Udsen) program. RAM is the primary missile of SSDS Mk 1. The OR was issued in May 1975, followed by a MoU for FSED in 1977 (Denmark joined in March 1979) and a production MoU in August 1987. RAM first flew in 1978. Progress since has been uneven; the missile has come close to cancellation several times.

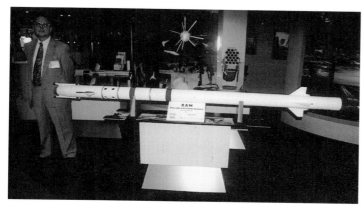

RAM on display, Dubai 1995. Note the pair of RF antennas in the missile's nose, at left. (S. Zaloga)

Unlike Sea Sparrow, RAM is a fire-and-forget weapon, guided initially by the RF (seeker) signal of its target (as obtained by SLQ-32), then switching to IR (but it can continue on RF if weather conditions preclude an IR lock-on). The point IR seeker is taken from the Stinger missile; the motor, warhead, and fuze from Sidewinder. The two-antenna RF seeker is new. Four tail fins keep the missile spinning as it flies, so that two canard control fins and two RF antennas can do the work usually done by four in a nonspinning missile. RAM can be fired as much as 12 deg off-bearing.

All installations use the 21-rnd Mk 49 box launcher. Proposals for modifications of the Sea Sparrow and Mk 13 launchers failed, and Hughes's vertical launcher was rejected for the last LHDs (to avoid introducing a unique system). Proposals have been made for launchers to be mounted alongside the standard U.S. 5in gun and atop the Contraves Sea Shield mount.

Procurement (U.S.): FY85, 30; FY86, 117; FY88, 240; FY89, 260; FY90, 580; FY91, 405 (580 requested); funding withdrawn FY92–93 (800 per year requested) but 495 bought FY93; FY94, 180 (240 requested); FY95, 240; FY96, 230 (including 30 Block 1); FY97, 100 Block 0 and 40 Block 1; FY98, 60 Block 1; FY99, 180 Block 1 (including 130 Block 0 retrofit kits). U.S. installation plan (as of June 1996): all LHA were done FY93–95; FY96, DD 972 and 987, LHD 1 and 3, LSD 48; FY97, DD 997, 973, 977, 978, 997, LSD 42, 44, 49, LHD 5; FY98, LSD 41, 43, DD 982, LHD 4 and 6; FY99, DD 985, 988, LSD 45, LHD 2, 7, and LPD 17; FY00, DD 969, 989, LSD 46, 52; FY01, LSD 47, 50, DD 992, CG 47, LPD 18/19; FY02, CG 48, 49, 50, LSD 51; FY03, CG 51, DDG 993–996. Destroyers and cruisers each get a single launcher; amphibious ships each get two. Missile unit cost (FY95) was $264,779; in 1987 it was expected that FY86 missiles would cost $145,000 each, cost averaging $100,000 for 4500 planned U.S. weapons. Low-rate production began in March 1989, with 500 ordered that June for 1992 delivery. RAM entered U.S. service on board the LHA *Peleliu* in June 1993; it entered German service in March 1994. In August 1995 RAM was tested in extended range and "around the corner" shots. As of June 1996, it had succeeded in 85 of 93 shots.

The first programmed upgrade is a new laser-proximity fuze developed by Santa Barbara Research and NWC China Lake. It is to enter service in 1996, replacing the original Sidewinder fuze.

The next stage, the Block 1 upgrade (RAM II), to enter service in 1999, deals with the problem of nonemitting missiles which home by IR or by semiactive radar seekers. The projected solution is an IR seeker that searches vertically, to LOAL rather than merely for terminal homing. The reticle (point) seeker is replaced by a new one with an 80-channel linear array backed by extensive signal processing electronics. This missile retains the original IR/RF capability. The IR mode and search pattern will be selectable from the launcher (e.g., in the all-IR mode, an expanded vertical search in flight, which would probably involve a 1-bit indication in the launch message). General Dynamics (Hughes) claimed that the improved missile would acquire even low-observable targets. A missile launched in RF mode will default to IR search if RF acquisition is lost. This program was initially known as IRMU (IR Mode Upgrade), and it was demonstrated over water early in 1990. A development contract was signed in December 1989. The IRMU feasibility study was completed in August 1990. An OpEval report was issued in September 1990. Approval to enter the engineering and manufacturing development (EMD) phase was granted in May 1994. Hughes is developing the seeker while BGT of Germany develops the signal processing.

The stage beyond, outside the scope of the current MoU, is a new dual-thrust motor for higher velocity, greater range, and higher-G terminal maneuvers. It would increase missile diameter. If the helical lands (rifling) now used to induce roll were removed from the Mk 49 launcher, it could be launched from this unit. An erodable spin vane at the rear of the missile would impart spin. This is a private Hughes-Hercules initiative. Hughes hopes to get funding in the late 1990s. The step beyond would be an uplink to engage nonemitting targets in bad weather.

As of late summer 1994, the RAM Project Office was considering using the RAM launcher for antitorpedo weapons, on the theory that the missile's SSPK was so high that all 21 rounds might not be needed. It might also be possible to fire Nulka and mine-clearance munitions from the launcher. These ideas reflected a new view that the RAM launcher was the SSDS launcher, and that SSDS was a spherical, rather than a hemispherical, problem.

Users: Germany (*Adams* class, Type 122, Type 123, probably Type 124, S143A/143B fast-attack boats; first installations: *Molders, Niedersachsen, Puma*), Japan (1900t frigates), Taiwan (*Perry* class), United States (LCC, LHA, LHD, LSD 41, and probably ultimately *Spruance* class). Interest has been expressed by Australia, Greece, Italy, Korea, the Netherlands, Norway, Spain, Turkey, and the UAE. Reportedly Italy is interested in modifying the Aspide launcher (but the failure of the RAM/Sea Sparrow combination may make that academic).

◆ Sea Chaparral

See Sidewinder (U.S. AAM below).

◆ Sea Sparrow (RIM-7)

Dimensions: 8 × 144 in; wingspan 40 in (25 in folded); tail span 24 in
Weight: 510 lb
Warhead: 77 lb blast-fragmentation
Propulsion: Boost-sustain solid-fuel rocket
Speed: Maximum Mach 2.5 (average 420 m/sec)
Range: 8–14 nm (16,000–28,000 yd)

Data apply to RIM-7M. RIM-7H: 66-lb continuous-rod warhead, boost-glide rocket motor, maximum speed 1600–1800 ft/sec (average 350 m/sec [1250 ft/sec]), range 1500–12,000 yd.

Sea Sparrow is a ship-launched self-defense variant of the Sparrow AAM. Its warhead is relatively large by short-range ship-defense missile standards; it was sized for the air-to-air mission against large bombers. All versions of the NATO Sea Sparrow Missile System (NSSMS) use the same Mk 91 FCS. The current

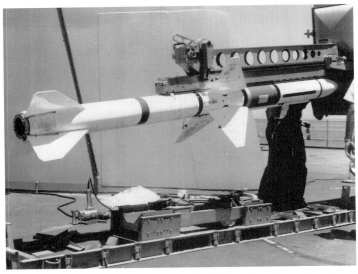

A Sea Sparrow being loaded into its Mk 29 launcher shows its clipped tail fins and foldable wings. (U.S. Navy)

Block II version (introduced 1978) uses the monopulse RIM-7M (a modified AIM-7M) missile. The missile has a new proximity fuze incorporating a target-range gate and a sea-range gate, the latter to keep the missile from detonating against the sea at low altitude. RIM-7M can discriminate between multiple targets in a stream attack, and also between different illuminators, most likely by sensing coding in the illuminator signal. Like AIM-7M, RIM-7M has an autopilot that can be set to vary flight path with target type (e.g., sea skimmer, helicopter, surface ship, aircraft); to some extent the autopilot can also be set at launch time to permit a ship to conduct multiple engagements. This version also has a self-destruct feature to protect friendly ships onto which the missile may inadvertently lock. Production amounted to 3227 rounds at a unit cost (FY89) of $156,000. U.S. production was to have ended in FY88 (200 RIM-7, 400 AIM-7), but further missiles were bought in FY89.

The jet-vane control unit of the vertically launched version of RIM-7M (prototype tested 1981, -7M version tested 1985) pitches the missile over onto a course toward the target. Missiles fired from vertical launchers begin to tip over 0.7 sec after launch and do not rise above 200 ft when fired against low-altitude targets. The missiles are fully tipped over by the time they are 250 ft from the ship. Missiles were originally provided with a delayed lock-on capability because, vertically launched, they would not immediately receive reflected illumination from a target.

The next version is RIM-7P, a -7M rebuilt for improved low-altitude performance, with an advanced reprogrammable (VLSI) missile-borne computer, an uplink capacity, and the ability to accept delayed lock-on. The higher-capacity computer allows the missile to execute a much greater variety of maneuvers. Instead of the usual up-and-over trajectory, RIM-7P can fly an offset path (the horizontal equivalent of up-and-over). For example, it can fly out in front of an approaching target. It also adds fuzing options. The combination of delayed lock-on and the uplink (to the autopilot) mimics SM-2 capability, albeit at much shorter range, hence U.S. interest in combining Sea Sparrow with SM-2 in Aegis ships. Unlike the VLS version of RIM-7M, the time delay (before illumination is needed) is no longer fixed by the missile's trajectory requirement; instead it is determined on the basis of target trajectory. For example, the target may be outside the seeker angle when the missile is launched. A time delay also allows the missile to maneuver to intercept a maneuvering target, if the illuminator is initially masked. The RIM-7P warhead weighs 85 lb. This version was operationally evaluated in June 1990, and production (of modification kits) was approved in October 1990. Known contracts (for AIM-7 and RIM-7) apparently amount to 4075 kits, presumably including FMS orders (plans originally called for 2850 rounds plus 1800 upgraded -7M).

RIM-7R, an interim step toward ESSMS with tail control and a dual-mode seeker, did not enter production. It has been superseded by RIM-7T, ESSMS (see separate entry).

The earlier Block 0 (interim point defense missile, IPDMS) uses the conscan RIM-7H (AIM-7E with a rapid run-up [RRU] modification, folding wings, and clipped fins [to double maneuverability from 15 to 30 G]). RIM-7H-1 is equivalent to -7E-1, and -7H-2 to -7E-2 (offering faster tracking, stronger flight-control responses, and an improved fuze for reduced minimum engagement range). Block I uses RIM-7H-5, an adapted -7E-5 with a modified fuze (point defense fuze fix), better reliability, and better resistance to spillover from other electronics on board a ship. Warm-up/reaction time is 8/9–16 sec. OpEval was completed in February 1974; full-scale development began in June 1978. Some of these missiles remain in service. Total production of the RIM-7H series, including kits to upgrade -7H-1 and -2 to -5, was 5033 missiles.

The successor weapon is ESSMS, which offers twice the performance and thus comes into the category of the Standard Missile (16–28nm).

Users: Australia (ANZAC frigates), Belgium (RIM-7M in *Wielingen* class), Canada (RIM-7M; delivery of six ship sets of launchers for "City" class completed 1987; delivery of 155 missiles completed 1988), Denmark (*Nils Juels* class [option for VLS version to replace current box launcher as of early 1994]; selected early 1994 for *Flyvefisken* class [three Mk 48–0 twin launchers in a standard container]), Egypt (probably RIM-7H), Germany (RIM-7M in *Bremen* class; VLS RIM-7M in F123 frigates), Greece (*Kortenaer* class; chosen for MEKO-200 frigate 1988), Italy (RIM-7H in *Lupo* class; being adapted for RIM-7M), Japan (RIM-7H, being replaced by RIM-7M, which entered license production about April 1991), Korea (21 RIM-7M ordered 1990 for KDX), Morocco (probably RIM-7H in *Descubierta*), Netherlands (*Tromp, van Heemskerck, Kortenaer* classes; VLS version bought for *Karel Doorman*–class frigates 1985, 256 VLS missiles bought 1988), New Zealand (ANZAC class), Norway (*Oslo* class, in a trainable launcher), Portugal (RIM-7M), Spain (RIM-7M), Thailand (VLS planned for *Naresuan* class), Turkey (RIM-7M in MEKO 200), United States (RIM-7M in carriers, AOR, AOE). The Thai PSMM 16 class, generally credited with Aspide missiles, may carry Sea Sparrow.

◆ Standard Missile-1 (RIM-66A, -66B, and -67A)

Dimensions: 13.5 × 176 in; span 42.5 in
Weight: 1240 lb (1390 lb for RIM-66B)
Warhead: 137-lb continuous rod
Propulsion: Boost-sustain rocket
Speed: Mach 1.25–3.5 (peak velocity 33% greater in RIM-66B)
Range: 35,000 yd, minimum 3000 yd for air targets; maximum intercept altitude 65,000 ft (maximum intercept range 50,000 yd, minimum altitude 60 ft, maximum altitude 80,000 ft for RIM-66B)

Data are for RIM-66A except as noted.

The Standard Missile replaced the earlier Tartar and Terrier, using as many parts in common as possible for, respectively, the medium-range (MR) weapon with a boost-sustain motor and the extended-range (ER) weapon with a separate booster and sustainer. Reliability improvements included all-electric design (hydraulic power for control surfaces was eliminated) and solid-state electronics with the first battery power in a U.S. missile (which drastically reduced warm-up time, from 26 sec to 1/15 sec). Those improvements in turn eliminated the requirement for shipboard check-out, missiles being shipped as "wooden rounds" good for a 3-yr no-test cycle. The Standard Missile also incorporated a single-sideband receiver (for improved ECCM and clutter rejection) and "Doppler offset" to improve discrimination among multiple targets. An increase from 12 to 19 guidance channels reduced ship-to-ship interference. While RIM-66A was an interim weapon that used the existing Mk 27 Tartar motor, RIM-66B introduced a new Mk 56 dual-thrust rocket motor, to achieve greater terminal maneuverability and greater range. Longer range meant a lengthier flight, and the electric battery had sufficient energy for 200 sec of operation.

The Taiwanese destroyer *Chien Yang* fires an SM-1 missile, 1989. The "golf ball" contains a W-160 fire-control radar. (Fu S. Mei)

Standard Missile (Medium Range) being fired from a Mk 26 launcher. The SM-1, SM-2, and Tartar missiles are virtually identical in appearance, although quite different in capability. (U.S. Navy)

A twin Standard Missile launcher on board a Taiwanese WJ-III (modified FRAM *Gearing*) destroyer. This type is unique to the Taiwanese navy. (Fu S. Mei)

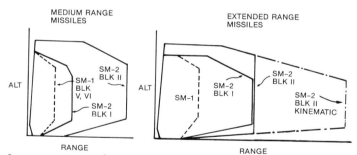

Improvements in the Standard Missiles' intercept envelopes resulted from the change from semiactive to command guidance. (General Dynamics)

Standard differed from its Terrier/Tartar predecessors in using an adaptive autopilot, that is, an autopilot that could adapt to changes in missile velocity (e.g., after burnout) and atmospheric pressure (e.g., as it climbed into thinner air). The missile continuously measures its own aerodynamics by sensing the strength of an intentionally induced roll oscillation. In 1971 it was claimed that the existing autopilot could deal with altitudes from sea level up to 100,000 ft, with payload variations of up to 1000 lb (i.e., with a fully burnt-out motor), and with speeds as great as Mach 5.

The original 1964 design allocated space and weight for an RF up/downlink for mid-course guidance and also for the inertial reference system for the autopilot, which it needed to exploit the link. Both capabilities were used in the SM-2 version of the missile.

From FY72 on, missiles were bought with a new adaptive proximity fuze, TDD (target-detection device) Mk 45. Earlier fuzes used a fixed cone-shaped sensing pattern whose length equaled the range cutoff. It could not deal with very small targets (the missile's blast might miss them altogether) or with crossing targets (which presented the fuze with a small effective length equal to body diameter). Mk 45 used a pair of beams to, in effect, measure target length; fuze delay was adapted to match. It was also specially adapted to low altitudes (it could trigger overhead bursts against surface targets), and it incorporated new ECCM features. Advanced development began in FY65, and the first fuzes were delivered to the fleet in 1973.

RIM-66A employs a conscan seeker, Mk 51 continuous-rod warhead, speed gate, analog guidance computer, and Mk 27 Mod 4 motor. However, it also has the Mk 1 autopilot and is all-electric. The Block II version of the missile reportedly survives in the French *Cassard* class. Block III (1194 missiles) was a follow-on, with unit cost $100,000 higher. Block IV (1665 missiles, in service 1968) was an upgrade with ECCM improvements, reduced minimum range, and shorter acquisition time against surface and crossing targets. Block III missiles were upgraded to Block IV from 1970 on.

Block V (RIM-66B, 2141 made 1969–83) substituted sequential plane scanning (SPS) for conscan; it reduced the effect of glint (target scintillation) in surface targets. The seeker head was driven directly rather than through gearing, and the new integrated-circuit autopilot reacted more quickly. This version has a Mk 90 blast-fragmentation warhead and a Mk 56 Mod 1 motor (which extends length 10 in). This is the version used by most export customers. Unit price is $495,000.

Block VI (RIM-66E) has a monopulse seeker (as in SM-2), a new proximity fuze (TDD Mk 45 Mod 4), and a digital-guidance computer. This version has a new dual-initiated warhead offering greater fragment velocity and density, to deal with targets closing at higher speed. Procurement began in FY80; acceptance trials were completed in March 1983. This version remains in production for export to, for example, Taiwan. All 22 remaining first-line FFG 7s are to receive Block VIB missiles (modified Block VI) to deal with small-RCS low-flying targets. Unit price is $601,500.

A few foreign ships have the ship-to-ship version, Standard ARM (RGM-66D), which follows an up-and-over trajectory to a range of 35–40 nm (minimum 7000 yd) carrying a 219-lb warhead (102-lb HE). The German navy reportedly bought Standard (Tartar) for its *Adams*-class destroyers specifically in the expectation of using a surface-to-surface version (which did not, in fact, materialize).

RIM-67A is SM-1(ER), with a different sustainer and an external booster (18 × 156.6 in, with 62.25in fins). Maximum reported range was 40 nm, but as early as 1971 a missile fired at White Sands intercepted an augmented target at 70 nm. The only surviving system is on board the Italian training cruiser *Vittorio Veneto*; see the 1991/92 edition for further details.

The Standard Missile concept was formally proposed in October 1963 by the Surface Missile Systems Project Office. Procurement began in FY67, a total of about 12,000 SM-1 (MR and ER) being made for U.S. and foreign service. U.S. procurement ended in FY85 (700 in FY84, 600 in FY85), but foreign demand led Hughes to reopen the line (171 in FY90, 242 in FY91, 153 in FY92/93). The U.S. decision to stop making new SM-1 missiles may have contributed to the French decision not to build a planned second pair of *Cassard*-class destroyers armed with this weapon. Proposals to arm U.S. frigates with derated versions of SM-2 have not been successful.

A Standard Missile land-attack version, SMASHER (Standard Missile Autonomous Strike Homing Round), was proposed by the NSWC for naval fire support. It would be fired from a standard Mk 41 VLS. It would use GPS for mid-course guidance, and an optical seeker for terminal guidance once it had reached a preprogrammed point. SMASHER would also have a new 500-lb warhead, and an enlarged missile could carry 1000 lb. This version, later called Standard Strike, played well in a January 1994 Lincoln Laboratory study, since it could rapidly attack time-critical targets such as tank columns.

At Navy League 1995, Hughes displayed further proposed versions: Standard Strike carrying a submunition payload (BATs) for shore attack; a target for ballistic missile defense weapons; and a supersonic low-altitude target (SLAT) to replace Vandal (converted Talos). SLAT was a modified Terrier, over 2000 surplus examples of which are in storage. At 10m altitude, Terrier range would be 40 km (22 nm); if the Mk 30 motor was replaced by the Mk 104 Standard Missile dual-thrust motor, that would increase to 64 km (35 nm). As a ballistic missile target, a converted Terrier could reach a maximum altitude of 85 km (280,000 ft) and a range of 275 km (150 nm); with the new motor, it could reach 168 km altitude (550,000 ft) and a range of 550 km (300 nm). Flight control would be by GPS/INS plus an off-the-shelf radar altimeter. These figures suggest how a Standard Missile might be expected to perform in a fire-support mode.

Users: Australia (*Perry* class, *Adams* class), France (*Cassard* class), Germany (*Adams* class), Greece (*Adams* class), Italy (ER in *Vittorio Veneto*, MR in *Mimbelli*, *Audace*, and *Impavido* clas-

ses), Japan (*Hatakaze* and *Tachikaze* classes), Netherlands (*Tromp* and *Jacob van Heemskerck* classes), Spain (*Perry* class), Taiwan (*Perry* and *Wu-Jinn III* classes), and United States (only *Perry* class [after NTU program is complete]).

Standard ARM users: Korea (PGM 352–356 [PSMM 5 class] and PGM 351 [*Asheville* class]; possibly also Iran (*Damavand*-class destroyer).

◆ Standard Missile-2 (RIM-66C)

SM-2 adds a programmable autopilot to the basic SM-1 missile, so that it can be command-guided into a homing "basket" near the projected position of the target. SM-2 was the first tactical missile to incorporate inertial navigation, to guide the missile from the launching ship up into the designated homing "basket." Semiactive illumination is needed only toward the end of the missile's flight. SM-2 is the basis of the Aegis system, which counters saturation by time-sharing illuminators. It is also part of the NTU to earlier missile ships.

SM-2 Block IV as displayed by Raytheon at the 1992 Navy League Show. The missile above it is Raytheon's wingless version of the Evolved Sea Sparrow Missile, with an IR seeker in its extreme nose (the nose cone is cut away to show the radar dish behind it). The missile in the background is "Box Office," an airframe proposed for AIM-9X. (Author)

Command guidance increases a missile's range in two ways. A semiactive missile homes all the way to its target: the illuminator must, therefore, provide enough energy for a sufficient amount to be reflected all the way back to the missile on its launcher. In contrast, SM-2 requires illumination only near its target. The illuminator must still provide sufficient energy to reach one way, but only a fraction of the way back. The combination of command and semiactive is preferable to pure command because tracking (both of missile and of target) is unlikely to be precise enough to bring the missile within lethal range at many tens of miles, while the target maneuvers violently.

The missile also gains range because it can fly a more energy-efficient path. When SM-2 replaced SM-1(MR) (without any change in rocket motor), effective range increased by 60%, from about 25 nm to about 40 nm. Altitude performance also improved.

SM-2 Block I (RIM-66C) introduced a monopulse seeker, which counters self-screening jamming. It has a Mk 115 blast-fragmentation warhead and a Mk 2 Mod 3 autopilot. RIM-66D is SM-2(MR) Block I for Tartar NTU ships. Block I procurement ended in FY83.

SM-2 Block II (RIM-66G) has an improved (Mk 56) rocket motor, to deal with faster and more maneuverable targets. It doubled effective range, probably bringing it up to the limit imposed by illuminator power. Block II also adds digital signal processing and a high-velocity fragmentation warhead (to kill targets passing at very high speeds). Block II (MR) was approved for service use in December 1983. RIM-66H is the vertically launched version; -66J is the version for Tartar NTU ships.

Block III missiles were procured in FY88/90 (RIM-66K for Tartar NTU, -66L for Aegis with Mk 26 launcher, -66M for Aegis with VLS). Procurement ended in FY90 with 710 missiles/ $390.214M (unit cost $549,000). Block III incorporates low-altitude improvements developed under a 1984 Standard Missile Improvement Program.

Block IIIA (RIM-66K-2, -66L-2, and -66M-2) production began in FY91; the plan released in 1990 called for 490/$250.126M ($510,000 each) that year, then 30 in each of FY92 and FY93 (unit cost about $630,000). The prototype SM-2 Block IIIA missile flew at White Sands on 2 March 1991. Improvements in this version include a directed explosion warhead (i.e., the missile rolls toward its target and then fires its warhead directly at it). At-sea operational and developmental tests were delayed to FY91 to await sufficient fuze design maturity.

Block IIIB production began with 100 modification kits in FY91 ($195,000 each), followed by a planned 66 kits and 300 missiles in FY92 and 79 kits and 300 missiles in FY93. Block IIIB incorporates MHIP (approved 17 July 1989). For details of MHIP (the combined IR/radar sensor), see the discussion of Sparrow below.

Total Block III procurement: FY93, 330 (combined Block II and III); FY94, 202; FY95, 202; plans (early 1995) call for 230 in FY96 and 235 in FY97.

Development of another new motor, the dual-thrust Mk 104, was announced in the FY86 budget. Mk 104 is presumably intended for an SM-2(MR) Block V, an unboosted equivalent to Block IV.

Total Standard Missile procurement (all versions): FY84, 1190; FY85, 1380; FY86, 1316. SM-2(MR) procurement began with 30 in FY80; FY83, 150; FY86, 846; FY87, 844; FY88, 1310; FY89, 1310; FY90, 940; FY91, 405; FY92, 330; FY93, 330. Unit cost was $415,000 in FY90 and $791,000 in FY92/93. Note that the FY91 budget request included 600 SM-2 Block IIIA missiles.

Users: Japan (*Kongo* class), United States (*Ticonderoga, California, Virginia, Arleigh Burke, Kidd* classes).

◆ SM-2 Aegis (ER) (SM-2 Block IV) (RIM-156A)

Dimensions: 13.5 × 256 in (booster: 21 × 72 in)
Weight: 3076 lb (total)

SM-2 Aegis (ER) is a boosted version of SM-2(MR) designed specifically for Aegis ships equipped with Mk 26 or Mk 41 launchers, to deal with very fast or very high-altitude targets. Added energy should make the weapon more agile, particularly at the edges of its flight envelope. The missile should also achieve greater range. Aegis ships could not use the regular SM-2(ER) configuration because their launchers are automatic (for high rates of fire) and, therefore, cannot accommodate the manual finning of the usual Mk 10 (SM-2[ER]) system. In 1987 the contract for SM-2 Block IV development was given to Raytheon; General Dynamics Pomona had been responsible for all SM-1/2 development up to that time.

Block IV is designed specifically for vertical launching, so the new missile's short (finless) booster uses thrust-vector control. Modifications to the missile itself include a slip-cast silica radome, a modified antenna with a new signal processor, an improved autopilot, and modified dorsal and tail fins (the latter with new actuators and a new clamp). Raytheon claims that the new aerodynamic surfaces will give considerable improvements in lift and control.

According to an official program description, the expansion of the missile envelope (to 200 nm range, 95,000 ft altitude) makes the HPIRS (high-performance IR sensor) program useful. Funded for 3 yr by the OSD BTI program, it is presumably intended to deal with low-radar-cross-section targets. HPIRS was added to the Navy FY90 budget. It is *not* MHIP. This version will be modified to deal with tactical ballistic missiles (e.g., those fired at an amphibious assault area) as the initial phase of the naval TMD effort (as Block IVA).

Hughes is developing the IR sensor for the Raytheon Block IVA missile (first guided firing was in April 1993). The 128 × 128 focal-plane-array imaging sensor (which can be grown to 256 × 256) is in a bump on the side of the missile, covered by a plate that protects it from the heat of high-speed flight at low altitude. When the sensor is needed, the protective cover blows off to reveal a sapphire dome.

The FY91 budget request included the first 300 production SM-2 Block IV missiles. The missile first flew in July 1991 at White Sands and had its first at-sea test in July 1994, from USS *Lake Erie.* Developmental Testing (DT) was completed late in 1994.

Users: United States (to be *Ticonderoga* [VLS ships only] and *Arleigh Burke* class); this missile can be fired by the Japanese *Kongo* class.

Block IVA is conceived as a dual-purpose AAW and antiballistic missile weapon for use at relatively short ranges (a lower-tier weapon in terms of ballistic missile defense). Tests have shown that its blast-fragmentation warhead should be effective against missile warheads (the fragments are now being optimized to kill hard ballistic missiles while retaining their capability against relatively soft cruise missiles and aircraft). To deal with faster targets, this version has a faster autopilot better integrated with the seeker. Primary fuzing against a fast ballistic missile is forward-looking predictive rather than proximity, with a forward-leaning proximity fuze as backup. The adjunct IR seeker significantly reduces miss distance. The step beyond, Tactical Aegis LEAP, is described separately.

As of mid-1996, a two-ship (probably CG 70 and CG 73) SM-2 Block IVA User OpEval was planned for September 1998. Planned procurement of missiles (ship installations) during current Five-Year Defense Plan: FY98, 48 (7); FY99, 106 (8); FY00, 146 (10); FY01, 155 (11). Ultimately 1500 SM-2 Block IVA missiles are to be bought. A reduction of $40M in FY95 delayed the program a year, so that this weapon will become operational in FY00 rather than in FY99.

◆ Stinger (FIM-92)/FlF-2

Dimensions: 2.75 × 60 in
Weight: 34.5 lb
Warhead: 6.6 lb (proximity fuze)
Propulsion: Two-pulse rocket
Speed: Mach 2.0
Range: About 5500 yd

Since 1984 the land-based Stinger has been issued to many U.S. warships and auxiliaries for point defense, particularly in Middle Eastern waters. For example, movies of the missile cruiser USS *Vincennes* showed a Stinger operator on deck. Target acquisition was initially entirely visual, but the Navy is now buying UPS-3 battlefield radars for this purpose. Compared to other hand-held IR missiles, Stinger is said to have a greater capacity to home on the forward aspect of an incoming target. Special features include a dual-color (IR and ultraviolet) seeker (for resistance to countermeasures) and a rosette-scan seeker (in Advanced Stinger) for target discrimination, for example, between an airplane and a flare.

Stinger was extremely successful in Afghanistan, against Soviet helicopters and ground-attack aircraft.

Recent procurements: FY84, 1205 Navy; FY85, 2360 Navy; FY86, 3439 Navy; FY87, 536 Navy; FY88, 425 Navy, 3067 Marines; FY89 request, none for Navy, 3115 for Marines. It was reported in April 1988 that purchases of Stinger by the Navy had ended, with about 150 fewer than the 685 originally planned. Because it was designed for use on land, Stinger incorporated no shielding against the electromagnetic radiation typically present on shipboard. This problem is typical of land-warfare weapons placed on ships without special adaptation. In addition, the missile's launch blast could damage the ship's structure.

Users: Denmark (to arm modernized *Falster* and *Willemoes* classes in a new twin mounting with an electronic receiver for target designation, replacing a 20mm gun), Germany (Type 332 and 343–class MCM ships; as Fliegerfaust 2 [FlF 2] in permanent ring mounts; Redege was Fliegerfaust 1), United States (issued as required, particularly for ships deploying to the Middle East). Some U.S. ships have permanent ring mounts, allowing the

A Stinger is fired from shipboard. Notice the supporting ring. (General Dynamics)

gunner to rest the launcher when not in use. Greece uses the predecessor missile, Redeye, on board *Kortenaer*-class frigates (they were also on board the Greek *Gearings*, now discarded).

◆ SDMS

Loral's (formerly LTV's) proposed short-range ship defensive missile is based on the ERINT (Extended-Range Interceptor) vehicle it developed for ballistic missile defense. As of 1996 the naval version is still only a feasibility study. SDMS uses a Ka-

SDMS at the 1992 Navy League Show. Developed by LTV, this weapon is now marketed by Lockheed Martin. (Author)

band terminal seeker and hits to kill. Midterm guidance is by updates (not necessarily periodic), using 180 thrusters distributed around the forebody of the missile. They are also used to steer the missile as it emerges from the vertical launchers, and for terminal steering; there are no jettisonable vanes in the jetstream. The missile uses a graphite-epoxy motor case. Dimensions: 10 × 182 in (670 lb); four can be accommodated in each VLS cell. ERINT made its first ballistic flight in June 1992.

◆ THAAD

The Army's Theater High-Altitude Air Defense, or upper-layer antimissile defense, missile may eventually be carried in Mk 41 VLS cells, as the Navy's contribution to ballistic missile defense. Lockheed won this competition in the fall of 1992. The naval equivalent of the lower layer would be SM-2 Block IVA. The Navy would currently prefer a LEAP version of the solid-fuel SM-2 to the liquid-fueled THAAD. Lockheed Martin has proposed an alternative, retaining the same kill vehicle but replacing the booster portion of the missile with two stages, the Mk 72 booster (of SM-2 Block IV) and a new second-stage booster (ASAS/XLV [Advanced Solid Axial Stage/Extended Length Vectorable] nozzle). The adapted Army missile fits a Mk 14 VLS canister. The all-solid-fuel missile exploits the full potential diameter of the VLS cell (in a Mk 21 canister). According to Lockheed Martin, it offers three times the downrange capability and over 1.5 times the velocity of the adapted Army missile. The Navy, however, remains cool to the idea. A deployable Army prototype version of THAAD is due for delivery in 1997.

U.S. MISSILE LAUNCHING SYSTEMS

Mk 10: For SM(ER) (originally Terrier) missiles; survives only (in Mod 7 version) on board the Italian *Vittorio Veneto*. The missiles are stowed horizontally without their booster fins, in 20-missile rotating rings. They are raised onto parallel monorails for ramming onto the launcher (through armored doors), and the boosters are finned manually before ramming. Rate of fire: 4 rnd/min (one missile every 30 sec per rail). Mod 7 has three rings (60 missiles) and fires both SAMs and ASROC (20 ASROC can be interspersed with the missiles on the two upper rings). This system was called ASTER. Weight: 546,734/361,994 lb. Complement: 16. Dimensions for a two-ring installation: 360 × 395 in (magazine, not counting launcher). Train rate: 30 deg/sec (elevation rate 20 deg/sec; limits +90/−10 deg).

Mk 13: Current standard SM(MR) launcher, with a single arm, first installed in late *Adams*-class missile destroyers. Mk 13 fires one missile every 10 sec (continuous salvo rate is one missile every 7.47–7.82 sec in the Mod 4 in the *Perry* class). The 40 missiles are stowed vertically, in two concentric rings (Mk 22, below, is in effect the inner ring of a Mk 13). Both the rings and the launcher rotate; the blast door is fixed. Train rate: 90 deg/sec (elevation rate 45 deg/sec); elevation limits are +95/−15 deg (+93/−15 for Mod 4). Diameter: 203 in. Weight (Mod 4): 134,704 lb empty. Mod 4 was designed specifically to fire Standard Missiles, which require no warmup, and, therefore, lacks the warmup connectors of earlier versions. This launcher can fire Harpoon missiles.

In addition to eliminating all warmup circuits and hardware, Mod 4 has a solid-state (rather than relay) control system and can automatically identify 7 of 64 possible types of missile in each magazine position (to handle different weapons). The missile automatically identifies itself to the guide arm as it is loaded onto the launcher.

Users: Australia (*Adams* and *Perry* classes), France (*Cassard* class), Germany (*Adams* class), Greece (*Adams* class), Italy (*Mimbelli*, *Audace* classes), Japan (*Amatsukaze*, *Hatakaze*, *Tachikaze* classes), Netherlands (*Tromp* and *van Heemskerck* classes), Spain (*Perry* class), Taiwan (*Perry* class), United States (*California* and *Perry* classes).

Mk 16: ASROC "pepperbox," carrying eight missiles in two-missile cells elevating separately. Maximum rate of fire is 3 missiles/min. Elevation limits: +85/−3 deg. This lightweight launcher is often criticized for its vulnerability to weather dam-

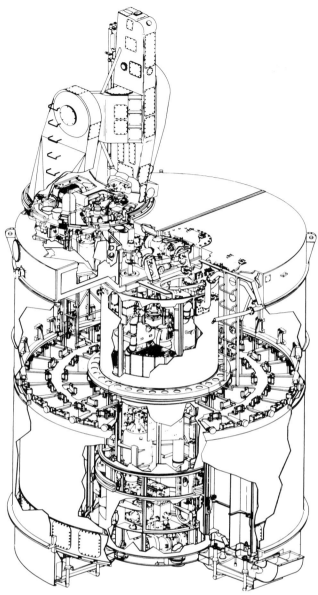

Mk 13 Mod 1 missile launcher. The missiles are carried in the two concentric rings surrounding the central column. (FMC)

Mk 16 is the standard ASROC launching system, shown on board the frigate *William S. Sims* (1986). Each pair of cells operates independently. (S. Terzibaschitsch and W. Donko)

age. Most versions are reloadable; in *Knox*-class frigates the magazine is under the bridge, abaft the launcher, and the missiles are stowed horizontally. This launcher is now extinct in the U.S. Navy, but it survives abroad.

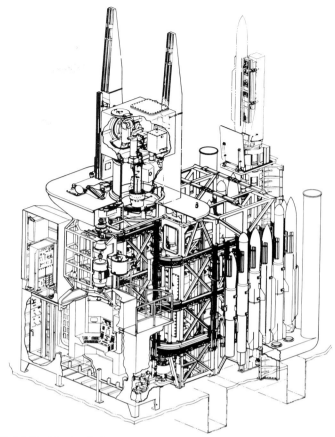

Mk 26 Mod 1 missile launcher, showing a variety of weapons (Standard, two kinds of ASROC, and Harpoon), and the strike-down hatch at the right, with a Standard Missile being loaded. The missiles are carried on a pair of vertical conveyors, one for each launcher arm. (FMC)

Mk 22: Lightweight single-arm SM(MR) launcher, for the Spanish *Baleares* class, carrying 16 missiles in one fixed vertical storage ring (the blast door revolves). Rate of fire: 7/min. Train rate: 85 deg/sec (elevation 45 deg/sec); elevation limits: +85/−10 deg. Magazine diameter is 146 in. Weight (empty): 94,003 lb.

Mk 26: Twin-arm dual-purpose (SM and ASROC) launcher, used in place of Mk 13 on *Virginia* and early *Ticonderoga* classes. Missile length limit is 200 in (diameter 14.75 in, weight 2200 lb, compared to 13.5 × 186.45 in and 1500 lb for Mk 13). Missiles are stowed vertically, in two parallel chains running fore and aft under the launcher. Rate of fire per arm reportedly approximates that of Mk 13 (in theory, two missiles every 10 sec). Train/elevation rates: 90/50 deg/sec. Versions: Mod 0, 24 missiles (193,022 lb/162,302 lb empty, largely for ASROC); Mod 1, 44 missiles (264,897/208,577 lb); and Mod 2, 64 missiles (337,031/255,111 lb).

Mk 29: NATO Sea Sparrow launcher (13,676 lb), firing 1 rnd every 2 sec. Train/elevation rates: 40/65 deg/sec; elevation limits +85/−5 deg.

Mk 32: Standard Missile box launching system, for *Asheville*-class gunboats (Mods 0 and 1) and for the Iranian destroyers *Babr* and *Palang* (Mod 2). It is fixed in train and elevates to 25 deg to fire up to 2 rnd/min (2 rnd/launcher, in a magazine forward of the launcher proper). Total weight: 22,420 lb. The Mk 134 launcher is 205 in long, with a 203in magazine.

Mk 33: RBOC chaff launcher.

Mk 35: Trident C-4 launcher for strategic submarines.

Mk 36: SRBOC chaff launching system using the Mk 137 launcher.

Mk 37/38/39: Launchers for CAPTOR mines from, respectively, surface ships, P-3 aircraft, and submarines.

A Mk 29 Sea Sparrow launcher on board the frigate *Van Kinsbergen*, 1990. (L. van Ginderen)

Mk 41: Vertical Launching System (VLS), first installed operationally on board the cruiser *Bunker Hill* (CG 52). FMC developed the vertical launch concept as part of the ASMS program (which became Aegis) in 1965–66, designing the basic eight-cell module in 1976; it then lost the production contract to Martin-Marietta. Compared to a rail launcher such as Mk 41, VLS stows 50% more missiles in the same space.

The system was originally designed to fire only Standard Missiles, using a 228in canister (which allowed for future expansion). However, it was decided that all VLS would also be able to launch Tomahawk missiles, so the standard canister was lengthened to 264 in. Standard Missiles are, therefore, loaded in short canisters with a 37.5in adapter; all canisters are 25 in² in

A Mk 41 reloading crane aboard USS *Cowpens*, September 1995. (Winter/Findler)

cross-section: Mk 13 for SM-2, Mk 14 for Tomahawk, Mk 15 for vertically launched ASROC, Mk 22 for Sea Sparrow, Mk 25 for ESSM quadpack. Maximum missile size is 22 × 257 in (222 in for the short module). Each canister has missile-specific adapters. Missiles are loaded and shipped in their canisters. Thus a quadpack must be shipped back after firing, even if several missiles have not been fired.

Launchers are assembled from modules (eight cells each, in two rows of four). Originally each group also included one five-cell module with a three-cell strike-down crane), for typical totals of 29 or 61 missiles. There is now considerable skepticism as to the practicality of underway replenishment with large missiles, so the cranes are being eliminated, increasing capacity to 32 or 64 missiles. Each module carries its own launch sequencer, motor-control panel, and gas exhaust system. When a missile is fired, it exhausts through the canister blowout cover into the plenum and then up through the deck between the two rows of cells. The plenum can withstand seven firings per cell plus a restrained firing from any other cell. (Work is underway to design a version that can withstand more firings.) The Mk 41 is said to cost half as much as a Mk 26 (per missile) and to require fewer crew (8 guided-missile mates on the *Bunker Hill*, 11 on an earlier Aegis cruiser).

Vertical-launcher cells ready for installation.

Rate of fire is reportedly 1 missile/sec.

Proposals to fit two SM missiles into each cell failed, but the new Evolved Sea Sparrow is being designed for quad-packing (four per cell).

In 1995 United Defense (formerly FMC) announced Cocoon, in effect a pair of Mk 41 cells with a bottom door for exhaust, which can be mounted to a bulkhead. The company reported U.S. Navy interest in Cocoon to replace the Mk 29 NATO Sea Sparrow launcher. Cocoon was offered to the RAN as part of the FFG 7 upgrade; United has also suggested VLS and adaptation of Mk 13 to fire ESSMs.

Users: Australia (ANZAC class: VLS-VL/RIM-7: eight cells), Canada ("Tribal" class, Mod T with 29 cells), Germany (VLS-VL/RIM-7 in *Brandenburg*), Japan (Mod 2 in *Kongo* class), New Zealand (ANZAC class), Thailand (VLS-VL/RIM-7 in *Naresuan*), United States (Mod 0 in *Ticonderoga* class, 61 cells each fore and aft; Mod 1 in *Spruance* class, 61 cells forward only; Mod 2 in *Arleigh Burke* class, 29 cells forward and 61 aft)

Mk 42: Countermeasures launching system.

Mk 44: Tomahawk armored box launcher (for Tomahawk Weapons System Mk 32). Mod 1 was the ground-launched system (GLCM), now obsolete, and Mod 2 is the shipboard launcher.

Mk 45: Tomahawk VLS for submarines.

Mk 46: Trident D-5 launcher.

Mk 48: Sea Sparrow VLS (using the Mk 164 launcher). This is essentially a short version of Mk 41, so it can accommodate quad-packed ESSMs. Mod 0 consists of two individual cells with exhaust uptakes between them, for on-deck installation. Mod 1 has paired cells with uptakes alongside, for bulkhead installation. Mod 2 is 8 or 16 cells concentrated in rows of four, with paired uptakes between pairs of rows, for in-deck installation. Mod 3 is a compact module, six cells with uptakes between the rows of 3. Mod 0 dimensions: total height 478 cm; total width 220 cm; depth 132 cm (16 cells weigh 15,942 kg). Dimensions include the dual manifold between the two cells. For the basic two-cell launcher, two canisters weigh 1450 lb, two missiles 1100 lb, exhaust control 725 lb, shipboard mounting interface 800 lb; the total for two cells is 4075 lb. The system as a whole requires one missile-launch controller (825 lb) and one electrical interface (242 lb). Each controller can accommodate two FCSs, 16 missiles, and 8 electrical interface units. Mod 1 (2 cells): 465 × 173 × 132 cm (13,278 kg for 16 missiles). Mod 2 (16 cells): 474 × 477 × 417 cm (17,648 kg). Mod 3 (6 missiles): 495 × 376 × 284 cm (8296 kg).

A Mk 48 vertical launcher aboard the Canadian frigate *Montreal* shows exhaust ducting. (H. and L. van Ginderen)

Mk 54 (RIM and Sea Sparrow) for LHDs was canceled in favor of a new EX-58.

Users: Canada (Mod 0 in "City" class), Denmark (Mod 3 in *Flyvefisken* class), Greece (Mod 2 in MEKO frigates), Japan (*Takao*-class destroyers, test ship *Asuka*), Korea (Mod 2 in KDX), Netherlands (Mod 1 in M-class).

Mk 49: RAM (RIM-116) box launcher (21 rnd). Total weight is 8960 lb. Working circle is 129 in, and elevation limits are −25/+80 deg. Because RAM is part of Weapon System EX-31, the launcher is often called EX-31.

Mk 49 RAM launcher, USS *Nassau*, 1995. (Author)

Mk 50: Launching system for SLQ-49 "rubber duck" decoy. Even-numbered Mods (0, 2, 4) include two Mk 166 launchers, one on each side (total weight is 600 lb). Odd-numbered Mods (1, 3, 5) include two Mk 166s on each side (total weight is 1200 lb).

Mk 52: Decoy launcher for the PBC patrol boat, including two six-barrel Mk 137 SRBOC launchers.

Mk 53: Decoy launcher, probably Mk 36 modified to fire Nulka.

AIR-TO-AIR MISSILES

Deletions: ASRAAM (AIM-132: not at present to be carried by Sea Harrier), AAAM (U.S., canceled 1992).

FRANCE

◆ Super R 530

Dimensions: 530F: 26 cm × 3.54 m; span 90 cm. 530D: 26 cm × 3.8 m × 87.5 cm (10.2 × 139.4 × 35.4 in [10.2 × 149.6 × 34.4 in])
Weight: 530F: 250 kg (551 lb); 530D: 265 kg (584 lb)
Warhead: 30+ kg (66+ lb)
Propulsion: Dual-thrust rocket (2-sec boost, 4-sec sustain)
Speed: 530F: Mach 4.5; 530D: Mach 5.0
Range: 530F: 35 km (38,300 yd); ceiling 21,350 m (70,000 ft). 530D: 45 km (49,200 yd); ceiling 24,400 (80,000 ft)

The semiactive R 530, broadly equivalent to the U.S. Sparrow, is the standard French heavy AAM, currently carried by Crusader carrier-based interceptors. The 530F version is carried by the Mirage F-1 fighter with its Cyrano IV X-band monopulse radar. The 530D (compatible with Doppler radar) is carried by the Mirage 2000.

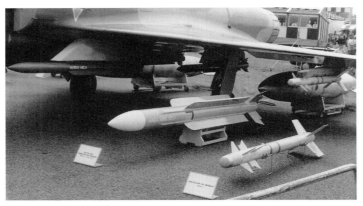

MICA, Super 530D, and Magic under the wing of a Mirage at the 1995 Paris Air Show. (Author)

The Super 530 missile can maneuver at up to 20 Gs (at 17,000–18,000 m in altitude) or 6 Gs (27,000 m altitude). The 530F version can snap-up (rising 9000 m to 27,000 m). The 530D can also snap-down.

Work began in 1958, and R 530 was in service in 1963. Design of the improved Super 530 began in 1968; the first guided firing was in 1975, and production began in 1980. The first Super 530D was delivered in May 1983, and the missile became operational (on board Mirage 2000 fighters) in mid-1986.

By 1990, 4857 R 530, 1486 R 530F, and 507 R 530D had been made or were on order (2330 530D/F had been ordered by 1994, 60% for export). There are 14 R 530 users; the missile was used in the Falklands (where it was fired at excessive range) and in the Iran-Iraq War. France ordered additional Super 530s in 1996 due to delays in the MICA program.

◆ **Magic (R 550)**

> **Dimensions:** 16.4 cm × 274.8 cm; span 66 cm (6.4 × 108.2 × 26.0 in)
> **Weight:** 89 kg; Magic 2: 90.7 kg (196.2 [199.9] lb)
> **Warhead:** 12.5 kg, including 6-kg HE (27.6 [13.2] lb)
> **Propulsion:** Single-thrust rocket, 1.9-sec burn
> **Speed:** Mach 2 +
> **Range:** 10 km; minimum range 300 m (range 1000–11,000 yd)

Matra's Magic is France's current standard IR-guided missile, conceived as a private-venture Sidewinder replacement. It is carried by Super Étendard strike fighters, Crusaders, and Indian Sea Harriers. Magic was first used in combat in the Iran-Iraq War in August 1980. In 1987 a Magic 1 cost $71,280; in 1991 a Magic 2 cost $93,600. As of 1990, more than 9500 had either been made or were on order, for at least 18 countries.

Magic 1 can be launched at airspeeds of up to 700 kt and is credited with a maximum maneuverability of 30 Gs. The IR seeker is nitrogen-cooled. The missile arms 1.8 sec after launch, so minimum range is 0.3 km. Typical range is 2.5 km (2750 yd) at medium altitude, or 10 km at high altitude.

The improved Magic 2 entered production in September 1984. It has a better detector (80–100 times as sensitive) and can be slaved to the aircraft's FCS. Maneuverability is increased to 50 Gs. In February 1990 a Magic 2 was fired by a fighter flying at Mach 1.3 at 20,000 ft, pulling 8 Gs, which was reportedly close to the edge of its flight envelope.

As of 1995, Thomson had produced over 10,500 Magic 1/2 missiles, 789 for export.

◆ **MICA**

> **Dimensions:** 16 × 310 cm (6.1 × 122 in)
> **Weight:** 110 kg (242 lb)
> **Warhead:** 12 kg (26.4 lb)
> **Propulsion:** Solid-fuel rocket
> **Speed:** Mach 4
> **Range:** 50–60 km

MICA is to replace both Magic 2 and Super 530, arming the next-generation French Rafale naval fighter and the Mirage

2000–5. The missile has two interchangeable homing heads, active radar (ADYA seeker) and IIR. Data above refer to the radar version. Like the U.S. AMRAAM, MICA has a preset programmable autopilot and an inertial reference system, for multitarget engagement using mid-course update. The seekers are designed to lock onto targets far off boresight at short range. Matra claims that its long wings particularly suit it to flight at high angles of incidence, for steep climbs and dives (snap-up and snap-down shots). The missile steers by a combination of aerodynamic (tail control) and direct-thrust control (using four vanes in its nozzle). Modes: multitarget engagement at long range (mid-course update), medium-range multitarget engagement (no mid-course update; radar FCS directs the missile to lock on after launch), dogfight, and self-defense. In the last mode the missile automatically locks onto targets as much as 90 deg off boresight, so a strike airplane need not turn away to engage an enemy aircraft. Matra is prime contractor, with radar guidance developed by Electronique Serge Dassault (ESD) and Marconi Defence Systems (which has a 30% share); the IR seeker is being developed by SAT and Matra. Matra points out that MICA is so light that it can be carried on wing as well as fuselage. Rafale should be able to carry six (wing tips and under body).

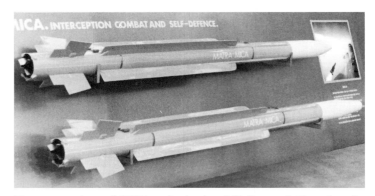

The two versions of MICA, radar (*top*) and IR (*bottom*). Note that the tail fins are very similar to those of Super 530. Control vanes are visible in their exhaust nozzles. (Author)

Studies began in 1979. Matra was awarded a development contract late in 1985, and air-to-air firings began in 1990, from a Mirage 2000. However, the program has encountered serious delays. As of 1994, over 2000 had been ordered, but it seems unlikely that operational missiles will become available until about 2002.

Users: France (for Rafale and Mirage 2000–5; planned deliveries [as of 1996] during the 1997–2002 plan period are 90 navy missiles in 2000–2002 and 125 air force missiles in 2002); Qatar (reportedly up to 1000 ordered, for Mirage 2000–5), Taiwan (for Mirage 2000–5).

GERMANY

BGT, which leads the European Sidewinder production group, is developing a successor missile, IRIS-T (IR Imaging Sidewinder-Tail Controlled), to a new German requirement for a Future Short-Range AAM. It is, then, an alternative to the British ASRAAM and a competitor for AIM-9X (like the U.S. missile, it was inspired by experience with AA-11). Like the U.S. Boxoffice, IRIS eliminates the steering canards of a Sidewinder in favor of clipped tail control fins, in this case individually electrically controlled deltas coupled to vanes in the missile's exhaust stream. Unlike the U.S. airframes, IRIS-T adds fixed mid-body wings for lift. Fixed vortex generators, for high angle of attack agility, replace the earlier canards. The two-pulse rocket motor initially produces limited thrust, so the missile can easily turn sharply in the required direction. The guidance system incorporates a strapdown inertial unit.

A mockup of IRIS-T displayed at the 1995 Paris Air Show. (Author)

The missile's new imaging seeker, suited to off-boresight angles as great as 90 deg, flew captive trials in 1993 and flew in a Sidewinder airframe in 1996. Unlike the imaging FPA of the U.S. missile, IRIS-T uses a linear array (InSb: two staggered rows [to cover gaps between elements] of 64 elements each); a mirror scans the image across it. BGT claims that such a detector costs only a fifth as much as a full staring array, combining its imaging ability (to reject countermeasures) with the image uniformity achieved by scanning, that is, by using the same detector over the whole focal plane (hence avoiding false targets due to different responses by different detectors in different places). To avoid this problem along the length of the array, the seeker uses LF filtering in that direction (the scan across the field is not filtered, as otherwise real targets would be filtered out). BGT argues that the greater theoretical sensitivity of the scanning array is offset by vibration and IR noise due to radome heating. Moreover, LF filtering cannot be applied to a 2D staring array, as it would wipe out real targets. BGT also claims that the linear array enjoys a wider dynamic range (because each element has more chip area to store a charge), hence can pick up weak targets before being saturated by the IR noise of the missile's hot seeker dome. Finally, because it has fewer elements, the linear array cools more quickly, hence needs less cooling gas.

As of 1995, BGT expected to begin a 9-month project definition study some time in 1996 after an MoU was signed with Sweden, Norway, and Italy (Germany would provide more than half the funds); it would be followed by a 54-month FSD phase beginning in 1997. The missile would enter service in 2002 on board Eurofighters (EFA 2000s).

JAPAN

◆ XAAM-4

This active AAM is to replace both Sparrow and Sea Sparrow in the JMSDF. The JFY95 budget included $600M for Mitsubishi to study a surface-launched version; development is to be completed in 1997. Presumably AAM-4 is intended to be comparable to AMRAAM.

RUSSIA

The primary AAM design organization is NPO Vympel. AAM development began in 1954, in a special design bureau (NII-2) which had been formed in 1946 to develop fighter radars. Yakovlev probably developed AA-3, Mikoyan developed AA-4, and Bisnovat (otherwise a jet aircraft developer) developed AA-5 (which was considered as an alternative to SA-N-1), but AAM development was consolidated in the late 1960s into OKB-134, renamed NPO Vympel (Pennant) in the 1980s. Novator (in Ekaterinburg [formerly Sverdlovsk]) is new (it may be possibly the Lyulev OKB). The seekers described below, under R-27, were developed by the Agat Moscow Research Institute.

It was reported in July 1996 that Fakel, otherwise associated only with SAMs, had recently displayed the mockup of a new tail-controlled IIR missile (AAM), 9M100, comparable in size to ASRAAM.

In March 1993 Russia was reported to be developing adaptive warheads for AAMs, that is, warheads that focus blast toward the target. They are carried by the Novator KS-172 (400km AAM), and possibly also by the AA-12; a variant now entering service shows six to eight small EO windows for sensors, which are thought to be laser fuzes used to sense the quadrant the target is in (however, they may also provide all-round proximity fuzing for a more conventional warhead).

The new carrier *Kuznetsov* will probably employ Su-27 (Flanker) fighters, which carry up to 10 missiles, including pairs of AA-10 A/B/C and four AA-8s (Aphids) or AA-11s (Archers). The Yak-38 (Forger) is no longer in service.

◆ AA-8 Aphid (R-60/Type 62)

Dimensions: 13 cm × 2.0 m; span 52 cm (5.1 × 78.7 × 20.5 in)
Weight: 55 kg (121 lb)
Warhead: 6 kg HE (13.2 lb)
Propulsion: Solid-fuel rocket
Speed: Mach 3.0
Range: 7 km (7650 yd)

AA-8 is the Russian equivalent of the modern versions of Sidewinder, replacing the earlier AA-2 Atoll (R-3S). This supplemental fighter weapon and strike aircraft self-defense missile is small enough to be carried on a twin-rail launcher, APU-60-IIM. There are both IR and semiactive radar versions. Data above refer to the IR type. There is some evidence that AA-8 lacks lethality. For example, in October 1988 an AA-8 fired by an Angolan MiG-21 failed to kill a British Aerospace 125 business jet carrying the president of Botswana. The missile cannot be launched head-on. R-60 was accepted for service use about 1975. It has been widely exported. The current version, the improved R-60MK, was designed for very short ranges (minimum range is 400 m; K means Kratkoe-deistviye, short range). This missile is now being replaced by R-73 (AA-11).

An AA-8 (R-60) missile on display at Farnsborough, 1990. In the background are AA-11s and an AA-10. (Author)

◆ AA-10 Alamo (R-27/Type 470)

Dimensions: 26 × 47.8 cm; wingspan 80 cm; finspan 97 cm
Weight: 350 kg
Warhead: 39-kg continuous-rod type
Propulsion: Solid-fuel rocket; boost-sustain in long-range version
Speed: Mach 4.0 (Alamo B: Mach 3.5)
Range: 0.5 to 130 km

Data refer to R-27RE, the current long-range two-stage version. The designation suggests that it was designed specifically for the Su-27. Work began in the early 1970s, and R-27 entered production in 1982. Guidance is inertial with mid-course update (at ranges up to 25 km/30 sec of flight time for the passive radar [and probably the IR], 50 km for the active radar), plus terminal homing (type indicated by suffix: A for active radar, R for passive radar, T for IR). A second suffix, E, indicates a longer booster, for greater range (maximum 130 rather than 80 km). The short boosters have smaller diameters (23 cm vice 26 cm) and shorter wings (77 cm vice 80 cm span). The only active-radar version is R-27AE, announced 1992, intended to engage small targets (such as cruise missiles) down to very low altitude (3 m).

An AA-10 (R-72R) missile on display under the wing of a MiG-29 at Farnsborough, 1990, with Aa-11s outboard. Note the characteristic inverse-tapered wings. (Author)

There is also a short-range IR-guided R-27PS for retrofit to MiG-27 strike fighters.

Target altitude can be 20 m to 27 km (66 to 88,600 ft). Typical launch range is 27 km (0.5 km above refers to an opening target). Maximum target acceleration is 8 g. The R1 version, in production since 1986, uses a 9B-1101K semiactive seeker (presumably monopulse). It locks on at altitudes between 20 m and 25 km at vertical separations of up to 10 km (for target airspeed of up to 3500 km/h, and acceleration up to 8 g). It locks onto a 3m² target at 25 km. The missile can be launched 1 sec after receiving target designation. The monopulse Doppler active radar seeker of the AE version incorporates a programmable computer with up to 32 kbytes of ROM and 32 kbytes of RAM; it weighs 1 kg. Maximum launch range against a 5m² target is 70 km; the missile locks on at 20 km. The radar is ready in 1.5 sec (after having been warmed up for 2 min). Dimensions: 200 × 600 mm (14.5 kg without radome).

The unusual configuration, with inverse-tapered wings abaft small strake foreplanes, and with the usual (but short-span) tail fins, was adopted to confer good maneuverability at high angles of attack.

The main versions are R-27R (Alamo A, 253 kg, 4.0 m long, 25 km launch range), R-27RE (Alamo C, 350 kg, 4.7 m long, 27 km broadside launch range), R-27T (Alamo B, 245 kg, 3.7 m long, 24 km broadside launch range, maximum 70 km), and R-27TE (Alamo D, 348 kg, 4.5 m long, broadside launch range 30 km, maximum 120 km). AA-10 is exported with the MiG-29 fighter (and presumably with the Su-27), so customers include China, Cuba, India, Iran, and Serbia.

◆ **AA-11 Archer (R-73/Type 72)**

Dimensions: 17 × 290 cm; wingspan 51 cm
Weight: 105 kg
Warhead: 7.4-kg continuous rods
Propulsion: Solid-fuel rocket
Speed: Mach 2.5
Range: 30 km nose-on; 0.3 km tail-on

This short-range dogfight missile was first reported in 1986. Performance, demonstrated when it became available to the West following the collapse of East Germany, considerably exceeded Western estimates and reportedly modified the decision to cancel AIM-9R in favor of AIM-9X. R-73 in effect bridges the gap between the short-range R-60 (AA-8) and the long-range R-27 (AA-10). Vympel sometimes calls it RMD (Short-Range Missile). It uses thrust vectoring for very high maneuverability. Target altitude is 20 m to 20,000 m; targets can be designated 45 deg off-axis. Targets can maneuver at up to 12 G. The modified R-73M/Type 72M (RMD-2) can attack targets down to 10 m, and can fire at nose-on targets at 40 km; targets can be designated 60 deg off-axis. At Farnborough in 1990 a Soviet aircraft designer credited this missile with a capability to maneuver at 60 Gs. This missile apparently introduced the off-boresight seeker to Soviet practice, hence the introduction of a helmet sight (to designate) in Su-27 and MiG-29. The export version is R-73E.

AA-11 (R-73, foreground) with AA-10 (R-27) behind it, at the 1992 Moscow Air Show. (S. Zaloga)

In April 1994 Vympel announced that it had already test-fired an AA-11 replacement with a new gimballed nozzle for thrust vectoring; it is broadly equivalent to ASRAAM or to AIM-9X. The design bureau also test-fired a rear-firing R-73 (range 12 km), using an underwing launch rail capable of turning 180 deg. There is some evidence that the "cobra" maneuver practiced at air shows by some Russian test pilots is used (in combination with the helmet sight) to toss an R-73 "over the shoulder" at a pursuing aircraft, while setting up the Russian fighter to escape. Note that the new Su-32FN strike fighter appears to show a rear-facing radar.

◆ **AA-12 (R-77/Type 170)**

Dimensions: 20 × 360 cm; span 35 cm
Weight: 175 kg
Warhead: 18 kg
Propulsion: Rocket
Range: Approx. 90 km forward-aspect, 35 km rear-aspect

Vympel's new missile is the Russian equivalent of AMRAAM, to attack look-up and snap-down targets. It uses the first active radar seeker in a Russian tactical AAM. The most unusual feature is its lattice tail-fins, which look like honeycombs perpendicular to the line of flight. Each honeycomb consists of a mesh of narrow wings. Similar fins are on the SS-N-15 ASW missile. They should retain attached air flow at angles of attack as high as 50–60 deg. Because individual vanes can be close without interacting, a large effective wing area can be obtained in a small space. At Mach 4, such a lattice can achieve 3 times as much lift as a monoplane wing in the same space. The lattice enjoys practically a constant coefficient of lift at varying angles of attack throughout the speed range, a particularly useful feature when the center of gravity shifts significantly in flight (due to fuel burnout). The lattice wing is also much smaller, hence has smaller hinge moments, and needs smaller actuators. Maximum target maneuver is 12 G. Further planned improvements are installation of an IR guidance system and an enlarged motor for maximum range of as much as 150 km (vs. AEW aircraft).

Novator's 400km air-to-air missile, R-72, shown at the 1993 Moscow Air Show. The dark line indicates the sensor of a proximity fuze. (S. Zaloga)

An R-77 (AA-12) missile shows its unusual honeycomb (lattice) tail fins, at the 1992 Moscow Air Show. (S. Zaloga)

AA-12 was first shown at Minsk in February 1992, and was first delivered in the fall of 1992; at Moscow in 1992 it was called AAM-AE. This missile was exported to Malaysia and to Vietnam for those countries' MiG-29s. NPO Vympel displayed a vertically launched version, for ships or ground troops, at Abu Dhabi in February 1993. In 1996 Fakel announced a naval version, the Poliment system (9M96 missile).

As of 1994, Vympel was working on an extended-range rocket/ramjet version of RVV-AE (R-77), RVV-AE-PL, weighing 225 kg versus 175 kg, and adding 40% to the original range of 110 km. A surface-launched version, RVV-AE-ZPK, lacks wings but has a large-diameter rocket motor.

◆ R-72/Type 172/KS-172 (No NATO designation)

Novator showed its new R-72 missile (export designation AAM-L, prototype designation probably R-172) at Abu Dhabi in February 1993. Like the shorter-range R-77, it combines commandable mid-course inertial guidance with an active terminal seeker. It has conventional tail fins and a large-diameter booster. Development began in 1991. An Su-27 can carry seven, but the intended platform is the Su-35. Dimensions: 0.514 × 6.0 m (750 kg with 75-kg adaptive fragmentation warhead). Maximum launch range is 400 km (216 nm), and the missile can be ordered to turn as much as 180 deg after launch. Target speed can be up to 4000 km/h (2160 kt); maximum target acceleration is 12.25 g; altitude can be 3 to 30,000 m. R-72 can engage targets with radar cross-sections as small as 0.05m² (AAMs). It can be catapult-launched between 700 and 2500 km/h (380 and 1250 kt) and between 50 and 17,500 m.

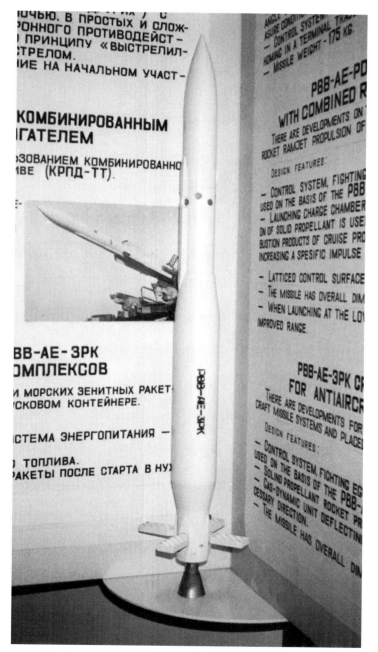

A model of the rocket-ramjet version of R-77, at the 1993 Moscow Air Show. (S. Zaloga)

◆ Air-to-Air ARM

See AS-17 air-to-surface missile.

UNITED STATES

The FY92/93 R&D program (as planned in February 1991) included a breadboard wide-band active array cued/supercued FCS and an integrated active array for guidance and fuzing for 8in-dia (Sparrow-size) missiles (a joint program with the Army and Air Force). A 200-element 5–18-GHz solid-state active array antenna had already been made under the FY90 program, and the integrated guidance-fuze concept tested. The FY91 program included new efforts at lock-on after launch guidance and also initial work on a diamond IR dome for future fast IR missiles (for FY93 survival tests). The FY95 program included a new start, a Passive/Active Fuze (PACT) to deal with fast highly maneuverable low observable low-fliers.

Effort is also being concentrated on more lethal warheads, which would make lighter and hence more maneuverable missiles more effective. One possibility is reactive fragments, which would burn as well as shatter a target. There is also interest in directional warheads (the program is the Combined Advanced Aimed Warhead/Advanced Aimed Fuze).

◆ AMRAAM (AIM-120A)

Dimensions: 7 × 144 in (wing span 21 in, tail span 25 in)
Weight: 335 lb
Warhead: 50-lb class
Propulsion: Solid-fuel boost-sustain rocket
Speed: Reported approx. Mach 4.0 (average 600 m/sec)
Range: Reported 60,000–80,000 yd

Hughes's fire-and-forget Advanced Medium-Range Air-to-Air Missile is intended to replace Sparrow. This much lighter missile may be carried in greater numbers; it also offers a fighter the ability to engage several targets simultaneously. A commandable autopilot set at launch time and then updated by data link flies the missile into a basket; terminal homing is by the missile's X-band pulse-Doppler seeker. AMRAAM provides F/A-18s with the capability to engage multiple targets, and is carried by the modernized Royal Navy Sea Harrier FA.2 fighter.

AMRAAM (AIM-120A) with Phoenix and Maverick in the background. (Hughes)

Hughes's FMRAAM as displayed at Farnborough, 1996. For a time it appeared that the product-improved version of AMRAAM would be a ramjet like this one, and if Hughes wins the British FMRAAM competition that may yet happen. (S. Zaloga)

With the decline of the F-14 program, an evolved AMRAAM is a potential Phoenix successor. The Navy supports development of a ducted-rocket propulsor (a ramjet version was proposed to meet the British medium range missile requirement, for a Skyflash follow-on). Other product improvements are replacement of current electronics by custom VLSI chips to reduce drastically the number of circuit boards (heat production is to be reduced by 90%) and replacement of the mechanical gyro by a laser ring gyro.

The first production AMRAAM missile was delivered on 26 October 1988. The program suffered from high unit cost and limited reliability. For example, USAF acceptances stopped February 1990 after failures due to vibration of the F-15s carrying the missile. In May 1991 the DAB (Defense Acquisition Board) approved low-rate AMRAAM production (1635 additional missiles). High unit cost seems to have stymied suggestions that a surface-launched version of AMRAAM could replace Sea Sparrow. On the other hand, Hughes and Kongsberg (then NFT) developed a mobile surface-to-air version, NASAMS (Norwegian Advanced Surface-to-Air Missile System) or ADSAMS. Each battery consists of three radars, three fire-control centers, and nine six-missile launchers, the controlling radars being based on the Hughes TPQ-36.

In 1982 Raytheon was chosen as a second-source supplier.

AIM-120B is a modified version for easier production. AIM-120C has clipped wings for stowage within the missile bay of the F-22; it has also flown on board F/A-18s. For some years there has been interest in a longer-range version using a ramjet, and Atlantic Research and Hercules have developed a variable-flow ducted rocket engine. Hughes has proposed a ramjet version for the current British FMRAAM (Future Medium-Range AAM) competition (against Meteor, an evolved version of a ramjet version [S225X] of an active Sparrow, the old Skyflash), using an Aerospatiale engine. Both the U.S. Navy and the Air Force have expressed interest, but have not made funds available. The British have justified FMRAAM on the ground that their new EFA fighter is not stealthy enough to get close enough to potential targets to use existing short-range weapons, and that it is better to concentrate on long-range shots. As of the fall of 1996, it appears that U.S. interest is more concentrated on very high missile acceleration, for quick kills at relatively short ranges.

The U.S. program originally called for 24,320 missiles. However, by early 1992 that had been cut to 13,038, of which 6752 had been funded through FY95. As of August 1992, plans called for about 6600 of the planned missiles to have warhead improvements for greater lethality. U.S. purchases: Air Force/Navy: FY87, 180/–; FY88, 400/–; FY89, 874/26; FY90, 815/85; FY91, 510/300; FY92, 630/191; FY93, 1000/140; FY94, 1007/75; FY95, 413/106. As of early 1995 the Navy planned to buy 115 in FY96 and 220 in FY97. Unit cost in February 1992 was $982,000, compared to a 1989 estimated export price of $475,000. Plans for European license production, as part of the agreement under which the United States would buy a European ASRAAM, fell through; all export missiles are U.S.-made. As of 1 January 1995, 5228 missiles had been ordered for export, the great bulk of them during 1994.

Users: Belgium (letter of offer issued for 400 missiles), Denmark (150 missiles and 70 launchers, ordered 1990 for F-16s), Finland, Germany (600 missiles in FY90), Israel (letter of offer issued, no numbers available), Italy (letter of offer issued for 33 missiles), Korea (at least 286 missiles), Norway (total of 1332 for NASAMS, operational 1995; sale of 100 AAMs approved but not yet delivered), Saudi Arabia (letter of offer issued, no numbers available), Spain (negotiating for 200 missiles), Sweden (100 for Gripens), Switzerland (letter of agreement, numbers not available), Turkey (156 missiles), United Kingdom (210 bought for Sea Harrier FA.2; letter of agreement for a total of 330), United States. In 1995 the U.S. government cleared AMRAAM for sale to Thailand. As of the fall of 1995, Malaysia and Singapore were negotiating to buy AMRAAM, but no action had been taken. AMRAAM was deployed to the Gulf in 1991 but was not used in action.

◆ Phoenix (AIM-54)

Dimensions: 15 in × 13 ft (span 36 in)
Weight: 1008 lb (985 lb for AIM-54A)
Warhead: 133 lb
Propulsion: Solid-fuel rocket (single-pulse)
Speed: Mach 5.0 (Mach 4.3 for AIM-54A)
Range: 80 nm (minimum 2.0 nm) (AIM-54A: maximum 72.5 nm, minimum 2.1 nm)
Launch Altitude: 60,000 ft maximum (-54A: 48,800 ft)
Missile Max Altitude: 100,000 ft (-54A: 81,400 ft)

Data apply to AIM-54C version.

Hughes's Phoenix is the longest-range AAM in operation. It is carried only by F-14 Tomcats, guided by their AWG-9 and APG-71 radars. The missile's autopilot flies it into a basket, within which it is semiactively guided on an intermittent basis. The missile uses its short-range X-band seeker for terminal guidance. Typically the missile flies an up-and-over trajectory, gaining momentum near the target for terminal maneuvers. On the other hand, reportedly the column of smoke made by the missile motor provides a target with considerable warning. Six missiles can share the single tracker-illuminator of an F-14 fighter. Although conceived as an antibomber weapon, Phoenix can shoot down antiship missiles: in June 1983 it was reported that Phoenixes shot down 11 of 11 Harpoons in a test.

Phoenix missiles carried by an F-14A fighter. (U.S. Navy)

Four engagements give some idea of AIM-54/AWG-9 capability. In one, an F-14 (at Mach 0.7, 31,500 ft) fired four missiles in close succession from 30nm range at four of five Mach 0.6 targets at 20,000–25,000 ft in a wave-front formation 20 nm wide, scoring one direct hit and three passes within lethal range.

In a second exercise, an F-14 attacked a simulated bomber using ECM at Mach 1.5 at 50,000 ft. The missile flew an up-and-over trajectory from a range of 110 nm, reaching a peak altitude of 103,500 ft, and flying 72.5 nm to hit the closing target.

In a third exercise a simulated MiG-25 Foxbat (an AQM-37A at Mach 2.2 at 82,000 ft) was hit from 35 nm, the missile climbing about 36,000 ft.

Finally, an F-14 at 10,000 ft killed a BQM-34A simulating a cruise missile that was flying at 50 ft, from a 22nm launch range.

AIM-54C (there was no -54B), the second production version, has digital rather than analog electronics. The missile can be programmed for better target discrimination in stream raids, for better capability against crossing targets, and for better capability against an opening target. It has better ECCM. Motor improvements offer greater range, altitude, and maneuverability. The fuze (TDD) is better adapted to small or very low-altitude targets in clutter such as chaff. AIM-54C+ (deliveries begun March 1986) adds internal heaters.

Development of a further improved AIM-54C++ began in August 1987. It has a high-powered TWT (adapted from that of AMRAAM, giving 10 times the power of the earlier version), a reprogrammable memory (RPM), and a new low-sidelobe antenna with better electronics. The RPM and new software were tested in shots in September and December 1989, and the full upgrade was first tested in August 1990. It was incorporated in new-production missiles and was also produced in retrofit kit form.

The basic concept of a very long-range AAM was developed in 1960, and Hughes was selected in August 1962. The first guided flight (from an A-3) was in May 1966. About 2500 AIM-54As were made in 1972–81, including missiles for Iran (some of which apparently fell into Soviet hands following the fall of the shah). No reliable reports of Phoenix engagements during the Iran-Iraq War have come to light; reportedly the Iranians used their F-14As as airborne radar-control platforms.

AIM-54C's engineering development began in October 1976, with first deliveries of development missiles in August 1979. Production began late in 1982, and AIM-54C was operational in January 1984. The 1000th AIM-54C (including more than 600 AIM-54C+) was delivered 27 October 1988. AIM-54C procurement: 45 for RDT&E, 90 pilot production, then 90 in FY83, 265 in each of FY84–86, 205 in FY87, 350 in FY88, 450 in FY89, and 420 in FY90 (last year procured). Deliveries from Raytheon (second source) began early 1988. In all, 2528 AIM-54Cs were bought. As of May 1991, 4213 missiles were on hand, but only 2000 were considered "warfighting capable"; most of the others were obsolescent -54As. Some Cs were found to have defective safing/arming circuits, and -54As were cannibalized for their rocket motors. Approximate unit costs: AIM-54A, $750,000; AIM-54C in FY83, $796,000, but in FY84, $681,000.

◆ Sidewinder (AIM-9)/Sea Chaparral

Dimensions: 5 x 112.2 in (canard span 15 in, wing span 24.8 in)
Weight: 188 lb
Warhead: 25 lb
Propulsion: Boost-sustain
Speed: Mach 2.5
Range: 10,000–20,000 yd

Data apply to AIM-9L version.

The Sidewinder is virtually the Free World's standard short-range AAM. It has also been copied by the Russians and by the Chinese. Several other countries have developed externally similar weapons. Sidewinder makes very few demands on the airplane carrying it. The seeker is normally caged to look dead ahead (in some cases it is slaved to the airplane's search radar). When an IR source enters its FOV, the missile generates a tone. In some aircraft the missile could begin to track the target before leaving the rail, generating a chirping tone in the pilot's earphones. These audio cues, standard for all Sidewinders, were essential since the pilot could not look away during a dogfight. Only with the advent of HUDs have Sidewinders introduced visual cues (a digital display of seeker-head position and an "in range" cue based on programmed launch-zone equations). Without such cues, it is very difficult for a pilot to know whether the target is actually within the missile's engagement zone. Tests during the Vietnam War showed that the missile often failed to hit its target for exactly that reason.

Sidewinder (AIM-9L). (U.S. Navy)

Developed by the U.S. Naval Weapons Center at China Lake, Sidewinder was made by Philco-Ford (then by Ford Aeroneutronics, which was bought by Loral). It was made under license in West Germany by Fluggeraetewerk Bodensee GmbH (now Bodenseewerk Geraete Technik, BGT).

Current U.S. versions are developments of the third-generation AIM-9L (the first generation was AIM-9B; the second generation, with a more powerful rocket motor, was AIM-9C/D/G/H; AIM-9E/J were rebuilt AIM-9Bs for the Air Force, combining the original rocket motor and 25-lb blast-fragmentation warhead with later-generation seekers). The -9B motor (Mk 17) burned for about 2 sec; range at high altitude was about 2.6 nm at Mach 1.7, decreasing to 4000 ft at low altitude. Minimum firing range for a subsonic airplane attacking another at the same speed and altitude is 3000 ft (reduced or increased by 300 ft for every 0.1 Mach difference in speed). The Navy AIM-9C/D had a 25-lb continuous-rod warhead (lethal radius 17 ft) and a new Mk 36 motor, which burned for 5 sec (it also used a longer-burning gas generator, 60 vs. 20 sec); range increased to 11.5 nm. The combination of a new seeker (which could be used at greater angles to a target's tail) and new broader-chord fins turned the relatively sluggish Sidewinder into a snap-shot dogfight weapon. AIM-9G had its seeker slaved to the fighter's radar. AIM-9H introduced double-delta wings for better maneuverability (and a new faster-tracking seeker).

AIM-9L, a joint-service weapon based on AIM-9H, was the version that proved so successful in the Falklands War, when British Sea Harriers used it to shoot down at least 25 Argentine aircraft. It introduced all-aspect attack capability (ALASCA), presumably homing from ahead on the heat plume visible behind the target. There is a new guidance and control group (DSQ-29) incorporating the forward-biased guidance introduced in AIM-9H: presumably proportional navigation (using a gyro as reference) has replaced the earlier pursuit navigation. Forward-biasing will cause the missile to hit an airplane near its cockpit, where the target is most vulnerable. It will make the missile tend to ignore any decoy projected aft. This version is capable of engaging violently maneuvering targets, and effective against fast aircraft even at medium range. It has a new active-laser proximity fuze (DSU-21). The warhead is a new 20.8-lb annular blast-fragmentation type, using preformed rod fragments.

A magnesium-fluoride window covers an argon-cooled indium-antimonide detector that operates in two colors (i.e., at both long and short wavelengths). Unlike previous missiles, this one uses a fixed reticule, with a moving tilted mirror (rotating Cassegrain system) performing a rosette scan. This version has an internal coolant tank, so it can be carried by Air Force aircraft (U.S. naval aircraft have coolant bottles in their missile launch rails).

AIM-9L/I is a modified AIM-9L, developed by BGT. One of four electronic modules is changed, for better countermeasures resistance, comparable to or better than that of AIM-9M. AIM-9L/I was tested for the first time at China Lake in the summer of 1990, achieving three successes out of three shots.

AIM-9M, the last U.S. production version, is a -9L with improved countermeasures resistance and clutter rejection. It incorporates a Hughes closed-cycle cooler and a new smokeless motor. Production began in 1981. Weight is 189.6 lb. Procurement of AIM-9M Plus (AIM-9M-8/9) upgrade kits began in FY93 with a contract for 1100 (to Raytheon). It has a new CCM seeker.

The previous AIM-9J had partially solid-state electronics and double-delta wings with more powerful actuators, plus a longer-burning gas generator (for flights lasting up to 40 sec, but not the 60 sec of the -9D and its descendants). Maximum range is reported as 15,850 yd. Overall range is sacrificed for high acceleration to deal with fast targets. About 6700 were delivered to the Air Force by Ford Aerospace about 1970. Some were rebuilt AIM-9B/E. AIM-9J1 is a new-build missile, -9J2 a converted -9B, and -9J3 a product-improved version. Dimensions: 5 × 120.9 in, span 22 in, weight 172 lb.

Current export versions are AIM-9N (a rebuilt -9J, formerly designated -9J1), with three redesigned circuit boards; and AIM-9P, a version of AIM-9M (which may be a rebuilt -9B/E/J). AIM-9P1 introduced a laser proximity fuze in place of the earlier IR fuze. -9P2 has a reduced-smoke motor. -9P3 has an IR fuze, a reduced-smoke motor, and a stronger warhead and guidance/control section; this version employs a new explosive that is less sensitive to high temperatures. -9P4 has increased IR acquisition

and guidance capability and an optimized fuze. -9P5 has better ECCM. Weight is 170 lb. There is also AIM-9S, originally AIM-9MX, a stripped version for Turkey (sale of 310 was announced January 1990).

BGT's AIM-9JUL1 combines highly reliable AIM-9L subassemblies such as the all-aspect seeker, the guidance electronics, and the coolant-bottle section with the control-servo section of the AIM-9J/N/P to form a new guidance and control unit, which is attached to the unchanged body of the AIM-9J/N/P missile. It offers performance and reliability comparable to that of AIM-9L at a significantly lower price. AIM-9TELL is a modernized AIM-9 with BGT's new seeker (Test und Experimenteleinheit Luft-Luft), developed for the ASRAAM missile, then rejected when BAe took over the program. TELL apparently gained support when AA-11 missiles were examined after the fall of East Germany.

AIM-9R (initially called a product-improved -9M) would have been the follow-on version, a -9L/M with a new near-visual seeker (to improve clutter and decoy rejection). It was conceived as an interim development pending the appearance of an entirely new AIM-9X missile. The Air Force balked at the price and did not want a missile without night capability (its F-16s could not fire Sparrows). It also feared that procurement would abort the AIM-9X program (which was intended to produce a missile suited to stealthy fighters like the coming F-22). Too, revelations of AA-11 performance suggested that AIM-9R was altogether inadequate. Russian-made decoys seemed effective against AIM-9M (3 were successfully decoyed during the Gulf War, out of 16 fired). Given the Air Force withdrawal, the Navy comptroller deleted AIM-9R from the FY93 budget, despite the aviation community's objections.

Another factor in any decision was the role of a helmet-mounted sight. As long ago as 1985, the Russians had introduced a very effective one in their MiG-29 and Su-27, to exploit a missile whose seeker could look far off-boresight. The Air Force in particular seems to have downplayed the significance of both missile and sight until U.S. pilots began flying MiG-29s in 1991. Using U.S. tactics, pilots flying the MiG with the helmet could acquire targets in 30 times the volume of air available to an F-15, and estimated exchange rates greatly favored the Russian fighter. German pilots flying MiG-29s against F-16s (which are more maneuverable) got the first shot most of the time, even though the F-16s were clean, whereas the MiGs were carrying belly tanks, six missile pylons, and two training rounds. Western tactics did pay off in many-on-many fights, in which limited target tracking by the MiG was a major disadvantage. As it happened, rigid Soviet tactics hardly exploited the combination. Apparently the U.S. Navy was far more insistent on obtaining an effective helmet-mounted sight and a very maneuverable dogfighting missile (the Air Force view favored long-range engagements with missiles like AMRAAM).

Ultimately both services agreed to use a seeker slaved to a helmet sight.

AIM-9X requirements are greater seeker capability (target detection against a blue sky at 8–10 nm, 4 nm against ground clutter); better data processing, and greater agility (with large gymbal angles to look over a full hemisphere). The airframe must fit inside the weapon bay of a stealthy fighter such as the F-22 and the next-generation JSF. Presumably it will use a long-wave IR (8–12 micron) staring seeker (for better sensitivity against a blue sky) to detect aircraft at all aspects, rather than rely on engine heat.

A series of black programs for a Sidewinder successor began in 1986; presumably their existence helps explain why the U.S. government abandoned plans to buy the British ASRAAM. Have Thrust remains classified. Top Hat was a U.S. test of the Hughes 128 × 128 HgCdTe FPA developed for ASRAAM. Box Office (Loral/Raytheon) and Boa (China Lake) were more agile airframes with digital autopilots, designed to fit within weapons bays. They are the alternative airframes for the AIM-9X fly-off, announced on 20 December 1994 (for completion in mid-1996): Hughes (using a modified Top Hat seeker in a 5.6 × 115in airframe) vs. Raytheon (using the Box Office airframe with a pro-

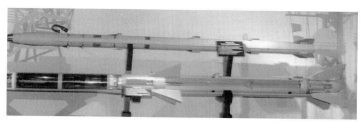

Box Office, as displayed by Raytheon at the 1993 Navy League show. Below it is a cut-away AMRAAM. (Author)

A model of Raytheon's AIM-9X candidate is shown at Farnborough, 1996. The nose rotates around the missile axis to track crossing targets. The airframe is Box Office. (S. Zaloga)

prietary wide-angle seeker) versus BAe's ASRAAM (which has a 60-deg off-boresight capability). Hughes is teamed with Texas Instruments and BAe. Raytheon is teamed with Honeywell (for the helmet), Lockheed Fort Worth, and GEC-Marconi.

The demonstration/validation fly-off may be limited to new seekers and control sections without new airframes; hopefully AIM-9X will use as much of the existing AIM-9 inventory as possible, certainly including the 5in motor, warhead, and safing/arming device. Even so, there is some fear that AIM-9X will be impractical and overpriced, perhaps twice as expensive as its predecessors. Some have suggested that high off-boresight angles are not really needed, that something closer to 20 deg than to the desired 90 deg would be quite sufficient. That might be provided at about $10,000 per missile, in the form of an autopilot (to solve problems of gyro tumble at high angles of attack), together with different seeker scan techniques and other forms of ECCM.

Of the airframes, Box Office is essentially a canard-less tail-controlled (electrically actuated) AIM-9M (using the Mk 36 Mod 11 motor). A future version might have a faceted low-observable body. Tail control makes the missile much more maneuverable, and the drastic reduction in drag (the tail is quite small) doubles the flight envelope. The autopilot makes for aircraft-style bank-to-turn tail control instead of missile-style skid-to-turn. A Look and Shoot program combined a Honeywell helmet sight with a Raytheon high-angle low Mach (number) (HALM) seeker on the Box Office airframe: a target 67 deg off-boresight (maneuvering at 3 G) was shot down. Box Office 2 added jet vane thrust vectoring, increasing maneuverability (turn rate 60–100 deg/sec, 5–7 times that of AIM-9M) to halve minimum launch range for off-boresight targets. For example, on 27 July 1994 an F-16 flying at Mach 0.87 shot down a QF-106 flying at Mach 0.87, maneuvering at 5 G, and 57 deg off-boresight. The missile achieved a 63-deg angle of attack (AIM-9M operates mainly at 10 deg or less), and turned in a radius of 880 ft. Dimensions: 5 × 122 in, tailspan 11 in, weight 185 lb, warhead 9.44 lb.

Boa is a simpler alternative with clipped canards: Boa-M is an AIM-9M with the smaller canards of a -9D and half-size tail fins, hence with reduced inherent stability. Late in 1990 a Boa-M hit an F-86 drone from a range of 2 miles (having been fired off center). This shot demonstrated not only the practicality of the re-

duced-size missile but also its greater agility. Dimensions: 5 × 123 in; tailspan 16 in, weight 205 lb, warhead 9.5 lb.

Hughes is offering a Box Office airframe with the IR detector built for the British ASRAAM, in a conventional hemispherical radome. Raytheon is offering much the same airframe, but with an unusual flat angled window which turns (about the missile axis) to cover the full hemisphere around the nose of the missile. It also offers a faster-burning motor. Raytheon's argument is that, at the high speeds now desired, any curved radome will heat unevenly, distorting the IR image at the detector. Better to adopt a flat window, the heat effect on which is easier to compensate. The flat window offers other advantages as well. It is relatively easy to make and thus to replace (missile windows suffer from debris hitting the airplane as it rolls on the ground); it can even be rolled up toward the wing when the airplane takes off, to avoid damage. It offers a very wide-angle view (AIM-9X is supposed to engage targets as much as 90 deg off boresight). Too, because it is off-center, it may be adaptable to a dual-mode (IR-radar) seeker. Raytheon's choice is based at least partly on the perception that, as of 1995–96, U.S. military attention was concentrated on short-range very high acceleration missiles for quick kills against targets that might not be detected until they were quite close. To this end, the company is offering a modified version of Box Office using the energetic ND-10 dual-pulse (boost-sustain) motor (162 mm dia rather than the 127mm of the existing Sidewinder) developed by Rafael for its new Python 4 AAM (Hughes is apparently limiting itself to the existing Sidewinder motor).

In FY85 Sidewinder flyaway unit cost was $55,000. Recent procurement by the Navy: FY84, 350; FY85, 1000; FY86, 2120; FY87, 627; FY88, 288; none in FY89. Total production run, approximately: prototypes, 361; AIM-9B, 80,627; -9C, 1019; -9D, 1036; -9E, 5000 (rebuilds); -9G, 2120; -9H, 7736; -9J, 10,000; -9L, 18,718; -9M, 25,007; -9P 4/5, 8956; -9A/B by BGT, 15,802; -9L by BGT, 17,026; -9P for Egypt under license, 1638 through 1993, production continuing; -9L under license by Mitsubishi, 4486 through 1993. Total U.S. production through 1993 was 146,810 missiles (but this may include some double counting).

Reportedly, it would take about four months and $18M to triple the current production rate under mobilization conditions.

In all, 452 Sidewinders were fired in combat in Vietnam, for a net single-shot kill probability (as published in 1980) of 0.18. In 1980, using AIM-9L, the U.S. Navy expected a single-shot kill probability of 0.50, the U.S. Air Force 0.285. That year OSD estimated that Sidewinder kill probability was 0.15 against a low-flying fighter and 0.30 against a high flier; comparable estimated figures against a bomber were 0.20 and 0.40. Recent experience suggests that these are rather conservative estimates.

Users: Argentina, Australia, Bahrein (-9P), Belgium (-9M), Brazil, Canada, Chile, Denmark (-9L), Egypt (-9L/-9P3), France (navy), Germany (-9L/M), Greece (-9P4), Indonesia (-9P), Iran, Israel (-9L), Italy (-9L), Japan (-9L), Jordan, Kenya, Kuwait, Malaysia (-9P4), Morocco, Netherlands (-9M), New Zealand, Norway (-9L), Oman (-9P/9P4), Pakistan (-9L), Philippines, Portugal, Saudi Arabia (-9L/P/P3), Singapore, South Africa, South Korea (-9P4), Spain, Sweden (-9L as RB 74), Switzerland (-9P3/P4), Taiwan, Thailand (-9P), Tunisia, Turkey (-9L/S), UAE, United Kingdom (-9G/L), United States, Venezuela, Yemen. AIM-9B was made under license by a European consortium headed by BGT (Germany, Italy, Norway, United Kingdom), and by Mitsubishi (since 1981).

Chapparal is a surface-launched version of Sidewinder. To reduce drag, two of the usual four wing rollerons are omitted. The naval version, Sea Chapparal, is used only by the Taiwan navy. It is fired from a 4-rnd turret, with eight more missiles stowed for ready use. The operator locks onto the target using a stabilized optical sight, and the system can be improved by adding a FLIR; targets can also be designated by other ship sensors. Range is about 2.2 nm.

The missile is MIM-72. Reportedly, the Taiwanese versions are MIM-72C, -72C/R, and -72F. MIM-72C, developed in 1970–74, has an all-aspect seeker, a larger warhead, and a radar (Doppler) proximity fuze. The addition of a two-color rosette-

Sea Chapparal on board a Taiwanese destroyer. (Republic of China Navy)

scan seeker (as in AIM-9L) and a smokeless motor resulted in MIM-72C/R (rebuilt MIM-72C) and the production MIM-72F.

Users: Taiwan (destroyers, *La Fayette*–class frigates, the LSD *Cheng Hai*, the new large transports, and the new replenishment ship *Wu Yi*; MIM-72C, -72C/R, and -72F versions). The Vietnam-era mountings are being refurbished. Plans to replace Chapparal with the indigenously developed Tien Chen have apparently been dropped.

◆ Sparrow (AIM-7)

Dimensions: 8.03 × 141.5 in (wing 24.65 in folded, 40.6 in open; tail span 24.3 in)
Weight: 510 lb
Warhead: 86-lb continuous-rod WEU-3/B
Propulsion: Rocket boost-glide
Speed: Mach 4.0
Range: Depends on guidance radar (24–28 nm air-to-air for AIM-7M).

Data apply to AIM-7M.

Sparrow (AIM-7) is the standard U.S. radar-guided AAM, supplemented by Phoenix (AIM-54) on F-14 fighters and by AMRAAM (AIM-120). As a semiactive missile, Sparrow requires a large illuminating radar on the fighter, and the firing airplane must illuminate the target all the way from launch to kill. However, because AMRAAM is so expensive, Sparrow development and production may continue for some considerable time.

Sparrows and a Sidewinder carried under an F-14. (U.S. Navy)

In Vietnam Sparrow's long range was something of an embarrassment since without very reliable IFF a long-range missile would inevitably destroy numerous friendly aircraft (which were, after all, the great majority of all aircraft in the area). Special attention to IFF procedure paid off heavily in the Gulf War, in which many air-to-air kills were made by Sparrows.

Sparrow single-shot kill probability in Vietnam was only 9%.

By 1980, however, the U.S. Navy estimated Sparrow's single-shot kill probability as 35%, and the corresponding Air Force estimate was 28.5%. OSD estimated 15% against a fighter at low altitude, 35% against a fighter at high altitude; corresponding figures against a bomber were 20% and 56%. Pre–Gulf War performance by U.S. Sparrows was, however, disappointing: five out of six missiles failed during engagements with Libyan aircraft in 1981 and 1989 and with an Iranian F-4 in 1987. However, in the Gulf War 23 Iraqi aircraft, 69% of the total, were shot down by Sparrows. Figures from Israeli combat use have not been published.

Current versions are all based on the post-Vietnam AIM-7F, proposed in 1963 as Advanced Sparrow III, an alternative to Phoenix. Development began in January 1972, and the first production contract was awarded (to Raytheon) on 31 October 1975. More compact modular solid-state electronics made space for a bigger motor and for a heavier warhead. This missile combined a new dual-thrust Mk 58 motor (3.5-sec burn, total impulse 30,800 lb-sec) for much longer aerodynamic range (with energy for snap-up shots) with new proportional-navigation guidance logic compatible with pulse-Doppler (rather than CW) fighter radars, such as AWG-9 and APG-65. The missile guidance unit is provided with a target range before launch, and it updates that range by calculating target speed (from Doppler: it compares reflected frequency with reference frequency, as received on rear-facing antennas). A range gate is used to reject decoys. Effective range depended partly on the power of the fighter radar: 38 nm from an F-14, 24 nm with the F-4 radar (the F/A-18 radar is presumably comparable).

AIM-7M (for monopulse) uses a monopulse seeker and adds an active (presumably laser rather than radar) fuze, the first missile-borne programmable digital computer in the series, and an autopilot. Because the autopilot can fly the missile a considerable distance before it requires illumination for guidance, missiles can be fired at several different targets in sequence, illumination being used only for mid-course and terminal homing. The autopilot can also fly the missile along an energy-efficient trajectory. The missile computer uses EEPROM memory; reprogramming requires that the missile be decanned, the computer pulled out, and its EEPROMs changed and burned in. A reprogrammed missile must be tested after modification. Full-scale production was approved on 12 December 1982, the first missile having been test-fired in April 1980.

In 1985 the U.S. Navy reportedly proposed a product-improved AIM-7X as an alternative to AMRAAM, using an uplink to the autopilot without the expensive active seeker. This version would have had improved low-altitude guidance (LAG), superior subclutter visibility, a new missile-borne computer and an internal digital data bus for a better interface to the airborne FCS before launch. The new computer uses ERPROM memory, so it can be reprogrammed from the data bus. In 1987 Raytheon won a $19.6M contract for this AIM-7P. Raytheon claims that the operational ready rate and reliability are double the specified requirements.

The next version, AIM-7R, was displayed at the 1991 U.S. Navy League show. The main advance is the addition of an IR sensor. Because the missile flies a proportional-navigation energy-efficient course, it tends not to point directly at the target; the radar dish points off to one side. That leaves room for an IR sensor in the nose. The seeker combination was developed under the joint Raytheon/General Dynamics MHIP (Missile-Homing Improvement Program). MHIP also applies to the Standard Missile (SM-2 Block IIIB, which has its IR sensor in a side fairing). MHIP required a considerable increase in computer capacity, mainly for IR signal processing. AIM-7R's requirements were developed while the AIM-7P computer was being redone. It was redesigned to free space for three IR processing boards. Total computer power is an order of magnitude greater than in the earlier -7M. The new front end is wholly retrofittable to existing -7M missiles. The tentative plan is to retrofit existing weapons, beginning with the earliest -7Ms.

Other proposed Sparrow improvements include advanced fuzing against low-observable targets (and a dual mode RF/IR fuze) and greater lethality by adding the effect of detonating unexpended fuel to the warhead.

Production: AIM-7F, 5000. Recent Navy procurement (including RIM-7): FY84, 695; FY85, 1671; FY86, 1948; FY87, 1716; FY88, 600 (none requested, directed because of delays in AMRAAM); FY89, 450 (last bought). The Navy plans to upgrade its AIM-7Fs to -7M standards. In March 1987 the reported requirement for Sparrow was 7988 for the Navy and 6321 for the Air Force. At that time the maximum production rate from two sources was 250 missiles per month. Unit cost (FY83) was $198,209.

Users: Canada (CF-18), Egypt, Finland (F/A-18), Greece, Iran, Israel, Japan, Korea (F-4), Kuwait (F/A-18), Saudi Arabia (F-15), Spain (F/A-18), Switzerland (F/A-18), Turkey, United States. Sparrow has been license-built by Selenia and by Mitsubishi. The Selenia Aspide (see above under SAMs) uses the AIM-7E airframe but with different internal components, both for air-to-air and for surface-to-air use. The British Sky Flash, which has been adopted by Sweden, is a modified AIM-7E, the dogfight version preceding AIM-7F.

SHIPBOARD GUNS AND GUN SYSTEMS

The terms *gun* and *mount* are often used nearly interchangeably in this section. In a few cases, the same gun (barrel and breech mechanism) is used in different gun mountings. The term *mount* (or *mounting*) is generally taken to include the guns it carries, so that one describes a weapon as, say, a twin 40mm mounting or a twin 40mm gun.

Deletions: Vickers 4in (Chilean *Almirante Williams* class retired).

AUSTRALIA

Late in 1995 the Metal Storm company of Brisbane announced a new kind of CIWS using multiple barrels, each of which could

be loaded with several rounds in tandem, to achieve a very high rate of fire, 45,000 rounds/barrel/min (albeit not sustained for very long). Firing is initiated by an electronic sequencer. The space between projectiles is filled with loose propellant. When the round nearest the muzzle is fired, the pressure of its propellant seals the next projectile into the barrel (using a proprietary mechanism) to prevent blow-by. The gun can be loaded in block form or with throwaway barrels (ceramics or plastic might be used if each barrel were loaded with 17 or fewer rounds). As of late 1995 a three-barrel version had been demonstrated and a 36-barrel version tested at 60,000 rnd/min to verify electrical and mechanical design; plans called for tests to the theoretical maximum rate of 1,620,000 rnd/min. Late in 1995 Metal Storm was seeking partners in North America and South Africa.

CHINA

China continues to use a derivative of the Soviet 130mm twin semiautomatic mount described in the Russian section; the Russian guns were used only on board "Kotlin"-class destroyers, which have been discarded.

◆ ENG-2

Caliber: 100mm/56
Rate of Fire: 25 rnd/min/barrel
Muzzle Velocity: 916 m/sec (3004 ft/sec)
Maximum Range: 22,500 m (24,600 yd)
Maximum Altitude: 15,000 m (49,000 ft)
Training Rate: 25 deg/sec (elevation 20 deg/sec)
Elevation/Depression: +85/−5 deg
Ammunition Capacity: 52 rnd ready-service
Weight: 34 t

This new twin autoloading 100mm gun has supplanted the single Soviet-designed 100mm/56 in Chinese production. It retains the original Soviet barrel and shell but uses a French-

Zigong (558), the first of a new variant of the Jianghu II–class frigate, displays a twin 100mm (ENG-2) gun mount forward, controlled by the Wok Wan director atop her bridge. She has the new type of Dardo-style (Type 76) twin 37mm guns fore and aft, but her only AA fire-control radar is aft. Note the Naja-style optronic director abaft and below the radar. The radar forward is probably Type 360, the Eye Shield successor (it has clipped ends; Eye Shield has elliptical ones). Just below it is a Type 756 surface-search radar. The UHF radar antenna on the funnel is the frigate version of Bean Sticks. Unlike other ships of this type, she lacks a Square Tie (Type 331) missile targeting radar, which is normally carried on a heavy platform (not in this ship) on the foremast under the search radars. As in a "Luda"-class destroyer, the radar on the Wok Won FCS apparently substitutes for Square Tie in missile targeting. Note also the absence of the usual Russian-style rectangular mesh IFF interrogator antennas, which are normally carried on the yardarm beneath the two search radars. Forward are a pair of Type 75 ASW launchers, and the new bow anchor suggests that the sonar has been relocated to the ship's forefoot. The small deckhouse aft probably contains controls for a VDS. (*Ships of the World*)

designed autoloader. It arms Jianghu II and III frigates and has been offered for export on board a projected frigate designated EF30. The mount is servo-controlled by a director. Traverse limits (left and right) 225 deg. Acceleration: 23 deg/sec²/in elevation, 20 deg/sec²/in traverse. Reportedly this mount suffers from lack of interlocks and is considered quite dangerous to its crew.

There has been some speculation that the Chinese would manufacture the French 100mm Compact gun or a derivative, having bought two from France.

Users: Bangladesh (Jianghu class), China ("Jiangwei," Jianghu III, some Jianghu I/II), Thailand (Jianghu class).

◆ NG15-2/Type 76

The gun in the locally produced version of Dardo is a twin 37mm (not 40mm), probably using the design of the Breda Compact Forty (the Russian 37mm from which the original Chinese 37mm was copied is derived from an earlier Bofors 25mm gun, so the Compact Forty design concept is applicable to it). For ballistics, see the Russian 37mm gun. Rate of fire is 360–380 rnd/bbl/min. Train (elevation) rates: 40 (50) deg/sec.

The Chinese version of Dardo is shown on board a Jiangwei-class (pennant number 539) frigate, 1992; the Rice Lamp director is on a short lattice mast above the helicopter hangar. The large radar to the right is Pea Sticks. (*Ships of the World*)

The Finnish SAKO 23mm gun mount. (SAKO)

The Chinese brochure for the Type 88C combat system (see the missile section above) lists the Compact Forty look-alike as Type 76A.

Users: China (Luhu, "Luda II," "Jiangwei"), Thailand (*Naresuan* class).

FINLAND

SAKO has developed a gun/missile launching system for the Finnish navy, to carry 2 × 23mm or 6 Mistral missiles, in each case with an on-mount operator using a joystick; it can also be con-

trolled by a ship FCS. Weight is 1700 kg (gun version) or 2200 kg (missile version); swing radius of the gun version is 1.570 m. Elevation limits: +80/−10 deg. Training rate is 80 deg/sec (elevation 50 deg/sec). The dispersion of the gun version is less than 3 mrad. The missile-carrying structure also carries TV and IR cameras (with monitors in the operator's cab) and argon bottles for seeker cooling; the missile version has an additional computer to control the launch unit system.

FRANCE

◆ 100mm MLE 1953, 1964, 1968, and Compact

Caliber: 3.9in/55 (13.5-kg projectile)
Rate of Fire: 90 or 40 or 10 (selectable) rnd/min
Muzzle Velocity: 870 m/sec (2850 ft/sec)
Maximum Range: 17,500 m; maximum effective range 12,000 m for surface fire, 6000 m for AA fire (19,100/13,100/6600 yd)
Training Rate: 50 deg/sec (elevation 32 deg/sec)
Elevation/Depression: +80/−15
Ammunition Capacity: 42 or 90 in magazine plus 18 in intermediate magazine, plus 6 in the loading train
Weight: 13,500 kg (29,750 lb)

Data refer to the export (Compact) version; only Malaysia uses the 90-rnd magazine.

Two 100mm gun mounts on board the destroyer *Duguay-Trouin*, 1982. (L. van Ginderen)

The standard French dual-purpose gun mount replaced, in effect, both the 127mm and the twin 57mm AA gun, firing a shell heavy enough for shore bombardment but light enough for a high rate of AA fire. It was the first French-designed fully automatic medium-caliber gun. The barrel is water-cooled (life 3000 rnd) and the fuze is set just before a round is loaded into the breech. Ammunition is fed from the main magazine below the gun into an 18-rnd intermediate magazine that elevates with the gun. From this magazine they are transferred down and around (in a horizontal fan) to be rammed into the breech. The intermediate magazine, which is more typical of smaller-caliber guns, brings the gun into action more quickly and makes for rapid access to alternative types of ammunition.

Model 1968 (22 t, 35-rnd ready-use magazine) is a somewhat lighter version of Model 1953. It trains at 40 deg/sec (elevation 25 deg/sec). Claimed maximum effective range is 15,000 m against surface targets and 8000 m against air targets (presumably the older mount is steadier than the Compact version). Model 1953 uses an analog FCS (CTA) with electromechanical computer, as does Model 1964. Model 1968 and the improved Model 1968-II (1970) use a digital FCS (CTD), in some cases integrated with the ship's SENIT CDSs. The CADAM (Cadence de tir Ameliore) program increased the rate of fire of these versions from 60 to 78 rnd/min.

Compact is a lighter-weight unmanned-mount export version. It can fire preselected 1-, 2-, 3-, or 6-rnd bursts.

At Bourget Naval in October 1990 Creusot-Loire showed a more reliable quick-reacting (10 sec from "power on" to first shot) Compact Mk 2. It has three selectable rates of fire (90 [reducible to 85], 45, and 20 [both of the latter are adjustable] rnd/sec). Barrel life is 6000 rnd (3000 heavy rnd). Any of three types

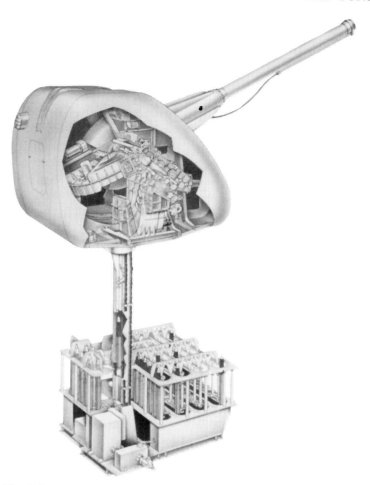

The 100mm Compact mount, showing the ammunition fan feed up the side of the mount and the conveyor that elevates with the gun. (Creusot-Loire)

of ammunition (capacity is 42/12/12 or 90/12/12 rounds of these types) is instantly selectable, and the loading system is reversible. Elevation rate is increased to 35 deg/sec. Standard deviation in firing is less than 0.5 mrad.

Creusot-Loire also showed a modernization program, 100TR (tourelle à technologie renovée) with a reduced radar cross-section. This version is considered good for at least 7 yr without servicing. Local wear is reduced by remotely locking the movable components when they are at rest (they unlock automatically when the turret starts up).

Work on a guided round was canceled. However, about January 1994 GIAT was considering extending 100mm range by using base-bleed; it was also looking at cargo-round options.

Users: Argentina (A69 class [Mle 1968]), Belgium (*Wielingen* [Mle 1968-II]), China (Jianghu IV class), France (carriers [Mle 1953], *Jeanne d'Arc* [Mle 1964], *Cassard* [Mle 1968-II], *Georges Leygues* [Mle 1968-II], *Tourville* [Mle 1968-II], *Suffren* [Mle 1964], *Aconit* [Mle 1968-II], A69 [Mle 1968-II], *La Fayette* [Mle 1968], *Floreal* [Mle 1953] classes), Malaysia (FS 1500 and *Musytari* classes), Portugal (MEKO, *Baptiste de Andrade* [Mle 1968-II], *Commandante Rivière* [Mle 1953] classes), Saudi Arabia (*Al Madinah* and *La Fayette* classes), Turkey (*Koln* and *Rhein* classes [Mle 1953]), Uruguay (*Commandante Rivière* [Mle 1953] class). China, Malaysia, Portugal (MEKO only), and Saudi Arabia use the Compact export version. Belgium and France have the CADAM conversion. The Royal Malaysian Navy let a contract in 1992 to update its 100mm guns to Mk 2 standard, for improved reliability (and with new software in the ammunition supply system).

◆ Coulverine II

Naval Guard (at Toulon) has developed a remote-controlled two-axis stabilized mount inspired by helicopter weapons. Targets are acquired by joystick on a below-decks console that incorporates an autotracker using video from the on-mount Grundig TV camera (5- and 50-deg FOVs). The two Coulverine prototypes carried M621 and M781 (20mm and 30mm) guns. The first Coulverine II, carrying an M693, ran sea trials on board *Ile d'Oléron* in September 1995. A version carrying a Mauser Bk 27 ran trials in May 1996. The mount carries 200 rnds of 20mm or 120 rnds of 30mm ammunition. All versions use a 1m-dia mounting ring atop which is an electrohydraulic container. Trunnion height is 1.23 m, overall height is 1.36 m, and loaded weight (20mm gun) is 580 kg. Elevation limits are −15/+60 deg; train and elevation rate is 55 deg/sec.

◆ DCN 25mm Gun

DGA/DCN displayed a 25mm mount, carrying a new GIAT M811 gun, at Bourget Naval 1992 (October 1992). The entire mount weighs less than 500 kg (1100 lb). Muzzle velocity is 1100 m/sec (3600 ft/sec), with an effective range of 2500 m (2730 yd). Elevation limits are +55/−15 deg. Rate of fire can be set at 125/400 or 125/650 rnd/min. The gun can fire single rounds, short (3-rnd) or long (8-rnd) bursts, or automatically. Weapon lifetime is 16,000 rnd plus 20% unloaded cycles. The GIAT gun, which weighs 105 kg (231 lb) fires all standard NATO 25mm ammunition. This weapon was designed to meet a 1992 requirement for a new Artillerie Nouvelle de Petit Calibre, but the French navy adopted the 30mm Breda. As of 1995 GIAT was still marketing this weapon.

◆ GIAT 20mm

Caliber: 20mm/90 (255-g projectile)
Rate of Fire: 650–720 rnd/min
Muzzle Velocity: 1050 or 1250 m/sec (3440/4100 ft/sec) (HE/AP)
Maximum Range: 10,020 or 6770 m depending on ammunition (10,960/7400 yd); effective range 2000 or 1200 m (2200 or 1300 yd)
Training Rate: Manual
Elevation/Depression: +60/−15
Ammunition Capacity: 300 (2 × 150-rnd magazines)
Weight: 336 kg (741 lb) empty
Working Circle: 2.23 m

The GIAT-CN-MIT-20F2 20mm/90 gun is based on the CN-MIT 20 M693 (Canon Mitrailleur 20mm Modèle 693), formerly the Hispano Suiza 820. The naval version entered production in 1983. There are also army and air versions. As of 1995, 150 had been made.

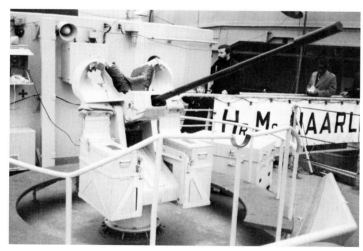

A GIAT 20mm gun (20F2) on board the Dutch minesweeper *Haarlem*, 1987. (R. Cheung)

GIAT also makes a Type 15A naval version of its M621 20mm/73 low-recoil gun, which is typically carried by helicopters and small aircraft. Muzzle velocity is 980–1030 m/sec (3215–3380 ft/sec), depending on the type of ammunition, and cyclic rate is 650 or 850 rnd/min. The naval mounting carries 160 rnd (weight

The French GIAT Affut 15 mounting for the 20mm M621 gun. The gun fires 750 rnd/min; the mount carries 160 rnd. Elevation limits are +45/−10 deg, and total weight (without ammunition) is 167 kg. (GIAT)

with/without ammunition is 222/184 kg, with elevation limits of +45/−15 deg). A collimator sight is provided. Recoil is minimized by a muzzle brake and a shock-absorbing mount. Total gun length is 2.207 m (86.9 in), and without the mount the gun weighs 47 kg (104 lb) in its aircraft version. Development began in the late 1970s, and naval installations began in the mid-1980s. Fifty have been sold.

Users:

> 20F2: Belgium (Tripartite minehunters), France (*Charles de Gaulle, La Fayette, Floreal, Foudre,* Tripartite minehunters, P400, CDIC, EDIC classes, *Monge;* but most 20mm in service are Oerlikons of U.S. or UK manufacture), Gabon (P400 class, *Gen. Nazaire Boulingui, Pres. El Hadj Omar Bongo*), Malawi (*Kasunga*), Morocco, Netherlands (Tripartite minehunters), Pakistan (Tripartite minehunters), Saudi Arabia, Senegal (PR 72M).
> Type 15A: Djibouti (two *Moussa Ali* class), Kuwait (PB37BRL boats), Saudi Arabia (40 ASD 12 class and two SM742 class), two other buyers unnamed; probably they are Gabon and Malawi (i.e., are not the F2s listed above).

French-supplied 20mm guns are used by the Belgian, Benin, Djibouti, Gabonese, Indonesian, Madagascar, Mauritanian, Morrocan, Dutch, and Senegalese navies, but many of these weapons may be older 20mm guns made in Britain or in the United States.

◆ GIAT AAT 52 and NF-1

Caliber: 7.5mm (NF-1, 7.62mm)
Rate of Fire: 700 rnd/min (900 in NF-1) (effective rates: 200–300, 250–300, respectively)
Muzzle Velocity: 832 m/sec (NF-1: 830 m/sec)
Maximum Range: 2000 m; effective range 1250 m
Elevation/Depression: +55/−30 deg
Ammunition Capacity: 200-rnd box
Weight: 17.6 kg empty (25.10 kg loaded) (NF-1)

These standard auxiliary weapons in the French navy and in the navies of the former French colonies are equivalent in function to the U.S. 0.50. The 7.5mm AAT 52 (Arme Automatique Transformable Modèle 52), the standard postwar French light machine gun, entered naval service in the late 1950s. The navy uses the heavy-barrel version (with a 23.5in barrel, rather than the 19.3in barrel of the light version). The belt feed and delayed-blowback action are derived from those of the wartime German MG42.

NF-1 is a NATO-caliber (7.62mm) version.

The French navy uses a standard pedestal mount (14A) bracketed to a bulwark (data above). There are also Creusot-Loire pintle mounts, designated P127A for the U.S.-supplied 0.50-caliber Browning M2 HB, CP 80A for the 7.62mm FN machine gun, and CP 52A for the NF-1. With a gun, P127A weighs 82 kg empty and 125 kg loaded. Elevation limits are +50/−15 deg.

Users:

> AAT52: Ivory Coast, Lebanon, Mauritania, Mauritius
> NF-1: Djibouti, France, Senegal

GERMANY

The prewar Krupp 105mm/45 survives on board the old Argentine *Murature* class. Most likely this is the 10.5cm SKC/32 firing a 15.1-kg (33.3 lb) shell at 785 m/sec (2575 ft/sec), with elevation limits of +50/−10 deg (weight 6.49 t).

◆ Mauser 40mm Guns

Mauser manufactured 40mm/70 Bofors guns under license in the 1960s, probably only for the German navy. The following were probably armed with these weapons: *Koln*-class frigates (now in Turkish service), Type 141 torpedo boats (transferred to Greece, Saudi Arabia, and Turkey), Type 148 missile boats, Type 332 and 343 MCM craft, Type 351 drone control craft, Type 340/341 patrol minecraft, Type 393/394 inshore sweepers, and *Rhein*-class tenders (now in Turkish service). One source claims that Types 141 and 148 were armed with Breda 564s. Mauser guns may also have been exported: to Belgium (*Godetia, Zinnia*), Brazil (*Schutze* class coastal minesweepers), and Denmark (*Daphne* class).

◆ Mauser Vierling (Drakon)/MIDAS/N 30/MN series

Caliber: 27mm/63 (1700mm barrels) (HE, TP, APFSDS ammunition)
Rate of Fire: 1700 rnd/min/barrel
Muzzle Velocity: 1200 m/sec (3940 ft/sec)
Training Rate: 80 deg/sec (elevation 80 deg/sec)
Elevation/Depression: +80/−10 deg
Ammunition Capacity: 1440 rnd (4 × 375-rnd magazines)
Weight: 4000 kg (including 850 kg of ammunition)

Data refer to MIDAS.

Development of Mauser's quadruple 27mm CIWS, using the gun of the Tornado bomber, began as a private venture in 1987, probably in hopes of gaining German navy support (RAM, the obvious alternative, was in deep trouble). As RAM's fortunes improved, the German navy lost interest in the gun alternative. A prototype was shown in 1989, the project was shelved early in 1990, but it was revived later in the year (with some funding from Diehl), and it is still being marketed six years later. Signaal collaborated in a version with an on-mount radar, MIDAS, but then withdrew, and the version without Signaal participation is Drakon (1994). It has been suggested that Mauser conceived Vierling to make use of surplus 27mm production capacity. Mauser is currently developing a 27mm Gatling for the European Fighter Aircraft; the company may promote a shipboard version.

Mauser has developed a prototype Naval 30mm Short-Range Gun System (N 30 SRGS) carrying one or two MK 30 Model F 30mm guns fed by two 225-rnd magazines, on a nonpenetrating deck mount developed from that of Drakon, driven by brushless servos (train/elevation speeds 120/90 deg/sec). Control can be remote, local, or manual. Effective range is 3 km (4 km with APFSDS). For other gun details, see the Italian Breda 30mm mount.

MN 27/30 GS are low-recoil stabilized nonpenetrating deck mounts, work on which began at the end of 1995; a pre-prototype was delivered for sea trials in May 1996. MN 27 uses the same revolver cannon as in MIDAS; MN 30 uses the MK 30 Model F

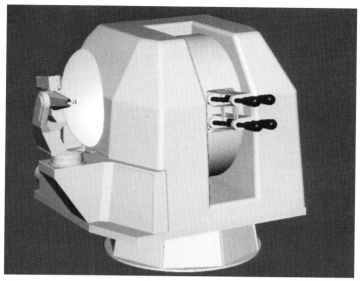

The Mauser-Signaal MIDAS close-in weapon. The version currently offered lacks the FCS radar. (Signaal)

gun of the N 30 system described above. Elevation limits are +60/−15 deg; train/elevation rates are 55 deg/sec.

◆ Rhinemetall 20mm Mk 20 Rh202

Caliber: 20mm/85
Rate of Fire: 1000 rnd/min
Muzzle Velocity: 1050 m/sec (HEI-T, TP-T ammunition) or 1100 m/sec (API-T ammunition) or 1150 m/sec (APDS-T) (3440/3770 ft/sec)
Maximum Range: 2000 m effective range (2200 yd)
Elevation/Depression: +55/−10 deg
Ammunition Capacity: 200 rnd, linked, in two boxes
Weight: 408 kg total; 74 kg ammunition (899/163 lb)
Working Circle: Approx. 2.45 m (96.5 in) radius

This low-recoil gun is essentially the World War II Mauser MG 151/20, which was made in South Africa from the 1970s on. It is gas-operated, fed by a belt from its right-hand side. As offered in 1973, it had only a speed ring sight, although a lead computing sight was offered as an option. The Rhinemetall version was developed in the early 1960s, and a naval version was announced in 1973 on the S.20 pintle fork mounting. Later a Wegmann AA mounting was announced (628 kg, limits +85/−15 deg).

Norway uses the same gun (made by Kongsberg) in a different mounting, KV-SK/20 (derived from the FK20–2 field-gun mounting). Elevation limits are +70/−15 deg, and the working circle is 1730 mm. Total weight is 400 kg without ammunition.

Users: Bahamas (*Protector, Marlin*), Barbados (*Trident*), Cyprus (*Salamis*), Equatorial Guinea (*Van Mill*, Wegmann mount), Germany (S.20 mount, Wegmann mount in Type 520 LCU), Greece (S.20 mount in Combattante, Wegmann mount in P 100 and "Osprey 55" classes, and apparently in a navalized twin land version in the *Jason* class; also in ex-U.S. LSTs), Indonesia (*Fatahillah, Dewantara*, patrol craft, Tacoma-type LST, Tripartite minehunters, police patrol boats), Ireland (*Eithne*), Nigeria (P20 class, Swifts, P-2000), Norway (on the locally designed mount: *Oslo, Hauk, Nordkapp* classes and MCM and amphibious craft; also in close-in protection for coast-defense guns).

The South African version of MG 151 was produced by Armscor as GA 1 Vektor in single (Casspir) and twin (Gemini) mountings. Casspir equips the South African "River"-class coastal minehunters and the T2212-class patrol boats. Elevation limits are +30/−7 deg, and loaded weight is 196 kg. The pintle mounting carries a 75-rnd box magazine. Gemini (503 kg loaded) carries two 100-rnd boxes.

ISRAEL

In mid-1995 Rafael announced completion of engineering development of a new Naval Stabilized Gun System (NSGS), also known as Typhoon, developed from its OWS 25 armored fighting vehicle overhead weapon station; the mount does not penetrate the deck. The pedestal carries a TV (daylight CCD or LLLTV, FOVs 3 and 10 deg) sight. The gun can be slaved to the LOS of a surveillance device (with the proper lead angle) or else simply stabilized and aimed from the bridge, using the TV sight. Typhoon can carry a variety of 20, 25, and 30mm electric- and gas-driven guns. On June 1995 sea trials on a "Super Dvora" carrying a 25mm Bushmaster and linked to an MSIS EO director, it was able to engage targets at 1000m at speed of over 28 kt. Stabilization accuracy with this gun is 0.25 mrad in traverse and 0.20 mrad in elevation, in Sea State 3. Elevation limits are +45/−20 deg. Carrying a 115kg M242 cannon and 200 rounds,

20mm Rhinemetall gun on board the Irish *Eithne*, 1986. (Author)

Typhoon mounted for tests on an Israeli patrol boat, carrying a triple 0.50-cal. Gatling gun and its optronic sensor (at left). (Rafael/Lockheed Martin)

Typhoon weighs 830 kg, is 1.6m high above deck, and has a swept circle of 1.9m radius.

At the 1996 Navy League show, Lockheed Martin displayed a version of Typhoon carrying a GAU-19/A triple 0.50-cal. Gatling gun, with a rate of fire of 1000 or 2000 rnd/min. The mount carries 800 ready rounds, all of which can be fired in a single burst. This version was tested aboard a "Super Dvora" in March 1996 (a pintle version had been tested in September 1995). An RFP for the definitive "Super Dvora" armament was expected in mid-1996. Loaded weight is 630 kg (1400 lb).

◆ TCM-20

The RAMTA TCM-20 twin 20mm AA gun is on board several Honduran warships. It is an adapted U.S. Army quadruple 0.50-cal. AA mount with two Hispano-Suiza HS 404 20mm cannon in place of the 0.50s; they are modified to fire HS 804 ammunition. Development began in 1969 and the weapon was first used in 1970. By March 1983, 700 had been delivered to Israel and seven other countries. Production has continued.

TCM-20 on Honduras "Swift" 105 ft 1990 (L. Montes)

Users: Argentina (air force), Chile (army), Haiti (army), Honduras (navy), Israel (army and air force), Kenya (army), and two others.

ITALY

In the fall of 1994 OTO-Melara and Breda combined as OTO-Breda.

◆ OTO-Melara 127mm/54 LW

Caliber: 5in/54
Rate of Fire: 45 rnd/min
Muzzle Velocity: 807 m/sec (2650 ft/sec)
Effective Range: 15,000 m surface; 7000 m antiair (16,400/7660 yd); maximum range 23,680 yd
Training Rate: 40 deg/sec (elevation 30 deg/sec)
Elevation/Depression: +83/−15 deg
Ammunition Capacity: 66 rnd (3 drums)
Weight: 37.5 t
Working Circle: 6.108 m (240.5 in)

This lightweight equivalent to the U.S. Mk 45 enjoys a higher rate of fire and is capable of higher elevation for AA use. The light weight is achieved by using light alloys and a fiberglass shield. The gun is fitted with a muzzle brake. It loads from two drums, a third being loadable while the gun fires. Each drum can therefore be loaded with a separate type of ammunition (surface, air, pyrotechnic, or chaff) selectable during firing. Two oscillating arms (which include fuze-setters) strip rounds from the vertical hoist and place them on loading trays. Reaction time is 5 sec. The ammunition is the standard U.S. semifixed type, the ammunition being brought together only at the bottom of the two fixed-structure hoists.

The Italian navy has awarded a contract for a new-generation "Alleggerito" mount (for year 2000 and beyond) using the electronics of the intermediate model (on *Kongo*) but weighing 30%

An OTO-Melara 127mm (5in)/54 gun on board the frigate *Zeffiro*, 1995. (Author)

less, with a low-RCS shield, redesigned mechanism, and modular magazine and hoist. Each drum is replaced by a 20-rnd automatic feeding device (AFD), one for propelling charges and two for projectiles; each AFD has its own hoist. Rounds are automatically assembled before they reach the gunhouse. Expected rate of fire is 40 rnd/min. The empty mount weighs 18 t (plus 2.5 t for lower ammunition hoists). Elevation limits are cut to +70/−15 deg; training (elevation) rates are cut to 36 (30) deg/sec. The crew is four rather than the five of the current Compact version. This version was announced in the summer of 1993. As of 1995, VSEL was promoting it for the Anglo-French-Italian "Horizon"-class frigate.

Users: Argentina (MEKO 360 class), Italy (*Mimbelli*, *Audace*, *Maestrale*, and *Lupo* classes), Japan (*Kongo* class), Korea (KDX 2000), Nigeria (MEKO 360), Peru (*Lupo* class), and Venezuela (*Lupo* class).

◆ OTO-Melara 76mm/62 Compact Mounting/Mk 75

Caliber: 3in/62
Rate of Fire: 85 rnd/min (Mk 75: 80)
Muzzle Velocity: 925 m/sec (3034 ft/sec)
Maximum Range: 8000 m surface; 4000–5000 m antiair (8700/4400–5500 yd)
Training Rate: 60 deg/sec (Mk 75: 65) (elevation 35 deg/sec)
Elevation/Depression: +85/−15 deg
Ammunition Capacity: 70 ready-service (drum magazine)
Weight: 7.35 t
Working Circle: 208 in (radius)

OTO-Melara's Compatto (Compact) is one of the most successful recent medium-caliber weapons, widely exported. The single 70-rnd feed drum surrounds the screw feeder hoist (6 rnd) leading up to a station below the left trunnion. Two rocker arms strip the hoist to feed a revolving 4-rnd feeding drum above the loading tray. The tray pivots back and up, taking a round from the loading drum, then moving to the breech so that the round can be rammed. The tray receives the spent cartridge case as the gun recoils, then feeds in the next round as the gun runs back out. The drum around the base of the hoist can be reloaded while the gun fires. Both rocker arms are needed to maintain a high rate of fire, one swinging up while the other swings down. Weight is minimized by using light alloys and a fiberglass shield. Recoil forces are reduced by about 35% by a small muzzle brake. There is a tank-type bore evacuator.

Mk 75, the U.S. version, can have one, two, or three loading drums (40, 80, or 115 rnd).

The "Super Rapido" (Super Rapid) version was redesigned for a higher rate of fire (selectable 1, 10, or 120 rnd/min; on trials, a gun achieved 139 rnd/min) specifically for antimissile defense. Some cyclic functions are now performed in parallel: a new round is rammed while the spent cartridge is ejected. To minimize vibration, the loading tray, which moves across the gun axis, is lighter (18 vs. 50 kg) and does not move as far (140 vs. 280 mm). Recoil length is shorter, for faster fire. Firing cycle time was cut from 0.7 to 0.5 sec. The ammunition feed was redesigned to make it easier to insert different types of ammunition, such as guided rounds. Dispersion at 1000 m was cut to

The OTO-Melara 76mm/62 Compact, on a fast-attack boat. (L. van Ginderen)

OTO-Melara's new non-deck-penetrating version of its 76mm gun, displayed in model form at the 1993 Navy League Show. (Author)

0.3 mrad (many small-caliber ASMD weapons have over 2-mrad dispersion at this range). The mount weighs 7.5 t and carries 85 rnd.

Note that in the Italian missile destroyers Super Rapido in effect replaces the Fast Forty as an antimissile weapon. OTO-Melara estimated that, using a Dardo FCS, Super Rapido could begin engaging incoming missiles at about 6000 m, the first rounds arriving at about 5500 m. Given the lethality of the rounds, a single gun might destroy four subsonic sea-skimmers, arriving on courses 90 deg apart, before any reached 1000 m.

Because the feed in the Super Rapido is quite different from that of the Compatto, the earlier guns cannot be converted to the later standard. However, a retrofit kit converts the earlier gun to 100 rnd/min.

OTO-Melara is now marketing a nondeck-penetrating low-RCS lightweight version of Super Rapido, carrying 50 ready-use rnd. It weighs 5.5 t without ammunition. Elevation limits are +70/−15 deg.

OTO-Melara developed a new prefragmented antimissile shell, AMARTOF, for the Super Rapido, filled with tungsten cubes rather than the spheres used in earlier shells. It has a lethal radius of 10 m. This lightweight (nearly 5 kg, 338 mm long) shell will also benefit from reduced time of flight to the burst point. It has a new mm-wave Doppler proximity fuze; an IR fuze is being developed. It was shown at Bourget Euronaval 1994.

There are two new SAP projectiles for surface engagement: SAPOM (6.35 kg, with 0.455 kg of Compound A3 HE) and extended-range SAPOMER (6.5 kg, 0.480 kg HBX-1). OTO-Melara

also offers a dual-purpose (antiship and AA) MOM (Multirole OTO-Melara) round. It has a proximity fuze and contains tungsten cubes embedded in the casing. An extended-range round is under development, and there is a new base-detonating delayed-action fuze.

Work on course-corrected 76mm shells apparently continues.

Fuchs Electronics of South Africa markets the M8953 programmable proximity fuze for the OTO-Melara 76mm gun, designed specifically for the Naschem HE preformed frag (HEPFF) shell, but also suitable for upgrades. HEPFF contains 8000 3mm-dia tungsten alloy balls, and can penetrate 8 mm of hardened aluminum. M8953 detects a missile at 5 m. The lethal area is 78.5 m², compared to 2 m/12.5 m² of older shells. The fuze is designed for ranges of 2–9 km. Described as a "fifth-generation" system, it operates in the UHF band to obtain a high Doppler frequency shift to discriminate between target and spin noise. The radiation pattern is optimized to look forward. The signal processor uses an FM technique to reject microphonic noise caused by projectile vibration. Enhanced filtering further reduces non-Doppler signals, including jamming, to provide relative velocity compensation. The fuze can be paralyzed: the projectile can be fuzed for impact hits against ship or shore targets, so there is no need to cycle the magazine to obtain appropriate rounds. Another South African company, Plessey Telument, markets another proximity fuze, the Intelligent Multi-Purpose Igniter (IMPI), which has a small radar sensor (Telemetric Enhancement Outfit) to improve accuracy.

ESD of South Africa upgraded the 76mm-gun drives (from hydraulic to electric) on the South African "Minister"-class fast-attack boats, the resulting weapon being ESD-76. The production contract was awarded in June 1995.

An older single 76mm/62 (from which the Compact mount was developed) survives on board the Italian *San Giorgio* class. It has a muzzle velocity of 850 m/sec, and fires 60 rnd/min. The older gun is recognizable by its angular gunhouse.

Users: OTO-Melara 76mm/62 Compact Mounting/Mk 75: Algeria (Bulgarian C-58–class patrol boats and Brooke Marine 37.5m patrol boats), Argentina (*Intrepida*-class FACs), Bahrein (FPB 62 and TNC 45–class missile boats), Brazil (Vosper design patrol boats), Canada (TRUMP upgraded frigates [Super Rapido]), Chile (*Sa'ar III* class), Colombia (FS 1500–class frigates), Denmark (*Nils Juels*, *Thetis*, *Willemoes*, and StanFlex 300 [Super Rapido] classes), Ecuador (*Wadi M'ragh* class and *Quito* class), Egypt (*Descubierta* class, *Ramadan* class), Germany (*Bremen*-class frigates and S143/143A/143B- and S148-class fast-attack boats), Ghana (FPB 57 class), Greece (*Kortenaer* class, *Rhein* class, P100 class, "Osprey 55" class, Combattante IIIN class, and *Jason*-class LSTs), India (see below), Indonesia (*Van Speijk* class), Iran (Combattante II class), Ireland (*Peacock* class), Israel (*Romat* class, *Sa'ar* III, IV, and 4.5 classes), Italy (*Animoso* [Super Rapido], *Audace* [Super Rapido], *Minerva*, *Sparviero* classes), Kenya ("Province" class), South Korea (Ulsan HDF-2000 and HDC-800 classes, *Donghae* class, PSMM 5 class, HDC-1150 patrol ships), Kuwait (FPB 57 and TNC 45 boats), Libya (Combattante II class), Malaysia (Super Rapido in ex-Iraqi *Wadi M'ragh* class), Mexico (*Manuel Azueta*), Morocco (*Descubierta* class, *Lazaga* class), Netherlands (*Karel Doorman* [Super Rapido] and *Kortenaer*-class frigates), Nigeria (*Erin'mi*, Combattante IIIB, and FPB 57 classes), Oman (new corvettes, "Province" and 37.5m classes, and *Al Munassir*; Super Rapido in corvettes and Al Mawj boats), Peru (PR 72–560 class), Philippines (*Cormoran* and Australian patrol-boat classes, both projected), Qatar (Combattante III class), Senegal (PR 72 MS class), Singapore (*Victory* class [Super Rapido], *Fearless* class), South Africa ("Minister" class), Spain (*Lazaga* class), Taiwan (rebuilt destroyers, *Lung Chiang*, and *La Fayette* classes), Thailand (PFMM Mk 16, *Kamronsin*, and MV 400 classes), Tunisia (Combattante III class), Turkey (FPB 57 class), UAE (Type 62, FPB 38, and TNC 45 classes), United Kingdom (*Peacock* class), Venezuela (*Constitucion* class).

Retrofit kits (for faster firing) have been supplied for evaluation to the Italian, German, and U.S. navies. The Royal Netherlands Navy bought at least two kits, and in spring 1996 the

German navy let a contract to modernize its guns to Super Rapido standard. This gun is manufactured under license in Japan, Spain, and in the United States (as the Mk 75).

About October 1991 Bharat Heavy Electricals Ltd. and OTO-Melara signed an MoU for the production of at least 100 76mm, all but the first batch to be made in India. Of the initial 18, 16 would be for the Indian coast guard and two for navy. The Indian navy opposed the deal on the ground that other projects should enjoy higher priorities, and that the requirement for a modern gun mount could be met by modernizing the existing Soviet-supplied 76.2mm weapon.

U.S. Mk 75 users: Japan (*Asagiri, Hatsuyuki, Minegumo, Abukuma, Yubari, Ishikari* classes), Saudi Arabia (PCG, PGG) and United States (*Perry, Hamilton, Bear* classes). Note that since FY86 OTO-Melara has supplied guns to the U.S. Navy in competition with the U.S. manufacturer, FMC. In U.S. and Saudi service the gun is controlled by a Mk 92 FCS and manning is three enlisted.

◆ **Breda-Bofors 40mm (Compact, Fast Forty, Types 64, 106/107, 564)**

> **Caliber:** 40mm/70
> **Maximum Recoil Length:** 100 m (3.94 in)
> **Rate of Fire:** 600 rnd/min/mount
> **Muzzle Velocity:** 1025 m/sec (HE) (3362 ft/sec); 1350 m/sec (APFDS) (4428 ft/sec)
> **Maximum Horizontal Range:** (HE) 12,500 m (13,700 yd)
> **Maximum Altitude:** (HE) 8700 m (28,500 ft)
> **Training Rate:** 90 deg/sec (elevation 60 deg/sec)
> **Maximum Elevation/Depression:** +85/−13 deg
> **Weight:** 5.5 t without ammunition (Type A; 7.3 t with ammunition; 5.3/6.3 t for Type B)
> **Working Circle:** 2.902 m (114.3 in)

Data are for the Compact Forty.

Breda's versions of the Bofors 40mm/70 were produced under license beginning with the Type 64 open twin mount in 1969. The enclosed Compact Forty (Type 70) twin mount is very widely used. It and other Breda versions of the Bofors gun employ extended feeds (rather than the clips typical of other Bofors guns) which greatly increase mount ammunition capacity. In this case ammunition is stowed in horizontal layers under the gun: 736 HE rnds in seven layers in Type A, 444 in four layers in Type B. In Italian service the usual FCS for the Compact mounting is Dardo. The Twin Fast Forty (prototype completed in summer 1988), externally identical to the Compact, employs a new recoiling mass (with half the recoil stroke, for a higher cyclic rate, 450 rnd/gun/min), digital servos (for more precise control), and a new upper magazine (200 rounds of APFDS) split between the two guns (in addition to the below-mount magazine of the earlier mount). In the antimissile role, the gun fires proximity-fuzed HE until the target gets to within 1000 m, switching automatically to APFDS in hopes of penetrating and fuzing the missile war-

A Breda twin compact 40mm gun mount on the carrier *Giuseppe Garibaldi*, 1991. (Author)

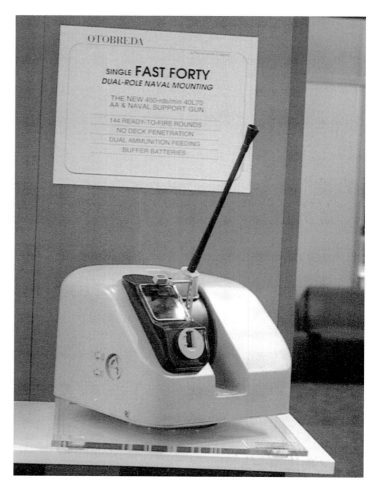

A model of the single Fast Forty, bought by Kuwait for the P37BRL boats, at Bourget Naval 1994. (Author)

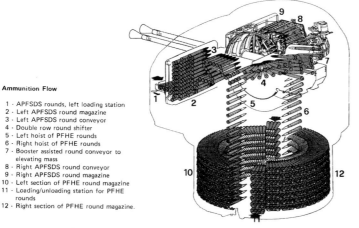

Ammunition Flow

1 - APFSDS rounds, left loading station
2 - Left APFSDS round magazine
3 - Left APFSDS round conveyor
4 - Double row round shifter
5 - Left hoist of PFHE rounds
6 - Right hoist of PFHE rounds
7 - Booster assisted round conveyor to elevating mass
8 - Right APFSDS round conveyor
9 - Right APFSDS round magazine
10 - Left section of PFHE round magazine
11 - Loading/unloading station for PFHE rounds
12 - Right section of PFHE round magazine.

Ammunition flow in the Breda twin Fast Forty (40mm) gun. (Breda)

head. A single version, using the same recoiling mass, appears not to have sold.

For open mounts, Breda's most noticeable addition is the Automatic Feed Device (AFD) which replaces the clip atop the gun. It was developed jointly with Bofors for the Breda-Bofors System 75. The AFD has also been installed in modernized mountings. Bazan makes a Spanish version of the single AFD gun, for example, for the *Descubierta* class. Breda also licensed its technology to Daewoo in Korea, which produced a new Twin 40mm/

A single Breda 40mm/70 on the Spanish frigate *Descubierta*, 1991, showing Breda's horizontal fan feed on top. Breda open twin mounts have similar feeds. (A. Raven)

This Israeli *Sa'ar II*–class missile boat shows single Breda 40mm guns with prominent autoloaders extending up from the gun platforms. This photograph seems to show the original radars, the French Neptune and the Italian Orion. (U.S. Naval Institute)

70 K(T) mounting, which fires at 330 rnd/min/gun, and carries 768 rounds of on-mount ready-use ammunition. It reportedly entered production in June 1994.

Breda also manufactured conventional open-topped 40mm mountings carrying air-cooled guns:

Type 64 is a twin mount, each gun carrying a 100-rnd automatic magazine. Total weight without ammunition is 7900 kg, and training and elevation rates are 85 and 95 deg/sec.

Type 106 is a twin 40mm/70; Type 107 is the corresponding single mount. Each gun carries a 32-rnd Breda autofeeder that elevates with the gun, or it can be loaded with the usual 4-rnd clip. Train and elevation speeds are both 95 deg/sec. Type 106 was used only by the German navy. Production of Type 107 ended in 1988.

Type 564 is a single 40mm/70 carrying a Model 1971 144-rnd automatic magazine; it is also marketed as the Breda-Bofors 350P. Total weight without ammunition is 3300 kg. Training and elevation rates are 80 and 45 deg/sec. The Breda 144-rnd automatic feed system is also manufactured under license by Empresa Nacional Bazan of Spain, for the Spanish navy. There was also a Type 520, equivalent to the Bofors 40L/70–520. Type 564 differs from Type 520 in having a digital servo system.

For defense against sea-skimming missiles, these guns use ammunition with a Fratelli Borletti proximity fuze that adjusts its fuzing range to the altitude, to avoid premature bursts. At 40 m above the sea, the burst range is 4.5 m; at 20 m, about 3 m; and at 5 m, about 1 m.

Users (Compact Twin 40): Algeria (Brooke Marine LSTs), Argentina (MEKO frigates and corvettes and A69 class), Bahrein (FPB 62, TNC 45, FPB 38), China (for Dardo in "Luda III" and "Jiangwei" classes; may be unlicensed), Colombia (FS 1500 class), Ecuador (*Wadi M'ragh* class), Egypt (*Ramadan* class),

Greece (P 100, "Osprey 55," and *Jason* classes), Iraq (*Wadi M'ragh* class, for sale), Italy (*Garibaldi, Vittorio Veneto, Maestrale, Lupo* classes), Korea (*Ulsan*-class 955–958, *Bukhansan* class), Kuwait (FPB 57 and TNC 45), Libya (Combattante II, *Ibn Ouf* class), Malaysia (ex-Iraqi *Wadi M'ragh* class), Nigeria (*Aradu*, Combattante III, FPB 57), Oman ("Province" class, *Nasr al Bahr*), Peru (*Daring, Lupo*, PR 72 classes), Philippines (*Cormoran* and Australian patrol-boat classes, both projected), Qatar (Combattante III class), Saudi Arabia (*Al Madinah, Boraida* classes), Thailand (PFMM Mk 16, MV 400), Tunisia (Combattante III class), UAE (TNC 45 class), and Venezuela (*Lupo, Almirante Clemente, Capana* classes).

The first Fast Forty sale was announced in the fall of 1995: single mounts are to be on board the eight new Kuwaiti P37BRL patrol boats, built in France.

For older types, users *include* but probably are not limited to the following:

Type 64 twin (100-rnd automatic magazine): Italy (*Albatros* class [also carries one single mount], *Piave*), Venezuela (*Almirante Clemente* class)

Type 106 twin (32-rnd autofeeder): Germany (underway replenishment ships), Greece (*Thetis*, Osprey 55, *Rhein* classes), Turkey (*Koln, Rhein* classes)

Type 107 single (32-rnd autofeeder): Congo (*Pirana* class), Israel (*Sa'ar II* class), Morocco (*El Bachir* and *Champlain* classes), Norway (*Storm* class), Portugal (*Cacine, Baptiste de Andrade* classes), Spain (*Barcelo*), Tunisia (P48 class)

Type 564 single (144-rnd magazine): Argentina (TNC 45, *Halcon* classes), Cameroon (*Bakassi*, P48 class), Chile (*Guacolda*), Ecuador (*Manta* class, rearmed with Emerlec 30), Egypt (*Descubierta* class), Finland (*Nuoli* class), France ("Patra" and Super "Patra" classes), Gabon (*Gen N.B. Kounba, N'Guene, Champlain* class LST), Germany (*Tiger* class), Libya (*Dat Assawari*), Malaysia (Combattante II, *Jerong*, PZ classes), Mauretania ("Patra" class, *Barcelo* class), Mexico (*Halcon* class), Morocco (PR 72, Osprey 55, *Vigilance, Lazaga*, and *Descubierta* classes), Norway (*Hauk, Snogg* classes), Saudi Arabia (*Jaguars*), Singapore (FPB 45 and Type A classes), Spain (*Descubierta, Lazaga* classes), Taiwan (*Perry* class), Thailand (*Ratcharit* class, *Prabarapak* class, PSMM Mk 5 class), Turkey (*Jaguar* and *Kartal* classes), Uruguay (*Vigilance* class), Venezuela (*Constitucion* class)

Total Breda production was about 100 single and 250 twin mounts; it is not clear whether the latter figure includes Compacts.

◆ Oerlikon/OTO 35 mm (Type GDM-C)

See Oerlikon 35mm guns below.

◆ Breda 30mm

Caliber: 30mm/82 (369-g projectile) (0.813 lb)
Rate of Fire: 800 rnd/min/gun
Muzzle Velocity: 1040 m/sec (HE) (3410 ft/sec); 1220 m/sec (APDS) (4000 ft/sec)
Maximum Range: Effective range 3000 m (time of flight 5.36 sec with HE round) (3300 yd)
Training Rate: 140 deg/sec (elevation 80 deg/sec)
Elevation/Depression: +85/−13 deg
Ammunition Capacity: 160 rnd
Weight: 1200 kg empty/1330 kg loaded (2640/2930 lb)
Working Circle: 2.72 m (107.1 in)

Announced in 1984, this Breda single mounting for the German Mauser MK 30mm Model F gun uses a dual feed and standard NATO ammunition (as in the U.S. GAU-8). A new locally controlled version was announced in 1986. It is gyrostabilized and joystick controlled using optics that are LOS stabilized. Aim-off is automatically calculated while the target is kept in sight. A twin compact version was announced in 1980, carrying 1100 (Type B) or 2000 (Type A) rounds. Training and elevation rates are 130 and 75 deg/sec. Elevation limits are +80/−13 deg, and the working circle has a radius of 2.523 m.

Breda single compact 30mm mounting. (Breda)

A model of the new Myriad close-in defensive weapon, at the Paris Air Show, 1989. The canted platform is similar to that employed in the Seaguard system (which Contraves manufactures). As in Seaguard, the director is separate from the mounting. (Author)

Users: France (standard small-caliber gun [Artillerie Nouvelle de Petit Calibre] adopted 1994), Italy (*Zara* [twin], *Corrubia*, CNL 39 classes for Customs Service) and Thailand (twin: *Kamronsin* and *Srinakarin* class). A planned purchase for the Venezuelan *Constitucion* class was canceled. The French guns are made in Italy, but GIAT makes their ammunition (Olin made the first batch, however).

♦ Breda-Oerlikon 25mm KBA

See Oerlikon (BMARC) 25mm, below.

♦ Myriad

> **Caliber:** 25mm
> **Rate of Fire:** 10,000 rnd/min
> **Muzzle Velocity:** 1270 m/sec (1285 m/sec for APDS-T)
> **Maximum Range:** Effective range 1000+ m
> **Training Rate:** 3.0 rad/sec (train 2.5 rad/sec)
> **Ammunition Capacity:** 2000 rnd (two boxes per gun)
> **Weight:** 7700 kg (including ammunition)

This CIWS, first displayed at Mostra Navale in Genoa in 1989, is a joint venture by Breda, Contraves Italiana, Elsag, and Selenia. It employs a pair of Oerlikon 7-barrel 25mm KBD Gatling guns, which fire the high-velocity ammunition of the Oerlikon KBB gun (KBD is the first Oerlikon Gatling gun). The AMDS (antimissile discarding sabot) ammunition uses a 14.5mm tungsten-alloy rod penetrator (mass 156 g). Each gun has two boxes of ammunition, so it can switch between AMDS and APFDS-T. Remaining velocity at 500m range is 1190 m/sec; time to 500 m is 0.41 sec. Remaining velocity at 1000 m range is 1113 m/sec (time to 1000 m is 0.84 sec). The gun has a new patented antihangfire safety mechanism, which precludes firing ammunition from an unlocked breech. Each gun weighs 1600 kg, including its 1000 rnd of ammunition. Like Sea Zenith, Myriad is mounted on a tilted platform, so it can engage zenith attacks.

The associated director carries a pair of radars, a Ka-band (35 GHz) set for acquisition and a W-band (95 GHz) set that takes over at short ranges. With a much narrower beam, the W-band radar suffers less from multipath. Gun and director are connected to a standard MAGICS console via a MHIDAS bus; as in Seaguard, many trackers and many guns can be interconnected through a single bus. The system can accept search-radar data and conduct its own threat evaluation before firing.

The Myriad program started in 1988; Myriad completed its first firing trials at Rome on 9 March 1995. It may be offered to the Italian navy to replace Dardo in new ships.

NETHERLANDS

♦ Goalkeeper (SGE-30)

> **Caliber:** 30mm
> **Rate of Fire:** 4200 rnd/min
> **Muzzle Velocity:** 3318 ft/sec (3900 ft/sec firing discarding sabot ammunition, MPDS)
> **Maximum Range:** Engagement range about 2000 m (2200 yd)
> **Training Rate:** 100 deg/sec (elevation rate 80 deg/sec)
> **Elevation/Depression:** +85/−25 deg
> **Ammunition Capacity:** 1200 rnd
> **Weight:** 14,018 lb loaded plus 7766 lb off-mount
> **Working Circle:** 100 in

This close-in weapon developed by Signaal and General Electric combines Signaal's Flycatcher land-based AA FCS (including its radar tracker), a new search radar, and the latter's 30mm seven-barrel GAU-8/A Gatling gun. Because the search (slotted array) and tracking radars are separate, the system can detect new targets while engaging an existing target, to deal with stream attacks. The system carries a TV camera, and it can be integrated with the IRSCAN IRST. Goalkeeper employs closed-loop spotting of the type used in Phalanx. Two fixed-program computers close servo loops for target tracking and perform ballistic calculations. A software-controlled computer controls the system. Work is currently proceeding on new tracking algorithms to handle evasive targets such as Exocet Block II.

The slotted-array X-band search radar (1.5 × 30/60-deg beam) scans at 60 rpm. The monopulse pulse-compression Cassegrain dish operates at X- and Ka-bands. The X-band beamwidth (2.4 deg) is greater than that of the acquisition radar, to assure very rapid handover without additional search. Both radars have standard anticlutter and ECCM features, such as pulse compression, pulse-to-pulse coherence (for Doppler-MTI tracking), frequency diversity, and flexible waveforms (adaptive transmission). Once the X-band tracker has acquired the target, the

Goalkeeper on board HMS *Invincible*, 1990. (E. Grove)

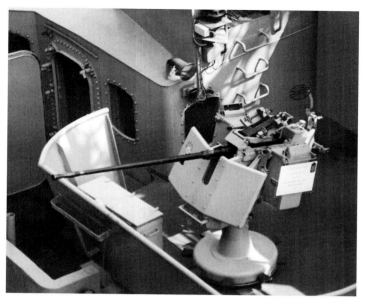

The Norwegian KV-SK/20 20mm mount (for the German Rh 202 gun) on board the frigate *Stavanger* in 1992. (Author)

0.6-deg beam of the Ka-band tracker takes over; Signaal claims that this narrow beam avoids reflection off the sea. The signal/noise ratios of the X- and Ka-band tracker radars are continuously and automatically compared to reject clutter and jamming. In automatic operation, the radar limits itself to targets in a 2–7-km range bracket, with radial speeds of over 150 m/sec. Total reaction time against a Mach 2 sea-skimmer, including automatic detection, IFF interrogation, 90-deg tracker slew, tracker elevation, X-band lock-on, and computer run-in, is about 5.5 sec, the engagement beginning at 1.5 km with maximum kill probability at 300 m.

The RNLN version has a 30-deg radar vertical beam width, compared to 60 deg in the RN version, on the theory that since the primary target is a sea-skimmer it is better not to spread the available energy. Programmed range is 8 nm, but the radar will detect targets at 16. The system tracks 30 targets, engaging the four most urgent. If there are more, it minimizes salvo length to engage as many as possible. The gun fires for about 0.2 sec/engagement, and can deal with two pairs of sea-skimmers about 5 sec apart.

Signaal first demonstrated the GAU-8/Flycatcher combination in November 1979, against targets at a range of about 1000 m.

A new nondeck-penetrating version was demonstrated in April 1994. With the addition of an ammunition slipring, the ammunition drum could be placed away from the gun, below or above deck.

At this time Signaal also announced an enhanced antiair/surface mode using new ammunition (Frangible Missile Piercing Discarding Sabot [FMPDS]) and new fire-control algorithms. FMPDS contains a brittle tungsten alloy penetrator, which breaks up soon after penetration, to destroy interior components, neutralizing an aircraft or surface target. The earlier MPDS ammunition is intended to penetrate missile sections and detonate the warhead, as in Phalanx.

The new penetrator also retains its energy about twice as long as MPDS, losing only half as much (an MPDS round hits at 1500 m/sec after losing 1040 m/sec, but FMPDS hits at 1980 m/sec, losing only 560 m/sec). There is also interest in long-rod penetrators. Reportedly the Korean KDX will have one Goalkeeper loaded with each type of ammunition, to combine the axial damage pattern of the kinetic penetrator with radial damage by HE.

Users: Korea (KDX), Netherlands (*Tromp, Karel Doorman, van Heemskerck, Kortenaer* classes), Oman (new corvettes), Qatar ("Vita" class), UAE (FPB 62), United Kingdom (*Invincible,* Type 22 Batch 3 classes); temporarily (in containerized form) on German *Bremen* class during the Gulf War.

NORWAY

Kongsberg (NFT) offers a manual mounting for the Mauser 25mm/73 Model E gun, based on its mounting for the Rhine-metall Rh 202 20mm gun. Elevation limits are +70/−15 deg. The gun weighs 109 kg and fires 900 rnd/min from boxes on either side. The Breda 25KBA is comparable.

◆ NFT Armored Turret

The projected Norwegian fast-attack boat will use a version of the new NFT armored turret developed for vehicles; it is also used (in more heavily armored form) in Norwegian coast defenses (carrying a Rhinemetall 20mm gun). The power-driven turret, which is controlled by joystick, can carry a 20- or 25mm gun. It can also operate manually if power is interrupted. The FPB version will carry more ammunition than the standard vehicle version described here.

The NFT turret was developed (with Hagglund of Sweden) for the M 113 armored personnel carrier; initially, this single-operator, welded-steel turret carried an Rh 202 cannon. Ultimately, it carried a Mauser 25mm Model E cannon with a coaxial 7.62mm MG 3 machine gun. The combat weight of this version (including 1000 rnd) is about 1000 kg. The bearing ring diameter is 1.2 m. Elevation limits are +50/−10 deg. Power train (not elevation) is up to 90 deg/sec. A newer version, with a higher profile (height 0.605 m above the vehicle roof), carries a dual-feed Rh 202 (200 rnd of 20mm) and a coaxial 7.62mm MG 3 (400 rnd) and weighs 850 kg. There are two speeds for manual train (there is no power option). Swept radius is 2.3 m.

RUSSIA

Gun systems are developed under sequential "A" designations (in a system apparently adopted in the mid-1960s), then redesignated in an AK series when adopted for service. The A series includes A-215, the 122mm rocket system.

Manufacturers: Yurga Engineering Plant makes the twin 130mm gun. Tulamashvod (Tula Ordnance Plant, Sporting and Hunting Guns Central R&D Bureau) is responsible for minor-caliber weapons (AK-630 and below).

◆ AK-130 (Lev)

Caliber: 130mm/54 (33.4-kg shell, 3.56-kg HE)
Muzzle Velocity: 850 m/sec
Maximum Rate of Fire: 35–60 rnd/min/mount
Maximum Range: About 23,000 m
Effective Range: Over 20 km
Elevation/Train Rates: 25 deg/sec
Elevation/Depression: +80/−10 deg
Ammunition Capacity: 180
Weight: 94 t

This fully automatic dual-purpose weapon may be triaxially stabilized. The barrels are liquid-cooled. The A-218 gun employs a ZiF-94 mounting (it is based on an earlier abortive A-217 on a 37t ZiF-92 single mount developed in 1967). Three types of rounds are advertised (A3-F-44, with a mechanical base fuze; A3-ZC-44 with a mechanical time fuze, and A3-ZC-44R with a proximity fuze). There may also be a laser-guided shell. The proximity-fuzed round may not have been introduced until the 1980s, as a means of dealing with cruise missiles. Lethal radius, against a cruise missile, is 8 m; against an airplane or helicopter it is 15 m. The complete round weighs 52.8 kg and is 1364–1369 mm long.

A standard Soviet twin 130mm mount.

The associated fire-control radar is Kite Screech (FCS T-91). The mount also has local controls.

According to a recent Polish account, difficulties with this mount nearly led to its replacement by a single 180mm gun.

Users: Russia (*Admiral Lazarev, Admiral Chebanenko, Sovremmennyy,* and *Slava* classes).

◆ SM-2-1 (56-SM gun)

Caliber: 130mm (5.1 in)/57.6 (33.5-kg shell with 20-kg cartridge)
Rate of Fire: 13–15 rnd/min/barrel (max)
Muzzle Velocity: 945 m/sec (3100 ft/sec)
Maximum Range: 27,800 m (surface); 16,000–18,000 (effective); ceiling 21,000 m
Train/Elevation Rates: 18 deg/sec (manual: 2.5–3 deg/sec)
Elevation/Depression: +82/−7 deg
Weight: 58.6 t

This standard postwar triaxially stabilized mount may have been derived from the wartime German 128mm fully stabilized AA weapon. Work began in 1943, the specification was approved in April 1944, and the SM-2 prototype was completed in 1949. SM-5-1 was an analogous mount, carrying two 100mm/70 guns in the *Sverdlovs*. According to one recent Russian source, late

Twin 130mm/58 mount on board a Chinese "Luda"-class destroyer. (U.S. Naval Institute)

Kotlins had a new mount, SM-62: +85/−5 deg, train/elevation rates 20 deg/sec, 14 men on the mount. This gun and mount are currently manufactured in China (PRC), the Chinese version differing from the extinct Russian prototype in lacking mechanical cross-level stabilization; the edges of the Chinese gunhouse are rounded, and there is no range-only radar (Egg Cup). The associated fire-control radar is Sun Visor.

Users: China ("Luda" class).

◆ AK-100

Caliber: 100mm/59 (15.6 kg shell)
Rate of Fire: 60, 45, or 15 rnd/min (322 ready-use rounds)
Muzzle Velocity: 880 m/sec
Maximum Range: 21,500 m (effective range 8000 m)
Training Rate: 35 deg/sec (elevation 30 deg/sec)
Elevation/Depression: −10/+85 deg
Weight: 35.7 t (empty)

A single 100mm gun on board the *Udaloy*-class destroy *Admiral Vinogradov*, 1990, with its Kite Screech control radar in the background. (S. Zaloga)

This automatic single-barreled water-cooled mount has optronic analog controls. Shells: A3-OF-58 with mechanical impact fuze, A3-ZC-58 with mechanical time fuze, A3-ZC-58R with proximity fuze. Lethal radius, using the proximity fuze, is 5 m against a cruise missile or 10 m against an airplane or helicopter. The complete round weighs 26.8 kg and is 1026–1033 mm long. The specification (TTZ) was approved in September 1967 and the gun was accepted for service in 1978. The gun is A-214 and the mount is ZiF-91.

Users: Russia (*Kirov, Udaloy,* Krivak II/III classes), Ukraine (Krivak III class).

◆ 100mm/56 (B-34)

Caliber: 3.9in/56 (15.6-kg shell, 28-kg fixed rnd) (34.4/62 lb)
Rate of Fire: 12 rnd/min
Muzzle Velocity: 900 m/sec (2950 ft/sec)
Maximum Range: 22,000 m (effective range 10,000 m) (24,000/10,900 yd)
Elevation/Depression: +85/−5 deg
Weight: 7.7 t (single mount)

This obsolescent single-shielded mount was made under license in China. The original maximum elevation was 40 deg. This mount was formerly used as a secondary battery for cruisers and was modernized in 1947. Electrically driven, the gun can fire in automatic, local, or manual modes. The breech is a horizontal sliding block. China now manufactures an autoloading twin version (see above).

The associated director is Wasp Head with (in a few PRC ships) a Rice Lamp radar.

Users: China (some Jianghu, "Jiangnan" class), North Korea (Soho, Najin, Taechong classes).

The 100mm T-55 tank gun (D-10T) is standard on "Yaz"- and "Vosh"-class river monitors; previous reports of 115mm guns were apparently incorrect.

♦ 90-K

Caliber: 85mm/52 (9.6-kg shell, 13-kg fixed round) (20.9/28.7 lb)
Rate of Fire: 15–18 rnd/min
Muzzle Velocity: 800 m/sec
Maximum Range: 15,000 m (effective range 8000–9000 m surface, 6000 m air) (16,400/8700–9800 yd)
Elevation/Depression: +85/−5 deg (elevation rate 8 deg/sec)
Weight: 5.3 t

This single mount apparently survives only in North Korea and Rumania. It (or a tank gun) arms the "Chong Jin," Korean-built "S.O. 1," and ex-Soviet *Tral*-class minesweeper/patrol boats.

♦ AK-726 and AK-176/AK-176M

Caliber: 3in (5.9-kg shell, 16-kg fixed round) (13/35 lb)
Rate of Fire: 100 rnd/min/barrel
Muzzle Velocity: 980 m/sec
Maximum Range: 15,700 m (effective at 11,000 m; ceiling 13,000 m; effective for AA at 6000–7000 m)
Training Rate: 36 deg/sec (elevation: 36 deg/sec)
Elevation/Depression: +84 deg/−2 deg
Weight: 26 t

Data apply to AK-726 (mount ZiF-67). The caliber is 3 in, not 76 mm. This mount, introduced in 1961, is semiautomatic, like the U.S. twin 3in/50; rounds are hoisted 30 at a time (per barrel) into the gunhouse. Standard stowage is 138 rnd/gun. The gun is not water-cooled, but standard practice is to use a firehose to cool down the barrel after an engagement. The turret has an unusually deep cleft, so the guns can be mounted aft of the center of the trunnion, for a high angle of elevation. Shells are A3-ZC/OF-62 with impact fuze and A3-ZC/OF-62P with proximity fuze. The full round weighs 12.4 kg (818 mm long). Lethal radius, using the proximity fuze, is 8 m against a cruise missile or helicopter. The associated fire-control radars are Hawk Screech and Owl Screech.

Development was ordered in April 1954.

Users: Algeria (Koni), Azerbaijan (Petya II), Bulgaria (Koni), Cuba (Koni), Ethiopia (Petya II), India (Kashin, Petya, Ugra), Libya (Koni), Poland (Kashin), Rumania (*Muntenia*, Tetal, "Tarantul" classes), Russia (Kara, Kynda, Kashin, Krivak I, Petya, Mirka, *Ivan Rogov*, Kapusta, *Smolnyy*, *Ivan Susanin*, *Arktika* classes), Syria (Petya III), Vietnam (Petya II/III), Yugoslavia (Koni, *Kotor* classes)

AK-176 is a more modern single water-cooled mount firing the same ammunition (at the same velocity) at 120–30 rnd/min (stowage 152 rnd). Elevation limits are −10/+85 deg. Train/elevation rates are 35 and 30 deg/sec. The mount can be fired

Twin 76.2mm/59 guns arm this Mirka-class ASW corvette. There are torpedo decoys stowed on deck aft, four RBU-6000 rocket launchers, and 40cm torpedo tubes. (U.S. Naval Institute)

either in automatic or in fall-back manned mode. The current version is AK-176M. The mount weighs 11.2 t empty (13.1 t loaded).

Shells are fed continuously from two sides. Each side contains a transporter (76 rnd), a chain hoist, and a pendulum which strips a round from the hoist and places it on the receiver of the elevating mass. The FCS is Vympel-221 with Kondensor-221 backup. This gun (A-221) was developed in parallel with a new 57mm gun (A-220) under a program begun about 1969; A-221 was first tested aboard a "Tarantul" on 23–30 November 1979 and was accepted into service as AK-176. A-220 was successfully tested in 1977–78 on board an "Osa" but did not enter service.

The associated fire-control radar is Bass Tilt.

Users: Azerbaijan (Svetlyak), Cuba ("Tarantul II," Pauk), Georgia (Grisha V, Muravey), Guinea (Bogomol), Guinea-Bissau (Bogomol), India (*Khukri*, "Tarantul," Pauk), Poland (*Kaszub*, "Tarantul"), Romania ("Tarantul"), Russia (Grisha, Parchim, "Nanuchka III/IV," "Tarantul," Matka, Dergach, Mukha, Pauk, Babochka, Muravey, Svetlyak, Slepen, "Vosh," Gorya, Ropucha II), Ukraine (Grisha V, Petya II), Yemen ("Tarantul").

◆ 81-K

Caliber: 3in/55 (6.6-kg shell, 11.2-kg fixed round) (14.6/24.7 lb)
Rate of Fire: 17–20 rnd/min
Muzzle Velocity: 815 m/sec (2675 ft/sec)
Maximum Range: 13,500 m (14,600 yd)
Elevation/Depression: +85 deg
Weight: Approx. 5 t

This weapon was introduced in the Soviet navy in 1936.

◆ 76.2mm/48 Single Mount (D-56TM gun)

Caliber: 76.2mm/48
Maximum Rate of Fire: 4–6 rnd/min (claimed 15 rnd/min max)
Muzzle Velocity: 680 m/sec (2230 ft/sec) (HE shell)
Maximum Range: About 800 m effective range, point-blank (about 870 yd)
Elevation/Depression: +30/−4 deg

A "Tarantul"-class missile boat of the Soviet Baltic Fleet fires her single 76.2mm gun. The radome atop her mast is Light Bulb, probably a missile data link. Below it is a Bass Tilt fire-control radar, and the big radome is Band Stand. The missiles are SS-N-2Cs. (TASS via SOVFOTO)

Two Shmel'-class gunboats, probably on the Amur, show their tank-type 76.2mm guns. The guns aft are machine guns; later ships of this type have the standard twin 25mm (over and under) mount. (TASS via SOVFOTO)

The PT-76 tank turret gun is found in Shmel'-class river monitors.

◆ AK-725 (ZiF-72)

Caliber: 57mm/75 (2.7-kg shell, 5-kg fixed round) (6/11 lb)
Rate of Fire: 100 rnd/min/barrel
Muzzle Velocity: 1020 m/sec (3345 ft/sec)
Maximum Range: 13.2 km horizontal, 6.7 km vertical (14,400 yd/ 22,000 ft); effective ranges about 9000 m horizontal, 5000–6000 m vertical (9800 yd/16,400–19,700 ft)
Elevation/Depression: +85/−10 deg
Train (Elevation) Rates: 35 (30) deg/sec
Weight: 25 t (without ammunition)

The barrels are water-cooled. The gun is recoil-operated. Unlike the various forms of ZiF-31B, this mount is fully enclosed, with a metal shield; ammunition supply is presumably fully automatic. Standard stowage is 1100 rounds. Control is generally by a Muff Cob radar director. The operational requirement (TTZ) was issued on 30 November 1956, the design was approved on 24 May 1958, the prototype was tested in 1960, and this mount entered service in 1963. In some classes, later units have the newer 76.2mm/60 in place of this weapon.

57mm Soviet-type twin mount on board the Indian frigate *Ganga*. (*Ships of the World*)

Users: Algeria ("Nanuchka"), Bulgaria (Poti), Cambodia (Turya), Cuba (Turya), Ethiopia (Turya), Georgia (Grisha I, Turya), India (*Godavari*, "Nanuchka II"), Indonesia (Parchim), Libya (Nanuchka), Lithuania (Grisha III, Turya), Rumania (Poti), Russia (*Moskva*, Kresta I/II, Grisha I/II/III, "Nanuchka I," Turya, Poti, Ropucha I, *Berezina*, *Boris Chilikin*), Yemen (Ropucha).

◆ ZiF-31B/Type 66

Caliber: 57mm/70 (2.8-kg shell, 6.3–6.6-kg rnd) (6.2/13.9–14.5 lb)
Rate of Fire: 150 rnd/min/gun
Muzzle Velocity: 900–1000 m/sec (2950–3280 ft/sec)
Maximum Range: 4500 m vertical (14,700 ft)
Training Rate: 30 deg/sec (elevation 25 deg/sec)
Elevation/Depression: +85/−10 deg
Weight: 10.8 t

Probably only the twin mount survives in Russian service, if at all; it entered service in 1958 on board modernized *Skoriy*-class destroyers (Project 31, hence the designation) and was a navalized version of the 57mm/70 M-50 used by the Soviet army. Like earlier Soviet naval AA guns, this one loads from clips. Heating and clip-feeding would probably limit its effective rate of fire to 90 rnd/min. The associated fire-control radar is Muff Cob. ZiF-31B was made in China as Type 66.

ZiF-71 was the corresponding single mount (train/elevation rates 50/40 deg/sec, weight 4.65 t); ZiF-75 was the quadruple. The ZiF-71 gun fires 170–210 rnd/min.

The PRC navy uses a water-cooled version of this weapon, designated Type 76 (see below). Muzzle velocity is 1000 m/sec (3280 ft/sec), and maximum horizontal and vertical ranges are 15,000 and 10,000 m. Rate of fire is 140–160 rnd/min, and elevation limits are +85/−5 deg. Maximum laying speeds are 25 deg/sec both in train and in elevation, but the mount can sweep (i.e., can move less precisely) at 40 deg/sec both in train and in

The Chinese cadet training ship *Zheng He* shows her twin Type 66 (ZiF-31) open gun mount forward, with a pair of Type 69 (AK-230) 30mm mounts abaft it. The top of the pilot house carries a Round Ball FCS radar; the mast carries Eye Shield and a pair of Type 756 surface-search antennas. (*Ships of the World*)

elevation. Total mount weight is 10,500 kg (23,140 lb). No working circle data are available, but the mount's length is 6.583 m and width is 3.36 m (height is 2.264 m).

Users: Bangladesh (Hainan [66]), Burma (Hainan [66]), China ("Luda" [76], Hainan [66], Haiju [66], Shanghai [66], Yukan [66], Daxin [66], Shengli [66]), Egypt (Hainan [66], Jianghu [66]), Guinea (T-58 [ZIF-31B]), North Korea ("Najin," Hainan [66], Tae-chong), Pakistan (Hainan [66]), Rumania (Shanghai [66], Croitar [ZIF-31]), Russia (T-58, Sasha, Alligator, Ugra, Don, Lama, Ingul, *Dobrynya Nikitich*, Uda, Manych, Okhtensky classes, all ZIF-31B), Vietnam (*Admirable* class [66]).

◆ 37mm (70-K/V-11M/V-47M/Type 76/NG15–2)

Caliber: 37mm/63 (0.74-kg shell, 1.8-kg round) (1.6/4.0 lb)
Rate of Fire: 160–180 rnd/min/gun twin; 130 rnd/min/gun single)
Muzzle Velocity: 880 m/sec (2890 ft/sec)
Maximum Range: 9500 m (10,400 yd)
Training Rate: (Manual, in V-11M) 19.6 deg/sec (elevation 15 deg/sec)
Elevation/Depression: +85/–10 deg
Ammunition Capacity: 5-rnd clips
Weight: 6170-lb single mount, 8375-lb twin mount

This obsolescent prewar weapon, derived from a prewar Bofors 25mm gun, is standard in the PRC navy in both single and twin versions. Twin mounts survive in other navies, for example, on board T-43–class minesweepers. The single guns were air-cooled, with the usual Bofors-type recoil springs surrounding the bases, and barrels had to be changed after about 100 rnd. The twin mount, introduced in 1948, is similar in layout to the standard U.S. twin 40mm of the time, with liquid-cooled guns. 70-K is the original single mount, V-11M the initial-production twin naval mount, and V-47M the later widely used twin mount with water-cooled barrels. Type 76 is V-47M built under license in China. NG15–2 is a Chinese version in which this gun is used in a mounting similar to that of the Breda Compact (see above).

Users (original 37mm type): Albania (Shanghai, T-43), Algeria (T-43), Azerbaijan (T-43), Bangladesh (Jianghu, Shanghai), Bulgaria (T-43), China ("Luda," Jianghu, Jiangnan, Shanghai, T-43,

A Russian twin liquid-cooled 37mm/63. (TASS via SOVFOTO)

LST, Yukan, LSM, auxiliaries), Egypt (Jianghu, Shanghai, T-43), Indonesia (*Burudjulasad*, *Multatuli*, *Teluk Amboina*), North Korea (Sinpo, Shanghai, S.O. 1, Chodo, *Tral* classes), Pakistan (Shanghai, *Nasr*), Rumania (M40, Shanghai, T-301), Russia (Alesha, Sasha, T-43, Polyarnik), Sierra Leone (Shanghai), Sri Lanka (Sooraya), Syria (T-43), Tanzania (Shanghai), Thailand (Jianghu), Tunisia (Shanghai), Vietnam (*Barnegat*, *Admirable*), Zaire (Shanghai).

◆ AK-630/AK-630M/AK-306

> **Caliber:** 30mm/54 (0.384-kg shell with 30g explosive)
> **Rate of Fire:** 4800–5000 rnd/min/mount (probably 1000 rnd/min effective rate; lifetime 8000 rnd)
> **Muzzle Velocity:** 890 m/sec
> **Maximum Range:** 8100 m (maximum altitude probably 500–600 m) (8860 yd; 1640–1970 ft) (effective range 4000 m)
> **Elevation/Depression:** +88/−12 deg
> **Training Rate:** 70 deg/sec (elevation 50 deg/sec)
> **Weight:** 1 t empty; 1.981 t loaded (AK-630M)

This six-barreled Gatling, using the AO-18 gun, has a mount similar to that of the twin 30mm weapon. Generally controlled by Bass Tilt (MR-123) or by a remote Kolonka II visual director, it is the standard current close-in defensive weapon. The mount stows 2000 rnd. AK-630M (1980) adds a 1000-rnd reserve bin. The gun fires in 400-rnd bursts, with a short cooling interval between bursts. Of all rounds 80% are within 11 mrad on each firing cycle.

A 30mm Gatling gun on board the cruiser *Marshal Ustinov*, 1989. (S. Zaloga)

This weapon first appeared in the summer of 1970. Development was ordered on 15 July 1963; the developmental designation for AK-630 was A-213. It was tested in 1971–73 and accepted for service on 6 January 1976. A-213M was the developmental designation for the improved AK-630M.

AK-630M1-2 (announced at Abu Dhabi in 1993) is a double (under-and-over) version of AK-630, firing 10,000 rnd/min, and carrying 4000 rnd. Weights: 2.5 t empty, 6.5 t loaded. Elevation limits are +90/−25 deg (elevation rate 50 deg/sec, traverse rate 70 deg/sec to +/−180 deg). This gun completed firing trials late in 1995.

AK-306 (1980, developmental designation A-219) is a lightweight (self-contained) version of AK-630 using the AO-18L gun, which is derated to 750–1000 rnd/min. Lifetime increases to 18,000 rnd. AK-630 weighs 1000 kg (without ammunition) but requires an additional 800 kg off-mount; -306 weighs 1100 kg altogether (less ammunition). It stows 480 rnd/mount, which can be fired in one burst. Control is by optical sight (OPU-1) only. There may also be a three-barrel version.

◆ 30mm Twin Mount (AK-230/Type 69)

> **Caliber:** 30mm/65 (0.36-kg shell, 1.0-kg round) (0.8/2.2 lb)
> **Rate of Fire:** Approx. 1050 rnd/min/barrel (effective rate 200–240)
> **Muzzle Velocity:** 1050 m/sec (3440 ft/sec)
> **Effective Range:** 4000 m (air targets)/2.2 nm (surface targets)
> **Training Rate:** 35 deg/sec (elevation 24 deg/sec)
> **Elevation/Depression:** +87/−12 deg
> **Ammunition Capacity:** Total 1000
> **Weight:** 1905 kg (Type A) or 1857 kg (Type B)

This weapon is widely used and widely exported. The unmanned mount is fully enclosed, stabilized, and power-driven. The gun tubes are liquid-cooled, and the NN30 guns are gas-operated. This mount is normally controlled by a Drum Tilt radar or by a remote Kolonka I optical director. The gun is a revolver, with a 4-rnd rotating breech. This weapon appeared in 1959, as a successor to the earlier twin 25mm.

Russian twin 30mm (AK-230) mount. Presumably, the tub at right is for local control.

A modified AK-230 is produced in the PRC as Type 69. Elevation limits are +87/−12 deg, and the mount trains at 70 deg/sec and elevates at 50 deg/sec. Total weight is 1800 kg (3967 lb): the weight figure above may include ammunition. Overall dimensions: 3.110 × 2.100 × 1.462 m.

◆ CADS-1 (Steelet)

See Kortik/Kashtan (SA-N-11) above. The NATO designation, CADS, means Combined (i.e., gun/missile) Air-Defense System.

◆ 30mm Grenade Launcher (BP-30)

This one-man single mount appeared in 1976. It fires a lightweight shell (28 kg) at low velocity (185 m/sec); it fires 400 rnd/min and the standard mount carries 400 rounds. Maximum range is 1.75 km. Presumably BP-30 is equivalent to the U.S. Mk 19 40mm grenade launcher.

◆ 25mm Twin Mount (2M-3M/Type 61)

> **Caliber:** 25mm/60 (0.25-kg shell, 0.7-kg rnd) (0.55/1.5 lb)
> **Rate of Fire:** 450 rnd/bbl/min; effective rate 270–300 rnd/bbl/min (also given as 150–225 rnd/barrel/min)
> **Muzzle Velocity:** 910 m/sec (2980 ft/sec)
> **Maximum Range:** 3000 m; effective range 2300 m (3300/2500 yd)
> **Training Rate:** 40 deg/sec (elevation 70 deg/sec) under hydraulic power (manual rates are 15 and 25 deg/sec, respectively)
> **Elevation/Depression:** +85/−10 deg
> **Ammunition Capacity:** 130 rnd
> **Weight:** 1585 kg (Type 61: 1735 kg loaded)

Widely used for light craft, this mount carries two superimposed guns, each on its own cradle. They are versions of a 25mm air-cooled Bofors gun, mounted on their sides, fed from the left (from the right in the Chinese version, Type 61). Unlike larger Bofors guns, they are normally belt-fed, from 65-rnd belts via quadrant trays; but the guns can also be fed from 5-rnd clips. The

A CADS-N-1 combined gun-missile mounting. Above each Gatling gun are four guide rails for missile tubes, which are loaded vertically from below.

Twin 25mm AA guns on board a P-6–type motor torpedo boat, about 1962. (TASS via SOVFOTO)

gunner sits on the right side. 2M-3 entered service in 1952; the standard version is the upgraded 2M-3M.

The twin 30mm mount (AK-230) was developed to replace this gun.

◆ ZU-23-2

Caliber: 23mm/81
Rate of Fire: 1000 rnd/min/barrel (cyclic); effective rate 200 rnd/min/barrel
Muzzle Velocity: 970 m/sec (3180 ft/sec)
Maximum Range: 7000 m; effective range 2800 m (7700/3000 yd)
Training Rate: Manual
Maximum Elevation/Depression: +90/−10 deg
Ready-use Ammunition: 50 rnd/gun (box magazine)
Weight: 893 kg (1968 lb)

This twin-barreled weapon was originally developed for the Soviet army. The barrels are air-cooled. Bulgaria produces the ZU-23-2F version, but no naval sales have been reported. Finnish

ZU-23-2 mounts on board the Latvian minesweeper *Imanta*, June 1995. (H&L van Ginderen)

ZU-23s are being replaced by a missile-gun version (see Finland, above).

Users: Finland (standard light AA gun), Iran (*Sumner* class, *Saam*-class frigates; replaces Sea Cat, other types), Poland (standard light AA gun). The Indian government armed some of its merchant ships with this weapon during the Iran-Iraq War.

◆ 14.5mm Machine Gun (2M-5/2M-6/2M-7/Type 82)

Caliber: 14.5mm/93
Rate of Fire: 550–600 rnd/bbl/min
Muzzle Velocity: 1000 m/sec (3280 ft/sec)
Effective Range: 2000 m vs. aircraft, 2500 m vs. surface target
Maximum Elevation/Depression: +90/−10 deg
Ready-use Ammunition: 150 rnd/gun (linked belt)
Weight: 600 kg
Working Circle: 1600 mm

Data are for 2M-7.

These twin 14.5mm mounts, carrying the KPV gun, superseded wartime 12.7mm mounts (carrying the DShKM-2B gun). Compared to the earlier gun, KPV could penetrate more than

A 2M-7 14.5mm mount on board the *Udaloy*-class destroyer *Admiral Vinogradov*, 1990. The ship carried four such mounts. (S. Zaloga)

twice as much armor (32 vs. 15 mm) and could fire 500 m further. Work began in 1944. The side-by-side 2M-5 open hand-operated mount (550 kg, working circle 1820 mm) was protected by an 8mm shield. Tested in August 1947, it entered service in 1952. 2M-6, a fully enclosed power-operated side-by-side twin mount, also entered service in 1952. Elevation limits were +85/−5 deg (train/elevation rates were 50/35 deg/sec under power, or 25/15 deg/sec by hand). This mount weighed 1560 kg; working circle radius was 1749 mm. Protection: 7mm face and sides (8mm and 14mm in the 2M-6T version). The contemporary over-and-under hand-operated 2M-7 (in service 1951) had 8mm armor. Numbers on hand in the Soviet fleet, 1991: 2M-5, 80; 2M-6, 39; and 2M-7, 500. There were also army triple (ZPU-3) and quadruple (ZPU-4) mounts. Apparently the KGB's Pchela (Project 125P) used an aircraft-style 14.5mm twin mount rather than any of the naval mounts.

Applications were:

2M-5: Project 123bis (P-4 MTB) and Project 180
2M-6: Project 191M (river monitor) and Project 1204 (Shmel' class river gunboat)
2M-7: Zhuk (Project 1400), Project 368T (Poluchat), Project 151 (TR-40 class), Project 361T (K-8 class), etc. This mount is often found on surface combatants as an anti-piracy weapon.

China built 2M-5 as Type 82 and also built the Russian army ZPU-4 as a naval mount. Type 82 fires API (990 m/sec muzzle velocity) and API-T (tracer) (1000 m/sec) rounds. Working circle radius is 1.757 m [69.2 in]. Total weight, without ammunition, is 600 kg [1320 lb]. Mount capacity is 150 rnds.

Russian-made KPVs (single, twin, quad) are used by Albania, Algeria, Angola, Benin, Bulgaria, Congo, Cuba, Ethiopia, Guinea, Guinea-Bissau, India, Iraq, North Korea, Madagascar, Morocco, Mozambique, Nicaragua, Poland, Rumania (including a quad version), Russia, Seychelles, Somalia, Sri Lanka, Syria, Tanzania, Vietnam, and North Yemen. Chinese-made guns are used by Albania, Bangladesh, Congo, and Pakistan (in a quad mounting, for example, on the *Gearing* class).

◆ **UTES-M**

> **Caliber:** 12.7mm
> **Rate of Fire:** 700–800 rnd/bbl/min (effective rate 100)
> **Muzzle Velocity:** 860 m/sec
> **Effective Range:** 1500 m vs. aircraft, 2000 m vs. surface target
> **Maximum Elevation/Depression:** +85/−12 deg
> **Train (Elevation) Rates:** 25–30 (15–20) deg/sec
> **Ammunition Capacity:** 200 rnd
> **Diameter:** 1388 mm
> **Weight:** 630 kg

This twin enclosed remotely controlled mount carries 12.7mm NSVT guns, which were adopted by the Soviet Army in 1972 to replace the KPV. UTES-M was adopted by the navy in 1976. Applications: Projects 1206 (Lebed), 1208 (Yaz), 1209 (Utenok), 1258 (Vosh), 1259 (Olya), 1400M/ME (Zhuk), 904 (Orlonok WIG), 1595 (*Neon Antonov* class), etc.

A UTES-M mount. Note the EO sight (with windshield-wiper) above the mount, which is standard. (*Ships of the World*)

SOUTH AFRICA

LIW is developing a 5t twin-stabilized 35mm dual-purpose gun (GA 35 DPG) for possible installation on board future South African corvettes, based on its eGLaS towed 35mm mount and GA 35 gun. The gun is locally designed, but appears to have been derived from the Oerlikon KCB, details of which may have been obtained via France. LIW is also considering a single locally or director-controlled version (Manned General-Purpose Gun) and a single version carrying four SAHV-3 missiles (Hybrid GPG).

SPAIN

◆ **Meroka/Sardin**

> **Caliber:** 20mm/120 (round weight 320 g, including 102-g projectile) (0.71/0.225 lb)
> **Rate of Fire:** 2 bursts/sec (9000 rnd/min during burst that lasts 0.080 sec)
> **Muzzle Velocity:** 1300 m/sec (4260 ft/sec)
> **Maximum Elevation/Depression:** +85/−15
> **Ready-use Ammunition:** 720 rnd (60/barrel) (2160 in future version)
> **Weight:** 4500 kg on mount; plus 421 kg off mount (9920/928 lb)

Bazan's CIWS is based on a Spanish army AA weapon. Targets are acquired by a Selenia RAN-11L/X search radar via a Selenia PDS-10 tactical-data console. The on-mount Sharpshooter radar FCS locks onto targets at 5000 m. It uses off-boresight tracking to handle low fliers. An optronic system (by Empresa Nacional de Optica, ENOSA) provides backup against jamming (it is being replaced by an Israeli LLLTV, tested in 1988). There is no closed-loop spotting.

Meroka. (Bazan)

The twelve 20mm Oerlikon gun barrels, firing a special hard-core penetrator, are arranged in two horizontal rows, very close together, slightly skewed to spread out a burst. Each row of guns is fed by its own belt, both of them from a magazine which can be reloaded while the gun fires. Meroka fires 2 bursts/sec, each consisting of four groups of three rounds (to limit recoil effects), lasting 0.08 sec. In theory, Meroka should enjoy a high burst rate without suffering the time-to-rate and time-to-stop problems of a Gatling. However, the mount reportedly suffers vibration problems, and the three adjacent barrels can interfere with each other, causing undue dispersion. Meroka is expected to begin hitting at 1500 m and to destroy targets at 500 m (550 yd).

Of 21 mounts in service, 18 are Mod 2A, which added the thermal imager to Model 2. Under an October 1995 contract Bazan is upgrading them to Mod 2A3 (the work is being done during regular 1996–97 overhauls; the prototype is on board *Navarra*). The current analog processor is replaced by three 32-bit digital processors on a bus (central, command, ballistics). A new digital firing circuit can fire the barrels in any desired sequence, using new independent electric firing pins in each barrel. This version has a fully automatic mode, BITE, and an on-board trainer. The next step, in the last two *Santa Maria*–class frigates, is Mod 2B, with a new RTN-30X radar and a new RAN-30L/X target acquisition radar. The prototype is a Mod 2(V) on board *Canarias*; another Mod 2(V) is on board *Principe de Asturias* (her other three guns are Mod 2As). Ultimately all Mod 2As will presumably be upgraded to Mod 2Bs.

Future Merokas will be redesigned for reduced RCS and greater on-board ammo stowage. The version in the next class of frigates (F 100 type) may combine light missiles with the guns. It is probably Sardin, Bazan's hybrid Meroka replacement.

Development began in 1975, Meroka was first installed in late 1986, and an upgrade program (to Mod 2A) was completed in 1992. Unit price (1994) is $3.42M.

Users: Spain (*Principe de Asturias, Santa Maria, Baleares, Mar del Norte, Mar del Sud* classes).

SWEDEN

Israel uses the 84mm Carl Gustaf antitank weapon, on board "Super Dvora"–class patrol boats.

◆ Bofors 6in

Caliber: 152mm/50 (101-lb shell, 71.8-lb cartridge)
Rate of Fire: 12–15 rnd/min/gun
Muzzle Velocity: 2950 ft/sec
Maximum Range: 28,000 yd
Elevation/Depression: +60/−10 deg
Weight: 113 t (no ammunition)

These weapons, aboard two Peruvian cruisers, are now the most powerful guns in service afloat, the cruisers having been brought back into active service when hostilities with Ecuador began. Unusually, the shell and cartridge case are stowed separately (for ease of handling) but are rammed together to form what amounts to a fixed round on a cartridge carrier before hoisting to the vertical sliding-wedge breech. The loading tray elevates with the gun for all-elevation loading. British observers criticized the design on the ground that ramming the shell and cartridge case together demanded extraordinarily close production tolerances.

Armor: 4.9in face and rear, 2in roof, 1.2in sides.

Work on this design began in 1937; these mounts first appeared on board Swedish *Tre Kronor*–class cruisers (1947).

◆ Bofors 4.7in/50 (120mm)

Caliber: 120mm/50 (21-kg HE shell; 40-kg complete rnd) (46.3/88.2 lb)
Rate of Fire: 45 rnd/min/barrel
Muzzle Velocity: 850 m/sec (2790 ft/sec)
Maximum Range: 13,000 m surface fire; 7000 m AA (14,200/7700 yd)
Training Rate: 25 deg/sec (elevation 40 deg/sec)
Elevation/Depression: +85/−10 deg
Ammunition Capacity: 104 rnd (52/gun)
Weight: 55 t (67 t including rotating platform and ammunition)

This gun survives in the two Dutch *Tromp*-class destroyers. The mount was considered extremely advanced when it appeared in 1950, and about 1953 the Royal Navy considered adoption. The mount was rejected: it was too heavy, too noisy, and not flash- or gas-tight. Reportedly, the Dutch navy found the mount too heavy (and vibrations too violent during rapid firing) for its destroyers.

◆ Bofors 4.7in/46 (TAK 120)

Caliber: 120mm (21-kg HE shell; 35-kg complete rnd) (46.3/77.1 lb)
Rate of Fire: 80 rnd/min
Muzzle Velocity: 800 m/sec (2620 ft/sec)
Maximum Range: 18,500 m (20,200 yd)
Training Rate: 40 deg/sec
Elevation/Depression: +80/−10 deg
Ammunition Capacity: 52 rnd ready use (plus 16 in mount)
Weight: 28.5 tonnes (without ammunition or flare launchers)
Working Circle: 6.33 m (249.2 in)

The barrel is water-cooled, and the gun has a vertical sliding breechblock. Each of two 25-rnd magazines is fixed to one side of the breech. The gun feeds alternately from each magazine into

The Dutch cruiser *de Ruyter* (now Peruvian) shows both the Bofors twin 6in and twin 57mm/60 (superfiring above the 6in turrets) guns. (U.S. Naval Institute)

The Dutch destroyer *Tromp* displays her twin 4.7in gun. This mount is to be refurbished for installation in a new AAW frigate (LCF class), and it may be reinstated in production for later ships of that type. The small objects visible above and below each barrel are light bulbs (the ship is on display). (Author)

A single Bofors 4.7in/46 on board the Finnish *Turunmaa*, 1986. (S. Terzibaschitsch)

the ammunition chamber of the autoloader. Since each magazine can be loaded with a different kind of ammunition, the gun can switch instantly without interrupting the loading cycle. The enclosure is 4–6mm steel for splinter protection. Development (on a private-venture basis) began in 1963, and the first prototype was tested in 1967.

Users: Finland (*Turunmaa* class and *Pohjanmaa*) and Indonesia (*Fatahillah* class).

◆ **Bofors 76mm**

> **Caliber:** 3in/50 (5.9-kg [13-lb] Mk 27 ammunition)
> **Rate of Fire:** 30 rnd/min

Muzzle Velocity: 823 m/sec (2700 ft/sec)
Maximum Range: 12,600 m at 30-deg elev (13,800 yd)
Training Rate: 25 deg/sec (elevation: 25 deg/sec)
Elevation/Depression: +30/−10 deg
Ammunition Capacity: 16 ready-use rnd on the sides of the hoist frame
Weight: 6.5 tonnes empty

This fully automatic single gun uses a Signaal WM 26 FCS, a "half-egg" incorporating a single TWS radar (for surface fire only).

Bofors 76mm gun on board the Norwegian patrol boat *Hvass*. The radome conceals a Signaal WM 26 fire-control radar, and the search radar above it is a Decca TM 1226. The missiles aft are Penguins and the gun aft is a Bofors 40mm L70. (G. Koop)

Users: Norway (*Storm* class), Singapore (110ft "Type B").

◆ **Bofors 57mm/70 Mk 2**

> **Caliber:** 57mm/70 (6.1-kg [13.1-lb] rnd)
> **Rate of Fire:** 225 rnd/min
> **Muzzle Velocity:** 1025 m/sec (PFHE; 950 m/sec for HCER) (3360/3120 ft/sec)
> **Maximum Range:** 17,000 m (18,600 yd)
> **Training Rate:** 55 deg/sec (elevation 40 deg/sec)
> **Elevation/Depression:** +75/−10 deg
> **Ammunition Capacity:** 120 rnd in cupola, 40 rnd ready to fire
> **Weight:** 6500 kg without ammunition (14,300 lb)
> **Working Circle:** 4.325 m (170.3 in)

Bofors claims that this gun is truly dual-purpose: that it is accurate and agile enough to destroy sea-skimmers (by using proximity-fuzed ammunition and by attempting to set off their warheads); and that, with penetrating (delayed action, for 2m penetration after passing through 20 mm of steel) HE rounds (HCER, or high-capacity extended-range), it puts more explosives into a surface target in the first 30 sec than any other gun of up to 100mm caliber. Bofors claims, too, that using better steel allows reduced shell thickness, so that the shell carries 40% more explosive than its predecessors.

Bofors 57mm/70 Mk 2.

A Bofors 57mm Mk 2 gun on board the Swedish corvette *Goteborg* in June 1995, with Elma ASW launchers and Philax chaff launchers (on the centerline) abaft it; note, too, the rocket pod on the shield. (H&L van Ginderen)

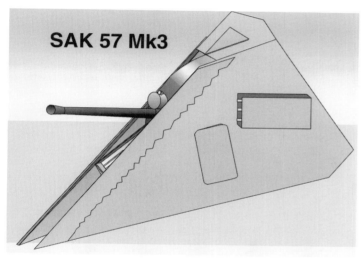

Bofors' stealthy Mk 3 57mm gun is shown in its tent-like shield. When not in use, the barrel folds down into the tent, to reduce radar cross-section. The triple 57mm chaff/flare rocket launcher on the side of the shield retracts back into it. This mounting incorporates its own FCS computer, as well as a gyro reference sensitive enough to detect hull bending (at up to 0.3 Hz) and an on-mount muzzle velocity radar feeding data to the FCS computer. The mount can be entered from below, so that personnel need not leave the ship's NBC citadel. The gun itself stows 120 rounds (three magazines, each reloaded in 8 sec, compared with 12 sec for Mk 2), with another 232 in special cassettes from which they can be fed automatically into the hoists. The 3P ammunition is a scaled-up version of that already in production for 40mm guns. This gun will also have a new base-bleed HC round. (Bofors)

The loader and the gun mount are two-sided, so that two types of ammunition can be handled simultaneously. Ammunition comes up from the magazine into two 20-rnd cassettes, mounted on a rail behind the gun. When filled, they move into position above and discharge their ammunition down into the ready-use magazines. There are also two intermediate cassettes, each holding 20 rnd, so that the cupola (turret) carries 60 rnd (two cassettes and the ready-use magazine above the gun itself) on each side, the total of 120 being sufficient for 15 or 20 engagements.

A new servo system greatly reduces aiming errors and damping time, for greater accuracy when engaging air targets. Mk 1 is a less sophisticated version. The rate of fire is 200 rnd/min, and elevation limits are +78/−10 deg (training rate 55 deg/sec, elevation 20 deg/sec). Ammunition capacity is 128 rnd plus 40 ready-use rounds in the dual hoists. Work on this mount and gun began in 1972. Compared to Mk 1, Mk 2 uses a special monobloc

steel barrel that does not require water cooling, and its turret has 10–20% lower RCS.

A new Mk 3, incorporating some elements of the 40mm Trinity program (see below), is under development. The gun will be housed in a tent-like low-observable gunhouse (cupola), from which the barrel will emerge only when needed; access will be from below. Launchers for 57mm flare and chaff rockets are also built into the cupola, emerging only as needed. A fixed muzzle velocity radar supplies data to the FCS computer, for better accuracy and to fully utilize the 3P ammunition (as in Trinity), programmable in six modes for aerial, surface, and ground targets. Bofors claims that this will be the first multipurpose ammunition for medium-caliber guns. Alternatives are a projected HCER (already in production) and HCER-BB (High Capacity Extended Range—Base Bleed, with a range of 21,000 rather than 17,000 m). Both types of ammunition are credited with extremely short times of flight and flat trajectories for higher hitting probability.

For easier integration, all interfaces with external units will be digital; its FCS computer will be integrated with ship sensors and C3I.

The gun itself will likely resemble Mk 2, with the same 120-rnd cassette arrangement. The mount will use selectable-length hoists, so that ammunition can be stowed far below.

Mk 3 was conceived for the future Swedish YS2000 stealthy corvettes; deliveries will begin in the late 1990s. There are already other prospective customers, including navies which may want to upgrade Mk 2 guns.

The earlier twin 57mm/60 (130 rnd/gun/min, muzzle velocity 3018 ft/sec, maximum range 15,880 yd) survives only on board the Peruvian cruiser *Aguirre*.

Users:

Bofors 57mm/70 Mk 1: Croatia (*King Petar Kresimir IV* class), Finland (*Helsinki* class), Ireland (*Eithne*), Indonesia (*Hajar Dewantara*, Lurssen FAC), Malaysia (*Spica-M*, *Perdana*, *Jerong* classes), Norway (*Nordkapp*), Rumania (*Cosar* class), Singapore (FPB 45), Sweden (*Carlskrona*, *Spica II*, *Hugin* classes), Thailand (*Prabparapak*), Yugoslavia (*Rade Koncar* class).

Bofors 57mm/70 Mk 2: Canada ("City" class), Gabon (Super "Patra" class), Indonesia (PB 57), Malaysia (new corvettes), Mexico (*Aquila* class), and Sweden (*Goteborg*, *Spica III* classes).

◆ Bofors 40mm L70/Trinity

Caliber: 40mm/70
Rate of Fire: 300 or 330 rnd/min
Muzzle Velocity: 1005–1025 m/sec (3300–3360 ft/sec)
Effective Range: 4000 m (4400 yd)
Training Rate: 85 deg/sec (elevation 45 deg/sec)
Elevation/Depression: +90/−10 deg
Weight: 2.8, 3, or 3.3 t without ammunition

The 40mm L70 was conceived by Bofors to replace the World War II L60 gun. The prototype was completed in July 1949; the first export sale was to the Netherlands, for cruisers, in 1953. All Bofors versions are single air-cooled guns: SAK 40L/70–315, which is hand-operated (2.87 t unloaded, working circle 3.31 m); SAK 40L/70–350, which is power (electrohydraulic) operated, gyrostabilized, and remotely controlled; SAK-40L/70–520, which incorporates the Breda autofeed device (AFD) and thus requires a crew of two (and has a GRP cupola); and SAK 40L/70–600, which employs the Trinity 99-rnd magazine (two more rounds are in the intermediate feed position and in the ramming position). All versions employ open-topped shields (sometimes topped by GRP weather covers). Models 315 and 350 use gravity-feed magazines like those of the earlier World War II Bofors 40mm/60. Versions produced under license by Breda since 1969 (see separate entry above) are power-fed.

A modified Model 520/R in service in South Korea and Morocco trains/elevates at 85/130 deg/sec (limits +83/−9 deg).

In August 1986 the West German navy awarded Bofors a contract to upgrade the existing German 40mm/70 guns, using the new high-capacity magazine and elevating mass that had been

Bofors 40mm/70 fitted with a new Trinity 99-rnd magazine, as in German service. (Bofors)

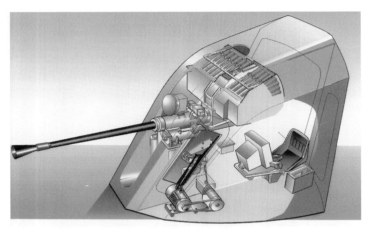

Bofors 40mm L70 Mk 3. (Bofors)

Single 40mm mount Mk 9 on board a British minesweeper. (A. Raven)

developed for the new Trinity version of the gun. The modernized guns have a higher rate of fire. Ships involved include the Type 343 minesweeper and the Type 148 missile attack boat.

The gun originally fired either armor-piercing (AP) or high-explosive with tracer (HE-T). Bofors developed the first production proximity fuze for a 40mm shell, for the L70 gun, beginning large-scale production in 1975 (40mm proximity fuzes are also manufactured by Borletti in Italy and by Thomson-CSF in France). Bofors has recently developed a similar fuze for the older

40mm/60, many of which are still in service. In 1982 the company announced a proximity-fuzed prefragmented HE (PFHE) shell specifically to engage low-flying aircraft and sea-skimming missiles. Lethal radius is 6.5 m against aircraft and 4.5 m against missiles. Bofors argues that, compared to a Phalanx-type penetrator (hittile), such a shell is more likely to destroy an incoming missile because it is much more likely to hit. If each shell is equated to a burst from a Gatling, the two rates of fire are not as different as they might seem. In theory, its Doppler feature protects the PFHE shell from from bursting prematurely when it nears the sea surface.

A high-capacity HE round (HCHE) uses a point delay fuze which allows the shell to penetrate a target for 0.3 msec (equivalent to 20 mm of armor) before bursting. Bofors claims that, given its large charge, the HCHE shell provides the blast effects of a conventional 57mm shell.

An Italian firm, SNIA BFD, has developed an armor-piercing fin-stabilized discarding sabot (APFSDS) 40mm shell, and this company has also developed a preformed fragmentation (PFF) round.

Bofors is currently developing a course-corrected 40mm shell, 4P GJC (gas-jet controlled), which the company is convinced will be needed to deal with next-generation maneuvering targets. The shell carries enough propellant to allow several corrections in sequence; a 5–10-rnd burst can be shifted about 50 m. The command link can also set (delay) the proximity fuze so that a shell can penetrate a target. This shell was first tested (against a static target) late in 1989.

Allied Ordnance of Singapore (AOS) is marketing a modified version, 40mm L70 NADM 330 (naval air defense mount, 330 rounds) in both local- and remote-controlled versions.

Trinity, begun in 1982, was a CIWS development of the L70 with an on-mount FCS. The name referred to the synergistic combination of ammunition, weapon, and fire control. Although the full Trinity system is now dead, elements will feed into the 57mm Mk 3 program. The prototype Trinity mount is on board the experimental attack boat *Smyge*.

The new 3P shell is slightly longer (for better aerodynamics) and about 25% heavier (1.1 vs. 0.88 kg for PFHE, with about 25% more explosive). Higher-energy propellant slightly increases muzzle velocity. Upon bursting, the 3P produces more than 3000 fragments, including 1000 tungsten-alloy pellets. The fuze is set, as it enters the breech, for proximity or point detonation, and with a set burst pattern: for example, a circular pattern for a high-altitude target or a fan for a sea-skimmer. There is also a new AP shell. A complete round weighs 2.8 kg, compared to 2.4–2.5 kg for older 40mm/70 rnd. To help absorb the greater recoil force due to the more energetic round, the gun has a muzzle brake. The gun is rated at 330 rnd/min.

A split 99-rnd magazine can carry two kinds of ammunition: 45 rnd to the left and 54 to the right of the gun, in 11 vertical rows; one side is used at a time, its outer row being emptied first. Two more rounds are carried in the gun. Bofors estimates 5–15 rnd per engagement. Claimed dispersion is 0.7 mrad. Claimed effective range is 2000–3000 m against a low-flying airplane, or 2500 m against a sea-skimming missile.

A simplified 40mm Mk 3, essentially Trinity without the FCS, was chosen for the Brazilian *Niteroi* upgrade. Mk 3 has a low-observable shield, an on-mount operator, and enough ammunition for 10 engagements. It uses the new 3P ammunition (see below). There are also two update kits using Trinity elements.

Update kit 1 is an electronics package on the lower part of the mounting for better accuracy and simpler maintenance. Kit 2 is a new elevating mass, carrying the new 99-rnd magazine and a new on-mount sight, plus Trinity features for accuracy and rate of fire. It is adapted to remote control.

Users: Brazil (Mk 3 in *Niteroi* modernization), Egypt (*Descubierta* [Bazan-built 350]), Finland (*Turunmaa* [350], *Rauma* [350], *Nuoli* [350], *Hameenmaa* [315], *Pohjanmaa* [350], *Teikka* [315], *Koskelo* [315]), Gabon (BATRAL [315]), Germany (*Tiger* [315], *Schutze* [315], *Lindau* [315], *Frauenlob* [315], *Frankenthal* [315], *Hameln* [350], *Wangerooge* [315], *Bredstedt* [315], *Sassnitz* [315], *Neustadt* [315]), Greece ("Hellenic 56" [350], *Jaguar* [350],

Nasty [350]; had 350 in *Gearing* class, now discarded), India (*Vikrant* [350]), Indonesia (*Fatahillah* [350 AFD], Lurssen fast-attack boats [350 AFD]), Malaysia (*Rahmat* [350], *Hang Tuah* [350; may be old 40mm/60, however], *Spica-M* [350], *Perdana* [350], *Jerong* [350], *Lerici* [315], *Lang Hitam* [315]), Mauritania (*Neustadt* [315], FPB 36 [350]), Norway (*Oslo* [350], *Hauk* [350], *Storm* [350], *Vidar* [315], *Horten* [315], *Nornen* [315], *Farm* [315], *Heimdal* [315]; some 315s may actually be 40mm/60 Mk 3), Peru (cruisers [350]; were also in *Friesland*-class destroyers, now discarded), Singapore (FPB 45 [350], Vosper Type A [350], *Landsort* [315]), Spain (*Descubierta* [Bazan-built 350], *Barcelo* [Bazan-built 350]), Sweden (Trinity: *Smyge*; other ships all use m/48, which is presumably 315), Trinidad/Tobago (CG 40 [315]), Turkey (*Kartal* [350], *Jaguar* [350], *Girne* [350], AB 25 class [315], *Rhein* [350], *Akar* [315], *Taskizak* [315], *Yuhasi Tolunay* [315], SAR 35 [315]). In other cases it is impossible to tell whether guns were made by Bofors or by Breda. Total Bofors production of 70-caliber guns was about 600 single mountings.

◆ Bofors 40mm L60 (and foreign versions)

Caliber: 40mm/60 (barrel length is actually 56 calibers) (0.9-kg [1.98-lb] shell)
Rate of Fire: 120 rnd/min (160 in U.S. mounts)
Muzzle Velocity: 800–880 m/sec (2620–2890 ft/sec)
Maximum Range: 10,000 m; effective range 3000 m (10,900/3300 yd)
Elevation/Depression: +90/−5 deg
Ammunition Capacity: 4-rnd clip

The Bofors 40mm/60 was made in Sweden before becoming the standard Allied heavy automatic AA gun of World War II; it survives in some numbers, both in single and in twin mounts. The first Swedish version was the single m/32; most mounts sold prewar were twin m/36s. In all, Bofors sold 435 mountings before World War II, customers including Argentina, Denmark, Finland, Greece, the Netherlands (the first customer), Poland, Turkey, and Yugoslavia. In addition, about 70 m/36s were made in Norway for Germany during World War II. Some of these weapons survive. Most existing 40mm guns, however, were made in Britain and in the United States during World War II. The original Bofors guns all used 4-rnd clips that were gravity-fed into the gun from above. All subsequent Bofors 40mm and 57mm

The U.S.-developed twin 40mm/60 remains in service in several navies. It is shown under test in 1943. (U.S. Navy)

guns continue to use the same basic gun mechanism, which is fed from above. Land-based (and some single naval) versions were air-cooled; naval twins were all water-cooled and power-operated.

All surviving British versions are single air-cooled mounts. Typically they accommodate 10 rnd (two clips plus two loose between the clips); it was claimed that a single loader could work fast enough for the gun to fire a 24-rnd burst. The first British naval version was the manually operated Mk 3. The hydraulically powered Mk 7 (elevation rate 45 deg/sec, weight about 3 t) has a gyro sight for its aimer. Mk 9 is a refurbished electrically powered Mk 9. The mount carries six 4-rnd clips, plus the clip on the gun.

The Australian Maribymong Ordnance Factory remanufactures Mk 3 and Mk 7 mounts as 40/60 AN, replacing hand and hydraulic drives with a new low-pressure oil-hydraulic system with a fully enclosed integrated power pack, controlled by a T-handle for rapid target acquisition coupled with slow and smooth tracking. The electrical box is relocated below decks. Time between refits is extended from 9–11 mo (Mk 7) to 6 yr. Weight without ammunition is 1500 kg (3350 lb). Elevation limits are +90/−5 deg. Training (elevation) rates: 40 (20) deg/sec. The 40/60 AN first went to sea on a *Fremantle*-class patrol boat in 1980; by early 1989, 30 were in service. This mounting has been adopted by the Thai navy.

Another wartime British 40mm mount, the Boffin (a single 40mm on a twin 20mm power mount), is to arm the new Canadian MCM craft. The weapons had been mounted on board the Canadian aircraft carrier *Bonaventure*, and were then used to protect Canadian airfields in Germany when the carrier was discarded. In August 1990 Mk 5C (Boffin) mounts earmarked for the mine-defense ships were diverted to the three Canadian ships going to the Persian Gulf: two each for the destroyers *Athabaskan* and *Terra Nova* and the replenishment ship *Protecteur*. They were supplemented by six 0.50-cal. machine guns on board each ship.

Users of British versions:

Mk 3: Egypt (*El Fatah*)
Mk 5: Bangladesh (*Umar Farooq*), Egypt (*El Fatah, Tariq*), India (*Betwa*)
Mk 7: Bangladesh ("River" class), Barbados (*Trident*), Chile (*Almirante Williams* and probably *Sumner* classes), Denmark (*Soloven* class), Greece (*Nasty*), Kenya (*Madaraka, Mamba* classes, both rearmed with 30mm BMARC GCM-A02), Libya (*Soloven* class), Malaysia (*Hang Tuah, Rahmat, Spica-M*, Vosper 103ft types, *Lerici* class), Mexico (*Azteca* class), Nigeria (*Makurdi* class), Norway (*Tjeld* class), Papua New Guinea (*Attack* class), Turkey (*Girne* class), United Kingdom ("Island" and "River" classes)
Mk 9: Bangladesh (*Leopard* class), Brazil (Type 22 frigates), United Kingdom (Type 22 Batch 1, some "Hunt" class)
40/60AN: Australia (*Fremantle* class), Thailand
Boffin (Mk 5C): Canada (new MCDVs, currently on board *Terra Nova* and *Protecteur*)

The U.S. Navy developed three principal Bofors mountings: a water-cooled twin mount (Mk 1: 13,000–14,000 lb), a quadruple (dual-twin) mount (Mk 2: 24,900 lb), and an air-cooled single mount based on the army's version of the gun (Mk 3). For the quadruple mount, elevation/depression limits were +90/−15 deg and training (elevation) rates were 24 (30) deg/sec. None of these weapons remain in U.S. service, but they were widely exported.

Mk 3 was originally a hand-operated gun for submarines and PT boats, but many of these guns were converted with power drive (4200 lb rather than the original 2440 lb, with performance comparable to Mks 1 and 2, above). The ultimate such conversion, Mod 9, has now been replaced by the 25mm Bushmaster; see the 1991/92 edition for details. During the Vietnam War the U.S. Navy also produced a single enclosed Mk 52 for riverine craft. None probably survive.

Users of U.S. versions:

Twin mount (Mk 1): Argentina (*Achomawi* class), Brazil (*Minas Gerais*), Ecuador (*Hualcopo*), Greece (*Cabildo*, LSM minelayer type), Indonesia (*Achelous*-class repair ship), Japan (*Chikugo*, *Miura* classes), Korea (*Dong Hae* class, LSTs [with single mounts], and LSMs), Mexico (Fast Transports, *Auk* class), Myanmar (PCER/*Admirable* class), Philippines (*Cannon* class, *Auk* class, PCE/*Admirable* class [with single mounts], LSTs [with single mounts], LSMs), Portugal (*Joao Coutinho* class), Taiwan (*Auk*, *Rudderow* classes, *Cabildo* class and other amphibious ships), Thailand (LSTs [with single mounts], LSM), Turkey (LSM and LST-type minelayers), Uruguay (*Commandante Rivière* class).

Quadruple mount (Mk 2): Argentina (*Cabo san Antonio*), Brazil (*Minas Gerais* [also one twin], *Belmonte*), Mexico (*Fletcher* [and twins], *Manuel Azuetz*, *Fabius* class), Peru (*Terrebonne Parish* class), Philippines (*Cannon*, *Auk*, *Admirable*, LST, LSM, *Achelous*-class repair ships), Taiwan (*Cabildo* class [with some single mounts]), Turkey (*Portunus*-class PB tender).

Single mount (Mk 3): Chile (PC 1638 class), Colombia (110ft class and PB Mk III class [Mod 9]), Dominican Republic (*Admirable* class, 110ft class), Ecuador (*Espada* class, PGM 71 class, ex-U.S. fleet tugs), France (P400, *Trident*, Combattante, *Foudre*, *Ouragan*, *Champlain* classes), Greece (*Aris*, *Thetis*), Haiti (*Henri Christophe*), Indonesia (Patrol Boats 860/861, LSTs), Iran (PGM 71 and Cape classes), Japan (*Atsumi* class and many MSA ships), Korea (*Asheville* class, HDC 1150, HDP 100, Wildcat, Sea Dolphin, Schoolboy, Sea Whale classes, probably also all other classes including FRAM destroyers), Mexico (*Admirable* class, *Huasteco* class), Norway (*Oslo*, *Vidar* classes and *Horten*), Pakistan (*Dacca*, *Madadgar*), Peru (river gunboats, *Terrebonne Parish* class), Philippines (LST class, *General Amilio Aguinaldo*; provision in the 77ft class for this gun), Portugal (*Baptiste de Andrade*, *Commandante Rivière*, *Cacine* classes), Singapore (LSTs), Spain (*Atrevida* class), Taiwan (destroyers, 32m patrol boats, LSTs [with some single mounts], LSMs, *Kao Hsiung*, *Patapsco* class, *Chin Siung* class, *Wu Yi*, *Amphion*-class repair ship), Thailand (PF 103, PSMM Mk 5, T 93, T 91 classes, LSSL), Togo (32m CNE type), Turkey (*Asheville* class, PGM 71 class, PC 1638 class, *Derya*, *Chanticleer*-class rescue ship, LST minelayers), Uruguay (*Commandante Rivière*, Paysandu, and Kondor II classes). This is probably the version of the 40mm gun used by the Japanese Maritime Safety Agency (*Tsugaru*, *Soya*, *Shiretoko*, *Izu*, *Daio*, *Erimo*, *Kojima* classes).

Daewoo of Korea has developed ADS (air defense systems) based on the U.S. Mks 1 and 3, the former in both basic and improved versions. The unstabilized basic version is locally controlled, with a dispersion of 10 mrad. The stabilized and remotely controlled improved version is credited with a dispersion of only 1 mrad. It carries an on-mount GSA Mk 3 gyro lead-computing sight and is controlled by a 16-bit microprocessor. An enclosed control cabin on its left side is balanced by a fairing covering power training and elevating gear on its right. Cages around the two loaders alongside the guns help them remain in place as the mount trains. Each gun carries the usual clip hopper, but alongside it is a 22-rnd magazine. Another 44 rnd/gun are apparently carried below decks. The single mount seems to have a similar configuration. The twin mount occupies No. 2 position on board Korean *Gearing* FRAM I destroyers. Single mounts arm at least some "Schoolboy/Sea Hawk"–class patrol boats.

The French DCN organization displayed a new 40mm/60 Mod E at the 1994 Bourget Naval show. France had been exporting an earlier Mod C. Mod E is derived from the existing French *army* gun mount, probably U.S.-supplied during World War II, hence equivalent to Mk 3. DCN adds new trunnions, electric motor drives, a plastic shield, and a 32-rnd rack; it is considering a remote-controlled version. Up to 400 mounts are available for refurbishment. As of late 1994 about 15 were being made, the first for Oman for P-400 patrol craft, for delivery in January 1995. Ex–French African colonies have reportedly shown interest. Mod D, a lesser upgrade, has been supplied to Oman for *Al Bushra*–class patrol vessels.

Bofors claims that the cumulative effect of modernizing the gun, its sight, and its ammunition improves kill probability against a typical fighter-bomber by 50–80% (e.g., kill probability at 1 km rises from about 18 to nearly 100%), based on a 9-rnd burst. Rate of fire is increased by about 50%, from 120 to 180 rnd/min; and the hopper at the top of the gun is enlarged to hold 20 rnd (2–3 targets can be engaged between reloadings; the rounds are still carried in clips of four, for easy handling). A new gun-mounted "U-sight" incorporates a laser ranger. Dispersion is cut to less than 4 mrad. Guns can be provided with power drives.

SWITZERLAND

In current Oerlikon guns, the first letter indicates cannon (K) or mount (G); the second, the caliber (A for 20mm, B for 25mm, C for 30mm, and D for 35mm); the third is a modifier (for guns, typically A, B, C). Thus a typical gun designation might be KDA. For gun mounts, the third letter is D or M, indicating the mount type. A modifier follows a dash; thus GDM-A is the first version of a power-operated (M) 35mm mount (GD). See United Kingdom, below, for the GCM series.

◆ Oerlikon 35mm (Type GDM-A and GDM-C)

Caliber: 35mm/90 (1.56-kg rnd, including 550-g shell) (3.43/1.21 lb)
Rate of Fire: 1100 rnd/min (550 rnd/gun/min)
Muzzle Velocity: 1175 m/sec (3850 ft/sec)
Effective Range: (Air/surface) radar control: 5000/8000 m (5500/8700 yd); optical control: 2500/5000 m (2700/5500 yd); local sight: 3000/5000 m (3300/5500 yd)
Training Rate: 120 deg/sec (elevation 130 deg/sec)
Elevation/Depression: +85/−15
Ammunition Capacity: 336 rnd
Weight: 10,500 lb without ammunition
Working Circle: 4716 mm (185.7 in)

Data are for GDM-C.

The gun is KDA or KDC. KDA was an Oerlikon design, a scaled-up 204GK (see KAA below), which appeared in 1959 as 353MK and then as GDF-001 and the improved GDF-002 (no KDB). It is license-produced in Japan. About 1969 OTO-Melara developed a naval mounting, which was designated GDM-A; it survives only on board the Japanese *Shikishima*, the ship designed to escort plutonium shipments. The Japan Maritime Safety Agency uses a single mounting (probably carrying KDA) similar to the 30mm GCM-A03-1 or -3 (see the British section below); it may be GDM-B. A slightly heavier naval version of the gun was developed as KDC, on the GDM-C mounting. It first appeared on board the Iranian frigate *Zaal* in 1971.

The Oerlikon twin 35mm gun (GDM-A). (Oerlikon)

The Oerlikon twin 35mm gun (GDM-C), developed in collaboration with OTO-Melara. (Oerlikon)

Both 35mm guns are gas-operated. High muzzle velocity and low drag make for short time of flight, for example, 6 sec to 4400 yd. The guns of GDM-C share a common trunnion, with 56 ready-use rnd on either side in a powered loader using two vertical hoists and a horizontal (quadrant) pusher to move rounds through the trunnions to the breech. The mount carries another 224 rounds, which can be dropped into the loader as the guns fire. KDA is belt-fed. The GDM-C mount is electrically controlled and biaxially stabilized, and the gun has a stabilized sight and joystick for local control. The gun can be manually controlled.

Users: Ecuador (FPB 45 class), Greece (Combattante II), Iran (*Saam*-class frigates), Japan (*Shikishima* and other JMSA ships), and Turkey (ex-U.S. destroyers, FPB 57 class).

◆ 35mm Millennium (35/1000)

Oerlikon's new four-chamber gas-operated revolver cannon was announced at Farnborough in September 1994. First test-fired early in 1995, it fires the new AHEAD prefragmented ammunition. A published drawing of a possible 35/1000 mount shows a considerable structure stiffening the barrel against vibration as it fires. The gun is belt-fed from the side from an ammunition box alongside the trunnion. Muzzle velocity is 1440 m/sec when firing APDS-T (armor-piercing discarding sabot) ammunition, 1180m/sec when firing HEI, or 1050 m/sec when firing the heavier AHEAD round (0.75 kg). Firing rate is up to 1000 rnd/min. The barrel is 2.766 m long (about 79 calibers; 3.03 m with muzzle brake) and weighs 100 kg. The entire gun weighs 450 kg and is 4.11 m long. Oerlikon's projected mounting would carry four short-range missiles together with the gun. As MDG-35, this weapon is a contender for the ILDS role in the Project Horizon frigate. Oerlikon's British partner is Royal Ordnance (agreement January 1995).

As a CIWS, Millennium differs in philosophy from existing weapons. The natural dispersal of the gun is used to distribute rounds in a plane through which an approaching missile is likely to pass. Time-fuzing is used to burst 18 AHEAD rounds to form a wall of 2736 fragments 10 m dia about 15–30 m ahead of the expected position of the missile and about 1.5 km from the gun. Oerlikon also claims that because Millennium has no on-mount FCS, it is far lighter and less expensive than its rivals. Nor does it require any deck penetration.

◆ Oerlikon 30mm

See United Kingdom (BMARC-Oerlikon 30mm) below. KCA is a four-chamber aircraft revolver cannon developed from the earlier 304RK, and adopted for the Swedish Viggen fighter.

◆ Sea Zenith (Type GBM-B1Z)

Caliber: 25mm/92
Rate of Fire: 850 rnd/bbl/min (total 3400 rnd/min)
Muzzle Velocity: 1335 m/sec (4380 ft/sec) (time of flight to 1000 m, 0.78 sec)
Training Rate: 2.5 rad/sec (elevation of 2.5 rad/sec) (143.2 deg/sec)

A Millennium mount, as proposed for Project Horizon. (Royal Ordnance)

Elevation/Depression: +127/−14 deg
Ammunition Capacity: 415 rnd/gun
Weight: 4600 kg above decks plus 2150-kg ammunition feed system (10,140/4740 lb); 2690 kg below decks

Sea Zenith is the four-gun weapon associated with the Swiss Contraves Seaguard system (see above under shipboard radars and FCSs). The guns are designated KBB-R03/L03. The ammunition supply is sufficient for 18 engagements (80 rnd each), and the guns can be reloaded while they fire. The unusual elevation arc (the mount axis is canted) makes it easier for the gun to engage very high targets; that arc is achieved by having the gun train in a plane canted at a 35-deg angle.

Reportedly this weapon was less than successful in Turkish trials conducted by the British. The guns were too close together (their rounds interfered, like those of some prewar triple turrets, so the shot pattern was too large). The mounting also vibrated excessively, probably because it was so flexible (to reach such extreme angles). Individual guns jammed during lengthy firings (such as those associated with relatively slow incoming missiles, about 5 sec long for a Mach 0.9 target), throwing the pattern off completely.

An alternative Sea Shield announced in 1989 is mounted entirely above decks and omits the very high elevation feature. No sales have been announced.

◆ Oerlikon (BMARC) 25mm (Type GBM-A01) and Breda-Oerlikon KBA

Caliber: 25mm/80
Rate of Fire: 570 rnd/min
Muzzle Velocity: 1100–1360 m/sec (3600–4460 ft/sec)
Elevation/Depression: +55/−10 deg
Ammunition Capacity: 140 rnd (2 × 70-rnd boxes)
Weight: 600 kg including ammunition (1320 lb)

This unpowered mount, carrying a KBA gun, was an outgrowth of the GAM series, developed about 1975. Because the gun is fed from both sides, the mount can be reloaded while firing from the other side. This mount is used only by the Seychelles, in the FPB 42 class.

A power-assisted Breda version, announced in 1988, was planned for Philippine patrol boats to be built in Spain, but these craft have not materialized. No other sales have been announced.

◆ Oerlikon 20mm (Type GAM-B01)

Caliber: 20mm/85
Rate of Fire: 1000 rnd/min
Muzzle Velocity: 1050 m/sec (3440 ft/sec)
Maximum Range: 2000 m (2200 yd)
Elevation/Depression: +55/−10 deg
Ammunition Capacity: 200 rnd
Weight: 92 kg without ammunition (90 kg of ammunition) (203/198 lb)

This manual mount carries a KAA cannon, essentially equivalent to the World War II Oerlikon (but with a higher muzzle velocity). It was mounted on board most British warships as a result of the Falklands emergency. The Royal Navy uses the GAM-B01 designation. Development of the GAM series began in 1974; GAM-B01 entered production in 1976. In 1991 BMARC began development of a Hybrid GAM, which could accommodate earlier 20mm guns: Oerlikon Mks 1SS and 2SS and British and U.S. Mks 2 and 4. It was scheduled to enter production in 1992.

A single World War II–type 20mm Oerlikon gun on board the Belgian minesweeper *Breydel*, 1985. (M. Loagie)

Oerlikon 20mm single mount as selected by the Royal Navy (GAM-B01). (Oerlikon)

Users: Argentina (Z-28 class), Austria (*Niederosterreich*), Bahrein (FPB 62–class fast-attack boats and 65ft Swiftships class), Chile (*Reshef*), Egypt (*Timsah II* class), Gabon (42m CNE boat), Guatemala (*Broadsword* type, 85ft type), Guyana (*Peccari*), Iran (Vosper Mk 5 and PF 103), Israel (Dvora and *Reshef* classes), Ireland (P21), Malaysia (*Lang Hitam*), Mauretania (*Patra* class, *Barcelo* class), Mexico (*Azteca* class), Morocco (*Lazaga*, "Osprey"), Nigeria (*Lerici*, Type 502 landing ships), Oman (new Vosper-Thornycroft corvettes, 37.5m class, *Nasr al Bahr* class, *Al Munassir*, CG 29, CG 27, and Haras classes), Papua New Guinea (AS 315 class), Saudi Arabia (*Al Souf* and "Explorer" classes), Senegal ("Osprey 55" and Interceptor classes), Singapore ("Swift" class, *Jupiter*), South Africa (*Reshef*, *Drakensberg*, *Tafelberg*), Spain (*Lazaga*, *Barcelo*), Taiwan (*Wu Yi* class), Thailand

(*Rattanakosin*, *Thalang*, *Bang Rachan*, T213, PS700 classes), Tunisia (103ft class), United Kingdom (*Fearless* class, *Sir Galahad*, *Fort Grange* class, *Diligence*, some "Hunt" class), Venezuela (*Capana*).

◆ Oerlikon 20mm (Type GAM-C01)

Caliber: 20mm/95
Rate of Fire: 900 rnd/min
Muzzle Velocity: 1050–1100 m/sec (3440–3770 ft/sec)
Elevation/Depression: +55/−10 deg
Ammunition Capacity: 200 rnd

This mount is very similar to GAM-B01 but the gun is a Hispano-Suiza 820 (Oerlikon KAD-B13–3). BMARC developed the new pedestal mount, which it called A41/820, in 1968–70 as a private venture, and production began in 1970.

Users: Libya (Thornycroft security craft), Singapore (Type A, Type B, Swift, *Panglima*, *Jupiter*), Trinidad (CG 40), Thailand (LST *Normed*).

◆ Oerlikon 20mm (Type A41A)

Caliber: 20mm
Rate of Fire: 800 rnd/min
Muzzle Velocity: 835 m/sec (2740 ft/sec)
Elevation/Depression: +50/−10 deg
Ammunition Capacity: 58 rnd
Weight: 225 kg (496 lb)
Working Circle: 1.7 m (66.9 in)

Type A41A, with its ammunition drum, is the closest current equivalent to the World War II Oerlikon. The other current Oerlikons are belt-fed from a rectangular box on the front of the mount. Developed by BMARC, it is an improved version of the wartime Mk 7 mount carrying a Hispano-Suiza HS 804 gun, which was originally designed for aircraft use and therefore has a very low recoil force. It appeared in 1968, and production began in 1970. A41A was dropped from the Oerlikon line but revived about 1980 because some customers liked its simplicity, ease of handling, and reliability.

This weapon has been manufactured both by Oerlikon and by BMARC.

Users: Brunei (*Perwira*), Egypt (*Timsah*, *Crestitalia*), Gabon (P400), Gambia (Tracker 2), Greece (Osprey), Guyana (*Peccari*), Ivory Coast (*Patra*), Kenya (*Nyayo*), Libya (Vosper Mk 7, *Garian*), Malaysia (*Duyong*, Brooke Marine 29m, PX/Improved PX, Vosper 32m), Mauritania (FPB 36), Morocco (P32), Nigeria (*Erin'mi*, intermarine patrol boats, Type 1300 LST, Lana), Oman (Brooke Marine type, Vosper 25m, *Al Mabrukah*, *Nasr al Bahr*, *Al Munassir*, CG 29, P 2000, Vosper-Thornycroft 75ft), Qatar (Combattante, *Damen Polycat*), Senegal (Tracker 2), Singapore (*Endeavour*), Thailand (*Sattahip*, T 213, *Chula*, *Sumidagawa*,

Yohomaha, Sriyanont, Halter boats), Trinidad (Vosper patrol craft), Tunisia (Vosper-Thornycroft patrol craft, P48), UAE (Keith Nelson, Camcraft 77- and 65ft, Posilipo, and CG 23 patrol craft).

♦ **Oerlikon and Hispano-Suiza 20mm (old types, including foreign versions)**

Caliber: 20mm/70 (122-g rnd)
Rate of Fire: 450 rnd/min
Muzzle Velocity: 2730 ft/sec (effective range 2000 yd)
Elevation/Depression: +75/−30 deg (Mk 10)
Ammunition Capacity: 60 rnd (drum magazine)
Weight: 970 lb (Mk 10) without ammunition
Working Circle: 106 in (Mk 10)

Data are for the U.S. Mk 10 mounting carrying a Mk 4 gun.

The Oerlikon 20mm drum-fed blow-back gun predates World War II. The wartime version was Type S. It was license-produced both in the United Kingdom and in the United States during the war, and most older Oerlikons still in use are probably of this type. These are the UK gun Mk 2 and the U.S. gun Mk 2/4 (in each case the gun is used in a variety of mountings). The rival gas-operated Hispano-Suiza 804 was adopted postwar by BMARC as A41A (see above), and a modified form was adopted postwar by the U.S. Navy as Gun Mk 16 (mounts Mks 51, 67, and 68, now extinct). HS 804 was rated at 750–800 rnd/min, and Mk 16 at 800 rnd/min. After World War II Yugoslavia adopted the Hispano 804 as the M55, the basis of the M71 and M75 mounts. The airborne equivalent, the Hispano-Suiza 404 (U.S. AN-M2), was quite successful during World War II. Both Oerlikon and Hispano-Suiza used 20 × 110mm cartridges (actually of slightly different dimensions); HS 804 achieved a slightly higher muzzle velocity (844 rather than 830 m/sec, firing the same weight of projectile). Postwar, both companies produced new weapons using more powerful cartridges: Oerlikon's 204GK and 5TG with 20 × 128mm cartridges, and Hispano-Suiza's HS 820 with 20 × 138mm cartridges. When Oerlikon took over Hispano-Suiza in 1972, 204GK became KAA, 5TG became KAB, and HS 820 became KAD.

British Manufacture and Research Corporation (BMARC) began to make Hispano-Suiza guns in 1939. After World War II, Oerlikon agreed that BMARC should market its weapons (up to 30mm caliber) in much of the world. BMARC was later bought up by Astra Holdings; when that company went bankrupt, the Oerlikon interest was bought up by Royal Ordnance, which concluded a marketing agreement with Oerlikon in 1993.

The standard British Oerlikon mounts at the end of World War II were the single Mk 7 and the twin Mk 9 and Mk 12. The corresponding U.S. mounts were the single Mk 10 and the twin Mk 24. Earlier single mounts, the U.S./British Mk 2, the British Mk 3, and the U.S. Mk 4, had adjustable heights. A few Mk 2 or Mk 4, many of them given to France and then re-exported, survive. Mk 7 was similar to Mk 3 but added an antivibration counterbalance weight.

All 20mm guns (except for Phalanx) have now been retired from U.S. service. In most cases they were replaced by 25mm Mk 88 Bushmasters.

Known users of British 20mm mounts:

Mk 7: Argentina (Type 42), Chile ("County," *Leander*), India (*Leander* class), Indonesia ("Tribal" and "Rover" classes), New Zealand (*Monowai*), Nigeria (*Obuma*), Pakistan (*Leander*; probably being removed from Type 21s), Portugal ("Rover" class), South Africa ("Ton," *Outeniqua, Drakensberg*), Sri Lanka (FPC), UK (Some Type 42, *Hecla, Bulldog,* "Ol").

Mk 9: Chile ("Tide" class), Croatia ("Ham" class), India ("Ham" class), Malaysia (*Mutiara* class), Yugoslavia ("Ham").

Known users of U.S. mounts:

Mk 2/4: Algeria (*Mangusta*, Baglietto T20GC), Argentina (A69, *Delfin, Lynch, Tionina*), Benin (PR 360T), Brazil (*Imperial Marinheiro, Parnaiba, Grajau, Tritao*), Burma (Y 301, *Carpentia,* survey ship 802), Chile (*Cherokee*-class tug, Batral-type landing ship, *Elicura*), Dominican Republic ("River"-class frigate, *Captain Alsina, Captain Beotegui, Cherokee*-class tug), Ecuador (LST, *Cherokee*-class tug), France (*Georges Leygues, Cassard, Suffren, Tourville, Aconit,* A69, *Circe, Durance, Garonne,*

Athos, Aramis, Leopard; being replaced by Breda 30mm guns), Greece (LST, LSM, ex-UK LCT), India (*Sukanya, Deepak*), Indonesia (*Teluk Langsa*), Korea (LST, LSM), Kuwait (OPV 310), Madagascar (BATRAM and EDIC types), Mauritania ("Patra" type), Mexico (APDs), Morocco (P 32, EDIC types), Pakistan (*Cherokee* type), Paraguay (standard 20mm), Philippines (PCE, *Aguinaldo,* LST, PGM, auxiliaries), Portugal (standard except for "Rover"), Senegal (EDIC), Seychelles ("Sirius"), Togo (coastal patrol craft), Tunisia (*Bizerte, Istiklal*), Turkey (LSM).

Mk 10: Argentina (*Commandante G. Irigoyen,* Dabur), Bahrein (Swift boats), Brazil (*Barroso Pereira*), Burma ("Osprey," Swift boats, river gunboats, CGC type, RPC, LCM 3), Chile (PC 1638 class, "Dabur," *Micalvi,* buoy tenders, patrol boats, river-patrol craft), Congo (*Pirana*), Dominican Republic (*Cohoes, Admirable,* PGM 71 classes), Egypt (Swiftships 93ft type), El Salvador (Camcraft and Swiftships patrol craft), Fiji (*Redwing* and "Dabur" types), Greece (Type 520, LCU, MCMs, *Patapsco* type), Honduras (*Chamelecon,* Swift 65ft type), Indonesia (BC 3001), Israel (standard 20mm type), Jamaica (standard 20mm), Japan (standard 20mm), Korea (MSC 289, "Fur Seal," Alligator, YO type, *Diver,* "Sea Dragon/Whale," some "Sea Wolf/Shark"), Liberia (*Sea Dolphin*), Mexico (all except APDs), Nicaragua ("Dabur" type), Pakistan (MSC 268 type), Peru (patrol craft), Philippines (*Admirable,* "Sea Hawk/Killer"), Saudi Arabia (standard in ex-U.S. ships), Spain (patrol craft), Taiwan (most units, being replaced by new guns), Thailand (standard type), Turkey (standard except as noted above and below).

Mk 24: Argentina (*Cabo San Antonio*), Belgium (*Aggressive* class), Burma (PCE, *Admirable,* PGM, survey ship 801), Ecuador (PGM 71 class), Ethiopia (EDIC-type landing craft), Iraq (*Ibn Marjid*), Italy (*Agave, Gaeta, Ajutant, Stromboli,* LCT 3 type),

A Yugoslav M 75 quadruple 20mm gun mount is shown aboard the Croatian patrol boat *Solta*; it replaced the single M 71 originally mounted in the boat's stern. (Zdenko Kinjerovac via Dr. Zvonimir Freivogel)

Korea ("Sea Hawk," "Sea Fox," MSC 268 class, *Mazinger*, "Sea Wolf/Shark"), Lebanon (EDIC), Morocco ("Osprey Mk II" type), Peru (*Maranon*), Philippines (*Auk, Admirable, Achelous*), Spain (ex-U.S. minecraft), Turkey (PC 1638, PGM 71, *Adjutant*, MSC classes).

The Yugoslav M55 is essentially HS 804 (650 rnd/min) with a new muzzle brake. M71 is the single mounting, M75 is a quad version, and there is also a triple version. Each gun carries a 60-rnd drum magazine and can fire 180 rnd in short succession but must then stop for 5 to 10 min to cool off. The single mount can elevate and train at 80 deg/sec (limits +85/−10 deg), and it weighs 460 kg (1014 lb) loaded. It is fitted with a reflex sight (RNS-M71T) with an FOV of 20 × 10.5 deg; the objective lens is 110 × 120 mm, and total weight is 3.5 kg (7.7 lb). The powered M75 has elevation/depression limits of +85/−10 deg and trains (elevates) at 80 (50) deg/sec. Effective range is 1500 m (maximum surface/air range is 4600/2000 m; with AP rounds 5500/4000 m). Working circle radius is 1.750 m, and loaded weight is 1900 kg (4190 lb). In the quad mounting, the guns are mounted two to a side, staggered one above the other, their ammunition drums protruding.

Users of the Yugoslav version:

> M75: Bangladesh (*Akshay*), Burma (PB 90), Croatia (*Hrvat-ska Kostajnica* [M75 vice original M71], PB 61, DTM21, *Faust Vramic, Silba* classes), Hungary (*Nestin*-class river minesweepers), Iraq (PB 90 class, *Nestin* class), Libya (*Spasilac*), Yugoslavia (Type 80, *Silba* class, *Mirna* class, *Nestin* class, DTMs, and Type PO transports).
> Triple 20mm: Honduras (*Hibures*), Yugoslavia (riverine command ship *Kozara*, DTK 211 and RTK 401–class landing craft).
> M71: Bangladesh (*Kaljevca, Shahjalal, Shahayak*, MFV 66, *Sanket*), Croatia (*Kralj, Mirna, Galeb*, Type 22, Type 21), Iraq (*Nestin* class), Libya (*Spasilac*), Sudan (*Kader* class, Type 15 class), Yugoslavia (*Mirna*, Type 20, *Botica*, Type 15, *Vikov Klanac, Nestin*, M301, *Silba*, Type 22, Type 21, *Vis*, PT 82, *Alga, Sabac*, tenders).

◆ AHEAD

This Oerlikon 35mm antimissile ammunition (Advanced Hit Efficiency and Destruction) was first shown at the Paris Air Show in 1991. The prefragmented heavy metal shell has a programmable base time fuze, set at the muzzle velocity gauge as the projectile leaves the muzzle. The gauge consists of three coils: the first two determine muzzle velocity precisely. The fire-control computer supplies target information. Flight time is calculated and the fuze is set by electro-induction as the projectile passes through the third coil. The projectile is set to burst ahead of the target so as to form a cone of pellets through which the target must fly. Oerlikon-Contraves claims that the pellets can defeat any front-end armor protecting a missile, drone, or RPV.

In 1996 Canada became the first customer (for land AA guns).

TAIWAN

Small and medium combatants are being armed with the Type 75 20mm gun, adapted from the U.S. M39 fighter weapon, a version of the German revolver cannon. Characteristics (of M39A3): projectile 3.56 oz (0.101 kg), muzzle velocity 2850 ft/sec, rate of fire 1700 rnd/min.

UNITED KINGDOM

In 1992 BMARC was bought out of receivership by Royal Ordnance PLC. The parent company, Astra, had collapsed after buying PRB in Belgium. See the Swiss section for BMARC/Oerlikon 20mm mounts.

◆ 4.5in Mk 6

Caliber: 4.7in/45 (55-lb projectile, 30–33-lb cartridge)
Rate of Fire: 10–12 rnd/min/barrel (theoretical rate 24 rnd/min/barrel)
Muzzle Velocity: 2460 ft/sec (derated to 2350 ft/sec in practice)
Maximum Range: 20,000 yd (maximum altitude 19,700 ft)
Training Rate: 25 deg/sec (elevation 25 deg/sec)

Elevation/Depression: +80/−15 deg
Ammunition Capacity: 80 shells, 45 cartridges in gun bay
Weight: 98,560 lb (revolving mass)
Working Circle: 218 in (radius)

The standard British postwar semiautomatic twin mount was from the outset for automatic aiming and for a high rate of fire. Shells (which can be of two types) are stowed in two magazines, with separate hoists to each gun (the gun has a single cartridge hoist). The mount had many novel features, notably the loading tray which recoils with the gun, and an unsuccessful power rammer. The Mk V gun has a vertical sliding breech-block. Barrel lifetime is about 750 EFCs. Welding was used extensively for the first time in British gun-mount construction. This mounting was also unusual in using hydraulic rams for elevation. Gunhouse plating is 0.375 in thick.

A twin 4.5in mounting Mk 6, on display at Whale Island, 1985. (R. Cheung)

Note that although the nominal caliber is 4.5 in, in fact the caliber is 4.7 in (120 mm), the earlier standard for British destroyers. The nominal caliber was changed to prevent the use of earlier (incompatible) ammunition in the new 4.5in semidual-purpose guns. Only the modern Mk 8 gun is really 4.5 in (114 mm).

A few single Mk 5 survive: in the Egyptian destroyer *El Fatah*, in the Indonesian "Tribal"-class, and in the Malaysian *Rahmat* (the gun may have been removed from this ship). Rate of fire is 14 rnd/min (firing cycle 4.3 sec), and maximum elevation is 55 deg. The single mount weighs 33,562 lb.

Users (Mk 6): Australia ("River" class), Bangladesh (*Leopard* class, Chile ("County" and *Leander* classes), India (*Leander* class), New Zealand (*Leander* class), Pakistan (*Leander* class), Peru (*Daring* class).

◆ 4.5in Mk 8

Caliber: 4.5in/55 (46-lb HE shell, complete round 80.5 lb)
Rate of Fire: 25 rnd/min
Muzzle Velocity: 2850 ft/sec
Maximum Range: 24,000 yd
Training Rate: 40 deg/sec (elevation 40 deg/sec)
Elevation/Depression: +55/−10 deg
Ammunition Capacity: 16 rnd
Weight: 25.75 t total (rotating mass 15.1 t)
Working Circle: 19 ft 11 in radius

This fiberglass-shielded unmanned single 4.5in mount is approximately equivalent to the U.S. 5in/54 Mk 45. For self-defense, rapid response was considered more important than rapid rate of fire in self-defense against missiles, since each proximity-fuzed shell should be quite lethal, and since there would not, in any case, be much time for many rounds to hit. For shore bombardment, the Royal Navy wanted 7.5 min (90 rnd) of sustained fire; water cooling was rejected because it would have added too much weight. Ready-service rounds are carried vertically, in an indexing feed ring, two spaces 180 deg apart normally being kept free for special types of ammunition, such as star-shell. Mk 8 can open fire in 10 sec from the shut-down state. The single type of HE shell is suitable for both air and surface action, the mode of the N97 fuze (direct action, proximity low- or high-altitude, and postimpact delay) being selected electronically just before the shell is rammed. There is also an N7 mechanical time fuze. Other shell types are illuminating, radar echo (chaff for I- or J-band, either as a decoy or for wind-finding), and practice. Vickers has developed a new base-bleed HE/ER (high-effect/extended-range) ammunition, to achieve 22% more range; in 1989 Vickers hoped ultimately to achieve over 30% more range, that is, over 31,200 yd. This shell is more accurate than a standard HE shell (because base bleed reduces drag) and it carries somewhat more HE (2.9 rather than 2.6 kg, out of the same 20.9 kg total weight). Rated barrel life is 3300 rnd.

A "Tribal"-class frigate displays her 4.5in Mk 5 gun, forward. The director is MRS 3, carrying a Type 903 radar. This particular ship, HMS *Mohawk*, no longer exists but three sisters survive in the Indonesian navy. (HMS *Excellent*)

Personnel: gun captain in CIC, supervisor and two loaders in magazine.

The gun was modeled on the army's 105mm Abbot howitzer; it has a muzzle brake and a fume extractor. Vickers designed the mounting. The prototype Mk 8 was built in 1966.

In 1995 VSEL received a contract to upgrade guns on board Type 23 frigates to Mod 1, which weighs 6 t less. VSEL then offered a Mod 2 for the Project Horizon frigate. It eliminates the feed ring; shells are loaded directly from the magazine, meeting the "fire from magazine" requirement. As of mid-1996, however, the Royal Navy clearly preferred a 5in or even a 155mm gun.

Royal Ordnance is currently working on course-corrected base bleed/rocket-assisted shells ("intelligent ammunition") for 4.5in, 127mm (for Project Horizon), and army 155mm guns using blow-outs at the shell base, controlled by a single microchip in the shell, using GPS for corrections. One option is a reconnaissance shell, which would eject a parachute-carried camera package. The new shells will be ready for marketing about 2003.

Users: Argentina (Type 42), Brazil (*Niteroi, Inhauma* classes), Iran (Vosper Mk 5 class), Pakistan (Type 21 class), Thailand (*Makut Rajakumarn*), United Kingdom (Type 42, Type 22 Batch III and Type 23 classes).

◆ 4in Guns

The World War II twin Mk 19 AA mount (elevation limits +80/ −10 deg) survives on board the Malaysian frigate *Hang Tuah* and the elderly Egyptian frigate *Tariq*. The old Mexican gunboat *Guanajuato* carries similar guns in single low-angle mounts. Ballistics: 2660 ft/sec, maximum range 19,850 yd.

◆ 3in Mk 6

This twin rapid-fire (95–113 rnd/gun/min) mount, designed to use U.S. ammunition, survives on board the Canadian frigates *Terra Nova* and *Gatineau*, which are to be discarded in 1997–98. It was considered more successful than the contemporary U.S. twin 3in/70. The guns are water-cooled. Ballistics: 15 lb shell, 3400 ft/sec, maximum range 19,500 yd. Elevation limits: +90/ −30 deg. Revolving weight: 83,150 lb (including 34 rnd/gun).

◆ 30mm (Type GCM)

Caliber: 30mm/75
Rate of Fire: 1300 rnd/min
Muzzle Velocity: 1080 m/sec (3540 ft/sec)
Maximum Range: 10,000 m (33,000 yd)
Training Rate: 75 deg/sec (elevation 50 deg/sec)
Elevation/Depression: +80/−15 deg
Ammunition Capacity: 160 rnd/gun (A03-01: 160 or 250 rnd/gun; A03-02: 250 rnd/gun; A03-03: 320 rnd/gun
Weight: 2000 kg (A02); A03-01: 2150 kg; A03-02: 2050 kg; A03-03: 1900 kg (4410/4740/4520/4190 lb)
Working Circle: 2520 mm (99.2 in)

The KCB cannon was developed by Hispano-Suiza as HS 831, an enlarged version of its gas-operated HS 820 (later KAD). In the United Kingdom, BMARC completed the prototype of a twin HS 831 mount with an operator's position on its right side, which it called A32. When Oerlikon took over Hispano-Suiza, the gun became KCB and the mount became GCM-A01 (a version with an enclosed operator's cab on its right side became GCM-A02). An improved series of mounts appeared in 1984 as GCM-A03 (-01 was the upgraded -A01, -02 the upgraded -A02, and a new remote-control version was GCM-A03–03). All versions are gyrostabilized and power-driven, with either local or remote control.

30mm GCM-A01 twin mount. (A. Raven)

Users: Brazil (probably retained on ex-British Type 22 frigates), Brunei (*Waspada*-class [A01]), Egypt (6 October, *Timsah*, "Crestitalia 70 ft" classes: A32), Jordan ("Hawk" class [A03–2]), Kenya ("Province," 32m classes and *Mamba* [A02]), Qatar (Combattante II class [A01]), Tunisia (Combattante III class [A03–2]), UAE (110ft class [A01]), and United Kingdom (Type 22 Batch II [A03–2], *Ocean* [A03] *Fearless* class [A03–2]).

◆ DS 30/SIGMA

Caliber: 30mm
Rate of Fire: 650 rnd/min
Muzzle Velocity: 1080 m/sec (3540 ft/sec)
Training Rate: 55 deg/sec (elevation 55 deg/sec)
Elevation/Depression: +65/−20 deg
Ammunition Capacity: 160 rnd
Weight: 1.2 t (with ammunition)

MSI's LOS-stabilized single mounting (which does not penetrate the deck) can carry a variety of 25mm and 30mm weapons, but it has only been sold with the Oerlikon 30mm KCB cannon (as DS 30B). The U.S. Navy tested a version carrying the 25mm Bushmaster as naval weapons system EX-39. The mount was conceived about 1980 by Laurence Scott (which then became Defence Equipment and Systems, and then MSI; the mount was named LS-30 and then DS 30) as a gun adaptation of its optical director. Power-operated, the gun is controlled by joystick (a director-controlled Mk II and a digital predictor-equipped Mk III never sold). The locally controlled version was later renamed LOCSIG.

DS 30B on board HMS *Berkeley*, March 1995. (H&L van Ginderen)

SIGMA (Stabilized Integrated Gun-Missile Array), announced at RNEE in 1993, is DS 30 with two short-range missiles (they can be Starburst, Mistral, or Stinger) atop its elevating mass. Total weight, including 150 rnd, is 1.6 t.

MSI announced a remote-controlled REMSIG version in 1994 (with local backup). It was bought by the Royal Malaysian Navy for the new *Lekiu* class. AUTSIG is an autonomous control version with an LLLTV (with 10:1 zoom lens) on the elevation axis of the gun. The TV feeds an autotracker, and the system computer calculates a lead angle. A below-decks operator's screen has overlaid symbology and text to indicate the engagement sequence, system status, tracking gate, range symbols, and text instructions. Targets are indicated either by the operator or by a remote target designation sight.

Users: Australia (*Huon*-class minehunters), Malaysia (new *Lekiu*-class corvettes), United Kingdom (Type 23, Type 22 Batch III, "Castle" class, *Sandown* class, "Hunt" class, *Fort Victoria* class, *Argus* [fitted for], *Guernsey, Lindisfarne*). Malaysia was the first export customer. DS-30 entered British service in 1987, having been ordered in 1985 as a 40mm replacement.

◆ L7A2

   Caliber: 7.62mm
   Maximum Rate of Fire: 625–750 rnd/min
   Muzzle Velocity: 838 m/sec
   Maximum Range: 1800 m
   Maximum Elevation/Depression: +45/−10 deg
   Ammunition Load: 200 rnd
   Weight: 10.9 kg (gun alone, empty)

L7A2 is the standard British light machine gun, and its role in the Royal Navy is broadly analogous to that of the U.S. 0.50. L7A2 serves as a policing weapon on board "Ton"-class minecraft, and the "Isles"- and "Castle"-class offshore-patrol vessels. It was also pintle-mounted on board larger ships, for example, for close-in defense. The gun, which is a standard air-cooled infantry machine gun, can be mounted on a pedestal, a buffered tripod, or a bulwark pintle.

This gun is based on the Belgian FN MAG.

Users (including the Belgian MAG): Antigua, Bahamas, Bahrein, Bangladesh, Barbados, Belize, Brazil, Cyprus, Ecuador, Gambia, Guatemala, Haiti, India, Indonesia (MSA), Ireland, Jamaica, Jordan, Kuwait, Malawi, Malaysia (Police and Customs), Mexico, Qatar, Seychelles, Sierra Leone, Singapore, Solomon Islands, South Africa, Sri Lanka, St Kitts and Nevis, St Vincent and the Grenadines, Surinam, Sweden, Thailand, Turks & Caicos, United Kingdom. Canada and the Netherlands use the heavy-barrel vesion, the Belgian-made FAL.

UNITED STATES

Although all four battleships were stricken in January 1995, by August it appeared that at least two would be restored to the Naval Vessel Register, and that the other pair, while used as museums, would be maintained in usable condition. The Navy stopped just short of demilitarizing the ships, blocking their gun barrels. For full details of the 16in/50 gun, see the 1991/92 edition; the ships are unlikely to see service in the near future.

The 8in/55 rapid-fire gun, and the 6in/47 guns are now extinct. Although the rapid-fire lightweight 8in gun (Mk 71) was considered as one of several options in a Naval Fire Support study, adoption seems unlikely. As of the summer of 1992, the U.S. Navy was removing and scrapping all 40mm Bofors guns (two quad mounts removed and refurbished during a refit of USS *Sphinx* survive, but are unlikely to see further service). Similarly, Mk 67 20mm guns are being scrapped; they probably survive only aboard six or eight auxiliaries (as of mid-1996). Both weapons are being replaced by standard 25mm guns. The Mk 68 20mm gun apparently survives on board small craft transferred abroad, such as to Honduras.

The program to develop new naval guns, at one time called WARSHIPS, has been reduced to near-term gun improvements. The Navy liquid-propellant gun project has been terminated for now, although the Navy retains a memorandum of understanding with the Army's liquid-propellant program, and the 155mm Lockheed Martin liquid-propellant gun remains a long-term candidate for the next-generation surface combatant, SC-21. The 60mm electrothermal program (using guided shells) was completed without leading to production.

◆ Naval Surface Fire-Support Program

The new OTH attack concept requires ships, including combatants, to be stationed as much as 50 nm offshore, while supporting troops well inland from the beach. A 1992 Dahlgren study considered both near-term (ca. 1997) and far-term (2010/2020) replacements (bomblet-carrying missiles and guns) for the 16in gun. Weapons that can be fired from a Mk 41 VLS include ATACMS, SeaSLAM, Beachcomber (a GPS-guided Patriot [16in dia] derivative, formerly proposed for the Assault Breaker program which produced the Army's ATACMS), Seabear (Skipper guided by fiber optics or IR), and SMASH (an SM-1 derivative; the SM Autonomous Strike Homing round, probably using GPS guidance). By late 1994 the Marines had concluded that they needed a gun range of at least 41 nm, and preferably 63 nm; the existing 5in/54 can reach out only to 13 nm. The most likely solution was the electrothermal gun (ETG); as of March 1992 FMC held the world record for muzzle energy (14 MJ) with its new 5in/54 ETG.

Late in 1994 it appeared that a 155mm gun, to be developed at Louisville, would be chosen, but that facility was ordered closed. The choice switched to an improved 5in/54 firing guided rocket-assisted shells. This program had already been approved in December 1994 to fill a gap until a new 155mm gun became operational, about FY01. Guidance cost would be drastically reduced by using GPS/inertial guidance instead of a seeker.

As of April 1995, a three-phase Naval Surface Fire Support program was planned:

   ■ Near term (to 2001): An improved Mk 45 gun (see below) will fire a new EX-171 Hammer GPS-guided rocket-assisted shell (competent munition) carrying at least 72 of the Army's dual-purpose XM-80 submunitions (shaped charges plus enhanced fragmentation, using a self-destruct fuze). As of mid-1996, the first long-range demonstration, using a pre-ATD guidance system built by Draper Labs, was scheduled for November 1996, to be followed by OpEval in November 1999. The pre-ATD round can survive 10,000 G and requires about 300 in^3 for its electronics. The 1999 tactical round will survive 15,000 Gs and will require about 150 in^3 for its electronics. Control of the pre-ATD shell will be by the canards developed for the abortive laser-guided shell; ultimately Hammer may be tail-controlled. A preplanned product improved version will have a terminal seeker (IR/MMW) and a tandem shaped-charge unitary warhead.

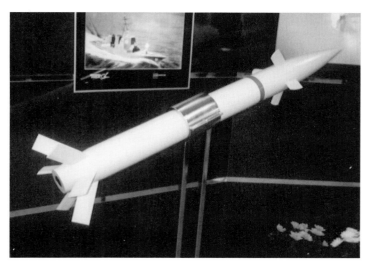

A model of the GPS-guided EX-171 Hammer round, displayed by Alliant Techsystems at the 1996 Navy League show. McDonnell-Douglas was the other partner in this project. (S. Zaloga)

Note that the existing 5in/54 rocket-assisted shell achieves a maximum range of 31,090 yd (23,690 yd for a conventional shell); Hammer is designed to achieve at least 82,000 yd. As CNO, Adm. Jeremy Boorda imposed a unit price limit of $35,000, far lower than that of the earlier laser-guided shell, which was driven down to about $40,000 in the mid-1980s. Hopes are that Hammer guidance technology can be packaged in 10 cubic inches, small enough to fit the standard NATO fuze screwed into the nose of a 76mm or 5in shell (or an Army/Marine Corps 105mm or 155mm howitzer, or 120mm mortar). Canard wings alongside the fuze would guide the shell. Hopefully this low-cost competent munition (LCCM) will cost $3000. It will use the type of micromachined circuitry already tested in the 60mm guided projectile (see the 1991/92 edition for details). A prototype is to fly in February 1998. Another concept (Best Buy) is to lengthen the extended range projectile beyond the 61.25in limit imposed by the Mk 45 gun by making it in two snap-together pieces (the tail includes the propellant), each of which can be rammed separately. Weight is limited by making the projectile out of graphite-epoxy composites. A triple-rammed 110in projectile could carry twice the Hammer payload to 115 nm. Yet another possibility is Rockwell's Scramshell, which propels the shell with a supersonic ramjet, accelerating it from Mach 3 (at the muzzle) to speeds as great as Mach 9. This technology may also be used for ship defense. Rockwell is proposing to use the same technology in a vertically launched Fasthawk missile (650-lb payload to 600nm range). The Navy is apparently also still interested in a vertically loaded 155mm gun. Finally, there is interest in a gun-launched UAV, Longlook, proposed by NSWC Dahlgren.

■ Medium term (to 2005): Missiles plus a next-generation gun. As of mid-1995, the main missile competitors were ATACMS, Sea SLAM (ship-launched SLAM), and a fire-sup-

port version of the Standard Missile, very large numbers of which are in inventory. The FY95 program included $11M to test the Standard strike missile.

■ Far term: Production and integration of a new gun.

Another element of this program is the attempt to link ships directly with forward-observer systems such as the Marine Corps' field artillery TDS. Forward observers and forward air controllers will have their own integrated GPS receivers and laser range-finders, hence will be able to transmit target coordinates to ships via digital links, for insertion into GPS-guided shells and missiles.

◆ 5in/54 Mk 42

Caliber: 5in/54 (70-lb shell)
Rate of Fire: 40 (derated to 28)
Muzzle Velocity: 2650 ft/sec
Maximum Range: 25,900 yd (Time of flight to 10,000 yd at 6-deg elevation is 15.8 sec.)
Training Rate: 40 deg/sec (elevation 25 deg/sec)
Elevation/Depression: $+85/-7.5$ deg
Ammunition Capacity: 40 (automatically loaded)
Weight: 145,930 lb (Mod 0)
Working Circle: 269in radius

Although no longer operational in the U.S. Navy, Mk 42 is widely used abroad. In all variants, the gun is fed by two parallel two-stage hoists, each extracting ammunition from a loader drum. Shells and cartridge cases are loaded separately into the drums, each of which holds 20 complete rounds. Shell and cartridge case are transferred together from drum to lower hoist, then to an upper hoist, and then to a transfer tray (on a cradle) that swings up parallel to the breech; the left and right hoists operate alternately, so that one places a round in the right cradle while the other descends to pick up another. Each transfer tray contains a fuze setter; it drops into position between rammer and breech to load the round. Having loaded, the tray pops up to avoid the gun's recoil, and an empty case tray moves into position to receive the ejected case. The entire process is mechanically complex, and the Mk 42 acquired a reputation for jamming during protracted firing, such as on the gun line off Vietnam: hence the current derating to about half the originally projected rate of fire. Mk 42 Mod 10 has a special troubleshooting status board.

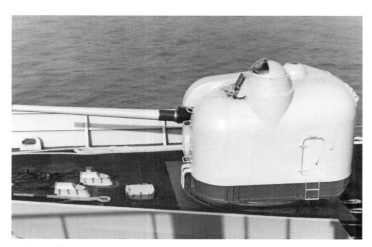

5in/54 Mk 42 mount, USS *William S. Sims*, 1986. (L. van Ginderen)

The 5in/54 Mk 42 has been manufactured under license in Japan (by the Japan Steel Works) since 1965.

Users: Australia (*Adams* class), Egypt (*Knox* class), Germany (*Adams* class), Greece (*Adams* and *Knox* classes), Japan, Spain (*Baleares* class), Taiwan (*Knox* class), Thailand (*Knox* class), Turkey (*Knox* class), United States (*Knox* class in reserve).

◆ 5in/54 Mk 45

Caliber: 5in/54 (70-lb shell)
Rate of Fire: Approx. 20 rnd/min (17 measured in test)

Muzzle Velocity: 2650 ft/sec
Maximum Range: 25,900 yd
Training Rate: 30 deg/sec (elevation 20 deg/sec)
Elevation/Depression: +65/−15 deg
Ammunition Capacity (on-mount): 20 (10 guided rnd)
Weight: 47,820 lb (no lower hoist)
Working Circle: 261 in radius

Mk 45 is the slower-firing, low-manning replacement for Mk 42. Compared with Mk 42, Mk 45 has a greatly simplified mechanism. There is only a single loader drum, and it includes the fuze setter. Some guns have no separate lower hoist; when a lower hoist is present, it feeds the drum. Rounds are loaded into a single cradle, which swings from the vertical up into position behind the vertical sliding breechblock. The round is rammed, and the block drops to close. The empty case is ejected when the gun counter-recoils, the empty case tray being mounted atop the slide. Misfired rounds are removed automatically, rather than manually, as in Mk 42. Personnel: gun captain, panel operator, and four ammunition loaders, all below decks.

5in/54 Mk 45 mount, USS *Vincennes*, 1987. (W. Donko)

Barrel lifetime is 7000 rnd, compared with 3070 for Mk 42.

Mod 1 was adapted for a new generation of guided shells (which, in the event, never entered service), with its loading station lowered to make room for these longer rounds, and an electronic fuze-setter added to the earlier mechanical unit. Ammunition type can be changed remotely. Development began in 1977, and production followed in 1982.

Mod 2 is the current export version.

Mod 3 is the likely designation of the near-term shore fire-support version, work on which began in April 1994. The prototype gun mount should be delivered in October 1998. The earlier two-piece barrel is replaced by a single-piece 62-caliber barrel, to make full use of a new high-energy insensitive propellant (barrel length is limited by a requirement that existing train and elevation drives not be stressed). A new high-pressure breechblock is fitted. New stronger base ring and trunnion supports will be supplied to absorb increased energy. Muzzle energy is doubled, increasing range from 13 to about 20 nm. Projectile ballistics is improved. This version is to be convertible to the electrothermal gun configuration already tested by FMC. In 1995, FMC estimated that the upgraded 5in/62 mount would weigh 50,000 lb without a lower hoist, or 24,600 lb with a four-flight lower hoist. A new NSFS control system is being added, providing an interactive display, a digital interface to the ship FCS, a digital interface to the new extended-range munition (to supply target coordinates), a GPS receiver, and an interface to ammunition recognition sensors. The new shell, about 60 in long, will have to be double-rammed (once for the projectile, once for the cartridge case), since the loader drum limiting length is 61.25in. That in turn will limit rate of fire to 10 rnd/min. DDG 89 is to be the first ship to receive the new version of Mk 45.

The longer barrel and recoil (to accommodate a more energetic charge) extend the range of a RAP shell from about 30 to about 45 nm (muzzle energy increases from 9.5 to 15 MJ). Improved gun interior ballistics and structure buy another 5 nm (muzzle energy 20 MJ). Conversion to the electrothermal operation would extend range to about 70 nm (25 MJ). In December 1994 the U.S. Navy announced that it expected to make an ETG decision by 1998; a prototype is to be delivered in 1997. An ORDALT package can be ready about October 1999.

A Mk 45 technical improvement program for existing mounts provides a lateral transfer cradle, an enhanced interface with the FCS, electric train and elevation drives, a new shield, and an index drive and lower hoist servo controls.

FMC's proposed Advanced Mk 45 mount (1990) offered a credible AA potential: higher rate of fire (to 40 rnd/min burst or 23 rnd/min sustained, via modified projectile handling), higher gun elevation and training rates, and better ballistic performance (increased muzzle velocity and tube length). Maximum elevation would be 70 deg. Gun shield radar cross-section would be reduced and reliability/maintainability improved.

An Ultra or Super Lightweight Mk 45 (1994) has 95% component commonality with Mk 45, but redesigning the hoist and eliminating the 20-rnd loader drum saves 2100 kg. It has a reconfigured operator console, new train and elevation regulators, and a lightweight reduced-signature shield. Estimated weight is 46,000 lb without a lower hoist, or 48,000 lb with a lower hoist. Royal Ordnance has proposed this weapon for the Project Horizon Anglo-French-Italian AAW frigate.

Users: Australia (MEKO frigates), Greece (MEKO frigates), New Zealand (MEKO frigates), Thailand (*Naresuan*-class frigates), Turkey (MEKO frigates), United States (*Ticonderoga, California, Virginia, Arleigh Burke, Kidd, Spruance, Tarawa* classes). U.S. cruisers from CG 51 on and *Arleigh Burke*-class destroyers have Mod 1. All foreign ships except the Turkish Track I MEKO frigates have Mod 2 mounts (these ships have Mod 1).

◆ **5in/38 Mounts**

    Caliber: 5in/38 (54-lb shell)
    Rate of Fire: 10–15 rnd/min/gun
    Muzzle Velocity: 2600 ft/sec
    Maximum Range: 16,500 yd surface; 11,900 slant (time of flight to 10,000 yd at 11-deg elevation: 22 sec)
    Training Rate: 25 deg/sec (elevation 15 deg/sec)
    Elevation/Depression: +85/−10 deg
    Ammunition Capacity: None on mount
    Weight: 95,700 lb
    Working Circle: 11 ft 11 in

Data are for the destroyer twin mount with 0.125in shield.

Single enclosed Mk 30 5in/38 mount aboard the U.S. Coast Guard cutter *Midgett*, 1987. (W. Donko)

The standard U.S. Navy dual-purpose gun of World War II survives in enclosed twin and single (Mk 30) and open single (Mk 37) forms. The twin mount crew, including loaders below decks, is 26 (13 on the mount itself). Barrel service life is 4600 rnd. Regunning time is 8 hr/gun, compared to about 1 hr for the 5in/54 Mk 42 or Mk 45. The mount carries no ready-use rounds. The enclosed Mk 30 weighs 40,900–41,000 lb. Training (elevation) rates are 38.74 or 34 deg/sec (15 or 18 deg/sec) for mounts with GE or Ford controls, respectively. The Mk 37 open mount trains (elevates) at 30 (15) deg/sec. A 5in/38 rocket-assisted projectile (Mk 57) developed during the Vietnam War is 51.5 in long and has a maximum surface range of 23,770 yd. The rocket burns for 40 sec, and the shell carries 3.5 lb of explosives. Corresponding figures for the standard 5in rnd (Mk 66) are 50.14 in, range 14,000 yd, and explosive content 7.9 lb.

Users:

> Twin mount: Korea (FRAMs), Mexico (FRAMs), Pakistan (FRAMs), Taiwan (FRAMs), Turkey (FRAMs), United States (*Iowa* class).
>
> Single enclosed mount: Brazil (*Garcia* class), Mexico (*Fletcher* class, fast transports).
>
> Single open mount: Taiwan (*Yu Tai*).

◆ 3in/50

Caliber: 3in/50 (15-lb shell)
Rate of Fire: 45 rnd/min/barrel
Muzzle Velocity: 2700 ft/sec
Maximum Range: 14,600 yd (time of flight to 6000 yd at 5-deg elevation: 12 sec). Maximum altitude is 30,400 ft.
Training Rate: 24 deg/sec (elevation 30 deg/sec)
Elevation/Depression: +85/−15 deg
Ammunition Capacity: No ready-use ammunition on mount (but each barrel can have 5 rnd in its loader). Typically 200 or 300 rnd in ready-service locker, another 1200 in magazine.
Weight: 31,435–32,400 lb, depending on version
Working Circle: 120in radius

Data are for the twin automatic 3in/50 Mk 33, once very widely used. It was developed specifically to deal with kamikazes; in 1945 it was the smallest gun that could fire a proximity-fuzed shell. Although there is no magazine as such on the mount, the loaders continually refill the 5-rnd revolving loading drums that actually feed the guns. There is no rammer as such; instead, the loader, which is an independent electrically driven device, catapults each round into the chamber, the breech-closing mechanism being triggered by the edge of the cartridge case as it trips one of the ejectors. Once a round is in the breech, the loader cycle stops until the gun fires and ejects that cartridge case. This unusual arrangement was adopted because the gun itself is the

earlier semiautomatic weapon adapted as simply as possible to automatic fire; in effect the loading and triggering cycle has been automated, without any basic redesign. That simple automation in turn limits the ultimate rate of fire. Because firing is automatic once a round has been catapulted into the chamber, the gun is unloaded whenever it is not firing: the loader has six slots, but only five can be occupied.

The original version of the twin automatic mount was Mk 27; Mk 33 is more common. Many mounts are enclosed in fiberglass gunhouses. There is also a single version (Mk 34), weighing, typically, 17,000 lb.

The barrel's life is 2050 rnd.

This gun is usually controlled by a Mk 56 director; others, with a Mk 34 (SPG-34) radar dish on the mount, are controlled by the Mk 63 system.

The 3in/50 automatic gun was provided to Japan under the Military Assistance Program (MAP). From 1957 on, the gun was manufactured under license by the Japan Steel Works.

Some surviving World War II ships are armed with the earlier single semiautomatic 3in/50 mount (Mk 26) from which this weapon was derived; Mk 26 has the same ballistics. Its rate of fire is 15–20 rnd/min, and because of the slower rate of fire, the barrel's life is rated as 4300 rnd. The working circle's radius is 96 in.

Users:

> 3in/50 automatic mounts (Mks 33 and 34): Brazil (*Ceara, Duque de Caxias*), Canada (*Annapolis* class), Colombia (*Boyaca, Asheville* class), Denmark (*Falster* class), Greece (*Asheville* and *Terrebonne Parish* classes), Indonesia (*Claud Jones* class), Japan (*Yamagumo, Minegumo, Chikugo, Isuzu, Miura* classes), Norway (*Oslo* class), Portugal (*Joao Coutinho* class), Spain (*Paul Revere, Terrebonne Parish* classes), Turkey (*Berk, Asheville, Falster, Terrebonne Parish* classes).
>
> 3in/50 semiautomatic mount (Mk 26): Chile (*Sgt. Aldea, Yelcho*), Dominican Republic (*Mella, Cohoes,* and *Admirable* classes), Ecuador (*Abnaki* class), Greece (*Aris, Patapsco* classes), Iran (PF 103 class), Mexico (*Auk* and *Admirable* classes), Peru (river gunboats, *Independencia*), Philippines (*Cannon, Auk, Admirable,* PCE/PCER, LSSL classes), Spain (*Anaga* class), Taiwan (*Auk* class, LSTs, auxiliaries), Thailand (PSMM Mk 5 class, LSSL, *Damrong Rachanuphat* class), United States (coast guard: *Reliance, Cherokee* classes), Venezuela (*F Larrazabel*).

◆ 3in/62 Mk 75

See OTO-Melara 76/62 (above, under Italy).

◆ 81mm Mortar Mk 2

Caliber: 81mm (53 lb for package of 3 rnd)
Rate of Fire: 10 rnd/min trigger; 18 rnd/min drop-fire, 45-deg elevation
Muzzle Velocity: 787 ft/sec
Maximum Range: 3987 yd
Elevation/Depression: +71.5/−30 deg
Working Circle: 108 in

This weapon can be mounted alone or in combination with a 0.50-cal. M2 machine gun, in a piggyback mount. In contrast to mortars for land service, it is either trigger- or drop-fired, and it can, therefore, be fired at 0 elevation. Mk 2's recoil mechanism reduces deck loads when the gun is fired. Mk 2 uses army ammunition.

Mod 1 is the piggyback version carrying the 0.50-cal. machine gun; total weight is 722 lb.

Users: Brazil (*Piratini*-class patrol boats and in river-patrol ships), El Salvador (77ft, 65ft, Camcraft classes), France (*Champlain* class), Gabon (*Champlain* class), Ivory Coast (*Champlain* class), Lebanon (EDIC III class), Libya (*Ibn Ouf* class), Madagascar (landing ships *Toky* and *Aina Vao Vao*), Malta (Swift), Morocco (*Champlain* class), Paraguay (*Itaipu*), Philippines (provision in 77ft class), Rumania (in VB 76 class), Saudi Arabia (PCG, PGG classes), Senegal (EDIC type), Sweden (Stridsbat 90 type),

The Japanese training ship *Katori* displays a pair of enclosed Mk 33 mounts forward, the superfiring one carrying a radome-enclosed SPG-34 radar for her Mk 63 FCS (the optical director is in the small band stand above the bridge). The destroyer alongside is *Nagatsuki*. (Author)

Over-and-under 81mm mortar and 0.50-cal. machine gun on board a patrol boat in Panama, 1983. (U.S. Navy)

A Mk 19 grenade launcher on its pintle mount aboard USS *Sirocco*. (Stuart Slade, DMS/Forecast International)

Thailand (PB Mk III and Swift Mk II classes), United States (PB Mk III/IV), Vietnam (ex-U.S. *Barnegat* class). Virtually all the 81mm mortars are probably of U.S. design (and, mostly, manufacture). Users of recoil-less rifles (probably U.S. Army types): Guatemala (*Broadsword* and 85ft type: 75mm), Iran (106mm in some of 32 Boghammer boats). Iran also uses the Soviet-supplied 107mm recoil-less rifle, in some Boston Whalers.

◆ 60mm Mortar

    Caliber: 60mm (49 lb for package of 10 rnd)
    Rate of Fire: 10 rnd/min trigger; 18 rnd/min drop mode, 45-deg elevation
    Muzzle Velocity: 500 ft/sec
    Maximum Range: 1850–2000 yd
    Elevation/Depression: +80/−20 deg
    Weight: 177 lb
    Working Circle: 114 in

This mortar is a smaller version of Mk 2. Some have seen service in the Persian Gulf on board patrol boats (PBs). During the Vietnam War it was used on board PBRs, which could not accommodate the 81. In many cases it is combined with an M60 machine gun in a piggyback combination. The 60mm mortar is descended from Mortar Mk 1, the Garrett (Kodak) trigger-fired mortar of 1945.

Users: Bolivia (PBR Mk II), Burma (PBR Mk II), Colombia (PBR Mk II), Costa Rica (105ft, 42ft, and 36ft types), Philippines (seven Mini-ATC type), Thailand (PBR Mk II), United States (PB III/IV, PBRs), Vietnam (PBR Mk II).

◆ 40mm Grenade Launcher Mk 19/EX-41

This short-range blow-back machine gun, developed during the Vietnam War, is used on board riverine and coastal craft and on larger ships to defend against saboteurs and boarders. It fires 400–450 rnd/min at a muzzle velocity of 800 ft/sec. Maximum range is 2400 yd (35-deg elevation), and effective range is 1780 yd (15-deg elevation). A 24-rnd box of ammunition weighs 21.5 lb. EX-41 is a prototype lightweight shoulder-fired semiauto-matic grenade launcher (using the same ammunition as in Mk 19) being built by NOL Louisville.

The current version is Mod 3. Procurement: 25/year in the late 1980s, then FY89, 350; FY90, 123; FY91, 321; FY92, 568; FY93, none. Many of the recently bought weapons are for the Marines.

◆ Emerlec-30/EX-74

    Caliber: 30mm
    Rate of Fire: 600 rnd/min/bbl
    Muzzle Velocity: 3543 ft/sec
    Maximum Range: 3500 yd
    Training Rate: 80 deg/sec (elevation 80 deg/sec)
    Elevation/Depression: +80/−15 deg
    Ammunition Capacity: 985 rnd/gun
    Weight: 4200 lb without ammunition
    Working Circle: 94 in

This ESCO mount carries one 30mm KCB Oerlikon gun on each side of a cab in which the operator sits. It was derived from a U.S. Navy mount, EX-74. ESCO (Electronics and Space Corporation) was a 1990 spinoff of the defense interests of Emerson Electric (hence the Emerlec name).

Users: Ecuador (*Manta* class), Ethiopia (Swift), Greece (Combattante IIIN class), South Korea (Ulsan HDF-2000 and HDC-800 classes, *Donghae* class, PSMM 5 class, "Sea Dolphin" class), Malaysia (FS 1500–class frigates, *Hang Tuah*, and corvettes), Nigeria (Combattante IIIB and FPB 57 classes, Abeking & Rasmussen and Brooke Marine–type patrol boats, and *Lerici*), the Philippines (*Katapangan* class), Saudi Arabia (*Sandown* class), Taiwan (*Lung Chiang* class).

◆ 25mm Automatic Cannon Mk 38 (Bushmaster)

    Caliber: 25mm/87 (1.1-lb rnd)
    Rate of Fire: Single shot, 100, or 200 rnd/min
    Muzzle Velocity: 1100 m/sec

Emerlec-30 gun mount. (Emerson Electric)

Maximum Range: 6800 m
Training Rate: Manual mount
Elevation/Depression: +55/−20 deg
Ammunition Capacity: 150 linked cartridges
Weight: Total gun weight (no mounting) 240 lb; total mounting weight 1250 lb
Working Circle: 151 in

The naval version of the Bushmaster "Chain Gun" is made by Hughes for the U.S. Army as M242. Procured by the Army as M242, the gun is designated Mk 38 Gun System, Machine Gun for naval service; the unstabilized hand-aimed pedestal mounting is Mk 88. Barrel life is 25,000 rnd; dispersion is 0.5 mil. The name derives from the use of a horizontal loop of externally powered standard industrial double-row roller chain, to drive the bolt back and forth. The length and width of the chain are determined by the length of the round and by the desired rate of fire. The chain runs at constant speed, carrying a shoe that drives the bolt. When in line with the bolt, the shoe pulls back and forth, locking and opening the bolt. When the shoe travels to one side (along the belt, perpendicular to the gun's axis), the gun has time to fire or to eject a fired cartridge (depending on where in the cycle this travel occurs). The feed to the gun is powered by the same motor that drives the chain.

The chain gun mechanism can easily be adapted to different calibers. There is current U.S. Navy interest in McDonnell-Douglas's Bushmaster II (30mm), which has about 70% parts in common with Bushmaster (I). A stabilized gun mount carrying it is designated EX-40 (in the system in which naval Bushmaster is Mk 38); EX-42 is an alternative mounting, possibly based on the British DS- series, since it can take a variety of weapons. Bushmaster III is 35mm, and Bushmaster IV is to be 40mm. Note that the 25mm gun tested in the British MSI mounting was designated gun system (MG) EX-39. It could also carry the 40mm grenade launcher and the M2 heavy machine gun. See also the minor-caliber gun mounts described below.

Development and procurement of the Chain Gun were approved in December 1971. In 1977 the CNO approved procurement to replace existing 20mm guns, which were difficult to support (they required overhaul every 6500 rnd) and did not use standard NATO ammunition; many existing rounds were considered unsafe.

25mm Bushmaster (Mk 38 gun on Mk 88 mount). (McDonnell-Douglas Helicopter Co.)

Procurement: FY86, 29; FY87, 25; FY88, 22; FY89, 57; FY91, 55; FY92 (last year procured), 55. It seems likely that more will be bought, since this gun has been chosen to replace all existing 40mm and 20mm weapons. It will certainly arm U.S. special forces boats (Mk III and *Cyclone* class) and the later LSD 42 class, and it is issued to ships deploying to the Middle East. Production of Mk 38 25mm cannon was drastically accelerated in 1987–88 to meet the needs of ships in the Persian Gulf, much of the work being done at NSWC Crane.

Users: Saudi Arabia (77ft class), Philippines (77ft class), United States.

◆ Minor-Caliber Gun Mounts (Mks 82, 93, 94, 95, 96, Valkyrie, STARC 25)/CLIP

The Special Warfare Command buys weapons for its small combatants, including the *Cyclone*-class PCs. NSWC Crane is responsible for CLIP (Craft Life Improvement Program) and also develops minor-caliber mounts.

The AMCGS program ended with the adoption of the surface mode for Phalanx. However, in April 1995, responding to congressional direction, NAVSEA sought an off-the-shelf non-developmental remotely controlled stabilized minor-caliber gun mount capable of taking a 25mm gun. Maximum weight, including 250 rnd, was set at 5300 lb (4500 desired), of which 4800/4000 would be above decks, and there would be no deck penetration. An optronic FCS, including an eye-safe laser and capable

The Valkyrie 25mm mount. (SEI)

Kollmorgen's STARC 25 is an adapted Bushmaster. Its sensor unit is fixed atop the gun. (Kollmorgen)

of night vision, was envisaged, to detect and recognize targets at 3000–5000 yd. An RFP for the Shipboard Stabilized Platform System (SSPS) was finally issued in the spring of 1996. The mounts being tested are STARC 25, Valkyrie, and the Israeli Typhoon. Current Crane projects are:

Mk 82–2, a stainless-steel mount for 7.62mm machine guns (weight 11 kg), suitable for an armored shield. As of March 1993, 4 had been tested and 52 more were being made for evaluation.

Mk 93, a stainless-steel machine-gun mount for the Mk 19 grenade launcher or the 0.50-caliber machine gun (M2HB). Weight with 100 rnds and a steel shield is 97.97 kg; elevation limits are +67/−27 deg, and working circle diameter is 1.29m. This mount is for a "Hummer" vehicle; it is interchangeable with the Army M64 but is corrosion-resistant. As of early 1993, 8 prototypes had been made.

Mk 94, a lightweight soft mount for the M2HB 0.50-caliber machine gun, made of aluminum and stainless steel; seven prototypes made as of March 1993

Mk 95–0, a twin 0.50 CLIP mount (27.3 kg), made of stainless steel and aluminum.

A CLIP contract has been awarded for a vertically stabilized 0.50. Weight with 200 rnd is 170 kg; elevation limits are +60/ −22 deg, and working circle diameter is 1.34 m. A similar round carrying a seat for the gunner weighs 297.87 kg with 200 rnd, and has elevation limits of +33/−30 deg.

Mk 96–0, a modified 40mm Mk 9–3 (power-operated stabilized mounting) with the 40mm gun replaced by a 25mm Bushmaster, and carrying a piggybacked Mk 19 grenade launcher. The one mount made for evaluation was cross-decked among *Cyclone*-class patrol boats off Haiti. Ultimately thirteen were ordered, one for each *Cyclone*. The gunner sits to the left of the 25mm gun on the powered mount, receiving target designation only through headphones. Possible add-ons are a stabilized sight and a night sight. Reportedly Crane is now working on a manually controlled stabilized version of the Mk 88 mounting.

Earlier abortive mounts are: EX-89, a commercial Emerson Electric mount for 25mm cannon for patrol boats; EX-90, a patrol boat mount for the General Electric GAU-12U; EX-91, a wheeled lightweight mount for a single 7.62mm M60 or 0.50-cal. M2HB machine gun (for the Marines); and EX-92, a 0.50-cal. gun mount XM-218 for the UH-1N helicopter.

Two new 25mm/30mm stabilized mountings were shown at Defendory in the fall of 1994: the E&S Valkyrie (in effect an Emerlec-30 successor) and Kollmorgen's STARC 25. The modular Valkyrie can accept any 25mm or 30mm gun plus unguided rockets and missiles such as Hellfire and Stinger. The mount is built around a stabilized set of trunnions mounted on a nondeck-penetrating rectangular barbette (1.37 × 1.93 × 0.5 m). Sensors (e.g., FLIR and laser ranger) can be mounted directly atop the elevating element. It carries system electronics as well as 12 batteries to provide power if ship power fails. The mount can carry either the 25mm cannon or proposed larger-caliber versions (30-, 35-, 40mm). An ammunition bay can be mounted on one side, a missile-launching bay (environmental enclosure) on the other, to carry, for example, a pair of Hellfires or four Stingers or a 7- or 19-rocket pod. The operator would be below decks. Alternatively, a manned cab can replace the missile bay. Initial sea trials were completed in November 1995.

Kollmorgen's STARC (Stabilized and Remote-Controlled) 25 is a stabilized remote-control version of the Mk 88 25mm mounting carrying one or two EO sensors atop it. The initial sensor was a single CCD daylight TV camera (FOV 12 × 9 deg), but Kollmorgen also offers an LLLTV or a pair of sensors to give either multiple FOVs (zoom lenses cannot be maintained boresighted) or day/night operation. A FLIR is being considered. Carrying 176 ready-use rnd (as in Mk 88), STARC 25 weighs less than 2200 lb. The below-decks electronics package (ballistics, autotracker, etc. using a 486DX processor programmed in "C") weighs 385 lb, and the control console 80–85 lb. Elevation limits are +60/−20 deg; train/elevation rates are 60 deg/sec (the gun has slewed at 120 deg/sec in tests). This mount was first fired in February 1995, and it completed the first of the three NAVSEA tests in mid-1996 (on board a 65ft PB; Valkyrie is next).

◆ GPU-5/GAU-13

This podded four-barrel 30mm Gatling gun (GPU-5 in GAU-13 pod), designed for the U.S. Air Force, was tested by the Marines in the fall of 1995 on board LCAC-66, to provide direct fire support. The Marines' effort was supported by Wright Labs of Eglin Air Force Base. The pod is mounted on a standard MAU-12 bomb rack on a cargo container (8 × 8 × 20ft box) in the well deck. An LCAC can accommodate four guns. They would be used both to deal with beach defenders and to destroy fixed obstacles. The pod is attractive partly because it is available at very low cost: the Air Force considers it surplus. When the Marines expressed interest, 48 were active and another 140 were stored at Davis-Monthan; all have now been turned over to the Marines (they cost $1.2M in 1981, which is $4.6M in current dollars). The pod is now being considered of MSC ship defense and for mounting on Marine ground vehicles such as the LAV. The system is to be guided/stabilized by an adapted EO missile or bomb seeker (from an AGM-65A/B or an AGM-130), which can track a target on the beach. The Marines call the armed LCAC a gun platform air cushion (GPAC). The success of the GPAC experiment implies that any store normally carried underwing on a standard bomb rack, such as a rocket pod, can ultimately be adapted to an LCAC. Other examples are machine guns and possibly even the 105mm (and projected low-recoil 155mm) guns of the AC-130 gunship. The concept recalls the World War II support landing craft, many of which were adapted beaching craft carrying weapons up to 5in caliber, as well as rockets (which LCACs can already carry, in the form of minefield breaching rounds).

◆ **Phalanx (Close-In Weapons System Mk 15)**

Caliber: 20mm/53 (0.22-lb rnd)
Rate of Fire: 1000–3000 rnd/min
Muzzle Velocity: 3650 ft/sec
Maximum Range: 6000 yd (effective range 1625 yd)
Training Rate: 126 deg/sec (elevation 92 deg/sec)
Elevation/Depression: +85/−25 deg
Ammunition Capacity: 989 rnd (1500 in Block 1)
Weight: 12,000 lb above deck, 466 lb below deck
Working Circle: 216in dia

Hughes's Phalanx is the standard U.S. Navy CIWS, using subcaliber (0.5 in) penetrators (originally depleted-uranium, now tungsten) to destroy or fuze incoming antiship missiles. It is now being modified to add a surface firing mode. The weapons system's designation covers the mount plus integrated radar; the mount proper is Mk 72. The Mk 15 *system* incorporates gun group Mk 16.

Phalanx combines a 20mm Gatling gun with a Ku-band search and track radar (*not* the VPS-2 range-only radar of the Army Vulcan system) that has two antennas but one transmitter, hence

Phalanx. (General Dynamics)

Phalanx (Close-in Weapons System Mk 15). The drum magazine is under the gun. (U.S. Navy)

(unlike Goalkeeper) cannot keep searching while it engages a target. The radar automatically detects and tracks incoming missiles. The radar uses unambiguous Doppler/ambiguous range, switching PRF to achieve range resolution in three range-coverage zones. The system decides automatically to engage, and the operator has a veto.

The gun fires continuously, but from a fire-control point of view, its stream of rounds is broken down into 10-rnd bursts. The radar tracks each as it goes out, predicting its point of closest approach to the incoming target, and corrects the aim of the following burst(s). The radar uses variable PRF with selected frequency-line tracking to measure the angular error of the projectile stream. The manufacturer, General Dynamics Pomona (now taken over by Hughes), claimed that this closed-loop spotting system improves system lethality by as much as an order of magnitude. Early specifications required that Phalanx detect a target at 5600 yd, acquire it at 4300, and open fire at 2500 (first potential intercept at 2000). The inner boundary (keep-out zone) was defined as 100–230 yd.

The depleted-uranium penetrators were replaced by tungsten, partly because the uranium is mildly radioactive (it must handled with gloves and lead-shielded when stowed adjacent to berths). The shift was made in 1989–90, when the price of tungsten fell below that of lead. Tests showed that tungsten rounds penetrated missiles and hit their guidance systems with greater mass intact.

Phalanx is sometimes criticized on the ground that it fires a much lighter round than Goalkeeper. The U.S. response is that lethality per round is much the same in both cases, since it takes a penetrating hitting projectile to fuse the warhead of the

CIWS Block 1, showing the new upper (search) antenna and the enlarged magazine. (General Dynamics)

A prototype Phalanx Block 1B shows its EO tracker (*right*) and its lengthened barrel with a barrel clamp. (Hughes)

incoming missile, which does the great bulk of the destruction; the heavier the round, the fewer rounds the gun can carry, for a given weight. Goalkeeper does enjoy the advantage of true TWS performance (Phalanx switches to rate-aided tracking of targets detected by the search radar when it shifts from search to track mode), but at a very high cost (including much greater weight and complexity). Moreover, full integration of Phalanx into SSDS should provide true TWS capability through other system sensors.

The system has a Mk 340 remote-control panel in CIC (which is the primary means of weapon control during an engagement) and a Mk 339 local-control panel in a local-control room (which is used to run the system operability test). Phalanx can accept remote target designation (e.g., from Aegis), and there is also a manual AAW mode, requiring a manual trigger command. Apparently the Japanese gun that shot down the U.S. A-6 during the RIMPAC 96 exercise was in manual mode.

The major recent development was the 16 October 1992 decision to provide a Phalanx Surface Mode (PSuM), rather than some new advanced medium-caliber gun, for large ships. Phalanx had always had a surface-engagement potential, but its use in that role was discouraged, partly because the fire-control system was ill-adapted to surface fire, and partly for fear that surface shooting would detract from the system's primary mission. Saudi Phalanxes do have the surface mode, using a TDS Mk 24 as designator. Phalanx is now being provided with an off-the-shelf Pilkington Optronics EO tracker specifically for surface fire. The initial Block 0 version suffered from sea corrosion. Special "maintenance shelters" had to be built to protect parts of the mount.

Block 1 (Baseline 0: CIWS Mk 15 Mods 11 to 14) can engage targets at steeper angles. The 2D scanning antenna of Block 0 is replaced by a four-plate back-to-back phased-array antenna. The radar switches through four alternative radar beams (extending up to the zenith), and gains data rate by back-to-back operation. The search volume increases enormously, since Block 0 was largely limited to low-altitude targets (it could detect high-angle targets at short range). The new radar detects targets at the maximum search angle of Block 0 out to maximum range. It uses multiple PRFs to resolve range ambiguity. This improvement presumably solves the problem presented by a helicopter, whose rotor blades provide Doppler, which would normally indicate high speed, but which in fact moves quite slowly. This version also has 50% more on-mount ammunition. A positive ceasefire function matches burst length to target characteristics, to conserve ammunition so that more targets can be engaged before reloading. Block 1 Baseline 0 was operationally tested at China Lake 3 December 1981–21 May 1982. Deliveries began in January 1988. Upgrades of U.S. systems to this version will continue at least through FY97. Note that this *CIWS* incorporates Weapon Group Mk 16 Mod 2 (Mod 1 was the original Phalanx gun with the original search antenna). Block 1 was successfully tested in 185 engagements in 1985–94, targets including 155mm shells and Vandal (ex-Talos) and BQM-34 drones, some of which popped up during flight.

Block 1 Baseline 1 replaces the hydraulic gun drive with a pneumatic one (4500 rnd/min) and increases search radar sensitivity. It was approved for limited production as part of the FY88 and FY89 production lots.

Baseline 2 (OpEval FY91) introduced an internal data bus, allowing it to self-test without requiring aircraft to fly toward it. An abortive Baseline 2A was to have added a second ammunition drum (as proposed by GE in 1989), for quicker reloading.

Baseline 2B (Block 1A) replaces the original CDC 469A computer with a new CDC AMP high-order language (HOL: ADA language) computer using R3000 RISC processors (said to be 100 times as fast as the current unit). The new computer accommodates new nonlinear spotting algorithms to deal with maneuvering targets. For example, an FFT is applied to the smoothed (Kalman-filtered) target track to extract regularities for prediction. The effect of greater computer power is to double effective gun range. This version integrates with SSDS via its data bus, hence can provide SSDS with search and track data from its radars. Production began with the FY95 contract. As of May 1996, fleet release was scheduled for later in the year. HOL processors were being delivered to the U.S. Navy but were not yet being exported.

Baseline 2C (Block 1B) is the antisurface mode version, including a lethality upgrade. Pilkington's IR sensor, fixed to the radar servo structure and dual-axis stabilized (using a Contraves system) is a modified version of the company's existing 8–12-micron High Definition Thermal Imager (HDTI 5–2F). It uses an 8-element SPRITE array to produce 525- or 625-line video. FOVs are 2 × 1.3 and 4.5 × 3 deg (horizontal resolution 72 and 161 microrad, respectively). The gun is controlled by one of two new stations, the local-control station and the remote-control station, which replace the former panels. Each receives FLIR video, which is used to acquire targets manually; they are then tracked by an SRT Electronics autotracker. Range is normally provided either by the Phalanx search radar or by another shipboard radar; but it can also be calculated automatically from the depression angle of the FLIR. The gun fires manually correctable 50-rnd bursts at surface targets, spaced by a 2-sec look-for-kill (visual) assessment interval. Since tracking is only by FLIR, the system radar continues to search for air targets; an automatic override ensures that air threats will take priority. However, the FLIR is now available to track air targets, overcoming multipath (targets are designated to the FLIR by the system tracker). About 20 Pilkington sensors are to be bought, cross-decked between ships. The first two HDTIs were delivered to Hughes in spring 1996. The lethality upgrade modifies both barrels and ammunition. Barrels are 38 lb heavier, lengthened (from 60 to 79 in, i.e., by 482.6mm, 24.1 calibers, from 76.2 calibers), and have a mid-length clamp to reduce dispersion to 1 mil. Wider lands in the new barrel should eliminate in-bore damage, which can cause the sabot to break up and the projectile to fly erratically. A new Enhanced Lethality Cartridge (ELC) uses the penetrator originally planned for the abortive 25mm round (which is 50% heavier: 105 vs. 70 g), with a more energetic charge for higher energy: such rounds impact with more than twice their current energy, the effect being similar to that of a 30mm round. R&D on this round was completed during FY95. As of mid-1996, however, the ELC round was not being manufactured because of the sheer number of existing conventional 20mm Phalanx rounds. Development of the PSuM ORDALT formally began on 12 July 1993. The first engineering development model was rolled out on 9 May 1996. TechEval is to be completed during FY97. Production of kits to upgrade existing guns to Block 1B is to begin in 1997.

Plans for a follow-on Block 2 were shelved in 1992 in favor of continued incremental improvement to Block 1. For details, see

the 1991/92 edition. A Baseline 3 incorporating a new Thomson-CSF transmitter was also abandoned.

In February 1992 NSWC Dahlgren requested industry proposals for a future CIWS, a 60 to 76mm gun firing long (12–15 caliber) rockets at a sustained rate of at least 200/min, with a total capacity of 40 to 50 rnd. The rocket airframe would include a terminal seeker, a mid-course command link receiver, a control system, a KE penetrator, and a sustainer motor; it would have to be extremely agile. System weight would be about 10,000 lb (Phalanx weighs 12,000).

Phalanx was proposed in 1968 as part of the early antiship-missile defense program prompted by the *Eilat*'s sinking; a feasibility contract was awarded to General Dynamics in 1969. Full-scale production was authorized in 1977, the first installation (on board the carrier *America*) following in 1980. The 400th system was delivered in 1985. Recent purchases: 18 in FY90, 15 in FY91, 14 in FY92, 12 in FY93. Unit cost including integration was $5.3M in FY93 (the weapon proper cost about $3.3M in FY90).

Users:

Block 0: Australia, Bahrein (on FFG 7 being transferred), Brazil (on LST), Canada, Israel, Malaysia (on LST), Morocco (on LST), Pakistan, Portugal, Saudi Arabia, United States. Total deliveries: 500.

Block 1: Australia, New Zealand, Egypt, Greece, Japan, Taiwan, Thailand, Turkey, United Kingdom, United States. Total deliveries: 335 (as of 1996). Many Block 0 are being upgraded to Block 1 standard.

As of 18 January 1995, the U.S. Navy had 140 Block 0, 89 Block 1 Baseline 0, 98 Block 1 Baseline 1, and 47 Block 1 Baseline 2 mounts. Distribution: Block 0: 4 AE, 1 AFS, 1 AGF, 2 AO, 4 AOE-1, 2 AOR, 1 CG-16, 3 CGN-25/26, 2 CG-47, 11 DD-963, 4 DDG-993, 38 FFG-7, 4 LHA-1, 6 LPD-4, 2 LPH-9, 3 LSD-36, 6 LSD-41, 1 LST. Baseline 0: 2 AE, 1 AOE, 1 CGN-38, 10 CG-47, 3 CV-63, 4 CVN-68, 4 DD-963, 3 DDG-51, 2 FFG-7, 1 LCC, 1 LHD-1, 2 LPH-9, 2 LSD-36, 3 WHEC. Baseline 1: 1 AOE-6, 1 AOR, 13 CG-47, 2 CV-62, 1 CGN-38, 2 CVN-68, 4 DD-963, 5 DDG-51, 7 FFG-7, 1 LCC, 1 LHA-1, 3 LHD-1, 3 LPD-4, 2 LSD-41, 4 WHEC. Baseline 2: 1 AGF, 1 AO, 2 CG-47, 1 CVN-65, 7 DD-963, 2 DDG-51, 7 FFG-7, 2 LPD-4, 1 LSD-41, 5 WHEC.

♦ Sea Vulcan 20/20P (JM61MB)/Daewoo 20mm ADS

Caliber: 20mm
Rate of Fire: 750/1500 rnd/min
Muzzle Velocity: 3380 ft/sec
Maximum Range: 6000 yd
Training Rate: 80 deg/sec (elevation 60 deg/sec)
Elevation/Depression: +55/−10 deg
Ammunition Capacity: 500 rnd
Weight: 318 kg empty, 465 kg loaded
Working Circle: 130 in

Data apply to Sea Vulcan 20.

Sea Vulcan 20 is a powered turret mount for a three-barrel M197 Vulcan machine gun, for use on small craft. Many components are identical to those used in the UTS turret of the AH-1 attack helicopter. The system is remotely controlled (by a Kollmorgen Mk 35 periscope director) with its own on-board ballistic computer (to process target-designation data from another source). Total weight is 800 lb empty or 1167 lb with ammunition, and training and elevating rates are 60 and 50 deg/sec, respectively.

Sea Vulcan 20P is a much simpler pintle mount (originally designed to carry a twin 20mm cannon) carrying the same three-barrel gun and a 300-rnd ammunition box. Total weight is about 500 kg without ammunition, and elevation limits are +75/−10 deg. In Japanese service, it is designated JM 61MB.

In Korea, Daewoo makes a version it calls the 20mm ADS (air defense system). Introduced in the 1980s, it is apparently a navalized version of the land-based Vulcan air defense system. It carries 750 rnd below decks, and is controlled by a GSA Mk 3 lead-computing gyro gunsight. Total weight is 1.2 t. Elevation/depression limits are +80/−5 deg, and training (elevating) rates are 70 (40) deg/sec.

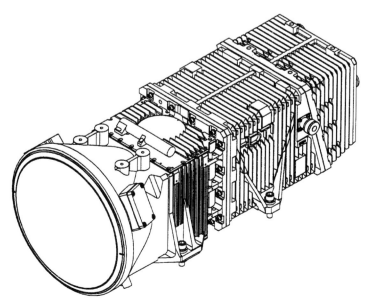

Pilkington's High Definition Thermal Imager (HDTI 5-2F) for the Block 1C surface mode upgrade. (Pilkington Optronics)

A JM61-M Vulcan mounting on board a Japanese minesweeper. (*Sea Power*)

Both the gun and the Sea Vulcan mount are manufactured by Lockheed Martin (which took over the GE naval weapons division).

Users: Honduras (Sea Vulcan in *Guardian*, 105ft and 85ft classes; retrofitted 1986–87), Japan (JM 61MB), Korea (Daewoo 20mm ADS in destroyers and "Sea Dolphin"), Saudi Arabia (Sea Vulcan in Jetfoil tender to royal yacht).

◆ 0.50-Caliber Machine Gun (M2)

This standard U.S. heavy machine gun is used on board many coastal craft. Total weight is about 87 lb, and total length is 65 in. The gun is recoil-operated, and it fires 450–550 rnd/min. Muzzle velocity is 2900 ft/sec (nominal), and effective range is 1500 yd. Maximum horizontal range is 7400 yd (35-deg elevation). A 100-rnd disintegrating-link belt weighs 30 lb. This gun is often combined with an 81mm mortar in an over-and-under mount.

An M2 machine gun on board a Jamaican coast guard cutter. (Jamaican Coast Guard via Lt. [sg] G. S. Reynolds)

Many surface combatants and auxiliaries have pedestal mounts on which shielded 0.50-cal. machine guns can be placed, for defense against small boats and swimmers. Sometimes these weapons are mistaken for larger 20mm cannon. Typically small ships carry two, destroyers and cruisers carry four, and larger ships carry eight of these machine guns.

A new soft recoil Mk 26 Mod 15 mounting, developed by NSWC Crane in the early 1980s, entered service during the Gulf crisis. Mod 15 was originally developed after the 0.50 began to appear aboard large ships in 1978. It was soon apparent that the

hard recoil of the existing version of the Mk 26 mount drastically limited accuracy. Mod 15 was developed in the early 1980s, and limited production was approved about 1985. However, it did not become important until ships in the Gulf began to encounter small attack boats in numbers.

FN Herstal of Belgium markets a ring mounting for this gun, M2HB-QCB.

The 0.50 gained importance with the introduction of a new explosive round, developed by Raufoss in Norway. Previous attempts to develop such a round for so small a caliber had failed because the 0.50-cal. bullet was too small to admit a mechanical safing-and-arming device (which was required to ensure safety, e.g., if rounds were accidentally dropped). Raufoss developed, in effect, a chemical safing-and-arming mechanism. The hard body inside the bullet is surrounded by explosive, and a detonating charge is packed into a cavity in the nose of the bullet. When the bullet hits, the hard body sets off the detonator before penetrating thin armor. However, if the bullet is merely dropped, the impact is insufficient to set off the detonating charge.

This multipurpose (MP) type of construction was originally applied to 20mm rounds, the first of which was fired in 1968. The 0.50-cal. version is in service with Norwegian, Danish, French (the best customer), British, and U.S. forces. It is produced under license by Olin, Pyrkal (British), and FN (Belgian). The round can penetrate 11 mm of armor at 950 m at a 30-deg angle. There are now also MP/T (tracer) and APS (which was first marketed early in 1989). The APS round can penetrate 20 mm of armor at up to 30 deg from the normal, at 400 m range. Compared to conventional 0.50-cal. rounds, the Raufoss round is much more accurate because of its weight and the different location of its center of gravity.

The effect of the Raufoss development is to extend some of the advantages of the 20mm cannon, until now the smallest that could fire an explosive shell, to the much lighter and more portable 0.50. Reportedly, the current trend is to improve armor penetration. In the past, 0.50-caliber AP rounds were merely hardened steel bullets, with limited performance (20mm RHA plate at 325 m). The most common current option is to use a tungsten core in an AP/Incendiary round (APHCI or APIHC). Here HC means hard core; tungsten alloy HC more than doubles penetration range.

◆ 7.62mm Mini-Gun (Mk 25)

This miniature Vulcan weighs 60 lb, including the drive motor and de-linking feeder. Total length is 30 in. Muzzle velocity is 2800 ft/sec, and effective range is 1200 yd (maximum 4000 yd). Cyclic rate is 2000 or 4000 rnd/min, and a 1000-rnd belt weighs 64 lb. This adapted aircraft GAU-2B/A is used mainly by Special Forces (SEALs).

◆ M60/Mk 43

Caliber: 7.62mm/85
Rate of Fire: 500–650 rnd/min
Muzzle Velocity: 2800 ft/sec
Maximum Range: 4000 yd (effective 1200 yd)
Ammunition Capacity: 1000 rnd (belt)
Weight: 24 lb empty

M60, derived from the wartime German MG42, has been the standard U.S. light machine gun since 1957. It is often mounted on board ships as a convenient defense against boarders and small craft, and it is used with the 60mm mortar in an over-and-under mount. It was also a major riverine weapon during the Vietnam War and as such may survive in Southeast Asia. The standard (basic) infantry model weighs 23 lb. There are also helicopter/aircraft models (M60C and M60D). Saco makes a kit to modify M60 into the lightweight (18 lb loaded) Mk 43 for the SEALs and the Marines. It has a shorter barrel and an improved hand guard.

Recent purchases (Navy funds, mainly for the Marines): 1384 in FY86, 1807 in FY87, 257 in FY88. M60E3 is 25% lighter than the original basic M60.

The U.S. Navy also used a Mk 21 machine gun, an earlier 0.30-cal. weapon (M1919A4) adapted to 7.62mm ammunition,

An M60 machine gun on board the USS *O'Brien*, 1980. (U.S. Navy)

in Southeast Asia, but those retained in its inventory are for war reserve use only. M240E1, a U.S. version of the Belgian FN light machine gun, has been adopted for Marine Corps light armored vehicles (LAVs), but thus far has not been used aboard ships. The British version of the same weapon (L7A2) is used on board British warships (see the UK section).

Users: Australia, Cameroon, Colombia, Costa Rica (some twin mounts), Dominican Republic, Grenada, Honduras, Korea (South), Marshall Islands, Papua New Guinea, Philippines, Thailand, Trinidad and Tobago, United States, Virgin Islands, West Samoa.

The German MG42 was produced postwar as MG52/59 and MG1, and in Yugoslavia as M1953. Users of these guns: Australia, Burma, Croatia, Denmark, Germany (Army), Greece (CG), Guinea-Bissau (some twins), Iran, Italy, Portugal, Saudi Arabia, Spain, Turkey (some twins), Yugoslavia.

◆ Antiaircraft Laser

Interest in laser AA weapons seems to have waned; for example, no laser was mentioned at the 1996 Navy League show, whereas TRW had displayed a model of its chemical laser at earlier shows. See the 1991/92 edition for details.

At the 1995 Navy League show it was reported that Hughes and Signaal were discussing development of a laser CIWS using Russian technology. Hughes would integrate the laser, which it had been studying for about a year, with the Phalanx and Goalkeeper mountings. This project builds on a three-month feasibility study by Hughes Electro-Optic Systems. Hughes noted that the Soviets had demonstrated high-energy electric lasers in the appropriate band, and that the technology was now available via the Lawrence Livermore Laboratory. The Phalanx derivative would use a 200-kW flywheel in place of the current Phalanx magazine, and a 500mm aperture solid-state laser in lieu of the Gatling gun. The flywheel's energy would suffice for 100 1-sec engagements before repowering (which would take 10 sec). Signaal had its own high-energy laser program; Hughes was particularly interested in exploiting Signaal's system engineering capability. As of the spring of 1995 neither company had managed to attract government funding.

ELECTRONIC WARFARE

This section combines airborne and shipboard systems, because so many now exist in versions for both applications. They share common signal processors and, therefore, common architecture, although the antenna systems are generally quite different.

Deletions: Canadian ULQ-6 upgrade program, UPD-501 (Canadian, defunct), DFS 2000 (German, no sales), FL 400 (German, no sales), Schalmei (German, no sales), MN-53 (Israel, apparently superseded entirely by NS-9000 series), G-100 (no naval sales), UA-1/2 (British, extinct), UA-11/12 (British, superseded by UAP), UA-14 and -15 (British), Warrant (British, abandoned), ALSS (U.S., program abandoned), DCJSS (nonexistent U.S. system, work abandoned 1987), LAIR (U.S. system, abandoned), PMTS (no sales), SLEWS (U.S., canceled 1992), ALQ-156 (Navy application probably died with A-6E), ASQ-191 (U.S., retired), WLR-13 (U.S., apparently never entered service), BTI-IRCM (U.S., superseded by tri-service program led by Army), IDAP (U.S., died when A-6E retirement was decided), Series 800 (U.S., no sale reported), SLQ-22/26 (U.S., out of service), SLR-21 (U.S., on PHMs which have all been stricken). For details, see the 1991/92 and 1994 update editions.

AUSTRALIA

◆ ALR-2001 Odyssey (Project 5140)

AWADI/ELTA's ESM system for the Australian P-3Cs uses a combination of wingtip (extended about 6 in), nose and tail radome, and under-body (blade farm) antennas. It provides a new sensor station 4 opposite station 3 (IRDS management atop a flat 19in rectangular screen), a display control processor, and a cockpit warner (to keep a pilot trying to get within photographic range of a ship from being shot down). The Harpoon OTH-T requirement includes radar fingerprinting and tracking. The system also provides COMINT capability from VHF up to microwave data link. Radar DF is by DTOA (digital time of arrival: accuracy better than 1 deg); COMINT DF is by interferometry. This system is reportedly derived from ELTA's EL/L-8300 (see separate entry below).

ELTA claims that Odyssey exploits operating principles and algorithms formerly seen only in ground-based systems. A prototype was delivered in 1994, and by mid-1995 nine installations had been completed.

ALR-2001 will probably also be installed on board Argentine S-2Es and on board Chilean P-3s scheduled for upgrade in Israel. Elements of ALR-2001 will probably also be used on Elta's new Spanish airborne ESM system.

◆ Type 133 (PRISM)

AWA Defence Industries of Adelaide's Passive Radar Identification System for patrol boats, which entered service in 1992, is intended mainly to counter smugglers who now have their own radar warning receivers. The 14-kg cylindrical mast unit, containing all RF processing elements, has four cavity-backed spirals near its bottom. Channelized CVRs cover 2–4 and 8–12 GHz (−75- and −73-dBm sensitivity, DF accuracy 10 and 8 deg; elevation coverage +35/−10 deg). The console houses the emitter processor, which can handle 350 kpps and can measure pulsewidth to within 0.5 microsec (range 0.05 to 1000 microsec); PRF range is 200 Hz to 350 kHz (PRI accuracy is 200 nsec, resolution 100 nsec). Circular or conical scan range is 1–40 sec (resolution 0.1 sec). A new emitter is reported within 1 sec (95% probability of detection if it is staring at the array) or within four scan periods. PRISM 133 can track 32 emitters simultaneously, and the operator library is 100 modes (mission library is 600 radar modes). The display is the usual polar plot with listed parameters (apparently for three emitters) on one side. The system provides both visual and audio alarms, and can provide emitter PRF in audio form.

PRISM I extends the frequency range to 2–18 GHz (sensitivity −73 dBm for 2–8 GHz, −67 dBm for 8–18 GHz); DF accuracy is 11 deg. This version can recognize complex radars. PRISM AD is a land-based air-defense version. PRISM II extends the frequency range down to 0.5 GHz (sensitivity −64 dBm for 0.5–2

GHz). A CM version can trigger an ECM system. PRISM III adds an IFM (resolution 4 MHz over the entire 0.5–18-GHz range) and uses a new array (bearing accuracy 10 deg for 0.5–2 GHz, 7 deg for 2–8 GHz, and 5.5 deg for 8–18 GHz). PRISM III (PA) adds a pulse analyzer. Pulsewidth resolution is 0.0002 microsec from 0.05 to 0.127 microsec, 0.02 for 0.128 to 1.28 microsec, and 0.05 from 1.20 microsec up. Anything over 128 microsec is classed as CW. PRF range increases to 10 Hz–500 kHz (PRI accuracy improves to 0.1 nsec; resolution is to four decimal places of PRF). Throughput increases to 500 kpps. This version can track 500 emitters, and the mission library is 2600 emitter modes. PRISM C (8–12 GHz only, DF accuracy 6 deg) is intended for commercial vessels navigating by taking bearings on specific radars ashore.

Type 133 is the first in a modular family intended for maritime, land, and air use.

First sea trials were carried out on board HMAS *Launceston* in February 1991, and the *Fremantle*-class systems were delivered in 1993–94. Type 133 will be bid for the Pacific Patrol Boat midlife modernization.

Users: Australia (*Fremantle* and *Huon* classes). The RAAF uses PRISM AD.

AWA also produces a series of CELTIC HF/DF sets; the RAN patrol boats will be fitted with CELTIC SAILOR, which covers 2–30 MHz (bandwidth 3 kHz with better than 25-Hz resolution). CELTIC can detect signals down to 50-msec duration, and can take 40 DF cuts/sec. It can detect surface waves at sea out to 250–300 km.

♦ Winnin/Nulka/Mk 234

The Nulka system uses the Winnin hovering rocket to carry an active jammer. The all-up round is 5.9 × 82 in (weight 110 lb), so it needs a special launcher.

Winnin moves sideways, to simulate a ship, while hovering; one of three tabs tips into the rocket exhaust, and thrust is reduced to balance off the reduction in decoy weight as fuel burns. Vanes turn the decoy toward the incoming threat. It collects threat and weather data, passing them by data link to the launching ship. A processor on the ship commands the decoy transmitter. Besides its RF transmitter, Winnin can carry an IR decoy. Although Winnin is usually launched in a precomputed direction, its movement can be remotely controlled. The system employs a decoy launch processor (DLP), which sets the decoy through an AWA-made launch interface unit (LIU). For U.S. trials, a standard Mk 24 decoy processor was used; the production Mod 2 will incorporate LIU functions, and will also have an optional interface to the SSDS fiber-optic bus. Presumably in the U.S. case the payload is controlled by SLQ-32A, which triggers the DLP. Winnin is launched and fully powered up in less than 10 sec; total endurance is over 55 sec.

Nulka was a joint project of the Weapons Systems Research Laboratory (Salisbury, South Australia) and the Government Aircraft Factories (Melbourne). Conceived in 1974, it first flew in 1981 and is being developed for the U.S. Navy (as "Hoveroc" or Cartridge Mk 234) under a 1986 MoU. Nulka completed U.S. technical and operational evaluation in 1992. It is to enter service on board U.S. amphibious ships in FY98, following a production decision planned for March 1997. The U.S. program, initially 90 ship sets and 450 decoys, was expanded in mid-1996.

AWA developed a 4-rnd box launcher (which the U.S. Navy designated electronic decoy launcher Mk 160 for trials), and there is also a 10-rnd version. As of 1995, the standard U.S. Mk 137 was being modified by the addition of a 2-rnd box launcher (at its rear end) as Mk 137 Mod 7 (2900 lb).

The Royal Australian Navy plans to fit each of six FFG 7s and eight ANZACs with four launchers (four Winnin each). AWA hopes to adapt Prism to trigger and control Nulka (its FCS can fit a slightly enlarged Prism, and Nulka can work with less than 10-deg DF accuracy). The U.S. Navy expects to begin buying production versions of Nulka in FY97, as part of the SSDS/QRCC program.

Nulka on display at Farnborough, 1996. The objects at the top of the decoy are motor-driven spin vanes used to roll the decoy to point its antennas at an incoming threat. The shinier section below the upper (payload) section contains the flight controls, an air data unit, and two two-axis gyros. Below it is the motor, with the thrust controls below that (the special vanes are visible at the bottom of the decoy). The motor provides sufficient duration to engage a threat detected at the ship's radar horizon, which would be about a minute at high subsonic speed. However, it lacks the endurance needed to counter a missile with reattack capability. Radiated power suffices to protect a ship with a large RCS. (S. Zaloga)

BRAZIL

♦ ET/SLQ-1

IPqM announced this 8–16-GHz noise/deception jammer, planned for the *Inhauma* class (atop the lattice mast) and for the *Niteroi* upgrade, in the spring of 1995. The dish with attached electronics box is mounted on trunnions, and the whole assembly is trainable, to track its target. Minimum peak pulse-radiated power is 1 kW, minimum CW radiated power is 175 W. Minimum receiver sensitivity is −30 dBW/m^2, minimum pulsewidth is 100 microsec, and PRF range is 50 Hz to 50 kHz. SLQ-1 is made by Elebra, and offered for sale by EMGEPRON, Empresa Gerencial de Projetos Navais, located at the Rio de Janeiro naval arsenal.

IPqM has also announced a 7–13-GHz chaff rocket similar in size to Shield: 101.6 × 1702 mm (20.3 kg launch weight).

CANADA

Lockheed Canada is now responsible for CANEWS (SLQ-501) and Ramses (SLQ-503) and is Canadian agent for Racal's Type 242 Kestrel (SLR-504). See the Netherlands section for Ramses and the United Kingdom section for Kestrel.

◆ CANEWS (SLQ-501)/LC 2000/Light Ship ESM

The 1–18-GHz (five-band) Canadian EW system is derived from Sphinx via the British UAA-1 (it uses the latter's IFM, accuracy 5 MHz) but incorporates a de-interleaving processor: two UYK-502 computers process up to 500,000 pps, classifying an intercept within 2 sec, using a 2000-mode emitter library including a small preprogrammed list of urgent threats. An operator can add a 128-emitter "regional" file of radars most likely to be encountered. Each band has its own eight-horn antenna (bearing accuracy better than 4 deg). The four low-band antenna horns for each octant are grouped together (the two highest-band antennas are side by side), with four Band 0 units between the pairs of boxes, and omnis to feed the IFMs.

CANEWS array, NCSM *Toronto*. (S. Slade, DMS/Forecast International)

LC 2000 in poster form at Bourget Euronaval 1996. (Author)

An upgraded CANEWS II under development by Lockheed, Computer Devices Co., and Software Kinetics for "City"-class midlife upgrades (CANEWS Configuration Update Program) is to undergo sea tests in 1996. It will probably add an auxiliary receiver to extend coverage up to 40 GHz; a new distributed network of 68040s and ASICs will deal with higher pulse density and more exotic emitters. This upgrade is intended to rationalize the three existing CANEWS versions ("City" class, TRUMP, and DELEX) and to improve bearing accuracy and sensitivity.

Lockheed announced a 2–18-GHz LC 2000/Light Ship ESM, a CANEWS derivative, in 1992 (sea trials were planned for 1995). Adoption of a single masthead unit carrying four wide-band antennas and a wide-band omni on top cuts weight from less than 200 kg to about 50 kg. Signal data are sent down to the processor by fiber-optic cable, to avoid the usual 6-dB waveguide loss. Although the system is to cost less than Can $1M, newer technology provides a processor (built around a 68040 programmed in ADA) that can handle over 500,000 pps, and the system provides 2-deg DF accuracy. New emitters are reported in less than 1 sec. The original baseline version tracked 128 emitters; a more powerful version (now advertised as baseline) handles twice the pulse density and tracks at least twice as many emitters.

A new Advanced MM-Wave ESM Subsystem uses a pair of four-port masthead boxes to cover the Ka-band (higher bands are optional); as in Light Ship ESM, signals are digitized at the masthead and data sent down to the processor by fiber-optic cable. Sensitivity is −60 dBm, and accuracy is 5 deg. Elevation coverage is +40/−10 deg. Pulse length can be between 50 nsec and CW. Upmast weight is 23 kg.

Users: CANEWS: Canada ("City" and TRUMP classes).

CHILE

◆ ITATA

ENAER's (Empresa Nacional de Aeronautica) microprocessor-controlled 3 MHz–18 GHz six-band air ELINT system was displayed at the FIDA show in 1984 and entered production in 1986. There are two operators, DF/signal selector (based in part on PRFs heard as audio tones) and pulse analysis (of strobed signals from the DF CRT). To handle the wide variety of bands, ITATA uses a combination of superhets and CVRs. The precision DF antenna is a servoed dish under the fuselage: 8-deg beam in S-band, 1.8 deg in Ku-band, with resolution less than 0.2 deg. Parameters (PRFs 0.092–12.83 kHz, pulse widths 0.05–24 microsec [resolution 0.05 microsec]; pulsewidth jitter can be measured) measured graphically on the CRT can be read out on LEDs and recorded in digital form. ITATA also measures emitter scan rate. The system can be locked onto a signal of interest, following it as it changes frequency. Compared to contemporary U.S. and European ELINT equipment, ITATA is quite bulky. Presumably it was developed because Chile was under an arms embargo; as soon as the embargo ended, it was easier to buy alternatives.

User: Chile (about 10 built, probably for six Beech 99 ELINT aircraft and three Beech 99A [Petrel Alpha] air force MPA). Although tested in an EMB-111AN maritime-patrol Bandeirante, apparently this system was not used in that airplane.

CHINA (PRC)

Most destroyers and frigates have pairs of Jug Pair ESM antennas on mast platforms. However, some ships have imported or copied EW systems. Installation does not seem systematic; ships are apparently fitted with what is available when they are being built. The new *Harbin* (lead ship of the Luhu class) apparently has a Signaal EW suite (Rapids/Scimitar). *Zhuhai* (166), the next to last Luda, seems to have Elettronica-type cylindrical antennas at the side of her forward superstructure, at the pilothouse roof level, together with four big rounded cylindrical radomes of the type in the Thai frigates.

At least one Jianghu III, *Wuhu*, appears to have a locally produced version of the Italian Newton Beta (Type 211 intercept, Type 318 noise jammer, Type 521 deception jammer), recognizable by four spherical radomes of the Italian system (no cylindrical ones). However, the ships bought by Thailand differ considerably from Chinese ships of this type, lacking spherical radomes and having instead large cylindrical radomes atop their bridge structures. *Siping*, a modernized Jianghu, appears to have boxes (for ECM?) abaft her bridge. Note that the boxes that seem prominent in some views of *Zhuhai* are apparently actually flag bags.

The Jiangwei class (at least in its export version) is credited with RWD-8 intercept gear, an NJ181-3 jammer, and a pair of PJ46 six-barrel decoy launchers. Chinese ships of this type have large numbers of decoy launchers mounted at the base of the foremast, on the 02 level. The intercept gear occupies radomes similar to those of Jug Pair (perhaps slightly taller), but the ship also seems to be carrying omni antennas higher up. The jammer has paired radomes of different sizes, in appearance a distorted version of Ramses with the radomes nearly touching, rather than some distance apart. This may be the EAJ-7 jammer.

Some ships reportedly have U.S. Mk 33 or Mk 137 decoy launchers.

CEIEC (China National Electronics Import and Export Corporation) makes Type 921-A (NATO Golf Ball), a derivative of the Russian Nakat (Stop Light), and RW-23-1 (NATO Jug Pair), a derivative of the related Nakat-M (Watch Dog). Both were originally made under license from the Russians. See the Russian section below for details.

◆ BM/HZ 8610

This Chinese derivative of the Russian Bell Tap typically uses two rows, each of eight monopulse ports, in sections clamped around a mast, for example, below a masthead radar (rows cover, respectively, 2–8 and 7.5–18 GHz, with elevation cover of +30/−10 deg). Accuracy: 5 MHz, 2.5 deg. Sensitivity is better than −70 dBW; dynamic range is 40 dB. The system can handle pulse widths between 0.1 and 99.9 microsec. It stores 500–1000 radar modes. Data are presented in both tabular and graphic (frequency vs. bearing) modes.

The manufacturer is Southwest China Research Institute of Electronic Equipment.

Users: Albania (Shanghai II, Huchuan, T-301 classes), Bangladesh (Hainan, Shanghai II, Hegu, Huangfen, and Huchuan classes), Burma (Hainan class), China (Haijui, Hainan, Shanghai, Hegu, Hola, Huangfen, Huchuan, and Type 206 OPV classes), Egypt (Hainan, Shanghai, Hegu classes), Gambia (Shanghai class), North Korea (Hainan, Shanghai, Huangfen, Soju, Taechong classes), Pakistan (Hainan, Shanghai, Hegu, Huangfen, Huchuan classes), Rumania (Shanghai, Huchuan classes), Sierra Leone (Shanghai class), Sri Lanka (Shanghai class), Tanzania (Shanghai, Huchuan classes), Tunisia (Shanghai class), Zaire (Shanghai class).

◆ BM/KZ 8608

This airborne ELINT system (1–18 GHz), designed for installation on board Y-8 (Xian-built An-12) aircraft, is made by Southwest China Research Institute of Electronic Equipment. Accuracy: 5 deg (1–8 GHz) or 3 deg (8–18 GHz); 5 MHz in frequency measurement. Dynamic range is 50 dB; sensitivity is −100 dBW. Maximum pulse density: 200,000 pps; PRF range is 100–20,000 pps (accuracy 1% up to 2000 pps, 2% above that). Pulse width range is 0.1 to 99.9 microsec. Since frequency measurement accuracy matches that of HZ 8610, both probably use the same IFM.

◆ Type 945PJ Chaff/IR Launching System

CEIEC's shipboard decoy system, made by the North East Research Institute of Electronic Technology (NERIET), employs groups of IR and chaff magazines, each with two groups of decoys (nine launch barrels per chaff group, three per IR group). For example, a Jianghu III–class frigate carries 10 magazines on each side, at her stern. The manufacturer claims the launcher is automatically triggered by the ESM system when hostile emitters are identified in the 7.5–18-GHz band. Reaction time is 5.5 sec from intercept to formation of chaff cloud. The controller can be on the bridge or in the CIC. Its computer sounds an alarm, displays threat bearing (digits and lamps), fires the decoys, and recommends an evasive course. The decoys can also be launched manually. The launcher is 500 × 250 × 370 mm (weight 36 kg empty [steel] or 26 kg [titanium alloy]). Each chaff cluster pro-

vides a 1500m² RCS, which lasts more than 60 sec. Average IR power is 950 W/Sr (3–5-micron band), lasting more than 40 sec.

◆ ERC-1

ERC-1 consists of 15 tubes in three layers, pointing forward, abeam, and aft, with a fire-control unit. The rockets are probably adapted from the Israeli (Rafael) long- and short-range types; they can be fired singly or in salvo. Decoy modes are attraction (persists in the air for 2 min), distraction (6 min), and dump (4 min). Although an IR decoy has been advertised, its existence is uncertain; the lack of such a decoy would explain the presence of an auxiliary IR sensor in the Taiwanese Hsiung Feng II missile.

Users: China (Luhu, some Luda class (including the one unit, *Kaifeng* (109), armed with Crotale).

DENMARK

◆ DL-6T/DL-12T

Danish Aerotech A/S developed this Sea Gnat launcher to meet a Royal Danish Navy requirement that a small ship (one launcher per side) be able to launch chaff on three bearings on each side (12, 40, 135 deg). Existing launchers fired on only one bearing; a large ship could cover multiple bearings by using multiple launchers. Tubes are nearly identical to those in a Mk 36 SRBOC launcher. A ship normally has one 20-rnd ready-use locker for each six launcher tubes. The computer uses a 68020 CPU (with math coprocessor) with 4 Mbytes of static RAM and a VME bus; clock rate is 25 MHz. Wind data, ship's heading and speed, and ESM data from the ship's ESM system are all input automatically. An optimum decoy pattern (given the loadout of decoys of different types) is calculated in 0.8 sec (acceptable overall system response time is 2–6 sec). The operator fires when the pattern is presented on a CDS console. The first production launcher was installed on a *Willemoes*-class attack boat in the spring of 1989; it proved quite successful during the subsequent Baltlant 90 exercise.

The DL-12T decoy launcher. (Danish Aerotech)

FRANCE

ELECTRONIC SYSTEMS

The French navy is apparently buying a new SSL type HF/DF, probably to support the Exocet Block II missile, which needs an approximate target range for fire control: it is probably best used in an indirect approach, dog-legging rather than merely following the line of bearing to the target. A future supersonic missile (ANNG) would also need this sort of data. The competing HF/DFs were the Thomson-CSF Altesse (on board the destroyer *Tourville*) and the new German Maigret, which won. Maigret lacks SSL capability, so probably a supplemental omni antenna is used to distinguish the surface from the sky wave. The accompanying precision UHF-VHF system will presumably be Thomson-CSF's Altesse/Enigme.

The new destroyer *Harbin* (Luhu-class prototype) displays new ECM systems at Vladivostok in mid-1996. The masthead radome is apparently the DESM used in some versions of Rapids; the corresponding jammer (Scimitar) is halfway down the foremast. The big radome further forward is probably also for a jammer (it cannot be for satellite communications, since it is shadowed by the bridge wing). Near the uptakes is an ERC-1 15-barrel chaff rocket launcher, with barrels in three layers. The big radome just below the jammer is for satellite communication. The object just outboard of the bridge is reportedly a TV camera used to control the forward 37mm guns (two similar objects are mounted on the after side of the hangar). The small radar antenna atop the mainmast may be used for helicopter control (however, a Racal Decca navigational radar antenna is mounted atop the hangar) or to acquire targets for the 37mm after guns. The search radar visible forward is a French Sea Tiger. (*Ships of the World*)

◆ DR 2000 (ARBR 16, ARAR 10, and ARUR 10, TMV 026, TMV 430)

DR 2000 is probably an X-band (8–10 GHz) derivative of an F (i.e., high S) -band analog submarine RWR (DR 875). It was adapted to fast-attack boats and to MPA. Although announced in 1977, this system is probably considerably older. Six DF antennas feed CVRs driving a circular analog CRT that displays emitter bearings and amplitudes. The CRT has two vertical rows (four each) of lights alongside, and a large knob, which is used to strobe a signal of interest to pass it to the pulse analyzer. DF accuracy is 5 or 6 deg.

The DR 2000S radome on board the Belgian frigate *Wandelaar*. (S. Slade, DMS/Forecast International)

Pulse analyzer outputs are pulse width, PRF, beamwidth, and scan rate. Initially the analyzer was connected to a hard-wired ARIAL 15 (analyze radar pour identification et alerte) containing a library of 15 emitter modes. The combination of detector, CRT, analyzer, and ARIAL 15, DR 3012 (TMV 026), is used to trigger Dagaie decoy launchers; it is analogous to the British Matilda. DR 3012 is absent from a Dagaie ship only when the launcher is controlled by the ship's CDS, fed by an ESM system.

Dalia (500 or 1000 [announced 1976] modes) is the programmable replacement for ARIAL. Identification is based on the characteristics of three consecutive pulses (giving estimated PRF). When a signal matches several in the library, all are displayed, each with a confidence level. Dalia displays parameters for the signal being analyzed, plus identities of up to four earlier signals, each displayed with its identifying number and three parameters (probably pulse width, scan rate, and PRF). For the signal being analyzed, six parameters are given, probably bearing, pulsewidth, power level, PRF, antenna scan period, and beamwidth. In German Type 206 submarines, DR 2000U originally had no automatic radar identification unit at all, so the Thorn-EMI SARIE was bought.

TMV 430 was a commercial designation for a small-ship ECM suite combining DR 2000, Dalia 500 or DR 3012, and an Alligator jammer.

DR 2000 Mk 2 was made for EMB-111s and German Sea Kings. Coverage was extended down to D-band (low S-band) and up to J-band (high X-band: 1 or 2–18 GHz). An added omnidirectional antenna fed an SHR for manual frequency measurement (an IFM in some units). This version probably introduced a pulse digitizer, for analysis. Total weight is about 90 kg.

DR 2000 Mk 3 has a higher-sensitivity antenna and RF amplifier (12-dB improvement), and a more powerful internal processor (pulse digitizer) with a capacity of several hundred-thousand pulses/sec. This version may incorporate an IFM.

DR 2000A (French navy ARAR-10; ARAR-10B in the Atlantique and originally in the British Nimrod: 2.3–11.1 GHz, using antennas on top of the tail fin) is for large MPA; DR 2000H for small MPA and helicopters, DR 2000S (French navy ARBR 16) for ships, and DR 2000U (French navy ARUR 10) for submarines. The pulse analyzers are ARAX 10, ARBX 10, and ARUX 1; the

frequency-measurement device (SHR tuning receiver) is ARAR-12A. ARUD 10 is associated with DR 2000U. In small combatants (Combattante IIIs and Argentine A 69s), ARBR 16/DR 2000S works with an Alligator jammer and Dagaie chaff launcher. The combination of DR 2000S with Dalia and Dagaie, as in a French navy A 69, is Sapiens 1 (Sapiens 2 and 3 are based on DR 4000; see below).

Users: DR 2000A: Abu Dhabi (eight Super Pumas), Brazil (DR 2000 in original EMB-111s, Mk 2 in 10 EMB-111 P-95B version; other aircraft being upgraded to this standard; also in six Cougar helicopters), Chile (six EMB-111s), France (Alize carrier aircraft [ARAR-12A in modernized aircraft], five Gardien MPA, Super Frelon helicopters), Gabon (one EMB-111), Germany (Mk 2 in Sea King helicopters), Indonesia (26 Super Pumas), Kuwait (six Super Pumas), Oman (two Super Pumas), Pakistan (Atlantique MPA), Saudi Arabia (six Super Pumas), Singapore (six Super Pumas). It is not certain how many Super Puma helicopters are fitted with DR 2000H.

DR 2000S: Argentina (A 69–type corvettes), Belgium (*Wielingen*-class frigates and Tripartite minehunters), Cameroon (*L'Audacieuse* class), China ("Luda"-class destroyer *Zhanjiang* [165]), Ecuador (three *Quito* and three *Manta* class), Croatia (four *Kobra*, one *Koncar* class), Finland (*Turunmaa* class), Germany (10 Type 143 [to be replaced by Octopus], 18 Type 331 minehunters [not certain], 10 Type 343 minesweepers, eight *Luneberg*-class tenders, two *Sachsenwald*), Ghana (two TNC 45 and two TNC 57 classes), Greece (10 Combattante IIIN, four Combattante II, six *Jaguar*, two *L'Audacieuse* OPV), Indonesia (four PB57, two PSK-5, two Tripartite minehunters, and four TNC 57 OPVs), Iran (12 Combattante II class, two now lost), Ivory Coast (four *L'Audacieuse*-class OPVs), Libya (10 Combattante II, one now lost, and LSD *Zeltin*), Madagascar (*Malaika*), Malaysia (four Combattante IIAL class), Mauritania (*El Nasr*), Morocco (*L'Audacieuse*-class OPVs), Oman (Brooke Marine 37.5m class), Peru (six PR72-560 class), Qatar (three Combattante III), Saudi Arabia (*Jaguar*, Durance classes), Senegal (*L'Audacieuse* class), Serbia (*Koncar* class), Tunisia (*L'Audacieuse* class), Turkey (*Jaguar*, Kartal classes), Uruguay (*Commandante Rivière* class), and Venezuela (six *Constitucion* class).

DR 2000U: Argentina (Type 209), Chile (*Oberons*), China (Ming class and Wuhan; first Han SSN), Colombia (Type 209), Denmark (Type 205 *Narhvalen* class), Ecuador (Type 209), France (all submarines), Germany (Types 205, 206, 206A), Greece (*Amphrite, Okeanos, Pontos, Posydon*; first four 209s have Sea Lion), Indonesia (Type 209), Pakistan (*Agosta* and *Daphne* classes), Peru (*Abtao* and Type 209 classes), Portugal (*Daphne* class), Serbia (*Sava* class), Spain (*Daphne* class), Turkey (*Atilay, Batiray, Saldiray*), Venezuela (Type 209). The earlier DR 875 may survive on board some older Type 209 submarines, such as those in the Turkish navy.

ARBR 16: Two *Clemenceau*-class carriers, *Jeanne d'Arc*, four (of seven) *Georges Leygues* class, three *Tourville* class, *Aconit*, *Duperre*, 17 A 69 class, *Commandante Rivière* class (being transferred to Uruguay), five *Durance* class, Tripartite minehunters, *L'Audacieuse*-class OPVs, *Ouragan*-class LSDs.

◆ DR 3000/4000 (ARBR 18/21, ARUR 13 and ARAR 13/ARBR 17/ARUR 11)

These digital successors to DR 2000 incorporate their own de-interleaving processors. DR 3000, conceived in 1985 for an abortive patrol airplane planned for the Central African Republic, is a lightweight, low-cost (comparable to that of DR 2000) version of DR 4000, which was designed for frigates. DR 4000 offered sufficient precision (2–3 deg) to support limited OTH-T. Two stacked six-port sets (with corresponding omnis for IFMs) cover two bands (C/G and H/J, 0.6–6.8 and 6.8–18 GHz). The omni is 260 (dia) × 415 mm; the stacked DF antennas fit into a 480mm circle (but can be split into port and starboard halves). Autotrack capacity is 15 (40 emitters can be tracked under operator control). Display modes: activity (PPI form with SENIT/NTDS symbols), signal data, and test/maintenance. A three-color code distinguishes threat levels. The console carries chaff and jammer controls. Library capacity is 2000 modes; identification is based on 10 parameters. The first preproduction units were delivered in November 1986.

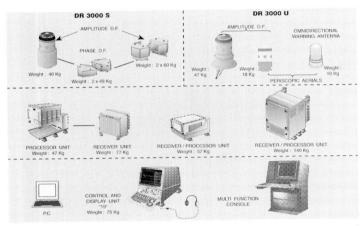

DR 3000S (surface ship) and DR 3000U (submarine) antenna arrays and below-decks equipment. The phase DF arrays are for interferometry. (Thomson-CSF)

ARBR 17, the French navy version, uses two eight-port DF arrays. It was first installed aboard the missile frigate *Cassard* (1986).

DR 3000 uses MMIC technology to cut weight while increasing sensitivity: the processor weighs 35 kg and the desktop console (with keyboard and trackball) another 42 kg (vs. 310 kg for the DR 4000 console, plus 25 kg for its IFM). This version reverts to a six-port antenna (1–18 GHz, accuracy 6 deg). Its ASIC-based window processor reduces interleaver workload by comparing received pulses with those already being tracked; capacity is 256 tracks. Library capacity is 4000 modes for 192 platforms. Pulse capacity is at least 1M pps. An IFM (which can measure frequency on a sub-pulse basis) is optional. Another option is a high-precision antenna (1-deg instantaneous monopulse accuracy, better using interferometry, to target OTH missiles; this is apparently the version sold to Pakistan for the Type 21 frigates). The S2 version in the *La Fayette* class (ARBR 21) uses four rectangular antennas and, presumably, interferometry; there is also a high-precision submarine version, using additional ports. DR 3000U has separate ESM and ELINT modules. Elevation coverage: +45/−10 deg; sensitivity is −68 dBm, dynamic range is 60 dB.

Variants: DR 3000A (MPAs: ARAR 12A or TMV 201), DR 3000S (ships: S1 is ARBR 18, S2 is ARBR 21), DR 3000U (sub-

A Saudi *Al Madinah*–class frigate shows DR 4000 elements at her masthead (omnis in a radome) and on the uppermost yardarm (two tiers, each of three DF spirals on each side). Between the DF spirals and the masthead radome are the open loops of Telegon VI with a V/UHF Adcock (vertical dipoles) below them. The collars below the yardarm are a pair of standard French navy UHF antennas (AN 192). The big rounded antennas conceal Otomat control dishes. The radar visible is Sea Tiger. The Dagaie launcher (without its "suitcases") is on the platform below the top of the superstructure.

DR 3000 arrays at Bourget Euronaval 1996. The upper array is the standard monopulse; the lower one is for interferometry, for higher-precision DF. (Author)

marines: ARUR 13), DR 4000A (ARAR 13A), DR 4000S (ARBR 17), DR 4000U (ARUR 11). Both ESM systems can be integrated with decoy launchers and jammers. SAPIENS 2 is DR 4000 (with IFM) plus Dagaie; SAPIENS 3 adds a jammer. NEWSY/NADS (French navy/Export) is ARBR 17/DR 4000S plus an ARBB 33 or Janet (export) jammer plus Sagaie and/or Dagaie. Sidewind combines the NADS central processor with DR 3000S, Salamandre, and Dagaie. DBI 3000 (brouilleur intègre) is DR 3000S plus Salamandre. These combination systems may vary in the choice of integrating processor.

A new lightweight DR 3000, for MCM craft and special warfare boats, was announced at Bourget Euronaval (October 1996).

Users:

DR 3000S: China (two destroyers, probably *Kaifeng* and *Harbin*), France (*Charles de Gaulle*, *La Fayette* class, and experimental boat *Iris*), Kuwait (PBR-37BRL class), Oman (Muheet-class light frigates: DR 3000S1), Qatar (DR 3000S1 in *Barzan* class), Pakistan (DR 3000S1X in Type 21 frigates), Saudi Arabia (DR 3000S2 in *La Fayette* class), Taiwan (*La Fayette* class). The French version in the *La Fayette* class, ARBR 21, is DR 3000S2, with improved DF accuracy for OTH missile targeting. DR 3000S1 is reported in Colombia, but photographs of the likely platform, the FS 1500–class frigate, appear to show the standard Argo radome.

DR 3000U: Brazil (*Oberons* and Type 209s: also reported as DR 4000U), France (*Le Triomphant*–class SSBNs), probably Pakistan (*Agosta 90* class).

ARAR 13: France (Atlantique Mk 1, Atlantique Mk 2).

ARBR 17: France (*Cassard, Suffren* classes, last three *Georges Leygues* class, *Floreal* class, *Bougainville*, *Foudre*).

DR 4000S: Saudi Arabia (*Al Madinah*–class frigates).

DR 4000U: Brazil (*Oberons* and Type 209s: also reported as DR 3000U), France (all submarines except *Le Tonnant* and the new *Le Triomphant* class), Pakistan (*Agosta* and *Daphne* classes), Portugal (*Daphne* class).

◆ **Altesse**

The French navy bought the V/UHF elements of this Thomson-CSF COMINT system; the HF element lost out to the German Maigret (see separate entry) in a French navy competition. Presumably the single HF test installation aboard *Tourville* will be (or has been) replaced by Maigret. Some examples of the HF/DF version may have been sold in the Middle East.

Altesse integrates interception, DF, and analysis functions to minimize processing time. A high-speed synthesizer offers quick scanning (up to 2 GHz/sec) to pick up fleeting signals. For DF, the receiver simultaneously measures the phases of signals in all five antennas, to deal with signals as short as 500 microsec (and even with 1-microsec pulse signals). Both direction and elevation of HF signals are measured; only direction is measured for VHF and UHF, since in those cases there is no sky wave. Modes: automatic scan (frequency-bearing plot, showing minimum and maximum frequency of signals at any given bearing), recurrent surveillance (frequency-bearing of preset targets, with technical data for analysis), and fixed-frequency (polar histogram in PPI format, with technical data; plus an azimuth-elevation plot for HF signals). For a particular signal, the system displays frequency step (for a frequency-hopper), bearing, center frequency, frequency range, signal level/duration, number of transmissions received and measured, and a measure of signal activity. Signals can be sorted into categories (fixed frequency, burst, frequency-hopping) and technical data (central frequency, bandwidth, signal level, duration, bearing) calculated as they are received. The display is a standard color CRT. For each frequency range, the system uses five vertical dipoles plus a sense dipole in the center. Thus it requires two nested arrays to cover 20–500 MHz with a third, mounted on the central sense dipole, to reach up to 1350 MHz. The HF (1–30 MHz) antenna is a pair of crossed circular loops. Instrumented bearing accuracy is better than 0.5 deg (1 deg in practice); SSL elevation accuracy in HF is better than 2 deg (typical range accuracy is then 10%). The processor can supply data directly to a ship CDS or to the TRC 6108 operator ter-

The Altesse V/UHF/DF antenna at Bourget Naval 1994. (Author)

minal. Altesse is based on Thomson's TRC 610 series of ELINT receivers.

The earlier-generation COMINT workstations are TRC 243 and 298 (HF and V/UHF). TRC 298 uses two fast frequency synthesizers controlled by two processors to handle up to 100 frequencies, scanning 1–10 sub-bands. These sets worked with separate Telegon (ARBR 11) HF/DFs and ARBR 15 V/UHF/DFs. The innovation in Altesse was to combine all COMINT functions. ARBR 12 is a Racal HF intercept set, presumably an alternative to the Thomson sets.

Thomson also offers a neural-net signal analysis receiver, TRC 641, to recognize standard modulation techniques (such as FSK) and alphabets stored in system memory, to demodulate signals in real time. This technique can deal with digital transmissions as well as classical analog voice signals. Thomson-CSF claims that modulation is successfully recognized 95% of the time for signals with signal-to-noise ratios better than 15 dB. Stored modulation types: NON, A1A, A3E, H3E, J3E, B8E, F1B, Multitone, noise, F3E, FSK2 to 34, BPSK, QPSK, FM-PSK, FM-FSK, AM-FSK, AM-PSK. Standard codes are also automatically recognized and signals decoded in real time. Basic alphabets recognized: Morse, RTTY (5 and 7), TOR ARQ, TOR FEC, TOR 1, TOR 2, TOR 4, FEC 100, ARQ 1A, Coquelet (8 and 12), Piccolo (32 and 34), CCITT 2 (Baudot), CCITT 5 (ASCII), Spector, CCITT 3. Other codes can be added via a PC. The system normally handles up to 19,200 baud. However, a "Ramburst" option allows storage of brief transmissions and their analysis without losing the first characters received. Measured parameters: center frequency, bandwidth, transmission start time; modulation parameters: type, index, speed, frequency shift (for frequency modulations), number of states (i.e., distinct characters transmitted); and demodulated signal parameters including code, alphabet, and statistics. The signal spectrum image (via FFT) is displayed in real time. The operator can use this data to sort for targeted signals.

◆ **BF**

Thomson-CSF's RWR employs two side spirals and two fore-and-aft pointing cones feeding a video unit via a modulator. Lamps indicate the quadrant of the threat and its type: pulse, CW, or ground TWS; an audio alarm is sounded for each threat recognized as such. Weight is 9.2 kg.

Users: France (Super Étendard, F1C), Libya (Mirage F1A), South Africa (Mirage IIIZ, Mirage F1A and F1C); may also be in Mirage F1E in Ecuador, Iraq, Jordan, Morocco, Qatar, and Spain, and in F1C in Greece, Jordan, Morocco, and Kuwait. A helicopter version is designated TMV 008H. Some BFs may have been replaced by Sherlocs.

◆ Remora/Barem

Thomson-CSF's pair of Remora jammer pods, DB-3141 (H/I-bands, 0.25 × 3.5 m, 175 kg) and DB-3163 (high bands and CW, 0.254 × 3.52 m, 175 kg) are recognizable by the vertical strip antennas at both ends. Each carries a single SHR with a TWT and fore and aft antennas. This system is apparently associated with the BF radar warner. Having received the warning, the pilot chooses to scan the SHR in one of six preset frequency ranges, comparing the signals it receives to threat data stored digitally. The pod can time-share to jam three threats simultaneously. A look-through receiver cuts off jamming (probably noise only) when the target radar ceases to transmit.

The Barem self-protection ECM pod. (Thomson-CSF)

The improved lightweight version, Barem (TMV 015: 0.16 × 3.45 m, 85 kg) which is associated with the Sherloc RWR in the MSPS system (see Sherloc entry below), uses separate reception and transmission antennas (two hemispheres, arranged vertically at each end of the pod). Compared to Remora, its threat library is more extensive and is easily reprogrammable and its TWT reacts more quickly. The pod records the parameters of radar signals it receives. It provides both noise and deception jamming. Modernized Super Étendards carry a Barem pod on a wing station, with a Phimat pod opposite, when Magic AAMs are not carried. MSPS (modular self-protection system), an integrated combination of Barem and Sherloc, apparently exists only in prototype form.

References to combat tests of both DB-3141 and Barem almost certainly indicate use by the Iraqi air force during the Iran-Iraq War.

◆ SAGE/SAPIENS

Thomson-CSF's SAGE interfaces between DR 2000/4000, chaff and jammers, and a TAVITAC combat system; in normal mode, the combat system coordinates EW activity. SAGE can also operate autonomously.

The Thomson-CSF/CSEE SAPIENS (surveillance alarm and protection, intelligence EW naval system) may be related to SAGE. SAPIENS 1 (small craft) uses DR 2000 and Dalia 1000 to control a Dagaie launcher. SAPIENS 2 uses DR 4000S with IFM. SAPIENS 3 is probably the system on board the Saudi *Al Madinah* class.

See also Sidewind, below.

◆ SAIGON (ARBG 1A)/Enigme (ABRG 2)

Dassault Electronique's Système Automatise d'Interception et de Goniometrie, for interception of VHF through UHF, equips the frigate *La Fayette* and is intended for the *Cassard* class. The antennas are eight short vertical dipoles. The VHF-UHF elements of Altesse appear to be the successor system, probably under the designation Enigme (ARBG 2).

◆ Sequoia

Thomson-CSF's high-precision interferometer array is installed on board *Aconit* and *Tourville*. It gives approximately 0.5 deg accuracy, for OTH-T. Sequoia corresponds to the British UAF/UAT of Type 23 frigates. It is the first of a new generation of specially adapted ESM sets. By way of comparison, DR 2000

gives 6–12-deg accuracy (typically 12 deg); DR 3000 and DR 4000 give 3–6 deg, typically 6 deg.

Sequoia is shown on board the frigate *Aconit* in 1992. (Author)

◆ TRC 281/284

Thomson-CSF communications jammers for, respectively, 2–30 and 100–500 MHz.

◆ ARBB 32/33

Electronique Serge Dassault's X-band systems were the first French-designed shipboard jammers. Design studies for ARBB 32 began in 1967, and two ARBB 32A prototypes and 10 production ARBB 32B were made in 1974–79. The only jamming technique seems to have been RGPO; ARBB 33 is more sophisticated.

ARBB 32B, the standard production version of this jammer, on the French frigate *Aconit* about 1994. The trainable device is mounted on a platform abaft the ship's main search radar. Presumably two horns behind the rectangular window keep it pointed at the threat, and the jamming horn is behind the circular window. An Electronique Dassault brochure dates the design studies for this device to 1967, and the series version to 1974. The ARBB 33A prototype differed in having two circular apertures without any housing. Clearly the jammer can train to handle only one threat at a time. Studies of a next-generation electronically steered system began in 1979, leading to a 1983 prototype. (S. Slade, DMS/Forecast International)

ARBB 33 on board the French destroyer *Cassard*. Note the shield to prevent interference with the nearby satellite antenna above. (*Sea Power*)

Users: Aconit, Georges Leygues class (first three units); originally also the *Suffrens* and the *Tourvilles*.

◆ ARBB 33/Salamandre (ARBB 36)

Electronique Serge Dassault began work on the ARBB 33 H-J band multithreat jammer in 1979, the prototype was completed in 1983, and production began in 1986 (the first unit was delivered in 1987). Each semicylindrical radome (height 2.2 m, diameter 1.2 m, weight less than 500 kg) paired port and starboard contain upper and lower dielectric windows covering, respectively, transmitting and receiving antennas. A Rotman lens (as in SLQ-32) forms thirty-six 5-deg receiving lobes on each side (to measure direction to within 5 deg). The corresponding jammer antenna is electronically steered (it was the first such jammer in France), with a higher gain than the planar antenna used in ARBB 32. A second array can be added on each side, so that the system can jam a total of four radars simultaneously. Alternatively, jammers can be time-shared among threats. Jamming power is over 100 kW, which Dassault claims suffices to counter target-

Salamandre arrangements in model form, Bourget Euronaval 1996. (Author)

The new Qatari FAC *Barzan* displays her three Salamandre jammer antennas (the big radomes spaced around her tower mast, below the platform carrying the MRR radar). The masthead carries the omni for her DR 3000S ESM set; one of two boxes carrying its DF spirals is visible at the end of the yard above and to the right of the nearest jammer antenna. The multitube launcher abaft the tower is Sadral. Two tubes of a Dagaie Mk 2 decoy launcher are visible above the bulwark further aft. (Vosper Thornycroft via *Ships of the World*)

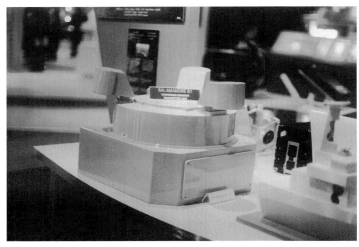

A scale model of the Salamandre transmitter unit (without receivers), Bourget Euronaval 1996. (Author)

designation radars as well as closer-in fire-control sets and missile seekers.

ARBB 33 has a unique reflex mode: it can operate independently of a dedicated ESM system, detecting and classifying a threat and reacting automatically (alternatively, it can be controlled by a CDS). The detector measures frequency, pulse width, PRF, and threat bearing (within 5 deg); reaction time in reflex mode is less than 500 msec (probably tens of msec). The reflex mode is needed because seeker lock-on can be extremely fast; typically the system receives ESM confirmation of its classification *after* the jammer has switched on. Primary techniques: continuous noise, pulsed noise, synchronous false echoes, asynchronous false echoes, and RGPO. In the latter case, jamming is coordinated with chaff firing, probably typically through the CDS.

Dassault Electronique's Salamandre is essentially a less elaborate export version of ARBB 33A. Because it is more compact, it can be air- rather than water-cooled. The receiver uses a pair of half-pie-shaped radomes clamped around the ship's masthead; it works with up to three phased-array transmitter antennas in cylindrical radomes (generally arranged around a ship's mast). Versions: (V)1 is ESM only, (V)2 has one jammer canister (providing 360-deg coverage by a combination of electronic and mechanical steering), (V)3 has three canisters (instantaneous 360-deg coverage), and (V)B is a jammer only. (V)1 and (V)2 are suitable for ships of under 1500 t; (V)2 is considered insufficient for a ship displacing 3000 t or more. Total weight of the (V)3 version is 800 kg.

The ESM subsystem uses wide-band phase interferometry for precise (within 1 deg RMS) DF in the E through J bands (C and D are available as options). The manufacturer emphasizes DF and tracking on the ground that direction is the only stable parameter of a modern threat; radar parameters may vary from pulse to pulse. Too, the better the DF accuracy, the easier it is to de-interleave pulse trains and thus to identify an incoming signal. Frequency, pulse width, and pulse-repetition interval are compared with a library of more than 2000 radar modes. Salamandre uses several TWTs, combining them for high radiated power against one target or using them separately to switch rapidly in azimuth and in frequency; it can operate despite the failure of any one TWT. The main jamming modes are continuous and pulsed noise, cover-pulse jamming (masking), synchronous and asynchronous false echoes, RGPO, and dual mode.

DCN selected Salamandre in preference to Janet or a Janet derivative for next-generation French ships; it will be integrated with DR 3000S, at least in the new French ships.

Users:

    ARBB 33: *Cassard, Suffren, Tourville* classes.
    Salamandre: France (as ARBB 36: *Charles de Gaulle* and *La Fayette* class; on board *Georges Leygues* as of 1995), Oman (Muheet-class light frigates), Saudi Arabia (*La Fayette* class).

◆ ARBR 10

This system, which dates from about 1959, has been replaced on board French warships by ARBR 16 or ARBR 17. The array consists of an omni and four directional antennas, presumably U.S.-type spinners, with preamplifiers, in two small radomes. The later cruiser version (ARBR 10F) may have added a third tall radome with an omni knob on top. The destroyer/frigate version, ARBR 10D, operated in the E4/J1 bands (X, C, and S-bands, 3–5–10 cm). It seems to have operated much like the higher-frequency part of WLR-1, with a dual display (panoramic, to indicate intercepted frequency, and analysis). The associated pulse analysis unit is ARAX 10, as in DR 2000.

    User: Portugal (*Joao Belo* class).

◆ Alligator

Thomson-CSF's small-ship X-band jammer was designed to work with DR 2000. Its antenna weighs 120 kg, its transceiver 320 kg. The receiver incorporates an IFM to measure the frequency of the radar to be jammed; Thomson claimed that it could begin to jam upon receiving a single pulse. Alligator is primarily a noise jammer, the intent being to blind the targeting or surveillance radar. However, its signal can be modulated in a preset (not reactive) pattern to confuse a missile. Alligator 5A, the jammer for surface craft, was introduced early in 1978.

    Users: Argentina (A 69 class), China (Luhu class [*Harbin*] and "Luda" hulls 17 and 18), France (A 69 class), Greece (Combattante II and III classes), Iran (Combattante II class), Libya (Combattante II class and *Zeltin*), Malaysia (Combattante II class), Peru (P-72 class).

◆ Janet

Thomson-CSF's shipboard I/J-band jammer, for the Saudi *Al Madinah*–class frigates, is associated with DR 4000. The first was delivered in 1985. A computer chooses tactics for automatic response; it can store received signals to recreate them for deception jamming. Janet is built of up to four modules, each incorporating an IFM receiver (to set frequency); two independent TWTs (one for noise, continuous and pulsed, and one for deception, including blip enhancement); and a two-horn antenna to acquire and track targets (using monopulse in azimuth). Each module contains jamming. Reception is sufficiently insulated from jamming transmissions so that the system can receive the signals it is attacking while jamming. It needs no look-through pause, hence can track frequency-agile radars. Each module is 1000 mm (dia) × 270 mm, and weighs 250 kg.

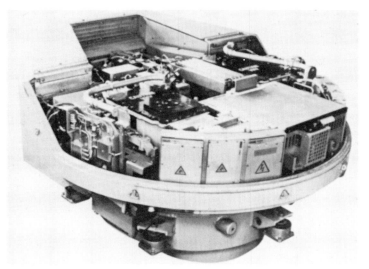

Janet. (Thomson-CSF)

◆ NEWSY/NADS/Sidewind/Cuirasse

NEWSY, the Naval Electronic Warfare System, uses a dedicated computer to integrate an ARBR 17 with an ARBB 33 jammer and chaff/IR decoy launchers (Dagaie, Sagaie). It combines deception jamming with chaff launching to pull away an incoming weapon. NEWSY is for *Cassard*-class frigates and the carrier *Charles de Gaulle*. CSEE's NADS is an earlier commercial version, on the Peruvian cruiser *Almirante Grau*.

CSEE's Sidewind is a smaller-ship derivative, using only a Mk 2 Dagaie as the decoy launcher. The system uses two 68020 processors and has a 19in raster-scan color screen. One processor interfaces with ship sensors and with the CDS; the other determines the appropriate jamming and decoy tactics. The display is a PPI supplemented by tables of up to 10 sets of threat characteristics. It includes recommended course to steer based both on weather and on the way the ship's RCS varies with bearing. The PPI shows threats, decoys, and relevant weather (e.g., wind direction compared to ship's course). Sidewind also offers a preview of the likely consequences of particular tactical choices ("what-if" facility). It automatically evaluates threats and recommends weapon assignment (hard vs. soft kill); it uses EW systems to respond to the worst threat (the operator has a veto).

The only announced user is Oman, in the new Muheet-class corvettes (to coordinate DR 3000S, Salamandre, and Dagaie).

Cuirasse adds a second processor and a hard-kill element to Sidewind, in the form of Sadral missiles. It also adds the Vampir ML11 IRST. See the OP3A/SARA system in the antiaircraft section.

♦ Sherloc/Shiploc/MSPS

Thomson-CSF's digital RWR uses a set of four antennas (wingtips and vertical fin) feeding channelized CVRs (2–18 GHz, extendable to 1–40 GHz) to feed a hybrid processor with a 100-mode library (including threat levels). Up to eight threats can be displayed simultaneously, either in CRT or in LED tabular form. Unknown signals can be recorded. Audio warnings (including synthetic voice) are generated. Total weight is 13 kg. The Franco-German Tigre helicopter radar/laser warner incorporates Sherloc. Shiploc is a shipboard version of Sherloc.

Users:

Sherloc: France (Crusader upgrade, C-160, C-135F), Iraq (Mirage F1E), Peru (Mirage 50), Saudi Arabia (Super Puma and Dauphin helicopters). Users other than France are probables. The French sale was announced in 1991. The earlier Serval is installed on Mirage 2000s.

Shiploc: Canada (MCDV class), France (Super Étendard and Crusader aircraft upgrades), Saudi Arabia (*Sandown* class).

Shiploc on the Saudi minehunter *Al Jawf*. (S. Slade, DMS/Forecast International)

♦ DDM/SAMIR

Matra/Sagem's IR missile launch (departure) detector was ordered into production on a crash basis in 1994, to protect French aircraft operating over Bosnia from IR-guided missiles such as SA-7 and Stinger. Each of two tail sensors offers 180 × 60-deg coverage. In a Mirage 2000, DDM 2000 (mounted on Magic missile pylons) is integrated with the Spirale decoy system. DDM-Prime (tail-mounted) is integrated in the Rafale's Spectra defensive suite.

SAMIR (Système d'Alerte Missile Infra-Rouge) is an alternative name.

A SAMIR missile launch warner, on SAT's stand at the 1995 Paris Air Show. It is mounted on the ESM antenna on the side of the upper part of the Rafale tail. (Author)

♦ Spectra

The integrated EW suite for the new Rafale fighter, Système de Protection Electronique Coutre Tous les Rayonnements Adverses, is being developed by a consortium led by Thomson-CSF (with Dassault Electronique and Matra). Spectra's antennas are electronically steered, and it incorporates digital RF memories, VHSIC, and artificial intelligence for threat recognition and response. The device's technology is MMIC on GaAs substrate. The overall system's weight is less than 180 kg. Spectra is intended for direct integration with other combat-system elements, that is, as part of the new generation in which RWR evolves toward ESM.

♦ Aircraft Expendables

Three active radar decoys are under development: Thomson-CSF's Spider (naval version LAD, fired from a Dagaie launcher; air version LEA [leurre électronique actif]) in collaboration with Matra; Spider II, a Thomson-CSF offensive (penetration) decoy; and ESD's CAMEL/BEL (Cartridge Active Miniature Electromagnétique Expendable). All are analog repeaters. Spider fits a flare container, covering the C- through Ku-bands (ERP about 10 W); it has a delta wing and relatively long endurance to provide a realistic target for Doppler radars. Spider II, operating over the L- through S-bands, has about 20-min endurance. Matra is developing LISCA (leurre infrarouge a signature et cinematique adaptee, a propelled IR decoy to simulate both an airplane's multispectral signature and its motion, developed with SNPE).

Super Étendards carry Matra Phimat chaff pods (108 mm × 3.6 m, 105 kg) on outer wing stations (with a Barem jammer under the opposite wing). These manually or automatically (via the BF RWR) triggered pods, which can carry 210 chaff packs, are also used by the French air force and by the RAF. Matra's replacement Corail (Contre-mesures Optronique et Radar Intègre par Leurrage) system, ordered into production in December 1989 for Super Étendards and Crusaders, is associated with the Sherloc RWR. It entered service in 1994, and was successful over Bosnia. Corail employs Alkan 5020 dispensers worked into standard pylons. Each pylon ("gondola") contains seven modules (each carrying 18 40mm chaff cartridges or eight 60mm IR cartridges, each 150 mm long). Each type of module carries an identifying chip that communicates with the decoy system. The system operates in manual, automatic, semiautomatic, emergency, and navigation (presumably target marker) modes. A somewhat earlier equivalent for Mirage F1s was SYCOMOR (Système de Leurrage EM et IR).

A new modular cartridge system for Rafale, Mirage 2000 (external extension of the internally mounted Spirale, equivalent to Corail), and for the F-16 can be fitted internally (in Rafale), in pylons (gondolas), or in pods.

♦ **Dagaie (AMBL 1)**

CSEE's short-range decoy supplements Sagaie on board French destroyers and larger ships. Small ships may carry only a single Dagaie, on the centerline. The trainable launcher carries 10

Dagaie Mk 2, showing the blocks of rocket tubes between the standard "suitcases." (Author)

Dagaie launcher. (Compagnie de Signaux et d'Enterprises Électriques)

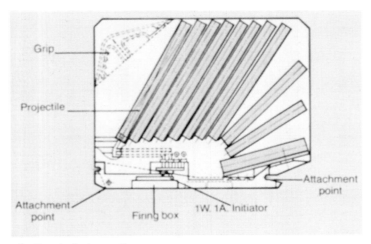

The Dagaie "suitcase."

A Dagaie Mk 2 long-range chaff round. (Author)

"suitcases," each 24 × 31 × 5 in (up to 110 lb). Each contains either IR (34) or radar (33) decoys fired by mortar. Given a warning signal, calculation time is less than 0.2 sec, and each launcher slews at 1.2 rad/sec. Each launcher can deal with up to five combined IR-radar threats (two suitcases each) in less than 10 sec.

In an IR suitcase (Type C), the initial-action IR charges operate very close to the ship, breaking up IR tracking. The 24 delayed-action IR charges extend the net operating life of the decoy, ensuring that the chaff cloud is co-located with an IR source. IR decoy duration is 30 sec, the emitting surface having an area of 360 yd² at an altitude of 45 ft. Individual decoys hit the water at 1-sec intervals, after having drifted with the wind. Type A and B chaff suitcases deploy clouds at different altitudes (maximums of 150 and 300 ft). Combining both types gives a very large cloud (RCS up to 24,000 yd²). A Type D suitcase gives a smaller cloud (3600 yd²) for small vessels. Radar bloom time is less than 2 sec; each suitcase forms 132 blooming points to form a 5500-yd² H-J band reflector lasting longer than 10 min.

There is also a six-suitcase version (990 rather than 1100 lb for the 10-suitcase type).

The system recommends helm orders for evasion based on the expected decoy disposition.

Dagaie Mk 1 is AMBL 1A in French naval service.

Dagaie Mk 2 (AMBL 1B, 1986) can fire 6–18-GHz chaff rockets (127 × 850 mm, 13 kg, carrying eight submunitions, in 3-rnd launchers replacing one, two, or three "suitcases") as well as mortar rounds because it has a digital/analog (hence programmable) computer (rather than pure analog). Rocket ranges are 250, 500, and 750 m (pressure-fuzed altitudes 50, 80, 100 m) and chaff duration is greater than 2 min (RCS is greater than 2000 m²). Dagaie MK 2 can be integrated with a computer CDS such as SENIT or TAVITAC.

Dagaie 3 (AMBL 1C) carries both suitcases and Sagaie-type rocket tubes. As of late 1996, this device is apparently no longer being marketed.

Dagaie was developed to meet a 1974 French navy requirement to counter low-altitude missile attacks distributed around the horizon, with a reaction time of 5 sec or less.

Users: Argentina (MEKO 360, MEKO 140, A 69 classes), Bahrein (TNC-45 and -62 classes), China ("Luda" hulls 17, 18, 165), Colombia (FS 1500 class), Ecuador (TNC 36 class), Egypt (Descubierta class), France (Clemenceau, Cassard, Tourville classes, Georges Leygues class [replacing Corvus; now in four of seven ships], La Fayette, Floreal, Commandante Rivière classes, Durance class), Ghana (TNC 57 class), Greece (nine on Combattante III class), Indonesia (TNC 57 FAC and OPV classes), Italy (for 12 ships, delivered in 1987; presumably, for MCM operations in the Persian Gulf), Korea (Mk 2 selected for KDX), Kuwait (FPB 57 and TNC 45), Malaysia (FS 1500 class), Morocco (two sold for the Descubierta-class frigate in 1979), Peru (ordered for the two ex-Dutch cruisers, but never paid for and therefore not delivered), Qatar (three double sets on Combattante IIIM class, four Mk 2 for Falcon-class corvettes), Saudi Arabia (eight sold in 1980 for the Al Madinah–class frigates, two Durance class, probably also on new La Fayette class), Taiwan (Mk 2 in Perry class), Thailand (two sold for the PFMM Mk 16–class corvettes in 1983, three on Ratcharit class), Tunisia (three sold for the Combattante III–class boats in 1981), and the UAE (10 for the Type 62–, FPB 38–, and TNC 45–class boats). The other three users are unknown; Italy was the first to order Dagaie Mk 2. It seems likely that the last two purchases were emergency procurements for the Gulf operations; the likely candidates include Belgium and the Netherlands, for minecraft or mine-support units. The other Descubierta-class corvettes (for Egypt and Spain) use the U.S. Hycor/Mk 137 system. Dagaie was removed from the Commandante Rivière class before transfer to Uruguay.

◆ **Sagaie (AMBL 2A)**

The long-range Système d'Autodefense pour la Guerre Infra-Rouge et Electromagnetique complements Dagaie. The 10-rnd rocket launcher (1900 kg, working radius 1.6 m), which is fired from CIC, trains and elevates. Each 40-kg (170 × 1740 mm) rocket carries a 24-kg payload; average speed is 250 m/sec. The

IR rocket carries parachute-suspended submunitions. Rockets are fired from their shipping containers. Range is 8 km for chaff and 3 km for chaff/IR decoys. In French service, Sagaie replaces the modified British eight-barrel Knebworth-Corvus system (Syllex). The prototype was tested in 1986.

At Bourget Euronaval 1996 CS Defense marketed an improved version, SP 210, as a universal multipurpose launching system, not only for countermeasures but also for ASW and for antitorpedo warfare. A poster showed it as the launcher of the STN Atlas low-cost ASW weapon (LCAW).

Users: France (Charles de Gaulle, Clemenceau, Cassard, Suffren classes), Italy (de la Penne and Maestrale classes), Saudi Arabia (the two new La Fayette–class frigates). Maestrale-class refits began about May 1991.

Sagaie. (Compagnie de Signaux et d'Enterprises Électriques)

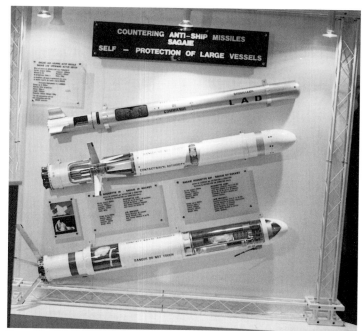

Some Sagaie rounds on display at the 1994 Bourget Naval show. At top is an active decoy, which would be suspended from a parachute. The other two rounds are standard IR (middle) and chaff (bottom) rockets. (Author)

◆ **NGDS**

At Bourget Euronaval 1996, CS Defense and Lacroix showed drawings of its new NGDS (presumably new generation decoy

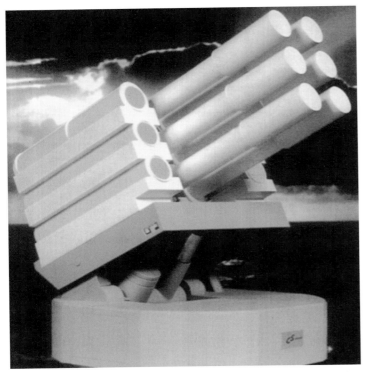

The new NGDS launcher, firing long-range and Dagaie Mk 2 rocket rounds. (CS Defense/Lacroix)

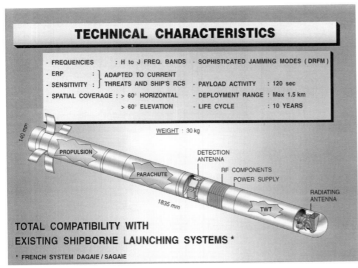

TECHNICAL CHARACTERISTICS

- FREQUENCIES : H to J FREQ. BANDS — SOPHISTICATED JAMMING MODES (DRFM)
- ERP : ⎱ ADAPTED TO CURRENT
- SENSITIVITY : ⎰ THREATS AND SHIP'S RCS — PAYLOAD ACTIVITY : 120 sec
- SPATIAL COVERAGE : > 60° HORIZONTAL — DEPLOYMENT RANGE : Max 1.5 km
  > 60° ELEVATION — LIFE CYCLE : 10 YEARS

WEIGHT : 30 kg

PROPULSION PARACHUTE DETECTION ANTENNA RF COMPONENTS POWER SUPPLY RADIATING ANTENNA TWT

1835 mm 140 mm

TOTAL COMPATIBILITY WITH EXISTING SHIPBORNE LAUNCHING SYSTEMS *

* FRENCH SYSTEM DAGAIE / SAGAIE

The French active jammer round, with Thompson-CSF electronics and Lacroix pyrotechnics. (Lacroix)

system), which could launch both existing Sagaie rounds and a new generation of longer rounds for distraction/seduction-confusion at 300–3000 m (chaff: REM NG; the equivalent Sagaie round, REM, is fired to 250–750 m), active seduction (LEA), IR (RIR: range 300–3000 m), and as torpedo decoys (LAT). The new launcher trains and elevates (Dagaie Mk 2 only elevates). The REM rocket (130 × <1500 mm, <30 kg) deploys in less than 12 sec at 2000 m, at an altitude of less than 150 m, with a duration of over 2 min. The RIR rocket (130 × <1800 mm, <30 kg) has a similar deployment pattern; duration is over 30 sec. The low-temperature round is spectrally matched to a ship target. An LEA round compatible with NGDS or Sagaie is 140 × 1835 mm (30 kg), can be fired to 1.5 km range, and covers the H–J bands over a sector larger than 60 × 60 deg. Operating lifetime is 120 sec. Thomson-CSF supplies the electronic components and coordinates soft and hard kill in a larger ship system. The LAT round (140 × 1830 mm, 26–40 kg) arrives at 1500 m range in 21 sec or at 3000 m range in 38 sec; duration is 3 to 10 min.

Barricade, as shown at Bourget Euronaval 1996. (Author)

CMN's model shows how Barricade would be mounted atop the bridge of a future fast-attack boat, with Salamandre on either side of the tower foremast. The radar above is MRR, and a CTM director is shown forward of the mast. Goalkeeper is aft, with a pair of 20mm A15 mounts abeam the uptakes. The antiship missiles are Exocet MM40s (presumably Block II). (Author)

◆ Barricade

CMN displayed this combined decoy and missile launcher at Bourget Euronaval 1996. It can carry 36 decoy rockets (such as Superbarricade) and 8 missiles (such as Stinger). Firing interval is less than 250 msec. Elevation limits: +70/0 deg (elevation rate 0.8 rad/sec; train rate 1 rad/sec). Missiles can be fired between +15 and +55 deg elevation. The system can be trained to within 1 deg accuracy. Total weight is 1 t, and the launcher requires a clear deck area 3 m in dia (the base is 1.64 m in dia, and the launcher is 1.838 m wide). Total height above deck is 2.594 m.

◆ Navalized Galix

In 1994 GIAT and Lacroix began work on a naval self-protection system derived from the Galix armored vehicle defensive aids system, for small craft. Feasibility studies began in July 1994 for Simmoneau Marine, which was responding to an unidentified customer. The prototype began sea trials in November. Initially the system will deploy stun or fragmentation grenades, illumination rockets (to a range of 1000 m), and obscurants versus IR, laser, visible light. Chaff and IR decoy payloads are under study. The system employs a deck-mounted 18-barrel 80mm launcher, with tubes splayed forward and on either beam in groups of six.

GERMANY (WEST)

ELECTRONICS

◆ Cerberus/ERWE/NRWE

German navy and Luftwaffe maritime strike and reconnaissance Tornadoes are equipped with Litton/TST ERWE II (Enhanced Radar Warning Equipment) digital radar warners, Telefunken Cerberus jammer pods, and Swedish BOZ-101 decoy pods. ERWE II employs a combination of E-J band monopulse CVRs, an SHR to detect CW signals in the E-J bands, and a special receiver for the C/D band (including missile guidance uplinks). The threat library can be updated in flight. The operator selects either terminal mode (smart analysis algorithm, identification and classification of threats) or bypass mode (high probability of intercept of scanning emitters [i.e., search radars] and real-time signal indication). The original ERWE (1979–84) employed an Itek ATAC computer, closely related to that in a U.S. ALR-67; ERWE II presumably uses an upgraded version and is integrated with the other elements of the airplane's DASS (defensive aids subsystem) via two interfaces to the 1553B buses.

A Litton/DASA replacement New Radar Warning Equipment (NRWE) extends coverage to K-band. The earlier CVRs are replaced by combinations of wide-band channelized receivers and intermediate bandwidth receivers (replacing the SHRs, to detect low-powered signals such as pulse-Doppler, CW, and missile uplinks). The new receivers are also intended to detect slow-scanning threats (e.g., interceptor aircraft). The receivers are backed by new amplifiers with wider dynamic ranges, which can distinguish weak CW signals against strong pulsed ones. Spatial screens and multiple temporal filters protect the processor from overload by limiting data flow from receivers to processors. Parallel processing increases throughput and speeds identification and classification.

The Cerberus jammer pod was derived from the Israeli EL/L-8202, itself a derivative of the U.S. ALQ-119 and ALQ-178 (Rapport). The current version is Cerberus III (1985); Cerberus IV, originally TSPJ (Tornado Self-Protection Jammer), began tests in 1994. The system can operate either under control of ERWE or independently.

◆ FL 1800B/FL 1800H/FL 1800S/FL 1800U/USK 800

DASA's FL 1800 is the standard German navy ESM system. Versions: 1800B for boote (small combatants); 1800H for helicopters;

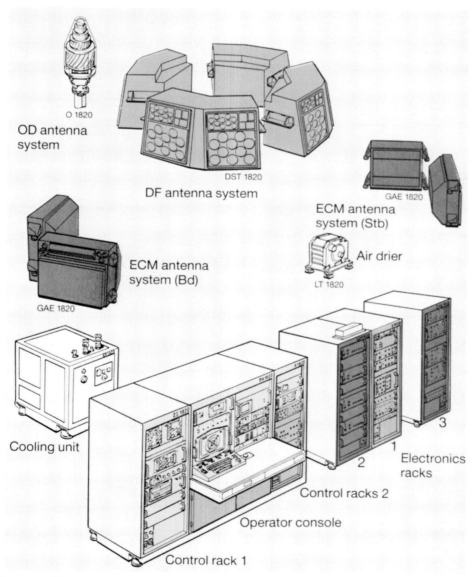

Elements of the German FL 1800S system. The OD (omnidirectional) antenna feeds an IFM. (AEG)

FL 1800S on board a German fast patrol boat. The DF antennas are below the Signaal "egg" radome, and the jamming antennas are above the sides of the bridge. (AEG)

FL 1800S on board the German frigate *Karlsruhe*, 1990. The omni antenna (for IFM) is carried between the STIR antenna and the Signaal "egg," and the usual pair of jammers is visible just above the bridge windows. The DF array is in the masthead radome. (G. Arra via *Ships of the World*)

1800S for ships and FAC; 1800U for submarines. At this writing only 1800S and 1800U have been adopted.

Covering 0.5–18 GHz in five bands for ESM, the digital FL 1800S was designed to engage a large number of close-in emitters automatically, for example, a missile attack in the North Sea or in the Baltic. In the DF array, each of eight panels contains, unusually, ten spirals for each band, offering protection against multipath (by measuring, in effect, elevation and also by more precise DF) as well as a degree of interferometric DF. Preprocessing limits data flow into the main system computer. The system can simultaneously jam several threats in different directions and at different frequencies (7.5–17 GHz), using eight TWTs and a beam-forming switching matrix. Each TWT can cover an individual threat, or they can be combined against a single threat. The system can provide both noise and deception jamming, and system ERP suffices to cover a frigate's RCS.

The submarine version, FL 1800U, is limited to ESM. Its antenna is Telefunken's USK 800. The top dome is an RWR (it can also accommodate an IFM). The bulbs below it carry DF spirals. USK 800/4, the only version thus far sold, is the full antenna; USK 800/3 is the omni only. Typical DF accuracy is 5 deg, the acquired DF values being integrated and the mean taken as the periscope antenna rotates.

A current FL 1800S upgrade to Stage II emphasizes signal processing. The CVRs of the original system are replaced by channelized receivers (nine sub-bands); two SHRs (for CW signals) are added, with provision for a future radar fingerprinting facility. A Racal Sadie parallel processor is introduced to handle the expected very high data rates. A new range estimation feature (to support RAM missile fire control) is introduced (using the amplitude of the received signal). A faster tracking processor promises almost pulse-synchronous jamming and a new switching matrix is provided. Modified displays provide a clearer color picture. The existing omnidirectional and DF antennas are modified.

The displays are a pair of side-by-side rectangular CRTs, one typically showing a B-scan of frequency against bearing, the other used to classify signals. The operator has a trackball.

Attempts to develop small-ship export versions of FL 1800 seem not to have been successful. See the 1991/92 edition for details of FL 400.

Users:

FL 1800S: Germany (*Adams, Brandenburg, Bremen*-class destroyers/frigates, *Alster*-class AGIs, S143A-class attack boats, Type 332 minecraft). The Step II upgrade is for the *Bremen* and *Brandenburg* classes (plus one base set) and for nine S-143A.

FL 1800U: Germany (Type 212 submarines).

◆ Maigret

In 1994 the French navy adopted the HF version of DASA's 1992 system (offered as Materiel Automatique d'Interception et de Goniometrie des Radiocommunications en Exploitation Tactique) in preference to the HF elements of Thomson-CSF's Altesse. The 1–500-MHz (extendable down to 250 kHz and up to 1 GHz) Maigret uses A 1284/1 Telegon 10 antenna or A 1288 antenna or A 1289 adapted to submarines. A switch connects the antenna either to the Telegon 10 DF or to an HF receiver (E 1800/3) or to a V/UHF receiver (single-channel E 1900/3 or 10-channel E 1900/S). All three connect to an audio frequency switch (for a headset and loudspeaker, which can be set on different channels for channel correlation) and to a computer with an emitter database for automatic identification. Maigret can process signals as short as 500 microsec. It operates in fixed-frequency, adaptive (searching two MHz bands for alerts), or linear modes. In HF, Maigret scans at approx 50 channels/sec. In V/UHF, E 1900/S scans at 3300 channels/sec in linear mode (E 1900/S) or up to 1 GHz/sec in adaptive mode; E 1900/3 scans at 330 MHz/sec in adaptive mode. Typically the system has a single color CRT operating in either PPI (frequency measured from center out, color indicating signal strength, symbols indicating emission type, e.g. voice/data/frequency hopping) or in histogram/A-scan modes. Tabular data on any particular signal can be called up. In the HF range, Maigret can display statistics of band occupancy. Bearing accuracy is 3.5-deg RMS (averaged over the entire azimuth, in 15-deg steps, and over the entire frequency band, with 10 uniformly distributed frequencies within each sub-band).

Users: France, Germany. Maigret had been adopted by "several" navies as of late 1996.

◆ Octopus

See the United Kingdom section below (Racal is the main contractor).

◆ SPS-N 5000

DASA announced this modular 2–18-GHz small-ship system, comparable to DR 3000, at the 1994 Bourget Naval show. It is an ESM system with an optional extension for ELINT (for which a real-time pulse analyzer can be installed). The RPA 2746 processor can handle 4M pps. The display can be a laptop computer. It shows bearing (vertical) against time (horizontal), colors indicating frequency band. A table at the right shows identifications by keyboard function number (by means of which data can be

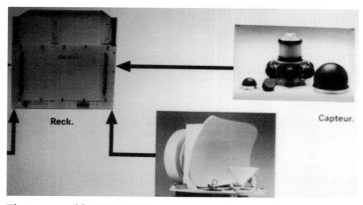

The two possible SPS-N-5000 antennas are shown in this 1996 poster: a wide-open six-port DF array (*top*) and a spinner (*bottom*) with a spiral on its back. The latter is a standard Condor Systems antenna. (Author)

The USK antenna planned for SPS-N-5000 is to be used to support the FL 1800U systems of the new German submarines. This four-port submarine version was on display at Bourget Euronaval 1996. (Author)

The innards of the submarine antenna are shown. The upper broad band consists of spiral strands (to cover both polarizations with adequate gain). (Author)

called up). An interferometer version may already have been sold. There is also a version using a dish antenna with log-periodic feed. The system can use a USK submarine antenna.

◆ Telegon/ASDF

Telefunken's (now DASA's) HF/DF systems (Telefunken Goniometers) break down into two series: odd numbers denote single-channel receivers, even numbers Watson-Watt three-channel (omni for sense, bow-stern, and port-starboard) receivers; Telegon 10 is interferometric. Most naval versions are Watson-Watts.

ASDF antenna. (AEG)

Telegon 12 UHF and HF arrays. This antenna is used in Maigret. (Daimler-Benz Aerospace)

The single-channel receivers sample different directions in sequence. Because they must tune only a single channel, they can scan rapidly through a wide frequency range (330 MHz/sec in Telegon 11) to deal with frequency-hoppers. A Watson-Watt must tune and match (in amplitude and phase) its three channels. The usual testing technique, sampling the output of the channels in sequence against a test signal, makes tuning too slow for very short signals, as in burst or pulsed communication. To exploit the Watson-Watt's inherent wide-open capability against such signals, Telefunken developed an alternative parallel calibration method using an internally generated calibration signal. A microprocessor compensates for amplitude and phase differences between the channels, and adjusts the gain control. Telegon 11 reduces the performance difference between the two types by scanning electronically in direction. Another vital next step, begun with Telegon 8, is to compensate for frequency-dependent quandrantal errors due to reradiation from the metal parts of the ship: the hull and superstructure dominate at 1.5–5 MHz; masts and other antennas dominate at 4–20 MHz.

Telegon 4, conceived in the mid-1960s, uses a flattened egg-shaped ferrite antenna (limited to ground waves) with whips radiating at angles to it (AK 1200). In Italian ships the egg-shaped radome was often enclosed in a circular cage, which in turn supports four vertical UHF dipoles (an Adcock) and a central sensing dipole. See the illustration of the Egyptian *Ramadan*-class missile patrol boat under the British Cutlass system. Telegon 6 is a modular version designed for the German armed forces. Subsequent Telegons are also modular; at least some share their receivers with ship communications.

Telegon 8 (PGS 1521) is a current digital system using the ferrite egg (plus an optional second array) to cover 10 kHz–30 MHz. It introduced the parallel calibration technique and is tuned either by hand or by keypad, achieving a resolution of 10 Hz (frequency accuracy better than 0.3 parts in 1 million). To compensate for reradiation errors, Telegon 8 divides its signals into 56 sub-ranges, for each of which it makes the necessary corrections. With corrections made, accuracy is 1 deg. This sort of processing (hence accuracy) is possible only because the system is digital, hence can treat signals from different directions at different frequencies individually. Telegon 8 can adjust to a 60-dB jump in signal level in less than 10 msec. Bandwidths are: 0.1, 0.3, 0.6, 1.5, 3, 6, and 10 kHz. Memory capacity is 30 frequencies. Development began in 1979, and series production began in 1981–82.

Telegon 10 (PGS 1720) adds two antennas (each of four vertical dipoles plus a sense dipole in the vertical mast) to the AK 1200 egg (0.1–30 MHz): A 1265V (VHF: 20–500 MHz) and A 1269U (UHF: 480–1000 MHz). Memory capacity rises to 100 channels. Frequency can be reset, accurate to within 10 Hz, in 1 msec. Because this is a modular system, it can be built with a more limited frequency range. For example, the ANZAC frigate version (PST 1720/PSI 1720) covers 10–500 MHz, using interferometric techniques at least for VHF.

Telegon 12 is a digital multimode VHF/UHF/HF (0.01 to 1000 or 3000 MHz) system. It combines four square-loop HF antennas (10 kHz–30 MHz) with five vertical VHF dipoles (30–500 MHz) and with five vertical arrays of UHF (500–1000 or 3000 MHz) interferometry antennas (in vertical rectangular boxes). Identical digital filters in the DF channels ensure accuracy and synchronism. Because all data are handled digitally by a general-purpose computer, the system can operate in small- or wide-aperture and in amplitude or phase-comparison modes, and it can time-share different modes to compare their outputs on a quasi-simultaneous basis. Signals as short as 0.5 msec are automatically detected. Dynamic range is 120 dB. Typical sensitivity is 13 dB in VLF/HF or 12 dB in VHF/UHF. The system can scan adaptively at up to 1.5 GHz/sec (Watson-Watt DF) or linearly at 10 MHz/sec (400 channels/sec) over channels 25 kHz wide. It can cycle through 1000 channels, displaying signals in up to 800 of them. Alternative displays are PPI, frequency scan (signal level and azimuth vs. frequency in B-scan format), azimuth histogram (for statistical analysis), and map (DF bearings overlaid on a map).

Of the single-channel series, Telegon 3 and 5 date from the 1950s, and none is likely to have survived. Telegon 7 covers 20–1000 MHz, using an E1900 V/UHF receiver (which is also used for communications). Telegon 9 (20–500 MHz extendable to 1000 MHz) can operate with Telegon 8 to cover the full 10 kHz–1000 MHz range. Telegon 11 (PGS 1655), the most recent member of the family, can use either the earlier egg and dipoles or new characteristic square loop antennas. Its V/UHF receiver is E1900/3 (scanning at 330 MHz/sec in wide-band). DF time can be 50, 100, 200, or 800 msec. The display is either synthetic video of a histogram of signal strength versus bearing or a conventional directional display with adjacent digital readout.

The related Advanced Shipborne Direction Finder (ASDF, PST 1288), introduced in 1985, suppresses reradiating fields using a new A 1288 antenna whose parallel-loop unit creates nulls directed at the presumed locations of fields reradiated by the ship. In theory, the alternative table look-up technique used in Telegon 8 cannot deal as well with very ambiguous signals. A 1288 also has the usual crossed loops. Telefunken claimed that this approach improves accuracy by at least half an order of magnitude. ASDF was designed so that it could be added to the Telegon 8 receiver, producing on-line correction data to be fed into the conventional HF/DF system.

CXA(2) is Telegon 12 adapted to British submarines.
Users:

Telegon (type not known): Brazil (*Inhauma* class), Colombia (FS 1500 class), Denmark (*Thetis, Nils Juel, Hvidbjornen, Willemoes, Falster, Agdlek* classes), Ecuador (*Wadi M'ragh* class), Egypt (*Descubierta* and *Ramadan* classes), France (*Durance* class and *L'Audacieuse*-class OPVs), Malaysia (FS 1500 class), Morocco (*Descubierta*), Thailand (Jianghu 053HT, 053HT[H], and *Naresuan* classes), Turkey (*Nusret*).
Telegon 4: Argentina (*25 de Mayo*, MEKO 140 class), Belgium (Tripartite Minehunters), Canada (*Mackenzie, Restigouche, St. Laurent, Protecteur* classes and *Bay-* and *Fort*-class OPVs), France (*Clemenceau, Jeanne d'Arc, Cassard, Suffren, Aconit, Duperre, Georges Leygues, Tourville* [except *Tourville* herself], *Commandante Rivière, A 69, Floreal* classes, LSDs *Bouganville* and *Foudre* and *Ouragan* class, and Tripartite Minehunters), Greece (*Kortenaer* class), India (*Sandhyak*-class AGIs, *Magar*-class LSTs, *Sukanya* and *Vikram*-class OPVs, *Deepak* and *Rajaba Gan Palan*–class AORs, *Tir*-class training ships), Indonesia (*Fatahillah* class, frigates *Ahmed Yani, Oswald Siahann, Siamet Riyadi, Yos Sudarso*, T-43 class), Italy (*Garibaldi, Vittorio Veneto, Animoso, Audace, Maestrale, Lupo, Minerva, Sparviero, San Giorgio, Gaeta, Lerici, Cassiopea, Etna, Stromboli* classes), Malaysia (*Musytari, Lerici* classes), Netherlands (*Tromp, van Heemskerck, Kortenaer, Karel Doorman, Poolster*, and Tripartite Minehunter classes), Nigeria (*Aradu, Lericis*), Norway (*Oslo, Sleipner* classes), Pakistan (Tripartite Minehunters), Peru (*Almirante Grau, Lupo, P-72* classes), Portugal (MEKO 200, *Joao Belo, Baptiste de Andrade, Joao Coutinho* classes), Spain (*Principe de Asturias, Perry, Baleares, Descubierta* classes), Tunisia (Combattante IIIM), Uruguay (*Commandante Rivière*), Venezuela (*Lupo* class).
Telegon 6: Argentina (A 69 class), Belgium (*Godetia, Zinnia*), Germany (*Adams, Hamburg, Bremen*, Type 143/143A/148 attack boats, Type 332/343/394 minecraft, *Rhein, Luneberg, Sachsenwald*-class tenders), Greece (*Rhein* class), Saudi Arabia (*Al Madinah, Sandown, Durance*, PCG, PGG classes), Singapore (*Landsort* class), Sweden (*Landsort* class), Thailand (*Ratcharit, Rattanakosin* classes), Turkey (*Koln, Rhein, Yildiz*, MEKO 200 classes).
Telegon 7: Iceland (OPVs).
Telegon 8: Bahrein (TNC 62 class), Germany (*Brandenburg*-class frigates, planned for Type 124 frigates), Ghana (TNC 57 class), Indonesia (TNC 57 class), Turkey (*Kartal, Dogan* classes), UAE (TNC 62, TNC 45, TNC 38 classes).

Telegon 10: Australia (ANZAC), Greece (MEKO 200), New Zealand (ANZAC).
Telegon 12: United Kingdom (all SSN, as CXA[2]; Telegon 6 is no longer in service); this may be the version in German Type 123 and Type 124 frigates.
PST 1288: New Zealand (*Leander* class).

◆ Expendables

At RNEE 1991, Chemring showed a 108mm chaff rocket for the German navy, with packaged chaff forward of bulk chaff, possibly for an unspecified single launcher.

◆ Giant (DM 19)/Mk 245

Buck Werke's IR seduction round is compatible with NATO Sea Gnat and now has the U.S. designation Mk 245 Mod 0. It sequentially deploys five mortar-propelled submunitions to a customer-defined range at individually set intervals (up to 20 sec), to "walk off" a seeker. Each submunition contains a three-part pyrotechnic payload: a mixture of warm smoke (for 8–14 microns), glowing particles (3–5), and gaseous radiation (4.1–4.5 microns) to simulate hull, stack, and plume emission signatures. Buck claims that Giant is effective against scanning and imaging seekers, including two-color types.

Users: Denmark, Germany (adopted 1990), Netherlands, Portugal, Spain, United Kingdom (adopted after September 1994 trials, in service 1995), United States. As of June 1996, Australia and Greece were in the process of adopting Giant. U.S. interest in Giant was strong enough to cause cancellation of the U.S.-designed Torch.

◆ Hot Dog/Silver Dog

The Wegmann-Buck Hot Dog/Silver Dog are simple adaptations of standard armored-fighting-vehicle 3in caliber devices (IR and chaff), in three- and six-tube launchers, in banks of 6, 12, or 24 tubes. Each round contains seven submunitions which it ejects in sequence to burst at ranges of 40 to 160 m. The rocket was developed with Plessey, and the IR material is the same as in that company's P6 round (see Shield, below). The other land-combat rounds are smoke, thermal smoke, and fragmentation grenades. The chaff cloud develops in 2 sec.

Users: Germany (Wolke/Hot Dog in FAC, Silver Dog/Hot Dog in MCM craft).

Hot Dog/Silver Dog decoy launchers. (Wegmann)

INDIA

◆ Ajanta

This new Bharat Electronics ESM unit is reportedly installed on board *Khukri*-class corvettes. It has a 1500-emitter library, and is used to trigger two 16-barrel chaff launchers, presumably of the standard Soviet small-ship type. Ajanta will also be aboard the *Delhi*-class destroyers. The associated jammer has not been named.

The Ajanta array is visible atop the mast of the corvette *Khanjar*, shown at the Indonesian fleet review of 1995. It replaces the Alenia array used on board the lead ship of the class. The same small cylindrical radome with a curved top was visible on board the carrier *Viraat* at about the same time. The radar is the Russian Positive E. (*Ships of the World*)

In 1986 India announced that its Armament R&D Establishment at Pune had developed a multibarrel medium-range chaff launcher, which either is or will be used on board Indian ships.

INTERNATIONAL

◆ Sea Gnat

This program began in 1973, the NATO Memorandum of Understanding (MoU) being written in October 1976 and signed in January 1977. The NATO program was begun in April 1977, the major cost-plus-fixed-fee contract being awarded in September, 1977. Integrated system firing tests followed in August 1978, with at-sea development tests in April 1979. For the Royal Navy, Sea Gnat was approved for production December 1985, with limited production in 1986.

Sea Gnat Mk 216 alongside its launcher, at RNEE 1991. (Author)

Mk 214 is a chaff seduction cartridge and Mk 216 a rocket-powered chaff distraction cartridge slowed by a drogue parachute. Mk 214 is 1.2m long and carries six sections of chaff, with a total RCS comparable to that of a ship. Mk 216 is 1.4 m long and carries three sections of chaff payload. Both proved very late (Mk 216 was not ready until 1995) and were reportedly well over cost. Mk 218, the IR version, was abandoned, largely in favor of Buck's Giant. These cartridges can be fired from standard U.S. decoy launchers. A remotely settable fuze was developed by the U.S. Army Harry Diamond Laboratory.

Estimated total orders, 1996: Denmark (1000), Netherlands (3500 Mk 214), Spain (1000 Mk 214), United Kingdom (about 3500 Mk 214 and 10,000 Mk 216), United States (about 46,000 Mk 214 and 14,000 Mk 216; Loral Hycor received a contract for 8000 Mk 214-1 and 8000 Mk 216-1 late in 1993).

Users: Australia (*Adams* and ANZAC classes), Denmark (*Nils Juel* class), Greece, Germany (Type 123/124 frigates), Netherlands (*Karel Doorman* class), New Zealand (ANZAC class, *Canterbury*, *Wellington*), Norway, United Kingdom, United States. The German designation is DÜRRAS/IRRAS.

ISRAEL

ELECTRONIC SYSTEMS

◆ ACS/RDR/TDF-500 series

Tadiran's new COMINT, radar DF, and HF/DF systems are intended for small business-type aircraft. The 20–500-MHz ACS-500 superhet (extendable to 1.5–1000 MHz) scans its 16 subbands in programmable sectors; it can ignore up to 127 channels and can display activity on up to 100 preset frequencies (signal level and time of reception). The associated TDF-500 HF/DF requires 10–300 msec to make a cut to within 2 deg. RDR-500 is an interferometric UHF (200–500 MHz) radar DF (accuracy 3 deg, pulsewidth range 3–100 microsec, PRF range 100 Hz to 5 kHz, elevation coverage −2/+7 deg). ACS/TDF-500 were reported in service by 1992, customer unknown. Tadiran's earlier radar ELINT system (RAS-2 Owl) is on board three Royal Thai Air Force Aravas, so these systems may be on the same aircraft.

◆ CR-2800

This Elisra (Tadiran subsidiary) 0.5–18-GHz ESM/ELINT system apparently competed with Elta's EL/L-8300. Maximum effective range is 330 km; the system can track up to 64 emitters simultaneously. Antennas: one omni (for IFM), four 10in cavity-backed spirals, and eight 3in cavity-backed spirals, for two frequency bands. All antennas are flush-mounted in pods or blisters. The directional antennas are grouped in four sets, each with adjacent amplifiers. For more precise signal data, for targeting, the system can be supplemented by an SHR and a rotating directional antenna. Total weight, in the basic version, is 300 kg. Reportedly, only three CR-2800s were made, two of which were installed on board Israeli Westwinds for maritime surveillance (the third was a ground-system prototype).

◆ C-Pearl/Kingfisher

Rafael's ESM system for submarines, small surface ships, and aircraft was introduced in 1991. The 40-kg radome-enclosed array comprises an IFM and three sets of DF ports (2–4, 4–8, and 8–18 GHz, extendable down to 0.5–2 GHz). Sensitivity is −60 dBm, and typical elevation coverage is 40 deg. Accuracy: 1.5 MHz, 1 deg (2 deg, 2–4 GHz). The inboard console weighs 125 kg. Signal processing is by distributed Intel microprocessors. Capacity (pulses/sec and library size) has not been published.

Kingfisher is probably an airborne version of C-Pearl, also first shown in 1991. It has somewhat different directional accuracy (1-deg fine DF [reduced to 2 deg for 2–6 GHz], 10-deg instantaneous DF).

◆ EL/L-8300

Elta's electronic reconnaissance system is used for both ground and naval operations. It first appeared on board a converted Israeli Boeing 707 in 1981. Nose to tail, the system consists of:

EL/L-8312A (ELINT section) for C–J bands (0.5–18 GHz, extendable to cover 70 MHz–40 GHz) using nose, tail, wingtip and forward belly omni antennas and determining direction (for triangulation within 20 sec of receipt of the first signal) by differences in time of arrival. The omni antenna feeds an SHR (accuracy 0.5 MHz, resolution 1 MHz), whose intermediate frequency output (at 50–70, 140–180, or 300–500 MHz) feeds a pulse digitizer. Limits: PRF 100 to 19,999; pulse width 0.1 to 99 microsec. Pulse data fed into the accompanying computer are four 16-bit words (pulse width, pulse amplitude, fine frequency, time of arrival, and status). The computer is EL/S-8610. The entire system can fit into a single 19in rack. There are one or two operators.

Supervisor/Control section (two operators).

EL/K-7032 (COMINT section) for the HF, VHF, and UHF communications bands (20–500 MHz, with frequency resolution 1 kHz; extendable to 2 MHz–1 GHz) uses microprocessor-controlled scanners (10-, 20-, 50-, or 100 kHz around a selected frequency, which can switch rapidly). Up to 300 signals can be handled simultaneously, three of them in the same frequency band. All are subject to automatic instantaneous four-channel DF (accuracy better than 2 deg). The antennas are blades in the belly of the airplane. There are four operators.

EL/L-8350 command and analysis station (Operations Section), controlling the system, with two EL/K-1150 V/UHF receivers and a computer controller. This section fuses COMINT and ELINT intelligence, and reports to the ground station (EL/L-8353) in real time.

Command-and-analysis suite.

A traffic collection unit (location not given) contains up to four EL/K-1150 and EL/K-1250 V/UHF receivers.

The airplane carries a threat library for fast analysis of intecepted signals. From 12,000 m it can detect signals emitted 400–450 km away. EL/L-8300 can handle up to 500 emitters.

About 1981 Elbit advertised a shipboard equivalent, EL/S-8300, using both spinners and monopulse DF antennas (an illustration shows a pair of cylindrical omnis atop a six-sided box, from each side of which protrudes a cylindrical-hemispherical radome, presumably covering spirals). There were also EB-series deception systems and an EL/L-8200 noise jammer.

An EL/L-8300 is supported by an EL/L-8352 postmission analysis station and an EL/L-8353 ground station.

System capabilities are suggested by the range of signals that can be simulated by the associated EL/L-8351 ground trainer: up to 270 distinct emitters, ranging over 100 MHz–40 GHz, one of three different antenna patterns, one of four scan patterns (circular, conical, bidirectional, or fixed), different scan rates (1–6 rpm circular, 20–50 Hz conical), variable effective power (over two orders of magnitude), and variable on-off time (20 sec up).

Users: Argentina (bought 1985, two on converted Lockheed L188W [Wave] Electras [reported delivered 1990], three on Boeing 707s), Australia (20 downsized versions bought 1989 for P-3C upgrade, as part of ALR-2001; see separate entry), China (on board ELINT Badgers), Indonesia (bought 1983, probably on one or more 737s equipped with SLAMMR radar), Israel (six on Boeing 707s), Singapore (four on Fokker Maritime Enforcers), South Africa (four on Boeing 707s), Spain (at least one modified Boeing 707), Thailand (two on C-130, with possibly four more to follow). In 1995 an Elta contract to upgrade Argentine S-2Es with new radars and ELINT equipment was announced; the ELINT portion is presumably related to the Elta-Australian ALR-2001, which is an EL/L-8300 derivative. Chile will probably install ALR-2001 on the recently delivered P-3Cs.

◆ NATACS

This 20–500-MHz (extendable down to 2 MHz and up to 1 GHz) Tadiran naval COMINT/DF system, announced August 1989, is derived from an earlier land-based system. It can incorporate a data link for multiple-station fixes. The antenna is a pair of stacked four-dipole Adcocks (vertical figure-8 loops) plus an omni (total 120 kg; 50 kg with alternative lightweight antenna). The SHR scans 1000 channels/sec (200 protected channels, at least 150 preset frequencies) with a minimum of 16 preset frequency search ranges. Frequency resolution is 1 kHz. IF bandwidths, which determine the degree of information extractable, are 10, 20, 50, and 100 kHz. Average DF accuracy is 1.5 deg (normal cut time 0.3 sec, fast mode 3 msec). AM, FM, and CW signals can be analyzed. Below-decks equipment is a search/DF station (including the SHR) and a monitoring operator's station (including monitoring receivers).

Users: Israel (*Sa'ar* 2, 3, 4, 4.5), Singapore (*Victory* and "Sea Wolf"-class fast-attack boats). The Singaporean systems may be CDR-1500s, using Neptune Intelligent Computer Engineering (Elnice) below-decks elements.

◆ NS-9000 Series

Elisra (originally AEL Israel) produced the first of these naval systems about 1978/79 for service in the early 1980s; they were announced at the 1981 Paris Air Show as the Elisra Compact Naval Electronic Warfare Suite. At that time Elisra claimed that it had supplied EW suites for destroyers (presumably Taiwanese Wu-Jinn II ships with Reshet CDS), frigates (presumably the South African *President* class), and FAC. The Elisra systems were renamed in the NS-9000 series in 1982. They were ESM devices, integrated with existing ECM. By 1985, they were in Israeli navy service (presumably replacing the ESM elements of MN-53) and had been exported to at least three countries, probably Chile, South Africa, and Taiwan.

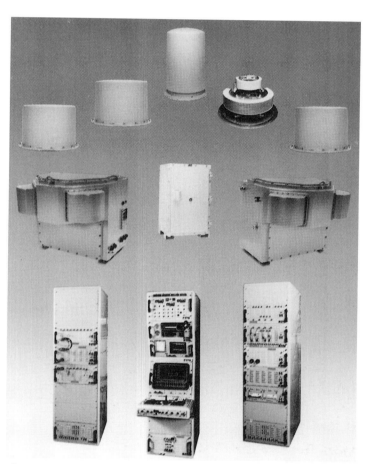

The NS-9003A/9005 integrated ESM/ECM system. The tall cylindrical radome is the ESM element (it is the sole antenna of NS-9010C). The object next to it is an RKR lens for DF (at bottom), surmounted by an array of receivers and by a biconical omni for IFM. The radome presumably covers a stack of such combinations, for different bands. This approach is similar in concept to that used in SLQ-32. Similar lens technology appeared in contemporary Rafael systems, against which NS-9003A competed successfully (Rafael used separate directional and omni antennas, however). The short cylinders are omni noise jammers. Below them are the directional MBATs. (Elisra)

NS-9001, an ELINT version of the NS-9003 ESM set, was introduced late in 1982. It was intermediate between the first and second generation. The lightweight NS-9009, for the Dabur class, may have been introduced at about this time.

The second-generation NS-9010 entered service in the mid-1980s and offered radar warning capability (preset alarms) as well as the usual ESM. It introduced a new RKR lens antenna. The corresponding ECM system, NS-9005, combined a conventional mechanically steered antenna with an exciter employing deception techniques.

Elisra exhibited third-generation versions of the earlier NS-9003 and NS-9005 (suffixed PR) at the 1989 Paris Air Show. The

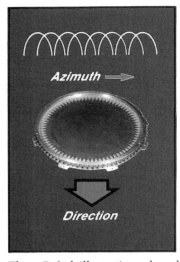

These Rafael illustrations show how the RKR lens/DF combination works. A wave striking the lens from any particular direction produces a signal that comes out of the plane of the lens at a particular point corresponding to that direction: the lens forms beams. Each of numerous parallel receivers, oriented vertically above the lens, receives signals from one beam. In effect, the receiver is channelized by direction rather than by frequency. This is much the same concept as in SLQ-32, except that points on the inboard side of the Rotman lens correspond to directions on the outboard side; the RKR lens covers the full horizon rather than a 90-deg sector. (Rafael)

ESM portion used the new RKR antenna. The main changes were concentrated in the ECM portion of the system: a multibeam array transmitting antenna (MBAT), high ERP, and very fast switching for transmission and deception. A fourth generation (integrated 9003A/9005 and a new 9010C) was announced in 1995.

NS-9001 is an automatic ELINT system (0.5–18 GHz); the display shows frequency versus bearing. DF accuracy: 1 deg in X/Ku-bands, 3 deg in S/C bands. Frequency measurement: 2-MHz resolution. Sensitivity: −70 dBm (omni), −80 dBm (sector). Modes: instantaneous DF (IDF), monopulse DF (MDF), and search (SDF). As built, the system was controlled by a 64-kword minicomputer, and it could handle more than 500,000 pps. ELINT features include magnetic recording of either the entire environment or of a specific emitter; intrapulse frequency analysis; time-domain video display; automatic emitter triangulation; and multiple display modes. This system was probably developed for the hydrofoil *Shimrit*, now discarded, which was launched in May 1981. She had a large tiltable and trainable radome atop a big fixed radome. However, published descriptions of NS-9001 refer to a fixed DF array and an omni. An SHR is optional. NS-9001 normally uses a cylindrical antenna carrying three layers of paired horns (for both polarizations); typically two are paired vertically, the bottom (largest) horns being carried individually or paired horizontally. Horns of different sizes can apparently be mounted alongside each other.

NS-9002 is a simulation van, which can generate up to 256 emitters (frequency resolution 1 MHz, PRF 125 pps up to 250,000 pps, scan rate 3 rpm to 100 Hz). The current version is NS-9002E. There is also a new compact NS-9002R.

NS-9003 is a computer-controlled 2–18-GHz ESM system using monopulse DF and an IFM; it can control decoys and a jammer (typically NS-9005). DF accuracy is 1 deg in X/Ku-bands and 3 deg in S/C-bands. Presumably this degree of precision was needed for missile targeting. IFM resolution is 2 MHz, and capacity is over 500,000 pps. Sensitivity is −70 dBm. Up to six radars can be blanked. This original version of the system used an Elbit EA-9170, a squat cylindrical DF array of horns in three layers; horns on the upper levels are paired side by side (probably to handle polarization diversity). Horns on the lower level are mounted individually. There were 18 wide-open elements (two horns each) for each of the two upper bands, and 12 for each of

two lower bands (horns of different sizes side-by-side). The IFM omni is a vertical masthead cone. NS-9003 was developed for the hydrofoil *Shimrit*. A corresponding submarine system, NS-9004, presumably preceded Timnex into Israeli service, but no longer exists. The third-generation NS-9003PR (1–18 GHz) uses

NS-9003 is shown on board a Chilean *Sa'ar* IV–class fast-attack boat. The DF array is in the squat radome in front of the search radar. Alongside the bridge are the two long tubes of a long-range chaff rocket launcher and two small multiple launchers for short-range chaff rockets. Similar short-range launchers are used by the South African and Israeli navies. This ship apparently lacks jammers. (Chilean Navy, 1992)

NS-9003PR/NS-9005 is shown on board a South African Minister-class strike craft. The RKR DF array at the masthead is surmounted by an IFM cone. The two spheres are directional jammers. Ships of this class originally carried a stubbier DF radome lower down, on the same platform as their FCS dishes. Presumably the later array was light enough to place further aloft. Corresponding Israeli boats use the aloft position for ELINT arrays. (South African Navy)

a new lightweight cylindrical antenna, tall rather than squat, offering an RMS DF accuracy of 2 deg. It uses RKR lens rather than multiport spiral or horn (amplitude comparison) DF technology. The lens assembly inside the radome may be surmounted by biconical omnis for IFM. However, there is often a separate conical omni. In a typical installation (a Sa'ar-class missile boat), the tall cylindrical DF antenna is mounted on the main radar platform; the IFM omni is at the masthead. In some cases it is mounted atop the antenna pot. Frequency resolution is 2 MHz and RMS DF accuracy is 2 deg. Sensitivity is −65 to −75 dBm (and can be increased to −85 dBm). Pulsewidth range is 0.1 microsec to CW. Capacity is over 500,000 pps, with a 5000-mode library. This system alerts the operator and automatically begins to jam preset threat signals. It also offers ELINT types of analysis: intrapulse analysis (i.e., analysis of pulse shape), PRF analysis, frequency profile analysis, and radar scan pattern analysis; and it can display the emitter signals in detail. Many installations include three shorter cylinders, which are probably the antennas of Rattler noise jammers.

Although described as NS-9003A/NS-9005, the ECM system of the Singaporean *Victory* class uses the radomes Rafael advertised for its SEWS system. The stepped masthead radome carries biconical omnis. The radome alongside the mast carries an RKF-lens DF array. The dielectric (RF-transparent) panels below presumably cover MBAT jammers. Below the masthead omni are the characteristic antennas (not visible in this photograph) of the NATACS ELINT system. (*Ships of the World*)

NS-9005 is a noise and deception jammer (2–18 GHz) using steerable antennas. Techniques are spot, barrage, or swept noise; or RGPO, RGPI, or AGPO deception; or false target generation. The original version used a pair of antennas in spherical radomes, probably plus the three fixed omnis of the earlier NS-9003/Rattler combination. It could handle up to eight threats. One third-generation NS-9005 PR (one exciter) can control four MBATs, each covering 90 degrees. With four trackers, it can time-share the exciter to deceive four threats virtually simultaneously; it can be expanded to 16 digital trackers. Elisra's MBAT uses a pair of semicircular (in plan) antennas projecting 90 deg apart from a box shaped like that of SLQ-32. Elisra claims that its new RKR lens technology (which Rafael claims is derived from its own MBAT) provides NS-9005/MBAT with high effective power at 7.5–18 GHz. The fourth-generation 1–18-GHz integrated NS-9003A/9005 also incorporates an MBAT transmitter. Up to 16 I/J-band (cover can be extended to 6–18 GHz) threats can be jammed simultaneously. Techniques include: noise, deception, false-target creation, tracker synchronization, look-through, and combinations. The single operator console carries a 19in color graphic display and a 9in alphanumeric display; it can also carry a video monitor. The operator uses a joystick, a full keyboard, and dedicated function keys.

NS-9007 upgrades existing manual EW equipment to automatic power-management suites. This was probably the designation of a modification to existing U.S.-supplied WLR-1s and ULQ-6s on Taiwanese Wu-Jinn II (Reshet CDS) destroyers.

NS-9008 is an automatic test facility.

NS-9009 is a compact system (2–18 GHz) developed for the Dabur class, and suited to small patrol boats of up to 200 t. The main cylindrical antenna carries six cavity-backed spirals with matched video receivers (for DF), with a pair of omnis on top splitting the spectrum into four octave bands. Base diameter is 50 cm, total height is 60 cm, and weight is 15 kg (inboard electronics add another 30 kg). Raw video from the two antennas is processed separately, then combined into sequences of digital words: DoA, band, pulse width, amplitude, and ToA. A preprocessor correlates these data with known signals to minimize the load on the system processor. An IFM can be added, mainly to set a jammer. The other available upgrade is low-noise RF amplifiers. Operating limits: over 200,000 pps; pulse width 0.1 to 10 microsec; PRF 0.1 to 50 kHz. DF accuracy is 8 deg, sensitivity −35 dBm. Displays: polar and tabular readout of up to six emitters; visual and audio alarms for specific threats. NS-9009 computes launch parameters for chaff launchers.

NS-9010 is a faster version of -9003 using distributed microprocessors and monopulse-switching DF (instantaneous DF is optional); the pulse density limit is over 250,000 pps. The fixed multibeam antenna (12 horns above 8 spirals) offers DF accuracy of 3 deg in X/Ku-band and 5 deg in S/C-band. In 1995, Elisra announced NS-9010C, a lightweight low-cost 1–18-GHz system (extendable down to 0.5 and up to 40 GHz) with a monopulse DF accuracy of 8 deg (3 deg optional) and a sensitivity of −65 dBm. Frequency resolution (by a digital IFM) is 3 MHz (accuracy 5 MHz). Amplitude: dynamic range 60 dB (resolution 1 dB). Pulse widths: 0.1 to 100 microsec (and CW); PRI 20 microsec (PRF 50,000) to 5 msec (PRF 200); scan rate 0.02 to 100 Hz. The 17in color display can show data in B-scan, PPI, or tabular form. The console carries a joystick and a few fast-action buttons. There is also a removable 40-Mbyte hard disk. Apparently a new feature of this system is a pulse preprocessor controlled in real time by the main system computer to respond to changes in the electromagnetic environment. NS-9010U is a developmental submarine version, formerly NS-9034. It will operate in a moderate pulse environment (about 100K pps). It will use six spiral antennas (2 to 18 GHz, 6-deg accuracy), an optional fine DF array (Elbit-supplied RKR lenses, 7.5–18 GHz, 1-deg accuracy for missile targeting), and an omni (2–18 GHz) on the periscope mast. Elevation coverage is +30/−10 deg.

NS-9025 is an airborne standoff jammer for naval and ground applications.

Users:

NS-9003/9005: Chile (*Sa'ar* and modernized *Leander* and "County" classes), Israel (*Sa'ar* 2, 3, 4, 4.5 classes), Malaysia (*Spica M* class), South Africa (*Minister* class). In many or most cases the original horn array was replaced by the taller RKR lens radome.
NS-9003PR/9005PR: Israel (*Chetz* and *Nirit*).
NS-9003A/9005: Israel (9003A with Rafael MBAT in *Eilat* class), Singapore (*Victory* class). In the *Victory* class the radomes are a squatter type advertised by Rafael (with an IFM knob on top), but reportedly the system is Elisra's.
NS-9009: Chile (*Dabur* class), Israel (Dabur and Improved Dvora classes; secondary ESM on *Sa'ar* 5, *Chetz*, and *Nirit*. This system may also be on board Daburs in Argentina. A photo of a boat in Sri Lankan service seems not to show any radomes at all.
NS-9010PR/9005PR: Israel (at least one *Sa'ar* 4.5), Peru (*Lupo* class). A Venezuelan modernization contract, announced in 1992, apparently was canceled due to lack of funds.

It was reported late in 1996 that India was buying an Israeli EW system for the *Viraat*. Presumably, it is an NS-9000–series device.

Note that ships previously listed as having MN-53 systems are now credited with NS-9000–series systems. NS-9003/9005 may have been sold to China for Jianghu-class frigates (some of which have spherical jammer radomes; *Siping* at least has box radomes which may be MBATs). The Chinese installations may also be locally produced versions of Newton.

◆ Rattler

Rafael's 2–18-GHz noise jammer probably began development in 1979–80. It is often controlled by NS-9003. It can engage up to three radars simultaneously by time-sharing one high-powered broad-band amplifier, excited by a lower-powered microwave source. Output power is reportedly greater than 400 W. Claimed effective range is 30–40 km. Up to 16 Rattlers can be ganged together on a single IEE 488 bus. Rattler was apparently used extensively in Lebanon in the early 1980s and in the Bekaa Valley strike of 1983. The antenna generally occupies a cylindrical radome, in some cases with a hemispherical top.

Users: Chile (*Sa'ar* 3 and 4 classes), Malaysia (*Spica M* class), South Africa (*Sa'ar* 4 class). Some Chinese Jianghus with large cylindrical radomes may be equipped with Rattler.

◆ SES-210E

Elisra claims that this 2–18-GHz digital small-combatant ESM system, announced in 1995, has been in service since 1992. Accuracy: 10 deg (2 deg optional), 3 MHz. The antenna assembly weighs less than 10 kg, and the system can control chaff launchers. Threats generate audio and visual alarms; the display is the usual PPI plus tabular data.

◆ Rafael MBAT (RAN-1010)

Rafael's Multi-Beam Array Transmitter (MBAT) is on board the *Sa'ar* 5 class. Reportedly Elisra's MBAT is based on Rafael technology revealed to Elisra when the latter integrated the Rafael transmitter with its NS-9003 system for the Israeli missile corvettes. Separate repeater, transponder, and techniques (deception) generator all feed the MBATs. Each air-cooled MBAT box contains a single horizontal circular RKR lens (fed from above by arrays of waveguides) with pairs of rectangular antennas on adjacent sides, 90 deg apart. The box can be mounted on trunnions, for stabilization. Rafael claims that using RKR lenses reduces system RCS. Each 7.5–18-GHz MBAT can jam several threats simultaneously. It can switch beams (to follow a target) in 150 nsec; each of 32 beams is 6 × 25 deg.

Users: The Israeli *Eilat* uses two nonstabilized MBATs based on RAN-1010. Elisra was system contractor (providing the NS-9003 ESM system), and Rafael was principal subcontractor. The larger Shipboard Electronic Warfare System (SEWS), of which MBAT is part, apparently has not been sold (note, however, that the Singaporean *Victory* class carries radomes identical to those in Rafael brochures advertising SEWS).

◆ TIMNEX 4 CH

Elbit's TIMNEX 4 CH is optimized for ELINT and OTH missile targeting rather than for threat warning. The mast carries a four-channel omni (stacked biconicals for IFM) above a high-band array of eight corrugated horns (8–18 GHz, gain typically 8 dBi), which lies above a low-band array of eight concave-horn spirals inside radomes (2–8 GHz, typical gain 3 dBi). DF resolution is 1.4 deg (accuracy 5 deg at 2–8 GHz and 3 deg at 8–18 GHz). The two DF arrays total 270 mm in height, and the omni on top is 220 (dia) × 280 mm; total weight is 200 kg. The original version lacks the IFM and may have smaller DF arrays. A miniature threat-warning array may be mounted above the submarine's periscope, feeding the same electronics as the main array: 2–18-GHz omni and 8–18-GHz DF array, accuracy 3–5 deg, resolution 10-deg RMS. System frequency range is expandable to 0.5–40 GHz. Frequency accuracy and resolution are 1.0 and 0.5 MHz. PRF and ToA are measured within better than 0.25%. Time of arrival resolution is 10 nsec, corresponding to 100,000 pps. System parameters are frequency, pulsewidth, PRF, modulation, amplitude, DoA, and ToA. Library capacity is 500 modes (up to 128 alarms and 100 platforms, upgraded from 64 modes and 32 alarms). The current Mk 2 (presumably [V]2) can carry 64 radar

tracks (full performance) or up to 128 if some processing delay is accepted. The computer was originally ROLM 1602B (16 bits, 64K words). Displays are alphanumeric, polar, and rectangular-coordinate.

Users: Australia (4CH [V]2: *Oberons*), China ([V]2 reported in all but first Han), Israel (4CH [V]1 in *Gal* class since 1982, [V]2 in *Dolphins*), South Africa (4CH [V]2 in *Daphne* class), Taiwan (4CH[V]2 in *Hai Lung* class; first user of this version). The Australian systems may have been replaced by the domestic (AWA) Mavis.

EXPENDABLES

Israel's chaff rockets were developed to complement the Gabriel missile. The Arab navies' Styx grossly outranged it, so the Israeli tactic was to induce the Arabs to fire first—and to miss—primarily using long-range AV-2 chaff rockets to produce false targets (RAM on the forward superstructures of the Israeli boats minimized their own bow-on radar signatures when the chaff was fired). Rockets were fired from a box on the bridge. Many Styxes went wild because Arab crews, panicked by targets popping up, failed to maintain a steady course for the 2 min required to run up gyros before firing. Even so, some missiles came quite close to the Israeli boats, hence the postwar development of short-range rockets and the associated jammers.

An Israel navy *Sa'ar* II displays her trainable decoy launcher (abaft the bridge, abeam the forward Gabriel launcher) and fixed short-range decoy launchers (on the side of the bridge). Her NS-9003 DF array is in the stubby radome on the same platform as her search radar, just below the yardarm. A spherical jammer radome is just visible beneath the fire-control radar dish. The fish of her EDO 780 VDS is visible aft. Note the triple Mk 32 torpedo tubes abeam the trainable decoy launcher. (Israeli Navy, 1994)

The long-range rockets were in fixed twin mounts on either side of the bridge structure. Short-range rockets were in sextuple launchers on converted 0.50-cal machine-gun pedestals (two launchers controlled by one bridge box). These devices survive on board Chilean and South African *Sa'ar* class fast-attack boats but have apparently been abandoned by the Israeli navy. The six-barrel launcher is now being marketed in the United States under the designation LADS. These launchers are used by Chile, South Africa, and Taiwan.

Many Israeli ships have pairs of 24-rnd short-range launchers fixed to their bridge structures in place of the earlier long-range tubes. Additional 24-rnd launchers are mounted abaft the bridge. Larger units have trainable and elevatable 45-rnd launchers, introduced about 1983, which fire 3D chaff clouds under computer

An Israeli *Reshev*-class fast-attack boat displays her trainable chaff launcher (among the Gabriel boxes amidships) and two pedestal-mounted chaff launchers (forward of her bridge). The ELINT array on the topmast is presumably NATACS. (Israeli Navy, 1994)

control (successive waves of chaff rockets are fuzed to "walk" the cloud away from a ship). This is the launcher atop the hangar of an *Aliyah* or on the quarterdeck (just forward of the gun) of a *Romat* or *Reshev*. The new *Eilat* has four 72-rnd stabilized launchers (elevation limits: +55/−15 deg, elevation/train rates 30/45 deg/sec). In at least some ships the 45-rnd launcher is replaced by a 14-tube launcher firing larger-diameter rounds, which are probably active decoys. Israeli FAC generally carry four single launchers for smoke rounds, to defeat EO weapons.

◆ ACDS/Deseaver

Elbit's Automatic C/M-Dispensing System, introduced about 1982, can launch up to 24 rockets in one salvo under local microprocessor control. Typically each fire-control unit (FCU) controls one 45-barrel or four to six 24-barrel launchers. The FCU is controlled either by a central computer (with 44 kbytes of EPROM and 12 kbytes of RAM; it has eight interrupt levels) or manually (as backup) via its front panel keyboard. In automatic mode, the missile threat is defined by the ship's CDS or her ESM/RWR system, with both of which the central computer communicates at 4800 bps (half-duplex). ACDS receives radar data (the display has a maximum range of 99,000 yd, with 1000-yd resolution; bearing resolution is 1 deg) as well as wind and ship course and speed. The main unit (with displays and a keyboard) reports back to the main tactical display and to the ship's active ECM units (for time correlation). There is also an optional remote-control unit. Payload interval is 150 msec to 8 sec; resolution is 150 msec.

Deseaver, the follow-on system, controls the three 72-rnd launchers of the *Eilat* class. It can operate in automatic, semiautomatic (operator has a single key to approve recommended action), or manual (operator must approve target designation and launch initiation) modes. The display shows both the threat and decoy deployment.

Users:

ACDS: Chile (22 systems), Israel (122), South Africa (28; 8 more scrapped), and Taiwan (208)

Deseaver: Israel (*Sa'ar* 5 class)

◆ Chaff Rockets

The long-range AV-2 of the 1973 war has a boost-sustain motor (range 10–12 km) and an altitude fuze. It is energized from the launcher (so no batteries are needed). Decoy targets appear 1–2 min after firing. The postwar short-range rocket has a single pulse motor and follows a preselected optimum-operation trajectory. A decoy is formed within 15 sec. In both cases, decoys persist for 10–15 min depending on the weather. Rafael's Beamtrap is a larger replacement for both long- and short-range rockets, fired from 24-, 45-, or 72-rnd launchers.

Characteristics of these Rafael chaff rockets are:

	Short Range	*Beamtrap*	*AV-2*
Weight	3.2 kg	6.6 kg	9.4 kg
Chaff	1.75 kg—1.3 kg		
Diameter	90 mm	115 mm	89 mm
Length	640 mm	804 mm	922 mm
Fin Span	125 mm	115 mm	179 mm

Users (of the Rafael two-rocket system): Chile, South Africa, Taiwan (AV-2 rockets). The short-range element of the system may survive in Israel on board Dabur- and Dvora-class patrol boats. Possible users: Argentina, Singapore, Sri Lanka, Thailand.

ITALY

At the British BARNEE show in September 1995 Elettronica displayed jammers it said could be used for Crosseye angle deception against a monopulse radar. Crosseye uses the interference pattern between a pair of linked transmitters a few meters apart to create a wavefront at an angle to the missile seeker, convincing it that the true target is at a different bearing. The technique has been known for many years, but has never, apparently, been implemented before.

Elettronica displayed this all-solid-state Nettuno 4100–series jammer antenna at Bourget Euronaval in October 1996. The company's brochure announced a new modular system under development, to combine RQN-5 ESM with either a traditional TWT-based ECM element or with a solid-state phased array, probably using Rx/Tx modules. (Author)

◆ Farad/Newton/SLQ-A, B, C, D/SLQ-01/SPR-A/BLD-727 and Nettuno/Nettunel (MM/SLQ-727)

Elettronica's ESM/ECM systems are modular. The core of the initial series, Farad, is ELT 123, essentially an RWR, providing DF processing and de-interleaving pulses; its pulse-recognition

Newton Beta jammers on board the Spanish frigate *Descubierta* in 1991. The large radome abaft the mast is for satellite communications. The ESM antenna (hat and cylinder) are just visible on the yard above the Signaal FCS "egg." (Raymond Cheung)

processor recognizes preprogrammed threats. It displays a threat strobe and a symbol indicating the threat family type. There is a small operator keypad, but no dedicated operator is needed. The supplementary ELT 261 is fed by the system's IFM. It maintains track files (hence recognizes scan patterns) and recognizes complex emission modes. ELT 261 contains the system ESM library, tracks selected emissions, controls jammers, and transmits digital data to a CDS. It provides a large-screen ESM display, with a keyboard, soft keys, and a trackball. The separate warning display can be deleted (or used as a bridge display) when ELT 261 is installed. The monopulse DF antenna is a collar surrounding a mast. ELT 261 is associated with four omni antennas: two cones ("witch-hats" for high frequencies) and two cylinders (covering half-cones). The mast elements weigh about 60 kg.

The associated jammers are ELT 361 (noise, to mask another ship, using an ELT 828 directional antenna in a spherical radome) and a separate ELT 521 (self-protection range deception, using a cylindrical [omni] ELT 814 antenna). ELT 521 uses a variety of deception techniques with programmable deception routines. It is capable of multiple-threat engagement (hence the use of omni antennas). Each ELT 828 weighs less than 50 kg, including stabilization.

The Italian navy version of Farad is SLQ-A. Export versions: Patrol (ELT 123 with or without ELT 261, ESM only); Attack (ESM plus deception jammer, with ELT 261 for target identification in enhanced version); and Coastal/High Value self-defense (ELT 261 driving a noise jammer; carries a deception jammer in enhanced version).

In the improved Newton, ELT 123 and ELT 261 merge into a single ELT 211 (about 450 kg). It chooses a preferred ECM reaction, and it can drive up to four jammers. Unlike Farad, it is connected directly to both the noise jammer (ELT 318) and to the ELT 521 deception set. Either can be switched to either the directional or omnidirectional antenna. The single operator at the console controls all ECM and ESM functions. The Italian navy equivalent to ELT 261 is SLR-4, which has a higher-capacity signal processor and an SHR to supplement the IFM, for better frequency discrimination. Some ships have SLR-3, formerly SPR-D.

A NATO version, bought by the Netherlands (as SLQ-01, because Ramses, SLQ-02, was not yet available) and by Spain, used a more powerful processor (ELT 311 vice 211) and a different jammer (ELT 511N vice 521).

China makes Newton Beta under license, using the component ELT numbers as Type numbers. This system shows the tactical situation with 6-deg resolution, hence cannot target missiles. Chinese designators: Type 211 ESM, Type 318 noise jammer, Type 521 deception, Type 923 omni, 981 omni, 929 directional antennas.

SLQ-B and -C are, respectively, lower- and higher-frequency Italian navy versions of Newton using different-sized versions of the cylindrical ELT 814 antenna. Frigates use SLQ-D, covering the full spectrum.

Versions of Newton (designating letter indicates the number of separate jammers) are as follows:

Newton Alpha: 100–500t ships. ELT 211 plus either ELT 318 noise jammer (ELT 814 antenna) or ELT 521 deception jammer (ELT 828 antenna).

Newton Beta: 250–1000t ships. ELT 211, ELT 318 (with two large ELT 814 antennas), and ELT 521 (with two ELT 828 antennas).

Newton Gamma: 1000–3000t ships: ELT 211, one ELT 318, two ELT 521s (two or three ELT 828 antennas), and two or three ELT 814. Gamma covers the 2–18-GHz range in four bands. The four outputs are displayed on two CRTs that can discriminate between pulse and CW signals. Two other CRTs display signal-analysis data, and a fifth gives D-band data. Several jammers are provided, including radar-angle jamming to confuse TWS radars.

Newton Lambda (SLQ-D/SLR-4): ELT 211, one ELT 318, and three ELT 521s, or two ELT 318s and two ELT 521s, in each case with four ELT 828 antennas. Lambda (rather than Delta) indi-

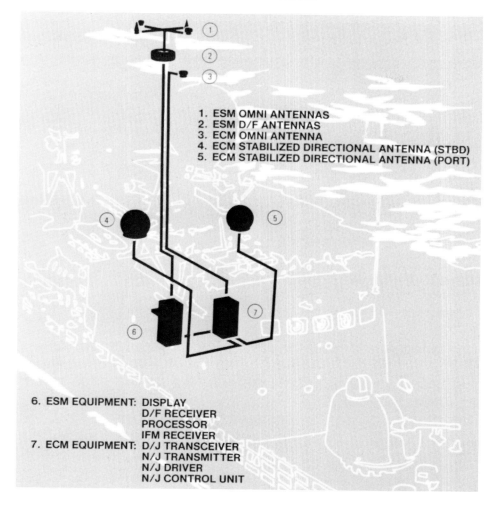

1. ESM OMNI ANTENNAS
2. ESM D/F ANTENNAS
3. ECM OMNI ANTENNA
4. ECM STABILIZED DIRECTIONAL ANTENNA (STBD)
5. ECM STABILIZED DIRECTIONAL ANTENNA (PORT)

6. ESM EQUIPMENT: DISPLAY
D/F RECEIVER
PROCESSOR
IFM RECEIVER
7. ECM EQUIPMENT: D/J TRANSCEIVER
N/J TRANSMITTER
N/J DRIVER
N/J CONTROL UNIT

Farad installed on board a typical fast-attack boat. (Elettronica)

The Italian submarine *Sauro* displays the antennas of her Elettronica Thetis ESM system (*left and right*), as well as her BPS-704 radar antenna. (*Ships of the World*)

cated the commercial *Lupo* application; the Italian navy's version is SLQ-D (i.e., Delta). Despite reports, this version was not exported to Iraq. Iraq received the Selenia INS-3, which (as of then) the Italian navy had not adopted; later the Italian navy did adopt it for *Minerva*-class corvettes.

Newton Epsilon: Five-unit system for the *Vittorio Veneto*, with ELT 211, two ELT 318s, and three ELT 521s (SLR-4, SLQ-B, SLQ-C).

Nettuno is a development of Newton Lambda adding a second console to ELT 211 for ESM analysis (with a larger threat library and a better computer, MARA 286). A next-generation Nettuno 2100 uses multiple RISC processors in place of the 286. Two high-band lens DF antennas improve angular resolution. The jammers feed four ELT 828s using lens antennas instead of the earlier dishes. In Nettunel, the Spanish version, three omni pots and one cone replace the earlier two pots and two cones. Nettuno 4000 is a new version using a jammer with a phased-array antenna. It presumably incorporates the "Crosseye" capability mentioned above.

Users: Farad: Italy (A1 in *Sparviero* class; patrol version in *Cassiopea* [probable], *Gaeta*, *Lerici* classes), Nigeria (*Lerici*), Thailand (coastal version in *Prabrarapak* and *Chonburi* classes). SPR-A in the Italian *De Christofaro* class is probably a related system. Similarly, it seems very likely that THETIS (MM/BLD-727), which is used only on board Italian submarines, is a related ESM system using a different antenna.

Newton Alpha: Morocco (*Lazaga* class), Spain (*Lazaga* class), Thailand (*Ratcharit* class). Elta may have manufactured a version of this system in Israel as MN-53 (now probably extinct), with omni jammers only.

Newton Beta: Australia (River class, as ELT 901), China (Jianghu IV/V), Egypt (*Descubierta* and Jianghu 053H[E] classes),

Passive elements of Nettuno are shown aboard the carrier *Garibaldi* in 1991. The flat plates surrounding the main masthead (in the background) are for the eight low-band DF spirals. The double cylinder on the platform below the radar in the foreground is one of two roll-stabilized lens antennas for high-band DF. The short yardarm below the DF spirals carries the four omnis: three cylinders and a cone, in this case pointed up, and visible behind the forward radar antenna. (Author)

The Nettuno roll-stabilized lens jammer on the carrier *Garibaldi*, 1991. (Author)

Morocco (*Descubierta*), Spain (*Descubierta* [and, originally, *Baleares* class, now modernized]), Thailand (Jianghu frigates, PFMM Mk 16 class). ELT 715 is the data-transmission unit used in the Moroccan version of this system, on board the *Lt. Col. Errhamani* (which has two large ELT 814s but lacks ELT 828s). The Chinese license-built version uses an ELT 939 transmission box (on board Jianghu IV– and V–class corvettes for China, Egypt, and Thailand). These ships have two ELT 814 antennas.

Newton Gamma: Ecuador (*Wadi M'ragh* class), Greece (*Kortenaer* class), Indonesia (*van Speijk* class: one large [centerline] and two small ELT 828s), Italy (*Lupo* class), Netherlands (early *Kortenaers*). Because SLQ-01 on board the Dutch *Kortenaer*-class frigates was replaced by Ramses only when ships were modernized, the two unmodernized Greek ships retain Newton (with two small cylindrical antennas, one on either side just abaft the bridge). The *Kortenaers* were completed with the Sphinx ESM system (but with some Newton ESM arrays, too), so in their case the two systems are probably tied together.

Newton Lambda: Italy (*Maestrale* class), Peru (*Lupo* class), Venezuela (*Lupo* class). The Venezuelan frigates may be refitted with Elisra equipment.

Nettuno/Nettunel: Italy (*Garibaldi, Mimbelli, Audace, San Giorgio*), Spain (*Principe de Asturias, Santa Maria* classes).

◆ Colibri (ELT 161)/ELT 263/NICE

Colibri, Elettronica's naval helicopter system, is an airborne equivalent of Farad, using an ELT 161 DF processor/warner (in-

stead of ELT 123) and an ELT 261 analysis (including IFM) unit; it can drive an ELT 361 noise jammer (requiring its own directional antenna) as well as an ELT 562 self-defense deception jammer. In an AB 212 the system employs two omni cones (one forward above the windshield, the other at the extreme tail), two half-cylindrical half-omnis (under the nose, facing port and starboard), and eight hemispherical DF antennas (spread around the helicopter, four in the nose, two amidships just below the engine exhaust, and two facing aft, on either side of the after cone).

Colibri DF antennas (small hemispheres) are visible on the nose of this Sea King (SH-3D) on board the carrier *Garibaldi*, 1991. The radar under the nose is probably APQ-706. Note the omni (a horizontal cone) above the windshield. The antenna above it is for a jammer (these aircraft carry both ELT 361 noise jammers and ELT 562 deception jammers). A similar antenna is mounted aft, abaft the step of the hull, with a pair of DF antennas nearby. (Author)

ELT 263, the corresponding MPA system, conceived for the Beech 200T, was announced in 1982. System memory suffices for the aircraft to locate an emitter by triangulation as it flies past. The system can transmit emitter location to a surface station. These systems are being withdrawn from service, partly because they do not offer sufficient precision to control air-to-surface missiles.

Claimed performance (range at which an emitter can be detected):

Flight Altitude	S-band	X-band
300 ft	34 nm	26 nm
1000 ft	50 nm	41 nm
2000 ft	63 nm	47 nm

NICE, Elettronica's New Integrated Computerized ESM system intended to replace Colibri and ELT 263, was announced at the Paris Air Show in 1989. Presumably it is a lightweight equivalent to Newton, substituting a single box for the previous separate DF and IFM/identification processors. Its DF antennas are cavity-backed spirals. NICE uses both wide-open and SHR receivers. It can detect coding within a pulse (i.e., pulse-compression coding). As of 1996, no sales had been reported.

Users: Colibri: Argentina (Sea Kings), Brazil (Sea Kings), Greece (AB 212, three of them fitted for ECM, 14 for ASW), Italy (AB 212, for special jamming; also ESM on board Sea Kings), Peru (AB 212 used for reconnaissance and Sea Kings), Spain (four ECM-equipped AB 212s, working with AB 212s carrying AS-12 missiles or torpedoes), Turkey (AB 204 and AB 212), and Venezuela (AB 212 with Sea Killer missiles). AB 212 helicopters ordered by Iraq were not delivered. Iranian AB 212s are probably no longer operational. The Italian cruiser *Vittorio Veneto* carries six helicopters, probably two ASW pairs (one dipping, one carrying torpedoes) and one ASUW pair (one EW, one Sea Killer shooter). Alternatively, there may be one Colibri helicopter per flight of three.

ELT 263: Algeria (two on Beech Super King Air), Finland (three on Learjet 35A), Indonesia (16 on Searchmaster), Spain (two on CASA-212; many others were retired), and the United Arab Emirates (four on CASA-212). Thailand replaced the ELT 263s on F.27 maritime reconnaissance aircraft with Argo 700s because the former was not sufficiently precise to target Harpoon missiles. Singapore, which had ordered ELT 263 in 1991 for its F.50s, decided instead to use the much more elaborate Israeli EL/L-8300. The Indonesian units are being replaced by Sky Guardian 2000, and as of 1996 Finland was about to replace the Learjets. South Africa retired its ELT 263s. Thus, of an estimated 84 made, no more than 27 remained in service in 1996.

♦ CO-NEWS/ELT 128

Elettronica's communications ESM systems both use stacked arrays of three sets of antennas (four vertical dipoles each) to cover HF, VHF, and UHF bands (probably 1–500 MHz, with breaks at about 30 and 200 MHz). CO-NEWS is primarily a V/UHF system with optional extension to HF; ELT 128 covers all three bands. The only obvious visual difference is that CO-NEWS has a considerably larger box at the base of the antenna.

Internally the two are quite different. CO-NEWS is a two-operator SIGINT system housed in a pair of large electronic cabinets, each of which has a QWERTY keyboard and a CRT (roughly 10 × 10 in on the left, 8 × 6 in on the right); the left-hand unit also carries numerous operator pushbuttons for control. DF processing is probably Watson-Watt for HF, Doppler for VHF, and perhaps interferometric at V/UHF. The display is used for signal analysis, presumably including some interpretation of the type of signal (e.g., AM or FSK) and possibly providing some fingerprinting. No data are available concerning the character of the frequency-scanning receiver.

ELT 128 is a less-capable automated system, presumably run by a minicomputer such as ND-160. It uses a remote receiver and has a single operator. This system is probably limited to Watson-Watt DF processing at all three bands. It can monitor AM, FM, SSB, CW signals, measuring DoA and signal strength, and giving a confidence level.

Users:

CO-NEWS: Italy (*Audace, Maestrale, Lupo* [Italian only] classes), Spain (*Principe de Asturias, Santa Maria, Baleares* classes). Note that the system in *Garibaldi* and the *Luigi de la Penne* class is the American/German Seagle, *not* CO-NEWS.

ELT 128: Peru (*Lupo* class), Thailand (MV400 *Chonburi* class), Venezuela (*Lupo* class). Some of the Italian installations listed above may be ELT 128s. This may also be the system in the Ecuadorian *Wadi M'ragh* class, which is usually listed as a Telegon (the characteristic Telegon egg is not visible in these ships).

♦ INS Series/RQN Series and MM/SLQ-747/IHS-6 (ALR-730/735)/Sea Petrel

These integrated shipboard (INS) and helicopter (IHS) systems combine a signal detector (RQN) with a pulse analyzer/warner (PAW), a pulse identification/display (RIN), and a directional jammer (TQN). They were developed by Selenia, whose EW division was bought by Elettronica in 1992. Elettronica considered the Selenia (by then named Alenia) architecture superior, and these systems are to form the basis of future Elettronica systems. For example, RQH-5(V) technology is now being inserted in Newton Gamma.

The intercept and DF antenna of an Italian INS-3 installed on the Indian frigate *Godavari*, 1986.

INS-5 is the latest of a series of Selenia jammers. They are generally mounted on masts, without radomes. (Selenia)

Work on RQH-5(V) began in 1984, with the first significant deliveries in 1989–90. The most important improvement is the substitution of linear for logarithmic amplifiers. A linear amplifier has a much more limited dynamic range, so it requires the insertion of an instantaneous automatic gain control (IAGC) act-

The Singaporean fast-attack boat *Sea Tiger* displays her SLQ-747 EW suite, comprising an Alenia ESM array at the masthead and characteristic Elettronica spherical jammer radomes below her Signaal "egg." The ELINT array part way up the mast is probably for the Israeli NATACS system. (*Ships of the World*)

ing on each pulse. On the other hand, the improved fidelity of such an amplifier makes for much better DF accuracy, typically 3 rather than 5 deg in a monopulse system (2.5 deg with calibration). The new family of systems also offer fine DF by interferometry and a new signal processor architecture. Ironically, prior to the merger, the Italian navy had permitted Alenia to export to Iraq and Libya, precisely because it bought its equipment mainly from Elettronica.

The only operational versions of the original Selenia series are IHS-6 (Selenia's alternative to Colibri) and its shipboard derivatives, INS-3 (the third-generation version) and INS-5.

INS-3 (1–18 GHz in two bands) employs a digital intercept receiver, RQN-3. The PAW-3 processor (ND-160 plus a hardware-based signal processor) maintains up to 64 emitter files and has 32 preprogrammed threat channels (with a 3000-mode library). Eight fixed DF antennas surround a conical omni; accuracy is 5 deg. Compared to the Elettronica antennas, this is more massive and the single cone is not separated from the stacked DF arrays. The 16in CRT of the RIN-3 display can show either a B-scan (frequency vs. bearing, with signals identified by track number and by standard NTDS symbol) or a PPI with range rings replaced by rings arranged by frequency band, that is, by degree of threat. In each case the screen also shows a list of track numbers with category symbols and a list of signal parameters: track number, band letter, frequency range in MHz, PRF, pulse width, identification.

INS-3 controls a 6–18-GHz TQN-2 jammer (noise and pulse) as well as chaff launchers. The standard directional dish is never enclosed in a radome. It uses four square antennas alongside the main dish to track its target in bearing and elevation by two-channel monopulse. Beamwidth is 3 deg; a second 6-deg beam is used against low-level targets, which cannot accurately be tracked because of multipath effects. A separate ULQ-2 can modulate the jamming signal for range and angle deception. The jammer antenna can also track a target passively, for other weapons. SLQ-747 combines the passive elements of INS-3 with Elettronica's spherical jammer radomes.

INS-3 was developed from IHS-6, which used a 0.65–18-GHz RQH-5 receiver (50 emitter tracks, 3000-mode library, expandable to 20,000 modes). Development began in 1975, primarily for task force EW and for standoff and stand-in jamming to support strikes. Parameters: frequency, pulse width, intrapulse structure, fine structure (for fingerprinting), jitter, stagger, PRI agility, scan pattern, amplitude changes (which can be displayed on a histogram). It can accept up to 20 new emitters every 20 msec. Options include a multibeam antenna for sectoral monopulse DF. INS-5 is a lightweight ship version using the same receiver. Compared to Colibri, IHS-6 has less impact on the helicopter or airplane airframe but loses some overall capability.

As indicated above, RQH-5(V) is a very different receiver. The corresponding system is Sea Petrel, which offers 2.5-deg DF accuracy (eight ports), and a sensitivity of −60 dBm. This receiver is combined with an Elettronica SHR in ST 2 (ALR-730; the ST

2 designation comes from the operational requirement number), the ESM system installed in modernized Italian Atlantic MPAs (it was the first fruit of the Elettronica-Alenia combination). Reportedly the combination was not altogether effective. In theory, the wide-open RQH-5(V) cued the superhets, but operator workload was excessive. SLQ-747 is another fruit of this combination: the INS-series is used to drive Elettronica's characteristic directional jammer.

Commercial variants of the new combination: Series 730 for MPA; Series 740 for fighters; Series 780 for ESM/ELINT/EW aircraft. ULR-741 is being developed for submarines as a potential BLR-727 successor using almost the same antenna.

Users:

IHS-6: Egypt (Commando helicopters, delivered 1980), Iraq (ASH-61 helicopters and supersonic aircraft).

RQH-5(V)/IHS-6: Italy (updated Atlantic MPA, as SL/ALR-730; EH-101, as SL/ALR-735); an RWR version for supersonic aircraft is SL/ALR-743. The current ALR-741 uses multiple RISC processors (ALR-730 used multiple CISC processors).

INS-3: India (*Vikrant, Viraat, Khukri,* and *Godavari* class), Italy (ex-Iraqi *Lupo* class; *Alpino* and *Minerva* class [SLQ-747]), Malaysia (ex-Iraqi *Wadi M'ragh* class), Singapore (*Dragon* class [SLQ-747 version] as refitted 1992).

◆ Breda 105mm Rocket Launchers (SCLAR)

SCLAR, which was funded as part of the *Maestrale* program, employs a digital microprocessor based on the Elsag ESA-24 to control each pair of launchers, setting train and elevation and choosing among stored decoy patterns. The first units were ordered in 1978. It seems unlikely that any ships were fitted with an earlier system, UCLAR, which employed the same 20-rnd launcher but lacked the local microprocessor.

Breda's 105mm rocket launcher, for both decoys and shore bombardment. (Breda)

The 20-rnd heavy launcher (1150 kg empty, 1750 kg loaded, working circle 1.38 m) carries four horizontal rows of tubes, either 24 × 81 mm or 12 × 127 mm. It trains at 60 deg/sec and elevates at 30 deg/sec (limits +55/−3 deg). Firing rate is about 1 rocket/sec. This launcher can also fire illumination and bombardment rockets. Rockets are carried in waterproof containers with frangible heads. Types: chaff distraction (range 12,000 m), chaff seduction (5000 m), illumination (4000 m), bombardment (11,000 m, either to support a landing force or to attack coastal targets).

Special bombardment (32 × 51mm HE rockets above 10 (two rows of five) 105mm rockets) and chaff-missile versions apparently found no buyers. See the 1991/92 edition for details.

A fixed (35-deg elevation, 45-deg train) L105 light six-tube chaff launcher was bought by Iraq, and will probably be retained in the *Wadi M'ragh*–class boats bought by Malaysia. The 5.2-kg rocket reaches a maximum altitude of 100 m at 300m range (4.426 sec after firing) and falls into the water at about 560 m (9 sec after launch). Bursting at 80 m, it creates an 800–1200m² cloud that lasts about 2 min.

Users: Argentina (MEKO 360H2 class, supplemented by Dagaie), Denmark (*Nils Juel* class, possibly not installed), Ecuador (*Wadi M'ragh* class), Italy (*Garibaldi, Vittorio Veneto, Audace, Maestrale, Lupo, San Giorgio* classes, *Stromboli* and *Etna* class AOR), Nigeria (*Aradu*), Peru (*Lupo* class), Turkey (FRAM destroyers and *Koln*-class frigates), and Venezuela (*Lupo* class). Reportedly in 1994 the Italian navy decided to standardize on NATO Sea Gnat and thus to abandon SCLAR. Similar considerations apparently led the German navy to abandon plans for SCLAR in the *Brandenburg* class.

JAPAN

The earliest modern Japanese naval EW systems were based on the U.S. BLR-1 scanning superhet system.

The somewhat later NOLR-1A and -1B were comparable to the U.S. scanning superhet WLR-1 system. NOLR-5, which is

EW systems on board the Japanese destroyer *Asagiri*. The masthead radar is OPS-28, the cruise-missile detector analogous to the U.S. TAS Mk 23; OPS-28 is used in conjunction with the radome-enclosed FCS 2-12E aft, which controls the Sea Sparrow (launcher on the stern). The fire-control radar forward is FCS 2-21A, and the air-search radar is OPS-14C. NOLR-6 combines equipment on both masts. (JMSDF)

EW systems of the missile destroyer *Hatakaze*. NOLQ-1 combines the masthead array, the antenna just forward of the main air-search radar (SPS-52C), and the flat array at the base of the big lattice mast. The 2D radar aft is OPS-11C, and the slotted array at the masthead is the OPS-28B antisea-skimmer set. (JMSDF)

probably equivalent to later versions of WLR-1 (e.g., WLR-1G), was a successor on board some frigates. It used a radome-enclosed antenna. ZLR-4/6, on submarines, is reportedly very similar to WLR-1G.

OLR-9 mainmast array (at maintop) and NOLR-6 mainmast array (radomes on platform) on board the destroyer *Amagiri*. The position of the cylindrical radomes varies among units of the class. The big radome is for Sea Sparrow fire control (FCS 2-12E). (*Sea Power*)

The big radome just above the Phalanx on board the *Amagiri* is an OLT-3 jammer (another is just visible on the other side of the ship). Somewhat similar radomes, aft on board older ships, are U.S.-type DF spinners. (*Sea Power*)

NOLQ-1 arrays on board the destroyer *Haruna*, with an OPS-11C radar above them. They presumably correspond to the lens antennas of SLQ-32. (*Sea Power*)

Two Japanese missile hydrofoils, PG-01 and PG-02, display ESM pots at their mastheads. No designations have been released, but these are probably Sanders SR-200s like those on the Peruvian PR-72s. (*Ships of the World*)

There was also a widely used OLR-3, a four-channel crystal video set (for 2–10 GHz) probably derived from contemporary U.S. airborne ESM sets used by ASW aircraft, such as the Tracker and Neptune (both of which entered Japanese service). It was installed in some destroyers sometime between 1958 and 1963. OLR-3A was later widely installed. Other OLRs (such as OLR-9) probably also use CVRs.

All of the earliest systems were limited to a maximum of 11 GHz, and were obsolete by the mid-1970s, as the threat (mainly antiship missile seekers) moved up in frequency toward 18 GHz.

As in the U.S. Navy, the next stage was an electronically scanned (in frequency) SHR, NOLR-6 (very similar to WLR-8), which appeared in the early 1970s, and covered the spectrum up to 18 GHz. It used a pair of rotating DF antennas to cover the radar bands, plus a circular dipole array on the foretop for DF in the V/UHF band. The corresponding submarine system is ZLR-3/5. OLR-9 is apparently the corresponding wide-open missile warning system, equivalent to the U.S. WLR-11. Frigates and destroyers mount OLR-9 with NOLR-6. Submarines carry both ZLR-3/5 and ZLR-4/6.

NOLR-8 replaced NOLR-6/OLR-9 beginning in JFY88, and is standard in ships built after JFY90 which do not have NOLQ-1.

The next-generation submarine system is NZLR-1 (submarines built after JFY88).

NOLQ-1, introduced in 1980, employs an IFM-based ESM element and a scanning SHR plus two OLT-2 jammers; it is similar in capability to the U.S. SLQ-32(V)2, for missile and helicopter destroyers. Typically it is combined with a separate deception jammer, OLT-3, and with Mk 36 decoy launchers. OLT-3, which is reportedly very similar to SLQ-17, is also used with the NOLR-6/OLR-9 combination.

NOLQ-2 (*Kongo* class) integrates the ESM set with the OLT-3 jammer and 4 × 130mm chaff launchers.

Note that there is no domestic patrol airplane system (P-2Js had HLR-101). SH-60Js have HLR-108. It is not clear whether it is closely related to the surface ship systems (in analogy to the relationship between ALR-142 and SLQ-32 in U.S. ships). The system in Japanese EP-3s is by NEC and Mitsubishi.

Some additional equipments are:

OPN-7B is a broad-frequency VHF/DF.
OPN-11 is a high-precision RDF (HF and VHF).
OLT-5 is a deception jammer.

KOREA

◆ ULQ-11K and -12K

These ECM sets for corvettes (four have ULQ-11K) and frigates (-12 on 18 *Donghaes*) are derived from ARGO Phoenix systems;

Commissioned in 1990, the escort *Abukuma* shows a new ECM suite that includes a pair of lens antennas on a platform above her forward fire-control radar. This combination is presumably NOLR-8. (*Ships of the World*)

some were sold to Korea by ARGO under the company's "Kodak" program.

NETHERLANDS

Systems are listed here because they were developed by Signaal. They were transferred to the British MEL company (which, with Signaal, was part of the Philips group) in 1985; Racal later bought the Thorn-EMI ECM division, which bought MEL in 1989 (MEL Canada was bought by Lockheed Sanders).

The S–Ku-band ESM system in the *Zwaardvis*-class submarines (now for sale) is designated SPR-06/00, using a BRR-05/00

The Korean frigate *Masan* (955) displays the antennas of her ULQ-11K system: an ARGO-style ESM pot above her bridge plus two jammers (in dark radomes) on either side of her tower foremast. The object just abaft the ESM pot is a Radamec EO director. Note the depth charge rails aft (six charges each), an unusual feature in a modern warship, but useful in shallow water. The light AA guns are Emerlec 30s. (*Ships of the World*)

receiver and an EIS-1 classifier. The system monitors all bands, but must be set to analyze in only one at a time (frequency, PRF, pulse width). It is not clear whether this is the AR-700 with which the class is usually credited.

♦ Ramses/Scimitar

Signaal's I/J-band Reprogrammable Advanced Multimode Shipborne ECM System uses a vertical pair of egg-shaped radomes on each side of the ship (350 mm dia × 1100 mm, 25 kg each). Each radome carries an identical Luneberg lens antenna; one of each pair tracks the threat the other jams. Because tracking and jamming antennas are well separated, there is no need to pause for look-through while jamming. Each pair operates independently, so two targets (one on each side) can be jammed simultaneously, each using one of a pair of TWTs in the RF cabinet, fed by one of two function generators in the processing cabinet (alternatively, both TWTs can be used against one threat while a jamming sequence for a second threat is set up). Both pulsed (deception) and noise jamming are available. Signaal claims that noise can be effective against target acquisition radars at ranges as great as 200 km.

Ramses on board NCSM *Toronto*. Note the baffles protecting the tracker from spillover from the jammer. (S. Slade, DMS/Forecast International)

A tracker slewed onto the designated threat bearing searches a small area for a signal matching the expected target signal in its own library. A tracker lock-on triggers a preprogrammed response, the waveform for which is produced by function generators in the processing cabinet.

Scimitar is a NATO version of Ramses, operating in the 8–16-GHz band to deal with missile seekers and target-indication radars. Power output is 1.0 kW in pulse mode and 100 W in CW mode, later increased to 1.5 kW and 150 W. Scimitar can jam several radars (with different characteristics) simultaneously, as long as they are all in its beam; presumably it has more TWTs and function generators than Ramses. Beamwidth (presumably identical to that of Ramses) is 7 × 7 deg (gain 23 dB); sensitivity is 60 dBm.

Users:

Ramses: Canada (modified version, as SLQ-503, in "City" class), Colombia (FS 1500–class frigates), Greece (*Kortenaers*), Malaysia (FS 1500–class frigates), Netherlands (as SLQ-02: *van Heemskerck*, *Kortenaer*-class frigates), Turkey (first group of *Yavuz*-class frigates, *Koln* class). An order to equip the Argentine MEKO 140 frigates was canceled because of the Falklands War. SLQ-503 operates with the Shinpads CDS, fed by CANEWS.

Scimitar: Argentina (*25 de Mayo*, MEKO 360 destroyers), Colombia (FS 1500 class), Malaysia (FS 1500 class and *Lekiu*-class frigates), Netherlands (*Tromp* class), Peru (*Almirante Grau*). The Peruvian installation may not have been completed for financial reasons. The Chinese Luhu-class destroyer *Harbin* appears to carry Scimitar.

♦ Sphinx/Rapids

Signaal's 1–18-GHz Sphinx (System for Passive Handling of Intercepted X-missions) apparently employs the same antenna as the A2 version of the contemporary MEL Susie, which uses a less capable processor. Signaal almost certainly originated the idea of wrapping the eight-port DF antenna around the base of its "egg." The three omnis are at the masthead. Each sector of the DF antenna has five antennas, including a horizontal cone. Bearing array diameter is 2.156 m (height 1.189 m, weight 560 kg). Frequency aerial diameters × heights: 250 × 268 mm, 185 × 251 mm, 357 × 335 mm, 610 × 415 mm, and 280 × 470 mm (one large cylinder and two pairs of smaller ones, all with vertical axes). Vertical coverage is 40 deg. Sensitivity: −65 dBm for the IFM, −40 dBm (37 dBm in J-band) for the bearing antenna (−65 dBm for the high-sensitivity bearing antenna). Dynamic range is 65 dB. Frequency is measured with 0.125% accuracy, and bearing to within 4.5 deg (5.5 deg for the high-sensitivity mode). Resolution: 5–10 MHz and 1.4 deg. Measurable pulse width is between 0.1 and 100 microsec, PRF between 100 Hz and 56 kHz, and scan period between 0.1 and 80 sec. Signals are divided into three strength levels.

The Dutch frigate *Van Kinsbergen* shows a Sphinx DF array around her foremast, under the egg-shaped radome of her Signaal WM25. The mast above carries the characteristic triplet of omni antennas for the system's IFM: one large cylinder (foreground), one small cylinder with a cone above (on the yard facing away from the view), and (on the yard facing forward) one small cylinder with a smaller one below it. The small cylinder lower down the mast is an Elettronica omni jammer. The surface-search radar is ZW-08. (L. van Ginderen)

The associated computer is SMR-4. Processing time is about 2.5 microsec per pulse (equivalent to 400,000 pps). Sphinx can track 14 signals, and can lock onto three of them. It can be provided with 12 preprogrammed threat warning channels. Sphinx automatically warns of radar lock-ons. It can blank out selected signals. The system's digital output can be passed to a CDS or an ECM system such as Ramses. There are three displays: a circular CRT (situation display) shows bearing versus frequency. Two alphanumeric displays show pulse-analyzer output and emitter identification.

Sphinx first appeared on board the Dutch Standard frigates, the first of which entered service in 1978.

Rapids (Radar Passive Identification System) was a next-generation successor, using an SR-MU computer with additional bearing and frequency analysis racks, and a cursive, rather than analog, display. MEL, which later marketed the system, claimed that it was descended from CANEWS. The 2–18-GHz spectrum is divided into four bands (2–4, 4–8, 8–12, 12–18 GHz). The bearing-frequency display has alphanumeric information alongside (radar track number, name, threat level, confidence level, function, category, platform, geographical position, scan type, minimum and maximum frequency, minimum and maximum PRF, mean pulse width, mean bearing, scan period, amplitude level, frequency agility indication, pulse jitter indication). Rapids is controlled by soft keys (on the display) and by a light pen.

The Dutch *van Heemskerck*–class missile frigates use a DF antenna similar to that of Sphinx. Bearing accuracy is probably 3.5 deg at 8–18 GHz; frequency accuracy is 5 MHz. Another version, in Turkish MEKO frigates and in Malaysian FS 1500–type frigates, uses the Anaren DESM antenna also used in Cutlass B1. The last two Turkish frigates use Cutlass B1. In this version, bearing accuracy (in free space) is 3 deg. Sensitivity in both versions is 60 dBm at 2–7.5 GHz, and 55 dBm at 7.5–18 GHz. As described in 1984, Rapids could track 10 signals, lock onto three of them, and threat warning capacity was six signals. Library capacity (presumably since increased) was 256 complex radars (64 platforms).

Users:

Sphinx: Argentina (*25 de Mayo*, MEKO 360 destroyers), Greece (*Kortenaer* class), Netherlands (*Tromp*, *van Heemskerck*, *Kortenaer* classes, also *Karel Doorman*, *Tjerk Hiddes*, *van Amstel*, *Willem van der Zaan* of *Doorman* class).

Rapids: Malaysia (FS 1500 class), Turkey (*Yavuz* class, with Ramses). The Chinese Luhu-class destroyer *Harbin* is apparently equipped with Rapids.

NORWAY

The sole specialized EW manufacturer, Nera A/S, abandoned this field in 1979, but the systems listed below are still in service.

◆ SR-1A and VR-1B/C

Nera's systems all cover the 2.5–18-GHz range, using four-port antennas (separate horns for vertical and horizontal polarization) in two bands: E-band to low J-band and upper J-band. The system is wide open: a two-gun CRT uses logarithmic time scales to display the entire range of PRFs (200 Hz to 10 kHz) and pulse widths (0.15- or 0.2–10 microsec) for identification. SR-1A adds a radome-covered dish (bearing accuracy 3.5 deg, rather than the 22.5 deg of the fixed ports) with its own CRT (showing a deflection pattern of multiple radial lines corresponding to the spinner's rotation, the longest giving the direction of the emitter; data can be read off as either true or relative bearing). The spinner can rotate at up to 500 rpm, the speed varying automatically to avoid synchonizing rotation with that of the transmitting antenna (and thus losing all signals).

SR-1A was probably developed in the 1970s specifically for the Norwegian missile boats and for German Exocet-firing fast-attack boats (Type 143 and variants); in the latter it was carried in a masthead radome. The earlier torpedo-firing Type 148 used the French DR 2000, which did not provide sufficiently precise bearings. This system was also installed on board *Oslo*-class frigates, presumably when they were fitted with Penguin missiles. It has since been removed from both types.

VR-1B is for submarines; -1C is the equivalent system for torpedo boats. Nera also produced a broad-band omni submarine radar warner, NE-10A, which was probably installed in conjunction with VR-1B. It covered the 2.5–11-GHz range, and gave an audible warning whenever it received a pulsed radar signal.

Users:

SR-1A: Norway (*Hauk*, *Snogg*, *Storm* classes).

VR-1B: Norway (*Kinn*, *Svenner*, *Utsira*, *Utstein*) and Spain (*Daphne* class).

VR-1C: Greece (*Jaguar* class). This system was bought by the Germans for *Zobel*-class torpedo boats.

POLAND

The first Polish-developed decoy system, Przpiorka, employed a standard helicopter-type Mars-4M 57mm rocket pod. It was installed on board the minesweeper *Tur* and the landing ship *Studzianki*. Both were out of service by 1991. The next step was a 70mm chaff mortar (Derkacz, in a fixed 12-barrel [3 × 4] mounting), total 63 kg, 530 × 360 × 475 mm. It was intended for Project 767 (*Lublin* class) amphibious ships; typically four mounts were placed together. The next version, Derkacz-2, com-

prised the fixed Dergacz (in somewhat enlarged form, 82 kg, 1230 × 585 × 510 mm) plus a single trainable 57mm rocket launcher (total weight 535 kg, 1445 × 1333 × 930 mm, carrying four [2 × 2] eight-barreled pods). The launcher covered a 290-deg sector, training and elevating at 40 deg/sec. It was placed on board the fast-attack boats (*Sassnitz* type) *Orkan* and *Piorun* (on the fantail). The triggering mast-mounted RWR is ORO-1, with two faces (at right angles) on each side. The next-generation system, Jastrzab, combines 81mm mortars (in 3 × 3 launchers, 60 kg, 524 × 500 × 322 mm, three on each side, 1.5–3.0-kg projectile, range 40–100 m), with 122mm rockets (pedestal carrying two arms, each with three frame launchers in a vertical line above it, and two below: 535 kg, 1733 × 1675 × 830 mm, train rate 0–40 deg/sec, elevation rate 0–20 deg/sec, training accuracy 0.35 deg, 10.0–12.2-kg projectiles [payloads 3.3–8.6 kg], effective range 800–2500 m [theoretical range 6300 m]). This system is designed to defeat EO as well as radar-guided weapons. Thus decoy types include chaff, IR, antilaser, and anti-EO (parachute or persistent smoke rounds). The triggering receiver is ORLO, which detects laser radiation as well as radar pulses. Projectiles are designated S00-81 and S00-122. This system was tested on board the frigate *Kaszub*, replacing Russian-type PK-16s, and was tested on board *Orkan* early in 1995.

RUSSIA

EW R&D is conducted by the Pleshakov Scientific and Technical Corporation (GosCNRTI) of Moscow. Some systems may be manufactured by Fazotron. Major airborne jamming systems often had flower names, such as Gardeniya.

Ships with central computers ("second captains") reportedly use them to process ESM data (e.g., for signal identification). Some Western systems, such as the airborne ALQ-78, had a similar architecture. The central tactical computer keeps track of jamming, decoy launching, and own-ship radar operation, to avoid mutual interference as it prioritizes tactical responses.

Many radars (e.g., Plank Shave, Strut Pair) can take precise ESM cuts for targeting, after which a very few pulses will be sent for precise ranging. They do not rotate quickly enough to search for signals.

In 1995 new small-ship and large-ship (2000 to 10,000 t) defensive suites, Vympel-R2 and Sprint, were reported.

Many export units were fitted with aircraft RWRs (SPO-2, SPO-3M). Reportedly they proved inadequate in Russian naval service, despite attempts to upgrade them.

Systems are divided into generations. The first, Nakat (Stop Light/Watch Dog), was derived from wartime German submarine RWR practice. The next stage was a simple jammer, Top Hat (Krab). The second generation integrated ESM and ECM in systems such as Side Globes (MP-403 Gorzuf) and Bell Shroud/ Bell Squat (MP-401). A typical third-generation system is Wine Flask (MP-405).

To make matters more confusing, it now appears that the same antenna can be used by several different systems, and that the same system can use a variety of antennas. Too, the wide-beam search systems associated with many jammers have not, apparently, been identified.

Note that Bell Crown, Bell Strike, Bell Thumb, and Fig Jar, often listed as ECM, are all data-link antennas.

◆ Amber Light

Reported submarine self-protection deception jammer, for use by a surfaced submarine (which would not be vulnerable to many ASW torpedoes, but might be attacked by radar-guided missiles). On Akula and Sierra classes. This set is carried with Rim Hat. This may actually be a radar/ESM combination used to ensure security when surfacing. See MPRK-60 in the addendum below.

◆ Bald Head/Squid Head

ESM in Alfa- and "Oscar"-class submarines, integrated with the Snoop Head search radar. Compared to the later Rim Hat, Bald Head lacks any separate RWR array; presumably the idea was to use the main ELINT spirals for both warning and ESM. Combining the radar and ESM masts reduces radar signature because the

Masts of an "Oscar"-class missile submarine: left to right, they are HF communications, Snoop Head/Bald Head (radar/ESM), Shot Gun (VHF/UHF communications), Park Lamp (VLF/LF receiver), and Pert Spring (satellite navigation).

two masts tend to create reinforcing echoes. This set is carried with Brick Pulp.

Squid Head is Bald Head plus the directional CVR antennas (for RWR) of Rim Hat. In some classes it replaced Stop Light. Presumably the main ESM system was not suitable for warning. Directional warning would have been necessary for submarines operating in a formation; otherwise, none of them would have been able to use radar for ranging, since omni warners would have picked up the transmissions, causing the submarines to dive. Hence the need for directional warners here and in Stop Light C, presumably associated with group tactics. Squid Head can be distinguished from Brick Pulp by its smaller overall size and by the array of cavity-backed spiral antennas at its lower edge. Installations: Tangos (Stop Light in early units), Russian

Squid Head (1) ESM antenna on board a Tango-class submarine. Antenna (2) is Quad Loop, a radio DF (the very similar Park Lamp, which has more loops, is a VLF/LF receiver). (3) is an HF whip and (4) is a periscope. (Sea Power)

Kilos, "Echo IV"'s. Squid Head may have replaced Stop Light C in the India class, now discarded.

◆ Bell Clout/Bell Slam/Bell Nest (Zaliv)/Brick Pulp (Zaliv-P) and Bell Bash/Bell Thump/Flat Track

Zaliv is the monopulse DF system associated with the Side Globes jammer (the Kynda class, now extinct, was unique in having Zaliv [MRP-11 and -14] but not Side Globes). Bell Clout/Bell Slam are the radomes of MRP-11 and -12, operating at 2.9–5.7 and 5.6–12.9 cm. Bell Bash/Bell Thump replaced Bell Clout/Bell Slam in later Kiev-class carriers and in some Kirov-class cruisers. Two Bell Thumps (mounted between the upper and lower Side Globes pairs) house antennas for MRP-11 and -12, replacing Bell Clout and Bell Slam. Each also has a small antenna, probably a set-on omni for the system. The pair of Bell Bashes (MRP-13) below the lower Side Globes pair presumably extend frequency coverage to Ku-band, so these three units cover about 2–18 GHz. It is possible that one of the two radomes covers a Ku-band jammer directed by the antenna in the other Bell Bash radome. In ships with Wine Flask, a Bell Bash/Bell

The Admiral Nakhimov (ex-Kalinin) shows the successor system to Zaliv. Wine Glass radomes (passive missile targeting) flank Bell Thump and Bell Bash; the radome in the middle is probably the Bell Crown data link. Bell Bash and Bell Thump have very similar radomes, but the structure under Bell Thump is taller. (Royal Navy)

Zaliv is shown on a Russian auxiliary. Almost hidden to the left is Bell Slam; to its right are Bell Tap and Bell Clout; the small radome on the mast is Shot Rock (communications). (Royal Navy)

Thump pair is assigned to each jammer (two Wine Flasks to a side of a ship).

MRP-14 and MRP-15 completed an extension up to 40 GHz and down to 0.5 GHz. The high-end unit (presumably MRP-14) is the array of spirals at the bottom of Bell Nip (see separate entry). Flat Track (presumably MRP-15), the low-end unit, too large to be covered by a radome, is a flat array of cavity-backed spirals, one on each of its three panels, angled like the sides of an octagon, each side covering a 60-deg sector. The arrays are paired vertically. Development was apparently protracted. Because both Flat Track and Bell Nip use vertically paired spirals to overcome multipath problems, it seems likely that similar techniques are used in earlier elements of the system.

The carrier *Kuznetsov* has a new, more highly integrated EW system. The large flat-faced housing with three flat circular (cavity-backed spiral) antennas is Flat Track. Atop it are a pair of Wine Flask jammers, each atop its EMS array (with monopulse DF antennas). Between the two Wine Flasks are two Bell Pushes, arranged vertically. The platform above carries the Bell Crown data-link antenna. The two large radomes below Flat Track are Wine Glass ESM sets for OTH-T (they replace the earlier Rum Tub). No NATO nickname has been reported for the two smaller antennas outboard; they may be K-band deception jammers cued by Flat Track. (Royal Navy)

This detail view of the *Kuznetsov* shows the Wine Glass (formerly Football B) and the probable K-band jammers more clearly (Flat Track is above them). (Royal Navy)

Bell Nest is a special high-end antenna (probably a version of MRP-12 or -13) carried by "Nanuchkas," which also have Bell Tap.

Dimensions (diameter × height, upper/lower) are: Bell Clout, 0.8 × 1.0/0.6 × 0.8; Bell Slam, 0.5 × 0.5/0.4 × 0.4; Bell Bash, 0.6 × 0.7 m; Bell Thump, 0.6 × 0.75 (plus a small radome less than 0.2 m in diameter alongside it, which presumably replaces Bell Tap as jammer set-on receiver); Bell Nest, 1.2 m total height.

Brick Pulp (Zaliv-P) is a submarine passive threat-intercept and -warning system delivered from the late 1960s on, beginning with the "Victor" and "Charlie" classes. The antenna is a cleaned-up and enlarged Stop Light B, with the same pimple for omni RWR. It is probably an enlarged Bald Head (including lower-frequency elements) plus an omni warner, presumably too tall to accommodate any integrated search radar. This system introduced spiral (vice horn) antennas for its CVRs. Since they have lower gain, the subsitution would imply the use of better amplifiers.

The previously reported Brick Group does not exist; its previously reported Brick Spit element was a misidentified snorkel head.

Users:

Bell Slam/Bell Clout: Russia (Kara, "Kashin" [Bell Slam only] classes).
Bell Bash/Bell Thump: Russia (*Gorshkov, Kirov* [*Admiral Nakhimov, Petr Velikiy*] class); was in *Novorossiysk, Minsk,* now stricken).
Bell Nest: Russia (some "Nanuchka" class).
Flat Track: Russia (*Kuznetsov*).
Brick Pulp (Zaliv-P): "Charlie I/II," "Echo III," "Echo V" (Echo modified for special operations), export Kilos (for Algeria, India, Iran, Libya, Poland, and Romania, and probably also China), "Victor I/II/III," Delta I/II/III/IV, "Papa" (now discarded). In Delta I/II, Brick Pulp was supplemented by Squid Head.

◆ Bell Nip (Kursk)/Bell Push

Bell Nip extends MP-403 down to K-band. Each of its pair of cones (presumably for Ku- and Ka-bands) sits atop a cylinder carrying two rows of spirals; the outputs of vertical pairs of spirals are combined to overcome multipath (due to reflection off the sea). That is particularly important to counter sea-skimming missiles. Each cone contains an omni receiver in its top, feeding a frequency-memory loop that the antenna below uses to transmit deception signals. In *Slavas*, Rum Tub, which is usually used for OTH-T, cues Side Globes; Bell Nip is mounted between the pair of Rum Tub antennas.

Bell Push, in the carrier *Kuznetsov*, is a pair of truncated cones, presumably equivalent to the omni and transmitter elements. This system was developed by Fazotron.

Users:

Bell Nip: Russia (*Admiral Gorshkov, Admiral Nakhimov, Petr Velikiy* [*Kirov* class], *Slava* class)
Bell Push: Russia (*Kuznetsov*)

◆ Bell Shroud/Bell Squat (MP-401 Start)

This small ship (destroyer/frigate) combination was designed to deal with the new (1960s) threat of Ku-band aircraft radars, for example, aboard A-6s. Compared to Bizan/Krab, Start offered a wider frequency range (reception in X- and Ku-bands, jamming in X-band), more jamming power (mean power over 1 kW), and better measurement of radar parameters (due to the addition of an IFM). The IFM was needed to control the PK-16 chaff launcher. Because it could measure frequency precisely, Start was used for electronic reconnaissance. Bearing accuracy was 15 deg. The system required two operators. It first appeared on board "Kashins" modernized as "tattletales," which would have been subject to air attack in the Mediterranean; it is also on board "Krivaks," which would face Tornadoes and Buccaneers in the North Sea and the Norwegian Sea. The usual outfit is two Bell Shroud for four Bell Squat. Bell Shroud is essentially Watch Dog with two additional rows of ports for monopulse DF of higher-frequency signals. Bell Squat contains a rotating antenna on top of a square flat plinth: thus it can deal with only one target at a time. In analogy to Top Hat, Bell Squat radomes presumably house separate air- and surface-jammer antennas. They are not externally distinguishable. The two Bell Squat radomes, one with a dimple on top and one flat, differ only because they were cast by two different factories, using different techniques. Approximate dimensions: Bell Shroud, 1.7 × 1.2 m; Bell Squat, 0.6 × 0.4 m.

The *Sovremennyy*-class destroyer *Boyevoy* shows a Wine Glass jammer with, below it, the two components of Bell Shroud. In most ships the small radome, with its bulb, is mounted above the large shroud. (S. Zaloga)

Bell Squat on the yard of the *Udaloy*-class missile destroyer *Admiral Vinogradov*, 1990. (S. Zaloga)

The current MP-401S version covers four radar bands using one active jammer. DF accuracy is 7.5 deg, and the system requires five personnel.

Users: Poland ("Kashin"-class destroyer), Russia (*Sovremennyy*, *Udaloy*, "Kashin"-mod, Krivak, *Ivan Rogov*, *Berezina*, and *Aleksandr Brykin* [missile transport]).

◆ Bell Tap

Bell Tap is a broad-band broad-beam (1.8–5.7 cm [roughly 5–18 GHz], 30–40 × 50–60 deg, sensitivity −65 dBW) radar warner and also a set-on search receiver for MP-403 (Side Globes) jammers. At least initially it had only an analog (directional and pulse analyzer) output. Dimensions: 0.4 × 0.3/0.25 × 0.3 m. The Chinese BM/HZ 8610 is a derivative using a much more directional antenna array and a digital processor (see separate entry). Note that, combined with Watch Dog, Bell Tap extends frequency coverage up to about 18 GHz.

Users: Algeria ("Osa I/II," "Nanuchka II"), Angola ("Osa II," Shershen), Bulgaria ("Tarantul II," Shershen, Pauk), Cuba ("Osa I/II," Pauk), Egypt ("Osa I," Shershen), Ethiopia ("Osa II"), Finland ("Osa II"), Germany (*Sassnitz*), India ("Nanuchka II," "Tarantul I" [except Cutlass E in 4], Pauk), North Korea ("Osa I"), Libya ("Osa II," "Nanuchka II"), Poland ("Osa," "Tarantul," *Sassnitz* classes), Romania ("Osa," "Tarantul," Epitrop classes), Russia (*Kirov* [except *Admiral Nakhimov*], *Petr Velikiy*, *Slava*, Kara, "Tarantul I/II" [not III], "Nanuchka," "Osa," Alligator I/

II/III/IV, Gorya, Natya, Babochka, Muraveyev, Pauk classes), Serbia ("Osa," Shershen classes), Syria (Osa I/II class), Vietnam ("Osa," Shershen classes), Yemen ("Osa," "Tarantul I" classes). In an "Osa," Bell Tap is mounted on the mast below the Square Head IFF antennas. In export "Nanuchkas," Bell Tap is mounted inside the Band Stand radome.

◆ Half Cup (Spektr-F)

IR laser warner detector array first seen in the *Udaloy* class (ships have four). This is probably the L-082 Mak array seen on a Backfire bomber (missile warner). It has 48 ports in a lower ring, with five rings spaced up the dome, to provide both bearing and elevation data. A control station supports 3–12 85-kg detectors; claimed effectiveness is 95% probability of detection of a single laser pulse. The associated countermeasure is a series of smoke bombs spaced around a ship's deck, to make laser guidance impossible; they resemble old-fashioned depth charges.

A Half Cup laser warner on the *Udaloy*-class destroyer *Admiral Vinogradov*, 1990. (S. Zaloga)

◆ Rim Hat (Kremlin-2)

An ESM system integrated with the Snoop Pair back-to-back submarine search radar. The four visible spirals at the bottom of the dome are for CVRs for radar warning. The big pot, hinged at one side (carrying the paired radar antennas), covers four tiers of spirals on a truncated cone, eight per tier, for IDF. The two Snoop Pair antennas differ; the one with the small feed is the conventional radar; the other, with a broad feed, is for data linking (for the P-100 missile) and for fine DF cuts on selected signals (accurate to within a fraction of a degree). The active elements can obtain a range on a target whose bearing is obtained by the DF cut. The paired radars nod, for example, to follow the P-100 missile. Rim Hat/Snoop Pair is associated with the 65cm torpedo tube, that is, with both the big wake-following torpedo and the P-100/SS-N-22 missile.

Users: Akula, Sierra, Typhoon classes, probably on some "Victor IIIs" (671RTMK version); reported on board Uniform and Yankee Notch classes, but that seems unlikely.

◆ Rum Tub (MP-404)

Long-range ESM set designed to target the SS-N-12 and -19 antiship missiles, using intermittent radar ducting. It probably provides the necessary signatures to the ARM versions of these missiles. Reportedly Rum Tub is based on compromised UAA-1 (British) and SLQ-17 (U.S.) technology. Rum Tub is a set of four radomes, divided into quadrants; each is split horizontally into a wider base and a narrower top, and each segment is further split into segments (five at the base, six at the top), each segment showing two square plates, one atop the other. The appearance is quite unlike that of earlier Soviet radomes. Rum Tub appeared about 1974; it was initially installed on board the first three *Kiev*-class carriers and the cruiser *Kirov*, the *Slava* class, and then on board the modernized cruisers *Kerch* and *Petropavlovsk*. Thus it is associated with the SS-N-12 and -19 missiles. Its presence aboard the two modernized cruisers (which lack long-range weapons of their own) may indicate an intention to use them as pickets (e.g., for target triangulation) to support missile-shooters. Other later Kara-class cruisers show empty platforms adapted to a radome of Rum Tub size. Wine Glass is the successor system.

Rum Tub, with Bell Nip antennas between the two quadrants. (Royal Navy)

Side Globes and Rum Tub radomes aboard the missile cruiser *Marshal Ustinov* at Norfolk, 1989, with Bell Nip (conical) radomes between the two sets of radomes (horizontally and vertically). (S. Zaloga)

In *Slavas*, Rum Tub apparently provides both OTH-T data and ESM support for Side Globes long-range jammers (there are no Bell Bashes/Thumps). Approximate dimensions: 2.1 m wide × 1.8 m high.

◆ Setka-3

This export jammer is probably related to MP-405 (Wine Flask). It can deal with eight targets simultaneously. Total power is 2.5 kW. There are two separate elements. The search set uses a four-quadrant antenna (four elements per quadrant). The jammer has a similar control antenna (also 16 elements) connected to a waveform generator and a series of amplifiers, each feeding one of eight jammer antennas (shown in a diagram as pairs at each quadrant, presumably electronically steered). Bearing accuracy is 10 deg, and reaction time is 0.1 sec. The search receiver arrays (which measure target altitude as well as bearing) for different frequency ranges are stacked vertically to form a pyramid or cone. An export X-band Sprint system for frigates (2000 to 10,000 t) may be related to Setka-3.

◆ Side Globes (MP-403 Gorzuf)

Like Krab and Start (MP-401), MP-403 was designed to deal with a combination of surface- and air-search radars and fire-control and missile-seeker radars. It could manually or automatically jam two threats simultaneously (masking, blocking, and directional jamming) tracking the target radar despite frequency agility on its part. It could also control PK-16 chaff launchers. The visible array consists of four radomes on each side of a ship, vertically paired. Each radome reportedly contains a jammer an-

tenna flanked by a pair of tracking antennas for monopulse DF. Presumably different pairs of Side Globes radomes are used for different bands. For example, the X-band element (2.95–3.6 cm, later extended to Ku-band) has a 15 × 15-deg beam and a 10–12-MHz jamming bandwidth. Bell Nip/Bell Push is probably the extension down into K-band, retained when Side Globes is replaced by Wine Flask (MP-405).

The associated search/set-on receiver is probably Bell Tap. Target direction is found by Zaliv (MRP-11/12: Bell Clout/Slam), operating in S/C- and C/X-bands, one of these monopulse DF antennas corresponding to a pair of Side Globe antennas. Carriers and *Slava*-class cruisers have one Bell Bash/Bell Thump associated with each Side Globes radome.

The system has two operators, and weighs (without antennas) 2730 kg.

Upgrades in the 1970s and 1980s provided a spectrum analysis capability (frequency measured within 1%) and interferometric DF using arrays of flat spirals (accuracy 2.5–5 deg). By this time systems combined broad-band IFMs with HF SHRs to reduce false alarms. This may refer to the use of Rum Tub (MP-404) in place of Zaliv.

The sheer size of the Side Globes radome suggests a very high gain antenna, and reportedly Soviet jammers produce very high effective radiated power (lethal to humans within 40–50 ft). Reportedly, too, the massive tower masts on which Side Globes is mounted conceal substantial cooling systems and also are intended to shield personnel from radiation. Side Globes appeared in 1967 (on board *Moskva*). Approximate dimensions: 1.8 × 2.2 m (length includes coned-in sections at base).

Gorzuf is a town in Asia. Wine Flask (MP-405) is the successor system.

Users: Russia (*Admiral Ushakov* [ex-*Kirov*], *Slava* class, Kara class).

♦ Stop Light (Nakat)/Watch Dog (Nakat-M)/Type 921-A/RW-23-1

These 1–10-GHz RWRs, which appeared about 1956, were derived from wartime German submarine practice. The antenna (probably in a version with extended frequency coverage) is an octagon with four tiers of horns, eight horns per tier (band). Reported bearing accuracy was 45 deg. Stop Light A is the basic version, offering a directional display and manual analysis, but no quick-threat warning. As a measure of its sophistication, a Foxtrot-class submarine decommissioned in 1994 had only a very simple CRT display, and its ESM library appeared to be limited to a sheet of blueprint paper listing the enemy radars to be expected in various bands (without any pulse characteristics). Stop Light B adds a dimple for an omnidirectional RWR. Stop Light C is a retrofit, in which a dome (presumably for directional RWR) replaces the dimple. The current Chinese version, Type 921-A (NATO Golf Ball), extends coverage to 2–18 GHz in four bands and substitutes transistors for the vacuum tubes of the Russian original. It offers a bearing accuracy of better than 30 deg. The solid-state control unit offers both a visual display and an audio alarm. The antenna unit is relatively bulky (56 × 61.5 cm).

Stop Light B (the A version lacks the pimple, presumably for an IFM, at the top of the array) (2) on board a Foxtrot-class submarine. The other antennas are (1) the Snoop Tray search radar, (3) the VHF whip, and (4) the HF whip. (*Sea Power*)

The name Machta has also been associated with Stop Light.

Nakat-M was the corresponding surface-ship warner, initially for *Sverdlov* and *Grozny* (Project 58, NATO Kynda) -class cruisers. Typically a ship carries one array on each side, each backed by a reflector. Watch Dog B added an omni antenna, presumably feeding a pulse analyzer (a dimple atop the cylinder).

The addition of the omni may have been connected with the use of a jammer (Top Hat). This version was probably called Bizan. Reportedly the Soviets considered the Top Hat/Watch Dog

combination equivalent to the U.S. WLR-1/3/ULQ-6. The version in a Krupny-class missile destroyer was Bizan'-4A. An improved version (presumably with the earliest Soviet digital processor) may have been installed, unsuccessfully, on the Kynda class.

The Chinese derivative, RW-23-1 (NATO Jug Pair), covers 2–18 GHz in four bands (a two-band version using six ports per band was displayed in 1987; it probably covers 6–18 GHz). Library capacity is 15 modes. The console has an operator desk, one large TV-type monitor, probably for signal analysis and tabular data, and a small PPI. Numerous operator controls suggests little automation.

Users:

Stop Light A: Albania (Whiskeys), China (Whiskeys).

Stop Light B: Algeria (Romeos), Bulgaria (Romeos), Cuba (Foxtrots), Egypt (two Romeos), India (Foxtrots), Russia ("Echo II," Foxtrot), Serbia (*Heroj*), Syria (Romeo). This system was replaced by Brick Pulp in submarines completed from the late 1960s on (Tango, "Charlie," "Victor," Yankee classes).

Type 921-A: China (Ming and Romeo classes), North Korea (Romeo class). At least in submarines exported to Egypt, this set has been replaced by other types.

Watch Dog A: Albania (T-43 class), Algeria (Polnocny class), Bulgaria (*Druzki*, Polnocny, T-43, Poti classes), Cuba (Polnocny class), Egypt (Polnocny, T-43 classes), Ethiopia (Polnocny class), Indonesia (T-43 class), Poland (Polnocny B class), Romania (Poti class), Russia (Riga, Polnocny A/B classes), Syria (Polnocny, T-43 classes), Vietnam (Polnocny), Yemen (Polnocny).

Watch Dog B: Algeria (Koni II class), Bulgaria (*Smeli*), Romania (*Marasesti*, Tetal, Cosar classes), Cuba (Koni class), Ethiopia (Petya II class), Guinea (T-58), India ("Kashin," Petya II, Polnocny classes), Libya (Koni and Polnocny classes), Poland (Polnocny C class), Russia ("Kashin I," Grisha I/II/III class, Mirka II, Petya I/II, Parchim II, Poti, Polnocny C, Polnocny B [MCM], Yurka, Ugra, Pinega, Malina, Lama, Don, Andizhan, Amga classes), Serbia (Koni I/IV), Syria (Petya III), Vietnam (Petya II/III).

RW-23-1: Bangladesh (Jianghu-class frigates), China (Luda [except 3] -class destroyers, Jianghu and "Jiangnan"-class frigates, Yukan-class LSTs, Fuqing-class AOR, T-43 class), North Korea (Wajin and Soho-class frigates), Pakistan (Fuqing-class AOR).

♦ Top Hat (Krab-11 and -12; also Gafel)

The first Soviet naval jammer appeared on board "Kynda"-class cruisers and "Kashin"-class destroyers; it was the basis for the later Side Globes system. The system incorporated a search receiver, presumably Bizan (modified Watch Dog). A separate trainable antenna (beam 25 × 25 deg) was used to locate the target radar, presumably on the basis of a coarse location by Watch Dog. The set-on element determined the number of enemy radars, their frequency, and their scan rate. The search receiver operated at 3–5.5 cm (5452–9980 MHz); the jammer operated at 3.0–3.75 cm (7997–9980 MHz). Krab was designed to deal with air- and surface-search radars, fire-control radars, aircraft-attack radars, and missile radar seekers. It could jam one target at a time. Jamming waveforms were continuous broadband noise (over a 12–20-MHz bandwidth) and modulated noise. There were two jamming antennas (presumably corresponding to Top Hat A and B radomes): one for surface targets (beamwidth 25 deg, gain 40 dB), and one for air targets (beamwidth 50 deg, gain 12 dB). Jamming power was 600 W, offering a theoretical range of less than 40 km against air targets. Reaction time was 60 sec. Radome dimensions: 0.4 × 0.36 and 0.58 × 0.54 m.

Top Hat can be recognized by its squared-off appearance, as contrasted with the rounded shape of Bell-series radomes.

Users: India ("Kashin," Polnocny classes), Libya (Polnocny [Top Hat A only]). With the retirement of *Moskva*, this system is now extinct in Russia. The carriers *Kiev* and *Novorossiysk*, now discarded, were sometimes incorrectly credited with four

Top Hat A and four Top Hat B radomes (they had Bell Thump and Bell Bash).

◆ Wine Flask (formerly Modified Football)/Wine Glass (formerly Football)/Half Hat (MP-405) and MP-407

MP-405 is the electronically steered modular successor to both Start (MP-401) and the Zaliv/Side Globes (MP-403) combination. It was the first Russian jammer able to generate continuous and randomly interrupted jamming signals, controlled in the 0.5–1.5-sec range. Waveforms: broad-band noise, repeater (deception), and combined (masker spot). Separate elements of this modular system (MP-405-I, -II, and -III) cover the Ku-, X-, and C-bands, each in four sub-bands. In small ships Half Hat is the ESM element and Wine Glass is the jammer. Each Wine Glass covers 15 × 30 deg with a mean power of 500–600 W. Reportedly the radome covers three flat phased arrays, each covering a 60-deg arc. The system is operated by two personnel (ESM situation and jammer control).

MP-407 also uses the Wine Glass radome for its jammer (it is not clear what the passive element uses). Techniques are repeater, masker, simulator, spot, and barrage. It is operated by three personnel.

Large ships combine Wine Flask and Wine Glass. Each Wine Flask radome covers a stack of four cylindrical antennas, the topmost of which is probably the broad-beam set-on element (30–40 × 50–60-deg beam). Each of the others shows two rows of antenna ports, presumably to provide limited vertical beam-steering. The four antennas on each side of a carrier are paired horizontally (with Bell Nip between them) and vertically, one vertical pair at each corner of a tower mast. Each jammer array sits atop an interferometric DF array, presumably MRP-11M-12M. Approximate Wine Flask dimensions: 0.6 × 1.2 m.

The main mast of *Neustrashimmyy* (1995) shows Half Hat above Wine Glass. Presumably the antennas on the yardarms are for data links. (H. & L. van Ginderen)

Wine Flask, the current jammer, is shown clearly on board the carrier *Admiral Gorshkov* (ex-*Baku*). The object next to it is the larger of two Bell Pushes, which appear to be the innards of Bell Nip (without the conical radomes). A second Wine Flask is barely visible to the left of the Bell Push. The pair of radomes (large and very small) at middle left is Bell Thump; a Side Globes radome is visible below it. (Royal Navy)

The carrier *Admiral Gorshkov* shows four Wine Glass jammers, on the two big platforms. Above the upper platform is one carrying Bell Thump and Bell Bash; a similar pair is outboard of the two Wine Glasses on the lower main platform. Above the upper platform is one carrying two Wine Flask jammers with Bell Push between them. Bell Bash/Bell Thump are the ESM associated with the jammers. This is an intermediate step leading toward the integrated system (ESM below jammer) in the *Kuznetsov*. (Royal Navy)

A Wine Glass jammer on board the *Sovremennyy*-class destroyer *Bezuderzhannyy* in 1993. At left is a Bell Squat, probably the deception jammer because it is closest to the Bell Shroud ESM array (not visible here). (Author)

MP-405 first appeared in the cruiser *Frunze*, completed in 1984, and in the carrier *Novorossiysk*. As of 1995, an improved MP-405M was being made, using existing antennas. Prior to the collapse of East Germany, MP-405 was to have been made there under license.

Users (Russia only): Half Hat: *Neustrashimyy*, sole "Nanuchka IV," all "Tarantul III," one "Tarantul I," "Dergach" class. At least some units of the following classes have it: "Nanuchka III" and "Tarantul II." Svetlyaks and Pauks may have this system, but available photographs do not show it. In a "Tarantul" or "Nanuchka III," Half Hat is mounted on a platform under the Light Bulb data-link antenna, with Wine Glass much lower.

Wine Flask: *Kuznetsov*, *Admiral Gorshkov*, *Kirov* class (except *Admiral Ushakov*), Only the carrier *Kuznetsov* has interferometric DF arrays rather than Bell Bash and Bell Thump. The entire jamming installation (modified Wine Flasks and Bell Nips) is carried on top of the upper of two Flat Tracks (which lack the higher-frequency flat arrays of the *Kuznetsov* installation).

Wine Glass: *Kuznetsov*, *Admiral Gorshkov*, *Kirov* class (except *Admiral Ushakov*), *Sovremmenny* class (except *Bezuprechnyy*, *Osmotritel'nyy*, Otchanny), later and refitted *Udaloys* (*Admiral Kharlamov*, *Admiral Levchenko*, *Admiral Pantaleyev*, *Admiral Tributs*, *Admiral Vinogradov*, *Simferopol*, in two radomes on mainmast platforms; may also be aboard *Marshal Vasilyevskiy*), *Neustrashimyy*, some "Nanuchka IIIs," sole "Nanuchka IV," "Tarantul III" class (and some "Tarantul I/II"), "Dergach" class. *Sovremmenny* was completed with four Wine Glass radomes, but the more usual complement is two, one on each side of the forward superstructure. A photograph of *Admiral Levchenko* appears to show Rum Tub on the jammer platform, with a small cylindrical radome outboard. *Sovremmennys* may have Start in addition to Wine Glass. They do not appear to have Half Hat on board.

EXPENDABLES

A spherical floating radar decoy, containing a corner reflector, is now standard in *Sovremmennys*, *Udaloys*, and Krestas. The Pacific Fleet's *Udaloy*-class destroyer that visited San Diego in 1990 had small drums (distraction decoys) located along her deck edges; they are equivalents to Rubber Duck (DLF/SLQ-49), that is, inflatable floating radar reflectors. In contrast, the short-range

chaff mortars are seduction decoys. The *Sovremennyy*-class destroyer that accompanied the *Udaloy* had no deck-edge drums, but that probably means only that the drums are new and have not yet reached all ships (they certainly are not on board all *Udaloys*). These drums are not the standard inflatable rafts common to modern Russian warships. It is not clear to what extent the drums are actually smoke generators (see Half Cup above).

◆ PK-2 (ZiF-121)

The trainable 152mm twin-tube launcher loads vertically from below decks, then trains and elevates to fire. It was conceived to fire an active decoy, not a chaff round: the firing cycle is far too slow for conventional chaff. The rocket-boosted round, which is about 1 m long, has an ogival head (in four petals) covering a parachute. Given the early state of electronic technology involved, this device was probably not particularly successful. Reportedly the Soviets preferred an active decoy to chaff on the theory that large-scale use of chaff would tend to jam their own radars. The launcher loads from below decks because such delicate devices would need heated stowage and, probably, some means of checkout. There may also be an IR decoy round, fired down into the water via what looks like a dud-disposal chute. There are also 140mm chaff (TSP-47, 36.1 kg, 7.73 kg of chaff), IR (TST-47, 37.5 kg, 2.6-kg IR decoy), and combined IR/chaff (TSO-47, 38.5 kg, 8.64-kg combined decoy) rounds, each 1.105 m long. Modes: confusion and distraction/dilution. This was the first Soviet decoy launcher, introduced in the Kara class (and then retrofitted to the "Kyndas" and Krestas), and for some time it was the only one carried.

PK-2 chaff launcher on board the cruiser *Kerch*, 1989. The chute visible to the left is used to drop duds over the side, and reportedly also to launch IR decoys into the sea. (Eric Grove)

Users: Russia (*Kuznetsov*, *Gorshkov*, *Kirov* class, *Slava* class, Kara class, *Udaloy* class, *Sovremennyy* class, *Berezina*).

◆ PK-10/KT-216

A lightweight 10-tube 120mm barrage decoy launcher is used in large numbers, to fire as many as 80 rounds at once. It first appeared in the *Udaloy* class in 1989. Rounds, currently offered by the Institute of Applied Physics Joint Stock Company of Novosibirsk are: SR-50 chaff (25.5 kg), SOM-50 IR (i.e., flare and aerosol: 25 kg), SK-50 chaff/IR (25 kg), each 1.226 m long. An RF/IR/laser/optical decoy is under development. The payload is contained in 9 to 14 packages with variable firing time. Decoys can form continuous, discrete, or compact aerosol clouds. The institute is working on smoke or aerosols to defeat optical and optronic sensors, to reflect or absorb laser radiation, to absorb low-temperature IR radiation, and to reflect or absorb RF radiation in the mm and cm ranges. One Krivak, *Bodryy*, has ten 10-

PK-16 on board the Algerian Koni-class corvette *Rais Kellik*, 1995. (H. & L. van Ginderen)

A PK-10 launcher on board the *Udaloy*-class destroyer *Admiral Vinogradov*. These launchers are also mounted horizontally. (S. Zaloga)

tube chaff launchers in place of the usual four 16-tube units. Unlike PK-2, PK-10 does not reload automatically from below decks.

Users: Russia (*Kuznetzov, Petr Velikiy, Chervonaya Ukraina, Udaloy* class, *Sovremennyy* class, *Neustrashimyy* class, modified *Krivak* class [and *Bodryy*], "Dergach" class, some "Nanuchka III" class, *Ivan Rogov* class, *Aleksandr Brykin*).

◆ PK-16

A fixed 16-tube 82mm chaff/IR decoy launcher of East German design was originally for light units; it is now mounted on board many larger ships. Rounds, all 653 mm long: TSP-60 chaff (8.3 kg) and TST-60U IR (8.5 kg). Modes: confusion and distraction/dilution.

Users: Russia (*Sderzhannyy, Neustrashimyy* class, *Krivak* I/II/III, Grisha V, "Nanuchka," "Tarantul," Pauk, "Matka," Turya, Mukha, Svetlyak, Gorya, *Ivan Rogov, Aleksandr Brykin*).

NAVAL SUPPORT ECM

As of 1996, the 120 Backfire (Tu-22M) and 80 Badger (Tu-16) bombers are supported by 75 Badger-H and -J EW aircraft and 24 Badger-A (Tu-16N) tankers. Reportedly, a typical antiship regiment of the early 1980s consisted of two strike squadrons (9–12 missile attack bombers each) and a support squadron (two to four Badger-H chaff layers, one or two Badger-J standoff jammers, and three to six Badger tankers). Without standoff jammer Backfires, these aircraft have either to fly out at subsonic speed or else to rendezvous with their subsonic Badger support aircraft.

Badger-H (Tu-16PP, postanevshchik pomiekh) carries up to 9000 kg (19,840 lb) of bulk chaff, sufficient for a 60nm-long cor-

ridor, in its bomb bay. The bomber measures the wavelengths of target radars; chaff is cut as it is dispensed. Badger-H has a pair of radomes like those of Badger-E (see below), plus a smaller radome just forward of the bomb bay; each probably houses a steerable antenna. Badger-H apparently replaced Badger-D (Tu-16Ye Yolka [fir tree], 1961), which had three steerable antennas under the bomb bay serving a threat analyzer/classifier inside, which controlled the bulk chaff cutter/dispenser at the rear of the bomb bay.

Badger-J (Tu-16P Bukiet [Bouquet]) is the complementary A-I band semiautomatic noise/deception escort jammer, using 12 receiver/jammer antennas on the nose, in a canoe under the bomb bay, in a blister immediately forward of the canoe, and usually in underwing pods. Bukiet apparently combines an SPS-22 deception jammer with an SPS-44 noise jammer. Flat-plate and podded antennas at the wingtips presumably locate emitters and monitor the effects of jamming. Some aircraft were apparently later rebuilt as ELINT platforms. Apparently Tu-16P and -16Ye were complementary programs, a total of 135 aircraft being converted (mainly from Tu-16KS missile carriers), beginning in 1961. Tu-16PP was separate.

A prototype escort jammer version of Backfire (Tu-22MP) appeared in 1992, equipped with a Miass jammer. As of 1996 it apparently had not yet entered service.

Jammers have flower names and SPS-series numbers (one- and two-digit numbers refer to sets for specialized jamming aircraft, including helicopters). Integrated systems have mountain names. Many devices also have L-numbers, for example, L-166 for a fixed-source IR jammer and L-028 for a decoy dispenser. The self-protection jammer pod for MiG-25/27 is the X-band (2.9–3.6 cm, 15W, coverage 60 deg in azimuth, 30 deg in elevation) SPS-141MVG noise ("thermal") unit, part of the first-generation SPS-130/140 Gvozdika series. The MiG-25RB has SPS-150 Lyutik. The next generation is SPS-160 Geran. For example, Fencer-D (Su-24M) has a BKO-2 Karpaty computer-controlled defensive ECM system employing an SPO-15S RWR, SPS-161/162 Geran active jammer, and APP-50A chaff/flare dispensers. The Tu-22M Ural self-protection system employs a Sirena 3 RWR, SPS-171 and -172 response (deception) jammers, AG-56 noise-jamming generator with automatic tuning, and chaff/flare dispensers. Sorbitsiya-S (probably in the SPS-170 series) is a wide-band jamming wingtip pod for the naval Su-27. It may be intended for cooperative countermeasures by several aircraft, for example to defeat monopulse systems. Gardeniya is a family of internal and podded jammers (3, 10, 20, 70 cm), an X-band version of which is used in the MiG-29. It may be related to Sorbitsiya-S and to a Shmalta podded system.

Naval electronic reconnaissance aircraft are:

An-12PPS (Cub D, first seen 1982) has very large teardrop fairings on the sides of its forward fuselage as well as a big tail fairing (replacing the tail turret) and a small radome atop the cockpit. Aircraft (eight in 1995) are, reportedly, assigned to the Baltic and Black Sea Fleets, although they have appeared over the Indian Ocean.

Il-20 Coot-A (surveillance, perhaps broadly equivalent to an EP-3): Radomes include a large canoe (10.3 × 1.2 m) under the forward fuselage for the 2cm Nit' (thread) side-looking radar, cheek radomes (about 4.4 × 0.9 m) on the forward fuselage for the phased-array Igla radar, and a twin array (probably for satellite communications) atop the fuselage just abaft the cockpit. There are probably also intercept antennas. The radars were both developed by Vega. Aircraft (14 in 1995) are assigned to the Northern and Baltic Fleets.

In 1995 the Russian navy reportedly possessed a total of 55 reconnaissance Badgers (-D, -E, -F, -K).

Badger-D (Tu-16RM: razvedchik morskoi, sea reconnaissance, first seen 1962) is a naval equivalent of Tu-16R, at least some aircraft having the big nose radome of the Down Beat missile target designation radar. The teardrop-shaped chin radome (for Puff Ball) under the nose was slightly enlarged. Two small radomes (not quite identical, for steerable antennas) were added at either end of the former bomb bay, and a larger one (somewhat larger than the chin radome) just forward of the center of the former bomb bay. Tu-16RM-2 (Badger-F, first seen January 1963) often operates with Badger-D and was probably a related program. It has a pair of large underwing radomes. Some also have the under-fuselage radomes of Badger-E; others have two large blade antennas on the lower fuselage just abaft the bomb bay (probably for the SPS-5 Fasol [bean] antisearch radar jammer), with a small radome forward of the bomb bay. Some have extra antennas over the cockpit or alongside the nose. At least one had a large tail cone replacing its tail-gun turret, presumably housing a Rezeda (reseda) or Fyalka (violet) jammer. Some have an internal noise jammer for strike support. The bomb bay may carry a camera pallet.

Badger-E (Tu-16R, introduced in the 1950s) is a modified Badger-A (bomber, with glassed-in nose) with three or four cameras on a bomb-bay pallet and a pair of radomes, fore and aft of the bomb bay, for two ELINT sensors. This and later electronic-reconnaissance or jamming versions retain the chin radome of the Badger bomber, housing an RPB-4 (Rubin 1) ground-mapping radar.

Badger-K (Tu-16Ye, 1981) differs externally from Badger-E in that its forward belly ESM radome is noticeably smaller than the after one. Some have enlarged chin radomes and/or blisters around the air intakes. The designation suggests that these aircraft are rebuilt Badger-Ds. A modified naval Badger-K (Tu-16 Azaliya, unofficially designated Badger-L, seen 1986) has a thimble radome protruding from its glassed-in nose, new blisters under the nose and around the air intakes, and a pair of under-wing pods, probably for self-protection chaff or flares. A larger flatter chin radome presumably houses a new ground-mapping radar. The radome of the Azaliya jammer replaces the tail turret.

All Blinders (Tu-22) have apparently been discarded, those in the Baltic Fleet having been replaced by 12 Fencer-Es (Su-24MR, mainly for imaging reconnaissance).

◆ **Sirena (SPB)**

Aircraft RWRs are numbered in an SPO series and are also often called Sirena (many aircraft, including the Tu-16 Badger, have Sirena 3). Most tactical aircraft, from MiG-21bis up to Su-24, have SPO-10 (6–20 GHz). Claimed accuracy is 12 deg. The system displays the type of threat and the direction of the most dangerous threat. A MiG-29 cockpit shows a small rectangular CRT or LCD above a series of lamps around the outline of a generic airplane: four to either side of dead ahead, and one to either side of the tail; six slits (probably lamps) presumably indicate threat type. The lamp display recalls early Vietnam-era U.S. RWRs. SPO-15 Beryoza (L-006) is the successor. The next-generation SPO-23 uses two or four four-beam azimuth antennas and can also use wide-angle azimuth and two elevation antennas, all to cover 4–18 GHz (elevation limits +/−30 deg) with a bearing accuracy of 10 deg. The system has a 128-threat library and weighs 18 to 30 kg. Output is digital, since it can feed a bus, such as a 1553B.

There are also dedicated ARM control units. TsKB Avtomatiki currently markets ATsU-1 and -2 pods, which detect emitters, generate target designation cues to the aircraft combat system, and use combat-system navigation data to estimate range to the target. ATsU-1 (216 kg) operates against pulsed and CW radars in one band; -2 (300 kg) handles pulsed emitters in one band and CW emitters in another. Scan zones are +/−32 × 0/−16 deg (accuracy 1 deg in bearing at over 100 km range). Each can detect up to 10 preset emitters and can cue two ARMs. There are also internal versions (SSR cueing AUTs: 2–18 GHz, +/−50 deg ARM scan zone, bearing accuracy 10 deg [3 deg at 4–18 GHz]). The SSR search receiver covers the full horizon (elevation cover +/−30 deg) with frequency resolution of 150 MHz (20 MHz in precision channel).

AIRCRAFT EXPENDABLES

Standard chaff/flare decoy calibers are 26, 50, and 140mm. A typical modern pyrotechnic dispenser, Vympel's UV26 (1985), broadly equivalent to the U.S. ALE-40, carries 64–512 × 26mm decoys, 32–256 × 50mm decoys, and 0–32 × 140mm decoys, which it fires in salvo or ripple patterns; it has 575 preprogrammed decoy-launching programs. A 128 × 26mm launcher weighs 35 kg empty. Platforms included the Yak-38M fighter, now retired. Modern bomber decoy launchers (APP-50MA/-50MR for Su-24 and UV-P1/UV-P2) are presumably comparable.

SOUTH AFRICA

The EW system of the modernized "Minister"-class fast-attack boats was developed by Grinaker Systems Technologies; the ELINT system is by Sysdel. Delcon was responsible for EW integration. A photograph of the first upgraded ship, SNS *Frederick Cresswell*, shows a Y-shaped topmast carrying small double ESM domes, with a small cylindrical radome at the split of the Y. The system covers 2–18 GHz, presumably in two bands (with sensing antennas in the small double radomes). An IFM is probably fed by omnis in the domes at the split of the Y. UEC provided the multiprocessor; the parameters are DoA, amplitude, amplitude change (to measure beamwidth), pulse width, PRF, ARP (antenna rotation period), bearing, bearing movement, frequency, and frequency shift (which would mean Doppler for an air target, or which might be used to detect frequency-hoppers). Library capacity is 20 threats (alarms), 50 possible threats, and 250 nonthreats. The ECM system can automatically sequence up to 70 decoys, and can control a total of 200. The earlier (NS-9005) noise and deception jammer antennas are apparently retained: a cylindrical omni on the radar antenna platform, and a pair of spheres on platforms below the missile guidance radar.

The ELINT system presumably uses the UHF dipoles (presumably an Adcock) on the pole mast below the Y.

Presumably the upgraded submarines (Project Orca) have a version of the same ESM system, a two-band 2–18-GHz type using the parameters listed above. The search periscope carries a radar warner (using a user-programmable threat library). The signal-intercept mast carries the DF and omni antennas of the main system in an enlarged head. Information is provided to the submarine CDS via the multifunction surface surveillance console; there is no separate ESM console. Typical warner ranges: surface ship 20 km (low band), aircraft 60 km (high band); corresponding intercept receiver ranges are, respectively, 30 and 80 km. The intercept receiver analyzes frequency (presumably using an IFM) and bearing movement.

SPAIN

Elsag Mk 1000 is apparently the Newton Gamma system in the *Descubiertas*. Mk 3000 is probably Nettunel, possibly with the U.S. S3000 added. Of new indigenous systems, Ensa's Deneb is an interface between Mk 1000 and the Tritan CDS in modernized *Baleares*-class frigates. Inisel's Kochab is a decoy launcher controller associated with Tritan.

An ELINT system, mainly for surveillance of the North African coast, was installed in a *Lazaga*-class fast-attack boat, *Alsedo*, in 1976. This equipment, which may have been an ex-U.S. Navy system, was transferred to *Alerta* (the ex-East German *Jasmund*) in 1993.

Aldebaran is associated with the Altair IR warning system being developed to control point-defense weapons, such as Meroka.

◆ Aldebaran/SLQ-380/SLQ-610/SLQ-620

Developed by the navy's CIDA research center, Aldebaran is the first entirely indigenous integrated ESM/ECM system. ESM elements are by ENSA, ECM by Inisel. Trials units (presumably breadboards built by CIDA) were delivered in 1989. ENSA's ESM element is probably EN/SLQ-610; Inisel's ECM element may be EN/SLQ-380. SLQ-380 may also be the Inisel Canopus jammer intended to replace ELT 311 and 511 on board the *Descubiertas* (under development beginning in September 1989). EN/SLQ-380 and EN/SLQ-610 operate at 2–18 GHz and are credited with -60 dB sensitivity, 8-deg DF accuracy, and a 2000-mode library. SLQ-610 can handle 800,000 pps. SLQ-610(V)2 and (V)3 probably offer better DF accuracy; (V)3 extends coverage down to 0.5 GHz. SLQ-620 is a down-rated version with 12-deg accuracy and a 1000-mode library. SLQ-610/620 is presumably intended to replace the ELT 114 and ELT 116 (Gamma) ESM element of the *Descubierta* class, and may also be selected for the *Baleares* upgrade.

◆ ALR-300/310

ENSA's (Ceselsa's) aircraft C–J-band RWR uses channelized CVRs. It can measure E–J-band (2–20 GHz) bearings to within 12 deg, using four spiral antennas; an optional omni blade antenna is used for C/D-bands (0.5–2 GHz). Signals are recognized by a microprocessor with a threat library (which can record up to 100 new signals in flight), and 15 threats can be displayed simultaneously. The (V)1 version weighs 20 kg. (V)2 adds an SHR and DIFM and a more powerful processor; weight increases to 38 kg.

ALR-310 is a simpler version for helicopters and light strike aircraft, substituting a single CVR for the channelized E-J band receiver of ALR-300. It, too, has an omni blade antenna for C/D-band (in this case, 0.7–1.5 GHz). DF accuracy is better than 15 deg, and total weight is 20 kg.

Users: Spain ([V]1 in Mirage 3, [V]2 in Mirage F1; [V]2 is to become standard in Spanish combat aircraft, presumably including the F/A-18; ALR-310 is in Spanish army helicopters).

◆ BLQ-355

Ceselsa's 2–20-GHz (five bands) ESM system is probably the version of Manta in the *Agosta* class. It employs an omni on the periscope plus a DF array. Capacity: 1M pps, 256 emitter tracks, 3000-mode library. The console has two screens, one in polar form and one showing the waveform.

◆ Elnath/SCR-390

ENSA's communications intercept/countermeasures system is probably EN/SCR-390, which uses an antenna similar to that of the Italian CO-NEWS. Elements: TSR-600 communications-band intercept receiver (SHR: scans 640 MHz/sec over 20–500 MHz [expandable to 1200 MHz], with resolution 5 kHz, sensitivity −107 dBm, and a 120-dB dynamic range); TRR-400 monitor receiver (20–500 MHz, extendable to 1200 MHz, 120 dB dynamic range, sensitivity −113 dBm, to measure signal parameters [AM, FM, SSB, CW signals]); TRX-800 signal classifier; TYK-610 special processor (68020 CPU, memory 5 Mbytes); and

TLQ-700 communications band exciter-jammer (100–500 MHz, expandable to 20–500 or 100–1200 MHz; ERP 1100 W; jamming techniques are single channel, barrier, multiple multiplexed channels, and responsive, generating AM, FM, AM and FM, FM tone, audio/data, and random noise in continuous and look-through modes; jamming can be omni or directional in one of four sectors). UYK-100 is the RISC ESM processor. All system elements interface with the SRY-1000 main computer/display, a SPARC-2 workstation (48 cm [1280 × 1024-pixel color] display, 380-Mbyte hard drive, 3.5in floppy). ENSA claims 100% probability of detection for emissions lasting 0.75 sec; its system can track up to 200 signals, correlated by time-frequency-direction. Post- processing analysis uses artificial intelligence techniques.

Users: Spain (*Principe de Asturias*), probably Thailand (*Chakkrinareubet*).

◆ Soccam/Taran

Inisel's 20–500-MHz modular COMINT/DF systems are, respectively, for surface and air platforms and use a common EW database management tool (Elios, EW ID and Operation System). Soccam (a Spanish acronym standing for adaptive modular communications observation and control system) has four monitor receivers (each with its own magnetic recorder), uses a 386 CPU (control/processing), and enjoys −100-dBm sensitivity. It demodulates AM, FM, and CW modes with 4-deg RMS DF. Multiple units can pool their data and their cuts by data link. Taran is basically an intercept version (with more limited DF); it is reportedly currently operational. It can fly on board large helicopters and medium fixed-wing aircraft such as the Falcon 20, F-27, and Bandeirante. Soccam, which may have become operational in 1993, is apparently intended for the future F100-class frigate.

SWEDEN

CelsiusTech (formerly PEAB) chaff/flare dispensers are for helicopters (BOH), for subsonic airplanes (BOP), for supersonic airplanes (BOZ), and for mounting inside an airplane's missile launcher rail (BOL). All are controlled from a dedicated data bus and have reprogrammable dispenser-program libraries. BOP 300 and BOH 300 fire standardized chaff cartridges. BOL releases its chaff like individually wrapped slices of bread. Because the dispenser is mounted in the wing, wingtip vortices help disperse the chaff. The BOZ pod is suspended from a 14- or 30in bomb rack; dimensions are 380 × 4000 mm (maximum loaded weight is 325 kg).

Users: Abu Dhabi (BOZ on Hawks), Austria (BOZ 100 on J-35s), Canada (BOL on CF-18s), Finland (BOZ on J-35s, probably BOL on F/A-18s), France (BOZ 100 on Jaguar and Mirage IV-P), Germany (BOZ 101 for Tornadoes), India (BOZ 100 on Jaguars), Italy (BOZ 102 for Tornadoes), Malaysia (BOZ on Hawks), Oman (BOZ on Hawks), Saudi Arabia (BOZ on Hawks), Singapore (presumably BOP 300 on Maritime Enforcer Mk 2, as this was the planned chaff system for that aircraft: up to eight units, each carrying two rows of three tubes each, with 16 separate dispenser programs), Spain (BOL and BOZ on F/A-18s), Sweden (BOH 300 on naval Vertol 107 helicopters [the standard box carries two triple rows of dispensers firing outboard, and one row of four dispensers firing aft], BOZ 100 pod [as BOX 9] on Viggens), Switzerland (BOL on F/A-18s), United Kingdom (BOL for Harrier GR 5 and Sea Harrier FA.2), United States (BOL as LAU-138/A [160 chaff packets] in F-14s, inside LAU-7 missile launch rails; initial contract for 290 dispensers let to Tracor in fall 1993 with another 110 ordered 1995; also on F/A-18s). BOL is also planned for the new EFA fighter.

◆ EWS 905 (PQ-859)/PQ-826

Saab-Scania's ESM/targeting system was introduced in the mid-1970s and announced in 1980. Its scanning antenna occupies a "doughnut" radome under the main search radar. Operating modes (all sector scans) are surveillance (slow scan: bearing, PRI,

The scanning dish occupies the "doughnut" visible under the slotted support. Above it (below the air search antenna) is a Susie wide-open DF array. (Saab)

pulse width, band, target scan rate displayed), alert (frequency band displayed), and decision (quick scan; bearing, PRI, and pulse width are displayed). Up to five threats can be shown simultaneously, with data on up to 50 emitters evaluated as less threatening stored for call-up. The system automatically commands chaff launchers and other self-defense measures.

Complementing the "doughnut" was a separate wide-open system (PQ-826 in Swedish naval service) served by a three-tier wide-open monopulse antenna. The two systems were linked through the ship's MARIL CDS. In the *Stockholm* class, both elements were replaced by an ARGO radome (see Phoenix below). The *Norkopping* class retained the RWR array. The *Hugin* class had only the doughnut, which they have retained.

User: Sweden (*Hugin* and *Norkopping* classes).

◆ 9CM and 9EW Series

PEAB's 9CM systems are integrated with 9LV/MARIL-series FCS/CDS systems. Each consists of a processor (ECM computer) fed by any of a variety of ESM systems, controlling a set of chaff launchers: typically Matilda/Philax (two sets of fixed launchers) for 9CM100; Rapids, Phoenix, or Cutlass with four sets of fixed Philax in 9CM200; Sceptre Lens (including a jammer) with a new eight-magazine trainable chaff launcher in 9CM300. 9CM300 employs new PEAB Luneberg lenses mounted on the fore and after surfaces of the mast (plus new omnis and laser-warning receivers). Versions incorporating a new medium-range distraction chaff rocket in fixed launchers (presumably Barricade) are denoted 9CM150, 9CM250, and 9CM350.

9EW is CelsiusTech's next-generation version integrated with 9LV Mk 3, announced 1987: 9EW300 (upgraded 9CM100) for FAC, 9EW400 (ex-9CM300) for corvettes and small frigates. This version can control a jammer.

Users: Australia (presumably 9EW400 using Sceptre-XL/SRBOC in ANZAC class), Bahrein (9EW250 in FPB 62 and TNC 45 classes), Denmark (presumably 9CM250 in *Nils Juels* and *Willemoes* classes, 9EW400 in *Flyvefisken*), Finland (9EW300 [Matilda-E/Barricade] in *Helsinki II* class, probably 9CM250 in *Helsinki*), Kuwait (probably 9CM100 in FPB 57, TNC 45 classes), New Zealand (presumably 9EW400 using Sceptre-XL/SRBOC in ANZAC class), Oman (presumably 9CM250 in "Province" class with Barricade decoy launchers), Singapore (9CM100 in *Land-*

sort class), Sweden (9CM100 in *Landsort* class and *Carlskrona*, 9CM300/9EW400 in *Goteborg* class), UAE (9CM200 in FPB 38 and TNC 45 classes), Yugoslavia (9CM100 in *Rade Koncar* class). 9CM100 was originally installed on board the Malaysian *Spica Ms* and the Swedish *Spica* class, now discarded. The Yugoslav *Kotor* class may have 9CM150. The Finnish *Hameenmaa*-class minelayers probably have 9EW300, and thus also probably have a 9LV Mk 3 CDS.

◆ YS 2000 SYSTEM

CelsiusTech is developing a 2–18-GHz EW system for the next-generation Swedish corvette (YS 2000). A lens like that of the *Goteborg* class feeds the processor developed for the Gripen fighter. About 100 amplifier-served feeders will form about 100 lobes (gain 10–20 dB, bearing accuracy about 0.5 deg, sensitivity −60 to 80 dBm). Probably the ESM lens will be mounted above a lens used for radar (PILOT) and as a broad-band data link antenna.

◆ Philax/Protean

This chaff system was developed jointly by MEL (as Protean), and also by the parent Swedish company, PEAB (now owned by CelsiusTech), as Philax. Conceived as a complement to the Matilda (Matilde) radar warner, it was first ordered for the Royal Swedish Navy in 1978 for the *Hugin* class. Each 40mm grenade weighs 0.37 kg and carries 0.175 kg of chaff. A salvo of nine grenades, fired together by a single ejection charge, gives the desired 1000m^2 RCS; each launcher has four cells (36 grenades each, total 16 such clouds). A seduction chaff cloud deploys in 5 sec at a height of 40–60 m (flight time 1 sec) and remains effective for about 20 sec. In the alternative distraction mode, flight time is 4 sec, and cloud RCS is typically greater than 300 m^2. Grenades can be made in several alternative chaff wavelengths.

Protean chaff launcher. (MEL)

Cells reload as units: total reload time is less than 1 min. Small ships carry two launchers, larger ones four. Grenades can be fired directly by Matilda, or manually on receipt of a Matilda alert.

A magazine can be replaced by three IR flare containers each holding 21 decoys (BEAB called the dual-mode system Philax 106; Philax 105 is chaff-only). The first five IR grenades form an initial decoy near the ship (about 10 m away), then two remaining groups of eight each are fired on varying trajectories, descending by parachute, to merge with the chaff cloud about 10–15 m above the sea surface. Reaction time is 2 sec, and the IR target is 150 m long. The decoy lasts about 25 sec. The IR payload is 4.5 kg, and the decoy works in both the 3–5- and 8–14-micron bands. The ammunition is made by Lacroix and Chemring.

At least 248 Philax and Protean had been produced by mid-1994; others may have been used by merchant ships during the Iran-Iraq War. This system may be license-produced in Korea. Unit cost is about $100,000.

Users:

Philax: Sweden (may survive in *Alvsborg* class and *Carlskrona*; in all others, replaced by EWS-900/Elma).

Protean: Egypt (October and *Ramadan* classes), Korea (KDX, *Ulsan*, *Donghae*, *Pohang* classes), Nigeria (*Erin'mi* class, may no longer be mounted). Protean was also reportedly sold to civilian shipowners during the Iran-Iraq War.

◆ EWS-900/900CA/900E

Saab's 40mm chaff launcher (0.38-kg rnd, carrying 0.20 kg of chaff) is now used mainly to fire Elma ASW bombs (see the ASW section). EWS-900 uses six eight-barreled launchers fired by compressed air, with two or more independent control boxes. Normally it is triggered by the ship's ECM computer (9CM/9EW system), but the extra boxes make it possible to fire chaff even if the ship's CDS is put out of action. Muzzle velocity is 70 m/sec, maximum height is 100 m, and dispersal begins in 0.6 sec. The current -900E uses four nine-barrel launchers.

Users: Finland (*Helsinki II* class), Sweden (*Goteborg* [900E], *Stockholm*, *Hugin*, *Spica II*, YSB, *Landsort* classes); probably in Singaporean *Landsort* class.

◆ Bofors Rockets

IR and chaff rockets (57 × 1385 mm, 16.5 lb, carrying 2–2.2 lb of chaff; and 103mm, carrying 5.8 lb of chaff to 10,000 m) can be fired either from flare rails rigged to Bofors gun mounts or from separate four-rail launchers. In the latter case, chaff firing is controlled by the ship's EW system; in the former, by the ship's gun FCS. Maximum velocity of the 57mm rocket is 420 m/sec (1400–1600m range at 30-deg elevation, time to bloom 30 sec; the cloud lasts at least 6 min).

Users: Bahrein (TNC 45 and FPB 38 classes [57mm launchers on deck]), Denmark (two triple 103mm rails on pilothouse in *Willemoes* class), Finland (*Helsinki II* class [rails on gun shield]), Indonesia (PSK Mk 5 class [rails on gun shield, probably 103mm]; these may also be the rails on the shields of the ex-British "Tribal" class), Kuwait (TNC 45 class), Malaysia (*Rahmat* [rails on gun shield], *Spica M* [103mm rails on gun shield], Combattante II [103mm rails on gun shield], *Jerong* class [rails, probably 103mm, on gun shield]), Singapore (Type A [57mm rails on 40mm gun shield]), Sweden (YS 2000 [gun shield], *Goteborg* [gun shield], *Stockholm* [six-cell 57mm launcher forward of bridge], *Hugin* [103mm rails on gun shield], *Spica II* [103mm rails on gun shield], *Carlskrona* [rails on gun shield], *Landsort* [rails on gun shield in some units] classes), UAE (FPB 44 class [57mm launcher on deck]). British-built ships may use a 51mm flare round, for which there is apparently no alternative decoy round.

TAIWAN

Dan Yang, a Wu-Jinn I *Gearing*, retains the U.S. WLR-1 and ULQ-6. At least some Wu-Jinn II *Gearings* (e.g., *Kai Yang*) seem to retain the AS-899A high-band element of WLR-1 and lack the WD-2A radome. They may also retain portions of the ULQ-6 jammer. Surviving WLR-1s have been modernized to cover the J-band, to deal with PRC missiles with J-band seekers (such as C801 and FL-1).

EW systems are designated in a Chang Feng (Long Wind) series:

Chang Feng I (probably formerly WD-2A) is an E-J band missile targeting/threat-warning receiver developed during the 1980s by CSIST, derived from Litton's Locator (see the U.S. section). It triggers AV-2 and SMOC-3 chaff rockets (the system designation may include the rockets). It equips at least 30 *Hai Ou*–type missile FACs and may also equip the two PSMM Mk 5 fast gunboats.

Chang Feng II (CS/SLQ-2) is a parallel destroyer system employing the Chang Feng I ESM set and the CR-201 chaff rocket (and, in some cases, AV-2). Ships carry their SLQ-2 radomes on their new lattice mainmasts. *Users:* Wu-Jinn I *Sumners* (three ships),

A Taiwanese (ROC) destroyer, firing her Hsiung Feng I missile, shows a CR-201 trainable chaff rocket launcher in the foreground. (Fu S. Mei)

the Wu-Jinn I *Gearings* (two ships) and the Wu-Jinn II *Gearings* (four ships). SLQ-2 includes a jammer.

Chang Feng III is the Wu-Jinn III (modernized *Gearing* class) EW system, integrated by CSIST. Reportedly it has not been entirely satisfactory. The ESM (including missile targeting) element is ARGO 680, using an antenna on the mainmast. The jammer is based on the Hughes Protector (MEWS/SLQ-31).

Chang Feng IV, in the *Perry* class, is probably the Raytheon Shield system; Raytheon claims that its Sidekick jammer (see the U.S. Navy SLQ-32 entry) was originally evolved to meet a Taiwan navy requirement.

AV-2/SMOC-3. Ships carry either pairs of twin Israeli AV-2 launchers or the modified SMOC-3, developed by CSIST in the 1980s (using a quadruple launcher and a different display/control unit). For details, see the Israeli section.

CS/CR-201 is the standard destroyer decoy rocket system, using four 16-tube 126mm launchers, installed in the early through mid-1980s; at least nineteen sets (four launchers each) were made. A new launcher (12 × 2 barrels) similar in appearance to the U.S. RBOC was displayed in October 1989. As in the Italian 105mm SCLAR system, there are both long-range distraction rounds and short-range break-lock rapid-bloom rounds (in this case, including IR decoys).

Chang Feng III ECM antenna on board a Taiwanese Wu Chin III destroyer, probably the *Liao Yang*, in 1992. (Fu S. Mei)

Masthead ESM radome associated with Chang Feng III, on board a Tai-wanese Wu Chin III destroyer in 1992. The large spherical radome houses a W-160 FCS antenna. (Fu S. Mei)

UNITED KINGDOM

For the Gulf War, Royal Navy helicopters (Lynx and Sea King Mk 5) were specially fitted with chaff and flare launchers. In addition, the Lynxes (which were used to attack surface units) had Yellow Veil RF jammers and Loral Challenger IR jammers.

ELECTRONIC SYSTEMS

As of 1992, the Royal Navy reportedly planned to standardize on the Thorn-EMI/MEL (now Racal) Manta/Sceptre series, for example, UAT (the program, Novation, calls for standardization in all possible areas). This program is complicated by Racal's absorption of the former Thorn-EMI EW division.

Racal is experimentally superimposing ESM and raw radar pictures on the same screen, on the theory that the two should no longer be separated in a ship's CDS. A window can display the table of emitter identifications. The company is also trying the standard Decca radar antenna as a precision ESM antenna, much as the Russians have done with many of their radars.

Racal's current (late 1996) view, which probably reflects the company's involvement in the Project Horizon frigate program, is that ESM and ELINT functions are merging, with the usual ESM identification of the type of emitter automatically supplemented by technical analysis (SEI, fingerprinting). Over the next five years systems will have to deal with the considerably worse multipath situations to be encountered close to shorelines, and they will need higher-gain antennas and more sensitive receivers, the latter mainly on the horizon (to pick up sea-skimmers). Elevation beam-shaping can improve gain. That suggests a csc^2 beam 5–10 deg wide above the horizon. As in the past, the new system will probably concentrate on 6–18 GHz. It is difficult to provide a single antenna of sufficient gain over the whole range.

Alternatives are: a vertical phased array (which encounters problems covering a broad band), a horn (which would be too large), and a horn with a controlled aperture (which can provide a gain of 17 dBi).

For the receiver, Racal's view is that the ideal is a channelized coherent receiver, in which incoming signals are matched to a variety of possible templates. That is not practical in any analog system, as the signal would have to be amplified and reproduced for each match. However, by digitizing the signal, operation is much simplified, since the digitized signal can be duplicated as often as needed. The receiver down-converts to baseband, then digitizes and feeds the digital signal into an ASIC chip. Racal's coherent channelized receiver, ZIFRA, offers as much as 6 dB improvement simply by its coherence. Channelization offers some of the sensitivity of an SHR (each channel is equivalent to an SHR). Coherent reception may be a way of detecting new long-pulse radars, such as Pilot.

Racal is prime contractor for the EW system of the Project Horizon frigate. The outcome of Project Definition Phase A (January–April 1994) was a system twice as expensive as existing ones. Phase B followed in August 1996, and as of December Racal expected a 12-month project definition contract to be awarded that month. Racal is to be responsible for radar ECM and ESM and for communications; CS Defense for EW C^2, decoy integration, and the operator interface; and Alenia for the radar ECM transmitter, CDS integration, and the EW workstation.

Racal is also responsible for ESM (F), the future suite for the follow-on carrier and the future escort. After a technology demonstration, the company expects to complete project definition by June 1997.

In submarines, the mast carrying the search periscope (often with a thermal imager) and the ESM array is now called the main tactical mast (formerly it was the self-protection mast, at least in SSBNs).

British warships are being fitted with a satellite downlink by means of which their ESM libraries can be quickly updated. In Type 42 destroyers, the relevant antenna is an upright cylinder with a rounded top, mounted under the Type 1022 radar on the foremast.

The Outfit designators UAI, UAO, UAQ, and UAV have not been used, to avoid confusion. The UAM designation was apparently reserved for a UAA replacement, but no such system was bought.

◆ ARI 18228 (Sky Guardian)/Mentor (UAG)

Marconi's Sky Guardian and Mentor digital RWRs are derived from the ARI 18228 RWR of the Sea Harrier FRS.1, which in turn was derived from the ARI 18223 of RAF Jaguars and Harriers. The Sea Harrier FRS.1 version has its antennas on the vertical fin, in the squared-off protrusion. It divides 2–18 GHz into four bands (centered on 3, 6, 10, and 18 GHz). The preprocessor takes not more than 10 microsec to reduce incoming signals to digital form. The processor uses a 128-mode library. The CRT can display several emitters simultaneously, and the system sounds an audio alarm when it recognizes a threat. Special algorithms limit bearing error to 7 deg or less. Separate channels intercept missile command signals. Sky Guardian (later Sky Guardian 100) was an abortive export version. Mentor 1/2/3, progressively more elaborate versions of ARI 18228 for ships, did not sell (see the 1991/92 edition for details). They had faster digitizers (to handle 1M pps), retained the limited immediate threat library, but added a larger reference library (3000 modes) through which an operator could search. Track capacity was 200.

The next step (Sky Guardian 200/300) introduced a new processing architecture. Mentor A and B are shipboard versions of Sky Guardian 200 and 300 announced in 1987. These sets divide the E-J bands into three CVR bands, each with its own preprocessor (digitizer). The outputs of all three go into an intermediate processor (for sorting, initial analysis, and rejection of some signals to avoid overload) rather than, as is usual, directly into the track processor. The third processor forms track files (i.e., measures PRF) and conducts library comparison. As the pulse rate rises, the system can throw out some information to avoid being

The ESM antennas occupy the prominent squared-off tail radome in this Sea Harrier FA.2 fighter. Aft-looking spirals are in the sides of the tail boom. The extended nose houses the new Blue Vixen radar. (British Aerospace)

overwhelmed. Radars locked onto the airplane (e.g., those that show no apparent scan rate) receive special priority. The track processor CPU is an 80386 (5 MIPS, 336K RAM/PROM/EE-PROM memory with 100% growth capacity). Overall response time is less than 1 sec from detection to identified display. The EEPROM library (capacity over 2800 modes/over 700 emitters) can be reprogrammed in about 60 sec on the flight line and can be updated in flight. Data for emitters encountered in flight can be recorded (and time-tagged, for location) for later playback and analysis. DF accuracy, using four broad-band spirals, is 10 deg or better in each band. MTBF is given as over 700 hr. Total weight is 24 kg.

Data can be displayed either on a 3in CRT (15 emitters with bearings or an emitter table showing band and PRF) or via the airplane central computer (as in Hawks), on a multifunction display or a HUD (as in the Sea Harrier FA.2). The system also provides the pilot with continuous threat audio (presumably at PRF frequency, giving an idea of the nature of the threat) and with synthetic alarm tones.

The version in the Sea Harrier FA.2 (ARI 18228/16) is probably extended down to C/D band (for Sea Eagle targeting against ships using S-band radars), as in ARI 18228; it may be extended up to K-band. The Royal Navy tested, but did not adopt, a shipboard Sky Guardian 200 in 1987. Reportedly it hoped to obtain something close to ESM performance at an RWR price. A French ARUX taken from a Nimrod was tried on board HMS *Fearless*, presumably in a parallel effort.

Sky Guardian 300 (for large patrol aircraft) adds an IFM and uses horn antennas for accurate DF (2.5 deg). For example, a CN-235 has two antennas above the cockpit and two in a duckbill on the tail, with each pair back to back, as in Orange Crop. This version uses a PC-type display with modes such as PPI (bearing vs. band) and B-scan (frequency-bearing).

Mentor A/B match Sky Guardian 200/300 performance but claimed MTBF is over 2000 hr. The PPI-type display uses color to indicate the character of each detected emitter (friendly, neu-

tral, hostile, or unknown). The display includes a table of emitter parameters (bearings, PRFs, relative amplitudes, and estimated identities). An adjacent display shows which automated warnings are set.

Sky Guardian 2000, announced 1993, is a lightweight version with a new processor architecture (parallel 68020s, no intermediate processor), an IFM and a new CPU; it can accept and process data from a laser warner. Library capacity is 1200 modes. Total weight is 13.0 kg and claimed MTBF is about 1000 hr. Sky Guardian 2000 began as an unsuccessful competitor to AWARE for a British army contract. Unlike earlier versions of Sky Guardian, this one is designed for integration with a jammer, such as Apollo, and also with a laser warner.

Mentor A*/B+ versions announced in the summer of 1993 use some Sky Guardian 2000 technology. Mentor A* (8–18 GHz, four spirals, 10-deg DF) includes a DIFM, previously only in Mentor B. It is still a radar warner, with a 4in monochrome display. B+ (2–18 GHz) uses four spirals and four horn antennas and offers 5-deg DF accuracy. It has a 14in color display with a keyboard and trackball for operator interaction.

Mentor 2000 is Mentor 2 (2–18 GHz extendable to 0.5–40 GHz, 3–6-deg DF using a six-port DF antenna, with a fine-DF option) married to the processor introduced in Sky Guardian 2000, using seven parallel 68020 CPUs in the processor plus one to manage the system, all programmed in ADA. Library capacity is 3000 modes, and track capacity is 200. When this system was proposed for the Royal Navy in 1989, it was claimed that it could search its 2500-mode library in 1 sec; standard Royal Navy systems needed 26 sec to search their 200-mode libraries. The developer, Marconi, claimed that this was the only ESM system that could overlay a synthetic picture on raw video. Sensitivity is −65 dBm, and dynamic range is 55 dB. A Falcon Equipment and Systems DS-301A communications-band ESM set (2–500 MHz, extendable to 1–1000 MHz) can be added. It includes both a surveillance receiver and a DF processor (using Adcock and Watson-Watt antennas, DF accuracy is better than 3.5 deg on the HF ground wave, better than 10 deg on the HF sky wave, and better than 3 deg on vertically or multiply polarized V/UHF).

Mentor 2001/2002 (announced at the IDEX 93 exhibition) add a 6–20-GHz multimode jammer (adapted from the Badger battlefield jammer, capable of handling 16 threats simultaneously, reacting in less than 0.5 sec) controlled from a common ESM/ECM console and (in 2002) a Shield decoy launcher. Jamming techniques are: spot, barrage, swept noise, power management and cover pulse, gated noise, RGPO, RGPI, false target, swept scan rate, LF noise, and inverse gain noise with false target. Adding a receiver controller upgrades Mentor 2002 from one to up to 20 receivers operating simultaneously on fixed or scanning frequency assignments. UAG is the Royal Navy version in the *Fort*-class AORs.

Users:
Sky Guardian 200: Abu Dhabi (Hawk), Austria (J-35), India (Sea Harrier and Jaguar [Maritime Attack]), Indonesia (Hawk), Malaysia (Hawk), Oman (Hawk), Spain (EAV-8A Matador), United Kingdom (Sea Harrier FRS.2 [ARI 18228/16], Jaguar, VC 10 tanker, some army Lynx). Sky Guardian is also on board some Sea King and Puma helicopters. As of 1991, reported production was 1230. Lynx installations are interim for AWARE 3.

Sky Guardian 300: Brunei (CN-235), Malaysia (CN-235).

Sky Guardian 2000: Indonesia (CN-235).

Mentor: United Kingdom (*Fearless*, "Hunt" class [*Berkeley, Cattistock, Chiddingfold, Ledbury, Quorn*], *Sandown* class, *Polar Circle, Fort Grange* class).

Mentor 2000: Malaysia (*Lekiu* class), United Kingdom (*Fort* class [as UAG]).

◆ ARI 18240 (Yellow Gate)

Nimrod MR.2 and British AWACS (E-3D) ESM system. See Loral EW-1017 in the U.S. section below.

◆ Ariel

Marconi's towed active decoy for Nimrod MPA was used during the Gulf War. Frequency coverage is 2–18 GHz. Jamming modes include noise and repeater. A new variant, not yet in service as of late 1995, adds a techniques generator on the parent aircraft, which communicates with the decoy via a fiber-optic link. Both versions use 100-kg pods, and can be deployed at speeds of 190 to 230 kt, towed at 130 to 360 kt, and can withstand maneuvers at up to 4 g.

◆ AWARE 3/4 (ARI 23491)

Ferranti's 2–18-GHz AWARE 3 RWR uses a pair of CVRs plus an IFM. Separate processors characterize the signal (by DoA, ToA, and frequency), classify it (using frequency, PRF, and scan rate [not pulse width], on the basis of a 1000-mode library; 2000 modes in AWARE 4), and manage tracks. System software must be loaded for each mission, so it is relatively easy to modify. Side-by-side displays are polar (up to 20 emitters) and tabular (bearings and identities of current threats plus, for a selected signal, bearing, identification [with confidence level], frequency, PRF [with jitter or stagger], scan period, and received power level). Bearing accuracy is better than 10 deg, using four planar spiral antennas. AWARE handles pulse-Dopper, pulse, and CW signals. It can feed a mission management system via a 1553B bus, or it can be a stand-alone system. Weight is less than 13 kg. AWARE 4 adds a new control indicator unit for airborne ESM in the front seat. Planned fixed-wing versions (AWARE 5 and 6) probably will not be built, since when Ferranti went bankrupt portions of the company involved in AWARE were divided between GEC-Marconi and Racal.

Users: Netherlands (Navy Lynx helicopters [AWARE 3], combat support ships [AWARE 4]), United Kingdom (army Chinook, Lynx, Puma, and next-generation helicopters).

◆ Hermes

Marconi Defence Systems' ESM system for Indian navy Sea King Mk 42B helicopters is derived from the ARI 18241/1 radar-homing-and-warning receiver fitted to RAF Tornado F.2 and F.3 fighters.

◆ MIR-2 (Orange Crop/Orange Blossom/UAN)

Racal's 0.6–18-GHz (four bands) ESM system was designed for the Lynx helicopter, to intercept and localize submarine burst transmissions. The front end is similar to that of RDL, but in-

stead of an operator attempting to identify a signal it has a simple hard-wired processor (based on pulse characteristics and PRI). In turn, the automatic pulse analyzer of some later RDL versions was based on Orange Crop technology. The display shows band, bearing (the scale is divided into 10-deg steps), and amplitude (three levels). Strobed signals are subject to pulse analysis (PRF is displayed digitally) and accurate bearing measurement (bearing is displayed on a 30-deg display calibrated in 2-deg steps; accuracy is 4.5 deg). The system uses six sets of paired spiral antennas (high- and low-band). Signal limits: pulse width 0.1–10 microsec, PRF 50–10,000 pps. Total weight without antennas is 30.7 kg.

Orange Crop on board a Sea King helicopter, HMS *Illustrious*, 1996. (Author)

A Type 669 jammer on board a "County"-class missile destroyer (second series). Type 668 has one jamming unit (rather than two) on each side, presumably sufficient to deal with one rather than two threats at a time. (R. Cheung)

Mk 1 (displayed in July 1978, the first contract following in October 1981) combines the RWR with a search radar receiver in an integrated unit. Mk 2 added track-data input and output and an optional radar-altimeter input. Mk 3 adds a PRF library for pulse analysis and a capacity to recognize important CW (missile-guidance) radars. Unit cost is about $350,000. The Ma and Pa program is a Royal Navy Orange Crop update to improve CW capability and visual and aural threat warning; the RWR is to be integrated into the Lynx CTS.

Users: Brazil (Lynx), Korea (Super Lynx), Spain (may be on Sea King AEW), United Kingdom (six in RAF, 183 on RN aircraft, two [as UAN (1)] on the "Castle"-class OPVs; UAN(2) was on board HMS *Argus* during the Gulf War). UAN (2) equips major British auxiliaries and amphibious support vessels. Orange Crop was installed on Sea Kings during the Falklands War. Podded Mk 2 (Orange Blossom) were installed on six RAF C-130s, for radar surveillance and self-defense warning. UAN, the Royal Navy surface-ship version, has radar blanking and its own dedicated power supply.

◆ Type 667/668

Type 667 is a high-powered S- and X-band (E/F and I-bands in ECM nomenclature) noise jammer, using two separate transmitter assemblies. Type 668 is a variant of 667 limited to X-band, to save internal space (e.g., in *Leanders* equipped with UA-13, which required two operator positions).

Users:

Type 667: Chile ("County" class), Ecuador (*Leander*), India (*Dunagiri, Himgiri, Nilgiri, Udaygiri, Talwar, Trishul*).
Type 668: Chile (*Leanders*), New Zealand (*Southland, Waikato*).

◆ Type 675(2) (Guardian)/ETW

Thorn-EMI's jammer was first bought in 1983. Each of two trainable stabilized units (port and starboard) carries a pair of boxes (each with two oblong antennas, one over the other, one for a jamming horn and the other for a DF antenna) and a DF receiver. The low gain of the horns probably limited Type 675(1) to point defense. The horns jam at up to 50-deg elevation. Guardian can either accept bearing and threat data from a ship's ESM system (via the CDS) or it can use its own channelized-receiver ESM, DF receivers, and threat/jamming techniques library. Type 675(1) was reportedly unreliable and difficult to maintain. Waveguide loss (the jammer TWTs are below decks) was reportedly excessive and frequency discrimination poor, but the Royal Navy considered power output sufficient and the system uses parameters other than frequency to recognize threats.

The "significantly better" Type 675(2) became operational in 1987 (the contract was let in March 1984). Its dish offers high gain for area defense (reported maximum range is 500 km/275 nm); Type 675 generates false targets to screen formations (Racal claims it is the only such threat dilution system in service). Type 675(2) is now being provided with its own threat warner, the Early Threat Warner (ETW). VSEL Combat System Division's new ECMIU (contract let November 1991) automatically transfers data directly between a ship's ESM system and Type 675(2) on board modernized carriers. Thorn-EMI's Set-on Correlator connects an ESM set with the jammer to reduce ambiguities in target identification and tracking. It ran a week of trials on board HMS *Liverpool* in April 1994.

A near-term upgrade provides a new floppy disk drive and an improved display. The shore development unit should enter service at Portsdown in March 1997, with the first ship fitting following in April 1997. From about June 1997 the system will receive a new UAT-type signal processor.

Four major upgrade options were evaluated between April 1992 and April 1993: (a) do nothing; (b) stretch the existing system; (c) add digital RF memory and false profiling; (d) add phased arrays. A project definition study should be complete in 1997, and HMS *Nottingham* will receive the first upgraded system in 1999. The major upgrade may be Type 695, otherwise described as the Type 675 successor.

Containerized Type 675(2) on board a Type 42 destroyer; a similar jammer is mounted on the other side of the container. The right-hand antennas are the receivers, the left-hand antennas the jammers. Type 675 and the commercial Guardian lack the dish antenna in the center of the mounting. (Thorn-EMI)

Users: United Kingdom (*Invincible* class, Type 42 Batch II [and Batch I *Cardiff*], Type 22 Batch III, *Argus*). In the Gulf at least some Type 42 Batch I destroyers, such as HMS *Nottingham*, had Type 675 instead of Type 670, on raised platforms between funnel and mainmast. Type 675(2) was planned for Type 23, but has not yet been installed, reportedly because of slow production and continued performance problems. As of late 1996, 19 were on board ships and one was a shore reference.

◆ UA-3 and UA-8/9/10 (Porker) and UA-13/SPR-02

The solid-state 2.5–11-GHz three-band UA-3, whose antenna is a stack of four horns (for each of three bands) feeding CVRs, was tested in 1959–60. A single CRT (bearing-amplitude) is switched among bands; an audio output provides PRF and, in effect, sweep rate, measured by aural comparison with adjustable reference signals. DF accuracy is generally within 10 deg, and can often be within 5 deg. Surviving sets probably employ EMI's YAF pulse analyzer, which handles one strobed signal at a time, plus (in some cases) an additional high-end antenna, to cover Ku (J)-band. UA-3 was the first RN set with a radar interference suppressor, needed as the number of systems multiplied.

The improved Porker adds omnis for a frequency channel (initially SHR, later IFM in at least some cases). It uses submarine-style cylindrical DF antennas (accuracy comparable with UA-3) with angled slots (to detect both polarizations: UA-8, 2.5–4.1 GHz; UA-9, 7–11.5 GHz; UA-10 for C-band). The omnis ultimately feed a CRT (frequency-amplitude). A signal displayed on either the bearing-amplitude or the frequency CRT can be fed into a pulse analyzer, YAZ, which measures pulse width, PRF, sweep rate, and modulation using an additional CRT. Using large bearing CRTs, operators in 1960 tests tracked up to five signals (differing in bearing and frequency) simultaneously. Analysis (by looking at and adjusting the CRT traces) took about a minute, compared to about 1 sec in later automatic systems. In the 1970s an automatic signal identifier, YAG (using MEL's SARIE II,

The foremast of a *Leander*-class frigate shows UA-13 at the masthead, surmounting Porker (visible as small cylinders, separated by flanges [baffles]). (A. Raven, 1988)

Abbey Hill (UAA-1) DF antennas under the platform of a Type 992Q radar antenna. The round objects on the small yardarm are presumably the associated omnidirectional antennas feeding the system's IFM. There are four tiers of DF antennas, corresponding to four bands. (A. Raven)

tested in November 1972), was added. Like YAZ, it analyzed one manually chosen (strobed) signal at a time. The similar YAW was for "County"-class destroyers equipped with the ADAWS CDS.

The 25–1400 MHz UA-13/SPR-02 extends Porker coverage to lower frequencies, probably with similar DF accuracy. It supplements YAZ with YAQ (for lower frequencies). Presumably UA-13 supported OTH Exocet targeting. It uses a conical omni antenna at the masthead, with projecting dipole DF arrays. In Dutch service it was designated SPR-02. Racal supplied the array, Signaal the below-decks electronics (the latter was probably eventually copied in some versions of the Soviet Bell Tap).

Users:

UA-3: Bangladesh (*Leopard* class).

UA-8/9/10: Chile (County and *Leander* classes), Ecuador (*Leanders*), India (*Dunagiri, Himgiri, Nilgiri, Udaygiri*), Indonesia (*van Speijk* class and "Tribal" class [UA-9/YAZ only]), Malaysia (*Hang Tuah*), Pakistan (*Leanders*). Some ships probably lack UA-10. The sets in Chilean ships are probably being replaced under the modernization program.

UA-13: Chile (*General Banquedano*), Indonesia (*Abdul Halim Perdana, Karel Satsuitubun*), Pakistan (*Zulfiquar*).

◆ UAA (Abbey Hill)/UBB/Susie

UAA was MEL's digital follow-on to Porker/UA-13, developed to a 1966 staff requirement (it began tests in 1975 and entered service in December 1978). It was the first British ESM set designed from the beginning to use an IFM and to integrate bearing and frequency information by tagging each pulse with ToA: the B-scan display shows bearing horizontally, frequency vertically.

A frequency-agile signal appears as a row of dots (variable frequency, constant bearing). The system also time-tags the end of each pulse, automatically measuring pulse width.

One advantage of the B-scan (as compared to a polar display, such as that in SLQ-32) is that it does not squeeze together lower-frequency signals, which in a polar display are generally near the center of the screen. The system sounds an alarm when particular pulses (recognized by a hard-wired comparator on the basis of frequency and pulse width) are received. Because there is no integrated processor to de-interleave signals and maintain tracks (for PRF and scan rate measurements), the operator still manually selects (in effect, strobes) a signal for analysis. The system measures signal parameters (including PRF) and provides them in digital form. The system automatically reacts to selected pulse trains. The operator can use a second display to identify signals by sorting through the on-line library (which is not the same as the alarm list). Analysis typically takes a few seconds. Results are displayed on a second CRT alongside the frequency-bearing unit.

Compared to Porker/UA-13, UAA doubles the number of DF ports per band to eight (DF accuracy is probably 2 deg) and adds high-frequency coverage (1–18 GHz) in the form of two more bands. Each CVR (DF receiver) covers 2 GHz. Reported IFM accuracy is 1.5 MHz.

UAA-2 has several times as many hard-wired alarms associated with particular pulses (but not larger numbers of programmed pulse trains, because, at least in its original form, it does not incorporate a de-interleaver, hence cannot analyze more than one signal at a time). It has a larger look-up library. Reportedly UAA-2 can sometimes localize emitters within 0.5 deg (presumably by interferometry). The updated UAA-2 enjoys drastically better reaction time because it has a de-interleaver (MEL's PTA, as in Manta/Sceptre).

Reportedly, both UAA-1 and -2 were very successful in the Gulf war. *Gloucester* was air-control ship for the northern Gulf. Her ESM set intercepted the Iraqi targeting radar whose operation indicated that Silkworms were about to be fired at the U.S. battleship *Wisconsin*. An officer on the ship later commented that it was fortunate that the set was being used in manual mode, since in automatic mode it might well have dismissed the brief Iraqi transmission as a false alarm.

Staff requirements for a further modification, initially designated UAA(3) and then reportedly UBB, were announced in mid-1994 (a Cardinal Points Specification was issued in September). Racal-Thorn received the contract in March 1996, calling for completion of the first unit in 1997. Equipment is to be installed with minimum disturbance during a 12-week availability. UBB will retain the current AYV antenna but add new inboard electronics based on UAT (see below). An important improvement is to be replacement of the current user-unfriendly MMI by a Windows-like environment. The upgrade will apply to eight Type 42 Batch II and III destroyers and to ten Type 22 Batch II and III frigates.

Susie is an export development of UAA, using a different DF array. Most installations use the 24-port Antenna A1 (24 antenna modules, the two upper bands sharing single antennas) or A2, designed to fit under a Signaal "egg." Each weighs about 170 kg. These arrays differ visually from the Signaal DF antenna (used in Sphinx/Rapids) in that each of eight radomes contains the antennas for the entire frequency range. Antenna gain is 5.5–7.5 dB (DF accuracy is 3.5 deg in fine mode). Like Sphinx/Rapids, Susie was designed to control a Scimitar jammer. Bands: 2–4, 4–7.5, 7.5–12, and 12–18 GHz. The system can recognize up to seven signals (five preset threats, on receipt of which a warning is sounded, and two signals to be blanked out automatically) on a pulse-by-pulse (band- and pulse width) basis. Susie-1, the simple version for FAC, has no IFM. Susie 1F (also known as Susie-2) has an IFM (accuracy 5 MHz) and can accommodate a threat library. Pulsewidth range: 0.1–100 microsec; PRI range is 10 microsec (PRF 100 kHz) to 10 millisec (PRF 100 Hz). DF receiver sensitivity is 30 dBm in fine range, 40 dBm in coarse range. Dynamic range is 50 dB. Susie 1F frequency receiver sensitivity is 40–47 dBm (optionally 65 dBm); receiver gain is 1–3 dB.

Users:

UAA: Brazil (Type 22 frigates [UAA-1]), United Kingdom (*Invincible* [UAA-2], *Ark Royal* [UAA-1], Type 42 [UAA-2 except UAA-1 in *York*] and Type 22 Batch II/III [UAA-2]). UAA-1 is being removed from Type 21 frigates sold to Pakistan.

Susie: Indonesia (*Hajar Dewantara* and *Fatahillah* class), South Korea (may be on board some *Po Hang* and *Donghae* class, which are otherwise credited with RDL-2), Sweden (*Norkopping* and *Alvsborg* classes), Turkey (*Dogan* class: Susie-1 in P 340-347). Unlike all the other ships listed, the Swedish ships lack the Signaal "egg" usually associated with its antenna; they have smaller-diameter arrays. These ships lack IFMs. Installations are all described as Susie-1, but some (not the Swedish ones) are probably -1Fs.

◆ UAD and UAK

These are British designations for the U.S. Classic Outboard. It is not clear whether they refer to SSQ-72 and -108, or to the carrier and Type 22 frigate versions. UAD-5 is a Racal COMINT system in the British version of Outboard. Reportedly, within a British task group, the frigate Outboards provide information to the carrier, which alone has a data-processing system on board.

◆ UAE

A U.S.-supplied threat-warner installed for Operation Corporate (Falklands War, 1982) on board three nuclear-attack submarines; also known as SANDMAN. Presumably it replaced UA-4. UAE is probably the U.S.-supplied S3000, which covers the 0.5–18-GHz band.

◆ UAF

Compared to UAA, UAF has a more elaborate eight-port antenna and a processor (de-interleaver: KS500, as in Cutlass). It is unusual in not having separate omnis; instead it shifts the IFM (in effect) among the DF channels, sampling the antennas in sequence. As in UAA, the main threat display is a B-scan, but in this case it can be overlaid with symbology. Typically a box around the point representing the detected signal indicates accuracy limits. Alongside it is a second CRT showing an emitter

UAF(1) array at the masthead of HMS *Norfolk*, with Type 996 radar above, May 1990. (A. Preston)

identification table (identity, bearing, threat significance) provided by the processor (and modifiable by the operator). Both displays can be collapsed onto a single screen. The operator can examine raw and processed data simultaneously, to extract parameters. The display is the high-definition color VU1400C. Thanks to its embedded computer, UAF was apparently the first British ESM set to include a built-in trainer.

Each of eight antenna groups is a stack of three rounded and approximately semicylindrical radomes (top to bottom, 12–18, 2–6, and 6–12 GHz) with a prominent horn below (wire-wrapped, for 500 MHz–2 GHz). Instantaneous bearing accuracy is 3 deg, but the system can use interferometry for fine DF cuts for OTH-T.

The contract was awarded in October 1983 (after a 1982 competition following the Falklands War) and first production sets were delivered in the fall of 1989, for installation on board Type 23 frigates. Reportedly Racal (which had bought Decca, the designers) won by default because MEL (which had designed UAA) considered its processor (PTA) as yet too immature. By the time UAF entered service its processor was considered inadequate to cope with growing pulse density. Reportedly, it was unable to correlate different pulses of pulse-agile radars (at a fixed bearing), carrying each as a separate emitter, hence overloading itself (the slightly later Sceptre apparently did not suffer from the same problem). Too, UAF reportedly suffered from interference by TV and other shore signals below 2 GHz. In February 1989 the major British EW firms bid to build UAF(X), which would use the existing antenna and front-end receiver. Racal, the UAF design authority, won the upgrade contract in 1993. KS500 is replaced by Sadie (see below); in addition to EWAM, the operator limits processor input using a digital filter. Band 1 RF performance is im-

UAF mast on board the modernized carrier HMS *Illustrious*, 1996. The radar is Type 996. Atop the mast is a UHF/DF array (a circle of short dipoles). Note the Type 675 jammer on the platform below the satellite radome platform. (Author)

proved. A July 1995 contract adds a new console processor (for better MMI), a new disk-drive package (floppy plus hard disk drive), and new software. HMS *Montrose* received the first upgrade in September 1995; the last was completed in April 1996.

Users: United Kingdom (*Illustrious* [as refitted 1993], Type 23 frigates). The pre-upgrade version is now designated UAF(1). The carriers are ultimately to have UAT (essentially the UAF front end married to Sceptre) instead of UAF. UAC, the submarine version of UAF, is now extinct, having been superseded by UAP (see below).

◆ UAS(1)/RX-740/RX-750

The Falcon Electronics RX-740 superhet microwave surveillance system (1–18 GHz) was bought specifically for the Armilla Patrol, to provide immediate warning of Silkworm attacks. It is an add-on to UAA-1. For example, it was aboard HMS *Sheffield* (on a rack adjacent to UAA-1) when that ship returned from the Gulf in March 1992, then was cross-decked to a ship going out to the Gulf. Frequency resolution is 10 kHz (100 Hz is available as an option). Dynamic range is 60 dB. The receiver can sweep continuously over a frequency range, or it can step between any two preselected frequencies and search over a preselected range (minimum 50 MHz up and down) around any set frequency. Up to 99 channel steps can be preselected, stored, viewed, and recalled. Scan time is selectable between 100 msec and 100 sec. The spectrum display width is variable from 1 MHz to 50 MHz in eight steps. UAS(1) is programmed as to threat band via a front-panel keyboard. It automatically activates a remote audiovisual bridge

warning unit. Purchases: 12 for the Royal Navy, 2 for the Royal Australian Navy. About 50 have been sold worldwide.

Falcon Equipment & Systems Ltd. (FESL) announced a follow-on 1–18-GHz RX-750 in 1994. Like its predecessor, RX-750 is a wide information bandwidth (500 MHz, resolution 1 kHz) superhet. Options include extensions (1–20 GHz, 0.5–23 GHz), frequency resolution of 100 MHz, and 250-MHz information bandwidth. RX-750 can use the existing RX-740 display and control system.

◆ UCB (EWCP)

The Electronic Warfare Control Processor is to integrate UAF/ UAT, the Type 675(2) jammer, and the Sea Gnat decoy (and, probably, DLH). Using a new dedicated console, this knowledge-based system is expected to present the ship EW director with a composite situation assessment and recommended courses of action, based on factors such as equipment status, threat priority, and expected interference with other systems. The composite tactical picture produced will be more useful to the ship's CDS. EWCP will also provide off-line planning tools (in this it is analogous to the U.S. EWCM). It is a step toward the fully integrated EW system planned for the Project Horizon Anglo-French frigate now in the concept stage.

The RFP was issued in the fall of 1991, and GEC-Marconi won the EWCP contract in 1996, to supply 14 UCB(1) outfits to the carriers and to selected Type 42 destroyers. The first will be delivered in 1998, probably to go on board *Ark Royal*.

◆ HF/DF Systems (FH Series)

These sets use the "birdcage" antenna developed during World War II, which has fore-aft and port-starboard coils, with an omni whip on top to resolve directional ambiguity. FH-4 (1944) is a dual-channel set with a common oscillator and a test aerial inside the main DF array (to maintain balance between the two directional loops). The use of a single local oscillator (for the SHR) insures that both loops are tuned to the same frequency.

A standard FH series HF/DF array at the foretop of a *Leander*-class frigate, 1988. Below the "bird cage" array are omnidirectional antennas and four antennas for DF, with omnidirectional antennas (for IFM) on the crosstree below them. They serve UA-8/9. (A. Raven)

The omni is switched in manually after a signal has been detected. Racal's 1–30-MHz FH-5 switches in its omni automatically, 50 times/sec, and so is better adapted to detecting short signals. Accuracy is about 1 deg against a surface wave signal. Sky waves are trickier because their apparent direction wanders; accuracy demands about 10 to 15 min of observation.

Surviving sets probably replace the original vacuum-tube receivers with more modern solid-state units, retaining the antenna and overall architecture. The Royal Navy used FH-5 into the 1970s; there were no later FH-series sets. A reported FH-12 may be a modernized FH-5 with solid-state receiver.

Users:

FH-4: Malaysia (*Hang Tuah, Rahmat*).
FH-5: Argentina (Type 42), Bangladesh (*Leopard* class), Brazil (*Niteroi* class; Type 22s [possibly only ex-HMS *Brilliant*]), Chile (County and *Leander* classes), Ecuador (*Leanders*), India (*Vikrant, Viraat, Leander, Whitby, Leopard* classes), Indonesia ("Tribal" class, frigates *Abdul Halim Perdana, Karel Satsuitubun* [others of this type all have Telegon 4]), Iran (*Damavand* and FRAM *Sumner* destroyers and Vosper Mk 5 class frigates), Pakistan (*Babur, Leander* class), Peru (*Aguirre, Daring* class), Thailand (*Makut Rajakumarn*).

◆ **EWRRF**

Early in 1994 the Royal Navy announced that it was seeking tenders for a contractor to coordinate development of an EW rapid-reaction facility (EWRRF) to support rapid two-way communication between the EW database of the RN EW Operational Support (RNEWOS) facility at RAF Wyton, naval units, and other EW data assets, for near real-time update of EW threat libraries on ships. This addressed a problem first encountered in the Falklands, when some ships had to have updates air-dropped to them. The broadcast will probably use SCOT channels.

◆ **Cutlass Family: Cutlass/Octopus/Porpoise/UAC**

Cutlass was Racal's first ESM system to use a de-interleaving processor (KS500, Cutlass), succeeding the manual analog RDL. Entering production in 1979, it was developed for a Middle East customer that considered manual systems inappropriate to the sort of intense electronic environment revealed by the October War of 1973, with up to 500,000 pps. Denmark was an important early customer.

These systems divide the 2–18-GHz range into two bands (2–7.5 and 7.5–18 GHz, each with monopulse DF and digital IFM). Library capacity is 2000 modes (400 radars); the operator can add another 100. Track capacity is 150, 30 per display page, ranked by threat. The display also shows the level of confidence of each identification. Total processing time is less than 1 sec. Selected digital data can be sent to other systems (e.g., antishipmissile fire control). Typically there are six ports, but there are also four- and eight-port versions. The small-ship version, Cutlass E, uses the same antenna as the earlier RDL. As of 1988, claimed frequency and bearing accuracies were 5 MHz and 5 deg over the 0.6–18-GHz range.

Cutlass B-1 uses the Anaren DESM antenna described below in the U.S. section for more precise DF (2-deg accuracy, sufficient to target antiship missiles such as Harpoon). The new antenna incorporates its own DF processor. Beside the usual data, this version collects intrapulse data: FMOP (frequency modulation on pulse) and PMOP (phase modulation on pulse), to identify pulse-compression radars. The same antenna-receiver-processor was used in the Signaal/MEL Rapids system. Having bought Thorn, which in turn had bought MEL (which had inherited the Signaal ESM line), Racal may try to convert existing Rapids units to Cutlass B-1s.

Octopus (for German S148-class fast-attack boats) is Cutlass B-1 plus a Scorpion jammer and an AEG threat analyzer/library.

Porpoise is a submarine version, originally for Type 209s. The highest-priority emitters trigger audio and visual alarms. Priority is based not only on the character of the emitter, but also on a calculation of the submarine's probability of detection, given the level of radar reflection from the masts, including the snorkel, and the sea state. The tabular display shows 25 tracks at a time.

An Egyptian *Ramadan*-class missile patrol boat equipped with Cutlass ESM gear, visible clamped to her mast above the big radome of her Marconi S1810 radar. The masthead array is the AEG Telegon HF/DF. The Cygnus jammer has not yet been mounted aft. (Giorgio Arra)

The titanium antenna head has an omni (for IFM) above two rows of ports (six per row, spirals for the low band and horns for the high band). Signals are amplified in the head proper before being transmitted into the hull of the submarine for analysis. Porpoise 2 is an improved version (DF accuracy 3 rather than 5 or 6 deg).

Users: Cutlass: Algeria (*Kalaat Beni Hammed*–class LSTs), Bahrein (Cutlass E in two TNC-45 [B-1 in *Abdul Rahman Al-Fadel* and *Al Taweelah*]), Brazil (B-1 in modernized carrier *Minas Gerais, Inhauma* class, ordered 1994 for two *Niteroi* class), Denmark (B-1 in *Nils Juel, Falster, Hvidbjornen,* Improved *Hvidbjornen, Willemoes* classes), Egypt (Cutlass E in *Ramadan* class, upgraded 1994/95), Germany (B-1 in S148 class, Octopus replacing DR 2000S in S143 class), Greece (B-1 in ex-German S148 class), India (Cutlass B-1 in frigates *Taragiri* and *Vindhyagiri,* Cutlass E in "Osa II" and in four "Tarantuls" [*Vinash, Vipul,* K-49, -50]), Kenya ("Province" class and *Madaraka* and *Mamba*), Kuwait (FPB 57 and TNC 45), Nigeria (Cutlass E in *Erin'mi* class, may be in refitted Combattante class), Qatar (Combattante III class supplementing DR 2000), Thailand (Cutlass E in *Khamronsin* class), Tunisia (Combattante IIIM class), Turkey (FRAM *Gearing*-class destroyers [Cutlass B-1 and Cygnus installed 1988–91], *Yildiz* class, MEKOs *Barbarossa* and *Orucreis* [B-1 version], minelayer *Nusret,* and *Tekirdag*), and UAE (TNC 62, TNC 45, and TNC 38 classes). UAF(1) is a Royal Navy version (see above).

Porpoise: Chile (Type 209), Turkey (Type 209-1400). UAC, now extinct, was a Royal Navy version. Some Turkish installations may have Sadie processors.

Minas Gerais has an array of eight VHF/UHF Yagis below the usual Cutlass B-1 antenna.

◆ **Sadie family: Kestrel (Orange Reaper/SLR-504)/Type 242/ Sabre/Sea Lion/Mermaid/UAP**

This is basically Cutlass with the much more powerful Sadie processor and with color rather than monochrome displays. In several cases, as in UAF, IFMs are in the DF channels, so no separate omni is needed. This architecture is adapted to a very dense pulse environment; the frequency given by a separate IFM may apply to the wrong pulse (IFM measurement takes a finite time, so the IFM may miss some pulses). Standard library capacity is 2000 modes (3000, plus 250 added by operator, in Sabre). Capacity is 1M pps (sometimes given as 500,000). In some cases, systems were apparently initially delivered with KS500 processors, the full Sadie not yet being ready; they were upgraded later.

Sadie (Segregation, Association, De-interleaving and Identification Equipment) is built around a special chip, both to solve the problem of tracking frequency-agile radars (mainly by using emitter bearing as a sorting parameter) and to handle double the pulse density. To do the latter, Sadie's EWAM (extended window-addressed memory) VLSI chip stores a window of values of each parameter (frequency, pulse width, bearing, modulation, expected ToA, and expected amplitude) for the set of emitters it is already tracking, checking any new pulse against them before track processing. Sadie typically consists of a segregator (containing the EWAM chip), known-emitter monitor (taking data from the segregator, including emitter track number and pulse record, accumulating parameters and performing scan analysis), three new-emitter analyzers (de-interleavers using 68020 CPUs), two processors, an ESM control processor (ECP), and an MMI, all connected by a VME bus. The processors use parameters from the segregator to calculate values for the key variables (based on exponential averaging). Peaks that do not come from main transmitter lobes are rejected. The ECP (programmed in Pascal) performs a full scan analysis on all monitored emitters, if required. Racal claims that this combination is particularly well adapted to handling both new scan bursts and pulse data smeared out by multipath, to produce apparently invalid parameter measurements (and, similarly, to dealing with missed pulses). The original EWAM used 2.5-micron CMOS technology, incorporates 27,000 gates, and can process 25 emitters at a rate of 500,000 pps; eight chips are mounted on a board to handle 200 radars simultaneously. The current Sadie V uses 1.5-micron technology to achieve 2–3 times the performance of its predecessor. As of the fall of 1996, no successor chip had yet been announced.

Kestrel, the 0.6–40-GHz helicopter version, uses the earlier MIR-2 antennas (bearing accuracy better than 3.5 deg, using pattern-correction techniques; but accurate frequency measurement [for identification] is emphasized over bearing accuracy).

UAP on board an *Upholder*-class submarine, 1994. The search periscope, forward, carries the warning array. The ESM mast, abaft it, carries a spinner above an array of spirals. (Author)

Elevation coverage is +/−45 deg. IFMs are supplemented by a superhet to handle CW signals. The interim Mk 1 has the KS500; Mk 2 has the full Sadie. Processing time is less than 1 sec, and track capacity is 400 (20 per display page: track number, bearing, frequency, PRF, pulse width, and scan rate and type).

The alternative bearing display shows the 25 highest priority emitters (lethality, type, and track number); it also gives fuller data for one track (bearing, status, time first and last seen, frequency [including frequency agility], PRF [including whether it is fixed or variable], pulse width, amplitude, scan rate and type, and identification). Preprogrammed threats generate audio and visual alarms. Output can be to a 1553B bus. Total weight is 47 kg.

Type 242, announced 1987, is a 0.6–18-GHz (extendable to 40 GHz) shipboard equivalent to Kestrel (the name is taken from the last three digits of the system's ARI designator). Its ECP can drive a Scorpion jammer, both elements being controlled from the same console. As in the big Royal Navy systems, displays are typically a pair of color raster-scan CRTs (color is used to denote some threats). The threat library is carried on dual floppy disks; the operator can write unknown signals onto the disks, for later review. DF accuracy is about 5 deg. Racal describes 242 as one-fifth the weight of its predecessors (as well as cheaper and more reliable).

The 0.6–40-GHz Sabre and the 0.5–18-GHz Sea Lion (for surface ships and submarines, respectively) are high-precision (2-deg bearing) versions developed from Type 242 for Harpoon targeting for the Royal Danish Navy. The Danes considered 2 deg necessary in order to distinguish individual targets on a crowded coast. Sabre uses amplitude comparison for 5–8 deg and interferometry (with two adjacent antennas) for 2-deg accuracy. To minimize size and cost, Sea Lion employs a dish antenna (it has no monopulse DF capability, but does have an omni on the submarine periscope for radar warning). Sabre was originally to have fed directly into the ship's command bus, without operator intervention. However, it was feared that in a dense pulse environment it could overload the ship's CDS. Therefore it was provided with a single operator screen (rather than the usual pair), so that the EW operator could filter system output. The 14in color raster display (also used in Sea Lion) is that used in the Royal Navy's UAF and UAP. In Sabre, sensitivity is −60 dBmi and dynamic range is 60 dB.

UAP, the standard Royal Navy submarine ESM set, was selected in 1987 (with sea trials in 1989). It combines UAF displays with the Sadie processor. Omni warning/IFM (2–40 GHz) and monopulse DF (four ports, 5-deg accuracy over 2–18 GHz) antennas are mounted on the search periscope, so that the submarine can conduct surveillance with just one mast exposed. In attack submarines, this mast is now being fitted with a GPS receiver. A separate dish on the ESM mast provides OTH-T accuracy. It is claimed that 95% of the ESM task can be done from the search periscope.

UAP(1) first went to sea in 1989. It was the first British system with an embedded trainer. A planned two-stage upgrade (2001–2002) will provide, first, upgraded processors with more commonality to other processors, correlators, and an improved data rate; the second phase will be an upgraded (presumably distributed) architecture. As of late 1996, 3 systems were ashore and 11 were at sea. UAP(2), which is not a parallel development, is the earlier UAC(1) with a new antenna. Of four deployed (on two *Swiftsures* and two *Trafalgars*), only HMS *Trenchant* retained her UAP(2) in December 1996, and it was scheduled for replacement by UAP(1) the following spring. A UAP(1) upgrade on offer for the Batch 2 *Trafalgar* offers ESM on a nonpenetrating mast and a targeting facility on a second mast. Like existing British submarine systems, this one would incorporate Telegon 12 HF/DF. As of late 1996 Racal expected a prime contract from the Batch 2 *Trafalgar* consortium at the end of February or early in March 1997. The first three systems are to cost about £15 million (the contract will include an option for two more). The UAP(3) version in *Vanguards* has six- rather than four-port ESM, and it lacks the targeting mast. It is mounted on the PSV-1 optronic mast.

Users:

Kestrel: Denmark (nine Lynx), United Kingdom (EH-101 Merlin as Orange Reaper/ARI 18242). The British version uses the helicopter's main display. The stand-alone Danish version (replacing MIR-2) uses a 20 × 7.5cm color CRT.

Type 242: Bahrein (with B-1 antenna in TNC 62s), Canada (*Protecteur* class [as SLR-504]), Oman ("Province" class, with RDL antenna and Scorpion jammer).

Sabre: Denmark (*Thetis*, StanFlex 300 classes).

Sea Lion: Denmark (Type 205 and 207 class; upgrade ordered 1995), Greece (first four modernized Type 209s), Norway (Type 207 and Type 210, except for four unmodernized submarines with VR-1B). Racal tried unsuccessfully to sell Sea Lion (as Mermaid) to Egypt for the Romeo-class upgrade.

UAP: United Kingdom (all SSNs have UAP(1); SSBNs have UAP(3), with antennas repackaged as part of the Trident Self-Protection Mast; it lacks the targeting mast). ISIDORA III is an export version, not yet sold.

◆ Griffin

Racal began work on this Sadie-based private venture 2–18-GHz RWR-ESM set in 1993 and announced it late in 1995. It introduces a new Filtronic IFM (frequency resolution 4 MHz) which is apparently sensitive enough to detect pulse-Doppler and CW signals. Capacity is 500,000 pps. Using four spirals and two wide-open dual Filtronic receivers, Griffin offers extra DF resolution over a forward sector (+/−30-deg azimuth × 10-deg elevation) by means of a proprietary ToA technique. Library capacity is 2000 modes. Frequency coverage can be expanded down to C/D-band and up to K-M band. Accommodated in a single 9-kg 1/2 ATR box, the system can feed a 1553B bus. Five versions are being marketed: naval helicopter ESM (17 kg), attack helicopter RWR (14 kg; the core of the proposed Integrated Defensive Aids system for Apache), fixed-wing aircraft RWR (14 kg), support helicopter RWR (14 kg), and fast-attack boat version (18 kg).

◆ Cygnus

Racal's directional jammer has approximately a 2-deg beam (30 dB gain); average ERP is 300 kW (480 kW in the middle of the frequency range). Because it was designed to work with simple ESM sets, Cygnus incorporates its own IFM (2 MHz accuracy) and its own pointing device, a pair of 8–16-GHz Anaren interferometers flanking the dish on its top and left side. They can work with pulsewidths down to 150 nsec. Using a special mechanism to differentiate target main from sidelobes, the system can avoid the need for a separate omni (for its IFM). Each interferometer consists of three arrays, coarse (40-deg FOV), medium (10 deg), and fine (2.5 deg). Error signals from the coarse array place the signal within the FOV of the medium "zoom" array, which in turn points the platform so that the target is within the FOV of the narrow beam. Each array is split in half, and lobe-switched to track the target. Anaren claims that its approach overcomes multipath effects over water, an effect proportional to antenna beamwidth. Jamming techniques include RGPO and false target generation. Cygnus 2 (7.5–18 GHz) uses a customer-defined ECM response code to respond to threats in its library, jamming emitters in threat priority based on the library.

Production began in 1977. Cygnus 2 went back into production in 1995 for the Egyptian *Ramadan* class.

Users: Algeria (*Kalaat* class LSTs), Bahrein (FPB 62– and TNC 45–classes, ordered 1984), Brazil (*Inhauma* class), Denmark (StanFlex 300 class), Egypt (*Ramadan* class, ordered 1978; upgrade 1995), India (frigates *Taragiri* and *Vindhyagiri*, and "Osa II" class), Kenya ("Province" class, and *Madaraka* and *Mamba*), Kuwait (FPB 57 and TNC 45), Tunisia (Combattante IIIM), Turkey (FRAM destroyers, *Yildiz* class, MEKOs *Barbarossa* and *Orucreis*, and *Tekirdag*), and UAE (TNC 62, TNC 45, TNC 38 classes). Cygnus was installed on board some Type 23s for training purposes (as of 1996 these ships have no jammers at all permanently installed).

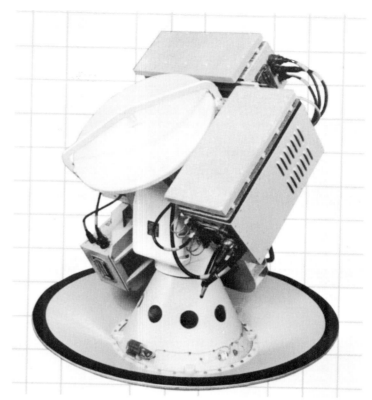

Cygnus jammer, with the two boxes of its Anaren tracking receiver above the disk and to the right. (Anaren)

◆ Manta/Sceptre (UAT)

MEL's rough equivalent to Cutlass used its Pulse Train Analyzer (PTA) instead of Racal's KS500. Now Thorn-EMI, which bought MEL, has been bought by Racal (as Racal Thorn), so both main lines of British shipboard ESM development have been brought under a single management. The land-based equivalent to these naval systems is Setter. The statement that these systems are derived from Rapids, with new Signaal technology, suggests that Signaal developed MEL's PTA. Compared to KS500, PTA had the important advantage of being able to perceive single frequency-agile radars as one—rather than several nearby—radar. Similarly, it is designed to handle PRF agility. Thus its tote display shows upper and lower limits on an emitter's frequency, PRF, and pulse width. Manta is the submarine version, Sceptre the surface-ship version. Each is modular; the versions are O, X, and XL. Each has an IFM (accuracy 6 MHz in the O version). Each has a base threat library capacity of 144 modes for automated alarms. The X version, now extinct, was roughly equivalent to Cutlass. It and the XL version added look-up libraries (6000 modes plus 100 operator-added ones in XL).

Sceptre O, for patrol craft, uses a single masthead array (for both omni and DF, accuracy 10 deg, elevation coverage −15/+30 deg). Dynamic range is 35 dB, and sensitivity is −40 dBm.

The 2–18-GHz XL series was reportedly developed beginning in the mid-1980s to regain MEL's position in the Royal Navy following Racal's UAF victory. Its alternative to Sadie is a proprietary Philips channelized digital receiver feeding fast (18 MIPS) de-interleavers working with transputers (for emitter recognition). Software is modular, much of it written in ADA for portability. Track capacity is 255. XL can deal with 1M pps (pulse widths 50 nsec–100 msec), with PRFs of 100 Hz–300 kHz and scan periods between 0.02 and 40 sec. Manta XL DF accuracy is 6-10 deg (2 deg optional, presumably by using a dish). Sensitivity is −40 dBm and dynamic range is 40–50 dB.

Sceptre Lens is Sceptre XL using a three-band (in two pairs of radomes) CelsiusTech lens antenna. Elevation coverage is +30/−10 deg, and bearing accuracy is 4.5 deg (with 2 deg available as an option). Sensitivity is −64 dBm, and dynamic range is 60 dB. The processor can deal with complex pulses. UAT (for Type

23 Batch 2) is essentially Sceptre XL with the antenna of the earlier UAF(1). It may also use the dual color displays of the earlier system. Carrier installations of UAT will begin with *Ark Royal*. Variants: UAT(1) replaces UAF(1) in Type 23 frigates and, presumably, in the carriers; UAT(2) and (3) are shore-based; UAT(4) has an interface with ADAWS 2000 for HMS *Ocean*; UAT(5) has an interface with ADIMP for eight Type 42 destroyers; and UAT(6) has an interface with CACS for Type 22 frigates. The new LPDs will get UAT(4) or UAT(5).

Users:

Manta XL: Australia (*Oberons*, to be fitted to *Collins* class as *Oberons* retire), Spain (*Agosta* class), Sweden (A-19 class).

Sceptre O: Saudi Arabia (chosen for old ex-U.S. MSCs, 1992).

Sceptre XL: Australia (ANZAC frigate), New Zealand (ANZAC frigate), Sweden (*Goteborg* class, as Sceptre Lens), United Kingdom (as UAT, for carriers and Type 23 Batch II frigates).

◆ Matilda/UAR/Matilde

MEL proposed Matilda in January 1984 as the simplest possible small combatant radar warner, focusing on what its study showed were the generic characteristics of locked-on missiles and fire-control radars: 7.5–16 GHz, low rate of change of bearing, constant pulse width, relatively constant signal strength. By responding automatically to any such threat (without consulting a library) Matilda's signal processing time was cut to less than 10 microsec, so that it could provide an alert within 1 sec of signal detection (for at least 30 sec warning of a subsonic threat). MEL argued further that chaff was the best instant countermeasure; it developed Protean specifically to work with Matilda. A processor voice module can give a prerecorded alarm. Four horns clamped to the masthead feed the system's four RF channels.

Matilda on HMS *Hecla*. The spiral antennas are at the ends of the two short cylinders clamped to the mast. (S. Slade, DMS/Forecast International)

The parent PEAB company marketed a more elaborate form of the system as Matilde. Missile/FCS emitters are automatically listed as Threat 1. All others are listed as Threat 2, and further classified by the operator, using a library in the ship's FCS computer. A 12in CRT can show either signal direction or alphanumeric signal data. Reportedly Matilde suffered an excessive false-alarm rate: it could not distinguish a locked-on radar from a powerful nearby scanning radar. It was therefore shelved for a time, to be revived by CelsiusTech (which took over PEAB). The system's Philax grenades are identical to those of Protean.

The Royal Navy ran initial trials in 1985. As of late 1996, UAR, the Royal Navy version, was no longer in service.

Users: Australia (*Success, Westralia, Tobruk*, and *Balikpapan*-class LCTs), Egypt (October and "Osa I" classes), Finland (as part of 9CM system: *Hameenmaa* and *Helsinki I/II* classes: Matilde), Greece (two ordered February 1987 for merchant-ship protection during Iran-Iraq War, later disappeared, may have been prototypes for Korean production), Jordan ("Hawk"-class FAC), Kuwait (as backup for Cutlass), South Korea (*Ulsan, Donghae, Pohang* classes: Matilde/Philax, now being made, apparently without license, in Korea, and specified for KDX), Singapore (*Landsort* class), Sweden (*Landsort* class). As of late 1993, total known production and orders amounted to 84 Matilda and 75 Matilde; unit cost is probably less than $100,000.

◆ RCM/Type 670

Decca (later Racal) introduced these jammers in 1975 to work with other Decca equipment, such as the RDL series described below. Separate training and elevating transmitting and receiving antennas are under a common radome (two radomes in larger ships).

Type 670 (in the radome) is visible just below the Type 1022 radar, HMS *Manchester*, Antwerp, May 1990. The material wrapped around the mainmast, at the same height as the big air-search radar, is intended to absorb its signals so as not to create misleading echoes. (L. van Ginderen)

The 8–10-GHz RCM-1 operates with RDL-2, using a high-power CW TWT for RGPO. The two-band (5–9 and 9–16 GHz) RCM-2 is capable of conscan deception. It has an IFM: upon target designation, the receiver searches a 100-MHz slot around the designated target frequency, to set the jammer on.

RCM-3 adds a processor and a memory loop to cope with frequency-agile radars. In its responsive noise mode, the IFM fast-tunes a local oscillator to the frequency of the incoming pulse. The only buyer was the Royal Navy (as Type 670 [Heather]) as an emergency response to the Falklands War (the Royal Navy had emphasized ESM but not jamming). Reportedly the IFM was excellent, but the TWT proved quite unreliable in service. About May 1993 the Royal Navy reportedly canceled an upgrade program, already under contract, and planned to withdraw Type 670 as an economy measure. Ironically, the upgrade program had been delayed by a special effort to maximize Type 670 availability for ships deploying for the Gulf War; this effort resulted in the best MTBF in the system's career, and the fully upgraded system was performing above specification by the second half of 1992. Type 670 modes are probably RGPO, conscan deception, and continuous/burst noise. The upgrade entailed improving guard circuits, mechanical components, and radome heaters.

Users:

RCM-2: Argentina (*Hercules* and MEKO-140 class), Egypt (October class), Malaysia (*Spica M* class, probably replaced by Rattler), Nigeria (*Aradu, Obuma*), South Korea (8 *Ul-*

san and 22 *Pohang*-class frigates), Thailand (*Makut Rajakumarn* and PF 103 class).

Type 670: Brazil (Type 22 Batch I), United Kingdom (Type 42 Batch I [except *Cardiff*], Type 22 Batch II).

◆ RDL

Decca's (later Racal's) Radar Detecting and Locating system was its first commercial, rather than Royal Navy, ESM system. As in Porker, the system is analog, the operator strobing a signal of interest to pass it into a pulse analysis CRT or an automatic pulse analyzer (APA-1C) with digital output. Parameters (pulse interval, pulse width, band) for up to five emitter modes (specific threats) can be entered by plug-in circuit cards. The pulse interval (PI) range is 10 microsec to 10 millisec; the pulsewidth range is 50 nsec to 100 microsec. APA-1C output can be passed in turn to an SRU-1 signal recognition unit (500-emitter library). The characteristic single-tier wrap-around antenna at the masthead is also used in Cutlass.

The basic 2–11.5-GHz RDL-1 incorporates the pulse analyzer. RDL-1BC is a version for fast patrol boats. RDL-2 extends coverage to 1–18 GHz, using some additional antennas. RDL-2ABC, for larger warships, amplifies the RF signal in the analysis channel to increase range and make visual pulse analysis (by two-trace CRT, to show either pulse width or PRF in two ranges) more effective; it also adds an SHR (feeding a frequency-amplitude display) to measure frequency. Up to three known frequencies can be suppressed, and SHR output is read out digitally.

More sophisticated versions with wider frequency coverage did not sell. Of several submarine versions, only UAB, for the Navy, entered service; it is now extinct.

Users: Argentina (RDL-2 in Type 42 destroyers, RDL-2ABC in MEKO 140 class, and RDL-1 in TNC 45 class), Bahrein (RDL-2 in FPB-38 class and -2ABC in two of four TNC-45 class), Brazil (RDL-2 in *Niteroi* class), Egypt (RDL-1 in October class, in addition to Matilda), Iran (RDL-2AC in Mk 5 frigates), Nigeria (RDL-2 in *Aradu* and TNC-57s, RDL-1 in Combattante IIIBs), Oman (RDL-2 in *Nasr Al Bahr*), South Korea (RDL-2 in 8 *Ulsan* class and 22 *Pohang*-class light frigates), Thailand (RDL-2 in *Makut Rajakumarn* and *Ratcharit, Prabrarapak,* PF 103, and *Sattahip* classes).

◆ RACAL COMINT System

Racal introduced a new shipboard communications intelligence system in 1989, based on the company's land-based equipment. Two alternative antennas are used: a single compact stack for 90–400 MHz and a stack of two separate antennas for 20–500 MHz. The simpler antenna covers civilian and military marine bands; the more complex includes land combat net radio frequencies as well as paramilitary bands. These systems now incorporate a computer-controlled Fast Acquisition Receiver System (FARS). Ranges of variable operating parameters, such as changes in signal level and target activity level, are preset, and FARS filters incoming signals, for example, to provide a display of the most recent active signals or of newly acquired signals.

In land applications, FARS has two alternative modes, scan and list. It can scan at 40 MHz/sec or it can address up to 250 selected (listed) frequency channels, at the rate of 160 channels/sec.

◆ SARIE

SARIE I and II are Thorn-EMI's signal-recognition processors, intended to supplement other ESM systems. SARIE I (ca. 1962/63) used a paper tape and an optical reader. SARIE II used magnetic tape to quadruple the library capacity of SARIE I; it can display up to six possible identifications of a received signal, along with the received parameters. It can make up to 1000 comparisons in less than 350 msec. In some British systems, SARIE automatically collected radar parameters from YAZ (see UA-8/9/10), but often emitter frequency had to be inserted manually. SARIE can handle PRF between 31 Hz and 19.5 kHz (accuracy 1 Hz up to 1 kHz, 100 Hz at 10 kHz); PRF jitter; pulse width between 0.1 and 99.9 microsec (in increments of 0.05 microsec); and scan period between 0.1 and 59 sec (in increments of 0.1 sec). SARIE was integrated with many DR 2000s (e.g., in German Type 343 minesweepers); presumably DALIA was often its replacement.

◆ Scorpion

Racal's wide-beam 7.5–18-GHz jammer doubles its effective power by measuring (using a mast antenna) and then steering a horn to match the polarization of the target radar (without such measurement and steering, the jammer has to waste half its power on the wrong polarization). The jammer can also modulate polarization angle up to +/−15 deg about the nominal angle, to deal with co-polar or cross-polarization radars. The basic jammer antenna is a wide-beam (40 × 40-deg) horn which can be tilted +/−60 deg to match polarization. It is used mainly to dilute an attack, confusing target acquisition. A steerable three-axis stabilized 8-deg carbon-fiber dish is used for point defense (jamming the radar of the incoming missile). The system time-shares a single TWT to meet up to eight threats (some Racal literature says five) simultaneously, providing a special series of up to ten different jamming modulations for each target. Modulations include continuous and burst noise, cover pulse noise, synchronized railing, and false target generation. Peak ERP is 160 kW in mid-band. Typically both antennas share a single radome.

Racal's Octopus (for German S148-class fast-attack boats) combines Cutlass B1 with a Scorpion jammer and an AEG threat analyzer/library. The German navy specified both antennas. In this version, Scorpion provides 150-kW midband ERP (50 kW minimum) and can jam up to 16 threats.

Users: Denmark (*Thetis* class), Germany (as Octopus, in the S148 class), Oman ("Province" class), Turkey (MEKO 200 Track II frigates). The version in the Omani ships is apparently limited to broad-beam antennas at the after part of the pilothouse struc-

RDL-2/3 intercept and DF arrays around the foremast of a Brazilian frigate, 1986. Each array is split to fit around the mast. (Author)

Scorpion uses the radome at right on a German Type 148 FAC. The radome at left is for the Anaren DF array of Cutlass B1; the combination is Octopus. The radar is Triton G. (Racal)

ture. The Turkish ships carry radomes (like the single radome in the German S148) on either side abeam their lattice foremasts. Photographs of the Danish ships do not seem to show the jammer(s) at all; they may be reserved for wartime fitting.

◆ Prophet/Sea Saviour

Racal's 6–18-GHz four-port helicopter or fighter RWR competes with Sky Guardian and AWARE; Sea Saviour is the ship version using the RDL array (elevation +40/−5 deg). A submarine warning version, Sprat, did not pass the project stage. As in the big Cutlass and Sadie systems, IFMs are inserted in the DF channels. Because the system measures the frequency of each incoming pulse, it can filter signals on a pulse-by-pulse basis (i.e., on the basis of frequency and pulse width), reducing the load on the deinterleaver (which has a 64-mode library), identifying emitters on the basis of frequency, pulse width, and PRF. Racal claims that filtering greatly reduces the false-alarm rate, the usual bane of RWRs. The simple LED display shows up to three signals at a time (the system can support two displays). Reaction time is less than 1 sec. The system can be extended down to S-band (3 GHz) and up to K-band, and the threat library can be expanded.

Users: Brunei (probably, for *Waspada*-class upgrade), Egypt (MiG-21s); Racal claims other unidentified buyers for Sea Saviour. In the British service, Prophet was superseded by AWARE.

◆ EP 4220

Thorn-EMI's 0.4–18-GHz (extendable to 40 GHz and above) channelized COMINT superhet has an instantaneous bandwidth of 1 GHz (to deal with frequency-agile emitters), but its accuracy and sensitivity are comparable to those of a narrow-band superhet. IF bandwidth is 80 MHz. Tuning can be quasi-continuous (using a spinwheel) or operator-selected monitoring (with up to 10-kHz tuning resolution). The receiver can also scan cyclically over up to 99 frequencies, continuing the scan after either a preselected dwell time or at a keystroke. Frequency ranges (in 36-MHz steps across a 1-GHz bandwidth) can be blanked out. Dynamic range is at least 60 dB. Real-time graphics displays are: Pan RF/IF, amplitude versus time, and frequency versus time. Display resolutions: amplitude 1 dB, frequency 1 MHz. Display facilities are zoom, freeze, and hard copy. This receiver can be connected to an EP4210 pulse analyzer (which measures intrapulse modulation).

◆ PALANTIR

This knowledge-based emitter identification system is the first fruit of a 1995 DRA program to develop NCTR for both picture compilation and threat warning. The parameters are frequency, PRI, pulse width, and scan type. A basic matcher using coarse parameter matches feeds a three-level (plausible, most strongly selected, and finally best choice) selector. Level 1 compares the observed range of each parameter against known operating range and agility (and scan type in the case of scan, for a simple filter by radar type). Each possible match is rated as either fully consistent, consistent, plausible, or not consistent. Then 29 combination rules are used decide whether there is any support for the possible identity. Level 2 selects the set of most strongly supported identities (presumably it can take platform data into account). Level 3 picks the best matches by detailed comparison. DRA claimed that, in tests against 900 simulated tracks (whose parameters were realistically corrupted and showed typical pulse sorting errors), PALANTIR performed significantly better than a typical conventional technique, both in terms of correct and unambiguous identities and in terms of limiting false alarms.

PALANTIR was developed on a SunSPARC station programmed in PROLOG, a standard prototyping and development software tool. Instead of rewriting the software in a conventional language, DRA is implementing PALANTIR on Psilogic's new PSIDRA, each of whose parallel nodes consists of two Sequential PROLOG processors using PowerPC CPUs.

◆ Expendables

Racal Radar Defense Systems, successor to Thorn-EMI, is reportedly developing a new naval expendable, which may have some CARMEN input (CARMEN was originally a joint venture with Thomson-CSF, and it lost to Siren in the Royal Navy competition). The Royal Navy bought U.S. GEN-X active airborne jammers on an urgent basis (under Urgent Operational Requirement 8/94) in mid-1994 for operations over Bosnia, NATO having ruled that only aircraft with self-protection jammers would be permitted there. The jammers, adapted to work with existing ALE-40 dispensers, entered British service early in 1995.

Note that Chemring provides Chaff Charlie (I or J band) for the standard 4.5in gun, and also Chaff Hotel manually released from helicopters. Both are for long-range confusion.

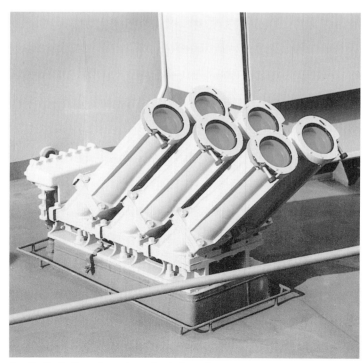

Outfit DLB (Sea Gnat launcher) aboard HMS *Westminster*. (S. Slade, DMS/Forecast International)

◆ DLA/DLB/DLJ (Sea Gnat)

The British Sea Gnat system uses a Thorn-EMI algorithmic processor (precomputed decoy patterns) to control U.S.-type Mk 36 launchers plus, in the case of DLA, a six-barrel Corvus launcher (see below). In DLA, each barrel of the six-tube Sea Gnat launcher is elevated at 30 deg; of two sets on each side of a ship, one is at a 30- and one at a 120-deg angle to the centerline. Corvus was required because Sea Gnat chaff rounds were delivered late; Sea Gnat was needed to provide an IR seduction round.

DLB eliminates Corvus, using pairs of barrels for the Mk 214-1 RF round, Mk 216 RF distraction round, and Mk 218 IR round. DLB* is an interim system with two Corvus barrels atop four SRBOC barrels (Corvus fired the N4 BBC distraction round; Mk 216 was not ready in time). DLJ has additional launchers to cover a large ship. DLJ(1), four DLB plus four U.S.-type SRBOC launchers, was converted to DLJ (2), which has eight DLB.

> Users:
> DLA: Type 42 Batch 3 destroyers *York* and *Edinburgh*.
> DLB: Type 42 destroyers, Type 22 and 23 frigates, *Intrepid*, *Fort*-class AORs (interim fit), *Oakleaf*, some *Appleleaf* class; was probably retained in Type 22 frigates transferred to Brazil. In Type 42s, this system has apparently superseded the U.S. Mk 36-1 (DLD) installed after the Falklands War.
> DLJ: DLJ(2) in carriers and *Ocean*, *Fearless*, and *Argus*; it was specified for the *Fort Grange* and *Fort Victoria* classes.

◆ DLC/Corvus and DLE/Shield

The Plessey-Vickers 102mm chaff-decoy rocket launcher has eight 1.6m tubes, all at a fixed 30-deg elevation: two sets of three at right angles, with a set of two above, bisecting that angle. The launcher weighs 585 kg (with another 42 kg in off-launcher electronics). Many launchers carry a single manually fired Attwell 2in rocket flare launcher atop them (there is also a single stand-alone rocket-flare launcher, manually trainable on its own pedestal). A pair of launchers (port and starboard) is considered sufficient to deal with three attacks. The prototype six-barrel version of Corvus went to sea on board HMS *Arethusa* in 1968. A new Plessey BBC (broad-band [G-K bands] chaff, 101.6 × 1580 mm, 21.8 kg with 6.8-kg payload) rocket, N4, replaced the earlier Knebworth in 1979. Its payload was the heaviest then available in a rocket of its dimensions. Rockets are manually preset for range (35 to 2000 m) and mode (distraction [long range, up to four clouds], dump [400m range, onto which a jammer moves a missile range gate], or centroid seduction [short range, to move the centroid of the net radar target off the ship]). Rockets are spin-stabilized, each tube having four right-hand spiral guides.

At a wavelength of 2.6 cm, 2.5 sec after bursting the chaff cloud RCS is 1200 m^2, equivalent (given reflection off the sea) to that of a 12,000m^2 ship. At a fuze setting of 1.5 sec or less,

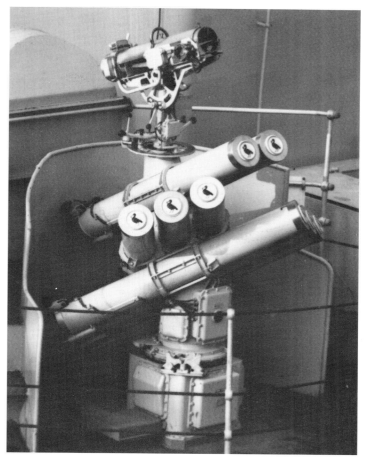

A Corvus launcher, with its rocket flare (illumination) launcher on top.

the cloud extends between 90 and 395 m in range, and between 25 and 138 m in height. It lasts for up to 5 min.

An associated IR decoy has a range of 40–160 m, carrying seven IR submunitions. One Plessey version uses the chaff rocket as a buoy, with the IR flare on top.

Plessey's (now GEC-Marconi's) Shield (Royal Navy DLE) was developed as a private venture after the Falklands War (the first sale, to Brazil, was made in 1983). It employs the same manually set rockets as Corvus, but each launcher carries two three-rocket modules, either parallel or crossed at an 80-deg angle. The crossed-barrel launcher is for corvettes or smaller ships. The Royal Navy's N5 or P5 rocket is N4 with inductive coupling and a modified fin assembly. P8 (102 × 1700 mm, 19 kg) is a BBC round with a larger payload (7.5 kg) and a programmable electronic fuze for remote automated operation; burst range is 50 m to 2.5 km. P6 (102 × 1630 mm, 17 kg) is an IR round using the same material as the German Hot Dog. It is a mortar rather than a rocket because it functions at short range. Each tube fires seven submunitions to walk the IR sensor away from the target, the first at 50 and the last at 250 m. Recoil indicates each firing to the launcher. The entire tube is thrown away after firing. Decoys are available in both the 3–5- and 8–14-micron bands.

Shield 2 is an automated export version using a Z-80 processor loaded with precomputed decoy patterns based on a large number of off-line simulations in a ShieldMOS simulator, adapted to the platform involved. The table in the system's EPROM computer card can accommodate up to eight threat types; the computer also takes into account such variables as wind speed and direction, sea state, and ship course and speed. Shield 3, which was probably first sold to Singapore in mid-1993 (for 45m patrol boats), substitutes a 68040 for the Z-80, employs an Ethernet LAN, and uses a plasma touch-screen for control.

In 1993 GEC-Marconi Combat Systems revealed initial studies of how Shield might be used as part of an integrated torpedo defense system.

Shield aboard NCSM *Toronto*. Note the light machine-gun mount (without a gun) in the foreground. In some cases the barrels are mounted in horizontal pairs, three high. (S. Slade, DMS/Forecast International)

Users: DLC/Corvus: Argentina (Type 42 destroyers), Bangladesh (*Leopard* class), Chile ("County" and *Leander* classes and AOR *Alm Jorge Montt*), Ecuador (*Leander* class), France (*Jeanne d'Arc, Aconit, Duperre, Dupleix, Georges Leygues, Latouche-Treville*), Greece (*Kortenaer* class), India (*Viraat*), Indonesia (*Fatahillah, Hajar Dewantara, van Speijk* [note that the Netherlands navy used SRBOC on these ships], and "Tribal" classes), Iran (Vosper Mk 5 and *Hangam* classes), Malaysia (*Rahman*), Pakistan ("County" and *Leander* classes; may be retained in ex-British Type 21s), and the United Kingdom (Type 42 destroyer *Birmingham, Resource,* and *Sir Bedivere, Fort Grange, Olwen, Rover,* and *Appleleaf* classes).

DLE/Shield: Brazil (*Inhauma, Niteroi* classes), Canada (TRUMP, *Restigouche, Protecteur* classes), Malaysia (*Lekiu* class), Pakistan (FRAM *Gearings* modernized with APECS II ECM suit), Singapore (*Victory* class [Mk 2] and new 45m class [Mk 3]), Thailand (*Khamronsin* class), and the United Kingdom ("Castle" class, *Sir Galahad, Diligence,* "Knight" class (LSLs), *Argus, Fort Grange, Rover*-class AORs, *Orangeleaf*). Brazil, Canada, and Singapore all use the automatic Shield 2 or 3 with P6 and P8 rounds. In 1989, unit price was about $250,000, plus $120,000 for radar absorbent cladding, without which the decoy is not sold. The first Royal Navy units were bought in the early 1980s.

♦ Replica (DLF[1]/Rubber Duck/SLQ-49)

Irvin's Replica is an inflatable buoyant structure supporting a 2.5m fabric-backed octahedral aluminum alloy tube corner reflector; to a radar, it looks very much like a ship. Unlike chaff, it is inherently broad-band; it is considered effective for up to 3 hr in Sea State 4. The decoy is carried on inclined ramps in two 1.14m long containers, similar to those used for liferafts, on inclined ramps. The two decoys are connected by a 4–5m line, container lids remaining connected as sea anchors, keeping the line taut and preventing the decoys from collapsing together. Replica can be set to self-destruct or can be activated by remote control.

Irvin Replica radar decoy, stowed (*left*) and deployed (*right*). (*Ships of the World*)

Reportedly Replica was inspired by a Soviet decoy, which is similar but spherical (about 2.5 m in diameter). DLF(2) is an improved version with a larger RCS. Proposed fitting to British warships has been reduced due to budget cuts. The Royal Navy calls Replica DLF or Rubber Duck. An RFQ for DLF(3) was issued in September 1991. The U.S. designation is SLQ-49. In April 1987 the U.S. Navy reportedly tested an air-launched version, comparable in size and shape to a Mk-46 torpedo.

Users: France, Italy (at least in *Mimbelli* class), Netherlands, Saudi Arabia (*Sandown* class), Spain (planned for minehunters), Thailand (*Kamronsin* class), United Kingdom, United States.

♦ DLH/Siren

On 20 July 1994 Marconi received an £80M contract for its I/J-band Siren active decoy, development of which had begun in 1982. It is fired from a standard 130mm launcher (dimensions: 130 × 1700 mm, 28 kg). The 2-kW Siren has a digital RF memory loop (DRFM) and hence can use software to control the signals amplified by its TWT. The loser in the British competition, the Thorn-EMI/Thomson-CSF CARMEN, had an analog memory loop. Marconi claims that Siren is more powerful than many onboard jammers. It activates 10 sec after launch, at a preset range of 400–500 m. It is parachute-borne, and stays aloft for up to 180 sec. Siren unit cost is about $50,000 (1994).

In 1989 Siren was evaluated by the U.S. Navy under the Foreign Weapons Evaluation Program. Compared to the long-life Nulka, Siren is conceived as a last-ditch decoy.

♦ DLK/Barricade/Super Barricade/Stockade

ML Aviation's (formerly Wallop Industries's) Barricade lightweight launcher fires spin-stabilized 57mm chaff and flare rockets from a stack of six open frames (3 rockets/frame). The lower three sets are angled at 60 deg to each other for full azimuth coverage by long-range Stockade rockets (range 400–2000 m, carrying 1 lb of chaff, dispersed centrifugally). The upper three fire short-range Pallisade rockets to 60 m from the ship for centroid seduction. Typically a ship has one set of 110-kg launchers on each side.

Barricade chaff launcher. (A. Raven)

Barricade Mk II is controlled by a microprocessor, which stores decoy firing sequences (distraction, dump/RGPO, confusion, seduction/centroid) and recommends a course to steer. Mk III, introduced at the 1991 RNEE exhibition, has updated electronics (storing up to eight preprogrammed reaction patterns), better tactical coverage, a better interface with a ship's CDS, more power supply options, and more commonality with Super Barricade. Launcher racks are lighter (95 kg) and stronger.

As DLK, Barricade is carried by frigates and destroyers on the Armilla patrol (Persian Gulf) because (with the failure of Sea Gnat Mk 218) it is currently the only IR decoy defense for British ships in that theater.

Super Barricade (Barricade Mk IV), which also has a tactical processor, fires a larger rocket (a spin-stabilized 102mm [4in] round) to 2000 m, to cover a larger ship. Of four sets of triple barrels, the lower two are trained 90 deg away from the rest so that a pair of launchers covers all four quadrants, firing medium and long-range Super Stockade in dump, distraction, and confusion modes. The upper two, firing Super Pallisade rockets in centroid deception mode, point along the same bearing, but at different elevation angles. They fire short-range Super Pallisade rockets in centroid deception mode. Development began in 1987.

The system's IR decoy is a flare rocket.

Barricade was privately developed, winning its first order in 1980 (for Omani FAC). Alenia integrated it with the mini-SADOC CDS of the *Minerva*-class corvettes; on this basis it developed an integrated retrofit package (command system and chaff launcher) for an unspecified Asian navy, almost certainly India (probably for "Tarantuls").

Users: Barricade: Algeria (*Kalaat*-class LSTs), Bahrein (two TNC 38s), Brunei (specified for new 80m corvettes, which have not yet been ordered), Chile (four *Prat*, four *Leander*, all with Corvus, and three FACs), Croatia (one *Koncar*, two "Osa I" class), Denmark (four *Falster* and two *Lindormen* classes, possibly also *Thetis*), Finland (*Turunmaa* class, *Helsinki* class, *Keihassalmi, Pohjanmaa*), Greece (two "Osprey" and two Improved "Osprey" OPVs), India (probably on "Tarantuls"), Ireland (one on *Eithne* [as flare launcher; no associated ESM]), Italy (eight *Minerva* class), Jordan (three "Hawk" class), Kenya (two "Province" class, *Madaraka, Mamba*), Malaysia (four Combattante II), Oman (four "Province," five Brooke Marine types, *Nasr Al Bahr*), Serbia (five *Koncar* and eight "Osa I" classes), Turkey (one *Nusret*-class minelayer), United Kingdom (seven "Island" class, two "Castle" class, 16 *Sandown* class, 12 "Hunt" class, *Hecla, Herald*). As of 1993, 130 Barricade installations were in service or on order. Unit price for a British naval contract was about $625,000 (probably including an associated Matilda RWR). Current cost for Barricade alone is probably $150,000 ($250,000 for Super Barricade). A total of 27 (each using two launchers) had been supplied to the Royal Navy by early 1991. It first bought Mk II in 1984, and Mk III entered service in 1990 (six were bought for "Hunt"-class minehunters for the Gulf War). Yugoslavia was to have received Barricades for four *Split*-class frigates, four Kotor-class frigates, eight Kobra-class corvettes, four Mornar-class corvettes, and 12 Koncar-class FAC. Only the systems listed above were delivered, split between Croatia and Serbia. The U.S. Navy evaluated Barricade in 1991 as an alternative to SRBOC for frigates, but bought none in 1992. There is, however, current interest in installation on board the PCs. No U.S. designation has been published.

Super Barricade: Australia (*Huon* class minehunters), Finland (*Hameenmaa*), India ("Tarantuls"), Malaysia (*Lekiu*-class frigates), Oman (two Muheet-class light frigates), Spain (eight modified *Sandown* class).

◆ Pirate

Pains Wessex announced this 130mm IR decoy at the BARNEE 1995 show. Unlike torch decoys, it produces a large "hot" smoke cloud. The cartridge contains nine submunitions (three air burst, six floating smoke generators). It emits in both IR bands (minimum mean values 1.0 kW/str in 3–5 microns and 4.0 kW/str in 8–12 microns), with an effective minimum mean area of 150 m^2, and a smoke duration of at least 60 sec (6 sec maximum time to full output). The launcher is Mk 36 Mod 1 (dimensions of decoy are 130 × 1134 mm, 18.6 kg). Pirate is a candidate for the NATO IR decoy, and it was bought by Turkey late in 1995.

UNITED STATES

To conform to JCS terminology, the U.S. Navy now calls ESM electronic support and ECM (including IRCM) electronic attack. Electronic warfare is now considered part of a broader "information warfare." ECCM is electronic protection. As outlined in previous sections, there is increasing interest in using electronic intelligence for tactical purposes. SEI (specific emitter identification, radar fingerprinting) is an important case in point. In the past, it was used (as HULTEC, hull-to-emitter correlation) to help track major Soviet combatant ships. Now it is seen as a means of tracking specific merchant ships (of over 500 t), for example, to help track shipments of illegal weapons, such as long-range missiles. The rub is that mass-produced commercial radars probably show far less variation (reflected in differences in fine pulse structure) than virtually handmade naval search radars. Late in 1995 the U.S. Navy received counter-proliferation money (as a FY96 new start) to find out whether SEI could be applied to merchant ships. Signals picked up by satellites and by receivers at choke points will be examined for Unintentional Modulation on Pulse (UMOP). If platforms can indeed be associated with particular UMOPs, special receivers are to be placed on board aircraft (EP-3, P-3, and ES-3 at a unit cost, respectively, of $125K, $270K, and $135K), in shore units at choke points ($750K), and on ships ($310K), in that order of priority.

Recent experiments by the Airborne Electronic Combat Services Program (AECSP, formerly FEWSG) suggest that relatively simple digital systems can greatly complicate ESM. For example, the digitized output of a modified APS-133 weather radar (a typical airliner radar), run through a scan converter (presumably to improve scan-to-scan integration) and displayed on a large screen, can detect ships (e.g., an amphibious group) at a range of 200 nm, yet the signals sent out by the radar are exactly those a typical airliner would produce.

Most antiship missiles use monopulse guidance. The alternative counters are deception (generally RGPO), a persistent active decoy operating away from the ship, and some means of confusing the monopulse system in angle as well as in range. A new shipboard ECM transmitter is being developed (FY96 new start ATD). Work is also underway on a new type of "photonic" EW beam-forming antenna. Electronic signals are replaced by light signals for easier processing (a brassboard linear array was built under the FY96 program, and a 16-channel optical brassboard under the FY97 program). The test of whether deception is working is whether the missile has reverted from lock-on to continued search. Some missiles confuse the deceiver by shaping their outputs to *appear* to have gone back to search mode while in fact still pointing their antennas at the target. An FY95 ATD uses Doppler to estimate the actual missile seeker pointing angle. EAGER (preferential acquisition decoy) is a new (FY96 ATD) active decoy, an electric helicopter (to avoid launch pyrotechnics) powered and controlled (via optical fibers) by the ship, via a 230m tether. Rotor diameter is 3 m; the vehicle weighs 36 kg (6.8 kg payload). Initial trials were conducted in the summer of 1996, and the full system is to be tested in September 1997. One great advantage of the helicopter is that it needs no pyrotechnic launcher, with attendant IR signature. An alternative is the SRBOC-fired FLYRT, a small electrically powered airplane that can also carry a jammer. An adaptive monopulse countermeasure ran at-sea tests in FY91, but seems not to have been successful.

Efforts to reduce ship RCS (see Outlaw Bandit, below) have led to work on a decoy adapted to limited RCS (a FY97 new start). One problem is that excessive decoy RCS may lead to detection if the decoy is prematurely triggered. Work on a new emitter location technique using the Doppler imparted to the emitter's signals by a helicopter's rotor blades began in FY96. The FY97 program included fabrication of an ADM of a new "smart skin array" to provide a very large aperture for aircraft ESM systems.

The current EA-6B may ultimately be replaced by a modified F/A-18. Its nose radar active array could be used as a high-gain directional receiver (capable of picking up and localizing enemy radar sidelobes) or as an X-band jammer. Podded wide-band antenna arrays (mid- and high-band interferometers and low-band spirals) would replace the usual wingtip missiles. Vertical low-band arrays would be in the nose. Signals down-converted in the pods would be transmitted to a fuselage processor. New jammer pods powered by internal ram-air turbines (for low drag) could be carried on the existing hardpoints. As of 1995, McDonnell-Douglas believed that two types of pod would suffice to cover the whole frequency band, rather than the seven types the EA-6B uses (which still leave some gaps). The problem of transmission through wing folds will probably be solved by digitizing signals at the wingtip pod and transmitting via fiber-optic cable.

Meanwhile the scope of ECM is growing. GPS has become more and more important; how easily can an enemy jam weak GPS signals in a limited battle zone? For example, an AECSP airplane carrying a 5W transmitter and flying at 24,000 ft jammed GPS signals within a 30-deg cone out to about 10 nm.

For its part, the U.S. services want to be able to engage in navigational warfare (the subject of a FY96 ATD), denying GPS and other navigational information to an enemy without losing their own access.

IR- and optically guided and controlled weapons, particularly those used by enemies to attack U.S. aircraft, are attracting more attention. Existing modulated-lamp countermeasures, which do not need any special warners, will probably not be effective against the new staring and imaging IR sensors. Too, a missile seeker may measure target temperature by comparing radiation at two or more wavelengths (colors or shades). No conventional lamp can overcome such measurement. A new strategy is needed. Besides triggering decoy dispersal, the new aircraft missile launch warner is to aim a mid-wave laser (a directional IR countermeasure, or DIRCM, a FY96 ATD) at the incoming weapon.

Operating at the appropriate wavelengths (with properly adjusted intensities), a tunable laser probably can solve the problem. It must first be tuned to the missile's seeker wavelengths. One possibility (closed-loop DIRCM) is to point the laser at the seeker. The radome over the seeker probably absorbs only those wavelengths it uses.

The demand for directional information rules out a nondirectional pulse-Doppler radar like the existing ALQ-156 (which had been part of the abortive A-6 defensive upgrade); to make the radar directional would be impractical, given the demands for antenna space on the skin of the airplane. That leaves staring IR and UV devices, both focusing on the missile's exhaust plume. Some favor UV in hopes that it will cut false alarms. For example, the aluminum in solid rocket fuel makes a very strong emission line in a part of the spectrum in which the ozone in the atmosphere blocks solar emission (an IR sensor may find it difficult to distinguish the sun from a missile plume). On the other hand, it is relatively easy to dope a missile motor to drastically cut smoke (UV emissions); IR emission is much more difficult to eliminate. In any case, detections must be filtered to eliminate, for example, missiles heading for other aircraft. A missile warner generally concentrates on sources whose intensity is increasing and which show constant elevation and bearing relative to the aircraft. Note that this logic is ineffective against a missile maneuvering *after* its motor burns out. As it happened, the choice fell on an IR system (see CMWS/ATIRCM, below).

Missiles with gyros can sense target motion; they will disregard decoys ejected aft. That demands a new generation of kinematic (powered or gliding) activated metal decoys. On the other hand, the shipboard equivalent of DIRCM, MATES, has not progressed beyond the prototype stage. Only now has the U.S. Navy found a satisfactory shipboard IR decoy, the German Giant (Cartridge Mk 245). Decoy launchers themselves produce hot spots, so one proposed FY97 project is to develop nonpyrotechnic decoy launch technology. The electric helicopter (EAGER, see above) falls into this category.

Optics and IR are also used to target weapons, such as light AA guns. Scanning at low power, a laser detects optics by reflection, then can automatically switch to high power to blind (jam) or destroy the optics. Both the Army and the Air Force have developed laser weapons of this type to (but not beyond) the point of FSD. Although a Navy antiperiscope project was dropped around 1985, probably the Navy has developed equivalents. Such devices are periodically denounced as inhumane (presumably cluster-bombing to suppress light AA fire is preferable). In 1995 Secretary of Defense William Perry announced that the United States would not deploy blinding weapons. That may not apply to devices intended to destroy EO sighting systems rather than human eyes.

A "fisheye" laser warner was completed in FY96, presumably for aircraft self-defense.

ELECTRONIC SYSTEMS

◆ **AAR-47**

Alliant/Loral's UV missile warner uses four sensors (elevation coverage greater than +/−30 deg). It filters for targets using a combination of spectral analysis and temporal algorithms, measuring the dynamics of the approaching object. It is effective up to 40,000 ft. AAR-47 automatically launches flares (e.g., from an ALE-39) and provides an audio and visual alarm for the pilot, either on a separate indicator or on the APR-39A display. Loral's laser-warning adjunct uses four 0.4–1.1-micron detectors around each UV detector. AAR-47 was approved for production in 1987 after OpEval and TechEval; in February 1988 the U.S. Naval Air Systems Command ordered its first 111.

See also the ATIRCM program described below.

Users: Australia (probably on Sea Hawks), Canada (C-130s, Sea Kings), United Kingdom (helicopters, transports), United States (known naval users: SH-60B [of Middle East Force, during the Gulf War], CH-46E, CH-53A/D/E, RH-53D, MH-53E, UH-1N, AH-1T/W, SH-2F/G, OV-10, P-3C [probably only AIP aircraft: two detectors at after edge of forward radome, two more aft, near the tail, integrated with ALE-47 decoy launcher], AV-8B [installed beginning 1992, with upgraded algorithms to cater for higher speed and maneuverability]). Estimated unit cost (1994) was $110,000. As of 1993, a total of 1185 had been made.

◆ **ALD-2 and ULA-2**

This 1–10-MHz (three bands) CVR-based airborne DF system was standard in many U.S. ASW aircraft of the mid-1960s (but note that the contemporary SP-2H had the narrow-band ALR-8); in P-3Cs it was superseded by ALQ-78. The four antennas drive the four plates of a CRT; DF accuracy is about 15 deg. The associated ULA-2 displays pulse width and PRF.

Users: Iran (P-3F), Spain (P-3A/B); probably also surviving S-2s in some or all of Argentina, Brazil, and Uruguay.

◆ **ALD-8/ALD-9**

ALD-8 is the E-Systems interferometer VHF/UHF DF of the original EP-3E ARIES I aircraft. It uses a pair of 73in crossed loops. ALD-8A (1980) was described as a time-shared semiautomatic system, that is, as capable of taking DF cuts in only one band at a time. ALD-9 is the Lockheed Sanders replacement, in EP-3E ARIES II and in the ES-3A ([V]2 version).

◆ **ALE-39/ALE-40**

The Goodyear/Tracor ALE-39 decoy (chaff, flare, expendable active) dispenser is standard on U.S. Navy aircraft. This 60-cartridge (expandable to 300) square container is typically attached to the side of an underwing pylon. It is being supplemented by the Bofors BOL. Decoys are launched in multiples of 10. Cartridges are cylindrical (36 mm [dia] × 148 mm, 273 g). ALE-40 is the Air Force equivalent, using square-section decoys. The (V)6 version is used on British Nimrods.

The standard U.S. Navy IR decoys are Mk 46 and its successor, MJU-8A/B. Alliant offers an alternative, KC001/KC003, which weighs 280 g (ejection weight is 180 g). Performance is probably typical: ejection speed is 25–50 m/sec, rise time is less than 0.2 sec. Peak output is not given, but a comparable flare designed for F-15s produces more than 50 kW/steradian. Recent developments include the MJU-29 thrusted decoy (which will simulate aircraft motion) and a two-color composition for decoys.

Tracor's ASTE (Advanced Strategic/Tactical Expendable) is now a joint program; both services are to use Air Force–type square-section decoys. A forward-fired IR decoy is to be 2 × 2.5 × 8 in. Tracor is also developing a covert decoy for use over populated areas, 1 × 2 × 8 in.

ALE-41 and -43 are bulk chaff dispensers, used to simulate Soviet support aircraft for fleet training. ALE-41 is a pod carrying 280–360 lb, sufficient for an 80nm corridor, in six precut 50-lb cartridges containing dipoles between Mylar films, spread by the wind as the tape unravels. The pod is programmed on the ground, controlled either by a cockpit switch or by the aircraft's radar detector. It was approved for service use in 1977. Lundy's ALE-43 cuts chaff in flight to suit threat radars, each of up to nine packages (320 lb) feeding a roller and cutter. It can be carried either in a pod or internally (as in an EA-6B).

◆ ALE-47

Tracor's biservice "smart" chaff dispenser is the second fully automatic U.S. dispenser system, derived from the ALE-45 on board Air Force F-15C/Ds. It replaces both ALE-39 and ALE-40. Earlier systems could drop decoys in preprogrammed sequences, but they could not shift from sequence to sequence. Nor could they be triggered automatically by the aircraft threat warner. The only difference between Navy and Air Force versions is the magazine (cylindrical- or square-section decoys). Like a ship-board decoy processor, ALE-47 accepts data on own-platform motion (such as air speed, altitude, and maneuvers) and on the threat, from the RWR. Reaction time is less than 100 msec. Modes: manual (using six preprogrammed sequences), semiautomatic (the system selects tactics but the crew initiates), and fully automatic. Tactics are programmable, for example, to take advantage of the range of new expendables now available (ALE-47 can program smart active expendables such as GEN-X). Development was somewhat delayed because this Air Force program, begun in 1983, was made a biservice program in 1986; Tracor won the program in 1988, when initial production was ordered. The main order, for 3800 systems, came in 1993.

Users: Finland (F/A-18), Kuwait (F/A-18), Malaysia (F/A-18), South Korea (F-16), Switzerland (F/A-18), Taiwan (F/A-18), Thailand (F/A-18), United States (Navy: F-14D and F/A-18; Air Force: F-16, F-22, C-17).

◆ ALE-50 (AAED)/FOTD

Raytheon's advanced airborne expendable decoy (AAED, a towed decoy carrying a simple repeater, to confuse monopulse radars) was developed for the IDAP program (A-6 upgrade) but is to be carried by F/A-18E/Fs (in triple launchers) and also by F-16s (Block 40/50 aircraft will carry a single dispenser in each of two weapon pylons, and the Air National Guard plans a two-decoy dispenser in the ALQ-184 jamming pod carried by early model F-16s) and by the B-1B (two aft quadruple dispensers: two decoys are launched together, to provide sufficient power). ALE-50's 2.75in-dia shell contains a receiver and a mini-TWT powerful enough to compete with the radar return of the airplane itself. Hughes is the follower producer. The 1990 cost goal was $10,000–$15,000 per expendable decoy (the decoy cannot be retracted even if it survives a missile engagement). A production decision is due late in 1997.

The next step, part of IDECM (see below), is a fiber-optic towed device (FOTD) or RFCM no larger than ALE-50. The fiber-optic cable would transmit jammer waveforms from a techniques generator in the airplane, for more sophisticated types of jamming; it would also transmit a waveform from an independent wide-band repeater (to be used if the techniques generator fails, in hopes of attracting a threat missile). The decoy would translate the light signal in the fiber-optic cable to an RF waveform, and TWTs in the decoy would amplify that RF for jamming. On 3 Nov 1995 ITT and Lockheed Sanders won the IDECM competition, using the Lockheed Sanders FOTD (the company had already developed FOTDs for black programs). An F/A-18E/F is to carry three such decoys. The Air Force is expected to adopt a higher-powered version to protect the F-15 and B-1. Sanders/ITT are to deliver 15 RFCM subsystems and 100 decoys in April 1998, for flight tests beginning that fall on board an F/A-18; the system is to undergo OpEval on board F/A-18E/Fs in spring 2000.

A helicopter towed decoy was a FY95 new start ATD.

The ALE-50 decoy is shown in action, and in its triple T-3 launcher. (Raytheon)

◆ ALQ-39/ALQ-190

These counter-surveillance decoys are deployed from aircraft, to bring them far enough from the fleet. Presumably they are associated with programs to deceive air- and space-borne surveillance radars. Initially that meant ship-based false target generators, to be used by seaborne deception groups steaming far from a battle group. Later it meant airborne counters to the (now extinct) Soviet space-based synthetic-aperture radars (SARs). Engineering development of the SAR countermeasure began in FY92. Airborne tests continued through FY95, when the countermeasure transitioned to FSED. CHAFFBUOY (ALQ-39) is a delayed-deployment chaff cartridge. AIRBOC (Air-Launched Rapid-Blooming Chaff, ALQ-190) deploys immediately upon being launched.

◆ ALQ-78

Magnavox's E/H/J-band P-3C ESM system replaced the ULA-2/ALD-2 of P-3A/B, and is now being replaced by ALR-66. A three-speed spinner in a radome under the port wing feeds two electronically tuned SHRs (high-precision, 7.3–10.75 GHz, and low-precision, 2.57–40 GHz; the band actually scanned can be more limited). Like the earlier WLR-1, ALQ-78 scans simultaneously in bearing (nominal DF accuracy 8 deg) and in frequency, the SHR locking on when a signal is detected, to measure pulse width and PRF (it could not originally do so when multiple signals are present, as it had no de-interleaver). In DF mode, the antenna is locked onto a single frequency while turning through 380 deg, to achieve 1-deg accuracy. The antenna can also be locked onto an emitter at a fixed frequency (for up to 31 sec) to measure scan pattern. The aircraft central computer (CP-901) was originally the emitter identifier, but a separate reprogrammable processor was added in the late 1970s to support Harpoon targeting and to reduce the load on the central computer. Further modifications (FY82) added a de-interleaver, which uses fine frequency information to help sort pulse trains. Note that the ALQ-78 spinner is used in some OTH-T versions of the replacement ALR-66. Production began in the mid-1970s. Estimated unit cost is $160,000.

This Japanese P-3C shows an ALQ-78 radome under its port wing root (to the right in this picture). (W. Donko, 1989)

Users: Australia, Canada, Japan (license production by Mitsubishi began 1981, was completed 1992), Netherlands, Norway, United States (some P-3C).

◆ ALQ-99

ALQ-99 is the tactical support jammer of the EA-6B Prowler, the standard U.S. Navy ECM airplane; it is also on the U.S. Air Force's EF-111 (which is to be replaced by the EA-6B). The development contract was awarded in August 1966. A replacement ADVCAP (Advanced Capability) version was developed but not funded; as of 1996 it appears that a more modest improvement will eventually be bought instead.

An EA-6B of VAQ-140 (1988) displays the leading features of the ALQ-99 system: the tail radome (for all-around view) and the underwing pods. The two strakes on the vertical tail are ALQ-99 receivers for Bands 1 and 2. The short stub protruding aft from the tail radome (the "beer can") is for ALQ-126, added during the ICAP-1 program. (U.S. Navy)

Initially the system was intended for strike support, jamming air defense radars. Then it was upgraded to jam the voice links between interceptors and their controllers. When the defenders adopted digital data links (which are more difficult to jam), the system was upgraded again to deal with them. In the late 1960s a new fleet defense mission was added: the system now had to jam Soviet long-range airborne targeting radars and, to a lesser extent, the missiles themselves. The system's receivers were used for surface surveillance. About 1985 the system was adapted to control HARM missiles, to physically attack enemy radars and to render enemy warships vulnerable to salvoes of antiship weapons by forcing them to shut down their defensive radars.

ALQ-99 was probably the first tactical jamming system controlled by a central computer, which reduces the processing load by using a preloaded threat radar map (and aircraft position at the time a signal is intercepted) to help identify the emitter. The computer is fed by amplitude-DF search receivers, most of them in the radome on the vertical tail, for a 360-deg FOV. Up to five jammers can be accommodated. To set them, the airplane has five SHRs (20-MHz tuning bandwidths). The jammers themselves are in self-contained pods, each self-powered (by a ram-air turbine) and containing its own exciter flanked by two transmitters. Each pod carries its own automatic frequency and direction trackers. Trainable and elevatable antennas underneath can track target radars while the airplane maneuvers. This degree of self-containment buys flexibility (the aircraft need not always carry the full spectrum of possible jammers, so some of its hard points can be used for fuel or for HARMs) and high total power.

Bands are: 1, VHF (64–150 MHz); 2, A-band (150–270 MHz, including some P-band radars); 3, B-band; 4, C-band (0.5–1 GHz); 5/6, 1–2.5 GHz; 7, 2.5–4 GHz; 8, 4–7.8 GHz (most of G- and H-bands); 9, 7.8–11 GHz (upper H-, I-, and lower J-bands); and 10 (J/K-bands, for which no jammer is as yet available), 11–20 GHz. The original EA-6B (1972) covered Bands 1, 2, 4, and 7. XCAP (1973) added Bands 5, 6, 8, and 9 to deal with newer high-frequency fire-control radars. ICAP-2 search-receiver coverage was extended to the lower edge of Band 8, at 4 GHz (rather than 3.5 GHz as before).

ALQ-99 was originally a semiautomatic system, partly because it appeared before computers had become particularly reliable. Problems with operator speed (due to an increasingly dense pulse environment) were first noticed in the ICAP-1 version (1977). Versions through ICAP-1 used analog processors to produce their jamming signals.

ICAP-2 (ALQ-99F, first flown in 1980) is a major redesign, built around a much faster computer (AYK-14). It is adapted to a computer mission planner (TEAMS). Aircraft location is given by CAINS (plus, now, GPS). The computer uses an automatic signal processor and reacts automatically as it encounters threats; the operator is now monitor rather than initiator. The analog exciters (jamming signal generators) are replaced by AIL's digital universal exciters. Pod antennas (30-deg beams) are now electronically steered, and output is about 1 kW/MHz. Instead of being limited to a single band, pods (185 × 28 × 18 in) are now generic, each carrying any two transmitters (for one or two bands). They vary only in weight (1014 lb, for two Band 4, up to 1089 lb, for two Band 9). The effect of doubling up within pods is to free two hard points for fuel tanks or HARMs without reducing the number of bands jammed simultaneously. This version also enjoys limited communications-jamming capability. One effect of increased automation was to drastically reduce the workload of the front-seat ECM officer (ECMO); the work is done largely by the two ECMOs in the back of the cockpit.

ICAP-2 has some major limitations: in pulse processing (reportedly no more than 50,000 pps), in the number of threats it can handle simultaneously (due to the five SHRs), and to changes in radar mode while jamming (it lacks any look-through capability).

ICAP-2 aircraft are currently in three distinct configurations, Blocks 82 (69 aircraft), 86, and 89 (56 aircraft).

The next step, ADVCAP, is currently in abeyance. It would have been better able to attack the command links used by integrated air-defense systems, using a new associated communications-band jammer (ALQ-149, see separate entry). Amplitude DF would have been supplemented by interferometry, for finer cuts useful in, for example, missile targeting.

A new receiver-processor group (RPG) would have increased capacity to over 1M pps. Increasing civilian use of the electromagnetic spectrum increases signal density and also makes it easier for a jammer to be seduced into action against a nontarget signal. RPG could have handled complex radar waveforms, such as coded and chirped ones. To jam them, ADVCAP offered a coherent countermeasures capability (COCM, i.e., against pulse-compression radars). Given a new look-through capability, RPG would have been able to jam reactively, quickly modifying system response to follow a frequency-hopping threat emitter. The only current means of dealing with such a threat is barrage jamming, which offers only limited power in the bandwidth the threat occupies at any one instant. Although a reactive jammer probably cannot follow pulse-to-pulse agility, it may well suffice to break track. RPG substituted a disk recorder for the digital tape of the earlier version, for greater signal density and higher speed. To deal with wider-band frequency agility, ADVCAP would have used faster scanners (SHRs) and a wider-band "universal exciter" upgrade (UEU). UEU technology satisfied the communications/radar exciter and ALQ-149 interface requirements. There was also a new Band 2/3 transmitter. A new high-power RF transmitter for Bands 9/10 has been in development by AEL Defense Corp since August 1991; it is a joint Air Force/Navy program (for the EF-111 and EA-6B).

To accommodate the improvements, ADVCAP would have used two, rather than one, AYK-14 computers. A third display, for the front ECMO, was added. Development began in 1983, and the ADVCAP prototype flew in 1990. However, the FY95 program eliminated ADVCAP funding.

FY95 EA-6B improvements were limited to a VHISC module for the existing central computer (AYK-14), a Have Quick radio (ARC-210), and improved navigational systems (GPS and a laser-ring gyro). These were not insignificant. The computer module would, for example, substantially accelerate processing, and might accommodate software for part of the required RPG capability. Better navigation would make it easier for the airplane to correlate emitters seen over land with those mapped out earlier, thus reducing its processing load.

Litton and AIL offered ICAP 2+, built around a single AYK-14. Capacity would increase to 250,000 pps, using a derivative of Litton's RPG (replacing three WRAs). Instantaneous SHR bandwidth would increase twentyfold, for faster jammer set-on. The Band 7, 8, 9, and 10 search antennas would be replaced. Although ICAP 2+ would still rely on amplitude-comparison DF, interferometry could later be added. ICAP 2+ would use much of the 150,000 lines of ADVCAP software already written (it needed a total of 120,000 lines). The system uses one AYK-

14 computer rather than the pair intended for ADVCAP. As of 1994, Litton and AIL expected that ICAP 2+ could be fielded as early as 1999 to offer 80% of ADVCAP capability for 20% of its price, at no net increase in aircraft weight. Both houses of Congress supported lower-cost alternatives to ADVCAP; on 10 May 1994 the House Armed Services Committee explicitly ordered the Navy to consider upgrades such as ICAP 2+.

In January 1995 the Defense Department submitted a plan for a low-cost EA-6B upgrade. The center wing box section would be replaced and the jammer hardbacks redesigned. The whole fleet would be upgraded to Block I FY89 configuration. This plan included the universal exciter (UEU), added a low-band (A/B-band) transmitter, and entailed the purchase of 300 UEUs, 135 Low-Band Transmitters, and 50 Band 10 receivers. The low-band transmitter accepts signals from the ALQ-99 pod exciter, amplifies them, and sends the results back to the pod for retransmission. This upgrade also adds a band identification receiver.

Little was apparently done. In 1996 Congress demanded more action. For example, the Navy was authorized to begin a reactive jamming upgrade in FY96, but as of mid-1996 it did not plan to begin work until FY99. Acting on the FY97 program, the Senate Armed Services Committee added money for 49 additional Band 9/10 transmitters (the House added money for 60), for 24 additional USQ-113 communications jammers (see separate entry), plus money for improved situational awareness (presumably by a computer upgrade) and for research into a universal exciter upgrade. The Navy was asked to submit a plan for a complete upgrade program, and to obligate funds for the reactive jamming upgrade by 1 June 1997.

As of late 1996, plans call for a common Block 89A configuration for all EA-6Bs, with GPS and ARC-210 radios and upgraded universal exciters, low- and high-band jammers, and USQ-113 communications jammers. First flight is scheduled for June 1997, with test and evaluation in FY98, installations beginning early in FY99, and IOC early in 2000. The next version, ICAP-3, is to have receiver improvements, an integrated USQ-113, and access to all-source (i.e., satellite-transmitted special intelligence) information.

◆ ALQ-108

Magnavox's IFF deception set originated in the early 1970s. It replaces or supplements the interrogator in AEW radars. Presumably its main function is to trigger hostile IFF systems to identify hostile aircraft more clearly. This system is installed in EP-3Es (which carry an APS-20 [AEW radar] derivative) and in U.S. E-2Cs. A derivative is reportedly on board German F-4s.

◆ ALQ-126/164 and ALQ-162

Lockheed Martin Sanders' E- through J-band pulse track-breaker is associated with the ALR-67 RWR. The current ALQ-126B was the first U.S. Navy/Marine Corps reprogrammable defensive jammer. RF memory duration is 4 microsec, for tactics such as RGPO and VGPO (other tactics include inverse conical scan, main lobe blanking, and swept square wave). Typical response time is 0.1 microsec. ALQ-126 emits over 1 kW/band. In an F/A-18, the forward high-band antennas are just aft of the radome (above and below the fuselage), with an aft high-band antenna atop the port fin; forward mid-band antennas are above and below the fuselage just forward of the air intakes (starboard above, port below), with aft mid-band antennas just forward of the vertical fins (above and below); and low-band antennas are positioned with the mid-band antennas, but on the other side of the airplane. Jammer beamwidth is typically 60 deg, pointed down at about 15 deg. Total weight is 190 lb (two units, upper and lower deck, connected by blind-mate connectors), and the maximum power requirement is 3 kVA. This system was last ordered for the U.S. Navy in FY89, and surge production for the Gulf War completed the U.S. program. However, ALQ-126/164 are still in production for foreign sales. The planned U.S. successor was ALQ-165.

Sanders's ECP 3434 improves performance against pulse threats while expanding system memory and increasing throughput. Five prototypes performed design T&E but not

OpEval; as of 1996 Canada wants two of the prototypes for its own OpEval.

ALQ-164 is the podded version for Harriers (16 × 85 in, 350 lb).

Because it does not jam CW radars, ALQ-126 is typically combined with Northrop's ALQ-162 (Shadowbox), the Compass Sail Clockwise jammer. It uses two vertically polarized antennas, covering 60 deg to either side in azimuth and 30 deg up or down in elevation; the system can also interface with other ECM antennas as required. Total weight is 40 lb plus two 0.5-lb antennas and a 1-lb remote-control unit; demonstrated MTBF is 335 hr (260 specified). Northrop beat ITT for this contract. Estimated cost is $75,000 to $120,000; 688 had been made through 1991. In 1994 Northrop proposed Shadowbox II, which would add a pulse-Doppler capability within the same footprint. It was demonstrated on an F/A-18 in February 1994.

Users:

ALQ-126/164: Australia (F/A-18), Canada (CF-18), Italy (Harrier), Kuwait (F-18), Malaysia (F/A-18), Spain (EF-18 and Harrier), United States (F/A-18 and Harrier; ALQ-126A in EA-6B for self-protection). A-7Es had ALQ-126A, which replaced an earlier ALQ-100, triggered by ALR-45 RWRs; this jammer may therefore survive in Greek and Thai aircraft (the Portuguese A-7Ps delivered about 1981 probably lack this system). Surviving U.S. A-6Es (now in storage) also have ALQ-126As.

ALQ-162: Canada (CF-18), Denmark (F-35, F-16), Spain (EF-18), United States (AV-8B and Army aircraft).

◆ ALQ-144

Sanders's helicopter IR countermeasure employs a cylindrical electrically heated graphite IR source surrounded by a modulator, mounted either on top of or under the helicopter. Deliveries began in March 1981; by January 1991 over 3000 had been produced.

Users: Jordan (AH-1S), Pakistan (AH-1S, UH-1B/H), United Kingdom (various helicopters and aircraft; bought 185 for Desert Storm), United States (Army [AH-1S, AH-64, UH-60], Air Force, Marines [AH-1W, UH-60], Navy [LAMPS III Block 1 upgrade, also H-3 and SH-2]). U.S. naval helicopters use the -144(VP) Phase Lock pair version. There are at least two other foreign users (FMS sales to five countries were announced in January 1994).

◆ ALQ-149

Lockheed Sanders developed this tactical communications jammer for the abortive ADVCAP version of the EA-6B. Coverage includes the 20–70-MHz band specifically requested by the Marine Corps. ALQ-149 shares the airplane's AYK-14 computer (to identify analyzed signals and decide responses) with ALQ-99; cooperative jam/look-through cycles allow simultaneous operation of both systems. ALQ-149 was originally planned for the ICAP-2 version of the EA-6B, but development was so protracted that it had to be delayed to the ADVCAP version. Reportedly, part of the problem (now remedied) was overambitious specification in frequency range. The Vietnam-era ALQ-92, which covers the low frequency bands, was removed some years ago; USQ-113 is being purchased as an interim solution (see entries). With the apparent demise of ADVCAP, the fate of ALQ-149 is unclear; seven EDMs were delivered in 1988.

◆ ALQ-157

Loral's microprocessor-controlled programmable IR jammer offers five jamming modes, each with wide preprogrammed frequency-agility range; more codes can be added to deal with new threats. Upgraded from 2- to 4-kW IR power, it may now be so powerful that large helicopters equipped with it can dispense with IR suppressors. Two emitters are used, one on either side (in a helicopter, of the vertical tail; in a P-3C, scabbed to the aft fuselage). The system weighs 220 lb, and MTBF is 215 hr (lamp MTBF is 330 hr). The prototype appeared in 1977, and it was approved for service use in August 1983; the first production

units were delivered in September 1984. Matador is a commercial version, to protect large aircraft.

Users: Saudi Arabia (probable), United Kingdom (probably some Lynx), United States (Marine Corps C-130F, P-3C, CH-46, CH-53E, probably some SH-3 in the Middle East). There are probably other Middle East customers. Export use includes both aircraft and patrol boats. The CH-43 version is (V)1 (probably 147 made); the CH-53 version is (V)2 (probably 114 made). At least 200 were either in service or on contract by 1988, and 200 had probably been exported by 1991 (first export sale was in 1985).

◆ ALQ-165 (ASPJ)

The ITT/Westinghouse Airborne Self-Protection Jammer (ASPJ) was designed to replace the combination of ALQ-126 and -162 on board upgraded F-14s, F/A-18s, and A-6s. The associated RWR is ALR-67. An unsuccessful OpEval (which some criticized as unrealistically severe) suspended the program, though ASPJ is being installed on board F-14Ds, has been exported, probably formed a major part of the basis of ITT's successful IDECM bid (see below), and may now be revived for the F/A-18. ASPJ splits its band (originally 0.7–18 GHz, later reportedly 1–35 GHz) into high and low components, each with its own receiver and TWT transmitter (operating in either pulsed or noise mode), all connected to a common processor. The F-14 ("common") version adds a high-band transmitter and a simplified receiver for aft coverage. ALQ-165 apparently differs from earlier systems in its ability to jam (noise and deception) multiple pulse threats, reportedly 16–32 of them, with an accuracy of 0.5–20 MHz; minimum receivable pulse width is reportedly 0.1 microsec. The anti-CW SHR element was to offer an instantaneous bandwidth of 1.44 GHz (resolution 5 MHz). The original design was criticized because it could not simultaneously jam enough radars, and the number of range-gate deception jammers (effective against "older pulse radars") was doubled in the production version. This system fit within 2.4 ft^3 (225 lb; 306 lb for the common version). A podded version for the Harrier weighed 380 lb. By late 1991 it appeared that required MTBF, then projected at 186–257 hr, with 30 min MTTR, would be exceeded by about 20%.

Reportedly the program suffered initially because it concentrated on head-on or tail-on threats relevant to fighters (with which the program managers were familiar) rather than on broadside threats faced by slower attack aircraft. It did win a 1986 comparison with the ALQ-126B/162 combination. Later it suffered a combination of what some described as unusually harsh OpEval tests and what some called a rather simplistic analysis: it was assumed that HARM and Tomahawk would destroy most enemy radars *before* aircraft equipped with the jammer faced enemy defenses. The great sophistication of ASPJ could hardly seem worthwhile in such an artificially low-threat context.

The ASPJ specification was issued in 1976, the ITT/Westinghouse team winning in 1981. The severe weight constraints imposed by the F/A-18 made development difficult, so that the final prototype was delivered two years late (early 1986). Initial production (100 in FY89) was divided between the partners, who competed for shares of the 150 ordered in FY90. Delivery of 20 preproduction (production verification, or PV) units began in the fall of 1989, the initial production contracts having been let in September 1987. The Air Force withdrew from the program in January 1990, citing a black program (now known to be a towed decoy) then underway.

In 1992 Congress decided to terminate the program after 95 had been bought. Installation was forbidden pending further tests. Finally money was released in September 1994 to install ALQ-165 on F-14Ds (unrestricted use was approved in mid-1996). All other jammers were placed in storage. After an Air Force F-16 was lost to an SA-6 over Bosnia early in June 1995, installations were authorized (in July) on board 12 Marine Corps F/A-18Ds (replacing their ALQ-126Bs) assigned to overfly the former Yugoslavia. These sets were declared operational on 25 Aug 1995. However, cancellation was not reversed, and a proposal to equip carrier-based aircraft with ASPJ was rejected. Installation on board Air Force F-16s was also considered. By the fall of 1995, the Marines were enthusiastic about ALQ-165 performance. The FY97 program includes 36 more ALQ-165s, and as of the fall of 1996 it seems likely that many F/A-18s will be equipped with it.

Users: Finland (for 57 F/A-18C and probably 7 F/A-18D, first delivered 21 Nov 1995), Korea (F-16), Switzerland (for 34 F/A-18C/Ds), United States (F-14D, F/A-18C/D). The export sales kept the production line open and thus made the recent procurement possible. Further exports seem unlikely, since the Navy opposes the transfer of the digital RF memory (DRFM) unit technology.

◆ ALQ-167 (Yellow Veil)

British Lynx helicopters operating in the Persian Gulf use this podded Whittaker Electronics (U.S.) 4–11-GHz (two bands: 4–8 and 8–11 GHz, outputs 2- and 4-kW ERP) device as a standoff jammer to protect British warships and merchant ships against antiship missiles and for self-defense. The pod replaces two Sea Skua missiles. Some Sea King HAS.6 carry it internally (the outward sign is a twin-horn antenna protruding from the fuselage forward of the port mainwheel sponson). The pod contains two oscillators (for the two bands), an amplifier, and a transmitter. Yellow Veil (ARI 23363/23379) is a version of a standard U.S./NATO training jammer. The original ALQ-167 was limited to noise jamming; ALQ-167A adds an RGPO mode and a capacity to radiate aft. Pod dimensions are 10 × 138 in (236–320 lb).

The long pod of Yellow Veil is carried by this Royal Navy Lynx helicopter. (Whittaker Electronic Systems)

Some F-14s (which lack any internal jammer) have carried ALQ-167 on the forward starboard Phoenix hard point, but this is probably only a training measure.

◆ ALR-8

This airborne ECM receiver equipped Atlantic MPA. A few may survive on board Italian aircraft. ALR-8 is a scanning SHR system, roughly analogous to the contemporary WLR-1, covering up to nine bands (50–10,750 MHz); in practice a typical installation included only four tuners at a time. ALR-8 included an auxiliary CRT for pulse analysis. In U.S. service, ALR-8 was generally installed with a wide-band warning receiver, ALR-3 (1–40 GHz in four bands).

◆ ALR-44

Sylvania's ESM receiver, in ARIES II EP-3Es, employs six channelized receivers to cover 0.5–18 GHz; one set of six tuners is shared by each pair of receivers, with a maximum of 18 tuners per ALR-44. The tuners are dual-conversion superhets (first IF 160 MHz, width 25 MHz; second IF 42 MHz, width 0.5 MHz).

There are six indicators. This set was also carried by earlier EP-3s and by EA-3Bs, now extinct.

◆ ALR-47/76/502

These Lockheed Martin Federal Systems (formerly IBM) ESM systems are comparable to ALQ-78, except that the spinner is replaced by a wide-open antenna system (two pairs of five-octave cavity-backed spirals at each wing tip) feeding two solid-state SHRs. The emitter identifier (comparator) feeds signal identity, parameters, and bearing to the aircraft central tactical computer in digital form. Presumably a library in the central computer is used to identify signals outside the short list in the comparator. ALR-502 is a version of ALR-47 for the Canadian CP-140 MPA. Target Acquisition Console Mk 105, using a version of ALR-47, was the passive targeting device for the Standard ARM antiship missile. Its comparator equivalent is a dual-memory (24 kwords) IBM System 4/Pi-type SP-0A. It can process several emitters simultaneously. In this case digital outputs are passed automatically to an FCS to preset the missile.

ALR-76 is a VLSI upgrade of (and form-fit replacement for) ALR-47 for the S-3B with a wider frequency range (using faster-scanning software-controlled multibandwidth SHRs: wide bandwidth for acquisition, narrow for analysis and interference processing). Software includes algorithms for reactive scanning, to improve the probability of intercept. Other algorithms mitigate the effects of CW and pulse-Doppler signals, which might raise pulse density beyond the system's capacity. ALR-73 uses a pulse processor (de-interleaver, 10 MOPS throughput) and a general-purpose control and correlation processor (CCP), with an aggregate memory of 448 kwords. The CCP holds the system mode library and provides processed data to the interface to the airplane CDS; Loral argues that because the system locates and identifies emitters, it can avoid re-reporting them to the CDS and so reduce the load on the airplane CDS. Increased identification capacity in a new comparator adds capabilities for threat avoidance (radar warning) and fleet surveillance. Interferometry improves directional accuracy. ALR-76 was adopted as ELINT cueing system for the EP-3E ARIES II upgrade. Lockheed Martin claims that the system is software-compatible with its passive ranging system (PRSS) and with SEI. Private-venture improvements include increased library capacity and extension to mm-waves.

Users: Canada (as ALR-502, in the CP-140 MPA; ALR-76 is aboard the *Protecteur*-class AORs and was installed, presumably for OTH-T, on board two Harpoon-armed frigates, *Restigouche* and *Terra Nova*, sent to the Persian Gulf in 1990; it is presumably equivalent to an upgraded Mk 105), South Korea (Mk 105 is probably on board four *Paek Ku*–class boats armed with Standard ARM Missiles), United States (S-3A/B, ES-3A, EP-3E ARIES II). ALR-47 was first delivered in 1971; estimated cost (in current terms) was $150,000. All U.S. aircraft listed, other than the S-3A, carry ALR-76, the development contract for which was let in July 1983. It costs about $250,000. The system weighs about 88 lb.

◆ ALR-60 (Deepwell)

GTE's computer-controlled five-operator communications intercept and analysis system (100–150 MHz) is for ARIES I EP-3E Orions. The receiver incorporates two separate digitally tuned modules. The CP-1131 16-bit computer (with 16-kword core memory) uses an external magnetic drum memory, MU-600 (16 Mwords: 64 tracks, each of 500 data blocks, each of 523 words; access time 17 msec, 2247 bit/sec; the drum spins at 1800 rpm). The improved ALR-60A uses an AYK-14 computer, but retains the drum. ALR-60 often works alongside ALR-52. Seven were made.

◆ ALR-66/85/93/606/ASPIS/SLR-600/Locator/Triton IV

This Litton (formerly General Instruments) digital series includes both relatively inexpensive RWRs (about $75,000) and quite elaborate ESM devices (typically $250,000) for OTH-T. All versions evolved from an E-J band (extendable down to C-D band) four-port RWR, which became the (V)1 version. It had CVR receivers and a 24-bit processor (de-interleaver: 8 kwords of

RAM/ROM, 1.2 MOPS) supporting a 3in digital display on the LAMPS I helicopter. Library capacity was 1000 modes (100 radars), and the CRT could display the 15 most critical threats at one time. The system measured pulse width (wide or narrow) and PRF (nine values) and indicated signal band (E, G, I, J). It uses scan type to distinguish fire-control from search radars. The system can detect and identify pulse-Doppler, CW, interrupted CW, LPI, 3D (short dwell time), frequency-agile, jittered/staggered PRF, and pulse-compression radars. DF accuracy was better than 10 deg (resolution 1.4 deg). Total weight is 59.4 lb. The contract was awarded late in 1974. In SH-2F/G helicopters, this set was replaced in the early 1980s by the (VE) version, a related type intended for export, with computer memory expanded to 9 kwords. The threat library could be reprogrammed on the flight line in 90 sec or in the air using a computer memory reloader. MTBF is 725+ hr. ALR-66(VE) was superseded by ALR-66A(V)1. Some helicopters used their radar antennas for fine DF cuts, as in the (V)2 and (V)3 versions described below.

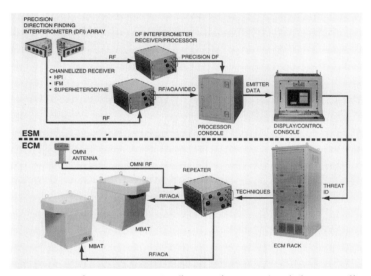

Triton IV combines precision DF (by interferometry) and electronically steered multibeam array transmitter jammers. (Litton)

(V)2 was a P-3B version (1980) specifically for OTH-T, using the airplane's APS-80 nose radar antenna (Little Look program; Big Look was part of the EP-3E) and a more sensitive receiver for fine DF cuts. It retained the original RWR capability, replacing the earlier ALD-2. This version had a CRT and a keyboard. The signal library was expanded, but the processor probably did not change. This and similar versions of ALR-66 seem to be unique among airborne radar detectors in sharing the main radar antenna with the on-board radar. Reportedly the shared-antenna technique has not been entirely successful, hence the spinner in (V)5.

ALR-66 was then adopted as interim for the P-3C, pending completion of AIL's interferometric ALR-77. When the latter was dropped as too cumbersome and too expensive, a version connected directly to the aircraft central computer, (V)3, was substituted (1984). The keyboard was deleted, the system now using the P-3C plasma display. Again, the main radar antenna (modified with an ellipsoidal subreflector) was used for DF cuts. It is supplemented by four dual-band C/D-band and four E/J-band (3 sub-bands: G/H, I, J) spirals mounted at the wingtips (45-deg elevation coverage). For high sensitivity, the E-J-band CVRs are mounted in the wingtips, close to the spirals. This version introduced an IFM (frequency measurement unit, FMU). To avoid mismatches between DF and frequency channels, an IFM is placed in each DF channel. The nose and spiral antennas are treated as two parallel channels, between which the system computer switches cyclically (the order of scanning, and the time spent in each channel, are computer-controllable). Emitters that the system decides represent lethal threats trigger aural

alarms. The system also tags the highest-priority emitter with its ELINT catalog number and displays PRF, pulse width, AoA, and frequency. The operator can call up similar data on any other emitter displayed. In targeting mode, the system measures emitter frequency, AoA, PRF, scan width, scan illumination, and beamwidth.

The next series, ALR-66A, has more computer memory (68 kwords, of which 28k are EEPROM/ROM; capacity is 1800+ modes, reprogrammable in 90 sec). Shadow time is less than 2 microsec, equivalent to up to 500,000 pps. Versions are A(V)1 for helicopters and A(V)3 for P-3Cs (this version was developed in 1987 specifically for Portuguese P-3Bs). The C-J band ALR-66(V)4, a high-sensitivity RWR version for the E-6A, is probably a variant. It has an SHR to detect to detect pulse-Doppler fighter radars as well as upgraded software and improved DF.

The export version is ALR-606; (V)2 (1988) is a maritime patrol version, a cross between (V)2 and (V)3, using the enlarged memory. Presumably it uses the airplane's radar antenna for fine DF cuts. It can track 35 radars simultaneously, displaying 15 at any one time. Monopulse DF accuracy is better than 15 deg.

As of spring 1995 a new series, which will probably become ALR-66B, had just completed developmental testing and was about to begin operational testing. It is derived from the (V)5 adopted for the abortive P-3C Update IV. The sensitivity of the wingtip antennas is increased by 25 dB in E-J bands (C-D were more sensitive to begin with) to increase range considerably. Too, RWR and fine DF can be conducted simultaneously. The system thus enjoys 100% probability of intercept even while targeting. The airplane central computer is unloaded to some extent by moving out some of the processing load. The B(V)3 version used in the P-3C AIP upgrade uses a belly antenna, Condor Systems' AS-105, for fine DF because the nose radar (APS-137) is not suited to this role. Antenna characteristics: 19- or 24in-dia radome, 200 rpm, csc^2 beam to 30 deg, beamwidth 2 deg at 18 GHz, probably 80 deg at 0.5 GHz, corresponding gains 26 and 4 dB. Litton unofficially calls this version ALR-66X(V)3. FSED began in 1991.

This version uses multilevel parallel processing to deal with very dense pulse environments. Signals are channelized (within frequency bands) to limit the bandwidth any one processor sees. High-speed pulse encoders digitize even overlapping pulses to reduce shadow time. A preprocessor sorts signals by frequency and AoA. Litton emphasizes the use of generic threat processing, which permits the system to identify types of emitters even though those emitters are not in the threat library. Generic processing is important because many Third World threat emitters (manufactured in the West or in the Third World itself) may not be carried in libraries filled with the characteristics of Soviet-made equipment. Lancer was an unsuccessful export derivative. Litton credits ALR-66B with an expanded data memory, and with the capacity to accept data in-flight on up to 10 emitters of interest (e.g., to take over surveillance from another airplane in flight). It can be connected to other aircraft primary sensors via its processor-interface structure (for 1553B buses or RS 432 or RS 232 connectors). The export version (1995) is ALR-606B(V)2.

The Korean ADACS (Automatic Data Collection System) is a low-end B(V)3 variant that can record the signals it receives, for ELINT. The DF antenna is the podded unit originally developed for ALQ-78.

In 1992, as a direct result of Desert Shield/Storm experience, the Navy asked for a version of ALR-66 to supplement the radars and sonobuoys (feeding SQR-17 analyzers) of mobile inshore underwater warfare (MIUW) teams responsible for coastal security. As of late 1995, an MIUW upgrade, from TSQ-108 to -108A, was in progress. It included not only a repackaged ALR-66 but also a modernized SQR-17.

Related systems are:

ALR-85: For the Taiwanese IDF and the CN-235 in Korea, incorporating a C/D-band DF and an IFM/SHR combination receiver (the IFM is better in a dense pulse environment, but the more sensitive SHR is a better detector of CW and pulse-Doppler signals). A Litton flier lists ALR-85 only as a C-130 system, widely used in the Far East. ALR-91(V)3 and (V)4 are comparable systems for F-5, F-4, and F-16 aircraft (they are derived from the Air Force's ALR-46 and ALR-69, respectively). Like ALR-93, below, they employ multiple 68020 processors.

ALR-93: A more sophisticated 0.5–18-GHz derivative of ALR-85, which Litton sees as the core for further developments, both for threat warning and for ESM. There is apparently a fine DF (interferometer) mode. Like -85, ALR-93 combines an IFM (in this case a wide-bandwidth [4 GHz] type protected by band-stop filters, capable of handling pulses as short as 100 nsec) and a multibandwidth SHR. The special-purpose ESM processor is replaced by one using 68020s for parallel processing. Litton stresses the system's ability to handle a very dense environment, using a unique multiparameter preprocessor. Library capacity is over 2000 modes. Litton describes this as a baseband system with shared resources, so presumably some processing functions (such as DF) are carried out on down-converted signals. The ESM version adds a directional dish for OTH passive detection and targeting, including passive ranging. This version also automatically displays radar parameters and does pulse analysis. ALR-93 also functions as an automatic data-collection system (ADACS), storing parameters or pulses in its memory, from which they can be extracted using a hand-held memory loader/verifier. In the fall of 1995, ALR-93 was being bid for an Argentine A-4 upgrade. The original ALR-93 may have been intended specifically for transport aircraft, but the current (V)1 is being marketed for tactical types (CN-235, F-16, F-5, Mirage). The (V)3 version is described as a lightweight ESM (rather than threat warner) unit for helicopters and small fixed-wing aircraft. The tactical version weighs 27 kg; the transport or tanker version, 49.3 kg including a second display for the cockpit. ALR-93(V)4 is an ELINT version using a lens antenna in addition to the spirals and omni.

ASPIS: A derivative of ALR-93 for Greek F-16s, ordered November 1990; the radar warning receiver is integrated with a chaff dispenser. Litton produced ASPIS in conjunction with Tracor and Raytheon (E-Systems). The system has a dual-bandwidth superhet, an IFM, and band-switching quadrant receivers. In 1995, Litton, Raytheon, and Tracor were marketing ASPIS as the Advanced Self-Protection Integrated Suite, using a range of pre-integrated hardware. Litton would supply the threat warner (including an advanced digital receiver) from its new series of federated systems (ALR-93 is the top of its line) and federated system controller; Raytheon offered the ALQ-187 active jammer; and Tracor offered a countermeasures dispenser such as ALE-40 or -47. Litton's advertisement mentions precision targeting and location capabilities, which implies that the system offers depression as well as bearing data (for passive ranging). The system's federated architecture makes it simple to add, for example, laser warners, a missile launch detector, and an IR jammer.

SLR-600 and Locator 1000 are shipboard versions of ALR-66(V)2, ALR-66(V)3, and ALR-66A(V)3. They combine a masthead DF dish (26.1 in [dia] × 16 in, 87 lb) for missile targeting with a pair of arrays (three each side) of cavity-backed spirals below it (for search and threat warning). The large-ship version includes a pulse analyzer. Its operator can display emitter data and change the priority assignment of different signals. A plasma touch screen shows both polar and tabular emitter data. Both large- and small-ship versions were offered covering E- through J-bands, with extensions down to C-band; it is not clear which frequency range was sold. DF accuracy, using the dish, is better than 3 deg.

Locator 1000 (originally Locator) introduced a new processor, probably the parallel unit employed in ALR-93. Options included an interferometer for fine DF, a supplementary SHR, and a laser warning receiver. MTBF is 1000 hours, and MTTR is about 30 min. As of 1995 this version was no longer being marketed.

Locator 2000, for larger ships, is Locator 1000 plus a deception (repeater/transponder) jammer. The integrated (ESM/ECM) high-resolution color display is controlled by keyboard and trackball;

it shows emitter data in both polar and tabular form. ESM coverage is 2–18 GHz, sensitivity is better than −60 dBm. DF accuracy: 2 deg (targeting)/8 deg (ESM warning). Elevation coverage is up to 80 deg. The system can handle over 1M pps (i.e., twice the capacity of the -66[V] series), with a 2500-mode library. Reaction time is less than 1 sec (i.e., time to detect and log a new emitter), and track capacity is more than 200 emitters. The ECM portion (7.5–18 GHz) employs 2 semi-omni antennas (6 lb, 7.5 in dia, for repeater jamming), 2 multibeam array transmitters (MBAT, 490 lb each, 30.7 wide × 34.5 high × 32.4 in) feeding flat circular lens antennas, an ECM rack (570 lb), and a repeater/switch (82 lb). This system can deal with up to 16 simultaneous threats, at frequencies between 7.5 and 18 GHz, with ERP up to 86 dBm. A photograph of a masthead installation has been published, but it is not clear which ship is involved. There are automatic interfaces with a laser warner, an EO warner, decoy launchers, ship emitter blankers, the ship gyro, and auxiliary sensors.

As of the fall of 1995, Litton had renamed Locator 2000 as Triton IV. In place of the spinner of Locator 2000, Triton IV uses interferometer arrays (DF accuracy 0.8 deg, sensitivity −71 dBm), one per quadrant, each containing three spirals plus a fourth slightly further apart. A special interferometer receiver/processor is used for precision DF. The fourth spiral on each quadrant array can be used for instantaneous amplitude-comparison DF. The associated channelized DF receiver feeds both an IFM and a superhet. A separate omni is used to obtain detailed signal characteristics, to be used by the system's deception repeater. The jammers are a pair of Rotman lens–MBATs. Litton Amecom offers the same interferometer in its lightweight LR-100 COTS-based warning and surveillance receiver (see separate entry).

Users:

ALR-66(V)3: Japan (P-3C, made under license by MELCO beginning 1986; equips about half of Japanese P-3Cs), United States (P-3Cs and B-52s carrying Harpoon missiles). The Japanese systems may be replaced by a new indigenous system, HLR-109. As of 1995, Litton was offering a (V)3 upgrade including the new wingtip antennas.

ALR-66(V)7: Sales not known (IFM/SHR version for C-130, may have been redesignated ALR-85). Another transport version was ALR-66(VC).

ALR-66(VE): Greece (A-7E; about 120 bought 1981), Morocco (50 bought 1980), New Zealand (A-4), United Kingdom (Special Operations C-130Ks [1994 program], also tankers), United States (LAMPS I helicopters; replaced by A(V)1 version), Venezuela (bought 1984). There was also an unidentified Middle Eastern customer (1984). The New Zealand version is sometimes mistakenly identified as ALR-93.

ALR-66A(V)1: Egypt (SH-2G), United States (SH-2G, SH-60F).

ALR-66A(V)3: Norway (P-3B), Portugal (P-3P, with belly antenna), United States (P-3C, as upgrade).

ALR-606(V)2: Brazil (S-2 upgrade), Greece (S-70B Hellenic Hawk helicopter), Pakistan (P-3C: 1989 version with podded DF antenna), Taiwan (S-2T and S-70C), Thailand (S-2s, now retired), Venezuela (probably CASA 212s).

SLR-600: Thailand (*Ratcharit* class).

Locator 1000: Taiwan (sold as Sea Hawk, now designated WD-2A).

◆ ALR-67 and ASR/ALR-45

Litton's standard 1–16-GHz U.S. Navy RWR uses four small spirals for high-band, and four low-band blade antennas, each with its own CVR, plus an SHR, mainly for CW signals. This system also has a separate digital display. ALR-67 uses a dual CP-1293 (system manager and pulse processor), a close relative of ATAC, the first computer developed exclusively for an RWR (ca. 1975). It is a 16-bit computer (machine cycle time 250 nsec [equivalent to 4 MOPS], minor cycle time 62.5 nsec, with 50 basic instructions). Emitter DoA is calculated on the basis of relative ToA at

ALR-67ASR components include four ambidextrous (both circular polarizations) spirals. Typically two are mounted forward, two aft, each feeding one of the quadrant receivers shown at upper right. Above them is the low-band integrated antenna, typically mounted in the nose. The large flat box is the countermeasures receiver. It includes a channelized receiver module, an RF electronics module (superhet side and RF distribution side), a control interface module, and a wide-band RF delay line. The box at upper left is the system computer, with the azimuth display alongside it. The small box with the cable emerging from it is the control status unit. The earlier versions of ALR-67 are physically similar but use simple circular spiral antennas. The equivalent of the countermeasures receiver is the special receiver. (Hughes)

the different antennas, which are far enough apart to make this feasible. The system is field-programmable. It now coordinates with onboard FC radars, data links, jammers, missile-detection systems, and ARM weapons, and can control decoy dispensers.

System capacity (in terms of pps) apparently sometimes proved insufficient during the Gulf War. Reportedly, too, there were some problems in reprogramming ALR-67 and ALQ-126 to deal with Persian Gulf threats. Not all aircraft had identical equipment; some could be reprogrammed directly, but for others new memory modules had to be inserted physically (tripling the time required). A new hand-held Advanced Rapid Reprogramming Terminal, which can be plugged into an aircraft to download fresh data into an ALR-67, will help solve the problem. The follow-on ASR version (see below) is designed for rapid reprogramming.

In 1990 Litton proposed ECP-510, which it had been developing for some years as an ALR-67 improvement, in effect halfway between ALR-67 and -67ASR. New ASIC chips increase system computing power (for a factor 5 increase in allowable pulse density). An interface with the host aircraft's INS allows the system to stabilize itself so that the display (and, in effect, the system's tactical picture) remains accurate during high-G maneuvers. Greater sensitivity increases detection range by a factor of 6 (10 when in the presence of a wingman's radar signals) and helps with LPI signals. Sensitivity can be selected by frequency band (the adjustment would be based on the expected mission threat environment). An IFM is used to identify emitters unambiguously. ECP-510 provides better directional information for passive weapon targeting. The displays are adapted to night vision. OpEval was completed in April 1992. The new version, designated ALR-67(V)2, was very well received, and a production run of 266 units (to supplement modified ALR-67s) was completed in October 1994.

Because ALR-67 was one of the first RWRs to incorporate a digital computer, it has software written in machine language, which is difficult to update with new threat emitters; NavAir has now contracted with Litton to rewrite (V)2 software in C, which will make it possible for Navy personnel to update it. A

contract to study passive targeting (DoA), that is, passive ranging, was let late in February 1994. It is described as a means of air-to-ground passive emitter location and air-to-air precision DF.

ALR-67 is in effect a digital version of the 1–14-GHz single-band ALR-45, which was supplemented by Loral's 0.5–20-GHz superhet APR-43 (Compass Sail Clockwise) to sense the missile's CW guidance signal. A-6Es and some F-14As still carry ALR-45s; they have probably been upgraded with threat processors. Some F-14As have ALR-50, which was an Air Force equivalent of ALR-45. Some A-7s had a digital version, ALR-45F (production of which began in 1981), using the computer and digital display developed for ALR-67; this first U.S. Navy digital RWR was intended specifically to target the digital HARM missile.

In September 1988 the Navy issued an RFP for an advanced special receiver (ASR) to upgrade ALR-67. Hughes/AEL/IBM (now Loral Federal) won: this version will be designated ALR-67(V)3. It increases frequency coverage, sensitivity, DF accuracy, signal-processing throughput (factor of 50 improvement), and memory (factor of 40). Unlike many RWRs, ASR displays threats in azimuth, independent of an airplane's maneuvers, to provide better situational awareness. Despite these improvements, the result is still an RWR rather than an ESM set.

The spirals are replaced by AEL's new ambidextrous spiral type, and they incorporate integrated signal detectors. The quadrant receiver backing each antenna down-converts the signal into the IF band, which is divided into 11 frequency channels. Frequencies were chosen to minimize interference by onboard jammers. Signals from the integrated low-band antenna are not down-converted. All of these signals are detected in the countermeasures receiver, which generates the digital words used by the system's new dual 32-bit computer. Measured parameters include amplitude, AoA, ToA, frequency, and pulse width. A separate fast-tuning SHR detects CW signals.

The channelized architecture of ASR is normally used in ELINT systems. Hughes claims that it allows ASR to distinguish weak signals even in the presence of strong radar or jamming signals from a nearby wingman. The ADA-programmable countermeasures computer (CC) manages external interfaces with jammers and with two 1553 buses. It uses dual-redundant HAC-32 multichip modules built around Intel 80960 32-bit CPUs. The system has a new EW bus controller. New active components throughout the system, beginning with the new antennas, allow end-to-end calibration and built-in test (BIT).

Complaints that ALR-67 was less effective than the Air Force's ALR-56 during the Gulf War made the ASR upgrade more urgent.

Applied Technology (now part of Litton) won the contract, initially for an EA-6B warning receiver, in 1975. In 1977 the Acquisition Review Committee (ARC) decided it would be standard for all front-line Navy tactical aircraft; production was approved in 1981, and the contract for the first 43 was awarded in 1982. Over 1200 were eventually made. ASR successfully completed hardware critical design review (CDR) in February 1991, and software CDR in March 1991. Tests were very successful; among other things they showed better than expected response time.

Late in September 1996 it was reported that software problems with ALR-67(V)3/4 would delay the limited rate production contract about 18 months, to spring 1998.

Users: Australia (F/A-18), Canada (CF-18), Kuwait (F/A-18), Spain (EAV-8B), United States (A-6E, AV-8B, F-14A, F-14D, F/A-18). (V)2 is to equip all F/A-18s (through the C/D model), F-14Bs and -14Ds, AV-8Bs, and the few modernized A-6Es. (V)3 is to equip the last two production lots of F/A-18C/Ds (Lots 19 and 20) as well as the F/A-18E/F. Deliveries began in September 1995. The version for F-14s and AV-8Bs is (V)4. Plans to equip EA-6Bs with ALR-67 were dropped.

◆ **ALR-68**

Litton designed ALR-68 for the German air force. It is carried aboard German F-4s and a modified version is part of the German

Sea King helicopter upgrade program, which also includes Seaspray radar and the Sea Skua missile. It is based on the earlier U.S. Air Force ALR-46, using the same ATAC computer as in ALR-67 but derived from the Air Force's ALR-46 rather than from the Navy's ALR-45. As such, it was the first operational European RWR incorporating a general-purpose processor. The (V)3 version used by German F-4Fs employs a 68020 and an ATAC 16. Litton is currently developing an ALR-68A version.

User: Germany (including Sea King helicopters).

◆ ALR-71

This countermeasures receiver for the EP-3E ARIES was developed by the Naval Avionics Facility, Indianapolis. The CRT output has five traces to show signal density and frequency. Presumably it is used to analyze spread-spectrum and frequency-agile signals.

◆ ALR-72

Sanders' VHF/UHF tactical communications interceptor was developed in the 1970s and is carried by EP-3s and by some special-purpose P-3s, such as Customs Service "slicks." The receiver is a computer-controlled 20–500-MHz SHR. The system uses a 20–200-MHz omni and two DF "farms" used for computer-controlled DF, one of seven and one of fifteen blade antennas. Intercepted signals are digitized and subject to frequency analysis. The output is passed through analog voice recognizers. Two independent subprocessors sample and analyze audio output, classifying by signal category and type.

◆ ALR-73

Litton's 0.5–18-GHz four-band E-2C passive detection system (PDS) uses broad-band wide-open DF antennas (52 in all, at nose, tail, and wingtips), each of which has its own IFM. The AYK-14 de-interleaver can simultaneously process signals from two bands, forming track files (pulse width, PRI, pulse amplitude, special tags) for identification by the airplane's central processor. The overall data load is cut by ignoring redundant emitters for a programmable period. DF (2-deg accuracy) is by phase interferometry. Probability of intercept is increased by monitoring both real and image sidebands. Unit cost is about $2M. This system was developed about 1980.

Users (all on E-2Cs): Egypt, Israel, Japan, Singapore, Taiwan, United States. ALR-59, an earlier SHR version (probably lacking any de-interleaver), may survive aboard some export E-2s.

◆ ALR-75

Andrews SciCom's (formerly Scientific Communications') modular 0.1–40-GHz ELINT (search/analysis) receiver was developed in the 1970s. It was carried by ARIES I EP-3Es and survives on board some special surveillance P-3s. A single panel controls up to eight frequency-synthesized superhets in any desired frequency combination. Signals are scan-demodulated and pulse analyzed, the results being displayed on a single CRT; there is also a separate dual CRT search/reporting display. The system memory retains characteristics of intercepted and analyzed signals. ALR-75 is integrated with a separate DF system.

◆ ALR-81

Condor Systems' SHR receiver (0.5–18 GHz with automatic mm-wave activity detection) is used with Litton's OE-320 directional antenna (see the EP-3E entry for details). Control and display modes include band scan, sector scan, dwell, manual, and threshold stop. Acquisition thresholds are programmed. Antenna/receiver control and display are integrated. There are two separate types of display, both digital: multimode DF/scan and RF/IF panoramic. The receiver uses one or two TN-613 tuners (step size 100 kHz, 0.5–8 and 8–18 GHz with 160-MHz IF [75-MHz bandwidth]). Signals are tagged with time and position using the airplane's INS (LTR-72 in an Orion). Receiver output is fed into the airplane's 1553B bus. The (V)1 version is in the ARIES II EP-3E. The (V)2 version has two operators. The (V)3 version, using a DF spinner, is in the ES-3A.

◆ ALR-82

NAWC's six-band receiver is used on the ES-3A.

◆ ALR-84

Carlisle receiver/processor, for ARIES II EP-3E.

◆ ALR-92

Microwave receiver for ES-3A.

◆ ALR-801

Condor Systems' 0.5–18-GHz (extendable to 40 GHz) MPA ESM system merges radar warning receiver functions with some SIGINT functions; in effect it brings some SIGINT capabilities into the ESM world. Its dish (2 deg $\times$ csc^2 to 20 deg over 2–18 GHz, typical gain 22 dB) is backed by a pair of spirals (60–70-deg beamwidth) to cover its whole bandwidth. The electronically scanned channelized SHR (IF 1 GHz, bandwidth 500 MHz) sends its channelized product to a digital frequency discriminator (an IFM). Frequency is measured to within 500 kHz and PRI to within 0.1 nsec. Condor's SP-103 processor has a 10,000-emitter threat library. Radar data are automatically integrated with the system's ESM data, for better target identification. Automatic DF and time difference of arrival software is available. Optional digital receivers deal with stealthy radars (FMCW and other spread-spectrum LPI types).

Condor's ALR-801 uses a single spinner for both ends of its spectrum: two spirals at left for low frequencies are backed by a dish to form a narrow high-frequency beam. Some antennas use a different approach, in which a log-periodic array (for lower-frequency signals) is superimposed on the dish. (Condor)

Users: Three unnamed countries, possibly including Chile (for P-3s).

◆ APR-39

This simple RWR, covering a series of high bands (using four spirals in hemispheric radomes) and C/D-bands (using an omni blade), was introduced in 1968 as Alert 1, for Army aircraft such as the UH-1 helicopter and the Beechcraft U-21. Later versions were adapted to small craft. The spirals feed two dual CVRs (one channel per spiral); the blade feeds another CVR. Versions differ in their high-band coverage and in their signal processing.

In the (V)1 version, the usual visual display (bearing, identity, radar mode) is supplemented by an audio tone whose frequency

APR-39 antenna, USS *Cyclone*. (S. Slade, DMS/Forecast International)

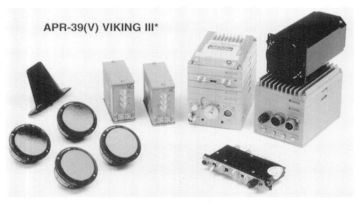

APR-39(V) VIKING III*

Elements of APR-39(V) Viking III: the four high-band spirals and the C/D-band omni are at left, with the two dual high-band receivers. To the right are the tuned RF receiver (TRF receiver) and, at right, the digital processor, in this case a modified CP-1597. Modifications are an improved user data mode (UDM) with 16 kbytes of emitter identification data storage, a modified video processor (for better pulsewidth measurement), and an advanced main processor unit (a 16-bit 10-MHz 80C186 running PL/M 86 software). The display is the box above the processor, and the controls are in the box at right front. Other versions lack the TRF. (Litton)

is proportional to the PRF of the intercepted signal. High-band coverage: F–I-bands and most of J-band. The system weighs about 3.63 kg and can be installed either internally or in a pod.

The (V)2 version has a new processor (Loral CP-480/APR-39[V]); memory is 19k (EPROM): signals are filtered by angle-gating or by PRI. Total weight is 6.5 kg.

The A(V)1 version has another, more capable digital processor (CP-1597) and it can feed a 1553B bus, for example, to provide video to a single integrated cockpit display. Threats are recognized on the basis of band, PRF, pulse width, persistence, and power level (i.e., proximity). A programmable user data module (UDM) using EEPROM chips contains parameters of threats for which visual and audio (synthetic voice) alarms are generated. Threats are prioritized for display. The 3in digital daylight display indicates whether a threat radar is searching or has locked on, and when radar lock is broken. It automatically separates threat symbols when they become too dense for the pilot to read. High band coverage is H–M bands (6–100 GHz).

A(V)2, the standard Navy and Marine Corps helicopter warner, has a digital signal processor based on three 80186 chips. High-

band coverage is C-K bands (2–40 GHz, extendable to 40 GHz). Receivers are CVRs and a YiG tunable crystal. Compared to A(V)1, A(V)2 has an expanded interface with countermeasures equipment and is flight-line reprogrammable. It is compatible with NVGs. Late in 1988 an Army/Marine Corps program was announced, to integrate A(V)2 with the AVR-2 laser warner and the AAR-47 IRCM for AH-1W helicopters.

A(V)3 is a special Army version for nap-of-the earth and night flights, using three 8085 chips in its processor.

The countermeasures interface makes A(V)2 the basis for more sophisticated integrated systems such as a threat warning system (TWS)/EW controller (EWC) version, which might incorporate a threat emitter data recorder (TEDR) and can communicate with an AAR-47 missile warner (triggering an ALE-39 dispenser) and jammers such as ALQ-136 and ALQ-162. Litton is now considering integration with an IR/EO sensor.

Litton's SIEWS is a 2–18-GHz shipboard system built around an APR-39A(V)2 receiver. Triton I, II, and III are export versions. Triton I is the basic RWR system, which can trigger chaff rockets. It can include a large ESM display. Triton II can include a fine DF (better than 2 deg) option for missile targeting as well as sensor fusion (presumably a joint radar/ESM display). Triton III adds a laser warner and can include a jammer. Note that Triton IV is a renamed Locator, a derivative of ALR-93 (see above).

Viking III is an export C/D and E-J band helicopter version of APR-39A (in effect a helicopter version of Triton) with a tuned receiver (TRF, presumably a tuned YiG crystal). Litton argues that the TRF not only improves detection of CW and pulse-Doppler signals, but it also makes it easier to resolve ambiguities between signals detected by the CVRs. A faster processor makes it easier to handle a dense pulse environment. The system controller (advanced main processor unit, AMPU) uses a 16-bit 80C186 microcontroller chip. The improved user data module (UDM) carries 16 kbytes of emitter identification data in EE-ROM form, accessible via a memory loader/verifier. A modified video processor unit (VPU) improves pulsewidth measurement. The system weighs 23.2 lb. Software is written in a commercial language, PL/M 86.

E-Systems developed (V)1, Loral (V)2, and Litton (General Instruments) A(V)1. By 1995, Loral was sole supplier of the A(V)1 and A(V)3 versions to the U.S. Army, for all U.S. and FMS requirements. However, Litton was advertising A(V)2 and two derivatives, Triton and Viking III.

In 1994, estimated unit prices were $19,000 for APR-39A(V)1, $27,000 for APR-39A(V)2, and $39,000 for APR-39A(V)3.

Users: Canada (CH-124 Sea King), Egypt (APR-39 in October class [replaced by Triton], Triton [ordered spring 1994] in two Jianghu-class frigates, two "Komar" and six October-class missile boats), Germany (Army PAH-1 helicopters), United Kingdom (Lynx and Gazelle helicopters), United States (Army helicopters; Navy OV-10, AH-1, H-46, UH-1, CH-46 helicopters; Marine KC-130R/F [A(V)2 version]; patrol boats), Yugoslavia (patrol boats). Other users reportedly include Australia, Bahrein, Korea, Sweden, Taiwan, and Turkey, plus at least one unidentified. A version of A(V)2 was ordered for PB Mk V and also for the U.S. *Cyclone*-class PCs. However, as the *Cyclone*-class mission evolved, it became clear that situational awareness rather than simply self-defense was needed, and APR-39A was dropped in favor of Privateer. A (V)1 version, proposed by E-Systems in 1985, equips U.S. Patrol Boats Mks III and IV; 44 were bought. It was exported to Egypt (October class) and Yugoslavia (patrol boats). Viking III was bid to Norway in the fall of 1995. As of January 1988, 6000 APR-39 had been delivered.

◆ ARS-5

Cubic's ARS-5 is a sonobuoy reference system, an interferometer normally used to locate the buoys of a field by measuring phase differences between signals received by antennas spread over an airplane. See the description of the S-3A tactical system in the Surveillance and Control section; ARS-5 is the version in the P-3C Update III. Because it contains its own embedded signal processor, it is an interferometric VHF DF. Cubic claims that it is designed for expansion into the ELINT DF role. The company also offers a stand-alone sonobuoy reference system (SRS) with similar potential.

◆ AVR-2

Perkin-Elmer's (now Hughes Danbury Optical Systems') laser-warning receiver, usually for helicopters, uses the display of the APR-39 RWR. AVR-2 employs two warning heads (four sensors) and a comparator, to estimate threat direction. It also characterizes the type of laser (range-finder, designator, missile guidance beam). Elevation coverage is +/−45 deg. Wavelength coverage is Bands 1 through 3, with potential to grow into Band 4. Total weight is about 20 lb. System development began in 1979, and production about 1990. AVR-2A(V) provides a training receiver (to be used in Army laser training ranges) as well as bus interfaces (RS-422, 1553B). It is also more sensitive. Development began in 1991, with first deliveries in 1994. The alternative Israeli Elisra SPS-65 (U.S. designation AVR-3) was apparently not adopted for U.S. service.

Users: U.S. Army (132 on AH-1F/1S, 252 on AH-64A, 60 on MH-60K, 206 on OH-85D), Marines (160 on AH-1W, 96 on UH-1N, 1 on V-22), Navy (19 on HH-60H, 24 on UH-1N).

◆ BLA-4

Monopulse radar DF set, part of the standard U.S. submarine suit.

◆ BLD-1

Litton Amecon's precision submarine interferometer ESM set is carried by *Los Angeles*–class submarines as a supplement to BRD-7, for tactical surveillance and OTH-T. It is also part of the WLQ-4(V)1 for the new *Seawolf.* BLD-1 is primarily an interferometer DF, but it also provides frequency and PRF on command. It works in two bands, with two receivers per band. The antenna is a square array with tapered upper sides, fitting below the cylinder of the BRD-7. The tapered upper portion of each side carries four spirals, apparently of two sizes; the vertical portion below carries three spirals, which may be of two sizes, so the antenna covers three or four bands. The system is controlled by a UYK-44 computer, and it is connected to a WLR-8 or WLR-1H. BLD-1 entered service in 1985. It was bought specifically for *Los Angeles*–class submarines with vertical launch tubes, that is, with the capacity to fire multiple Tomahawk antiship missiles (non-VLS *Los Angeles*–class submarines are limited to the much less precise BRD-4).

◆ BLR-6

This crystal-video submarine RWR survives on board Turkish *Tang*-class submarines. Presumably it complemented a superhet BLR-1, much as BLR-10/12 supplemented the later WLR-1 on board submarines.

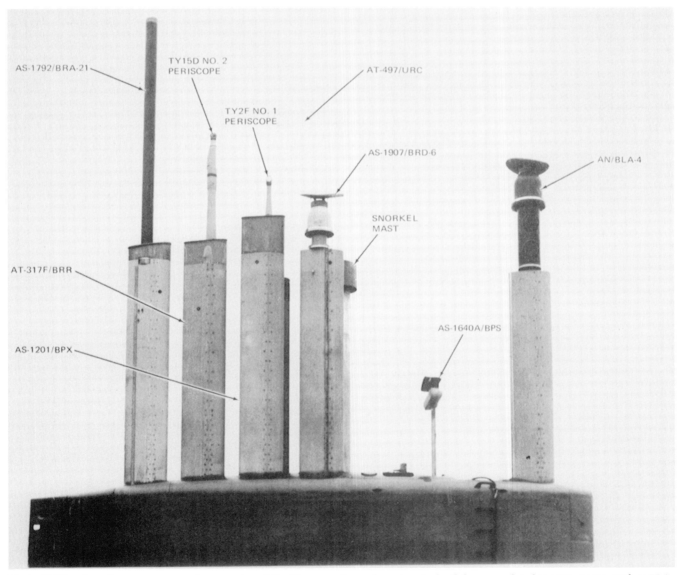

Typical U.S. submarine antennas are shown on board the *Sturgeon*-class submarine *Archerfish* as completed in 1971. Some, such as BLA-4, are still in service. Others, such as BRD-7, presumably fit much the same space as their predecessors. Note the fairing covers above BLA-4, BRD-6, and the radar antenna (AS-1640A). The button atop the Type 15 periscope houses ESM units (for WLR-8 and -10). (U.S. Navy, declassified upon presentation to the U.S. National Archives)

◆ BLR-10/12

These RWR systems supplemented WLR-1 and thus may be present in submarines equipped with that system. BLR-10 is a wide-band DF; BLR-12 is mounted on Type 8 (attack) periscopes.

◆ BRD-7/8/9

These communications DF sets have some signal analysis capabilities. There is a periscope-mounted omni antenna. BRD-8 is a more sophisticated version, with a spectrum analyzer. BRD-9, probably for *Seawolf*, is physically larger and covers a wider frequency range, but uses the BRD-7 antenna atop a new Integrated ESM mast (IEM), which incorporates BLD-1 functions. BRD-7 probably entered service in 1970. Initial procurement (FY73 and before) was 28 systems, followed by purchases for the *Los Angeles* class. Development of a new RCS reduction radome (RCSR) was completed in FY92, and in mid-1992 the Navy announced that it was buying several (in 1991 it had issued an RFP for 12, with an option for 12 more). The follow-on system will be part of ASTECS (Advanced Submarine Tactical ESM Combat System). Unit cost of a BRD-7 is probably about \$3.2M. About 100 were made.

A new monopulse periscope DF system is being developed for the Type 18 periscope.

◆ BLR-13

This two-channel ESM set (feeding a CRT showing frequency and amplitude) is used with the Type 15 periscope; it appeared in the 1970s. In broad-band mode it distinguishes between a frequency-hopping and a sweeping radar. In narrow-band mode it uses a tunable YiG filter for precision frequency measurement.

◆ BLR-15

RWR for Type 8 periscopes. BLR-15A (1978) has three CVRs for three bands; it operates in omni (warner) or DF mode. This set is similar to the earlier BLR-12.

◆ EWCM

The electronic warfare coordination module is part of the carrier/large combatant command system (NTCCS-A), supporting the OTC and his EW coordinator. With the rise of standard Tac-series computers, EWCM has now been subsumed into JMCIS.

◆ IDECM

The Integrated Defensive ECM system is the ALQ-165 successor, for the F/A-18E/F (possibly to be retrofitted to the -18C/D). As a joint program, IDECM includes the Air Force F-15 and B-1B, although it is primarily for the F/A-18. ITT and Lockheed Sanders won the contract in November 1995, ITT having offered a system based on ALQ-165 (it was a contract requirement that IDECM use the wiring and antennas originally intended for ALQ-165) but incorporating jammer technology developed for the Army's helicopter Advanced Threat Radar Jammer (ATRJ, the ALQ-136/ALQ-162 replacement). IDECM will add to this core Sanders' integrated towed decoy (see above). It will be integrated with ALR-67, with the new CMWS (see separate entry), and with the ALE-47 expendable launcher, and thus with the new family of decoys developed under the Air Force–led ASTE program. An initial request for information (RFI) was released in December 1993, followed by a formal RFI (which also serves as a draft RFP) on 23 August 1994.

◆ JASS

Joint Airborne SIGINT System is conceived as a standardized suite of scalable modular systems for aircraft such as the EP-3, ES-3, U-2, RC-135, and the Army Guardrail. DARO, the new airborne reconnaissance office, sees JASS as part of a larger Joint Airborne Surveillance Architecture (JASA) to handle the 2010 threat. As of late 1995, DARO had already awarded a prototype high-band sensor/processor contract to TRW (for delivery in July 1997). This work was based on TRW's earlier Senior Smart U-2 program, stopped late in 1994 in favor of DARO's current multiplatform approach. The first high-band modules are to be in-

stalled on board EP-3s. A draft RFP for the low-band portion of the system was distributed in mid-October 1995. The program office is located at Wright-Patterson Air Force Base. As of late 1995, there was some criticism that money for JASS had come from planned upgrades of existing ELINT platforms, crippling them until JASS was ready, which would be in about a decade.

◆ JETS

The Joint Emitter Targeting System, administered by NavAir, is intended to improve the accuracy with which antiradar missiles can be targeted, both in bearing and in range, compared to the existing HARM targeting system. The requirement is sufficient accuracy for HARM or to hand off to a SAR radar to target JSOW, or to target JSOW or JDAM directly. Ultimately fully passive emitter location would make it possible to attack enemy radars with GPS-guided weapons. NavAir will allow the use of a modified RWR, replacement of an RWR by an RWR-ESM combination, or an independent ESM-targeting system. As in ASW, a moving platform that measures bearing precisely as it moves also, in effect, measures range (e.g., by triangulation) if the target does not move. The more precise the bearing and the more accurate the measurement of platform motion, the more accurate the range measurement. Current techniques include frequency-Doppler (carrier-Doppler), time-Doppler, and rate-of-change of phase. Frequency-Doppler measures the change in frequency of a coherent threat radar due to own-aircraft motion, in effect the range rate due to platform motion (as in Ekelund ranging by submarines). Time-Doppler measures the apparent change in PRF as the platform moves (but may be ineffective against an older radar that cannot maintain PRF precisely). Rate-of-change of phase can be used against a noncoherent radar. A differential ToA technique uses several wide-open antennas. These techniques require extremely precise digital clocks and digital frequency measurement devices, as in the ALR-67 Advanced Special Receiver. Examples are the ALR-67 DoA upgrade, Texas Instruments's ASQ-213, and Anaren's passive-emitter locator.

Attempts at fully passive ranging date back at least to the Vietnam War, when some A-6s were fitted with special systems (TIAS) intended to support Shrike missiles by measuring the change in target bearing as the airplane maneuvered. Some new systems benefit from Doppler DF techniques, which offer very high precision even in relatively simple systems.

The Lockheed Martin/Anaren Passive Ranging Sub-System (PRSS) exemplifies current ideas. It was developed with the cooperation of the Air National Guard, NAWC, and NRL as an adjunct to a standard RWR. Tested on an F-16, it offered range within 20%. PRSS uses both the aircraft inertial navigation system (INS) and a digital RF memory (DRFM) of the type typically used in jammers, to measure frequency (or phase) precisely (hence to permit Doppler RF). PRSS takes a succession of measurements of emitter frequency (to within a few Hz, i.e., Doppler) or electrical phase (to within a few deg) as the airplane maneuvers. That series of data is compared to a set of possible series compatible with the maneuvers (as measured by the INS) and with various emitter locations; only one will fit completely, and that will locate the emitter. If several variables are used (e.g., frequency, phase, ToA), the location process can be made more robust. Tests began in August 1993, using recorded data for postflight analysis; real-time tests began in the fall of 1994. At a range of 40 nm, 60 sec of flight time cut location error to less than 300 ft. At a range of 20 nm, even 10 sec suffices nearly to eliminate location error (3 sec of maneuvers locates a target within about 20%).

Litton has demonstrated a similar capability using the ALR-69 on an F-15; the Navy's ALR-67 would have a similar potential (there is an ALR-67 DoA improvement program).

Lockheed Martin also offers a Targeting Avionics System (TAS), which initially estimates range by measuring elevation angle. It improves its range estimate by precisely measuring target azimuth. By the fall of 1996 the company had demonstrated 1 deg accuracy, and was hoping to reach half a degree. This degree of accuracy suffices for HARM, but not for JSOW, which is the weapon JETS is intended to aim. The current TAS prototype occupies part of an underwing pylon on an F/A-18; presumably the HARM missile would be suspended from the pylon. In a 29 October 1996 demonstration, an F/A-18 located a simulated ground radar while flying at 12,500 ft. Because the location was stored in the airplane's computer, it could dive to a position shielded from the radar (at 2500 ft, behind two mountain peaks) before firing its HARM. TAS has been selected for fleet evaluation in 1997 as part of the Naval Technology Insertion Program; a single pylon will be provided for trials, possibly including carrier operations. The manufacturer has obtained permission to brief TAS to countries that have purchased F/A-18s.

Texas Instruments' approach, exemplified in the Emitter Location System (ELS) it developed for the Tornado, is to measure direction to the emitter very accurately. As an airplane flies a steady course, a series of such measurements allows it to triangulate the emitter (errors due to unsteady aircraft motion are filtered out mathematically). In ELS, preprocessors calculate the AoA of each pulse, then arrange the data in clusters by AoA and frequency. Six MIL-STD-1750 computers sort the pulse reports and calculate the range to each emitter. This system uses interferometers in the leading edges of the wing roots of the Tornado (the rest of the wing cannot be used because it can swing back and forth). In this case, beside the advantage of much greater precision, the interferometer rejects multipath reflections off the airplane's large air intakes. A podded version of ELS became Texas Instruments' HARM targeting system (HTS).

JETS includes the use of SEI techniques to identify specific land targets and aircraft and to avoid decoys.

The requirement was announced on 21 March 1995. A formal RFP will probably follow about mid-1996. The program may include networking with offboard sensors, including those on satellites. JETS would be installed on board the Navy F-18E/F and EA-6B and the Air Force F-15 and F-16. An improved version of the Texas Instruments ASQ-213 HARM targeting pod (deliveries of which, to the Air Force, began in September 1993), displayed at Navy League 1995, was probably intended to meet this requirement.

This program succeeds ERASE (Electromagnetic Radiation Source Elimination). The feasibility of an F/A-18 precision radar target system was demonstrated under the FY93 program.

♦ LAMPS III BLOCK II ESM (ALQ-?)

Loral Federal Systems (ex–IBM Federal Systems) has adopted a Loral/AEL miniaturized version of the APR-50, used on the B-2, to replace ALQ-142 in the Block II LAMPS upgrade (SH-60R). It uses interferometric DF. As displayed in October 1994, a flat panel carries multiple spirals for each frequency band, somewhat irregularly spaced: five high-band, five medium-band, three low-band. As of early 1995, no designation had been assigned.

A LAMPS III Block II interferometer array, as shown at Navy League 1995. (Author)

♦ Outlaw Bandit/PCMS

The Passive Countermeasures System is intended to reduce ship RCS and IR signatures below those of decoys. Previously black, the program was revealed (as Outlaw Bandit) in 1993. Sheets of RAM cover flat areas of the superstructure, and special material is applied to masts, ducts, and stanchions. Radar-absorbing blankets cover fueling stations and other equipment. Portholes are covered by a gold-impregnated plastic film, to keep radar signals from entering compartments, where they might be reflected from internal corners. Antennas are modified to reduce their reflectivity outside narrow desired bands (work on SPG-62, for example, was conducted during FY93). An *Arleigh Burke* requires only about a third as much radar-absorbing material as a *Ticonderoga*, because of its better shape. These measures leave a ship reflecting strongly along a few particular bearings (radials): the ship's CDS must take this into account. IR signature reduction explains why the big bow numbers of U.S. warships are now painted in gray, which has a much smaller IR signature than the earlier white numerals.

The Outlaw Bandit OR was issued in the fall of 1987, a formal acquisition plan following in the fall of 1991. Full-scale production was approved in July 1993, after a successful OpEval on USS *Wadsworth* (22–25 February 1993). By that time interim installations had already been completed on 39 ships. Outlaw Bandit cost about $2.9M for a frigate or $6M for a cruiser. During FY93 the *Ticonderoga*-class PCMS completed developmental testing, and the *Spruance*-class version completed production acceptance test and evaluation. The *Kidd*-class version was designed under the FY93 and FY94 programs. The FY96 program included measures to reduce installation cost and to simplify RAM material maintenance.

As of the spring of 1996, the program called for the following installations to be completed by FY2001: 24 FFG 7 (21 in FY95 and before, 1 each in FY96/98), 21 DD 963 (20 in FY95 and before, 1 in FY96), 4 CG 47 (3 in FY95 and before, 1 in FY96), 18 DDG 51 (7 in FY95 and before, 6 in FY96, 5 in FY97), and 3 DDG 993 (the first in FY97).

Note that similar programs exist in several other navies (such as the Australian, Canadian, Israeli, and British). These programs can be contrasted with special hull shaping, as in the French *La Fayette* class (which also uses RAM extensively).

♦ SLR-16 and SLR-23

See SSQ-72/108, Classic Outboard.

♦ SLR-22

See SLQ-34.

♦ SLQ-20

Seesaw II augments the shipboard-countermeasures capability of ships deployed to particular areas. It uses a log-periodic antenna mounted on SPS-49(V)1 radar antennas, replacing their AS-2182/UPX IFF antennas. That suggests that SLQ-20 is a generalized IFF interrogator capable of triggering foreign aircraft IFF transponders, for identification and tracking. Official U.S. comments at the time of the *Vincennes* incident (1988) strongly suggest that the use of such foreign IFF data was standard operating procedure. SLQ-20 first appeared in 1968. Most surface combatants equipped with SPS-49 radars can carry it. The modernized SLQ-20A is generally listed as an important "littoral warfare" program, and as of 1995 an air-to-air version was under development.

♦ SLQ-32/Sidekick/Shields/ALQ-142/AIEWS

Raytheon's SLQ-32 is the standard U.S. Navy ECM system. It was the successful competitor in the Design-to-Price Electronic Warfare System (DPEWS), beating the Hughes SLQ-31 (which in turn became the basis for a major Taiwan navy ECM system). The competition emphasized very high probability of intercept for self-defense; SLQ-32 became the first wide-open U.S. system, replacing earlier scanners. To achieve good directional accuracy

SLQ-32(V)3 on board the missile destroyer *Dahlgren*, 1986. The upper antennas cover Band 3, the middle (larger) ones Band 2. The flat plates cover DF lenses; the semicircular radomes cover semi-omni antennas. The lowest plates cover Band 3 transmitter antennas for jamming (they are missing from the [V]2 version). The two flanking radomes cover lens antennas for improved Band 1 DF accuracy, for antiship missile targeting. Unlike (V)1 and (V)2 versions, this one is roll-stabilized. (Author)

SLQ-32 integrated polar display, showing own-ship and friendly emitters in the center circle, hostile missiles in the broad middle ring, and hostile nonmissiles (such as ships) in the outer ring. That arrangement corresponds roughly to frequency, since missiles (with the smallest available space for antennas) generally operate at the highest frequencies, and the least urgent threats, ships, operate at the lowest. Engagement data and further emitter data for analysis and identification are displayed around the edges of the 8 × 10in CRT. (Raytheon)

SLQ-32(V)2 (*above*) and Sidekick (*below*) on board a *Perry*-class frigate. (Raytheon)

LAMPS III helicopters carry ALQ-142, an airborne version of SLQ-32 which transmits its data down to the ship. The forward antennas are behind the flat plates on either side of the nose; a similar flat plate is behind the bulge visible aft. (Sikorsky)

without scanning, it uses a beam-forming lens rather than the amplitude comparison common in foreign navies. As a consequence, its antennas are relatively heavy, hence must be carried lower in the ship. They may, therefore, suffer more from reflection off the sea. Presumably to limit this problem, the more sophisticated versions of the system use stabilized antennas. The boxes surrounding the antennas caused some internal reflections, and radar-absorbing paint had to be applied.

Each position on the inboard side of the beam-forming Rotman lens corresponds to a beam direction: a signal fed into the appropriate position on the inboard side produces signals all along the outboard side, with appropriate phase differences adding up to a beam in the desired direction. Because the system is linear, the same lens can serve many inboard elements, forming numerous beams simultaneously. Similarly, it converts an incoming beam in a particular direction into an output, inboard, at the element corresponding to the appropriate direction. Each element enjoys the same gain, given by the total aperture.

Detractors point out that the accuracy of the Rotman lens is limited by multipath (including reflection off the ship itself). On the other hand, any system mountable at the masthead (to minimize multipath) is likely to use amplitude comparison for DF, a technique far less precise than the beam-forming offered by the lens. To the extent that the ultimate goal is radar/ESM correlation, an ESM system working with a narrow-beam radar such as SPY-1 needs better accuracy (the Rotman lens is limited to about 2 deg). Ironically, SLQ-32 was chosen over SLQ-31 because it offered a higher probability of detection at short ranges (with its high-gain antenna, SLQ-31 was optimized for long range), yet the follow-on AIEWS (see below) brings interest back to longer ranges.

Probably to control cost and increase applicability throughout the fleet, SLQ-32 was conceived as a stand-alone system with no direct connection to (or requirement to receive data from) a ship's CDS. Thus although SLQ-32 entered service in February 1979, the interface with NTDS and with ALQ-142 entered service only in 1982. The CORT Perry-class frigates introduced an EW fire-control mode in which SLQ-32 could directly and automatically cue the ship's FCS, causing a missile to be run up on the rail and the STIR guidance radar to slew onto the indicated bearing. EW integration is being extended to other fleet units.

SLQ-32 is modular. Its simplest version (Band 3 only) was a missile warner (H–J-bands). Band 2 covers aircraft radars (E-through I-bands), that is, the precursors to a missile strike. Band 1 is lower frequencies (B–D-bands) using spirals rather than a lens. Band 1 includes such major Soviet air-search radars as Top Sail and Sky Watch, and so originally served to warn that a major Soviet unit, which might be able to fire missiles, was present. With the rise of the Maritime Strategy in the 1980s, there was considerable interest in improving DF accuracy (for missile targeting) by changing to a different antenna in this band. ARGO-Systems began producing Band 1 improvement kits under a January 1985 contract. Operational test and evaluation of the SLQ-32 improvements for OTH detection (OTH-D Low Band improvement) was completed during FY88. Some of the changes increased Band 1 DF accuracy by about an order of magnitude, for better OTH missile targeting. Unfortunately, the new antennas created serious electromagnetic interference problems, which became evident just as Band 1 lost much of its importance with the end of the Cold War. Tests of a corrective began in 1994.

The Band 2 DF antenna uses a linear array of 38 vertical horns to cover 90 deg. They feed nine receivers through a Rotman lens (built up of parallel plates in stripline form). Effective beamwidth is therefore 10 deg. The Band 3 DF antenna uses 66 horns to cover 90 deg, feeding 17 receivers through another lens; each beam is therefore 5.3 deg wide. These antennas are mounted in a stabilized box, the flat lens-fed arrays pointing out at 45 deg to the centerline of the ship. The FY85/88 programs improved higher-angle coverage (HAT) for Band 3, to counter high divers. A stack of semi-omnis (in semicircular radomes) directed out on each beam feed IFMs.

A new track file is opened if three or more identical pulses are received within a programmable interval (up to 32 msec). PRF, scan type, scan period, and frequency are all extracted.

The system's jammer interposes a TWT between an outboard lens position and the corresponding horn antenna, amplifying jamming signals generated on the other side of the lens, which imposes the appropriate phases. No beam-switcher is needed to pass high microwave power, and total jamming power is the sum of the power of the TWTs. For each 90-deg sector, 35 horns (each with its TWT) form 32 beams, with a reported total radiated power of 1 MW. Jamming modes include RGPO and AGPO, the latter jamming CW missile-guidance radars. It is claimed that the system can jam 75 hostile threats simultaneously, each with a separately tailored countermeasure.

Versions:

(V)1: Simplified version for amphibious ships and auxiliaries, Band 3, missile warning, only; most were upgraded to (V)2. The antenna assembly weighs 1560 lb.

(V)2: Full-band passive version. The stabilized antenna assembly weighs 2400 lb. Band 1 lens antennas (AS-3316) are 25 × 13 × 18 in (30 lb).

(V)3: Jammer version of (V)2, for major combatants (jams on H-J bands). Antenna weight is 5000 lb.

(V)4: For carriers, replacing SLQ-17; it works in conjunction with the WLR-1H narrow-band receiver. This version passed its OpEval on board the carrier *Kitty Hawk* in January 1994. The major improvements are a digital memory for faster threat evaluation and improved interference suppression (presumably between the jamming and sensing elements). Some components are as much as 300 ft apart. The system uses two computers, each near one set of transmitter/receivers, which are connected by fiber-optic cables for fast data exchange. The wide separation between components is due entirely to the broad beam of the carrier, which complicates coordination between elements of the system.

(V)5: Jammer version of (V)2 with a separate Sidekick jammer, for *Perry*-class frigates and *Spruance*-class destroyers, bought after the *Stark* attack. The jammer is similar in concept to that of (V)3, but with lower radiated power. Raytheon had developed such a system for the Taiwan navy some years earlier, and took only three months from request to first installation (October 1987).

There are also major upgrades, SLQ-32A and SLQ-32B, so an upgraded SLQ-32(V)2, for example, will be SLQ-32A(V)2.

Shields (Ships High-Power Electronic Defense System) is an export derivative of SLQ-32, announced in 1989; there are two versions, (V)1 for small ships and (V)2 for mid-size ones such as frigates and destroyers. Like SLQ-32(V)5, Shields has a separate lens jammer, presumably Sidekick. Shields was designed, developed, and tested for an unspecified export customer, probably Taiwan.

ALQ-142 is a repackaged SLQ-32(V)1/2 for LAMPS III helicopters, using four Rotman lens array antennas. The threat library is carried in the helicopter's AYK-14 computer. This system was chosen for its compatibility with the shipboard ESM/ECM system of the ship operating the helicopter.

SLQ-32 (V)1, (V)2, and (V)3 all use UYK-19 computers, originally with 64-kword memories. There have been three upgrades. First the (V)3 version was increased to 96 kwords. Then all versions were increased to 128 kwords, primarily to accommodate CDS integration (although this was not done in all ships, the new configuration was made standard). The latest digital processing unit (DPU) upgrade is to 512 kwords, and in the (V)4 version there is an adjunct processor (256 kwords) as well as the main unit. The 512-kword version includes an embedded 20-Mbyte hard disk. The display console memory has been upgraded as well, from 4 kwords (16-bit words) to 16 kwords. The 512-kword upgrade is part of a larger Phase B upgrade that increases Band 3 sensitivity and suppresses interference.

The upgrade program began in 1987 with Phase A, which merged with Phase B (see above). Phase C, an active jammer upgrade involving both hardware and software, is also called ADCAP. It increases the number of targets the system can engage simultaneously and adds pulse-on-noise and programmed power attenuation. A digital radio-frequency memory unit and digitally tuned oscillators are being developed for the (V)3 and (V)4 versions. There are also improved circuits for prolonged CW emissions. Some of the active countermeasures improvements are part of programs for improved antiship missile deception ECM (ASM/DECM) and for counter-targeting countermeasures. ADCAP completed development/operational testing on board USS *John Rodgers* in September 1994. It is designated SLQ-32A(V).

Phase D became SADI/DDI (shipboard automatic decoy integration/DECM decoy integration), which integrates SLQ-32A with the Mk 36 decoy launcher. Under SADI/DDI, the operator at the DCC console can manually or semiautomatically control a Mk 36 SRBOC launcher. DDI completed at-sea operational and technical evaluation during FY93. The corresponding software package, under test as of spring 1995, is Revision 17 (R17). It introduces a deceptive ECM/decoy integration algorithm to replace the earlier basic decoy algorithm. It recommends either active countermeasures and decoy employment to EW operators and TAOs, or automatically implements approved tactics based on tactical scenario, as selected by the TAO. The new software uses Windows-type software to reduce operator workload. It offers improved emitter identification, and maintains a world-wide-threat database. A single software baseline will be used for both DDI and non-DDI consoles. The console is being modified by NSWC Crane to control additional decoy launchers and the warning siren required by DDI. It can operate either automatically or semiautomatically.

Phase E replaces the existing processors with a fully distributed system running in ADA language, using 68040s. Interfaces for Ethernet and Safenet 2 data buses (LANs) allow integration into the new generation of LAN-based naval CDS. The FSED contract was awarded in FY92, and the critical design review was completed in June 1994. Phase E includes a Band 3 Improvement (ECP 206; 10 to be bought each year from FY93 through FY96, with 19 in FY97), the digital processor upgrade (22 per year in FY93 and FY94), and some rapid development contract (RDC) upgrades (ECP 469 and 470) to correct problems due to spillover from other shipboard electronics and to reflections off the sea surface (16 bought in FY93, 10 FY94). Another current passive improvement is the tactical emitter feature (TEFE). The effect of greater processing power is to reduce response times and markedly improve DF and frequency measurement.

Perhaps more important, the effect of opening up the system architecture is to make it much easier to integrate new kinds of elements, such as MATES. The opened-up SLQ-32B becomes the first phase of the next-generation AIEWS (see below). It is to begin operational tests in 1996. In effect, SLQ-32B reversed a 1991 decision to support AIEWS by limiting SLQ-32 to improvements that would directly affect fleet readiness and warfighting.

SLQ-32 arose out of a DPEWS RFP issued in October 1973; OpEval was conducted in February–September 1976, and its selection was announced in February 1977 (the first units were delivered in June 1978). Hughes became second-source supplier in 1990 (24 systems awarded to each of Hughes and Raytheon), but Raytheon again became sole-source supplier in December 1993 (Lot 15, eleven SLQ-32s). Unit prices, as of early 1989, were $335,000 for (V)1; $600,000 for (V)2; about $5.4M for (V)3; and about $7.2M for (V)4. As of the end of 1993, 548 SLQ-32s had either been made or ordered. Sidekick production began with a prototype in 1987, followed by 10 units in each of 1988 and 1990, and then by an order for 28 (including seven for Taiwan, with an option for three more) in 1993.

AIEWS (Advanced Integrated Electronic Warfare System), for a time known as SLQ-54, is the successor to SLQ-32. AIEWS is to incorporate Precision ESM, for passive FCS, and it is to be an open-architecture system using the new generation of commercial-based processors (UYQ-70).

Current ECM efforts, most of which would feed into the AIEWS program, are: closed-loop ECM for real-time effectiveness (1989–91); antidiscrimination decoy (Long Duration Decoy, 1991–93); IR Decoy (IRCM, 1992–94); false range/Doppler imaging (Counter-SAR, 1992–94); ASDCs (1993–95, emerging from RAIDS and Console MMI work); small-ship compatible decoy (the small UAV, as well as improvements to current expendable decoys); advanced missile simulations/counter targeting); and coherent-delay. AIEWS will probably also include counter-ARM techniques. The advanced threat warning receiver may be carried as a separate program for coherent ESM.

It is not clear to what extent AIEWS will differ from its predecessor. For example, NRL's call for multibeam transmission through the full angular sector available to the system appears to demand a lens antenna. Like SLQ-32, AIEWS is to attack both missile seekers and targeting radars. To deal with increasingly frequency-agile seekers, it will need wide instantaneous operating bandwidth. It will also need polarization diversity. To avoid spillover into the ESM part of the system (reportedly a problem in SLQ-32[V]3), it will need low transmitter sidelobes

and low quiescent transmitter noise. Of course, all this will have to be done with reduced RCS.

In 1995, SLQ-32 Phase E was considered AIEWS Phase I (for completion in 2000), to be followed by Phase II (ESM: better RF front end, correction of digital and video processing shortfalls, to be fielded in 2006) and then by Phase III (enhanced ECM and onboard IR countermeasures, presumably derived from MATES, to be fielded in 2008).

In June 1996 the SLQ-32 upgrade program was virtually canceled, and money allocated for it reprogrammed to accelerate AIEWS; only minor SLQ-32 improvements will now be carried out. The earlier Phase I (SLQ-32 Phase E) and Phase II will merge as Increment I, to enter service in 2001; Phase III becomes Increment II (to begin 1999, and to enter service in 2004). As of the fall of 1996, Northrop Grumman had received an ATD contract for an advanced active/passive array. Two contracts were let for assistance in defining AIEWS requirements: one to Lockheed Martin Ocean, Radar, and Sensor Systems (with Litton Amecom for the passive element, Lockheed Martin Sanders for the jammer, and Computer Sciences Corporation for control/processing software and the CDS interface), the other to Hughes Aircraft (with ITT Avionics for RF countermeasures, Lockheed Martin Tactical Data Systems for IR countermeasures, and AEL for special signal receivers). An RFQ is expected about April 1997, and the Navy hopes to award an EMD contract later in FY97. The winning team must offer both RF and IR countermeasures. In FY99 the Navy will decide whether to exercise the IRCM option.

Users: SLQ-32: Australia (*Adams* and *Perry* classes with [V]2), Egypt (*Knox* class), Greece (*Adams* and *Knox* classes with [V]2), Saudi Arabia ([V]1 in PCG and PGG classes), Taiwan (*Knox* class), Turkey (*Knox* class), United States. SLQ-32(V)4 is planned for all carriers, but in 1995 CV 62 and CVN 68, 69, and 71 still had SLQ-29 (using the Hughes SLQ-17 jammer); CVN 69 was refitted with SLQ-32(V)4 in FY96. All active cruisers have the (V)3 version. From DDG 68 on, *Arleigh Burke*–class destroyers also have this version. The *Kidd* class has the (V)5 version (DDG 996 got the upgrade to A[V]5 in FY96). *Spruance*-class destroyers are to have their (V)2s replaced by (V)5s (originally they would have had [V]3s; as of 1995 that had been done in DD 969, 973, 976–979, 983, and 987. *Perry* class frigates are having their (V)2s replaced with the (V)5 version: as of March 1993, 51 sets of Sidekicks had been ordered. It was installed in FFG 36 and FFG 52 in FY96, and is to be installed in FFG 57 and FFG 61 in FY97. The amphibious flagships and the LHAs/LHDs all have the (V)3 version (LHD 5 is to upgrade to A[V]3 in FY97). Lesser amphibious ships and underway replenishment ships generally have the (V)1 version, but the AOEs and AORs have (V)3 (the AOE 1 class has [V]2 or [V]5). As part of SSDS, LSD 42, 44, 45, and 48 all got SLQ-32A(V)1 in FY96. *Knox*-class frigates were upgraded from (V)1 to (V)2. *Bear*-class Coast Guard cutters have (V)1 (the *Hamiltons* retain WLR-1, which is probably more useful to intercept illicit signals).

Shields/Sidekick: South Korea (KDX), Taiwan (*Perry* class), Thailand (planned for carrier *Chakkrinareubet*).

◆ SLQ-34/SLR-22

This cover and deception system appeared in the early 1980s. SLQ-34 uses two small antennas, one for reception and one for transmission (about 30 lb each, approximately 20 × 15 × 15 in). SLR-22 is the associated threat receiver.

◆ BGPHES (SLQ-50/ULQ-20/ES-3A)

E-Systems' Battle Group Passive Horizon ESM System (ULQ-20) functionally replaces the autonomous carrier-based EA-3B. It reduces cost and complexity by using remote control: the airplane functions as an extension of carrier ESM, transmitting its data down to the carrier via a special wide-band data link (Link 11 is also installed). Thus the BGPHES airplane, the ES-3A, is broadly analogous to a LAMPS helicopter. The system is controlled primarily from the carrier, although the ES-3A does carry two operators. BGPHES can also operate with the Air Force TR-1. An ES-3A can detect surface targets to 450 nm and air targets to

The ES-3A (BGPHES) prototype. (Lockheed)

700 nm; flying higher, a TR-1 extends these horizons to 650 and 900 nm.

The ES-3A is fitted with belly blade antennas (for radio intercept/DF), with a canoe (probably housing radar DF antennas), and with a pair of cylindrical radomes (for radar DF). It retains its FLIR and its ALR-76. The APS-137 radar is probably modified for BRIGAND. GPS is installed. EP-3 digital processing and display systems are added (computers, mass memory, digital tape, color displays, and keyboards with trackballs). The single AYK-10 of the S-3 is replaced by three AYK-14s. The net effect of conversion is to exchange nearly 6000 lb of new electronics for 3000 lb of ASW equipment. The new electronics spaces, mainly in the former weapons bay, are air-conditioned, which adds more weight. The copilot is replaced by an EW combat coordinator (an NFO). Two EW operators replace the two acoustic-sensor operators of the S-3.

Sixteen aircraft were converted to form two squadrons, VQ-5 and VQ-6 (at Rota and Guam), supplying two-airplane detachments for carriers. The ES-3A became operational in mid-1992.

The Navy is acquiring ten RS-6BN intelligence-gathering payloads, similar to the Air Force RS-6B, to be shared among the 16 aircraft.

Development of the SLQ-50 surface terminal, for installation in SSES, proved more difficult. After the 15-rack XN-1 version (incorporating a UYK-44 computer) was tested on board USS *Eisenhower* in FY87, the Navy asked that the system be downsized and integrated with other shipboard ESM. The program was split into a local element (using existing sensors) and the airborne monitoring element, which controlled the airborne sensor package. An XN-2 version of the local element failed its tests in the summer of 1993. Some of the problems were traced to differences in the hardware architectures of the two elements. In December 1993 the BGPHES program manager realized that an existing SSES upgrade program (SSEE) intended for smaller ships already performed the local monitoring role. The surface terminal was split into linked SSES and airborne control/monitoring elements, sharing a common track database management system. SSEE employs two racks of equipment and a standard analyst's work station—and the now-standard JMCIS computer environment. It also became apparent that the Air Force had already developed an airborne monitor/control station for use with U-2s. Fortunately it, too, was compatible with the COTS computer standard, JMCIS. The combination successfully extracted data from an Air Force U-2 in land-based tests in April 1995.

The revised system was tested on board the carrier *John F. Kennedy* in 1995, leading to procurement in FY97 and initial installation in FY98 (a total of 25 systems is planned).

BGPHES is a development of E-Systems' Airborne Remotely Controlled ESM System. Formally, it was an outgrowth of the Navy/NSA CHESS (Combat Horizon Extension System Survey) of 1978, followed by the Senior Jump concept demonstration of 1979, using a U-2R payload and USS *Harlan County*; the same system was deployed on board USS *Nimitz* in 1981, and a formal OR approved.

◆ SRD-502

This DF system, made by Southwest Research Institute (SwRI), is used on board the Canadian "City" class. This MF/HF/VHF/UHF system uses four nested antennas incorporating active elements: a dipole array (UHF Adcock) above small double loops (VHF: six outputs from the eight loops) above larger double loops (MF) plus monopoles parallel to the mast to form an omni; the lower array is also electronically switched to provide HF/DF. Each DF array has eight elements. In this and other SwRI DF arrays, the eight loops are interconnected to form six outputs: four coaxial space loops and two simple loops. No sense omni is needed; the array can measure direction unambiguously independent of elevation, hence it can work against sky waves or VHF from aircraft. It cannot, however, measure elevation angle reliably (due to reflection off the sea) and hence cannot do single-station location.

SRD-502 arrays on board NCSM *Toronto*. (S. Slade, DMS/Forecast International)

The AS-5157/SRD-502 array is 14.8 ft high and 6.67 ft in diameter (580 lb). Below-decks elements are a command/control interface (J-5165) in the equipment room, and a DF display group (OD-5016) and a DF data-processing group (OL-5014) in the CIC. The interface unit is connected both to the display and processor and to a sonobuoy processing system. The operator console distinguishes between sky and ground waves and conducts automatic search routines (e.g., band search, stored frequency search, and monitoring and DF of the 121.5- and 243-MHz guard channels). The console shows two small screens above a large one. The uppermost shows the IF spectrum and can be used for signal acquisition, for example, to decide how to set the tuning window. Although it can detect frequency-hopping signals, the system is not fast enough to DF them. The large lower screen is the primary MMI. Displays include an azimuth histogram for DF, as well as signal history, scan file, set-up, and self-test. The small middle window is used for tuning, for example, showing the IF outputs from the two receivers (as a Lissajous pattern). An azimuth histogram allows the operator to distinguish multiple targets in the IF passband, that is, multiple targets at much the same frequency. The data-processing group can accept remote tasking from the ship's CDS.

SwRI began with land-based DF systems (its first SSL system was a land Wullenweber of the mid-1970s) and was responsible for the DF element of the U.S. Outboard system (SRD-19) and for parts of Combat DF (SRS-1). It produced the British Cluster Sentinel (AU-506) as well as other naval and land systems. SwRI

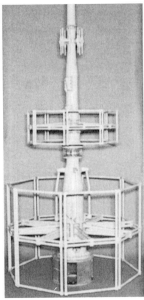   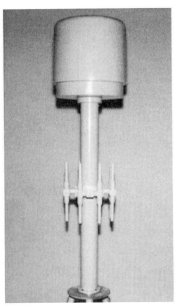

Southwest Research Institute (SwRI) DF antennas: (*left to right*) AS-5157/SRD-502, AS-3506/SRS-1 (Combat DF), AS-3112/SRD-19 (Classic Outboard), and SwRI Model 7401. Note that the Combat DF antenna lacks the low-band UHF elements of the Outboard antenna. (SwRI)

systems generally employ nested open-loop DF antennas (e.g., eight loops in SRD-19). The company has developed its own computer algorithms for DF, sensitivity enhancement, digital signal processing, spread-spectrum signal processing, and multiple-target DF techniques

◆ SRD-503

SwRI built this COTS HF/DF for the Canadian navy, for use on board TRUMP destroyers (the prototype was completed just before the Gulf War). The designation is SwRI's; it is *not* in the standard AN series. SRD-503 (SW-1, 2, 3, etc.) uses dome-enclosed ferrite loops and a top-loaded monopole to measure ground wave signals. It is similar in appearance to the radome of SwRI Model 7401. The system uses SwRI processing, flat-panel color displays, etc.

◆ SRS-1 (Combat DF)

Combat DF is a less elaborate (own-ship) version of Outboard (SSQ-72/108) for missile targeting, using a simpler VHF/UHF (partial) DF antenna, AS-3506. Compared to Outboard, it lacks any intelligence function. Combat DF operates over a broader band, and was conceived primarily to support the Tomahawk antiship missile. Block 0 is basic step-search signal acquisition and DF against communications signals. Block 1 adds a modular subsystem, the foundation for future automated signal acquisition. To at least some extent SRS-1 superseded SSQ-72, which in turn has largely been superseded by SSQ-108, more of which were bought than SSQ-72 and SRS-1 combined. Presumably that development reflects the greater interest in connectivity (as symbolized by the emergence of JOTS) and the growing importance of OTH data not only for targeting but also for other operations.

Sanders is the major contractor. SwRI makes the AS-3506 DF antenna (7.77 ft high × 4.5 ft dia, comprising an upper array of eight dipoles and a lower array of eight double loops). As modified the array extends coverage down into the HF range.

Combat DF encountered severe cost, scheduling, and technical problems, and for a time was close to cancelation. About 1988 it was very nearly combined with BGPHES to save it.

The prototype installation was aboard *Wasp* (LHD 1). Plans currently call for Combat DF aboard the *Wasp* class and on board selected *Arleigh Burke*– and *Spruance*-class destroyers.

◆ SSQ-70

SSQ-70 is a system for collecting operational intelligence.

◆ SSQ-72 (Classic Outboard) and -108 (Classic Outboard I/II)

Outboard, the netted HF/DF and signal-exploitation system for OTH-T, was conceived in 1973 and approved for service use in 1974; Sanders Associates received a multiyear procurement contract in February 1975. Plans originally called for two Outboards

AS-3112/SRD-19 antennas, part of the Classic Outboard suite, are shown at the masthead of a British Type 22 frigate: the DF array covers the VHF range in three bands. The upper two are covered by Adcock arrays, the lower by closed loops. The entire array is 85 in high. The two cylindrical objects below the array are UHF receive and transmit antennas. (A. Raven)

SRD-17 (AS-3202) deck-edge antenna, USS *Mississippi*, June 1988. (Stefan Terzibaschitsch)

per carrier battle group; 24 were ordered for missile cruisers and destroyers (to match 12 deployable carriers). Outboard is now fitted to U.S. and some British ships. The related cryptologic combat-support console (CCSC, for battle group commanders) and cryptologic combat-support system (CCSS, for all Aegis ships) were developed by Unisys, which is also responsible for the cryptologic interface unit (CIU) which sanitizes the special information produced by Outboard for use by the ship's CDS.

Outrigger, often mentioned with Outboard, was shorthand for a variety of more highly classified intelligence sources, provision of which (to Outboard stations) could improve Outboard performance.

SSQ-72(V)1 comprises the SLR-16 HF receiver, SRD-19 DF, and the local monitoring station (LMS), which recognizes signals. The (V)2 version adds the SLR-23 automated narrow-band acquisition system and SYQ-8 for target identification. SLR-16 automatically seeks and acquires signals, selecting those of interest for further analysis while avoiding set frequencies of no interest. SRD-19 provides sufficiently accurate DF for targeting. Production was completed in 1989; as of 1994, it was estimated that six remained in U.S. service.

SSQ-108, superseding SSQ-72 and parallel to SRS-1, has two phases: Outboard I (SSQ-108[V]1) consists of SRD-19A, the SLR-16A countermeasures receiver, the OK-324/SYQ system supervisor station (SSS), the LMS, and tactical intelligence (TACINTEL) communications. The SSS provides the interface to the ship CIC and to offboard systems (other Outboards, the shore HF/DF Bullseye net, and the Combat DF system). Outboard II (SSQ-108[V]2) adds SLR-23 and an OK-324/SYQ modification kit.

Outboard has been installed on board 36 selected DDs, CGs, and CGNs. The major contractors are Unisys, Sanders (which is responsible for the DF portion of the system), and SwRI.

A joint US/UK Outboard upgrade program was announced in 1995, to provide 16 new systems for *Spruance*-class destroyers and 12 for the Royal Navy. An EDM is due in 1996–97. Developmental and operational tests are planned for FY98, with low-rate initial production to begin that year. The British systems are planned for the new Project Horizon frigate. Contractors: Lockheed Sanders and SwRI in the United States, Siemens-Plessey in the UK.

SRD-19 operates in the communications band (LF/MF/HF/VHF), using standard communications antennas for target acquisition and reference, for example, a 10–30-MHz inverted cone, a 35ft 2–35-MHz whip, and two broad-band discages. For LF/MF-HF DF it uses 24 small deck-edge antennas in three groups of eight. These antennas are electronically switched in sequence to form receiving beams. They form the sort of large array that, ashore, can be used for single-station location by measuring the AoA of sky-wave signals. There is also an Adcock-type masthead VHF/DF array (AS-3112/SRD-19: two sets of eight dipoles each and eight crossed loops: 6.8 ft high, 4.5ft dia, 155 lb). The latter array includes both a wide-open directional system and a wide-band target acquisition/reference system.

Other known users include: Greece (one), Germany (three), Netherlands (two), Norway (two), Spain (one), Turkey (one), United Kingdom (three SSQ-72 [to be replaced by 108(V)2] on Type 42 destroyers; SSQ-108[V]2 on carriers and three Type 42 destroyers, SSQ-108[V]1 on six Type 22 Batch II frigates; plans to install on the projected LPH and LPD were dropped in 1993 for lack of funds).

◆ SSQ-74 (ICADS)

A van-mounted radar and communications simulator, SSQ-74 is called ICADS (Integrated Cover and Deception System). SSQ-74 may be temporarily installed on a destroyer's weather decks; ICADS has a gross weight of 18,000 lb (1974). This system is now being modernized.

◆ SSQ-80A(V)

SSQ-80A is a portable (carry-on) two-operator three-rack automated communications signals collection, analysis, and exploitation unit, for signals between lower MF/HF and V/UHF. An automated radio frequency management system (RFMS) distributes collected signals, protecting the system from local interference and also conditioning the received signals for analysis. Audio distribution, recording, and storage are also automated, and the system incorporates a computer database (e.g., of technical data references, threat profiles, and activity summaries). Output may be by printer, paper tape punch, or cryptographic device. Major contractors include Engineering Research Associates (ERA), Electronic Support Systems, Inc. (ESSI), and Cubic Communications.

◆ SSQ-82 (MUTE)

Multiple Unit for Transmission Elimination controls a ship's electronic emissions. By centralizing control, it makes full electronic silence possible. In this sense, as an antitargeting device, it is an ECM.

◆ SSQ-95 (AEB)/Tactical Buoy Simulator (TBS)/LURES/Lifeline

Litton's Active Expendable Buoy is similar in size to an A-size sonobuoy (124 × 914 mm, 17.3 kg) and contains a receiver, power supply, TWT, programmable signal processor, and deployable antenna. It is reusable. AEB is deployed from aircraft or ships. The buoy counters enemy command/control; an advanced multipurpose buoy, under development in the early 1990s, was intended to counter surveillance and targeting radars and missile seekers. Dalmo Victor received a contract for 45 test buoys in June 1984, and successful OpEval was completed in FY87. However, the expendable buoy was considered too expensive to be worth producing, so the program was revised to make it recoverable. The recoverable version was tested in the summer of 1991. The production version was developed by Litton and Magnavox. Litton received a $19M contract for five prototype and 200 production buoys in September 1993, to be completed by November 1996.

By April 1994, Litton was producing a floating active seduction decoy, the Tactical Buoy Simulator (TBS), for an undisclosed foreign customer (probably Taiwan), to be used on "frigate-sized ships." Fired from a Mk 36 SRBOC launcher, it hits the water at a nominal range of 150 m, surfaces, erects its antenna, and lures an inbound missile. TBS has a 5-yr shelf life.

In 1995 Litton announced a new LURES version of AEB, some of which had already been delivered. The company expected full-scale production the same year for an unnamed client, again probably Taiwan. The Litton Urgent Response Electronic Seduction round (130 × 1123 mm, 24 kg) can be fired by a Mk 36 chaff launcher to 150–250 m from ship, where it deploys an antenna (1.7 m above water) to transmit in C/X-band (7.5–16 GHz). It is conceived as an emergency blip enhancer, attracting an incom-

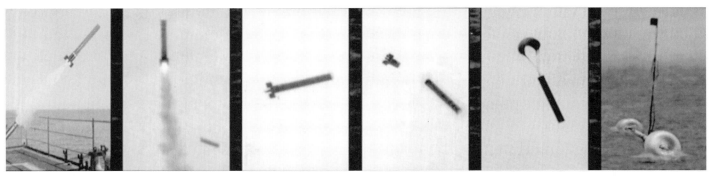

LURES deployment from a standard chaff launcher. The object that looks like a flag is a cylindrical omni transmitting antenna. (Litton)

ing antiship missile away from the target ship. The round includes a modular MMIC receiver, a digital controller, a fiber-optic delay line, and a TWT transmitter. Unlike active airborne decoys (Nulka, Siren) it has a long life (over 1 hr), and it does not require any support by a shipboard system. Reaction time is 15 sec, and system delay (in response to a received signal) is under 400 nsec. Effective radiated power (ERP) is 1 kW (option 2 kW), using a seawater battery. Sensitivity is greater than 45 dBm, dynamic range is greater than 60 dB, input pulsewidth range is 100 nsec to CW. LURES can be retrieved, refurbished, and reused five times, or it can be set to scuttle after 1 hr. Field tests were completed in September 1994.

Also in 1995 Litton advertised Lifeline, a man-portable I/J-band active electronic decoy in a small towed or remotely controlled boat. In the towed version, the decoy is controlled by a fiber-optic data link in the tow cable. It employs a pair of separate receive/transmit omni antennas on a mast, with the electronics package in the boat's hull. Sensitivity is greater than −45 dBm, and dynamic range is greater than 60 dB. Input pulse width can be from 100 nsec to CW, and system response time is less than 400 nsec. A lead-acid gel-cell battery suffices for over 1 hr, with an ERP of at least 1 kW (2 kW optional); alternatively, the decoy can be powered by an external generator. The electronic package weighs 39.2 lb without batteries or 105 lb with batteries. A photograph shows an MMIC receiver, a fiber-optic delay line, and a high-power transmitter on a standard circuit board, so operation is probably mainly range-gate deception. Lifeline is expected to operate in sea states up to 5.

◆ ULQ-6

This deception repeater, which appeared in 1959 (as an adapted ALQ-32 airborne jammer), was conceived to defeat the conical-scan seekers of early Soviet antiship missiles, such as AS-1 and then SS-N-2. Originally it covered only the I-band, but ultimately that was extended to G–I bands. During the 1960s and 1970s it was the standard U.S. deception (self-protection) jammer, two (port and starboard) being placed aboard each ship from destroyers up. The associated ESM system is WLR-1.

The array consists of fixed upper and lower elements, with a trainable element between them, providing a pair of omni jamming beams plus a trainable beam. Originally the system included no target tracker, the operator using a single ECM receiver antenna (on the trainable element) both to receive target pulses and to indicate that the array was pointed correctly. Surviving installations flank the trainable conical ECM antenna (located above the jamming horn on the trainable array) with a pair of skewed DF horns, for target tracking. The ECM horn may be either wide (low gain: 17 or 18 deg, depending on antenna version) or narrow (high gain: 8 or 9 deg). Tests showed that ULQ-6 could jam three threats (pulse trains) per array.

The first version, ULQ-6A (1 kW) produced a false target, and thus could function as a track-breaker. The next version, ULQ-6B (late 1960s) added RGPO capability in the form of swept audio. Peak power increased to 25 kW (1 kW average). The equivalent carrier version was probably ULQ-6C, with a narrower beam.

ULQ-6 aboard NCSM *Algonquin*, 1992. (Author)

During the mid-1970s, the U.S. Navy encouraged buyers of U.S. destroyers (which were equipped with ULQ-6) to adopt the SLQ-30 upgrade, which added a channelized receiver to ULQ-6B and -6C, at a cost (in 1975) of $250,000. It used the SLR-12 receiver, the spinning DF antenna of which was carried in a small separate radome (19in dia, 31.9 in high). Presumably the extra antenna was needed to extend system coverage to higher frequencies.

Users: Brazil (*Garcia* class), Canada (TRUMP and older frigates), Iran (*Sumner* class), South Korea (FRAM *Gearing* and *Sumner* classes), Mexico (FRAM *Gearings*), Spain (*Paul Revere* class).

◆ ULQ-16/SP-2060/EFE

Condor's (formerly Electronic Support Systems Inc.'s) precision pulse analyzer for ESM in ASW aircraft (such as P-3Cs) and warships (e.g., on *Spruances*, working with SLQ-32, and on submarines) accepts signals at 160 MHz (baseband frequency, moved from the actual signal frequency by mixing upon reception). There are one automatic and five manual modes (time base, delayed time base, single sweep, self-test, and falling raster). ULQ-16 measures PRF/PRI, pulse width, pulse amplitude, scan time/rate, illumination time, and bandwidth, and compares signals to those in its memory. ULQ-16 entered service in 1984, and over 600 were bought.

The AIP upgrade of U.S. Navy P-3Cs employs a Condor SP-2060 (ex-EP-2060) to replace the earlier ULQ-16. SP-2060 de-interleaves pulse trains, measures pulse parameters precisely, and uses an internal library to identify emitters. Parameters measured are: PRF, amplitude, pulse width, antenna scan rate, ToA, stagger intervals, and pulse group intervals (for some forms of pulse-compressed signals). Floppy disk drives are used to load emitter libraries (over 2000 emitters) and to store observed signals. There are two separate units, a main processor and a control display carrying a numeric keypad. Both show synthetic video.

Typical displays include an automatic listing of signal activity, a time interval analysis (to show pulse width and subpulse intervals), and amplitude (as a radar beam scans past the detector) showing, in effect, beam pattern. As of the fall of 1995, Condor claimed several foreign sales.

SP-2065 (ex-EP-2065), which equips EP-3Es and ES-3As, adds some features. A hardware frequency synthesizer is used for precision measurements and pulse gating. A separate high-resolution display shows real video of pulses and pulse trains simultaneously on four time bases, so that pulse width and PRF can be read off simultaneously (as on an IP-1159 pulse analyzer). Pulses can be displayed in real time while they are being processed automatically. The device accepts dual video inputs, displaying and processing them independently.

Comptek's private-venture Emitter Feature Extractor (EFE; formerly the Precision Pulse Analysis System, or PPAS) was another proposed replacement for ULQ-16. Although it was not bought by the U.S. Navy, it was sold to the United Kingdom and to Taiwan, as well as to some U.S. labs. More details of EFE have emerged than of ULQ-16 or SP-2060, but the latter presumably offers broadly comparable features.

EFE is designed to be embedded in a larger ESM/ELINT system, which can control it via NTDS, 1553, IEEE-488, or RS-232 interfaces. Comptek claims that EFE employs unusually effective algorithms for emitter identification even in ambiguous situations (the emitter library can be developed on a PC and downloaded into the EFE), and for emitter pulse-train separation (for multiple complex pulse trains, even in very corrupt signal environments). Presumably such sorting is simplified by the system's ability to make very fine-grained measurements of pulse shape, since often in a frequency-agile system pulse shape will not change as frequency does. Such measurements may also make it possible to recognize multiple receptions of a single pulse due to multipath. Computer-aided displays make analysis more effective. EFE has a real-time data display for tracking, parameter-to-parameter analysis, and spectrum analysis. Waterfall plots can be offset by automatic pattern determination.

Operation is manual or automatic. In manual mode, the EFE displays a stream of pulses in real time, and the operator controls the trigger mode and time base. Alternatively, the operator can display a static buffer of pulses while controlling the time base and display window. Pulses can also be filtered prior to display, to reduce the complexity of the display. In automatic mode, EFE de-interleaves pulse trains and measures PRI, pulse width, and scan rate. In this mode the operator can perform manual or assisted analysis on specific pulse or emitter buffers. The processor software includes the Comptek SLIDE pulse train de-interleaving and PRI estimating algorithm, which the company claims is particularly well adapted to dense pulse environments, and to staggered PRFs (up to 100 levels). The SCAN analysis algorithm performs a time-domain scan analysis to determine lobe center and beamwidth, and scan rates from 0.1 to 100 Hz. Both SLIDE and SCAN are described as highly tolerant of dropped pulses and noisy data. The associated threat library has 2000 entries; it uses weighted parameters to increase confidence in identification. EFE uses a VMEbus architecture with 8 Mbytes of memory, expandable to 32 Mbytes. Pulse measurement characteristics are: ToA within 2.5 nsec (stable to one part in a billion, to one part in 100 billion with optional rubidium time standard); pulse width to within 40 nsec (single pulse; 13 nsec if averaged over several pulses); amplitude to within 23 mvolt (linear video) or 2 dB (log video); minimum measurable pulse interval is 100 nsec; maximum measurable PRF is 4M pulses/sec at burst rate; and noise riding threshold is adjustable to 83% of input level.

◆ USQ-113(V)

Rockwell's software-controlled VHF/UHF communications monitor/jammer is likely to become standard in EA-6Bs, given the demise of the ADCAP program and the associated ALQ-149. Applications include shipboard communications jamming. The jamming element is UST-104 (-104A for ships and large aircraft, -104B for tactical aircraft and ground vehicles).The basic version covers 20–500 MHz, but some are more limited (to, e.g., 100–500

MHz or 225–400 MHz). The receiver element can monitor one or more signals to gather intelligence or for jamming. USQ-113 can function as a radio (it was derived from ARC-171) either for normal voice or data communications or for deception. In jamming mode, USQ-113 can time-share power among several signals at rates and dwell periods tailored to voice or data-link signals. It can concentrate on a particular data-link frequency. It can use noise, time, or deception jamming, or it can be linked to an external modulator, optimized against a particular network. Transmission is omnidirectional.

Procurement began under the FY90 program (70 units, half planned for EA-6Bs). USQ-113 was carried by some EA-6Bs during the Gulf War, but most examples earmarked for such aircraft were mothballed. EA-6Bs were again using USQ-113 in the summer of 1994. By 1995 there were plans to insert ALQ-149 technology to create an "advanced" USQ-113, perhaps including the ALQ-149 analyzer. Rockwell Collins is now in partnership with Lockheed Sanders, which owns ALQ-149. USQ-113 is likely to be included in the planned EA-6B Block 89A Warfighting Upgrade.

Under the FY90 program the Marines began to place this jammer aboard UAVs, to disrupt communications from the rear echelons of enemy troops (it replaces the earlier ULQ-19 [RACJAM]).

Estimated unit price is $650,000 to $840,000. Procurement: FY90, 70; FY96, 30 for EA-6Bs; FY97, 24 for EA-6Bs.

◆ WLQ-4 (Sea Nymph)

GTE-Sylvania's automated ELINT system for the *Sturgeon* class replaced the earlier manual WLR-6 (Waterboy). A modernized version equips the new *Seawolf*. Search, acquisition, signal processing, logging, and reporting are all automatic, controlled by a UYK-20. The system consists of a receiver-processor group (the computer, four receivers, a pulse-analyzer CRT, a PRI analyzer, and a threat warner), a threat-warning group, and a carry-on signals exploitation augmentation group; it can be supplemented by an additional receiver group (two more receivers and a PRI analyzer). Each pair of receivers comprises one S-band SHR (1.976–4.024 GHz) and a five-SHR VLF/HF set (1 kHz–32 MHz, IF 79.545 MHz, bandwidth 200 kHz for frequencies above 2 MHz). This must have been among the earliest systems using microprocessors extensively (40 of them, using 50,000 lines of code; the UYK-20 uses another 400,000 lines of code).

Development was approved in July 1974. The first full ship installation was completed in March 1979. By the time OpEval was complete (November 1979), 19 preproduction models had been approved. Full production was approved in September 1980. The U.S. FY84 budget included upgrades of existing systems to WLQ-4E configuration. The FY85/86 budget included concept definition of a next-generation WLQ-4(). A repackaged WLQ-4(V)1 will be installed on board new *Seawolf*-class submarines. Through 1993, 37 systems were completed or on order: 34 for the *Sturgeon* class, one for *Narwhal*, and two for the *Seawolf* class.

◆ WLR-1

These ELINT (superhet) systems use a combination of omni and DF antennas. In all versions but WLR-1H, DF is by spinners in radomes. The omni antennas are the "sword" and "derby." The system covers nine bands, only one of which can be processed at a time, using a tuner that down-converts to a single processing/display band. The display carries a pair of multigun CRTs, one for signal acquisition and one for analysis. The acquisition CRT raster-scans (across in frequency, down in time) as the tuner scans the chosen channel. Signals appear as bright dots along the scanned line, so a consistent signal appears as a vertical line. The operator can stop the frequency scanner at the indicated frequency. The spinning antennas show received signals as blips on A-scans (in this case, intensity vs. port or starboard bearing). Their high gain compensates for the very limited time they spend on any one bearing. Once signal frequency is identified, the appropriate spinner can be stopped at the indicated bearing.

A "sword" antenna typical of those feeding the WLR-1 pulse analyzer. This is on board a British ship, but U.S. "swords" (i.e., monopoles emerging from ground planes consisting of a few wires) are identical. WLR-1 also employs higher-frequency "derby" antennas, which are analogous in design. (A. Raven)

It picks up all pulses from that direction, so pulse parameters (including PRF) can be measured on the analysis scope. Against a persistent signal, for example, from a distant airplane, the system's high gain in both frequency and direction make up for the limited time it spends open in each frequency and in each direction. However, this sort of system would not easily pick up a very brief signal, such as that from a missile seeker. Hence the addition of WLR-3 (see below).

WLR-1G is the ultimate version of the original WLR-1, with solid-state tuners. It covers nine bands: 50–100, 90–180, 160–320, 300–600, 550–1100, 1010–2600, 2575–4450, 4406–7375, and 7300–10,750 MHz. The first ten *Spruances* were fitted with -1G as an interim measure.

WLR-1H is a radical redesign cutting coverage to six bands; -1H eliminates everything below 550 MHz, and adds a 10–20-GHz high band. Presumably this change reflects the rise of J-band radars. The most important new feature is fast (100 microsec) and simultaneous electronic scanning of its frequency bands, for much greater probability of intercepting short signals. WLR-1H can therefore capture and analyze many emitters simultaneously, whereas WLR-1G and its predecessors are limited to one at a time. Signals are digitized; up to three can be de-interleaved in each band. Each tuner is microprocessor-controlled, and a central processor manages the system as a whole. WLR-1H retains the individual signal manual analysis capability (for which WLR-1 was valued) and adds a threat library and an automatic search and signal identification mode. The signal analysis display uses six sweeps and can store up to eight frequencies per band for display. Limits: pulse width, 1–50,000 microsec; PRF 20 Hz to 2 MHz; bandwidth 20 MHz. An alphanumeric screen (54 lines, 80 characters each) displays its emitter file, its threat alarm file, emitter classification parameters, and candidate matching radar/platform data. WLR-1H can track 300 emitters. Threat library capacity: 1500 radar modes, 300 radars, 150 platforms, 80 threats. Parameters: frequency, PRI, pulse width, AoA, scan type, scan period, pulse amplitude, beamwidth.

The (V)3 version adds wide-open fixed antennas for coarse DF (both amplitude comparison and interferometry). The servo-controlled spinners are retained for fine DF. Alternatively, the high-gain spinner can be used to acquire a signal at longer range, or for passive tracking. The additional units are port and starboard antennas in three tiers. Each low-band antenna has three elements; each of the two higher bands uses four elements (three for DF, one for elevation).

Work on WLR-1H can be traced back to 1979 contracts let to ST and to ARGOSystems for upgrades including improved signal processing equipment. In 1981 ST began work on upgrading the WLR-1G signal acquisition interface, and ARGOSystems began work on improvements to -1G signal processing units. Improvements in -1H are officially listed as a new Signal Acquisition System (SAS) or an upgraded SAS (depending on which model of WLR-1 is replaced), a Signal Processing Unit (SPU), an Emitter Classification Unit (ECU), BITE, and Enhancement Modules (DFEMs). In September 1983 WLR-8(V)4 was canceled in favor of WLR-1H, which cost only half as much. This choice largely reflected the nature of the procurement process; a modification to an existing system had to pass many fewer hurdles than a wholly new system. It could, therefore, be developed much more quickly: -1H was actually a generation or more *ahead* of WLR-8(V). The kit that upgrades a WLR-1 to -1H standard costs about $900,000, this low cost reflecting the rapid fall in electronics prices. Too, a WLR-1 could be upgraded relatively easily, whereas WLR-8(V)4 installation required a shipyard availability.

Existing WLR-1, -1B, -1D, -1F, and -1G in U.S. service are being replaced by -1H. WLR-1Cs are being upgraded to -1H standard. On carriers, WLR-1H works with SLQ-32(V)4 to provide precise signal data for ELINT. One version was designed for *Permit*-class submarines. By the end of 1993 ARGOSystems had produced over 100 WLR-1H (the last U.S. purchase was probably 11 in the FY92 program).

Users (WLR-1):

> On board surface ships: Australia (-1F on *Adams* class, possibly upgraded to -1H), Brazil (*Garcia* class [sometimes listed as SLR-2, but that equipment was superseded by WLR-1]), Colombia (*Dealey*), Germany (-1B in *Rhein* class), Indonesia (-1C: *Claud Jones* class), Iran (*Sumner* class), Korea (FRAM *Gearings*), Mexico (FRAM *Gearings*), Pakistan (*Gearing* [without APECS] class), Spain (*Paul Revere* class), Turkey (*Rhein* class, *Dixie*-class tender, *Berk* class [WLR-1C]), United States (-1H with SLQ-32[V]4 in carriers, flagship *La Salle*, ex-carrier -1H in six long-endurance *Hamilton*-class Coast Guard cutters).
>
> On board submarines: Taiwan (Guppy II), Turkey (*Tang*, Guppy II, and Guppy IIA classes), United States (*Cheyenne, Columbia, Greeneville, Flasher, Gato, Greening, Haddock*).

◆ WLR-3/WLR-11/ALR-52

These radar warners were conceived to supplement WLR-1, which did not cover the new high missile-seeker bands (above 10 GHz) introduced in the late 1960s and early 1970s. Both WLR-3 and -11 employed an additional spinner antenna (scanning at 300 rpm). WLR-3 used a pair of CVRs, whose output was displayed on the WLR-1 CRT. Coverage extended up to 10.75 GHz.

ALR-52 is an airborne version of the WLR-3 successor, WLR-11 (7–18 GHz), one of the earliest ARGOSystems sets. It retained the spinner (in ALR-52 for 1–18 GHz) but added an IFM to the scanning superhet. The digital processor (de-interleaver) developed for WLR-11 (and used by ALR-52) evolved into ARGO's AR-700. Sorting parameters are frequency, pulse width, and time of arrival/bearing. WLR-11 could track 300 signals, using an 80-mode library. Like WLR-11, ALR-52 uses a spinner, but coverage is expanded to 0.5–18 GHz using separate octave modules. Each of two operator stations can select any band (the video processor gives priority to one if both select the same band, but displays all intercepted signals at both). In an updated version, one position is replaced by an interface to a digital computer.

Users:

> WLR-3 (on board surface ships): Brazil (*Alagoas* and *Sergipe*), Pakistan (*Garcia* class), Turkey (*Muavenet*)
> WLR-3 (on board submarines): Taiwan (Guppy II)
> ALR-52: United States (EP-3E ARIES I and Deepwell)

◆ WLR-6 (Waterboy)

This Sylvania manual ELINT set was originally designed for SSNs; about 40 were made. It survives mainly on board surface ships.

Users: Australia (*Adams* class), Brazil (*Garcia* class), Japan (a ruggedized Watkins-Johnson commercial version of WLR-6, covering the range from VLF to 40 GHz, equips four [ultimately 10] Japanese submarines of the *Yushio* class).

◆ WLR-8/10

WLR-8 is a submarine SIGINT system using seven electronically swept octave-band SHRs to cover 50 MHz–18 GHz. It was conceived in 1968 as a replacement for WLR-1. Signals are automatically classified and recognized, on the basis of PRF, frequency, modulation, pulse width, amplitude, and scan rate. The system can be directed to search particular frequency segments on a priority basis. It can be manually or computer-controlled, and can use any WLR-1 antenna.

All but the lowest-frequency band (which is varactor-tuned) are YiG-tuned. Three more tuners are available as reserves, or for expanded frequency coverage. The display is a five-trace CRT; the upper two, which can be switched to any tuner, show amplitude versus frequency. The next two are A-scans for manual PRF (actually PRI) measurement. The last is used for signal analysis. A PS-300 computer is used for system control, signal acquisition/analysis, and file processing.

WLR-8 was probably conceived for the *Los Angeles* class, which had much less internal space than the previous *Permit/ Sturgeon*, and thus could not accommodate WLQ-4. In 1971 GTE-Sylvania won a design competition, beating Watkins-Johnson, ITT, and Loral. The submarine version was approved for service use in 1973. After protracted development, the surface-ship version was canceled in September 1983 in favor of WLR-1H, leaving only the submarine versions. (V)1, which was not built, was the basic computer-aided surveillance system. (V)2 added automatic signal acquisition, parameter measurement, and a threat-alarm function (Scan Lock). (V)3 and (V)4 were abortive surface-ship versions (a single [V] was made for the carrier *Enterprise*). Later all versions were redesignated, the basic submarine version being (V)1. (V)2, for the *Los Angeles* class, covers 550 MHz–20 GHz. (V)5 is for *Ohio*-class strategic submarines.

The current major upgrade is the High Probability of Intercept Field Change Kit developed by ST Research. This staring wideband system (about 2–40 GHz) fits within the existing WLR-8 chassis; it can handle 2M or 3M pps.

A typical unit price was $541,000 in FY90. GTE is currently prime contractor, with an ARGOSystems receiver and IBM improvements.

WLR-10 is the corresponding threat warner, sharing the same mast with WLR-8.

◆ WLR-14/WJ 1140

Watkins-Johnson automatic signal acquisition and processing system for submarine electronic intelligence collection, a version of the company's WJ 1140. WJ 1140 uses a series of parallel tuners to cover the frequency bands 0.5–1, 1–2, 2–4, 4–8, 8–12, and 12–18 GHz, and coverage can be extended down to 40–550 MHz, and up to 18–40 GHz. The associated antenna systems are L-4/A/RS-160 (40–550 MHz), L-6/A, and L-5/A (18–40 GHz). L5/ A consists of fixed horns looking up into a spinning reflector. L-6/A is a spinning-horn antenna in a radome, scanning at 0 to 2000 rpm; the antennas can also be manually steered from the control console. They have a relatively broad pattern and are circularly polarized. The system also employs conical omnidirectional antennas. WJ 1140 can employ a C-204 analysis control unit (ACU), which measures signal parameters and identifies signals automatically, based on ToA, amplitude, pulse width, and AoA. ACU tuner modes include fixed, band scan, limit scan, and sector scan. The ACU can automatically scan through the tuners at either an automatic scan rate or under operator control. Displays include pulse-by-pulse and average PRI formats, which can be used to determine the detailed characteristics of a signal consisting of a multiple pulse train, such as a phase-coded pulse-compression signal.

WJ 1140 is reported to have been installed on board the Korean destroyer *Jeong Buk*, presumably replacing the earlier U.S.-sup-

The Korean destroyer *Jeong Buk* is reportedly equipped with the WJ 1140 signal-collection system (the commercial version of WLR-14), presumably using the directional HF antennas visible here above the usual U.S.-type ESM radomes. (*Sea Power*)

plied WLR-1, and using much the same antennas (a pair of lower-frequency antennas has been added). This system is presumably used for radar ELINT. Compared to later versions of WLR-1, WJ 1140 lacks automated signal analysis, but some additional processors may have been added. The later Watkins-Johnson receivers all had automated signal analysis, as in WLR-1H.

Watkins-Johnson produced a series of later multituner receivers to replace WJ 1140: WJ 1240, 1440, and 1740. WJ 1440 in particular has had naval application. WJ 1240, which covers 0.03 to 40 GHz, has independent digital control and parallel displays for its bank of tuners, for simultaneous surveillance of several channels. WJ 1440 was derived from WJ 1740; it has microprocessor-controlled memory scan, allowing the operator to store up to 16 scan-control matrixes, the controlling computer automatically scanning through any preselected series of them. A tuner-integrated local oscillator synchronizer (TILOS) improves overall stability and frequency accuracy.

The current successor to WJ 1140 is WJ 36500 (which is currently under naval contract for testing, although it has been built to commercial specification).

WJ 36500 (SIRS, signals intelligence receiving system) is a 15-channel SHR covering 30 MHz–40 GHz (although it can be extended to higher frequencies). It can be provided with a DF antenna, and can be used for ELINT with a monitor or tape recorder or processor. It has multiple interactive operator stations, using a 1553B bus (LAN) to distribute signals to a variety of tuners, chosen according to application. Such an architecture makes tuner replacement relatively simple, compared to the redesign required in the unbussed systems of the past.

Users: Denmark (two AGIs), Germany (AGIs), South Korea (*Jeong Buk* and KDX class), United States (Coast Guard "Island" class).

◆ WLR-18 (Classic Salmon)

This Watkins-Johnson COMINT system (5 kHz–2 GHz) is standard on *Los Angeles*–class submarines. It uses an existing antenna, the communications sleeve on the standard Type 18 periscope. WJ-32770-X is similar. It is built around a WJ-9195 Rapid Acquisition Spectrum Processor (RASP), which scans the 20–512-MHz (extendable to 2–1400 MHz) spectrum at a rate greater than 1 GHz/sec (with resolution of 25 kHz), and displays the signals intercepted on a digitally refreshed display. The system typically employs three types of operator station: the supervisor station (including the RASP), and two collection operators. The supervisor uses the RASP to locate signals of interest, then hands them off to the collection operators, who actually operate the miniceptor (WJ-8607) receivers; they can also scan for signals. The system can support up to eight miniceptors (20–512 MHz, extendable to 2000 MHz) and two dual receivers (for 5 kHz–32 MHz), a total of 12 channels.

◆ WSQ-5 (Cluster Spectator)

The Watkins-Johnson carry-on ELINT system for *Los Angeles*–class submarines covers the range from UHF up to mm-wave (30 MHz–40 GHz). It is normally coupled to WLR-18, using an existing antenna, the BLA-4 omnidirectional bicone atop the Type 18 periscope. This automated system reduces the workload, and presumably the volume, of those it replaces. That would be important, since a *Los Angeles* probably has less free internal volume than a long-hull *Sturgeon*, a type that had been enlarged specifically to make room for a new electronic reconnaissance system, and which is likely to be retired in the near future. WSQ-5, a multi-operator system, includes a signal acquisition system, automated interaction with a series of superhet tuners, signal processors, a means of automatic emitter identification, and automatic data logging and storage (with capability to monitor an advanced tape recorder). It uses distributed 80386-based processors on a LAN. Work on the advanced development model began about 1986, and several have been delivered. WSQ-5 *does not* replace WLR-8/WLR-1H, which are basically threat warners with little or no ELINT capability.

◆ ARIES/EP-3

The first EP-3B "Batracks," flown by VQ-1, were modified from P-3A airframes in 1969 to replace the EC-121s previously used for naval electronic intelligence gathering. Unlike the earlier aircraft, they were conceived as airborne equivalents of such seaborne automated intelligence collectors as the unfortunate USS *Pueblo*; the P-3 airframe provided the necessary space and weight capacity. The two aircraft chosen had served on black CIA missions over China, Burma, and Tibet in 1964–67; a third black P-3 became the first EP-3A, initially testing a SAM warner intended for B-52s.

The VQ aircraft were initially "ferrets" mapping the radars that would have confronted naval strike aircraft trying to attack the Soviet Union and its allies from the sea and, to a lesser extent, determining the characteristics of Soviet naval radars. During the Vietnam War they monitored North Vietnamese radars and radio traffic. As the Soviet fleet spent more time further out at sea, particularly in the Mediterranean from 1967 on, VQ aircraft spent more of their time collecting data on Soviet naval radars and naval radio circuits. Radar "fingerprinting" (i.e., the

An EP-3E ARIES II of VQ-1 ("World Watchers"). This version can be distinguished from the earlier ARIES I by its numerous underwing blade antennas. The wingtip pods contain ALR-73 antennas. As of late 1996, only the ARIES I aircraft were still active. (U.S. Navy)

identification of specific details of radar signals with specific hulls) presumably became more important with the rise of interest in OTH-T from the mid-1970s on. The EP-3s have also been identified with RINT (radiation intelligence), the attempt to detect unintentional emissions. For example, after the Vietnam War it was revealed that U.S. aircraft had detected trucks on the Ho Chi Minh Trail from the unintentional emissions associated with their ignitions (mainly distributor caps).

After the two EP-3Bs, 10 P-3Bs were modified to EP-3E ARIES (Airborne Reconnaissance Integrated Electronic Suite: three ARIES I, seven ARIES I Deepwell; four for VQ-1, six for VQ-2 in the Atlantic), with identical external configurations. Both the EP-3Bs and -3Es had large belly radomes (often said to contain the antenna of an APS-20 radar), a ventral canoe abaft it, a large dorsal canoe extending forward from the vertical tail, and a modified tail radome (MAD removed). The location and number of blade antennas (dorsal and ventral) varied from airplane to airplane. All of these aircraft seem to have retained their original nose and tail radars. The canoes all concealed rotating DF antennas. For example, the broad ventral canoe probably housed the antenna of the ALD-8 communications DF.

The first ARIES aircraft entered service in July 1971; the original EP-3Bs were modernized to near -3E standard. These aircraft operated in both the radar and the communications bands, and were capable of transmitting back data they acquired. They lacked much analytic capacity, and were intended mainly to acquire data for later analysis.

The EP-3E belly radome contains the 12 × 6ft antenna (AS-4074) of the OE-319 group, operating at 0.37 to 18 GHz, and transmitting at 0.37 to 10 GHz (maximum power 500 kW). The antenna can scan (continuously or in sector mode) and it can oscillate in elevation. Presumably this is a much-modified APS-20 search antenna equipped with the associated ALQ-108 IFF spoofer, and provided with a much more flexible signal generator. OE-319 is Big Look (ALQ-110 radar signal-analysis program). It is probably set up for BRIGAND (bistatic) operation, partly to gauge the performance of the radars it detects, and it would certainly provide precision DF. This radar is probably also carried by WP-3A/3D weather reconnaissance aircraft.

Bistatic Radar Intelligence Generation and Analysis, New Development (BRIGAND) is a technique for detecting the signals reflected by objects near a target radar; in effect it picks up a distorted version of the target's own radar picture. It was developed by VQ-1 technicians in 1960, using the highly directional antenna of an APS-20 to feed a very sensitive radar receiver (an APR-9). The detailed view of the nearby ground clutter makes it possible to locate the target radar more precisely. BRIGAND also reveals nearby objects. For example, even if only one ship in a group is radiating, back-scatter reveals the others. BRIGAND is also effective against airborne radars and IFF transponders.

An EP-3E shows its characteristic belly radome (for the Big Look antenna) and its ventral canoe. (Lockheed Aeronautical Systems Co.)

In active mode, OE-319 can localize an emitter (for identification) by searching its line of bearing.

ARIES I aircraft have the ALR-52 ELINT system (see separate entry). Deepwell adds the ALR-60 central-computer COMINT system.

Because these aircraft were P-3B conversions, they lacked internal buses and central computers. About 1980 they were fitted with AYQ-14, an interactive signal processing system intended to facilitate collection. It employed a single AYK-14 computer and up to six data-collection computers (CP-1563: 10 kwords of ROM, 10 or 14 kwords of RAM, all 16 bits), which converted the digital data from sensors into words usable by the central computer. It also included a pair of plasma displays and two tape recorders.

Lockheed received a CILOP contract in June 1986 for the first of 12 further P-3C conversions (EP-3E-II ARIES II). The first CILOP aircraft was delivered to the Naval Air Test Center in July 1990. However, after the first five had been completed, the contract was shifted to NADEP Alameda (the last aircraft are being done by NADEP Jacksonville, Alameda having been closed). The U.S. Navy planned to standardize the three current EP-3 configurations: EP-3B Batrack and two versions of EP-3E (ARIES I and II) by 1995; VQ-2 is being upgraded to ARIES II standard.

The great change in ARIES II is a much higher degree of automation, which makes it possible for the crew to analyze the signals collected, and therefore to make decisions as to which signals to pursue. Thus there is now an EW combat coordinator, corresponding to the TACCO of an ASW P-3C. Besides a conventional aircrew (pilots, flight engineer, navigator, communicator) an ARIES II carries 15 specialists: a secure communications operator, a data recorder/flight technician, an EW combat coordinator, a BRIGAND (mainly precision radar location) operator, a LAB operator, an ESM supervisor, a radar/ESM operator, a manual ESM operator, a scientific/technical operator, a special systems evaluator, and five special systems operators. Here "special" clearly means COMINT, probably cryptologic support. The manual ESM operator would use a spectrum analyzer to dissect signals of particular interest. The LAB operator was originally intended to test experimental modular equipment; LAB now probably refers to a particular piece of equipment, since the airplane also carries a scientific/technical operator. The latter may be a radar fingerprinter.

ARIES II substitutes a more powerful mission computer (AYK-14) for the ASQ-901 of the P-3C, and introduces a bus architecture (1553B bus). There are no longer separate COMINT and ELINT suites, since all acquisition sensors can report to the computer and, through it, control any monitor sensor. The display is the Lockheed Sanders IP-1515. Communications signals are typically acquired by a Carlisle ALR-84 and monitored by the Magnavox ARR-81 computer-controlled receiver (1 kHz–500 MHz). The main airborne communications-band DF is ALD-9. Radar signals are acquired by the Sylvania ALR-44 (0.5–18 GHz) of earlier versions, and the earlier ULQ-16 spectrum analyzer remains. A high-gain OE-320 directional antenna feeds each Condor Systems ALR-81 pulse analyzer. The big belly antenna and its ALQ-108 remain from the earlier suite. The IBM ALR-76 ESM/RWR is added at the wingtips.

The Magnavox ARR-81 COMINT receiver is microprocessor-controlled, using a 64-bit serial word for digital tuning. Its multiple radio receivers each have 20 preset channels, to search separate frequency ranges. Different versions have differing numbers of receivers: 0–2 × R-2143, 2–4 × R-2144, and 0 or 8 × R-2282. R-2143 is a 1–32-MHz double-conversion receiver (IFs 79.545 MHz and 455 kHz, with selectable bandwidths of 0.5, 3.2, 8, and 16 kHz). Maximum tuning time is 10 msec. R-2144 is a dual-conversion tuner for 20–500 MHz (IFs 21.4 MHz with selectable bandwidths of 8, 25, 50, 250, and 500 kHz). Maximum tuning time is under 5 msec. R-2282 is an alternative VHF/UHF double-conversion tuner.

Litton's OE-320 DF antenna group covers 0.5–2 and 2–18 GHz. It scans at 0–200 rpm, and can be limited to a 15-, 30-, 60-, or 120-deg sector centered on the airplane centerline. The antenna can be manually or automatically slewed to a signal of interest, and its elevation angle is adjustable. Antenna diameter is 23.75 in, and gain (depending on frequency) is 1.7–27.4 dB.

Other added equipment includes GPS navigation and FLTSAT-COMM capability.

The major external differences between ARIES II and earlier EP-3s are extensive "farms" of blade antennas beneath the wings and rear fuselage and the ALR-76 antennas at the wingtips. A small DF radome lies abaft the ventral canoe.

The next step is to make better use of available offboard information correlated with what the airplane's own sensors can detect, for better situational awareness. In common with other current programs, the ARIES II upgrade (SSIP, sensor system improvement program) emphasizes open architecture and the use of existing equipment (NDI, COTS, GOTS). That suggests that it will ultimately add a new data bus and a new central processor. Presumably SSIP makes it easier for an EP-3E to receive (and transmit) satellite intelligence broadcasts of various types, sent in different formats. SSIP reflects the jointness lessons of the Gulf War.

The 1994 budget included the $300M SSIP, comprising three projects: Story Book, to improve signal processing to deal with more sophisticated (presumably LPI) radar and radio waveforms (it replaces ULQ-16 with the Condor Systems ES-2065 and also replaces ALR-44/81); Story Classic, to improve the existing intercept sensors and upgrade cryptologic workstations; and Story Teller, to make it easier to pass information to other platforms, for all-source data fusion. About a quarter of ARIES II mission avionics will be replaced. Much of the program is new software. Two SSIP packages were bought in FY94, four in FY95, and six in FY96. The ES-3A is to be similarly upgraded.

There were also two P-3B and two P-3C Special Projects aircraft, which gather intelligence but which appear unmodified (they are sometimes described as "small cousins" of the EP-3s, which they resemble internally). The absence of canoes suggests that they lack the fine DF capability and high-gain reception of the EP-3E, but retain the ability to do detailed signal recording and, now, analysis. This program is currently called Reef Point. Three replacement aircraft had been delivered by the fall of 1993, with the fourth scheduled for FY94. The new program replaces the previous variety of configurations with a single standard one. Released details of the conversion: installation of standard Navy systems for increased capability and reduced operator workload (and common logistics); installation of special mission equipment as specified by intelligence agencies and by OpNav; and update of RF distribution hardware for selected intelligence-gathering subsystems. Total program cost was $102.5M. These aircraft are reportedly operated by VPU-1 (Brunswick, Maine) and VPU-2 (Barbers Point, Hawaii).

The JMSDF is the only other operator of a P-3 SIGINT version; it is not clear to what extent its aircraft correspond to the EP-3E. Like the EP-3E, the Japanese EP-3 has had its MAD boom removed. It has a very different radome configuration, with two widely spaced dorsal teardrop radomes and a somewhat smaller ventral radome (from which prominent blade antennas protrude) where the EP-3E has its large radar antenna. The JMSDF's first EP-3, converted by Kawasaki, was rolled out in July 1990. It carries NEC's LF and Mitsubishi's HF systems. Replacing the current EP-2J, it covers a wider frequency range and, because it flies higher, a larger area. The JMSDF expects to buy a total of six to replace the two current EP-2Js.

Several quite different aircraft were designated EP-3A. The Naval Research Lab designated its electronic warfare simulator/evaluator an EP-3B (it is now designated an NP-3D). There are also EP-3Js (ex-P-3Bs) used to simulate jammers in fleet exercises.

◆ ASTECS

The Advanced Submarine Tactical ESM Combat System is planned for the *Seawolf* and, presumably, the New Attack Submarine classes. It integrates threat warning and intelligence-gathering in the same system, which is also directly connected to the submarine's CDS and hence to its JMCIS database. It also includes organic OTH-T as is currently offered by the high-precision DF (BLD-1) of the later *Los Angeles* class. The system is to reside in a row of five electronics racks, two of which carry dual CRTs and keyboards, and one of which carries the printer. The ELINT function is reflected in the presence of two sets of narrow-band radar tuners (there is also a wide-band receiver section). A V/UHF communications receiver is used for COMINT. The system is 92% NDI/COTS hardware (i.e., it uses TAC-series computers) and 90% NDI/COTS software. Because it is integrated with the submarine's CDS, it can display JMCIS data with which to correlate its own observations.

Typically one set of screens might show tasking, the other signal alerts and a summary of emitters being received, plus an early warning panel. If no threat was present, the early warning display might be replaced by one showing identifications of emitters, with confidence levels. Alternatively, DF plots can be displayed. Other displays include: signal exploitation, communications signal analysis, receiver control, Morse code translator, contact manager, TRE, geographic situation, and noninterest signals.

The OR was issued in October 1991. ASTECS was awarded to a Lockheed Martin team in the fall of 1995. The other members are GTE (signal distribution, submarine physical integration, training features, NDI/COTS adaptation), ST Research (wide-band radar subsystem, Integrated ESM Mast interface, radar man-machine interface), Engineering Research Associates (communications subsystem), Condor Systems (narrow-band radar subsystem, SEI, early warning subsystem, photonics mast interface, radar MMI), and Delfin Systems (security engineering, contact management, signals exploitation).

◆ Counter Communications

This is a projected carry-on replacement for the SSQ-74 van cover and deception system that now equips fleet deception groups. Vans are disliked because they take up too much deck space on board small combatants, and because they add too much RCS and topweight to other ships. Moreover, they are recognizable. The new system will be installed internally. It will incorporate an open architecture, hence will be able to simulate any radar within its radio frequency coverage through a computer-controlled modulation system. Inital operations will include a capability to simulate the two radars identified by the C&D program sponsor.

◆ MEWS/SLQ-17/SLQ-29

Hughes' Modular Electronic Warfare System provides the jamming element of the Taiwan navy's Chang Feng III. It is based on SLQ-31, the unsuccessful alternative to SLQ-32, and is related to the larger U.S. SLQ-17. The main difference between the two systems is Hughes's concentration on one high-energy beam for long range versus Raytheon's preference for lenses to form numerous beams simultaneously. Hughes always described SLQ-17 as a false target generator rather than as a source of protective noise.

The jamming antenna is a curved slotted waveguide feeding a parallel, nearly semihemispherical reflector (a multiple-feed parabolic torus). Hughes claimed that this configuration provided stronger beams on the broadside, where the ship cross-section is greater and therefore where more jamming power is needed to overcome reflections from that cross-section. The single jamming beam is steered by shifting the signal generator among the feeds, using multiport electronic switches. In an idealized description (probably not quite comparable to the Taiwanese system) published in 1982, the antenna had ten feeds to produce 10 20-deg high-gain beams (10 deg for the two beams pointing abeam). At this time, Hughes emphasized that such a system could be installed in low-cost but upgradable form. For example, in five-beam form it might accommodate two four-port electronic switches, one feeding three ports and also the second switch. The second switch fed the other two ports, two of its outlets being unused. In an expanded version of the array, each of the two original switches would feed four ports, and a third switch would feed two more. The system could be further ex-

The SLQ-17 box is shown aboard USS *America* (now decommissioned) in 1995, with a satellite dish just above and inboard of it. This two-band system uses pairs of receiving horns and pairs of toroids for its jammers. Behind the top and bottom broadside windows are horizontal trainable pairs of horns forming trackers (a large pair over or under a small pair). The vertical combination of two separate trackers in each band presumably overcomes multipath. Behind the middle window are a pair (side by side) of jamming toroidal antennas with multiple feeds (along the inside element of the toroid), for beam steering. Each upper side window covers a large torus above a smaller one. The lower side windows cover the tracking horns associated with the side toroids, the vertical pair being adjacent rather than split between two windows. (Author)

panded by adding a fourth four-port switch, using three of its outlets and the two previously unused outlets of the third switch to drive a second series of beams elevated above those of the 10-beam array, doubling elevation coverage by forming four 40-deg beams and one 20-deg beam. This growth could be catered for by allowing for additional torus antennas in the system radome, additional cable runs, and additional switches and their driver cards. Hughes argued that such preplanned improvement using hardware identical to that already in the system would be relatively inexpensive.

At least three Hughes SLQ-17s remain active, on board CV 62 (to decommission FY97) and CVN 68 (to recore/refit 1998–2001) and 71; CVN 69 was refitted with SLQ-32 in FY96, and CVN 70 already has SLQ-32(V)4. This system is also aboard the laid-up CV 61 and CV 66. In these ships, the jammer is combined with WLR-1H and WLR-11 to form SLQ-29.

◆ AMD

The activated metal decoy was developed specifically for Desert Storm. No details are available. However, the name suggests some means of causing metallic chaff to produce an IR signature by undergoing a chemical reaction.

◆ CMWS/ATIRCM

Common Missile Warning System is intended mainly to deal with man-portable IR-guided AA missiles. It has been consolidated under the Army's Advanced Threat IR CM system, which was originally designed to protect helicopters. Originally the Navy was lead service for the fast aircraft equivalent, PMAWS-2000 (passive missile approach warning system). When the Navy dropped funding, the Air Force took over. OSD merged the Army and Air Force programs because the Army had the more stringent requirement, and reportedly because the Air Force tended to overspecify (its program would have failed operational testing). When the programs were merged late in 1994, the Army had just selected Lockheed Sanders' IR system, and the Air Force was about to issue its RFP. When the program was recompeted, Lockheed won again. This system uses a Loral missile warner based on AAR-47.

The outstanding feature of the program is the requirement that it sense not only the approach of a missile, but also the direction of approach, to control a directional IRCM (DIRCM) jammer. By the fall of 1994 DIRCM had been tested successfully against live missiles, using a Loral IR lamp (not a laser) whose light was focused by a mirror. For this test, the jammer was triggered by a modified AAR-44 warner mounted on a mock helicopter fuselage hung from a cable. The jammer would ideally be built around a laser, but in 1994 no small 2.5–5-micron laser existed. ARPA therefore let contracts to Lockheed Sanders and TRW to demonstrate diode-pumped lasers using nonlinear crystals capable of radiating in the 2.5–5 band. Feasibility demonstrations (with output of a few watts) were scheduled for the summer of 1995, with a follow-on contract (10–20 W) to be awarded in the fall of 1995.

Meanwhile the Naval Research Laboratory has been developing its own DIRCM, based on a new holmium thulium–doped YAG laser, which transmits simultaneously in three wavelengths in the 3–5-micron window, and which is tunable simply by turning a crystal. As of late 1994, four such lasers were considered sufficient to protect an F-14 or C-130, and work was proceeding on a single laser powerful enough to provide such protection. The goal was a laser that could fit within 1 ft^3 (it already fits within 2 ft^3). The laser cavity had already been shrunk from 55 to 17 cm in length. The system, in a pod on a P-3, is triggered by a Fly's Eye detector (initially one color, but being developed for two colors), which hands off a target to a pointer/tracker taken from the Army ATIRCM program. Each Fly's Eye has a 60 × 60-deg FOV (being expanded to 80 × 80 deg). Unlike existing Air Force systems, which can jam a seeker only after it has been identified, the NRL system uses a generic jamming code that requires no identification. It is expected to fly on a P-3 pallet in 1996.

There is also an issue of size and coverage. In theory, a DIRCM should be able to protect against threats from any direction, so multiple units are needed. Martin Marietta/Denver is working on a novel electronically steered ball lens, fed by optical fibers; selecting the activated feed(s) points the beam. This is apparently a Luneberg Lens at optical frequency. If viable, it would provide a DIRCM sensor only 4in in diameter; three such could cover a fighter.

The Army's ATIRCM uses a jam-head with three windows: a large one for Bands 1 and 2, a midsize one for an IR missile tracker, and a small one for new Band 4 threats. It is too large to be installed in a fighter; NavAir has begun an EW Advanced Technology (EWAT) effort to develop a fast jet DIRCM, working with Sanders, the Air Force, and the Army to shrink ATIRCM.

Plans currently call for delivery of 16 CMWS for flight tests to begin in 1997, followed by the first 34 production items to begin in late 1998 (and to be completed in the fall of 1999).

In effect CMWS competes with Nemesis (AAQ-24), a SOCOM/RAF program to protect C-130s and helicopters, based on the AAR-54 IR warner. It is scheduled to enter production by the end of 1996. Litton and Daimler Benz Aerospace have developed another MWS, MILDS (missile launch detection system), using UV sensors. In contrast to the usual central processing system, MILDS places a signal processor behind each antenna. Other systems will probably be developed for the F-22 (using IR for high altitude) and to meet a British fast jet specification (which, like CMWS, will compare IR with UV sensors).

In addition to DIRCM, there is a new Air Force "smart" decoy program, ASTE (Advanced Strategic/Tactical Expendables), the fruits of which will presumably be available to naval aircraft. It includes a forward-firing flare and a nonburning IR decoy for Special Forces. Tracor won this contract in November 1995. A similar Army program, AIRCMM (Advanced IRCM Munitions) was at the demonstration/validation stage late in 1994.

◆ MATES

Multiband Anti-Ship Cruise Missile Defense Tactical Electronic System is a module to add to SLQ-32 and AIEWS. Loral won the NRL advanced technology demonstrator competition, using the same signal processor and algorithms as those developed for a canceled Air Force test program (LIFE, Laser IRCM Flyout Experiment). Presumably cued by an IRST, MATES uses EO ima-

ger/trackers (such as FLIRS) to track an incoming IR-guided missile or bomb (including a laser-guided weapon, which uses an EO seeker), then jams it using a laser. The laser first directs a low-power beam at the incoming weapon to identify its seeker type, hence select the best jamming waveform (modulation). Presumably the laser can attack the sidelobes of the IR sensor; possibly, too, it can in effect paint a false image on a staring IR sensor. The laser is partly tunable, and the system as a whole attempts to measure the effect of jamming (see the discussion of the directed IRCM above). The breadboard version is quite massive, but an operational version might weigh as little as 300 kg. To achieve the required agility, the laser beam is directed by a mirror.

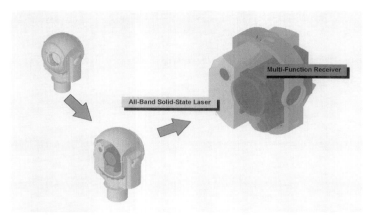

Lockheed Martin's above-decks MATES jammer combines an all-band solid-state laser (left) with the multifunction receiver at right. This is probably the configuration that will be offered as part of AIEWS Phase Two in the spring of 1997. (Lockheed Martin)

MATES overwater shore tests, at Chesapeake Bay, were conducted between December 1994 and January 1995, the system breaking lock on all the airplane-carried sensors tested. A 1995 ship test was successful. MATES inspired the decision to proceed with an ATCD of defense against an imaging IR seeker in an antiship missile under the FY96 program.

Note that about 1984 Loral supplied an aircraft-type IR countermeasure to protect the yacht of a foreign head of state, perhaps Brunei, from weapons such as SA-7s.

◆ Advanced Digital Receiver

Litton Applied Technology announced this new receiver early in 1995; it is likely to be incorporated in a variety of naval systems, such as ALR-67ASR. It was intended to deal with an increasingly dense pulse environment by adding additional pulse-identification parameters (IMOP [chirps, phase coding, etc.] and UMOP, partly for specific emitter identification), better time correlation (using a crystal clock), and extremely precise time and frequency measurement to support passive-emitter location (see JETS, above). For example, accuracy on the order of nsecs makes it possible to locate an emitter direction to within a few degrees, comparing times of arrival at different antennas. Doppler location requires frequency measurement precision of a few Hz. The new receiver began early in 1994 as an IR&D project (Litton Applied Technology, Litton Ameecom, Mercer Engineering Research Center) to develop a common module that could be fitted to all existing Air Force and Navy aircraft without affecting related aircraft systems or wiring. In Litton's view, unambiguous identification of emitters requires fusion of a wide variety of techniques (clock de-interleaving, UMOP and IMOP analysis, classic RWR, and emitter location). The Litton receiver replaces existing IF receivers in ALR-67ASR and -69 (Air Force). It employs a high-speed A/D converter and leading edge (of pulse) detector, a digital processor, and a Litton R-4600 processor. RF down-conversion is channelized.

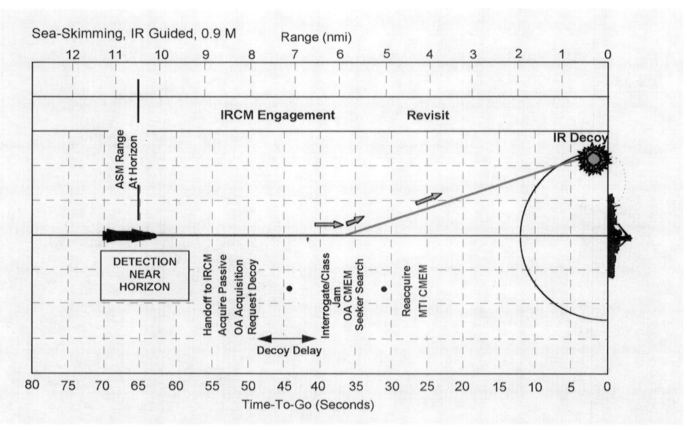

A typical MATES engagement begins with handoff by a designation system. The threat is prioritized and then acquired, first passively (by the multifunction receiver, picking up the exhaust plume or skin heat) and then actively. MATES is analogous to other shipboard jammers: it seeks to lock the incoming weapon onto a decoy. In this engagement diagram, CMEM is the vital countermeasures effectiveness monitor, which decides whether to keep jamming. (Lockheed Martin)

◆ AR-700/AR-740/APECS

AR-700 was the follow-on to the AR-600 (Phoenix) series, incorporating a new 12-bit digital IFM (DIFM), accurate to within 2 MHz (3 MHz for 8–18 GHz). Conceived for submarines, it was also installed on board many surface ships and aircraft. The signal processor is the ASP-32 (200 tracks) of Phoenix II. It probably handles about 1M pps. Library capacity is 990 modes (100 radars). The processor can handle frequency agile (+/−5%), stagger (up to eight positions), jitter (+/−10%), chirp, and CW signals. AR-700S5 is the submarine version. DF accuracy (monopulse DF) is 10 deg in S1 and S2, 8 deg in S3 and S4, and 5 deg in S5. Sensitivity: −40 dBm in S1 to S3, −60 dBm in S4 and S5. Estimated cost is $3.5 to 4.75M. The associated surface-ship jammer is APECS.

AR-700A uses the more powerful ASP-2000 (500 tracks). It can handle a maximum pulse density of 1.5M pps (it can sustain 1M); maximum reaction time is 1 sec (excluding scan time measure-

ment). PRFs can be between 12.3 and 250,000, pulse widths between 0.1 and 99.9 microsec.

AR-700A(V)1 is a 2–18-GHz system offering accuracies of 4 MHz and 5 deg, with a sensitivity of −60 dBm, and a capacity of 1.5M pps. AR-700(V)2 extends coverage down to 0.5 GHz (extension up to 40 GHz is optional). In the submarine version, the periscope antenna provides 5-deg bearing accuracy, and a separate ESM dish antenna provides 2-deg precision with sufficient

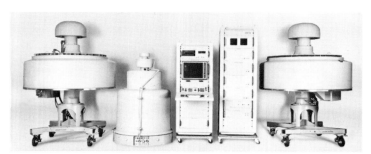

Elements of the ARGOSystems APECS II surface-ship EW system: the two stabilized air-cooled jamming antennas flank the ESM "pot," the system display/processor, and the jammer transmitter. Many systems have monopulse DF spirals in place of the DF elements of the pot. (ARGOSystems)

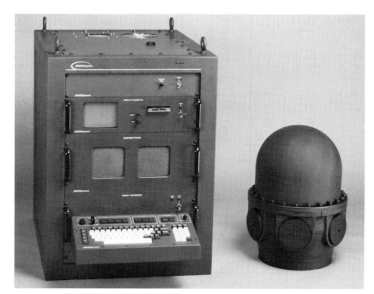

ARGOSystems's AR-700 ESM system for submarines, with the indicator on the left and the antenna on the right. Three DF ports are visible on the antenna. (ARGOSystems)

The Phoenix AR-700 masthead ESM array on board the Norwegian frigate *Stavanger* in 1992. (Author)

This ARGOSystems jammer was displayed at the 1993 Navy League Show. The vertical circular plate at the right is the beam-former. Two such modules, oriented like this, and pointed 90 deg apart, fit within each big cylinder of an APECS II jammer (the smaller cylinder above it holds a cooling fan, with a heat exchanger below the big cylinder). (Author)

sensitivity for missile targeting beyond the horizon. The surface-ship version offers interferometric DF (0.7-deg accuracy); instantaneous accuracy is 2 deg. The processor can handle 3M pps. AR-700A(V)3 adds an electronic warfare operator's console (EWOC), a specialized high-performance workstation with a relational database.

The system measures frequency, bearing, PRF, pulsewidth, scan period/rate, amplitude, time first seen/since last seen, CW indicator, frequency agility, chirp (indicator), stagger (2- through 16-position), and jitter. The associated library lists 1000 emitters. The system identifies new signals within 1 sec of interception. In a MEKO frigate, the system uses monopulse for instantaneous DF (5-deg rms), but it uses interferometry for fine DF (1-deg rms in the two high bands, 1.5 deg in the low band). However, accuracies quoted for the surface-ship version of AR-700A(V)2 are 2 deg (instantaneous) and 0.7 deg (interferometric).

APECS (Advanced Programmable Electronic Countermeasure System) is the corresponding surface-ship jammer. APECS I uses the ASP-32 processor and a pair of phased array modules, port and starboard. APECS II uses ASP-2000 and provides signals with polarization diversity, to counter monopulse threats. Compared to APECS I, it is easier to install (because its signal generator is self-contained, so it requires neither external waveguide nor water cooling), and can handle complex signals. For example, it can deal with frequency/PRF-agile seekers by tracking the leading edges of their pulses, not waiting until the full pulse has been received before sending the countering signals.

In a Portuguese MEKO frigate, APECS II employs a masthead omni antenna and a pair of monopulse (cavity-backed spiral) DF antennas. Each of the ESM antennas is a stack of three: for 0.5–2, 2–8, and 8–18 GHz, each stack consisting of four cavity-backed spirals.

The APECS II jamming antennas are a pair of big stabilized air-cooled cylinders, each of which covers a pair of Rotman-Turner lens antennas fed by a bank of mini-TWTs. Among its techniques, the system provides cross-polarization (automatic polarization tuning) jamming to defeat monopulse seekers.

Because control is software-based, ECM tactics can be tailored to specific threats. The two basic operating modes are transponder (in which the appropriate response signal is preset) and deception (in which the response signal is constructed in response to the details of the received signal). The two techniques can be run in sequence, and the entire system can operate fully automatically, semiautomatically (the command to radiate is under operator control, but everything else is automated), or manually. The ECM system employs ARGO's own frequency-memory loop (FML). Each of the two ECM transmitters covers 180 deg with 30 overlapping time-shared beams, sufficient to noise-jam 8 or deceive 16 threats (of which eight may be frequency- and/or PRF-agile). Maximum ERP is 230 kW. The associated ECM library contains 255 technique parameter sets.

Noise techniques are spot/barrage, swept spot, and cover pulse. Deception techniques are RGPO (using frequency memory loop or video count-off), false target generation, angle deception (by swept scan rate or low frequency noise [to defeat conscan radars]), and automatic polarization tuning.

Each of the two monopulse receiver units is 87 (high) × 71 (wide) × 64 cm (weight 57 kg); the omni unit is 48 (dia) × 72 cm (36 kg); each of the two transmitters is 165 (dia) × 183 cm (500 kg).

The first APECS II was delivered in 1986. The system was selected in 1987 for the Dutch *Karel Doorman* class (at a unit cost of $3.75M) in place of a more expensive Signaal system.

The version for the Australian *Collins* class is AR-740. It extends coverage up to mm-wave (18–26 GHz) and provides fine DF (interferometry) for Harpoon targeting.

The aircraft version of AR-700 was installed successfully on board an Indonesian CN-235 in 1994. At that time ARGO had bids into Brunei, Indonesia (which took Sky Guardian, on cost grounds), Turkey, and the UAE.

A miniaturized version of the mast assembly, 6.5in dia and 11.8 in high, has been developed.

Users:

Surface ships: Finland (*Helsinki II* and *Pojanmaa* [last without APECS jammer]), Greece (APECS II/AR-700 in MEKO 200 class), Korea (APECS II selected for KDX), Netherlands (APECS II in M-class units *Abraham van der Huist, Van Galen, Van Nes, van Speijk*), Norway (AR-700 in *Oslo* class), Pakistan (APECS I in *Babur* and FRAM destroyers *Alamgir, Taimur, Tughril*), Portugal (APECS II/AR-700 in MEKO 200 class; may replace ARBR 10 in *Commandante Rivière* class), Thailand (four FPB).

Submarine version: Australia (AR-740 in *Collins* class), Egypt (four Romeos, probably reordered as AR-900s; see below), Germany (six submarines, probably Type 206A [Ginny]), Greece (four submarines refitted to fire sub-Harpoon), Netherlands (*Zwaardvis* class), Sweden (A-17 [AR-700-S5] class), Turkey (*Doganay, Dolunay, Yildiray*).

Aircraft version: Thailand (F27, with fine DF for Harpoon targeting).

◆ AR-730

This new modular ESM system, operating over the 0.5–18-GHz range, is intended for MPA. In its RWR version, it uses monopulse DF antennas with CVRs. In the ESM/ELINT version, it adds an omni antenna (feeding digital IFMs) and a rotating directional antenna, for precision DF. It can also accommodate an SHR to operate over the 0.5–2-GHz band.

◆ AR-900/CLOAC

This new lightweight system, announced in 1993, introduces a new ESP processor that can handle 10M pps (also reported as 4M pps, 500 tracks). It splits the 2–18-GHz spectrum into two bands (2–6 and 6–18 GHz), each with its own DIFM (accuracy 3 MHz in low band and 6 MHz in high band). Frequency resolution is 1 MHz. The monopulse DF array uses eight broad-band spirals (accuracy 3.5 deg in low band, 2 deg in high band; 1 deg with interferometry). An omni antenna feeds DIFM receivers. The electronic signal processor (ESP) can handle 4M pps. It identifies an emitter within 1 sec of signal acquisition, using a 5000-mode (500 radar) library. Displays: activity, tactical (PPI), frequency-bearing, frequency-amplitude, and frequency-PRI. Sensitivity is −65 dBm. Pulsewidth range is 0.1 to 99.9 microsec (resolution 0.1 microsec), amplitude range over is 60 dB (resolution 0.5 dB), PRI range is 2 to 10,000 microsec, that is, PRF between 100 and 500,000 (resolution 0.1 microsec). AR-900 can handle all polarizations and scan types; threat, steady, and CW signals. Signal types detected and classified are conventional pulse trains, frequency-agile trains, FM on pulse (pulse-compressed), jittered PRI, staggered PRI (2–16 positions), and pulse-Doppler. The unusual width of the bands probably makes it easier to handle variable-frequency signals, such as those produced by pulse-compression radars. The antenna unit is 14.6in dia × 23.3 in (28 kg).

The AR-900S submarine version uses a new low-RCS radome.

AR-900 is the core of a new generation of systems: CLOAC (compact lightweight omnidirection advanced CM), APECS III, and MPA Avionics. It has already been exported to Egypt, for the Romeo submarine refit program. The CLOAC jammer (7.5–18 GHz) has 64 overlapping time-shared beams and can track 16 threats; maximum reaction time is 1 sec.

ARGOSystems AR-900 ESM system, showing the array in front of its radome, the shock-mounted processor, and the operator console at right. (ARGOSystems)

◆ AR-7000

ARGO's modular system reportedly combines ELINT, COMINT, and ESM capabilities over 20 MHz–18 GHz. The ELINT element uses four SHRs: 0.1–1 GHz plus three for 0.5–18 GHz, feeding a digital pulse analyzer. The COMINT element uses up to 20 receivers (up to five operators) to monitor the 20 MHz–1 GHz band; it uses a set of phase-matched receivers and arrays for each of two bands (20–500 MHz). The ESM element is ap-

parently AR-700A (0.5–18 GHz in three bands using DIFMs, with a combination of monopulse and interferometric DF, and a 5000-mode library).

◆ ARGO Phoenix I/II

ARGOSystems's ESM/DF system (1–18 GHz in five bands) for ships of fast-patrol-boat size and larger was announced in 1984, but Phoenix I probably dates from the mid-1970s. These systems employed ARGO's proprietary analog IFM. Phoenix I covered 2–12 GHz (2–4, 4–8, 8–12) using three IFMs. It was later extended to 18 GHz by adding a fourth IFM. Signals were processed by a DSA (digital signal analyzer), a 4-bit slice processor using software written in the Forth language. Signals could be identified manually or automatically. This version had a 10-signal memory (it could track up to 10 PRIs). The associated dish antenna, in a characteristic can-shaped radome, could spin or sector-scan or point. There was also a land-based version, the Cueing Sensor, for Germany.

An ARGOSystems ESM antenna (probably Phoenix I) on board a Korean *Ulsan*-class frigate, with a Radamec HWK 409-029 EO director visible behind it, and an Emerlec 30 mount below. Similar radomes can be seen on baord Colombian FS 1500–type frigates, Finnish *Helsinki*-class fast-attack boats, New Zealand *Leander*-class frigates, and Swedish *Stockholm* and *Spica II* classes. (*Sea Power*)

Phoenix II is an upgrade using the ASP (advanced signal processor), a 68000-based unit that can track up to 200 emitters. The unit is controlled by a MicroVax computer. This version can also cover an additional low band (0.5–2 GHz). Many of the versions sold had additional monopulse (spiral) antennas for warning, and were designated Phoenix 2U. In these units, the pot contains the spinner, with a monopulse array at its bottom, and with omnis on top (0.5–8 GHz with 8–18 GHz above them).

Phoenix IV is a fully automatic version.

The initial series of ARGO systems is probably derived from WLR-16 (AR-627), a monopulse DF system with an analog IFM and a pulse de-interleaver, developed about 1976. It divided the 0.5–18-GHz range into six bands. All output was digital. Presumably ARGO used its experience with WLR-16 in developing its part of WLR-1H. The ARGO company itself originated at Stanford, where the U.S. Navy supported work on an IFM introduced from England sometime after 1956. When antiwar activists forced Stanford University out of defense research during the Vietnam War, the IFM group formed ARGOSystems.

Users: Phoenix I (AC 672): Denmark (one), Finland (land unit for tests), India (four for Type 1500 submarines), Iran (ordered but not delivered), Korea (numerous units for surface ships, probably the basis for ULQ-11/12), Netherlands (*Walrus* class), New Zealand (four for *Leander*-class frigates), Taiwan (four, probably designated ARGO 680/681). Note that AC 672, for the Indian submarines, is often described as Phoenix II. The report of four sales to Taiwan is puzzling, since it does not correspond to any particular class. It seems more likely that ARGO 680/681 is the masthead radome that equips Wu-Jinn III–class destroyers.

Phoenix II: Finland (six, for *Turunmaa* and *Helsinki* classes [Farol]), India (geolocation units for the army), Sweden (*Stockholm* class [Carol] plus 12 without the monopulse warner, for the *Norkopping* (*Spica II*) class, plus three for A-14-class submarines [Alice]). This system may also have been sold to Colombia (FS 1500 class, with Scimitar jammer). The reported installation on board Peruvian *Lupo*-class frigates seems less plausible.

An associated AR850 for land users sold well.

◆ DASS-2000

Loral announced this defensive aids subsystem for MPA in 1995. It employs a central defensive aids manager (a RISC 4000-based computer) to form a tactical picture, using various warning system outputs, and to determine the appropriate defensive responses on that basis. The computer is designed so that it can work with a wide variety of existing warners and countermeasures, some of which Loral would supply. It can also communicate with other aircraft systems, such as ESM and the aircraft TDS. For example, it can combine their outputs with its own data to form a more useful picture. DASS-2000 is part of the BAe/Loral proposal for the RAF Nimrod MPA replacement. Loral also offers a much more limited DASS-type subsystem based on its version of APR-39.

Loral's DASS-2000 brochure shows a typical PPI display, apparently using a full-size computer screen rather than the usual small plasma panel. Emitters are identified by letters and seem to be placed at bearings around the aircraft. The aircraft ESM system probably contributed a series of numbered targets indicated by range and bearing. The operator can call up data on any specific emitter (typically frequency, PRI, PW, power level, complex emitter code [CEC, an indication of signal complexity, e.g., frequency-hopping], range [presumably by SSL techniques], bearing, and identification). Panels on the other side of the display were marked with the various sensors and defensive measures available to the operator (radar warner, missile warner, laser warner, chaff, flare, decoy, jammer, IRCM). Note that, if the system is linked back to the aircraft central tactical system, it can use its own multipath data to extract a target's altitude from the system's active radar range.

◆ Digital ESM Receiver (DESM)

Anaren's DF receiver is a component of the Racal Cutlass B1 and also of a version of the Signaal Rapids. A complete one-band (7.5–18 GHz) array has a diameter of less than 10 cm (the full two-band [2–18 GHz] masthead unit is 60 cm in diameter × 101 cm and weighs 60 kg). Anaren claims that these small dimensions reduce vulnerability to multipath. The 32-element circular array feeds a Butler Matrix, which produces phase shifts at its five output channels proportional to different multiples of the AoA: $1\times$, $2\times$, $4\times$, $5\times$, and $8\times$. They are compared to a reference channel. The $8\times$ channel provides the most precise information, but it is ambiguous because every 45-deg shift in AoA produces an equivalent result. The other channels resolve this ambiguity. Thus the masthead unit requires only five amplifier channels in each band. From top to bottom, the masthead unit consists of a Band 2 antenna, a Band 2 matrix, a Band 1 antenna, and a Band 1 matrix, with amplifiers and other electronics below in the flared bottom of the radome.

Each pulse is represented by a 55-bit word, giving frequency, bearing, amplitude, pulse width, and ToA. Bearing accuracy is better than 2 deg, and elevation coverage is $+40/-10$ deg. Good directional accuracy makes it possible to use AoA as a parameter in de-interleaving trains of pulses, and 2 deg is the level of precision needed for missile launching.

Minimum recognizable pulse width is 200 nsec in the 2–7.5-GHz band and 100 nsec in the 7.5–18-GHz band; bearing resolution is 1.4 deg (8 bits), pulsewidth resolution is 25 nsec (12 bits), and ToA resolution is 1 microsec (16 bits).

◆ EW-1017/ARI 18240/1

Loral's ESM system for MPA was adopted for the British Nimrod MR.2 under the designation ARI 18240/1. EW-1017 is on board German Atlantic MPA and also the British version of the U.S. AWACS (E-3). This system uses 16 cavity-backed spiral antennas in wingtip pods, forming two sets (eight each) for high- and low-frequency bands; system coverage is probably 2–18 GHz. The front-end receivers are also in the pods. The hybrid SHR operates broad-band for acquisition and then narrow-band for identification and DF. The system uses several parallel processors (sometimes described as an array processor) to deal with large numbers of pulses. It has a stand-alone display in Nimrod and, presumably, the German Atlantic, but it feeds the central tactical display of the E-3A. As of early 1996, Loral was engaged in upgrading this system for the RAF.

◆ FERRET

GTE's austere submarine ESM set uses an Israeli front end to cover the entire 1–40-GHz range. The narrow-band (1–18 GHz) subsystem uses up to four SHRs for precise analysis. Claimed DF accuracy is 5–10 deg. Frequency resolution: 125 kHz (narrow-band), 5 MHz (broad-band).

Users: South Korea (Type 209s and Tolgorae-class midgets).

◆ Guardian Star/BLQ-501

Sperry Marine's Guardian Star is based on the electronically scanned ESM antenna of the U.S. Type 18 periscope, on *Sturgeon* and the new *Seawolf*-class submarines. In this application, it has no specific designation, and it uses standard military processors, and so on. The display is the one Sperry developed for its anti-collision shipboard radar.

Guardian Star Mk 3(V). (Sperry)

The current Mk 3(V) divides 2–18 GHz into high and low bands, with frequency resolutions of 3 and 2 MHz (accuracy 7.2 and 3.6 MHz, 5- and 10-deg DF). Sensitivity is −60 dBmi, and dynamic range is 55 dB. The system can operate in up to 1M pps, and it can track and display 250 emitters, detecting and identifying an emitter in less than 1 sec. Elevation coverage is +30/−30 deg, using an antenna array 30 cm high (9.3 kg: six-port cavity-backed spirals plus an omni). Library data can be loaded from a bubble memory cartridge.

Users: Canada (as BLQ-501, in *Oberons*), Venezuela (*Almirante Clemente* class upgrade; three units delivered, but only one ship was upgraded due to cost of complete refit).

◆ HFS-200/100

SwRI's shipboard COTS HF/DF systems use AS-145 (SwRI designation) antennas in ships' superstructures. HFS-200 uses six antennas and is equivalent to the 24 deck-edge antennas used in Outboard. It is capable of SSL, if the height of the ionosphere is known. As of early 1996, one was being tested on board a U.S. Aegis cruiser. The system is calibrated partly by measuring the responses of scale-model antennas on a brass model to scale sky waves; a computer applies these calculated responses to the full-scale array. The array provides both azimuth and elevation, but any such system suffers from multiple modes. SwRI solves that problem by processing the outputs of the antennas separately, using the variation in each output over time. This superresolution technique is analogous to the interferometry used to improve the precision of ESM arrays. In effect time variation substitutes for the spatial variation that a larger array would detect. HFS-200 will compete against a Lockheed Martin Sanders system based on Spartan.

HFS-100, now operational on board two U.S. noncombatants, is a simpler ground-wave system using four AS-145 antennas. If a sky-wave signal persists, HFS-100 can find its direction by averaging over time (i.e., by using a histogram). HFS-100 became operational about 1992.

◆ LR-100

Litton Amecom's lightweight 2–18-GHz (extendable down to 0.4 GHz and up to 40 GHz, and also to the ultra-low band, 70–400 MHz) ESM set was designed for UAVs but may also be used on board SEAL craft. All electronics are packaged in a VME box. Four 12in interferometer arrays in "split diamond" configuration offer DF accuracy of 0.8 deg; amplitude comparison DF accuracy is 10–15 deg. There are also alternative arrays for band extension. A superhet (500-MHz bandwidth), unusual in a radar warner, gives sufficient sensitivity (−71 dBm) to detect back- and sidelobes as well as main lobes of threat radars, giving the system more opportunities to detect any given emitter. If there are fewer than 10 emitters, it revisits any emitter within less than 300 msec. In high density conditions (over 40 emitters, including 10 pulse-Doppler or CW), the superhet scans its entire spectrum in less than 2 sec, so it provides warning of any new emitter within 2 sec. Frequency is measured to within 2 MHz (resolution 0.625 MHz). Pulsewidth range is 100 nsec to 409 microsec and CW (resolution 25 nsec); PRI is 2 microsec to 50 msec (resolution 3 nsec). Data given: DoA, time of initial detection, time of last update, identification, min/max/average frequency, average pulse width, average PRF/PRI Type/Deviation, and frame rate.

The superhet is software-controlled. In RWR mode, it inspects programmed threat frequencies many times a second for rapid warning, sampling other frequencies more slowly. In ESM mode, scanning is more uniform (although a designated frequency range may be visited more frequently as a Task Dwell). Task Dwells may be used to measure scan rate or to make pulse-to-pulse measurements as an ELINT function. In tests against 32 simulated emitters (1.5M pps), LR-100 detected all RWR threats within 2 sec and ESM/ELINT signals within one radar-scan period. These tests included identification of complex scan patterns.

MTBF is 1500 hr; MTTR is 15 min. The prototype was delivered in 1995, with the first production unit following in 1996.

As of the fall of 1996, three contracts for LR-100 had been let: for the Advanced SEAL Team Delivery System (a small submarine) and for demonstrations on board Hunter and Predator UAVs. LR-100 was successfully tested on board the new SEAL boat (PB Mk V), and Litton expected a formal developmental and operational test (DTOT). This system was incorporated in both the Lockheed Martin (F-16U) and McDonnell-Douglas (F-15U) offers to the UAE for its 1996 fighter competition. A more capable LR-500 is being tested on a U.S. F-15.

◆ MD-103A

Delfin's VHF/UHF (25–1000 MHz) digital intercept/DF system is aboard about 50 U.S. warships (Aegis ships and frigates) and was sold to Korea and also to some other foreign navies. No official designation was ever supplied. Modules: IF processor, DF processor, display processor. The system has 99 channels, which can be scanned at up to 8/sec; two can be set as priority channels. It has 16 search bands, and maximum search rate is 16 steps/sec. Minimum step size is 1 kHz. Automatic delay time is settable as 0 to 99 sec. Modes are: PAN, spectrum/falling raster, and DF. In PAN mode, the receiver is tuned to a specific center frequency, and a histogram shows activity within a set bandwidth (200 kHz or 2 MHz, resolution 5 or 30 kHz, respectively). In the spectrum/falling raster mode, the system rapidly scans a wide frequency range, displaying activity at various frequencies in a waterfall pattern (vertical scale 2 min to 1 hr) with a graph of output along the bottom. The operator specifies center frequency, sweep width, sweep sensitivity, and time duration; the system scans at up to 20 MHz/sec. The operator may switch to PAN or DF mode for any particular signal of interest. DF is by pseudo-Doppler augmented by proprietary digital signal processing. The operator selects integration time (0, 0.25, 0.5, 1, 2, 4, or 8 sec) and the display is a PPI with numerical indication of direction. The display is a flat electroluminscent panel.

DF accuracy (0.25-sec integration time) is 3 deg, with 1-deg resolution. Minimum pulse length (10-deg accuracy) is 10 msec. IF bandwidth is 15 kHz in AM or NFM mode, 150 kHz in WFM mode, and 2.8 kHz in SSB mode.

The antenna is MA-104, a pair of nested four-dipole Adcock arrays (VHF and UHF) with a central whip for sensing. The fat UHF dipoles, each pinched in the middle, are mounted part way up (or else atop) a mast. The entire antenna weighs 25 lb.

◆ Peace Peek

E-Systems's SIGINT system was supplied for five German navy Atlantic aircraft.

◆ Privateer/Zeus

This new open-architecture COTS/GOTS-based ESM/ELINT suite for the *Cyclone*-class patrol boats (initially PC 7), superseding APR-39A, was integrated by NISE (the Naval Command, Control, and Ocean Surveillance Center). Zeus is the export version (to which data below apply). The cylindrical antenna array (20in dia) comprises a Condor ESM element (about 1½ ft tall) above an SwRI LF-UHF COMINT element (AS-506 antenna for MBS-506 system, about 3 ft tall). The full system may also include a crossed-loop HF/DF antenna (AS-145) for lower frequencies. Below-decks elements all use VXI (VME extension for instrumentation/VME) backplanes. The main computer is a VXI version of the HP 743 (128 Mbytes of RAM, over 100 MHz clock speed). Below decks are a COMINT case, an ESM rack, and a VXI DF processor rack (for the ELINT element, using SwRI's PS-516 processor and a 1-Gbyte hard disk). There is one operator. Some of the software is used in other EW systems. NISE claims that the system is scaleable to other platforms, such as submarines and patrol aircraft.

The 0.5–40-GHz ESM element uses a DF spinner and a fast-tuning superhet receiver; DF accuracy is better than 1 deg for 18–40 GHz, 1 deg for 12–18 GHz, 1.6 deg for 8–12 GHz, 3 deg for 2–8 GHz, and 5 deg for 0.5–2 GHz. RF bandwidth is selectable (50–500 MHz). Maximum pulse density (burst) is 2M pps. Modes are: CW/pulse/complex jitter/stagger/IMOP/UMOP;

The prototype Privateer installed on board a *Cyclone*-class patrol boat, July 1995. (SwRI)

measured parameters are RF, PRI, PRF, pulse width, amplitude, scan rate, and scan type. The emitter library is programmable.

The ELINT element covers 10 kHz–30 MHz with 1-Hz resolution and 20–1200 MHz with 10-Hz resolution; DF accuracy is 3 deg for ground waves (however, SwRI's MBS-506A operates at 0.5 to 2000 MHz with 10-deg DF accuracy). Typical tuning time is 3 msec. The superhet can scan up to 100 channels/sec, with 250 preprogrammed channels, 51 standard LF/HF bandwidths (100 Hz–16 kHz) and 15 standard V/UHF bandwidths (1–240 kHz). Modes are: lower and upper side-band, intermediate side-band, CW, AM, and FM. DF modes are manual, automatic frequency scan, automatic band sweep, and archived data retrieval. Inside the ELINT dome are ferrite loops for HF and dipoles for VHF and UHF (three stacked arrays with vertical polarization).

Optional upgrades, presumably realized in Privateer, are a two-slot VXI spectrum analyzer (10 kHz–1.6 GHz, displaying up to 5 MHz using up to four traces, with windowed drag and drop features), a VXI digital tape recorder (bandwidth DC to 25.6 kHz, for up to eight channels, with a capacity of 4–20 Gbytes), VXI noise reduction filtering, and a 16-channel A/D and D/A converter (sampled at 4–48 kHz, 16 bits, 80-dB dynamic range, with eight C40-compatible ports). The system can be upgraded to handle burst transmissions and frequency hoppers.

Installations in the *Cyclone* class began in 1995, and should be complete by mid-1998.

◆ S3000

EM Systems's surveillance (ELINT) system is installed in British nuclear submarines. It uses a high-gain scanning antenna plus an omnidirectional antenna and IFM receiver; the operator selects scanning, sector-scan, or pointing modes for the directional antenna. There are an associated threat library and an automatic threat-alarm feature. Coverage is 0.5–18 GHz.

The Privateer antenna. (SwRI)

◆ Sandpiper

Condor's general-purpose HF to mm-wave ELINT collection system is used by the U.S. Navy (no designation is known) and by several foreign navies. It combines a tunable IFM subsystem (for high probability of intercept) with up to 24 SHR tuner channels, narrow- and wide-band recording subsystems, single or multiple operators, auto and manual analysis, and distributed processing using Ethernet/GPIB/RS-232 interconnections.

◆ Sea Sentry

Kollmorgen's ESM system for submarines and surface ships was announced in 1980. Only Version III, for submarines, entered service. Sea Sentry III (Kollmorgen Model 962U) uses both the periscope and its own antenna (multiple arrays and microwave receivers on a mast). The General Instruments DF/threat processor has a 128-emitter threat library, and it can be supplemented by additional ELINT information collected by the submarine. Up to 35 emitters can be processed simultaneously, and 15 displayed. The user assigns a priority to each threat radar, CW (fire-control) radars having the highest. Threat surveillance is automatic, and there are two modes: (a) surveillance, as a wide-open receiver providing all-round cover; and (b) search, in which frequency is measured and direction is more accurately measured. The system handles both CW and pulse signals, displaying threat identity, bearing, range, and other signal data on its CRT.

Kollmorgen claims that Sea Sentry III is the first completely automatic broad-band radar threat detection and analysis system integrated into a submarine's surveillance periscope. Signals in the 100 kHz–1 GHz (mainly communications) range are detected and identified. For the 1–18-GHz range, DF accuracy is better than 10 deg. The system's mast carries three omnis and four DF spirals (each feeding its own microwave receiver). A four-digit LED displays the threat's center frequency (within 15 MHz). Threat characteristics are presented on a radar parameter digital display.

Users: Argentina (TR1700 class), India.

◆ Seagle/AS-505

This SwRI/Rohde & Schwartz ELINT system equips the Italian carrier *Giuseppe Garibaldi*, the *Mimbelli*-class destroyers, and, in modified form, the Greek intelligence-collector *Hermis*. SwRI (Southwest Research Institute of San Antonio, Texas) is responsible for the AS-505 antenna and probably for some of the DF elements of the system; Rohde & Schwartz is responsible for below-decks elements. The antenna resembled that of SRD-19 (Outboard), but has only four loops in its bottom (HF) array (it has eight dipoles in each of its middle [VHF] and top [UHF] arrays). Where Outboard used to have four loops, it has monopoles.

◆ Cluster Sentinel/AU-506

Submarine ELINT system by SwRI, for three British SSNs. However, the name suggests U.S. intelligence involvement. This antenna (AU-506) employs ferrite loops and dipoles inside a radome. The processor is by ERA, now the E-Systems division of Raytheon. Presumably Cluster Sentinel replaces the earlier CXG.

◆ Seaking

Condor Systems' black (i.e., probably intelligence-related) U.S.-sponsored export system.

◆ Seawatch

Condor Systems' submarine masthead monopulse DF array is connected with a photonics mast program. A published photograph shows a four-port DF array using "ambidextrous" distorted spiral antennas for each port, and a spiral-wound cylindrical omni above them. The claim that this is a high-accuracy system suggests that it employs some form of ToA or phase processing. It can be integrated with a Condor ESM system.

◆ Small-Ship ESM

NRL's COTS-based 0.5–18-GHz system uses a dual-aperture spinner (both elements using log-periodic arrays) inside a radome. The MMIC SHR is in the pedestal under the dome. Major new features are the lightweight antennas, using metallic reflectors on composites, the MMIC receiver, extensive use of COTS components, and a special digital ESM processor (advanced sig-

Seagle antennas occupy the masthead of the destroyer *Francesco Mimbelli*, 1995. Below them are the low-band DF spirals of the Nettuno ECM system, the stabilized high-band DF array of which is also visible, on the square mast platform (the other array is on the mainmast, pointed diagonally away from this one). (H. and L. van Ginderen)

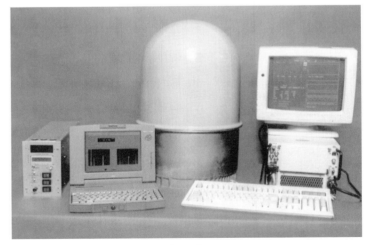

NRL's Small-Ship ESM System. (NRL)

nal processor) using sampling to help identify complex signals. Digital sampling measures the detailed form of each pulse, to detect UMOP; given other U.S. interests, it seems likely that this system was developed mainly for radar fingerprinting (the SEI program described elsewhere). UMOP is also a way of tracking signals whose frequency and other characteristics vary widely over time, since it reflects physical characteristics of the radar transmitter and antenna, which do not vary over time. The advanced processor has been under development since 1981. The light weight of the antenna and receiver (50 lb total for the pedestal) makes masthead mounting practicable, and the processor can withstand carrier landings. As of the fall of 1996, six prototypes were in service in shipboard, land, and air applications. Should the SEI pilot program prove successful, presumably this system will enter production (as of the fall of 1996 there was interest in producing more).

NRL's 0.5–18-GHz MMIC EW receiver was conceived to detect subtle emitter characteristics (such as UMOP) normally lost when signals are digitized, over a broad bandwidth (1000 MHz). At the same time receiver size, power demand, and cost were cut dramatically. MMIC Phase II uses NRL-designed chips in a triple-conversion superhet (160-MHz output, first local oscillator with 1-MHz oscillation, second and third stages driven coherently rather than separately tuned). Characteristics (conventional receiver data in parentheses): tune step 1000 (10) kHz, tune speed 40 (5) msec, noise figure 14 (12) dB, dynamic range 60 (55) dB, IF bandwidth 75 (50) MHz, dimensions $11 \times 8 \times 1$ ($29 \times 17 \times 8$) cm, weight 138 (6124) grams, power draw 25 (86) W, cost $10,000 ($120,000). The next step would be an entire receiver, of somewhat more limited performance, on a single chip.

SEI demands that the detailed shape of the incoming pulse be characterized and stored. Because the pulse lasts so short a time, digitization requires very frequent sampling, typically at a rate of 1 GHz with great dynamic range (typically 70 dB, to capture the rise and fall of the pulse). In a typical developmental system, a 500-MHz signal is sampled at the rate of 500 Mega-samples/sec, data going into a digital signal processor which carries out FFTs.

SEI requires some means of filing signal parameters for later identification of the specific platform to be tracked. NRL has developed an algorithm to cluster multiple emitter features for simpler identification.

◆ **Spartan**

Lockheed Sanders's low-cost HF/DF system (Scalable Processing Architecture for Real-Time Analysis), announced 1995, is for Coast Guard units. It uses small antennas distributed around a ship, rather than the classic masthead array (a similar antenna system is used in the Lockheed Martin shipboard HF surface-wave radar). It can handle both sky- and ground-wave signals as well as mixed-mode signals, and it is designed to participate in an HF/DF net. The system uses COTS components (with a VME backplane) and it displays data on JMCIS (i.e., TAC-3) hardware. The first systems are on board the two TAGOS surveillance ships turned over to the U.S. Coast Guard. Claimed accuracy is better than 3 deg (0.5 to 30 MHz) on AM, BFO, LSB, USB, and CW signals. The receiver can either scan automatically in frequency or it can listen at a keyed-in frequency and bandwidth (and threshold and dwell time). Characteristics of targets of interest can be stored for automatic selection during scanning.

◆ **SR-200**

Lockheed Sanders's IFM system breaks the 0.5–18-GHz spectrum down into four bands (0.5–2.0, 2.0–4.0, 4.0–8.0, 8.0–18 GHz, with optional extension to 40 GHz) and offers sufficient precision for OTH-T. The array comprises an omni and a rotating multihorn (for multiple bands) DF antenna. The display is either a PPI or tabular, or ESM data can be overlaid onto a radar display. There are three receivers: IFM, tuned RF (TRF), and logarithmic video, the latter for pulse analysis. The IFM is fed only by the narrow-beam spinner; the others are fed by the omni. The design emphasizes angular accuracy, since bearing can be used to estimate range as the platform moves. Rated accuracy, from low to high bands: bearing, 7.5, 5, 4, 2 deg; frequency, 9, 9, 17, 21 MHz. PRF range (for each band, respectively): 75–100 Hz, 125 Hz–100 kHz, 250 Hz–100 kHz, 500 Hz–100 kHz. Pulsewidth range: 0.2–100, 0.2–100, 0.1–100, 0.1–100 microsec. Capacity: 500,000

The Peruvian PR 72–class FAC *De los Heros* has the antenna of her SR-200 ESM system at her masthead. (Peruvian Navy)

pps; can display 58 active tracks. In 1980 tests, at 3-GHz directional accuracy was better than 2 deg in one pass, and better than 1 deg in multiple passes.

Users: SR-200: Peru (two *Darings* and six PR-72s) and one other customer (11 sets); SR-200B (base-band) was sold for land use. The unnamed user was probably Japan, for missile hydrofoils.

◆ **SwRI Model 7401**

SwRI's simple HF/VHF DF employs a radome-mounted loop and omni above an eight-dipole Adcock array; it is 1.5 ft in dia $\times$ 5.69 ft high (83 lb) and employs some active antenna elements. This was announced about 1988. Elements have sold, but not the entire system. Limits: 0.5–1000 MHz.

◆ **Varo LWS**

The U.S. Navy is now testing this laser-warning system (reportedly for the 0.1–0.4-micron band).

◆ **WJ 8957 (SCANS)**

The Watkins-Johnson signal collection-and-analysis system (for 1–2000 MHz) was adopted for the Royal Australian Navy's *Collins* class, and is currently being considered by the Royal Navy. In the Australian ships it is coupled to a WJ 34901 antenna intercept and acquisition system. An RF data bus distributes signals to three positions: two for intercept/collection, one for early warning. A separate DF antenna feeds a tasked precision DF system. Typically one intercept position deals with FSK, Morse, and AM/FM signals; the other deals with tactical voice signals. Each is equipped with two HF receivers (5 kHz–30 MHz) and three V/UHF receivers (20–1400 MHz), all feeding the same display. The early warning position has an HF receiver and a V/UHF receiver, both feeding a spectrum processor and a display. It deals with special signals. The spectrum processor and the DF system both feed into the system CPU. The DF antenna is a series of stacked arrays (with a pair of HF loops at the bottom) inside a radome; total height is 29.5 in (dia is 16.5 in). Bearing accuracy is 3 deg (internal display resolution is 0.1 deg). This is an interferometer system, with integration times of 100, 200, and 500 msec and 1, 2, and 5 sec.

◆ **WJ 8958 (DFS)**

The Watkins-Johnson shipboard DF systems (1 MHz–2 GHz) for ships and submarines are currently in service both in the United States and abroad but are not as yet assigned any official U.S. nomenclature. The fiberglass radome (18×31 in, 125 lb) contains a stack of three quadrature dipole arrays (1100–2000, 330–1100, and 45–330 MHz) and a pair of crossed ferrite loop arrays, plus the appropriate preamplifiers and RF switches. This is essentially the same antenna as that described above (in WJ 8957). Below 45 MHz, the antenna finds signal direction by Watson-Watt (amplitude comparison) techniques, using the ferrite arrays. Above, it uses dipoles and interferometry. Bearing accuracy is 3 deg; bearing resolution is 0.1 deg. Elevation coverage is 45 deg.

Users: South Korea (planned for KDX class).

♦ WJ 32500

Ship or submarine ELINT signal collection system (0.5–12 GHz, covering the COMINT and ELINT bands). Typically it has five operator positions: three for COMINT (Morse or HF, voice/VHF/UHF, and special signals in HF-SHF), one for telemetry, one for ELINT, and requires nine racks of electronic equipment.

♦ WJ 34901

Watkins-Johnson DF antenna, covering 2 MHz–2 GHz, using loops and monopoles to achieve an accuracy of better than 3 deg within a radome 16 in wide and less than 31 in high. It can be used by both surface ships and submarines. This antenna is under Navy contract, but it has not yet been delivered.

♦ ZS-1015(S)

Lucas Zeta of San Jose, California, has supplied this communications signal intercept and Adcock (two-channel) DF system to one unnamed Northern European navy. The system is software-intensive (so that all functions can be concentrated in a single workstation, using a single raster-scan screen), all data being collected and stored in a relational database. This system can handle more than 10 emitters simultaneously, and the system can handle up to 3000 channels/sec. Up to four ships can participate in a DF net, and the system is designed to provide ESM reports directly to a ship's CDS. There is also a land-based version, ZS-1015, which can cover 0.5 to 3000 MHz.

An earlier, and presumably related, ZS-1010(S) covers 20–100 MHz or 100–1000 MHz using two or three nested four-dipole Adcocks (correlative interferometers) to achieve an instrumented accuracy of better than 1 deg (better than 2 deg in DF, with 0.1-deg resolution). The system can handle signals as short as 4 msec. Frequency resolution is 100 Hz. There are two receiver channels, and intercept speed is up to 3000 channels/sec. Like ZS-1015, this system can handle more than 10 emitters simultaneously.

♦ Expendables

Recent decoy programs have included development (design completed FY95) of a rigid inflatable RF/IR decoy for use from Mk 36 launchers, presumably as a possible replacement for the current Rubber Duck (see the British section). Thin-ring chaff was successfully demonstrated against a mm-wave radar during FY94.

♦ SADIS (Processor Mk 24)

Comtek's Semi-Automatic Decoy Integration System special-purpose decoy launch processor and display is the standard U.S. Navy interface between SLQ-32 and Mk 36 decoy launchers. The contract was let in 1988, and units entered service in 1989. SADIS incorporates its own Mil-Spec computer, based on an 80286 processor. Base memory is 64 kbytes, but it is expandable; the box has eight slots, of which only four are used at present (including the I/O card). The internal bus is an 8-bit wide Intel Multibus (specified by the user), which is described as somewhat slow for the processor. Using an 80386 CPU, Mk 24 Mod 3 is the Nulka FCS.

♦ CAMLAC

Hycor's Computer-Aided Master Launcher Control for Mk 36 Super RBOCs uses a microprocessor with ROM, with sufficient space for 10 tactical engagement sequences programmed by user. Another eight are programmed at depot level, and cannot be changed on board ship. The display is a plasma panel. Wind (speed, direction) and threat (type, range, direction) are entered either manually or via interfaces with the ship combat system; appropriate sequence is automatically selected. CAMLAC seems to replace the standard U.S. Navy launcher control (Mk 158 Mod 1 or 2), which shows status but fires manually. There is also a standard bridge launcher control (Mk 164 Mod 1 or 2).

Cartridges listed: Mk 182 Mod 1 chaff, Mk 193 Mod 1 practice, Mk 191 Mod 0 test.

♦ SCIP/ALEX

Tracor's Shipboard Countermeasures Interface Package controls Mk 33 and Mk 36 chaff launchers; it can handle any known chaff cartridge. It receives threat data (from the ship RWR), ship heading and speed data, and launcher status and loading data, all of which are entered into its RAM. The system can incorporate its own anemometer for wind data, and its own inclinometer for roll. The system's ROM contains its engagement algorithm. It can operate either manually (recommending reactions to the threat) or automatically. SCIP also indicates the appropriate course to steer. The control console can be located either on the bridge or in CIC.

Users: Egypt, Singapore, and one other; as of late 1992 a sale was pending in Asia.

Tracor offers both 113mm and 130mm cartridges: 113mm seduction and distraction chaff and seduction IR (TDSC-, TDDC-, TDIR-113) and 130mm seduction and distraction chaff and seduction IR (TDSC-, TDDC-, TDIR-130). There are also 66mm and 76mm smoke/obscurant grenade launchers.

Hycor's ALEX (Automatic Launching of Expendables) would appear to be an alternative designation for SCIP. ALEX automatically detects which type of decoy is in which tube, and also automatically detects duds and selects the best alternative available; it can also prompt the crew to load the appropriate type of decoy into each tube.

♦ AAED

The next-generation active-airborne expendable is under development by Naval Research Laboratory. Forward-fired, based on the 2.75in rocket, it uses an autopilot to fly relatively slowly ahead of the airplane. Naval Air Systems Command is developing a 600-lb pod (based on the current 2.75in pod) to carry both AAED and chaff/flare decoys. NRL remains the prime contractor for the decoy, with a Teledyne CME payload, Garret guidance, and Atlantic Research propulsion.

♦ GEN-X

Texas Instruments's generic expendable jammer is to be carried in existing chaff/flare dispensers. In 1986 the design objective was a unit price of $3000. The standard expendable size is 1.63in dia × 5.8 in (the Air Force cannot use Navy expendables because the Air Force's chaff chutes are rectangular in section). Compared to POET, GEN-X can operate over several frequency bands.

GEN-X expendable jammer in combat. (Texas Instruments)

Thus an airplane need not carry many different types of active expendables and can devote valuable chute space to chaff and flares.

In September 1987 the Naval Air Development Center awarded Texas Instruments a contract for 288 of these decoys, to be delivered by September 1989 ($19M). The Navy has an option for up to 30,000 such jammers. As of September 1987, Texas Instruments had already delivered 25 test decoys, as part of the competition leading up to the 288-decoy award.

Texas Instruments won the GEN-X production competition (over Raytheon) in April 1992.

♦ POET

Sanders's Primed Oscillator Expendable Transponder (AN/AM-6988/A) is a small active system. POET was developed in the late 1970s in response to a suggestion by the Defense Science Review Board that the Navy take the lead in developing expendable microwave decoys; POET was one of the first active expendables. It is launched via the standard chaff/flare dispenser. POET has a single antenna and is limited in frequency coverage. As of 1986, POET was the only expendable jammer in the U.S. inventory and was being manufactured at the rate of 2300 per month. POET fits within standard expendable dimensions, 1.4 in (dia) × 5.8 in.

POET is to be replaced by GEN-X.

♦ Samson

Samson is the expendable decoy developed by Brunswick and produced by Israel Aircraft Industries (IAI). Samson's success in the Bekaa Valley in 1982 prompted the U.S. Navy to buy 100 for operational evaluation. The decoy is a glider, carried on a standard aircraft hardpoint, that dispenses chaff or generates false targets as the plane flies toward the target. This decoy was the outcome of a series of studies and prototypes for the U.S. Air Force; when U.S. support ended, the Israeli Defense Ministry took over.

Brunswick developed the Model 150 Maxi Decoy (tested 1973) for carriage, with folded wings, in the external-stores rack of a strike aircraft. Three Maxis could be carried in each of a Phantom's Sparrow-missile positions, and two could be carried on a 750-lb hard point. Maxi was a high-subsonic glider, but Model 290P (1974) was self-propelled, with a circular rather than square-section fuselage. That model in turn led to the design of the cylindrical-fuselage unpowered Samson 1, manufactured under license by IAI. The U.S. Navy bought 100 Samsons in 1985, for further OpEval, and in 1987 bought another 1000, plus 1500 of the improved TALD.

♦ TALD (ADM-141)/ITALD/MALD

The Tactical Air-Launched Decoy was developed from Samson and shown for the first time in 1986. There are two main versions: the active/passive ADM-141A (with a Luneberg lens to increase RCS) and the chaff-dispensing ADM-141B. In addition to the lens, ADM-141A (RF TALD) carries emitters mimicking fighter radars and ECM systems. ADM-141B (chaff TALD) carries 80 lb of chaff, which it releases in 40 increments. Its total weight is 400 lb. There is also an IR TALD for IR-missile training.

The decoy weighs 450 lb and achieves a 10:1 glide ratio, so when it is launched from 40,000 ft at 250 kt it flies for 68 nm.

The Brunswick TALD decoy. (Brunswick)

TALD under the wing of an A-7E of VA-76. (U.S. Navy)

Launched from 2000 ft, at the same speed, it flies 14 nm. In either case, it can execute preprogrammed turns to simulate aircraft.

Both TALD and Samson are carried like 500-lb Mk 82 bombs, their swept wings folded back; over 20 can be carried in the multiple ejectors of a typical attack bomber or fighter. Compared to Samson, TALD has a square (rather than round) cross-section for greater chaff capacity, a better active emitter, a better chaff dispenser, and a wider carriage-and-release envelope. TALD has a digital flight-control system, programmed with 20 flight speed profiles and 20 lateral (maneuver) options. During the Gulf War, the U.S. Navy launched 137 TALD decoys from A-6, A-7, F/A-18, and S-3 aircraft. Most were used to force Iraqi radars to remain active (and thus to succumb to antiradar missiles), but in at least one case an Iraqi fighter locked onto a TALD and gave chase.

The Navy ordered its first batch of 500 TALDs from Brunswick in December 1985. TALD entered service in 1987. In November 1987 the Navy ordered another 600, with an option for 1000 more, production to be split between IMI and Brunswick. As of March 1992, 4000 TALD had been bought in three lots. In September 1992 a contract (the most recent) for 1480 TALD was awarded to IAI. Reported unit price is $15,000 to $18,000.

ITALD (ADM-141C) is a self-propelled version of TALD, powered by a Teledyne CAE 312 turbojet, with an improved IR signature and a more realistic flight profile. It was first displayed at Farnborough in 1990, and hardware was delivered in April 1994. The manufacturer, Brunswick, claims that ITALD will cost only 2 or 3 times as much as the unpowered TALD. Launched at 20,000 ft, ITALD should achieve a range of about 175 nm, most of that at 20,000 ft and at Mach 0.8. Alternatively, it can fly in at very low level at Mach 0.73 and then pop up to 10,000 ft about 100 nm from its launch point. ITALD has a more realistic flight profile and a better IR signature than TALD. ITALD production funds ($2.5M) were added to the FY96 program in mid-1995. The Navy has considering equipping TALD with the inertial guidance planned for the ABF or AIWS. For the ARM mission, Brunswick is considering a mm-wave seeker.

As of 1995, the Navy planned to buy 220 (rather than the original 1500) ITALD, freeing funds to develop a more compact AMRAAM-sized decoy (MALD, miniature air-launched decoy). MALD is intended to force threat radars to radiate, revealing them as targets for antiradar aircraft. ARPA is managing this ACTD as a joint program. A solicitation to industry was issued in December 1995, and an RFP was released in July 1996. The only stated requirement was a unit cost of $30,000 or less. Teledyne Ryan won the $24.4M 30-month MALD ACTD program in December 1996 with a 45-kg device (about 6 × 90 in with a 24in wingspan) powered by a Sundstrand engine developed under ARPA's Small Engine Advanced Program. A total of 32 systems will be delivered. MALD will include a lethal version for defense suppression.

In December 1996 it was reported that the Japan Defense Agency was about to buy ITALD from IAI (not Brunswick) for its fighters.

♦ Mk 33/34 (RBOC)/RBOC II

RBOC was the Hycor Rapid-Blooming Chaff launching system. Mk 33 was for frigates or destroyers (four launchers); Mk 34, for corvettes, fast patrol boats, or hydrofoils (two launchers). The launcher itself was Mk 135. The first 11 sets of Mk 33 were delivered early in 1972. This system has now been replaced in U.S. service by Mk 36, but it was exported. These launchers were either automatically or semiautomatically controlled by the ship's ESM system. Each was a six-barreled mortar fixed in position: barrel elevation angles were 55, 65, and 75 deg (in pairs). The standard Mk 171 chaff cartridge provided short-range protection, to about 150 yd (slant range). For longer ranges (about 1000–1500 yd) a rocket motor could be added to the cartridge.

Loading a Mk 33 RBOC. (U.S. Navy)

Mk 36 SRBOC launcher. Versions exist with the tubes either splayed, as here, or in rows of two. (Hycor)

Decoys included chaff (2–20-GHz range), an IR decoy (HIRAM), and a combined decoy (Gemini, a parachute-suspended flare). In 1977 a typical cartridge outfit for two six-barrel launchers was 32 Mk 171 and 16 HIRAM, plus two Mk 173 test cartridges.

Loral (Hycor) continued to market RBOC and to produce improved rounds, such as LOROC, for the 4.4in RBOC after the U.S. Navy shifted to the 5.1in SRBOC launcher. Its RBOC II launcher has been sold to foreign navies for small warships. Unlike RBOC, the RBOC II tubes can be extended to accommodate longer rounds (see below).

RBOC is normally controlled manually from the CIC (using Master Launcher Control Mk 158) or from the bridge (using Bridge Launcher Control Mk 164). However, RBOC II can be controlled automatically by an ALEX system (see separate entry).

♦ Mk 36 (SRBOC)/MBL-9

The six-tube Super-Rapid Blooming Chaff launcher fires 130mm cartridges. Mod 1 (two groups) is for ships under 140 m long; Mod 2 (four groups) is for larger ships. All use Mk 182 cartridges, which climb to 244 m. Cartridge types: NATO Sea Gnat, Super Chaffstar, Super HIRAM III/Super HIRAM IV, Super Gemini (RF/IR).

Laguna Aerospace of Irvine, California, advertises MBL-9, in which three tubes are added to the usual Mk 36 (elevation angles are 45 deg [tubes 1, 4, 7], 52.5 deg [tubes 2, 5, 8], and 60 deg [tubes 3, 6, 9]). One stated advantage of the enlarged launcher is that it can launch Mk 2 torpedo countermeasures cartridges without sacrificing missile-defense rounds. The associated FCS is ARES.

Users: Australia (*C. F. Adams,* ANZAC, River, and *Perry* classes and *Tobruk*), Bangladesh (Jianghu 053H1 frigate), Belgium (*Wielingen* class), Brazil (FRAM *Gearings*), Canada (*Annapolis* and *Restigouche* classes), China (three Jianghu 053HT class), Denmark (*Nils Juel* class), Ecuador (FRAM *Gearing*), Egypt (*Descubierta* class), Germany (*C. F. Adams* and *Bremen* classes), Greece (FRAM *Gearings,* Kortenaers, MEKO 200s), Japan (surface combatants, down to frigates), South Korea (FRAM *Gearings,* KDX, *Ulsan* class, 13 of *Pohang*-class frigates [with Protean; some have Protean only]), Mexico (FRAM *Gearings*), the Netherlands (*Tromp, Karel Doorman, Jacob van Heemskerck,* and *Kortenaer* classes), New Zealand (ANZAC and *Leander* classes), Norway (*Farm, Nordkapp, Nornen* classes), Pakistan (*Brooke* class), Portugal (MEKO 200 and *Joao Belo* classes), Saudi Arabia (PCG and PGG classes), Spain (*Principe de Asturias, Perry, Baleares, Descubierta,* and *Paul Revere* classes), Thailand (*Makut Rajakumarn* and PF 103 class), Turkey (MEKO 200, FRAM destroyers [except *Kilic Ali Pasha, Kocatepe*], *Muavenet,* and *Yildiz* class), the United Kingdom (*Invincible* class, Type 42 destroyers, Type 22 Batch 1 and 2 frigates), and the United States.

♦ FLYRT

NRL's Flying Radar Target is a small electric-powered airplane fired out of a Mk 36 tube, deploying its wings in flight (the boost motor separates 1.5 sec after launch) and using a very clean airframe and a lift-to-drag ratio of 20.5:1 to achieve long endurance. It can carry a jammer. The program began in 1991, and FLYRT was successfully demonstrated in September 1993. Mentions of a contemporary FLIRT (Flying IR Torch) may be misprints.

♦ HIRAM

Hycor's IR Anti-Missile Decoy for RBOC launching (112 × 417 mm, 4.1 kg) is a spar buoy sufficiently bright to duplicate the radiant intensity of even a large ship. HIRAM-2 (8 × 39 in, 29.4 lb, extending beyond the mortar muzzle) uses liquid (similar to JP-5) rather than solid fuel, to burn longer (1 min vs. 0.5 min) with a brighter and higher flame (3m high). It will strike the water about 150 m from a ship in 5–7 sec. HIRAM was announced in 1980 for deployment in 1981.

◆ **Standard U.S. Chaff Cartridges**

Mk 171 appeared in 1974. RCS was about 7 times that of earlier rocket decoys (Mk 76). Mk 171 could be made for any frequency between 2 and 20 GHz. Hycor markets it as Chaffstar.

Mk 182, which entered service in 1977, was the corresponding SRBOC round, carrying about 4 times the payload of Mk 171 in two stages (macrocassettes for first-stage deployment, plastic-wrapped packages within each macrocassette for second-stage deployment). RCS is about 13 times that of the old Mk 76.

The next stage is Mk 214, NATO Sea Gnat, development of which was completed in 1986; it offers about 26 times the RCS of the original Mk 76.

Mk 186 (Torch) is the standard IR decoy, replacing the earlier SOID. It burns on hitting the water. Mod 2, recently developed, provides improved flame characteristics. It completed developmental and operational tests during FY94. There is also an Advanced Torch Decoy (Mod 3). These cartridges will probably be superseded by Giant (Mk 245).

◆ **Chaffstar II**

Announced in 1986, Hycor's cartridge (112.3 × 1067 mm, 18.2 kg) produces a much larger chaff cloud than Chaffstar I (Mk 171: 112.3 × 412.1 mm, 4.15 kg) and must be launched from an RBOC II launcher with a barrel extension. Muzzle velocity is 200 ft/sec, and the typical cloud is 328 ft (100 m) in diameter, with an area of 7850 m^2. Payload weight is 8.2 kg.

◆ **LOROC**

Hycor's long-range cartridge uses a booster rocket to gain range; it must be launched from an extended-barrel RBOC II. It is designed to burst 1.0–4.5 km from a ship for distraction. Dimensions: 112 × 1200 mm, 14.75 kg, payload 2.3 kg. This round outranges the only current U.S. Navy chaff rocket, Sea Gnat Mk 216 (maximum range is reportedly 1.5–2.0 km). The U.S. Navy abandoned its long-range chaff rocket program in 1974 due to technical problems, and by the late 1970s all surviving chaff rockets (adapted Zuni aircraft rockets) had been landed. LOROC has been exported to several foreign navies. It cannot be adopted by the U.S. Navy because the United States no longer uses the 4.4in caliber mortar.

ANTI-SUBMARINE WARFARE

SONARS AND UNDERWATER FIRE-CONTROL SYSTEMS

Deletions: SQS-504 (Canadian, extinct), SQS-507/HS-1000 (Canadian, no sales), New Dipping Sonar (Canadian: competition won by FLASH, but EH-101 helicopter canceled), DUBA 1 (French, extinct), DUBA 2 (French, extinct), IP 64 (Italian, ships discarded), DLB-1 (Italian, extinct as *Alpino* retires), LWS-20/30 (Dutch, extinct sonar intercept receivers), Pegas (Buck Toe: Russian, extinct), Bottle Cap (Swedish, no sales), 9TCI210 (Swedish, extinct), Type 164B/174/176 (British, probably extinct), Type 2023/2061/2062 (British, extinct with decommissioning of *Resolution*-class SSBNs), Type 2052 (extinct with the decommissioning of the older British nuclear submarines), Type 2057 (canceled with Type 2080 in favor of a new Type 2087), Type 2075 (would have been the first integrated British sonar, was canceled 1991 when the second batch of *Upholders* was canceled; the prototype is not being retained [as had been reported] as a technology demonstrator; presumably Ferranti abandoned the corresponding FIS 3), Type 2078 (planned new SSN sonar, abandoned in favor of an Anglo-French suite). Dolphin-1000 series (British, no sales reported), FISCS (British, no sales reported, and company dissolved), PMS 46 (British, extinct), PMS 56 (British, no sales reported), Sea Hunter (British, no sales reported), Sea Searcher (British, no sales reported), SP2110 (British, no sales reported), SWS 35/40 (British, no sales reported), DCH (British, ships discarded), Series 4 (British, no sales reported), BQQ-8 (U.S., long dead), SQS-11 (U.S., probably extinct), QCU-2 (U.S., probably extinct when removed from Portuguese *Joao Coutinho* class), HIPAS (U.S., loser in LF airborne sonar competitions), Osprey (U.S., loser in LF airborne sonar competitions), SQR-13 PADLOC (long dead), SQQ-89I/SQY-1 and SSATS/LFA/RMES (U.S., canceled 1991 as unaffordable within the planned FY94 budget; existing SQQ-89s will be upgraded instead), SQS-54 (U.S., extinct), BGMSS (U.S., canceled), Lightweight Sonar (U.S., test completed, no production), EDO 1102/1105 (Peruvian *Abtao* class retired). For details, see the 1991/92 edition.

AUSTRALIA

◆ ASSTASS

The RAN now emphasizes surface (e.g., antismuggler) surveillance rather than ASW; the Australian Surface Ship Towed-Array Surveillance System team conducted a new project definition study. Arrays are to be acquired from 1996/97 to 2000/1, the first going on board the fifth ANZAC frigate. Tested on board HMAS *Darwin* off Western Australia in February 1995, Kariwara (see below) tracked targets at own-ship speeds up to 21 kt, and therefore may be chosen for ASSTASS. In a mid-1995 trial on board the frigate *Newcastle*, Kariwara successfully tracked HMAS *Adelaide*, the oiler *Westralia*, an S-70B-2 helicopter, and a P-3C Orion.

◆ Kariwara/Narama

The Australian-developed Kariwara thin-line towed array can be used by both surface ships and submarines. Small diameter was specifically desired so that the array could be stowed in a submarine casing when the submarine entered shallow water (the alternative larger-diameter array is usually clipped to a submarine fin, hence can be torn off by underwater obstructions). The 40mm-dia array consists of 2in hydrophones embedded in a ropelike matrix made in continuous lengths. The buoyant polypropylene rope core in which the electronics are embedded is surrounded by a gel-filled weave of electrical conductors and Kevlar fibers, the whole being covered with a polyurethane sleeve. The full array consists of an acoustic section 70 m to over 2000 m long with a tow cable at least 50 m long, a 150m vibration isolation section, and a 50m drogue tail.

Sections of the wet end were tested on board the submarine *Oxley* in 1982. *Otama* received the first clip-on operational test version in April 1987. The first analog production versions were delivered late in 1991, to equip the Australian *Oberons*. GEC-Marconi developed a digital version for the *Collins* class and perhaps also for ASSTASS.

The pre-Kariwara array, SESTAS, uses Sonartech's single-cabinet SAAPS (Submarine Acoustic Array Processing System), which also handles the Type 2007 flank array. One operator looks at output from either flank or towed array. The display provides, on one screen, a gram at top, then ALI, then a time-bearing plot below it.

Note that Thomson Sintra Pacific and DSTO are working to adapt the *Collins*-class towed array for passive aircraft detection and location, using narrow-band processing (Doppler changes most rapidly at the airplane's closest point of approach). Altitude can be determined from the way in which Doppler varies systematically, for example in the signal from the airplane's turbo-props.

Thomson Pacific's alternative, Narama, was announced at Bourget Naval in 1992. It differs from Kariwara in being optimized for surface, not submarine, use (it is towed at higher speed, and shallower). Like Kariwara, it uses extruded threads; diameter is 25–50 mm (up to 5 km long, with up to 1000 channels, using analog or digital telemetry, over copper wires or fiber optics). Optimum operating speed is up to 15 kt, but the array is usable at 20 and can survive at over 30. Narama ran successful sea trials about the end of 1992, and was successfully tested on board an Australian *Oberon*-class submarine. Thomson claims that it is cheap to produce using an automated process, and that it may be attractive to geophysicists who need 5km arrays.

The first two *Collins*-class submarines have Kariwara; equipment for the last four is to be decided by competition between Kariwara and Narama.

◆ Krait

AWA's small ship towed array sonar uses the Shearwater fast acoustic processor (see below under airborne ASW) and a new thin-line (25mm, 32- or 64-hydrophone) low-noise streamer. Krait weighs less than 2 t and total footprint is 3 m². The 32-hydrophone version operates at 200–400, 400–800, and 800–1600 Hz; the 64-hydrophone version at 100–200, 200–400, and 400–800 Hz. The array is streamed at 2–20 kt, at 10–50 m. Operator aids include noise cancellation and autodetect and -track. Krait is conceived primarily as an OTH surface-ship detector; typical claimed shallow-water ranges are over 40 km for a trawler, over 50 km for a small surface warship, and over 65 km for a merchant ship. Claimed MTBF is 1000 hr, and MTTR is 30 min.

◆ Mulloka

This Australian-developed replacement for British hull sonars such as 177 and 184 was developed specifically for the main Australian operating area of the 1960s and 1970s, southern waters with short inherent range. Hence the choice of a relatively high frequency (transmission, 6–11 kHz; passive, 3.5–14 kHz), to produce a series of very narrow beams to achieve solid coverage out to about 10 kyd (but virtually nothing beyond). A 96-stave (25 spot transducers per stave) cylindrical transducer transmits randomly (to reduce warning to submarines) for 1–4 sec and then listens. Honeywell produced the transducer.

The RAN shifted to Spherion when it became more interested in northern areas, where the water is shallow but where the inherent range can be quite long, hence the preference for lower frequency (and a vertically steered beam). However, some reports suggest that Spherion is preferred mainly because it is both much less expensive and much more compact (Mulloka is both heavy and massive, and it may be difficult to accommodate).

The Mulloka prototype was completed in 1975 and the initial production contract was let in 1980.

Users: Australia ("River" class and first two *Perry*-class frigates).

◆ PIPRS

Ping Intercept Passive Ranging System was developed by the Australian DSTO Sonar and Surveillance Group, using existing MicroPUFFS arrays in Australian *Oberons*. Essentially a transient processor, it is made by Sonartech (Sydney). PIPRS is a cooperative program with Canada, which also uses MicroPUFFS.

CANADA

In the fall of 1996 the Canadian Department of National Defence announced plans to equip the "City"-class frigates with a low frequency (probably 1–2 kHz) Towed Integrated Active-Passive Sonar (TIAPS). Contracts for the experimental development model (XDM) should be under way by February 1997, with delivery of the passive element expected by February 1999, and sea trials beginning in April 2002.

In Canadian service the U.S. MicroPUFFS is designated BQR-501. The Singer-Librascope FCS now on the *Oberons* is designated BYG-501. The British Type 162 is SQS-501 and the British Type 502 (only in HMCS *Gatineau*, controlling Limbo) is SQS-502.

Gatineau probably has the last surviving example of the Canadian ASROC FCS. ASWDS probably became extinct with the reconstruction of the "Tribals" and the installation of SQS-510 on the two West Coast *Restigouche*-class frigates. See the 1991/92 edition for details.

◆ SQR-501

The Canadian towed array (CANTASS) uses a U.S. SQR-19 wet end feeding a Canadian (Computing Devices) UYS-501 signal processor using a 68020 central executive processor. It can track up to 240 signals. The system has three consoles (two primary search/monitor operators and a supervisor analyzing collated information), each with two high-definition (1152 × 1536 pixel) monochrome monitors. Display outputs include LOFAR, DEMON, and broad-band in beam- and bearing-stabilized modes.

The requirement was stated in 1981, and CANTASS was developed in 1983–87, running sea trials in 1987–90.

Users: Canada (12 "City" class and two *Annapolis* class, in place of their VDS).

◆ SQS-503

This 8–12-kHz hull sonar was developed by Canadian EDO of Cornwall, Ontario, from the abortive U.S. (EDO) SQS-5 7–15-kHz TRDT (rather than RDT) scanning sonar (pulse widths 5, 14, 35 [60 kW], and 100 msec), and scanned at 100 cycles/sec (6000 cycles/min). Range scales were 2, 4, 6, and 8 kyd. SQS-5 was first tested in 1955.

Users: Canada (*Gatineau*), France (*Foch*-class carriers).

◆ SQS-505/509/510/Type 5051

SQS-505 is the standard Canadian surface-ship sonar. Its 36-stave (10 elements/stave) cylindrical transducer (4ft dia × 4 ft) produces 36 10 × 10-deg beams at 6.4, 7.2, or 8.0 kHz (bandwidth 400 Hz divided into sixteen 25-Hz channels for each beam). Modes: ODT, triple RDT (TRDT), directional transmission (DT), ASPECT, and swept FM (wide-band mode). Pulse lengths: 2.5, 10, 40, 480 msec. Source level: 126 dB (ODT), 135 dB (TRDT, DT). Signal processing: matched filter with time, function automatic gain control (TFAGC) and frequency, function AGC (FFAGC) or incoherent (wide-band) processing. Nominal range is 200–32,000 yd (range scales 2, 4, 8, 16, 32 kyd). Target Doppler can be up to 40 kt. Passive operation: 10 kHz. Track capacity is five targets. One of two CRTs shows targets detected actively (with 5- or 12-ping history) or raw video or a range-Doppler format (seven successive A-scans with Doppler); the other shows a passive "waterfall" and alphanumeric readouts. Targets are classified by Doppler, by a separate steerable audio channel, or by ASPECT. Data can be transferred to the ship's CDS in digital form.

The (V)6 version for the "City" class has new transmitter and receiver (source level 133 dB, pulse length 10 or 40 msec). Active frequencies match those of earlier versions, but passive frequency is reduced to 4.5 kHz and there is a steerable passive mode. Separate control consoles are eliminated, since this version feeds data directly into the ship's SHINPADS combat system bus. There is no separate console, since the SHINPADS consoles substitute. This version includes a computer-aided detection and tracking feature developed by Westinghouse Canada.

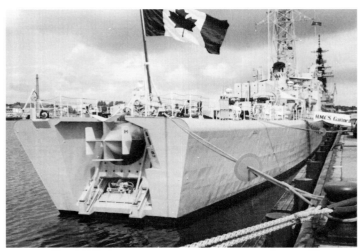

SQS-505 VDS on board HMCS *Gatineau*, August 1988. (S. Terzibaschitsch)

SQS-505 was developed in both hull and VDS forms. The hull dome is 14 ft long, and the towed body (SQA-502 hoist) is 18 ft long and weighs 14,000 lb (10,000 lb submerged). The earliest version was (V)1 (hull)/(V)2 (VDS). The TRUMPs have (V)4/(V)5, which have some digital circuitry added, better integration of the hull sonar and VDS, and an integral digital FCS computer. Memory was added so that the sonar could retain a longer ping history. BITE was also added. This version can retain 20 ASPECT pulses ([V]3 is the AOR version to replace SQS-503). The "City" class has (V)6 with a separate towed array.

SQS-509 is a low-frequency (4.8, 5.4, 6.0 kHz active, 3.125 kHz passive) version developed while the Royal Netherlands Navy developed PHS-36 with Canadian Westinghouse assistance. The SQS-509 transducer is reportedly very similar to that of the Dutch sonar. Power output is increased by about 2 dB; transducer size is increased by a ratio of 4:3. Source level: 137 dB. Pulses: 10 and 40 msec. Doppler limits: 40 kt. Nominal range matches that of SQS-505.

CDC's SQS-510 is a redesigned SQS-505 with a new UYS-501 programmable signal processor but with the existing transducer and transmitter power supply. It resulted from parametric studies conducted by DREA (Canadian Defense Research Establishment Atlantic) in the early 1970s, which showed that the most significant gain in performance could be had by upgrading the sonar receiver and display. In this system, both control and tracking processor use 68020 CPUs. The transmitter is modified to receive stave firing signals from the new pulse generator, which synthesizes CW and FM pulses, and distributes time-delayed versions to the staves to form a transmitting beam. Pulses: CW or FM; durations 10–500 msec, FM sweep width 100 to 750 Hz. Defaults: 400 msec CW, 300 Hz sweep/320 msec FM. Transmit modes: ODT, narrow beam (10 deg), and broad beam (38 deg).

There are 72 active receiving beams. Stave outputs are passed through a zoom filter that selects the frequency band of interest (allowing for +/−50 kt of Doppler) and digitized (sampling rate 20.48 kHz, dynamic range 138 dB) for the UYS-501, which forms beams and automatically detects targets. Some data go into a separate tracking processor (capacity 100 tracks). The sonar can display up to 16 operator-defined tracks.

The sonar normally time-shares its active and passive (2.2–8.6 kHz) modes. When it is pinging, maximum passive frequency is limited to 5.5 kHz to avoid interference. In listening mode, 36 beams are formed. Inputs are integrated over time (nominally 7 sec) and normalized to allow transient detection. Passive track capacity is 36 targets.

Each of two color synthetic-video displays (1536 × 1152 pixels) is divided into a 1024 × 1024 acoustic area and a set of smaller alphanumeric areas for target and parameter data. Acoustic displays: B-scan (and magnified B-scan), Doppler scan (range/Doppler/bearing), A-scan, A-scan history, classification (high resolution, 0.6 yd, A-scan for selected range and beam), passive waterfall, ray path, BT data.

SQS-510 significantly outperforms SQS-505.

Westinghouse Type 5051 (announced June 1992) is an improved commercial version of SQS-505, combining the SQS-505 transducer and hull outfit with a new digital (vice analog) transmitter (from the abortive SQQ-89[I] program) and a new digital signal processor. Versions are 5051-5 (5 kHz nominal: 4.8, 5.4, 6.0 kHz), -7 (7 kHz nominal: 6.4, 7.2, 8.0 kHz), and -10 (10 kHz); the latter has a new transducer (24 staves, 144 elements, 0.6 × 0.6 m, 24 17 × 17-deg beams). Modes: ODT, TRDT, DT (single beam directional), and dual-pulse at a source level of 224–233 dB. CW pulse widths: 2.5, 40, 100 msec. FM pulses: 40, 100, 500 msec (linear or hyperbolic FM or CW-FM hybrid). Receiver bandwidth is 1–15 kHz (dynamic range 120 dB; 36 or 24 beams with one steered beam for tracking). The parallel-array processor is dynamically configured by software for active-passive operation. Doppler speed limits are +/−40 kt. Accuracy: 1% in range, 1 deg in bearing, 0.5 kt in Doppler. The passive processor admits signals over any 2-kHz band within the transducer bandwidth.

The two higher-frequency versions have a mine-avoidance mode. They transmit at 8 (5051-7) or 10 (5051-10) kHz, using 1-msec FM pulses (bandwidth 1 kHz); receiver beam width is 8 × 10 deg, and minimum range is 300 m.

The system can incorporate a 6–10-kHz VDS (Fathom Oceanology Model 15–1000, 1.525m dia × 4.572mm long, 3600 kg), which can be launched at up to 16 kt (and towed at 30) on a 270m faired cable.

Display modes of the single 19in high-resolution monochrome monitor are: A- and B-scans, Doppler (two targets: Doppler vs. range), Passive, and Spectrum. Passive is a dual waterfall; the screen is divided into two sections, an upper one of 128 lines, each representing 85 msec of integration time, and the lower of 128 lines, each representing 32 lines of the upper display (2.7 sec). Alternative integration times are 341 msec and 10.9 sec. A bright pulse along the line indicates noise at that bearing. Spectrum displays 256 lines of LOFAR data (87 sec). Range scales are 500 yd to 64 kyd. The screen can also be split into two displays: A-scan/Passive, B-scan/Passive, B-scan/Doppler, and A-scan/B-scan.

Target reliability is 2000 hrs MTBF.

In effect, 5051 supersedes the HS-1000 series formerly advertised by Westinghouse Canada. Work began in 1990. No sales had been announced as of mid-1996.

Users:

SQS-505: Belgium (*Weilingen* class [505A]), Canada (TRUMP and "City"-class frigates [being upgraded to -510], *Protecteur* [retrofit] class), Greece (*Kortenaer* class, being upgraded to -505F), India (first four *Nilgiri* class, including VDS), Netherlands (*Kortenaer* class). The Indian sonars almost certainly do not have SQS-505 signal processors. A 1992 contract adds a mine-avoidance capability to Canadian SQS-505s. This entails adding a new Westinghouse signal processor and a new transmitter module. SQS-505 was developed in 1966–69 for the "Tribal" class.

SQS-509: Netherlands (last four *Kortenaer* class).

SQS-510: Canada (*Annapolis, Nipigon*; refitted "City" class [begun 1995]), Portugal (MEKO frigates; replaces SQS-17/DUBA-3 on *Commandante Rivière* class [contract July 1991]).

◆ CTS-36 RDN

C-Tech's 36- or 39-kHz (33 kHz optional) hull sonar is derived from a family of commercial fish-finding sonars developed since about 1970. The 540-element (270-channel) 450 (dia) × 910 mm (17.7 × 35.8 in) transducer transmits in ODT (270 50W channels), sector, and SDT (36 elements/sector are driven) modes. Source level is 220 dB (there are five discrete power levels: full, −H5 dB, −H10 dB, −H15 dB, and off); pulse length is 1–150 msec. Pulses can be CW or FM (chirp). In search mode, a 12-deg receiving beam is scanned through an operator-selected sector.

In tracking mode, each of three independent 6 × 6-deg receiving beams is locked onto a target. Search MCC mode uses a 30-deg receiving beam to maintain contact with a nearby target. Beam elevation is continuously adjustable electronically between +8/ −24 deg, stabilized for roll and pitch. Targets are detected automatically. Doppler filter resolution is 1.25 kt over 20 kt. The range scales are 250, 500, 1000, 2000, and 4000 m. There is a separate steerable audio receive beam (800-Hz bandwidth). Display modes: PPI, B-scope, and bearing-time for tracking, all oriented true north or to the ship's bearing. The display is either a seven-color 1280 × 1024-pixel CRT or a CDS console. Claimed MTBF is greater than 500 hr.

CMAS-36 is a simplified 36-kHz (39 kHz optional) version for shallow-water mine and obstacle avoidance, using the same transducer, with ODT, search MCC, and surveillance (searching a 76-deg zone centered on the bow) modes. Source level is 223 dB, and pulse lengths are 0.2 to 15 msec.

The first CTS-36 sonar was delivered to Denmark in February 1991.

Users: Bangladesh ("River" class), Canada (CMAS-36 in "Tribal"-class ships sent to the Persian Gulf in 1990, possibly as C-Tech Spectra-Scan 3000), Denmark (*Flyvefisken* and *Thetis* classes).

♦ CSAS-80/CSS-80AS/CIDS

C-Tech's 80-kHz harbor-surveillance sonar competes with Saab's Bottle Cap. It uses technology similar to that in CTS-36 to search a 6-, 12-, or 24-deg conical field that can be tilted 24 deg up or down. Targets are automatically detected and tracked, and static targets can be suppressed automatically. Range scales are 250, 500, 1000, 1500, and 2000 m. The related CSS-80AS searches a 3 × 360-deg cone that can be stepped through a vertical sector of 15 deg. Transmission is ODT (4 deg vertical); the receiving beam is 17 (adjustable to 3) × 5 deg. Source level is 211 dB; pulse length is 1–20 msec. Bearing resolution is 0.56 deg. The transducer can be up to 2000 m from the dry-end electronics.

Users: Sweden (contract awarded July 1991, first delivery February 1993), United States (CSAS-80 is the basis of the Coastal Intrusion Detection System, CIDS, which also employs an X-band radar and TV and IR cameras; the associated C3 is CDC's ISIS). CSAS-80 was under consideration by Kuwait just before the August 1990 invasion, and has been considered by at least one Asian country. As of mid-1996, CSAS-80 was being considered by about five potential customers.

CHILE

See Germany for TGS, the fire-control upgrade for *Oberon*-class submarines.

CHINA

Sonar equipment was listed as a high priority in the 1956 12-yr national scientific program. Soviet submarine sonars were copied in the early 1960s, after which Chinese designs appeared.

No. 706 Institute developed integrated sonars for nuclear submarines (SQZ-3I and -3II), which were installed in 1970 and certified in 1975. At the same time the Acoustic Research Institute of the Chinese Academy of Sciences, Jiangning Mechanical Plant, and Shanghai 22nd Radio Plant developed an SQC-1 scouting (presumably passive search) sonar and an SQW-3 ray tracer for nuclear submarines. These submarines also had a TS-1 mine-avoidance sonar. Dongfeng Mechanical Plant and the Acoustic Research Institute developed an SQZ-D integrated sonar for diesel submarines.

Surface sonars are:

SJD-2 is an unknown type, presumably a copy of Soviet equipment.
SJD-3 is a copy of the Russian Tamir.
SJD-4: Attack sonar.
SJD-5: The Type 5 (SJD-5 or EH-5) searchlight sonar (on the Jianghu class; Type 053HT) is a developed Soviet Tamir 11.
SJD-7: The French DUBV 23 made under license for "Jiang-

wei"-class frigates and probably installed in some export frigates.
SJD-9: Probably a license-made French DUBV 23. The Chinese bought the DUBV 23/43 combinations originally ordered for the French *Cassard* and *Jean Bart*. One was installed for trials, the other used as a pattern for production for the later "Luda" class. (Note, however, that the prototype Luhu-class destroyer *Harbin* has what appears to be a Raytheon-type fish, suggesting that she may be fitted with a DE-1167-series sonar.)
SJD-11: This bulbous bow sonar was tested in 1971, when it successfully detected a submarine under poor water conditions at an own-ship speed of 18 kt. It was associated with an ASW rocket launcher.
SJC-1B: "Scouting sonar," presumably a passive search set.
SQZ-3: Sonar system of the Han- and Xia-class submarines.
SQZ-A: Ming-class sonar system.
SQB-2: Passive ranging sonar, presumably related to the French DUUX 5.

At Abu Dhabi, a frigate offered by CSSC had a 507H hull-mounted bow sonar. No details are available, but it was not too large. Note that in 1988 the Chinese displayed two new sonars, perhaps operating at lower frequencies, at ASIANDEX in Beijing (ESS-1 and -2).

There may also have been VDS for seaplanes or helicopters. The Chinese account cited above mentions SKD-41 and -42A "aerial hoisting sonars."

FINLAND

♦ PTA/HDS

Sonac's 78m (including VIMs) small-combatant array carries 24 hydrophones, each of which has an integral electronic unit to filter, amplify, and digitize its output; two fiber-optic signal channels in the 600m tow cable eliminate electromagnetic interference. The cable is towed from an active depressor, which keeps the array clear of underwater obstacles, and can also steer the array to penetrate and follow thermoclines. Maximum array depth is 100 m; tow speed is 3–12 kt. The short tow cable improves maneuverability in shallow water. It is usable because the system automatically cancels the screw and engine noise of the towing vessel. VIMs in the array and the faired tow cable cut turbulence interference.

The two primary displays are broad band (30-min waterfall) and narrow band (10-min history). There is also a true motion display. A screen can also be used to show paravane depth and BITE information. The system can sound an alarm when transients are detected; it can analyze and record for replay; it can also track designated targets. The processor is 595 mm (W) × 1812mm (H) × 1070mm (D) and carries a tracker ball and two screens. Optional features are a data recorder, display printer, BT, interface with radar for information on surface targets, exchange of data with another PTA system, target classification and identification, and an interface with the ship's CDS.

Sonac's Hybrid Dipping Sonar adds a new medium-frequency CW/FM active component, PTA (see below). The system forms 16 passive beams, and processes a single beam in both modes. Total weight is 150 kg, including transducer and display.

Work began about 1989, and the prototype entered service in 1993. The target weight was 1 t, but the system weighs about 2 t.

User: Finland (PTA in *Rauma* class).

FRANCE

SONARS

With the merger of Sintra-Alcatel into Thomson-CSF in 1987, Thomson Sintra became the sole supplier of French naval sonars. Thomson later began a joint venture with the sonar division of the former British Ferranti company to form Thomson Ferranti Sonar Systems (TFSS). In mid-1996 it was announced that GEC-Marconi (which took over Plessey's sonars) and Thomson Sintra would form a new joint venture, based in the Netherlands,

Thomson Marconi Sonar NV (TMS), in which Thomson would have a 50.1% interest. The product lines of the two companies are to be combined as an NG line of hull sonars:

NG/S, for small/medium ships (Spherion)
NG/C, for medium/large ships (Type 2050)
NG/CZ, for large ships (Type 2050, presumably with an LF transducer, and with more inboard equipment)

At Euronavale 1996, TMS announced two sonars, MFS Horizon and CAPTAS 20. MFS (medium-frequency sonar) Horizon offers standard processing and twin-screen X-Windows display for either a 2050 or a Spherion array (2050 requires two rather than one processing cabinets). CAPTAS 20 is a new passive/active towed array employing ceramic-ring omni transducers. The (V)1 version is an active sonar with a concurrent passive torpedo alert function. (V)2 adds a long (VLF) passive towed array.

CAPTAS 20(V)1 (TSM 2651) uses a 1.4–2.2-kHz active transmitter (TTB) towed on a 350m faired cable. The transmitter in turn tows a 400m neutrally buoyant cable, from which is towed a short array comprising a 120mm × 45m LF array with right/left ambiguity resolution for targets bearing 30 to 150 deg port or starboard (with 85mm electronics elements) buffered from the cable by an 85mm × 20m VIM. In the (V)2 (TSM 2652) version, the LF array tows a VLF array comprising an 85mm × 20m digitization module from which extends a 40mm × 120m acoustic element (10 Hz–2 kHz). The acoustic element in turn tows a 100m rope tail.

CAPTAS 20 and the Horizon hull sonar are integrated as MUROSS (Multirole Sonar System), under the control of a single ASW (ASW Tactical Assistance) console. This combination provides two 6–8-kHz active channels with special processing for mine/obstacle avoidance (as in the U.S. Kingfisher) and for active short-range torpedo detection. The 1–5-kHz passive element of the towed system is used for medium/long-range torpedo detection/classification and to intercept surface-ship sonar signals. The ASWTA fuses sonar data and provides facilities for situation assessment and aided decisionmaking. It sends its tactical picture to the ship's CDS.

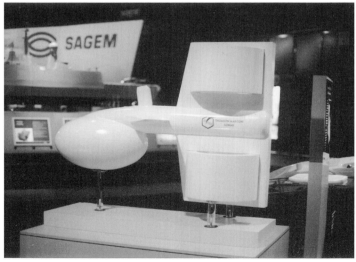

A model of the CAPTAS 20 active pinger is shown at Bourget Euronaval 1996. The bulge at left is the counterweight; the two flooded-ring transducers are at right. The tow point is the stub to the left of the fin carrying the transducer. (Author)

See the United Kingdom section for Type 2050 details.

French Lynx helicopters using dipping sonars have a mission computer that can handle up to 15 way-points (it is being upgraded to 100) with up to six moving or sonar targets. It can accept geographic, radar, or grid coordinates, providing the pilot with bearing and range and with the next way- or hover point. The standard tactic is to dip at the last known target contact ("jumping on the contact"). It is estimated that, with a reliable sonar range of 1500 yd, one Lynx in daylight or two at night can keep contact with any submarine. With a reliable range of 3000 yd, the French navy estimates that a Lynx can maintain contact with a 35-kt submarine in daytime or a 22-kt submarine at night (night dipping is slower, using a complex autopilot). In 1991 the helicopter system was integrated with GPS. These helicopters typically carry Mk 46 torpedoes.

◆ DMUX 20 (formerly DSUX 20) (TSM 2233)/Scylla

The first fully integrated French submarine sonar, DMUX 20, the DSUV 22 successor, feeds the SUBICS CDS. It corresponds broadly to the U.S. BSY-1. The arrays are those of Eledone. The passive cylinder, the sonar interception unit, and the active sonar all feed a signal processor and then a data processor. Similarly, the towed array (plus any flank array) feeds a signal processor and then its own data processor. Both data processors feed the tactical information bus, on which are interchangeable Colibri double-screen operator consoles. Signal processors use massively DSPs (TMS 320C30s) for beam forming and FFTs. Data processors (postprocessors) use 68040 CPUs for automatic detection (by ALI in the case of passive contacts) and tracking. Thus the output of the system to the CDS bus comprises processed data (contacts), but the sonar system retains raw (digitized) acoustic data in the form of FFT outputs at the signal processors, to make up for processing errors. Console operators correlate outputs from the two sonar elements, operating at low and very low frequencies. For example, a frequency line seen by one sensor may coordinate with one seen by another, so the combination may be meaningful to a track manager. This system can track 48 targets (acquired automatically or manually). The operator can designate up to four noise sources for spectral analysis. Narrow-band sonar jammers can be automatically rejected. This system includes a sonar performance monitor. It can also accommodate a passive ranger (TSM 2255) and a mine-avoidance sonar, each presumably having its own processors feeding the common sonar system bus.

The sonar filters the plots sent through to the CDS bus by automatic CMA (contact management analysis). Concurrent passive processing techniques are broad and narrow band and transient.

The new Australian submarine HMAS *Collins*, rolled out of its assembly shed on 28 August 1993, displays elements of her French sonar system: the intercept transducer projecting above the bow, the flank array, and the three ranging arrays along her casing (superstructure). (Australian Submarine Corp. via Rockwell International)

The Scylla sonar of the Australian *Collins* class is probably a variant of the integrated TSM 2233 rather than of the earlier unintegrated Eledone. Its 2000 hydrophones are distributed among seven arrays (bow cylinder, two PVDF flanks, sail active array, passive ranger [three arrays on each side], towed array, mine-avoidance sonar, and intercept array [two elements, fore and aft]). Total array surface is about 70 m², compared to 10 m² for typical current sonars (for diesel submarines) with three to five arrays. The system performs 60 acoustic functions (compared to 16 in a typical existing type), including nulling to defeat jamming, self-noise cancellation, and automatic detection (none of which is currently common).

DMUX 20 trials (on board the experimental submarine *Dauphin*) began in 1989.

Users: Australia (*Collins* class), France (*Amethyste* class), Pakistan (*Agosta 90* class).

◆ DMUX 80

The new integrated SSBN sonar suite is unique in French submarine practice in including a large spherical ceramic bow array. The other elements are a PVDF flank array, an acoustic intercept array, and a towed array. Each array feeds its own combination of signal and data processors. As in DMUX 20, operators decide which tracks to merge, for example on the basis of broad- and narrow-band data. The system does automatic as well as interactive TMA. The system's 14 electronic cabinets accommodate 28 DSPs and 65 CPUs with a total processing power of 6 GFLOPS, plus 14 data processors (total 140 MIPS). Program software amounts to 2M lines of code (100 Mbytes). Sonar data input rate is 256 Mbytes/sec; sonar data output (to the CDS) is 3 kbyte/sec.

Users: France (*Le Triomphant* class).

◆ DSBV 1

This 5–40-kHz passive torpedo-detection sonar shares a dome with DUBA 3 in the *Commandante Rivière* class. DSBV 1 presumably shares some of the components of Velox (DUUG 1).

Users: Portugal (*Commandante Rivière* class), Uruguay (*Commandante Rivière* class).

◆ DSBV 61A/DSBV 62C/Anaconda (FLUTE)

DSBV 61 is a three-octave digital surface ship towed array (about eight modules, 50 hydrophones, acoustic section about 80 mm × 300 m [984 ft], total 365 m including VIMs) towed on a 1000m cable. The system includes two consoles (plus alphanumeric readouts) and five processing cabinets (presumably one LOFAR processor, one DEMON processor, and three beam-formers). The operator can select channels for audio, LOFAR, and DEMON processing. The system includes a torpedo warner.

DSBV 62C is a more compact version for the *Tourville* class, with one console and one processing cabinet.

The requirement was stated in the mid-1970s, Thomson Sintra delivered the prototype in mid-1980, and DSBV 61 was approved for production early in 1985. The first array was installed aboard *Primauguet*, commissioned November 1986.

Anaconda is the export version.

Users: France (seven *Georges Leygues* class, streamed from a DUBV 43C VDS body; DSBV 62C on three *Tourville* class, plus one shore-training unit for each version), Netherlands (*Karel Doorman* class: Anaconda, streamed at a critical angle; uses a Mangouste Mk 2 processor).

◆ DSBX 1 (SLASM)

Système de Lutte Anti-Sous-Marin was developed as the French ASW system of the 1990s, adding a 10t towed fish (with 90t handling gear) to the existing hull sonar. The fish (5.5 × 1.8 [W] × 4.6 [H] m; the composite shell weighs 2 t) contains a pair of 1-kHz transmitters (12 transducers each) pointing to port and starboard, plus a DUBV 43 sonar. Like the early DUBV 43, it can operate to 600 m. The ship's towed array acts as receiver (and also as torpedo detector). A slight difference in frequencies allows the array to distinguish returns from port and starboard. Other automatic inputs will be sonar intercepts and helicopter-

laid sonobuoys, both active and passive. All elements feed a common set of processors and displays, the operators choosing an optimum configuration (depending upon both physical oceanographic circumstances and the tactical situation).

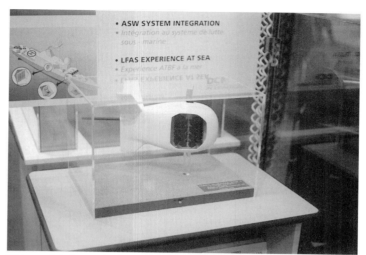

This model shows the lightweight ATBF fish, with its omni pinger. It is one of a family of possible SLASM fishes. (Author)

A model of the ATBF pinger array. (Author)

A lighter SLASM 2 is to equip *Georges Leygues*–class frigates on their midlife modernization. However, SLASM may be superseded by the Franco-German LFTASS, should that materialize. The main difference between the two is that SLASM uses a directional transmitter, whereas the lighter LFTASS would have to be omnidirectional. A 30-month definition-phase MoU was signed in mid-1996, leading to a production MoU in 1999.

DCN offers a range of ATBF2 lightweight SLASM (1–1.5 kHz) for export; it includes a 1t towed active body (transmitter range 30 km), a 2t body (60 km), and a 4t body (over 100 km).

Tourville, the first ship fitted with SLASM, began sea trials early in April 1995 after a 14-month refit at DCN Brest. Trials were completed in March 1996, and the system was formally accepted. *De Grasse* installation is to be completed by September 1996.

TSM 2670 is an experimental LF VDS sonar using an omni transmitter and a dual linear receiver. Data are all transmitted by fiber optic.

◆ DSUV 2

This passive low-frequency (i.e., sonic) keel (bow) array works with the DUUA 2 active pinger in the submarine's sail, for which it can function as scanning receiver (this combination is broadly equivalent to the unintegrated sonars of the early postwar German submarines). Beams are formed by a scanning compensator. The original system used only a paper recorder: each scan was represented by a horizontal line, dark spots indicating noise levels (as the paper unrolled, a vertical line indicated a target). Later a CRT (waterfall) was added. The system can automatically track a single operator-selected target, for which audio can be extracted for classification. The compensator receiver is designated GC 02. The original DSUV 2 was a small array of 36 spot hydrophones descended from prewar French arrays; DSUV 2H uses a GHG-style 64-stave array. Both use the same analog receiver system.

Users: DSUV 2 in *Daphne* class in Pakistan, Portugal, South Africa, and Spain. DSUV 2H in *Agosta* class in France, Pakistan, and Spain (array later integrated into the DSUV 22 system) and in Type 209 submarines, probably in Colombia, Ecuador, and Peru.

◆ DSUV 22 (TSM 2233 Eledone)/ Type 2040 (Argonaute)/Octopus

This digital sonar is similar in concept to the contemporary U.S. BQQ-5, in that it was intended specifically to feed digital track data to a computer-driven FCS (in this case, DLT D3A). A digital beam-forming version of the previous passive bow array (DSUV 2H) feeds a digital tracker and a signal processor. The TSM 2263 bow array has 128 preformed beams (combining adjacent beams, directional accuracy is 0.1 deg). Autotrack capacity (in the current version) is 48 noise sources and 8 sonar emitters; the operator can initiate tracking on four noise sources and four sonar emitters. There are two versions, with 32 staves/64 hydrophones (TSM 2271R) and with 64 double staves (1.25/3.5 m [49.3/137.8 in] dia × 0.8/3 m, operating at up to 12 kHz in two or three frequency bands (e.g., 1–5 and 5–12 kHz for the smaller version).

Generally there is also an aft-looking passive array.

As in earlier systems, the passive array can be the receiver for an active searchlight pinger (DUUA 2D); the searchlight can also function separately in single-ping analog mode. Eledone (TSM 2233) is the export designation. Type 2040 (Argonaute)/Octopus is a modified version for the Royal Navy and the Royal Netherlands Navy. Scylla is the version in the Australian *Collins* class (see above).

Eledone active array, typically located in the submarine sail. (Thomson Sintra)

Using a MITRA 1500–series computer (as in Beluga and Remora), track capacity was 4–12, with 1–2 noise sources subject to spectral analysis. The later Type 2040/Octopus was credited with 12.

Typically the system's self-noise monitor (QSUA-4A) sounds an automatic alarm if the cavitation noise level rises above a preset value. The displays show broad-band noise levels throughout the length of the submarine.

Versions beginning with Octopus are federated. Additions can include a passive ranger (TSM 2255/DUUX 5), an intercept sonar (TSM 2243), and a mine-avoidance sonar (TSM 5423). Each element of the system is separate. However, a CRT displays signals from different sensors (or from different operating modes) simultaneously in different colors, for correlation and, therefore, classification. For example, the display can easily distinguish between a helicopter's sonar (which shows up only on the intercept sensor) and a ship's hull sonar (which will be accompanied by propeller sounds, visible on the combined display). Tracks cannot be combined at the sonar level (DMUX 20 integrates the arrays, using them all simultaneously).

Octopus and Type 2040 were integrated with CDS (respectively, the Dutch SEWACO VIII and the British DCC). The most recent version of Eledone is integrated with the French SUBICS II CDS.

Eledone was conceived to meet the requirements of the *Agosta* class (as defined in 1971); it was developed in 1971–76 and approved for service use in 1976 as DSUV 22. Octopus was developed specifically for the Dutch *Walrus* class (it was ordered in 1979). Type 2040, a further development, won the British 1982 competition for Batch I *Upholder*-class submarines.

Users:

DSUV 22: France (*Agosta* class), India (six sets bought May 1991 for delivery 1997–99, probably for Type 1500 submarines), Pakistan (*Agosta* class), Spain (*Agosta* class, retrofitted to *Daphne* class [with 32- rather than 64-stave bow array]). *Agostas* have the 64-stave version.

Eledone: Argentina (Type 1700), China (Han and some Ming class; may use separate bow [TSM 2272] and flank ranging [DUUX 5] systems; built under license by the China Na-

Eledone passive attack (bow) array. (Thomson Sintra)

tional Electronics Import & Export Corporation of Beijing).

Octopus: Netherlands (*Walrus* [64-stave] and *Zwaardvis* [32-stave] class, the latter now for sale, the first example of Eledone/CDS integration). SUBICS II (TSM 2295) is reportedly functionally identical to Octopus/SEWACO VIII.

Type 2040: United Kingdom (*Upholder* class, for sale). Integrated with DCC CDS. The 64-stave bow array has three rather than two tiers of transducers per stave. The submarine also has flank arrays, a towed array, and an intercept sonar, Type 2019 (PARIS). Type 2040 requires four processing cabinets for its four modes (adaptive, active, passive, intercept).

◆ DSUV 61

A towed array for French SSBNs, used primarily for evasion, DSUV 61 is comparable to BQR-15 and Type 2023. Tests were conducted in 1974–77, the first installations following in 1977–78. *Le Tonnant* and *L'Inflexible* were completed with this array, and the four earlier units were retrofitted. The current version is DSUV 61A; a 61B is being developed.

◆ DSUV 62/Lamproie (TSM 2933)

This attack submarine towed array (50 or 80 mm × 100 m [328 ft] on a 400m cable), used for passive fire control rather than evasion, is related to DSUV 61. Up to 64 noise sources can be tracked, and up to eight designated as potential targets. Processing: narrow (LOFAR and DEMON), wide band, and audio. The processors are TMS 320C30 DSPs and 68020 and 68040 CPUs in a MIMD-type system. Thomson Sintra claims second convergence zone performance for this array.

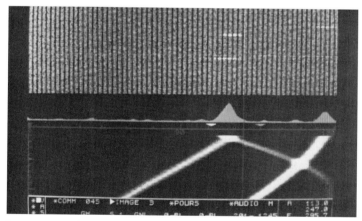

Lamproie combined narrow- (*top*) and broad- (*bottom*) band display for initial detection. The upper display is a LOFARgram, showing frequency (horizontal) plotted against time (vertical). The graph below is a series of time integrals of the highlighted areas of the LOFARgram. The lower (broad-band) display is a waterfall, showing potential target tracks, bearing (horizontal) being plotted against time (vertical). (Thomson Sintra)

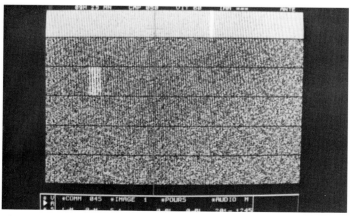

The Lamproie classification (LOFARgram) display, showing a series of six different frequency bands (separate horizontal bands) simultaneously.

Lamproie, the export version for both submarines and surface ships, uses a short (74 m, including VIMs at each end) array cased in Kevlar. The processor can operate simultaneously in several frequency bands, permitting comparison among different harmonics of the same signal. It provides automatic threat (i.e., torpedo) warning. Lamproie can track targets either automatically or manually, and can automatically reject narrow-band jammers. The display is the usual pair of high-resolution color CRTs. The array can be towed at up to 32 kt and at depths as great as 1000 m (3280 ft). For a surface ship, the wet end can be a critical-angle tow or it can be towed from a VDS fish or other depressor (for shallow water).

Thomson Sintra received a research contract in 1975–76 after it began work on DSUV 61. The prototype was completed in 1979, and DSUV 62 was approved for production in 1981. The first installation was on board the submarine *Rubis* early in 1983.

Users: Australia (*Collins* class [Lamproie]), France (*Agosta* [62A], *Rubis* [62A], *Amethyste* [62C] classes; total of at least 14 ordered), Pakistan (*Agosta* class, planned for *Agosta* 90), Spain (DSUV 62 tested on *Siroco* and *Mistral* 1991, to be on other *Agostas* as modernized; as of mid-1995, *Mistral* was still fitted for DSUV 62C, but it had been removed).

◆ DUAV 4 (HS 71/73) (TSM 8251)

Sintra-Alcatel's dipping sonar for the Lynx (WG-13) is light enough to leave weight for the helicopter to carry antiship missiles such as AS 12, AS 15TT, and Sea Skua. The sonar operates at 21, 22.5, and 24 kHz (source level 119 dB) in three modes: (a) fixed-frequency active (around 20 kHz) to measure bearing, range, and Doppler (for speed); (b) variable-frequency (to detect motionless targets); (c) passive, at 10 to 20 kHz. HS 73 uses a coherent processor to reject reverberation echoes in shallow water. Transducer depth is typically 140 m (460 ft) on a 160m cable (maximum depth is 495 ft). Maximum effective range is about 6000 yd.

DUAV 4 UPG (TSM 8253), the new upgraded version, is probably the modernized Swedish version described below. It has a new processor, improved MMI, and operator assistance functions for shallow-water classification.

Development began in 1968–69, and the sonar entered French navy service in 1975 with the commercial designation HS 73 (HS 71 is the export version). This sonar was first exported in 1978. Reportedly, DUAV 4 has not been particularly successful, and it has been replaced in French service by HS 12 (see below). Production ended about 1987.

Users: Netherlands (12 on Lynx Mks 27/81) and Sweden (14 on KV-107s, 1975, at least eight of which are being upgraded under a June 1992 contract with Thomson Sintra). Reportedly, the Dutch navy plans to replace its DUAV 4s with HS 12s, but funds are not yet available. The Swedish upgrade involves improved signal processing and MMI, using a SADANG processor. The acoustics, already optimized for the Baltic, will not be changed. The prototype upgrade was ordered 1988 and delivered April 1992. South Africa bought both the Super Frelon and the Puma; some may carry dipping sonars. Israel bought the Super Frelon and may have bought some French dipping sonars. The Libyan Super Frelons are reported no longer flyable.

◆ DUBA 3

This 22.6–28.6-kHz (21.4 or 29.8 kHz at reduced power) attack (searchlight) sonar controls 305mm mortars; SQS-17 (which shares the same dome) is the associated search sonar. Peak power is 4 kW (source level 126 dB), pulse lengths 10–30 (11–33 yd) or 100 msec (100 yd). Sonar outputs are elevation (target depth), bearing, and radial speed (Doppler of a single ping).

Users: Portugal (*Commandante Rivière* class), Uruguay (*Commandante Rivière* class).

◆ DUBA 25 (TSM 2400)

This 8/9/10-kHz digital hull sonar was specially designed for use in coastal waters (on the continental shelf). It was designated an attack sonar because it was associated with the Bofors ASW

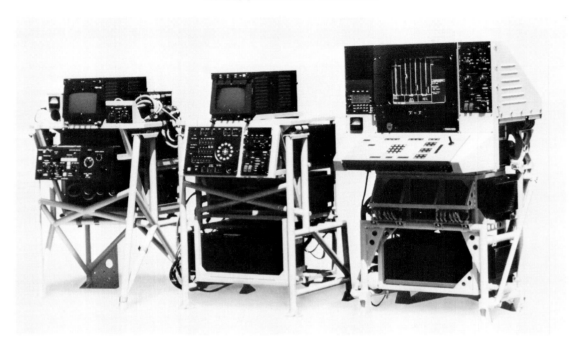

The Thomson Sintra family of helicopter dipping sonars. They are (*left to right*) DUAV 4, HS 12, and HS 312. (Thomson Sintra)

launcher of the A 69 class. The 1.1m (1500 kg) -dia 36-stave cylindrical transducer (nine elements/stave) produces 36 beams (each 10 deg wide). Pulses (CW or FM) are 30 or 90 msec long. Range scales are 3, 6, and 9 kyd. The display is a PPI. The operator can filter one preformed beam to reject a narrow frequency band centered on the transmission frequency, to reduce clutter and reverberation (limiting returns to those sufficiently Doppler-shifted). For attack, special fine-bearing circuits are used, together with an auxiliary B-scan showing one beamwidth and one-eighth of the full range scale.

Development began in the late 1960s, Thomson Sintra received the R&D contract in 1970, and development was complete by 1974.

Users: France (C70AA and A 69 classes). DUBA 25 was adopted for the destroyers because they could not accommodate the big DUBV 23/43.

◆ DUBV 23/43

This 4.9–5.4-kHz (four frequencies) hull/VDS combination was designed to counter quiet, deep-diving diesel submarines, that is, relatively slow targets, to achieve reliable direct-path ranges of 10–15 km, without seeking bottom-bounce or convergence-zone performance, and to support the Malafon standoff missile and the Lynx torpedo-delivering helicopter (which reacquires the target using its own dipping sonar). Tactical-data processing was limited to a noninteractive display. Modes: ODT, strip surveillance, sector surveillance, passive search at sonar frequency, panoramic attack, and directional (pseudo-searchlight) attack. The 48-stave transducer produces 15-deg beams and has a power output of 96 kW (pulse lengths 4, 30, 150, and 700 msec). Reported performance: 50% probability of detection of a 200ft target at 8000 yd, or against a periscope depth target at 14,000 yd. Accuracy in range is 150 yd +/−1% of the range scale; accuracy in bearing is 1 deg; and accuracy in speed is better than 0.4 kt on the 0–10-kyd scale, or 1 kt on the 0–30-kyd scale. Reportedly, the French consider this sonar superior to the U.S. SQS-23.

The 24-stave transducer (192 elements, 8/stave) in the stabilized fish can operate either independently or synchronized with DUBV 23, in scanning or in attack mode. Frequency, beamwidth, and power output match those of DUBV 23. Work began in 1988 on a modification (DUBV 43C) for deeper operation (700 m), using a new transducer (developed by GERDSM), with a new signal

DUBV 43 fish, on board the experimental destroyer *La Galissonière.* (U.S. Naval Institute)

processor (UTCS). This increase adds four months to the period during the year when the sonar pair can cover the full depth of the Mediterranean. Tow speed is 4–24 kt. More recently, an adjunct signal processor (UTCS) has been added.

The DUBV 23/43 requirement was issued in 1963/64; Sintra-Alcatel used DUBV 24 as a building block. DUBV 23 was developed in 1964–67, and the upgraded DUBV 23D was tested in 1977. DUBV 43 was approved for service in 1969, and an upgrade program was begun in the early 1970s. Tests followed in 1977.

China makes the DUBV 23/43 combination under license (DUBV 23 is SJD-7).

Users:

    DUBV 23: China (Modified Luda class, "Jiangwei" class), France (*Suffren*, first four *Georges Leygues* class [last three have DUBV 24C], *Tourville* class, *Aconit*).

    DUBV 43: China (Modified Luda class), France (seven *Georges Leygues*, three *Tourville*, two *Suffren* classes and *Aconit, La Galissonière, Duperre*). DUBV 43C may still be limited to the *Georges Leygues* class. In the last three ships of the *Georges Leygues* class (D 644–646) and in *Dupleix*, the fish tows a DSBV 61A array.

◆ **DUBV 24**

The 5-kHz DUBV 24 is a slightly less powerful version of DUBV 23 using the 24-stave (8 transducers/stave) transducer developed for the unsuccessful commercial SS 24 to form 24 beams (15 deg wide). DUBV 24 was one of the first French preformed-beam sonars. Modes are: ODT (with six audio beams), TRDT (three-ping), single-beam RDT, searchlight transmit-receive for attack, ODT for attack (to deal with fast targets), and passive. SS 24 (hence, probably, DUBV 24) source level was 223 dB (ODT)/232 dB (RDT). It used three frequencies around 5 kHz.

Users: France (last three *Georges Leygues*–class frigates).

◆ **DUUA 1A/B/C**

This 13.5–30-kHz (six bands; high-power element at 17 kHz; passive 2–40 kHz) submarine searchlight sonar forms an 8.5 × 8-deg beam. Pulse widths (high power): 8, 20, and 150 msec (power levels 100 or 400 W). Range scales: 2, 4, and 6 km. The transducer can scan manually or automatically. Of three transducer mountings, MSS-1 and -2 scan in azimuth at 15 deg/sec; MSS-4 scans at 30 deg/sec. Elevation limits are −100/+30 deg: MSS-1 and -2 scan at three speeds (maximum 9 deg/sec); -4 does not scan in elevation. A is the basic version; B is a double sonar; and C is an intermediate sonar.

Users: France (*Daphne, Agosta* classes; not on nuclear submarines), Pakistan (*Daphne, Agosta* classes), South Africa (*Daphne* class), and Spain (*Daphne, Agosta* classes).

◆ **DUUA 2A/B/D**

Thomson Sintra's 8-kHz searchlight pinger was conceived for the modernized *Daphne* class (development completed 1966).

DUUA 2A occupies the bow sonar dome of the French *Daphne*-class submarine *Sirene*, 1995. (H&L van Ginderen)

The DUUA 2D is the pinger of the Eledone system. DUUA 2B is a passive adjunct placed in service in 1979. The flat octagonal array (88 transducers: outer rows of six and eight, with six inner rows of 10 each, beamwidth about 10 deg) can tilt and rotate on its MSS-5 mounting. The pinger can operate in searchlight mode (as a tracker) or its scanning beam (4 or 8 deg/sec between −H175 and +175 deg, elevation limits −30/+15 deg) can be received by the associated passive array (DSUV 2H or Eledone), or it can be an intercept sonar. Pulses are CW or FM (30–500 msec, depending on mode, 30 kW, 1.5 kW in reduced-power mode). Range scales are 3, 6, 12, or 24 km. The console has a single CRT, for an A-scope (range vs. amplitude).

DUUA 2B is housed in a smaller sonar dome, operating in either narrow band (500 Hz at 2–15 kHz) or broad band (2.5–15 kHz).

The 5-kHz DUUA 2D (source level 215 dB in search mode, 4 kW peak power) can be used as a passive receiver (1–6 kHz) if the main hull array fails. It incorporates an 8–11-kHz underwater telephone. Unambiguous range is 100–1400 m.

Users: Colombia (Type 209), Ecuador (Type 209), France (-2A in *Daphne*; -2B and -2D in *Agosta* and *Amethyste* classes), Pakistan (*Daphne* class; -2B in *Agosta*; -2D in *Agosta* 90), Peru (Type 209), South Africa (*Daphne* class), Spain (*Daphne* class; -2B in *Agosta* class), Venezuela (Type 209). As of 1994, a total of 22 DUUA 2A, 14 DUUA 2B, and 8 DUUA 2D in service; some submarines carried both -2A and -2B. These figures do not count -2Ds integrated into foreign Eledone and successor systems.

◆ **DUUV 23**

This SSBN predecessor to Eledone, sonar multifunction (SMF), uses a digital beam-former working with a big bow cylinder nearly identical to that of DUBV 23 (modified for the pressure of great depths). It is not an integrated sonar, but it seems to have been the first French multifunction sonar to serve a digital CDS. Operation is mainly passive, and the system offers no analysis and no CMA. As in Eledone, there is a separate active element, in this case a cylinder rather than a planar array. The SSBNs also carry separate passive ranger (DUUX 5) and towed array (DSUV 61). Attempts to develop a flank array for these ships were abandoned after trials on board *Narval* about 1970 revealed excessive self-noise. About a decade later the discovery of PVDF and great improvements in processing made flank arrays practicable, and they became a priority for the next-generation SSBN *Le Triomphant*. DUUV 23 was originally designated DSUX 21.

Users: France (*L'Inflexible* and *Le Redoutable*-class SSBNs).

◆ **DUUX 2A/B/C**

This 5/7/12/18-kHz passive triangulation range-finder was developed in the late 1950s; until 1980 it was standard on Type 209 submarines. Direction is determined by the delay (phase difference) in reception between three transducers on each side (20–36m baseline), as measured in a correlator/integrator using variable delay lines. Over a 90-deg arc on each side, accuracy is 1.5 deg in azimuth and 1% in range at 1–5 km (2.5% at 5–10 km, 5% at 10–20 km, and 10% at 20–30 km). DUUX 2C was a special version for the German navy.

DUUX 5 is the successor.

Users: Argentina (Type 209), Brazil (*Oberon*), Chile (*Oberon*), Ecuador (Type 209), France (*Daphne* [2A], *Rubis* [2B], *Agosta* [2B], *Redoutable* classes), Germany (Type 206 [2C]; 2A was tested on board the experimental *Wilhelm Bauer*), Greece (Type 209), Pakistan (*Agosta* [2B], *Daphne* [2A] classes), Peru (Type 209 [2C]), Portugal (*Daphne* class), Peru (Type 209), South Africa (*Daphne* [2A] class), Spain (*Agosta* [2A], *Daphne* [2A] classes), Turkey (Type 209), and Venezuela (Type 209). The British designation was Type 2005; it was replaced in Australian and Canadian service by MicroPUFFS. A total of 120 were supplied to 14 navies for eight classes of submarines.

◆ **DUUX 5 (FENELON)/TSM 2255**

This 2–15-kHz third-generation (digital, with integral microprocessor) replacement for the DUUX 2 range-finder automatically detects and tracks up to three contacts in a 120-deg sector on either side of the submarine (bearing accuracy 0.3 deg abeam, resolution 2 deg abeam and 4 deg at 60 deg fore or aft of the beam, range accuracy 5% at 10 km). A fourth target can be tracked by means of an acoustic intercept receiver (the computer apparently limits the system to four noise sources and two sonar emitters). Target course and speed are automatically calculated from range and bearing. DUUX 5 can do LOFAR and DEMON processing simultaneously at several frequencies between 2 and 10 kHz, to handle multiple targets. Displays include a 20-min target track history, to assist in classification. Data can be transferred automatically to the submarine's FCS.

DUUX 5 array, one of three on each side of the submarine. (Thomson Sintra)

DUUX 5 display. Each half covers a 120-deg sector, with bearing running along the horizontal axis and time along the vertical. Radiated noise spectra can be displayed vertically on the right-hand side. (Thomson Sintra)

Two types of spot transducers are available. Maximum baseline is 48 m. The current TSM 2255 version is integrated with Eledone/Scylla. Array size is 0.2–1.0 × 0.2–0.6 m. This version can track eight noise sources and eight sonars.

DUUX 5 was developed for French nuclear attack submarines. The development contract was let in the mid-1970s, the prototype being tested in 1977.

Users: Argentina (TR-1700 class), Australia (TSM 2255 in *Collins* class), China (Han class SSN, Xia class SSBN, one modified Romeo [two sets exported 1983; this sonar may be locally produced]; probably on Ming class), France (*L'Inflexible* and *Redoutable* class SSBNs, TSM 2255 in *Amethyste*-class SSNs), India (Type 1500 class), Norway (probably in *Ula* class), Pakistan (TSM 2255 in *Agosta* 90 class), Spain (*Agosta* class, replacing DUUX 2). The advertised export version of the Chinese Romeo includes both DUUX 5 and an enlarged chin sonar dome (presumably carrying a French cylindrical array). DUUX 5 may also be part of the sonar suite of the E58G design offered for export (carrying six C801 missiles).

The French navy may also use DUUX 3, which measures vertical AoA based on time difference of arrival.

◆ **Diodon (TSM 2630)/Sorel (TSM 2630)/Salmon (TSM 2640)**

The 11/12/13-kHz TSM 2630 sonar (Diodon hull version, Sorel VDS version) was conceived as a half-cost alternative to DUBA 25, using the same display, but operating at higher frequency for reduced size, and with 24 rather than 36 staves (48 preformed beams). It was an early application of digital technology. Bow transducer and VDS share common information handling and signal processing but can transmit independently. Pulses are CW and hyperbolic FM (20 or 80 msec, maximum source level 123 dB, can operate at reduced power; range scales 2–16 kyd). Operating modes: ODT, RDT, SRDT (sector RDT), and SDT. Signal processing: linear integration filtering (to accommodate Doppler speeds of up to 30 kt) and coherent processing (of FM pulses, which can show fine target structure, with range definition of 1.5 m). One target can be autotracked, using a pair of adjacent steered beams. One beam or an adjacent pair (for tracking) can have their echoes Doppler-enhanced, to eliminate reverberation. As in DUBA 25, a separate attack display shows a 20-deg sector over a quarter of the full range scale, centered on the position of a surveillance marker on the PPI. The special display gives range to within 1% and bearing to within 1 deg. A separate Doppler display (1 kt resolution) is used for target following.

Sorel medium-frequency VDS fish. (Thomson Sintra)

Built-in fault-detection equipment can isolate a fault to within five circuit boards. Estimated MTBF is 500 hr, and MTTR is 15 min.

The Sorel fish is launched/recovered at 4–10 kt and typically operated at 14 kt (maximum tow speed is 20 kt).

TSM 2365 is an upgrade kit for Diodon, incorporating Spherion (TSM 2633) features (36 preformed beams). It is probably being incorporated in the modernized Saudi *Al Madinah* class. A Mangouste 40-MOPS signal processor, a proprietary BALUS proc-

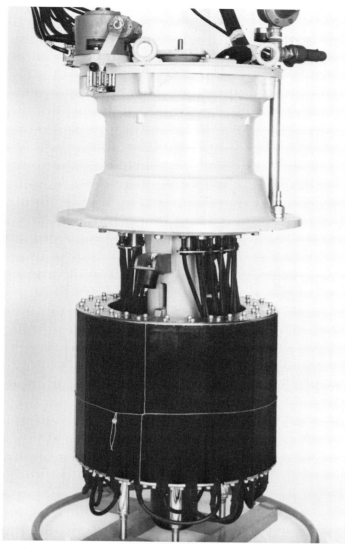

Diodon hull array. (Thomson Sintra)

The French Salmon VDS fish. A model of the standard handling equipment is in the background of the side view. (Author)

essor (using 68000-series CPUs), and an RS6000 COTS processor are inserted. The modernized sonar uses two new 1280 × 1024-pixel consoles with keyboards and rollerballs, offering enhanced analysis of sonar echoes. The modified sonar has two FM (hyperbolic and TRDT) and one CW modes. Improved processing in hyperbolic FM and coherent processing in the TRDT mode increase the figure of merit by 7 dB in both modes, increasing range by 25–45%. New functions include ADT; ray path/probability of detection calculation; target simulation for training. Modernization also adds a torpedo alert (Albatros) and an interactive computer-aided classification and identification system (Inca). Range scales: 1, 2, 4, 8, 12, 16 km.

The 12-kHz (three-frequency) Salmon is a lightweight (550-kg fish) higher-powered (217 dB: CW and FM pulses; ODT only) dismountable Sorel for small patrol ships, also using a 24-stave transducer (290mm dia, 150 kg) with 48 (24 using CW) preformed beams. Maximum instrumented range is 12 kyd. Three targets can be tracked simultaneously. Launch, operating, and survival speeds match those for Sorel. Maximum depth is nearly 300 ft. The towing/handling mechanical assembly weighs 5.2 t.

The modernized TSM 2643 uses a 24-stave (7 elements/stave) cylindrical array operating at two frequencies around 19 kHz to produce 36 preformed beams. As in Spherion, it offers 64-track capacity and double-zoom target analysis to measure the apparent length and aspect of a target as well as an integrated ray tracer and range predictor. Range scales are 2, 4, 8, 12, and 16 km. The VDS version weighs 7630 kg.

Spherion (see separate entry below) is an upgraded version of Diodon with a spherical rather than a cylindrical transducer.

Work began in 1969, and Diodon ran sea trials in 1971. Salmon development began in the late 1970s, the first test following in 1985. Reported unit cost (1994) is $3M.

Users:

Diodon/Sorel: Argentina (A 69–class corvettes), Ecuador (*Wadi M'ragh* class), India (TSM 2630 with Sorel in *Nilgiri* class), Malaysia (ex-Iraqi *Wadi M'ragh* class: TSM 2630 version), Portugal (*Baptiste de Andrade* class), Saudi Arabia (TSM 2630 with Sorel in *Al Madinah*-class frigates).

Salmon: Denmark (*Thetis* and *Flyvefisken* classes), Finland (one ship, probably *Hameenmaa*), Singapore (*Victory* class [not EDO 786, as has been reported]), Sweden (*Stockholm* and *Goteborg* classes, the latter with the TSM 2643 version).

◆ FLASH (TSM 8260)

The Folding Light Acoustic System for Helicopters opens its array underwater to produce 24 preformed beams at three frequencies below 5 kHz (the U.S. ALFS version reportedly operates at 1.2–5.6 kHz). The associated processor can handle 8 or 16 sonobuoys. Thomson Sintra and STN Atlas are developing a scaled-down version for the NH 90 (Lynx successor) shipboard helicopter.

Users: France (presumably to replace HS-12 on Super Frelons, using a French processor), United Kingdom (Type 2095, using a

Ferranti processor), United States (ALFS, using a Hughes dry end). FLASH won the Canadian NSA (New Seaborne Aircraft) competition, but the helicopter was later canceled.

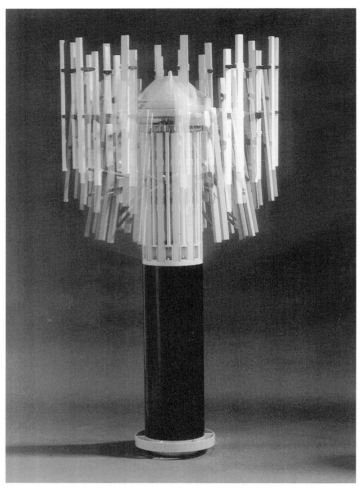

A time-lapse photograph shows the FLASH array in different stages of extension. (Thomson Sintra)

FLASH and its reeling machine. The array has been folded. (Author)

◆ HS 12 (TSM 8252)/SS 12/DIP 12/HS 312 (TSM 8240-1-2-3)/ SS 312/Gudgeon (TSM 2362)

Thomson Sintra's 11.5/13/14.5-kHz (7–20-kHz passive) helicopter dipping sonar was developed from the company's small-ship SS 12 VDS. The associated processor is TSM 8251. The 12-stave

transducer produces 12 preformed beams, usually displayed as four quadrants, each showing (in CW mode) target range and Doppler (up to 40 kt). In sector mode, the three beams are shown for target tracking (two targets simultaneously). In FM mode, range is so precise that target motion can be seen from sweep to sweep. Rated maximum range is 10+ km. Maximum depth is 300 m (figure of merit 175 dB) and a typical reel rate is 5 m/sec.

HS 12 on a Lynx helicopter. The dipping body and winch are on the left, the control panel on the right. (Thomson Sintra)

Thomson Sintra claims that HS 12 is currently the lightest helicopter sonar in the world (508 lb: 121-lb transducer/dome, 42-lb cable, 158-lb hydraulic winch, 187 lb for display, control, and processing). The 33-lb sonar dome is 10.3 in in max dia and 33.7 in long. HS 12 can be removed from any helicopter in less than 45 min.

SS 12 is a 13-kHz (three frequency ranges, source level 212 dB) hull and VDS equivalent for FAC and corvettes, competing with TSM 2640 Salmon. Range scales are 2, 4, 8, and 16 km or kyd. The variable-depth fish can operate at 600 ft and at speeds of up to 16 kt.

HS 312 is HS 12 integrated with a four- or eight-sonobuoy processor based on SADANG. An SS 312 small-boat towed version (February 1991) attracted no buyers.

Gudgeon (TSM 2362 for hull or VDS, probably an HS 312 derivative), announced in 1992, uses an unusually tall 0.2m-dia transducer, presumably to form beams in the vertical, for example to avoid surface or bottom reflections. The 12-stave (6 elements/stave) cylindrical transducer produces 18 bearing-stabilized preformed beams at about 13 kHz. Track capacity is 64, and range scales are 1, 2, 4, 8, 12, and 16 km. As in Spherion, this sonar offers double-zoom target analysis to measure the apparent length and aspect of a target, as well as an integrated ray tracer and range predictor. As in other sonars in this series, transmission (CW and FM) is ODT only (but RDT and TRDT are options). Targets are automatically detected (passive ones by ALI) and tracked; the display shows synthetic video or multiple pings. The system includes an acoustic path tracer and performance predictor.

Users:

HS 12: Finland (two on Cougars, others on at least six Mi-8 and -14 helicopters; two more ASW Super Pumas ordered 1991), France (at least 30 on board Super Frelons and Lynxes, with more as DUAV 4 is replaced on board Lynxes; total probably 60), Indonesia (two Pumas), Saudi Arabia (12 Dauphins), and Singapore (on at least five of 22 planned Super Pumas). Other Cougar/Super Puma naval operators who may use HS 12 are Brazil (six, plus nine on order), and Saudi Arabia (six). Not all of these helicopters necessarily carry sonars. The Finnish installation is interesting because other operators of Soviet naval helicopters may follow suit. It is not clear whether any of the reported eight Iraqi Super Frelons (with sonars) survive.

HS 312 (TSM 8240–43): Chile (three Super Pumas), China (three for Super Frelons, with more being made locally for further Zhi-8 Super Frelons, for Zhi-9 Dauphin IIs for shipboard operation, and for Harbin SH-5 flying boats), France (four), India (24 on Mk 42B Sea Kings), Thailand (nine, Chinese-built, on Zhi-9 helicopters), UAE (seven upgraded Pumas and seven shipboard Panthers, all ordered 1995). The Chinese sonars may be HS 12s; if they really are HS 312s, that would seem to imply an additional sale of French sonobuoys. HS 312 was announced as the standard sonar of Super Puma naval helicopters, but they apparently carry HS 12 instead. Some sonars listed as HS 312 may in fact be HS 12s, sometimes upgraded (FoM 177 dB).

SS 12: China (both prototypes: they are on board Haijui-class patrol boats 688 and 697 [sold 1987]).

Gudgeon: Singapore (*Fearless*-class patrol boats).

◆ Alura

DCNI's onboard classification system uses software designed to run on standard computers. It accepts one, two, or four-channel analog input or digital input (stored signals) at up to 1, 2, 5, 10 or 20 kHz, performing spectral analysis (256-, 512-, 1024-, or 2048-point FFT). Modes are baseband, zoom, one-third octave, and demodulation (DEMON); display modes are waterfall (broad-band), instantaneous spectrum (spectrogram), average spectrum (LOFARgram), and transfer function (instantaneous/average). Cursors: simple, cross (comparison of two frequencies), harmonic, modulation, and Doppler. Audio channel: real-time or postprocessing, with variable filter and speed. Classification software differentiates automatically between different types of noise and separates out essential components (stationary sources, lines, broad-band, transients). Alura uses two CPUs, a RISC processor, and a C30 DSP. DCNI claims that Alura is the first system designed not only for passive classification but also for self-noise monitoring and acoustic maintenance (to allow shipyards to measure a ship's radiated noise).

Users: France (all SSBNs and SSNs and *Georges Leygues* class). Alura is used both for self-noise measurement (15 channels can be switched among its four) and for sonar analysis.

◆ INCA

The new (1995) Thomson Sintra/SAES INCA (Interactive Classification Aid) module can be integrated with any sonar; it works on the basis of the spectral character of radiated noise. INCA can be used at a shore site supporting MPA, using mass-stored mission data. INCA spectrally analyzes (LOFAR, vernier, DEMON, ALI, or spectrogram) current or stored signals (speeds: 8, 4, 2, 1, $\frac{1}{2}$, $\frac{1}{4}$, $\frac{1}{8}$ real-time). It gathers classification parameters based on spectral and/or audio analysis. It then selects possible matches from its stored "album" of signatures, and provides the user with a confidence level for every hypothesis (it sorts hypotheses by confidence level).

◆ PFAS (TSM 2253)

PVDF Planar Flank Array Sonar consists of 32 or 64 polyvinylidene fluoride (PVDF) panels (each 0.42 × 1.13 × 0.1 m), each acting as a single 10 Hz–3 kHz transducer (frequency depends on panel size; narrower staves are effective to 5 kHz). The array as a whole forms 64 beams. The system automatically detects and tracks up to 64 targets (plus eight operator-initiated ones). The 30m flank array prototype uses a 2.5–3 kHz beam-former to produce 5-deg wide beams which can be steered through 60 deg in the vertical to avoid surface noise. To overcome self-noise, the array uses an electronic noise-canceller, driven by an accelerometer on the hull. Flow and vibration noise are reduced by averaging the noise pattern, in effect, over a wide surface. Thomson Sintra claims that this array is the first to be applied directly to the hull. PVDF was announced in 1988. A continous sheet of alternating piezoelectric film and metallic electrodes replaces conventional ceramic hydrophones. Trials showed a better signal-to-noise ratio than conventional hydrophones, with response up to 5 kHz (and a theoretical limit of 10 kHz). Sea trials of the

A planar array on a French submarine. (Thomson Sintra)

production version began in September 1992 on board the French nuclear submarine *Saphir*.

In the *Le Triomphant* class, PVDF is used for a WAA-type beam-forming passive ranging array (earlier passive rangers used triplets of spot hydrophones). Unlike spot hydrophones, PVDF need not be mounted in fairings protecting it from flow noise (but which themselves create drag and add flow noise). Thomson Sintra expects to use PVDF in future semiconformal bow arrays, to replace the current cylinders and spheres.

Users: Australia (*Collins* class), France (*Le Triomphant* class, for passive ranger), Norway (one *Ula*-class submarine, a previous generation type, TSM 2285).

◆ Spherion (TSM 2633)

Thomson Sintra's Spherion, announced in 1985, derives its name from its spherical shape, which is covered by 160 spot transducers. Like TSM 2630, it is offered in both hull and VDS forms. The 10–13-kHz (three or four spot frequencies) VDS, using a Salmon transmitter (217-dB ODT, 227-dB directional mode; there is also a sector directional mode) and a 1.15m sphere (1830 kg: 36 preformed 10- or 15-deg beams stabilized in azimuth and elevation) came first. Pulses are CW (768 Doppler channels) and FM (pulse-compression ratio 300:1). Track capacity is 25. The system measures apparent target length, inclination, and Doppler. System weight is 6000 kg.

Spherion array. (Thomson Sintra)

Spherion B (TSM 2633) is the 6–8-kHz hull version, also producing 36 preformed beams. This version also uses a 1.15m sphere (1860 kg). Track capacity is 64. Range scales: 2, 4, 8, 16, 24, 32 km. A double-zoom target analysis function measures apparent target length and aspect. This version includes an integrated ray tracer and range predictor, and it transmits its data to the ship's CDS. The Mk 2 version for the ANZACs has a TRDT mode to increase its source level by 6 dB, and incorporates a torpedo warner. In 1993, reported cost was $3.5–4M ($6–6.5M for the hull-VDS integrated version).

Users: Australia (ANZAC class, using Spherion B), India (last two *Nilgiri* class and two *Delhi* class; two delivered March 1991), Malaysia (*Lekiu* class), New Zealand (ANZAC class, using Spherion B), Norway (*Oslo* class, with both hull transducer and higher-frequency VDS), Saudi Arabia (*La Fayette* class), Taiwan (*La Fayette* class).

◆ **TSM 5421/5423/5424**

Thomson Sintra's TSM 5421 mine-avoidance sonar is typically mounted in the upper bow of a submarine, scanning mechanically at 8 deg/sec over a 60- or 120-deg sector which can be swung over a 175-deg arc on either side. The cylindrical transducer (0.5 × 0.5 m) transmits a 30 × 15-deg beam and receives on ten preformed beams (each 3.2 × 15 deg). Range scales: 50, 150, 500, 1500 m. There is also a passive mode (38 kHz, 8 × 40-deg manually directed beam) to receive special pinger signals. Large obstacles are detected at 1000 m, and small ones (such as moored mines 1 m in diameter) at 600 m (12-dB reflection index).

TSM 5423 uses a pair of arrays at right angles, each 0.6 × 0.15 × 0.15 m, to cover a 60 × 30-deg sector in detection (mine bearing) and classification (mine depth) modes. Range is 650 m for a −12dB target. This is the standard mine-avoidance sonar of the DMUX 20 integrated system.

TSM 5424 (Petrel) is an analogous surface-ship sonar, also using two arrays (the vertical one much longer than the horizontal below it) at right angles. In obstacle avoidance mode, it automatically detects obstacles in 3D, provides a CPA, and offers a preferred heading to the helm. Coverage is 60 × 12 deg, steerable over +/−180 deg in heading; range is over 500m. The sonar can be used at up to 12 kt. As of the fall of 1996, Petrel was under development. See also the Mine Warfare section below.

UNDERWATER FIRE-CONTROL SYSTEMS

◆ **DLT/DLA/TSM 2072**

Direction Lance Torpilles and Direction de Lancement d'Armes are, respectively, submarine and surface-ship digital torpedo FCSs built around standard CDS computers. The submarine D (digital) series replaces earlier analog (S-series) TDCs. Surface-ship types are in an L-series corresponding to the D-series from which it is derived. D3A (IRIS 35M computer) is typical. It tracks eight targets and guides two torpedoes while preparing a third for firing. The three side-by-side displays are: tactical situation, firing path, and alphanumeric data. There are two keyboards; typically two operators sit at the console in the control room, with a third in the torpedo room. Recent DLAs use 15M125 computers (they may be D3Bs).

The surface-ship equivalent is L 5, as in the Saudi *Madinah* class. It can display two target tracks but can control only a single torpedo (if both targets must be attacked, one torpedo must be fired on a preset track). The computer is a 15M125.

S4E is the surviving version of the analog submarine system (the surface ship equivalent is L 4C). It controls Z 16, E 14/15, and L 3 torpedoes. Roughly equivalent to the U.S. Mk 106 or TDC, S4E bases its solution on a series of bearings plus occasional single-ping ranges. Control room elements are the RZ-1 bearing relay (from sonar), the GZ-2 bearing plotter, the PRR-2 track plotter, the CONJ-1 computer, and the QLT-3 torpedo ballistic computer. The relative target track derived from the bearing plot is plotted on the PRR-2, from which track data are derived for the CONJ-1, which corresponds to the position-keeper element of U.S. analog submarine FCSs. Apparently ranges are inserted only at this stage.

Agosta CIC, showing the torpedo FCS display (DLT), DUUX 5, and the panoramic (integrated) sonar displays. (Thomson Sintra)

TSM 2072 integrates DLT-D3 or the Signaal M8/Sinbad with a submarine sensor system. It manages acoustic and nonacoustic tracks, compiles and evaluates a tactical picture, and controls weapons (German, U.S., French, or British). Software written in C and ADA runs on 68020 and 68040 CPUs using a VME bus. The workstations can be Colibris or MOCs. According to Thomson Marconi, as of the fall of 1996, this system was operational at sea, most likely on board French-built submarines.

Users: Argentina (L 4C in A 69 class), France (D3B in *Amethyste* class [replaces D2B], D3A in *Agosta* class and modernized *Daphne* class, D4A in *Le Triomphant*, D1A in earlier SSBNs; L4C in *Georges Leygues* class [D 640–643], *Cassard* class, *Tourville* class, *Aconit* class, A 69 class; L 5 in later *Georges Leygues* class [D 644–646]), Portugal (L 4C in *Joao Belo* class, S4E in *Daphne* class [some may have D3A]), Saudi Arabia (digital DLA in *Al Madinah* class), Spain (D3A in *Agosta* class, S4E in *Daphne* class), Pakistan (D3A in *Agosta* class), and Uruguay (L4C in *Commandante Rivière* class).

◆ **SYVA/SYTIT**

DCNI's SYVA is a stand-alone towed-array TMA/tactical advisor for surface ships and submarines. It acquires sonar track data and own-ship data, displays tracks in azimuth and in frequency, and does track management (creation, labeling, exchange, and removal). It conducts TMA, displays the tactical situation in PPI form (including tracking selected targets, recommending course, evaluating threats, showing go/no-go areas, displaying acoustic advantage, and providing torpedo alerts), and it can provide system control. SYVA incorporates software written for the earlier Digilog SYTIT (Système de Traitement des Informations Tactiques), which it supersedes in surface-ship applications. It is adapted to SLASM. It can handle more than 300 tracks, and can designate five targets simultaneously. It offers multiple TMA techniques and interactive aids. Software is modular, comprising an MMI, an external system interface, an applications toolkit, and common services. The toolkit contains TDAs, tactical situation synthesis, TMA, and environment data processing. The interface to external systems accepts data from sonars, from Aidcomer, from the ship's CDS, and from a target classification system such as Alura. Common software services are supervision/ communications/data management, media storage/replay/ simulation, and history/recording/graphic/interface tools. Basic software is written in UNIX, X-Windows, Motif, and TCP-IP.

The current processor is a ruggedized SunSPARC, but in December 1996 SYVA is to be rehosted on an AIX workstation (PowerPC).

SYTIT survives in submarines. It employs 68000-series processors for graphics and system control and a SPARC processor. The submarine version, SYTIT(M), uses fully militarized equipment, and its pair of monochrome (showing yellow and green by switching polarization) CRT consoles typically flank a larger PPI display console.

SYTIT is still being marketed, as SEXTET (Exploitation Tactique de l'ETBF) with a 3D acoustic processor, ETIA (Exploitation et Traitement des Informatives Acoustiques). The submarine version shares ETIA with the surface version.

Users:

SYVA: France (*Tourville* class, *Dupleix, La Motte-Picquet, Primauguet, Latouche-Treville, Aconit*).
SYTIT(M): France (submarines).

GERMANY

Sonars

Virtually all German sonars are produced by Krupp Atlas Elektronik GmBH (KAE), which later became Atlas Elektronik and which in 1994 merged with other firms to become STN (SystemTeknikNord) Atlas Elektronik. Both companies had been members of the Electronics and Systems Technology Division of Bremer Vulkan; the new company remains part of the Bremer Vulkan Group.

Note that CSU is a commercial designation, meaning compact sonar for U-boats. The German navy uses DSQS and DBQS designations.

German submarine sonars fall into four generations: (a) unintegrated suites consisting of passive arrays (based on the wartime GHG) and trainable active planar-array attack sonars (counted by STN as two generations, prototype and production); (b) integrated sonars (CSU 3, for third-generation compact sonar U-boat) in which both arrays and a sonar intercept receiver feed a single console; (c) Standard Sonar 80 (ASO 80, CSU 83: DSQS-21 and DBQS-21D in German navy service) added a passive ranger (PRS in its stand-alone version), a spectral (LOFAR/DEMON) processor (sonar information processor: SIP 3), and applied beam-preforming; and (d) Standard Sonar 90 (DSQS-23, DBQS-21DG) in which all arrays, including towed and flank arrays, feed a common bus; it provides integrated TMA.

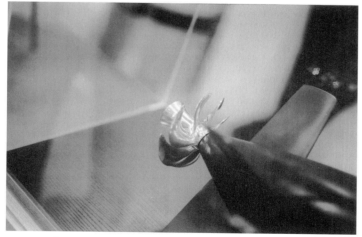

Sonar performance involves silencing. The model of the new German Type 212 submarine displayed at Bourget Euronaval 1996 showed this unusual silenced propeller. (Author)

◆ Unintegrated Sonars (GHG, AN 407, AN 410)

These analog sonars combine a 1–10-kHz passive conformal array (GH, Gruppen-Horch, listening array) descended from the wartime GHG with a trainable active planar array attack sonar

in the sail. The initial AN 526 had horseshoe-shaped bow arrays (288 elements in 96 groups of three each, covering a 300-deg sector) and 19-element stern arrays. Unfortunately, individual staves could easily be knocked out of alignment and were difficult to replace. The successor cylindrical AN 5039 is no longer in service, all submarines built with it having had their sonars replaced. Signal processing was analog only; the display was a CRT, typically alongside that of the active element. In at least some cases, hydrophone output was in six bands between 350 Hz and 3.2 kHz, all six being displayed above the main PPI as an aid to frequency analysis and classification. The single scanning beam was formed by delay lines and a compensator. The sonar could scan continuously, or it could track one target, using sum/difference circuits to keep it within 1 deg of the appropriate direction. Using a correlator, it could autotrack.

The AN 407 (M1H) 8–12-kHz active element is a trainable and elevatable planar-array sail transducer consisting of six brick-shaped elements, each containing six radially polarized ceramic tubes (active surface area about 1000 cm^2). It can operate independently, or its echoes can be detected by the passive array. AN 407 has a single CRT, presumably an A-scan.

Associated with these sonars were French sonar intercept receivers (DUUG 1A/AUUD 1C) and passive rangers (DUUX 2C) and Signaal fire controls (M 8/8).

Users: Argentina (Type 209s), Greece (later four Type 209s). The Greek boats are being fitted with CSU 83.

◆ CSU 3 and PRS 3 Series

The single CRT of the integrated third-generation system can switch between the active and passive sonars and a German-made ISK sonar intercept receiver. There is also an audio channel. For example, an operator may identify a target by its sonar emission, then switch to the passive array for long-range tracking, and to the active array for short-range fire control. The active mode is displayed in 30-deg sector waterfalls. The intercept function can display up to eight pulses in the center of the CRT, plus data on bearing, frequency, signal level, and signal duration on one pulse. These pulses can also be presented on the audio channel. The 0.3–12-kHz passive bow array is a 24-stave (three elements/stave) cylinder (2.8m dia) with four analog trackers. Its beam can depress for bottom bounce. Effective frequency coverage of the initial version, CSU 3-2, is limited to about 3.5 kHz because it uses a scanning mechanical beam-former. CSU 3-4 has a digital beam-former, hence can pick up higher-frequency signals, up to 10 or 12 kHz. Neither version has a narrow-band analyzer.

The overlapping preformed beams of PRS 3-15. (KAE)

CSU 3-2 uses the 8-kHz (35-msec pulse) AN 410 planar active array of the later version of the unintegrated sonar: it forms overlapping 20-deg beams over a 110-deg sector, operating in ODT and RDT modes. CSU 3-4 uses a 96-stave cylinder (1m dia) to form beams digitally over a 30-deg sector (range 10 kyd). The 1–100-kHz intercept receiver uses three P7 hydrophones; it

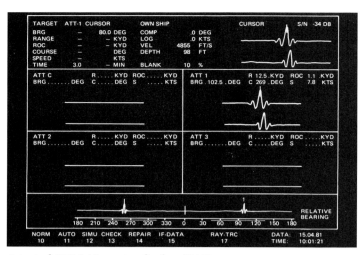

A typical PRS 3-15 ranging display. (KAE)

measures frequency, pulse rate, and amplitude. Its only display is the main CRT.

Specially intended for shallow water, this sonar system provides target elevation angle to estimate range and optimum sound ray path.

The PRS 3-15 (60 hydrophones/array in 15 staves) 2–8-kHz passive ranger (three arrays on each side) could replace the French DUUX 2 of early Type 209s. Tracking can be either manual or automatic (using the four ATT channels of CSU 3-4, which can be assigned by the main sensor). Targets can be tracked over a 170-deg arc on either beam (45–135 and 225–315 deg relative to the bow). PRS 3-15 directional accuracy is about 0.5 deg. As in the U.S. PUFFS system, range is measured by the curvature of the wavefront as indicated by time delays between the arrays. Course and speed are automatically calculated. STN claims that interference effects and other disturbances common in narrow-band systems are suppressed by using wide-band preformed beams. Effective range is 15 kyd. PRS 3-4 is a smaller version with 40 hydrophones/unit.

Development of CSU 3 began in 1963–64. The first units (CSU 3-2 passive only) were installed in German Type 205 submarines in 1966–68, after which an improved version was exported. PRS 3, roughly contemporary with CSU 3, was developed in 1961–65 and tested in 1965–66.

Users:

> CSU 3-2: Ecuador (two Type 209), Greece (four later Type 209), Indonesia (two Type 209), Peru (six Type 209), Turkey (six Type 209), Venezuela (two Type 209), and Yugoslavia (*Heroj* and *Sava* classes).
>
> CSU 3-4: Argentina (three TR 1700 class), Australia (CSU 3-41 in six *Oberons*), Canada (CSU 3-41 in three *Oberons*), Chile (two Type 209), Germany (18 Type 206, of which 12 were modernized with CSU 83), India (two SSK-1500), Israel (three Type 206), Sweden (five *Sjoormen* class), and Yugoslavia (two *Sava* class, probably bought through Italy). In all, 48 CSU 3 were made, not counting those for the German navy, so the two Argentine units as yet unbuilt were probably earmarked for the later CSU 83. The Type 206s originally had unintegrated sonars.
>
> PRS 3-4: Colombia (Type 209), Indonesia (Type 209), Germany (Type 206), Yugoslavia (*Sava* class, possibly standalone in *Heroj* class).
>
> PRS 3-15: Germany (Type 206A), Greece (Type 209), India (Type 1500), Israel (Type 540), Korea (Type 209), Norway (Type 210), Sweden (modernized submarines with CSU 83), Turkey (Type 209/1400), Venezuela (Type 209).

◆ Standard Sonar 80/ASO 80 (DSQS-21)/FAS 3-1/TAS 83-1

This series of submarine and surface-ship sonars share digital beam preformers and standard BM 802–series color displays (red for new targets, green for targets already being tracked, and gold for passive surveillance).

Console for a DSQS-21 sonar, showing a ray-trace indicator on the upper display and a PPI below it. (KAE)

CSU 83 sonar coverage, including three passive arrays on each side. (KAE)

The submarine version, CSU 83 (DBQS-21 for the German navy), uses CSU 3 arrays (including the passive ranger and intercept array) and two 0–12-kHz self-noise monitors (sail and engine room), the single BM 802 console replacing the earlier single monochrome CRT. Any of the three main sonars can initiate a track (spectral data are included in the track file). Passive autotrack capacity is eight targets using a dual-mode tracker (short integration time for short-range tracking, long integration time for long-range detection). The system's spider-web bus carries raw rather than processed acoustic data (German wire-guided torpedoes can supply their own raw video to the same bus). The active sonar feeds the bus directly; the passive sonar and ranger feed it through processors. The system's LOFAR/DEMON spectrum analyzer (SIP 3, the sonar information processor) initially had a paper gram recorder, but now has a CRT console (also used for passive ranging) to supplement the main system console. SIP can analyze data from four targets simultaneously, displaying them one by one. It offers automatic line tracking (ALT), automatic maneuver detection (by detecting line shifts), and high-resolution target bearing measurement. It may also be part of the automatic tracker and its spectral analyzer is used in some active sonar modes. The sources of signals detected could be identified using a mass storage signature library. SIP 3 can be retrofitted into the earlier CSU 3-4.

Intercept parameters in CSU 83 include pulse spectra and modulation type.

PSU 83 (DBQS-21F) is a modernized passive version of the old unintegrated small-submarine sonar using the old AN 526 horse-shoe array (bow and stern-sector); the key development seems to have been a beam-former suited to arrays of arbitrary shape, such as the horseshoe. It has the same automatic tracker as CSU 83 and has a single BM 802–series console. Bearing rate is measured on the waterfall (bearing-time) display. Target bearings are constantly predicted for emergency snapshots. The console can display ray traces. A high-quality audio channel is available for target classification. Further options: intercept sonar; flank array (using LOFAR processing); DEMON detection, tracking, and analysis; active pinger; passive ranger (PRS); own-noise analysis (ONA); mass storage for target data and display recording; sonar graphic recorder (bearing-time and frequency-time waterfalls); and on-board sonar trainer. STN Atlas markets the associated FCS as FSU 83; the integrated two-console (one for torpedo control) system is OSID 83.

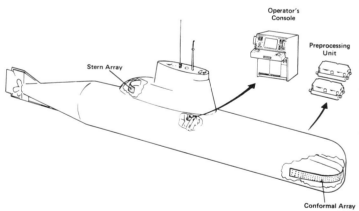

PSU 83. (KAE)

Increased interest in low-frequency (under 100 Hz) signals led to development of a supplemental stand-alone 48-stave (144-hydrophone) LF (10 Hz–2.5 kHz) flank array, FAS 3-1, with its own signal processor (eight broad-band, eight DEMON, and eight LOFAR channels). Protected from flow noise by a shell and backed by plastic to absorb structure-borne self-noise, the array on each side of a submarine can be 20 to 48 m long, depending on submarine length; a typical 30m array covers a 160-deg sector (bearing accuracy is 1 deg in the 90-deg beam sector). Typical maximum range is 50 kyd. There are two consoles (tracks and signal processor).

TAS 83 is a stand-alone clip-on towed array (150–1200-Hz broad-band, 10–1200-Hz LOFAR, 600–1200-Hz DEMON) using some FAS 3-1 technology suited to CSU 83, typically with an 80m acoustic aperture (128 beams covering 5–175 deg on each side, 2-deg bearing accuracy and resolution) on a 300m cable. TAS 83-2 (TAS 83-1) provide 8 (4) × 8-line multiline LOFAR trackers (MLT), 8 (4) broad-band detection and tracking chan-

nels, 16 (4) LOFAR classification channels, 8 (4) DEMON classification channels, one (no) target-related broad spectral analyzer, and one (no) transient noise detector (TND). TAS 3-2 was the corresponding surface-ship array.

DSQS-21/ASO 80, the corresponding hull and variable-depth sonars for surface ships, is intended primarily to operate in shallow water, often with a cluttered bottom. Versions are: DSQS-21A/ASO 86 (96 staves, 3.0m dia, 96 beams; 1.0m-dia VDS transducer) is for large destroyers, DSQS-21B/ASO 85 (64 staves, 1.8m dia, 64 beams; 1.0 or 0.58m-dia VDS transducer) for destroyers and frigates, DSQS-21C/ASO 84 for corvettes (32 beams hull and VDS; 1.0 or 0.58m-dia VDS transducer), and DSQS-21D/ASO 83 (32 staves, 0.95m dia, 32 beams hull and VDS [0.58m dia]; single display) for small ASW patrol vessels. In each case a Z suffix, as in DSQS-21BZ, indicates that the transducer is electronically stabilized against roll and pitch. Pulse lengths: 5 and 50 msec CW; 50 msec FM; and 5/50, 50/50, and 300/300 msec CW/FM. Range scales: 2-32 kyd in five brackets. On the PPI display, fixed navigational points (such as cliffs) are shown in yellow, approaching targets are in red, and retiring targets in green. Targets are detected automatically. New plots are correlated with past tracks to reduce the false-alarm rate and to distinguish new targets (a box around the expected next position of each target is examined; if it is empty, the track is dropped as unconfirmed). Track display capacity: three active or passive. As in CSU 83, there is a sonar-intercept facility. However, there is no integral spectrum analyzer. Estimated unit cost is $4M.

Work on the standard modular sonar began in 1974, following Krupp-Atlas feasibility studies for a sonar for Type 122 frigates begun in 1972. R&D was conducted in 1976–79, and DSQS-21BZ was tested in 1979. CSU 83 (DBQS-21DN) was tested in 1985 on board a German Type 206 submarine. The first CSU 83s were installed on Brazilian Type 209/1400 submarines.

Users: DBQS-21 (CSU 83): Brazil (two Type 209), Colombia (two Type 209 as refitted), Denmark (-21F in two Type 205 and in three Type 207 bought from Norway; also reported as PSU 83 in ex-Norwegian units), Egypt (PSU 83 in modernized Romeos), Germany (12 Type 206A, Korea (Type 209), Netherlands (stand-alone FAS 3-1A in *Zwaardvis*, for sale, and probably in *Walrus*), Norway (-21N in *Ula* class, -21F in *Kobbens*), Sweden (*Nacken, Vastergotland* [with FAS 3-1], and *Sjoormen* [midlife modernization of two units was funded under the FY87/91 plan]), Turkey (CSU 83/1 in new Type 209/1400 submarines, with TAS 83 towed array), Venezuela (Type 209s refitted to 206A standard 1990–92). The Norwegian version omits a passive ranger (Norway probably used DUUX 5). Germany, Korea, Turkey, and Venezuela all use the four-console version of ISUS. Chile reportedly bought SIP 3 to enhance Type 2007 flank array performance in its *Oberons*. The Dutch *Zwaardvis* and probably *Walrus* classes have hybrid flank arrays introduced in 1981, using a commercial Interstate Electronics Corp. spectrum analyzer, an HP-1311A display unit, and TNO's Interfas Type JO116 electronic unit.

DSQS-21/ASO80 Series: Argentina (ASO 80 series in 10 MEKO frigates), Brazil (four *Inhauma* class, ASO 84-2), Colombia (four FS 1500–class, ASO 84-2), Germany (DSQS-21 in three *Adams* and eight *Bremen* classes), Iraq (DSQS-21C [ASO 84-41] in *Wadi M'ragh* series, now for sale), Italy (DSQS-21B in ex-Iraqi *Lupo* class), Malaysia (two FS 1500 class, ASO 84-5), Nigeria (replaced PHS-32 in *Aradu*), Taiwan (10–15 DSQS-21CZ sonars in refitted non-SQS-23 destroyers and DSQS-21CZ for the modified *Perry* class) and Thailand (DSQS-21B in PFMM Mk 16s [*Ratanakosin* class]; DSQS-21CZ in the frigate *Makut Rajakumarn* [replacing PMS 26], in the U.S.-supplied PF 103 class [replacing SQS-17], in the three new *Kamronsin* class, and in the last two frigates to be built in the PRC).

◆ **Sonar 90/ASO 90 (DSQS-23)/CSU 90 (DBQS-40)**

Sonar 90 is a fully integrated follow-on to Sonar 80, reporting compound tracks (rather than tracks associated with only one sonar) to CDS. It incorporates integrated TMA. The system is built up of modules, each containing 40 E-format boards or 20 DE-format boards or a mixture of the two, each module being fitted for one main task. For example, an electronics cabinet accommodates two, four, or six modules, some of which are spares. The system uses EPR 2300 32-bit processors (with 68030 CPUs) and TMS and ADSP 2100 DSPs; a typical signal processing board carries a 30-MIPS array processor for mass computations (such as FFT, filtering, and normalization) using three DSP macrocells, each incorporating ADSP 2100s with 240 kbytes of high speed local RAM. Only 70 different types of boards make up the total of 500 in CSU 90.

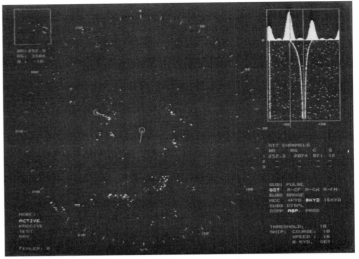

ASO 90–series active-sonar display, showing both a PPI and a B-scan centered about a bearing of interest. The circle at the very center of the PPI shows own-ship course and speed. (KAE)

ASO 90–series transducer. (KAE)

The arrays of CSU 90 match those of CSU 83, but with an integral flank array. The hull arrays feed a common bus with three consoles: one for the active sonar (with its eight ATTs);

one for passive arrays (eight ATTs for the DEMON analyzer fed by the cylindrical or other arrays, and eight ATTs [each with eight automatic line trackers, ALTs, for the LOFAR analyzer fed by the flank and towed arrays]); and a third to compile the tactical picture using TMA (and for passive ranging using PRS).

The system forms up to eight compound tracks, which can pass through the optional TMA analyzer; the analyzer can also evaluate other sensor data to form a more complete tactical picture, which is displayed on a tactical-underwater-situation display (TUD).

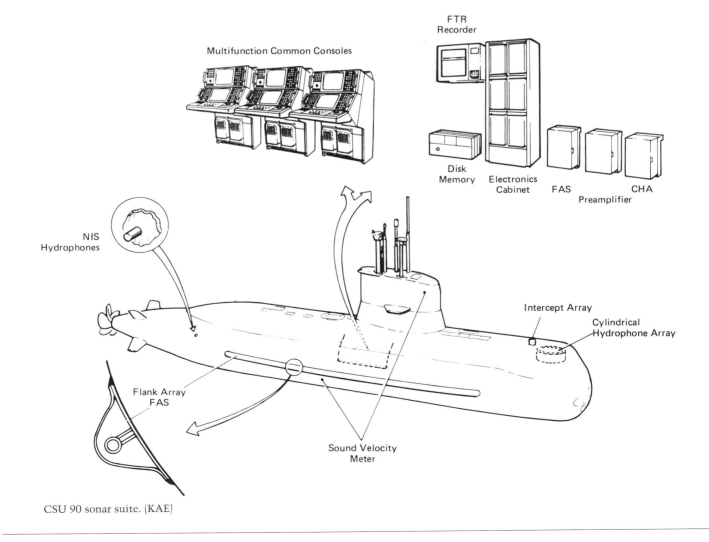

CSU 90 sonar suite. (KAE)

An Acoustical Passive Classification (APC) module replaces the earlier SIP 3. It has a disk mass memory (as its library) and can provide automatic warning channels. The Germans regard such identification as the most difficult sonar problem.

Unlike ASO 80, ASO 90 can operate actively and passively simultaneously, using a 1-kHz passive channel (fully passively it can use either the narrow channel or wide-band). It can use two CW frequencies in a single ping. Transmission is still analog. Pulse lengths: 5, 50, 300 msec in CW and FM and combinations of the two, for example, CW 50 msec followed by FM 50 msec. CW and FM are processed in parallel for fast target data generation. The CW pulse gives Doppler. The FM pulse gives target length and aspect angle (ALADIN, the German acronym for display of extended targets by interferometry). The ALADIN display shows raw sonar data (in the form of B-scans [with precise angular variation] in two adjacent sonar beams, with amplitude vs. range alongside each B-scan) plus a table showing target Doppler, speed (as calculated on the basis of aspect), length, aspect (angle to sonar), whether any radar ESM is being received, and the system's decision as to whether the target is a submarine. Target classification (sub likely, possible, or unlikely, with a confidence level) is based on Doppler, change in target position, target shape and size, target aspect angle, and any correlation with a radar contact, using either several CW50/FM50 pulses or one CW300/FM300 pulse.

Active modes: ODT and TRDT (tri-beam) for search (using 5- and 50-msec pulses and combinations); S-ODT (sector ODT) and S-TRDT for convoy protection search in company with other ships; and SDT (sector search mode for attack), mainly using 300-msec pulses. The PPI display shows Doppler and amplitude as well as range and bearing. A five-ping history can be shown for each target. Track capacity: 30, of which 10 are automatically chosen (or operator-chosen) as likeliest and are displayed and passed to the CDS. They are automatically tracked (ATT). Two Kalman filters for each target smooth tracking and make it highly accurate; they are selected by a maneuver detector. As in ASO 80, correlation ("geometric processing") is used to weed out false targets. Action commands for up to 10 targets can in turn be automatically transferred from the CDS to the sonar, on whose consoles they can be displayed. Range scales: 2, 4, 8, 12, 16, 24, 32, 48 kyd (24 nm).

Both active and passive modes can be displayed on the two screens of the console. Wide- or narrow-band passive data are presented in waterfall and B-scan form. Up to 20 passive targets are internally tracked, one of which can be selected by the operator for automatic target tracking. A "newly appearing target" alarm (active and passive) makes it easier for the single operator to handle passive as well as active operation. In active mode, a torpedo is recognized on the basis of fast target movement (air bubbles); in the passive mode, by the sudden appearance of a fast-increasing noise level.

The optional 1–100-kHz sonar intercept receiver can use both the main cylindrical array and a separate intercept array. Measured signal parameters: bearing, frequency, pulse length, PRI (range setting), and pulse amplitude (for range estimation). Up to eight signals can be displayed on the PPI and passive displays, and up to 10 can be automatically classified for torpedo and other warnings (which can be shown as strobes on the PPI).

The versions correspond to those of ASO 80: ASO 96 (LF, 2.5m cylinder, 1.0m VDS transducer), ASO 95 (1.88m cylinder; 1.2m in ASO 95-2; 6–9 kHz [three frequencies], 1.0 or 0.58m VDS transducer), ASO 94 (0.95m cylinder, 96 staves [six transducers/stave], 6–9 kHz [three frequencies], 1.0 or 0.58m VDS transducer), ASO 93 (0.58m HF cylinder, 0.58m VDS transducer), ASO 92 (0.7 × 0.3m HF conformal array). Each stave has six transducers. ASO 94 and above have 32 or 64 preformed beams, electronically stabilized against 25-deg roll and 8-deg pitch (ASO 93 has 32 beams). Passive coverage: 2–11 kHz wide-band (usable only when the sonar is not active), 1 kHz narrow-band. The 12-kHz VDS system (0.58m transducer, 32 beams) is designated VDS 2-100 or -180, depending on cable length (100 or 180 m). Operating speed is 6–18 or 6–20 kt, respectively; survival speed is 25/30 kt. A towed array can be either an integrated element or a stand-alone system.

Users:

DBQS-40 (CSU 90): Brazil (bow array and processor in *Oberons*, replacing Type 187 sonar; Type 2007 feeds into CSU 90 processor; planned for completion 1998, but only *Tonelero* completed, due to lack of funds), Chile (*Oberon* modernization [bow array, intercept sonar, and new processor]; possibly Type 209 modernization; ordered August 1993), Germany (Type 212 submarines), Greece (Type 209 modernization [including flank array]: Project Neptune), Israel (*Dolphin* class now building), Italy (Type 212U submarines), Sweden (*Gotland* [A-19] class). The German navy CSU 90 version was originally designated DBQS-21DG or DBQS-90FTC (for flank array/towed array/[automatic] classification). It ran its first sea trials on board a Type 205 submarine in early 1992.

DSQS-23: Germany (F123 *Brandenburg* class). The DSQS-23B of the new *Brandenburg* class probably corresponds to ASO 96. She has an intercept sonar and provision for a TAS 6-3 towed array.

◆ PSU 1-2

This small submarine digital passive sonar presents information from its 64-beam cylindrical transducer on a CRT in true or relative bearing. It can autotrack four targets; two can be transferred to the FCS and one to the plotting table. Selected parameters are displayed on the associated digital indicator (TPD 3). The operator classifies the target by listening on the audio channel coupled to the bearing cursor.

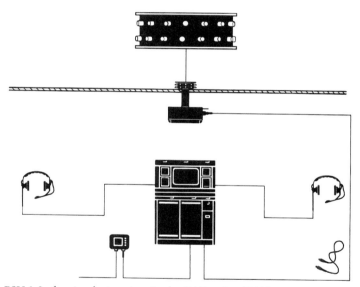

PSU 1-2, the simplest system in the KAE series. (KAE)

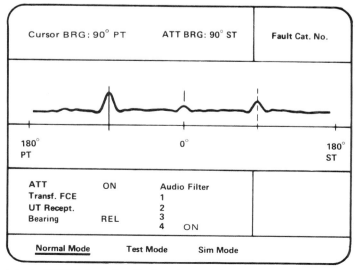

A typical PSU 1-2 passive display, showing three targets.

Users: Colombia (probably on two SX-506-class midget submarines), Korea (*Tolgorae* and SX-756-class midget submarines), Pakistan (four SX-756), and Yugoslavia (six *Una* class). The Yugoslav boats also have a Krupp Atlas PP-10 active sonar. Argentina is sometimes listed as a user, but she has no known midget submarines.

◆ TAS 90 (TAS 5-2, 5-3, 6-2, 6-3)

TAS 90 is a series of 15 Hz–1.2 kHz (broad-band around 2.4 kHz) submarine (clip-on)/surface ship towed arrays compatible with Series 90 sonars, analogous to TAS 83 for CSU 83. TAS 6-2 uses an 80m acoustic aperture (three frequency bands) in a 240m body on a 1000m cable. TAS 6-31 uses the same cable and aperture, but at higher frequency (four bands) in a shorter towed body (200 m). TAS 6-3 uses a 165m aperture (in a 320m body) on a 1000m cable (three bands). TAS 5-3 uses a 330m aperture (three bands, lower frequency) in a 490m body on a 1500m cable. Finally, 5-2 uses the long body (four bands) on a 2000m cable. The array is conventional, with preamplifiers in the body and without multiplexing; it uses two wires per channel. The nested array has 72 channels; the HF part has at least three hydrophones per group, the LF part fewer. The surface-ship version has either a single console (TAS 6-2), a double console (TAS 6-3, 6-31, and 5-3), or two double consoles (TAS 5-2).

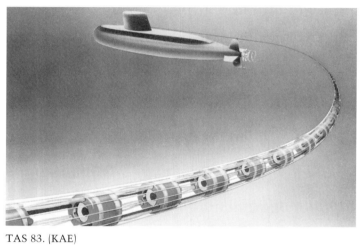

TAS 83. (KAE)

A prototype was tested at sea in 1990, and development was completed early in 1993. An experimental version was leased to Sweden.

Users: Germany (Type 212 submarine and modernized Type 122 and Type 123 frigates), Italy (Type 212U submarine). The frigates will probably get long apertures, for better LF performance (the Baltic has minimum loss at 200–600 Hz).

◆ ACTAS ASA 92

STN's 1.5–2-kHz active array uses an omni body (two transducers, 2.3 × 0.8 [W] × 1.1 m [H], 230 kg) on a 400m cable, from which is towed a twin-line array (for right/left resolution) on a 250m cable (120mm × 40m hydrophone section, with 70mm × 20m VIMs at each end). Targets are automatically detected and tracked (range, bearing, speed, course) and the digital data transferred to the ship's CDS. ASA 92 was probably derived from a German experimental LFA program of the early 1990s, culminating in sea trials in the Baltic and the North Sea aboard the test ship *Planet*. ACTAS sea trials began in mid-1996.

◆ LOPAS

Allied Signal ELAC's Low-Cost Passive Sonar is a digital upgrade to early German export submarines with analog sonars, an alternative to PSU 83. Its modular beam-former uses time-shifts to form 96 preformed beams, which are sampled digitally at the beam-former output. Given this digital data, the system com-

puter can automatically track eight (ATT) targets simultaneously, storing 15 min of track history. An associated signal processor can perform FFTs, with a normal resolution of 100 Hz for target detection (and 0.25 Hz for LOFAR processing, for classification). The single console has a 14in color monitor. Displays include bearing-time (waterfall), polar, bearing-amplitude, bearing-amplitude history, bearing-frequency history, FFT bearing-frequency of the 96 beams, and FFT applied to a single channel (e.g., in an ATT channel or selected by cursor); the system can also display the sound-velocity profile (SVP).

◆ TGS

STN Atlas (originally AEG Telefunken) developed this FCS for the Chilean navy, to adapt German-supplied SUT torpedoes to British-built *Oberon*-class submarines. A CDT digital computer replaces the earlier analog fire-control computer in the torpedo guidance console (TGC) of the TCSS Mk 9 system. It accepts sonar data, displays a tactical picture, and automatically monitors and controls the wire-guided SUT. A torpedo distribution unit in the torpedo room is connected to the main computer by a standard V24 interface. TGS entered service in 1992.

◆ ELAC 1BV/2

ELAC's stabilized 8/10/12/14.9-kHz searchlight sonar has two transmitters (search and high power: pulse width 5–50 msec). Source levels: 131.5 dB (8.2 kHz), 133 dB (10 kHz), 134.6 dB (12 kHz), 136 dB (14.9 kHz). Beamwidths (at 3-dB points) at these frequencies: 12.6 deg, 9.6 deg, 8 deg, 7.5 deg. Range scales: 1500, 3000, 6000, and 12,000 m. Consoles indicate target direction, elevation angle (for ASW mortar FCS), Doppler/range, and coarse Doppler/range.

This was the first modern German surface-ship sonar. ELAC (Electroacoustic GmBH), now a division of Honeywell, no longer produces complete sonars.

Users: Greece (*Thetis* class) and possibly Israel (early *Sa'ar* class).

FIRE-CONTROL SYSTEMS

◆ Hagenuk TFCS

Hagenuk's analog torpedo FCS was developed for the first postwar German torpedo boats to control unguided forward-fired Mk 8** (British-supplied) torpedoes. It used a two-man optical target designator (*Zielsaule*)/computer; it is not clear whether target data were entered automatically from the ship's plot (CIC), which accepted radar and own-ship data. Target angle and torpedo spread angle were cranked in centrally and corrected at the tubes (typically, the forward tubes were splayed 9.5 deg from the boat's centerline, and the after tubes 15 deg from centerline). Maximum torpedo gyro angle was 30 deg. Torpedoes could be fired in salvo, either all four at a time or two (fore or aft groups) at a time. Personnel: two at the target designator, two at the tubes, one at the plot, and one at the radar.

Users: Chile (*Guacolda* class), Greece (*Jaguar* class), and Turkey (*Kartal* class). Although German-built boats are sometimes credited with wire-guided torpedoes (such as Seal), they carry forward-firing tubes that probably cannot fire such weapons.

INDIA

◆ APSOH (HUS-001/HUS-002/HUS-003)

Bharat's 7.5–9.0-kHz (passive around 4.0 kHz) advanced panoramic sonar hull-mounted (APSOH or HUS-001) uses a 32-stave (13 elements/stave) cylindrical array (895mm dia × 914 mm, 2000 kg) forming 32 full beams and 64 half-beams for active and passive channels, spaced 11.25 deg apart. Transmit beams are 9 × 12 deg (+/−1 deg). Transmit modes: dual contra-rotating directional (DRDT), sector contra-rotating directional (SRDT), single directional (SDT), omni, omni interlaced with RDT (O-RDT). Pulses: 5 and 40 msec CW, 40 msec LFM (linear FM), 160 msec SFM, 160 msec CW. APSOH uses a postdetection pulse-compression (PDPC) receiver and a polarity coincidence correlator (PCC) receiver. Output power: 32 kW peak (20 kW nominal);

source level 222 dB omni, 232 dB RDT. Range scales: 4, 8, 16, 32 km. Display resolution is 7.8 m at the lowest range scale, 1.4 deg in bearing, Doppler 1 kt. Passive processor integration times: short-term average 160 msec, long-term average 2560 msec, spoke suppression 10.24 sec and 40.96 sec (ELCA). The sonar can correct for own-Doppler up to 32 kt.

APSOH conducts simultaneous active/passive search and track. It can track two targets simultaneously in active (semi-automatic) mode, one in passive (automatic) mode.

Transducer data are similar to those of the British Type 184, from which APSOH was presumably adapted. Unlike 184, this sonar has digital output for direct insertion into a CDS. The displays are raster-scan memory-aided units showing an eight-ping history, with a 50-Hz refresh rate. A photograph of associated equipment shows three workstations, each with a rectangular (nearly square) CRT, one with a small alphanumeric display above and a numerical pad above the main CRT. They include the output of a classifier processor using an A-scan to bring out target highlights (ASPECT). There is also an audio channel. The system includes a microprocessor-based monitoring system.

HUS-002 is a dual array (hull and VDS) sonar operating at 6.0 to 7.5 kHz, with the same beamwidths as in HUS-001. Both hull and VDS arrays have 32 staves each (nine elements in the hull array, seven in the VDS). Dimensions: hull 1220 × 1229 mm, VDS 1220 × 890 mm. The arrays can operate separately or interlaced. Power level: 122 dB ODT, 132 dB RDT.

HUS-003 is an advanced version of HUS-001, with a digital beam-former, higher rated power amplifiers, two independent displays, integrated BITE, and PC-based video recording.

Bharat offers two types of transducers, whose dimensions and characteristics do not quite match those listed above. Type 1 (TAS 051) is probably related to the HUS-001 transducer, but has 12 elements per stave. It can operate at 6.7 to 9.7 kHz. Maximum input per stave is 1.2 kW. Overall dimensions are 1168 × 1209 mm, total 1300 kg; the acoustic zone is 895 × 1020 mm. TAS 052 (Type 2) probably corresponds to the hull array of HUS-002, with nine elements per stave. It operates at 4 to 9 kHz, with maximum input per stave 1.2 kW as above. Maximum dimensions are 1282 × 1168 mm, acoustic zone 1219 × 1041 mm.

Developed by the Naval Physical and Oceanography Laboratory (NPOL) at Cochin, APSOH was first installed on the Indian frigate *Himgiri*, presumably in place of a Canadian Westinghouse SQS-505. It also now equips the second and third *Godavari*-class frigates.

INTERNATIONAL

◆ ATAS (TSM 2681/82/83)

Active towed-array sonar employs a 3-kHz (three frequencies) flex-tensional FM transducer (25 kW peak power; ODT with 25-deg vertical beam) towed up to 900 m astern of a ship, with 40m triple array (each 88mm dia) receiver (0.5-deg resolution broadside) towed on a 300m cable, with a 20m VIM. Because the receiving array is actually three arrays in a single fairing, there is a triangle of receivers at each point along its length. By always selecting the pair farthest apart horizontally, the system resolves right/left ambiguity. Weights: transmitter, 200 kg; on-board electronics, 280 kg; handling system, 7 t; tow cable (23 mm × 900 m, 1.5 t). There are now three versions: (V)1 purely active (towable at 16 kt, 235m depth), (V)2 active or passive (adds the 120m Lamproie array with a 20m separator from the LF array, and with a 100m rope tail), (V)3 simultaneously active and passive (with another cabinet and a second display, so both modes can operate simultaneously). There is also a torpedo-warning function. Claimed direct-path range is 20 km. Range scales: 8, 12, 16, 24, 32, 64 km. Track capacity: 64 in active mode, 12 in passive mode. ATAS produces 96 preformed beams. Developed by BAe, ATAS is now a joint project with Thomson Sintra, which supplies the signal processor and a two-screen console adapted from that of the Spherion sonar. Total weight is 11 t.

Users: Pakistan ([V]1 in Type 21 frigates), Taiwan ([V]2 in *La Fayette* class). Reportedly ATAS is being considered for the projected Spanish F-100 class.

ATAS transducer body in 1990, showing the vertical stack of flextensional transducers. (Author)

ISRAEL

◆ CORIS

Rafael's passive linear arrays, named after a fish, were announced in 1992: they were probably 3–4 yr from service at that time. Unlike existing systems, they use the entire array for all frequency bands, and they attempt to provide the same beam width at all frequencies. CORIS-TAS is a towed array for surface ships; CORIS-5 is a flank array for submarines; CORIS-M is a moored surveillance version. CORIS-TAS is a critical-angle array operating in four low-frequency bands (10–1600 Hz). Resolution at low frequency is 0.3 Hz. It employs two interchangeable 19in color monitors (search and track/classification, only one of which is manned when the submarine is cruising). Processing modes are: broad-band, narrow-band (LOFAR), and DEMON. Eight targets can be tracked automatically; own-ship noise is canceled out by ignoring the beams pointing at the ship. Rafael claims that jammers can be rejected automatically. CORIS-5 is the corresponding flank array, modular to allow for different submarine lengths. Although in theory it covers the full 360 deg around the submarine, detection probability is greatest in the 120-deg sector on either side of the submarine. Detection bandwidths are 10–1500 Hz for narrow-band, and 10–1000 Hz for broad-band; dynamic range is 70 dB. Both arrays are intended primarily to track surface targets; the CORIS-5 brochure appears to claim second or third CZ performance.

ITALY

Early in 1995 Alenia and Whitehead merged their underwater activities as Whitehead Alenia Sistemi Subacquei SpA (WASS). Alenia was part of Alenia Elsag, itself part of the state-owned IRI-Finmeccanica Group; Whitehead was part of the FIAT CIEI Group.

It seems likely that the SEA-90 sonar project will be abandoned, now that Italy has decided to buy the German Type 212 submarine with the CSU 90 system.

SONARS

◆ D-100 Wolves

Whitehead Alenia's submarine retrofit/upgrade preformed-beam sonar was announced in 1996. It employs a standard CTI two-screen display with independent 1280×1024-pixel color monitors, a standard array (parallel) signal and data processor, and a pressure-resistant front-end signal conditioner (16-bit digitizer), its interface (outside the pressure hull) to an existing array. To limit noise, the link between conditioner and signal processor uses fiber optics. The digital beam-former uses time-delay interpolation and is effective up to 10 kHz; beam spacing depends on array geometry. There is also an independently steerable beam and an audio beam with spectral analysis and DEMON. Other features are automatic detection (with CFAR), TWS, TMA, sonar data fusion, and interactive acoustic classification.

◆ D-102 Stratos

Whitehead Alenia's short tethered sonar system is a stand-alone 12–30-kHz sonar offering torpedo alert, obstacle avoidance, and ASW surveillance and attack capabilities. Pulses are FM and CW, 25–200 msec long. Passive operation is PCDC. Beams: transmission, 45×40 or 20 deg; reception, 3.3×25 or 15 deg. The towed unit has separate transmitting (20 staves, 4 elements/stave) and receiving (120 staves, 6 elements/stave) arrays, the former with wider diameter (1000×200 mm), wrapped around the cylinder at the bottom of which is the transmitting array (230×400 mm total). Data are transmitted to the signal processor by fiber optics. Estimated performance: mine typically detected beyond 300 m at ship speed over 20 kt, in a 60-deg sector on either bow; submarine typically detected at over 3000 m at over 20-kt own-ship speed; torpedo typically detected at over 1500 m at own-ship speed over 20 kt, over the whole horizon. The body is towed at a depth of less than 20 m at a ship speed of up to 25 kt, up to Sea State 4.

◆ IPD 70/S and MD 100/S and SARA

This sonar combines a 220 Hz–7 kHz conformal array (46 barium titanate hydrophones) wrapped around the lower part of the bow, for long-range detection and classification, with a 36-stave 8–15-kHz cylindrical target-tracker in the upper part of the bow (which contains TS-100 underwater telephone). The arrays are largely independent; each can handle four passive targets simultaneously, using its own digital beam-former and a shared high-resolution compensator. The MF array ranges by single narrow-beam 9-kHz pings (10 deg, peak power 10 kW, source level 130 dB). This array can also search actively (ODT or RDT). The current IPD 70/S digital (presumably beam preforming) version uses

IPD 70/S transducer. (USEA)

a pair of Elsag ESA-24 computers and a two-screen console based on that of the NA-18 AAW FCS. IPD 70/S can be integrated with a CM 10 range predictor (FOM evaluator).

The MF array also feeds a 3–15-kHz sonar interceptor. Submarines equipped with IPD 70/S were also generally fitted with 2.5–80-kHz Velox M5 sonar interceptors, primarily to detect active-homing torpedoes approaching from astern. However, these units may have been replaced by Alenia IN 100A LF (directional and omni) and ISO 100 HF (omni) intercept sonars. Measured parameters are bearing, frequency, pulse length, and repetition rate.

MD 100/S is the accompanying passive triangulation ranger (three arrays/side), comparable to the French DUUX series, capable of tracking four targets simultaneously within a 120-deg beam sector on each side. The sonar deduces target course and speed from the range and bearing data it measures. It was added to the *Sauros* when they were modernized. The version in the *Primo Longobardo* class is integrated with IPD 70/S.

An associated LOFAR/DEMON spectral analyzer, SARA (Selenia's spectral analyzer and classification system), uses the bow array and pairs of LF transducers on the flanks (probably from MD 100/S); lines are detected automatically or manually, and are automatically compared to a signature library. As of mid-1995, SARA may still have been developmental.

Work on IPD 70/S began in 1978, preproduction trials following in 1981. MD 100/S trials were conducted in 1983–85, and systems ordered for the improved *Sauro* class; late in 1986 the Italian navy decided to upgrade the *Sauros* themselves with digital IPD 70/S (vice IPD 70) and with MD 100/S.

Neither IPD 70/S nor MD 100/S was ever exported (the designation SISU was sometimes used).

Users: Italy: *Sauro* (retrofit; SEPA Mk 1 FCS), *Salvatore Pelosi* (with BSN-716[V]1 and SEPA FCS Mk 3) and *Primo Longobardo* (with BSN-716[V]2).

FIRE-CONTROL SYSTEMS

◆ APS Series

Whitehead's airborne presetter for A244/S is supplied in two configurations: APS 101, for helicopters with dipping sonars, and APS 102, for fixed-wing aircraft and helicopters without such sonars, both of which drop the torpedo in forward flight. APS 101 uses dipping sonar data to calculate the appropriate presets; it displays estimated hit probability.

◆ SEPA FCS

The SEPA FCS controls A184 heavy and, in the case of the Mk 2 surface system, A244 lightweight torpedoes. Mks 1 (submarine) and 2 (surface ships) can handle four targets simultaneously. They use a two-man CCRG (computation, display, and control) console built around a ULP 12/M minicomputer, with large circular CRTs. In Mk 2 the CRTs are flanked by vertical pairs of rectangular alphanumeric screens. Mk 3 uses militarized ULP microprocessors. It adds a third operator position. Apparently Italian practice is to use passive sonar data (interpreted by BSN-716) to form a long-range tactical picture, then switch to short-range sonar for fire control. FCS Mk 3 uses the short-range sonar picture for weapons control. It incorporates a sonar performance predictor, to interpret sonar data; it predicts counterdetection range and conducts threat evaluation and target designation. The fire-control portion of Mk 3 guides up to six A184 torpedoes.

A planned fully integrated system, SICS, has apparently been abandoned with the adoption of CSU 90 for the Italian version of the German Type 212 submarine.

SEPA is Societa di Elettronica per l'Automazione, part of the FIAT group.

Users: Italy (Mk 2 in *Mimbelli*, *Audace*, and *Maestrale* classes, Mk 3 in submarines [replaced Mk 1 in *Sauro* class]), Peru (Type 209s, Mk 1 replacing M 8 in all but the last two boats, *Antofagasta* and *Casma*). Mk 1 entered service in 1979, and Mk 2 in 1982 aboard the *Maestrale* class. Mk 1 may also have been installed in Indian Type 1500 submarines carrying A184 torpedoes.

JAPAN

Japanese submarines are equipped with license-built U.S. SQS-36J active sonars. Some surface ships have SQS-35J VDS. OQR-1 is reportedly a Japanese version of SQR-19.

Work is proceeding on new tactical passive and active and on surveillance towed arrays. A submarine-towed array, included in the ZQQ-5B system, was tested on board the submarine *Okishio* in 1987. An improved LF active sonar is to use a new transducer and improved anechoic baffling. Work on submarine CDS automation reportedly includes applications of artificial intelligence. The contractors are Mitsubishi and Kawasaki. The new trials ship *Asuka* has a flank-mounted active/passive bow array and a new towed array. The bow arrays extend back as far as the tower foremast.

◆ HQS-102/103

These are license-built versions of the U.S. AQS-13 (for the Sea King) and AQS-13F (for the SH-60J).

◆ OQS Series

The OQS Series are hull sonars for surface ships.

OQS-1/2/12/14 are license-built versions of the U.S. SQS-4/29; OQS-12 and -14 are developed versions, in the *Isuzu* class. OQS-12 is a modified SQS-31. Like some U.S. versions of SQS-4, OQS-12 or -14 can support a VDS operating from the same sonar stack, using an OQA-1 hoist and fish equivalent to the U.S. SQA-10. The current VDS is SQS-35J. In *Shirane*, the VDS is used to tow an array. *Users* (OQS-12): *Isuzu* class (OQA-1 VDS hoist).

OQS-101 is an indigenous-design 3-kHz hull sonar, equivalent to U.S. SQS-53. It is the hull sonar of the *Shirane* class.

OQS-102 is a new hull sonar for the *Kongo*-class Aegis destroyers; it is comparable to SQS-53C.

OQS-103 is a license-built SQS-23 bow sonar. It is being replaced by OQS-4. *Users:* Later *Yamagumo* class, *Chikugo* class.

OQS-104 is an indigenous LF design, in the *Asagiri-*, *Hatakaze-*, and *Hatsuyuki*-class destroyers, and the *Yubari-* and *Ishikari*-class frigates. OQS-4 is probably similar to SQS-23. Compared to OQS-3, it has improved electronic components and better signal processing.

SUBMARINE SONAR AND COMBAT SYSTEMS

From the sixth submarine in the *Uzushio* class (*Takashio*) onward, the separate TDC was eliminated in favor of a system in which detected target data are processed digitally and shown on a CRT. In the *Yushio* class, the computer/display system, ZYQ-1, is greatly enlarged. For the first time in a Japanese submarine, it automatically links detection and weapons systems. It also handles submarine operations data. The system is also described as the SCDS, or submarine computer-data system. Installation of ZYQ-1 required an additional 350 t of submarine displacement (from the 1850 t of the previous class to 2200 t). From the *Nadashio* on, Harpoon fire control is added to the computer system. The *Harushio* class has a new version of the basic system, presumably ZYQ-2. Growth to 2400 t accommodates decoys and a towed array.

ZQQ-1 in the *Uzushio* introduced a new Japanese-produced sonar array, a 10ft-dia DIMUS cylinder consisting of three tiers of staves, in the bow of the submarine. The system is used for search and for precision (presumably passive) ranging and as a sonar intercept receiver. The *Uzushio* has been broken up, and the other unit with this sonar, *Makishio*, is a target services training ship. ZQQ-1 and its successors are manufactured by Oki Electric.

ZQQ-2, a modified ZQQ-1, was introduced in the *Isoshio*, the third unit of the class. Three submarines of this type are in service, one (*Isoshio*) as a training ship.

ZQQ-3 was introduced in the *Takashio*. She and later submarines have an MF active sonar, SQS-36(J), midway up their sails, to supplement the bow sonar.

ZQQ-4 was introduced in the *Yushio* class. In 1987 the *Okishio* of this class was the first Japanese submarine with a clip-on towed array, a purchased U.S. BQR-15. It will also be fitted on three other *Yushio*-class submarines. In these submarines the active sonar is closer to the base of the sail, below the sail planes. Like the earlier sonar systems in this series, ZQQ-4 employs a cylindrical bow array.

ZQQ-5, for the *Harushio* (2400t) class, is a new type of system, combining a bow array with a flank array and a Japanese-produced retractable (rather than clip-on) towed array (ZQR-1). From the second unit on, the system is the modified ZQQ-5B. This class will also be fitted with a torpedo decoy system. The *Yushio* class is being upgraded to ZQQ-5B on refits. ZQQ-5 was developed by Hughes and Oki.

An *Uzushio*-class submarine shows the characteristic cylindrical transducer of recent Japanese submarine sonar systems. (*Ships of the World*)

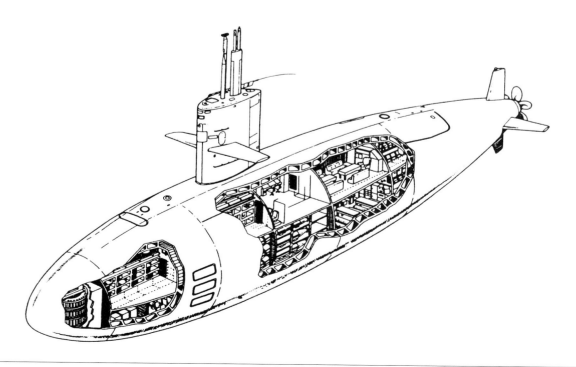

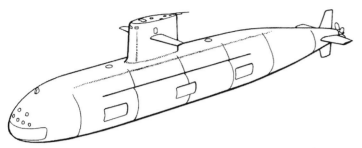

The new Japanese *Oyashio*-class submarine marks a departure from earlier *Barbel*-like hull forms and incorporates a WAA-type passive ranger. (*Ships of the World*)

The new 2700t submarine (*Oyashio* class) will have triple ranging arrays on its flanks. It is not clear whether these are the flank arrays credited to ZQQ-5/5B. The submarines equipped with these sonar systems lack the extended parallel-beam section that is generally needed to accommodate a triple ranging array. The *Oyashio* hull resembles that of a Type 209 or a *Collins*, with six torpedo tubes above the sonar window. Note, however, that the triple arrays seem to be curved like those of the U.S. WAA, rather than flat as in the Australian submarine or in European practice.

NETHERLANDS

In 1990 the Signaal sonar division was amalgamated with that of Thomson Sintra; the Signaal surface-ship sonars are no longer offered for sale as such.

SONARS

◆ CWE-10N/PAE-1 and M5 FCS

Van der Heem's 10.5/11-kHz searchlight and 24-kHz (variable between 5 and 50 kHz) attack searchlight sonars share a dome and are associated with the Signaal M5/1 FCS. Pulse widths for both are 0–50 msec (also reported as 100 and 200 msec, respectively). CWE-10N peak power is 10 kW; instrumented ranges are 1, 2, 3, 4, 6, 8, 12 km. PAE-1 peak power is 250 W; instrumented ranges are 1, 2, 3, 4, 6, 8 km. Total installation weight is 3200 kg, compared to 3800–6000 kg for the contemporary ELAC 1BV series (which was also used with M5).

The manufacturer was van der Heem, part of the Philips group; it was absorbed into Signaal (which was part of the same group).

M5 was originally an analog system broadly analogous to the U.S. Mk 105, controlling the Bofors 375mm ASW launcher, working with a separate M9 torpedo FCS. Initially, M9 used the M5 analog computer as its position-keeper. Target course and speed were displayed on a vertical CRT, and target depth was shown on a paper printer. By 1966 M5/1 was using the digital computer of the M9/6 as its position-keeper. This combination kept the searchlight sonar on the submarine target and held the last target range and bearing in the event that contact was lost.

M5/4 (1961) merged rocket and torpedo control functions in one digital system with two fixed-program computers. It has three separate plots: ASW (search sonar/radar), surface targets (search sonar/radar, attack sonar, passive sonar), and summary. ASW and surface plots are on standard four-operator SEWACO-type horizontal consoles. An operator at the ASW plot controls depth-charge racks directly, but torpedoes and ASW rockets are normally controlled by computer.

Users:

CWE-10N/PAE-5: Argentina (*25 de Mayo*), Peru (cruisers), Turkey (*Koln* class). PAE-1 is installed only on board the frigates.

M5: Greece (*Thetis* class [M5/4]), Turkey (*Koln* [M5/1] class).

◆ PHS-32

Signaal's 9.3/10.5/11.7-kHz (600-Hz bandwidth) preformed-beam sonar uses an SMR-Mu computer and a 30-stave 730mm-dia transducer (10 spot transducers/stave, 60 preformed beams, each 12 × 12 or 20 deg, switchable during reception; bearing accuracy 1 deg). Pulse lengths: 12.5, 25, 50, 100, and 400 (optional long pulse or FM mode only) msec. Range scales: 1, 2, 4, 8, and 16 kyd; range accuracy is 0.5–2% of full-scale range (range gate is $\frac{1}{16}$ of the range scale). This is an ADT sonar (track capacity four targets). In passive mode, up to four targets can be displayed in a 20-min time-bearing (waterfall) format. Tracks are filtered sufficiently smoothly for fire control. An FFT processor extracts Doppler data in each preformed beam; the B-scan display is connected to a memory storing that data. Signaal argued that the time-bearing waterfall made detection more likely than a conventional PPI, since the operator did not have to search ever-widening circles. Modes: ODT, TRDT, LP (long pulse option), MCC (beam widened in the vertical to maintain close contact), and LISTEN (passive). During sea trials in 1978, in bad weather (Sea State 4, ship rolling up to 25 deg, and pitching up to 10 deg), a submarine was automatically tracked out to 14,000 yd.

The display includes a ray-path predictor, using a sound-velocity profile from an online XBT. PHS-32 incorporates BITE. It was reportedly the first operational sonar to use advanced digital signal processing (FFT and pulse compression).

The transducer, made by Graseby, can be fixed or retractable. Total weight of the fixed hull outfit is about 7000 kg. The retractable hull outfit weighs about 2500 kg and can be lowered or retracted at up to 24 kt.

PHS-32 was a private-venture development. Design work began in 1974, hardware contracts were awarded from 1975 on, and the first unit was tested in 1977–78.

Users: Korea (*Ulsan* class and some *Donghae* class, a total of 25 sets), Indonesia (*van Speijk* class, training frigate *Hajar Dewantara*, *Fatahilah*-class frigates, and the PB 57–class patrol craft *Andau* and *Singla*), Netherlands (*Tromp* class, replacing old EDO sonars), and Nigeria (MEKO 360–type frigate *Aradu*).

◆ PHS-36

This 5.5/6.7/7.5-kHz bow sonar was intended as a 36-stave successor to PHS-32, developed to a late-1970s requirement (and first tested 1979–81); the competitors were a Signaal sonar (incorporating some SQS-509 technology) and a French sonar, Tarpon. The Dutch government compromised, buying the Signaal dry end (Signaal would have bought the transducer abroad in any case) and the French wet end (ironically, a 32-stave transducer). There are 32 preformed beams (15 deg wide, 5-kW pulses; source levels in Tarpon were 220 dB ODT and 227 dB directional); the

PHS-36 (Tarpon) hull array. (U.S. Naval Institute)

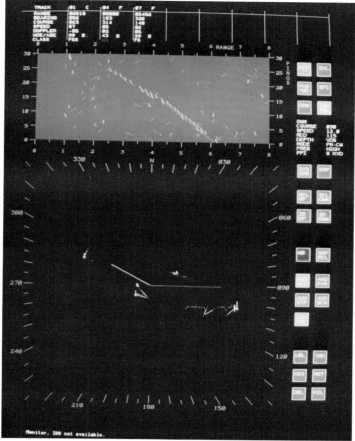

A PHS-36 sonar CRT shows a PPI display (*lower part*), a range-correlation display (*upper green part*), a track table (*top*), and light pen–operated controls (*right*). The operator selects the closely related pictures needed for the specific task: e.g., sonar tracks and surface-search radar tracks can be combined on one display. The processor conducts FM and CW processing simultaneously to cope with both noise- and reverberation-limited conditions. The main sonar-processor functions are autodetection, autotrack initiation, and autotrack processing. The operator does not form part of the detection chain. This CRT is part of a General Operator Station (GOS) console, which also has access to the ship's tactical data-handling system (the Sewaco VII CDS of an M-class frigate). (Signaal)

sonar operates in four active modes and one passive mode. As a measure of PHS-36 requirements, Tarpon offered a maximum instrumented range of 32 kyd and both Doppler (768 cells formed by FFT) and pulse compression (maximum ratio 300:1 for an FM pulse) processing.

Users: Netherlands (*van Heemskerck* and *Karel Doorman* classes; reportedly selected 1995 for new AAW frigates).

◆ SIASS

Signaal's Submarine Integrated Attack-and-Surveillance Sonar System employs a 96-stave passive cylindrical bow array (four transducers/stave: 96 preformed beams), a cylindrical active transmitting array, triple (25-transducer, arranged 5 × 5: total 32 preformed beams on each side) passive ranging arrays (using wavefront curvature) on each flank, and a four-element HF acoustic-intercept array (the big bow array is used for LF intercepts). They are probably essentially CSU 3-4 and PRS 3-15 arrays (Signaal always bought its wet ends from outside suppliers).

There are 28 broad-band tracking channels: four each for the cylindrical and flank arrays (on eight preselected frequencies), four for the active sonar, and 16 for the HF and LF intercept sonars. Normally the passive-ranging sonar is slaved to the main bow cylindrical array: range is calculated automatically once a broad-band contact enters the ranging sector. In at least some cases, tracking is based on the automatic association of inputs from different sensors operating in different frequency ranges. Active modes are single-ping (directional) and single- or multi-

ple-ping ODT. Each sonar has an electronic classification library of up to 300 specific platforms (100 ship classes, 100 sonar types). The system as a whole can store up to 35 tracks, carrying out TMA on up to 20 of them.

Each of the 160 preformed beams is subject to simultaneous complex FFT analysis (LOFAR), the system computer holding 15 min of history on each (total 2 Mbytes). Targets can therefore be detected (and tracked) by ALI: different targets can be tracked simultaneously in wide- and narrow-band. There are also enhanced classification channels, Zoom-LOFAR (high-resolution vernier analysis) and DEMON (blade and shaft rates).

The HF intercept sonar operates up to 100 kHz, and uses an FFT processor to detect, classify, and correlate contacts. It incorporates a threat library and can generate automatic warnings.

Work on SIASS began in 1978, and production models were completed in 1982/83.

Users: Taiwan (*Hai Lung* class). Reports of installation on board Dutch submarines are incorrect; this sonar was devised because the French government refused to release to Taiwan the Octopus used on board *Walrus*-class submarines. The associated CDS is Spectrum, which is related to the SEWACO VII of the *Walrus* class.

◆ ALF

The RNLN tested this low-frequency active sonar (developed by TNO Physics and Electronics Lab, TNO-FEL) on board HNLMS *Tydemans*. ALF demonstrates capabilities planned for the next-generation Dutch LCF frigate and possibly on some *Karel Doormans*. Its Thomson Sintra transmitter is based on the Tonpilz projector used in SLASM (2t body, 2.5 m high, housing two columns of six Tonpilz transducers to form an omni array). The receiver is a pair of 130m arrays supplied by Ferranti Thomson Sonar Systems in the UK. TNO supplied the signal processing algorithms, which run on a Sun 470 and an array processor. Total weight including the winch is 17 t. Development work began at end of second quarter 1992. This is an exploratory program; as of 1996 no formal requirement had been issued.

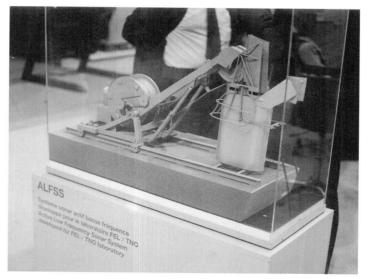

This model of the ALF towed body and handling gear was displayed at Bourget Naval 1994. Half the Tonpilz transducers inside the fish point to port and half to starboard to produce an omni signal. The fish tows a dual array, not visible here. (Author)

UNDERWATER FIRE-CONTROL SYSTEMS

◆ M8 Series

Signaal's (HSA's) submarine-torpedo FCS introduced a fixed-program solid-state digital computer into its M8/1 version (1960). It handles several targets in parallel (three in the M8/24 version), cycling both position-keeper and torpedo ballistics functions among them. Because M8 handles several targets at a time, it displays its tactical data on a PPI (range scales 5/10/20 km or 5/10/20/40 kyd) rather than on dials. Like earlier single-target systems, it accepts a mixture of passive and active sonar data, as well as radar and periscope data. The maximum own-ship speed is 40 kt, and the maximum target speed is 60 kt. M8 can control straight-running, homing/programmed, or wire-guided torpedoes. Special-purpose computers added an automated plotting capability for TMA.

The Royal Netherlands Navy let the M8 development contract in 1955. The successor system, SINBADS (originally M8/41), is a full submarine CDS (see the CDS section for details).

Users: Argentina (M8/24 in Type 209s), Ecuador (M8/24 in Type 209s), Germany (M8/8 in Type 206 class), Greece (M8/19 in Type 209s), Netherlands (M8/7 in *Zwaardvis* class, for sale), Turkey (M8/24 in first two Type 209s).

◆ M9 Series

M9 is an ASW FCS built around an SMR-S computer and a standard Signaal three-operator horizontal console. Although primarily intended to control the Bofors 375mm ASW rocket, it can also control Mk 32 torpedo tubes via a Mk 264 Mod 1 control panel. An earlier system, also designated M9 (and now extinct), was a digital surface-ship torpedo ballistic computer (1958) using the position-keeper of the M5/1 system.

Users: Egypt (*Descubierta* class), Indonesia (the frigate *Hajar Dewantara* and the *Fatahilah* class and possibly the two fast ASW attack craft), Malaysia (the FS 1500–class frigates), Morocco (*Descubierta* class), Nigeria (*Aradu*), and Spain (*Descubierta* class). The Indonesian *Hajar Dewantara* and the FAC are unique in this group because they carry SUT dual-purpose wire-guided torpedoes, which are fired from tubes facing aft. Other ships carry Mk 32 tubes.

◆ M11

Signaal's surface-ship antiship torpedo FCS is reportedly related to the original M5 and M9, using a fixed-program digital position-keeper. The main system sensor is a Signaal "egg." Data below refer to the VM11/2 version, which was designed about 1966 to control Seal wire-guided torpedoes. Maximum range is 30 kyd (maximum firing range is 20 kyd); minimum range is 300 yd; and maximum torpedo course change is 14 deg/sec (maximum boat course change is 8 deg/sec). Maximum closing is 50 kt. The system can compensate for 30-deg rolls (at up to 25 deg/sec) and for 10 deg of pitch (at 15 deg/sec).

Users: Argentina (*Intrepida* class [TNC 45 type]), Germany (S143 class), Greece (working with Vega, controlling wire-guided torpedoes in Combattante II and III attack boats: probably VM11 version; probably also ex-German S143 class).

NORWAY

Simrad (established 1947), the only sonar manufacturer, originally produced fish-finding and whaling sonars; in 1975–76 it announced a series of searchlight naval sonars (SU, ST, SQ-D, and SK3-D). The searchlights being ineffective against submarines, Simrad shifted to scanning sonars (SS hull and ST towed series).

See the Mine Warfare section for SA950, which also has an ASW application.

Reportedly Simrad sonars are used by Taiwan (in minehunters and in antifrogman PCLs).

◆ SQ Series

The 24-kHz SQ3-D/SF has five range scales (maximum 2500 m; 4-kW peak power, which can be increased to 8 kW). It can search automatically, the array (beam 12 × 16 deg) training through 360 deg in bearing and through 90 deg in elevation. The usual sonar speed of a *Hugin* is 22 kt.

Users (SQ3-D/SF): Finland, Norway (SQ3-D on *Vidar*-class minelayers), Sweden (*Carlskrona*, *Hugin* class, probably also the MCM support ship *Skredsvik* and the Swedish coast guard ships *Gotland* and *Karlskrona*).

◆ SS105

This 14-kHz scanning sonar uses a 48-stave array (48 preformed receiving beams, each 10 deg wide, with split-beam processing in each beam). Transmission modes are ODT and TRDT, and the range scales are 2–16 km (total output 15 kW). LEDs indicate target range, relative/true bearing, and own-ship's speed, and there is an 11in CRT (PPI). The dome can be fixed or retractable (using an unusual pivoting mechanism), and the sonar can be used at speeds of up to 25 kt.

Users: Finland (*Turva* and *Kiisla* classes), Norway (*Nordkapp* class; provides data to NAVKIS CDS).

◆ SS240 Series/ST240

This 24-kHz patrol boat scanning sonar uses a cylindrical array (42cm dia, 300 kg) to produce 64 preformed beams (8 × 12 deg). Transmission modes: ODT, sector (30, 60, or 120 deg), RDT (output 7 kW). CW pulse lengths are 1.3 to 200 msec; FM pulse widths (1.9-kHz bandwidth) are 1.3, 2.6, 5.2, and 10.4 msec. Range scales: 0.5, 1, 2, 4, 6, 12 km. Both transmission and reception beams may be tilted from +10 to −20 deg. An MCC mode uses a broad vertical beam for both transmission and reception. The true/relative motion PPI shows echoes in eight colors to indicate signal strengths.

SS242 is the fixed-transducer version.

ST240 ("Toadfish") is a lightweight VDS (towed at speeds of up to 16 kt) or dipping version.

Developed from SS304, SS240 was announced in 1986.

Users: Finland (*Helsinki II* class; may be VDS of *Kiisla* class; SS242 in *Tiira*-class patrol boats), Sweden (at least 13 ordered, mostly to refit the *Hugin* class with ST240 for search and SA950 as an attack sonar for the Elma system; both feed a single console). Taiwan may use this sonar in minehunters and in antifrogman PCLs.

◆ SS245 Series

This 24-kHz preformed-beam (32 beams, each 10–14 × 13–17 deg, interpolated to form 64 display beams) hull sonar uses a 432 × 280mm 300-kg array of seven circular 27-transducer rings, arranged so that the spot transducers form a checkerboard to generate a more even pattern. Transmission modes: ODT, sector, RDT, MCC (as in SS240). Transmission and reception beams are tiltable (+10 to −20 deg) in 19 steps. Source level: single beam 218–223 dB, omni 211–216 dB. Modes: CW short, normal, long (pulse width 1.25–200 msec; in omni mode maximum pulse width is 90 msec); FM-0, -1, -2, -3 (one, two, four, or eight pulses, lengths 1.25, 5.00, 20.00, and 80.00 msec, bandwidth 800 Hz). Range scales: 500, 1000, 1500, 2000, 4000, 6000, 8000, and 12,000 m. In passive mode the sonar can perform DEMON analysis. The display is a 20in raster-scan color monitor. Data can be shown in relative or true motion (zoom or ASPECT or Doppler analysis). Versions are SS245 (hoistable, no dome), SS246 (hoistable, with GRP dome), SS247 (fixed, with GRP dome), SS248 (hoistable transducer and dome), and SS249 (hoistable, with inflatable rubber dome).

◆ SS304 (Spira)

This 34-kHz patrol boat (down to 150 t, up to 40 kt speed) sonar uses an 85-deg wide array of 17 preformed receiving beams (narrow in the vertical, for shallow water) and a single 9 × 7-deg transmitting beam (source level 232 dB); the transducer turns to cover 360 deg; it can be tilted (within +15/−105 deg). Maximum instrumented range is 4000 m. The 512-line 14in raster-scan CRT uses six colors (three for symbols, three for echoes).

SS304 was developed from the SM600 fish-finder, demonstrated to the Norwegian navy in December 1982 on board a fishing boat.

Users: Finland (*Helsinki*, *Turunmaa*, and *Kiisla* classes), Sweden (*Goteborg* and *Stockholm* classes [with Salmon]).

◆ SS575/576

This new 57-kHz digital sonar uses a 256-element spherical array (64 preformed beams, each 11 × 11 deg). It can transmit on 1–64 beams (ODT). The transmitting beam can tilt between +10/−90 deg. Pulse widths: CW (0.6–160 msec; 60 msec in ODT mode), FM (0.6, 2.5, 10, or 40 msec, bandwidth 1.78 kHz in each case). Modes: CW short, CW normal, FM-0 (one pulse), FM-1 (two pulses), FM-2 (four pulses), FM-3 (eight pulses), FM-auto. Range scales: 250 m, 500 m, 1, 1.5, 2, 4, and 6 km. Power output is 25 W per transducer (total 6.4 kW). Signal processing: ASPECT, Doppler. The display is a 20in high-resolution color CRT with zoom mode. Presumably SS575/6 was inspired by Spherion, which is now in the *Oslo* class; it is likely to be adopted for the new Norwegian FAC. SS 575 is the standard transducer; SS 576 is mounted on a stalk. Both versions are hoistable.

◆ SU Series

This 12/14.5/18/24-kHz searchlight sonar tilts +20/−110 deg; at 18 kHz the beam is 10.5 × 12 deg. The center frequency is set to one side of the receiving filter band, leaving more room for positive (approaching) than for negative (retiring) Doppler. Peak power is 4 kW (8 kW with an optional second transmitter). Range scale is 3.5–9 km; range is displayed on a chemical (paper) recorder. An optional PPI can pulse the sonar at 75 or 150 to 500 m, for high-resolution survey work. SU-RS is the azimuth-stabilized version for survey work.

Users: Australia (SU-2 in *Flinders*), Ireland (*Emer* class [24-kHz version]), United Kingdom (Island and *Hecla* classes, with 2034 sidescan).

◆ Terne Attack Sonar

This stabilized searchlight tracking sonar has a maximum instrumented range of 3000 yd and a depression angle of 35 deg (with a maximum instrumented depth of 1000 ft). The minimum depression angle is 5 deg. The range scales are 1000 and 2500 yd. The sonar incorporates a horizontal-range and depth computer. It can be controlled by a scanning sonar, which triggers it in range and controls it in bearing. For example, as tested by the U.S. Navy in the early 1960s, the Norwegian attack sonar, designated SQA-16 (depth determining group), was controlled by an SQS-31 or -32.

RUSSIA

Sonars and sonar "komplexes" are developed by Okeanpribor in St. Petersburg. They are designated by code-name and by MG and MGK number. At least in a submarine, the K indicates a combination of passive, active, sonar intercept, and communications functions. Many submarine sonar complexes are named after rivers; FCSs are named after cities. Many surface-ship sonars are named after metals. A few sonars numbered in an earlier

An Okeanpribor poster, displayed in 1995, shows typical arrays. Note that the submarine array is for reception only, whereas the surface-ship array is for both reception and transmission. (S. Zaloga)

GAS series (Russian initials for sonar) survive. NATO assigned nicknames are somewhat confusing: since systems were identified mainly by reception of sonar signals, the same name can cover several different sets.

With substantial recent improvements in passive sonar operation, submarines typically use their passive sets for primary detection and their active sets to regain contact. That may occur at such short range that HF sets such as Mouse Roar may be useful.

Generations of surface-ship sonars can probably be associated with foreign sources. Moose Jaw (Orion) and Mare Tail are probably versions of the British Type 177 (at different frequencies). The roughly contemporary Bull Nose is probably derived from Type 184. The next generation reportedly derives from French scanning sonars (which themselves derive from U.S. practice, quite different from British): Horse Jaw, Bull Horn, Horse Tail. The first really big Soviet sonar was the 6m-dia cylindrical Rubin, designed about 1960 for the "Papa"-class submarine.

According to recently published Russian accounts, a new generation of ASW weapons (and, surely, sensors) was ordered developed under a 1960 decree, specifically to deal with U.S. strategic ballistic missile submarines. It included Shkval (but see below), RPK-1 (Vikhr, NATO FRAS-1, now extinct), RPK-2 (SS-N-15), the first Soviet air-dropped ASW torpedo, AT-1, and the SET-65 submarine-launched ASW torpedo. The corresponding sensors were presumably the first-generation LF submarine and surface-ship sets, such as Kerch, Rubin, and Orion. The reference to AT-1 suggests that the 1960 program included the second-generation (BM-series) broad-band sonobuoys and the May (Il-38) ASW airplane that used them. Because priority initially went to submarine systems, such as RPK-2, surface-ship weaponry was badly delayed. Hence the decision to arm the Kara I (Project 1134) "ASW cruiser" with antiship missiles; nothing else was available. The only surface-ship system to appear even approximately on time was Vikhr, aboard the ASW carrier *Moskva*. Note that, contrary to contemporary reports, it was conceived with (though probably not fielded with) a torpedo payload as alternative to its nuclear depth bomb.

SS-N-14 (RPK-3/RPK-4) and the corresponding medium-frequency Piranha sonar appear, then, as a follow-on program probably dating from the mid-1960s. One might speculate that they were needed because the earlier systems could not be accommodated on board anything much smaller than a large cruiser. These systems appeared in the early 1970s aboard cruisers (Kresta II/Kara, Projects 1134bis and 1134A) and frigates (Krivaks, Project 1135). The corresponding ASW corvette was Grisha (Project 1124), armed with unguided rockets (RBU-6000) and with ASW torpedoes.

It now (late 1996) appears that a new generation of ASW sensors and weapons was conceived in the late 1960s, using LF narrow-band technology (probably built around a common signal processor). It included the new LOFAR sonobuoy, RGB-16 (Type 75) and, probably, the first Soviet towed arrays (e.g., in the "Victor III" class) and the Rubikon and Skat submarine sonars. The corresponding MPA airplane was Bear F Mod 2/3 (Tu-142MK with Korshun system).

The corresponding ship system was based on a Ka-27 helicopter, which would prosecute convergence-zone contacts obtained by the new LF hull and towed sonars. This combination is roughly analogous to the contemporary U.S. *Perry* class/LAMPS I combination. However, the helicopter may also have been seen as a targeting device for RPK-6/7 (SS-N-16 with torpedo). About 1972 design work began on ships equipped with the helicopter and sonar, successors to the existing ASW frigate and corvette: respectively, *Udaloy* and *Neustrashimyy*. Both designs escalated rapidly in size, so that by 1982 the decision had been taken to develop *Neustrashimyy* in parallel with the revised Krivak III.

◆ Ajax (Ayaks)/Irytysh

Sonar of the new Project 885 (*Severodvinsk*) submarine, incorporating a spherical bow array so large that the torpedo tubes have been moved back (as in U.S. submarines) to fire around it. The associated system (komplex) is Irytysh.

The new *Severodvinsk* is to have the first Russian spherical sonar, Ayaks (D. Markov).

◆ Akula

The flank array in a "Victor III" is about a third as long as the submarine, probably inspired by the British Type 186/2007. It was reportedly the first such array on board a Soviet submarine. There is also an unnamed passive ranger, presumably equivalent to the French DUUX 2. Similar systems are probably on board other modern SSNs. Russian (not export) Kilo-class submarines may have a related flank array, and a flank array is part of Skat-3.

◆ Arktika MG-100 (NATO Pike Jaw)/ Arktika-M MG-200/Leningrad

Arktika was the 13–16-kHz diesel-electric attack (searchlight) tracking sonar associated with the Leningrad mechanical analog FCS. Presumably Arktika was the first Russian sonar capable of autotracking (it could also be manually steered). The combination of Arktika and Leningrad was the first to provide Russian submarines with the option of firing torpedoes without exposing a periscope. Leningrad can position-keep two targets while calculating torpedo ballistics for one. It can operate continuously for up to 8 hr; MTBF is 1200 hr. Unlike contemporary Western systems, it turns torpedoes through two gyro angles in sequence. The torpedoes of a spread therefore emerge in parallel, and thus can hit despite errors in target range (the single gyro angle applied by standard Western systems causes the torpedoes of a spread to diverge, so much beyond the estimated range the target is unlikely to be hit). Reported typical range is 4 kyd (2.0 nm).

Users: Bulgaria (Romeo class), China (Romeo and probably Ming classes), Cuba (Foxtrot class), Egypt (unmodernized Romeo class), India (Foxtrot class), Korea (North: Romeo class), Libya (Foxtrot class), Russia (Foxtrot class), Syria (Romeo class).

◆ Bronza (MG-345)

This 6.5/7/7.5-kHz sonar suite comprises a dipper or VDS and a hull sonar. Range scales are 4, 8, 16, and 32 km. Typical submarine detection ranges: 4.6 km for hull array, 5.5 km for towed array, 7 km for dipping array. The transducer can be towed at up to 150 m. The use of a metallic name, like Platina, suggests that this is an integrated combination, unlike the separate hull and dipping sonars of, say, a "Grisha."

Users: Bulgaria (Pauk class), Cuba (Pauk class, with dipping sonar), India (Pauk class, with dipping sonar), Russia (Pauk class).

◆ Feniks-M MG-10 (NATO Trout Cheek and Shark Teeth)

Feniks was equivalent to the wartime German "Balcon" array (an earlier array, laid flat against the side of the hull, was called MARS). In a Foxtrot, the improved Feniks-M array (broadly equivalent to the German GHG or the U.S. BQR-4), which is carried on the upper part of the bow, surrounds a Hercules (MG-15) cylindrical transducer (Romeos lack the active transducer; they may have an omnidirectional pinger [equivalent to the old U.S. BQS-4], which uses the Feniks array as a receiver). Feniks-M was tested on board two Whiskeys in 1958, and was deployed on board Foxtrots, Romeos, and production Novembers (Project 627A; the 627 prototype had the earlier combination).

A Feniks passive array lies behind the sonar window on the bow of this Foxtrot-class submarine, on display in London, 1995. Inside the passive array is a Hercules scanning sonar, the combination forming Tuloma. The domes above Feniks house sonar intercept arrays. Windows on the submarine's sail cover arrays for underwater acoustic communication. Not visible here is the narrow forefoot window covering an Arktika fire-control searchlight sonar. (Author)

In early nuclear submarines, Feniks-M was called Shark Teeth; there is no evidence that it was any different from the array on board a diesel submarine. Its sonar window was often faired more completely into the bow. Apparently it was assumed that the same array was part of the Kerch system, since "Charlie" and "Victor I" were credited with Shark Teeth plus a Pike Jaw (Arktika) successor called Shark Fin, a MF attack sonar.

Users:

Feniks-M: Bulgaria (Romeo class), China (Romeo and probably Ming classes), Cuba (Foxtrot class), Egypt (unmodernized Romeo class), India (Foxtrot class), Korea (North: Romeo class), Libya (Foxtrot class), Russia (Foxtrot class), Syria (Romeo class).

Feniks: Albania (Whiskey class), North Korea (Whiskey class).

◆ Hercules MG-15 (NATO Wolf Paw)

The first Russian scanning sonar, this HF system appeared in 1957; it was roughly comparable to the U.S. QHB/SQS-10 family. The NATO Wolf Paw code-name applies only to the surface-ship version. Petyas listed below may have Titan/Vychegda rather than Hercules. Vychegda (see below) was probably a tiltable searchlight attack sonar using much the same transducer, since it received the same NATO code-name. Hercules-2M, the surface version in the "Kynda" class, was designated GAS-372. Tuloma (in Julietts and Foxtrots) is probably an integrated combination of Feniks and Hercules.

Users: Bulgaria (Poti class), Cuba (Foxtrot class), India (Foxtrot class, Petya class), Libya (Foxtrot class), Romania (Poti class), Russia (Foxtrot class), Syria (Petya III class), Vietnam (Petya II class).

◆ Kerch/MGK-100 and -300 (NATO Shark Teeth/ Shark Fin and Squid Arm)/Brest

Kerch combines a 4m LF cylindrical array (Shark Teeth) with an MF attack sonar (Shark Fin) below the waterline in the bow, with another in some sails. Given its date of origin, and the later emphasis on fully digital operation, Kerch almost certainly employs a mechanical commutator. This sonar was introduced in the Alfa (Project 705) class as part of the Yenisei MGK-100 complex. It was also on board "Charlie"-class submarines, and it may have equipped some modernized "Echo II"-class submarines. In an "Alfa," the passive cylindrical array (about 80 staves, six double transducers per stave) lay atop a trainable elevating active array (eight elements above six), so in effect the sonar could be trained both horizontally and vertically.

The Soviets reportedly considered Kerch equivalent to the U.S. BQQ-2. Late-production Foxtrots reportedly had only the passive element of the Kerch system (i.e., a Feniks-M derivative), which NATO code-named Shark Teeth E, retaining their earlier active pingers.

Shark Fin may be the MG-14 medium-frequency active sonar listed among the sonars on board a "Charlie"-class missile submarine, in addition to the Kerch system. It first appeared on

A model of the bow of an Alfa-class submarine (Project 705) shows the Kerch sonar, with its underslung active element and a quadruple sounder at left. The latter was presumably used for bottom-mapping navigation. The SSBN equivalent of this sonar has its planar transmitting array above the receiving array. In these submarines the receiving array may be conformal rather than cylindrical. (Rozvoorouzhenie)

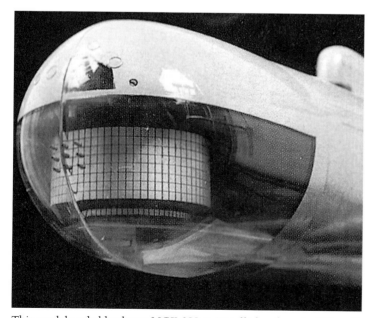

This model probably shows MGK-300 as installed on board a "Victor"-class submarine. (Morphysiprobor)

board "Echo II"– and "Charlie"-class missile submarines. It then appeared on board many SSNs, as well as Tango-class ASW submarines. Reported performance: active range 2.0 nm, passive range 4.0 nm (8 kyd).

"Victor I," Yankee, and Delta I/II/III–class strategic submarines apparently used the related MGK-300 complex (one source credits the Yankee class with MGK-100, and MGK-300 may be a modernized version). In at least some cases (such as "Victor I") MGK-300 probably uses a 6m-dia Rubin (MGK-200) sonar (introduced on board the Project 661 "Papa"-class submarine).

According to a recent Russian account, the main advances represented by MGK-300 were: adoption of multiple operating modes, reduced frequency, increased capability in passive and active modes, the use of reversible (presumably active/passive) transducers, and the ability to adjust reception parameters to match water conditions (which suggests depression or elevation of the beam for bottom-bounce or perhaps convergence zone detection). A photograph of the console shows a big circular CRT.

At least in SSBNs, the associated FCS is Brest, which receives its data mechanically and can position-keep and develop attack solutions for two targets simultaneously (rather than on a single target, as in Leningrad). This analog system can accommodate ballistics for seven types of torpedo.

NATO applied a different code-name, Squid Arm, to the Alfa-class sonar suite, which included a Mouse Roar HF obstacle-avoidance sonar, which was common to many later classes. A recent Russian book lists Alfa with an Okean sonar system including the Yenisei passive sonar.

◆ MG-7

This 300-kHz dipping sonar is used by major warships to detect swimmers and by small minesweepers for mine avoidance. There is no known NATO code-name.

◆ MG-70

Ice-monitoring sonar, at least in "Victor" class.

◆ Orion (NATO Moose Jaw)

This enormous LF hull sonar was probably intended to achieve convergence-zone capability, at least in the Mediterranean. It may be a lower-frequency derivative of the British Type 177, details of which would have been obtained by the well-publicized Soviet spy ring at Portsmouth, which was working just when Type 177 was being developed. Instrumented range is 40 km (about 44 kyd).

Users: Russia (first two *Kirovs*).

◆ Pelamida (NATO Shark Tail)

This "Victor III"–class towed array is reportedly 8 cm × 80 m long, with 50 hydrophones, operating at 20–200 Hz; it is streamed on a 756m cable (37.5mm dia). In a "Victor III," the array has full DEMON processing. Probably the tail and the flank array share a processor, as in some U.S. submarines. This sonar may be called Pithon.

◆ Platina MG-335 and Piranha MG-335MS (NATO Bull Nose/Steer Hide)

This MF hull/towed sonar is integrated with 53cm torpedo tubes used for self-defense, and in this sense corresponds to the U.S. SQS-56/Mk 309 panel/Mk 32 tubes in a *Perry*-class frigate. Typically it can search out to 130 deg to either side of the bow. Claimed ranges are 4–6 km in direct path and 25–30 km in convergence zone.

Krivaks have a related sonar (code-named Bull Horn by NATO), Piranha (MGK-332). The K in the designator suggests that Piranha includes both the bow sonar and the Mare Tail VDS. The bow array operates at 4.5, 5.0, 5.5 kHz with 380-Hz bandwidth (CW and FM pulses); pulse widths 30, 60, and 120 msec. The same consoles control RBU-6000 and process data from its smaller attack sonar (which is in a separate dome about 60 ft abaft the main dome). Krivak III has a solid-state version. Estimated ranges: 3 nm passive, 5 nm active (10 kyd). These figures correspond to SQS-23 performance. Grishas are credited with an

A Russian "Victor III"-class submarine displays her towed array pod atop her vertical fin. This particular submarine had fouled the towing cable of a U.S. towed array, and her crew was trying to break the cable. The submarine was trimmed down by the bow, so her unusual double propeller (two four-bladed propellers in tandem, turning together) is visible. This type of propeller was adopted by many early steam-torpedo and destroyer builders as a way of transmitting considerable power with cavitation and without accepting unduly large propellers. The scale of the pod and fin are clear from the figure of the Russian crewman trying to cut the cable. This photograph was taken in the fall of 1983. (U.S. Navy)

The Platina control console. (Rozvoorouzhenie)

MGK 335MS sonar system, working with an "Elk Tail" VDS. The *Sovremennyy* is credited with an MG-335 sonar, almost certainly actually MGK-335. MGK-335MS is a digitized version currently offered for export.

MGK-335 has a two-way underwater communication mode.

Users:

Platina: Poland (Kashin), Russia (*Kuznetsov, Admiral Gorshkov, Slava, Sovremennyy*, and modernized Kashin classes).

Piranha: Russia (Krivak class, Grisha class). This may be the version in *Sovremennyys*.

◆ Polinom (NATO Horse Jaw/Horse Tail)

This Orion successor is probably an all-round scanning sonar rather than a sector scanner. The use of a single designator for both bow and towed (Horse Tail) sonars suggests that it is an integrated system like Platina. In the *Kiev* class, Polinom replaces both Moose Jaw and the MF Bull Horn. It is credited with instrumented ranges of 30/60/120 km, that is, with multiple convergence zone range in the Mediterranean. Polinom is reportedly based on compromised French technology, and is probably, in effect, a lower-frequency equivalent to DUBV 23. Unlike earlier Soviet VDS fish, that used in Polinom is saucer-shaped.

Users: Russia (*Kuznetsov, Admiral Gorshkov*, last two *Kirovs, Udaloy* class).

◆ Rubikon MGK-400 (NATO Shark Teeth)/Uzel

This modular hybrid sonar, introduced in 1974, uses analog beam-formers but apparently introduced narrow-band digital signal processing (probably DEMON rather than LOFAR) to Russian practice, at least for diesel submarines. Accurate frequency measurement made it easier to discriminate against reverberation and also made it possible to measure range rate by Doppler shift. The passive element employs a new dual-channel electronic switch (commutator), for better DF accuracy. The main LF bow transducer is a tapered passive cylinder (truncated cone: 7 transducers/stave) apparently similar to that of MGK-200. The active element of the system is in the sail. The associated mine-detection sonar (NATO Mouse Roar) is Arfa (MG-519); the sound velocity meter is MG-553, and the cavitation detector is MG-512. These auxiliary sets are probably also included in the Skat system described below. Some Tango-class submarines (which have MGK-400) also have towed arrays. MG-53, a passive set carried by some Kilos, may be a flank array but is much more likely to be a sonar intercept set.

A model of MGK-400EM at Dubai, 1995. (D. Markov)

Estimated performance: 6 nm active, 9 nm passive.

MGK-400EM is a fully digital version using a digital beam-former, enjoying twice the range of the basic sonar but using the same arrays and the same equipment volume. The manufacturer, Okeanpribor, currently offers -400EM-01 and -02 as upgrades of existing Foxtrot-, Romeo-, and Whiskey-class submarines. MGK-400EM can autotrack four targets but the system still can engage only two.

Two targets can be autotracked, data from the autotrackers being fed automatically (mechanically) to the Uzel digital torpedo FCS, which is built around a 100-KOPS computer. Like the earlier Brest, it can engage two targets simultaneously, in this case using wire-guided torpedoes (whose paths are shown on the system's CRT). Three targets can be tracked manually. Uzel weighs 2.8 t, takes 3.5 min to warm up, and has an MTBF of 2000 hr.

Users: Algeria (Kilo class), China (Kilo class), India (Kilo class), Iran (Kilo class), Russia (Kilo and Tango classes). MGK-400 was introduced in the Tango class. MGK-400 is identified here with Shark Teeth rather than (as is usual) with Shark Gill because as a hybrid sonar it seems closer to the MGK-100/300 family than to the digital MGK-500.

◆ Shelon/Argun (NATO Elk Tail and Rat Tail)

These are probably the two helicopter dippers (NATO Elk Tail [Ka-25 helicopters: 14–16-kHz OKA-2] and 14–15-kHz Rat Tail [Ka-27 helicopters]) on board Grisha-class ASW corvettes; these ships also have Titan hull sonars. Unlike a ship with a conventional VDS, a ship using a dipper must stop, dip, and only then run. Such craft are best suited to "sprint and drift" operation, and they are designed to retrieve their dippers very rapidly. OKA-2 has a maximum active range of 5500 m and can reach 18,500 m in passive mode.

◆ Sheksna

Sonar of the sole Babochka (Project 1141) -class ASW hydrofoil.

◆ Shtil' MG-35

This sonar is listed on board Kresta II and Krivak III, in combination with a Titan II bow sonar and, in the Krivak, a Vega towed sonar. It is also listed on board the "Zhenya"-class minesweepers. The name suggests that it is a fire-control set, perhaps a successor to Vychegda.

◆ Skat (MGK-500) (NATO Shark Gill)/MGK-540

This sonar added to the earlier combination of functions "infrasonic [i.e., VLF] frequency band detection," which implies the presence of a VLF flank array (later a towed array was added). The system is also described as automated, which implies both digital beam-forming and a higher degree of integration. In a Typhoon-class SSBN, Skat is described as a digital sonar capable of tracking 10 to 12 targets.

A model shows the MGK-540 active-passive array. Note the flank array sections alongside the pressure hull. (Rozvoorouzhenie)

Associated sonars are: MG-512 cavitation monitor, MG-518 upward-looking fathometer, MG-519 mine detector, MG-553 sound velocity meter, NOR-1 ice lane detector, and NOK-1 surface warner (to ensure safe surfacing).

The ultimate development of this series of sonars, MGK-540, automatically detects, ranges on, and tracks targets in broad- and narrow-band at frequencies ranging from audio down through LF to "infrasonic" (LOFAR region); targets are automatically classified by signature. This sonar also automatically intercepts and tracks narrow- and broad-band sonar signals, measuring their parameters for identification. Using a new acoustic data link, it can exchange information and target identification. The sonar has an integral performance estimator/ray tracer and BITE, and it incorporates self-noise monitors.

The arrangement is very different from that of the earlier sonar. There is no separate active element. Instead, there is a cylindrical transducer (nine transducers per stave, about 30 staves) in the chin position, plus a double series of long horizontal staves mounted as a ring around the pressure hull.

Skat was introduced in "Victor II"-class submarines; "Charlie II" has Skat-M. Victor III has Skat-KS. Apparently only in this class the transducers of the cylinder are wrapped around a sphere that houses the processing elements; this is *not* a spherical sonar. This arrangement suggests that as an interim type (pending availability of Sierra/Akula), "Victor III" lacks internal space which in other designs is used for the sonar processor. Skat-1 is MGK-503 in Akula-, Sierra-, and Typhoon-class submarines; in their case the active/passive bow transducer is apparently a truncated cone like that in MGK-400. Skat-2 is in Delta IV (Project 667BRDM) submarines. Oscar and Akula II apparently have Skat-3 (MGK-540).

◆ Tamir (NATO Perch Gill [Tamir-5L,-5LS], Stag Hoof [Tamir-5N, -5NS], Stag Horn [Tamir-10], and Stag Hoof [Tamir-11, -11M])

Tamir-5LS, an active 24-kHz searchlight sonar introduced in 1947–50, equipped first-generation postwar Soviet submarines. It was probably copied from British sets supplied in wartime. The corresponding surface ship set was Tamir-5N. Tamir-10, for small surface ships, appeared in 1950, Tamir-11 (MG-11) and -11M following in 1952. They may have had tilting searchlight transducers, as in contemporary Western attack sonars associated with ahead-thrown weapons.

Users:

> Tamir-5LS: Albania (Whiskey class), North Korea (Whiskey class).
> Tamir-11: Albania (T-43 class), China (some Shanghai class), Egypt (Hainan, Yurka, and T-43 classes), Korea (Taechong class and Hainan class), Poland (modified *Obluze* and *Krogulec* classes), Romania (*Kronstadt*, Cosar, Musca, M-40 classes), Russia (Yurka class), Vietnam (Yurka class).

◆ Titan MG-312 and MG-332 (NATO Bull Nose)

This MF scanning search/target indication sonar was introduced in the "Kashin" (Project 61) and Petya (Project 159) classes. Titan also appeared on board the new BPKs (Kresta and Kara classes). It was first tested in 1960, and probably operates at 7.5 kHz with a 7500-yd keying interval. The timing and the frequency suggest that this sonar may have been derived from the compromised British Type 184. Some ships, such as "Krupnys" converted for ASW in the late 1960s, received Titan-2 (MG-332) sonars. Presumably Platina (MG-335) integrated the Titan hull transducer with a towed transducer. Vychegda is the attack sonar associated with Titan, supporting RBU-6000.

◆ Vega MG-325 (NATO Mare Tail) and Pike (NATO Mare Tail)

This MF VDS, the first in Soviet service, is associated with the Orion (Moose Jaw) hull sonar in the first two *Kirovs*, and with Titan-2 (MG-332 Bull Nose) in frigates and destroyers. It was probably based on the British Type 177 (reportedly it uses the same sort of stepped-frequency transmission). Mare Tail was tested in 1966 on board a Petya I trials ship. Pike is the version on board Krivaks (Pike-MK is on a Krivak III). Mare Tail (probably Pike) may be carried by some Mi-14 helicopters. Estimated performance: 4.0 nm active (8 kyd), 2 nm passive.

◆ VGS-3 (NATO Foal Tail/Lamb Tail)

Dipping active/passive sonar of the Ka-28 helicopter.

◆ Vychegda MG-311 and MG-322 (NATO Wolf Paw)

This was the planar-array attack sonar (for RBU-6000) which worked with the Titan search sonar in "Kashins" and other ASW ships of the 1960s. The NATO code-name suggests that it used a Hercules transducer in tilting searchlight form. Active range was 5 km (about 5500 yd).

MG-322, which is probably a new version of Vychegda, is the main hull sonar in Konis (MG-322T version) and is also in Indonesian (ex-German) and probably Russian Parchims. Parchims also have MG-329 (presumably a scanning search sonar) and possibly an MG-16 mine-avoidance set.

◆ Zvezda M-1 (NATO Ox Yoke/Ox Tail)

Neustrashimyy-class integrated sonar suite, comprising a bow sonar, flank arrays on a bow dome extended back along the keel, and a towed active sonar. This sonar may be broadly comparable to SQS-53C, with digital reception *and* transmission. A drawing of the export version of a *Udaloy*-class destroyer (presumably equipped with this type of sonar) shows a sonar window in the forefoot and a side panel further aft, possibly analogous to the U.S. SQQ-23 PADLOC (passive location by triangulation).

Foal/Stork Tail dipping sonar of an Mi-14 (Haze) helicopter. (Royal Navy)

Dipping sonar of a Ka-27 Helix helicopter. (Royal Navy)

◆ Burya

The FCS of the Smerch-2 (RBU-6000) and Smerch-3 (RBU-1000) systems can control up to four launchers. Versions for different classes are indicated by suffixes giving the project number of the ship. Control is analog.

◆ Drakon

This small-ship analog underwater FCS controls both torpedoes and RBU-6000. It may accept data from other ships in a group, for example for coordinated rocket firing. Drakon is aboard, for example, Pauk-class ASW corvettes. The system can operate continuously for 12 hr. Total weight is 2.7 t.

◆ Purga

This large-ship underwater FCS controls both torpedoes (to ranges of 50 km, against targets 30 km apart) and RBU-6000/ 1000 (to 8000m range); it is on board the *Neustrashimyy*. Maximum target speed is 60 kt. Calculation/weapon setting time is 15 sec; readiness time from "off" position is 40 sec. Weight is 2000 kg. Purga can operate continuously for 24 hours, and service life is 20 yr. There are both analog and digital versions.

SOUTH AFRICA

The International Maritime Technology (IMT) company of Simonstown has developed a towed array, intended as a technology demonstrator. It was used in 1988 to find the flight-deck voice and data recorder from the South African Airways 747 that crashed in the Indian Ocean. This device might form the basis of a future South African navy sensor.

The South African *Daphne*-class submarines are being modernized with new locally produced sonars. Only the original medium-range active sonar has been retained.

SWEDEN

SONARS

◆ SonTak

Sonartaktisk beslutsstoed is the standard sonar decision aid (to determine which sonar is best suited to current conditions, at which depth [if it is a VDS], and how sonars in a task group can best be combined) on board Swedish submarines, corvettes, and minesweepers. It uses an MIU 2000 personal computer connected to one or two probes (conductivity, pressure, temperature, to calculate a sound velocity profile). It can collect hydroacoustic forecasts from the shore-based BAeSEMA HAIS system and to send their information to HAIS. The computer runs two programs, the sonar tactical decision aid (SonTak) and a hydroacoustic database (HYDAB). HYDAB is used to classify passive contacts, including pings from active sonars. New information can be entered into MUSAC, the naval intelligence and analysis center, where the master hydroacoustic database is located.

These systems were installed in 1995.

FIRE-CONTROL SYSTEMS

◆ Spider/GII

The Spider FCS for the Tp 45 lightweight torpedo is based on the earlier GII tactical plotter (electronic chart table), which is also the basis for the Swedish COOP MCM system. It uses 80386/ 80387 CPU and math coprocessor and a Texas Instruments TMS 34010 graphics processor; it has a keyboard, up to three trackballs, and a touch-panel that has its own simulated trackball. Maps are shown on a 1024 × 1024-pixel 12in AC plasma screen. Software is modular: master and tactical plotting indicator (TPI) in GII, with torpedo fire control (TFC) and the appropriate interface added in Spider. Master manages the internal bus and mass storage (hard and floppy disks). One TFC can handle up to four torpedoes simultaneously.

◆ TORCI

PEAB's fast-attack-boat torpedo FCS can engage two targets simultaneously with long-range wire-guided torpedoes. Its fixed-program solid-state computer projects ahead target positions (position-keeps) and continuously calculates a torpedo interception course for each target, taking own-ship maneuvers into account. A PPI fed by the search radar shows the tactical situation, projected target course, and torpedo course already run (dead-reckoned on the basis of commands sent) and intercept course. A tracker operator maintains track using bearing- and range-correction handwheels to keep the target centered on a B-scope (the surface search radar has no TWS memory). The console also shows projected torpedo running range. When targets are designated optically, torpedoes are fired along the LOS, with course corrections as the ship and target move. Torpedoes are normally guided automatically by the system, but they can also be steered manually using port/starboard buttons.

TORCI appeared in 1959, and was a very early example of solid-state electronics (using discrete devices).

Users: Denmark (*Willemoes* class), Norway (*Snogg* class), and Sweden (*Spica II* class).

◆ 9TC302

The digital FCS for Swedish ASW helicopters controls Tp 42 wire-guided torpedoes. A small data-transmission unit aboard the helicopter continuously and automatically transmits target course and speed to another helicopter or ship so that the latter can attack without transmitting. When controlling other platforms, the master helicopter uses its on-board radar to monitor the position of the cooperating units as well as to provide target data against periscopes or surfaced submarines. The Tp 42 torpedo can also be used against surface vessels.

The production version was first delivered in May 1981. Deliveries were completed in 1983, an evaluation system having been delivered in 1978.

UNITED KINGDOM

Submarine sonars normally operate passively. A "captain's key" (which must be kept in the captain's sight at all times) has to be inserted in order to ping.

Late in 1994 GEC-Marconi received a contract from DRA for a reconfigurable (single- or multiline) experimental towed array.

◆ Type 162 and 162M

"Cockchafer" 50-kHz bottom-profile sonar detects bottomed submarines. It sweeps a narrow beam across the sea bed and detects the shadow of an object. Three quartz-strip transducers, each producing a 3 × 40-deg fan beam, are mounted horizontally, flush with the hull near the bow: one on the keel and one on either side, tilted down at a 25-deg angle. The shadow is shown on a chemical range recorder. Range scales are 300 and 600 yd (Type 162M adds a 1200-yd scale). Range accuracy is better than 2%.

Cockchafer entered service in 1948. It is currently manufactured by Kelvin-Hughes and by A B Precision (Poole) Ltd.

Users: Bangladesh (*Leopard* class), Brazil (Type 22s), Canada (as SQS-501), Chile (County class, *Leanders*), Ecuador (*Leanders*), India (*Leanders*, possibly other ships), Indonesia ("Tribal" class), Iran (*Saam* class), Pakistan (Type 21s, *Leanders*), United Kingdom.

◆ Type 170B

The 15–25-kHz "four-square" attack sonar is associated with the Limbo mortar, returns in its four beams (in diamond arrangement) being compared to autotrack the target in bearing and in elevation. Depth settings for fire control are derived from the tilt angle. Accuracy is 0.5 deg in bearing and tilt, 5 yd in range. Maximum range and depth, about 2000 yd and 1200 ft, correspond to a 1945 Admiralty policy that near-term weapons and sensors should deal with 15kt diesel submarines capable of diving to 1000 ft (these figures were changed in 1950 to 25 kt and 1500 ft). The Type 170 operator scans in depth and bearing, centering the beam using a CRT. It is flanked by separate paper recorders for bearing and range, with a fire-control unit alongside the range recorder. Type 170B can accept visual and radar data (e.g., the location of a submarine periscope). A planned means of correcting for water sound profile was never developed.

The Type 170/Limbo FCS staff requirement was stated in 1948, preliminary trials of the "four-square" transducer having been conducted in 1947. The first production 170Bs began trials in June 1954. A solid-state Type 170M entered service in 1974. Ships already fitted with Type 170 could be converted to 170M during normal refits, as the transducer was not changed.

Type 199, the VDS version of Type 170, is now extinct.

Users: Chile (ex-HMS *Achilles* has 170B; the other *Leanders* have had their Limbos removed but may retain the sonar), India (*Leanders*), Indonesia ("Tribal" class), Iran (Vosper Mk 5 frigates), Malaysia (*Rahmat* and *Hang Tuah*), Pakistan (*Leander* class). Many ships in which Type 170 was the primary sonar were reequipped with PMS 26 (see that entry).

◆ Type 177

The first British scanning sonar (6, 7.5, or 9 kHz) uses a flat sector-scanning transducer (12 vertical strips, 10 transducers each, in pairs driven by separate transmitters, to produce five 10-deg transmitting beams in a ripple sequence equivalent to RDT; there are four 14-deg receiving beams). Transmission is a series of ripples (five pulses each): long (150 msec), medium (20 msec, 225 Hz above base frequency), and short (5 msec, 225 Hz below base frequency), for a total of 875 msec, with a pulse interval depending on the range scale: 7.5 sec/5 kyd, 15 sec/10 kyd, 30 sec/20 kyd. Four pings are needed to classify a target. For example, a full dual sweep (80 deg) takes 8 min (4 min at 10 kyd, 2 min at 5 kyd). This was acceptable against a 15kt submarine, but not against a fast one; hence the shift to Type 184. Expected performance (isothermal water, Sea State 1–2): range to a beam-on submarine (own speed 12 kt), 18 kyd. With a negative temperature gradient and Sea State 2–3, range would fall to 8 kyd, and to only 3 kyd with a surface layer and Sea State 4–5. Bearing accuracy: 5 deg on Doppler display, 1 deg on sector-scan display. In effect this is a simple preformed-beam (electric delay network) sonar like the German GHG rather than a mechanically scanned sonar like contemporary U.S. sets. It is roughly comparable to the U.S. SQS-4 series.

The displays are paper range recorders for the separate beams, plus a CRT for the Doppler display and a CRT for the sector-scan display.

This sonar was designed in 1949 and accepted for service in 1957.

Users: Chile (*Condell* and *Lynch*), and Indonesia ("Tribal"-class frigates).

◆ Type 184 and 184M/Graseby G750

This 6/7.5/9-kHz sonar, replacing Type 177 (but using 30% of the same components, and modifying 30% of existing components), marked the first operational British use of a cylindrical array (3.5 × 3.5 ft, 32 staves, 13 BaTi transducers/stave; some 7.5-kHz units may have had 4 ft × 46in arrays). All-round scanning offered a sufficient data rate to handle fast submarines. Effective range is somewhat less than in Type 177 because the sonar beam does not revisit any particular sector as often. Type 184 introduced simultaneous active (against submarines) and passive (for torpedo detection) operation, and multitarget tracking. Important innovations were the echo Doppler display and the use of fixed transmission intervals with a dual-frequency system. A CRT made for better target recognition and tracking and an all-around and continuous torpedo alarm. Doppler was found particularly valuable against a fast submarine.

Transmission is RDT, using sets of 12 staves excited in phase to create an 11.25 × 10-deg beam scanning around the array in about 1.6 sec. Pulse width is 45 msec with a source level of 136 dB (originally 75 msec for a special Doppler sector, for narrower bandwidth); there is also probably a long 150-msec pulse for long range. Range scales/pulse intervals: 5 kyd/7.5 sec, 10 kyd/15 sec, and 20 kyd/20 sec. To avoid reverberation, reception is blanked out for the first 5 sec in short-range mode and for the first 10 sec (8 kyd) in the longe-range modes. Beam-forming networks produce eight split receiving beams (the complexity of the networks precludes any finer division of the incoming signal). Comparison of the phases of signals received in each half-beam improves accuracy within a beam to about 1 deg. The sonar also forms a scannable 90-deg-wide Doppler sector consisting of four 22.5-deg beams (bearing accuracy is about half a beamwidth, or 10 deg) using 21 Doppler filters (maximum Doppler 40 kt). Passive targets (mainly torpedoes) are displayed around the edge of the PPI. One electronic marker measures range and range rate for transmission to the ship's FCS; another is manually set in range and bearing. It can be used to select an audio channel.

Passive performance (45kt steam torpedo): 6 kyd at own-ship speed of 18 kt, 3 kyd at 24 kt, 1.5 kyd at 30 kt, in each case about twice that of the predecessor Type 176.

The retractable dome, which can accommodate Type 177 as an alternative, is 64 × 157.25 × 61 (deep) in.

Modified versions: Type 184M (export version Graseby G750), solid-state electronics; 184P, solid-state Doppler display; 184S, solid-state PPI. In 1985 Graseby began the Royal Navy Type 184P modernization, based partly on its own G750 program; by April 1989, 29 ships had received partial modernizations. Ultimately the transmitter, PPI, Doppler display, and passive elements were all replaced. The eight-sector beam-former was replaced by a 16-sector beam-former for better performance (less noise surrounds the target in any one beam). Using 31 Doppler filters in each Doppler channel, the modified sonar can measure speed up to 40 kt with 3kt precision. Modernization included the 16-sector modification and replacement of more than half the vacuum tubes by solid-state electronics. BITE was added. The program was protracted, and it is not clear how many sonars were fully modernized before Type 184 was withdrawn from British service.

Type 184 was conceived in 1955 primarily for self-protection (combining 177 and the antitorpedo 176 in a single time-shared transducer), but also for future ASW ships. Tests against fast submarines (HMS *Explorer* and then USS *Nautilus*) showed that something very different was needed. Type 177 searched too narrow a sector too slowly: fast submarines quickly cleared the search zone.

Users: Chile ("County" class, *Leander* class [some 184P]), Ecuador (*Leander* class [184P]), India (*Godavari* [G750], four *Nilgiri* class [G750]), New Zealand (three *Leander* class [G750]), Pakistan (*Leander* class, Type 21 frigates). The *Nilgiri* sets are being (or have been) replaced by Canadian Westinghouse SQS-505s (hull and VDS); the last two units have French Spherion sonars.

◆ Type 187

The MF/LF (10 kHz active, 2.5 or 10 kHz passive) searchlight attack sonar of *Oberon*-class submarines has a 5ft wide flat transducer rotating within a 72 × 192 × 57.5 in (high) dome, using split-beam techniques to achieve a bearing accuracy of about half a degree. It incorporates a low-power mine-detection sonar. In theory, targets initially detected by 186/2007 would be tracked passively by 187, which would shift to active pinging for the attack.

Type 187 trainable sonar transducer with its sonar dome removed, on board a British *Oberon*-class submarine, 1988. The individual spot transducers can just be distinguished; the sonar is trained broadside. (A. Raven)

Some *Oberons* may retain their Type 719 trainable hydrophones (one at the fore end of the keel, one at the after end of the sail).

Users: Brazil (*Oberon* class), Chile (*Oberon* class). Type 187 is being replaced by CSU-90 bow arrays in modernized Brazilian and Chilean *Oberons*.

◆ Type 189

Type 189 is a cavitation indicator.

◆ Type 193

See the Mine Warfare section.

◆ Type 195/2069 and PMS 26/27

The standard British 9.5/10/10.5-kHz helicopter dipping sonar uses a four-stave (13 elements each) flat-faced transducer (10.8 × 38.4 × 7.3 in, 45 lb in a 120-lb fish on an 800ft cable) covering a 90-deg sector. As in Type 177, the staves are excited in turn to sweep the beam across the sector; a delay-line network produces three 30 × 4.7-deg (at 10 kHz) receiving beams (phase comparison within each beam improves bearing accuracy to 3 deg). Pulse widths are 5, 25, and 40 msec (original source level 129 dB, peak power 6.5 kW). Range scales: 3, 6, 9, and 12 kyd (accuracy 1.5% of scale). The sonar typically pings twice in each 90-deg sector, then takes 3 sec to train 90 deg. It was designed for a 6000-yd range under average conditions (3000 yd against a submarine below the layer, or 8000 yd if both transducer and submarine were below the layer), but performance improved considerably when quiet gas-turbine helicopters entered service. On-board electronics dead-reckons between dips so that the helicopter can maintain contact as it approaches its target. A Doppler display is used for initial detection. A BT in the fish measures the sound-velocity profile.

Plessey's Type 195 was conceived in the late 1950s and entered service in 1966. Production of the final 195M version ended in 1985.

Type 2069 is an upgraded 195M, to operate at greater depth (1000 ft) and to be integrated with an AQS-902 processor.

Plessey's PMS 26 and 27 small-ship 9.5/10/10.5-kHz sector-scanning sonars are based on the Type 195 helicopter dipper, with the same 90-deg instantaneous coverage, but they can depress their beams for MCC (the transducer, in a retractable dome, is 44.5 × 99.6 × 53 cm deep, 100 kg). In the current Mod 1 solid-state version, pulse widths are 250 msec and 1 sec (modes CW and FM); there is also a short CW pulse for short range. Range scales are 3, 6, 12, and 18 kyd (effective range is about 4.5 km). There is a passive mode, and options include passive tracking, a 20-kHz transducer, an underwater telephone mode, and an interface to a CDS.

PMS 26 was marketed as a replacement for Type 164/174, which were often used in combination with a Limbo control set (170). Because PMS 26 cannot track in depth, Type 170 probably survives in ships refitted with it. PMS 27 is the same sonar using a different hull outfit suited to ships down to 750 t.

Users:

Type 195: Australia (Sea King Mk 50), Argentina (seven Italian-built Sea Kings and two Lynxes), Canada (31 CH-124s; replaced by AQS-13), Egypt (18 Sea King Mk 47s), India (10 Sea King Mk 42), Pakistan (six Sea King Mk 45s, now removed), and the United Kingdom (150 Type 195M on Sea Kings). The improved Type 2069 is operated only by the Royal Navy (60 purchased for Sea King HAS.6).

PMS 26/27: Denmark (*Nils Juel*–class frigates, fishery-protection ship *Besketerren*), Indonesia (probably ex-"Tribal"-class frigates), Iran (probably Vosper Mk 5 frigates), Ireland (*Eithne* [PMS 26L]), Malaysia (probably frigates *Rahmat* and *Hang Tuah*), Mexico (probably two, applications unknown), Nigeria (*Obuma* and Vosper Mk 3 and Mk 9 frigates), Turkey (patrol boat *Girne* and probably also AB 25 class), Venezuela (two *Almirante Clemente*–class corvettes).

◆ Type 2001/2020/2027/2032/2074

The standard British active-passive SSN bow sonar, now in its third generation (2001, 2020, 2074), uses a eyebrow array running back about 20 to 22 ft from the bow on either side of the submarine. Details that follow are for the original 2001, but are probably reasonably accurate for successors. In this sonar the array consists 24 flat panels (each 2 × 6.75 ft, carrying 56 transducers, tilted at an angle of 20 deg to the vertical). This array produces a total of 24 active search beams (about 10 × 16 deg). Normally, the beams tilt down 20 deg to compensate for the array's shape, but they can be tilted another 20 deg for bottom bounce. As in the major contemporary surface-ship sonars (177 and 184), the 3.25-kHz active beam (source level 137 dB) is rippled from one end of the array to the other in a sequence of 24 long (200 msec/20nm+ scale) and 24 short (100 msec/10 nm) pulses. These pulses are Doppler-filtered, originally using fifteen 8-Hz filters (equivalent to a total of 30 kt). To catch short-range targets, a ripple of 20-msec pulses (at 3 kHz) follows the main long pulse. It is processed in a 40-Hz filter (the Doppler for 10 kt). Echoes from long and short pulses are displayed separately. To overcome any problem of splashover from one beam to another, the system has an alternative low-power ODT mode. A separate active attack/classification mode (on one beam) uses a long FM pulse (1.25 sec at 3.5–3.8 kHz) which can be used for ASPECT; a separate attack/ASPECT display is mounted between the two main CRTs, so that either search operator can cue the attack/classification operator.

Type 2001 operates passively at 1.5–2.3 kHz; 2.5 would have been better but then the sonar would also have suffered from reverberations from active transmissions. For greater precision, a second passive channel, at 5.5–6.5 kHz, was provided (with the second harmonic of the main active frequency, about 6 kHz, blanked off). For passive operation, the sonar forms 47 beams, each 10 deg wide, at 5-deg intervals (in active operation only half the beams were used). Passive signals are displayed on the main initial-detection displays, and there is also an audio channel for the sector-display operator.

Because the beams were formed by delay lines, they could not be geographically stabilized to cancel out own-ship motion (digital beam-formers eliminate this problem). The main displays, then, were stabilized in 5-deg steps. Only the sector display (for attack) was continously gyrostabilized.

The next-generation Type 2020 (which incorporates considerable 2016 technology) uses steered preformed beams with the 2001 array. It is mainly a 2–16-kHz passive sonar using bottom bounce and CZ modes. The active frequency may be raised to 5.5–5.7 kHz. Features include automatic tracking for reduced workload. There is a manual override. Displays include three CRTs (two in sonar, one in the control room) and two multipen paper track printers. There is no depression/elevation display. BITE and fault-monitoring were incorporated for the first time in a British submarine sonar. The Type 2020 requirement was stated in 1976–77, Plessey receiving a contract in 1977, and the first production delivery following in October 1982 for HMS *Tireless*.

A more completely upgraded Type 2020, designated MODEX or 2020EX, uses two Ferranti universal raster-scan displays for both passive and active data, replacing the earlier cursive PPIs. Reportedly, the universal screens make for faster operator reactions during close contact or in torpedo evasion. The printers are retained for mission analysis. Plasma touch-panel displays replace the earlier keyboards. Reportedly 2020 MODEX is Type 2043, part of the Trident submarine suite (Type 2054).

Type 2027 is a passive ranger using the 2001/2020 array (*Swiftsure, Trafalgar* classes), estimating range on the basis of multiple propagation paths. That probably means measuring the depression/elevation of the same tonal received over the different paths, then using a sonar propagation model to find the distant point at which those paths converge.

Type 2032 uses 15 detuned bow array transducers for LOFAR passive detection; it is equivalent to the U.S. linear array wrapped around submarines' bows. It was first delivered in March 1989, and all 13 had been delivered by March 1991.

Type 2074 is a further upgrade of 2020EX/2054 (Phase II Upgrade) first delivered in mid-1990. Part of 2076 (see below), it is almost certainly a processor or software upgrade (unit cost, about £1M, will not buy new arrays). Plessey received the development contract in February 1988. Early in 1995, GEC-Marconi Naval Systems sonar division (the Plessey successor) won an order for 2074LRE (possibly LF Receiving Equipment).

Users: United Kingdom (2001 in chin position [2001BC version] in all but last two units of *Swiftsure* class; 2020 retrofitted to *Splendid* and *Spartan* and in all *Trafalgars*; 2032 in all SSNs; 2074 in *Sovereign, Superb, Sceptre, Spartan, Splendid*, and all *Trafalgars*).

◆ Type 2004

A submarine hull-mounted sound velocity meter.

◆ Type 2005

The French DUUX 2A passive range-finder.

◆ Type 2006/2012/2018/2030/2035/2047

Sonar signal analyzers: Type 2006 is the U.S. AN/BQQ-3 LOFAR set. Type 2012 is probably a successor. Type 2018 is a submarine DEMON analyzer with LOFARgram output (DIANA). Type 2030 is Spectral Dynamics's two-channel spectrum analyzer with waterfall display (U.S. AN/BQR-22). Type 2035 is a BQR-23 16-channel waterfall processor used with the Type 2024 array. Type 2047 is Plessey's wide-band (5 Hz–3.2 kHz) hard copy (pen output) analyzer producing up to 12 LOFARgrams simultaneously, replacing Type 2035. Type 2047(AC) is a 16-channel processor for the 2024 array. It is on board four *Swiftsure* class.

◆ Type 2007

This 1–3-kHz preformed-beam flank array (24 hydrophones on each side) is a primary long-range search set; it is for initial detection, bearing resolution, and limited TMA. The addition of a TAPS processor converts Type 2007AA to Type 2007AC, with greater sensitivity and better target discrimination. Note that, although the 2007 processor can be switched to a towed array, the Canadians preferred to buy a separate towed array dry end. The requirement was stated in the late 1960s, and the array was developed by British Aerospace; the first unit entered service in 1971. Later units were manufactured by Graseby Dynamics.

Users: Australia (*Oberon* class), Brazil (*Oberon* class), Canada (*Oberon* class), Chile (*Oberon* class), United Kingdom (*Swiftsure*, first five *Trafalgar*).

◆ Type 2013

Type 2013 is a bathythermograph (BT).

◆ Type 2015/2021/2025/2060

Expendable bathythermographs (XBT). Type 2060 is the surface ship set to replace 2015.

◆ Type 2016/2050

This 5.5/6.5/7.5-kHz Type 184 replacement was the first British sonar to incorporate significant computer signal processing, in the form of digital preformed beams and automatic detection and tracking (using an FM1600B computer with 64 kwords of memory). The 64-stave (12 elements/stave) 6ft mechanically stabilized cylindrical array (which can retract into the hull) produces two sets of beams, one nearly horizontal (consisting of 32 pairs of beams, for tracking) and one dipped at 7 deg, to penetrate below the surface layer. An auxiliary 12-element vertical array can be rotated around the main transducers to monitor propagation characteristics. Operating modes are ODT and SDT (for tracking). Total transmitter power is 44 kW.

Each of the three side-by-side consoles has a circular CRT, keyboard, and rollerball, with alphanumeric readouts above. Typically the center CRT is used for a surveillance PPI; its data can be passed to the ship's CDS, and it is also used to monitor system performance. The left-hand display is used for classification/tracking (Doppler B-scan as well as A-scan for target details, using ASPECT). This CRT can show a blow-up of part of the surveillance display, either in B-scan or as a cut through the beam in a vertical plane. The right-hand console is passive (including all-around torpedo warning, as in 184, with an automatic torpedo alarm to the CDS). It is normally used for passive target tracking (bearing-time waterfalls show target histories) and to show frequency ranges. Normally, the operator sits at the center PPI, supported when necessary by an operator at the left-hand (tracking) display.

The sonar uses five electronics cabinets for receivers (four active, one passive), two others for transmitters, and another for T/R control circuits. The signal processor occupies three separate cabinets with another for computer spares.

Plessey's Type 2016 was introduced in the Type 22 class following trials of a test sonar using Ferranti's methods of computer-aided detection (work on which began in 1967) in HMS *Matapan* in 1971–76 and tests of an operational prototype on board HMS *Broadsword* in 1978. In the Falklands it was able to overcome multiple reflections and, thus, to distinguish an Argentine submarine on the bottom. Type 184 seemed to have no such capability. However, because 2016 signals are digitally processed, it lacks an analog (audio) circuit, which the Royal Navy considers an invaluable aid to target classification.

Type 2050 is Ferranti's 64-beam upgrade combining the same transducer with a new signal processor based on that of the FMS 21 export sonar, incorporting Curtis architecture. Type 2050 is credited officially with an excellent software-based ability to reject bottom echoes, for good performance over the continental shelf. The system uses the same type of console as Type 2054; it incorporates 25 M700 microprocessors. Four electronic cabinets replace the twelve of 2016, including one for target classification and one for data-display handling.

The planned 4.5-kHz Type 2050 transmitter was badly delayed, so the program is being carried out in two phases. The first, now sometimes called 2016/50, provides only a new receiver. It requires one rather than two operators. It can track up to 40 targets simultaneously, using linear FM or CW pulses; it also operates passively (in broad- and narrow-band modes) for torpedo detection. The bow dome version in a Type 23, 2050NE, uses the same transducer. Confusingly, the Type 22 and Type 23 versions of 2016/50 are officially designated 2016H22 and 2016HN, though both have been called 2050.

The ultimate version has a much larger 4.5-kHz (or lower frequency) transducer, and therefore is limited to ships with bow domes; unlike 2016/50, it will reach convergence zone in the Atlantic. The test ship was HMS *Scylla*, and the first two will be on board the Type 23 frigates *Monmouth* and *Iron Duke*, which are also the first with the full DNA (SSCS) command system (*Iron Duke*, completed at the end of 1992, was operational trials ship, since she was the first to combine 2050 with an operational CDS). It seems likely that, like SQS-53B/C, 2050 will provide so many passive tracks that automatic TMA (which can be provided by DNA) will be necessary to sort them. Ultimately the full Type 2050 is to equip all Type 22 Batch III (circa 1996) and all Type 23 frigates. Type 22 Batch IIs will receive only 2016/50.

In November 1995 the Royal Navy released an RFP for a preproduction wide-band passive array subsystem for Type 2050.

Unit cost of Type 2050 is about $4–5M (1990). In 1986, 2016 cost $3.5M, plus about $2M for computers. A total of 27 Type 2050s (out of 41 projected) had been bought as of February 1990. Trials of 2050 began in 1986 on board HMS *Jupiter*. The first production unit was delivered in mid-1987. Ferranti's export version was designated FMS 21.

Users: Brazil (Type 22 frigates [2016]; 2016/50 in ex-*Broadsword* and ex-*Brilliant*), New Zealand (*Leander* class [2016/50]), United Kingdom (*Invincible* class [2016], Type 42 Batch I [2016], Type 42 Batch II and III [both 2016/50], Type 22 Batch II [2016/50], Type 22 Batch III [2050], Type 23 [2050]). Note that 34 Type 2016 were bought for Type 22 and Batch 3 *Leander*-class frigates, for later Type 42 destroyers, and for *Invincible*-class carriers.

♦ **Type 2018**

Type 2018 is a submarine DEMON frequency analyzer with LOFARgram output (DIANA).

♦ **Type 2024**

This SSN clip-on towed array typically uses the Type 2030 spectrum analyzer, the Type 2035 processor (which is being replaced by Type 2047), a Plessey beam-former, and a Scientific Atlanta waterfall display. The Ameeco wet end was designed by AUWE. This system is being fitted with the new broad-band TAPS processor. In the Falklands War, HMS *Conqueror* used her array to track the Argentine cruiser *Belgrano* from beyond the horizon, keeping station for two days. Reportedly there was some fear that following the cruiser into somewhat shallower water would cause the array to foul and then to tear off, denying the submarine her ability to track. During the 1980s at least one such array was actually lost to an underwater obstruction. Type 2024 is being replaced by Type 2026.

The contract was let in 1970, followed by preprototype tests in 1974 and service in 1975.

Users: United Kingdom (*Superb, Sceptre, Splendid*).

♦ **Type 2026**

This British/Dutch second-generation attack submarine clip-on (to the port tail fin) towed array was developed in tandem with 2031(I) to replace 2024. The Royal Navy calls it Integrated Sonar Phase I. Compared to 2024, it has more sensitive hydrophones, a stronger cable, a new broad-band LF processor, and an updated narrow-band processor. The processor can be switched to classify signals from the intercept sonar and the Type 2008 underwater telephone. The three large CRTs of the display may cover three octaves. The Dutch version uses an Ameeco wet end, a Marconi beam-former, and a Signaal display processor. Type 2046 is the successor.

HMS *Turbulent* tested a reelable version (the prototype for Type 2044, for the *Vanguard* class), the winch for which was housed in a hump visible aft, above the waterline. Presumably, the array itself was stowed in the narrow space between pressure and outer hulls.

The R&D contract for this array was awarded to Marconi Underwater Systems in 1977–78, and 2026 was tested in 1983–85, entering British service in 1987. The Royal Netherlands Navy bought five arrays late in 1985.

Users: Netherlands (*Walrus* class), United Kingdom (first five *Trafalgar* class).

♦ **Type 2031**

The British five-octave surface-ship towed-array sonar is used both tactically and for surveillance, hence is designed for very long range (probably at least 3 CZ in the Norwegian Sea), attained by a combination of low frequency (hence a long array, reportedly 89 mm × over 500 m, or twice the length of SQR-19) and powerful broad- and narrow-band processing. With the demise of the *Leander* class, the only version in service is Type 2031Z, employing Curtis computer architecture for compactness (reducing weight by 60% and power by 80%, and also drastically cutting cost). The Curtis processor is a very fast special-purpose fixed-program digital computer with over 100 Mbytes of memory. A Logica tracker, introduced 1983, uses image processing to enhance LOFARgrams produced by 2031Z. It seeks buried tonals by integrating *along* a line (which may vary in frequency, due to Doppler) rather than along a fixed frequency (as in ALI); it can also follow the line across different beams as the target maneuvers. The host computer uses a parallel array of 16 68000-series CPUs. The tracker automatically detects, tracks, and classifies contacts. It is to be on board all Type 23 frigates. As of June 1992, eight had been made and six were at sea.

The equivalent submarine sonar is Type 2046.

The initial 2031 R&D contract was awarded to GEC Avionics in 1971/72, four being installed on board modified *Leanders* in 1982. In 1983 this version was superseded by the Curtis-architecture 2031Z.

Users: United Kingdom (Type 22 Batches II and III, Type 23).

♦ **Type 2033**

Hydrographic survey-ship sonar.

♦ **Type 2034/2053/Sonar 3000 PLUS**

Dowty's (Waverley) dual (left- and right-hand arrays) 110-kHz (100-msec pulse) sidescan sonar has been in British service since 1976. The current version of the towed body ("towfish") is Mk 3. Range scales are 75, 150, and 300 m (PRFs of 10, 5, and 2.5 pps). Over 50 units are in current use by the RN Hydrographic Service.

Sonar 3000 PLUS (RN Type 2053) is a family of sidescan devices developed from 2034, and Sonar 3010 has been proposed as a mine locator (analogous to the U.S. Klein Mk 24; see the Mine Warfare section). It adds a higher frequency (300-kHz) mode for short range and high precision (37.5m scale) and can mark a target.

♦ **Type 2040**

See Eledone in the French section above.

♦ **Type 2041**

Upholder-class passive ranger (U.S.-supplied MicroPUFFS).

♦ **Type 2046**

This designation applies both to a towed array (using fiber optics to transmit data back to the submarine) and to its three-octave Curtis architecture (see Type 2031) core processor/display. Type 2046 uses two FMS 13 processors housed below the four adjacent operator positions, each with a CRT and a flat electroluminescent panel beneath it. Display formats include multibeam waterfalls (for detection) and LOFARgrams (for classification). Compared to Type 2024, Type 2046 reportedly provides an improved narrow-band search capability.

The first of 27 arrays was delivered in 1987. Ferranti developed a processor update in 1991; the production contract followed in March 1992, with successful sea trials in the summer of 1994, and delivery completed in June 1996. This Build Standard 2 combines inputs from bow and towed sonars to track targets. It introduces color displays, transputer-based signal processing, and new tactical software written in ADA.

Reportedly at least some submarines (such as HMS *Triumph* and HMS *Turbulent*) carry two Type 2046s each. Probably most British nuclear submarines now have 2046 in place of 2024 or 2026. Type 2046 was also installed in the *Upholders*, which are now for sale.

♦ **Type 2048 (PMS 75)**

Plessey's Speedscan converts a Type 193M minehunting sonar into a sidescanning sonar. The transducer is trained 90 deg on the beam, and Speedscan records the echoes obtained. Its beam-former transforms these data into a map of a strip of the bottom, using three pings for each point in the map. Type 2049 was BAe's unsuccessful competitor to 2048. One prototype was delivered to either the Royal Netherlands Navy or the Royal Danish Navy for trials.

♦ **Type 2051 (Triton)**

This digital passive sonar is a British equivalent to Eledone, employing a bow array (with 32 preformed beams), a broad-band processor, and a two-octave narrow-band processor (an upgraded FMS 12) feeding four Ferranti multipurpose displays. The same narrow-band processor could also handle the outputs of a pair of flank arrays or of a clip-on array. The first fully integrated British sonar, Type 2051 was conceived for *Oberon* upgrades, the active-passive bow array going into a new streamlined low-noise dome to replace Type 187. Plessey was design authority, and R&D was conducted in 1982–84.

Users: Canada (*Oberon* class). British *Oberons*, similarly modified, have all been discarded.

♦ **Type 2054**

Plessey's active/passive/towed passive Trident submarine sonar suite employs a Type 2043 active/passive bow sonar (effectively Type 2020EX), a Type 2044 reelable towed array, and a Type 2045 intercept sonar. These subdesignations are no longer used. Signal processing is entirely digital, the signals being transformed to digital form before being passed to the beam-former. There are five consoles, each with two 17in display screens and touch-sensitive plasma control panels. Plessey (whose sonar division is now part of Marconi) was responsible for the bow sonar, the beam-former, and the signal processor; Marconi for the intercept sonar; and Ameeco for the towed array. In March 1993 GEC-Marconi and Ferranti-Thomson were asked to bid for an integrated stern arc cover system, to assure SSBN security prior to surfacing. Type 2054 includes a Sub-Harpoon missile capability.

The requirement was issued in 1983; Plessey was chosen early in 1985. The preproduction version was completed early in 1989.

Users: United Kingdom (*Vanguard* class).

♦ **Type 2063**

Submarine self-noise monitor.

♦ **Type 2064**

Reportedly, minehunter tracker.

♦ **Type 2065**

Experimental retractable thin-line array.

♦ **Type 2067**

Underwater tracking system.

♦ **Type 2068**

Gresham-CAP's sonar-environment prediction-and-display system (SEPADS) (sonar ray-path predictor) is used with surface-ship towed arrays. 2068 incorporates a library of oceanographic information on a 50-Mbyte hard disk and a series of sound-propagation loss models (each taking about 1.5 sec to run) to predict ranges and to estimate the optimum array depth. The associated computer is a commercial Digital PDP-11/44, and the prediction is updated every 4 to 6 hr.

♦ **Type 2072**

This submarine broad-band linear passive flank array (30 × 3 m, about 3.3 × 98.4 ft), for the last two *Trafalgars*, supersedes 2007. The display incorporates an FMS 12 narrow-band processor, to detect very low frequency tonals.

♦ **Type 2076**

Ferranti-Thomson's Phase III submarine suite for the *Trafalgar* and projected *Trafalgar* Mk 2 classes (plans to refit the *Swiftsures* were dropped) is the first Royal Navy sonar incorporating large-scale flank arrays with three passive ranging spots on each side. There are also the usual bow, towed, obstacle avoidance, and intercept arrays; Type 2079 is probably the bow element. This integrated sonar will incorporate INMOS T9000 transputers, the type used in AQS-950 FLASH. Its interfaces with SSCS are to be updated with Phase 6 and 7 software to support 2076 functionality. Other elements of the update include a new fiber-optic Tactical Weapon System Data Highway and the Submarine Acoustic Warfare System (SAWS, Project Teluma), a knowledge-based tactical aid providing course recommendation and decoy management.

The 1 February 1994 announcement of a £180M contract for full development and initial production ended a 3-yr competition with GEC-Marconi and began a 5–7-yr development cycle. The initial order is for four outfits, with an option for three more. The first shore trial integration system was delivered late in 1995. Type 2078 may be an alternative designation for the next-generation SSN sonar.

♦ **Type 2077 (Parian)**

Plessey won the contract for this LPI submarine obstacle-avoidance sonar early in September 1989; it beat the Ferranti FMS 52. Type 2077 is a high-definition LPI sonar, probably equivalent to the U.S. MIDAS of the *Los Angeles* class. As of

1989, the Plessey system had not yet been tested as a unit. However, it uses proven arrays and components, some of the latter identical to those of the Hydra selected for Swedish submarines and to those of the British Type 2074.

Users: United Kingdom (four *Swiftsures* and seven *Trafalgars*).

◆ Type 2081/Subpack

This submarine hull environmental sensor suite (nominally a 2068 successor) is probably intended at least partly as a wake sensor, given the level of security involved. Parameters measured include conductivity (using an inductive cell), temperature, depth, fluorescence (by shining a single-pulsed Xenon lamp through seawater flowing over the detector), and bioluminescence. Type 2081 employs two sensor packages in titanium cylinders (280 mm × 450 mm [deep], 28 kg) hard-mounted forward of the sail, each with its own hull penetration. Because Type 2081 is a spot sensor, it may be intended mainly to provide a submarine with some measure of its environment, and thus of its vulnerability to nonacoustic sensors. However, a 1994 photograph of HMS *Spartan* shows a "classified mast" somewhat more than sail height, most likely an experimental wake sensor, on the starboard after side of the sail. The photograph suggested a series of access doors running up its height, presumably to take in water for sampling.

Type 2081 development began in 1979, with a production contract awarded in 1992, for 1993–95 delivery of 13 units. Chelsea Instruments also produces an export version, Subpack.

◆ Type 2087

The future Type 23 sonar suite supersedes both 2057 (next-generation towed array begun 1987) and 2080 (future LF sonar suite announced 1990); the designation was chosen to indicate the fusion of the two (as yet there are no 2083–2086s). The staff requirement, ST(S) 7590, calls for a LF (down to 500 Hz) towed transmitter and a wide-aperture towed array (down to 100 Hz). Active pinging would be used to detect quiet submarines and also for bistatic operation with other LF sonars. Type 2087 is also to provide HF intercept capability to cue J-SSTD (Sonar 2070); the 2087 array handling system must include a winch subsystem for the towed SSTD decoy. Type 2087 is to be integrated with the Type 2050 bow sonar and with the Type 2095 dipper on the Merlin helicopter, so the project includes automatic track association. Type 2087 may also appear on the Project Horizon frigate.

The program began in 1993, and an ITT (RFP) was issued 20 June 1994 for a 15-month feasibility study phase, to be followed by a 6-month risk assessment phase. Three teams responded:

BAeSEMA team: MacTaggart Scott (handling), Ultra Electronics (signal processing), Logica (passive data processing, MMI, operability), AT&T Advanced Technology Systems (active data processing), and GECO Defence (towed array).

GEC-Marconi Naval Systems (Sonar Division): partnered with Ferranti-Thomson Sonar Systems and Thomson Sintra, all now brought together as TMS (see the international section above).

Babcock Thorn Ltd (later Babcock Rosyth Defence Ltd): Westinghouse (now Northrop Grumman), Indal, STN Atlas Elektronik, Data Sciences, Northern Telecom, Reliability Consultants, Thorn, and BSYS Marine.

Although only two contracts were to have been let, early in 1995 all three consortia received feasibility study contracts. In September 1996, ITTs for second-stage project definition were given to all three consortia. At about the same time a fourth team offered the Allied Oceanics LFATS (see separate entry). Two 24-month project definition studies are to be awarded early in 1997.

◆ Type 2090 (IBIS)

Ultra Electronics/Sippican bathymetric information system and sonar performance predictor takes data from SBT (submarine bathythermograph), XSV (expendable sound velocity), and XCTD (expendable chemical trace detector).

◆ Type 2093

Type 2093 is a replacement for Type 193. See the Mine Warfare section.

◆ Type 2094

Planned replacement for Type 2053 oceanographic sonar, now being competed.

◆ Type 2095 (AQS-950)

Thomson Sintra's FLASH replaces the Type 195 helicopter sonar for the Merlin helicopter (EH-101). Ferranti-Thomson's signal processor incorporates INMOS T9000 Transputers (T9s), which have 10 times the throughput of the earlier T800s.

◆ SIU

The Sonar Interface Unit federates the existing British submarine sonar suites that were designed as combinations of discrete units. The SIU allows any console to display and process data from any of the arrays. As mounted in HMS *Turbulent*, the SIU connects Types 2007AC, 2008, 2019, 2020, and 2026.

◆ FMS 12/13/15

Ferranti's modular narrow-band passive sonars, incorporating Curtis architecture, were announced at RNEE 1983, and FMS 12 was tested in 1984. All versions use multiple Argus M700 microprocessors (plus signal-processing Transputers in FMS 15) and consoles incorporating touch screens, trackerballs, and four special-purpose keys. There is a simple multiple-beam (waterfall) display for surveillance, and a high-resolution vernier (frequency) display for classification. Self-noise can be processed out. Optional improvements are automatic target detection and classification, automatic communication with a submarine's tactical system, hard-copy output, and a color display. The associated beam preformer produces 32 beams. The second digit indicates the number of octaves. FMS 15 incorporates automated TMA.

The reported FMS 12 frequency range is 10–384 Hz and 384–768 Hz.

Users:

FMS 12: Canada (in Type 2051, in *Oberons*), United Kingdom (Type 2072).

FMS 13: United Kingdom (in Type 2046).

FMS 15: Korea (eight sets: six for Type 209 submarines, two for shore training), New Zealand (FMS 15/2 for *Leander* and possibly ANZAC-class frigates using Dowty wet end; one delivered 1991 to trials ship *Tui* to work out tactics).

◆ FMS 52

This short-range, dual-frequency, high-definition preformed-beam sonar, for submarines, harbor surveillance, or surface ships, uses a steerable array covering up to 90 deg (bearing resolution is 3 deg). Presumably the beam-former is the same as that used in the other FMS sonars (32 beams). Announced in 1989, FMS 52 had just lost out to the Plessey alternative in the Type 2077 competition, but was adopted by the German navy for the new Type 212 submarine.

Users: Germany (Type 212 submarines), Israel (*Dolphin* class), Italy (Type 212 submarine), Korea (Type 209 submarines).

◆ SubTASS/Hydra

MUSL's (formerly Plessey's) towed array is the submarine version of the earlier Plessey COMTASS or Hydra. The 63mm array is 125 m long, towed on a 1000- or 1500m 25mm cable. It operates in three frequency bands. The operational version is probably a derivative of either COMTASS 2 (adding narrow-band surveillance) or COMTASS 3 (adding automatic detection). The surface version has been marketed as an antiship detector, for example, for drug surveillance, but without much success. The process employs Series 5 cards (see below).

The Swedish submarines apparently also received a Plessey flank array, a new 10 Hz–6 kHz type announced in 1989. Each standard module (2.0 m long, 1.2 m high) contains up to 12 Plessey patented large-area hydrophones embedded in a special resin fairing. The upper frequency limit depends on beam-forming electronics and array spacing. Each hydrophone incorporates its own preamplifier and, thus, can be connected to a long cable array without loss of performance. The Swedish towed and flank arrays use Plessey beam-formers but the SIP 3 signal processor of the submarines' CSU 83 systems. The Swedish contract was awarded in March 1988, and the first arrays were delivered late in 1989.

Users: Canada (*Oberon* class, as SQR-502), Sweden (fitted in conjunction with the CSU 83 sonar suite: *Nacken* and *Vastergotland* classes and *Sjohunden* and *Sjolejonet*). The Canadian version is a hybrid, with more than 2000 ft of cable stowable on the pressure hull under the casing. However, the array proper is still clipped to the end of the tow cable. By varying the length of the two, the submarine can vary the position of the array. For example, the submarine can run in the layer, streaming the array below it. The Canadian wet end is made by Hermes, and is about 100 m long.

◆ ESSFOUR/ESSFIVE/ Series 5

GEC-Marconi/GECO's new towed array systems are for small submarines and for small surface ships, respectively, using Series 5 card processors (see separate entry below) in a single-shelf single-operator configuration with two 21in color monitors (1024 × 1024 pixels) and a trackermouse. They display narrow-band, broad-band, and DEMON data. Each channel can have up to 2560-Hz bandwidth. The four-octave array consists of a 100m (52mm dia) acoustic section (51 hydrophones) with a 20m VIM (three VIMs for a surface ship) and a 30m rope tail on a 70m cable (1500m for a surface ship). The system forms 21 beams per octave to cover 180 or 360 deg. Signals are detected by their energy, using 1-, 2-, or 4- sec integration. Gain is 0 to 42 dB in 6-dB steps. In narrow-band mode, resolution is 0.03–1.7 Hz. The analysis band is 10 to 1280 Hz wide (in octave steps), using a 1- or 4K FFT. For DEMON, the input band is 640 to 1280 Hz wide in any chosen octave, and the analysis bandwidth is 80, 160, or 320 Hz. Options are a line enhancement algorithm, broad-band correlation, tracking, a wider operating bandwidth, and an image disk recorder. The submarine version can accommodate a flank array.

◆ TCSS Mk 9

Torpedo Control (Submarine) survives in modified form only in the Chilean *Oberon* class, in which a German-supplied computer provides some picture-keeping services as well as a wider variety of torpedo ballistics. See the German section above.

UNITED STATES

Heavily censored U.S. budget documents list a variety of programs for SSBN security, both acoustic and nonacoustic: LMFAS/LFAA/SBP (low/medium and low frequency active acoustics/submarine bistatic processor), presumably underwater forms of BRIGAND (see the EW section; they were tested at sea in FY94); the Buoyant Cable Antenna Extended Frequency System (BCAEFS) and Buoy Extended Frequency System (BEFS) to detect radar usage (presumably while submerged); ATOMS (Automated Threat Overflight Monitoring Systems) for early warning/LR detection of threat aircraft, presumably via towed arrays. Project JADE is probably a laser warner. CRIMSON minimizes some form of propagation; most likely it allows the submarine to seek areas in which lasers would be less effective. LIGHTHOUSE reduces submarine detectability by some passive means, possibly wake or turbulence. There is also an entirely unspecified RAMPART project. Some of these code-names may apply to particular acoustic phenomena. Others may apply to MAD or to UEP. The SSBN security project also develops TDAs for submarine security (TDASS).

Recent U.S. R&D programs for hull/machinery improvement show considerable interest in electromagnetic silencing (including UEP/ELFE) and in reducing submarine wakes (such as turbulent wakes) through better maneuvering control. Under the FY94 program, the active and passive magnetohydrodynamic wake of a submarine was measured and compared to predictions, presumably for nonacoustic detection.

The FY94 program included completion of design and development of a five-line multidimensional (volumetric) towed submarine array, described as the enabling technology for a "dramatic improvement in the passive detection, classification, and localization of diesel-electric submarines in shallow water." There is also apparently increasing interest in correlating and comparing signals at different frequencies in order to detect and classify diesel submarines. Thus the FY94 program included completion of integration testing of a 250-channel adaptive cross-channel device for this purpose. Another step in this direction (FY96) is an acoustic classifier combining echo structure clues with clues based on plausible target tracks. The FY97 program includes demonstration of a real-time capability to process data from multiple receiver arrays (active and passive) for autonomous target association and automatic operator alerting.

Automated Fleet Towed Array Sonar (AFTAS) and Real Time Transient Processor (RATTRAP), conceived as aids to submarine operation in shallow water (where very fast reactions might be needed), were developed as ADM modules about June 1995, converted for fleet use, and began at-sea evaluation in mid-1996. Both COTS systems moved from concept to installation in nine months.

Pilot Fish is a black program, reportedly a seabed active sonar for bistatic use by a submarine (the name, however, suggests a UUV).

As of 1995, the U.S. government was finally allowing export of towed arrays for diesel submarines.

CAVES, probably conformal acoustic velocity estimation system, is a developmental "smart skin" sonar using numerous sensors buried in a submarine's anechoic coating; the name suggests that they detect sound by their movement rather than by pressure. Interest in CAVES suggests that advances in computing power over the past decade have overcome the great problems that precluded development of a conformal bow array for *Seawolf*. Limited to portions of the hull amidships, CAVES may replace the heavy WAA. The current ARPA SubTech program includes a multistatic active sonar (using distributed sources) and a leave-behind acoustic source (coded so that it could not be exploited by others).

To deal with quiet diesel submarines, work is proceeding on active classification using medium-frequency (i.e., SQS-53, BQQ-5) sonars. An automatic detector/tracker (ADT) and normalizer already exist. The echo classification and tracking (ETC) baseline system, then, combines ADT with a multi-ping classifier. It is to be used in ALFS and in SQQ-89 Block II. The next step is a shallow-water *single*-ping classifier coupled with improved bistatic sonar, in a shallow-water automatic detection/classification (SWADC)/ETC baseline system (to be completed about FY98). It is to appear in SQQ-89 Block III and possibly in the COTS-injected version of BSY-1 (see the A-RCI program below). An improved version may be used for a projected SH-60R/ALFS upgrade. The next step (about FY97–99) is a classifier that can adapt to the local environment, for SQQ-89 Baseline IV (for SC-21). Meanwhile wide-band technology is to be developed in the LBVDS program, for possible use in SQQ-89 Block IV (SC-21). LBVDS development is likely to be completed about FY01/02.

As projected in mid-1995, a real-time classifier was to have been ready by late FY96, and the EC-84 improvement to SQS-53 was due in FY97. This program includes the ALFS dipping sonar (FY99). To succeed, it has to draw on exploratory (6.2) R&D to discriminate submarine/nonsubmarine contacts, to minimize false contacts, and to reduce clutter.

Existing submarine navigation systems expose the submarine to detection when she uses either GPS or some form of bottom sounder to update her inertial navigation system; updates are required every few days. It now emerges that the U.S. Navy has been developing a gravimetric alternative for some years; pro-

U.S. Hull Sonar Transducers

Sonar	Transducers	Frequency	Staves	Dimensions	Wt
SQS-30	TR-114	10.0	48	45.92 × 45.735	10,250
SQS-29	TR-115	8.0	48	64.5 × 53.149	11,000
SQS-32	TR-116	14.0	48	40.5 × 41.395	3,730
SQS-29/30	TR-255	8–10	48	56.7 × 49.6	10,000
SQS-10	AT-349	20.0	48	18.8 × 25.8	1000
SQS-11	AT-354	25.5	48	18.8 × 23.9	800
SQS-17	TR-166	12–14	24	19.0 × 35.75	
SQS-23	TR-208	5.0	48	100.5 × 63.0	
SQS-26	TR-313	3.5	72	192.0 × 69.0	60,000
SQS-30B	TR-195*	10.0	48	24.375 × 32.5	
SQS-35	TR-229*	11.9–14.1	24	19.5 × 29.0	
SQS-36	TR-204	13.0	24	19.0 × 35.75	

Dimensions are diameter × overall height. Early transducers are all magnetostriction types. Asterisks indicate ceramic transducers. TR-166 is made of ammonium-dihydrogen-phosphate. TR-196, for SQS-17A, used redesigned inductors (3 in 1) and had a mounting plate (the overall height increased to 38 in). TR-195 (SQS-30B above) is the smaller-scale transducer used in SQS-4-series VDSs (SQA-10 fish and hoist). TR-204 and -313 are made of barium-titanite. TR-208/208A is lead-zirconate-titanate. TR-229 is the transducer used by both SQS-35 and SQS-38. TR-231 is the MCC part of the SQS-38 transducer, not the entire transducer. This list is not complete, but it does give some idea of relative sizes. SQS-10 and -11 have two independent sections, each of 48 staves, stacked vertically.

totypes were installed on board the test ship *Vanguard* and on board two SSBNs in the mid-1980s. The technique employs a gravimeter, using known gravity anomalies to locate the submarine. These gradiometers measure local changes in underwater terrain. Efforts are currently underway to miniaturize these devices for commercial and UUV purposes.

HELICOPTER SONARS

◆ AQS-13/18

Allied Signal's 9.25–10.75-kHz (9.23, 10, 10.75 kHz in -13F) helicopter dippers are the most widely used in the West. The cylindrical transducer scans on reception (AQS-13B introduced preformed beams [16], and -13G/18 has 32 preformed beams). A pinger below the cylinder transmits a 360-deg ODT pulse (only 180 deg in AQS-13A; pulse widths 3.5 and 35 msec, supplemented by 200 msec FM in AQS-13E, by 200 and 700 msec FM in AQS-13F [source level 216 dB], and by longer pulses, up to 4 sec, in AQS-13G/18; the latter has a source level of 217 dB). Range scales (in the original version): 1, 3, 5, 8, 12, and 20 kyd; typical range 4000 yd. The dip cycle is 2–3 min; with the helicopter hovering at 50 ft, the transducer is 450 ft below the surface.

AQS-13C added a sonobuoy interface. AQS-13E added APS (adaptive processing sonar mode) to improve performance by 20

An SH-60F carrier inner-zone ASW helicopter dips its AQS-13 sonar. (Sikorsky)

dB in shallow water (reverberation-limited) or by 13 dB in noisy deep water, using the long cosine-squared (rather than rectangular) FM pulse and FFT processing; the associated sonar data computer (SDC) also processes sonobuoys. The SDC automatically detects contacts and displays them as synthetic video on the system CRT.

The AQS-13F is the U.S. SH-60F version (for carrier inner-zone protection). It can process four LOFAR or three DIFAR buoys. In addition to the four pulse lengths, it has an MTI mode, a passive mode (500-Hz band between 9 and 11 kHz), and a single-sideband underwater telephone mode (8 kHz). The dipping body is lowered at up to 16 ft/sec, and raised at 22 ft/sec; operating depth is 450 ft when the helicopter is hovering at 50 ft. Weight: 775 lb for AQS-13, 625 lb for -13B (which saved 200 lb by using hybrid microcircuits).

AQS-13G is a lightweight (600 lb, 194-lb fish) digital version adopted by the German navy as AQS-18. Signal processing improvements include multi-ping correlation and a lower noise floor; figure of merit (FOM) improves by 14 dB. Allied Signal is considering adding performance prediction and obstacle avoidance features. A lead-acid battery pack is carried in the sonar "fish," but there is no capacitor to store energy between pings. Instead, the helicopter recharges the battery between transmission cycles. The power level is reportedly twice that of AQS-13B, and the high-speed winch (22 ft/sec average) limits the dip cycle to no more than that of the earlier sonar, although the depth can be much greater (cable length is 1000 or 1500 ft).

AQS-13 was developed from the AQS-10 of 1955.

Users: AQS-13: Brazil (eight Sea Kings; six survivors being equipped with AQS-18), Canada (31 of 44 CH-124A Sea King delivered), Greece (16 AB212), Iran (seven Sea King and seven AB212), Italy (25 Sea Kings and 27 AB212), Japan (71 of 167 Sea Kings, as HQS-101; the other aircraft are for SAR), Peru (nine Sea Kings and six AB212s), Spain (10 Sea Kings and 11 AB212s [four more AB212 are for ESM; -13Bs being replaced by -13Fs in Sea Kings]), Turkey (AB212s), United States (175 SH-60F Carrier Inner Zone Helicopters [AQS-13F]; SH-3 Sea Kings are being retired), Venezuela (nine AB212, three delivered 1990). It is not certain whether all the naval AB212s listed above have dipping sonars; like Lynxes, some may be limited to weapons delivery, using data links and MAD (the only other important light ASW helicopters, Alouette IIIs, HD500s, and Wasps, are so limited). AQS-13 has been offered to the Royal Australian Navy for the S-70 Seahawk.

AQS-18: Brazil (six for SH-3D Sea Kings, for delivery to be completed by December 1996), Egypt (SH-2Gs), Germany (Sea King and Lynx), Greece (S-70C[M]), Italy, Japan (SH-60J), Korea (Super Lynx), Portugal (Lynx), Spain, Taiwan (10 S-70s). There is also one undisclosed Asian customer, presumably Singapore.

The Greek version omits all sonobuoy capacity (receiver, on-top indicator, mission tape recorder). Non-NATO versions generally lack sonobuoy processing capability.

◆ AQS-14

See the Mine Warfare section.

◆ AQS-22 ALFS (Airborne Low-Frequency Sonar)/AQS-23

Hughes's ALFS is to replace the AQS-13 series on board SH-60F and rebuilt LAMPS helicopters. It combines the French FLASH wet end with a Hughes dry end incorporating a UYS-2 processor. See the French section for details of the AQS-22 wet end. Its beams have a fixed depression angle; reportedly Hughes is working on a controllable depression angle (which would be very valuable in shallow water) for the U.S. Navy. ALFS operates in any of five frequency bands, to minimize the effect of helicopter self-noise. The operational requirement was for 35 consecutive 4-sec pings/dip (a 10% duty cycle); the sonar is powered directly by the helicopter rather than via a battery pack. Pings can be up to 4 sec long.

FLASH being tested on board a U.S. Navy helicopter. (Thomson Sintra)

The Hughes dry end processes sonobuoys concurrently with active or passive sonar operation. It is required to handle eight omni or four directional buoys with constant resolution over their full bandwidth, that is, in broad-band and in explosive echo-ranging as well as in LOFAR mode (actual capacity may be 16 DIFARs plus the sonar). The operator can select full-band, eighth-band, or quarter-band verniers. There is also an embedded trainer. BITE is intended to localize a problem to a single card within 2 min with 95% confidence. A shallow-water upgrade (SWUG) concentrates on target recognition decision aids and on signal processing for reduced reverberation.

The cable was originally to have been 2500 ft long, but as of mid-1992 it had been reduced to the 1500 ft of the AQS-13F that ALFS replaces.

AQS-23 is Hughes's export version, using a new UYS-5 Common Acoustic Processor not as subject as UYS-2 to U.S. export controls.

The ALFS/UYS-2 combination was selected in December 1991. The first EDM was delivered to the navy in March 1995. This sonar is scheduled for TechEval in 1996.

◆ HELRAS/LFATS

Allied Signal's HELRAS is, in effect, an LF equivalent to AQS-13, with an ODT pinger extending from the bottom of the array of receiving staves. In this case, however, the pinger consists of 8 or 10 stacked projectors (presumably flex-tensional), which can focus the beam in the vertical, for example to achieve a shallow grazing angle (in the air, the stack collapses and is folded inside the fish). As in FLASH/ALFS, the receiving staves are deployed from the dipping fish in umbrella fashion. HELRAS was originally a 1.2-kHz system, but the version offered in 1996, HELRAS-2, operates at 1.38 kHz (219 dB source level). It uses an AQS-13G/18 dry end. Pulses are long CW and coded; processing is digital, including multi-ping correlation. Total system weight is about 320 kg. Dipping depth is 460 m. In trials in the Timor Sea it achieved a range 500 times water depth (typically about 100 m); it has functioned in water as shallow as 50 m, and in the Tasman, Ionian, and Ligurian Seas has demonstrated ranges of 30–70 km. It has also proven effective in a Norwegian fjord, overcoming reverberation effects of the sheer walls. HELRAS first flew (in 1.2-kHz form) in December 1987 on board an Italian navy SH-3D. As of mid-1996 a localization/attack mode was under development. During exercises in the fall of 1995, the Italian navy used this very long range (50–80 km) sensor as a kind of underwater AWACS, vectoring helicopters equipped with conventional short-range dipping sonars.

LF Active Towed Sonar (LFATS) is a shipboard equivalent of HELRAS by Allied Signal in cooperation with Digital Systems Resources (DSR), using COTS processing and control equipment. The transmitter, towed on a 335m cable, consists of four vertically spaced platters, each carrying four transmitter disks. The receiver array is four lines streamed from the towed body. Source level exceeds that of HELRAS-2. The system produces composite cardioid beams that can be steered to resolve left/right ambiguity. The complete system including handling gear and processor weighs 3750 kg. LFATS can work with HELRAS in multistatic mode. It can operate at 15 kt, and can survive at

An Italian Sea King deploys the Allied Signal (Bendix) HELRAS long-range dipping sonar. The dots below the fish are the active elements, strung out. (British Aerospace)

Allied Signal's HELRAS low-frequency helicopter sonar. (FIAR)

30. Allied Signal Oceanics claims the LFATS offers 2–5 times the performance of ATAS at a much lower cost and at less than half the weight. FSED began June 1993, with tests due for late July 1996.

Based on trials, Allied Signal claims the following search rates in nm²/hr (HELRAS/LFATS): Timor Sea (100 m deep), 4613/3547; Norwegian Sea (250 m), 4111/2938; Ligurian Sea (2033 m), 4358/3338; and Ionian Sea (1968 m), 5110/4330.

Users: Italy (HELRAS-2 adopted for Italian EH-101). LFATS was a late entrant in the British 2087 competition, proposed by Devonport Management/Strachan & Henshaw/Allied Signal in mid-1996. At that time it was also being promoted in Australia, the Netherlands, Norway, Sweden (YS 2000), UAE, and other Middle East countries.

SUBMARINE AND SURFACE-SHIP SONARS

◆ A-RCI

Lockeed Martin's Acoustics-Rapid COTS Insertion is intended to transform and unify U.S. submarine sonar processsing and submarine combat systems. It is to be built around the fiber-optic ATM (asynchronous transmission mode) bus (LAN) planned for the new attack submarine and is to employ new COTS-based signal processors (MPP, see below) and a new common display workstation based on UYQ-70 components but with a footprint adapted to submarines. Installation will be incremental, with the initial delivery in November 1997. Ultimately all U.S. submarines may be fitted with the ATM backbone (see the New Attack Submarine network in the Tactical Data Systems section). The effect of the ATM is finally to permit free circulation of raw acoustic data as well as processed data, as had been hoped for in BSY-1.

Clearly, installation of a full ATM backplane into existing submarines would be very expensive. The initial product, an MPP processing a pair of towed arrays simultaneously, fits the existing SSN 688I architecture as a stand-alone sensor. In the New Attack Submarine, it is an element to be integrated into the submarine's distributed co.nbat system. In earlier submarines, the step beyond installation of MPP is to modify the CDS with a local ATM connecting the new workstations to the existing central computer (UYK-7 or -43). As in a surface-ship CDS, the effect is to unload some central computer functions. Whether the central computer will be eliminated altogether is open to question, however, because so much has been invested in its CMS-2 code, which is difficult to migrate to another computer.

Ultimately, the effect of the ATM and the new COTS-based workstations is to construct a single standard submarine CDS/sonar processor which is easy (and, more important, inexpensive) to modify for different classes (applications) because its software is so modular. It should also be easy to import new applications such as UUV control, again because computing power, hence software, is so modular.

◆ BQG-4 (PUFFS)/MicroPUFFS (BQG-501/Type 2041)

This submarine passive ranger measures the curvature of the wave front of the detected sound, comparing ToA. PUFFS employs three vertical transducers: bow, amidships, and aft; range accuracy depends on the ratio between the range and the length of the installation (three equally spaced 6ft vertical hydrophones along a 250ft baseline, operating at 200 Hz–8 kHz, should get a range accurate to within 2% against a snorkeling submarine at 10–15 kyd). The surviving version, BQG-4A, is a modified -4 with BITE and improved sensitivity, reliability, and maintainability. In U.S. service, PUFFS was associated with the now-extinct Mk 45 nuclear torpedo. The torpedo had no seeker, and the firing platform had to detonate the torpedo at the appropriate range. TMA using a single sonar was not precise enough, but PUFFS could provide a good enough range. Adoption of Mk 45 was actually predicated on the success of the PUFFS tests. PUFFS was proposed in 1953, was developed in 1956–60, and was produced in 1960–66.

The submarine *Wahoo* shows three vertical PUFFS hydrophones. MicroPUFFS and WAA use 2D hull arrays instead. (U.S. Navy)

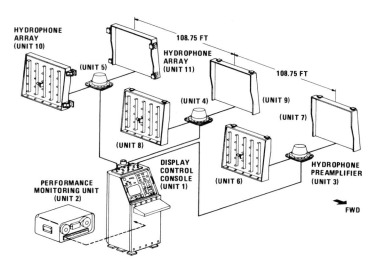

MicroPUFFS arrays. (Sperry)

Sperry's MicroPUFFS is a microcircuited version, using baffled hydrophone arrays, developed specifically for the Royal Australian Navy (1972–76). The three hydrophones on each side of the submarine (five staves, five transducers/stave) each form five continuously processed preformed beams; targets are tracked automatically. Ranging is by cross-correlation of the same signal as received by the three arrays, the two time differences being converted into bearing and range data. The range solution is, therefore, both instantaneous and continuous. Each triplet of hydrophones covers a 150-deg sector. In an Australian *Oberon*, the hydrophones are 108 ft 9 in apart. Sperry estimated that the range error on a target directly abeam at 6000 yd would be about 2.5%, rising to about 11% 60 deg off the beam. The error would be about 5% at 12,000 yd (directly abeam).

Sperry claimed that, compared to PUFFS, MicroPUFFS could more efficiently reject background noise because it used correlation and preformed-beam techniques. Early sea experience sug-

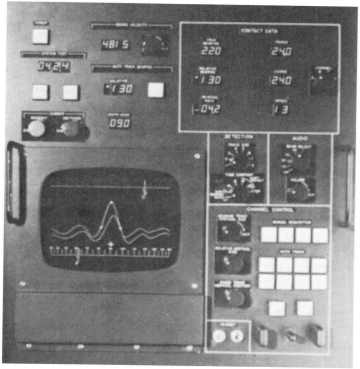

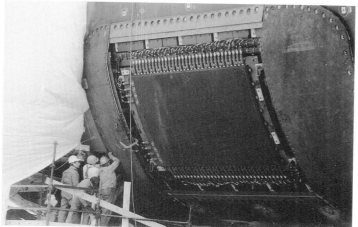

A wide-aperture array on board USS *Seawolf*, at her launching. Note the extensive connections needed for beam-forming. (S. Slade, DMS/Forecast International)

MicroPUFFS display. The CRT shows two correlograms, one for each pair of adjacent arrays on one side. The upper line shows 150 deg of bearing on the starboard side; the lower, 150 deg on the port side. Targets appear on one or the other, and a control stick can be used to position a cursor on the target. When the operator aligns the peak of a correlogram with three dots on the display and presses a button, the system begins to track the target automatically in bearing. The operator can begin to track automatically in range when the peaks of the two correlograms are aligned (i.e., when triangulating on the same target). Contact data are displayed in the upper right-hand side of the panel, including true bearing, relative bearing, bearing rate, and range. Target's course and speed are indicated continuously through TMA. (Sperry)

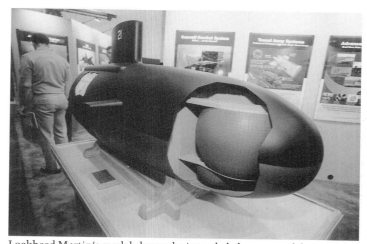

Lockheed Martin's model shows the intended placement of the receiving and transmitting spheres in the bow of the new *Seawolf*. The first WAA element is just visible beneath and abaft the bow plane. (Harry Gerwin)

gested that MTBF might be as great as 3600 hr, with 30 min (or less) MTTR.

Users:

BQG-4A: Turkey (*Tang* and Guppy III classes).
MicroPUFFS: Australia (*Oberons*), Canada (*Oberons*), United Kingdom (*Upholders*, as Type 2041; now for sale). In the Canadian ships, MicroPUFFS is visible in the form of six red-outlined soft patches along the sides of the upper casing (Stations 15 to 18a-19a, 64b to 69a, and 103 to 110, all port and starboard).

◆ **BQG-5/WAA (Wide-Aperture Array)**

Lockheed Martin's WAA is the successor, in effect, to PUFFS and MicroPUFFS, consisting of three large conformal arrays on each side of a submarine. Larger array size should enable both lower-frequency operation and directivity both in depth and in azimuth, so that WAA should be able to exploit bottom- and surface-bounce paths and the CZ propagation path. The concept was tested as early as 1971; by 1980 WAA was considered an essential element of any post–*Los Angeles*–type submarine because it was capable of passive ranging out to Mk 48 range. It is also valued as the most precise means of measuring bearing and bearing rate, for quicker TMA without any own-ship maneuver and at longer ranges (due in part to its 10-dB FoM). For example, in each of five modeled shallow-water environments, WAA provided a TMA solution before a submarine could detect a target on her spherical array. Because it is a beam-forming system, WAA can track multiple targets simultaneously. WAA is sometimes called RAPLOC (rapid passive localization), the "rapid" differentiating it from the much slower TMA. Finally, WAA overcomes flow noise (eliminating flow noise striping).

Bow arrays for the BSY-2 sonar of the *Seawolf* class: the big sphere is the passive element. Note the framework for the conformal array surrounding the spheres. (U.S. Navy)

The great barrier to deploying WAA is its weight. It employs 404 hydrophones per subarray (six in all), compared to 10 per subarray in the SSN version of PUFFS, BQG-2A. Its electronics require eight standard cabinets. Although plans called for fitting

WAA as a stand-alone system in *Los Angeles*–class submarines beginning with those authorized in FY89, these ships have only very limited weight margins. WAA is also part of the BSY-2 system of the new *Seawolf* class, and will surely be installed on board the New Attack Submarine.

On 27 December 1995 NAVSEA awarded Lockheed Martin a contract for a lightweight, low-cost version of BGQ-5A. The new version halves hull penetrations and is light enough for installation on board 688i-class submarines. It employs A-RCI inboard components including the MPP processor. Each array now consists of six 56-channel elements with outboard electronics combining their outputs into 16 optical fibers which pass into the hull. Inboard electronics comprises a conventional receiver cabinet feeding into a beam-former/processor cabinet (two VME drawers for beam-forming and two for postbeam-former processing) and two control display workstations (CDWS). The prototype is to be delivered early in 1999.

CAVES is the WAA follow-on for the New Attack Submarine. *Augusta* (SSN 710) tested an EDM model beginning in July 1987.

◆ BQQ-5/BQQ-6

The current U.S. standard SSN sonar is a digital (DIMUS) suite built around a 15ft spherical active-passive bow array, BQS-13 (1241 TR-155E/BQ hydrophones operating actively at about 3.5 kHz and passively at 0.5–5 kHz) and a UYK-7 computer. Unlike the earlier U.S. spherical sonar, this one uses preformed receiving beams (DIMUS), which offer a multitarget tracking capability absent in earlier analog-beam-forming sonars. Parallel beam-formers, CV-3011 and CV-3010, are used for active and passive reception, each forming a total of 600 beams (each 6 × 7.2 deg) over 60 azimuth positions at each of 10 elevation angles (+19/−53 deg). The passive beam-former feeds a spectrum analyzer (CP-1124), a feature absent in earlier U.S. spherical bow sonars. Its output goes to the UYK-7 system computer and to a classification postprocessor (CP-1125) before display. There is also a broad-band processor (CP-1122).

The digital active beam-former generates waveforms for transmission. The transmitter, however, uses an analog beam-former and therefore cannot rapidly or randomly shift beam position (a desired feature that was not realized until the advent of SADS in BSY-1). Active modes: ODT, sector search, tracking (using three or six contiguous beams in an analog beam-former [compensator]) in split-beam mode. The operator can listen to target echoes from the analog compensators, active beam-former, or active tracker processor.

The sphere is supplemented by a chin array (104 DT-276 hydrophones) that replaces the BQR-7 of the earlier BQQ-2. Its beam-former, CV-3035, forms 24 port and 24 starboard beams (and two noise beams, to reject self-noise) by time-delay compensation. When a towed array was added, CV-3035 could be switched to form its beams. Note that at least in the successor sonar system, BSY-1, the chin array is replaced by a triple line of hydrophones similar to the earlier BQR-7, mounted relatively high in the bow of the submarine.

Filtered tracking data go to the UYK-7 for automatic tracking. Displays: three dual-CRT synthetic-video consoles (initially OJ-274, for broad-band waterfall, narrow-band, active, or classification displays [UYK-7 outputs] selected by the operator, who also sets system operating mode; it is joystick-controlled), one raw video display (IP-1124: any of six modes on a 10 × 10in CRT; later versions have IP-1125 or -1417), and a performance-monitoring and fault-location console (OJ-275).

Associated with the main arrays (and sharing their displays) are a BQS-14 mine-avoidance sonar and a WLR-9 intercept receiver.

BQQ-5A added a towed-array broad-band processor (ICC/TABP) and a second bay to its UYK-7. OJ-431s replaced the OJ-275s, and a second raw video console was added (in the *Los Angeles* version only). New active and passive signal processors were introduced. BQQ-5B incorporates SHAB, a steerable hull-array beam-former for the chin classification array. It uses improved control display consoles (ICDCs, OJ-462) and has a single

analog display. BQQ-5C, the main current version, is an upgraded -5B with expanded DIFAR reception (multiple interface unit/digital spectrum analyzer, with three UYK-44 in one cabinet) and a UYS-1 spectrum analyzer. There are four OJ-544 digital displays (three in some *Sturgeons*). This version requires a total of 57 electronic cabinets (32,000 lb). Software amounts to 311 kwords. BQQ-5C passed its OpEval in June 1984.

BQQ-5D introduces a multi-array signal beam-former and conditioner (CV-3984) as well as new broad- and narrow-band processors, the latter incorporating three UYK-44s (and replacing the earlier multiple interface unit/digital spectrum analyzer). This version was designed to work with the TB-23 thin-line array and it incorporates some BSY-1 technology. It completed OpEval in November 1988 and was certified for service in May 1989.

BQQ-5E replaces the UYK-7 computer with a UYK-43 (with an embedded memory set, EMS, in place of UYH-1 disk memory). System design is focused on the localization process. The system incorporates TARP (towed array passive ranging) using the TB-29 thin-line array. It can handle both thin and fat towed arrays, but only one at a time (the next version will be able to handle both simultaneously). BSY-1 technology is included in the form of an under-ice/mine-avoidance sonar, MIDAS (BQS-24). ECP-7001 (FY95–96) provides LF active interference rejection (so that the sonar can operate actively and passively simultaneously), dual towed array processing (TB-16 and -29), and full spectrum processing. The corresponding improvement to BSY-1 is ECP-1000. The BQQ-5E contract was awarded in December 1988.

Future planned improvements include an LF adjunct (LFA, presumably using a towed array as receiver), TAP (towed array processor), full spatial vernier processing (SVP) for the TB-29, dual towed array processing (presumably using TB-16D and -29 simultaneously, as in BSY-2), and a color display for the ICDC.

First deliveries in the Acoustic Rapid COTS Insertion (ARCI) program for BQQ-5/6 and BSY-1 are planned for November 1997.

In BQQ-5 through -5D, versions were (V)1 for *Los Angeles* and (V)2 for *Sturgeon*; (V)3 was used for the now-extinct *Permit* class (with BQS-11 bow sphere) in versions through -5C. BQQ-5E(V)3 is the current *Los Angeles*–class version. -5E(V)4 is a version for Trident submarines, replacing BQQ-6 (see below). As of mid-1996, existing BQQ-5s were being brought to -5D standard. IBM Federal Systems (now part of Lockheed Martin) received contracts to convert existing BQQ-5s to -5Es in October and November 1992.

BQQ-6 is, in effect, a passive-only SSBN version for Trident submarines (later ones have a version of BQQ-5E), using a 944-element bow sphere, two flank arrays (100 transducers), an HF array (three line hydrophones on a tracking pedestal), and a towed array. BQQ-6 requires 33 electronic cabinets and 430 kwords of software. About 73% of BQQ-6 components are common with BQQ-5. BQQ-5E(V)4 is a version for later Trident submarines, enjoying greater commonality with BQQ-5, using a thin-line array. Work on integrating BQQ-5E and CCS Mk 2 into Trident submarines began under the FY88 program, reflecting a decision to backfit ships with complete systems rather than make incremental improvements.

Concept formulation began in January 1969, and elements of the system were tested on board the *Pogy* (SSN 647). The prototype system was installed on board the *Philadelphia* (SSN 690). BQQ-5 was approved for service use in April 1979; an improvement program began in FY80.

Users: United States (*Los Angeles, Ohio, Sturgeon, Narwhal* classes).

◆ BQQ-9 (TASPE)/TABIDU/ACORN

Rockwell International's broad-band towed-array signal processor is built around an expanded UYK-20A computer and a UYS-1 spectrum analyzer and has a single sonar-operator display console and no remote console. It was adopted specifically for the SSBNs' long BQR-15 (SPALT 9080) array, which replaced TB-23 when the latter failed its tests. It can operate either as a stand-alone system or as a part of a federated submarine combat system. As such it was adopted in 1984 for the first 10 *Ohio-*

BQQ-5 uses a spherical bow array directly descended from the BQS-6 which equipped earlier U.S. submarines. The first BQS-6 is shown on board the attack submarine *Thresher*, building at Portsmouth Naval Shipyard, April 1960, with the lower hydrophones in place. The triple row of hydrophones wrapped around the sphere is not visible. (U.S. Navy)

class submarines as well as for pre–*Ohio* class units. TABIDU (Towed-Array Broadband Interim Display Unit) is a private-venture COTS version for the next five *Ohios*; it uses the new FFT technology developed for FAAS. Since only the interface with the array is custom-built, TABIDU can, in theory, process signals from any free world array. Rockwell received a contract for seven units (for five submarines) in January 1994.

ACORN is a commercial version of TABIDU (1995). Rockwell stated that it was in production for ship and land-based export use for unspecified customers. As of the spring of 1995 Rockwell had just completed a sea test with an ACORN tactical processor for the Royal Australian Navy, using the Kariwara array, in hopes of providing it for the *Collins* class. Unlike TABIDU, ACORN can include a beam-former as well as processors for narrow-band, broad-band, torpedo detection and tracking, transient detection, and TMA. For example, one ACORN box could form 200 beams as well as about 800 channels of narrow- and broad-band signals.

Rockwell offers a proprietary transient detector, mainly for torpedo detection. Instead of using a priori information on particular transients (templates), Rockwell prefers to search for short-term events that differ from the ambient noise pattern. A human operator then decides whether the alert is real. In five at-sea tests (three U.S. surface ships, two U.S. submarines) Rockwell claimed that its algorithms offered detection capability at least as good as an operator's, often considerably better, with no worse false-alarm rate. Once the operator confirms that an alert is a torpedo, the system autotracks.

Users: United States (BQQ-9 in SSBN 726–735 and probably in SSN 642 and 645; TABIDU in SSBN 736–740).

◆ BQR-2B/21

This early postwar 0.5–15-kHz passive sonar employs 48 staves (43in line hydrophones) in a 68in circle. BQR-2 uses a compensator to scan among 24 18 × 30 deg (at 5 kHz) beams preformed by delay lines. Bearing-time information is recorded for the 0.7–1.4-kHz band, and the target-follower (BDI) is accurate to within 0.1 deg. There are two consoles (stacks) for simultaneous acquisition and processing of multiple targets and independent, continuous, recorder scanning. Sweep rates: manual or 4 rpm for each beam (recorder beam 1 or 10 rpm). Modes: MTB (maintain true bearing), GTT (generate target track), ATF (automatic target following), and automatic on-target slewing. About 1960 BQR-2B was credited with a range of 15–20 nm against a snorkeling Guppy in the deep Atlantic.

BQR-21 is a preformed-beam solid-state version using the BQR-2 array to preform 96 beams. It has three CRTs, two for passive waterfall data (averaged over long, intermediate, or short periods) and one for system mode or fire-control data. One analog beam-former (whose beam can be set manually or can autotrack, as in BQR-2) is retained, its cursor presented on the digital displays. The digital beam-former has four ATF channels, so as a whole the system can track five targets. Compared to BQR-2, BQR-21 enjoys reduced self-noise, partly through the installation of an array baffle.

The Honeywell West Covina division received the BQR-21 development contract in June 1972, with sea trials of the first development model following in 1974. Procurement ended in FY82, a total of 66 having been purchased (59 tactical units, 8 trainers, and 1 configuration control unit).

Users:

BQR-2: Taiwan (Guppy II), Turkey (*Tang*, Guppy IIA, Guppy III).

BQR-21: United States (SSN 642 and 645).

◆ BQR-7

This 50 Hz–5 kHz conformal passive array (52 hydrophone groups, each of three hydrophones, running back about 45 ft from the submarine's bow to cover a 270-deg arc) has a single scanning compensator (there is no target follower), operating at 1 or 20 rpm to drive a chart recorder in the 0.5–2-kHz band. Overall system accuracy is about 1 deg, but sometimes with a

3-deg offset to take signal integration time into account. The associated bearing-deviation indicator is accurate enough for passive fire control. In 1960 it was estimated that, on board a quiet submarine, a BQR-7 would be able to detect a snorkeling Guppy at 75 nm.

Users: United States (SSN 642 and 645).

◆ BQR-15/SPALT 9080

The first operational U.S. submarine towed-array sonar, this short (150 ft) 3.5in array carries 42 hydrophones on a 2200ft cable. It forms 46 beams on fixed bearings with digital outputs plus two analog beams steerable to any of 23 bearings, and a third steerable to any one of 92 bearings. Each signal is electrically independent of the others. The large array diameter is due in part to the use of a relatively simple technology, twisted pairs to carry the hydrophone outputs. The array proper weighs 950 lb. This array uses a BQR-23 narrow-band processor and BQQ-9 or TABIDU for broad-band processing. It requires nine electronic cabinets.

When TB-23 failed its tests, BQR-15 was modified with a new thin-line (1in) wet end, AT&T's SPALT 9080 (now being marketed as 9080). It offers more than 200 channels and a dynamic range of 60 dB. Each channel has its own data transmitter, using pulse-code modulation and digital serial time-division multiplexing over the coaxial cable. In stand-alone form, 9080 would use a standard U.S. Navy digital beam-former and signal conditioner. It is long enough to offer both full-beam and half-beam pairs (for triangulation) over the surveillance frequency range.

BQR-15 was introduced largely to give strategic submarines the ability to detect targets on aft bearings, hidden in the baffles of the bow sonars. In addition to submarine signatures, BQR-15 can receive underwater telephone signals (from UQC-1 and WQC-2).

Users: United States (*Ohio* class [SPALT 9080] and SSN 642/645 [probably the short version]). The JMSDF tested this array on board the submarine *Okishio* in 1988–89, to integrate it with ZQQ-5 or -5B, and the current Japanese ZQR-1 is probably essentially BQR-15.

◆ BQR-19 (Top Hat)

Raytheon's mast-mounted short-range navigational sonar for SSBNs is designed for evasion while surfacing. Its array is a 24-stave cylinder (DT-374/BQR-19 hydrophones), and inboard electronics consists of three cabinets, weighing a total of 1000 lb.

◆ BQR-20A/22/22A/23

Spectral Dynamics's narrow-band BQR-20A processor is the SQQ-23 passive receiver. The similar BQR-22 can be connected to a dual-channel hard-copy (LOFARgram) recorder. BQR-22A adds a remote range-rate indicator. Scientific Atlanta (the parent firm of Spectral Dynamics) produced the BQR-23 towed array signal processor, which is used with BQR-15 arrays and as part of BQQ-5. It provides at least 64 LOFAR channels simultaneously in real time, with a visual display.

Work began in the late 1960s; the BQR-20 contract dates from 1971, and BQR-22 from 1974. The original BQR-23 contract was awarded in 1974. Scientific Atlanta has proposed that BQR-20 be replaced by the more capable BQR-23.

Users:

BQR-20/22: Greece (*Adams* class: signal processor for SQQ-23 sonar), United Kingdom (as Type 2030), United States (*Los Angeles*– and *Sturgeon*-class submarines; BQR-22A(EC15), the latest version, is used in ASWOCs serving P-3C Beartrap squadrons).

BQR-23: United Kingdom (as Type 2035) and United States (*Los Angeles, Sturgeon, Benjamin Franklin, Ohio* classes).

◆ BQS-4

The successor to SQS-4 for submarines, the 7-kHz BQS-4 consists of seven vertically stacked cylindrical transducers inside a passive sonar (BQR-2 or -21) that acts as receiver. Vertical stacking permits beam movement in the vertical plane. Typical range is 6–8 kyd.

Users: Taiwan (Guppy II), Turkey (*Tang,* Guppy IIA, Guppy III), United States (SSN 642 and 645).

♦ BQS-14/15/MIDAS (BQS-24)

The HF under-ice and mine-avoidance sonars use sonar domes in the sail. Direct descendants of the wartime FMCW mine-avoidance sets with separate transmit and receive arrays, they are part of BQQ-5 and its successors. Hazeltine's BQS-14 employs a cylindrical transducer with 30 dual staves, as well as a projector (TR-215/BQS), an HF transducer (TR-217), and seven LF transducers (TR-216). Internal electronics occupy six cabinets, and the system as a whole weighs 2200 lb.

BQS-15 uses three line projectors, tracking pedestals, two HF transducers (TR-282), four LF transducers (TR-281), and four cabinets of inboard electronics, for a total of 3300 lb. MIDAS is a BQS-15 derivative modified by the Arctic Submarine Laboratory for short-pulse multibeam operation so that it can use adjacent transmit and receive arrays.

Users:

    BQS-14: United States (*Sturgeon* class).
    BQS-15: United States (*Los Angeles* class).
    MIDAS: Unites States (late *Los Angeles, Seawolf, Ohio* classes). Specifications were finalized in FY89, and development began in FY90.

♦ AMDS

The Advanced Mine Detection System for submarines is being developed by Westinghouse, Sonatech, and Loral (formerly IBM) Federal Systems. It was to have completed engineering development by end of first quarter of 1994. It employs commercial processors, including IBM RISC System/6000 and SKY (based on Intel i860) and 0.5-micron VHSIC circuitry. Loral is responsible for displays, processing, operator-machine interface, and transmit and receive arrays. The final design review was completed in May 1992, and the prototype was to have been tested in a submarine chin array in 1995.

♦ QBE-3

This 18–25-kHz searchlight sonar, with a typical range of 1 kyd (max indicated range 5 kyd), was standard aboard U.S. 83ft Coast Guard cutters transferred abroad. QBE is a converted passive sonar in a fish-type retractable dome, using a 15in-dia transducer. In the U.S. World War II system of designations, QB denoted a sonar with a rochelle-salt transducer.

User: Turkey (83ft Coast Guard class).

♦ SQQ-14

See the Mine Warfare section under countermeasures.

♦ SQQ-23

See SQS-23 below.

♦ SQQ-25

This high-definition 3D sonar is found on board the submarine rescue ships *Ortolan* and *Pigeon.* SQQ-25 uses a 7-kHz chirp. Active range is 2500 yd; passive 1000 yd.

♦ SQQ-28

The LAMPS III shipboard processor was later extended to LAMPS I support, for *Perry*-class frigates assigned to Naval Reserve units. SQQ-28 can process all buoys up to and including VLAD (SSQ-77). Capacity is eight omnidirectional or four directional/active buoys. The system incorporates an automatic acoustic target tracker that is twice as fast as manual techniques, averaging 10 min to determine target course. There are multiple display formats and automated detection aids. MTBCF (i.e., between critical faults) is 670 hr; MTTR is less than 1 hr. SQQ-28 shares displays with the SQR-19 towed array.

Users: United States (*Burke, Ticonderoga, Spruance, Perry* classes).

♦ SQQ-34

The CV-ASW module, part of a carrier's CDS, is a semiautomated system, the primary source of external data to the battle group ASW commander. It also provides all information for the carrier's own ASW aircraft (S-3, SH-3, and SH-60F). This system was originally the CV–Tactical Support Center and was renamed in 1979.

♦ SQQ-89

General Electric's (now Lockheed Martin's) integrated surface-ship sonar and fire-control suite is analogous to the submariners' BQQ and BSY series. It now requires about twice as much source code as Aegis. SQQ-89 was conceived under the ASW Combat System Integration (ASW-CSI) project, to handle the large number of passive contacts provided by the SQS-53B/C sonar and the SQR-19 towed array. The other major system sensor is the SQQ-28 LAMPS III processor.

In the original SQQ-89, each acoustic subsystem uses a UYS-1 processor. It has its own UYQ-21 control console, and it feeds data into SQQ-89 via a UYK-20 computer and an OL-190/UYQ-21 acoustic-data converter, which supports a pair of OJ-452/UYQ-21 dual-screen consoles (the two screens can show different frequency ranges, or can split between broad- and narrow-band displays). Individual consoles can switch from one sensor to another, but cannot mix sensors. Versions differ in the number of OL-190s (one in a *Perry,* or two [master and slave] or three) and therefore in the number of OJ-452s. For example, in the (V)3 version, three OJ-452s are lined up together, separated from the fourth by an equipment rack. Two of the three consoles working together might be used for SQS-53 (one active and one passive) and one for SQR-19, with the fourth also used for SQR-19. One SQS-53 console might be switched to SQQ-28 when a helicopter is launched to prosecute a contact. An operator can switch between an SQR-19 display showing a CZ contact and an SQQ-28 display showing a LAMPS helicopter prosecuting that contact.

Any two sensor outputs can be displayed side by side on two consoles, for visual correlation by the sonar supervisor. For example, a passive (SQR-19) and an active (SQS-53) picture of the same contact can be shown side by side. The supervisor's role is somewhat analogous to that of the track supervisor in a ship CDS, but he does not have a dedicated console (only versions now in development provide the supervisor with a dedicated console, and there is some disagreement as to whether that is a wise development).

Side-by-side comparison was impossible in earlier systems, which relied on paper LOFARgrams and lacked any electronic memory. SQQ-89 achieves its high performance because several operators can see the same displays together; a total of seven to nine people work the ASW problem together. Moreover, the system uses LAMPS III as a sensor, fully equivalent to the hull sensors because the data link has such a wide bandwidth and, thus, can transmit sonobuoy data so fully.

Operators at the consoles detect targets, that is, decide that what they see on the screen corresponds to a real target. That automatically inserts the target data into the system's track memory, carried in the embedded Mk 116 Mod 5 or later FCS, or in a *Perry*-class weapons alternate processor (WAP). The FCS or WAP connects SQQ-89 to the ship's CDS, accepting external or nonacoustic track data and providing the CDS with acoustic track data. Unlike a submarine CDS, SQQ-89 lacks any equivalent to MATE; that appears only with the new USQ-132 TDSS (see separate entry).

As SQQ-89 developed, the distinction between sensors and fire control disappeared, as in Aegis: thus in (V)4 and later versions, an acoustic console replaces the specialized Mk 116 FCS console. The latest improvement to the SQQ-89 series is the insertion of an acoustic video processor (AVP) into the lower drawer of the UYQ-21 to provide better graphics. This is display, not signal processing, technology. The major current development is the transition to an open COTS architecture.

SQQ-89 includes SIMAS (UYQ-25), which helps estimate the effective range of the passive sensors. Each version also includes

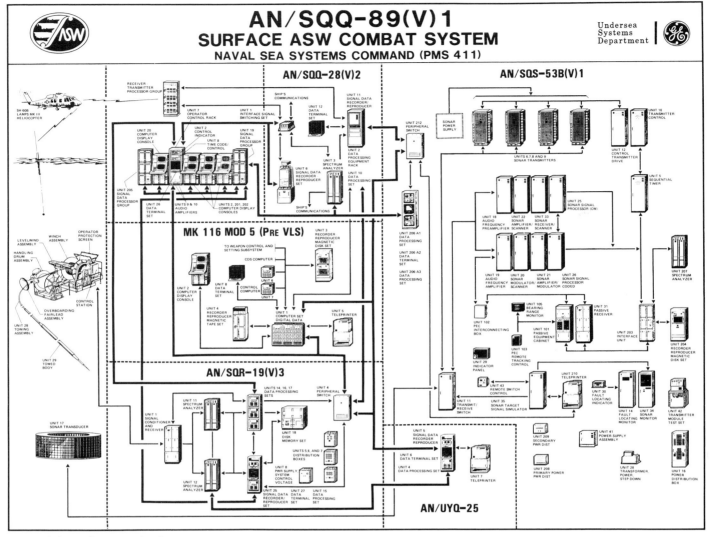

SQQ-89(V)1 configuration. (GE)

an on-board trainer, SQQ-89T(V). Versions of SQQ-89 differ in the versions of Mk 116 around which they are built.

As a step toward an open architecture, two LANs are being installed in the (V)6 version as part of an adjunct subsystems upgrade: a display LAN (D-LAN) and a signal LAN (S-LAN). The D-LAN is connected to the system displays, to a new passive adjunct processor (PAP), to new workstations (TDSS [see below], SIMAS II, and AP), and to the existing SQQ-89 system (via an interface processor). S-LAN is connected directly to the system sensors via interface units, to the AP, and to a new system-level recorder (SLR, USH-XX). The system receives nonacoustic data (CDS, JMCIS) via the SQQ-89 interface processor. Because SI-MAS is now integrated into the D-LAN, the system's common integrated tactical picture includes environmental data. SIMAS II and SLR apparently also greatly improve self-noise data collection.

The COTS adjunct processor initially hosts the MSTRAP automated torpedo detector and enhanced VLF processing (LO-FAR). Later it is to add bistatic processing for the SURTASS LFA pinger, MF bistatic processing, and improved active sonar classification. A development contract for an acoustic intercept receiver (tested in prototype form in mid-1995) was let early in 1996.

This version adds a console with a free-standing 19in CRT for the ASW Evaluator, a dual-screen console for the sonar supervisor, and two standard acoustic workstations (a TAC-3 and a UYQ-65). Each of the acoustic workstations can show any acoustic/tactical plot generated by the AP or SIMAS data. The sonar supervisor and evaluator can view the compiled tactical picture, using 19in CRTs driven by the TDSS.

Versions:

(V)1 for DD 965, 980, and 992 uses Mk 116 Mod 5 (with a three-bay UYK-7 computer and an OJ-452 display) with SQR-19(V)3, SQS-53B(V)1, and UYQ-25A(V)2. There are four OJ-452(V)8/UYQ-21(V) consoles (three plus a running spare) in the sonar-control space, with an OJ-452(V)11/UYQ-21(V) in CIC near the weapons-control panel (Mk 329). Of two UYS-1 spectrum analyzers, one is connected directly to SIMAS. Of four UYK-20 computers, three are used for the spectrum analyzers and one for the signal conditioner and receiver (feeding into a UYH-2 disk memory set). First installation was in the *Moosebrugger* (DD 980).

(V)2 is the two-console version without any integrated SQS-53 or Mk 116. (V)2 CG is for CG 54 and CG 55 only, with SQR-19(V)1 and UYQ-25; and (V)2 FFG is for FFGs 7–9, 11–13, 15, 28, 29, 32, 33, 36, 38–43, 45–49, 53, and 55–61, with SQR-19(V)2 or -19A(V)2 and UYQ-25A(V)2. First installation of the FFG version was in USS *Curts*.

(V)3 with Mk 116 Mod 6 has two variants: (V)3 CG for CGs 56–64, with five consoles in sonar and SQR-19(V)1 or -19A(V)1, SQS-53B(V)2, and UYQ-25 or -25A(V)2; and (V)3 DD for DDs 963–964, 966–968, 970, 971, 973, 975, 981, and 991, with four consoles in sonar and SQR-19(V)3/A(V)3, SQS-53B(V)1, and UYQ-25 or -25A(V)2. A(V)3 for CG 65 only uses Mk 116 Mod 7 with SQR-19B(V)3, SQS-53B(V)2, and UYK-25A(V)2. A(V)3 is the first version with a UYK-43 computer (instead of UYK-7). First installation was in the *San Jacinto* (CG 56). This version is very similar to (V)1.

AN/SQQ-89(V)2
FY86 EQUIPMENT CONFIGURATION

Undersea Systems Department

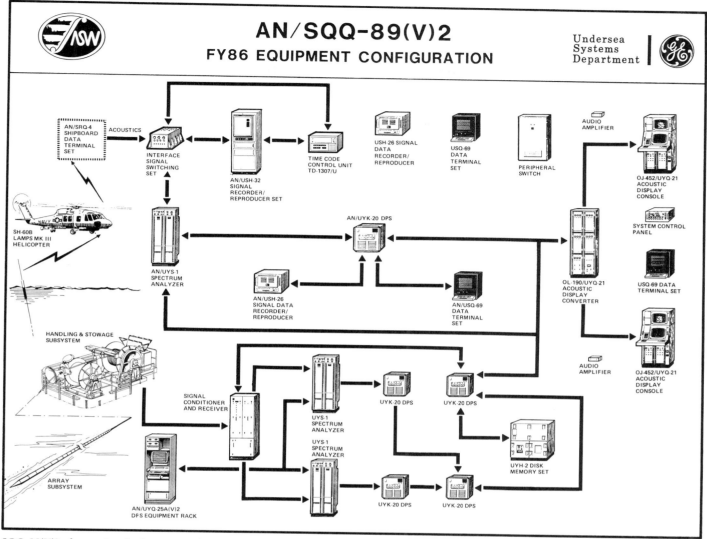

SQQ-89(V)2, the version for frigates, without a large hull sonar. (GE)

(V)4 for DDG 51 (the *Arleigh Burke*) only uses Mk 116 Mod 7 with five consoles in sonar and SQR-19B(V)3, SQS-53C(V)1, and UYQ-25A(V)2. Three acoustic-data converters serve six OJ-452s: four for the acoustic operators, one for the sonar supervisor (SS), and one for the ASW-control system operator (ASWCSO). The system is connected to two OJ-451/UYQ-21s in CIC, for the ASW evaluator (ASWE) and the fire-control operator (FCO). There are three UYK-43(V)7 computers: one for the weapons-control system (WCS), one for command and display (C&D), and one for the Mk 116 Mod 7 (which uses nearly 215,000 lines of computer code). UYQ-21 display formats include NTDS-style PPI as well as bearing/frequency analysis and TMA.

(V)5 with Mk 116 Mod 8 is for DDs 966–968, 970, 971, 973, 975, and 980–982; it uses SQR-19(V)3 or -19A(V)3 and SQS-53B(V)1. Ships are to be upgraded to this standard after FY90. The equipment in CIC and in sonar control corresponds to that in the (V)3 destroyer version. The computer is UYK-43(V)8.

(V)6 uses Mk 116 Mod 7 or (for DD) Mod 7/VLS. Variants are (V)6 CG for CGs 68–73 and (V)6 DDG for DDGs 52–58, both with SQR-19B(V)1 and SQS-53C(V)1; and (V)6 DD for DDs 978 and 985–988, with SQR-19B(V)3 and SQS-53C(V)2. The equipment configuration matches that of (V)3 (for destroyers and cruisers) and (V)4 (for Aegis destroyers). The computer is UYK-43(V)7.

(V)7 with Mk 116 Mod 7 is for CGs 66–67, with SQR-19B(V)1 and SQS-53B(V)2. The equipment configuration matches that of the (V)3 cruiser version. The computer is UYK-43(V)7.

(V)8 with Mk 116 Mod 8 for VLS ships and Mod 9 for non-VLS ships is for DDs 969, 972, 974, 976, 977, 979, 982, 983, and 997,

with SQR-19B(V)3 and SQS-53B(V)1. The equipment configuration matches that of the (V)3 destroyer version. The main computer is UYK-43(V)8 and (V)9. A projected A(V)8 version has OJ-653/AVP instead of OJ-452 displays and has a UYK-43(V)9 computer.

(V)9 for FFGs 14, 20, 30, 31, 34, 37, 50–52, and 54 works with SQR-19B(V)2. The equipment configuration matches that of the (V)2 frigate version.

(V)10 is a redesigned (V)6 for DDG 51 Flight IIA, without the SQR-19 array, but with UYS-2 (EMSP) and UYQ-65 (AIDS). The main processor is UYK-43(V)7.

(V)11 is the future projected FFG version, with UYQ-65 display.

(V)X is an open-architecture COTS version compatible with LAMPS III Block II (SH-60R) and with the new Acoustic Intercept capability and SSTD. Presumably it is the (V)6 Adjunct Subsystems upgrade described above.

Prior to (V)6, destroyers and frigates all have SQQ-28(V)2; cruisers and Aegis destroyers have SQQ-28(V)3. SQQ-89(V)5 and later all have SQQ-28(V)9, a version that shares a UYK-44 computer (signal-data processing unit, SDPU) with the SQR-19 array. All versions from A(V)3 onward use UYQ-25A(V)2; only (V)2 and (V)3 use UYK-20 for SIMAS (the others use the non-MIL-STD 9020C version).

SQQ-89 R&D began in FY76, with interface definition in FY78. Concept formulation was completed in FY79, and FSD in FY81. Initial operational tests were conducted on board the *Moosebrugger* in FY84, and the first production model was in-

AN/SQQ-89(V)4 SURFACE ASW COMBAT SYSTEM

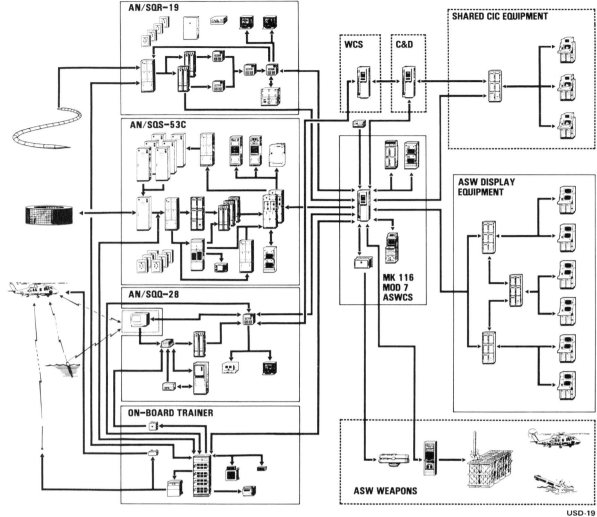

SQQ-89(V)4, the fully integrated version of the system, in which the Mk 116 element is nearly vestigial. (GE)

stalled in FY86; full-scale procurement began in FY87. Design of the UYK-43B version was completed during FY86.

The Adjunct Upgrade was first installed on board USS *Hayler* in the summer of 1995, including prototype TDSS, SIMAS II, SLR, and AP/MSTAP. The second prototype (with limited SI-MAS II and SLR functionality) was installed on board USS *Mitscher*.

Currently planned upgrades to SQQ-89 include: display improvements, bearing ambiguity resolution (for [V]6 and A[V]6 versions, FY98), a shape filter, an improved normalizer, shallow-water waveforms (to enter service in FY01), SIMAS II, the MSTRAP torpedo alertment processor, LFA bistatics/TACTASS (using the SURTASS pinger), an echo tracker classifier (ETC), active evaluation display improvements, an acoustic intercept receiver, SQS-53 bistatics, EER and ALFS bistatics.

Most improvements are planned as part of a series sequential SQQ-89(V) block upgrades. The baseline Block 0 is equivalent to SQQ-89(V)6 for towed-array ships or (V)10 for ships without towed arrays, such as Flight IIA *Arleigh Burke*–class destroyers. The (V)6 version entered service in FY92 and (V)10 in FY96. This version included the SQS-53 digital receiver and Kingfisher. Note that funding for anything beyond Block I is uncertain because of the intense pressure in the Navy budget. However, the Block structure does give a good idea of what is wanted. In what follows, note that medium means SQS-53.

Block I: Torpedo Alertment Upgrade with open-system architecture and the adjunct processor, to enter service FY97.

Block II: Shallow Water Upgrade with preplanned product improvements to Block I, including vastly improved shallow-water classification, an interface to the remote minehunting system (for some ships); it also introduces SURTASS processing improvements. It is to become operational in FY99.

Block III: Multistatic Upgrade to provide full littoral capability by adding an MF bistatic processor, a below-the-layer MF passive array, full LAMPS III Block II capability, and an undersea warfare (USW) dedicated data link for multistatic processing. It is to become operational in FY01.

Block IV: This will probably be the SC-21 (future surface combatant) baseline.

Users: United States (*Arleigh Burke, Ticonderoga, Spruance,* long hull *Perry* [FFG 7, 8, 15, 28, 29, 32, 36–61] classes). The following *Perry*-class frigates are not expected to receive SQQ-89: FFG 10, 24, 27, 31, 34, 37, and 54. Ships fitted include FFG 7, 8, 9, 15, 20, 28, 29, 32, 36, 38, 39, 48–52, 55–61 plus five others. From the *San Jacinto* (CG 56) on, newly completed Aegis cruisers have SQQ-89 as initial equipment. Unit cost (FY90) was $27–28M. SQQ-89 installations, as of 1995: CG 47, 13; DD 963, 18; and FFG 7, 28. UYQ-25A(V)2 installations: 13 for the CG 47 class, 12 for the DD 963 class, and 21 for the FFG 7 class.

◆ SQR-17

DRS's shipboard sonobuoy/array processors display data in broad- or narrow-band form and also as hard-copy (e.g., LOFARgrams). The main console has three screens, a central 19in acoustic-data display flanked by 9in screens for menu prompts, selection of operating mode, and sensor status monitoring. The system incorporates both an SKR-4 LAMPS I link receiver and an ARR-75 sonobuoy receiver (to handle over-the-side buoys). In its SQR-17A version, it uses a UYS-1 acoustic processor.

The basic (V)1 version is a four-channel (LOFAR) LAMPS I sonobuoy processor, which can also be used to process data from buoys dropped over the side. It incorporates a 14-channel RD-420 tape recorder. (V)2 adds an interface for a towed array; its digital multiplexer encoder/decoder (DMED) converts 32 channels of towed-array-hydrophone data, plus own-ship course and speed and track-bearing data into high-density digital format for recording on an upgraded RD-420A. (V)3 is a next-generation version, the first fleet ASW processor to incorporate FDALE (frequency domain adaptive line enhancement), to improve detection of weak lines buried in broad-band noise. A(V)1 and A(V)2 are next (sixth)-generation eight-channel (eight LOFAR or two DIFAR/DICASS) systems, totally integrated, with 28-channel RD-420B tape recorders. They add DIFAR, DICASS, and VLAD processing. The computer can conduct TMA (MATE/MLE). Existing systems were modified beginning in 1988 to provide torpedo warning. This version can feed data directly to an ASW FCS, such as the WAP of a *Perry*-class frigate or FFISTS in a *Knox*.

SQR-17 evolved from the SQS-54 LAMPS I processor (now extinct).

Users: Egypt (*Knox* class), Greece (*Knox* class), Taiwan (*Knox* class), Thailand (*Knox* class), United States (*Ticonderoga* [CG 47–8 only], *Kidd, Perry* [short hull/LAMPS I/SQR-18] classes; also used by MIUW units [16 bought 1989]). As of 1995, an MIUW system upgrade was in progress. DRS was providing a new acoustic processor. A total of 97 SQR-17s had been bought by 1989.

◆ SQR-18

EDO's 735ft (3.25in dia) array consists of 32 vibration-isolated hydrophones (eight modular hydrophone sections) in a 170ft acoustic section (2.7in dia), mounted on spacers between three wire ropes in an oil-filled polyurethane tube. The A(V)1 version is towed from an SQS-35 VDS fish (containing preamplifiers) on a 730m cable. A(V)2, which uses the SQR-19 array-handling system (OK-410), is towed from a 5300ft critical-angle tow cable (to reduce the effect of own-ship noise on the array). EDO developed an own-ship noise canceller which made it possible to use a short-scope tow cable, the array being held down by a special depressor. A projected A(V)3 uses EDO's AMSP parallel processor.

The current beam-former/processor is a two-screen DRS unit (which processes and displays four beams at a time) related to

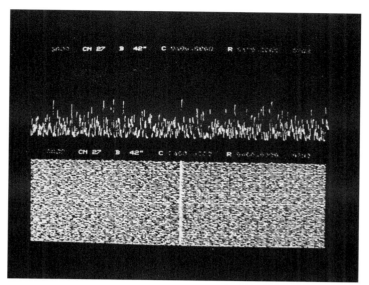

SQR-18 LOFAR and ALI display. (EDO)

SQR-17. It operates in broad- and narrow-band simultaneously, tracking by means of automatic target-following circuits and an automatically stabilized tracker beam. All processed data are stored and displayed electronically; the system does not use LOFARgrams. Signal measurements (frequency and amplitude of tonals, harmonic ratio, and tag frequencies) are shown as alphanumerics. SQR-18As have been fitted with EDO's ALICE (adaptive line canceler and enhancer), consisting of an embedded post-beam-former interference canceler (EPIC) and an SQR-17 adaptive line enhancer (ALE). EPIC cancels a companion ship's sound so that submarines can be detected when a towed-array ship is escorting a very noisy ship. The EDM was completed in February 1982.

Produced by EDO, and later also manufactured by Gould (which also made SQR-19, and whose array division was taken over by Lockheed Martin), SQR-18 was the first U.S. surface-ship tactical towed array. The SOR for it was stated in FY73, work having begun under the FY68 program. Contracts for two prototype arrays were awarded in August 1974. For a time, SQR-18 was to have been replaced altogether by the superior SQR-19; but development continued as insurance against any problems in the -19 program, and the -18 is now an alternative standard.

Users: Egypt (*Knox* class [A(V)2]), Japan (six units bought, but reported in eight *Asagiri* class), Netherlands (two units), Taiwan (*Knox* class with SQR-18A[V]1), United States (some *Perry* class, with A[V]2).

◆ SQR-19/TAS-2019

The current standard U.S. Navy tactical towed array, generally installed as part of the SQQ-89 suite, uses a 16-module (eight VLF, four LF, two MF, two HF, nested, each about 40 ft long, consisting of 48 equally spaced hydrophones) 800ft (3.5in dia) array covering seven octaves, with another 100 ft of other elements towed on a 5600ft (3.25in dia) cable, at depths as great as 1200 ft, to achieve ranges that cover multiple CZs. Each hydrophone module contains its own amplifier; data are multiplexed for transmission up the tow cable. In addition to the acoustic aperture, the array includes separate heading, depth, and temperature modules (HDTMs) monitoring ambient water conditions at its outboard end and a telemetry drive module (TDM) and three VIMs on its inboard end. There is also a drogue. There is no tow fish or depressor. The handling device is OK-410/SQR.

SQR-19 automates many of the detection, classification, and contact-management functions performed manually in SQR-18, so that two operators and a supervisor can detect contacts reliably even in high-density conditions. Data are processed into 43 beams. Features include computer-aided detection (presumably based on ALI), visual alerts, optimum search display formats, special classification display formats, and special data-process-

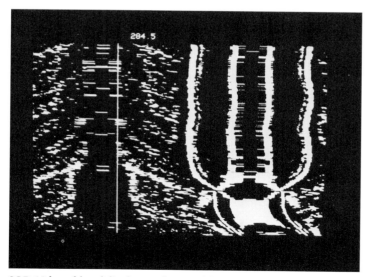

SQR-18 broad-band display, with waterfall (for target motion in bearing) at right. (EDO)

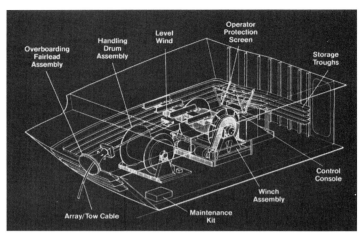

Typical towed array handling gear (OK-410/AN/SQR-19). (Gould)

ing techniques. Processing modes: narrow-band, broad-band, DE-MON. The basic display formats are search (bearing-time waterfall plus some integrated line data), classification (LOFAR display), and true bearing (bearing-vs.-time tracks, based on detections). The system employs a pair of UYS-1 processors sharing a common memory and two OJ-452/UYQ-21 displays (typically embedded in an SQQ-89) plus four UYK-20 computers. Each UYS-1 is connected to a UYK-20 (and cross-connected to another); and the two UYK-20s communicate with each other, for signal processing and data processing. Display and control are run by another pair of UYK-20s, sharing a common UYH-2 mass memory, which communicate with each other and with the other two UYK-20s and the UYS-1s. They in turn communicate with the UYQ-21 system's two consoles.

Versions ([V]1 through [V]3) differ in which versions of OJ-452 and the OL-190 acoustic data converter they use. SQR-19B uses a LAN and UYK-44 rather than UYK-20 computers.

SQR-19 continuously monitors its own performance and can be reconfigured around failed elements without being taken out of service. Consequently, it has an estimated availability of 0.993 (which means all but 3.5 hr out of a typical 210 days during a year), with an MTBF (1995) of 710 hr, a maximum fault-detection time of 1 min, and an MTTR of less than 20 min. The array itself is modular, for quick replacement of faulty elements, and it has an MTBF of better than 2000 hr.

The engineering development contract for SQR-19 was awarded in December 1977, the first ship installation (DD 980) following in November 1981; full-scale production was approved on 26 December 1984. Development was protracted, reportedly mainly because of problems with the dry end. The original 490ft (1700-lb) array had its acoustic aperture doubled in length (2× version, with eight VLF modules added) after experience in 1983 showed that it was necessary to go to much lower frequencies to detect quieter new Soviet submarines. The 2× version was tested in FY87. SQR-19 is made by Lockheed Martin (successor to the original manufacturer, Gould) and Westinghouse. GE (now part of Lockheed Martin) was responsible for the dry end and for system integration.

TAS-2019 is an export version announced in 1995 by Lockheed Martin, using the U.S. Navy wet end and a COTS/VME processor, typically with the standard OK-410 handling gear. The software involved is U.S. government–controlled.

Users: Canada (wet end only in SQR-501 system; 15 sold under FMS), Spain (*Perry* class, as SPAINTASS), United States (*Ticonderoga, Arleigh Burke, Spruance, Perry* classes). As an indication of numbers made, as of March 1995 Lockheed Martin had delivered 125 SQR-19s.

◆ SQS-17/35/36/EDO 700/701/EDO 780/790 series

EDO's 12/13/14-kHz SQR-17 small-ship scanning sonar (scan rate about 3500 rpm) uses a 24-stave array (19in dia, in a 100in dome; the beam-former rotor taps eight staves at a time). Transmission is ODT only (pulse widths 16, 35, 60 msec; source level

134 dB, peak power 1–6, 22, or 30 kW). SQS-17A and -17B differed slightly in frequency.

SQS-17 was conceived in 1954 to replace QCU for ships such as the 173ft PC. It was the first modern sonar manufactured in France (under license); experience with it led directly to the modern French scanning sonars.

EDO's SQS-36 is in effect a preformed-beam version of SQS-17 developed under a 1966 contract; SQS-35 is a VDS equivalent developed from the EDO 700 VDS (in turn the solid-state EDO 700E of 1972 used SQS-35 technology). The related SQS-38 is extinct. The 13-kHz SQS-35 uses a 24-stave transducer (9 transducers/stave, 12 preformed RDT beams, 24 reception beams, peak power 30 kW). SQS-35V is a solid-state version. SQS-36 is a hull version (11.9/13/14.1 kHz with an MCC mode using the two lowest transducers on each stave to depress the beam; nominal range is 12 kyd).

SQS-35(J) is NEC's license-built version.

The 13-kHz EDO 700/701 uses a 495 × 787mm 24-stave transducer (397 kg; hoist and towed body weigh 8250 kg).

EDO 780 (1976) is a lightweight 11.9/13/14.1-kHz VDS derived from SQS-35; it is the first of a series of 24-stave (24 preformed beams) hull and VDS sonars using the same basic console, transmitter, receiver, and data-storage and control unit. Pulse widths: 10, 30, 60 msec CW, 60 msec FM. Range scales: 2, 4, 8, and 16 kyd, with 32 kyd added in the lower-frequency sonar. Accuracy is 0.5 of the range scale, 1 deg in active bearing, and 0.5 deg in passive bearing. For the HF sonars, the passive band is 5.8–10.6 kHz; for the lower-frequency sonar, it is 2.8–5 kHz. There are eight acoustic-intercept bands. EDO 786 (1979) is a hull version of EDO 780 based on SQS-38, the hull equivalent to SQS-35. Source levels (780/786): SRDT, 232/226 dB; TRDT, 226 dB; DT 224–232/218–226 dB; ODT, 217 dB; MCC, 199/201 dB. Weight: inboard, 2188/2176 kg; outboard, 7300/1365 kg. EDO 796 is a 6/7/8-kHz hull sonar. Source levels: SRDT, 231 dB; TRDT, 225 dB; DT, 231 dB; ODT, 216 dB; MCC, 210 dB. Weight: inboard, 2436 kg, outboard 3045 kg.

The dual CRT shows processed rather than raw video. Alternative displays are: ray-path predictor; active detection (range vs. bearing); active search (six-ping history to make weak targets stand out visually); active track classification (sector scan range vs. bearing and target Doppler side by side); passive search (bearing vs. time waterfall; either long-time for slow targets or short-time for fast ones); and passive track classification (BDI for high-accuracy tracking and target spectral analysis side by side). Display data are all stored internally, so that alternative displays can be called up at will. Tracking is by ball-located cursor on a display. The displays were based on experience with BQQ-5. Compared to SQS-56, they show more attention to passive detection, with waterfalls (time vs. bearing displays).

EDO 796 differs from earlier EDO sonars in using a standard Israeli console.

Users:

SQS-17: Iran (PF 103–class corvettes [probably removed]), Philippines (*Auk*-class corvettes), Portugal (*Commandante Rivière* class), Taiwan (*Auk*-class corvettes), Turkey (PC 1638 and PGM 71 classes), Uruguay (*Commandante Rivière* class). This sonar was installed on board Iranian PGM 71–class gunboats (now lost) and was probably installed on board exported World War II–era PCs modernized in the 1960s with fixed Mk 32 tubes. It was on board Greek and Philippine *Cannon*-class frigates, now discarded.

SQS-35: Japan (*Shirane* class, *Takatsuki*-class destroyers, and *Minegumo*; five *Chikugo*-class escorts), Spain (*Baleares* class). Deactivated in U.S. ships 1991, but may be reactivated in some export *Knox* class (it had been used to tow SQR-18 arrays).

SQS-36: Japan (submarines, as SQS-36J).

EDO 700/701: Brazil (EDO 701 in Vosper-Thornycroft frigates), Japan (presumably MSA).

EDO 780/790: Indonesia (*Claud Jones* class [786], replacing SQS-42), Israel (780 on four *Sa'ar II* class, 796 on *Eilat* class), Korea (786 on frigates).

◆ SQS-23/SQQ-23/PAIR/PADLOC

This 4.5/5/5.5-kHz scanning sonar is in effect a scaled-up SQS-29 (see below), also using a 48-stave array (two transducers each, to form 96 channels; the beam can be depressed electronically) with a commutator scanning at 150 Hz (versions through -23C have two scanners, fast [738.8 rpm] and slow [54 or 13.5 rpm]). Separate scanners form transmission beams for RDT and for SDT (using a 9.25-deg beam); there is also an RDT mode. Any of the three can use an MCC (broadened vertical) beam. There is also a handkey mode for communication (using four staves about 90 deg apart). Principal operation modes: search (RDT), search-analyze (long-pulse SDT beam on operator's chosen bearing), attack-RDT (operator controls width of pulse sector and slaves sector bearing to CRT tracking cursor; the target is tracked but the operator can observe a broad area around the target); and attack-SDT (for the late phase of an attack, when the operator concentrates on the target). Pulses are CW and FM (pulse lengths 2 [later 5], 30, and 120 msec and 4.3 sec [-23H long-pulse wide-sector RDT mode transmitted at 60 kW]); source level (early version) is 244 dB. Range scales: 1, 2.5, 5, 10, 20, and 40 kyd. SQS-23 was the "reliable 10,000 yd sonar" specified for ASROC ships designed in the late 1950s. It is currently credited with a maximum range of 14–15 kyd under ideal conditions; the LORA version (see below) has a limited CZ capability (probably only in the Mediterranean).

SQS-23 installed as a bow dome, USS *Barry*, 1959. This ship was the test installation. (U.S. Naval Institute)

The main improvement programs were TRAM (test, reliability, and maintenance, splitting the transmitter into groups each driving eight staves, and offering rotating-beam SDT), MIP (modest improvement program, reducing CRT clutter caused by background reverberation and providing an FM transmission mode), and LORA (long-range addition, largely by self-noise reduction, including a rubber dome, to give a CZ/BB capability in the Mediterranean for Atlantic Fleet ships only). Many SQS-23s have been modernized using Raytheon's solid-state transmitters (SSTs); see the entry for the Raytheon DE 1191 below.

SQS-23A introduced the three frequencies (-23 operated only at 5 kHz), which could be varied by 250 Hz to avoid intership interference; it used piezoelectric rather than magnetostrictive

transducer elements (the TRAM version is -23E). SQS-23B (5 kHz only) introduced SDT (the TRAM version is -23F). SQS-23D reverted to three frequencies (4.55, 5.05, 5.55 kHz, 380-Hz bandwidths) and introduced an FM slide (400-Hz bandwidth) pulse, the fast scanner, and TRAM. SQS-23G is the TRAM version of -23C.

SQS-23H is SQS-23D with a solid-state transmitter with fault localization; three solid-state cabinets replace 21 vacuum-tube cabinets and 10 motor generators. The transmitter uses solid-state linear amplifiers and has automatic fault localization. Each of the 48 channels powers a complete stave. Solid-state version of other TRAM variants are -23J/K/L.

SQQ-23 (PAIR, performance and integration refit) is a solid-state version (ODT: 160 msec at 160 kW, 5.6 sec RDT at 4.3–5.7 kHz [60 kW]) adding passive tracking by a second transducer (in a separate dome, 60 ft back from the first) and PADLOC (passive-active detection and localization). It has a second operator console and BITE. SQQ-23 uses rubber rather than steel domes for better sonar transmission. The single-dome SQQ-23B is now extinct.

SQS-23 was the LF replacement for SQS-4, associated with the ASROC stand-off weapon, was first installed in 1958. SQQ-23A was evaluated in FY71 and entered service in FY73.

Users: Australia (*Adams* class: SQS-23F [with DE 1191]), Colombia (*Boyaca*), Greece (SQQ-23A on *C. F. Adams* class [three plus option on three DE 1191]), Italy (*Vittorio Veneto* [SQS-23G]), Japan (*Haruna*, *Takatsuki*, *Yamagumo*, and *Chikugo* classes, mainly as OQS-3), Korea (five FRAM I and two FRAM II [eight DE 1191 bought, not clear whether all refitted]), Mexico (two FRAM Is), Pakistan (SQS-23D in four FRAM Is [with DE 1191]), Taiwan (12 FRAM Is, two *Gearing* FRAM IIs [12 DE 1191 bought]), and Turkey (two ex-*Carpenter*-class ships, seven FRAM Is, one *Gearing* FRAM II).

◆ SQS-26/53

This 3.5-kHz scanning sonar (receiving at 1.5–4 kHz, in four bands/seven channels) was the culmination of U.S. hull sonar development; its solid-state SQS-53 version is now standard. The 72-stave (eight elements/stave) array (5-deg beams), about 16 ft (dia) × 5 ft, is comparable in size to a 60ft personnel boat. Like SQS-23, SQS-26 is mechanically scanned (hence can track only one target at a time) and its transmitting beam is formed in an analog scanner. Beams can be electronically depressed for BB and CZ propagation in the Atlantic as well as in the Mediterranean. Full potential performance (20 kyd direct-path range, BB and CZ ranges) was reached only after a 1970s improvement program which increased source level and replaced the original steel dome with a low-loss rubber one. Transmission modes: ODT and variable-depression. Receiver processing modes: search, tracking, SSI/TDI.

There are two sonar signal processors (coded and CW pulses) and three consoles (surface channel, A-scan, and target tracking). The surviving versions are GE's SQS-26AXR (*Garcia* class) and -26CX (*Knox* and *California* classes). In 1996 Alliant announced an upgrade program for foreign navies operating SQS-26, presumably equivalent to EC-16 (see page 630).

SQS-53A is a solid-state version of -26CX using the same transducer, with digital output (using UYK-20s and UYQ-21s) but still using mechanical scanning. Passive improvements under the Quick Reaction Fleet Improvement program (begun 1975) were: wide-band passive transducer elements (addition of a diode bridge to the standard elements, begun FY78) and a passive equipment cabinet (PEC, incorporating a UYS-1) to provide narrow-band passive processing. Without the PEC, the sonar had to use an SQR-17 or -18 for passive processing.

EC-16 is a GOTS upgrade for the *Kidd* class and the first nine *Ticonderogas*; the prototype was tested in October 1994 on board USS *Scott* (DDG 995). It opens system architecture (for future quick upgrades) and replaces the old analog electronics in the receiver (for better Doppler resolution) and control/display (it provides a color display with Windows format and 12/16/30-ping track histories). Tactical displays include bottom topography, wrecks, and environmental support (ray traces and perform-

Installation of an SQS-53 sonar dome. (U.S. Navy)

ance prediction). Digital interfaces with CDS and JMCIS are improved. Although the analog transmitter remains, waveforms are modified to match those of Kingfisher and of SQS-53C. The net effect is to reduce system footprint, removing 15 cabinets and 25,000 lb; the use of GOTS cut development time and cost by about two-thirds. Maintenance training is likely to be cut from 29 to 5 weeks, and maintenance hours by 500/yr.

SQS-53B (SQS-53 improvement program Phase I) is a preformed-beam version of -53A, hence offers multiple-target tracking (on a TWS basis only) and substantially better passive (including narrow-band) performance. Receiver modes: PPI, preformed beams, SSI/TDI. This version incorporates QRFI plus a digitized broad-band receiver in place of an earlier unreliable analog device. Active improvements are a digital sector scan indicator (DSSI), wide-sector track (WST), fast automatic gain control (FAGC), and SIMAS (UYS-25). SQS-53B offers improved data association (for detection, classification, and tracking of simultaneous multiple active and passive contacts). SQS-53A analog controls and displays are replaced by standard Navy digital components (two OJ-452, one OL-190) for integration with SQQ-89. As in -53A, the system is controlled by a UYK-20. Reliability and maintainability are much improved (some years ago MTBF was 200 hr, and the target was 500 hr), and manning is cut by 60%. A SQS-53A/B product improvement program (PI) replaces the -53B receiver subsection with -53C digital components. EC-84, for SQS-53B on *Spruances* and *Ticonderogas*, is an expanded version of the EC-16 GOTS upgrade program for SQS-53A.

SQS-53C (Phase II of the SQS-53 improvement program) replaces the analog transmitter beam-former with a more powerful broader-band digital one (one amplifier per transducer, beam shape and pointing controlled electronically; the beam is stabilized in all active modes). This change offers the same sort of accelerated active search provided by SADS in BSY-1. As in a phased-array radar, multiple targets can be tracked automatically by quickly creating beams in different directions. The system's Westinghouse-developed active adjunct processor detects and tracks targets, handling up to 100 active and passive target tracks. Reaction time is also much improved.

During trials in USS *Stump*, the EDM model of SQS-53C regularly demonstrated Second Convergence Zone capability. The ship regularly detected targets at own-ship speeds that were formerly considered transit speeds. The ship was able to detect targets at extended ranges in shallow water, using the sonar's improved waveforms (to overcome reverberation) and frequency agility. Earlier analog systems tend to suffer from alignment problems, and offer many fewer waveform options. Reportedly SQS-53C has a stealthy (presumably spread-spectrum, hence the significance of the wider bandwidth) waveform. Pulses are FM

and CW, and transmission modes are ODT, RRDT (random/rotationally directed transmission) and TRDT.

As in -53B, the displays are UYQ-21s. UYS-1 processes both active and passive signals. UYK-44 is the control computer. Compared to SQS-53B, -53C has half the space and weight devoted to shipboard electronics, largely thanks to the use of SEM cards. Even so, -53C needs 31 electronic cabinets and 37,000 lb of inboard electronics. By way of comparison, the 3.5-kHz version of Westinghouse's 21HS, in effect a COTS version of -53C, requires only about 13,000 lb of inboard electronics, most of it in four cabinets. MTBF is 765 hr (MTTR 1 hr).

The (V)1, (V)2, and (V)3 versions may differ slightly in their transducers.

An SQS-53C passive subsystem modernization (PSM) program replaces the current analog/digital converter and two passive beam-formers with COTS, reducing three cabinets to three VME chassis in one cabinet. The first modified sonar was tested on board USS *Cole*. A decision as to whether to include PSM in the SQQ-89(V)X COTS version was scheduled for June 1996.

Ongoing near-term efforts include an attempt to improve SQS-53C shallow-water classification capability by 50%, work on full-spectrum passive processing, and the development of SQS-53 bistatic capability with SQR-19, with other SQS-53 platforms, and with ALFS. A mid-frequency towed array testbed (TARS) is being developed as a deep receiver adjunct for the SQS-53 transmitter, to detect deep targets. Integration with SQS-53 is to begin in FY97.

SQS-53D (the digital receiver version of SQS-53A/B) is an upgraded sonar for the *Spruance, Kidd,* and *Ticonderoga*-class ships. It should enter service in FY97 as part of SQQ-89 (V) Block I. Ten were ordered from Lockheed Martin in December 1996.

All SQS-53 sonars have been modified to incorporate Probe Alert for one-way acoustic communication to submerged submarines; in this mode, the sonar concentrates on projecting encoded signals into the water. Probe Alert entails modifications to the A-scan console, the sequential timer, and the transmitter control unit. First delivered in 1986, it is the latest of several attempts to use these LF sonars for underwater communication. Many SQS-53s have had the Kingfisher mine-avoidance modification; see the discussion of Kingfisher for SQS-56 below.

SQS-26 feasibility studies began in 1955, and the prototype XN-1 model was installed in 1961. Initial production contracts were let in 1961, that for the definitive SQS-26CX being let in October 1964 (the first was delivered in December 1967 and entered service on board the *Knox* in 1969). The sonar was approved for service use only in November 1968, after considerable difficulties, and for some years SQS-26 could only rarely achieve its theoretical performance (SQS-23 often did better in service).

Delivery of SQS-53A began in October 1972.

Hughes received the contract for the SQS-53B EDM in June 1979. It first demonstrated its new narrow-band passive capability in November 1982.

The first SQS-53C EDM was installed on board USS *Stump* in August 1986.

The unit cost of an SQS-53B was $6.3M in FY87, compared to $3.4M for SQS-53C.

Users:

SQS-26: Brazil (*Garcia* class [AXR]), Egypt (*Knox* class [CX]), Greece (*Knox* class [CX]), Taiwan (*Knox* class [CX]), Thailand (*Knox* class [CX]), Turkey (*Knox* class [CX]), United States (*California* [CX], *Knox* class [CX]).

SQS-53: United States (*Virginia* [-53A], *Ticonderoga* [-53B], *Arleigh Burke* [-53C], *Spruance* [-53A and -53B], *Kidd* [-53A], -53B is being retrofitted to existing *Spruance* and *Ticonderoga* class ships; -53C will be retrofitted to *Spruances* and *Ticonderogas*).

◆ SQS-29 Series/SQS-39 Series/SQS-43 Series

These MF scanning sonars use mechanical commutators (scanning on reception at 150 Hz [9000 rpm]) and 48-stave (nine elements/stave) transducers (beams 10 × 15 deg). The 16-contact rotor scans at 3000 rpm, the outputs of each group of eight staves going to separate left/right beam-forming networks. The phase difference between the two networks is used for target tracking, a technique called SSI (sector scan indicator). There are two video (search and tracking) and one audio (classification) receiving channels, each with its own scanner. An MCAR (multiple-channel aural reception) modification provides broader-beam reception to improve the capability against fast targets (three beams 7.5 deg apart instead of the single 10-deg receiving beam). Transmitting modes: ODT (source level 117 dB), RDT (source level 133 dB; includes 30–300-deg sector scan, oriented around the bow), ASPECT (acoustic short-pulse echo-classification technique: a burst of short steered pulses gives an indication of a target's shape), MCC (depressed-beam, using windings on the middle and next two above elements in each stave, or on the middle and next two below elements [for depth finding]), and passive search (using the outer edge of the PPI, with a sweep rate used for the 5-kyd range scale). Pulse lengths: 2, 7, 30, or 120 msec (4–50 kW). Range scales: 1, 2.5, 5, 10, 15, and 30 kyd. Typical nominal ranges (for targets in the layer): 7500 yd for SQS-29/30 and 6500 yd for SQS-31/32. SQS-29 can detect a target below the layer at about 2100 yd.

Versions are: SQS-29 (8 kHz), SQS-30 (10 kHz), SQS-31 (12 kHz), and SQS-32 (14 kHz). Because of differences in wavelength, SQS-29 and -30 use a larger transducer than SQS-31 and -32; it uses a 145in dome (100in for SQS-31 and -32). Some sonars in this series (mainly SQS-31 and -32) were modified for operation with SQA-10 VDS; the hull and VDS transducer could operate alternatively off the same stack. The fish accommodated a full-size (48-stave) SQS-31 or -32 transducer or a half-size SQS-29 or -30 transducer.

Although not redesignated, SQS-29 series sonars may have improvements associated with the SQS-39, -43, and -49 versions: TRDT (8000 yd nominal range), SDT, and MARK (maintenance and reliability kit). MARK increased maximum power to 134.4 kW and also improved preamps.

SQS-39: SQS-29 with SDT and MARK.
SQS-42: SQS-32 with SDT and MARK.
SQS-44: SQS-29 with SDT and MARK.
SQS-45: SQS-30B/C with SDT and MARK, and capable of running a VDS off the same stack.

These are all modified versions of SQS-4, tested in 1951 in its 14-kHz version. It entered fleet service in 1954; 250 were made. The VDS version was first studied in 1960–61. Some SQS-4s were installed on board submarines, and many SQS-4s and modified versions were transferred to Allied navies.

Users: Indonesia (SQS-45, -39, and -42 in *Claud Jones* class), Iran (SQS-42 and -44 in FRAM II destroyers), South Korea (SQS-29 series in FRAM II destroyers; VDS in *Dae Gu* only), and Turkey (*Berk* class). SQS-4 sonars in the Taiwanese navy were replaced by Krupp-Atlas DSQS-21s.

◆ SQS-55

This special HF (100-kHz) DIMUS (electronic lens) sonar was developed and used by the Naval Coastal Systems Laboratory, Panama City, to track underwater objects at short range. It forms an array of 60 2 × 10-deg beams. Pulse width is 1 or 2 msec; range scales are 300 and 600 m. Source level is quite high, 218 dB. SQS-55 probably dates from 1972.

◆ SQS-56 (DE 1160)/Kingfisher/DE 1163/DE 1164

Raytheon's 6.7/7.5/8.4 kHz (bandwidth 400 Hz, FM or CW) direct-path private-venture solid-state digital (preformed-beam) active-passive hull sonar uses a 36-stave transducer (121.9 cm [dia] × 96.5 cm, 2268 kg, 36 preformed beams). DE 1160B (details below) operates at 30 kW peak power (7.2 kW average). DE 1160C (SQS-56) operates at 90 kW and adds another transmitter unit and a dummy load. Both sonars use the same transducer and receiver. The beam can be depressed/elevated at 12.5 or 25 deg. Transmission modes: ODT (5.0–160-msec pulses, source level 218 dB), Single RDT (5.0–2180-msec pulses, 232 dB, over a 20–120-deg sector), TRDT (5.0–1940-msec pulses, 227 dB), and WRDT (wide: 5–700-msec pulses, 30–120-deg sector, 225 dB).

Reception modes (600-Hz bandwidth): search (12.5-deg depression/elevation, resolution 2-deg and 2 yd/2.5 kyd scale or 16 yd/20 kyd scale) and tracking (two independent steered 20-deg beams, range gates 625 and 1250 yd, tracking using SSI and TDI; one 14-deg independent audio beam, accuracy 0.5 deg in azimuth, 1.1 yd in range, and 2 kt in Doppler). A 3–6-kHz passive mode uses 18 preformed beams (18 × 21 deg). Active track data are shown on an expanded B-scan (20 deg in bearing × 625 or 1250 yd), and both long- and short-term passive averaged data can be shown separately, in waterfall form. Total system weight is 11,600 lb for DE 1160B and 12,800 lb for DE 1160C.

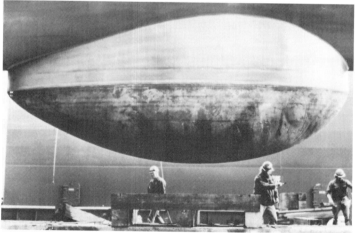

SQS-56 transducer and its sonar dome.

DE 1163 is a VDS version of DE 1160B (peak power 35 kW, average 7 kW). DE 1164 combines DE 1160 and DE 1163 in a single integrated sonar. DE 1160LF is a larger LF (probably 3.5 kHz) version; 1164LF is the corresponding integrated sonar.

A DE 1160/SQS-56/1167 Improvement Program (IP) is intended to improve shallow-water performance, increase range, and add a capability to detect and avoid small objects (Kingfisher, see below). Greatly increased computing power in a fully digital system makes it possible to subject the same signal to several different types of processing in parallel, overlaying the results to combine the merits of different types of receivers, for improved range and better shallow-water performance. The improved sonar also offers computer-aided detection and tracking. Raytheon sees this version as its third-generation sonar, DE 1160 being its second generation. The system uses 68000-series general-pur-

The standard dual control of a DE 1160 sonar. The lower screen is a dual B-scan (range vs. bearing). (Raytheon)

DE 1164 fish shown after it had been streamed and recovered by the Italian frigate *Maestrale*, March 1982. (Raytheon)

pose processors and TMS320-series digital signal processing elements; processing load is less than 50% of maximum available and bus load (less than 0.2 Mbytes/sec) also allows for future growth. Functions include weapon preset evaluation. The sys-

tem is rearranged around an Ethernet bus to provide an open architecture. A new two-screen (19in, 1280 × 1024-pixel color) multifunction operator console carries a graphics processor and an applications processor (6 MIPS, 6 Mbytes of memory) supporting the system's real-time operating system. A new VME controller cabinet combines all sonar signal and control processing (separate array processor [beam-former], sonar signal processor, and sonar system processor [controlling the dual transmitter] feed each other and each feeds the system bus; there are also two hard disks). Source levels: 232 dB at 7.5 kHz, 238 dB at 3.75 kHz; pulse length: 5 to 160 msec; bandwidth (CW/FM): 6.25–2000 Hz (maximum target Doppler 40 kt). Beamwidth is 10 deg (resolution 1.25 deg), using linear time-domain beamforming (sidelobes −30 dB).

Future improvements are to include TMA, integration of non-acoustic data (radar, ESM), sonobuoy processing, integrated onboard testing, integrated BT, and an integrated VDS.

Alenia markets the improved DE 1160 as the DMSS-2000 dual-mode sonar system.

Kingfisher is a mine-avoidance modification developed by the U.S. Navy Underwater Sound Laboratory and Raytheon for operations in the Persian Gulf. Its special PCC (polarity coincidence correlator, a right-left correlator) receiver feeds an auxiliary display console, on which the operator sees three adjacent 10 × 16-deg beams in A-scan form; they are also made audible (it turned out that identification was largely by ear). The beams are too wide to distinguish easily between small objects. The Sound Lab added an electronic range recorder, showing up to 80 pings on seven beams, to give a picture of the area ahead of the ship. It draws a horizontal line—in effect, an MTI line. The special beams are then trained on the suspicious object. This system was used by USS *Nichols*. Similar modifications were adopted for SQS-53 and were considered (and probably tested) for AQS-13 sonars. Kingfisher was developed in parallel with the installation of Plessey Mirror Sonars in bulbous bows strapped onto the forefeet of some U.S. frigates.

Engineering design was completed in October 1977, following 1975 tests. Production began in 1979. DE 1160B is the export version. DE 1160C provides more power (with an extra electronic cabinet). Spain has upgraded her 1160Bs to 1160C standards. DE 1164 is the corresponding VDS, which can be trailed at depths as great as 600 ft. Spain designates the sonar being installed in the *Baleares* class as SQS-56LF rather than DE 1160LF. It is being produced largely by Inisel, under license.

DE 1160 was designed to match the Canadian SQS-505. The first major application was to the U.S. *Perry* class. The entire DE 1160 series was designed to share common computer hardware and software, common displays, common transmitter amplifiers and power supplies, common circuit cards, and common interface units. Unit cost (1988) is $3.5–4.5M.

Users:

DE 1160/SQS-56: Australia (SQS-56 in *Perry* class), Greece (four DE 1160 in MEKO 200s), Italy (four DE 1160B in *Lupos*, one DE 1160LF in *Garibaldi*), Morocco (one DE 1160 in *Descubierta*), Saudi Arabia (four DE 1160B in PCG class), Spain (six DE 1160B/C for *Descubierta* class, five DE 1160LFs for *Baleares* class, and six SQS-56SPs for *Perry* class), Taiwan (six SQS-56s), Turkey (SQS-56 in MEKO 200s), United States (SQS-56 in *Perry* class).

DE 1163/1164: Greece (four VDSs for MEKO 200s), Italy (Hull/VDS in *Maestrale* class, DE 1164LFs in *Mimbelli* class, DE 1164 hull/VDS in *Alpino* class [replacing SQS-43]). The Chinese Luhu-class destroyer *Harbin* displays a VDS similar in form to that of DE 1163, and may have a DE 1164 or DE 1167LF sonar.

◆ SQS-58/DE 1167

Raytheon's 12- or 18-kHz (2-kHz bandwidth) small-ship pre-formed-beam hull/VDS sonar (hull, fish, or combined) is in effect a smaller version of DE 1160/SQS-56, using a 36-stave transducer (selectable 10 × 13-deg sum beam for listening). Pulses are 1-kHz FM slides (6.25, 50, 100, 200 msec). Range active search mode: interlaced ODT (215 dB, limited to 5-kyd scale to maximize data rate on the most urgent threats) and TRDT (225 dB: 12 transmissions in sequence to cover 360 deg, usually 200-msec pulses [can use 50 msec]). Evaluation mode: ODT (all but 100-msec pulses). Range scales: 2, 4, 8, 16 kyd (resolution 8–64 yd; 256 range cells in the display). Tracking accuracy is 2 deg (by comparing half-beams). The display can show a three- or six-ping history. Passive mode: 4.5 kHz (2-kHz bandwidth). Display formats: active search B-scan, sector B-scan showing target Doppler, passive waterfall (showing both short- and long-term averaged data). Only one operator is required. The hull sonar weighs 4375 kg (12 kHz) or 3920 kg (18 kHz); the VDS weighs 10,260 kg. Service rate: 1 hr of service is required for 60 days of operation. MTTR is 30 min. The sonar uses BITE.

The 7.5-kHz (7.5- or 12-kHz VDS) DE 1167LF is intended for larger ships that cannot accommodate DE 1160 B/C. The 7.5-kHz hull array is 48 in in diameter, compared to 28.2 in for the 12-kHz array. The 7.5-kHz VDS fish weighs 50,300 lb; the 12-kHz fish, 23,550 lb. Some parts are made in Italy by Elsag.

DE 1167 (MOD) is used to modernize existing SQS-23s: the receiver and console and a new 48-kW solid-state transmitter (SST) are added to the existing dome and transducer, adding a minimum of 10 dB in performance.

SQS-58(XN-1), on Raytheon's test ship *Sub Sig-II*, is a DE 1167. In 1988 the unit cost of a DE 1167 was $2M.

Users: Egypt (two DE 1167LF/VDS in *Descubierta* class), Italy (eight DE 1167 in *Minerva* class; probably also in the two modernized *Audace* class, replacing EDO 610; the total purchase was nine DE 1167LF and four DE 1167), Japan (four DE 1167LFs, presumably for the MSA), and Korea (26 DE 1167s [application not known, may have been bought in place of EDO sonars]). The *Minerva* sonars were the first to be made in Italy.

◆ Lightweight Broad-band VDS (LBVDS)

The FY96 new start program is intended to counter slow submarines and mines in shallow water. Lockheed Martin Ocean Systems received a demonstration contract about April 1996, to build a prototype for completion in 2001 (the projector and receiver are to be fabricated during FY97).

◆ SADS

Submarine Active Detection System is part of the BSY-1 sonar suite. It provides the accelerated active search (random beam positioning) originally wanted in BQQ-5 by replacing the analog transmitting beam-former (scanner) of BQS-13 with a fully digital unit (one amplifier per transducer), as in SQS-53C, with which it shares some waveforms.

◆ 21HS

Northrop Grumman's (formerly Westinghouse's) 21st Century Hull Sonar is intended both for export and as part of the planned COTS version of SQQ-89. The system comprises a processor cabinet, sonar transmitter cabinets (one for 10 or 13 kHz, transmitter plus amplifier for 5–7 kHz, transmitter plus three amplifiers for 3.5 kHz), T/R switch (integrated with the amplifier and transmitter in the 13 kHz version) and up to three color raster-scan display consoles using X-Windows graphics (console and processor are combined in the 13-kHz 21HS-13 small-ship version). By way of contrast, SQS-53C uses a total of 31 electronics cabinets (seven in the transmitter group, 16 in the receiver processing group, and five [including two main operator consoles] for the operators). The system typically uses 216 transducers (36 staves) to create 36 beams (it covers 300 deg), but it can use an existing transducer. Typical array diameters are 10 ft (3.5 kHz) and 4 ft (7 kHz); the system can also accommodate a VDS. An upgraded SQS-53 would retain its original power amplifier and transmitter, but upgraded SQS-26 and -56 would receive new transmitters. Modes: SD (surface duct), VD (variable depression), ODT (omni), RRDT (random rotating directional), TRDT (tribeam), Track, Obstacle Avoidance. Waveforms are CW, FM, and SW (shallow water: short wide-band pulse). Source level is 220–235 dB. Pulse widths: 20, 100, 500 msec; Northrop Grumman is seeking an export license for pulsewidths of 1 sec or more. FM band-

widths: 100, 350, and 700 Hz. FM pulses can be processed coherently or they can be pulse-compressed (PDPC mode, postdetection pulse compression, in which slices of the pulse are detected separately by replica comparison, then pulse-compressed). The system can also detect both broad- and narrow-band radiated noise. It can handle up to 100 target tracks. MTBF is to be over 1100 hr (MTTR under 1 hr). Work began in 1993, and the system was announced in 1995, when a trial using the SQS-53C transducer of a U.S. destroyer, probably *Hayler*, was planned for 1996.

◆ SIMAS (UYQ-25)

Sonar In-Situ Mode Assessment System is a sonar performance predictor (essentially a very sophisticated ray-tracer) incorporated in SQS-53 and SQQ-89. It is particularly valuable for passive operation since it provides an operator with an estimate of CZ range and also with likely signal strength from various CZs (as well as from alternative signal paths, such as bottom or surface bounce). SIMAS is embedded (rather than separate) in SQQ-89(V)4 and later versions.

The original UYQ-25 of 1978 used a UYK-20X(V) computer, a USQ-69 data terminal, and a teleprinter. It was programmed by magnetic tape and weighed 1165 lb. UYQ-25A (1986) uses a DTC I desktop computer (HP 9020) with 16- and 55-Mbyte disk drives and can incorporate a spectrum analyzer (HP 3582A). UYQ-25A(V)1 (with spectrum analyzer) is used for SQR-18A(V) acoustic predictions and equipment-mode selection. UYQ-25A(V)2, for SQR-19 (part of SQQ-89), has no spectrum analyzer. UYQ-25A(V)3, with no spectrum analyzer, is for SQR-18(V).

◆ SWALAS

Shallow Water ASW Localization and Attack System is a planned future program, probably conceived as an extension of the bistatic ADAR/AAA sonobuoy. However, the Fleet recommended that nonacoustic sensors be included. Presumably that meant laser radar on board helicopters and other ASW aircraft.

This project completed its Milestone 0 evaluation in February 1994. Milestone 1 slipped from February to October 1995 due to the extended COEA (nonacoustic). Milestone 2 is scheduled for February 1999.

◆ SURTASS (UQQ-2)

See the Surveillance and Control section.

◆ TB-16/BQ

This 3.5in (240 ft with 186ft acoustic aperture, 1300 lb) submarine array is towed on a 2600ft (0.37in) cable. The array comprises two VIMs, one transverse VIM, one sensor module, five acoustic modules (including a spare) with a total of 50 hydrophones, and one array-stabilization module. Hydrophone signals are amplified, conditioned, and modulated, then frequency-multiplexed for transmission to the submarine via the tow cable. The modular design of the array allows for complete interchange of acoustic module positions within the array, including the spare, provided no two with the same channels (indicated by part number) are used in the same operating configuration, and proper channel cards are substituted in the LF receiver processing the signals transmitted by the array.

TB-16A (1403 lb with a 450-lb cable, 1982) has reduced self-noise, so that it can be towed at greater speed (or at the same speed with greater sensitivity). TB-16B (in production 1987) embodies ECP 59 to further reduce flow noise. TB-16D replaces analog with digital signal transmission. The current version is TB-16E, a refined TB-16D (contract for 69 units let to Lockheed Martin in December 1989). The next version, TB-16( ), to be TB-16F, adds some nonacoustic capability to detect array shape, depth, heading, and elevation angle (which earlier versions did not measure; in the past, ship heading was used as array heading). Compared to a thin-line array, the shorter but thicker TB-16 should suffer less self-noise at a given speed but should also be effective only at higher frequencies. Note that BSY-2 incorporates both TB-16D and the long thin-line TB-29.

The tube running down one side of the submarine *Olympia* houses a towed array; there is no space within the single hull for anything so massive. Such stowage in turn limits the maximum length of the array. (U.S. Navy)

Typically, TB-16 is stowed in a tube running outside the pressure hull, the reel, cable, and winch being located in the forward main ballast tank. The array is streamed out of a tube leading from the port horizontal stabilizer. This installation was designed for SSN 637–class submarines, the early 688s being fitted with a permanently streamed (clip-on) array. The 688s were later provided with reelable arrays using tube stowage, operational experience having shown that the fixed array could be damaged during high-speed runs.

TB-16 is the production version of TB-16(XN-1)/BQ, an improved version of the Tuba II (BQH-4) array, offering a much wider frequency range than the earlier nonretractable STASS (BQR-25). It was developed under a 1973 contract. The array was originally made by Chesapeake Instrument Co., which was then taken over by Gould, and then by Martin-Marietta (which became Lockheed Martin), the current manufacturer. Production (by Lockheed Martin and predecessors): 131 TB-16, 56 TB-16A, 45 TB-16D, 65 TB-16E (as of March 1995), 40 STASS.

◆ TB-23/BQ

The 4× (four times the TB-16 aperture) thin-line towed array has an overall length of 4000 ft (2450 lb), probably including about 3000 ft of cable; maximum diameter is 1.1 in, except 1.14 in at intermodule couplings, 1.15 in at VIMS, and 1.2 in at array-termination module. Allied Signal Oceanics' 98-hydrophone array consists of two VIMs, one environmental module, four LF modules, two MF modules, and two HF modules, plus an array-stabilization module and an array-termination module. Apparently tests were not altogether successful (see BQR-15/SPALT 9080 above), and installation has probably been limited to *Los Angeles*–class submarines; this array is being superseded by TB-29. TB-23 was tested in 1987. By March 1995 Lockheed Martin and Granite State Manufacturing had delivered 50 units.

◆ TB-29 (formerly TB-12X)

This new, long, thin, submarine towed array is part of BQQ-5E and BSY-2. The original TB-12X designation indicates an array with an acoustic aperture 12 times as long as that of TB-16. That probably means about 2500 ft (12 TB-16s would be 2880 ft long, but the TB-16 acoustic aperture must be shorter than the total array length). The aperture is so long that it can be divided into sections for passive ranging (TARP, towed array range processing). TB-29 is described officially as a quantum improvement in long-range detection and localization.

TB-29 is part of BQQ-5E, superseding the TB-23 of BQQ-5D, on board *Los Angeles*– and *Ohio*-class submarines. In the new *Seawolf*, TB-29 is combined with the shorter TB-16D. Prelimi-nary sea trials were run during FY89, when the final TB-12X specification was drawn up. A full-scale development contract was awarded in the second quarter of 1990, with sea trials in October 1990 and October 1991, and TechEval and OpEval in 1993. Reportedly WAA has gained in importance because TARP was less than completely successful.

◆ TARP

Towed array range processing uses the array to measure the curvature of the wavefront it detects, as in PUFFS, but on a much larger scale. In theory, the curvature measures range. The British version of this technique, also in current use, is range-focusing. Reportedly, problems in U.S. trials of TARP led to demands for WAA despite its size and weight. A recent British paper suggests that TARP is fundamentally flawed in that the wavefronts encountered by long towed arrays are rarely planar. Instead, the details of propagation (including reflections off surface and bottom and convergence-zone refraction) must always be taken into account. In theory, then, TARP should always incorporate a ray-tracer. Again, in theory, the pressure measurement at each hydrophone in the array can be compared with the predicted pressure field associated with a target at a variety of ranges, depths, and bearings; the best match indicates target position. This matched-field processing approach requires high bandwidth and much more computation than conventional TMA, since the pressure field from each of numerous points must be calculated very rapidly. Range resolution may be poor, and accuracy depends on the precision of the acoustic propagation model. On the other hand, unlike TMA, matched-field processing begins instantaneously, as the pressure field is measured.

◆ UUVs

ARPA is developing unmanned (autonomous) underwater vehicles, mainly for use from submarines in the Pathfinder (mine avoidance), submarine escort/decoy, and UUV-deployed hydrophone array (remote surveillance system, RSS) roles. See the Mine Warfare section for the mine-avoidance role. Escort/decoy (tactical avoidance system, TAS) is a submarine simulator that will decoy the threat and communicate intruder information. DARPA awarded the TAS contract to Martin-Marietta in February 1990.

By late 1994, NUWC Newport had built an experimental 26.5 × 292in UUV (5200 lb), capable of 0–12 kt. There was also a 21in UUV used for mine reconnaissance experiments (see the Mine Warfare section), and at least two 44in-dia Scout vehicles built in 1990. The objective is a 21in-dia vehicle with an endurance of 24–30 hr, suitable for TT launch and recovery. The main difficulty is energy storage (high density, low power output). Thus the original OR for the mine surveillance system, which called for a 4-kW motor and a 96-kWh capacity (i.e., 24 hr, but at very low speed), was considered difficult to meet; eventually a 3360-kWh capacity will be needed. That will probably require a fuel cell.

Under the FY94 program, a new shallow-water acoustic communications capability (5 kbps at 1 nm between a tactical-size UUV and a static platform) was demonstrated; range was later extended to 3 nm. A tethered remotely operated vehicle (TROV) was launched from and recovered to a *Los Angeles*–class submarine in FY95. A Stirling engine for UUVs (75- and then 100-hr wick combustors) was built and tested in FY94/95.

◆ EDO 610 Series/CWE-610

This LF (6-, 7-, or 8-kHz) preformed-beam (10 × 10-deg beams) hull sonar uses a 36-stave transducer (1245 × 1067 mm, 2500 kg). Modes: ODT, search (120-deg sector), attack (50-deg sector). Range scales: 2, 4, 8, 16, and 32 kyd. Maximum target Doppler is 40 kt. There is also a passive display.

Development began in 1963, for the Royal Netherlands Navy, of the first EDO sonar designed specifically for a foreign customer. EDO 610 reflected the company's experience with SQS-26BX, and was intended as a more compact alternative to SQS-23; SQS-505 is derived partly from this sonar. The prototype was completed in 1966. EDO 610A appeared in 1972, and 610E is a solid-state version incorporating SQS-38 experience. In 1995, EDO offered Brazil a new 610M sonar to replace the existing 610E. Although reports stated that only the cabling would be retained, presumably 610M retains much the same transducer (to limit hull work), replacing the entire inboard electronic package.

This sonar is designed to work with the EDO 700/701 VDS (see SQS-17/35 above).

Users: Brazil (610E in all Vosper Mk 10 frigates; ASW ships also have EDO 700E VDS), Italy (*Audace* class [610A]), Peru (*Lupo* class [610E]), Venezuela (*Lupo* class [610E]).

♦ EDO 900

This submarine mine-avoidance sonar uses a 368mm transducer to transmit continuous FM signals, the echoes from which are shown on a 7in ship-centered CRT. There is also an audio channel.

Users: Germany (Type 206 submarines).

♦ EDO 1110

This submarine flank employs a linear transducer array forming 96 broad-band beams or 48 narrow-band beams to cover the 135-deg sector on each side (with reduced accuracy at the ends). It operates at 300–1500 Hz (0–250 Hz for DEMON). The amplitude-interpolation tracker has 16 ATTs (combined broad- and narrow-beam); there are also three high-precision trackers (combined broad- and narrow-band and DEMON), so the system can track a total of 19 targets simultaneously, using LF beam-preforming, split-beam correlation (for accurate pointing), and spectral analysis (broad- and narrow-band interpolation). Tracks can be maintained even when targets cross the submarine's path (passing from the FOV of one array to the other). Bearing accuracy is 0.4 deg; frequency accuracy is 0.32–1.30 Hz. The operator selects broad-band search, narrow-band search, narrow-band search LOFAR, high-quality tracker analysis, or intercept sonar analysis formats on either of two color displays (19in, 1024 × 1024 pixels). On each format, the top area provides cursor readouts such as frequency, bearing, and rpm. The bottom area provides tracker data, system status, and BITE information. Outboard weight is 4500 lb; inboard weight is 1513 lb.

This system was announced in 1985.

Users: Israel (Vickers 540 submarines); delivered 1991. In 1996 Rafael announced that it had developed a software-driven adaptive noise cancellation system for this flank array, which is not decoupled from the hull; it claimed a 15–20-dB signal-to-noise improvement equating to greater range and better narrow-band classification.

The EDO 1110 control-indicator with explanations of the display formats (at right). In the broad-band search display, the large center portion contains target bearing versus time and target energy amplitude versus bearing, the latter from the submarine's shorter-range cylindrical array. Narrow-band search data from any one of the 48 narrow-band beams are shown in both ALI and LOFAR formats. Time history of all the beams is stored in memory, so beams can be switched instantaneously. Left-hand data are selected by the operator (narrow-band and DEMON tracks, processed audio, or DEMON analysis). (EDO)

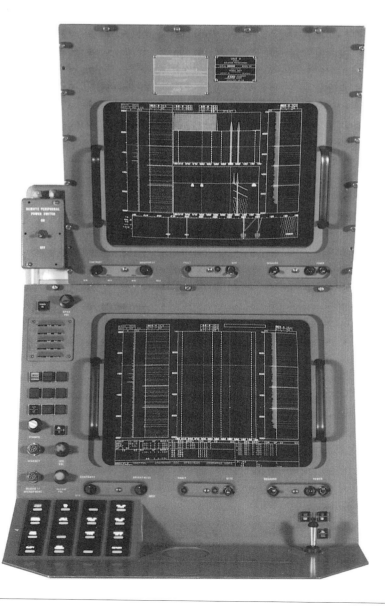

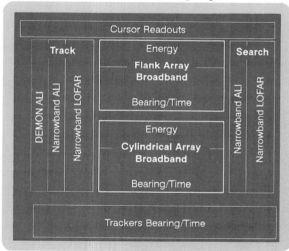

Broadband Search Display Format

Narrowband Search Display Format

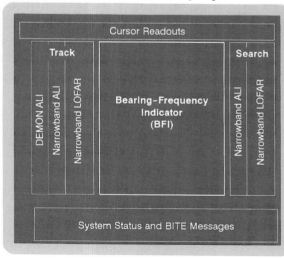

◆ EDO 1550/Avitek-500 Series

This 72–87-kHz CTFM obstacle-avoidance sonar scans over +/−30/60/180 deg sectors at 25 deg/sec using a 60 × 17.5-deg transmitting beam and a 2.5 × 17-deg receiving beam. It splits the 3–1500-yd range interval into 80 or 128 cells. EDO 1550 is the upgraded version.

Users: Netherlands (submarines), Norway (submarines; first two delivered for *Kobben*-class March 1993), United States (deep submergence vehicles, some submarines).

◆ Raytheon DE 1191

This hull sonar combines features of the DE 1190 transmitter, the DE 1160 receiver and display, and a new LF transducer. The solid-state transmitter (DE 1190 SST: 12-, 24-, 36-, 48-, 72-, and 96-kW versions) is sold as an SQS-23 upgrade. DE 1191 includes a 48-kW transmitter (14-dB improvement over SQS-23; peak power 120 kW) and eliminates 40 cabinets and boxes of vacuum tubes and 10 motor generators, leaving five cabinets and saving 450 ft^3. DE 1191 uses the same dome and transducer as SQS-23, so no drydock work is required for installation. Typically the SST is installed first, then the more expensive receiver/display. Features include memory-refreshed B-scan and multi-ping storage.

The DE 1191 transmitter costs \$1M. By November 1989 Raytheon had sold 80 transmitters.

Users: Australia (three for DDGs), Germany (three for DDGs, later replaced by DSQS-21s), Greece (three, plus an option on three, for FRAMs), Pakistan (six for FRAMs), Korea (eight for FRAMs), Taiwan (12 for FRAMs), and the United States (48 for ships with SQS-23 sonars, the only survivors of which are probably the four DDGs transferred to Greece).

UNDERWATER FIRE-CONTROL SYSTEMS

◆ Mk 101/Mk 106

These early postwar analog FCSs can handle only a single target at a time. They consist of a position-keeper (to determine target course and speed) feeding a ballistic computer (angle solver). Once target course and speed have been determined (based on intermittent observation, and assuming that they are constant), a fire-control solution is continuously computed and continuously applied to the torpedo gyros. The electronic Mk 101 can project ahead evasive (curved) target motion once a torpedo has been launched. Mk 101 also differed from its predecessors in that it did not restrict own-ship maneuvers during the analysis period (in this case, 20 min). A new Angle Solver Mk 18 was introduced to handle wire-guided torpedoes (it position-keeps for the torpedo). It can change torpedo course in 2-deg increments and enabling run in 100-yd increments. Limitations: torpedo speed 15–60 kt, torpedo run 300–35,000 yd, target speed 0–40 kt, own-ship speed 0–40 kt, target range 0–35,000 yd, torpedo depth 0–1400 ft. Like its predecessors, Mk 18 is still an analog computer with special components for particular sets of torpedo ballistics, in this case for torpedoes Mk 14 Mods 3A and 5, Mk 16 Mods 6 and 7, Mk 27 Mod 4, Mk 28 Mods 2 and 3, Mk 37 Mods 0 and 1 (the last with the angle solver modified), Mk 39 Mod 1, Mk 45 Mod 0, and standoff mines Mk 27 Mods 0–3. Mod 4 handles the Mk 48 torpedo, using a separate tone generator to produce the necessary digital guidance signals.

Although wire guidance theoretically allows for dog-leg courses, such tactics required a much more elaborate plot or computer, permitting the operator to visualize the tactical situation, hence are not available to Mk 101.

Mk 106 is a simpler system built around the wartime torpedo data computer (TDC) Mk 4, modified for electrically rather than mechanically set torpedoes (however, it retained a mechanical setting capability for older torpedoes). TDC Mk 4 accepts torpedo speed settings of 18–55 kt and values of torpedo run differences from −100 to +150 yd; torpedo spreads can be up to 900 ft forward and aft of the estimated target midpoint. Like Mk 101, Mk 106 can track targets at ranges up to 30,000 yd, and can set torpedoes for travel up to 15,000 yd. In surviving versions, max-

imum target depth is 1000 ft, and maximum target speed is 40 kt. Surviving versions incorporate a Mk 18 Mod 3 angle solver (in Mod 14) or a Mk 37 torpedo director (in Mod 16 or 17), to control a single wire-guided torpedo. The version capable of controlling Mk 48 apparently has not survived.

Contracts for Mk 101 and the parallel surface Mk 102 were let in 1948, and Mk 101 entered service in 1952.

Users:

> Mk 101: Turkey (*Tang* class [Mod 18]). This version can control Mk 48 wire-guided torpedoes.
> Mk 106: Taiwan (Mod 16 in Guppy II), Turkey (Mod 14 in Guppy III, Mod 17 in Guppy IIA).

◆ Mk 105

This postwar Hedgehog/depth charge FCS for destroyers and frigates, first tested in 1952, was built around Librascope's Mk 5 attack director. As in the submarine TFCS, it consists of a position-keeper to project ahead target position (using rate-aided tracking on a straight-line basis) and a ballistic section. Like Mk 101, it can handle an evasive (turning) target, the turn angle of which is entered manually. Target turns are detected by comparing observed position with projected straight-line position. The projected target track can also be used to help regain contact after an attack. Target depth is entered manually.

The associated Mk 1 A/S attack plotter (ASAP) shows the attack situation on a CRT: own-ship course, the path of each sound beam, and the position of the underwater target when contact is made. Because the target blip persists, the CRT shows a series of such blips in succession; the target course is estimated by drawing a line through them. The CRT also shows firing range and forward bearing for a Hedgehog, so that the correct train and firing time can be estimated.

In FRAM II destroyers Mk 105 is combined with a special panel (Mk 264) that enables it to fire lightweight torpedoes from Mk 32 tubes. In these ships maximum target range is 6000 yd and maximum target speed is 30 kt. The small-ship Hedgehog version is probably limited to 3000 yd (target speed and depth 25 kt and 1200 ft).

Users: Indonesia (*Claud Jones* class), Iran (*Sumner*, PF 103 classes), Korea (FRAM II *Gearing* and *Sumner*-class destroyers), Taiwan (FRAM II *Gearing* and *Sumner*-class destroyers), Turkey (*Berk*, PC 1638 classes).

◆ Mk 111/114

These systems use SQS-23 and -26/53 sonars to control Asroc and ASW torpedoes (but not Hedgehog, which requires a separate Mk 105). Because its early digital computer was unreliable, Mk 111 was superseded by the analog Mk 114. As in Mk 105, each system combines a single-target position-keeper (feeding a CRT display) with a ballistic section in the form of an attack console (Mk 38 in Mk 111, Mk 53 in Mk 114). As in Mk 105, target course curvature can be taken into account. The ship's GFCS tracks the outgoing Asroc for spotting corrections.

Despite its reliability problems, Mk 111 enjoyed an advantage over the analog Mk 114 because it could be reprogrammed (rather than physically changed) to accommodate new weapons such as the Mk 46 Mod 1 torpedo (about 1966). Because the firing panel had to be changed physically, the opportunity was taken to make human-factors engineering improvements to follow Mk 114 practice.

In a Mk 53 attack console, the plotter screen (a 20 × 20in CRT) can represent 4 × 4, 10 × 10, or 20 × 20 kyd; it displays own-ship and target positions, a weapon in flight, and a water-entry point. As in Mk 105, persistent blips show target and own-ship courses. The operator can align the cursor with the target images to read off target course and can adjust cursor length to measure target speed. This type of manual analysis was preferred to computer analysis because it automatically smoothed data (contemporary computer capacity was not sufficient to provide filtering). CRT readouts are passed automatically to the associated ballistic computer. Corresponding rate-aided target-tracking data (position-keeping) are sent back to the sonar as a check on the accuracy of the solution (the predicted target position appears on the sonar PPI, and the sonar operator uses his controls to transmit corrections back to the FCS). Once a satisfactory track has been found, the sonar operator can concentrate on searching for more targets, in what amounts to TWS operation. The upper unit of the attack console displays some sonar data, which can help an ASW officer decide attack tactics.

The computer section to the right of the CRT includes a weapons-mode selection panel, a torpedo preset panel, and the firing panel. Dials also show attack parameters, ballistic data, and weapons-control information generated by the computer, as well as Asroc weapon status. The torpedo presets (in the Asroc missiles) are set manually, but are sent along the same data path as the ballistic computer outputs.

The plotter and the ballistic computer are separately manned, the ASW officer standing behind both operators. The ASW officer estimates target depth, usually selecting best submarine depth to avoid detection; depth has little effect on the overall solution.

A modernized Mk 114, not put into service (but available for export), replaces the attack console with a digital Mod 4 unit developed by Ocean Technology Inc. (OTI) as part of an abortive FF 1052–class ASW upgrade. OTI developed much of the Mk 116 software to work within SQQ-89. Mk 53 Mod 4 was conceived as a downsized and modified equivalent. It has two embedded UYK-44s, each with a corresponding color CRT: one mainly to maintain track files (as in later versions of Mk 116), the other for ballistics and system control. Mod 4 also includes a second graphics generator that can drive a remote monitor (e.g., a large-screen display) and it can accept inputs from remote peripherals. No at-sea test of Mod 4 as such was conducted (it was, however, tested at NOSC). This version was planned for missile cruisers, but installations may have been abandoned when the ships were scheduled for striking. However, it may later be installed on ships already transferred abroad, for example, to Taiwan. The Pakistan navy has expressed interest in Mod 4.

Mk 111 limits: range 35,000 yd (computing limit 32,000 yd, target depth 1400 ft, target speed 35 kt).

Users:

Mk 111: Greece (*Themistocles*, ex-DDG 15), Pakistan (*Tughril*), Taiwan (*Fu Yang*, *Huei Yang* [with Mk 105 Mod 10], *Kai Yang*), and Turkey (*Yucetepe* [with Mk 105], *M. Fevzi Cakmak*).

Mk 114: Brazil (*Garcia* class), Egypt (*Knox* class), Greece (*Adams* class and *Knox* class), Italy (*Vittorio Veneto* [Mod 21]), Japan (Asroc ships), Korea (FRAM I destroyers), Mexico (FRAM I destroyers), Pakistan (FRAM I destroyers), Taiwan (FRAM I destroyers, *Knox* class), Thailand (*Knox* class), Turkey (FRAM I destroyers and *Knox* class), United States (*California* class).

◆ Mk 116

Librascope's all-digital surface-ship FCS has evolved from a stand-alone system into the heart of SQQ-89 (in Mod 5 and later versions). Early versions such as Mod 1 are built around a digital fire-control switchboard, to which are connected the SQS-53 sonar, ASWO command/control console (a standard OJ-194), CPS (computer processing subsystem, a three-bay UYK-7), and WCSS (Weapons Control and Setting Subsystem, via a Weapons Control Panel Mk 329 Mod 1, which selects system mode [attack, training, local test], weapon type and launcher [including TT barrel], and also search depth, search mode, or gyro angle presets for Asroc or TT torpedoes; it includes the launch key). The UYK-7 stores the target's track history and displays target symbols on the ASWO PPI. TMA is conducted on the ship's dead-reckoning tracer. The system is connected to the ship's CDS, from which it can take target data. A target can also be inserted manually, at the ASWO console. The sonar provides two more target channels. The system can attack two targets simultaneously (with Asroc and with torpedoes). The post-firing display on the PPI shows the computed water-entry point for Asroc; the depth-

charge symbol is retained and position-kept for 30 min. In a torpedo attack, by Asroc or tube, the torpedo symbol is retained and position-kept for its run time.

Mods 0/1/2/4 are the original versions for, respectively, the *Spruance, Virginia, Kidd,* and *Ticonderoga* classes, controlling both ship-launched weapons and a LAMPS helicopter. As of 1975, WCSS MTBF had been tested at 1200 hr and was probably 3255 hr; average MTTR was 0.20 hr, maximum 1.08 hr.

Mod 5 is a radically different version integrated with SQQ-89, incorporating an OJ-452 acoustic display console. It accepts all the contacts (and associated data) generated by SQS-53B, correlating them with each other and with manually entered data inputs from the CDS to generate track files with at least a 70% probability that all contacts reported back to the CDS are unique. Mk 116 aids the operator in target classification and annotates the contact range after the first tagged active contact is returned to the ASW control system. In passive mode, Mk 116 estimates contact range and recommends maneuvers for TMA to improve that estimate. It creates track files accurate enough for fire control. Using up to four bearings (or combinations of bearing and range plus passive bearings) to determine a contact's course and speed, it must produce track files of sufficient quality that the CO/TAO can determine that the target is within active sonar range (as predicted by SIMAS). The attack that follows is based on active confirmation of the estimated range. Mod 9 is a conversion with a UYK-43B computer.

Mod 6 (introduced in CG 56) is Mod 5 adapted to the requirements of the vertical launching system. Mod 8 is a conversion with a UYK-43B computer. Mod 7 (Mod 10 for non-VLS ships) uses the UYK-43B instead of UYK-7 (for the *Spruance* class, for CG 65 and later cruisers and for *Arleigh Burke*–class destroyers). It adds integrated acoustic-performance prediction and sensor supervision. The system automatically accepts and correlates both acoustic and nonacoustic (radar, ESM, link) data. This version is the first to be compatible with TDSS (see below). There are two OJ-452 consoles. Reliability: MTBCF 875 hr, MTTR less than 1 hr. Mod 10 is Mk 116 Phase II.

Mk 116 Phase III is the open-architecture version.

Mod 1 was approved for service use in October 1980. Mod 5 was evaluated on board the *Moosebrugger*, August–November 1982.

Weights of versions: Mod 5, 6200 lb; Mod 6, 5000 lb; Mod 7, 7600 lb; Mod 8, 4700 lb; Mod 9, 5900 lb.

Users: United States (Mod 0 in *Spruance* class, being replaced; Mod 1 in *Virginia* class; Mod 2 in *Kidd* class; Mod 4 in *Ticonderoga* class; Mod 5 in *Spruance* class as modernized with SQQ-89; Mod 6 in VLS *Ticonderoga* class [CG 65 and later]; Mod 7 in *Arleigh Burke* and later *Ticonderoga* class [CG 65 and later; also in modernized *Spruances* with UYK-43B computers]; Mod 8 in modernized VLS *Ticonderoga* class [with UYK-43B computers]). DD 965 had the first production Mod 5. DD 978 is the lead ship for the Mod 7 computer program. DD 977 is the Mod 8 prototype. DD 976 is Mod 10 prototype (planned for non-VLS ships, DD 963/CG 47/DDG 993 classes).

◆ Mk 309 Fire-Control Panel

Despite its designation, this is a compact ASW FCS, optimized to fire torpedoes to drive off an approaching submarine (it also provides the bridge with evasive maneuvering advice). Tactics are chosen from a look-up table embodying a firing doctrine developed from 40,000 tactical simulation runs ashore to develop optimum ship-evasion courses. The panel receives three synchro inputs: target range and bearing and own-ship course. Target speed and aspect are entered manually. The panel displays maximum, optimum, and minimum torpedo-firing ranges and recommends a lead angle. The operator enters torpedo presets and fires the weapon.

A Mk 309 upgrade (i.e., replacement) prototype (to incorporate Mk 46 Mod 5 and Mk 50 torpedo characteristics) was completed in 1992. The current Mod 2 digital upgrade, developed by NUWC Keyport, uses a VME rack with a pair of interchangeable CRTs (tactical display replacing the old pair of wheels over data entry panel). The boards inside are also interchangeable.

Mk 309 was conceived for the *Hamilton*-class Coast Guard cutters; its design reflects the limitations of the computers of the late 1960s (the Mk 309 designation was assigned in 1968). Mod 0 weighs 75 lb; Mod 1 weighs 340 lb. The other torpedo control panel, Mk 264, is only a part of a larger underwater FCS; it is used to select the Mk 32 barrel and preset initial search depth, search floor, and gyro angle.

Users: Australia (*Perry* class [Mod 1]), Morocco (Mod 0 in modified *Descubierta*), Saudi Arabia (Mod 0 in *Badr* class), Spain (*Perry* class [Mod 1]), Taiwan (*Perry* class [Mod 1]), Thailand (Mod 0 in *Ratanakosin*), United States (*Perry* class [Mod 1]). Presumably Mk 309 Mod 0s were removed from U.S. Coast Guard cutters when other ASW equipment was landed.

◆ USQ-132/TDSS

Northrop Grumman's Tactical Decision Support System is part of the SQQ-89 Adjunct Subsystems upgrade, replacing the old dead-reckoning tracer (which provided the only geographical picture of the overall ASW problem, and was therefore used for TMA). It is used to form a fused tactical picture (including air and surface traffic) from both onboard and offboard sources, and offers TMA aids somewhat like a submarine's MATE (using different formats, however). Contacts can be displayed in both true and relative formats. The main horizontal 37in color CRT is supplemented by a 19in supervisor's vertical CRT. The TDSS dual display station (DDS) in CIC supports two remote displays (one at sonar control and one in CIC for the ASW Evaluator; see the SQQ-89 Adjunct Subsystems discussion above). Inside the station are a Hewlett Packard 747I/100 RISC processor and a 2-Gbyte hard disk drive, with a digital tape drive and a CD-ROM drive. It incorporates automated charts. TDSS uses Unified Build (UB) software designed to work with JMCIS systems. The DDS is 148 × 101 × 148 cm (500 kg).

USQ-132 shows both its large horizontal display and its secondary display. (Northrop Grumman)

The TDSS computer receives own-ship data (including SQQ-89 track data and real-time CDS tracks) from the UYK-43 computer of the Mk 116 Mod 7 system, and external data from NTCS-A and the SQQ-89 performance predictor via D-LAN. TDSS operators overlay this data on their ASW summary plots. Inputs from the CDS, NTCS-A, and ASW Control System (SQQ-89) are displayed on the tactical summary plot. Sonar performance prediction, bottom contours, coastlines, and objects of interest can all be displayed, overlaid onto the geographical summary plot. For ASW search and detection planning, sonar detection zones, areas of uncertainty, sensor bearing errors, and counterdetection ranges (all based on SQQ-89 performance prediction) can all be displayed. TDSS provides algorithms to help automate TMA, analogous to submarine MATE algorithms (e.g. Bearing Doppler, Ekelund Ranging, Speiss [Single Leg Bearing], hyperbolic fix, time-bearing, time-frequency, evaluator, and strip plots). TDSS also improves weapon safety by indicating NOTACK zones, Mk 50 ship safety barriers, weapon acquisition areas, weapon-entry, and torpedo-intercept points.

Northrop Grumman sees the DDS as the core of a COTS tactical data management system providing operator alerts and other TDAs.

TDSS was originally the Contact Management System (CMS), for *Spruance*-class destroyers. Because TDSS is a tactical advisory system, it can run on TAC-series computers rather than on Mil-Spec machines. For example, although TDSS displays weapons safety zones, weapons are still fired from the Mk 116 Mod 7 OJ-452 console. TDSS was a rapid prototype system. The stand-alone version was tested in FY93. A full-up version with a bidirectional interface to Mk 116 Mod 7 passed its preliminary and critical design reviews in May and July 1994, entering service in 1995. The TDSS prototype was installed on board USS *Stump*, and the second was placed on board USS *Cushing*. Presumably TDSS will ultimately be placed on board Aegis ships, too.

◆ FFISTS

See the Surveillance and Control section for details.

SUBMARINE PERISCOPES

Because sonar may be limited in its ability to detect and track surface craft, periscopes are often the submarine's primary surface-search sensors. Most submarines have two types, a wide-angle search periscope and a narrow-angle attack scope. A submarine commander obtains the surface picture by making a quick sweep with the search periscope, the duration of the sweep determining both the quality of that picture and the extent to which the commander exposed the submarine to detection. Much of the submarine officer's training (e.g., in the British "perishers'" course) is devoted to the ability to form a coherent surface picture after the briefest sweep.

Many periscopes incorporate stadimeters, which measure the angle between the horizon and the top of an object of known height; from this angle the range can be calculated. In some cases the stadimeter is turned horizontally to estimate target course by comparing apparent with known length (given a known range). Many attack periscopes incorporate range-only radars that supplement their optical range-finders. The alternative, particularly in optronic masts, is a laser range-finder.

Some search periscopes are binocular, with duplicated windows at the top. At one time many search periscopes provided for air search, but now air warning is more usually the function of an RWR atop the search periscope.

Two major developments are associated with the post-1945 revolution in submarine design and performance, the combination of high underwater speed and indefinite submerged periods (snorkeling when required). Search and radar periscopes had to be extendable at relatively high speeds (the U.S. Navy called for periscopes extendable at 14 kt). Images had to be specially stabilized against the resulting vibration. Sextants for taking navigational fixes had to be incorporated in search periscopes. This requirement is losing its urgency with the rise of GPS.

Optronics is an outgrowth of television and FLIR technology. Periscopes were initially provided with sensors such as image intensifiers (LLLTV) to extend their usefulness to lower light levels. However, as with surface-ship and aircraft applications, the potential of converting the image into an electromagnetic signal is much greater since the image itself can be processed to extract all of its information content and even to merge it with other relevant data.

Ultimately, however, optronics can have revolutionary consequences. The periscope need no longer be connected physically to the attack center (the viewing post). The submarine can therefore be rearranged. The optical sensor can even be placed in a towed body. At the least, the mast need no longer penetrate into the pressure hull; it can telescope. The body of the mast need no longer be pressure-tight, and it can be nonmetallic (nonradar-reflecting). Moreover, there are considerable advantages (both in drag and in radar cross-section) to be gained by using a noncylindrical mast (which is acceptable if the head, rather than the entire mast, rotates). Thus far, faith in optronics has not reached the point of abandoning all conventional periscopes, however.

Ultimately it might be imagined that adopting optronics would allow elimination of the submarine's sail, with enormous advantages in drag and noise, but that has not yet happened. One reason is that the sail is needed for other reasons, such as surface navigation (e.g., when entering port) and to support a snorkel.

Since the optronic image is captured for later use, observation need no longer coincide with exposure. Although an optronic head may be relatively large, then, it may be able to scan quite rapidly. Too, an optronic sensor can be quite light and therefore relatively easy to stabilize and even to control in an autotrack mode.

The submarine commander is no longer the operator of the periscope sensor, just as he is not the operator, but rather the supervising user, of the various other acoustic and nonacoustic sensors on board a submarine. The skipper could obtain the full tactical picture without having to concentrate all attention on the necessarily fleeting periscope image. Manufacturers offering digital optronic or photonic periscopes tend to suggest radically revised arrangements for submarine control rooms or operations rooms, for example using a large screen display surrounded by relevant database readouts (e.g., the characteristics of the ship shown on the screen, to the extent that the expert computer system connected to the data can identify the contact). The single screen could also present acoustic or merged tactical picture data.

A conventional or LLLTV camera can be inserted in the bottom of the periscope, taking the same image as the eyepiece, on much the same principle as a single-lens reflex camera. However, an IR camera is best placed at the top of the periscope since thermal photons traveling all the way down the tube would suffer from added noise. Moreover, the optical components of the periscope will not focus or reflect IR radiation as they do light. The IR sensor must be cooled, and the coolant led up a very narrow periscope tube (or else a very compact refrigerator must be incorporated in the small periscope head).

Existing optronic periscopes employ a camera analogous to the window of the periscope, fixed rigidly to a tube that the observer rotates. However, there is no reason for the observer to memorize the scene as quickly as the periscope can be turned. In principle, the sensor can make a very quick scan (or even look simultaneously in several directions), and the image can be stored either digitally or in a video recorder, for display as desired on a CRT. The newer sensors can provide images of optical periscope quality.

FRANCE

First-generation ballistic missile submarines have MRA-2 stellar navigation masts. French SSNs still use the old ST5 attack periscope; SSBNs have no attack periscope, only the search types and the star-trackers.

◆ PIVAIR (SPS)/SMS

SAGEM/SOPELEM's optronic/optical periscope carries an ESM antenna and the gyrostabilized unit for both conventional optics and the 8–10-micron CT-10 IR camera. Besides the usual binocular optics, the base of the mast carries a sextant, a 35mm camera, and the IR monitor. PIVAIR uses a micromonitor in the ocular box (displayed in the eyepieces); it can also feed a remote monitor. Optical magnification is 1.5× or 6× (12× optional) (FOVs: 26, 9, 4.5 deg at elevation +80/−10 deg). These masts are two-axis LOS-stabilized, using a gyro in the periscope head (hence the ability to handle 12× magnification, which is quite unusual in a periscope). FLIR FOV is 3 × 6 deg. Automatic IR modes: quick-look (one revolution in 5 sec, with the panoramic picture retained in memory), and panoramic search. Typically in IR mode the mast can detect a patrol airplane or helicopter at 10 nm. The SAT-made IR camera uses a 96-element HgCdTe linear array scanned across the FOV. It is being replaced by an IRCCD camera (288 × 4 elements).

The standard sensor head is 320mm in dia, on a 200mm tube (250mm in SPS-S); the attack version has a 140mm head on a 180mm tube.

This mast combines L and MRA-2 functions in one mast.

A mocked-up submarine at Bourget Euronaval 1996 offers a dramatic comparison between the head of SFIM's modified attack periscope (*left*) and a standard SAGEM search periscope (*center*). Presumably very short exposure compensates for the greater size of the search head. (Author)

Search Mast SAGEM (SMS) is an export nonpenetrating mast based on PIVAIR (SPS). Reportedly it is a conversion of a dedicated ESM mast. The TV LOS elevates between +80/−10 deg, and the IR LOS between +30/−10 deg. There are four TV FOVs (32/16/8/4 deg) and one (9 deg) or two (13 and 5 deg) IR FOVs. The TV camera is a black-and-white CCD (color is optional) operating at 0.4–1.1 microns; the IR camera operates at 8–12 microns, using a closed-cycle cooler. The entire mast is covered in RAM; the sensor head is 320 mm in dia and it weighs 280 kg. Claimed MTBF is 1250 hr (3600 for TV only); MTTR is 30 min (inboard)/8 hr (outboard).

SMS was tested on board the French submarine *Psyche* (September–December 1992), on board the Swedish *Gotland* (March–September 1993), and on board a Norwegian *Kobben*. It has been or will be tested on board a Korean Type 209. In 1992, SAGEM claimed that it had delivered a total of 25 periscopes since 1980, beginning with PIVAIR for SSNs and SSBNs. These periscopes may be installed on modernized Spanish *Agosta*-class submarines.

SAGEM made IMS-1, a nonpenetrating IR-only periscope, for Danish *Narhvalen*-class submarines. The two-axis stabilized (LOS) cooled IR head carries the company's 8–12-micron 288 × 4-element IRIS CCD (elevation limits +30/−9 deg, FOV 5.4 deg for search, 7 × 5.4 deg for imaging). The periscope can scan manually, or it can scan the horizon in less than 5 sec at constant elevation (then retracting), or it can do panoramic surveillance at 15–20 rpm. The horizon scan picture is recorded for replay submerged. The monitor displays a processed IR picture, threats being displayed as alarm spots (the mast acts as an IRST). The mast can be used at submerged speeds up to 12 kt. The sensor pod (208mm dia, 180 kg) is carried on a 235mm mast.

Optoradar Mast SAGEM (OMS) is gyrostabilized in one (rather than two) axis, carrying both TV (elevation +50/−20 deg; FOVs 32 and 4 deg) and IR (elevation +50/−20 deg; FOV 9 deg) cameras and an X-band (9.2–9.5 GHz) LOS-stabilized navigational radar (range scales 4–32 km, angular accuracy 2.5 deg, five-target ADT). The sensor pod is 370 mm in dia (weight 450 kg); MTBF is 1000 hr (3600 for TV only).

There is also a SAGEM attack periscope (APS).

SAGEM received its first optronic periscope contract in 1976. *Users:*

SPS: France (*Amethyste* class [only *Casabianca, Emeraude, Rubis, Saphir*], *Le Triomphant* [M92/SPS-S version with high-sextant mode]; probably on *L'Inflexible* and *Le Redoutable* classes).

IMS: Denmark (*Narhvalen* class).

OMS: France (*Le Triomphant*).

◆ SOPELEM Periscopes

Optical attack and search periscopes are manufactured by SFIM (which absorbed SOPELEM). The standard search periscope can incorporate a gyrosextant, a range-only radar, and an RWR. There is generally an integral 35mm camera (containing 250 frames of film in the case of PIVAIR, described above). Principal types are:

Attack Periscopes
ST3 for the *Daphne* class.
ST5 for the *Agosta* and *Amethyste* classes. Magnifications 1.5× and 6× (corresponding FOVs 30 and 7 deg); elevation limits +30/−10 deg. The operator is provided with a seat.

Search Periscopes
M41 for the *Daphne* class.
J, for the *Agosta* class, incorporates the APA-4 attack-radar antenna and the AUD omnidirectional ESM antenna. Magnifications: 1.5× and 6× (corresponding FOVs: 20 and 5 deg).
K, for the *Amethyste* class, incorporates a light intensifier. Magnification is 5×, FOV 10 deg, elevation limits +10/−10 deg. Daylight magnifications are 1.5× and 6× (corresponding FOVs: 36 and 9 deg); elevation limits +80/−10 deg. PIVAIR (above) for French SSNs, is designated Type K', a Type K with a fairing.
L, for SSBNs, omits the sextant (SSBNs have a separate MRA-2 star-tracker periscope).

Production of M/ST3 ended about 1975 after 50 were made. J/ST5 production ended about 1985 with 40 made, but may re-open.

SFIM has modernized the standard SSN optical attack and search periscopes with a CCD day video channel (with recorder) and a night image intensifier above the window; the prism is flipped to switch from optics to the CCD element. A laser ranger can be fitted. Compared to ST5, the new version offers better light transmission and an adjustable LOS; it is also stealthier. The LOS-stabilized head offers 12×, 6×, and 3× magnifications. J95 is an analogous version with 1.5× and 6× magnifications (FOVs 5 and 20 deg) carrying an electronic stadimeter, a night (image-intensified) channel, and a DR 3000 radar warner antenna. The last French navy conversion was completed about June 1996. These periscopes, ST5 95 and J95, have been adopted for the Pakistani *Agosta* 90B; the first new-build periscopes are to be delivered during the last three months of 1997.

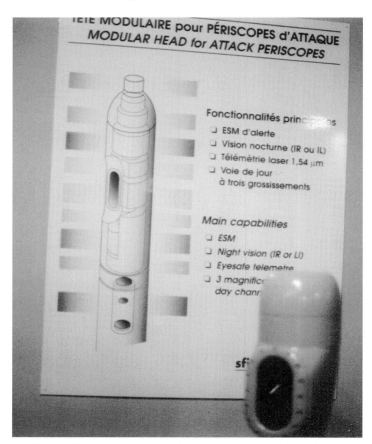

SFIM's modified attack periscope is shown with and without its casing. SFIM sees this version as part of a modular series, one version of which is shown in the diagram. (Author)

Eloptro of South Africa has upgraded the M41 and ST3 periscopes of that country's *Daphne* class; the prototypes are on board SAS *Emily Hobhouse*. The tubes are retained, but optical performance is greatly improved by reducing the number of optical elements, reducing field curvature and chromatic aberation, and so at least doubling transmittance. Larger exit pupils further improve performance in poor light conditions. Both periscopes are fitted with split-image range-finders. The search periscope was also fitted with day and LLLTV channels (a still camera can be installed) to provide quick-look to minimize periscope exposure (the image is captured in the control room console) and a view for the entire command team.

GERMANY

All periscopes are made by Carl Zeiss, which has manufactured over 200 (for 15 navies) since resuming production in 1958.

◆ StaS C/3

Zeiss's first postwar production periscope is a dual-purpose instrument (search/attack) with magnifications of 1.5× and 5.6× (FOVs 40 × 30 and 10 × 7.5 deg, elevation limits +90/−15 deg).

User: Denmark (*Narhvalen* class). This periscope was removed from Norwegian and Danish Type 207 submarines; it was also installed on German Type 205s, now discarded. In all, 30 were made.

◆ AS C 17/NavS (SERO 12)

AS C 17 (24 units) is the fixed-eyepiece attack periscope (with direction indicator in the eyepiece) of the German Type 206 and 206A; NavS (22 units) is the navigational periscope of the same type (in the snorkel mast).

Fixed eyepieces were adopted so that the control room could be made narrower, for higher underwater speed. Magnifications: 1.5× and 6×, FOVs 38 × 28 and 9.7 × 5 deg (elevation +90/ −15 deg). Entrance and exit pupils are 10.5/7 and 22 or 24/4 mm for the two magnifications. Tube diameters: 42–180 mm and 178–180 mm. AS C 17 contains a stadimeter. SERO means sehrohr, periscope in German. This is probably the periscope of the Israeli Type 540 (*Gal* class).

◆ AS C 18/BS 19

AS C 18 and BS 19 were, respectively, the attack and search (beobachtung) periscopes of the early Type 209 export submarine (21 of each were made).

Magnifications: 1.5×, 6×; FOVs respectively 40 × 30 and 9.5 × 7.5 deg (LOS elevation +75/−15 deg). Entrance pupils are 10.5 and 24 mm, exit pupils 7 and 4 mm. Tube diameters: 52–180 mm and 60–180 mm.

Users: Argentina, Colombia, Ecuador, Greece (Type 209/ 1100), Peru (*Islay, Arica*), Turkey, Venezuela (*Sabalo* had her AS C 18 replaced by AS 40, but retained her BS 19). These periscopes were first installed on the Greek *Glavkos* in 1971.

◆ AS 40/BS 40 (SERO 40)

AS 40 and BS 40 (12 and 11 units, respectively) introduced electrical control. These power-rotated binocular periscopes have electrically elevated prisms. Magnification and other functions are controlled electrically, by pushbuttons. The ocular box shows true and relative bearing, elevation angle, target height, target range, and ESM data. In most cases search and attack periscopes are identical. Magnifications: 1.5× and 6× (FOVs 36 × 28 and 8 × 6.5 deg, prism elevation limits +75 [reduced to +60 when an antenna is fitted]/−15 deg). Entrance/exit pupils: 21/ 14 and 36/6 mm. Options are a laser ranger, TV, and an integrated 8–12-micron FLIR (in BS 40 Stab IR: 96 × 4 CCD detectors, FOVs 12 × 9 and 4 × 3 deg).

40 Stab is an LOS-stabilized version (at least 11 made) using a two-axis gyro and a 16-bit microprocessor.

Users:

AS 40/BS 40: Greece (Type 209/1200), Indonesia (Type 209), Peru (later Type 209s). First installed 1978 on Greek *Posydon*.

40 Stab: Chile (Type 209), Korea (Type 209), Taiwan (*Sea Dragon* class), Venezuela (Type 209/1400 as refitted). First installed 1983 on Chilean *Thomson*.

◆ SERO 14/15

The current Zeiss production periscopes (SERO 14 search, SERO 15 attack) have magnifications of 1.5× and 6× (FOVs 36 × 28, 8 × 6.5); SERO 14 adds 12× (FOV 4 × 3 deg) and a zoom capability. Elevation limits are +75/−15 deg (SERO 14) and +60/ −15 deg (SERO 15). SERO 14 incorporates an IR camera (8–12-micron, 180-element U.S. modular detector, FOVs 14.2 × 10.6 and 4 × 3 deg). SERO 15 incorporates optical (stadimeter) and laser (Neodymium-YAG) rangers. SERO 15 Mod IR adds a 3–5-micron camera. Diameter is larger than in the 40 Stab series.

Users: Germany (Type 212), Norway (*Ula* class). Prototype masts were installed in U-1 in 1982–83.

◆ OMS-100

Zeiss's optronic mast carries a FLIR and a TV, the outputs of which are displayed on a control-room monitor. A laser range-finder can replace the usual range-only radar antenna. GPS and ESM can also be added. The 7.5–10.5-micron FLIR (96 × 4-element digital CCD detector) has 12.4 × 9.3/4.1 × 3.1-deg FOVs; its LOS can be elevated within the −15/+60 deg range. The television channel (three-chip color CCD camera) offers 30 × 22.7 to 3.5 × 2.6-deg (zoom) FOVs. The 220mm-dia head weighs 280 kg. The control and display weighs 300 kg, and the hoist weighs 2500 kg. As of 1994, this mast was being tested in the Type 206 submarine U-21. Zeiss tested its first EO mast on U-1 in 1977, followed by tests of an improved model on U-1 in 1984, and then by the SERO 14/15 series.

RUSSIA

Periscopes are designated in a PZKG series. Submarines generally carry two, one for the CO, the second either for air defense (SS, SSN, "Charlie"-class SSGN) or multipurpose (SSBNs and "Oscar"-class SSGNs). Magnifications (Kilo-class type): 1.5×, 6× (FOVs 32.16 × 25.5, 7.5 × 6 deg). In this case outer diameter is 180 mm and length is 11.475 m (230 kg). The mast power-rotates at 10 to 20 deg/min. A periscope camera has a 36-shot magazine and exposure is set manually.

UNITED KINGDOM

Barr & Stroud, a division of Pilkington Optronics, is responsible for submarine optical periscopes. Attack periscopes are designated in a CH series, search periscopes in a CK series. There are three current types: 127mm periscopes for small submarines, which may have only one periscope, and 190mm and 254mm for larger ones. Large diameters were adopted to increase stiffness and so to reduce vibration at high speed. Current periscopes are fitted with a patented device permitting use at up to 16 kt, although 12 kt is more usual. At least in the latest search periscopes, the optics are arranged to reduce the effects of vibration by splitting the optical path at the point at which the periscope enters the submarine's sail.

The standard periscope TV vidicon tube is a 16mm monochrome SIT unit. The image intensifier is a 50/40mm Mullard Type xx 1332, providing a gain of up to 30,000 times. Its auxiliary large-aperture (110mm, 4.3in) window remains below the surface in daylight (to avoid glint). Magnification is 6× (7-deg FOV); elevation limits are +15/−7.5 deg. This device has been installed in Canadian *Oberon*-class submarines, and the Australian and Chilean *Oberons* are likely candidates.

The alternative 8–13-micron-band FLIR (installed since 1978) uses the same 110mm window, but this time one made of germanium.

The standard laser range-finder is a NdYAG accurate to within 10 m, using a 10-nsec Q-switched pulse.

Barr & Stroud periscopes in service:

CK024/CH074: Australia (*Oberons*), Brazil (*Oberons*), Canada (*Oberons*), Chile (*Oberons*)

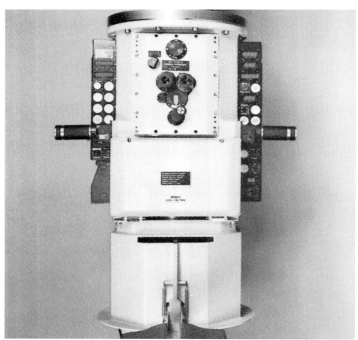

Standard Barr & Stroud eyepieces for the 254mm attack periscope and the 254mm search periscope. (Pilkington)

CK027/CH077: Netherlands (*Zwaardvis*, for sale)
CK030: Denmark (Type 207), Norway (Type 207)
CK031/CH081: Italy (first pair of *Nazario Sauro*)
CK032: Yugoslavia (*Una* class midgets)
CK033/CH083: United Kingdom (*Swiftsure* class)
CK034/CH084: United Kingdom (*Trafalgar* and *Upholder* classes: 1.5× and 6×)
CK037: Korea ("Cosmos" class)
CK038/CH088: Sweden (190mm: *Sjoormen, Vastergotland, Gotland* classes)
CK039: Pakistan (SK-756)
CK041: Korea (*Tolgorae*)
CK043/CH093: Australia (*Collins*)
CK051/CH091: United Kingdom (*Vanguard*, CH091 to be replaced by thermal imager)
IRO28J: Japan (*Harushio*, with thermal imager)

Sweden is to install Barr & Stroud periscopes (unidentified type) in the new *Gotland* class.

In 1995 Pilkington said that 128 of its periscopes were in service, of which 34 had IR cameras and 24 are remotely controlled.

In the *Vanguard* class, the periscope has a conventional eyepiece but also a TV camera, and the eyepiece is a deck above the control room. The periscope is therefore normally operated remotely, the TV image being viewed on a control-room console. Pilkington sees this as a natural step toward a fully optronic nonpenetrating periscope. The *Vanguard* installation continues a long series of efforts, beginning with what Pilkington claims was the world's first thermal-imaging periscope, delivered to the Royal Navy in 1977. It was followed in 1981 by ARTIVIS, a Quick Look Round (QLR) demonstrator, to the British MOD. Operating in both visual and IR bands, it made a 360-deg scan every 0.7 sec. The operator could view any three sectors within the acquired panorama. The company delivered a laser-ranger periscope in 1982, and its first remote-controlled periscope for the *Upholders* in 1986. This class also had the first periscope fully integrated into the CDS, using the ship's 1553 bus. In 1988 Pilkington delivered what it claims was the world's first nonpenetrating IR periscope, the first of five to an unnamed navy, probably Japan (for the *Harushio* class).

Pilkington claims that HMS *Vanguard* now has the most complex sealed EO pod ever built for a submarine.

◆ CK034/CH084

These 254mm instruments (70mm upper tube in the attack periscope) have magnifications of 1.5/3/6/12× (FOVs 24, 12, 6, 3 deg) and 1.5/6× (FOVs 32 and 6 deg) respectively. Both are quasi-binocular. The search periscope carries a sextant (AHPS 4), which automatically prints out the observed altitude, bearing, and time of observation. The attack periscope (CH084) is fitted with an image intensifier, a FLIR, and a stadimeter (with automatic computing).

◆ CK043/CH093

The CH093 254mm search periscope has an image intensifier and LLLTV rather than the thermal imager of the earlier CH084; both its image intensification and optical channels are stabilized. The corresponding 190mm attack periscope is CK043.

◆ CK040

This combined-purpose (search and attack) 127mm periscope for small submarines accommodates an image intensifier and a stadimetric range-finder. Unlike the larger-diameter periscopes, CK040 has a monocular eyepiece, and the LOS is not stabilized. It lacks provisions for range conversion or transmission and cannot accommodate an ESM antenna, a TV camera, or a FLIR. CK040 cannot be power-driven. There is no true bearing scale and no digital bearing readout; CK040 has only a relative bearing scale. Like the larger-diameter Barr & Stroud periscopes, CK040 has a heated window and eyepiece and a microphone. This type of periscope was sold for midget submarines (see the list above).

◆ CM010

This private-venture production-standard optronic mast incorporates a Ferranti Thomson dual-screen workstation and a McTaggert Scott mast hoist. The workstation manipulates images and generates synthetic video for the submarine CDS, in exact analogy to a sonar console. The sensor head unit (SHU) carries electro-optics in a sealed pressure vessel; the optronics processor is below decks. Sensors are an IR camera, an HDTV monochrome camera, a broadcast-standard color camera, and ESM and GPS. FOVs are 3, 6, and 24 deg (elevation limits +60/ −15 deg. Mast diameter, 340mm, can be reduced to 220mm if reduced maximum elevation (50 deg) is accepted. Programmable scan modes are intended to retain image resolution while minimizing mast exposure. The mast can carry a family of sensor heads, CM011 through CM014. Work began in January 1993, with sea trials scheduled for 1996.

The SSN 20 optronic periscope project lapsed with the SSN 20 project. See the 1991/92 edition for details.

UNITED STATES

Kollmorgen and Sperry Marine manufacture all U.S. Navy periscopes. Attack submarines carry one attack (Type 2F, replacing Type 2D) and one search (Type 18 and 18B, replacing Type 15, which in turn replaced Type 8) periscope. Type 15 introduced search receivers integral with the periscope. *Sturgeon-* and early *Los Angeles*–class submarines are equipped with Type 15D. *Ohio*-class strategic submarines are unusual in carrying two general-purpose periscopes, Types 8L and 15L.

Unlike Barr & Stroud, the U.S. Navy did not increase periscope tube diameter to counter vibration at high speed. Instead, a hydrodynamic fairing surrounds the outside of the periscope. Because it does not require a larger periscope diameter, this approach would have been a major advantage in the large U.S. post-1945 submarine modernization (Guppy) program.

◆ Type 2

The original Type 2 attack periscope was introduced in 1942. It had a long slim (1.4in) neck and a very small head; a range-only radar, ST, was added during the war. A new Type 2D (1959) incorporated postwar advances in optical design and optical coating and is the basis of current U.S. attack periscopes. It contains a tilting head prism (elevation +74/−10 deg) and has two magnifications (6× and 1.5×; FOVs 8 and 32 deg). The stadimeter at the periscope head can be used at both powers, and the head window and eyepiece are electrically heated to avoid fogging and ice formation. A camera adapter can be fitted. Overall length is 45 ft 2.875 in (optical length 43 ft 3 in), and the outer tube diameter is 7.5 in.

Typical U.S. faired periscopes aboard a *Los Angeles*–class submarine off Norfolk, October 1986. (Jürg Kürsener)

◆ Type 8L Mod (T) and Type 15L Mod (T)

This combination equips *Ohio*-class strategic missile submarines, Type 8L to starboard (carrying the ST range-only radar) and Type 15L to port (carrying WLR-10 ESM). Elevation limits are +60/−10 deg, and magnifications are 1.5× and 6× (FOVs 32 and 8 deg). Each periscope is 46 ft long. Television camera and still-photographic camera attachments are available.

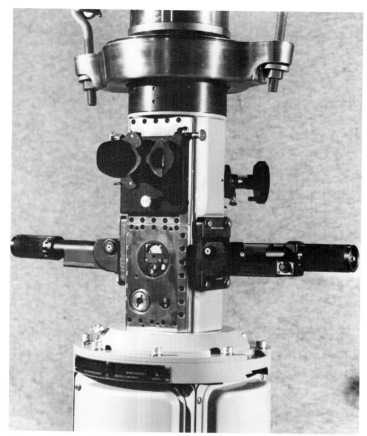

The eyepiece of a Trident submarine's periscope (probably Type 15L). (Kollmorgen)

Sperry Marine was selected to design Type 8J Mod 3 for the new *Seawolf*-class submarine.

◆ Type 18

The current U.S. search periscope carries ESM intercept antennas above its gyrostabilized optics and can provide image intensification and LLLTV for low-light operation. Train is power-assisted. Type 18B has an overall length (to top of radome) of 36 ft 10 in (optical length 36 ft from the center of the eyepiece to the zero-elevation line of sight at the prism in the head). Type 18D is 42 ft overall (optical length 41 ft 4 in). Magnifications: 1.5×, 6×, 12×, 24× (FOVs 32, 8, 4, 2 deg). Elevation limits: +60/−10 deg. The LLLTV provides a 525-line format interlaced 2:1, 30 frames/sec, using a minimum of 16 gray scales; the sensor is a silicon-intensified target vidicon. Periscope functional modes are day, night, visual, TV/visual, IMC (image-motion compensated), camera, and gyro.

The most important new feature of Type 18 was its very high maximum magnification, originally 18×, allowing the submarine to observe targets from beyond detection range. Kollmorgen won the competition for this periscope against Itek mainly because it could allow the use of a camera without removing the periscope faceplate. Ultimately that led to the common use of TV cameras, whose images are piped throughout the submarine and recorded (the system is called Pereviz).

Sperry Marine's Type 18 Periscope ADF Group is the associated ESM system; it has been adapted to surface craft as Guardian Star (see the EW section). It is a UYK-44-based system with a touch screen. There is no formal AN-series designator. Production is competed on an annual basis, and AEL recently won the second production lot.

◆ Type 22 (NESSIE)

Sperry Marine's Naval Electronic System for IR Exploitation is a second-generation optronic periscope for the *Los Angeles* class incorporating a 3–5-micron FLIR, LLLTV, and an EHF satellite communications antenna. Hughes received a contract for the IR

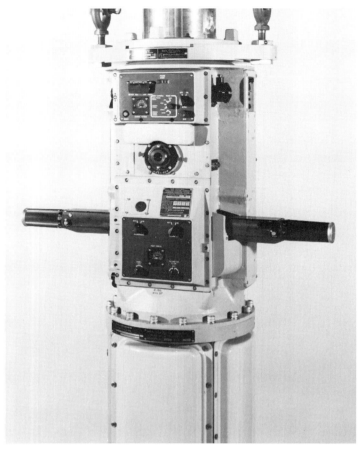

The eyepiece of a Type 18 periscope, as installed on board *Los Angeles –* class submarines. (Kollmorgen)

sensor in April 1996. The initial low-rate production run may be for as many as six masts. No details of Types 19, 20, or 21 have appeared. Presumably at least some were abortive optronic masts.

♦ **Model 76**

Kollmorgen's 7.5in export periscope is made in both search and attack versions; both have binocular eyepieces with split LOS-stabilized optics. Magnification: 1.5× and 6× (FOVs 32 and 8 deg); elevation limits are +74/−10 deg in the attack version and +60/−10 deg in the search version. Both versions carry stadi-meters, transmitting range electronically to the FCS. The attack version carries a broad-band RWR with a display on the control unit of the periscope. The search version can carry a sextant, LF communications antennas, a satellite navigation antenna, and an ESM early-warning antenna. Optional features include a 12× telescope, power rotation, and a television camera feeding a re-mote unit (carrying a 9in CRT).

Kollmorgen's intensifier is mounted in the mast, rotating 90 deg to enter the main optical path of the periscope. The com-pany's 8–12-micron SPRITE (12/4-deg FOV, 0.2-mrad beam-width) can be mounted between the optical head and the ESM antennas. Kollmorgen offers a television stadimeter (with auto-matic range computation if target masthead height is dialed in). The alternative radar ranger uses a slotted-waveguide antenna below the optical window. The laser ranger is mounted in the base of the periscope, opposite the viewing optics, with a swing-ing mirror (as in a single-lens reflex camera) to bring its beam into the main optical path. A sextant uses the periscope synchro to read off its line of elevation from the deck plane, the target-bearing transmitter to measure the target's direction relative to the submarine, and a built-in vertical reference to determine tilt and cross-tilt angles so that the sextant can measure star alti-tudes relative to the true horizon. The corrected altitude angle, bearing angle, and time are displayed and printed.

Individual users have their own model numbers.

Users: Argentina (four TR-1700 class), Brazil (Type 209/1400), India (Type 1500 *Shishumar* class), Israel (three *Dolphins*), Italy (two *Salvatore Pelosi* class [Model 322, with radar ranger], two *Primo Longobardo* class [Model 323, with laser ranger], second pair of *Nazario Sauro* class [Model 324]), Netherlands (four *Wal-rus* class), Sweden (three *Nacken* class), and Turkey (six Type 209/1200, four Type 209/1400 [Model 374]).

♦ **Universal Modular Mast/Model 86/Model 90**

The Universal Modular is to equip the *Seawolf* and the New Attack Submarine. Kollmorgen is responsible for the optronics, Loral Librascope for the display, and Riva Calzoni for the two-stage mast structure. Models 86 and 90 are commercial versions, probably using Alenia dry ends with MAGICS or CTI consoles. The U.S. Navy version carries an 3–5-micron FLIR, color and high-definition monochrome TV (optical FOV 22.8 or 10 or 4.4 deg, elevation limits +74/−10 deg), ESM, and a GPS receiver. The RFP for an operational optronic mast was issued in January 1992, and Kollmorgen won the contract for the first three pro-duction systems in May 1995. It teamed with Riva Calzoni late in February 1988, and under ARPA auspices it built a prototype mast for the test submarine *Memphis* under a 1988 contract (18 months of trials were completed in 1995).

Model 86 has two windows in its head (color CCD TV above eight-element 8–12-micron SPRITE FLIR [FOVs 10 and 4.4 deg, elevation limits +55/−10 deg]), and prisms can direct the op-tical path down to a light-intensifier. A mirror behind the FLIR window directs the thermal path down the axis of the periscope to a thermal camera. The entire photonic system is two-axis sta-bilized. The head should be capable of a sector scan in less than 2 sec, and a full scan in 5 or 6 sec (or less using a black-and-white camera).

Model 90 is an optronic adaptation of a conventional 190mm periscope, combining a direct-view optical channel (1.5×, 6×, 12×, 18×, elevation limits +74/−10 deg) with a FLIR (limits +55/−10 deg), a television camera, an optional laser ranger, ESM, and GPS.

TOM (tactical optronic mast), OMS (optronic mast sensor), and COM (compact optical mast) are Model 90 derivatives. TOM and OMS use a rotating masthead sensor package carrying a day-light color TV, a 3–5-micron FLIR, and a two-axis LOS stabilizer. To this can be added a monochrome TV (which may be image-intensified for night viewing), an 8–12-micron thermal camera, a laser range-finder, a GPS antenna, and an RWR. The sensor module is mounted on a rotating unit carrying the slip ring and rotary electrical joint, as well as a rotating mirror. Because the only link down into the hull is cable carrying video, the console, which is used to integrate IR, visual, and ESM data, has two high-definition CRTs, the upper for the CO, the lower (which can window to display different sensor data simultaneously) for the station operator. A more advanced version of TOM, developed for ARPA, was installed on board the test submarine *Memphis*.

OMS is a simpler stabilized mast carrying a television and ESM sensor. COM is a very compact mast for special applica-tions such as midgets and small submarines. Its sealed rotating housing, with a hemispherical dome on top, carries an LLLTV or high-resolution monochrome TV with single-axis stabiliza-tion and optional GPS and ESM.

As of early 1994, Model 90 was reportedly in production for at least one export customer.

SONOBUOYS AND SIGNAL PROCESSORS

Most Free World sonobuoys are built to a standard A-size (4 × 36 in) to fit the buoy ejectors of such aircraft as the Nimrod, P-3 Orion, and Atlantique. B-size is 6 × 60 in (ERAPS size); C-size (9 × 60 in) was used only by Britain; and D-size is 3 × 15 in (projected for submarine underwater signals). E-size probably refers to a projected D-size sonobuoy. F is a dwarf (A/3) size (4 × 12 in) now used by the Royal Navy and for some French buoys. The U.S. Navy has tried an A/2 size (4 × 16.5 in), which may be designated "F." G is A/2 size (4 × 18 in), but it was discarded because a filler was needed between two buoys in a launch tube: hence the choice of the 16.5in length.

An artist's concept of a next-generation submarine control and imaging center, fed by a nonpenetrating optronic periscope. (Kollmorgen)

The other major factor in sonobuoy operations is the number of available VHF radio channels (for the link with the airplane), typically either 31 or 99, typically between 136 and 173 MHz. As sonobuoy range decreases because of submarine quieting, the number that must be laid to gain contact (or to search an area) increases; therefore, more channels are needed. About 1984 the major improvement was the increase from 31 to 99, as reflected (in the U.S. Navy, for example) by replacement of the 31-channel ARR-72 receiver with the 99-channel ARR-78.

LOFAR is spectral analysis using time integration to pick up stable narrow-band signals amid the surrounding noise. CODAR measures the time difference between reception of the same signal by two buoys. It finds the direction of a signal relative to the two omni hydrophones that pick it up, given knowledge of the spacing of the buoys (which were dropped at specified points by intervalometer). If the time of the signal's origination is known, CODAR also gives a range.

Although a submarine may emit strongly at only a very few frequencies, acoustic conditions on a given day may make it easier to detect some harmonic of one of those lines. Typically, then, a searching airplane drops XBT and background noise buoys, and then the LOFAR processors are set for the line sought. The great advantage of adopting a more flexible processor (such as AQA-7) is that the buoy can offer either narrow- or broadband performance, LOFAR or CODAR (Julie-Jezebel).

DIFAR, directional LOFAR, uses two beam patterns, at right angles to each other: it measures two components of the signal it detects and sends two LOFAR signals (corresponding to its two beams) up to the monitoring airplane, plus an omni sense signal to resolve the 180-deg ambiguity in the two beams (much as in HFDF). From a signal-processing point of view, one DIFAR buoy equals two LOFAR buoys. Signal processing includes comparison of the two signals, generally using an arctan function to derive an angle. Target direction can generally be found within about 10 or 15 deg.

Processor capacity is generally measured in LOFAR channels. Two such channels equate to a DIFAR channel, and up to eight may be needed for a Barra buoy. Two LOFAR channels also suffice for a DICASS directional active buoy (one for a range-only buoy), but not for the British CAMBS (eight LOFAR channels equate to three CAMBS channels).

DEMON (demodulated noise) extracts very low frequency signals which are reflected in the modulation of flow noise. LOFAR/DIFAR typically applies to machinery noise (including noise made by auxiliaries), whereas DEMON is generally used to extract blade rate (i.e., propeller turn counts) from flow noise (direct LOFAR analysis is impossible because there is too much random noise).

DIFAR cardioid processing is a more sophisticated directional technique than conventional DIFAR processing. Instead of processing the directional beams separately (incoherently), each is added to or subtracted from the omni signal before processing, forming four cardioid (heart-shaped) beams, each pointed in a direction with a null opposite. That more than doubles the processing load, but the null excludes enough noise to add about 2 dB of processing power.

ANODE (Ambient Noise Omni-Directional Evaluation) uses a DIFAR buoy to measure noise. The pure omnidirectional signal is compared with a root-mean-square average of the two directional signals. If the noise is really not directional, the two should match exactly, but directional noise (e.g., from nearby shipping) will unbalance the two. Typically the comparison is matched against frequency, largely to determine which frequency ranges are best for buoy operation (i.e., which do not suffer from highly directional ambient noise). ANODE is commonly used by airborne ASW platforms, but more rarely in postmission analysis.

Command-activated pinging buoys, either omnidirectional (range-only, or RO, also called CASS, for command-activated sonobuoy system) or directional (e.g., the U.S. DICASS and the British CAMBS), are airplane equivalents to sonars, using CW and FM pulses. Typically, the pulse length can be varied by command; a longer pulse gives longer maximum range but can suffer from reverberation.

When sonobuoys are launched from within an airplane's pressure cabin (as in the British Nimrod), the crew sets them at launch time. The U.S. P-3C carries them externally, in sonobuoy launch containers (SLCs) set before flight time. If the launchers are inside the pressure cabin, then the cabin must be depressurized if multiple buoys are to be launched (the Nimrod uses a 6-rnd launcher) or else launched one by one through a special pressurized launcher. An airplane intended to launch buoys from high altitude (e.g., while monitoring a large field) must almost inevitably use external launchers.

In the case of the P-3C, the aircraft tactical system is aware of which buoys are set in which way and selects the ones it wants. This method becomes less satisfactory as the number required to prosecute a contact grows toward the total on board, and as the buoys themselves become more flexible in their operation (so that setting involves more tactical judgment, made at the scene of prosecution). The alternative solutions are a command downlink and remote setting on board the airplane.

Deletions: UYS-502 (Canadian, out of service), HIPADS/HAPS (Canadian, aborted when EH-101 canceled), SSQ-75 ERAPS

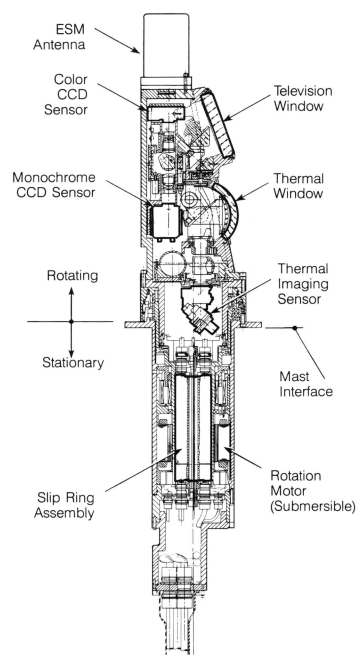

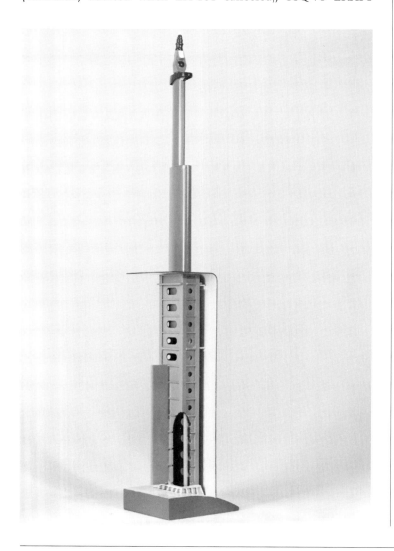

Kollmorgen's Model 86 nonpenetrating periscope (*left and above*). (Kollmorgen)

(United States, development program completed FY93 without production), SSQ-79 (not produced), SSQ-101 (not produced), SSQ-102 (terminated FY91), SSQ-103 (low-cost buoy proved too expensive; canceled), ASUTAA (United States, abandoned), IPADS (United States, version of AQA-7, program ended), United States advanced development projects (AE, ETSS, ITSS, TAS, all abandoned). See the 1991/92 edition for details.

AUSTRALIA

SONOBUOYS

◆ Barra (SSQ-801/SSQ-981)

Sonobuoys Australia's A-size (914 mm × 123.8 mm, 12.7 kg) narrow- and broad-band (10–2000 Hz) sonobuoy employs 25 hydrophones in a horizontal planar array consisting of five outstretched arms, to form 60 horizontally steerable beams. An internal magnetic compass provides a bearing reference. Array depth is either 21.5 or 128.5 m, and operating life is 0.5, 1, 2, or 4.5 hr. Fifty VHF channels are available. The volumetric array promises high gain and rapid localization of a contact, but the price is a heavy processing load: modes include 12-beam (eight

The range of sonobuoy sizes. (Sparton)

B-size   Stretch A   A-size   G-size   F-size   A/6

Standard A-size sonobuoys being loaded. The vanes protruding from their heads are rotochutes, which slow the buoys as they descend. (U.S. Navy)

LOFAR channels) and four-beam (quadrant, four LOFAR channels). The current processors are AQS-901 (RAAF Orion or RAF Nimrod) or the combination of a UYS-503 sonobuoy processor and an AQA-801 side processor in a helicopter (RAN Sea Hawk).

GEC-Marconi's (formerly Plessey Marine's) British version is SSQ-981. The manufacturer claims that it has been able to reduce unit cost. Dimensions match those of the original SSQ-801, but weight is reduced to 11 kg. Life span is 1, 2, 3, or 4 hr; operating depth is 21.5 or 121 m. Compass resolution is 0.36 deg, and accuracy is 1.0 deg at less than 65 deg in latitude.

Barra sonobuoy. (Plessey)

Sonobuoys Australia is now developing E (enhanced) Barra with an onboard VLSI processor, allowing it to operate without a dedicated Barra airborne acoustic processor. The same in-buoy processor also forms part of a completely new buoy, as yet unnamed, that the company is developing under a contract from the DSTO.

The program began in 1969 as Project Barra, full development being approved late in 1974. The production rate for the Royal Australian Navy in 1981–89 was 2000/yr, but as of 1989, it was rising to 2500/yr, to provide for exports to the Royal Navy. As of mid-1994, total Barra production was about 48,500. Unit cost in 1994 was about $5500 for the RAF.

Users: Australia, United Kingdom.

SIGNAL PROCESSORS

◆ Shearwater/FTAAS

AWA's new fast-time acoustic processor for postmission analysis can replay mission tapes at up to 32 times real-time speed, and can process 32 channels simultaneously. The basic eight-channel module is mounted in a 19in rack (a 32-channel system requires four such modules). Capacity: 32 DIFAR or eight Barra or eight frequency-azimuth (FRAZ) or eight power-bearing or 32 sound velocity (BT). Displays: LOFARgrams, frequency-azimuth, power-bearing (as in Barra), histograms (ALI, for example), and Delta Y Plots. AWA's earlier FTAAS, in RAAF service since 1990, operates at 8 times real-time (16 channels).

CANADA

SONOBUOYS

The Royal Canadian Navy uses DesJez (destroyer Jezebel). A ship can monitor a sonobuoy barrier laid by helicopter. The current standard practice is to use one dipper to direct another helicopter to attack. A sonobuoy helicopter can detect *and* attack. The abortive EH-101s were intended to function that way. On the TRUMPs, there are two helicopter spots because both are needed: Alfa with a dipping sonar, Bravo with sonobuoys and torpedoes. The "City" class is intended to use Bravo only.

The only current sonobuoys are SSQ-536 and SSQ-53D. SSQ-53D(1), made by Hermes, is more sensitive than SSQ-53D. An improved -53D(2) entered production late in 1992.

SIGNAL PROCESSORS

◆ UYS-501

This single-instruction multiple data (SIMD) parallel processor has eight identical arithmetic modules in parallel; the central executive processor is a 68020. UYS-501 has up to five independent signal processor I/O interfaces. It is built up of 59 cards in two racks. Memory comprises 4M 32-bit words of DRAM (expandable to 64M complex [64-bit] words); the cache memory is 32K 32-bit words in fast SRAM. Output is 32 MFLOPS; UYS-501 can compute a 1024-point complex FFT in 160 microsec.

◆ UYS-503

Computing Devices Co.'s airborne signal processor uses denser memory components than its predecessors. It suffices for all buoys except the complex broad-band Barra. The current (V)5 can process 32 DIFAR buoys, can simultaneously process buoys and a dipping sonar, and has acoustic fusion algorithms that combine passive tracking with other acoustic data. Besides LOFAR, it can detect and track on the basis of broad-band and transient signals. A new color display reduces operator workload. Earlier versions store 20 min of LOFAR data from each buoy (four DIFAR or eight omnidirectional) in four modules (one unit). Alternatively, each module can handle one DICASS (CW/FM) or one range-only (CW only) buoy. UYS-503 can also process expendable bathythermograph buoys or a dipping sonar (one "slice" per 90-deg sector). Each 44-lb unit includes eight standard buoy receivers.

Computing Devices Co. was formerly Computing Devices of Canada.

Users: Australia (S70 helicopter RAWS system, with a Side Barra Processor), Canada ("City"-class sonobuoy processor; *not* part of the recent sonars; selected for the abortive EH-101 program with the French FLASH wet end), Japan (probably in the SH-60J), Sweden (*Goteborg* class and sonobuoy craft), United Kingdom (Nimrod 2000 processor, as A627), and the United States (SH-2G). It may be used by the Royal Norwegian Navy, and it was the favored processor for the Fokker Maritime Enforcer Mk 2.

◆ SBP 1-1 (AQA-801)

CDC's Barra side processor works with UYS-503; it can also function as a stand-alone processor. Each of its four subprocessors can handle one Barra or eight LOFAR or four DIFAR or DICASS buoys. Typically three operator-chosen beams per Barra buoy are LOFAR-processed, plus 360-deg broad-band (simultaneously in the 50 Hz–1-kHz and 1–2-kHz bands). By selecting only some beams, the operator can avoid considerable background noise. SBP stores 20 min of LOFAR data on each frequency channel; the operator can call up and display the stored data on the CRT. The unit includes a patented demultiplexer that allows digital sonobuoys to be used with a standard analog receiver. A second SBP 1-1 can be connected in parallel to double the processing capacity.

The first SBP 1-1 was delivered in the summer of 1984.

Users: Australia (Seahawk helicopters), Japan (1992, for SH-60J; this sale may also have involved the UYS-503); the RAF Nimrods and RAAF P-3Cs all use the GEC AQS-901, which processes Barra without any special additional unit. Test units were bought by Canada and Sweden.

CHINA

A recent Chinese account of military technology claims that a passive omnidirectional sonobuoy (SKF-1) was production-certified in 1967. An "aerial nondirectional sonar buoy" (HF-1) was design-certified in 1972. The wording suggests that SKF-1 was placed in the water by a ship, but that HF-1 was air-dropped.

FRANCE

The French navy expects to use the Lynx successor, NH-90, in a LAMPS-like mode, using a repackaged SADANG 1C processor aboard the ship. It will carry up to 50 buoys, using an eight-buoy launcher (8 A- or 16 F/G-size buoys), receiving and retransmitting signals from 16 of them simultaneously. NH-90 is to handle VLAD buoys and HARP arrays (see the U.K. entry below) as well as Barra. These are digital rather than analog buoys, and SADANG will have to be modified to handle them (a digital buoy requires more memory in the processor). It can accommodate the beam-former required by Barra (and especially by HARP). The helicopter will also carry an active sonar (probably FLASH) with 1500 ft of cable and 10,000-yd reliable range, and with multiple-target automatic tracking capability, and a MAD.

The French navy currently uses A-size only for DICASS and range-only active buoys. LOFAR buoys are all F (A/3) -size. An F-size DIFAR buoy, TSM 8062, was shown at Bourget Naval 1992. As yet there is no interest in array buoys (VLAD, SVLA, etc.). The DSTA 3 active buoy is no longer in service; the last ones were used in the Bay of Biscay in 1991. It has been replaced by TSM 8030/8050. Production of the TSM 8030 DICASS buoy began late in 1986. Development of the successor DSTV 7 began in 1985 (see below).

SONOBUOYS

◆ DSTV 4L/M (MSR 810) (TSM 8010)

Thomson-CSF's 31-channel A-size omni LOFAR buoy (10 Hz–20 kHz, 124 × 914 mm, 8 kg or less) corresponds to the U.S. SSQ-41. Conceived as the passive counterpart to the active DSTA 3,

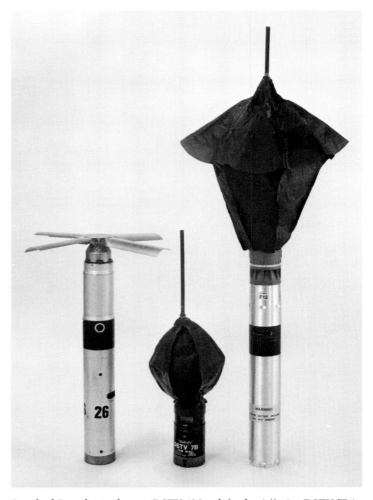

Standard French sonobuoys: DSTV 4M at left, the A/3-size DSTV 7B in the middle, and a range-only active buoy at right. The buoy on the left shows the rotochute that slows its descent. The other two show the inflated floats that keep their radio antennas above the surface. (Thomson Sintra)

DSTV 7X mini-Jezebel (LOFAR) buoy. (Thomson CSF)

it was produced in Italy by Misar as MSR 810. DSTV 4L operates at 65 or 330 ft (with an additional 990ft option in the 4M version), and has a lifetime of 1, 3, or 8 hr. The F-size -4M version is more reliable and more sensitive. DSTV 4N is the corresponding ambient noise buoy. The successor buoy is DSTV 7.

DSTV 4L was tested in 1968 (procurement began in 1970, and production ended early 1989); DSTV 4M procurement began in 1986. Total production of DSTV 4 for the French navy was reported as 130,000, plus 5,000 Italian-made MSR 810 (DSTV 4L). A total of 20,000 DSTV 4L were made.

◆ DSTV 7 (TSM 8030)

DSTV 7 entered service in 1989. DSTV 7 versions correspond to radio channels: 7B is the first 33 of 99, 7C is channels 34–66, 7D is channels 67–99, and 7E is a true 99-channel buoy. An A/3-size (124 × 304 mm, 4.5 kg) version of DSTV 4M, DSTV 7 incorporates a radio-frequency synthesizer so that radio channels need not be set before flight: they can be set manually on the airplane. DSTV 7A is limited to the 31 channels of the previous generation. DSTV 7B, 7C, and 7D can select from among a preselected 34 of the total of 99 channels. Frequency range of the buoy is 10 Hz–20 kHz (optionally 5 Hz–20 kHz); the hydrophone depth is 20 to 100 or 300 m. Lifetime is 1, 3, or 8 hr. The buoy can be dropped from 150–10,000 ft, at 80–250 kt.

As of mid-1989, 30,000–40,000 TSM 8030 had been made. About 3000 DSTV 7 were reportedly made between 1989 and March 1992, at a unit price of $8500.

◆ TSM 8040

Thomson Sintra's A-size (124 × 915 mm, 17.6 kg) DICASS buoy operates at 6.5, 7.5, or 9.5 kHz with either CW pulses (0.1–0.5 or 1 sec) or 1-sec FM pulses; pulses can repeat with intervals of less than 1 sec. Beam modes are ODT, cosine, or sine. Depth, remotely selectable, is 20 m or 150 m (450 m optional). The buoy reports on one of 31 VHF channels, and it is controlled by UHF (291.4 MHz). Power is supplied by a lithium cell, with an operational life of 30 min at 20 m, 20 min at maximum depth (50 sec of emission).

Production began in 1986.

◆ TSM 8050

Thomson Sintra's F-size range-only buoy (6.0/6.71/7.5/8.4/9.4/ 10.5 kHz) transmits CW (four pulses in a train, total duration

100 msec) or FM (one 320-msec pulse), in each case with an 11-sec recurrence rate. Hydrophone depth is 20 or 150 m (TSM 8050A) or 20 or 450 m (TSM 8050B). Operational life is 30 min, using a lithium cell and a magnesium/lead-chloride battery. The buoy reports by 12-channel VHF at a power level of 0.25 W (compared to 1 W for the passive DSTV 7). Presumably the lower power level is acceptable in a buoy used to localize a submarine detected by a relatively large field of passive buoys (some of which might have to be monitored from a considerable distance). Production began in 1989 for Lynx helicopters (18 buoys each).

◆ TSM 8060

This family of A-size (124 × 914 mm, 9 kg; 99-channel) DIFAR buoys began development in 1986; all major components are tailored to a future F-size version. TSM 8062 was displayed at Bourget Naval in 1992. Depth is 30, 120, or 300 m; lifetime is 1, 3, or 8 hr. As an interim measure, SSQ-53D is being manufactured under license.

A project to develop a low-cost buoy comparable to the abortive U.S. LCS appears to have failed.

SIGNAL PROCESSORS

◆ LAMPARO (TSM 8220/8251/8252)

This first-generation digital processor is a repackaged SECBAT (TSM 8200), the extinct sonobuoy processor of the modernized French Atlantique. It can handle eight LOFAR channels and can also do DEMON processing. With the advent of SADANG (see below), TSM 8200 was redesignated SADANG 2000; TSM 8230 processor technology was inserted, so that TSM 8202 and 8203 could handle, respectively, 32 and 64 buoys.

LAMPARO (TSM 8220) was announced in 1986. TSM 8251 is the version used with the DUAV-4 dipping sonar; TSM 8251 (for the HS-12 dipper) handles both the sonar (equivalent to four LOFAR channels) and sonobuoys.

Users: TSM 8220: Brazil (EMB-111 and probably modernized S-2), Chile (EMB-111 and probably AS365F helicopters), China (as part of HS-312 in Zhi-8 helicopter), Netherlands (Lynx), Saudi Arabia (AS 365F); probably other AS365F and AS332F Super Pumas.

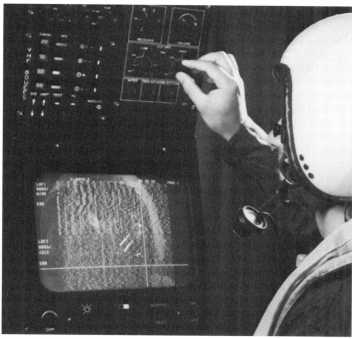

LAMPARO LOFARgram display. The curved white area is a reflection from the pilot's helmet; the display proper shows the usual vertical lines, spread out over the frequency spectrum. The operator seeks lines that remain stable over time. (Thomson Sintra)

◆ DSAX 1 (SADANG, TSM 8210)/TSM 8230

This modular system is intended primarily to handle DIFAR buoys. It is built around a data bus carrying 1–4 TSM 8230 signal processors (each to handle 16 LOFAR or 8 DIFAR buoys), each with its own VHF buoy receiver, multiple data processors, multiple video processors, and multiple RAM-ROM; also an I/O port and system management block. The bus design made it easy to upgrade from LOFAR to sufficient DIFAR capability. There is also a UHF controller/sonobuoy localizer. The system connects to the 1553B aircraft bus. It provides both a CRT and an optional graphic recorder for hard copy. The original TSM 8230 (in SADANG 2001A) required five ATR boxes; the current version (in SADANG 2001C) fits into a single 50 × 30 × 25cm (25 kg) box, using a VME bus, Texas Instruments DSP (signal processor), and 68000-family CPUs. Two processors can be ganged together in a single console, so one console can handle 32 LOFAR (two can handle 64).

SADANG NG (Nouvelle Génération) is intended specifically to use active buoys against quiet submarines in shallow water. Capacity is 16 DIFAR and 16 DICASS for one operator, 32 to 64 DIFAR and 16 DICASS for two. Facilities include autotracking, data fusion (using similar or dissimilar sensors), computer-aided classification, and mixed processing of passive and active buoys.

Announced in 1989, SADANG means Système Acoustique de l'Atlantique Nouvelle Génération. The contract was awarded in 1978. Once the name SADANG had been announced, Thomson Sintra renamed the export SECBAT (MPA LAMPARO) described above as SADANG 2000 (for two operators). It also announced a SADANG 1000 for small MPAs, with one operator (TSM 8221/8222, 8/16/32 buoys). Presumably TSM 8221 used the earlier SECBAT processor, whereas TSM 8222 uses the new DIFAR processor. SADANG itself became SADANG 2001. A repackaged stand-alone TSM 8230 (LAMPARO 1001) will be the processor for the NH-90 and EH-101. SADANG is also part of the AMASCOS MPA system (see under aircraft systems in the Surveillance/Control section above).

Users: TSM 8210 (DSAX 1): France (Atlantique Mk 2), Pakistan (SADANG 2001C in upgraded Atlantic Mk 1). SADANG 2001C is to replace 2001A.

◆ TMS 2000

Thomson Marconi announced this MPA system at Euronavale 1996. Presumably it combines features of SADANG and AQS-960. Capacity is 8, 16, or 32 channels (up to 32 DIFAR per unit), with two main and up to six auxiliary processes per channel (multiple independent bands at multiple resolutions). Thus it can combine narrow- and broad-band processing, swaths, transients, and DEMON. It offers manual or automatic noise nulling and full cardioid processing on all DIFAR buoys, with computer-aided automatic detection, tracking, and association/classification. Active capacity is 16 DICASS in multistatic as well as monostatic mode (for shallow water), with ping-to-ping integration and automatic handling of pulse sequences, as well as reverberation suppression and elimination of stationary artifacts (FM mode). A Geographic Energy Plot (GEP) fuses passive and active information. An Acoustic Localization Plot (ALP) shows synthetic data in geographic (PPI) form (sonobuoy positions, coastlines, bottom features). The two plots can be overlaid.

◆ Calcuta

DCN Ruelle's new acoustic processing and control system controls a VHF sonobuoy receiver and displays the outputs of four of eight buoys simultaneously (10 Hz–50 kHz: LOFAR, DIFAR, CODAR, DEMON, RO, DICASS). An alternative early warning eight-way LOFAR switched analysis (time-sharing) increases capacity to 48 sonobuoys. The processor is a TMS 320C31 controlled by a 25-MHz 68EC030 CPU using Windows display software; 16-bit data are acquired at varied sampling rates. The display is a 640 × 400-pixel electroluminescent screen. Input is eight analog sonobuoy channels; output is via dual 1553B or RS422 or RS232 port. The associated buoy receiver is RR229.

◆ Mustang

Thomson Sintra's standard modular parallel (MIMD) digital signal processor and data processor uses VME racks connected by Ethernet and two types of cards: signal or data processing and I/O data transfer. Each board is considered one or more logical nodes; Mustang can incorporate more than 500 nodes. Local 32-bit 8-MHz rings (outside the VME bus) are used within one VME rack, typically between calculating nodes and I/O nodes; some I/O nodes are also connected to the special high-speed data link (10-MHz 16-bit Artery) connecting particular racks. VME and Ethernet buses are used for system synchronization, debug, and data outputs. Thus data flows into an I/O node connected by local ring to calculating nodes and to an I/O node connecting the rack by Artery to another rack, which has its own local ring. The VME bus carries results to an I/O node. General-purpose signal-processing nodes use standard commercial TMS 320C30s and Motorola 96002s (local memory 1–8 Mbytes), CAROUSEL ASICs (50,000 gates) which control communication with the 32 Mbyte/sec (between two CAROUSELs) local ring, and PEPSI ASICs which control communication using the Artery. There are also special FFT (56 MFLOPS per board) and time domain beam-former (using a FAUVETTE ASIC with 100,000 gates, and with 1 Mwords [24 bits/word] of local memory; board performance is 48 MFLOPS) nodes. Data-processing nodes use 680x0 or SPARC CPUs, with large local memory (2 Mbytes for a 68020). I/O nodes can input or output at 160 Mbits/sec. Overall processing power is 20 to 7500 MFLOPS.

By the end of 1991, 80 Mustangs were in use in 15 French and export programs, including sonars and EW. Mustang+, with a new FFT board (placing a Sharp LH9124 chip set on a mezzanine above each 320C30 to do a 1024-point FFT in 120 microsec), appeared in 1994. Mustang++ (1995–96) at least doubles performance but is adapted to the original software. The general-purpose signal-processing board now has four rather than two TMS 320C-series processors.

Mustang is the latest of a series of Thomson Sintra parallel (SIMD) signal processors, beginning with CAFI in 1973, and including the 16-bit fixed-point Mangouste (1983, 20–175 MFLOPS) and the 32-bit floating-point Mouflon (1988, 50–1000 MFLOPS).

INDIA

In 1978 Hindustan Aeronautics Ltd. reported that it was producing a sonobuoy for the Indian navy, based on a design by the Naval Physical Oceanographic Laboratory at Cochin. The buoy is retarded by rotochute, and it lowers its transducer to a depth of 30 m. Lifetime is 8 hr, power being provided by a nickel-cadmium battery; and data are transmitted by VHF (162.25–172.5 MHz). Presumably, the buoy is A-size, to fit Western-supplied helicopters and aircraft, and its long life suggests fully passive operation.

The new Advanced Light Helicopter is to be built in separate sonobuoy and dipping sonar versions.

ITALY

◆ BI Series

Olivetti's A-size Julie-Jezebel omni buoys operate on 31 (BIT-3) or 41 (BIT-8) channels, replacing SSQ-41. Hydrophone depth is 65 or 330 ft (lifetime 1–3 hr). BIR is intended for light helicopters (4.5 × 24 in, 65 ft depth, 1 hr lifetime). These buoys are intended specifically for the Mediterranean, with its shallow surface layer. Work on these buoys began in the mid-1970s, and they entered service in 1979–80; about 12,000 were manufactured through 1986.

◆ MSR 810/910

MSR 810 is a license-produced version of the French DSTV 4L/M LOFAR buoy. Misar is currently developing MSR 910, a range-only active buoy.

JAPAN

Japanese equivalents to the U.S. SSQ-41B (LOFAR) and SSQ-53 (DIFAR) are Oki's HQS-6B and -12; the acoustic reference buoy (equivalent to SSQ-57) is HQS-21B, and the SSQ-47/50/62 equivalents are HQS-31/32/33B.

KOREA (SOUTH)

In July 1992 it was reported that Korea wanted Motorola's sonobuoy technology as part of P-3 offsets; Gold Star Precision would make the buoys.

RUSSIA

It is very unlikely that the following catalog is complete; rather, it is an indication of past progress and of past design practice.

Surface ships can monitor sonobuoys. For example, in a Krivak III, the monitoring antennas (Long Fold) are at the ends of the foremast yardarms. On the newest ASW ships (*Neustrashimyy*, *Udaloy*, and Krivak III), Ka-27PL data are data-linked to the ship CDS, as in a LAMPS III.

The Soviets used explosive echo-ranging extensively.

They also had an active ranging buoy (range reportedly 1850–5550 m), which is *not* listed in the entries that follow. Reference has been made to RGB-NM and RGB-N buoys for the Ka-25, neither of them clearly identified.

Different generations of buoys coexist, and may be used together (e.g., LOFAR for initial detection, then old broad-band buoys for localization, possibly using explosive echo-ranging). Short-range buoys are typically dropped across or near the expected target track, at variable depths. Russian publications describe square and circular sector barriers, the latter to be used when more time is available.

No data on sonobuoy processors has been released, but Bear F Mod 4 (Tu-142MZ) carries a second-generation system, Zareche, ordered in 1974 (installed in the mid-1980s), to deal with quieter submarines. Presumably it has finer frequency resolution than its predecessor, using the same buoy. Zareche may also rely more heavily on Julie techniques.

◆ RGB-16/1 and Type 75

This equivalent to SSQ-41B (Julie-Jezebel, 2 Hz–5 kHz) is also called RGB-1; presumably it is one of the current generation of small buoys (120 × 1260 mm, 9 kg, similar to NATO A-size), operating on 24 channels (170–200 MHz). The six-element hydrophone can be set to 20, 150, or 300 m depth, and lifetime is not less than 4 hr. The buoy can be launched from 150 to 2000 m at an aircraft speed of up to 600 km/hr. RGB-16 was exhibited by the Ukrainian "Slavutich" design bureau at IDEX 95.

Typical aircraft loads: May (Il-38) carries 216 RGB-1 for search (nine fields, 24 buoys each), or 144 RGB-1 and 10 RGB-2 (and two AT-1 torpedoes or 10 PLAB-250–120 depth charges or a nuclear depth bomb) for search/attack.

Bear-F (Tu-142) aircraft and Ka-25 and -27 helicopters process their sonobuoys on board. Ka-25 originally carried 12 broad-band buoys without a processor. It now carries three Type 75 Series S. The larger Ka-27 carries 12 Type 75 Series S buoys. Presumably it was specially designed to accommodate the processor and the LOFAR buoys, which were back-fitted into the smaller Ka-25. However, a recent Russian publication refers specifically to a device offering an aural presentation of sonobuoy data, which would mean broad-band operation.

Presumably this generation of buoys includes a broad-band equivalent to BM-1 and an echo-ranger.

◆ RGB-25 (Type 25 or RGB-2)

This directional counterpart to RGB-16/1 (alternative designation RGB-2) uses a rotating array like that of early British passive directional buoys, rather than the pair of orthogonal channels common in the West. The array rotates at 4 rpm, and (as in the West), the buoy has an onboard magnetic compass. The 230 × 1855mm (45 kg) buoy operates on 10 channels. Acoustic and radio frequency ranges match those of RGB-16/1. Paddle hydrophone depth is 20 or 150 m. Operating life is not less than 45

min. Radio output power is 20 W (0.75 W in RGB-16/1). The buoy can be dropped at speeds of 350 to 600 km/hr, and from altitudes between 200 and 2000 m.

Russian (actually Ukrainian) sonobuoys are shown at Dubai, 1995, with the RGB-25 directional array at left (and the buoy itself next to its array, with the much smaller RGB-16 and RTB-92 alongside it). The poster above the directional array advertises a 900-Hz flextensional transducer capable of radiating at least 2 kW down to a depth of 120 m; dimensions are 465 × 210 × 1070 mm (170 kg). (S. Zaloga)

◆ RGB-56/64

These large omni broad-band buoys detect targets at 2–4 kyd. RGB-56 (8.75 × 48 in, 60 lb) operates at 4.4–6.4 kHz; RGB-64 (6 × 37 in, 33 lb) operates at 3–11.5 kHz. Both use an 18-channel AM (49.2–53.45 MHz) data link, each buoy being preset before launch. The buoy transmits only when target noise (in effect, integrated over its bandwidth) exceeds a preset threshold (intensity is given as one of seven levels). The monitoring helicopter or airplane continuously tunes over the channels, automatically locking onto a transmitting buoy and locating it using a VHF/DF built into the sonobuoy receiver. The operator can listen, for example, for a turn count, and then resume tuning or can hand-tune, obtaining a rough fix by comparative listening, or estimating submarine speed by turn-counting. The threshold procedure extends the buoy's life, which (in RGB-56) could be as great as four to five days (given battery strength; the buoy was designed, however, to scuttle in 24 hr).

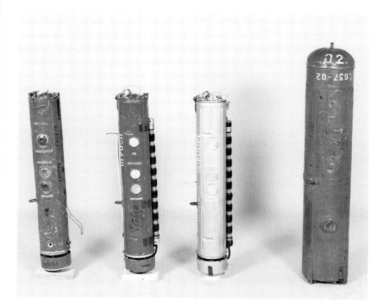

Standard Soviet sonobuoys: three RGMB (RGB-56) on the left, RGBN (RGB-64) on the right. All are still in use. (U.S. Navy)

U.S. observers noted that RGB-56 had the beam pattern (17 deg in the vertical) appropriate to bistatic operation with an active sonar, the transmission biasing necessary to prevent transient interference, and a center frequency (5 kHz) and band pass well suited to such operation. Presumably that really meant explosive echo-ranging.

An equivalent buoy made under license in Romania, R-500, exists in both air-dropped and anchored form. The anchored long-life version is 340 mm × 1.55 m (maximum width 430 mm, length including anchor 2 m); total weight less anchor is 98 kg (including 57 kg battery). A small boat typically drops a line of 18 buoys. Each transmits for up to 4 sec at a time and has a maximum rated range of 10 cables (0.5 nm). The anchored version can be used in depths up to 70 m (230 ft), and it lasts 7 to 20 days. The receiver, R-550E (for helicopters) or R-550N (for patrol boats), is credited with a DF accuracy of 30 deg, using four dipoles.

RGB-56, first seen in September 1959, was the first Soviet sonobuoy; RGB-64 was a miniaturized follow-on. In 1962 U.S. naval intelligence reported Soviet interest in a directional listening equivalent. RGB-56 components had appeared, by that time, in a variety of old mine, buoy, and paravane casings, presumably to monitor U.S. and NATO exercises.

There were also marker buoys (RBM-100 and -200).

◆ RTB-92

This BT buoy was shown at IDEX 95. It is somewhat larger than the companion RGB-16: 150 × 1260 mm (14 kg), using two radio channels (170–200 MHz); readings are taken down to 400 m. The buoy can be dropped from 200 to 2000 m, and at speeds of 150 to 600 km/hr.

◆ BM-1

This 1968 follow-on to RGB-64 (6 × 47.5 in, 33 lb) uses a line hydrophone and a 29-channel VHF FM data link (171 MHz, with

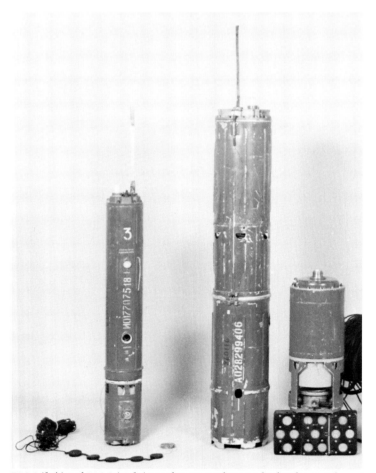

BM-1 (*left*) and BM-2 (*right*) sonobuoys, with BM-1 hydrophone at lower left and BM-2 array at lower right. (U.S. Navy)

channels 150 Hz apart). Like RGB-56/64, buoys transmit only when they receive a sound signal above a preset threshold. The associated radar is Wet Eye, in May ASW aircraft; these buoys are also carried by Bear-F. Internal electronics is solid-state with printed circuits. BM-2 (1969: 9 × 57 in, 97 lb) is the corresponding directional buoy.

SWEDEN

The Royal Swedish Navy uses moored sonobuoys, deployed from specialized surface craft, as mobile hydrophone arrays. The buoys are locally manufactured but are descended from about 50 Dowty buoys purchased several years ago.

UNITED KINGDOM

SONOBUOYS

Early in 1997 the British Ministry of Defence expects to let two parallel contracts for two-year project definition studies of a Future Active Surveillance System for Nimrod 2000, under SR(A) 903. This system will use separate transmitting and receiving buoys, and it may use explosive sound sources. A planned parallel passive project was dropped because current DIFAR buoys seem satisfactory.

A pair of new buoys, to staff requirements ST(A)902 (passive) and ST(A)903 (active), are intended for the Nimrod replacement, Nimrod 2000. Digital uplinks are being developed to overcome the transmission problems of the current analog radio links. A digital DIFAR is being developed as HIDAR, and a 20-bit LOFAR buoy has been demonstrated. There is also interest in placing GPS receivers on buoys to improve localization accuracy, and to allow aircraft greater freedom of maneuver (compared to that allowed by current RF techniques). DRA's experimental active sonobuoy, announced in 1991, probably illustrates current thinking. Its ten flex-tensional transmitters can be packaged in A-size. It stores a total of 64 sec of sonar waveforms at 1 kHz; modes include CW, FM, and pseudorandom noise. Its battery suffices for 200 ping-sec (which can probably be upgraded to 500), operating at 300 Hz–10 kHz at a source level of 210 dB. Radio command range is 8 km. This buoy was used as the pinger in British HARP (Horizontal Array Random Position) experiments analogous to the U.S. STRAP program described below. HARP uses three or four pingers and 12 or 13 LF passive buoys plus one DIFAR buoy (containing a compass) to orient the entire array. HARP is probably to be the Nimrod 2000 sonobuoy system. It is covered by an MoU signed in 1989, BURLAP (British-U.S. Random LF Array Program).

SSQ-947B is the British version of the U.S. SSQ-47B RO buoy.

LOFAR production has stopped in favor of Barra (SSQ-981).

SSQ-991 (GEC-Marconi) is a pinger (with radar reflector) intended as a reference point for Type 195M dipping sonars.

◆ SSQ-904/SSQ-905/SSQ-906/SSQ-907/SB112

This 31- or 99-channel mini- (5 in × 12 in, 10 lb, i.e., F-size) Jezebel (LOFAR) buoy (10 Hz–6 kHz) is made by Ultra Systems (formerly Dowty) and by GEC-Marconi. SSQ-904 operates at a depth of 60, 300, or 450 ft, with a lifetime of 1, 4, or 8 hr. It can be dropped from 50 to 10,000 m, and at speeds of 60 to 325 kt. SSQ-905 is a calibrated version.

SSQ-906 is a 99-channel 9.6-lb low-self noise version with better LF performance (4 Hz–6 kHz). Buoy response is shaped to an inverse ambient sea noise curve to overcome average sea noise. Recent brochures show a minimum frequency of 2 rather than 4 Hz. That is so low that, in theory, the buoy can pick up blade rate directly, rather than via DEMON processing (2 Hz is 120 rpm). The manufacturer described this buoy as providing the lowest-frequency coverage in NATO. Hydrophone depth is 30 or 140 m (other combinations can be provided) and lifetime is 1, 4, or 6 hr. The buoy can be dropped from altitudes of 150–30,000 ft and at speeds of 60–300 kt. SSQ-907 is a calibrated version; SSQ-907A is a calibrated version of SSQ-906A. SB112 is a special moored version by Ultra.

SSQ-904 resulted from MoD studies of the late 1970s (and from a 1978 Dowty proposal for a dwarf buoy for helicopters);

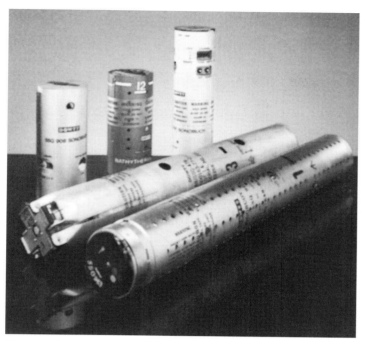

Ultra sonobuoys, with three miniatures in the background and standard A-size buoys in the foreground. The buoy on the left is the SSQ-906 omnidirectional passive type; it is flanked by a BT buoy and by SSQ-954B. The two buoys in the foreground are an Ultra-made SSQ-47B and SSQ-963A CAMBS. (Ultra)

production began in 1980. SSQ-906 was introduced in 1988. As many as 288,000 SSQ-904s may have been produced by mid-1994 (this figure may include SSQ-905, -906, and -907). As of 1989, Plessey and Dowty had contracts for a total of nearly 90,000 SSQ-906 buoys. Unit price was about $800 in 1994. The success of this buoy led in turn to the 1984 proposal for the G-size SSQ-954, which entered service in 1985.

For the RN and RAF, production has apparently ceased in favor of the SSQ-954 DIFAR buoy; the most recent reported SSQ-906/907 contracts were issued in November 1987, for 48,893 SSQ-906 and 5941 SSQ-907 (both to Plessey, now GEC-Marconi), for delivery in 1988–91.

Users: Australia, France (SSQ-906), Sweden (probably SB112), United Kingdom (for Nimrod and Sea King helicopter; presumably also for Merlin). This buoy is probably used by the Indian navy.

◆ SSQ-937

This three-channel F-size XBT buoy gives temperature down to 1000 ft (sink rate is 5 ft/sec). The six-channel SSQ-937A measures down to 1500 ft in 6–12 min.

◆ SSQ-954/SB113

Plessey's (now GEC-Marconi's) 99-channel G-size DIFAR-LOFAR buoy has hydrophone depth settings of 30, 140, or 300 m; lifetime is 1, 4, or 6 hr. DIFAR compass accuracy is within 5 deg. The buoy can be dropped at speeds of 50–300 kt from altitudes of 150–30,000 ft. Compared to SSQ-954 and -954A, -954B uses one rather than three buttons to select frequency, depth, and lifetime (they can also be selected remotely). SB113 is Ultra's special moored version of SSQ-954B. SSQ-954 appeared in 1985. In July 1993 the British Ministry of Defense asked for bids for 60,000 SSQ-954 buoys, for delivery in 1994–99.

◆ SSQ-963 (CAMBS)

Ultra's 31-channel A-size Command Active Multi-Beam has separate omni transmission and preformed-beam directional receiver arrays. There are three selectable depths, and lifetime is 1 hr, with automatic or command scuttling (shelf life is 5 yr). The buoy can be launched from altitudes of 200–8000 ft and at speeds of 60–300 kt.

SSQ-963A (CAMBS III) represents an unspecified but radically different technical approach from two earlier generations, most likely FM pulses. It costs about a third as much as CAMBS II but has better acoustic performance. CAMBS V (Ultra contract about the end of 1995 for up to 8735 buoys for delivery 1997 through 2000–2001) will probably incorporate GPS and a digital uplink.

AIRBORNE SIGNAL PROCESSORS

GEC makes postmission analyzers. As of mid-1994, both the Canadian navy and the RAF had received GEC-Marconi Naval Systems Fast Time Replay Mission Support Analysis Processors based on Series 5 processors: the RAF had the briefcase-size CRISP, and the Canadians had both CRISP and CHIP 19in shelf-size units.

◆ AQS-901

GEC Avionics's three-operator signal processor, which uses a 99-channel receiver, is adapted to the Barra buoy. Each of two elements, connected by data bus, can process eight LOFAR (or one Barra) buoys, using a GEC 920 ATC computer (2048-point FFT in 11.25 millisec). AQS-901 also controls and processes CAMBS active buoys (setting pulse width, pulse type, and PRF). The displays are CRTs and paper gram recorders. An operator can be alerted automatically when a potential target exceeds a preset threshold.

AQS-901 was first delivered in March 1979. Production ended in the fall of 1986.

Users: Australia (P-3C: 60 bought), United Kingdom (Nimrod: 83 bought). Production figures suggest two per airplane plus spares. This is probably the processor in the RNZAF P-3Ks.

◆ AQS-902 (LAPADS)/AQS-920 Series

GEC-Marconi's Lightweight Acoustic Processing-and-Display System exploits improved computer technology to shrink AQS-901 by about 80%. AQS-902A, a digital equivalent to the U.S. AQA-5, processed only four LOFAR buoys, with an A-scope for wide-band (search) mode and paper grams for narrow-band (classification/tracking) mode, an unusual combination for helicopters. AQS-902B adds a CRT display. TATTIX (ASN-902) is two AQS-902B plus a console for tactical integration. AQS-902C doubles processing power (four DIFAR buoys or eight LOFAR or four LOFAR and one BT buoy). It also has a CRT; the equivalent of TATTIX is TPS, the Tactical Processing System. AQS-902D-DS is an upgraded system capable of handling a dipping sonar (it has been upgraded further to AQS-902G-DS; see below). AQS-902F can process four LOFAR, one BT, and four range-only buoys; or four DIFAR and two DICASS; or four VLAD buoys.

AQS-902G-DS has a 12in CRT and a sonar processor. It has 12 verniers (800, 400, 200, 100, and 25 Hz wide) that can be positioned anywhere in its displays, and it can display 12 LOFARs simultaneously. A harmonic cursor allows the operator to compare a line with its harmonic. Up to 1.5 hr of LOFAR history can be stored, for line enhancement. One of the CRT formats, the acoustic localization plot (ALP), allows the sonar operator to check the validity of data before passing them to the observer's tactical plot. It replaces the separate tactical plot of many airborne systems, so that one piece of equipment does the job normally reserved for two. The tactical plot of the range and bearing information derived from the buoys provides current and predicted target information and track.

AQS-920 is an upgraded export version. AQS-924 can handle four 10 Hz–2.4 kHz omni or pseudo-omni buoys (passive or RO) or two directional buoys (DIFAR or DICASS, including single or triple cardioids) plus one calibrated buoy or BT. AQS-924 doubles the number of omni channels. The system can handle 10 narrow bandwidths or resolutions. The display covers a time history of up to 64 min. The maximum number of analyses processed is eight BBAs (broad-band analyses: 688 cells) plus 24 VWs (vernier widths, i.e., narrow-bandwidths: 180 cells). Passive processing modes include CODAR, DEMON, ambient-noise measurement (ANM), and signal-to-noise ratio (SNR). The processor can also handle an active dipping sonar. Buoy data can be processed simultaneously in wide- and narrow-band modes. Narrow-band outputs can be either LOFARgrams (on a CRT) or automatic line integration (ALI, with integration time 3.75, 7.5, 15, or 30 sec, and automatic alerts). For classification, the system provides harmonic multipoint dividers, so the operator can compare the same line in several harmonic forms. For localization, there are narrow-band frequency/bearing trackers, semiautomatic CPA/Doppler fixing, and the acoustic localization plot (ALP).

Total system weight, excluding the sonobuoy receiver, is 52.5 kg, including one or two 625-line CRTs and a hard-copy unit (for LOFARgrams).

AQS-902A (for Royal Navy Sea Kings) entered service in 1980.

Users: Brazil (AQS-928 reported in 11 S-2, 1990), Greece (LA-PADS in 14 HU-16B), India (902C: 12 Sea Kings; contract announced September 1984), Italy (update of Atlantic Mk 1 with AQS-902C), Netherlands (probably 902B in two Fokker Maritime Enforcers), Nigeria (probably 902B in two Fokker Maritime Enforcers), Pakistan (Atlantic Mk 1 modernization with AQS-902), Peru (probably 902B in one Fokker Maritime Enforcer), Philippines (probably 902B in three Fokker Maritime Enforcers), Spain (probably 902B in three Fokker Maritime Enforcers), Sweden (six AQS-924s ordered in 1984 for patrol boats, AQS-928 ordered for similar installation in 1990, plus probably three AQS-902 on aircraft), Taiwan (32 Turbo-Tracker conversions with AQS-902F/AQS-928, ordered 1991), United Kingdom (902D: Sea King HAS.2 and HAS.5 helicopters; 112 being replaced by 902G-DS in HAS.6 version; a further upgrade contract to work with the Type 2069 sonar was announced in 1994). In all, over 440 have been ordered. AQS-928 was selected in 1990 for a planned upgrade of the Turkish S-2 force, but the aircraft were taken out of service instead (they have been offered for sale).

◆ AQS-903/AQS-930/GEMMA/AQS-960

GEC Avionics' AQS-902 successor can process Barra and CAMBS buoys, using a pipelined distributed processor to provide 8 times the processing power of AQS-901 for each of 16 buoys (offering several verniers simultaneously). It includes an ALP. Weight is only 160 kg.

AQS-930 is the export version, with 16 (AQS-932), 32 (AQS-934), or 64 (AQS-938) LOFAR channels, each equivalent to half a DIFAR, to one-eighth of a Barra, or to one-quarter of a DICASS. CAMBS capacity is, respectively, 3, 6, and 6. Weight (66.5, 74.5, or 82.5 kg) includes two 12in 625-line acoustic display CRTs.

Added processing modes (compared to AQS-924/928) are four-cardioid rather than triple cardioid, and Barra broad-band. Added detection aids are narrow/broad-band AGC (automatic gain control), broad-band power/bearing (DIFAR/Barra), and display enhancement. Additional classification aids are predictive (ratio) dividers and recorded data recall. Added localization/tracking aids are broad-band bearing trackers, automatic/manual CPA/Hyfix, and a coordinated tracker for multiple contacts. The LOFARgram display can show up to 60 min of history. These processors can handle dipping sonar data.

GEMMA, the GEC Avionics MPA Mission Avionics, is built around AQS-903/930. In April 1992 GEC Avionics and Boeing agreed to share ASW technologies for the U.S. and British patrol airplane replacement programs (Boeing was later chosen for Nimrod 2000).

Assuming that the announced alliance survived, the acoustic processor will be GEC-Marconi's AQS-960, based on the Advanced Signal Processor (ASP), which GEC-Marconi supplied to the UK Joint Acoustic Analysis Center (JAAC) early in 1994. It uses energy-mapping techniques, which suggest a broad-band operation designed to detect the flow noise of a diesel submarine or a very quiet nuclear submarine. ASP uses the same DEC Alpha CPU as the Kestrel 6000 radar.

ASN-990 is probably an export designation for GEMMA.

Users: United Kingdom (EH-101 Merlin).

◆ AQS-950/951

These Ferranti/Thomson Sintra acoustic processors incorporate SADANG 2000 technology. AQS-950 is the processor used in the British version of the ALFS sonar, Type 2095. It may be part of the processor suite of the French Atlantique 2 MPA. The related AQS-951 was proposed (1995) for the British Nimrod replacement.

◆ Series 5/SPUD/CHIP/CRISP

GEC-Marconi's Series 5 acoustic analysis cards are currently in Royal Navy and foreign service. The system's vector (DSP) arrays are linked by a dual 24-bit 13.3-MHz synchronous data bus (SDB: 40 Mbit/sec). An IEEE 796 bus connects them to the SCSI, I/O processor, data acquisition device, and an 80386 control processor. Another SDB bus links the control, data, and display processors. The signal processing subsystem is connected by LAN to the control/data processing subsystem. As of late 1995 the six standard cards were:

A 16-channel analog input card, sampling each channel at up to 100 MHz with 16-bit resolution and 42 dB switched gain as well as automatic gain ranging.

An I/O processor card, with 24-bit parallel interface, with three processor nodes, each containing a 10-MHz Motorola 56000 DSP, 64 kwords of 24-bit external DSP SRAM, and a universal bus interface to the SDB, plus a universal bus interface to connect all three nodes to the IEEE 796 Host Bus.

A vector processor card for signal processing (8 Motorola 56000 DSP elements, each with 64 kwords [24-bit] SRAM external DSP memory and universal bus interface to the IEEE 796 Host Bus; total of 80 MIPS maximum processing capacity); DSP programs are downloaded to the DSPs from a controlling microprocessor to configure the card for the required processing.

A control processor card, interfacing directly with the IEEE 796 bus; 80386 CPU plus optional 80387 coprocessor, 8 Mbytes of RAM/ROM/EPROM, SCSI bus controller, serial links and a LAN interface.

A video processor card, interfacing directly with the IEEE 796 bus, containing an 80386 CPU, two 82786 high-performance video coprocessors, 8 Mbytes of video memory, and immediate access to video data.

A special interface card for customer-specified interfaces, controlled by 80386 via the IEEE 796 bus.

A related Fast-Time In-Depth Acoustic Analyzer (CHIP) provides eight independent channels running at 8 times real-time for postmission analysis. Resolution is 0.0025 Hz across a 15360-Hz-input bandwidth. SPUD is a related 64-channel (16-kHz bandwidth using 4k, 2k, or 1k FFTs) device currently used for trials and laboratory work. A 13in portable unit (CRISP: Compact Reconfigurable Interactive Signal Processor) can handle four DIFAR (omni and steered cardioid with bearing extraction) or eight LOFAR channels using simultaneous broad- and narrow-band analysis. Spectral analysis bands are 2400, 1200, 800, 400, 200, 100, 80, 40, 20, 10 Hz with cell widths of 0.0125 to 3 Hz. DEMON input bandwidths are 300, 600, and 1200 Hz (analysis bands are 40, 80, and 200 Hz). Cell width is 0.05 to 0.25 Hz. LOFAR bands are 19200, 9600, 4800, 2400, 1200, 800, 400, 200, 100, 80, 40, 20, or 10 Hz; cell widths are 0.0125 to 24 Hz.

Users: Canada (CRISP in Air Force, SUBTASS in Navy), France (probably SSN/SSBN navigational sonar), NATO (main sonar and SPUD/CHIP in test ship *Alliance*), Sweden (Hydra flank and towed array systems), and United Kingdom (CRISP in RAF; SPUD/CHIP in RN, RAF, and DERA; Type 2074 sonar; SSN data analyzer; submarine navigational sonars). Series 5 is also used in data analyzers and display processors aboard two surface units.

UNITED STATES

SONOBUOYS

Current U.S. policy is to use directional buoys (DIFAR, DICASS) only and not to purchase omnidirectional buoys. Although more expensive than the omnidirectional type, the directional units are not needed in the same quantities. The problem is that, in peacetime, MPA must often track submarines for protracted periods. In wartime (for which the systems were designed), tracking would continue only long enough to make an attack. Thus it was common for a patrol airplane to drop as many as 60 buoys while tracking a submarine during an 8-hr period. In recent years, tracking has required such great expenditures that some have suggested that a period of prewar tension (requiring sustained tracking) would exhaust sonobuoy reserves. The low-cost sonobuoy was proposed in part as a solution to this problem since in theory it could be made and used in great quantities at affordable prices.

Sonobuoy stowage on board a P-3C of VP-22, NAS Adak, November 1987. (Jürg Kürsener)

With the end of the Cold War, the emphasis has shifted from DIFAR (SSQ-53) to active sonobuoys and E²R (no longer explosive echo-ranging; now it is "Extended Echo-Ranging") using an active sound source and passive SSQ-110 buoys. In 1994 the only buoy in production was the active SSQ-62C.

Plans for E²R appear to envisage three phases. Initially the sound source is apparently an uncoded pinger or a miniature depth bomb, as in the old Julie system. The improved EER system substitutes a new buoy, ADAR (air-deployed active receiver), for SSQ-110, to deal with shallow as well as deep water; it will also be a passive buoy to detect submarines operating at high speed. Shallow-water operation presumably requires vertical beam-forming. The final stage is the advanced EER (AEER), using a new sound source to handle poor water conditions; presumably it is to be coded for better detectability. A choice between the two candidate sound sources, the air-deployable LF projector (ADLFP) and the advanced ranging source (ARS), is due in FY97. Work on an advanced receiver begins under that year's program. AEER is to reach low-level production in FY98.

Current programs are the Acoustic Intercept System (AIS), a full-spectrum acoustic processor; and the Generic Acoustic

Stimulator System (GASS), which is an ocean, sensor and target-modeling combination that will couple with all ASW trainers. A new type of active buoy, using a slotted cylinder projector and high-power density electronics, was tested during FY95.

Sonobuoy purchases, as of February 1992:

	FY91	FY92	FY93
SSQ-53	216,736	—	—
SSQ-62	19,865	10,947	—
SSQ-77 VLAD	—	97,325	124,800

The total U.S. Navy sonobuoy purchase in FY89 was 376,000, including 15,000 SSQ-36 XBTs. That fell to 294,990 in FY90. For later years, only dollar amounts (in millions) are available:

	FY94	FY95	FY96	FY97
SSQ-53	37.1	—	8.9	14.7
SSQ-62	—	22.3	—	—
SSQ-110 (EER)	0.4	37.0	—	—
SSQ-86 (DLC)	—	2.4	—	—

Figures for FY96 and FY97 are those submitted in the January 1995 budget.

In FY95, the Navy had about 150,000 passive buoys on hand. A planned extension of shelf life from 5 to 6 yr would bring the inventory to a steady level of about 100,000. On the other hand, active buoys, needed to track diesel submarines, were in short supply. Probably only 25,000 were on hand, against a requirement for 125,000. In June 1995 the Navy asked that the programmed FY96 funding for SSQ-53 be shifted to active buoys (SSQ-62C), as otherwise it would run out of active buoys in FY98.

◆ STRAP

The sonobuoy thinned random array processor (STRAP), tested in May 1991 on board P-3Cs, forms beams from the outputs of all its buoys in real-time (the buoys in effect form a single sensor). The coefficient applied to each buoy output in each beam depends on precise location of the buoy (better than those available from the airplane's interferometer), which changes as it drifts. STRAP uses two arrays (to cross-fix targets), each comprising 20 SSQ-53D and four PAEL (prototype array electronic location) buoys. Buoy hydrophone depth varies, so STRAP forms 3D beams. Each sonobuoy transmits raw acoustic data plus timing chirps from the PAEL buoys. The retransmitted chirps measure buoy distances from PAEL buoys. Directly transmitted PAEL chirps locate the two STRAP arrays relative to each other.

Two Hewlett-Packard HP 3565 front-end processors in the P-3 strip the chirps from raw acoustic data (arriving at up to 70 kbyte/sec) to calculate conventional or adaptive beam-forming coefficients. Beams are processed by three AP Labs VME workstations, each containing a SPARC 1E main processor (12.5 MIPS, 1.5 FLOPS) and a SPARC 1E graphics processor. Nine SKY Computer Warrior digital signal processing boards and two Mercury Computer MC860 boards are distributed among the three VME stations, adding 234 MFLOPS of throughput. The workstations and three operator positions, each with a 19in color monitor using Update IV symbology, are connected by an Ethernet LAN. Targets are automatically detected by ALI. System output is a PPI-type display. In addition to 320 Mbytes of Sun and VME memory, the system has 3.54 Gbytes of disk capacity and 4.4 Gbytes of 8mm videocassette.

◆ MCSS

The active moored buoy (moored CASS) is deployed over the side; the hydrophone is deployed at a depth of 20–700 ft. MCSS is rechargeable for continuous operation and is tunable to one of three channels.

◆ SSQ-36 (XBT)

This A-size expendable bathythermograph has a cable probe down to 1000 ft. Although not a sonobuoy, the XBT is essential to sonobuoy-field operations and therefore is listed here. Lifetime is 5 min, and SSQ-36 reports on one of three RF channels.

◆ SSQ-41

The standard Western 31-channel A-size (14 lb) omnidirectional Julie-Jezebel (LOFAR) buoy uses a line hydrophone (10 Hz–20 kHz) at a depth of 60 or 300 ft, with a lifetime of 1, 3, or 8 hr. The 31- or 99-channel 14- or 15-lb SSQ-41B (Jezebel wide-band) operates at up to 10 kHz (with improved dynamic range) at a depth of 60–1000 ft. It can be launched at up to 370 kt and at altitudes as high as 30,000 ft. Sparton currently advertises the extended-frequency (5 Hz–2.4 kHz) SSQ-41N. SSQ-41 is the most widely used Western buoy.

◆ SSQ-47B/SSQ-522

This 12-channel HF active (range-only: 13, 14.2, 15.4, 16.6, 17.8, and 19 kHz) A-size sonobuoy (29 lb) uses a hydrophone at a depth of 60 or 800 ft and has a life of 30 min, emitting automatically keyed CW. Control is possible from 0–10 nm and from 500–10,000 ft, at up to Sea State 5. The last U.S. Navy production orders were in 1982; in 1988 this buoy was manufactured only for foreign military sales.

SSQ-522 is Sparton's designation (hydrophone depths 80 or 600 ft). More than 275,000 had been delivered by the end of 1989. By 1992, this buoy was no longer in Canadian service.

Users (SSQ-522): Italy, Japan, Korea, Netherlands, Norway, Spain, Taiwan, United Kingdom. Japan, Norway, and the United Kingdom are license producers.

◆ SSQ-50 (CASS)/SSQ-62 (DICASS)

These command-activated 31-channel sonobuoys use CW and FM pings (6.5, 7.5, 8.5, 9.5 kHz, lengths and intervals selectable from one of four preset acoustic channels). The omni CASS has been superseded in U.S. service by the directional (reception, not transmission) DICASS, but it survives in foreign navies. Hydrophone depth is 60 or 1500 ft and lifetime is 1 hr (30 min for SSQ-50B and -62). The current 34-lb SSQ-62B adds a third depth (89, 396, or 1518 ft). Its surface unit employs a seawater battery; the submerged pinger uses a lithium battery. The new 86-channel SSQ-62C offers a fourth transducer depth (90, 400, 1500, and 2500 ft, of which the latter three are commandable). It also includes electronic function select (EFS) for radio channel selection, and it has a more powerful radio transmitter. SSQ-62D will have EFS, thermal rather than lithium-sulfur-dioxide batteries, and families of depths (shallow: 50, 150, 300 ft; deep: 90, 400, 1500 ft).

The SSQ-62 successor, an improved DICASS, is SWALAS, currently under initial development.

The DICASS feasibility contract was let to Sparton in 1968. SSQ-62B was last bought in FY91; about 244,111 -62A and -62B were made through 1994. Unit price (FY90): $1050–1150. Early in 1995 Sparton received a contract for 20,581 SSQ-62CX buoys, for completion by January 1997. Magnavox also makes SSQ-62C, having delivered 1186 by January 1995.

Users (DICASS): Australia, Canada, Netherlands, Norway, United States.

◆ SSQ-53 (DIFAR)

The A-size directional Julie-Jezebel (directional LOFAR) buoy is very widely used. The original 31-channel 26-lb SSQ-53 (10 Hz–2.4 kHz) had only a single hydrophone depth (90 ft). SSQ-53A added a second depth (1000 ft) and a variable lifetime (1 or 8 hr). The directional and omnidirectional transducers are multiplexed: a single line carries all data up to the transmitter in the buoy. The 99-channel 22-lb SSQ-53B added a third depth (100, 400, 1000 ft) and a third lifetime (1, 3, or 8 hr). The hydrophone suspension was improved to reduce low-frequency mechanical noise. Operating parameters are chosen by push button (verified by light-emitting diodes on the buoy). The sonobuoy can be launched at up to 370 kt and from as high as 40,000 ft. SSQ-53C was a dwarf (G-size) version. SSQ-53D has its frequency range extended to lower frequencies. It also enjoys lower self-noise, largely by decoupling the hydrophone from the rest of the buoy assembly. The new SSQ-53E is probably -53D (Low Noise). Tests in 1970 showed that the version of SSQ-53 then in use could

locate targets within about 13 deg, although buoys could suffer badly when swamped by strong shipping noise at CZ ranges (the buoy's point hydrophones automatically combined direct, BB, and CZ sound paths).

SSQ-530 is a 31-channel Canadian (Sparton) improved version of -53A (90, 330, 1000 ft, lifetimes 1 or 4 hr).

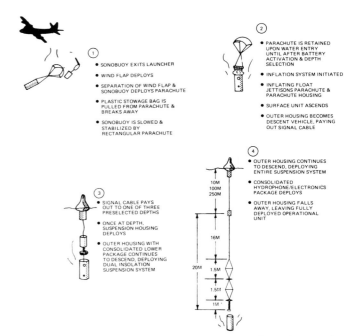

Typical deployment sequence of an SSQ-53 sonobuoy. (Sparton)

SSQ-53 was standardized in 1969 after competitive testing begun in September 1967; Magnavox received the first production contract in 1968, and by 1969 Sparton, Magnavox, and Hermes all had contracts. SSQ-53B was delivered early in 1984. In 1989 unit price was $240, a figure Magnavox reached by using a robotic production line. Orders: February 1990: 65,435 from Sparton, 72,268 from Magnavox; March 1990: 52,621 from Hermes. The 1991 unit price was $357 (some lots were as low as $298). SSQ-53D superseded -53B after FY89 (it entered service in 1991). Orders (January 1991): 138,871 from Sparton, 30,000 from Magnavox, 47,865 from Hermes. About 1,550,000 DIFAR buoys had been made by 1994. No SSQ-53 production was included in the FY92/93 budget. However, 16,000 were included in the FY94 request; presumably they are the initial SSQ-53Es. An SSQ-53E production order is likely to be let in 1997, for delivery in 1998.

Users: Australia, Canada (made by Hermes), France (Hermes buoy made under license by Thomson Sintra), Germany, Japan (made under license by NEC), New Zealand, Norway, Spain, United Kingdom (made under license by GEC-Marconi and by Ultra Electronics), United States.

◆ SSQ-57A

Sparton's low-cost passive A-size buoy (14 lb) is used for calibrating ambient sea noise, for monitoring exercises, or for collecting acoustic intelligence. In each case, its smooth response (to 20 kHz) is important; a narrower-band buoy would miss important parts of the spectrum. Mechanical design is similar to that of SSQ-41. Hydrophone depth is 60 or 400 ft (lifetime 1, 3, or 8 hr). The buoy can be launched from 100–30,000 ft at 45–370 kt, into seas up to Sea State 5.

Sparton currently offers SSQ-57M, a 99-channel, moored, long-life, air-delivered 2/3rds A-size version for use in shallow water. Hydrophone depths are 15/30/60 m. This is a LOFAR-calibrated version. SSQ-57B is also a LOFAR-calibrated version.

Production began in 1968, and procurement ended in FY89 with an order for 42,552 from Magnavox. Foreign users include Australia.

◆ SSQ-58A (MIUW)

This 31-channel 50 Hz–10 kHz omni moored buoy (with a flow shield) is an element of the movable MIUW surveillance system. The mooring and hydrophone assembly are suspended from a 36in-dia, 24 in deep, foam-filled fiberglass float. MIUW is deployed over the side of a boat in 40–110ft depths (600 ft with an optional deep mooring kit). Minimum hydrophone depth is 20 ft. The buoy can survive in tidal currents of up to 3 kt and in surface currents of up to 6 kt. The buoy carries a 12V commercial rechargeable lead-acid battery; lifetime between recharging is 100 hr. A radar reflector sits atop its quarter-wave antenna. A navigational warning light can be enabled or disabled as required. As of 1989, MIUW was in limited production by Sparton.

SSQ-58A buoy for MIUW. (Sparton)

◆ SSQ-77 (VLAD)

The A-size 99-channel 10 Hz–2.4 kHz vertical-line-array DIFAR buoy (29 lb) forms a beam angled down in the vertical to avoid surface shipping noise and to exploit the bottom-bounce channel. Its single DIFAR hydrophone (at the phase center of the array, to provide bearing data) is supplemented by nine omnis and two geophones. The entire array is carried in a faired cable, the fairing reducing cable noise ("strum"); the array is held vertical by a terminal weight and is stabilized in direction by a 15ft drogue, a water-filled plastic bag acting as a sea anchor. The buoy does vertical beam-forming (beam elevation is preset). The signal format is, then, identical to that of an SSQ-53, so VLAD can be processed by any existing DIFAR processor. Depth is 1000 ft; lifetime is 1 or 8 hr. SSQ-77A was the first production 99-channel buoy.

VLAD buoys were initially manufactured in alternative BB and horizontal-beam versions, and were unpopular because users were unfamiliar with BB operation. Current SSQ-77Bs can be set to either beam angle before being launched.

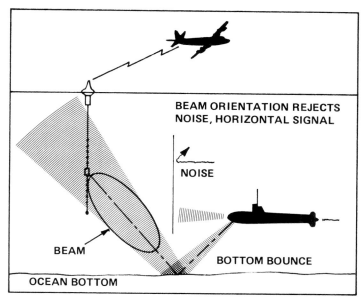

Operating geometry of the SSQ-77A VLAD buoy. (Sparton)

The first 2000 service-test models were bought in FY76, the buoy was approved for service use late in FY78, and production began in FY80 with 1000 units, followed by 7000 in FY81 and by 23,000 in FY82, by Magnavox and Hazeltine. Sippican acquired rights to manufacture SSQ-77A from Hazeltine in March 1984, beginning full-scale production in 1986. Recent procurement: FY87, 98,812; FY88 request, 51,663; FY89 request, 34,874; FY90; FY91, none (end of SSQ-77A production, January 1990); FY92 request, 97,325 (beginning of SSQ-77B production, April 1992); FY93 request, 124,800. Apparently none were requested after FY93. In March 1992 85,138 buoys ($58.6M) were ordered from Magnavox and Sparton, followed by 88,948 SSQ-77B from Magnavox in March 1993 ($34.1M), all delivered by December 1994. Unit cost (FY92) was $650–700.

◆ SSQ-101 (ADAR)

This A-size buoy is the receiver of the improved EER system. The lead platform is the S-3B; the P-3C will follow. The buoy deploys a horizontal array and has a digital uplink. As of mid-1996, ADAR was in the E&MD phase. The corresponding sound source is SSQ-110.

◆ SSQ-90

An active multiple ping (AMP) B-size (103-lb) buoy, SSQ-90 is currently in limited production.

◆ SSQ-110

SSQ-110 is the sound source of the current Extended Echo-Ranging (EER) system. It uses some of the mechanical components of SSQ-62 (DICASS), as well as the same command format. It is a delivery vehicle for two Navy-designed and -fabricated explosive sources; the buoy holds the charges at the water surface until commanded to release. The charges then release independently to detonate automatically at the appropriate depths. Made by both Sparton and Magnavox, this buoy entered production in 1996. The EER capability is to be incorporated into the S-3B and SH-60. A shallow-water sound source is being evaluated.

◆ SSQ-113

NUAMP is an A-size array buoy deployed by P-3s. It is similar to SSQ-62B (DICASS), except for the suspension and the array of projectors. This nomenclature was assigned in 1992. The buoy is made by Sparton.

Of other recent SSQ-designated equipment, SSQ-103 was the abortive low-cost sonobuoy. SSQ-104 and -105 were probably abortive sonobuoys. SSQ-106 is a fire-detection device, SSQ-107 is a simulator control device for the SSQ-91 combat-simulation test system (control console, Link 4, and Link 11 consoles), SSQ-108 is Outboard II (see the Electronic Warfare section), SSQ-109 is a minehunter machinery control system, SSQ-111 is a cryptologic combat-support system (see the Electronic Warfare section), SSQ-112 is a cryptologic signal simulator set, SSQ-114 is a radio frequency management system associated with SSQ-108, SSQ-115 is a maintenance/trainer/communications control center, and SSQ-116 is a simulation control subsystem.

Airborne Signal Processors

◆ AQA-3/4/5

These analog (time-compression) devices with paper (gram) readouts (four 3in-wide grams, for four buoys) were the first airborne LOFAR (Jezebel) acoustic processors. They could obtain a line of bearing to a pair of omni buoys using CODAR. Analysis (by a parallel bank of matched narrow-band filters) takes a finite time, so these systems collect a short sample, then transfer it to a secondary analysis device while collecting the next sample. In AQA-3/4, the secondary device is a magnetic tape (about 5in dia) rotating slowly past record and erase heads. Analysis heads rotate rapidly around its inside surface (Bell Labs considered AQA-3 the earliest example of recording on one side of a medium with pickup on the other side). The faster the pickup rotational speed (which is fixed by strength of material), the narrower the bandwidth per filter and thus the greater the signal-processing efficiency of the system as a whole. The compression ratio is the ratio of recording speed to pickup speed.

The next step, in AQA-5, was a solid-state system, Deltic (Delay-Line Time Compressor), using a digital memory and a delay line. The product of clock rate and delay-line length, the multiplication factor, measures overall capability (in terms of resolution or multiple buoys). Compared to AQA-3 and -4, AQA-5 enjoys an increased compression factor of about 17. This is still an analog device (digital analyzers use FFTs).

AQA-3 and -4 can handle four buoys (four LOFAR or two CODAR in AQA-3, four LOFAR or two LOFAR and two CODAR in -3A and -4). AQA-4 is similar to -3 except that it uses a single internal band to cover both broad-band and narrow-band signals. Frequency range: 10–200 Hz. Note that this was not the entire LOFAR range (which extended up to 300 Hz).

AQA-5 can handle up to eight buoys: eight LOFAR, or six LOFAR and one CODAR, or four LOFAR and two CODAR, or two LOFAR and three CODAR, or four CODAR. Frequency range: 10–300 Hz.

AQA-3 and -4 were made by Western Electric. AQA-5 was made by Western Electric and Emerson (which delivered its first in 1964). At least 650 AQA-5s were made.

Users:

AQA-3/4: Argentina (six S-2E), Brazil (possibly in eight S-2E), Italy (eight S-2Fs), Korea (14 or fewer S-2E), Peru (nine S-2E), Spain (two P-3A, probably replaced by AQA-7), and Uruguay (3 S-2G). The Argentine aircraft have been fitted with tactical computers, but apparently not with new sonobuoy processors, since 1982. S-2Es introduced a coordinated tactical navigation system to solve tactical problems, combining memory, display, and automatic computation. They had ASW data links (2.2-GHz AKT-19), transmitting their sonobuoy data down to the operating ship for analysis. Presumably, the Argentine and Brazilian carriers have this capability. Of S-2s previously listed, late in 1996 the Brazilian air force declared all its aircraft no longer airworthy, and it seems unlikely that they will be rewinged. The Italian aircraft are gone. The Korean aircraft are being replaced by P-3Cs, and may no longer be in service. The Peruvian and Venezuelan S-2Es are no longer in service. It seems unlikely that the Uruguayan aircraft are used for ASW rather than for general surveillance. The processors of the Argentine aircraft may have been replaced.

AQA-5: France (*Alizé* carrier ASW aircraft), Germany (Atlantic), and Pakistan (Atlantic). The German AQA-5s

were upgraded when the airplanes were modernized in 1979–84. The Pakistani units are being replaced by SADANG 2001C. It is not certain whether AQA-5 was exported to Iran, for the P-3F. All U.S. and NATO P-3s were refitted with AQA-7.

The earlier AQA-1 indicator (*not* an analyzer) is used only by Iran (P-3F: to process active buoys). An improved AQA-5, WAP II (Wide-band Acoustic Processor II), was used on board some frigates to process SQR-15 towed-array data. WAP III is used by IUWGs (Inshore Underwater Warfare Groups) in TSQ-108 vans.

◆ AQA-7(V)

This was the first U.S. digital sonobuoy analyzer and the first capable of handling DIFAR buoys. Frequency range is 10 Hz–2.4 kHz. Sonobuoy signals are routed to a frequency translator compressor (FTC), where the frequency band of interest is translated to a processing band, sampled, and time-compressed independently in eight channels. FTC outputs are spectrum-analyzed to provide target bearing (for a DIFAR or DICASS buoy) and to supply both paper (LOFARgram) and CRT displays. Unlike earlier analog processors, AQA-7 can operate in multiple modes: over the entire LOFAR range (10–300 Hz) or its upper or lower halves or, in coarser setting, over 80–2400 Hz (or high or low halves). The integration times were as follows: normal, 80 sec; medium, 2.5 min; long, 5.0 min for the normal band (corresponding times for the extended band were 40 and 80 sec and 2.5 min). Two grams on each processor (two AQA-7s on board a P-3C) are available for DEMON. As a measure of frequency resolution, a weak signal can be dominated by a stronger one within 0.8 Hz (6.4 Hz in the extended-frequency mode): the DIFAR bearing computer sees only the interfering signal. Similarly, AQA-7 cannot distinguish two signals of roughly equal strength within 0.2 Hz (1.6 Hz in the extended-frequency mode). In this case, the computer would yield a bearing equal to the vector sum of the two sources.

With eight LOFAR channels, each of two AQA-7s on board a P-3C can simultaneously process up to two CASS active buoys, or one DICASS active buoy. A P-3C can process eight channels of acoustic information simultaneously on dual signal-data recorders (SDRs) and another eight channels on the bearing-frequency indicator (BFI). Electronic processing made available automatic line integration (ALI) for automatic target detection. First on board P-3Cs, AQA-7 was later installed on board P-3A and P-3B under a DIFAR Retrofit program, as only it could process DIFAR buoys.

AQA-7 was first delivered in 1969. Versions are paired, two to a P-3C. Five generations appeared through 1989, major improvements being single and then triple vernier, provision for DICASS, and provision for passive tracking. AQA-7 was made by Magnavox.

(V)1, (V)2, and (V)3 use two frequency-multiplier-storer units instead of the FTC introduced in (V)4.

(V)4/5 (1975) introduced single vernier analysis. Its TS-3542 analyzer processes time-compressed signals by conducting a narrow-band search for frequency lines of interest; the signal's amplitude at each frequency increment is supplied to output as a digital word. Two complete DIFAR analyses are conducted in less than 1.25 sec with decreased time required for range signals. Its input consists of 16 time-compressed signals, two real-time signals, plus clocks and control lines from other parts of the AQA-7(V) system. Output information is stored in shift registers and supplied as required.

(V)6/7 added triple vernier capability (simultaneous examination of three portions of the spectrum), at the suggestion of the Operational Test and Evaluation Force (January 1979). This and later versions use analyzer TS-3807, whose input is 72 time-compressed signals.

(V)8/9 (1980) added DICASS capability.

A(V)10/11/12 (1984) are A(V)8/9 with passive tracking algorithm (PTA—see LAMPS) added. This version also has a new interactive control panel (ICP).

UYS-1 is the successor system.

Users: Brazil (plans to buy 10 P-3A/B), Greece (P-3B TAC-NAVMOD II with [V]10/11), Japan (70 P-3C with [V]8/9; 40 to

One side of an AQA-7, showing both the CRT screen and the paper (hard-copy) display. Each can be used to interpret LOFAR buoy data. The screen can show data integrated over time, frequency interval by frequency interval. The hard-copy printer provides a record of sound at each instant of time, the operator deciding that a line is present by what amounts to visual integration. (U.S. Navy)

be converted to Update III, with UYS-1), Korea (eight P-3C), Morocco (plans to buy three P-3A/B), Netherlands (13 P-3C Update II.5 with AQA-7[V]8/9), Norway (P-3C), Pakistan (three P-3C with AQA-7[V]11D, embargoed), Portugal (six P-3P), Spain (seven P-3A/B), Thailand (AQA-7[V]8/9, removed from P-3Ts for training, will be reinstalled), United States (AQA-7[V]11/12 in 108 P-3C Update I/II/II.5, all to convert to Update III, with UYS-1). Apparently the Chilean P-3s had their AQA-7s removed before transfer. Thus far no AQA-7s have been sold to update other aircraft (some were on board S-2s, but they were removed when the aircraft were transferred).

◆ OL-82/OL-5004

Sanders's FFT sonobuoy processor differs from its predecessors in lacking any paper printout (the S-3A was intended to detect targets largely by ALI). Frequencies are presented logarithmically rather than linearly. The system's entirely digital output is particularly well adapted to data-bused systems, in which data pass from console to console in digital form. OL-5004 adds vernier displays and can measure ambient sea noise.

Users: Canada (OL-5004 in Aurora MPAs), United States (OL-82 in S-3s).

◆ UYS-1

The design of this standard acoustic signal processor (ASP) emphasizes programmability (for multiple applications). Processing rate is 10–20 MFLOPS, with a total input/output rate of 1.25 Mwords/sec. Program memory is 128k 32-bit words, expandable to 256k with an engineering change. Bulk storage is up to 1024k 32-bit words, organized in 64-bit double words with eight error-correction code bits. I/O is organized in up to eight programmable channel pairs (combination of NTDS and Proteus). Demonstrated MTTR is 12 min; predicted MTBF is 775–1100 hr, depending on configuration. Capacity is five DIFAR channels.

Three ASP can be ganged together as Tri-ASP.

UYS-1 was designed for upgrading, given the very rapid evolution of computer technology. For example, as of 1984 ASP memory technology was already in its fourth generation, having evolved from 4k (bits per chip) to 64k. Improvements between the start of production, in 1981, and 1984 included doubling central processor control memory (2k to 4k words), doubling arithmetic processor storage (2k to 4k double words), doubling arithmetic processor working storage (2k to 4k words), doubling program storage (128k to 256k words), and improving programmability using distributed program architecture microcode. Many of these improvements resulted from the replacement of 1k static memory by 4k read/write memory, cutting the net number of modules.

In the 1990s, ASP software was upgraded to match a simplified and improved programming method (Signal Processing Graph Notation, SPGN) developed for the more powerful UYS-2. SPGN was demonstrated in a program called ECOS (EMSP common operating system). The ASP Common Operational Support System (ACOS) is a programming methodology by which acoustic engineers can implement signal processing graphs into ASP (UYS-1) code without extensive computer training. ACOS Phase I SPGN applications development tools were implemented in FY88.

Lockheed Martin Loral is developing a COTS field retrofit, UYS-1A, which can be executed in less than 30 min. Throughput increases from 60 MOPS to 4 GFLOPS, bulk memory from 4 Mbytes to 16 Mbytes, and I/O channels from 8 to 32. A preprocessor with 400 Mbytes of memory and 2 Gbytes of mass storage (removable SCSI hard disk) are added. A VME Card Cage assembly accommodates a COTS system controller board and up to three COTS processor boards (such as i860, C40, PowerPC, and SHARC). It can also accommodate high-speed interface boards.

Production began in 1981, the 250th unit being delivered in October 1984. The initial requirement, as stated in 1981, was for 500 units. In all, more than 1800 were delivered. In aircraft form, UYS-1 is 57.32 × 23.44 × 11.19 in, weighs 240 lb, and requires 1530 W of power.

Users: Japan (30 P-3C Update III), Norway (six P-3C Update III, more planned), Saudi Arabia (plans six P-3C Update III), United States (140 P-3C Update III, S-3B, SH-60B, BQQ-5C [Tri-ASP for Expanded DIFAR], BQQ-9, BSY-1, SQS-53B/C, SQR-19, UQQ-2; also used by Air Force and Army).

◆ UYS-2 (EMSP)

AT&T's Enhanced Modular Signal Processor was conceived as a family of parallel processors, EMSP A (35 in^3, burst multiplication rate 400 MFLOPS), B (30 in^3, 200 MFLOPS), C (25 in^3, 150 MFLOPS), D (15 in^3, 100 MFLOPS), and E (5 in^3, 25 MFLOPS). AT&T claims that UYS-2 embodies four important advances: (a) graphical programming using a Very High Order Language written symbolically or pictorially; (b) a true-data flow architecture to accommodate devices transmitting data at quite different rates (i.e., to process different devices in parallel); (c) a distributed operating system, which automatically optimizes the computer's operation; and (d) data-networking to support multisensor processing and sensor fusion. An EMSP is built around six functional elements (FE) implemented as standard electronic modules (SEMs): a scheduler (up to 8000 nodes/sec; capacity 65,000 queues and 32,000 nodes); a global memory (intelligent memory providing storage and memory management, two or three 32-Mbyte units plus 16 Mbytes of nonvolatile storage), a command program processor (UYK-44 in SEM-B, 68020 with math coprocessor in SEM-E); an arithmetic processor (16- or 32-bit format, up to six 360-MFLOPS units); an input signal conditioner (16 or 32 analog channels); a data processor programmable in ADA (using a 68020 CPU with math coprocessor); and an I/O processor (two Proteus channels [360 kwords/sec, 34-bit words], 12 analog channels, two transmitter channels; ports for one or two 1553B buses; the SEM-E version has a 68020 CPU with math coprocessor). The FEs are connected through a 16 × 16 Data Transfer Network (DTN). The DTN is unidirectional and asynchronous, with full access to and from each connected device; no data flow blocks any other. It carries 32-bit words at a rate of 7 Mwords/

sec (SEM-B version) or 10 Mwords/sec (SEM-E version). DTN can be supplied in various sizes: 2–16 ports, 8–64 FEs. Data refer to the current UYS-2A as used in ALFS, with two arithmetic processors and two global memory modules. Performance in the ALFS configuration: graph, 720 MFLOPS; sonar channels (32), 610 MOPS; data processing, 130 MOPS; global memory, 130 Mbytes; local memory, 80 Mbytes. It can handle 16 buoys, with 16 analysis bands (verniers) per buoy, simultaneously. In April 1991 a SEM-E UYS-2 (seven arithmetic processors, six global memories, and a 64-channel signal conditioner) demonstrated a 54-DIFAR capability during integration testing of a P-3C Update IV program at Bell Laboratories.

UYS-2's Navy-supported Signal-Processing Graph Notation (SPGN) is a very high order language expressed in flow charts. Each chart consists of a series of primitives (operations) connected by data-flow arrows and affected by control arrays. Typical primitives are beam-formers, FFTs, FIR filters, normalizers, and thresholders. AT&T claims that this graphical technique offers a substantial reduction in initial programming costs and also a sixfold reduction in software-maintenance costs. Coding is entirely separated from hardware details, so programs are easily transported from machine to machine (AT&T successfully ran programs written for the SEM-B version on the SEM-E version).

Modular design made EMSP one of the first DoD VHSIC insertion programs (a new arithmetic processor with 46% more throughput than its predecessor entered production in 1988 for the BSY-2). Formal approval for production was granted in August 1989. During 1989 there were some attempts to kill EMSP (UYS-2) on the grounds that commercial processors could outperform it. EMSP had, after all, been conceived a decade earlier. Although UYS-2 has 6 times the processing power of UYS-1, some potential user programs bought UYS-1 instead for fear that UYS-2 would be canceled. Exponents of EMSP could point to the virtue of standardization, and also to the machine's capacity for later improvement. In April 1989 it was decided that the SEM-B version would be limited to about 180 machines, out of a total planned purchase of 750–1000. Later UYS-2s would be built of the larger SEM-E cards (6 × 6in), which hold 3 times as many microchips and other components as SEM-Bs, and they use high-density gate array and memory devices.

MTBF is 1250 hr for the largest configuration or over 4600 for the smallest; predicted MTTR is 0.25 hr.

The first destroyer UYS-2 is to go aboard DDG 79 in FY98 (the sonar then becomes SQS-53C[V]4).

Users: United States (ALFS, SURTASS, BSY-2 for submarines, SQQ-89; would have been in Update IV P-3s, but the program died). NAVSEA claimed that in the P-3C, one UYS-2 was equivalent to 14 UYS-1s in the same size box. UYS-2A is in ALFS and in SQQ-89(V)10; DDG 51s are fitted with one or two UYS-2As, and DDG 993s with one.

◆ UYS-5

Hughes's Common Acoustic Processor is an exportable VME-backplane substitute for UYS-2, initially intended mainly for the AQS-23 sonar. Throughput is 132 MFLOPS/17 MIPS. In sonobuoy-only configuration, it can handle 16 or 32 DIFAR (growth to 64) using one or two operators. Alternatively, it can handle a dipping sonar and 8 or 16 DIFAR channels. Postprocessing facilities are contact frequency alert, acoustic target tracker, closest point of approach (calculation), and acoustic spatial data fusion.

◆ ASAP

Lockheed Martin's (formerly Martin-Marietta's) advanced systolic array processor is proposed as a fast-time analyzer, for example, for the 20 shore-based ASWOCs. ASAP is a massively parallel processor; the manufacturer claims 300 MOPS on each computer board. The range of equipment based on ASAP includes a generic workstation (SMS-20V), a neural network computer (SNAP), and a variety of special boards. ASAP can be programmed in ADA and can incorporate a VME bus.

Lockheed Martin also has a linear mapped array processor (LMAP), which may be offered as a coprocessor for UYS-2.

◆ AAP-640/AAP-400/AAPS

BBN's COTS-based parallel-processor VME-backplane Advanced Acoustic Processor series uses a new multiprocessor software architecture, the Signal Processing Engine (SPE). The backplane carries multiple Quad-Skybolt processors (each with 64 Mbytes of local memory, connected via their own VSB bus) plus a 68040 system manager (MVME 166) and a Sparc 10 display host computer, each with 64 Mbytes of local memory and a 2-Gbyte hard drive, connected by their own Ethernet bus.

Program modules include conventional and adaptive beam-formers, spectral analysis, LOFARgram generation, DIFAR and cardioid processors, correlators of various sorts, post-detection pulse compression, and A-scan generation. A typical display shows three windows: a Data Display (DD) extending across the top of the screen, a Tactical Display (TD) at lower left, and a Classification Display (CD) at lower right. DD shows a series of A-scans, amplitude versus time, for matched filter outputs from each sensor or array beam. TD is a PPI-like view of sensors, sources, previously detected target locations, bearings, and detection ellipses overlaid on a bathymetric chart. CD magnifies selected A-scans and also shows the output of various classification tools. Any data manipulation on one display updates all three. Any window can be expanded to the full screen. AAP-400 can handle 32 DIFAR buoys simultaneously (in cardioid form). The system retains 60 min of raw data for each buoy. DIFAR bearings are shown on the TD.

The version number (as in AAP-400) indicates the computing power (400 MFLOPS). AAP-640 is a more powerful device using a 20-slot VME backplane and a 19in monitor. Like AAP-400, it is designed to handle 32 DIFAR buoys (or 128 beams from a deployable array), all in real-time. It is *not* a beam-former for an array of buoys (as in STRAP); it handles buoys one by one, incoherently. It can interact with an operator quickly enough to match the ping rate of a typical underwater sound source, 3–5 min. The system is auto-triggered (to detect an incoming sound source). A separate computer classifies contacts using a neural net. AAP-640 is now being tested by the U.S. Navy aboard a P-3C. It is fully ruggedized, and can also be placed aboard a ship.

AAP-400 was tested at Patuxent River in 1992. One was installed on board a British Nimrod patrol aircraft in the summer of 1995 for trials intended to develop specifications for next-generation U.S. and British active sonobuoys. During the trials, AAP-400 handled multiple DIFAR buoys at the same time as a Barra buoy. AAP-400 had already been flown over 20 times in U.S. shallow-water ASW trials. Two of the current AAP-640 were delivered to Warminster early in 1995 under a 1994 contract.

Rockwell and BBN are marketing a follow-on processor as the Advanced Acoustic Processor System (AAPS).

◆ AMSP/2

EDO's Advanced Modular Signal Processor (Series II) is made up of three hardware modules: digital signal processors, crossbar data-transfer network, and mass-storage memory. Each crossbar is a bus for up to 15 devices. Each connector can be programmed to be directional (so that data flow in a direction determined by software), and data can be transferred both port to port and in a broadcast mode (to any N ports). Destination ports can be programmed on line. All of the elements on any crossbar effectively communicate simultaneously, and the system can change its internal relationships as it executes a problem. The crossbar communicates with each processor at 7.2 Mbytes/sec via first-in/first-out (FIFO) buffers. They, in turn, communicate with the manager module at 28.8 Mbytes/sec. Each processor has its own memory unit so that there is no need to switch in and out of a central (global) memory during processing.

AMSP uses a tree architecture. For example, one input into a crossbar might communicate with another five devices on one side of the next crossbar; they communicate with another eight on the other side, which also communicate with seven more on the other side of the next crossbar, and so on. In contrast to some other parallel processors, each processing element operates independently because it need not send its product directly to (or receive input directly from) any other element. This programmed flexibility makes it possible for the AMSP crossbar network to simulate virtually any network topology.

The entire processor communicates with other equipment via an Ethernet bus.

EDO claims that the use of a few simple modules greatly reduces both cost and technical risk. Special PC-compatible programs are available to develop the subprograms used in the processors. AMSP was first developed as a coherent processor for the EDO 780 export sonar (1983). It was also adopted for the SQR-18A(V)1 and SQR-18(V)2.

♦ BEARTRAP

This special P-3C squadron tests prototype ASW tools and collects acoustic and nonacoustic data on diesel and quiet nuclear submarines; its name derives from its Cold War mission. About 1994, for example, BEARTRAP was installing a new COTS-based superprocessor (APEX) using the new Futurebus+/VME computer standard, for quick integration of new sensors and algorithms using new computer boards. Much equipment is palletized.

♦ FAAS/FTAS/SPAS

Rockwell's shore-based postmission analysis processor (FAAS) for French navy Atlantique MPAs is part of a new family using standard (modified commercial VME) common hardware in 19in racks with paired CRTs, usually stacked vertically: spectrum analyzer, beam-former, acoustic display. Presumably FAAS is the unit Rockwell advertised in 1995 as the Sonobuoy Fast-Time Analyzer (FTAS), details of which follow. This system is probably related to the open-architecture Signal Processing and Analysis System (SPAS) announced in 1994, which has the same capabilities. The single rack version is the Rockwell Tactical Processing System. FTAS processes 16 LOFAR or 8 DIFAR buoys (32 bands) at up to 16 times real-time, using 4k-point complex or 8k-point real FFTs. It stores 1 Gbyte of acoustic data (expandable to 4 Gbytes), operating at 1.6 GFLOPS. Beside standard narrow-band and DEMON analysis, it can use short integration times (down to 0.08 sec) to detect transients and intercept active sonar emissions; short-time integration is also needed for HYFIX (hyperbolic fixing of a signal). Thus it can accept acoustic data at up to 20-kHz bandwidth, with selectable vernier bands up to 10 kHz. It incorporates 20 line trackers (ALI) and a harmonic family detector. The beam-former of the equivalent shipboard system can handle any array geometry (hull or towed). It performs broad-band (STA, ITA, LTA), DEMON, and narrow-band (LOFAR, ALI, FRAZ) processing on all beams. It places multiple operator-selectable search-and-classification verniers on all beams; it provides 20 broad-band and narrow-band trackers; short-term narrow-band and nonstationary broad-band alerting; an FCS interface; an interface to a passive array (analog or custom digital, active blanking optional); and an optional remote tactical display.

As of 1992, Rockwell had delivered acoustic processors to the Australian, Dutch, French, UK, and U.S. navies. These include special-purpose multichannel acoustic signal processors, such as the U.S. BQQ-9. In March 1994 Rockwell Collins France sold 10 OPS-100F acoustic processors to the French navy for F70- and F67-class frigate modernizations. Deliveries began in January 1995, followed by successful sea trials in May 1995. This COTS system uses 19in VME racks. It simultaneously processes four passive buoys (LOFAR, DIFAR, BT, CODAR, DEMON, NPL, SVP), autodetects transient events, and alerts its operator. In U.S. ASWOCs and carrier ASW modules Rockwell's UQX-5 has been replaced by Scientific Atlanta's FQX-3.

♦ FQX-3 (FTAS) and SPS 1000

Scientific Atlanta's new fast-time analyzer uses commercial hardware to achieve a processing speed of 8.5 GFLOPS (with 32-bit, i.e., 1500-dB dynamic range). It can handle two missions simultaneously, matching flight history to buoy and target history, accepting up to 32 acoustic channels, processing in 64

channels at 1, 2, 4, 8, or 16 times real-time. Processing options are LOFAR, DIFAR, DEMON, ANODE, Cardioid, Null Steer (to null out noise), and XBT. The system can display up to 16 LOFARgrams (frequency-time), bearing-frequency, or ALI, either separately or in split-screen format. Alternatively, it can show absolute sound power level (which is used in Julie systems and also to measure submarine signatures). Up to 1024 independent vernier bands (up to 16 per channel) can be presented. The standard monitor shows up to 1600 lines of data in LOFAR format. On-screen aids include Doppler, Lloyd's Mirror, CPA, and harmonic cursors (to identify higher harmonics of a detected line, as a means of confirmation). These systems convert up to 419,000 samples/channel of acoustic data to digital (12-bit) data; the cutoff frequency can be set at any of five values. Disk storage amounts to 8 hr of 64-channel data (800 Mbytes of history, with a 9-Gbyte working memory disk file). A typical system has up to 32 thermographic printers (to print out LOFARgrams). A typical FTAS has a pair of large acoustic monitors, flanked by tactical display workstations (using VAX 3100s with desktop monitors, keyboards, and trackballs).

FQX-3 typically employs a pair of SunSPARC workstations with 1600 × 1280-pixel high-resolution color displays plus a pair of terminals for tactical displays including mission tracks. The system is designed to integrate acoustic data with other mission data. It provides multiple cursors and ten-point electronic dividers for analysis.

SPS 1020, a scaled-down version of FQX-3, uses a single workstation and display (typically two screens, one for acoustics and one for tactical or alphanumeric data). The operator can simultaneously analyze up to 16 frequency regions of interest (at different FFT resolutions; bandwidths are 5 Hz–81 kHz) across the same overall frequency band of interest. Tonal dynamic range is 110 dB, and the system computes and displays 3200 spectral points per channel (for lowest possible minimum detectable signal; this resolution was previously available only on hard copy, monitors being limited to 800 FFT points). To show all 3200 points, the display must pan across the frequency spectrum. Alternatively, it can show the whole spectrum with 1600 FFT points. Vertically, 1100 lines of data are displayed. Higher-frequency bands can be translated down to be made audible. The system handles 16 analog LOFAR (buoy) or DEMON inputs (center frequency 0 to 20.48 kHz, analysis bandwidth 40, 80 or 160 Hz), and offers transient detection/analysis, and Data Zoom. Playback rate is up to 16 times real-time. Of two independent signal processors, one is used for time domain data (including gain and low-pass filtering prior to analog/digital conversion). It performs frequency translation and DEMON processing. The other controls frequency-domain data and timing; for example it performs FFTs, spectrum averaging (for automatic detection), and dynamic spectrum equalization (DSE). It controls the video interface. Up to 65 acoustic files can be stored for playback. Contact analysis aids are Lofix (Comparative LOFAR fixing: position based on signal strengths from up to three LOFAR buoys), CZ fix (based on buoys holding convergence zone contacts; if there are only two buoys, the system generates a hyperbola from which the operator must determine target ambiguity), manual fix (based on a single point or sensor entry), Doppler (based on measured Doppler or direct entry), Hyfix/LOP (based on hyperbola from dynamic change over two or more buoys), DIFAR fix (using multiple buoys), Target class (enables the operator to build a target summary sheet from up to 21 sources and frequencies), and data summary files (index of target classification files). Geographic aids: range/bearing cursor, variable range circle, variable range box, fixed circle, CZ plot, box ellipse, expanding circle. Computation aids: ETA/ETD (estimated time of arrival/departure), CPA/LLOYD (Lloyd's Mirror measures target depth by using multipath effects), predicted static point, predicted dynamic point, intercept point, course/speed. The system also provides environmental data (BT, sound velocity profile, sea noise).

SPS 1020 was developed for the Spanish air force, which moved its P-3s from Jerez (near Rota) to Moron at the end of the Cold War. At Jerez, the P-3s had shared the facilities of the TSC at Rota. After the move, a new acoustic mission support center was needed. The SPS 1020–based system for it was commissioned on 25 April 1996.

FQX-3 replaced Rockwell's UQX-5 in U.S. service; the first two were shipped in December 1992. Earlier Scientific Atlanta fast analyzers, particularly the GD-850 series, are used by the French, German, Italian, Japanese, Portuguese, and Swedish navies for postmission (sonobuoy) analysis and, in some cases, to process towed array data.

◆ Neural-Net Signal Processor

GTE is developing a neural-net sonar-signal processor in hopes that it will be a much less expensive VME-architecture alternative to a future UYS-2 upgrade.

◆ MPP

Digital System Resources' COTS Multipurpose Processor is part of A-RCI, described above. It is envisaged as the first of a series of real-time signal processing equivalents to COTS computers (TAC series), the hope being that successors can be installed with minimal software impact. A software layer (MPP middleware) isolates applications software from processor hardware. MPP includes the requisite special-purpose interfaces (in its initial application, to towed arrays) plus signal conditioners, beamformers, detectors, postdetector processors (classification and transformation into display-ready data) in a VME-backbone militarized water-cooled cabinet with a footprint similar to that of a SEM-B UYS-2. The prototype uses Mercury signal processors (four i860s on a board) and Force 5 CPUs; a later version may use PowerPC CPUs or SHARC 21060s. MPP is expected to feed the new common display workstation (UYQ-70 equivalent) via a fiber-optic cable.

MPP arose out of a 1991 small-business (SBIR) proposal for an architecture adapted to software migration as hardware developed. The MPP contract was signed in March 1994. Part of a larger program to insert COTS systems into submarines, MPP was sponsored by the New Attack Submarine Program and by the Submarine Combat Systems Program. Its initial application is to upgrade BQQ-5s (and possibly -6s) to process two towed arrays simultaneously; it replaces Tri-ASP signal processors on *Los Angeles* (and possibly *Ohio*) -class submarines. As the COTS insertion program gains momentum, MPP may replace UYS-1 altogether in these submarines.

NONACOUSTIC ASW SENSORS

The only current nonacoustic sensors in widespread Western service are MAD and radar (to detect exposed periscopes and snorkels, not traces of submerged submarines). MAD is particularly valued as a terminal attack sensor since, despite its relatively short range it has a very low false-alarm rate. The Soviets were apparently unique in using it as a search sensor.

A major nonacoustic sensor of the past, the snorkel-exhaust "sniffer" (AUTOLYCUS in Britain) is apparently extinct, partly because it could not distinguish a submarine from a diesel merchant ship or, for that matter, from the downwind trace of a city or industrial area.

The search for a viable nonacoustic sensor continues, with current interest in surface-piercing blue-green laser radars (LADARs). For many years the Soviets were credited with interest in wake-sensing (thermal, chemical, and hydrodynamic), and current U.S. and British interest in environmental sensors (2081 and TOMS) may reflect similar interest, or at least interest in overcoming nonacoustic detectors.

AUSTRALIA

◆ LADS

Not conceived as an ASW system, the Laser Airborne Depth Sounder is an underwater survey system said to be able to penetrate 50 m of water under all sea conditions. The stabilized laser scans a 240m-wide swath at a rate of 168 pps, producing a grid pattern of spots 10 m apart.

LADS was developed by DSTO in the mid-1970s, and a contract for an operational version was awarded to the Australian company BHP Engineering Pty Ltd. in May 1989. Sweden showed interest in LADS as a means of detecting small submarines in very shallow water under poor acoustic conditions.

CANADA

At Brighton in March 1993, OpTech of Canada showed a programmable LIDAR, which could use different scan patterns for MCM and ASW. OpTech provided the laser in the Northrop ALARMS. In 1987 the company provided a 200-Hz (PRF) laser with a coverage rate of something under 3 km²/hr for MCM, or 48 for ASW. A 400-Hz LIDAR (1995) should about double these rates. A future 2-kHz LIDAR should give 30 km²/hr for MCM, 450 for ASW. In 1988 the company tested a 10-kHz LIDAR (35 km²/hr for MCM). Maximum ASW depth is probably about 50 to 70 m. The display is color-coded for depth.

An earlier OpTech LADAR (Larsen 500), operational for survey work in 1985, demonstrated mine detection down to about 100 ft in the late 1980s, using a pulsed beam and backscatter to determine the position of the water surface.

◆ AIMS (ASQ-504)

The Advanced Integrated MAD System was devised by CAE Electronics, Ltd., of Canada. Unlike other helicopter-borne MAD gear, AIMS is carried on board the helicopter; CAE claims that this arrangement frees the crew of the operational restrictions associated with towing a conventional MAD body. Moreover, because the MAD detector is not towed, it is very easy for the helicopter to shift from dipping sonar to MAD operation. The company also claims increased detection range, with a sensitivity of 0.01 gamma in flight. Total weight is 50 lb.

The integration in AIMS is between a very sensitive magnetometer and an advanced compensator to take into account the magnetic field of the aircraft (as well as geological magnetic noise). CAE has been developing sensitive compensators since the 1960s; CAE's AN/ASA-65 is currently the Free World's standard MAD compensator, with 900 units in service.

Detection is by optical pumping of directionally oriented cesium, and interference from the helicopter is canceled out by compensating upon takeoff, the compensating terms being computed in 8 min using an on-board vector magnetometer.

Users: Australia (P-3C upgrade, S-70B-2 helicopters), Canada (CP-140), Taiwan (S-2T), United Kingdom (242 units for Sea King and Lynx HAS.8 helicopters and for Nimrod MR.2 aircraft).

See the 1991/92 edition for details of the earlier ASQ-502.

FRANCE

◆ DHAX 1/DHAX 3/Mk 3

Thomson-CSF's DHAX 1/3 use four/six cesium-vapor paramagnetic resonance cells.

Crouzet's MAD Mk 3 uses electronically pumped NMR rather than the optically pumped U.S. and Canadian systems based on electron spin resonance. The company claims extreme simplic-

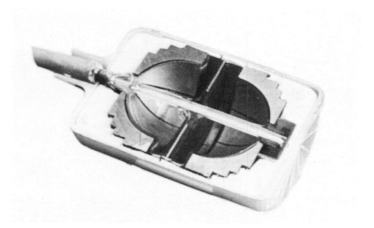

Crouzet MAD sensor, cut away to show its cavity. (Crouzet)

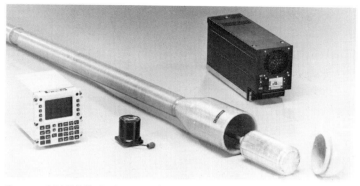

Crouzet MAD Mk 3, showing the probe and its casing. (Crouzet)

ity and reliability for this approach: there is no optical exciter; because the system uses a liquid rather than a gaseous medium, nothing need be vaporized before the MAD can operate. Moreover, the output is easily read as a resonant frequency. Crouzet also uses a distinctive signal-processing technique. Instead of threshold detection, the system compares the received signal with a model of the expected target signal, a method the company calls MAD-SADE (Self-Adaptive Detection/Estimation). A simple dipolar model of the target suffices, and the SADE method gives both a confidence level and a fix of the target's position. Experiments both in the Mediterranean and in the English Channel in 1979–80 showed that MAD-SADE improved net detection probability and that, for a given probability, the method increased detection range, so that in about 60% of cases the airplane detected the submarine before passing over it. Sensitivity is within 0.1 gamma. This system was tested in 1983, and production began early in 1985.

Users: Italy (Atlantic Mk 1 [DHAX 1]), France (Atlantique Mk 2 [Crouzet Mk 3], Lynx [DHAX 3, towed]), and Pakistan (Atlantic Mk 1 [DHAX 1]). In the Atlantique, twin sensors are used in tandem, to detect any change in the aircraft's signature, canceling it out. In helicopters, Crouzet Mk 3 is towed on a 70m cable. Crouzet's attempt to market a MAD buoy apparently failed. Crouzet Mk 3 was tested in French Navy Lynx helicopters.

JAPAN

♦ HSQ-101

The MAD in P-2J aircraft is probably related to the U.S. ASQ-10 (the contemporary PS-1 carried ASQ-10A). The later P-3 and SH-60J both carry versions of ASQ-81.

RUSSIA

The Soviets experimented extensively with nonacoustic submarine detectors, apparently with no great success. The standard surface-ship suite of the late 1960s included an MI-110R IR wake detector (there was no NATO code-name). There may also be a turbulence or temperature or chemical wake detector; many submarines have protrusions from their sails which appear to be nonacoustic wake detectors.

In contrast to Western navies, the Soviet Union reportedly considered MAD a search sensor, to detect submarines passing through relatively narrow straits. Presumably, this practice explains intense Soviet interest in submarine degaussing. Such a practice would recall the Anglo-American MAD barrier flown over the Straits of Gibraltar during World War II. MAD was used in that case because the layering of the water (caused by the interpenetrating Atlantic and Mediterranean currents) precluded conventional acoustic search.

Reportedly, the helicopter MAD, which is towed on a long cable, is designated APM-60. Effective range is 300–700 m.

♦ Amethyst

Bear-F Mod 4s carry this ASW LIDAR, which uses a blue-green CO_2 laser. It scans from side to side (out to a 45-deg angle) as the airplane moves forward, covering a 100m-wide swath. The pilot

must maintain constant altitude (100 m) and ground speed (100 m/sec, about 200 kt); Amethyst must be shut down whenever the airplane turns. Each line in the display (representing one scan) deviates up and down to indicate range (in effect, depth). Lines are spaced a meter apart (in scale). Very high projections or deep troughs extend over adjacent lines, creating a shadow effect. The back-and-forth scan forms a green line on a standard Russian 525-line screen, measuring 20 × 25 cm, with a frame rate of 100 Hz (corresponding to the rate of forward motion; each screen corresponds to a 500m-long swath). Because the screen is relatively short, the image is compressed vertically. It is somewhat distorted toward the sides because the beam slants so steeply there. The system is calibrated to 50 m depth, but is said to be ineffective below 100 ft (about 30 m). Apparently some operators learn to interpret it within about 15 min, but others never do. That is reminiscent of sonar recognition, which also involves inherent talents. The series of images is automatically recorded on a standard 3-hr videotape.

The drastic limits on aircraft motion suggest that the system is mechanically range-gated, perhaps by a disk rotating in front of the receiver. Much must depend on the sensitivity of the receiver, so it probably burns out if it is *not* protected. Hence the injunction against turns (which drastically change the angles and ranges to the sea surface). Aircraft speed is tightly limited (within about 1%) because the system must process only one pulse at a time, inserting that range into the horizontal scan. If the airplane moves too quickly, part of one line is inserted into the next (presumably the equivalent of the STA problem in radar).

UNITED STATES

The heavily censored released version of the FY92/93 program (February 1991) mentioned four main nonacoustic projects:

NA-1/16: Clipper Shale, a possible submarine wake-sensing system. At-sea tests with an improved Clipper Shale were scheduled for April–June 1993.

NA-4: High-powered laser (technical review expected October 1993). This is presumably a blue-green LIDAR similar in concept to the mine-detecting Magic Lantern.

NA-17: Spotlight. The name suggests bioluminescence.

NA-20: For the SH-60B helicopter (to be developed for fixed wing aircraft as well).

LIDAR (designated ATD-111, to indicate an advanced technology demonstrator) was to have been part of the LAMPS III Block II upgrade, but apparently it encountered severe problems. As of late 1995, the program was still alive, but only barely so.

The censored account of the FY96 R&D program includes a reference to a nonacoustic device as an enabling technology for airborne detection in regions of high geological noise, to be field-tested.

Work is proceeding on periscope detectors, both airborne and shipboard. The FY97 program includes a demonstration of a coherent processor and electronically steered phased array for periscope detection and of a LIDAR for shipboard periscope detection (LIDAR is apparently to be used to reduce the false alarm rate inherent in a periscope-detecting radar).

A nonacoustic submarine tactical sensor system (STSS), tested at sea in FY91/92, may have been intended to counter possible foreign airborne nonacoustic systems.

TSUNAMI is a congressionally mandated CIA program to study nonacoustic detection (reportedly entirely unsuccessful). Congress feared that the Navy was unenthusiastic about technologies that might nullify its sea-based deterrent; it wanted an entirely independent audit of nonacoustic technology. TSUNAMI may have been inspired by the Soviet technical disinformation program revealed by CIA Director John Deutsch in the fall of 1995.

There may also be a separate DoD black nonacoustic program. Its only known element is April Showers, an ASW version of Kaman's Magic Lantern.

The magnetic array sensor (MARS) is a joint program with Norway to develop a fiber-optic magnetic bottom sensor, suitable for shallow-water underwater surveillance. This will be the first fiber-optic magnetic sensor array to be evaluated as an ASW surveillance sensor. The array was installed in FY92, and field tests were conducted in FY96.

Beginning in FY88, the United States funded work on a MAD buoy. An MoU with France (i.e., presumably with Crouzet) to develop and test a MAD buoy carrying an NMR sensor was signed 4 Dec 1990.

Westinghouse has demonstrated an underwater vehicle carrying a laser. The Westinghouse SM2000 runs 8 to 150 ft above the bottom, covering a 10–210ft swath, depending on water quality. Resolution is 0.5 in at 100 ft. SM2000 uses an Argon ion gas laser, wavelengths 0.488 and 0.5145 microns at 1.5 W.

The object at the base of the sail of some *Los Angeles*–class submarines is a Total Oceanographic Measurement System (TOMS), carrying salinity, temperature, etc. sensors. Presumably it helps the submarine commander avoid areas in which the submarine might be particularly visible to some nonacoustic sensors, and it may also detect some submarine wakes. It is equivalent to the British Type 2081. In FY94 TOMS roll-on/roll-off capability was installed on board all *Los Angeles*–class submarines. Test and evaluation was completed very successfully in FY95.

◆ ASQ-10

The MAD in P-3A/B and late-production S-2 aircraft, this saturable-core magnetometer was introduced about 1960.

◆ ASQ-81

Texas Instruments' MAD is currently the standard U.S. Navy system. It uses optically pumped metastable helium. In 1979 it was reported that ASQ-81 had triple the effective range of earlier MADs, about 3000 versus 1000 ft. However, other reports suggest that the range of the earlier MAD was only doubled. ASQ-81 incorporates an improved means of maintaining alignment with the earth's magnetic field and has automatic target detection, which ASQ-10 lacks.

The helicopter version can be towed at 10–140 kt and can be reeled at 50 or 200 ft/min, the limiting length of the cable being 80–180 ft. ASQ-81 can typically be turned on in 1.5 min, and sensor noise in-flight is generally about 0.24 gammas. Gain can be set at 0.1, 0.2, 0.4, 1, 2, 4, 10, 20, or 40 gammas full-scale.

Versions are (V)1 for the P-3C, (V)2 (towed) for the SH-3H and SH-2D helicopters, (V)3 for the S-3A, and (V)4 (towed) for LAMPS III helicopters.

The towed ASQ-81 MAD "bird" on board a LAMPS III helicopter, USS *Hue City*, 1995. (S. Slade, DMS/Forecast International)

ASQ-81 entered service in 1970.

Users: U.S. and foreign operators of the P-3C and SH-3; the U.S. Navy for the S-3, SH-2, and SH-60; Germany and the Netherlands for the Lynx helicopter; Japan for the HSS-2 helicopter; and Korea, Spain, and Taiwan for the 500M/500MD helicopter.

◆ ASQ-208(V)

This is a digital version of ASQ-81. The microprocessor used to compensate for the aircraft's magnetic field has a three-channel filtered display and threshold processing. Existing ASQ-81 wiring is retained, but signal recognition is improved. As in the existing unit, targets are automatically detected. However, in this version a range/confidence estimate is provided. Aircraft electronics is simplified. Texas Instruments offers both inboard and towed versions.

MISSILES

Deletions: Ikara (Australian, no longer in service).

CHINA (PRC)

◆ CY-1

> **Dimensions:** 41 cm × 5.5 m (16.1 × 216.5 in)
> **Weight:** 700 kg (1540 lb)
> **Propulsion:** Rocket
> **Range:** 5–18 km (5500–20,000 yd)

This ballistic antisubmarine missile was first displayed at ASIANDEX in November 1986. No details were given, other than that CY-1 will be fired from a multicell launcher on board surface ships. Externally the missile resembles Asroc, and CY-1 is credited with Asroc-like performance. However, unlike Asroc, CY-1 reportedly may be carried by helicopters and MPA. CY-1 is intended to engage submarines operating at 150–300 m depth at speeds up to 33 kt. It carries a lightweight homing torpedo, probably A244.

No platforms are definitely known. CY-1 may fill some of the box launchers in recent destroyers and frigates, and it may possibly be an alternative load in the six-tube launcher in "Jiangwei"-class frigates.

FRANCE

◆ Malafon

> **Dimensions:** 651 × 5877 mm; span 3190 mm (booster: length 2135 mm, span 1800 mm) (25.6 × 231.4 × 125.6; 84.1 × 70.9 in)
> **Weight:** 1000 kg (2200 lb) after booster separation; booster: 330 kg (727 lb)
> **Warhead:** L 4 homing torpedo
> **Propulsion:** Glider, after boost; booster burn time 2.8 sec, impulse 35,000 kg/sec (77,140 lb/sec)
> **Speed:** 280 m/sec at end of boost, decreasing to 100 m/sec during flight (918 ft/sec, decreasing to 328 ft/sec)
> **Range:** 3000–15,000 m; maximum 20,000 m (3300–16,400 yd; maximum 21,900 yd)

ASQ-81 MAD stingers on a line of P-3 Orions. The radomes below the MAD boom carry the rear antenna of the APS-115 radar, so that a 360-deg search can be maintained without the drag associated with hanging a radome below the airplane. (U.S. Navy)

This ship-launched standoff weapon carries an L 4 homing torpedo and uses a gun direction radar for guidance. The missile is tracked using two flares in its wingtips. Malafon is a glider gyrostabilized in roll and pitch; at the end of its flight (800 m short of the predicted position of the submarine), it is commanded to level off, the torpedo is unlocked, and the missile is braked by parachute. The torpedo continues on and enters the water.

Malafon is stowed without its wings and tail fins, the booster fins being folded. One missile is usually held on the launcher, ready to be fired, and the missile can be launched within 30 sec. A second launch can follow 60 sec later, and then the firing rate can be up to one every 90 sec. Typically a ship carries 13 missiles; the launcher proper weighs 10,500 kg.

MILAS. (Author)

Malafon on its launcher. Reloads are stowed in the deckhouse on the right. (U.S. Naval Institute)

Development began in 1956, and the missile was first tested in 1958, with initial operational tests in 1964. As of 1978, it was reported that 370 Malafons were in service and that further missiles were being manufactured to replace those expended in training. Malafon's guidance systems were modernized in 1986–87 by Sfena and now use solid-state components instead of vacuum tubes. As a result, Malafon should remain in service to the end of the century.

Users: France (*Suffren, Tourville* classes and *Aconit*).

◆ MILAS

> **Dimensions:** 460 mm (1060 mm with boosters) × 6 m (18.1 [41.7] × 236 in)
> **Weight:** 800 kg including torpedo (1760 lb)
> **Warhead:** Murne or A290
> **Speed:** 300 m/sec at 20 m in altitude (984 ft/sec at 66 ft)
> **Range:** 40 km (time from launch to splash at about 20 nm is less than 3 min) (44,000 yd)

MILAS, a development of Otomat Mk 2 by Matra and OTO-Melara (with a homing torpedo in place of the usual warhead), is the planned replacement for Malafon and also the planned Italian standoff ASW weapon, replacing Asroc. The basic requirement was formulated in the late 1970s, when the French naval staff reversed a decision to abandon standoff weapons in favor of helicopters. Tactical experience showed that a helicopter's reaction time was about 15 min; the French navy asked for a CZ standoff missile. Like Otomat, MILAS can receive mid-course guidance instructions.

Maximum range is nearly 60 km in a straight line. For a flight of 35 km, the elapsed time is less than 3 min. Cruise altitude is 200 m. It is estimated that in-flight course corrections can increase the probability of target acquisition by as much as 15% at long range. After turbojet cutoff, the delivery system, retarded

by a parachute, separates from the torpedo, and another parachute lowers the torpedo into the water. Given its limited dimensions, MILAS will probably be carried in a deck container (canister launcher) rather than in the magazine used for Malafon.

A formal Franco-Italian requirement was formulated in 1985, MILAS was chosen in the summer of 1987, and a French-Italian development MoU was signed in September 1987. The first development firings were carried out in June 1989. The program was somewhat delayed by the decision to roll A-290 and Murene, the two planned payloads, into a single Impact torpedo. The first all-up MILAS was fired 21 April 1994, from the trials ship *Carabiniere*. The French and Italian navies have both indicated an initial requirement for 200.

MILAS will arm French F 67–class destroyers (probably 12 launch units each), replacing Malafon; it will also arm seven C70 during midlife refits (6–8 launch units each) and will be added to Italian *Maestrales* and other major Italian warships during their midlife updates. All future French and Italian ASW warships will be armed with this weapon. In addition to France and Italy, another NATO navy is reportedly interested.

INTERNATIONAL

◆ NLCAW

The NATO low-cost ASW weapons project was inspired in part by the experience of the Falklands. False contacts were numerous, and in many cases the only sure means of classification was to fire a weapon (a real submarine runs away). Since weapons are increasingly expensive, the preferred technical approach seems to be a rocket- or mortar-thrown intelligent depth charge or low-cost, low-performance torpedo. The program also presumably builds on work done during the 1980s on a homing depth charge, to be fired from the standard Terne or Bofors 375 launcher. The system consists of a simple rocket or mortar (i.e., ballistic) launcher, a semi-intelligent weapon, and an FCS. In at least some cases, the weapon is also to be deliverable by helicopter.

A former European participant in the program considered it remarkable that, a year after laughing off the requirements (Pk, range, price), industry was able to meet them. The surprise was just how many weapons already met the specifications; the NATO group brought the weapons-makers together with those producing the standoff missiles or rockets. For example, Whitehead produced a torpedo with a diameter of about 8 in, with a very reasonable kill probability, and with a unit cost of about $50,000; three torpedoes could be fired out of a standard Bofors 375 mortar, and the Whitehead weapon was not much larger than a standard A-size sonobuoy. The existence of really cheap ultra-lightweights called into question the rationale for standard lightweight torpedoes.

Sweden's Elma was rejected because its range was much too short. The most widely used unguided weapon, the Bofors 375, was rejected because it was not sufficiently accurate; its six-shot salvo was credited with a Pk of less than 0.5, although it was considered useful as a means of forcing a submarine to flee.

Ultimately the NATO group dwindled to Germany and Norway, which continued development, initially in hopes of holding unit cost to $50,000, about a tenth the cost of a new lightweight torpedo. It would be projected by rocket, with a maximum air flight range of 8 km when launched from surface ship, and a range of up to 500 m against the target from point of water entry. The Germans were somewhat less optimistic, partly because they had a very demanding mission-abort requirement in mind; they hoped for a weapon about half the caliber of a conventional lightweight torpedo at about half its cost. The German version was developed by STN Atlas (which is responsible for all German heavy torpedoes) with Dynamit Nobel AG (warhead), Honeywell ELAC (sonar), and Rheinmetall (booster and parachute).

As of the fall of 1994, the German LCAW was to have been fired from a 10-rnd launcher similar to the French Sagaie decoy launcher. It was envisaged as electrically powered (dry thermal battery and a small permanent-magnet motor driving contra-props, 30kt attack speed), 140 mm × 2300 mm, 56 kg including a booster and a 4.5-kg warhead (shaped charge). An air-dropped version without a booster would be 140 mm × 1400 mm, 36 kg. Upon entering the water, the weapon would sink vertically, using its PVDF side-looking arrays (one near the nose for transmission, one in the afterbody for reception) to search a cylindrical volume. The long side arrays would provide beams directive enough to reject reflection from the surface and the bottom. During this phase the nose array would act as an echo sounder, allowing the weapon to work in very shallow water. Once a target had been detected, the motor would start, and the torpedo would turn to the horizontal and run along the appropriate bearing. The nose array would take over as the torpedo seeker. The weapon would attempt to strike the target at right angles, for maximum shaped-charge effect. Current German plans call for buying 1000 LCAW about 2002–2006.

In September 1992 Norway offered an A200 variant, A200/N, which was far less expensive that the German weapon. Whitehead was teamed with NFT (now Kongsberg: prime) and with Diehl as principal subcontractor. The ship version, with a drag-reducing nose cone, would be carried by a ballistic rocket, for example, from a RAM launcher. Including the booster, A200/N is just over 2 m long. The trajectory is modified over the last 50 m to ensure that the torpedo drops into the water as close to perpendicular as possible. Simulations showed a 70–85% chance of hitting an 8kt submarine running at 15 to 300 m at a range of up to 8000 m. Kongsberg envisages modular launch adaptors for the air version, to be placed on external hard points or in bomb bays. See the Italian section below for details of A200.

The Norwegians and Germans funded a joint Phase 2 (April 1994–October 1995), the main issue in which was a more powerful warhead. As of late 1996 it was not clear whether either the German weapon or A200 would be bought by either navy.

RUSSIA

Missile systems designated in an RPK series. RPK-1 Vikhr' (NATO FRAS-1/SUW-N-1) is now extinct.

♦ RPK-2 Viyoga

This submarine system (missile 82R, fired from 21in torpedo tubes) was developed by the Novator (Lulyev) OKB, inspired by the U.S. Subroc. Authorized under the same 1960 decree that produced the Shkval torpedo, the 53cm version (length 8.2 m) was scheduled for completion in the fourth quarter of 1965. A 650mm version (length 11.3 m) was developed in parallel, for completion in 1966. The 53cm version was designated SS-N-15 by NATO. Both versions carried nuclear depth bomb payloads. Guidance is presumably inertial, based on prelaunch sonar data (U.S. practice was to track the target passively, then use a single ping to obtain an accurate range; this method reduced the target's warning time). In the U.S. weapon, the warhead had to be nuclear because the combination of the single ranging ping and the sound of the motor firing underwater provided the target with some warning. Analysis showed that a submarine could escape the acquisition range of a Mk 44 torpedo launched in this way, but that it could not escape the lethal volume of the warhead. In the 1960s the antiship threat presented by a possible Soviet Subroc was a major factor in driving U.S. antimissile-defense projects.

An unusual feature of the missile is its honeycomb fins, like those of R-77. Range was originally 8–10 km, but an improved version can reach 40 km (25 nm). RPK-2 entered service in 1969, equipping "Victor I/II" (Project 671 and 671RT) and Alfa (Project 705) -class submarines.

♦ RPK-3 Metel (NATO SS-N-14 Silex)/URPK-3, URPK-4, and URPK-5

> **Dimensions (85R):** 7.205 m vice 7.2 m or 7200 mm (full depth, including underslung weapon, is 135 cm)
> **Weight:** 3930 kg
> **Propulsion:** Solid-fuel rocket
> **Speed:** Mach 0.95 (290 m/sec)
> **Range:** 30 nm (4 nm minimum); 50 km max

Raduga's missile is based on its P-120 (SS-N-9) antiship weapon. This command-guided rocket-powered missile is broadly equivalent to Malafon or Ikara. Reportedly the original versions were 60R (carrying a 5-kT nuclear depth bomb) and 70R (carrying an AT-2U homing torpedo). A new torpedo-carrying version, 84R, carried the AT-2UM torpedo. UPRK-3/4 Rastrub-B/A (missile 85R) is a "universal" (antiship and antisubmarine) version with a 185-kg antiship shaped charge in its body, carrying a lighter-weight torpedo with a 60-kg (rather than 100-kg) warhead, probably APR-2E. RPK-3 is the cruiser version, using the guidance system of the SA-N-3 (Grom-M) missile and the KT-106 launcher. RPK-4 is the Krivak version, using the Musson FCS and the KT-100 launcher. UPRK-3/4 launchers are KT-106U and -100U. The *Udaloy* version uses the Drakon FCS. The cruiser *Kirov* has a unique twin reloadable launcher. In Krivak III and modified *Udaloy* (as planned) and in *Frunze* and *Kalinin* as built, this weapon was superseded by a TT-launched SS-N-15 (82R).

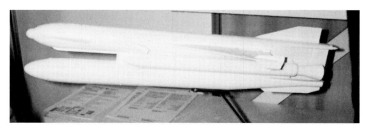

A model of the 85RU (SS-N-14) missile, at the 1993 Moscow Air Show. (S. Zaloga)

There is also a coast defense version (which may not have been deployed by the Russians).

Against targets in direct-path range, detected and tracked by hull sonars, the missile is commanded to drop its torpedo immediately above the submarine position. Krivaks are limited to this mode. Against a more distant target (e.g., detected by an airplane cooperating with the ship, or in the convergence zone), the attacking ship sends a helicopter to the estimated submarine position. The helicopter uses sonobuoys and a dipping sonar to localize the submarine, hovering almost directly over it. The missile is fired directly at the hovering helicopter, which orders the torpedo dropped at the appropriate moment (presumably via a link back to the launching ship). Without the helicopter, attack range must be limited roughly to the horizon, about 10 nm. The missile typically flies at 400 m (15 m in antiship mode). Flight range is 50 km (minimum 5 km vs. a submarine, 10 km vs. a surface ship). Submarines can be engaged at depths between 20 and 500 m.

Note that when Krivaks first appeared carrying the trainable launcher for this missile, it was assumed that they were intended for antiship work; the unseen missile in the container was tentatively designated SS-N-10. This designation was not shifted to the ASW missile that actually occupied the container, probably in the belief that an alternate (nonexistent) antiship weapon could occupy the launch container.

Modified versions: URPK-5 Rastrub-A system (85RU with KT-100U launcher in Project 1135M ships, 1980) and probably

URPK-4 Rastrub-B system (85RU with KT-106U launcher and probably Drakon command system in Project 1155 [*Udaloy*] -class ships).

◆ RPK-5 Leevyen/UDAV-1 (RBU-10000/12000)

The Leevyen (heavy rain) system fires the 89R ASW missile from the KT-129 six-barrel launcher (NATO RBU-10000) in one Project 1124 ship (Grisha class) and from a 10-barrel launcher (NATO RBU-12000) in larger ships. The new launcher was first observed on board the carrier *Gorshkov* in 1989; the same launcher appears on board the new cruiser *Nakhimov* (ex-*Kalinin*). It is presumably the replacement for RBU-6000. It has 10 larger-dia tubes in the familiar horseshoe arrangement. Range: 216 m to 10,000 m.

Half-scale models of RPK-8 and UDAV-1 rockets at Euronaval 1996. The 111SG and 111SZ UDAV-1 rounds weigh 250 kg; 111SO weighs 196 kg. (Author)

RBU-12000 on board the *Admiral Gorshkov* (ex-*Baku*). (Royal Navy)

UDAV-1 is an antitorpedo system using the same launcher, coupled to a flank-array warning sonar and its own FCS. It was announced at Defendory (October 1994) by the Splav State Research and Production Enterprise of Tula. Three layers of projectiles form the antitorpedo barrier; all are carried in 300 × 2200mm rockets: an outer layer of acoustic decoys (111SO missiles), a middle layer of depth charges suspended from buoys (111SG missiles, probably with acoustic fuzes), and an inner layer of explosive charges (111SZ SG missiles). The decoy weighs 201 kg, the depth-charge rockets 232.5 kg. Rockets are similar to those fired by RBU-6000. Each magazine holds three salvoes (30 missiles). The range envelope is 100–3000 m, and munitions

can be launched within 15 sec of detection. The associated sonar entered service about 1990. The current version is UDAV-1M. Claimed probability of hitting a torpedo with one salvo: 0.90 for a straight-runner, 0.76 for a homer. This system is aboard *Kuznetzov*, *Gorshkov*, and the cruisers *Admiral Lazarev* (ex-*Frunze*) and *Admiral Nakhimov* (ex-*Kalinin*).

The UDAV-1M *System* may also be designated RKPTZ-1.

◆ RPK-6/7

These 53cm (RPK-6) and 65cm (RPK-7) successors to RPK-2 entered service in 1981 and 1984. The Vodopod system (83R missile) uses a torpedo warhead (UMGT-1) and the Vodopei system (84R missile) presumably uses a nuclear depth bomb warhead. An improved version is URPK-6 (Vodopod/Vodopei-MK, using 83RN and 84RN missiles). The associated surface ship systems are Veder (86R missile, torpedo) and Vspletsk (86R missile, presumably with a nuclear depth bomb). Projected range with the Orlan (UMGT-1) torpedo was 100–120 km (54–65 nm). The current RPK-6 payload is APR-2E; the current RPK-7 payload is the short 53cm torpedo.

The RPK-6 surface version arms the missile cruisers *Frunze* and *Kalinin*. In these ships it is fired like a torpedo, dives into the water, stabilizes itself, and then ignites. In effect it replaces SS-N-14. It may have been chosen to arm the Krivak III and modified *Udaloy*, although the appropriate torpedo tubes were not fitted. *Neustrashimyy*, which has torpedo catapults like those of French ships, may have the 65cm RPK-7.

◆ RPK-8 Zapad (RBU-6000 launcher)

This system fires a 90R missile (212 × 1832 mm, 112.5 kg, 19 kg HE), which has a separable acoustic homing head (as in the new air-launched S3V depth bomb), from the RBU-6000 launcher. The warhead is a shaped charge. It is carried by, for example, *Neustrashimyy*, and is probably a scaled-down RPK-5. Effective range is 600–4300 m, and the round can dive to 1000 m. It is effective against torpedoes and swimmers at depths of 4–10 m. The homing head can make up for an error of 130 m in the aiming of the rocket. System response time is 15 sec, and single-salvo kill probability is given as up to 0.8.

◆ Medvedka

Splav's small-ship rocket-thrown torpedo (40 × 535 cm, 750 kg) is fired from an elevatable (for range, 1.3–23 km) but not trainable quad (2 × 2) launcher (9.5 t, 5.8 × 1.8 × 2.4 m) singly or in two-shot salvoes. Development began in 1987 and trials began in 1993 aboard the Project 1141 ASW craft *Aleksandr Kunakovich*; first deliveries were expected in 1996.

◆ S3V (KAB-250PL)

This guided depth bomb, advertised at the 1992 Moscow Air Show, is designed to attack targets down to a depth of 600 m (1968 ft). It is guided by an active pinger in the nose, actuating tail fins; the bomb can glide at an angle as great as 60 deg to the vertical. Diving speed is 16.2 m/sec (53.1 ft/sec). Dimensions are 211 × 1300 mm and weight is 94 kg (19-kg shaped-charge warhead). Compared to a conventional PLAB bomb, kill probability is 1.2 to 1.5 times higher in shallow (less than 200 m) water and 4 to 8 times higher in deeper water, down to 600 m.

UNITED STATES

Efforts to revive the Sea Lance (UUM-125A) program, canceled in 1989, failed. Tomahawk/Mk 50 has not attracted Navy funding.

◆ Asroc (RUR-5A)

Dimensions: 13.25 × 177.4 in (33in fins)
Weight: Mod 3, 949–57 lb; Mod 4, 1071–73 lb
Warhead: Mod 3, Mk 44 torpedo; Mod 4, Mk 46 torpedo
Range: Maximum about 10,000 yd (minimum range is 900 yd)

Asroc was conceived as part of a system including a reliable 10,000-yd sonar, SQS-23. It has now been retired by the U.S. Navy, but survives abroad. Note that some ships have Asroc launchers but no missiles. The Mk 112 box launcher is trainable, but it fires at a fixed 45-deg elevation, two of the eight cells elevating together. Range is determined by fixing the point of booster separation. In *Knox*-class frigates two cells of the Asroc box were modified to fire Standard surface-to-surface (later Harpoon) antiship missiles. As of 1993 all Asroc box launchers had been removed from the only U.S. ships then carrying them, *Spruance*-class destroyers. Asroc is no longer carried by U.S. ships with Mk 26 launchers. The nuclear version of Asroc (W44 warhead) was retired by September 1989.

A torpedo-carrying Asroc being fired. (U.S. Navy)

A standard Asroc box launcher on board the Japanese destroyer *Harayuki*, 1989. (W. Donko)

Asroc can also be fired from the Mk 10 launcher of the Italian cruiser *Vittorio Veneto*.

Users: Brazil (*Garcia*-class frigates), Canada, Egypt (*Knox* class), Germany (*Adams* class), Greece (*Adams* class, *Knox* class, and FRAM I destroyers), Italy (*Vittorio Veneto*, from ASTER launcher), Japan (*Asagiri, Hatakaze, Hatsuyuki, Tachikaze, Amatsukaze, Takatsuki, Yamagumo, Minegumo, Abukuma, Chikugo* classes), South Korea (FRAM I destroyers), Mexico (FRAM I destroyers), Pakistan (FRAM I destroyers), Taiwan (FRAM I destroyers, *Knox*-class frigates), Thailand (*Knox* class), and Turkey (*Carpenter* class and FRAM I destroyers). Total production, 1960–70, was about 12,000. Of U.S. ships with Mk 26 launchers, the *Kidd* class is being fitted with vertical launchers; as of late 1996 it was not clear whether early *Ticonderogas* would be similarly refitted.

◆ Vertical Launch Asroc (VLA: RUM-139A)

VLA is Asroc redesigned modified for firing by the Mk 41 vertical-launching system. Compared to Asroc, VLA has increased range (to exploit the greater direct-path range of SQS-53, compared to SQS-23) and can carry a somewhat heavier payload (Mk 46 or Mk 50 homing torpedo). Dimensions are 14.1 × 192.6 in (maximum fin span 27.4 in), and warshot weight is 1409 lb (1371 for exercise shot). As of 1987, the Navy demanded a minimum range of about 5 kyd and a maximum range of at least 15 kyd. The missile is controlled by a digital autopilot (DAC), which uses a thrust vector control (TVC) to pitch it over into the appropriate elevation (initially 40 deg, then 29 deg). Trajectory height is minimized to avoid errors due to high-altitude wind. As in conventional Asroc, range is controlled by thrust cutoff and then airframe separation. Compared to conventional Asroc, VLA is more maneuverable (thanks to its autopilot).

This weapon had been expected to enter service in 1989, but in 1988 Sea Lance was adopted as the single standoff weapon for both submarines and surface ships. VLA was demoted to interim status, but it was revived in 1990 as the primary surface-ship standoff ASW weapon, Sea Lance (both versions) having been canceled.

VLA was approved for production late in March 1993. The current low-rate initial production (LRIP) order is 300 for the U.S. Navy, and 60 for the Japanese. Forty more were requested for FY94.

Combined at-sea development and operational tests of VLA were conducted by the *Hewitt* in December 1988.

Users: Japan (*Kongo* class), United States (*Ticonderoga* class [VLS ships only], *Arleigh Burke*, and modified [with VLS] *Spruance* class).

TORPEDOES

Torpedoes use active or passive acoustic or wake-following (wake-homing) guidance or else rely entirely on gyros (as straight- or pattern-runners). Except for wake-following (which uses pingers looking more or less straight up), active seekers are generally used only against submerged submarines, which are often far too quiet to attract passive torpedoes. The water's surface acts as a mirror: an active homer near the surface can be attracted into it. The bottom can also act as a mirror, complicating performance in shallow water. Generally an active seeker depends on Doppler to distinguish a real target from surrounding clutter (it may be unable to deal with a hovering submarine). Many submarines have anechoic coatings that drastically reduce reflected signal strength. The usual counter-countermeasure, adopted in the 1970s (for example, in Mk 46 NEARTIP) is to code the seeker signal to make the echo easier to distinguish. As in a pulse-compression radar, coding improves the torpedo's signal-to-noise ratio without increasing the peak power that would offer the target longer-range warning.

A submarine detecting the approach of an active torpedo will try to escape at high speed. The rule of thumb is that the torpedo must be at least 50% faster. However, at high speed water flow over the sonar dome in the nose of the torpedo becomes very noisy. The U.S. Navy sought to solve this problem in Mk 48 by

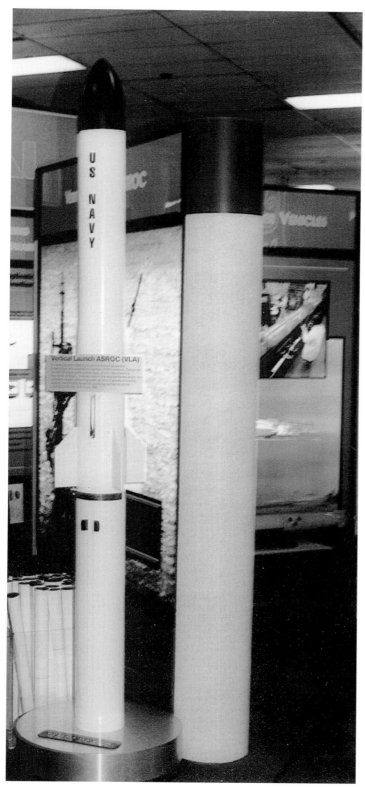

A model of Vertical Launch ASROC, displayed at Navy League 1993. (Author)

with a broader depth-band will search a greater volume at a fixed depth, generally following a snake path.

Passive homing is generally used against surface ships (which in any case do not provide much of an echoing target (distinct from the surrounding surface, that is). Note that a ship radiates noise not only from her propeller but also from her bow. Passive seekers can also be used against relatively noisy (e.g., snorkeling) submarines. That was satisfactory in the 1950s and 1960s, when an attacker was unlikely to detect diesel submarines unless they snorkeled. It became less attractive as passive detection (by submarines and surface ships, not by torpedoes) improved by going to lower frequencies, that is, wavelengths too long for easy inclusion in a torpedo seeker: hence the U.S. view that ASW torpedoes should be primarily active. Many European designers preferred what they called a covert approach, homing passively at relatively low (quiet) speed. They argued that, unless alerted, a submarine commander would generally operate at low speed. Because a very quiet torpedo might well catch the submarine unawares, there was no need for very high pursuit speed. Hence the preference for inherently quiet (but low-speed) electric motors. The covert approach becomes less attractive as submarines become quieter, even when snorkeling. Future ASW torpedoes will probably use active seekers (electric motors may often be retained to limit torpedo self-noise). Torpedoes described as dual-purpose (antiship as well as ASW) may be able to switch to passive homing, but in some cases merely disable the ASW seeker to operate as straight- or pattern-runners.

Early acoustic torpedoes used hard-wired signal processors and two- or four-beam energy comparison (left-right or a combination of left-right and up-down); one broad beam might encompass both submarine and noise or decoys. The torpedo sonars of the 1960s formed more (hence narrower) beams, which made it easier for them to distinguish a submarine against surrounding noise. In some passive systems (such as the French E 14), phase comparison replaced energy comparison. The torpedoes of the 1970s had software-controlled seekers and signal processors (which could handle different beams differently). They could be Doppler-enabled, changing tactics depending on the target's speed.

Active and passive seekers are limited to relatively high frequencies, hence relatively short ranges. Shipboard and submarine sensors operating at much lower frequencies can reach out much farther. Many torpedoes therefore have mid-course guidance in the form of a wire (which can also be used to correct the course of a nonhoming torpedo attacking a maneuvering target, as in the heavy Swedish torpedoes). In its simplest form, wire guidance is one-way, commands being issued by the firing ship (whose FCS dead-reckons the position of the torpedo). Some recent systems use a two-way wire, the operator receiving the picture generated by the torpedo-borne sonar. The torpedo can, for example, be used to probe beyond a bubble screen the target may have set up to hide itself from a long-range sonar.

Wake-following is an alternative antiship technique. A torpedo can be set to turn through a fixed angle each time it crosses the wake, so that it follows a sinuous path toward the ship, around the wake (assuming that the torpedo enters the wake at an acute angle). If the torpedo can detect both wake boundaries, it can run up the wake itself, wasting less time turning back and forth. The technique is effective because the wake's boundaries can be detected relatively easily by, for example, an upward-looking HF sonar. Too, a surface ship's wake extends many ship lengths aft, and it is very difficult to simulate. Wake-following was invented in Germany during World War II (as a variation on pattern-running), and it has been tried out by most of the major torpedo manufacturers since then.

Wake-nibbling is an alternative to wake-crossing. The torpedo detects and follows the edge of the wake. It therefore wastes much less of its forward motion than a wake-crosser. (See the Italian A184 below.) Wake-nibbling (edge-following) is far more difficult to implement than wake-crossing.

Thus far wake-following seems to be limited to antiship weapons, probably because it is easy to aim a torpedo at a line on the surface (a wake), but very difficult to aim at a cone (a submarine

running it out to a position near the target under external (wire) control at a high "transport" speed, at which its own sonar was unlikely to function. Then it was ordered to slow to attack speed, at which its sonar was effective. The British Spearfish is similar in concept. Note that maximum usable sonar speed has increased with improvements in domes and signal processors.

The torpedo's acquisition range (set largely by its ping rate) and the look angle of its seeker define the band in depth it sees at any instant. A torpedo with a narrow depth-band usually follows a spiral (helical) search path, covering only a limited volume for a given endurance. Given the same endurance, a torpedo wake) in the volume of water. It would also be difficult for the submarine torpedo to be sure that it was turning back into the wake as it tried to run down toward the submarine.

Straight- and pattern-runners generally can be turned through an adjustable gyro angle after leaving the tube. Effective range is limited by the accuracy of the torpedo and by the ratio of the torpedo's speed to the target's speed. In the past, the main method of torpedo warning was visual observation of its wake, so it was often argued that a wakeless (electric or oxygen) torpedo could be fired at a faster or more distant target, in the expectation that evasive action would not be taken. The main countermeasure to such torpedoes was zig-zagging (whether or not the torpedo was detected), in the hope that the attacker would be unable to anticipate the target's maneuver.

Weapons fired beyond effective single-target range were said to be fired "into the brown," that is, into the mass of targets in hopes of hitting one at random (this was also called a "browning shot"). Pattern-running is an attempt to increase the efficacy of such a shot by causing the torpedo to weave back and forth in the mass of target ships until exploding under one of them. The most common pattern-runners zig-zag (the French designated their pattern-runners in a Z series); but the Germans, Italians, and probably the Soviets produced aerial torpedoes that circled. Pattern-runners are still an economical way of attacking convoys from a safe distance. Wake-following was conceived as an improvement on pattern-running.

Deletions: Murene and A290 have been replaced by a Franco-Italian Impact (EU 90) project. The U.S. Mk 15 is probably extinct (the last platform is the Mexican *Cuitlahuac*, which is unlikely to carry any).

CHINA (PRC)

Chinese torpedoes are designated in a Yu (fish) series; the current production antiship torpedoes are Yu-4A and -4B.

In 1988 it was reported that the PRC program to manufacture the U.S. Mk 46 Mod 5 has been delayed because of difficulties in translation to metric units. Reportedly, the current PRC lightweight torpedo is the Italian A244, about 40 of which were acquired. However, a recent Chinese account of 1989 tests of a light acoustic torpedo is illustrated by a weapon that resembles Mk 46 rather than Mk 44/A244, albeit with an enlarged nose and what looks like a magnetic proximity fuze (a clean circular metal plate on the side of the torpedo abaft the homing section). This is probably a new weapon, possibly Yu-5.

◆ Yu-1

This straight-running thermal torpedo for torpedo boats was planned as a license-produced version of a Soviet HTP torpedo, presumably 53-57. The Chinese decided to substitute compressed-air propulsion for safety. Production was ordered in 1962, but a prototype assembled in 1966 failed its tests (it ran deep, its power output was unstable, and the motor tended to flame out). These problems were solved only in March 1970, the torpedo being type-classified in September 1971. Dimensions: 533 mm × 7.8 m, 3.5 km/50 kt or 9 km/39 kt; 400-kg warhead.

◆ Yu-2

This copied Russian 45cm RAT-52 rocket torpedo is the only standoff weapon the H-5 (Il-28 copy) can carry. RAT-52s were imported in 1954, and in 1958 the Chinese had complete drawings. The first two were completed in July 1960, but they failed in air drops. Then all Soviet aid was withdrawn, and the project was suspended. It was revived in 1964, and type-classified in June 1971 (it remains in service). As an indication of Yu-2 capabilities, a 1957 Soviet manual estimated that eight RAT-52 hits would sink a *Midway*-class carrier or an *Iowa*-class battleship; one to two would suffice for a *Gearing*-class destroyer. The weapon was quite inaccurate, however: it would take 58 shots (dropped from 7000 m, about 23,000 ft) to make eight hits. RAT-52 dimensions were 450 × 3897 mm (627 kg, warhead 243 kg), performance (in water) was 550–600 m at 58–68 kt. This contact-fuzed weapon could be dropped from altitudes above 1500 m at speeds up to 800 km/hr. Gyro-guided once in the water, it tended to porpoise,

to break up upon hitting the water at high speed, or to lose its heading. Range from bomber to target, most of it in the air, was considerable: RAT-52 was the direct predecessor of the later antiship missiles since the bomber launching it could operate from beyond the conventional AA range of the target. RAT-52 was withdrawn from Soviet service in the mid-1960s but Yu-2 probably survives in both China and in North Korea.

Yu-2 is a Chinese version of the old Russian RAT-52, shown here with an Il-28T torpedo bomber. (TASS from SOVFOTO)

The Chinese and North Koreans probably also have the standard postwar Soviet aerial torpedo, 45-56NT (450 mm, 970 kg, 200-kg warhead, 4000 m at 40 kt, droppable from 1000 m at 360–420 km/hr).

◆ Yu-3

This submarine-launched electric torpedo was the first PRC ASW weapon, a tremendous step beyond the earlier straight-runners. Work began in 1965, in conjunction with the new SSN design (a water-slug torpedo-ejection system was designed specifically for the new submarine). Components were first tested in a lake in the fall of 1969, and small-scale production began in 1971. However, the homing system was far from ready. The first version used a mechanically scanned transducer, which could not overcome much flow noise, so the torpedo had to slow near its target. A preformed beam seeker solved the problem. Yu-3 was approved for production in 1984. The next year work began on the improved Chinese Sturgeon II, which was successfully tested in January 1991. Performance: 23 kt/8 kyd; warhead: 272 kg.

◆ Yu-4

This is a submarine-launched antiship homing torpedo. Work began in 1958, when a Soviet SET-53 acoustic torpedo was bought. Manuals were translated, and work began on the electric motor, but in 1963 priority shifted to the simpler Yu-1. Work resumed in 1966, and five pilot models were completed in 1971. They were too slow. Two parallel programs began in 1976. The Dong Feng Institute Factory proposed an all-passive weapon, which became Yu-4A. The Northwest (Xi Bei) Industrial University proposed a passive/active weapon, Yu-4. Both were approved for production in February 1984. Performance: 35 kt/11 kyd; warhead: 272 kg.

◆ Yu-5

Yu-5 may be an improved passive acoustic homer. Reported performance 35 kt/16.2 kyd; warhead: 272 kg.

◆ C43

In January 1990 the PRC announced first tests of a new Type C43 heavy dual-purpose (submarine/surface ship) torpedo off the Fujien coast in the Taiwan Straits. It is said to have wire mid-course and active/passive terminal homing. C43 was developed by the Electronics Industry Division under the Chinese Academy of Sciences (Academia Sinica), with technical assistance reported from IBM, NEC, and Wang Computers. As of mid-1990, C43 was not yet in production, but it is presumably intended to replace the current Yu-4/5.

FRANCE

French submarines are currently armed with the F 17 Mod 2 for offensive action, with L 5 Mod 3 for self-defense against attacking submarines, and with the SM 39 Exocet missile. The Spanish *Agosta*-class submarines are being modernized (beginning with *Galerna*, in 1993); they will carry F 17 Mod 2.

As of mid-1992 DCN was experimenting with a laser-radar TDD operating in the 0.45–0.55-micron (blue-green) "window." It uses a pair of 50cm "eyes" (emitter and backscatter receiver); it can probably also detect a wake. The range is 0.8–10 m, the FOV is 11 × 11 deg (2 × 2 m at 5 m). Transverse resolution is 50 cm, image rate is 100 Hz (13 × 13 pixels at 17 kHz).

An indication of the current production rates of torpedoes for the French navy is that the 1984–88 budget called for orders for 70 torpedoes in 1984/85 and for an additional 190 in 1986–88, with 278 torpedoes delivered in 1984–88, and another 170 after 1988. These figures must all be for heavy torpedoes since Impact is not yet in production. Reportedly, the initial production rate for Impact is to be 20 per year.

◆ E 12/E 15

> **Dimensions:** E 12: 550 mm × 7.0 m (21.7 × 276.0 in); E 15: 550 mm × 5.9 m (21.7 × 232.3 in)
> **Weight:** 1650 kg (3637 lb); 1387 kg (3057 lb)
> **Speed/Range:** 25 kt/12,000 m (13,000 yd); 25 kt/12,000 m (13,000 yd)
> **Warhead:** 330 kg (727 lb); 300 kg aluminum tolite or HBX-3 (660 lb)
> **Powerplant:** Nickel-cadmium battery (120 cells), 50-kW motor

Alcatel's E 12 was developed on the basis of wartime German technology (such as the T-5 homing torpedo) that fell into French hands in 1944–45. E 15 is the export version of E 12. Both E 12 and E 15 are submarine-launched passive-homing torpedoes, for use against surface ships or against submarines at periscope depth (target depth down to 18 m [59 ft]). The torpedo has a contact or magnetic fuze. Maximum homing range is about 700 m (770 yd). The E 15's homing system duplicates that of E 14; the hull is a lengthened form of that of the E 14.

See the E 14 entry below for a modification program.

Users (E 14/E 15): France (*Daphne* class), Pakistan (*Daphne* class), Portugal (*Daphne* class), South Africa (*Daphne* class: E 15), Spain (*Daphne* class).

◆ E 14

> **Dimensions:** 550 × 4279 mm (21.7 × 168.5 in)
> **Weight:** 927 kg (2043 lb)
> **Speed/Range:** 25.5 kt/5000 m (5500 yd) (40-kW motor)
> **Warhead:** 200 kg tolite (440 lb)
> **Powerplant:** Nickel-cadmium battery (80 Amp-h)

CIT-Alcatel's submarine-launched passive-homing torpedo is in effect a shorter version of E 12, designed primarily to arm small French antisubmarine submarines, now extinct. It is also usable by ships (the French navy used it alongside L 3). E 14 uses contact or passive magnetic proximity (range about 4 m) fuzing. This weapon is intended for use against surface ships (at up to 20 kt) or against submarines at about periscope depth, using run depth settings of 6–18 m (20–60 ft); E 14 can run at depths as great as 300 m (984 ft). Compared to E 12, E 14 trades endurance for a more powerful warhead.

This torpedo has the same propulsion and hull as L 3, but E 14 homes passively, using a bank of four transducers operating by phase comparison within a 1-kHz bandwidth at about 25 kHz. Enable range is 350 m (383 yd); average acquisition range is 500 m (550 yd); maximum range is about 800 m. The battery has 76 cells (E 15 has 120).

E 14 was introduced in 1960, and about 1000 were made. Some were upgraded to become E 15 Mod 2s.

In 1990 CNIM announced that it was modernizing French L 3, E 14, E 15, and Z 16 torpedoes to E 15 Mod 2 standard, adding the AH 8 homing head and silver-zinc primary battery already operational on the F 17 Mod 1 torpedo. As modified, the torpedo searches at 25 m depth and has a detection range of 2000 m; attack depth is 6–18 m (presettable), and maximum depth is 300 m. Performance is 31 kt/12,000 m, and the warhead is 300 kg of aluminum tolite. Those torpedoes are lengthened to 5900 mm (232.3 in).

Users: Portugal (*Daphne* and *Commandante Joao Belo* classes), South Africa (*Daphne* class), Spain (*Daphne* class), Uruguay (*Commandante Rivière* class).

◆ E 18

> **Dimensions:** 533 × 5230 mm (21 × 205.9 in)
> **Weight:** 1230 kg (2711 lb)
> **Speed/Range:** 35 kt/18,000 m (19,700 yd)
> **Powerplant:** Battery

E 18 is a submarine-launched passive torpedo. Maximum depth is 500 m (1640 ft).

Users: Spain (*Agosta* class), probably also France and Pakistan.

◆ F 17

> **Dimensions:** 550 mm × 5.9 m (21.7 × 232 in)
> **Weight:** 1410 kg (3108 lb)
> **Speed/Range:** 35 kt/22,000 yd
> **Warhead:** 250-kg HBX-3 (equivalent to 500-kg TNT) (551 [1100] lb)
> **Powerplant:** Zinc-silver oxide battery

DTCN's passive wire-guided torpedo was introduced in 1973. Mod 1 (data above) is for submarines only. It was developed into F 17P (polyvalent, i.e., to be fired by either surface ships or submarines, 1985) and then into Mod 2 (1988). Some F 17s are converted E 18 torpedoes. A less expensive F 17S series is extinct.

F 17 torpedo tubes on board the Saudi frigate *Al Madinah*. Western navies have found it is easier to operate a surface-launched wire-guided torpedo from stern tubes, the wire running out as the ship steams away. That arrangement applies also to several U.S. attempts to combine wire guidance with surface ships and to the Italian A184. (Thomson Sintra)

Mod 1 is set to search either for surface ships (6–20 m) or submarines (30, 100, or 200 m). Its diving limit is over 500 m (1640 ft). A proposed upgrade with a new passive seeker would have a rated detection range of 2000 m, a search depth of 25 m, and a preset attack depth of 6–18 m; performance would be better than 31 kt/12,000 m. The warhead would be 300 kg of aluminum tolite.

F 17P Mod 2 (for submarines only) is 550 × 5620 mm (21.7 × 221 in), weighs 1320 kg (2909 lb), and has speed/range of 35 kt/32,000 yd. Search depth is settable at 6–20 m against surface ships and 30 or 60 m against submarines. F 17P Mod 1, for surface ships, is 550 × 5910 mm, 1428 kg, 35 kt/20,000 yd.

F 17 Mod 2 is 533 × 5384 mm (21 × 212.0 in), weighs 1397 kg (3079 lb), and has a speed/range of 40 kt/20,000 m (22,000 yd) (because of its more powerful 85-kW motor). Alternatively, it can run 18,000 m at 28 kt plus 11,000 m at 40 kt. Mod 2 searches at one of four depths (attack/ceiling depth, preset at 6–20 m, 30 m, 100 m, and 200 m). A special shallow-water mode can be

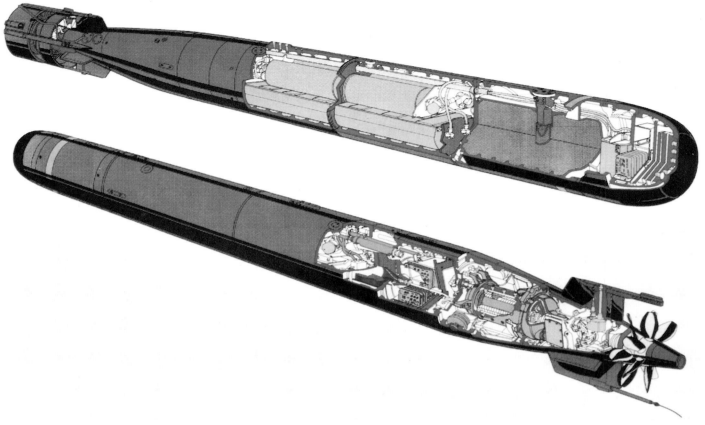

F 17 Mod 2. (DCN)

preset before launching (sonar scan is limited in elevation). It can be launched down to 400 m, and maximum operating depth is 600 m (1968 ft). Maximum trim angle is 40 deg, and maximum turn rate is 12+ deg/sec. The warhead is 250 kg of HBX-3 (equivalent to 450 kg of TNT, according to DCN). The torpedo carries 18,000 m of guidance wire. A typical French submarine torpedo tube has a dispenser for another 4000 m (8000 m in German-built submarines such as Type 209). Spain has an agreement with SOFMA to convert 16 E 15 torpedoes to F 17 Mod 2 standard.

In 1994 DTCN announced a wake-following sensor, AWD (made by STN) for the F 17 torpedo, mainly as an anticountermeasure terminal homer. AWD had been publicized for many years, without any indication as to its role, and it seems likely that French and German torpedoes are already equipped with it. F 17 adds a 15cm section to carry the upward-looking wake sensor. The export announcement suggests that the French believe their torpedo countermeasure system can deal with this threat.

Thomson Sintra has tested fiber-optic (as opposed to the current wire) guidance for torpedoes. The first trial, using 2 km of cable, occurred on 22 December 1987; a second trial (20 km) was conducted on 9 February 1988. The tests were mainly to determine whether information could be transmitted over very long distances without error; in these tests the information transmission rate was 41 Mbit/sec. Thomson Sintra claims that these were the first experiments of their type.

Unit price (1987): $750,000–$1.2M.

As of 1994, a total of 350 F 17 had been made, but others may have been converted from existing E 18s.

Users: France, Pakistan (F 17P in *Agosta* class), Saudi Arabia (F 17P in *Al Madinah* class), Spain (F 17 Mod 2 in *Agosta* and *Daphne* classes; had used F 17S in *Barcelo*-class FAC, now discarded).

◆ L 3

Dimensions: 550 × 4320 mm (21.7 × 170.1 in)
Weight: 910 kg (2006 lb)
Speed/Range: 25 kt/5000 m (5500 yd)
Warhead: 200-kg HBX-3 or TNT (440 lb)

Powerplant: Nickel-cadmium battery (40-kW motor, two contra-props)

This active acoustic submarine- or surface-launched antisubmarine torpedo (for target speeds up to 20 kt) uses a contact or active-acoustic (range 20 m) fuze. L 3 is usable in depths down to 300 m (984 ft). The torpedo's pitch angle is limited to +10 to −40 deg. Acquisition range is 1000 m (1100 yd), using a 32-kHz active seeker. The torpedo runs at 30 m (98 ft), executing a sinuous (snake) search after reaching its enable point.

This torpedo was introduced in 1960, and it was first displayed in 1968. L 3 was manufactured by DCN, which now offers a modification package (see E 14 entry above) including a new homing device, AS 15, instead of the earlier AS 3. About 600 L 3s were made.

French surface ships generally carry a combination of L 3 (short-range) and L 5 (long-range) torpedoes, both launched by compressed-air catapults rather than from torpedo tubes (two in an A 69, four in a larger ship).

Users: France (*Daphne* class), Pakistan (*Daphne* class), Portugal (*Commandante Joao Belo* class and *Daphne* class), South Africa (*Daphne* class), Uruguay (*Commandante Rivière* class).

◆ L 4

Dimensions: 533 mm × 3.13 m (21 × 123 in)
Weight: 525 kg (1157 lb)
Speed/Range: 30 kt/5000 m (5500 yd)
Warhead: 150 kg (331 lb)
Powerplant: Battery

This lightweight active (32-kHz AS 4T seeker) antisubmarine torpedo is designed to attack submarines running at or below 20 kt. L 4 is used by aircraft and as the warhead of the Malafon missile. Average acquisition range is 1000 m (1094 yd); L 4 has a circular (helical) search pattern. This torpedo is produced by DTCN and entered service in 1964.

A modernized version can operate in shallow water, and another version is suitable for launching from surface torpedo tubes (3.3 m long, 570 kg [130 in, 1256 lb]).

User: France (as Malafon payload).

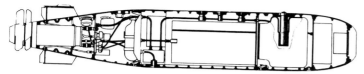

L 4 BS torpedo. (Direction des Constructions Navales)

◆ **L 5**

> **Dimensions:** 533 mm × 4.4 m (21 × 173 in)
> **Weight:** 935 kg (2061 lb) (Mod 4, Mod 3 is 1300 kg)
> **Speed/Range:** 35 kt/7000 m (7700 yd) (Mod 4: 10,000 yd)
> **Warhead:** 150 kg (330 lb)
> **Powerplant:** Silver-zinc battery

DTCN's active-passive torpedo was a response to the major increase (approximately quadrupling) in sonar range associated with the new standoff weapons of the 1960s (such as Asroc, Malafon, and Ikara). The program began in 1960; compared to E 14, L 5 was expected to have twice the capability against both surface ships and submarines. In the same volume, L 5 achieves 10 more knots and greater range, partly by adopting a silver-zinc battery and a two-rotor electric motor (of twice the power). This torpedo is also more difficult to countermeasure. L 5 was initially conceived as two torpedoes, one primarily ASW and one, of greater range, primarily to attack surface ships.

Mod 1 is a ship-launched antisubmarine or antiship weapon. Mod 2 did not enter service. Mod 3 (5500 mm long [216.5 in], 1300 kg [2865 lb]) is submarine-launched against submarines (replacing E 12 and E 14). Because Mod 3 was deemed insufficiently effective against surface ships, the wire-guided F 17 was developed. Mod 4, a simplified Mod 1, can be launched either by submarines or by surface ships, to attack fast submarines. Mod 4P is dual-purpose. The data above refer to Mod 4. Mod 4 has both acoustic and contact fuzes. Maximum operating depth is 500 m (1640 ft). L 5 entered service in 1971.

Users (L 5): Belgium (Mod 4 in *Weilingen*-class frigates), France (Mod 3 in submarines, Mod 4 in *Cassard, Georges Leygues, Tourville*, A 69 classes, Mod 1 in *Suffren, Aconit* classes, all from catapults), Libya (from Super Frelon helicopters), Pakistan (Mod 3 in *Daphne* class), South Africa (*Daphne* class), Spain (Mod 3/4 in *Agosta* and *Daphne* classes).

◆ **Z 13/Z 16**

> **Dimensions:** 550 × 7120 mm (21.7 × 280 in)
> **Weight:** 1715 kg (3780 lb)
> **Speed/Range:** 30 kt/10,000 m (10,900 yd)
> **Warhead:** 300 kg (660 lb)
> **Powerplant:** Battery

DTCN's submarine-launched straight- or pattern-runner was based on captured German technology (particularly that of the LUT torpedo). Z 13 has contact and magnetic fuzes. Running depth, set prior to launch, can be as deep as 18 m (59 ft), and the torpedo can be fired from 180 m (590 ft). Z 13 entered service in 1960; Z 16 is the export version.

TORPEDO LAUNCHERS

◆ **KD 59**

Compressed-air catapult launcher for heavy torpedoes, typically in the superstructures of French destroyers. A double athwartships set of KD 59E launch cradles is provided with 10 L 5 Mod 4 torpedoes and a device to transfer torpedoes from side to side.

Users: France (*Cassard, Suffren, Georges Leygues*, and *Tourville* classes). The *d'Estienne d'Orves* (A 69) class has four conventional fixed torpedo tubes for L 3 or L 5 torpedoes. The *Commandante Rivière* class has triple rotating 21.7in tubes for L 3 torpedoes.

◆ **K66A**

This heavy pneumatic surface-ship torpedo tube, for the F 17 torpedo, is presumably only on board the Saudi *Al Madinah*

class. Torpedoes up to 6.516 m long are fired at 15 m/sec. Overall dimensions: 8.421 (6.832 with doors open) × 1.027 × 1.364 m; 2285 kg.

◆ **K 69**

New launcher optimized for the Impact torpedo, in single (KU 69), double (KD 69), and triple (KT 69) versions, for launch at 0–30 kt. These launchers are compatible with the Mk 46 torpedo. KU 69 is offered in both breech-loading and clamshell (top-loaded) versions. Dimensions: 3.2 × 0.7 × 0.915 m (350 kg).

Daphne-, Agosta-, and *Le Redoutable*–class submarines have 21.7in tubes; the nuclear attack submarines and *Le Triomphant* have 21in tubes. The *Agosta* class can fire either 21- or 21.7in torpedoes. These tubes employ pistons to expel torpedoes, a system introduced by the German navy during World War II. The piston is actuated by air, so this mechanism, like pure air ejection, suffers from depth limitations. Its advantage is that it is covert: no air bubble is released.

GERMANY

German two-way wire-guided torpedoes transmit back raw acoustic data. Other such torpedoes, such as later versions of Mk 48, transmit back processed data, that is, acoustics as seen by the torpedo sonar processor.

The *Thetis* (now Greek) and *Koln* (now Turkish) corvette and frigate classes are all equipped with 21in torpedo tubes, probably initially for U.S.-supplied Mk 37s and British Mk 8s. It is unlikely that they can launch modern German wire-guided weapons. In the *Thetis* class they have been adapted to fire lightweight ASW weapons.

STN Atlas makes an AWD wake-detector for heavy torpedoes. The only known application is to the French F 17.

By 1993, about 1400 torpedoes had been produced by or ordered from STN Atlas, a figure consistent with the production estimates given below. These figures suggest that many buyers of German-built submarines received ex-British Mk 8 and ex-U.S. Mk 37 torpedoes in addition to their STN weapons.

The current German long-term defense plan includes a lightweight torpedo to replace Mk 46, UAW 90 (U-Boote Abwehrwaffe 90: 500 units), which is to enter the development phase in 1999–2011. The number 90 presumably reflects an earlier determination to buy a new torpedo in 1990 (see the Impact entry below for the reported choice at that time, between Murene, A 290, and Mk 46 Mod 5).

◆ **DM1 Seeschlange**

> **Dimensions:** 533 × 4150 mm (4620 mm including wire reel) (21 × 163.4 [181.9] in)
> **Weight:** 1370 kg (3020 lb)
> **Speed/Range:** 33 kt/6000 m; maximum range 12,000 m (6600/13,100 yd) (4 nm wire)
> **Warhead:** 100 kg (220 lb)
> **Powerplant:** Silver-zinc battery (contraprops)

This wire-guided (one-way link) short ASW torpedo (for the Type 206 class) entered service in 1975 after tests in 1972–73. It has much in common with Seal, but only about half the battery capacity, to limit length and accommodate an active sonar. Reportedly the seeker is limited to two dimensions; the firing submarine tracks the target in depth. The initial design concept, a single universal homing head, suited to both active and passive homing, was realized in the later SUT (see below). Both Seeschlange and Seal have preset search programs to be used in the event the guidance wire breaks before the target is acquired, as well as reattack logic (e.g., circular search in the event of target loss). Fuzing in both torpedoes is combined impact and proximity.

Wire guidance was adopted specifically to suit Baltic conditions, especially the shallow water and the very long detection ranges provided by modern radars and sonars.

The name means Sea Serpent. In all, 250 DM1/DM2 torpedoes were made.

Users: Germany (Type 206 submarines).

◆ **DM2A1 Seal**

> **Dimensions:** 533 × 6550 mm (6080 mm in the original DM2) (21 × 257.9 [239.4] in)
> **Weight:** 1370 kg (3020 lb)
> **Speed/Range:** 33 kt/20,000 m (22,000 yd); also a lower-speed setting (9.9nm wire)
> **Warhead:** 250 kg (551 lb)
> **Powerplant:** Silver-zinc battery (contraprops)

Seal is the passive antiship equivalent of Seeschlange, in service in 1969. Like Seeschlange, it is wire-guided (in this case, two-way); it has a larger warhead suited to antiship attack. The long range keeps the attacking platform out of counterattack range. Fuzing is a combination of impact and proximity. When fired from surface platforms, these torpedoes are launched back over the stern, the tail pointing forward, the wire reeling out over the stern.

Users: Germany (Type 206 submarines and Type 143 fast-attack boats [whose tubes are being deleted in favor of RAM missiles and mine rails]).

◆ **DM2A3 Seehecht/DM2A4**

> **Dimensions:** 533 × 6600 mm (21 × 259.8 in)
> **Weight:** 1370 kg (3020 lb)
> **Speed/Range:** 35 kt/20,000 m (22,000 yd) (16.5nm wire)
> **Warhead:** 260 kg (573 lb)
> **Powerplant:** Battery

This is a two-stage AEG/Elsag upgrade of existing Seal/Seeschlange torpedoes. DM2A3 is a seeker/self-noise upgrade, using a new 3D Alenia seeker, new two-way wire guidance, and a new course-attitude reference gyro system (using pressure cells to maintain depth). The torpedo uses distributed 16-bit processing (e.g., separate ones for guidance, fuzing, attitude control,and data communications), with a total program length of about 520 kbytes.

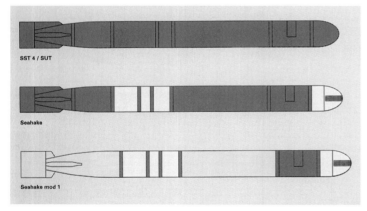

Planned development of DM2A3 (Seahake) and DM2A4 (Seahake Mod 1) from SST-4/SUT, showing the new sonar array in Seahake and the new high-speed propulsion system in DM2A4. Given the considerable commonality between DM2A3 and SST-4/SUT, the earlier torpedo can be modified to Seahake using a conversion kit. The shrouds aft are symbolic; both SST-4/SUT and Seahake use conventional propellers (Seahake has new low-noise contraprops). (STN)

DM2A4 is a propulsion upgrade with a new electric motor. The heavy torpedo propulsion study is still ongoing, but the German navy had to choose a powerplant in order to get torpedoes in time. DM2A4 is expected to have a wake-homing antiship capability. The export version will be Seahake Mod 1.

Series production of DM2A3 began in 1989. Some will be modified DM2A1 (reportedly the German navy plans to upgrade 115 to 170 DM2A1). The first upgraded DM2A3 torpedoes were integrated into Type 206A submarines in the third and fourth quarters of 1994. As of late 1994, it had been decided to defer DM2A4 entry into service to 2004 (rather than 1998), due to slowed funding.

Users: Germany (DM2A3 in Type 206A, DM2A4 in Type 212), Norway (DM2A3 in *Ula* class [100 ordered 1989]). Current German plans call for 146 DM2A3 (production 1994–98) and 73 DM2A4 (possibly not to complete definition phase until 2005).

◆ **SST-3/SST-4 Seal**

> **Dimensions:** 533 × 6080 mm (6550 mm including wire reel) (21 × 239 [260] in)
> **Weight:** 1414 kg (3116 lb)
> **Speed/Range:** 35 kt/24,000 yd; 23 kt/56,000 yd (9.9nm wire)
> **Warhead:** 260 kg (573 lb)
> **Powerplant:** Battery

This surface ship/submarine antiship homing torpedo was developed because the German navy refused to sanction the export of DM1 or DM2. The seeker is fixed in bearing. SST-3 (1972) can be fired from a depth of 100 m (330 ft). The improved SST-4 has three speeds (35 kt/12,000 yd; 28 kt/22,000 yd; 23 kt/40,000 yd). Mod 0 is impact-fuzed; Mod 1 (used only by Argentina) is proximity-fuzed for under-the-keel explosions. SST-4 entered service in 1980, and was the weapon fired by the Argentine submarine *San Luis* in the Falklands.

Reportedly 400 SST-4s were made.

Users: Argentina (Mod 1 for Type 209s and TR-1700s; also in *Intrepida* class; used with the U.S. NT37C), Brazil (Type 209s and *Oberons*), Chile (Lurssen fast-attack boats, Type 209s, possibly *Oberons*), Colombia (Mod 0 in Type 209s), Ecuador (probably Mod 0 in Type 209s), Greece (Combattante II/III and *Jaguar* class), Indonesia (probably superseded by SUT), Peru (Mod 0 in Type 209s), Turkey (Mod 0 in Type 209 submarines and *Kartal*-class attack boats), and Venezuela (Mod 0 in Type 209 submarines). This torpedo was probably license-produced by IPTN of Indonesia from 1978 through about 1986. Brazil also bought Tigerfish for its submarines, and Indonesia adopted the dual-purpose SUT. This torpedo was probably also supplied to Denmark and Norway, which ultimately adopted the Swedish Tp 61.

◆ **SUT**

> **Dimensions:** 534 × 6390 mm (21 × 252 in)
> **Weight:** 1414 kg (3116 lb)
> **Speed/Range:** 34 kt/12,000 m; 23 kt/28,000 m (13,100/30,600 yd) (the speed for 28,000 m is also reported as 18 kt, and the range for 23 kt as 18,000 m)
> **Warhead:** 260 kg (claimed equivalent to 500 kg TNT) (573/1100 lb)
> **Powerplant:** Battery

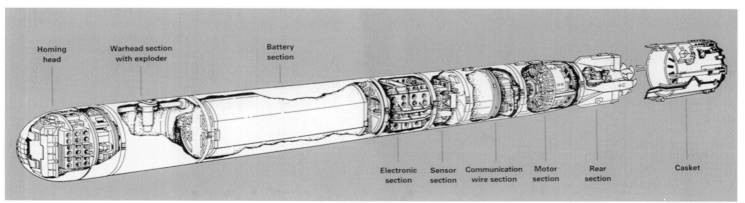

DM2A3 Seehecht. (STN)

This dual-purpose (surface and underwater target) wire-guided torpedo derived from SST-4 has active/passive terminal homing (active at 2000 m and passive at 4000–6000 m, according to 1978 claims by the manufacturer). The 2D seeker is fixed in bearing, but incorporates some sanitized DM1/DM2 features. The seeker/control incorporates reattack logic. Torpedo attitude is controlled by a free gyro acting directly on the control surfaces. As in SST-3/4, the guidance wire is effectively one-way. Reported minimum running depth is 10 m. Compared to Mod 0, the impact-fuzed SUT Mod has slightly improved software. Mod 1 is an unofficial proximity-fuzed upgrade for one unidentified Far Eastern customer, probably Indonesia. Mod 2 has a steerable 2D seeker with wider FOV, a magnetic fuze, and two-way wire guidance (an "audio channel" sends its sonar data back to the submarine, as in German navy torpedoes).

An IPTN-made SUT torpedo being loaded into an Indonesian Type 209 submarine. (IPTN)

SUT was announced in 1975, ran trials in 1976, and entered service in 1980. In 1986 Indonesia signed a contract for license production.

In October 1994, unit price was $1.6–2.0M. Reportedly in 1987 RoK bought 48 SUT Mod 2 for unit price of about $1.6–1.8M; a second batch of Mod 2 will be delivered 1997 for about $1.8M each.

Users: Chile (Type 209s; Mod 1 in *Oberons;* estimate 95 bought), Colombia (Mod 0 in Type 209s; also reported as SSTs), Greece (Mod 0 in Type 209s; estimate 112 bought), India (Type 1500s), Indonesia (probably Mod 1 for both Type 209 submarines and *Hajar Dewantara* and PB 57–class surface ships; both imported and built under license), Korea (Mod 2 for new Type 209s), Taiwan (200 Mod 2 ordered 1988 from Indonesia for *Sea Dragon* class). Reported sales total 439, possibly excluding production for Taiwan. Chilean Type 209s and Indian Type 1500s may have SST-4s.

◆ G7e

Dimensions: 53.3 cm × 7.0 m (21 × 275.6 in)
Weight: 3870 lb
Speed/Range: 30 kt/8200 yd
Warhead: 617 lb
Powerplant: Battery

In the designation, "G" indicates 21in dia, and the length is 7 m; e indicates electric propulsion. The data above refer to one version of the wartime German weapon. Wartime German steam torpedoes may also survive.

Users: Denmark (submarines; used as late as the late 1970s, may still exist), Finland (retained German torpedoes as a war reserve to equip fast patrol boats and the two corvettes), Italy (made by Whitehead until the early 1970s, may remain as war reserve), Norway (coastal forts, wire-guided), and Yugoslavia (probably in submarines).

TORPEDO LAUNCHERS

Virtually all German-designed submarines have swim-out torpedo tubes, a type selected by the main design organization, IKL, because it was more compact and also more efficient than any positive-ejection alternative. Compactness was particularly prized because of the tonnage limit imposed on the new German submarines. The standard MaK tube is 750 mm (29.5 in) or 775 mm (30.5 in) in diameter (the wider tubes are the four closest to the submarine's centerline). There are four sections: a narrow-diameter inboard tube (2.5 m long), a section (of the same diameter) penetrating the pressure hull (1.2 m long), a conical section (0.3 m long), and then a maximum-diameter outboard section (3.75 m long for 775mm tubes, 3.5 m long for 750mm tubes). These tubes are installed in a hull with a circular shape that greatly reduces flow into the tubes and, thus, makes swim-out much easier. The larger bow diameter is needed to provide sufficient flow as the torpedo accelerates out of the tube (less space is needed for the initial flow over the propellers). As of early 1988, MaK had made 786 tubes since 1961.

Swim-out does impose some limitations. Since the torpedo leaves the tube at very low velocity, the launching submarine must move slowly and cannot maneuver freely while firing. Cavitation in the tube (because of the drag of water flowing between the tube wall and the torpedo) may reveal the submarine. Because the torpedo does not fill the tube, it may hang up (as reportedly occurred on board an Argentine submarine on trials during the Falklands War). A swim-out tube cannot be used for energetic internal-combustion torpedoes because their toxic exhausts will vent into the submarine. Finally, a swim-out tube cannot easily launch missiles (although for a time at least Whitehead was offering a compact electric motor to swim Harpoon capsules out of tubes).

The new German Type 212 submarines will have positive-discharge hydraulic tubes. One piston, which pushes the water out, is provided for each nest of three or four tubes, and one hydro-accumulator can be provided for each tube. This system launches torpedoes at a minimum speed of 12 m/sec at any depth, at a submarine speed of up to 12 kt. The firing interval, for a six-torpedo salvo, is 5 sec. Alternatively, the system can fire three double shots at an interval of 10 sec. It takes less than 5 min to refill the accumulators. Work on this design began in 1983, and a prototype in a simulated submarine-section was under test until the end of June 1988.

An alternative, apparently adopted for the new Israeli *Dolphin*-class submarines, uses a hydraulically impelled thrust arm. This version achieves maximum launch speed (better than 10 m/sec) in about 1.5 sec and can run at a lower speed (0.2 m/sec) to launch mines. Development work began in 1986, and work on a prototype began in 1988. Because the thrust arm does not fill the tube, torpedoes can also swim out of it. Tube diameter is 710 mm (28 in), leaving a 90mm (3.5in) hydraulic cylinder at the bottom.

MaK supplied an air-expulsion system for existing swim-out tubes (III, IV, VII, VIII, which are fitted to lay mines) in Greek submarines, specifically to fire sub-Harpoon missiles.

INDIA

In 1986 India announced that an NST-58 torpedo, developed by the Naval Science and Technology Laboratory in Vishakhapatnam, was in production to replace the lightweight A244/S in Indian service. No details were provided, but it is generally assumed that NST-58 is an A244/S derivative.

There is also a program to develop a heavy torpedo.

INTERNATIONAL

Thomson-CSF and MUSL plan a joint study of advanced torpedo sensor technology. European torpedo-makers (other than MUSL) plan a joint heavyweight torpedo propulsion project.

◆ Impact (EU 90)

Dimensions: 324 mm × 2.6 m (12.75 × 102.4 in)
Weight: 250 kg (551 lb)
Speed/Range: 38 kt search, 53 kt attack; endurance over 10,000 yd at maximum speed (6 min at maximum speed, or 12 min at mixed speeds, gives approximately 10,000 yd at 53 kt and probably about 12,000 yd at mixed speeds)
Warhead: 50-kg shaped charge (110-lb)
Powerplant: Aluminum-silver oxide battery (two-speed 136-HP engine-driving pump jet)

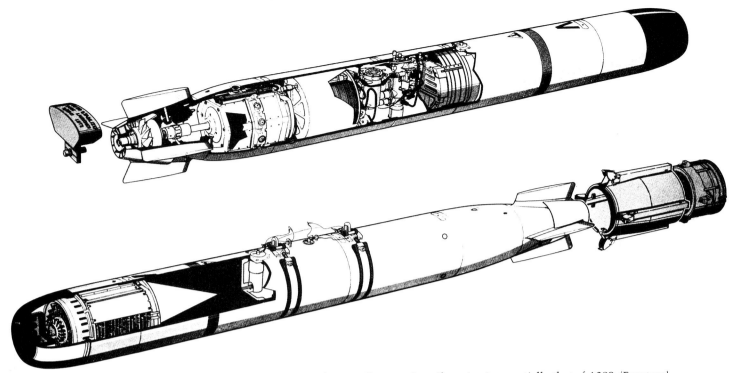

Eurotorp's Impact lightweight torpedo replaces both Murene and A184. The pumpjet tail section is essentially that of A290. (Eurotorp)

Eurotorp's Franco-Italian active-passive multifrequency lightweight torpedo supersedes both Murene and A290. It retains the Murene seeker (but without the flank transducers originally planned) and Mangouste acoustic computer (now with 68020 CPUs). The guidance computer uses X86-series CPU chips. Software has been written jointly by Whitehead and DCN, and the after end is mainly A290. Eurotorp claims it has the first variable-speed (rather than two- or three-speed) electric torpedo motor (made by STN: speed [29 to over 50 kt] is software-controlled). Eurotorp sees Impact as far more than a simple combination of Murene and A290, but rather the product of a careful rethink of both (hence, e.g., the elimination of the flank arrays in the nose, since the new acoustic head provided better beam definition). Performance roughly matches that planned for Murene.

Compared to Mk 46, Impact must be supplied with much more information, such as protection zones for friendly ships and

a bathythermal profile. That requires a special control console. Alternatively, Impact can be fired in a degraded mode, with much less information. Eurotorp emphasizes Impact's capability against submarine countermeasures, thanks in part to its ability to use multiple sonar frequencies (Mk 46 is more limited). On the other hand, Impact is likely to be extremely expensive. It was reported (prematurely) in October 1991 that Murene was being built at a rate of 20 per year, at a unit cost of about $1.7M. The collaborative project was announced in 1990 (the name Impact was chosen in 1992). Development has been protracted. Thus although in October 1992 Eurotorp hoped to run qualifying trials in 1994 and to begin production for the French navy in 1996, in fact the 1997–2002 defense plan (1996) listed 150 torpedoes for delivery by the end of the plan period in 2002. The first 50 are to be ordered under the 1997 program. A Chilean order for Murene was canceled because the projected delivery date, 1997, was not acceptable. On the other hand, Eurotorp hoped to sell Impact to Germany as a Mk 46 replacement, claiming that in a German evaluation Murene and A290 were first and second, with Mk 46 Mod 5 well behind. The company considers Mk 50 roughly equal to Impact, but argues that its propulsion is more dangerous (and, moreover, that it will not be released for general export).

Plans originally called for 350 torpedoes for the French and Italian navies, but that seems unlikely; as of 1996 only 20 preproduction weapons had been made.

ITALY

◆ A184

Dimensions: 533 mm × 6 m (21 × 236 in)
Weight: 1265 kg (2788 lb)
Speed/Range: 36 kt/10,000 m or 24 kt/25,000 m (11,000/27,300 yd)
Warhead: 250 kg (550 lb)
Powerplant: Silver-zinc battery

Whitehead's heavy wire-guided torpedo (usable by both submarines and surface ships) is wire-guided, with digital active and passive terminal homing using two semicircular arrays, one in the vertical and one in the horizontal plane, for wide sector coverage. It demonstrated a wake-following capability in 1987 U.S. Navy trials. Reportedly, A184 is a wake-nibbler rather than a wake-crosser. The current version is Mk 3. A new TOSO homing head (developed from that of the German DM2A3/4) is being installed, beginning in 1996. It can handle several targets simul-

Impact, at Bourget Euronaval 1996. (Author)

taneously. The new version is also more fully digital; sonar data are digitized close to the transducer.

The requirement was issued in 1971, and A184 entered service in 1974 in both submarines and surface ships. Estimated unit price (1996) is $1.0–1.25M.

Users: Italy (submarines, *Maestrale* class) and three unnamed users, probably China (PRC), India (Type 209s), and Peru (some Type 209s), all in submarines. Peruvian interest in A184 stems from disappointing tests of SST (reportedly unable to maintain

depth under wire control) after the failures in the Falklands. This torpedo may form the basis of the new Chinese heavy torpedo.

◆ **A244 and A244/S**

Dimensions: 324 mm × 2.75 m (12.75 × 108.3 in)
Weight: 220 kg (235 kg for A244/S) (485/518 lb)
Speed/Range: 30 kt/6000 m (6600 yd)
Warhead: 34 kg (blast) (75 lb)
Powerplant: Lead-acid battery

This Mk 44 Mod 2 replacement uses a single-frequency Elsag AG70 passive/active seeker. A244/S uses a CIACIO-S programmable triple-frequency active/passive seeker (probably with adaptive preformed beams and variable search patterns and maneuvers). The pulses are coded FM slides. The manufacturer claims that by analyzing the structure, Doppler, shape, and time-space coherence of returning echoes its computer can reject clutter, multipath, or mirror effects (from the surface or the bottom), and echoes from the bottom, and can even distinguish submarines from natural formations on the bottom. Mod 1 is for helicopter launch, Mod 2 for aircraft.

The A244 requirement was issued in 1968; the torpedo entered service in 1975, followed by the improved A244/S in 1984 (Mod 1 was ready for delivery in 1987).

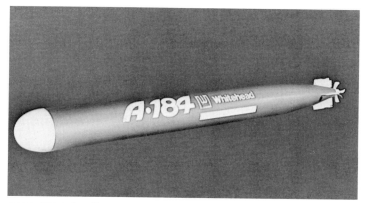

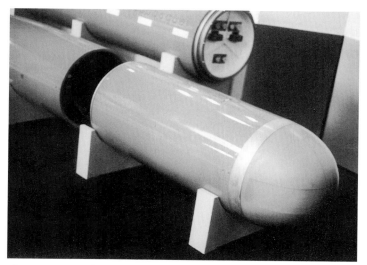

A184. (Whitehead)

The A184 nose clearly shows the paths along which the seeker trains and elevates (along the centerline). Presumably it is locked in the elevated position for wake-following. (Author)

The tail of an A184 shows the cable reel and the propeller guard used when the torpedo is loaded. (Author)

A244/S Mod 1 at Bourget, 1994 and 1996. The tail view shows the control tabs inside the shroud, which is typical of both this torpedo and the U.S. Mk 44. (Author)

Work on CIACIO began in 1964 after Selenia gained experience with the Mk 44 seeker during license production. CIACIO 60 (60 kHz) was completed in 1966 and CIACIO 30 (30 kHz) in 1968; CIACIO-S appeared in 1972 and underwent live trials (using Mk 44 torpedoes) in 1975 and very shallow water trials in 1977–78.

Eurotorp (the Impact consortium) now markets A244/S Mod 1. Estimated unit cost of an A244 is 70% that of a Mk 46, that is, about $140,000; A244/S probably costs $145,000. Reportedly about 2300 A244s had been made as of late 1994.

The Indian NST-58 is apparently an A244 derivative.

Users (A244/S except as indicated, with reported numbers ordered): Argentina (540), China (about 50), Ecuador (A244: 72), Greece (from helicopters: 24), India (NST-58, an A244 derivative; total about 450), Indonesia (36), Iran (12), Italy, Libya (but the ships that carried this weapon no longer exist; ordered 200, may have received no more than 12), Nigeria (18), Pakistan (MPA: 12), Peru (A244: 72), Singapore (200), Sweden (limited numbers for evaluation, possibly 80), Taiwan (reportedly 120), Turkey (from helicopters: 50), UAE (probably about 24), Venezuela (150), and Yugoslavia (tubes for *Kotor*-class not delivered, torpedoes probably used by Croatian naval helicopters). Malaysia bought *Wadi M'ragh*–class corvettes originally built for Iraq; they carry tubes to launch A244/S torpedoes. China may make A244/S under license. In the case of Iran, presumably A244/S was bought to supplement U.S.-supplied Mk 44 torpedoes for the two FRAM *Sumners*.

◆ LCAW (A200)

Whitehead's low-cost antisubmarine weapon is a very simple torpedo intended mainly to help classify targets. Dimensions: 123 mm × 883.4 mm (11.3 kg, 2.5-kg PBX shaped-charge warhead). The torpedo can be dropped over the side from a compressed-air launcher. An air version, A200/A, designed to be dropped from an A-size sonobuoy dispenser, is 914.4 mm long, with a sonobuoy-type rotary air brake (12 kg). Performance: 18 kt for 3 min (range 2+ km; electrically propelled). LCAW has an inexpensive wide-band active sonar seeker with mid-course guidance. Development began in 1987, and technical tests were completed in 1992.

The A200 low-cost ASW weapon is shown at Bourget Euronaval, 1996. The control computer is in a linear section alongside the battery pack. Note that A202 (1223 mm, 16 kg) has a larger warhead (5 vice 2.5 kg, semidirectional and therefore equivalent to a 14-kg omnidirectional TNT warhead) and incorporates a free-run gyro (for its straight run) between its warhead and its battery pack. (Author)

A202 is a 16-kg version for frogmen (fired from a bazooka-like launcher as "Medusa") or from midget submarines. As of 1996, Medusa had been ordered by Italian navy Incursori special forces and the midget version was being developed for an unidentified foreign navy.

TORPEDO LAUNCHERS

◆ B.512

Whitehead submarine torpedo tube.

◆ B.515/ILAS-3/SPS 104

ILAS 3, the standard Italian lightweight-torpedo launching system, consists of a Whitehead SPS 104 FCS system (for torpedo presetting and launch control) and two sets of B.515 triple tubes. In its most elaborate form, SPS 104 incorporates a computer. It displays the tactical picture and torpedo presets and automatically transmits the order to fire; it can be integrated into a larger FCS. SPS 104 exists in three versions: (a) manually controlled via a remote-control panel in CIC; (b) controlled directly by the CDS; and (c) connected directly with the sonar (for a ship without a CIC), computing target course and speed and choosing optimum presets. The panel selects the tube and presets and fires the torpedo. Firing is by compressed air, and the tubes have heaters. Whitehead also makes a lightweight FCS in two versions: (a) for helicopters with dipping sonars, and (b) for MPA and helicopters without dipping sonars.

Users (ILAS-3): Argentina (MEKO 140/360, possibly Type 42 destroyers), China (Luhu- and some Luda-class destroyers and Jianghu IV–class frigates), Ecuador (*Wadi M'ragh* class), India (*Delhi, Godavari*, and *Leander* classes), Italy (*Giuseppe Garibaldi, Mimbelli, Maestrale*, and *Minerva* classes; *Lupo* and *Audace* classes probably have Mk 32), Malaysia (*Lekiu* class and ex-Iraqi *Wadi M'raghs*), Peru (*Lupo* class), Singapore (*Victory* class), Venezuela (*Lupo* class).

◆ B.516

Whitehead heavy torpedo tube for surface ships, firing aft over the stern (for wire guidance). There is also a B.516/A version.

Users: Italy (*Maestrale* class).

JAPAN

Japan currently uses Mk 44 and Mk 46 lightweight torpedoes and Type 80 heavy torpedoes.

◆ Type 80

Type 80 is a wire-guided ASW torpedo comparable in size to the U.S.-supplied Mk 37, but with better performance; speed is over 30 kt. Type 80 is about the same size (19in dia and short length) as Mk 37. Type 80 was developed from the GRX-1 experimental torpedo, but it also drew on data from the ongoing GRX-2 program. Research began in JFY65, the designation Type 80 being applied in JFY80. Production began in JFY84. At that time the equipment designator G-11 was applied. Performance: 34 kt/16 kyd, 22 kt/36 kyd; warhead 150 kg.

This torpedo is carried by the *Uzushio* and *Yushio* classes. Type 80 replaced the Japanese version of Mk 37, Mk 37-0-N.

◆ Type 89 (ex-GRX-2)

This new standard heavy (submarine) thermal torpedo is roughly equivalent to the U.S. Mk 48. Reported maximum speed is 70 kt, with a range of 30,000 m (32,800 yd); also 40 kt/50 kyd; warhead 300 kg HE. It was developed in parallel with the electric (silver-zinc) GRX-1. Development was protracted; as of 1983 GRX-2 was to have been ready for designation (standardization) in JFY85, but that occurred only in JFY89. Despite the delay, Japan did not seek license production of either Mk 48 or Mk 48 ADCAP.

The current R&D program includes work on counter-countermeasures improvements for this weapon.

◆ GRX Series

These are experimental torpedoes. When a torpedo is adopted for service, its GRX designation is replaced by a Type number indicating the JFY in which it is applied. The current research program includes a new torpedo-launching system.

GRX-4 is a new lightweight torpedo broadly comparable to the U.S. Mk 50, with a shaped-charge warhead, a SCEPS powerplant, and a propulsor. A development contract was awarded to Mitsubishi Heavy Industries in March 1987, apparently as an alternative to a Japanese production program for Mk 50. Its shaped-charge warhead was tested successfully against a double-hull submarine section in July 1989; apparently the guidance system is designed to ensure that the torpedo hits at right angles to its target. Performance: 55 kt/12 kyd; warhead 45 kg HE.

GRX-4 supersedes GRX-3, an earlier experimental air-launched, electric, lightweight torpedo developed as an alternative to Mk 46. Begun in 1975, GRX-3 was abandoned as too large and too heavy.

The two current developmental torpedo programs are GRX-5 and -6.

TORPEDO LAUNCHERS

The standard submarine tube in the *Uzushio* class is HU-602; it was succeeded by HU-603 in the *Yushio* class and by HU-603B in the new *Harushio* class. From the fifth *Yushio* (*Nadashio*), the HU-603 tubes are fitted to fire Harpoon missiles as well as torpedoes (the earlier units were later modified). HU-603 can also launch torpedoes at greater depths than can its predecessor.

The Japanese version of the U.S. Mk 32 triple tube is designated Type 68.

KOREA

The South Korean ADD defense development agency has signed an agreement with Eurotorp for assistance in developing a lightweight ASW weapon. The ADD program, which has reportedly encountered problems, envisages a White Shark 533mm heavyweight (possibly based on a reverse-engineered Mk 37) and a Blue Shark 324mm lightweight. Pending development, German torpedoes were bought for the Type 209 submarines.

RUSSIA

Ship- and submarine-launched torpedoes (with the exception of air-delivered torpedoes) are developed by the Gidropribor Central Scientific Research Establishment in St. Petersburg and made by the Dvigatel plant there (except SAET-60 and SET-40, made by Dagizel). They were also made in Ukraine, and since the breakup of the Soviet Union the Ukrainians have advertised 53-65KE. Lightweight air-launched torpedoes (AT, APR series) are developed by the OKBs responsible for guided bombs; UMGT-1 (developed by Gidropribor) was the first (thus far, probably the only) lightweight intended for both ships and aircraft. Submarine torpedoes are spindle-set; there is apparently no Russian equivalent of the NATO electric-setting umbilical.

Reported capacity: at least three weapons per tube, more in large submarines. Examples: "Victor III" (24), Sierra (40), Akula (40, including 12 limited to 53 cm), Kilo (18). Some of these figures probably include weapons in tubes, which are not always loaded in peacetime. The Mike-class submarine was credited with six weapons in tubes (two cruise missiles, two Shkvals for quick defensive snapshots, and two SAET-60M) and another 16 (6 cruise missiles, 10 torpedoes) in racks. Shkval is probably an alternative to 53cm straight-running nuclear torpedoes (BGTs, large [*bolshoi*] "escape/evasion devices") in nonreloadable tubes. They would be fired down the noise strobe of an approaching wire-guided torpedo, in hopes of forcing the launching submarine to evade. Two Shkval or BGT per submarine is probably standard.

The older export diesel submarines (Whiskey, Romeo, Foxtrot) fire *only* straight-runners (presumably 53-39 and 53-56V, with 53-51 in Russian service only) and SET-53. Because SET-53 is a passive torpedo, it is likely to be effective only against surface ships and fairly loud snorkeling submarines. Dvigatel's modernization program would presumably provide a capability to attack more deeply submerged quiet submarines.

Both the 65cm torpedo and 53-65KE have been offered for coast defense.

Torpedoes are generally designated by caliber (cm) and by year of introduction. Calibers are 40 cm (16 in), 45 cm (18 in), 53 cm (21 in), and 65 cm (25.6 in). NATO designations followed Soviet practice but generally did not match Soviet designations; wher-ever possible both designations are given below. In at least some cases, NATO projected Soviet developments that did not occur, or which did not enter service. Too, in some cases torpedo caliber was misestimated, causing additional confusion. Sometimes the Soviets used drastically abbreviated designations which did not include caliber. Air-launched weapons used a different format. E indicates electric propulsion; U sometimes indicates a "universal" torpedo suitable for surface and submerged targets. GTs were "evasion devices," torpedoes to be fired back at her pursuers by a submarine under attack (M, *maliy*, for small; B, *bolshoi*, for large). Weapons no longer in Russian service are included because they probably survive in the navies of former client-states.

The designations below suggest that few if any entirely new torpedoes entered service during the 1980s. However, NATO reported a new generation, including at least a 53-83E passive homer, TEST-83 active/passive ASW torpedo, and 53-83W wake follower. It is not clear to which Russian designations (if any) these NATO designations corresponded. Dvigatel currently offers to replace the Type 2050 passive seeker of SET-53ME and the passive Type 2056 of TEST-71 with an active Type 2541 (range 1500 m); UTEST-71 already has the new seeker. The same seeker can be installed in SET-65E. In each case, installation can be done at a local torpedo maintenance facility.

Gidropribor mentioned an SET-92K torpedo at Abu Dhabi in 1993, but gave no details.

◆ **65-73 and 65-76 (Kit) and DST-92**

> **Dimensions:** 650 × 9140 mm (25.6 × 359.8 in)
> **Speed/Range:** 50 kt/54,000 yd; 30 kt/109,000 yd (50,000 and 100,000 m, respectively)
> **Warhead:** 500 kg (1100 lb) in 65-73; nuclear in 65-76

Data apply to 65-73. Run depth for both torpedoes is 14 m (46 ft). This torpedo, which is probably an enlarged 53-65, probably became operational in 1981. Type 65 has attracted very considerable attention in the West because it has the sort of warhead required to sink a carrier and because wake homing is virtually impossible to counter by means of a towed or thrown decoy. Presumably, the torpedo is fired on a gyro course toward the expected target position, the wake-homing feature considerably enlarging the effective target length and thus making very long firing ranges (as indicated above) useful. In this sense the 65cm torpedo might be regarded as an underwater cruise missile, supplementing antiship cruise missiles flying through the air.

This torpedo marks a drastic change in Soviet torpedo size and, therefore, can be fired only by recent submarines. It seems likely that the 65cm torpedo was designed because 65cm tubes had already been selected for "Victor II" and later submarines, to fire the SS-N-16 ASW cruise missile.

"Victor III"–class submarines are fitted with four 65cm and two 53cm torpedo tubes, the two smaller-dia tubes to the sides of the four larger ones. The continued use of smaller-dia tubes suggests that some special 53cm weapon, which cannot be fired from the larger tube (i.e., using a liner), is carried. The most likely candidate would be Shkval.

From "Victor II" onward, most Soviet submarines have tubes with 65cm diameters, so it would be reasonable to imagine that the Soviets have produced 65cm weapons in all three major torpedo categories: antiship and nuclear (as here), and electric antisubmarine. To limit the arsenal to existing smaller-caliber weapons (fired, presumably, using unwieldy tube liners) would be to disregard the considerably greater volume (e.g., for endurance, guidance, or both) offered by the larger torpedo caliber.

NATO listed a dual-purpose (presumably electric) 65-83 or E65-83. The existence of this torpedo is speculative.

Several other 65cm weapons have been advertised. DT (1993: 11 m, 450-kg warhead, total 4500 kg) has a gas turbine powerplant. DST-90 or -92 (11 m, 557-kg warhead, 35 kt/50 km, mean run depth 20 m, maximum firing depth 100 m) estimates the range to the target from the reduction in the width of the wake as it crosses back and forth. DST-96 (11 m, 445 kg, 50 kt/50 km) is a projected successor. NATO's estimated characteristics for a 65-76 successor were length 9.1 m, warhead 900 kg or 50 kT.

The sensor end of a 65cm wake-follower, taken from a Gidropribor video at Bourget Euronaval. (Author)

♦ **53-27L**

Dimensions: 21 × 276 in
Weight: 3800 lb
Speed/Range: 43.5 kt/4570 yd
Warhead: 550–600 lb
Powerplant: Air-steam

This torpedo was carried postwar by motor torpedo boats. The L may have indicated manufacture at Leningrad. Running depth was 16–40 ft. It may be the 53cm weapon used by PRC and Bangladesh torpedo boats, and by some North Korean craft.

♦ **53-38/53-38U/53-39**

Dimensions: 533 × 7200 mm (21 × 284 in)
Weight: 1615 kg (3560 lb)
Speed/Range: 44.5 kt/4000 m, 34.5 kt/8000 m, 30.5 kt/10,000 m (4400/8700/10,900 yd)
Warhead: 300 kg (661 lb)

Data are for 53-38. 53-38U: 533 × 7450 mm (21 × 293 in), 1725 kg (3800 lb), 400-kg (882-lb) warhead. These were the standard surface and submarine air-steam torpedoes in service at the outbreak of World War II; 53-38U was an improved version of the basic weapon. There were several major wartime modifications. A magnetic proximity fuze (NVS) entered operational service about 1943. Running depth was 16–40 ft. The improved 53-39 entered service in July 1941. It had a more powerful engine and increased air and fuel (kerosene) capacity, and had a new MO-3 gyro adjustable for angled fire (0- to 90-deg port or starboard). Data: 533 × 7488 mm (21 × 294.8 in), 1780 kg (3923 lb)

with 317-kg (699-lb) warhead, performance 51 kt/4000 m; 39 kt/8000 m; 34 kt/10,000 m (4400/8700/10,700 yd). 53-39PM was a pattern-running version.

♦ **53-51**

Dimensions: 533 × 7800 mm (21 × 307 in)
Speed/Range: 51 kt/4000 yd; 39 kt/10,000 yd
Warhead: 400 kg (882 lb)

53-51 was the postwar Soviet submarine torpedo, a straight- or pattern-runner. Maximum launch depth was 106 m (348 ft); maximum operating depth was 14 m (46 ft). The exploder was impact or magnetic (proximity).

♦ **53-56V and 53-56VA**

Weight: 1900 kg (4188 lb)
Speed/Range: 51 kt/4000 m, 41 kt/8000 m
Warhead: 400 kg
Powerplant: Air-steam (piston)

These are standard air-steam powered export torpedoes for Shershens and, probably, Foxtrots and Romeos. 53-56V is a submarine weapon. Data above refer to it. 53-56VA is a torpedo-boat weapon. Both torpedoes have pattern-running modes based on the wartime German FAT. The exploder is an inertia-pendulum with 4 deg of freedom, so that it can work at any impact angle. The mechanical FCS on Romeos and Foxtrots is designed to work with 53-56, and probably cannot easily be adapted to alternatives. These torpedoes are spindle-set. 53-56VA data: 533 × 7490 mm, 1750 kg (21 × 295 in, 3859 lb), 51 kt/4000 m, 39 kt/8000 m, 310-kg warhead. NATO 53-70VA is an assumed successor: 35 kt/11 kyd, with a 562-kg warhead. This torpedo may not exist.

♦ **53-57 (NATO 53-56) and 53-61**

Dimensions: 533 × 7688 mm (21 × 305 in)
Weight: 2000 kg
Speed/Range: 51 kt/9000 m, 45 kt/18,000 m
Warhead: 305 kg (671 lb)
Powerplant: HTP/fuel (open cycle)

53-57, the first operational Soviet torpedo with an HTP engine, was a modified 53-51. In effect it was the first modern Soviet unguided antiship torpedo; it could be fired by both surface ships and submarines. It was the standard straight-running antiship torpedo of the 1960s. Run depth was 2 to 14 m. 53-61 was an improved version: 15 km at 55 kt or 22 km at 35 kt, running at 15 m, with straight-, pattern-, or circular-running. 53-61M of 1963 added a passive homer. It may have been the prototype wake-follower (see 53-65, below, which is generally described as the first Soviet thermal antiship homer).

A nuclear version of 53-57 (developed as T-5, Soviet service designation unknown) carried a 15-kT warhead. The NATO designation was 53-59. Reported length was 7200 mm (283.5 in); reported performance was 50 kt/11,000 m or 32 kt/21,000 m. Operational in 1959 or 1960, this torpedo was almost certainly the primary weapon element of the November-class SSN weapons system, the submarine being fast enough to reach a firing position off the bow of the fast target (e.g., an aircraft carrier). The torpedo exploded at a set range as indicated by the propeller turn count. The propeller count was also used to arm the warhead after the torpedo passed a set enabling range. An anticircular turn mechanism protected the firing submarine.

At one time it was suggested that this torpedo was also the first Soviet naval strategic nuclear weapon because it could be set to swim into enemy harbors.

There is some evidence that Soviet nuclear torpedo warheads were unsafe. In February 1972 a Soviet submarine off the North American coast suffered crew casualties because of radiation leakage from torpedo warheads. The two nuclear torpedoes on board the Whiskey-class submarine that grounded in Sweden in 1981 had noticeable radiation signatures.

53-57 could be carried by surface ships. For example, the standard torpedo load of a "Kashin" (Project 61) -class destroyer was a mix of 53-57 and SET-53 (ASW homing) torpedoes.

◆ 53-65 (NATO 53-68)

Dimensions: 533 × 7945 mm
Speed/Range: 68 kt/12,000 m or 44 kt/22,000 m (also given as 45 kt/18,000 m)
Warhead: 305 kg
Powerplant: Kerosene fuel burned in oxygen; multipiston engine

This wake-following torpedo replaced 53-61. It reportedly introduced both a new powerplant (probably semiclosed-cycle, using oxygen to enrich reused exhaust gas) and wake-homing into Soviet practice. 53-65 was the first Soviet thermal torpedo capable of homing (wake following would not be much affected by torpedo self-noise). Run depth is 5–14 m; maximum launch depth is 100 m. This weapon became operational in 1968. 53-65 was upgraded in 1969 to 53-65M (NATO 53-68), with an improved passive homer. 53-65K is a 53-61 upgraded to -65 standards, usable by surface ships as well as by submarines (19 km at 45 kt, run depth 12 m, warhead 304 kg). The export version is 53-65KE: 533 × 7945 mm, 2070 kg, 307.6 kg HE, up to 45 kt at 4–12m run depth, to 19,000 m.

The 53-65K version is apparently currently standard in Russian surface warships and submarines. There may also be a 53-65KYe version.

A nuclear version (NATO 53-68N), which carries a 20-kT warhead, became operational in 1970. 53-68N can be launched from as deep as 106 m (348 ft), and it can run down to 300 m (984 ft). Estimated performance: 45 kt/14 km. As in the earlier thermal nuclear torpedo, 53-68 is a straight-runner using propeller turn count to measure the distance to a preset detonation. Note that 53-68 is sometimes described (in Western sources) as a modernized version of the nuclear 53-56.

The NATO designation for a successor piston-engine wake-following torpedo, 53-83, probably applies to UGST (see below).

Users (53-65KE): Algeria, China, India, Iran, Poland, Romania, and Russia. Unit price (1996): $600–800,000.

◆ SAET-50 (NATO ET-80 [50])

Dimensions: 530 × 7454 mm (20.9 × 293.5 in)
Weight: Over 1600 kg (over 3520 lb)
Speed/Range: About 23 kt/7000 m (7650 yd)
Warhead: 375 kg (827 lb)

The first Soviet antiship homing torpedo was probably based on the wartime German "Gnat" (T-5), using the body of the existing ET-80 electric torpedo of 1942 (Gnat was based on the German G7e, which also formed the basis of ET-80). Developed in 1946–50 as SAET-2, it was accepted into service in 1950 (hence its SAET-50 designation). Although clearly no longer in Russian service, it may survive abroad. Its Soviet successor was SAET-60. SAET-50 can be set for circular or sector search. In the latter mode, the torpedo turns to one side for a period of several seconds. If no target is detected, the torpedo swings back onto its initial straight course. The torpedo sonar consists of four nickel-plate (magnetostrictive) transducers operating at 25 kHz and forming a line across the nose of the torpedo. SAET-50M could reach 29 kt.

◆ SAET-60 and SAET-60M

Dimensions: 533 × 7800 mm (1855 kg)
Speed/Range: 42 kt/13,000 m (SAET-60M: 35 kt/15,000 m)
Warhead: 400 kg (881 lb)

SAET-60, which entered service in 1965–66, was the second Soviet antiship homing torpedo. The nuclear version is NATO ET-80 (66). SAET-60M (sometimes rendered SAET-M) followed in 1969 (adding a second speed setting, 35 kt/15,000 m, and had a 300-kg warhead). The powerplant is a 46-cell silver-zinc battery. Operation is passive at 25 kHz. The exploder is impact or acoustic proximity. Running depth is 5–14 m. Reportedly the current version is SAET-60M.

Reported estimated details of the nuclear version (NATO ET-80A [66]): 533 × 7700 mm, 35 kt/10 km, 20 kt/40 km, 20-kT warhead. Maximum running depth was 305 m (1000 ft). A deep run would tend to increase the area affected by the nuclear burst, thus reducing the effect of any aiming error by the submarine.

The straight-running electric torpedo reported in previous editions as NATO E53-66 apparently did not exist.

◆ SET-53 (NATO ET-80A [60])

Dimensions: 53 cm × 7.8 m
Speed/Range: 23.3 kt/6 or 7.5 km, depending on battery
Warhead: 100 kg (220 lb)

SET-53 was the first Soviet ASW homing torpedo; it was the standard weapon of the 1960s. SET means Somonavodyashchayasya Electricheskaya Torpeda, or self-guiding electric torpedo. Work began in 1950; it was intended to engage targets moving at not less than 9 kt and at 20–200m depths. This weapon also had an electronic (magnetic) proximity fuze (range 5 m). It was tested in Lake Ladoga in 1954–55, with formal state trials between August and October 1957; it was accepted into service in 1958 as SET-53. The formal designation was presumably SET-53-58. According to Western sources, ET-80A could acquire a cavitating submarine (21 dB at 24.8 kHz) at about 700 yd. The torpedo could be set to run as deep as 325 ft, although it could dive to 500 ft when homing and could attack a target either above or below its set depth. The exploder was a modified version of the wartime German active magnetic TZ-5 (with two additional horizontal receiving coils), with a range of 20 ft (above, below, or alongside). Warhead weight was small presumably because electronics were so bulky. SET-53M was an improved SET-53 adopted in 1964. Warhead and operating depth did not change, but performance was improved to 29 kt/14 km. This version may have incorporated pirated British Mk 20 active/passive technology. Dimensions: 533.4 × 7800 mm; total weight 1480 kg. SET-53MKE is an export version: 24 kt/15.4 kyd.

According to Gidropribor, this was the most widely produced of all Soviet torpedoes. It was supplied to users of all the first-generation postwar submarines (Whiskey, Romeo, Foxtrot) and thus is in service in China and in North Korea. The Chinese Yu-4 presumably began as an attempt to copy SET-53

◆ SET-65 (NATO ET-80[67] Enot) and SET-65M (NATO ET-80A[76] Enot-2)

Dimensions: 533 × 7800 mm (21 × 307 in)
Weight: 1850 kg
Speed/Range: 40 kt/15,000 m; also given as 35 kt/10 km, 24 kt/20 km
Warhead: 250 kg

This active/passive acoustic submarine torpedo, currently standard, was the successor to SET-53/SET-53M with 1.7 times the speed, twice the range of SET-53. With active/passive guidance, this was the first serious Soviet ASW torpedo. Maximum depth was 200 m. The true designation is probably SET-53-65. Details of an export SET-65E, which arms export Pauks (Project 1241PE), were published in 1993: 53.3 × 780 cm (307.1 in), 1700 kg with 205-kg warhead. It is stored in a nitrogen-filled container to achieve a shelf life of 18 months. SET-65Ch of 1972 (reportedly 21 × 307 in, 45 kt/15 km, 460 m depth, 250-kg warhead) was a converted 53-65 body. Performance was also reported as 35 kt/10 km and 24 kt/20 km. SET-65 became operational in 1967.

There is probably a nuclear version with a 20-kT warhead.

SET-65. (Rozvoorouzhenie)

♦ **SET-72 (E-280) and SET-80/USET-80 (NATO E53-79A)**

> **Dimensions:** 53 cm × 6950 mm
> **Speed/Range:** 40 kt/8 km, 29 kt/10 km
> **Warhead:** 100 kg (weight 1005 kg)
> **Propulsion:** Electric

SET-72 (data above, run depth 20–400 m) is the standard dual-purpose active-passive shipboard 53cm ASW torpedo. SET-80/USET-80 (40 kt/15 km, 1000 m depth, 80kg warhead) is its submarine-launched successor. A recently announced TE-2 may be a follow-on. A Russian source credits SET-72 (not E-280) with an 80kg warhead, 41 kt/8 km, and a diving depth of 750 m.

♦ **TEST-71 (NATO 53-71)/TEST-96**

> **Dimensions:** 533 × 7935 mm (21 × 312.4 in) (length 8260 mm including wire reel)
> **Weight:** 1820 kg (1840 kg including wire reel)
> **Speed/Range:** 35 kt/25,000 m (also given as 20,000 m) (Performance also given as 40 kt/15 km or 25 kt/20 km)
> **Warhead:** 205 kg

The standard wire-guided torpedo was developed from SET-65. TEST means teleupravlyayannaya torpeda, teleguided torpedo. The current version, for both submarines and surface ships, is TEST-71M; the export version is TEST-71ME. Diving depth is 400 m. Data above are for TEST-71ME (performance is for TEST-71). TEST-71ME searches at 24 kt and attacks at 40; maximum range is 15–20 km. Homing can be shut down and the torpedo reaimed to overcome decoys. Depth limits are 2 and 400 m. There is a 1445-kg practice version.

The predecessor weapon, probably no longer in service, was TEST-68 (29 kt/24,000 m, maximum depth 250 m, 200-kg warhead), probably a converted SET-65. NATO designated this weapon ET-80A (the same designation was also used for other torpedoes). NATO's TEST-83 is probably TEST-71M. The surface-ship version of TEST-71 (NATO ET-80A-67) may be designated TEST-77E or TEST-E. There is probably a nuclear version.

Probably all buyers of Kilo-class submarines received TEST-71ME as standard equipment. UTEST-71E is TEST-71ME with a wake-following capability. TEST-96 is UTEST-71E with an improved seeker. It was announced at Abu Dhabi in 1993. USET-80 is a follow-on to TEST-71.

Users: Algeria, China, India, Iran, Poland, Romania, and Russia. Estimated unit price (1996): $400–600,000.

♦ **UGST/UDWT (probably NATO 53-83)**

> **Dimensions:** 533 × 7200 mm
> **Weight:** 2200 kg
> **Speed/Range:** 50 kt/20 km or 35 kt/35 km
> **Warhead:** 200 kg

This "universal" thermal torpedo, a TEST-71ME follow-on, which uses a pumpjet propulsor and has flip-out tailfins, was announced at the LIMA 1995 show. The monopropellant axial-piston powerplant may be derived from that of the U.S. Mk 48, which was compromised in the 1980s. The seeker has alterna-

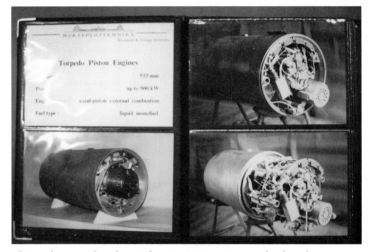

These photographs of torpedo piston engines were displayed at Bourget Euronaval 1996 by Morteplotekhnika, which develops torpedo engines. Presumably one powers UGST. The printed description, of an axial piston engine with monopropellant fuel, with an output of up to 500 kW, is certainly reminiscent of the Mk 48 powerplant. (Author)

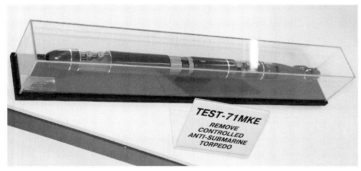

A model of TEST-71MKE shows the dark nose window for the transducer, the dual elements of the proximity fuze, and the cable reel abaft the rudders. (D. Markov)

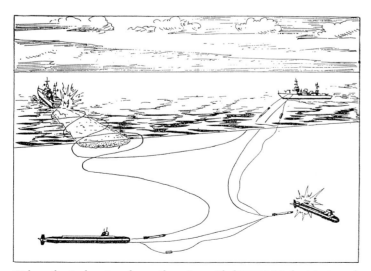

Gidropribor's drawing shows the wire-guided TEST-96 electric torpedo fired by submarines and surface ships against a submarine and (as a wake-follower, at left) against a surface ship. Note that a wire dispenser is fired with the torpedo. (Gidropribor)

Morteplotekhnika's photographs of torpedo turbines may include the 65cm powerplant. The caption indicates that this engine produces 1200 kW (1600 HP), and that the corresponding 53cm powerplant produces up to 700 kW. (Author)

tive ASW (active pinger) and wake-follower modes. The warhead has both proximity (electromagnetic and sonar) and impact fuzes. The torpedo can be wire-guided. Maximum operating depth is 500 m. The design is modular (presumably using an internal bus), to simplify updates. Unit price (1996) is $800,000–$1M.

◆ AT-24

This designation, used in the 1994 update, is probably an erroneous transcription of AT-2U (the Cyrillic U looks like a Y, hence something like a 4). See AT-2 below.

◆ BGT

Dimensions: 53 cm × ?
Speed/Range: 55 kt/15 km

This straight-running nuclear torpedo was designed for quick return shots by submarines trying to evade attackers. Shkval is probably its successor.

◆ Shkval (VA-111)

Dimensions: 533 × 8200 mm
Speed/Range: 200 kt/12,000 yd

The replacement for the BGT is a cone-shaped rocket torpedo that uses some of its exhaust gas to form the supercavitating bubble in which it runs. Shkval is a straight runner, designed originally to carry a nuclear warhead, with two burst settings. Shkval-like underwater projectiles are now being offered in a variety of sizes, down to 1 m length. It has also been reported that research is underway to increase speed to over 500 kt. Shkval was considered effective against submarines moving at up to 50 kt at depths as great as 400 m. A nonnuclear version is currently advertised.

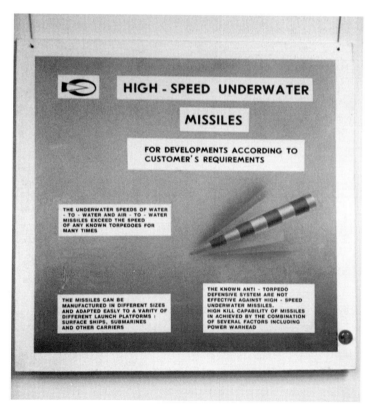

This poster, displayed at Dubai in 1995, apparently represents Shkval. (S. Zaloga)

Estimated unit price (1996): $1.25–$1.5M.
Shkval was developed under a 13 Oct 1960 decree authorizing a program of exotic ASW weapons to counter U.S. SSBNs. Other weapons authorized by this decree were Vikhr' (RPK-1, NATO SUW-N-1), Vyoga (RPK-2, NATO SS-N-15), Purga, and the air-launched AT-1 and AT-2 torpedoes. Of these, only the Purga rocket torpedo (350 × 6740 mm, 875 kg, 5 km range, 10m/sec search speed, 27m/sec [52.5 kt] transit speed) did not enter service. Shkval design requirements were a range of 15–20 km at a speed of 100 m/sec (194 kt). The draft design was accepted in 1963, the first experimental vehicles were fired in 1964, and Shkval was accepted into service in 1977.

Inclusion in the anti-Polaris program suggests that Shkval was intended to destroy an SSBN engaged in missile firing. However, according to a recent account of Shkval development, interest in a high-speed underwater rocket forming a cavity (the shell met the water, hence caused friction, only at nose and tail) in which to run dates back to the early 1950s, the object being to counterattack ASW ships attacking with depth charges. A diesel submarine fitted with a modified Katyusha rocket launcher hit a target at 500 m range. The project was abandoned as potential enemy ships were fitted with ASW rocket launchers that outranged the underwater rocket. However, sufficient interest remained to inspire development of a new type of hydromotor. This technology matured at the end of the 1950s, just as reports were received of a fast new U.S. torpedo, EX-8 (presumably the nuclear Mk 45). Reportedly the Soviet government then approved development of an underwater rocket capable of more than 100 m/sec, to be used for counterattack. BGT would seem to have been an interim weapon.

A follow-on system in development offers a 60kt acoustic search speed and a 300kt transit speed.

◆ 45-36NU/45-36ANU

Dimensions: 18 × 224 in
Weight: 2000 lb
Speed/Range: 45 kt/4400 yd (air version 41 kt/3280 yd)
Warhead: 440 lb

The standard World War II torpedo boat and air-dropped torpedo may survive on board North Korean–built torpedo boats. The reinforced ANU could be dropped at speeds of up to 200 kt (360 km/h).

◆ AT-1 (NATO E45-70A) and AT-1M (E45-75A)

Dimensions: 450 × 3900 mm (17.7 × 153.5 in)
Speed/Range: 28–30 kt/10,000 m (11,000 yd)
Warhead: 90 kg (198 lb)

AT-1 is a standard air-delivered weapon and the payload of the SS-N-14 missile. It is designed to attack submarines below 20 m depth. It circles at 27 kt at a set depth (20–200 m), accelerating toward the target once it locks on. Alternatively, it may execute a helical (up and down) search down to 305 m (1000 ft). Acquisition range (reportedly passive) is 500–1000 m; torpedo range is 5000–10,000 m. AT-1 can be dropped at 20–500 m.

The replacement, NATO's E45-75A, is probably AT-1M (which entered service about 1973). Reported performance increases to 38 kt/9000 yd. A modernized lengthened (4600 mm, 181 in, 840 kg) version later appeared.

AT-1MV, the current version, is used *alongside* APR-2E.

AT-1 was originally PLAT-1, explicitly an ASW torpedo, to distinguish it from the very fast AT-1 antiship torpedo, a RAT-52 successor: 45 × 393 cm, 530 kg (70-kg warhead), 89–98 kt/5000 m, launched at 500 m altitude.

◆ AT-2 (NATO E53-72A)

Dimensions: 533 × 4600 mm
Weight: 840 kg
Speed/Range: 40 kt/8000 m
Warhead: 100 kg (202 lb)

A 53cm equivalent to the air-launched AT-1 torpedo conceived under the 1960 anti-SSBN decree, AT-2 is a standard bomber weapon and its AT-2UM version arms the 84R version of SS-N-14. Data refer to AT-2UM. Homing range is 1000 m, maximum depth is 400 m, and speeds are 23 kt search and 40 kt transit. The original AT-2 was probably 3900 mm long and had a maximum operating depth of 300 m and speed/range of 38 kt/9000 yd; warhead weight may have been 90 kg.

◆ MGT (NATO SET-40-63 or SAET-40)

Dimensions: 40cm × ?
Speed/Range: 28 kt/6 km, also given as 25 kt/6 km
Warhead: 80 kg, also given as 50 kg

This submarine-launched evasion (passive homing anti-escort) weapon appeared in 1961; it was fired from the 40cm tubes of Soviet missile submarines. It was *not*, as often stated, an ASW torpedo; it loitered to find an approaching escort, and its run depth limit protected the firing submarine. SAET-40 was sometimes described as a scaled-down SAET-50.

◆ UMGT-1 and UMGT-1ME (NATO 40-79)

Dimensions: 40 cm × 3.5 m (16 × 138 in)
Weight: 850–950 kg (1873–2093 lb)
Speed/Range: 41 kt/8 km
Warhead: 60 kg
Powerplant: Seawater battery

This weapon was developed as the RPK-6 payload and for air launch by bombers, presumably Bear-Fs, as Project Orlan. At least during the development stage, the acoustic seeker operated at 12 kHz with a maximum range of 1200 m (1300 yd); the acoustic proximity fuze had an effective range of 1.5–3 m. Operating patterns: loiter (circular run, using passive homing), active homing, and a straight-line run-out at assigned depth. Maximum depth was about 400 m. The design of the on-board computer incorporated LSI but test weapons used discrete transistors. Maximum depth is 500 m. The torpedo can be braked by either a conventional parachute or a rotorchute (2.5m dia, with four 0.7m blades). In URPK-6, UMGT-1 is replaced by the APR-2 rocket torpedo.

UMGT-1ME was formerly called APSET-95 (40 × 384.5 mm, 650–720 kg, 60-kg warhead, up to 50 kt). NATO 40-79 was probably incorrectly identified as a thermal torpedo.

◆ SET-40 (NATO E40-65A [MGT-2])

Dimensions: 400 × 3850 mm
Speed/Range: 29 kt/7500 m (also given as 8000 m)
Warhead: 60 kg
Powerplant: Silver-zinc batteries

SET-40 was the first Soviet lightweight torpedo, for firing from small surface ships (light frigates and corvettes) and (probably later) from submarines. Work began in the second half of the 1950s, probably originally on a 345mm weapon. Like the U.S. Mk 44, SET-40 uses an active pinger (acquisition range 640 yd, as indicated by the seeker ping rate). This weapon uses an active acoustic proximity fuze (frequency reportedly 650 kHz) similar to that of the contemporary French L 3. Maximum operating depth is 200 m (660 ft). SET-40M was a modernized version (1968) capable of diving to 400 m. This weapon may also have been designated SET-U or USET; the former would indicate a modified (strengthened) torpedo, the latter a dual-purpose one. USET/SET-U is credited with a 30-kg warhead. This torpedo is reportedly based on AT-1.

◆ SET-73 (NATO E40-75A [MGT-3])

Dimensions: 400 × 4500 mm (15.9 × 177 in)
Speed/Range: 30 kt/14,000 yd
Warhead: 80 kg

The 400mm active/passive dual-purpose (antiship and antisubmarine) torpedo is not nearly as ubiquitous in Russian service as is the lightweight (324mm) torpedo in the West. It is carried only by small corvettes (Poti and Pauk classes), by the older light frigates (Mirka and Petya), and by submarines with 40cm tubes. The newer light frigates (Grisha and Parchim classes) carry 53cm weapons. That allocation may imply that the 40cm torpedo has never been altogether satisfactory.

Some sources indicate that the proper designation for NATO E40-75A is SET-72; SET-73 is taken from a Russian source.

◆ USET-95

Dimensions: 40 × 470 cm
Weight: 650 kg
Warhead: 80 kg
Propulsion: Electric

This torpedo, announced in 1993, can be launched by both surface ships and submarines; it follows surface-ship wakes and homes actively and passively on submarines.

◆ APR-2E

Dimensions: 35 × 370 cm (14 × 146 in)
Weight: 575 kg (1267.3 lb)
Speed/Range: Maximum speed 63 kt
Warhead: Equivalent to 100 kg (220 lb) of TNT

This new solid-fuel ASW torpedo was first shown (in poster form) at the 1992 Moscow Air Show. APR means aviatsiya protivo raketny, airborne ASW rocket. APR-2 is dropped by aircraft and ASW helicopters (CFE documents released in 1990 show that it is the standard weapon of Mi-14 [Haze] ASW helicopters) and is a missile payload for SS-N-15 and Medvedka. As it sinks in the water it listens; it ignites and attacks when it detects a target, a concept much like that the Germans have adopted for their version of the NATO low-cost torpedo. E probably means export version.

An APR-2E aerial torpedo, with a KAB-500 Kr guided bomb alongside. (S. Zaloga)

Homing is by a correlation-phase system with maximum range of 1500 m (1640 yd), pattern 90 × 45 deg, maximum resolution (signal/noise) 0.4, bearing accuracy up to 2 deg. Endurance is 1–2 min (listed as combat mission fulfillment time). Kill probability (with a designation error of 300–500 m) is 70–85%. Maximum depth is 600 m (1968 ft) and maximum target speed is 80 km/h (44 kt).

An APR-3 with a hydrojet (rather than a rocket) propulsor is under development. This version will enjoy double the acoustic acquisition range of APR-2.

An earlier APR-1 ASW rocket torpedo dates back to the late 1950s. It did not enter service.

◆ UTST-95

Dimensions: 32.4 cm × 2.8 m
Weight: 250 kg
Speed/Range: 40 kt/approx. 7 km
Propulsion: Thermal (Otto) fuel

Gidropribor's lightweight universal homing torpedo is the first Russian small-diameter thermal weapon. It is probably the Medvedka payload. This torpedo was announced at UDT 95. The active seeker operates at about 30 kHz.

SWEDEN

Swedish lightweight torpedoes do not use seawater batteries because the salinity of the Baltic varies so much.

The planned future lightweight weapon is 40cm ASW Torpedo 46 for Submarine 2000, Surface Attack Vessel 2000, and helicopters. It is to be particularly maneuverable and effective in shallow water, and to have an active/passive homer, and probably a new type of powerplant. The torpedo manufacturer is Swedish Ordnance, product of a merger of FFV and Bofors.

◆ Type 42 Series

Dimensions: 400 × 2440 mm (2620 mm with wire dispenser) (15.75 × 96.1/103 in)
Weight: 250/298 kg (550/657 lb)
Speed/Range: 25 kt/20,000 m; 33 kt/10,000 m (22,000/10,900 yd)
Warhead: About 50 kg (110 lb)
Powerplant: Battery (two-speed motor)

This lightweight passive electric ASW torpedo (with secondary antiship capability) can be launched by submarines, surface ships, and helicopters. Uniquely among modern lightweight weapons, it uses wire guidance (to bring it into a homing basket under the difficult acoustic conditions of the Baltic). As in the U.S. Mk 48, wire guidance makes it worthwhile to provide a higher run-out speed. Type 42 has both impact and proximity fuzes.

Type 42 entered production about 1976. Type 422 (298 kg, 1983) has an improved wire data link and a better signal processor. The export version, Type 427, incorporates some Type 617 technology. A special "incident" version has a less lethal warhead, to force a submarine in Swedish waters to surface. This development parallels that of Elma and Malin (see unguided weapons below).

Users: Sweden (Type 421 in *Nacken* class, Type 422 for helicopters). An export Type 427 is described as "in service" since 1982. The customer was probably Finland, for helicopters.

◆ Type 43X0/Type 431/Type 432

Dimensions: 400 × 2850 mm (15.9 × 112 in)
Weight: 350 kg (280 kg in helicopter version) (771 [617] lb)
Speed/Range: 35 kt/10 kyd, 25 kt/22 kyd, 15 kt/32 kyd
Warhead: 50 kg
Powerplant: Silver-zinc battery; three-speed motor

This improved Type 427 introduced data programming at transmission (so that the wire carries more data), an autopilot, and a three-speed motor. The new digital computer, which is programmed in Pascal, is smaller than its predecessors. Signals sent to the torpedo control speed, depth, and course and provide target data. The torpedo reports its position, speed, course, depth, homing system parameters, and target radiated noise. The on-board computer calculates expected target position and can independently initiate one of several search patterns if the guidance wire breaks.

Type 43 also differs from Type 42 in being of modular construction, to accommodate a special warhead or battery. The basic air-launched version, Type 432, has a lighter battery than the ship-launched version (Type 431); capacity is 4.2 rather than 5.6 kWh. In both cases, the battery is more durable than that of Type 42, capable of 30 rather than 10 exercise firings between overhauls. The Type 43X0 export version can be delivered with a different battery.

Development was ordered early in 1984, and Type 431 entered service in 1987.

Users: Pakistan (for Type 21 frigates, ordered 1994), and Sweden (corvettes and *Vastergotland* class submarines).

◆ Type 45/Type 46 (Grampus)

This torpedo, originally Type 43X2, combines the Type 43 hull (400 × 2800 mm, 310 kg) and three-speed motor (4.2 kWh AgZn battery) with a new seeker and a better signal processor. Wire guidance is intermittent rather than continuous: periodically the shipboard FCS updates (reconfigures) the torpedo guidance system, for example, for reacquisition and reattack. The two-way wire carries torpedo sonar data back to the launch platform. Reported performance: 40 kt/10 kyd, 25 kt/22 kyd, 15 kt/32 kyd.

The first Type 45 order was announced at Defendory in October 1990, to enter service on the *Goteborg* class. This torpedo project probably benefited from Swedish experience with A244/S active torpedoes bought that year. Reportedly the Swedish navy was very impressed by the torpedo's ability to detect and attack a bottomed submarine in difficult underwater terrain, that is, on the bottom next to a steep rise. Estimated unit price (1996): $600–800,000.

On 1 July 96 the Swedish Defense Material Administration (FMV) signed a contract with Bofors for a new Tp 46 (Grampus) 400mm wire-guided (probably copper rather than fiber optics) torpedo, to attack deep-diving submarines. In effect it is a Tp 45 mid-life upgrade. Requirements include a variable-speed propulsion system (there are three options) with a maximum speed of 45 kt, offering a very low-speed option in which the torpedo examines a bottomed submarine, sends back data, and accelerates if the submarine attempts to attack. Development costs are to be shared with Denmark, which rejected previous lightweight torpedoes on the ground that they would be ineffective in the Baltic.

◆ Type 61 (Tp 61)

Dimensions: 533.4 × 7025 mm (21 × 288 in)
Weight: 1765 kg (3890 lb)
Speed/Range: 45 kt/20,000 m (22,000 yd) (some sources claim maximum speed is over 60 kt)
Warhead: 250 kg (551 lb)
Powerplant: Hydrogen peroxide/alcohol (350-kW 12-cylinder engine)

FFV's long-range wire-guided antiship torpedo is fired from both submarines and surface ships. The manufacturer claims that wakeless HTP propulsion offers 2 or 3 times the range of conventional thermal or electric torpedoes. Course and speed are maintained within 0.3% during the run to the target. Wire guidance is necessary to exploit the very long range of the torpedo; Sweden was one of the first countries to employ submarine-launched wire-guided torpedoes operationally. Longer-ranged versions (613/617) have terminal acoustic homing (wake homing in at least some cases). Inertial and acoustic proximity fuzes are available.

Data above are for Type 61 (1968); Type 612 (swim-out, 1975: 533 × 7500 mm [21 × 295 in]) was the first production version. The current Swedish navy service version, Type 613 (533 × 7025 mm, 1765 kg [21 × 277 in, 3890 lb]), incorporates a digital computer that can be programmed to suit particular environmental and threat conditions. Adoption of a two-speed motor increased range by about 50%, to 30,000 m (32,800 yd) (low speed is 25 kt/32.8 kyd). This improvement was exploited by the introduction of terminal homing and, therefore, two-way wire guidance. Production began in 1983, first deliveries following in 1984.

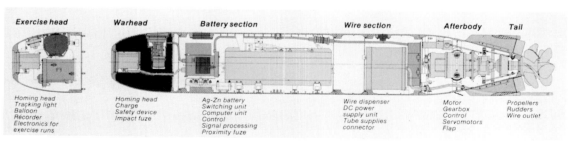

Type 43 torpedo. (FFV)

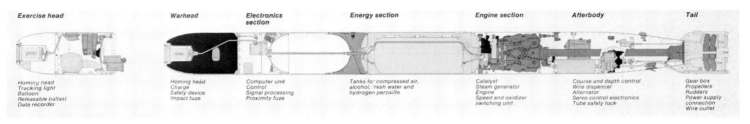

Type 617 torpedo. (FFV)

Type 617 (announced 1982, in service 1984) is the export version of Type 613. Length is 6890 mm (271 in); weight is 1860 kg (4099 lb); and estimated performance is 60 kt/30,000 m (33,000 yd) (also given as 45 kt at 33 kyd). The warhead weighs 240 kg (529 lb).

Type 61 is unique among modern Western wire-guided torpedoes in being suitable for forward firing from surface ships (the German torpedoes, A184, and the abortive surface-launched version of the U.S. Mk 48 all had to be fired aft, over the stern). Presumably, Type 61 accelerates fast enough to carry its wire clear of the firing ship.

Users: Denmark (Types 613 and 617), Norway (Type 617), and Sweden (Type 613). In December 1993 Norway signed a 2-yr contract with Bofors to modernize Type 617 torpedoes.

◆ Tp 62/Type 2000/T96

Dimensions: 533 × 5990 mm (21 × 236 in)
Weight: 1314 kg (2896 lb); exercise version 1182 kg
Speed/Range: 60 kt/33 kyd, 40 kt/49 kyd

This next-generation wire-guided, HTP-fueled export torpedo is powered by a new 7-cylinder axial-piston semiclosed-cycle swashplate steam engine driving a pumpjet. Unlike Tp 61, Tp 62 is quiet enough to deal with submarines as well as surface ships. The on-board computer controls safe/attack volume, search pattern, and torpedo behavior in the event the guidance wire breaks. The new AT-96 preformed-beam seeker can operate passively or actively, and there may also be a wake-following mode. The seeker tracks multiple targets to reject false ones, including acoustic countermeasures and environmental noise. Target data, such as elevation and bearing and data for ECCM (not raw acoustics) are transmitted back down the copper or fiber-optic wire, which can carry 80 types of message. Fuzes are contact and acoustic proximity. In 1992 Torpedo 62 was described as 30% lighter than Type 613. The tail section (presumably related to that used by Spearfish) is made by GEC-Marconi.

Calculated shelf life is 20 yr, assuming power-up testing every 2 yr, and EPROM refreshment every 3 yr; torpedoes must be reprepared every year. Type 62 was announced in 1990. The manufacturer, Swedish Ordnance, was formed in 1991 by merging FFV with Bofors. It received a Swedish government advanced development contract in April 1991. Test firing began in 1993, with tests in the Swedish Coastal Fleet in 1994–96.

In mid-1995 the U.S. government estimated that Tp 62 production would begin in 1997, and that the peak rate would be 96 weapons per year. The Royal Swedish Navy would receive 600 torpedoes in 1997–2003, and 300 would be made for Denmark and Norway.

Type 2000 was the commercial designation used during development; T96 is a tropicalized export version.

In mid-1994 Alliant bought U.S. rights to Bofors torpedo propulsion technology; the company believes that the 7-cylinder twin-sinusoidal cam engine, running on HTP, is applicable to lightweight as well as heavyweight torpedoes.

TAIWAN

The 1995 Taiwan budget announced design work on an indigenous submarine torpedo, WS-X-T, begun in 1993; concept design was completed in FY94 and FY95. It is to match at least Mk 48 (not ADCAP) performance. WS designators for the torpedo and Taiwanese mines come from the name of the underwater systems laboratory of CSIST, Wang Hsiang.

UNITED KINGDOM

◆ Mk 8**

Dimensions: 21 × 264.85 in
Weight: 3452 lb
Speed/Range: 45.5 kt/5000 yd or 41 kt/7000 yd
Warhead: 805 lb (torpex) with magnetic proximity fuze
Powerplant: Burner-cycle (steam torpedo)

This straight-runner was fired at (and sank) the Argentine cruiser *Belgrano* in the Falklands War in 1982, the guided Tigerfish not having a reliable antiship mode at that time. It was a standard postwar British MTB weapon and was probably supplied to many countries to supplement ASW torpedoes. Mk 8** is often called Mk 8 because earlier versions are long gone. It appeared in 1927. Normal depth setting is 40 ft; maximum depth is 200 ft.

Users: Brazil (*Oberons*), Chile (*Oberons* and *Guacolda* class), Greece (the "Nasty" class and ex-German *Jaguar*-class torpedo boats), and Turkey (the *Kartal* and *Jaguar* classes). This torpedo may survive as a war reserve weapon in other navies (most likely Australia, Canada, Denmark, the Netherlands, and Norway), and it was probably supplied to buyers of German-built submarines. It was withdrawn from British service in 1985, when Tigerfish was accepted as an effective antiship weapon.

◆ Spearfish

Dimensions: 21 in × approx 19.5 ft
Weight: 1850 kg (4077 lb)
Speed/Range: 65 kt/24 kyd, 29 kt/50 kyd
Warhead: 300 kg (661 lb)
Powerplant: HAP-Otto fuel (pumpjet propulsor, turbine engine; HAP is hydrogen ammonium perchlorate)

Like Mk 48, MUSL's heavy dual-purpose torpedo uses wire guidance and dual speeds (transit and attack). Its turbine engine achieves its best speed (reportedly 81 kt in a Scottish loch) at shallow depth, so the reported tactic is an up-and-over shot, with transit mainly at shallow depth. Alternatively, the torpedo can run out slowly and quietly, then search passively in a glide, accelerating to the highest speed at which it can ping effectively. Marconi claimed in 1981 that in active mode the torpedo could measure the size and aspect of the target. It could therefore hit at an optimum point along the submarine's length. Too, it might be very difficult to decoy, since a real target would not suddenly change size and shape.

Multiple receivers (presumably arranged around the sides of the torpedo nose) are some distance from the acoustic transmitter, for better directivity. Spearfish reportedly uses some Stingray technology (presumably seeker and logic), but in 1981 it was reported that it has 5 times the computing capacity of the smaller weapon.

Spearfish. The pumpjet has a shroud. (Marconi)

Speed at depth is considerably reduced (by way of contrast, a swashplate like that of Mk 48 loses endurance but not speed at depth). An endurance of 21,000 m has been reported. The Sundstrand monofuel turbine was the losing competitor in the U.S. Mk 48 contest. Reportedly, early in 1980 Marconi decided to increase Spearfish's speed (by replacing pure Otto II fuel with HAP-Otto fuel, increasing power from 550 to over 1000 HP) to deal with Alfa-class submarines. Feasibility studies for this Tigerfish replacement were conducted in 1977–79, leading up to Naval Staff Target (later Requirement) 7525. Reported requirements were a maximum speed of 55 kt, a diving depth of 3000 ft, and significantly improved self-noise, acquisition range, and lethality. Spearfish was chosen in 1980–81 (announced September 1981). It appears that Marconi offered a considerable savings if the Stingray and Spearfish programs were combined into a single British torpedo program. By the fall of 1989 the expected RN purchase had risen from 770 to over 1000. Marconi received an order for 100 initial-production torpedoes. Then the Ministry of Defense suspended orders in hopes of convincing other European navies to adopt Spearfish as a standard weapon. Finally Marconi was asked to tender (for return 8 April 1993) for a Spearfish production batch. Reportedly, as of 1992 only 20 development weapons had been delivered, and Spearfish was carried on board only HMSs *Trafalgar, Trenchant,* and *Talent* (together with Tigerfish: presumably reports that the two are totally incompatible are false). The original planned in-service date was December 1987; the actual date (using production torpedoes) was March 1994. The delay was assessed as due to propulsion (9 months) and reliability assurance (62 months). The main production order was given in February 1994. Unit cost was £1M for the first 100, then £1.5M for the main order (£594M). Total cost for production and development was £1664M. No totals are known, but the main order was reportedly for about 350 torpedoes.

◆ Stingray

> **Dimensions:** 325 mm × 2.53 m (12.75 in × 98 in)
> **Weight:** 267 kg (588.5 lb)
> **Speed/Range:** 45 kt/10,000 yd (also reported as 8,200 yd); max depth 2500 ft (755 m)
> **Warhead:** 45-kg (99-lb) shaped charge
> **Powerplant:** Magnesium/silver-chloride seawater battery (pumpjet)

MUSL's lightweight torpedo uses a preformed-beam active/passive seeker. MUSL claims that Stingray was the first lightweight torpedo to incorporate a programmable general-purpose computer rather than a hard-wired special-purpose device. It can be software-modified for different water environments and for different targets. The computer selects a search mode (for deep or shallow water, for example, in either case a snake rather than helix) and a ping mode (CW or FM). In shallow water, Stingray runs at a fixed height above the bottom. Observed target data can be compared to stored characteristics; the computer calculates an interception path that takes into account the target's potential speed and maneuverability. At short range, Stingray uses highlights in the target's sonar image to measure target speed and aspect, so that it can make a terminal maneuver (a sharp turn) to hit at right angles, for maximum shaped-charge effect. By way of contrast, according to MUSL, a conventional torpedo shifts between passive and active modes (if at all) using a preset homing criterion, or at a preset point. Search is probably a snake pattern (rather than the helix of earlier torpedoes) at a single depth. Note that it is not considered advisable to place two Stingray in the water simultaneously, as they will attack each other.

In March 1981 the torpedo was credited with depth performance equal to that of an Alfa-class submarine, then thought to be about 800 m. The torpedo is negatively buoyant: to avoid crashing into the bottom, it must accelerate quickly (reportedly it pulls out of an air-drop dive in less than 4–5 sec, to avoid hitting a shallow bottom). The rudders are located in the wash of the propeller for immediate effectiveness. The seawater battery, which drives a single-speed pumpjet, takes about 1.5 sec to fill with seawater and start after the torpedo enters the water. Thereafter, unlike most such torpedoes, it takes in no more wa-

Stingray torpedo (practice version) showing the pumpjet just forward of the parachute housing. (Author)

ter: there is no water scoop to make self-noise. The hot, partly spent electrolyte is recirculated by internal pump, and controlled amounts of cooled seawater are run into the battery. Recirculation limits the effect of variations in water temperature and salinity, for example, when operating in river estuaries, ensuring a more consistent output through the weapon's run. Battery output is controlled by varying recirculation rate and water input. If the torpedo enters at too shallow an angle, the battery does not fill quickly enough, and the torpedo, which is tail-heavy when not filled, may porpoise.

When Stingray was offered in 1981, the U.S. Navy found its speed unacceptable. Gould offered an alternative electric variable-speed powerplant with a maximum speed of 62 kt. That figure may indicate the sort of performance expected of the current U.S. Mk 50.

Stingray has now replaced all ex-U.S. torpedoes in Royal Navy service; the Mk 46s retained as a war reserve have been sold to Alliant for reconditioning and resale. Stingray studies began in 1964, the NSR 7511 staff requirement being issued in June 1968. Marconi received a contract for a seeker feasibility study in August 1969. The company apparently proposed something more, a torpedo that would modify seeker operation as it ran and that would be adaptable to a very wide range of water conditions. A design contract followed in 1977. Production began in April 1981, with orders for 280 and then for 550. Some Stingrays were sent to the South Atlantic in 1982 (HMS *Antelope* had four on board when she was sunk), but they were not used. The torpedo officially entered service in 1986; the British government placed an order for 2500 Stingrays in January 1986. On 19 Oct 1985, in its first live-warhead test, a Stingray dropped from a Nimrod aircraft destroyed a double-hulled submarine, HMS *Porpoise,* moored at a depth of 65 m in the Mediterranean. Total running time to the target was about 3 min. The extent of damage to the submarine seems to have been surprising. The torpedo was expected to cut a small-dia (albeit fatal) hole in both hulls, after which the submarine would have been raised for examination. Instead, it was so completely destroyed that it could not be raised. This result may indicate the power of all current lightweight torpedoes equipped with warheads made of modern explosives.

The SCEPS powerplant upgrade program was canceled in 1991. See the 1991/92 edition for details.

GEC-Marconi received an upgrade contract (Stingray Life Extension [SRLE], sole-source RFP issued July 1995, contract announced 10 July 1996) to extend the life of the torpedo to 2020. Initially it applies to a batch of 50 to 100 Stingray Mod 1. Improvements include a digital correlator, a new on-board processor, a variable-speed motor with a new battery, and probably some Spearfish signal processing technology. The contract may also include new controls with electrical rather than hydraulic actuators. The contract also covers continuing software development, with an emphasis on quiet shallow targets.

At DSA 96 Hawker Batteries showed a lightweight seawater-activated magnesium/silver chloride battery for Stingray.

Users: Egypt (ordered 1984 for Sea King helicopters and *Descubierta*-class frigates), New Zealand (at least 40 ordered for *Leander*-class frigates), Norway (at least 50 ordered for *Oslo* class), Thailand (ordered 1984 and 1990 for Fokker F 27 Maritime Enforcer aircraft and *Rattanakosin*-class corvettes, and for *Makut Rajakumarn* frigate upgrade; all other major Thai surface warships are now being converted to fire Stingray), and United Kingdom. The reported British war stock requirement was reportedly cut from 2500 to 1500 torpedoes due to the end of the Cold War. As of 1991, estimated total Stingray program cost was £2044M (about $3.5 billion); if that amounts to 2500, unit cost including R&D is about $1.4M. About 1988 a U.S. estimate of the unit cost of this torpedo was $440,000. The reported 1986 contract cost for one 2450- or 2500-torpedo batch, £400M (i.e., about $200,000 per torpedo) probably does not include major government-furnished elements.

◆ Tigerfish (Mk 24)

Dimensions: 533 × 6464 mm (21 × 254.5 in)
Weight: 3420 lb
Speed/Range: 35 kt/14,000 yd; 24 kt/31,600 yd; max depth (est.) 2000 ft
Warhead: 750 lb (magnetic proximity fuze for surface targets; impact fuze for submarine targets)
Powerplant: Twin silver-zinc batteries (two-speed motor)

This two-speed (parallel/series battery connections) wire-guided torpedo runs out blind and slows to search speed, using retractable wings to provide lift at that speed and to improve roll control. The active seeker is a narrow-beam narrow-band (CW) sonar; there is also a passive antiship mode. Control surfaces are hydraulically powered, using a pump slaved to the propeller shaft. This torpedo has a proximity fuze.

Tigerfish is not fast enough to engage fast nuclear submarines,

Tigerfish shows its retractable wings (between the two battery compartments). Note also the extra horizontal surfaces at the tail, just forward of the propellers. (GEC-Marconi)

so during the 1980s the Royal Navy planned to supplant it in first-line ASW service with Spearfish. Now that most threat submarines are diesel-electric, Tigerfish is fast enough. A 24-kt attack speed would correspond to a submarine speed of 16 kt (the 35-kt approach speed would allow the torpedo to deal with faster targets, say up to about 23 kt).

Development was very protracted, beginning in 1959 as ONGAR. After it failed trials, Marconi received a guidance and control contract in 1969; the company was also asked to develop an alternative Mod 1 antiship seeker. Trials in 1973–74 showed that although performance was satisfactory the torpedo was unreliable. Because the problems were concentrated in the guidance system, GEC-Marconi received an overall system contract in 1974. Even though Mod 0 failed provisional fleet acceptance trials in 1979, it was issued to the fleet beginning in August 1980 because there was no alternative in sight. In 1982, two of three Mod 1 torpedoes fired at the burnt-out hulk of the LSL *Sir Galahad* did not hit because their batteries failed. In 1983 Marconi received the Consolidation (i.e., get-well) Program contract. In 1985 test shots showed a satisfactory 80% reliability. Part of the get-well program was replacement of the existing wire dispenser with a pair of dispensers, one on board the submarine. The submarine can now take evasive action after firing without breaking the guidance wire. Some Stingray technology has also been incorporated into the modified weapon, Mk 24 Mod 2, and all 600 war-stock Mk 24s had been modified by 1987.

At DSA96 in Kuala Lumpur, Hawker Batteries showed a new silver-zinc primary battery for Tigerfish.

Unit cost for Tigerfish Mod 1 (1987): $840,000.

As of 1994, total production (including licensees) was 788 torpedoes. Reported unit cost is about $500,000.

Users: Brazil (Mod 1 [dual purpose]; first export sale, for both Type 209s and *Oberons*), Turkey (40 Mod 2 bought late 1991, with more expected, in preference to the DM2 series for the new Type 209/1400 submarines), and United Kingdom (standard SSN/SSBN torpedo). There is a swim-out version for the after torpedo tubes of *Oberon*-class submarines.

TORPEDO LAUNCHERS

◆ Submarines

Strachan & Henshaw has been the prime submarine torpedo-tube contractor since 1972.

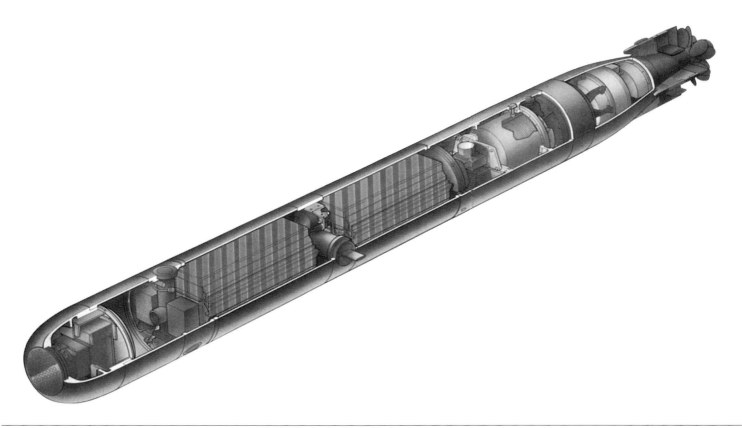

The *Oberons* have dual-pressure gear, in which lower-pressure air was used for control, and the limited supply of HP air used exclusively to eject the torpedo.

HMS *Dreadnought* introduced the U.S.-type water-ram system, which is independent of depth. HP air pushes a piston, which in turn pushes a water piston that pushes water into the torpedo tube. The next stage is to use a rotary (water) pump, driven by an air turbine, as the prime mover. This is more compact than the earlier water-ram system and has been, therefore, adopted in the British *Upholder*-class diesel-electric submarines. This system is also used by the Dutch navy, and it has been adopted for the Australian *Collins*.

SURFACE SHIP SYSTEMS

◆ STWS Series/PMW49A

STWS-1 is an underwater weapons system including an adapted U.S. Mk 32 torpedo tube, firing Mk 44 and Mk 46 torpedoes only. Normally, AIO target data are fed into the STWS, but it can also take sonar data directly, and data can be fed in manually in a backup mode. Operating modes: manual, aided manual, automatic. In the automatic mode STWS-1 uses sonar data to compute an FCS solution, which may take time, hence the provision for a manual mode for snap-shots. In the aided manual or automatic modes, STWS displays the course to steer to get to the point at which a torpedo will be within acquisition range of the target, and it also shows the distance to run to the firing point. The PWO (Underwater) selects which torpedo to fire (STWS-2 carries both Stingray and US Mk 46) and the torpedo search-pattern parameters (range, depth, course).

STWS-1 appeared about 1975, in effect as a replacement for the Limbo long-range mortar. STWS-2 (1981), which can fire the Stingray torpedo, incorporates the PMW49A triple torpedo launcher, which carries four prominent hatches and a control box (muzzle to breech) on each tube. The foremost hatch (No. 1) contains the Stingray lanyard solenoid unit. Hatch No. 2 contains the Stingray battery port cover remover. Hatch No. 3 contains the Mk 46 lanyard solenoid unit, and Hatch No. 4 contains the plug puller unit. Large boxes between Hatches 1 and 2 are distribution boxes. A pipe running along the length of the upper tube is the charging hose (torpedoes are fired pneumatically, from air flasks locked into the tube breeches). Torpedoes are fired when the tubes are trained 45 deg from ahead. There is a training handle at the breech end of the tube, although tubes are normally trained remotely. Muzzle doors are electrically operated, with a box at each muzzle. STWS-2 is exported as PMW49A. In this form it uses an Ultra (formerly Dowty) ATLAPS presetter/controller using distributed microprocessors.

STWS-3 is the current twin-tube system. The export designations are LWL 1 (lightweight fixed launcher) and DMTS 90 (deck-mounted torpedo system). The export DMTS retains Mk 46 capability; STWS is Stingray only.

Users:

STWS-1: Argentina (Type 42), Brazil (first two Type 22, *Niteroi, Inhauma* classes), Ecuador (*Leanders*), Nigeria (*Aradu*), Pakistan (unmodified Type 21s)

STWS-2: Brazil (last two Type 22), Thailand (*Khamronsin* class), United Kingdom (Type 22, some Type 42 [TT removed in many to save topweight])

STWS-3: United Kingdom (some Type 42 Batch II/III [with twin TT, to save topweight] and Type 23).

In Type 23s, the external tubes are replaced by MTLS (magazine torpedo launching system), located inside the hull for better weather protection and for minimum torpedo handling. The torpedo is launched directly from the magazine space, necessary settings being fed in from the operations room via the ship's data bus (combat system highway). By co-locating the launcher with the magazine, MTLS also serves the helicopter hangar. This arrangement was first tried in the U.S. *Knox* class, whose design was also an attempt to reduce manning. MTLS is manufactured by J&S Marine (now Cray Marine).

◆ Plessey Torpedo Launchers

Plessey Naval Systems (now part of GEC-Marconi) is developing a new series of universal lightweight torpedo tubes (i.e., with connections for Mk 44/46, Stingray, A244/S, and Impact). The designations are PMW 53 (three-barrel), PMW 54 (two-barrel), and PMW 60 (one-barrel). The current Mk 32 cannot fire Impact without major modifications to accommodate the torpedo's different connectors.

UNITED STATES

The current standard submarine torpedo caliber is 21 in; 19in weapons were developed only so that they could swim out of 21in tubes using air ejection (i.e., limited in firing depth). The new *Seawolf* class has 30in tubes. The increased caliber permits silent (i.e., swim-out) firing of existing weapons, but a 30in weapon (now abandoned) was planned. Greater diameter would have made for much better acoustic performance since the area (and, therefore, presumably the gain) of the nose transducer would be about doubled. A 30in torpedo might also enjoy a more favorable length:diameter ratio, for better hydrodynamic performance. The New Attack Submarine is to have 21in tubes.

Reported recent R&D efforts include a lightweight (33% lighter than aluminum) composite low-signature 21in torpedo hull; new forms of propulsion; and new seekers. HYDROX (hydrogen-oxygen) is a very high energy density closed-cycle powerplant being tested in a 21in torpedo (FY96). It apparently promises Mk 48 ADCAP performance in a lightweight weapon. The U.S. Navy is seeking an environmentally benign alternative to Otto II fuel. At the same time it is developing a new generation of lightweight motors and batteries (such as an aluminum primary battery with an electrolyte management system, a high energy density aluminum silver oxide battery, and an inexpensive multicell aluminum hydrogen peroxide battery). Under the FY95 program test and evaluation of a 1600-element high-resolution polymer array, a torpedo conformal array, and a broad-bandwidth array were completed.

◆ Mk 14/23 Series

> **Dimensions:** 21 × 246 in
> **Weight:** 3209 lb
> **Speed/Range:** 31.1 kt/9000 yd or 46 kt/4500 yd
> **Warhead:** 643 lb
> **Powerplant:** Steam turbine

Mk 14 was the standard U.S. submarine torpedo of World War II, remaining in use through the 1970s. It was probably supplied to many Allied navies on board ex-U.S. submarines, and may also have been supplied to users of German-built submarines. Although early Mk 14s had magnetic exploders, all surviving examples are contact-exploded.

About 13,000 Mk 14 torpedoes were manufactured during World War II (with others built prewar), together with 9700 of the simpler one-speed Mk 23 version (46 kt only). Mk 14 was declared obsolete in the late 1950s or early 1960s, when U.S. submarines were all assigned to the ASW role and when the hydrogen-peroxide Mk 16 became available in quantity to provide the few antiship weapons required. However, it was reactivated in 1969 and was withdrawn again only as dual-purpose Mk 48s became available.

Some Mk 16s may also survive, apparently having been exported after withdrawal from U.S. service. In the late 1970s, for example, the Royal Danish Navy used Mk 16 alongside Mk 14 and G-7e, favoring Mk 16 for surface shots because of its long range at high speed (46 kt/14 kyd).

Users: Peru, Taiwan, Turkey (Mk 23), in ex-U.S. submarines. It may also be used by other navies.

◆ Mk 37 and NT37 Series/Seahuntor

> **Dimensions:** 19 × 161 in
> **Weight:** 1690 lb
> **Speed/Range:** 23.8 kt/8000 yd or 15.8 kt/18,000 yd
> **Warhead:** 330 lb
> **Powerplant:** Battery

Data apply to Mk 37 Mod 0.

Mk 37 torpedo. (U.S. Navy)

Alliant's Seahuntor torpedo. (Alliant)

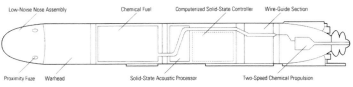

Seahuntor. (Alliant)

This wire-guided antisubmarine torpedo homes passively or actively (or in combination); operating modes are predicted-intercept, corrected-intercept (i.e., mid-course corrected run), and bearing-rider. The torpedo follows a preset horizontal search pattern (left or right circle or snake). Vertical search can only be upward from the running-depth ordered, within preset limits. Mk 37 was always a single-purpose torpedo because its homing system was ill-adapted to surface targets, and because it was too slow to catch fast surface ships. Speed is preset as high or low. Data above refer to the Mod 2 version.

The wire-guided submarine Mod 2 carries its internal wire reel in an extender section between the afterbody and the tailcone. The torpedo can be command-enabled, receiving course changes in 2 deg/signal increments. It sends status signals (fin velocity switch activation, enable acquisition, and loss of target) back down the guidance wire. Preset operating depths are 200, 150, 100, and 40 ft. Anticapture (antisurface-homing) circuits are disabled when the torpedo runs below 200 ft in deep water or when it homes passively. The torpedo can be set to run at constant depth (40, 100, 150, or 200 ft) while homing (before terminal maneuvers), when above 100ft depth in deep water, or when in shallow water. A helical snake search pattern is used when water depth is greater than 150 ft (2700 ft dia, 1000 ft maximum depth). Active acquisition range is 900+ yd at 900 ft depth.

Mod 3 is a refurbished free-runner specifically for the Spanish *Baleares* class, probably with similar homing characteristics (length 135 in, weight 1430 lb. Range: 23,500 yd/17 kt, 10,000 yd/26 kt. The torpedo can combine periods at both speeds. Depth limits: 4–1000 ft. Trajectory: snake or circle search under gyro control followed by helical search in depth.

NT37 is a Mk 37 rebuilt by Alliant (formerly Honeywell, which bought Northrop's torpedo division—hence the NT designator). Work began in 1968. The original NT37 had new batteries, a more powerful motor, a quieter propeller, and a new acoustic panel.

NT37C (certified for service in 1973) replaces the silver-zinc battery and motor with the 90-HP Otto fuel engine of a Mk 46-1. Speed increases by 40%, and range by 125% (endurance by 80%), presumably equating to 18,000 yd at 36 kt, or 40,500 yd at 23.8 kt (maximum speed is also reported as 33 kt). High speed made NT37C an effective straight-running antiship torpedo. Modes: (a) straight high-speed run with depth control; (b) delayed homing, the torpedo running straight but searching if it misses (or beginning its search at a preset range); and (c) full passive homing, as in the original Mk 37.

NT37D is NT37C plus a new solid-state (vice vacuum tube) acoustic panel.

NT37E is NT37D plus a new digital programmable (rather than analog) guidance system (whose autopilot can be programmed to take the torpedo to specific geographical coordinates, e.g., for a harbor attack). The system incorporates additional antiship run patterns. NT37E has a self-noise-reduction nose assembly (with baffling to protect the transducer from engine and hull noise, and with a new nose shape to reduce flow noise), a solid-state acoustic panel (to replace the vacuum tubes of the original Mk 37), and a new digital (vice analog) autopilot (which can be programmed to navigate the torpedo to specific geographical coordinates). These modifications increase active detection range by 50–90% and passive detection range by 100–200%, partly because with less flow noise the acoustic system can be made more sensitive. Performance also improves at higher speed and in shallow water, in both cases thanks to noise reduction.

NT37F (first ordered 1991) is NT37E with some guidance improvement. The manufacturer claims that major service work is reduced from an 18-month cycle to once every 6 yr, partly through the introduction of a self-testing acoustic panel and a more reliable control system. Reported performance: 36 kt/20 kyd, 25 kt/45 kyd.

According to a 1996 U.S. Navy report, NT37 offers wake-following capability in at least one version (reportedly not yet sold).

Seahuntor (Sea-hunting Torpedo) is NT37G, a longer (190 vs. 177 in) next-generation version with a larger warhead (up to 75% heavier than that in Mk 37, in a 200in version of this torpedo), a proximity fuze, increased speed (about 165% of that of Mk 37, using a modified two-speed Otto engine), increased range (150% more than in Mk 37), and new electronics (including a new guidance package and a new sonar; active and passive homing ranges are double those of Mk 37). Reported performance: 38 kt/20 kyd; 27 kt/25 kyd; reported warhead 225 kg. Late in 1995 Alliant was offering Mod 2 (wire-guided) and Mod 3 (free-running), with lengths of 4.77 and 4.11 m (weights 840 and 822 kg), both with 150-kg warheads and multispeed engines. At Navy League 1996 Alliant displayed a half-length version.

Unit cost for Seahuntor (1996) is $750–900,000.

Some Mk 37s were rebuilt as Submarine-Launched Mobile Mines (SLMM Mk 67; see the Mine Warfare section). Others became Standoff Weapons Mk 31 for the SEALs, to be used from Swimmer Delivery Vehicles Mk IX (operational FY87), to attack ships in harbor. The SEALs also have both limpet mines and Underwater Demolition Weapon EX-33, a 1200-lb charge that can be laid under major or nested ship targets in harbor.

Design on Mk 37 began in 1946. Evaluation of the first pilot lot (30 torpedoes, 1955–56) led to the first production order (for 90). Mk 37 was accepted into service in 1959; Mod 1 was the first major U.S. submarine-launched wire-guided torpedo. The first Mod 2 was delivered in March 1967. Work on NT37 began the next year. Norway ordered NT37C conversion kits in February 1976, and by 1977 NT37C was in service in several NATO and South American navies. The NT37E nose and acoustic panel were first tested in 1980, developmental and operational tests of NT37E following in 1982 and 1983. NT37F was first ordered in 1991. Estimated unit cost of NT37 (1992): $400,000–$450,000.

Work on Seahuntor began in 1992, and the weapon was tested in September 1993.

Users (Mk 37): Argentina, Brazil, Greece, Peru, Spain (Mod 3, in *Baleares* class frigates: 12 per ship, launched through the transom), Taiwan, and Turkey. Torpedoes in Greek and Peruvian service may have been retired with the demise of U.S.-built submarines in those navies.

♦ Mk 44/A44/KT44

Dimensions: 12.75 × 100 in
Weight: 425 lb
Speed/Range: 30 kt/6000 yd
Warhead: 75 lb
Powerplant: Seawater-activated battery (30-HP motor)

Data are for Mod 0. Mod 1 is 101.3 in long, 433 lb, with a 73-lb warhead.

Mk 44 torpedo, showing its characteristic shroud forward of the propellers.

This pure active homer has an acquisition range of 1000 yd (max; 650 yd average). Operating depth is 50–1000 ft. The helical search pattern has a 440ft dia. Prelaunch fire-control settings: mode (surface or air/Asroc), initial search depth (50, 150, 250, 450, 650, or 900 ft), search floor (150, 250, 450, 650, or 900 ft), and dive/climb angle (4.5, 6, or 7 deg). After a runout of about 1000 yd (Mods 1–4 only, not Mod 0) or initial dive (at a 30-deg angle), the torpedo may execute a flat search turn at the initial search depth; it then runs up or down through the helix, then runs the other way after a flat turn. It continues up and down along the helix until it exhausts its 6-min endurance.

At least one operator, the RNZAF, considered Mk 44 its only effective torpedo for use in shallow water (less than 300 ft deep). The RNZAF considered Mk 46 Mod 2 ineffective in shallow water and considered even Mod 5 unsatisfactory in this environment.

In 1986 Honeywell offered a modernization kit, replacing the magnetostrictive transducers with a planar array (rather than an acoustic window) of ceramic ones incorporating a preamplifier. The analog transmitter and receiver are replaced by digital devices. Claimed improvements include tripled volume search rate, a 75% increase in detection range, and a reduction in minimum shallow-water search depth by 47%. The addition of a notch filter reduces boundary-layer attacks. A new range gate reduces acoustic false alarms. A new search mode is added for intermediate water depths. MTBF increases from 160 to 3000 hr. The South Korean designation for the upgraded torpedo is reportedly KT44.

A44 is a Mk 44 upgraded (at 30% of the cost of a new torpedo) by the South African Institute for Maritime Technology (IMT of Simonstown). It is virtually a new torpedo (196.8 kg, 2573 mm long), with a 300mm 45-kg shaped-charge warhead (to penetrate 40mm of steel behind a 1.5m water-filled double hull), and a new homing system (76% hit probability against a 16kt target when air-launched, 50% when deck-launched). Claimed acquisition range is now over 1000 m in deep water and over 700 m in shallow water. Counter-countermeasures include spatial filtering, decoy-triggering pulse, multifrequency multimode (FM, Doppler, short-pulse) sonar, and logic features. The sonar scans 98 × 16 deg. Speed is 32 kt, endurance 6 min. Maximum operating depth is 1000 m, minimum 10 m. Modes: circular search, direct run-out, sector shot. Presets are target range, commanded course, initial search depth, search floor, attack mode, and (optionally) target depth and speed. The modular design allows for later upgrade, and the software-based control system allows for customized tactics. In-water tests of the seeker (target acquisition, long-range homing), control algorithms (including lost-

target procedure), and search pattern began in 1996. IMT also offers a form/fit/function replacement for Mk 44's vacuum-tube electronics, with the same functional capability but with much better reliability. This modification allows for future upgrades to torpedo logic and adaptation to specific tactical needs.

Designed primarily to attack submarines with speeds of up to 17 kt (i.e., postwar diesel-electric types), Mk 44 was formerly NATO's standard lightweight homing torpedo, the payload for which Asroc and Ikara were designed. Development began about 1952 and was completed in 1956. Production began in July 1958, a total of 10,583 being made under the FY59–65 programs (the last was delivered in December 1967). In U.S. service, Mk 44 was replaced by Mk 46 from about 1967 on. This weapon was manufactured under license in Canada, France, Italy, Japan, and the United Kingdom.

Users: Australia, Brazil, Canada, Chile, Colombia, Germany (as DM4), Greece, Indonesia, Iran, Italy, Japan, Korea (South), Netherlands, New Zealand, Norway, Pakistan, Philippines, Portugal, South Africa, Spain, Thailand, Tunisia, Turkey, United States, Uruguay, and Venezuela. In many cases Mk 44 is retained only as a reserve weapon. The upgrade kit was bought by Korea and reportedly also by Pakistan.

Many users may be unable to operate Mk 44 torpedoes because their batteries may have expired. For example, New Zealand had to retire its Mk 44s in March 1993. However, this retirement was ordered after a decision not to renew the batteries.

♦ Mk 46 and Mk 46 NEARTIP

Dimensions: 12.75 × 100 in (15.3in fins)
Weight: 508 lb
Speed/Range: 12,200 yd/45 kt at 50ft depth; 10,100 yd/45 kt at 1500 ft depth
Warhead: 96 lb of H-6
Powerplant: Otto-fuel piston engine

Data apply to Mod 1 as delivered (1968). This active or passive/active lightweight torpedo uses a fixed-program digital computer with autopilot (into which presets [homing mode, initial search and ceiling depths, search pattern, and course heading; some versions also have a search floor, to avoid hitting a shallow bottom] are inserted). Initial depth is one of six options, depending on the depth and course of the target submarine. Surface-launch ceiling is automatically set at 50 ft, to keep the torpedo from attacking the launching ship, but it is selectable for other modes. Course headings are programmed only for snake search (5 for a surface tube but 12 for a helicopter, so the latter can attack in any direction from the hover). At least in the current Mod 5, information can be entered up to 0.25 sec before launch, and there is no warmup prior to firing.

Active homing range is 1600 yd maximum (1300 yd average) with a 30-kHz sonar. In passive/active mode, which provides

Alliant torpedoes are shown at Navy League 1996: Mk 46 at top, then the pumpjet Mk 50, and at bottom the new half-length version of Seahuntor. (S. Slade, DMS/Forecast International)

The front half of a Mk 46 (top) shows (right to left) the sonar transducer, then (behind the thin strip of torpedo body) the casting carrying the power transistors and the printed wiring board of the sonar transmitter, then the four printed wiring boards of the receiver, then a covered section containing the warhead, then the control group's 22 printed wiring boards, housed in a casing. The control group contains the torpedo's gyro pendulum (to control its attitude), its course gyro, its pressure transducer (to sense depth), and its pressure arming/safing switch. The bulkhead visible abaft the control group is the front end of the torpedo's fuel tank. The hybrid lightweight torpedo is shown below Mk 46. (Author)

antisurface target capability, the torpedo initially seeks a passive target. It switches to active mode if it receives no target noise during a short preset time. The primary search modes, snake and circle, both flat, contrast with the helix modes of earlier torpedoes. Presumably, this change reflects Mk 46's longer sonar acquisition range, which provides a wider FOV at any depth. Surface tubes are generally programmed for snake search but can select circle under urgent or close-attack conditions. Aircraft and Asroc launches are automatically set for circle. Helicopter-launched torpedoes can be set to circle or snake.

The passive mode was demonstrated when a Mod 5 destroyed a surfaced submarine. Mk 46 can presumably then be used in an alternative antisurface-ship mode; torpedo-carrying missiles such as Asroc can be employed against surface targets. They generally drop their torpedoes outside effective CIWS range.

The computer carries search and reattack tactics and controls vertical beamwidth for search: narrow for shallow water (and during the attack phase), to avoid bottom and surface reflections, and broad in deep water. Turned on once the torpedo has passed its preset enable distance, it provides control signals and a time base, and controls the active sonar and interprets its outputs, setting a range gate. A second valid echo in the gate verifies that a target is present, and the computer begins to send pitch commands to the autopilot. Comparison with later torpedoes, such as Murene, shows what the computer does not do: it does not track several targets simultaneously to decide which is worth attacking (and which is a decoy), and it uses preset tactics. The difference is presumably entirely a function of the much greater power of newer computers.

Operating depth is 20–1500 ft.

Mod 1, the first major production version, introduced the 5-cylinder swashplate engine and Otto monopropellant. Its main limitation was that it began to search immediately upon hitting the water, hence could not be used by a helicopter with dipping sonar detecting a distant contact. A stronger hull (for greater depth) and better counter-countermeasures were introduced in 1968. Computer logic changes (1969) improved performance against slow and/or periscope-depth targets (masked by reverberation). Mod 1 Phase 2 (1971) incorporated Mod 2 improvements (except HATS), including better shallow-water performance and ECCM.

Mod 2 (1970) has additional computer logic improvements (for reattack after losing contact or rejecting a decoy) and a new au-

topilot. For single-helicopter attack (HATS, the helicopter attack tactical system), it provides a run-out (modes are air/Asroc, without a run-out, and HATS). The modified autopilot adds further gyro settings (95, 120, 150, 180 deg in addition to the earlier 0, 35, and 70 deg) so that the helicopter could launch while hovering into the wind regardless of target bearing. This version introduced PBXN-103 explosive (Mk 103 warhead), 27% more powerful than its predecessor.

Mod 4 is the payload of the CAPTOR (Mk 60) mine. Work on this version began in 1973.

Mod 5, NEARTIP (the Near-Term Improvement Program), is very nearly a completely new torpedo, employing either entirely new or greatly modified seeker (sonar transducer, transmitter, and receiver), guidance, and propulsion, largely to deal with Soviet submarines with anechoic coverings. The torpedo has a new slow (quieter) search speed (which increases endurance 30–50% in terms of time) (30 kt/16 kyd) and its sonar sends out new coded pulses for better signal-to-noise performance and better use of target Doppler. Signal-processing logic was improved, particularly to reject false targets. At the same time, reverberation effects in shallow water were reduced, so self-noise could better be measured and disregarded. All operation is now digital, with improved stability and precision and an improved digital computer. Improved search and reattack patterns are stored in the computer's EPROM, for better countermeasures resistance (discrimination) and target acquisition and reacquisition. A second roll pendulum improves pullout from dives and is also better for shallow-water launch. Once the torpedo has locked onto its target it still attacks at the same sort of high speed provided by the original Mk 46. The fuze is revised to function even if the torpedo struck the target at a shallow angle. Work on this version began in 1974. It was tested successfully in 1979.

Mod 5 requires overhaul at 4- and 8-yr intervals (engine teardown every 4 yr).

Alliant (ex-Honeywell) offers a retrofit kit to convert Mod 1 and Mod 2 torpedoes to Mod 5 standard. A third less expensive than a new Mod 5, it includes a Mod 2 transducer, a new receiver and transmitter, a new digital-computer control system, and a two-speed valve for two-speed propulsion.

The U.S. Navy introduced the first of two shallow-water modifications in 1984, to improve performances against slow submarines at periscope depth in both deep and shallow water. Such targets provide little Doppler (which the torpedo uses to distinguish them from background noise) and the torpedo may be confused by reflection (both of its pulses and of its self-noise) from the surface. The torpedo was fitted with a more coherent transmitter and better steering logic. This version was successfully tested in Eckernfoerde Bay in 1987, confirming that it met the NATO 40m requirement.

Honeywell (now Alliant), the manufacturer, developed a further shallow-water modification, Mod 5(AS), beginning about September 1989 (it entered production about 1990). Mod 5AS(W), an improved version, is entering service between October and December 1996.

The high cost of the new Mk 50 encouraged the U.S. Navy to modernize some Mk 46 torpedoes. Alliant's Mk 46 SLEP program (1000 torpedoes, total $8M) began fleet introduction early in FY96 and should be completed in 1998. The after seal is replaced and shallow-water performance somewhat improved (better bottom avoidance, endurance, and resistance to shallow-water countermeasures). The guidance system is modified to prevent CCM software from being copied. This is probably the Mod 5AS(W) version described above. See also the Hybrid Torpedo program described below.

Mod 6 (1989) was an abortive CAPTOR upgrade version, a slightly improved Mod 5 forebody with a Mod 4 afterbody. Mod 7 was a surface-ship torpedo defense version. Although 172 were converted, the torpedo failed its OpEval.

Mk 46 is now virtually the standard NATO lightweight torpedo; exports began in 1972, and Mod 5 alone was bought by nine navies. In U.S. service it replaced Mk 44. Compared to Mk 44, Mk 46 is much faster, dives deeper, has 60% greater maximum acquisition range, and can be dropped at up to 500 kt. The final Development Characteristic was issued in June 1956. Mod 1 was successfully evaluated in November–December 1965. Honeywell became second-source supplier in July 1965 and became single-source supplier in 1969. It made about 9200 Mod 1 in 1965–69 (the 5000th Mod 1 was delivered in March 1967). Many Mod 1s were later modernized to Mod 4 or Mod 5 standard. Mod 2 was produced through 1981, including 950 units made for the Royal Navy beginning in 1972. Total production, for FY80 and previous years, was 11,646 torpedoes. The Mod 5 program began in October 1972, OpEval being completed in February 1978. The initial contract was awarded in July 1979 (for 570 torpedoes under the FY79 program, under a planned 3-yr program for 2274 torpedoes) and the last in February 1987. Purchases in later years were: 253 in each of FY81 and FY82, 440 in FY83, 1200 in FY84, 1565 in FY85, and then 500 each in FY86, FY87, and FY88, for a total of 5881 new-build Mod 5s. The first NEARTIP (Mod 5 conversion) kit contract, for 600 kits ($18.5M), was awarded in February 1978. Contracts for another 5140 kits were let in 1979–83 (total 5740). Additional Mod 5s were made for the Dutch and British navies. In September 1990 the U.S. Navy let an FMS production contract for 331 torpedoes (including 245 for Spain, 40 for Brazil, completed at the end of 1992). Taiwan ordered 160 Mod 5s in 1993. Egypt ordered 80 at about this time. Early in 1994 Australia ordered 50 to 100 Mod 5s. In 1994 Alliant received a $15.84M contract to make Mod 5s for Turkey and Mod 2s for a new South American customer (probably Chile). Early in 1995 recent Mod 5 upgrade kit sales were: 36 to Canada, 70 to Australia (with another 180 expected). The 1995 contract also included the first sale of the HOTTorp exercise torpedo. The company received another contract early in 1995 to build 204 Mod 5s and 70 upgrade kits for export, for delivery between September 1995 and February 1997. Mitsubishi manufactures this torpedo under license in Japan (coproduction approved July 1982). Although Mk 46 production for the U.S. Navy ended in 1990, the U.S. government currently plans to support the weapon through 2017. Alliant is actively marketing Mk 46, and it bought back surplus British torpedoes (freed by Stingray purchases).

About 1986 the U.S. Navy's reported objective was a total of 5500 Mk 46-5 and 3000 Mk 46-4 torpedoes. In mid-1995, the U.S. Navy had about 14,000 lightweight torpedoes on hand (about 300 Mk 50 and 9500 Mk 46 active plus 4000 Mk 46 being cannibalized or in deep storage); it needed only about 8000.

Current unit price is about $250,000.

Users: Australia (468 bought prior to 1974; has a mix of Mod 2 and Mod 5), Brazil (unknown number of Mod 2 bought before 1988; Mod 5 bought November 1989 for delivery 1988 and 1989; 131 bought 1990), Canada (428 Mod 1 bought; 200 Mod 5 kits bought 1981, 150 Mod 5 kits bought 1992), Chile (bought in preference to Impact), France (100 bought; 93 Mod 5 kits bought 1981), Germany (204 Mod 2 bought 1978, Mod 5 bought for new *Brandenburg* class; carried by MPA as well as by ships; Mod 2s now being upgraded to Mod 5[AS]), Greece (100 bought prior to 1974; has Mods 1/2 and 5), Indonesia (48 Mod 2 bought 1984), Iran (694 bought, 280 of them prior to 1974, and 414 in 1975), Israel (Mod 5 in *Eilat* class, also has Mods 1/2), Italy (Mod 2), Japan (Mod 5 made under license by Mitsubishi), Korea (South: Mod 1), Mexico (probably in *Gearings*), Morocco (12 Mod 1 bought 1984), Netherlands (all now Mod 5: 168 bought before 1974, 50 in 1979; modification kits bought 1981), New Zealand (six Mod 2 bought before 1974), Norway (not certain), Pakistan (Mod 5 reported, for *Gearings*), Portugal (Mod 5 on MEKO 200 and *Baptiste de Andrade*–class frigates), Saudi Arabia (52 Mod 2 bought 1978), Spain (231 Mod 5 bought 1988 to supplement Mod 2 bought earlier; 118 Mod 5 kits had been bought 1981; 200 Mod 5 bought 1990; total of 500 Mod 5 on hand in 1991; 245 made under last Mk 46 contract 1991), Taiwan (five bought pre-1972, 50 Mod 2 in 1973, 150 in 1978; now has Mod 5), Thailand (100, some of them Mod 5), Turkey (Mods 1 and 5), United Kingdom (950 bought before 1974, 500 in 1979; all either expended or returned to Alliant for resale), United States. Belgium plans

to buy 65 Mod 5 to replace L 5 torpedoes, on board *Weilingen*-class frigates. This torpedo has been approved for export to China (PRC) and to Yugoslavia (February 1992). China had already recovered some Mk 46s, but reportedly her attempt at reverse-engineering failed because Mk 46 was designed to Imperial (ft/in/lb) rather than to metric standards. The PRC Mk 46 program fell afoul of the 1989 arms embargo. Reportedly, too, the Japanese Mk 46 program has encountered difficulties. The figures above may not be complete for some navies, probably because some torpedoes were provided as direct aid rather than as FMS purchases. Portugal hopes to substitute Mk 46 Mod 5 for the current French L 3 torpedoes on board the *Commandante Rivière* class.

◆ Lightweight Hybrid Torpedo (LHT)

This program responds to the new littoral threat and to the end of the Cold War. The Navy argues that Mk 46 vehicle performance suffices, but that the sophistication of Mk 50 guidance is badly needed in the confusing shallow water environment. The new Lightweight Hybrid Torpedo combines Mk 46 warhead and propulsion with the Mk 50 seeker array and transmitter, a new COTS receiver, COTS-based signal processor, and COTS-based tactical processor. A new COTS-based command/control unit will link the torpedo controls with the processor. A Mk 48 ADCAP fuel-control valve will provide greater speed variability, to include the low search speed of Mk 50. Maximum speed and depth will not exceed those of Mk 46. Compared to a Mk 50, the signal and tactical processors move from mid-body to the front end. An open system architecture should make for easy technology insertion. Changes to the Mk 46 after end are limited to those needed to connect it to the new digital front end. In 1993 the torpedo program office and NUWC developed a control and acoustic technology vehicle (CATV) with an Alliant interface between the Mk 46 after end and the Mk 50 front end. CATV entered the water less than 9 months after the contract was signed, and proved quite successful. The Mk 46 control system had enough dynamic range to compensate for the extra weight of the Mk 50 nose array.

Alliant's mock-up of a lightweight hybrid torpedo is shown between Mk 46 (top) and the short version of Seahuntor (bottom), at Bourget Euronaval 1996. (Author)

An Alliant/Hughes team won the development contract in June 1996. As envisaged in 1995, the program would call for delivery of 35 vehicles within 18 months of contract award, for in-water tests. The planned program calls for 2000 modification kits for delivery in 1999–2010 (full production would begin in 2002).

The hybrid program begins a process of increasing commonality in torpedoes, since it uses some Mk 48 and Mk 50 hardware as well as the new shallow-water algorithms being developed for Mk 48 ADCAP (see below).

Mk 46 torpedo. (U.S. Navy)

Mk 48 torpedo, showing the pumpjet. (Westinghouse)

◆ Mk 48/ADCAP

Dimensions: 21 × 230 in
Weight: 3480 lb
Speed/Range: 55 kt/26 kyd, 40 kt/40 kyd (reportedly 10 nm of wire)
Powerplant: 500-HP Otto fuel swashplate engine

This heavy wire-guided active/passive torpedo runs out at high transit speed (reportedly 55 kt) and then slows to ping and attack (reportedly at 40 kt). Press reports that the torpedo accelerates as it attacks suggest that it speeds up from 40 kt as it approaches its target, that is, as the target signal strength increases enough not to be drowned out by increased flow noise. Published figures more than a decade old suggest an acquisition range of 4000 yd (compared to 1000 for Mk 37) and a diving depth of 2500 ft. Mk 48 has also been described officially as the only U.S. torpedo capable of reaching the Alfa's depth, reported as 800 m (2624 ft). The torpedo has a pumpjet to provide high speed without so much noise that the weapon would be unable to home, or that the target would be alerted soon enough to escape easily. Existing torpedoes (Mod 1 and later) use a swashplate piston engine using Otto II (nitrogen ester with oxidant) fuel. Compared to the rejected turbine alternative, the swashplate is noisier but more efficient, particularly at maximum depth, where the combustion products are ejected against considerable back pressure. Torpedo noise was not the determining factor at this time, as the United States enjoyed both the sonar and the weapons advantage.

Aside from the active and passive homing modes, there is a nonacoustic mode, presumably a straight- or pattern-running shot at a surface target, the only intelligent element of the torpedo being its fuze. Numerous published photographs showing Mk 48s blowing substantial ex-warships in half strongly suggest that the torpedo uses a standoff (proximity) fuze for under-the-keel explosion.

Mod 3 (1977) adds a two-way (rather than one-way) wire link (TELCOM), allowing the torpedo operator to exploit the torpedo's sonar. It transmits 14 torpedo and target parameters each second.

Mod 4, a transitional step toward ADCAP, has ADCAP electronics and adds a fire-and-forget mode.

Mod 5, a modification kit, was another interim step toward the new ADCAP version.

ADCAP (advanced capability) is an extensively modified version with greater speed and endurance and a new seeker. The fuel rate to the swashplate engine is increased to add power (and more allowance is made for speed variation); more fuel is carried, in space liberated by a more compact computer. In 1996 the U.S. Navy reported ADCAP performance as 65 kt/20 km (22 kyd). Performance has also been reported as 65 kt/30 kyd, 40 kt/50 kyd. The new nose (transducer, electronically steered sonar with beam-former, and new signal procesor) improves acquisition range, including range at high torpedo speed. A wider sonar field of view reduces the need for the torpedo to maneuver (and this to lose net forward speed) as it approaches a target.

ADCAP was inspired by tests that showed that the basic Mk 48 structure could operate at the depths achieved by the new Soviet Alfa-class submarine, and that targets could be recognized at the necessarily high torpedo speeds involved. The forward-looking sonar had adequate vertical coverage.

When first developed, ADCAP was so different from Mk 48 that a new designation, Mk 49, was initially assigned to it. Presumably, the use of the Mk 48 ADCAP designation justified a simplified development process, just as current electronic equipment often retains earlier designations despite radical improvements.

A Quiet ADCAP program was canceled in February 1992 because the expected Soviet threat was unlikely to materialize and because it was encountering technical problems. It was replaced by the ADCAP MODS program, suited to shallow-water operation against quiet diesel submarines: a guidance and control (G&C) software block upgrade and a torpedo propulsion upgrade (TPU), both of which were restructured in 1993–94. There is also an upgrade to the analog sonar transmitter. Shallow-water tests showed that ADCAP had only limited capability, but also that software upgrades could make a considerable difference. Existing software is written in the CMS-2 programming language rather than in the now-standard ADA. Software Block Upgrade II (in CMS-2) is the first to improve shallow-water capability. Block IIA is rewritten in ADA. Ultimately a more powerful computer will use new sonar waveforms and processing techniques. Blocks III and IV, written in ADA, are adapted to the new TPU. Block II development included 90 in-water developmental test runs in the Gulf of Mexico, the last of which was completed in October 1993. The current modified guidance and control unit (with Block IIA software) was tested beginning in October 1993, with fire-control integration tests beginning in 1995. Block III software developmental tests were scheduled to begin in January 1996, with Block IV developmental tests beginning November 1997. The advanced sonar waveforms and computer processing are due for fleet introduction in 1998.

Propulsion quieting (TPU) is needed both for better signal-to-noise ratios in shallow water (where sound reflects off the bottom and the surface) and to reduce any warning the torpedo provides to its target. A contract for the TPU prototype

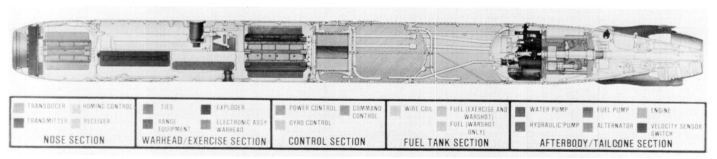

TRANSDUCER	HOMING CONTROL		TIES		EXPLODER		POWER CONTROL	COMMAND CONTROL		WIRE COIL	FUEL (EXERCISE AND WARSHOT)		WATER PUMP		FUEL PUMP		ENGINE
TRANSMITTER	RECEIVER		RANGE EQUIPMENT		ELECTRONIC ASSY WARHEAD		GYRO CONTROL				FUEL (WARSHOT ONLY)		HYDRAULIC PUMP		ALTERNATOR		VELOCITY SENSOR SWITCH
NOSE SECTION			**WARHEAD/EXERCISE SECTION**			**CONTROL SECTION**			**FUEL TANK SECTION**			**AFTERBODY/TAILCONE SECTION**				

Mk 48 Mod 4. (Westinghouse)

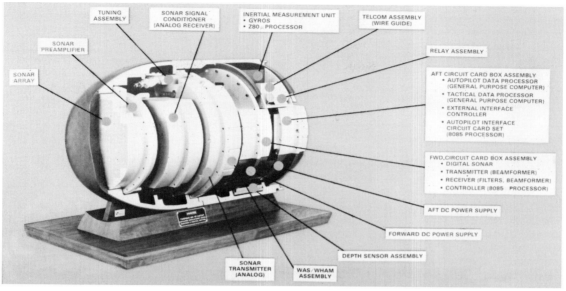

Mk 48 ADCAP's guidance section. (Hughes)

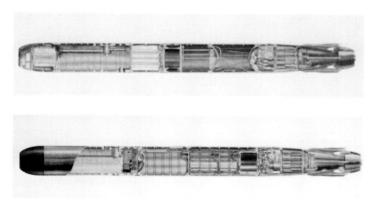

Mk 48 Mod 4 (a) and ADCAP (b). ADCAP has much greater fuel stowage, made possible by shrinking the size of the computer between the warhead and the fuel tank. (Westinghouse)

was awarded in September 1993 (15 were made under the FY94 program).

Mk 48 began as a development of the RETORC II (Research Torpedo Re-Configuration) research program begun in 1956. Development characteristics for a new torpedo (at that time designated EX-10) were set in 1960 (400% of Mk 37 range, 150% diving depth, twice speed, 17% greater acquisition range). The existing Mk 37 was credited with only 10% effectiveness against a 20kt submarine. The proposed Mk 48 was credited with 40% effectiveness against a 35kt submarine, and work was accelerated after system tests on board the submarine *Permit* in the Pacific in 1964. In 1967–68 further contracts were awarded to modify the basic torpedo for antiship as well as antisubmarine use, the single-purpose Mk 47 antiship torpedo project having been abandoned. Mk 48 entered service in 1971. In 1991 the GAO reported an average 75% hit rate during weapons training and accuracy tests. The ADCAP OR was issued in 1975, and the program was accelerated in September 1979 in view of the demonstrated characteristics of the Alfa-class submarine. Hughes received the contract to develop the torpedo's digital guidance and control electronics in August 1979. The first test run was made on the Canadian NANOOSE range early in 1982, using an ADCAP inertial system. TechEval began in August 1986. The first warshot (which sank a decommissioned destroyer) was reported in July 1988. In 1985 it was decided to accelerate production. The 1985 Five-Year Defense Plan called for 1890 ADCAPs, and 123 were included in the FY86 budget. At that time the reported Navy objective was 4659 Mk 48 torpedoes, of which 4000 had been funded through FY87; the cost per Mk 48 was

then $2,239,515. A March 1988 objective for ADCAP modification kits (for Mk 48 Mod 5) was 1062.

Production of Mk 48: 3059 were procured through 1980, then 144 in FY80, the same number in each of FY81–84, and 108 in FY85 (total 3887). The first near-term upgrade Mk 48 Mod 4 was delivered to the U.S. Navy in December 1980. ADCAP procurement: 30 in FY85, 123 FY86, 50 FY87, 100 FY88, 320 FY89, 260 (cut from 320 requested) FY90, 240 FY91 (cut from 320 planned), then 108 in each of FY92–94, none thereafter. ADCAP production ended in December 1995. About 1300 modification kits are planned (first delivery October 1996, program to be completed by 2003). Unit cost as of February 1992 was $2.1M. In 1996 reported unit cost was $1–1.5M.

As of mid-1995, the U.S. Navy had about 4000 Mk 48/ADCAP on hand, of which 3000 were active (about 1000 ADCAP and 2000 Mk 48 [mostly Mod 4]); but with the decline in submarine numbers only about 2000 were needed.

As of 1994, estimated quantities of modification kits were: 37 in FY95, 85 in FY96 (cut to 51 in mid-1995), 177 in FY97, 230 in FY98, 289 in FY99. Low-rate initial production (of hardware, not software) was approved in April 1995.

Users: Australia (127 supplied 1979, 27 ordered 1980), Canada (48 ordered 1985, 13 in 1988, 26 Mod 4 ordered 1989 for 1991 delivery), Netherlands (100 supplied 1980), Turkey (10 ordered 1990 for two *Tang* class [cannot be fired by other Turkish submarines]), and United States (only current ADCAP user). In 1995, the Royal Australian Navy was seeking a Mk 48 replacement for purchase in the late 1990s, ADCAP being a likely choice.

◆ Mk 50 Barracuda

Dimensions: 12.75 × 111.5 in (total length may grow to 115.5 in)
Weight: 771.2 lb
Warhead: Shaped charge
Powerplant: Closed-cycle thermal (SCEPS)

Mk 50 was developed specifically to counter Soviet Alfa-class submarines and future deep-divers, which were beyond the reach of existing lightweight torpedoes. Reported performance is 55 kt/14,000 yd, which was to have been increased by a new (probably abortive) version of the SCEPS powerplant (1990) to 70 kt/18 kyd. Official statements that Mk 50 searches at reduced speed suggest dual-speed operation like that of Mk 48. It was officially stated in 1987 that Mk 50 homes actively (FM pulses) at twice Mk 46 range (the OR required a homing range of 3000 yd). There is also a passive mode. Reportedly the seeker operates at 25 kHz and there are two digital signal processors.

The SCEPS (stored chemical energy power system) powerplant incorporates a block of solid lithium and a tank of sulfur hexa-

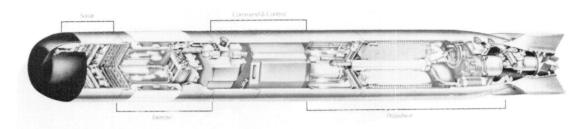

Mk 50 Barracuda torpedo: the exercise version. (Honeywell)

fluoride. When the torpedo is fired, electric squibs melt the lithium. A reaction with the sulfur hexafluoride creates heat (to produce propulsion steam) and a solid ash, which has less volume than the reactants, and so does not have to be dumped outside the torpedo during its run. The torpedo's engine, therefore, does not have to fight increasing water pressure at greater depths. Garrett, which developed the system, said that it is easier to produce than the Otto-fuel power plant of a Mk 46.

Reported minimum launch depth is 40 m (the torpedo can operate in less than 10 m depth), and maximum operating depth is 1100 m (about 3600 ft).

Development began with a technical-assessment phase (February 1972–September 1978). The Honeywell/Garrett design won in 1981, and FSED began in 1983. As of 1988, the reported objective for production of Mk 50s was 7743 torpedoes plus 160 for research and testing. Estimated unit cost was $250,000, compared to $180,000 for Mk 46 at a high production rate. However, a 30 June 1991 Selected Acquisition Report showed a total program cost of $8971.7M to buy 7851 torpedoes (average $1.14M per torpedo). Actual procurement: 39 in FY87, 16 in FY88, 140 in FY89, 200 in FY90, 265 in FY91, 218 in FY92 (246 requested), 212 in FY93 (264 requested), 24 in FY94. Production was completed in July 1996 (522 torpedoes from Alliant, 541 from Westinghouse). Mk 50 procurement was suspended pending completion of a "bottom-up" defense review (it was the only program suspended this way), on the ground that Mk 50 had been designed to deal with deep fast targets, whereas the most likely future targets would be slow and shallow. The decision was taken to terminate production, but Congress authorized a final FY94 batch. The FY92/93 budget (February 1991) unit price was $1.06M (FY92). Mk 50 guidance/control technology is being injected into the new hybrid torpedo program, it having turned out that Mk 50 was much superior to Mk 46 Mod 5AS against future slow/shallow targets.

Plans for a new warhead were presumably dropped with the end of the Cold War. The projected VLA version of Mk 50 was terminated in February 1992; VLA will use the Mk 46 torpedo instead. Work is continuing on improvements for shallow water, near-surface, and zero Doppler conditions, and for bottomed-target recognition. Thus far the U.S. Navy has refused all requests for export (e.g., from Germany).

TORPEDO LAUNCHERS

◆ Mk 25

Mk 25 survives only on board Spanish *Baleares*-class frigates, which use it to launch Mk 37 torpedoes. It was designed to fire both homing torpedoes (originally Mk 35, later Mk 37) and fast straight-runners (Mk 16). Torpedoes are launched by air pressure, and the tube has provision for electrical torpedo setting. Barrel length is 247 in (overall length, with the muzzle door open, is 279 in), and total weight is 1900 lb/barrel.

◆ Mk 32

The standard lightweight torpedo (12.75 in) launcher on board numerous U.S. and foreign frigates, destroyers, and cruisers is normally fired remotely (electrically), but all versions prior to Mod 15 have provision for local emergency firing. Mod 15 lacks any such provision. Torpedoes are ejected by air. Trainable tubes have interlocks that prevent firing when they are not trained outboard. Mods 9 and 15 have interlocks requiring that the muzzle doors be open before the torpedoes can be fired. These launchers are manufactured abroad under license, for example, by MUSL.

A Mk 32 triple tube on board the nuclear cruiser *Mississippi*, June 1988. (S. Terzibaschitsch)

The two main versions are the triple trainable Mods 5–8 and the twin fixed Mod 9 (*Knox* and Canadian "City" classes). Mods 5–9 are controlled and the torpedoes within remotely preset by Mk 264 or Mk 309 firing panels. Mod 5 or 6 (ex-Mod 2 or Mod 7; or ex-Mod 0) is the version for ships with Mk 102, 105, or 111 FCS; Mods 7 and 8 (ex-Mod 2 or 0) equip ships with Mk 114 or Mk 116. Mod 2 was a redesigned Mod 0 with new training gear, barrels (fiberglass liner inside metal rather than all-fiberglass), and securing mechanism. ORDALT 7020 (November 1970) modified Mods 5–9 to indicate the type of weapon loaded without visual check. It prevented inadvertent firing of the weapon when the torpedo selected was not the same as the torpedo loaded. ORDALT 7658 (January 1971) to Mods 5–9 was interim deletion of the no-run-out presetting capability when launching a torpedo from the lower barrel. A Mk 46 launched in this mode was likely to acquire the wake of the firing ship and would probably attack it. Mod 17 (*Perry* class) and Mod 18 (*Virginia* class) are conversions of Mod 5 and 7, respectively, to fire Mk 50 as well as Mk 46 torpedoes.

Mod 14, for the *Spruance* class, is similar to Mod 7 but with faster response, controlled by Torpedo Setting Panel Mk 331 (of FCS Mk 116) or Weapons-Control Panel Mk 329, or by a local bulkhead-mounted control box. Mod 15 is an unmanned version, also similar to Mod 7, with a positive weapons-away indication for each barrel, and heated and remotely controlled muzzle doors.

Mod 16 was the abortive Mk 46 SSTD version, planned for carriers and major amphibious ships.

Typical weights (Mod 5): 2230 lb empty, 3110 lb with Mk 44 torpedoes, 3754 lb with Mk 46, 4450 lb with Mk 50.

Note that at least one Mod 5 was delivered to the PRC before the 1989 cooperation cutoff.

SUBMARINE TORPEDO TUBES

Pre-World War II pneumatic tubes survive only on board former U.S. Guppy-type submarines in Taiwanese and Turkish service. These tubes (Mks 32 and 34 bow tubes, Mks 33 and 35 stern tubes) were modified postwar for electrical torpedo setting. Launching velocity varied with conditions but was typically 50–60 ft/sec. Maximum air pressure was 600 psi. Barrel lengths: bow tubes, 251 in, stern tubes 276 in. Because the tubes are pneumatic, maximum firing depth is 200 ft.

All postwar bow tubes (including Mk 43s in the Turkish *Tang* class) are hydraulic so that they can fire at any depth (*Tang* class Mk 44 stern tubes are swim-outs). They use air-actuated piston pumps, typically one for every bank of two or three tubes (water cylinder, air cylinder, piston). Typical performance for the initial version: 1500 psi impulse, launch speed 32 ft/sec, barrel length 252 in. Operational U.S. versions are all operated from a control panel: Mk 63 for *Sturgeons*, Mk 65 for the *Benjamin Franklin* class, Mk 67 for the *Los Angeles* class, and Mk 68 for the *Ohio* class.

Mk 69 is the 30in tube for the *Seawolf* class.

UNGUIDED WEAPONS (MORTARS AND DEPTH CHARGES)

Deletions: 305mm mortar (France: removed from Portuguese ships, no longer supported by French navy, so probably inoperable in Uruguayan ships), Menon (Italy, extinct), RBU-900 (Russian, extinct), and Squid (United Kingdom, extinct).

CHILE

Cardoen, the Chilean explosives manufacturer, produces a fast-sinking AS-228, externally similar to the U.S. "teardrop" depth charge of World War II. Depth of burst can be set at any of 19 figures between 100 and 1600 ft. Cardoen also manufactures miniature antidiver depth charges that can be set to explode between 4 and 12 m.

CHINA (PRC)

◆ 250mm Rocket Launcher (EDS-25A)

Although similar in concept to Russian RBUs, this weapon seems to differ in detail. As employed on board "Luda"-class destroyers, it has 12 tubes: an outer shallow horseshoe layer of seven, with five inside (two on each side, one in the middle). The mount elevates and trains. A five-tube version (equivalent to RBU-1200) is carried by Jianghu-, Jiangdong-, and Jiangnan-class frigates. This weapon became operational in 1972.

ITALY

◆ MS 500

Misar's 500-lb ASW bomb/mine was designed specifically for the Atlantic MPA, which Italy operates. In the depth-bomb mode, its acoustic proximity fuze detonates it at the closest trajectory point to its target, so it requires no depth presetting.

NORWAY

◆ Terne III

This rocket-fired depth charge system uses a stabilized searchlight sonar to search for, detect, and track the target in depth. It places weapons 20 yd apart in a line perpendicular to the target's course. Fuzing modes are time (0.3 sec after water entry), contact, and proximity (Doppler to detonate 20 ft from the target). In the current Mk 8/10, range is 400–5000 m; the 21cm × 2m rnd weighs 120 kg (explosive charge equivalent to 70 kg). The six-barrel launcher elevates to 47–77 deg to fire. It can be reloaded in 30 sec, and six salvos are available in ready-use stowage. The deck opening, which is covered by two weather hoods, is 3.6 × 5.0 m.

Developed by the Norwegian Defense Research Establishment with U.S. assistance, Terne was introduced about 1960 in its Mk 3 version.

User: Norway (*Oslo* class).

The Norwegian frigate *Narvik* shows her prominent enclosed Terne III launcher between her forward twin 3in/50 gun and her bridge. The radar above her bridge is a French DRBV 22, with a Signaal WM-24 above. The radar aft is a Mk 91 controlling NATO Sea Sparrow missiles. (U.S. Naval Institute)

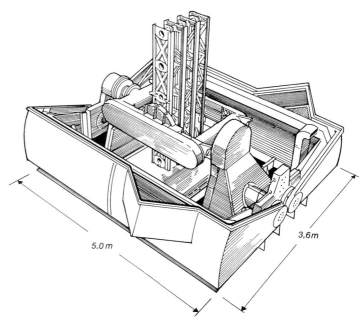

The Terne launcher. (Kongsberg)

RUSSIA

RBU is the Russian designator (Raketnaya Bombometnaya Ustanovka, or Rocket Depth Charge). Former MBU designators reflect an earlier, erroneous Western belief that these weapons were mortars like the British Limbo. A full ASW rocket system (RPS) consists of the RBU (launcher) plus the RGB (rocket), the UDB (depth fuze), and the PUSB (firing control device). The figure in the designation is usually the nominal range in meters.

◆ RBU-1000 (Smerch-3)

This six-barrel lightweight short-range version of RBU-6000 fires impact/time-fuzed RGB-10 rockets (195 kg, 100 kg explosives) in ripples (two, three, or six rounds at once). Arranged in a horseshoe, the barrels load vertically and automatically, one by one. The mount is remotely trained and elevated (to control range). Maximum target depth is 500 m. Smerch-3 is controlled by a Burya FCS, to attack torpedoes at close range and submarines at greater ranges. Loadouts: 60 rnd (5 salvoes/launcher) in a Kara or Kresta II, 48 rnd (4 salvoes/launcher) in a Kashin. RBU-1000 was introduced in 1962–63.

Users: Russia (*Kirov*, Kara, Kresta I/II, Kashin, *Udaloy*, *Sovremennyy*, *Berezina*).

◆ RBU-1200 (Uragan System)

This five-barrel launcher (three above two; 1.4m barrels) is controlled by the Uragan FCS (elevation limit 51 deg, loading angle 40 deg, elevation rate 18 deg/sec). The RGB-12 rounds (252 × 1228 mm, 71.5 kg, 32 kg HE, lethal radius 6 m). Sinking speed

RBU-1000 rocket launcher on board the cruiser *Kerch*, 1989. This device is mounted on the ship's quarter, firing aft. Kresta II– and *Sovremennyy*-class ships carry RBU-1000s in similar positions, which would be very reasonable if the weapon had a secondary antitorpedo (e.g., deployed noisemaker) role. The U.S. Navy experimented with a rocket-launched antitorpedo noisemaker, NAE, about 1948, ultimately discarding it because the launcher, Mk 31, presented too many hazards. Towed noisemakers were preferred. Other Russian classes engaged in ASW lack any equivalent to RBU-1000 aft. Most carry a towed torpedo decoy. (Eric Grove)

is 6.85 m/sec (depth settings are 10–330 m). Flight time is 3–16.3 sec. At the maximum range, 1450 m, bombs are spread over a 70 × 150m area. The launcher elevates for range but is fixed in train (except for loading, in Pauks).

A PRC-manufactured equivalent uses 40kg (88-lb) rockets with 3kg (6.6-lb) warheads, to extend range to about 2000 m (2200 yd).

RBU-1200s on board an SO 1–class subchaser, 1968. (SOVFOTO)

Users: Bangladesh (Jianghu class), China (Jianghu, Jiangdong, Jiangnan, Haijui, Hainan, Shanghai classes), Cuba (Pauk class), Egypt (Jianghu class), Finland (*Turunmaa* class), India (Pauk and Natya classes), North Korea (Soho, Hainan, SO 1 classes), Pakistan (Hainan class), Romania (*Democratia*, Shanghai, and Kronstadt classes), Russia (Pauk, Mayak, Natya classes), Thailand (Jianghu class), and Vietnam (SO 1 class).

◆ RBU-2500 (Katyusha: Smerch-1 System)

This 16-barrel (two horizontal rows of eight) manually loaded projector trains and elevates; it fires RGB-25 rounds (312 × 1340

mm, weight 85.0 kg, including 26 kg of HE; lethal radius 5 m). Range is 550–2700 m (flight time 3–25 sec). Sinking speed is 11 m/sec (depth settings 10–320 m). The load-out in a Riga-class frigate was 128 rounds (4 salvoes/launcher). Smerch-1 may be coded as D-13.

RBU-2500 being loaded. (TASS)

Users: Bulgaria (*Riga*), India (Petya class), Romania (Tetal and Poti classes), Russia (Petya III class), Syria (Petya class), and Vietnam (Petya class).

◆ RBU-6000 (Smerch-2)

The twelve barrels are arranged in a horseshoe, automatically loaded when they are elevated into the vertical position, barrel by barrel. They fire RGB-60 rockets (212 × 1830 mm, 110 kg, 25 kg HE) to 5700–6000 m (maximum submarine depth 500 m), in a ripple (1, 4, 8, 12) controlled by a Burya FCS (which can also control Smerch-3, RBU-1000). The empty launcher weighs 3100 kg. Loadouts: 144 in Kresta II and Kara (6 salvoes/launcher), 192 in Kashin (8 salvoes/launcher). This weapon can be used for shore bombardment. It was introduced in 1960–61. The bomb can be fitted with the guidance system of the S3V depth bomb. See also RPK-8.

Users: Algeria (Koni class), Bulgaria (Koni class), Cuba (Koni class), India ("Kashin" class), Libya (Koni class), Poland ("Kashin" class), Russia (*Kirov, Slava*, Kara, *Udaloy*, "Kashin," *Neustrashimyy*, Krivak, Parchim, Grisha, Petya II classes), Yugoslavia (*Kotor* and Koni classes).

DEPTH CHARGES

Many ships still carry depth charges and throwers, and similar equipment was widely exported. All depth charges (which can be dropped from aircraft or launched from ships) are cylindrical. The old BMB-1 spade-and-arbor type is now rare. In BMB-2, the depth charge fits within the mortar barrel. Standard internal and external rack capacity is 10 charges.

The standard types are B-1, 4VB, M-1, and 4VM.

| | | WEIGHT | | |
	Dimensions	Total	HE	Settings
B-1	44 × 72 cm	166 kg	135 kg	20–210 m
	(17 × 28 in	366 lb	298 lb	66–689 ft)
4VB	46 × 73 cm	163 kg	115 kg	15–210 m
	(18 × 29 in	359 lb	254 lb	49–689 ft)
M-1	26 × 43 cm	35 kg	25 kg	10–50 m
	(10 × 17 in	77 lb	55 lb	33–164 ft)
4VM	19 × 63 cm	22 kg	16 kg	10–25 m
	(7.5 × 25 in	49 lb	35 lb	33–82 ft)

RBU-6000.

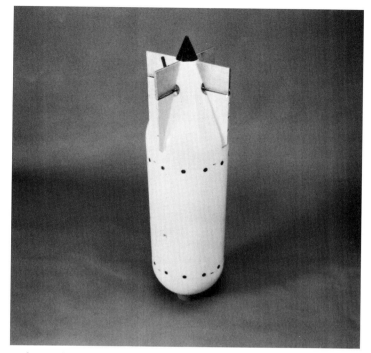

Saab's guided depth bomb. (Saab-Scania)

A nuclear depth bomb is carried by helicopters and aircraft as an alternative to a homing torpedo. Reported weight is 700 kg and estimated yield is 200 kT.

The standard aircraft depth bombs are PLAB 120 (123 kg with 64-kg warhead) and PLAB 250 (250 kg with 133-kg warhead). There is also RBK-100 PLAB-10K, a 125-kg cluster bomb carrying six small depth charges.

SPAIN

◆ ABCAS

This low-cost ASW weapon (Arma de Bajo Coste Anti-Submarina) completed an 18-month project definition phase in November 1991. It carries 24 rockets (six across) in a stabilized launcher (2 m high, 1.80m dia). The rockets, cheap enough to be fired at an unconfirmed target, would be fired in salvoes. Range is 1–8 km. The rockets have shaped-charge warheads, to penetrate pressure hulls. Three prototypes were built for trials: one of the warheads, one of the stabilizer, and one to test the rocket motor.

SWEDEN

Saab/FFV has developed an active high-frequency (100–200-kHz FMCW) sonar seeker driving moveable fins for a depth charge dropped by an airplane, helicopter, or ship. In tests, all depth charges fell within the area of uncertainty. The Swedish version is applied to a standard ship depth charge (Model 33, about 50 cm in diameter, 300 kg). Saab has considered numerous applications, including Mk 11, the Bofors 375mm charge, and Elma.

The standard aircraft depth bombs are (HE weight in parentheses): 60 (50), 120 (80), 160 (110), and 205 (140) kg. No designations are known. All use SAM 204 hydrostatic fuzes.

◆ Bofors 375mm Rocket Launcher

The vertically loaded four-barrel version trains and elevates at 18 deg/sec (elevation limits +15/+90 deg). Eight rockets (two more salvoes) are carried on the rocket table below. Rockets are fired at 1-sec intervals, and it takes 3 min to reload all four tubes. The original long-hoist version (with intermediate hoist stage) weighs 7.3 t. A later short-hoist version (no intermediate stage) weighs 7.6 t. The later two-tube version (1967) exists in two versions: Type A (3.2 t, four rockets on rocket table) and Type B (eight rockets on rocket table, replenished by pushbutton trucks, two rockets at a time, from one or more six-rocket storage tables). This version trains and elevates at 30 deg/sec. It elevates to +90 deg, but can fire only between 0 and 60 deg.

The French version of the Bofors 375mm rocket launcher. The flare-launching racks are alongside the rocket tubes. The guns are twin 57mm/60s, also a French version of a Bofors original. (L. van Ginderen)

The French six-barrel Model 1964 version, built by Creusot, usually carries six rails for illumination rockets. It can be reloaded in less than 60 sec. Total system weight, including remote control, is 16 t (5.7t launcher, 10.1 t of ammunition [36 rockets]). Rated range is 1600 m, the French navy using rounds with 100 kg of explosive.

Rocket Types	M/50	Type E	Type F	Type N
Weight	250 kg	250 kg	242 kg	230 kg
Charge	100 kg (220 lb)	107 kg (236 lb)	107 kg (236 lb)	80 kg (176 lb)
Min Range	370 m (405 yd)	670 m (732 yd)	1400 m (1530 yd)	1530 m (1670 yd)
Max Range	875 m (957 yd)	1660 m (1815 yd)	2230 m (2439 yd)	3600 m (3940 yd)
Terminal Sinking Speed	10.9 m/sec (35.8 ft/sec)	10.2 m/sec (33.5 ft/sec)	9.2 m/sec (30.1 ft/sec)	
Time of Flight[a]	14.2/19.4	16.0/25.3	19.3/28.5	24/36

[a]Min/max range to 100m submarine depth, sec.

In the Swedish version, range (300–3600 m [330–3900 yd]) is adjusted by selection among four types of rocket (for varying velocity: M/50, Type E, Type F, Type N), by firing one or both concentric rocket motors, and by elevation. Depth of burst is set either by time (STIDR) or by acoustic proximity (ZAMBO) fuze; there is also an impact/time combination fuze (STIDAR). Lethal radius is about 15 m (16 yd).

Nonrecoverable training rockets are Types L (M/50) and M (for Type E), both 80 mm. Recoverable practice rockets are M/53 and Types H, K, and P (for M/50, E, F, N).

Although there is some question as to the continued value of this weapon for ASW, in the Belgian navy at least a line-of-bearing shot is the standard quick-reaction antitorpedo measure, presumably in hopes that the explosion will derange the torpedo homing system.

This system was originally developed for the Royal Netherlands Navy, which placed it in service in 1954.

Users: Belgium (four *Weilingen* class), Brazil (six *Niteroi* class), Egypt (two *Descubierta* class), France (17 *d'Estienne d'Orves* class), Greece (five *Thetis* class), Indonesia (three *Fatahilah* class), Japan (as Type 71: six *Yamagumo* class, three *Minegumo* class, two *Yubari* class, one *Ishikari* class, and four *Isuzu* class), Malaysia (two FS-1500s), Morocco (one *Descubierta* class), Nigeria (two *Erin'mis*), Spain (six *Descubierta* class), and Turkey (three ex-German *Koln* class). Brazil, Egypt, Indonesia, Malaysia, Morocco, Nigeria, and Spain use the two-barrel version; Greece, Japan, and Turkey use the four-barrel; all others are six-barrel.

◆ Elma/ASW-600/ASW-601/ASW-604/KAS-2000

The Saab/FFV lightweight ASW system employs four nine-barrel nonmagnetic LLS-920 mortars (at fixed 30-deg elevation) firing 100 × 267 mm (4.2-kg [3.9 × 10.5 in, 9.3-lb]) shaped-charge contact-fuzed M83 grenades to a range of about 250–300 m (267–330 yd). Dispersion (over 80 × 10 to 80 × 100 m) is controlled by a hand lever that splays the tubes. A full salvo is spread over 2 sec to limit deck loads. The sonar tactical display in CIC shows the predicted impact area and own-ship and target locations; it can be used to steer the ship to the aimpoint. Grenades sink nose-first. Each has a unique nose latch which keeps it from tumbling through the water, and which holds it to the submarine hull at right angles, for maximum effect. The shaped charge, developed from that in the Carl Gustav antitank rocket, is intended to force the submarine to surface. The mortar is based on Saab's proposed Philax chaff launcher; it has an alternative decoy function.

In January 1985 the system was ordered modified to engage targets in water only 10 m (33 ft) deep. Later the bombs were modified to arm upon hitting the water, to engage even shallower targets.

ASW-600 (1992) fires longer (465 mm, 5.7 kg) M90 grenades to 600 m, with a more powerful charge and flip-out fins for better flight stability. Export variants may reach 1000 m. There is also a coast defense version.

ASW-601 (1995) uses two trainable mounts, each carrying a pair of nine-barrel launchers. Normally the barrels are at fixed elevation, but there is also a triaxially stabilized elevatable version. ASW-601 was bought by Japan for trials. ASW-604 (1995) carries the same M90 grenade in one or two 20-rnd helicopter launchers; all can be dropped in a single pattern.

KAS-2000 (formerly KAS-90) is an ASW-600 follow-on announced in 1994 for the new YS-2000 corvette. To reach a maximum range of 1200 m (possibly 2000 m), the mortar is replaced by a rocket booster fired from a gyrostabilized six-barrel launcher

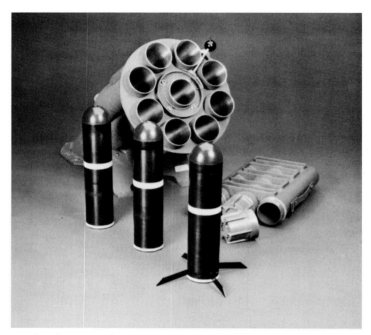

An Elma (ASW-600) launcher with its new M90 grenades. Range exceeds 400 m, and the grenade is armed virtually instantly upon entering the water. (Saab-Scania)

to a predicted impact point. Target data are transferred to the 15–16-kg 127mm (5in) grenade at firing time. The launch velocity (about 120 m/sec) is measured precisely and transmitted to an on-board computer (using chip technology like that in the Strix guided mortar round), which calculates the time to deploy the braking ballute (which, with elevation, determines range). At minimum range (150 m), the ballute deploys only 10 m from the launcher. Water impact slows the grenade to 70 m/sec (it detects the water by measuring the change in the index of refraction). Then it slows to 8 m/sec by jettisoning its rear section, turning on a nose-mounted active planar transducer like that of a torpedo. The same launcher can fire ECM and acoustic decoys, in both cases active and passive. Development began in mid-1996.

Elma development began in mid-1983 to counter midget submarines in Swedish coastal waters. Elma was first delivered a year later. ASW-601 completed trials on board the *Hugin*-class attack boat *Styrbjorn* in 1996. The Royal Swedish Navy plans to replace ASW-600s with -601 in all the *Hugins*, in 7 *Landsorts*, in 6 corvettes, and in 12 coastal artillery boats.

Users (ASW-600): Finland (*Helsinki II* class), and Sweden (fast patrol craft and *Landsort*-class minesweepers).

◆ Malin

This "incident weapon," announced in 1983, is a magnetic limpet mine that attaches itself to a submarine, emitting a traceable signal until removed. Malin makes tracking easy, and it is a nuisance that cannot be removed unless the submarine surfaces and sends someone out to find the mine on the hull. It is reminiscent of the U.S. "clicker" of the 1950s, a magnetized noisemaker that could be dropped on a submarine and that could generally be removed only if the submarine surfaced. Malin was devised to counter supposed Soviet midget submarines operating in Swedish waters.

◆ SAM 204

SA Marine's helicopter-dropped depth charge has a hydrostatic fuze (variable from 15–80 m [49–262 ft] in depth) and a variable charge (50–250 kg [110–550 lb] of high explosives). The fuze is unusual in being immune to transient pressure waves caused by other explosions, so depth charges can be dropped in salvo. Unlike the fuzes of other air-dropped depth charges, this fuze is set in the cockpit.

UNITED KINGDOM

Nuclear depth bombs have all been retired.

◆ Air-Launched Depth Charge Mk 11

Dimensions: 11 in × 4 ft 7 in (body section is 3 ft 2 in long)
Weight: 320 lb
Warhead: 176 lb

Data describe Mod 3, with a stronger outer case to withstand high-speed drops and helicopter vibrations. In the Falklands, Mk 11 was the only British weapon capable of attacking the surfaced Argentine *Santa Fe* (Sea Skuas merely passed through the submarine's sail). Many navies had already abandoned depth bombs on the theory that they could never catch fast diving submarines.

Users: Brazil, Chile, Egypt, India, Pakistan, and United Kingdom. France obtained some Mk 11s in 1988, but the U.S.-supplied Mk 54 is her standard depth bomb.

A Mk 11 depth bomb (with an A244/S torpedo behind it) at Farnborough, 1992. (Author)

◆ Limbo (Mortar Mk 10)

This triple-barreled hand-loaded mortar varies its range (between 400 and 1000 yd) by opening gas vents. It is aimed by a combination of roll and pitch (which is also used to stabilize the mounting). Rounds are spaced by a short time delay in firing. To make underwater trajectory predictable, the FCS fires so that the time-fuzed (preset depth) 390-lb (207 lb Minol) shells always enter the water at the same angle. A pair of Limbos produces triangular patterns above and below the estimated position of the submarine. One mounting and a magazine holding 17 salvos (51 bombs) weigh about 35 t. Lethal range is about 5 yd, but at up to 50 yd, light fittings will be shattered and pipes cracked. Serious psychological effects can be expected at even greater ranges.

Limbo was the ultimate development of World War II British ahead-thrown ASW weapons, beginning with Hedgehog. The associated sonar is Type 170.

Users: Canada (*Gatineau* and *Terra Nova*), Chile (*Gen. Banquedanoo* and *Ministro Zeuteno*), India (*Leanders*), Indonesia ("Tribal" class), Iran (Mk 5 frigates), Malaysia (*Rahmat* and *Hang Tuah*), and Pakistan (*Leander* class).

A Limbo mortar, 1986. (R. Cheung)

UNITED STATES

It is not clear whether a post–Falklands War U.S. initiative to develop a depth bomb fuze (SAM-104) for Mk 82 bombs bore fruit. However, in 1995 the RNZAF adopted a Mk 82 Snakeye with a mechanical time fuze (0.25-sec delay) as its standard depth bomb (first tested 23 March 1995). This weapon was needed because Mk 54 depth bombs had long since been discarded as expired. All nuclear depth bombs have been retired. Earlier U.S. depth bombs survive in other navies, but are not used by the U.S. Navy (see below).

◆ Hedgehog (Projectors Mk 10/11 and 15)

This 24-spigot mortar fires fast-sinking impact-fuzed rounds. Mk 10/11 is fixed in train and elevation, but the spigots can be rolled back and forth to stabilize them against the roll of the ship and to move the point of impact in train (by up to 25 deg). Mk 15 is stabilized and power-trained. Maximum bomb velocity is 175 ft/sec, and a typical flight time is 10 sec, plus 18.2 sec to sink to 200 ft. The bombs form an elliptical (Mk 10) or circular (Mk 11) pattern in the water. The standard post–World War II installation is two firing together. Typical pattern dimensions:

Fixed Mk 11 hedgehog on board USS *Cassin Young* (museum ship), 1986. (A. Raven)

Hedgehog Mk 15. (Author)

Mk 10, 195 ft wide and 168 ft in range at an average range of 283 yd; Mk 11, 267ft circle at 267 yd; Mk 15, 279ft circle at 265 yd. Total weights, including the usual six reload salvos, are 28,720 lb for Mk 10/11 and 26,785 lb for Mk 15.

Mk 10/11 was the standard U.S. World War II standoff mortar.
Users:

> Mk 10/11: Indonesia (*Samadikun* only), Korea (two FRAM II *Gearing*s and two FRAM II *Sumner*s), Taiwan (two Wu-Chin II *Gearing*, three Wu-Chin I *Sumner* FRAM IIs), Thailand (one *Cannon*, two *Tacoma* class), and Turkey (two *Berk* class). The equivalent British Hedgehog is extinct.
> Mk 15: Turkey (*Kocatepe*, PC 1638 class).

◆ Mousetrap (Projector Mk 20)

This 8-rnd (two sets, four rails each) Hedgehog equivalent (with the same warhead) uses rocket propulsion to avoid the mortar's

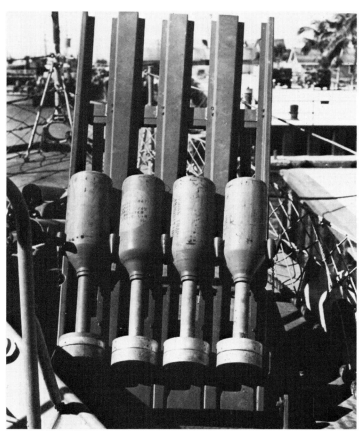

Mousetrap. (National Archives)

need for deck strengthening. Mk 20 forms a pattern about 80 yd wide at 300 yd. This World War II weapon was installed on board many patrol craft supplied to U.S. allies through the early 1970s. The 16-rnd Mk 22 is extinct.

Users: Iran (three PGM 71 class [probably removed]) and Turkey (*Girne*, 12 AB 25 class, four PGM 71 class, and four U.S. 83ft cutters). Mousetrap may also be on board other U.S.-supplied or license-built PGM 39/71 series gunboats: Brazil (six) and Dominican Republic (one).

DEPTH BOMBS AND DEPTH CHARGES

The standard shipboard depth charge was the fast-sinking (14.5 ft/sec and later 22.7 ft/sec) teardrop-shaped Mk 9 (17.7 × 27.6 in, 340 lb, 200 lb HE); fins spun it to stabilize it while it sank. Settings: 30, 300, or 600 ft. Mk 14 is an influence-fired version using an acoustic pistol.

U.S.-type streamlined (teardrop) depth charge, on board USS *Cassin Young* (museum ship), 1986. (A. Raven)

Some slow-sinking (8.5 ft/sec) cylindrical Mk 6 depth charges (17.7 × 27.6 in, 420 lb, 300 lb HE) may survive. Burst depth can be set at 30–1000 ft.

The air-dropped Mk 54 depth bomb (13.8 × 52.5 in, 354 lb, 250 lb of Torpex or HBX) became standard in NATO. It is used by at least the French, German, Italian, and Norwegian navies, and probably by most others using U.S. weapons. Note that this weapon may no longer be in service. New Zealand had to discard it as time-expired sometime in the 1980s.

COUNTERMEASURES

For a surface ship faced with passive homers, the usual countermeasure is a towed noisemaker. Although the noise level must suffice to fool the approaching torpedo, it cannot be allowed to blank out sonar operation: the output of the decoy must be controlled. Too, there is always some fear that, having attracted (but not destroyed) a torpedo, the noisemaker will merely lead it closer to the ship, hence current interest in thrown decoys (see, for example, the U.S. SSTD program). There is always some hope that a noisemaker will trigger not only the torpedo seeker but also any sonar proximity fuze, but the decoy designer cannot be sure what sort of fuze the torpedo employs.

Countering a wake-follower seems far more difficult: no noisemaker can simulate a wake. However, a wake-follower might be seduced by a dummy wake built up out of bubbles laid down by a line of thrown decoys.

The alternative is a direct-kill countermeasure, an antitorpedo weapon. Several such programs since World War II, both in Britain and in the United States, have died because it has proven so very difficult to find and kill a small torpedo.

For a submarine, self-propelled submarine simulators may mislead the sonar operator and may attract passive-homing torpedoes. Transponders, either hull-mounted or ejected, can confuse an active pinger. Finally, a submarine may eject bubble-

Lacroix displayed this notional sonar jammer, suspended from a float, at Bourget Euronaval 1996. (Author)

makers, which will create a screen between the boat and an active pinger. Since the bubbles reflect pings, the torpedo will be unable to see through the screen and may home on the screen itself. The bubble screen may also hide the submarine from a longer-range sonar. In that case, a torpedo with a two-way wire may be steered around the bubble, to look beyond.

In a submarine-versus-submarine engagement, the targeted submarine will want, first, to break track. She must accelerate, making noise. To cover that acceleration, she can create a bubble screen. She can also fire back (without wire guidance) at the pursuing submarine in hopes of escaping while the latter evades (or of forcing the latter to maneuver violently enough to break guidance wires). Hull-mounted transmitters may be used to break lock, just as a surface ship would use a radar lock-breaker and chaff launchers.

Underwater training targets are, in effect, submarine simulators and are, therefore, viable decoys, although they are not generally so described. Some of them are listed in the U.S. systems below.

CHINA

A recent Chinese account of military development mentions an SQK series of countermeasures, comprising an SQK-1 bubble screen, SQK-2 LF jammer, SQK-3 HF jammer, SQK-5 mobile decoy, and SQK-6 towed decoy. SQK-2 and -3 passed design certification in 1987.

◆ EAJ-1

This 15–40-kHz antisonar and antitorpedo jammer (118 × 800 mm, 8 kg) for surface ships and submarines hovers at depths of 30, 60, and 100 m (100, 200, and 330 ft). It can be launched at depths to 200 m (660 ft).

FRANCE

For some years Lacroix has displayed developmental torpedo countermeasures and sonar jammers to be fired from its Sagaie decoy launcher. Initial studies (by Lacroix and Thomson-CSF) were conducted in 1984, with preliminary trials between December 1984 and January 1985. The decoy can carry a pyro-acoustic noisemaker, a gas generator (to create a bubble curtain), and a jammer. At UDT 1995, for example, CS Defense proposed firing six decoys from Dagaie, or 10–12 rounds from Sagaie; these launchers might also fire STN's LCAW.

DCN St. Tropez and Lacroix are both currently developing soft-kill decoys compatible with Sagaie. In 1990, in connection with the abortive Spartacus system, sketches showed a rocket-deployed decoy floating from a buoy in the path of an oncoming torpedo. A sequence of three such decoys was expected to seduce the torpedo far enough away from the ship so that it could not circle back to reattack. The Lacroix torpedo decoy shown at that time weighed 50 kg and carried 25 liters of bubble-generating or pyroacoustic noise-generating material. It could reach 50–200 m in less than 3 sec. Although no wake-follower decoy was shown, it seems likely that a line of bubble-generators could simulate a wake pointing away from the target ship.

At Euronavale 1996 Lacroix displayed a Sagaie-fired Roquette LAT (torpedo lure) set for range (up to 3000 m; 21-sec flight time to 1500 m, 38 sec to 3000 m) and depth, with a lifetime of 3–10 min (payload 26–40 kg). An offboard sonar jammer would float from a balloon in the water (flight time less than 10 sec, duration 3 min, 126 × 1000 mm, 20 kg).

These decoys are part of a Franco-Italian SLAT program.

As described in 1986, the jammer would be deployable about 20 sec after alerting, 3800 m (4160 yd) from a ship, to operate for 4–8 min. As of 1988, Lacroix was designing a 130 × 780mm (5.1 × 30.7in) round (50 kg [110 lb]), operating in less than 3 sec, at ranges of 10–200 m (11–220 yd), carrying a 25-liter payload of bubble generators, pyroacoustic noise sources, or an active decoy that would respond to the torpedo's sonar and emit Doppler-shift-compensated false echoes. Safare-Crouzet and Thomson Sintra are developing an electro-acoustic decoy.

Reportedly, a self-propelled antitorpedo direct-kill (kinetic-energy) weapon is under consideration.

◆ DUUG-1/AUUD-1/Type 197 (Velox)

The first-generation Safare-Crouzet 2–80-kHz broad-band sonar intercept receiver uses four transducers feeding a CRT to indicate the direction of a received sound. The associated loudspeaker emits a tone keyed by the sonar the system intercepts (to indicate PRF, warning of a shift from search to attack scale). That precludes aural classification. Although the original Rochelle Salt transducers were rated at 10–40 kHz, they were resonant at 18 kHz and their response fell by 16 dB at 30 kHz. That made the system ineffective against homing torpedoes at 30–80 kHz. Too, the transducers were very directional at higher frequencies, so direction was not accurately indicated. Too, since one of the four CRT plates was fed by the after transducer, the display was often dominated by cavitation noise. At 14–19.5 kHz, bearing accuracy was 10–13 deg. Sonar frequency is measured on the CRT of the associated AUUD-1; the combination is similar to that of contemporary ESM devices. DUUG-1B presumably used different transducers to extend the effective frequency range to 2–80 kHz (but the U.S. Navy credited it with a frequency range of 5–40 kHz, and 20-deg bearing accuracy). The limitations of DUUG-1 explain the need for the multiband DUUG 2/Type 2019.

DUUG-1 entered French service in 1953. The British reluctantly adopted it (as Type 197, with different transducers) because they could not afford to develop a satisfactory acoustic intercept system of their own (to obtain sufficient gain, the British planned to use four 4ft vertical stacks of transducers covering 5–75 kHz). Type 197 was superseded by Type 2019 in British service. DUUG-1 was replaced by WLR-9/12 in U.S. service.

Users: Argentina (Type 209), Australia (*Oberon* class), Brazil (*Oberon* class), Canada (*Oberon* class), Colombia (Type 209), Chile (*Oberon* class), France (*Daphne* class), Germany (Types 205 and 206), Greece (first four Type 209), Italy (*Enrico Toti* class), Pakistan (*Daphne* class), Peru (Type 209), Portugal (*Daphne* class), South Africa (*Daphne* class), and Turkey (*Tang* class). Probably this set was also installed on early Type 209s, before the German equivalent became available as part of the CSU 3 suite.

♦ DUUG-2 (PARIS)/Type 2019/TSM 2243

Unlike DUUG-1, this French-British-Dutch 2–80-kHz set (recently expanded to 1–100 kHz) is directional (using a PPI display) and breaks the sonar spectrum into bands (2–7.35, 7.35–27, and 27–80 kHz in the French export version) in each of which it has adequate sensitivity. Target emissions are analyzed using tunable low/high-pass filters. The most recent versions add a display of pulse shape and measure of pulse parameters. The system can track up to eight sonar emitters. PARIS (Passive/Active Range-and-Intercept Sonar) typically uses the submarine's own passive transducer for LF reception and a dome forward of the sail for MF/HF reception.

According to the catalog of the 1996 Bourget Euronaval exhibition, the latest version of PARIS is DUUG-5, and TSM 2243 is an improved commercial derivative. Data above are for TSM 2243. Its current version uses TMS 320C30, 68020, and 68040 chips in MIMD configuration.

Plasma displays of an upgraded Type 2019 in Royal Navy service, with PPI at left and waterfalls at right. (Thorn-EMI)

Type 2019 (reportedly 1.75–14.5 kHz, but possibly up to 30 kHz) is the British version, with a reported bearing resolution of 3 to 5 deg. It probably differs from the original French version in incorporating a computer like that in contemporary ESM sys-

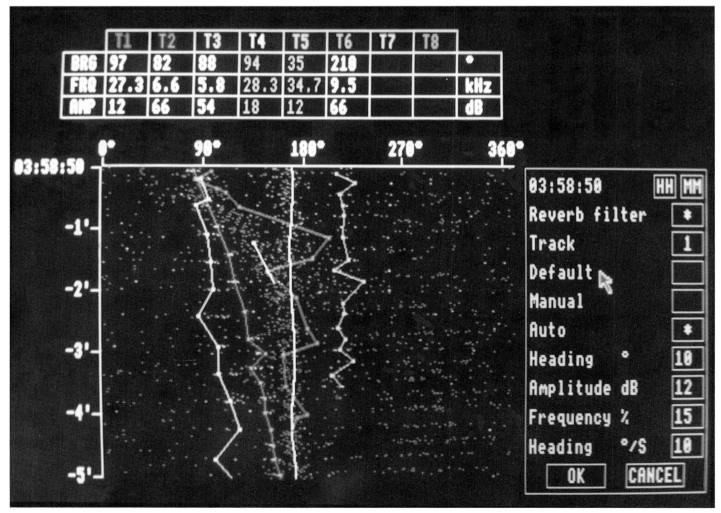

Track data extracted automatically by an upgraded Type 2019 in Royal Navy service, with a track table above the tracks superimposed on the rather faint dots of the waterfall actually detected. (Thorn-EMI)

tems. The dual-CRT display probably corresponded to standard British EW practice, with bearing versus frequency on one side and pulse identification alongside. In service, 2019 apparently suffered a high false-alarm rate, perhaps due to multipath. In November 1993 Thorn Automation received a contract to upgrade the twelve sets on board *Trafalgar*- and *Swiftsure*-class submarines. Drumgrance's new sonar processor intercept unit (SPRINT) is to reduce the false-alarm rate. The CRTs are replaced by plasma panels and the numerous (about 50) analog controls with soft-keys (e.g., to call up bands and change frequency and functions). Digital processors and data recorders were updated. A 1553B interface allows 2019 to communicate directly with the submarine's CDS. Thorn-EMI developed improvements to algorithms for signal processing, for extended frequency coverage, and for short-pulse detection; to sonar parameter extraction; to automatic pulse-to-pulse association and track management; and to classification.

Type 2029 was probably an abortive separate automatic digital sonar-intercept device.

The PARIS project (with Thomson Sintra as prime contractor) began in 1965, a prototype being built in 1968–69. The Royal Navy placed its contract in 1973, testing a prototype in 1974–75 and ordering its first sets in 1977.

Users: France (*Agosta* and *Rubis* classes), Netherlands (all submarines, superseded LWS-30), Pakistan (*Agosta* class), Spain (*Agosta* class), and United Kingdom (as 2019: all SSBN and SSN, to be replaced by new Type 2082). In the *Upholder* class, an active pinger was added to 2019.

◆ DUUG-6 (Velox M5/M6)

The Safare-Crouzet stand-alone sonar-intercept system was intended to replace DUUG-1/AUUD-1/Type 197. Velox M6 is a similar unit intended for integration into a centralized combat system.

Users: France (*Agosta, Rubis,* and SSBN classes), Italy (*Salvatore Pelosi* and *Nazario Sauro* classes), Pakistan (*Agosta* class), Spain (*Agosta* class), and probably the Netherlands. About 70 DUUG-6 were made. Users may have included early Type 209s.

◆ DUUG-7A (Velox M7)

Safare-Crouzet's 2.5–100 (extendable to 500) -kHz system autodetects and autotracks (up to eight tracks) sonar signals, measuring bearing, frequency, strength (in dB), pulsewidth, and PRF. Signals are characterized as CW, FM, or DEMON. Bearing is shown both as a number (within a degree) and graphically, by an indicator lamp lit (like that of a radar warning receiver) around a submarine sketch (within 15 deg), for a quick response. The console shows the last two intercepted signals. M7 will also detect ultrasound communications and acoustic noise generated by surface ships. Bearing accuracy: 12 deg at 2.5 kHz, 10 deg at 5–7 kHz, 7 deg at 7–50 kHz, 12 deg at 50–70 kHz, 16 deg above 70 kHz. Frequency resolution is 10 Hz–9.99 kHz and 100 Hz from 10–99.9 kHz. Measurable pulse duration: 40 msec–5 sec from 2.5–5 kHz, 10 msec–5 sec from 5–10 kHz, 2 msec–2 sec from 10–45 kHz, 1 msec–1 sec from 45–100 kHz. Dynamic range is over 90 dB (resolution 1 dB) from 2.5–45 kHz, and 80 dB (resolution 1 dB) from 45–100 kHz. Typically a submarine has three centerline arrays, forward of the sail, and at the fore and after ends of the sail. They can be supplemented by a VHF extension (up to 250 kHz, without bearing measurement) at the after end of the sail and by a VLF extension (down to 500 Hz) in the bow. Velox M7 entered service in 1992.

◆ SLAT/ALBATROS/SATAR/SPDT-1 and URDT-1

Système de Lutte Anti-Torpille is for ships not equipped with SLASM (see above), such as carriers, AAW destroyers, and general-purpose frigates. Directional (presumably at least dual-line) towed arrays will provide torpedo warning, and the countermeasure will presumably be one of the Sagaie-launched types described above.

In 1995 Thomson Sintra advertised the ALBATROS torpedo warning system, using a SATAR processor (developed with Safare-Crouzet) and either an existing hull array or a towed array with port/starboard discrimination. SATAR (Ship-borne Automatic Torpedo Alert Receiver) detects in broad-band, preclassifying based on specific torpedo characteristics, such as energy

The Velox M7 display, showing data for a previous intercept above data for a current intercept. Angled lines on the drawing of the submarine indicate baffles. (Safare-Crouzet)

fluctuation and frequency signature. All detected targets are passively tracked. Before passing an alert to the ship's CDS, the system classifies a target (one at a time) using LOFAR/DEMON data and a neural net (SYCAT). There are two operator displays: a broad-band waterfall and a LOFAR/DEMON display of all tracks in preclassification and classification processing. In an interactive mode (the operator decides whether to confirm that a contact is a torpedo), this display is the LOFAR/DEMON waterfall (gram) of the beam being classified, steered by the operator.

SATAR is apparently a follow-on to Safare-Crouzet's SPDT-1 (Sonar Passif pour la Detection des Torpilles, official designation URDT-1), which entered service in 1990. It uses a similar two-screen display (LOFAR for classification above waterfall for detection), but apparently is not as automated. It reportedly detects a torpedo at 10 km or more under favorable conditions.

Users (URDT-1): France (*Jean Bart, Georges Leygues, Suffren* class, *Aconit*).

◆ SALTO

DCNI's antitorpedo system comprises a REALTO (Recepteur d'Alerte Torpille) beam-forming/analysis processor (fed by an ALTO towed warning array and also by the ship's usual arrays, via another processor) feeding two single-screen consoles (or one two-screen console) and the CONTRALTO reaction element (firing decoys and determining appropriate evasive maneuvers). The system provides both visual and audio warnings. All elements use VME consoles tied together by an FDDI LAN.

The CONTRALTO decoy/jammer with its rocket. (DCNI)

REALTO has two elements, a Chaine de Traitement Sonar (CTS) for array and signal processing, and a Chaine d'Exploitation Sonar (CES) for track extraction, classification, display, and storage. CTS is based on a MIMD (multiple instruction, multiple data) ABACUS computer in two cabinets connected by two Lotus 40-Mbit/sec buses. Its CRESUS processing module carries a T800 transputer, two Motorola 96002 floating-point coprocessors, and a pair of Lotus interfaces. Other boards are used for data acquisition and I/O, multiplex/demultiplex, high-speed recording, and audio generation. Apparently spectral analysis comes before beam-forming. It is followed by normalization, surface-noise cancellation, averaging, clustering, bearing extraction, then energy detection and automatic tracking/classification. CES uses a single VME rack in one of the two cabinets. In semiautomatic mode the system displays panoramic and sector narrow- and broad-band data in bearing-time, panoramic, sector, or individual track formats.

The 32-element ALTO array (85 mm × 30 m, towable at up to 30 kt) forms 3 × 32 beams (32 up, 32 left, 32 right, the upward-looking beams being used to reject surface noise). The receiver/processor automatically detects and tracks in broad-band in each beam, classifying them as torpedoes based on broad- and narrow-band signal characteristics, DEMON, transients, and apparent motion. An audio beam channel has left/right ambiguity resolution and surface noise subtraction.

Decoy deployment (dropping and throwing) is semiautomatic,

on operator command. CONTRALTO uses a rocket-powered decoy (range 200 to more than 3000 m) compatible with Sagaie/Dagaie. There will also be mobile decoys. Studies of a hard-kill weapon are proceeding. No wake-following decoy now exists.

DCNI's simulation shows that SALTO offers a much better chance of escaping a torpedo than mere warning. For example, if a torpedo is detected at 3000 m, they claim that probability of escape with SALTO is about 95% (the curve has a knee there, offering the same probability of escape for any greater warning range) versus escape probability with warning of only about 4–12%. The knee in the warning curve comes at about 5000 m, but even a 6000m warning gives a probability of escape of only about 25–38%. Even at 2000 m, SALTO gives about 72–84% chance of escape.

ALTO ran prefeasibility and exploratory development sea trials in 1984–90. By October 1994 it had progressed through ALTOR1 and ALTOR2 prototypes to a production ALTOR3 with fully automatic track classification. CONTRALTO ran sea trials about 1990. The system was integrated with the SLASM of the first ALTO system on board an F 67–class frigate early in 1995. The SALTO prototype ran sea trials against French and foreign torpedoes (40 separate runs) about 1990–95.

The carrier *Charles de Gaulle* will be the first ship fitted, provided development and production funds materialize. SALTO is planned for the French version of the Project Horizon frigate and in *Georges Leygues*–class frigates (F 70) as modernized.

GERMANY

◆ TAU-2000

The Type 212 torpedo countermeasure system combines the usual bow array and intercept array with a control unit (in the CDS) and four TCM launch containers with hinged covers, each housing 10 devices (five jammers and five decoys) in self-contained tubes (typically two containers each port and starboard forward of the sail). The thermal battery powered TAU (Torpedo Abwehr Uboote) device (127 × 1200 mm, 18 kg) switches between jammer and decoy functions. It can operate on all sonar frequencies, with highlight simulation, natural Doppler, omni coverage, high jamming power, sophisticated target simulation, with on-board processors and integrated AD/DA converters. The jammer is used to break contact, followed by a decoy. Multiple devices (effectors) are needed for any one engagement.

TAU-2000 was developed for the German Type 212 submarine by a consortium (Allied Signal ELAC, HDW, STN Atlas Elektronik); HDW integrates the system into the submarine. A prototype TAU has already been run. System trials are scheduled for 1998–99, with production preparation and procurement in 2001.

◆ Marine Target Simulator

This modified (and lengthened) Mk 37 torpedo was first shown by Honeywell Regelsysteme (Germany) at Defendory in October 1990. Development began in 1989. Endurance is 4 hr at 8–9 kt and 1 hr at 12–15 kt; the device tows an array of transducers and hydrophones and carries transducers in its body.

INDIA

Bharat Electronics advertises a towed decoy (TOTED), using a fish that appears similar to that of the British Type 182. The fish is towed about 400 m aft. Beam pattern is at least 140 deg in the horizontal, at least 80 deg in the vertical. Minimum source level is 88 dB. Interference with own-ship or other sonar can be avoided by using filters selectable from the system's front panel. Modes are noise versus passive, CW versus active, noise/CW against a mixture of types.

INTERNATIONAL

As of 1994, six European NATO nations were negotiating an MoU for an 18-month study (Project Group 37), in parallel with U.S.-UK J-SSTD and French SALTO, to begin in 1995. A draft RFP was circulated to companies in France, Germany, Italy,

Spain, Norway, and Netherlands in June 1994. All six have been conducting joint feasibility studies since 1991. As of 1994, the Dutch and the Germans had recently completed national SSTD studies.

ISRAEL

◆ ATC-1

Rafael's towed acoustic torpedo countermeasure is so compact that it can go on board merchant ships: 800 kg for launch and recovery gear, 190 kg for shipboard electronics, 10 kg for remote control, and a 25-kg towed body (30 × 120 cm). An upgrade will add passive elements (one on the towed fish for very short range detection, and a towed array for long range detection and identification, e.g., an 8m array might detect a torpedo at 2 kyd). ATC-1 was announced in 1986. As of July 1992, it was in use by the Israeli navy; none had yet been exported.

◆ Scutter

Rafael's submarine-launched torpedo decoy (101 × 1020 mm, 7.8 kg) was announced in 1991. It is not preprogrammed, but generates deception signals based on the torpedo pings it receives. Scutter operates for 5–10 min at 10–300 m depth. Using a nose propeller, it maintains depth or simulates a diving or rising submarine, and it can respond to several signals simultaneously. Rafael proposes a ship-launched version, to be fired from a standard chaff launcher.

ITALY

◆ C303/309/310

Whitehead's family of torpedo countermeasures comprises a mobile decoy and a static floating jammer. C303/s, the submarine version, employs a 123.8 × 1125mm (10.2 kg) decoy and a 123.8 × 1125mm (5.5 kg) static jammer, both of which are stowed encapsulated in expendable cartridges filled with water-soluble fluid. The mobile decoy, powered by a lithium thermal battery, is based on the A200 LCAW torpedo. Its projector (repeater) and hydrophone are physically separated, to avoid spillover, and it simulates target length, target highlights, Doppler, and range rate. Alenia claims high speed and long endurance. The jammer, which is also powered by a lithium thermal battery, covers a wide bandwidth and produces high emitter power to mask both the target echo and the target's radiated noise. Typically C303

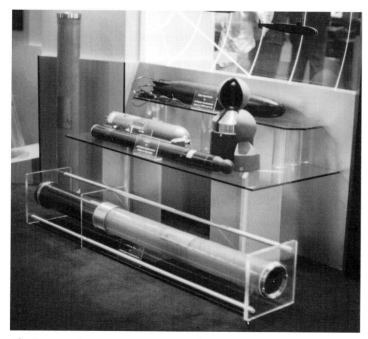

Alenia acoustic countermeasures are shown at Bourget Euronaval 1996. The large object with the round head is the ISO 100 intercept receiver. Behind it is the C303/s mobile decoy (target emulator). Below it are the static sonar jammer (*foreground*) and an associated air bottle. (Author)

is launched from the signal ejector in the submarine's sail (at 40 m/sec), but Whitehead is proposing a multitube external launcher, typically 21 tubes port and 21 starboard, each carrying both jammer and decoy. Launching of the two types is sequenced under control of an on-board console. Standard operating depth is 20–400 mm. Work on this system began in 1990.

C309 is a static surface-ship jammer or decoy, 76.2 × 750 or 1125 mm, 6 or 10 kg, respectively. Both are powered by lithium thermal batteries. The jammer masks target signature and echo; the decoy is a repeater that can simulate ship length, radiated noise, highlights, Doppler, and range rate. C310 is another surface-ship system, combining a static C310J jammer (76.2 × 750mm, 6 kg) with a mobile target emulator (123.8 × 1150 mm, 10.2 kg) similar to that used in C303. Both C309 and C310 use trainable multibarrel deck launchers; the C310 version carries 12 jammers and 6 decoys (fired, respectively, at 45-deg elevation and horizontally, four and two per engagement). Whitehead claims that a ship should have a 70% chance of escape against a torpedo detected at 1000 m (90% for 2200 m). C310 was announced in 1996.

The mobile submarine simulator is being tested by the U.S. Navy under the Foreign Comparative Testing Program.

◆ ISO 100

Alenia's wide-band sonar intercept receiver covers 40 deg in elevation. It can be autonomous or completely integrated with the main sonar. Outputs are bearing (within 5 deg), frequency (within 4%), and pulse length (within 2 millisec).

◆ BSS

Whitehead Alenia's torpedo-sized target (534 × 6000 mm) is currently used to test the Impact lightweight torpedo. It tows a 49m acoustic tail (16 independent transducers) and can reply to any sonar code or pulse length in real-time, also providing a time/frequency code for 3D tracking ranges. It is controlled by an underwater telephone link. BSS automatically evades when it detects an attacking torpedo. A silver-zinc battery feeds a 110-kW counter-rotating DC motor, which drives contraprops; speed/endurance are 14 kt/30 min, 21 kt/15 min, and 28 kt/7 min. Operating depth is 10–400 m, and maximum pitch angle is 30 deg.

RUSSIA

Romeos have a sonar intercept set (MG-23) using a transducer in a small dome above their bows. Foxtrots add a second set (MG-13), presumably working at higher frequency, using transducers in the "Fez" (NATO name) dome above the main one. The version in a November was MG-13M. The Kilo-class sonar-intercept system is probably MG-53.

A noisemaker (acoustic decoy) on board a Russian Krivak-class frigate, 1990. Most Russian decoys are not buoyant, and they are streamed with separate floats. (H. J. Verhoefen)

The sonar-intercept set in a "Victor" or later submarine is "Chanel," an ironic reference to the Anglo-French-Dutch PARIS (Type 2019). It uses three ("Victor I") or five ("Victor III," backfit to "Victor I and II," and also in Sierra and Akula) signal receivers around the sail, linked to a computer; the associated jammer uses two transducers aft of the main bow sonar (for deception in range and direction); the system also launches small-diameter decoys.

There are 40cm (400 × 4500mm, 497 kg) and 53cm (MG-74: 797 kg) submarine-launched simulators (decoys). The 40cm decice operates in noise or echo mode, transmitting typical submarine signals. MG-74 can also produce selective spot jamming signals. Two MG-74 can occupy one torpedo rack. Like Russian torpedoes, this device is spindle-set.

MG-74. (Rozvoorouzhenie)

An airplane-dropped decoy, possibly a version of MG-74, is intended to support submarines trying to break through ASW barriers. It is carried by Bear-Fs.

See ASW weapons above for UDAV-1 (under RPK-5).

SWEDEN

Bofors exhibited this 5in minitorpedo (countermeasure) at UDT 1995. It is controlled by the GII FCS. The poster above showed it both as a hard-kill torpedo countermeasure and as a floating sonar decoy. It is also adaptable as a direct-kill mine countermeasure and as a training device. (S. Slade, DMS/Forecast International)

UNITED KINGDOM

A 1991 Ferranti brochure mentions air-launched torpedo countermeasures.

◆ Unifoxer

This towed World War II broad-spectrum (5–50-kHz) torpedo decoy is reportedly retained as a war reserve because they can similate the noise of, for example, a convoy. They were used by merchant ships and some auxiliaries during the Falklands War. Unifoxer (replacing the earlier pair of Foxers) is typically towed towed 350 yd astern at 10 kt (maximum tow speed 20 kt). Broadband operation tends to interfere with sonars; narrow-band decoy operation is practicable because homing torpedoes tend to operate on fairly narrow bands.

◆ Type 182/Graseby G738

This tunable narrow-band noisemaker, using a magnetostriction transducer, was designed to protect destroyers and frigates at up to 25 kt and larger ships at up to 18 kt. To decoy passive torpedoes, it emits modulated white noise (at 20 dB above the ship's radiated level) at 20–80 kHz. To jam (not decoy) active homers, it produces a signal like that of a CW sonar: a modulated (1 msec

A Type 182 decoy and its handling crane on board the frigate *Andromeda*, 1985. (R. Cheung)

on, 1 msec off) high-intensity tone swept 4 times/sec over 20–80 kHz. Both modes can be transmitted simultaneously. Shipboard signal generators are duplicated so that the system can operate even if one fails. The fish (21 × 79 in, 163 lb) is designed to be streamed 400 m astern. Typically, two towing drums are arranged side by side at the stern, the decoy itself being handled by davit.

Graseby G738 is the export version, and GI738 is a solid-state version. As of 1983, GI738 had been exported to both Argentina (for MEKO frigates) and India.

◆ Type 2042

Self-protection (presumably sonar jamming) submarine system.

◆ Type 2066 (Bandfish)

Dowty's (now Ultra's) decoy (102 × 995 mm, 12 kg; it is *not* known as Amulet, as has been reported) is programmable before launch; it floats in the water while emitting active pulses to confuse an oncoming active-homing torpedo. Shelf life is 5 yr. A surface-launched version is the British thrown decoy in the joint SSTD program.

◆ Type 2070 (Talisman)

U.S./UK surface ship self-defense program, initially a British national project.

◆ Type 2071/2058 (TARTT)

Gearing & Watson's programmable submarine noise augmenter, for exercises and for self-protection (decoy, i.e., jammer) is based on a hydrosounder driven by a digital signal generator (DSG) which can store up to eight programs, repeat prerecorded signals, and produce 11 signals simultaneously (single tones, swept tones, bands of random noise, modulated noise, or pulses). Type 2058 (TARTT) is a towed version (in Type 182 decoy dimensions) carrying a UWS300F hydrosounder.

Users: France (one *Agosta* class), United Kingdom (three *Resolution* class, *Upholder, Swiftsures, Trafalgars,* planned for *Vanguards*).

◆ Type 2082

Thorn-EMI's 2019 replacement retains the existing array but adds a new processing cabinet that communicates with the Type 2074 multifunction console and also with a separate command display. Type 2082 greatly improves signal extraction (using frequency-domain processing), automatically detecting signals and initiating tracking (Thorn developed track extraction software for the 2019 upgrade). Tracks are passed directly to the submarine CDS. Type 2019 is the last stand-alone British submarine sonar before the advent of the fully integrated 2076. Development was completed by mid-1993 and deliveries to equip all SSN were completed by 1995.

A Bandfish decoy is loaded into a submarine signal ejector. (Dowty)

♦ Temula

Although apparently the reported Amulet decoy does not exist, there have been references to a Temula (anagram of Amulet) soft-kill SSTD decoy; Ferranti received a contract to retrofit Temula to RN SSK/SSN in 1991.

UNITED STATES

Later *Los Angeles*–class submarines (from SSN 751 on) are all being fitted with dihedral fins aft, each accommodating a 6in countermeasures launcher at its end. The last *Ohio*, USS *Wyoming*, departed for sea trials in 1996 with 16 decoy launchers in her turtleback, but none under her sail; this is probably the new standard configuration.

Past attempts to develop a surface-ship acoustic warfare system (AWS) have foundered on the failure to develop a reliable torpedo warner. MSTRAP (see below) may finally have succeeded. One element of this program was a series of SRBOC-launched devices, the electronic ADC Mk 6 torpedo decoy (1977) and the mechanical Mk 7 sonar jammer and Mk 8 torpedo decoy. Presumably these devices were abandoned as it became clear that the Soviets were using wake-following torpedoes. EX-10 was a next-generation (1983) surface-ship torpedo decoy.

Reportedly, the prominent pipe-lattice structures at the sterns of U.S. aircraft carriers are intended to widen their wakes as a counter to Russian wake-crossing torpedoes. In theory, the wider the wake, the more time the torpedo takes passing back and forth across it and, therefore, the less overall advance it can make up

the wake. Again, in theory, that should protect a fast ship from a torpedo approaching very much astern. It appears that this technique cannot be applied to smaller warships.

♦ ADC Mk 1

Acoustic Device, Countermeasure (5 × 72.75 in, 41.3 lb) is a submarine-launched sonar countermeasure powered by a sea-water battery. Mod 1 is a 6in version. Mk 1-0 was probably introduced about 1973.

Hazeltine decoys at Navy League 1995. (Author)

♦ ADC Mk 2

ESCO's submarine-launched electro-acoustic torpedo decoy (3.0 × 39.5 in, 7.6 lb) hovers using a small propeller and emits signals at a preset depth. ADC Mk 2 was introduced in 1978; more than 3000 were delivered in 1978–90, and over 2000 more were ordered for delivery 1990–94. Mod 1 is the 6in version.

♦ ADC Mk 3/ADC Mk 4

ORs for complementary CSA Mk 2-launched torpedo countermeasure and sonobuoy countermeasure/sonar jammer (and for CSA Mk 2 itself) were issued in December 1976. ADC Mk 3 OpEval was completed in FY88; Bendix (now Allied Oceanics) received a $13M contract for 367 Mk 3 (6 in, 125 lb) in 1989. ADC Mk 4 (6.25 × 106 in, 100 lb) began development (by Hazeltine) in 1988. It completed TechEval and OpEval in July and November 1993, respectively, and a production contract was awarded in the spring of 1994.

♦ ADC Mk 5

As of 1991, this sonar countermeasure (6 × 106 in, 110 lb) was in early development by Bendix (now Allied Oceanics), with delivery of 20 EDM units planned for 1994–95.

♦ ADC EX-9

This CSA Mk 2–launched replacement (6 × 96 in, 100 lb) for Mobile Submarine Simulator Mk 70 is for SSBNs.

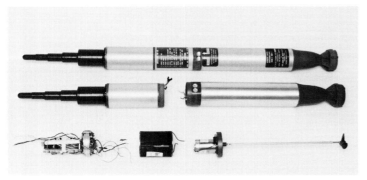

ADC Mk 2 Mod 0. The acoustic projector is at the top. It contains the ceramic transducers and impedence matching networks. Adjacent to it is an electronics section (the object exposed at top left) containing the signal generation and amplification circuits. Power is provided by the seawater battery (*center left*). At bottom left are the motor and propeller of the hovering module, which also provides the decoy's buoyancy as it hovers in the water. The hover motor is pressure-controlled to maintain nearly constant depth. Dimensions are the standard 3 × 39.5 in of a submarine's signal tube (weight 7.5 lb). (Hazeltine)

◆ BLR-14 (BSAWS)/SAWS/SDWS

Sperry's basic submarine acoustic warfare system uses WLR-9/12 to detect torpedo pings, WLR-14 to classify them, and the submarine sonar's preformed beams to track them; it automatically alerts the submarine and semiautomatically releases decoys.

Submarine Acoustic Warfare System is a successor using WLR-9/12/17, WLR-14, and a special-purpose signal-tracking receiver. It can employ a hull-mounted jammer (GNATS/NAU) and 3in (ADC Mk 2 Mods 0 and 1 and NAE Mk 3), 5in (ADC Mk 1 Mod 0), and 10in decoys (Mk 57 MOSS). Under the FY96 program, development of a multibeam torpedo rapid automatic classification system (MTRACS), enabling the submarine to use her towed and spherical arrays for torpedo classification and localization, was completed.

A SAWS successor, SDWS (Submarine Defensive Weapons System), is being developed. A new sonar intercept system (NSIS/WLY-1) replaces WLR-9/12/17; a new CMC2 processor/command system replaces WLR-14; the decoys, to be fired from a new quiet launcher, are ADC Mk 4 and a special-purpose NLQ-1 (whose designation suggests a counter to nonacoustic threats such as UEP; it completed its initial developmental tests in June 1993). The system will also deploy a hard-kill countermeasure, SMTD (submarine torpedo defense weapon). Unclassified descriptions do not mention a new sonar jammer.

The key NSIS requirement is full 360-deg coverage without shadows, using small transducers distributed over the hull. Each is individually processed, its video brought inboard by fiber optics. It is expected to recognize an oncoming torpedo for early acquisition, classification, and tracking. Compared to the WLR series, WLY-1 is to have extended frequency coverage, better pulse-to-pulse association, and to be able to detect shorter pulses. The NSIS/WLY-1 TOR was issued in September 1985 and the draft OR in September 1986. WLY-1 was to have been installed and tested in FY90, but the program slipped and Norden (now part of Northrop Grumman) did not receive a contract for the ADM of the new receiver until January 1992. A prototype was installed on a submarine in FY93 for sea tests in FY94 (developmental tests were completed during FY94). Two EMD models were ordered in FY96, and the system is to be ready for full-scale production early in FY01.

Generic Sonar is a successor program, presumably including obstacle avoidance and directional jamming. The wet end is being developed by Lockheed Sanders (four arrays, four spots each [electronically steered beams], two forward and two aft, for active HF or passive wide-band operation [not both simultaneously]). The dry end is being developed by NUWC Newport.

CMC2 is to be based on an "expert systems" approach. ARPA is working with Loral on automated decision aids, including SEAPACS, the Submarine Engagement Automated Planning &

Control System. The TOR was issued in March 1986. The ADM was to have been completed in FY93.

A new electromagnetic Countermeasures Torpedo Tube Launching System/Quiet Launcher (CTTLS/QTLHNR) was to have replaced the noisy gas generators (Mks 72 and 77) used in CSA Mk 2 Mods 0 and 1. The launcher, based on ARPA-developed technology, completed its developmental tests in August 1992.

The SMTD prototype was built during FY93, but the program lagged (developmental tests are expected about FY99).

◆ BLQ Series

This countermeasures generation preceded the current one. Their characteristics, though obsolete, give some idea of what decoys are expected to achieve.

BLQ-1: Fixed jammer to jam three ship or torpedo sonars simultaneously. Controlled from within the submarine, it listened for 5 sec and transmitted for 25. Delivered in December 1960, it failed its OpEval.

BLQ-2: Mobile decoy and jammer against surface-ship sonars (submarine simulator), carrying a sonar repeater/jammer and a beacon simulating the beat of a submarine propeller; it was launched from a submarine torpedo tube and followed a preprogrammed course (30–60 sec at 12 kt, then 19 min at 6–9 kt, at a depth of 50–300 ft). The first five were tested successfully in 1956, but BLQ-2 was never made in large numbers. The successor was the 10in-dia BLQ-9 (speed 8–10 kt at 50–400 ft). Initially a sonar repeater (blip enhancer), BLQ-9 later carried a sonar noise jammer. It also emitted submarine sounds at 0.1–1 kHz and simulated a submarine wake (which itself can be a sonar target) by passing seawater over lithium hydride. Six BLQ-9s were stowed in a modified torpedo-stowage cradle and ejected via the torpedo tube using temporary liners. The successor is MOSS (see below). It and BLQ-9 are characterized as contact-breakers.

BLQ-3–6: Small (3 × 39in) hovering devices ejected from the submarine's signal gun. BLQ-3 and -4 were jammers; BLQ-5 and -6 were sonar repeaters. They differed from their predecessors, the NAE series, in that they responded to sonar signals rather than being preset to emit over a given frequency range. Coverage of the full range of frequencies (7–70 kHz) required two separate devices. They were tested in breadboard form in 1962.

◆ CLAMS

Librascope's countermeasure launcher acoustic module set is a predecessor to the CSAs described below. It is carried by both strategic and attack submarines.

◆ CSA Mk 1

Countermeasures set, acoustic (6.5 × 87.54 in, internal diameter 5 in), is a quick-reaction external gas generator system for SSBNs (launcher Mk 139). This nomenclature was introduced in 1973.

◆ CSA Mk 2

Librascope's ADC Mk 3/Mk 4 launching system (launcher Mk 151) remotely selects and launches individual ADCs. OpEval was completed during FY88, and the first production contract let during FY89. Mod 0 is for SSBNs, Mod 1 for the *Sturgeon* class, and Mod 2 for the *Los Angeles* class. This has been a very protracted program; the original OR dates from December 1976.

◆ CSA Mk 3

Countermeasures-launching system for the new *Seawolf* class. An unclassified 1987 data sheet shows capacity for up to 16 decoys, up to 6 × 106 in in size.

◆ Fanfare (T Mk 6)

The standard U.S. towed torpedo decoy of the 1950s and 1960s survives on board many older Allied ships credited with the later Nixie (SLQ-25). The characteristic installation includes a small spray shield protecting the towing winch. Two decoys are provided per installation.

Fanfare on board the destroyer *Cassin Young*, showing the dual winches, each with its fish, and the spare fish between them. (A. Raven)

◆ MOSS Mk 57/MMD (ADC EX-11)

The 10in mobile submarine simulator (about 1000 lb) is a dual-purpose sonar and torpedo countermeasure, mainly for SSBNs, intended to simulate a full-size submarine. It is fired quietly from a Mk 136 catapult launcher inserted in a standard 21in tube. Each Trident submarine carries two launchers and six MOSSs; each attack submarine carries one launcher and four MOSSs. MOSS was provisionally approved for service use in June 1979, Gould having received an initial production contract for 36 in August 1977.

The successor, which can be fired from a countermeasures launcher, is the 6in mobile multifunction (i.e., vs. both sonars and torpedoes) device (MMD), ADC EX-10. MMD also replaces ADC Mk 6. A TOR was issued in March 1986, and the draft OR in February 1988. This device completed its first developmental tests in January 1993. An EMD model is due in FY98.

◆ NAE/FTC

NAE, originally a World War II sonar-countermeasures designation, is now the generic term for a noisemaker (the current version is NAE Mk 3). The launcher is the standard U.S. 3in signal tube (maximum size 3 × 39.5 in).

FTC, the false-target canister, creates a false target by making bubbles, for example, by letting seawater pour over lithium hydride. It is the submarine equivalent of a chaff round.

◆ Nixie (SLQ-25)/SLQ-36

Aerojet's towed noisemaker (towed body 6 × 37.05 in, 7.31in tail fin diameter, 46 lb) is generally installed in paired form, so that a decoy is available if one is destroyed by a torpedo. Nixie is about half the size and weight of Type 182. Evaluation was completed in December 1970, and production began in 1974. The FY88–91 programs included 421 engineering change kits (for the towed body and for the power amplifier).

SLQ-36 (1983) is the combined countermeasures tow (CCT), comprising an improved Nixie, a magnetic countermeasure, a wake-homing-torpedo countermeasure (presumably an acoustic counter to the torpedo's upward-looking sonar), and a towed torpedo detector. The magnetic countermeasure is presumably intended to detonate torpedoes using magnetic exploders (SLQ-25 would presumably have dealt with acoustic exploders).

◆ SLQ-33

Honeywell's towed acoustic simulator (body: 27.36 × 117 in, 1950 lb) with van-mounted electronics is for battle group cover and deception. Specifications for a product-improved version were completed in FY87.

◆ SLR-24/TWS-2000

Lockheed Martin's passive torpedo detector (for the U.S.-UK joint surface-ship torpedo-defense program) proved successful

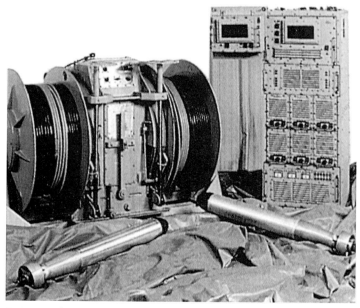

SLQ-25A, showing a pair of Nixie fish and their winch. Northrop Grumman currently advertises SLQ-25B, a modular SSTD system, consisting of Nixie, a fiber-optic towed array (2in dia × 210 ft on a 0.688in × 1600ft cable), MSTRAP, and a SRBOC-launched expendable decoy, either rocket- or mortar-propelled. The towed TB-14A pod is 6 × 47 in, 58 lb. (Northrop Grumman)

but procurement was suspended when the system as a whole failed its OpEval. As of March 1995, three SLR-24 had been delivered for installation on board carriers. The system combines Northrop Grumman (ex-Norden) inboard electronics (now MSTRAP, see below) with a short Lockheed Martin towed array (earlier interest in hull arrays was abandoned).

In 1995 Lockheed Martin announced TWS-2000, a torpedo warner based on SLR-24 technology but using COTS computers for beam-forming and signal processing. The associated workstation has two 19in high-resolution color monitors.

In 1996 Lockheed Martin bid a 3X version of SLR-24 for the Swedish YS-2000 corvette sonar requirement (the longer tail gives HF, MF, and LF coverage). This is a COTS version with three COTS (Tac-4) workstations. The U.S. Navy has also tried the 3X array for ASW.

The SLR-24 OR was issued in March 1985. See SSTD below.

◆ SSTD

Surface Ship Torpedo Defense has been restructured several times, following several program failures. Initially it was a three-phase program inspired by the advent of the Russian 65cm wake-following torpedo: (a) SLQ-25A enhanced Nixie, (b) U.S. national program to defeat wake-followers (using SLR-24 and Mk 46 Mod 7 torpedoes), and (c) the U.S.-UK program to defeat all torpedo threats, including straight-runners. Of these elements, the first improved Nixies entered service in 1988. The U.S. national system failed its Phase II OpEval, causing suspension of SLR-24 production; modified Mk 46 torpedoes reverted to their original role, and in FY93 money for the U.S. national program was withdrawn. At about the same time an antitorpedo torpedo apparently also failed (FY95 R&D funds were eliminated).

In April 1994 the U.S. national and U.S.-UK programs were merged as the U.S./UK SSTD Joint Project (J-SSTD). That followed a major cut in planned U.S./UK out-year funding. The RFQ for J-SSTD was issued in the summer of 1994. Due to limited funding, one rather than the planned two demonstration/validation contracts was awarded: in 1994 it went to the Westinghouse team; partners were AT&T (detect, localize, classify), Librascope (soft kill and combat control), Ferranti Thomson (sensors and DCL), and Ultra Electronics (soft and hard kill). To reduce risk, the hard-kill element, the antitorpedo torpedo (ATT), was removed from the program and reprogrammed as a FY97 Advanced Technology Demonstration (ATD). By late 1996, this ATD had reportedly been put aside. Although the public rationale was that the main diesel threat, the Iranian Kilos, was not operational, it seems likely that interest was shifting toward the pressure-wave technique described below.

SSTD uses a Northrop Grumman (ex-Westinghouse) Multi-Sensor Torpedo Recognition and Alertment Processor (MSTRAP), a COTS-based open-architecture computer in a Mil-Spec enclosure, which is now being embedded in SQQ-89. The sensor for the stand-alone version will still probably be SLR-24 (it encountered difficulties in the OpEval, and was to undergo Phase II OpEval in FY96). Note, however, that Northrop Grumman showed its own fiber-optic towed array at UDT 1996. The soft-kill element is LEAD, the Launch Expendable Acoustic Device, using the acoustic payload of ADC Mk 2 or the British 2066 Bandfish coupled to a rocket or mortar cartridge, to be fired from a standard SRBOC launcher. As of the spring of 1995, full-scale development was to have been completed by the end of FY96, with first production in FY97. However, it was also reported (in April 1994) that the soft-kill system would be operational in some form as early as May 1995. It was claimed officially that the COTS approach cut development time by two-thirds and acquisition cost by three-quarters. Westinghouse received a contract for preproduction MSTRAPs (3 with an option for 20) in May 1994. Then a batch of 14 was bought.

Perhaps the most exotic current antitorpedo scheme employs focused pressure waves, which are used in oil-field drilling to penetrate mud, against both torpedoes and mines. At the 1995 U.S. Navy League show United Defense displayed a drawing of a 5 × 4 transducer array on a ship's transom. In theory, the shock wave would penetrate and destroy the torpedo's warhead and electronics, much as earlier proposals for high-power microwaves envisaged the destruction of incoming missiles.

Tests of the SSTD system, comprising MSTRAP and the LEAD decoy (and using the SQR-19 array) are due early in 1997.

◆ WLR-9A/9B/12/17

Norden's submarine acoustic intercept receivers (AIRs) typically comprise sail- or dome-mounted quadrant hydrophones, a receiver-processor (to detect pulses automatically and measure frequency, pulse width, pulse-repetition rate, bearing, and signal strength), and a display group (raster-scan CRT and digital readouts, with threat identification from a library of ship, submarine, and torpedo sonars). The current versions may also recognize important transients, such as those associated with weapon firings.

WLR-9A, which replaces WLR-9, is more sensitive, is automated, and measures more signal parameters (-9 did not measure pulse width or repetition frequencies) for library lookup; it also adds a third band to the two in -9 (LF and HF), presumably to deal with torpedoes with medium-frequency pingers. Some installations are apparently limited to HF (two sub-bands rather than a single band) and MF, the main hull arrays being used for LF. WLR-9B encodes sonar parameters and sends them to the submarine's BQQ-5B for further processing and display. B(V)3 introduces a new receiver-processor. During the last few years, WLR-9s were modified for two surface ships for proof-of-concept tests (look-through own sonar).

WLR-12 is similar to -9A but has a new LF hydrophone with a wider frequency range. It lacks an MF hydrophone.

WLR-17 is a WLR-9 variant, probably for the *Ohio* class.

Work on these systems began in the late 1960s following the failure of WLR-2 and -5 (Velox was bought instead). At that time the U.S. goal was to cover 1.1–70 kHz with frequency accurate to within 10% and bearing to within 5 deg.

◆ Mk 28

This target for warshot torpedoes is a converted torpedo body. The Mod 2 half-length version, introduced about 1985, was presumably based on a Mk 37 torpedo body.

◆ Mk 30

The current standard U.S. submarine target simulator (21 × 245 in, 2700 lb) can be fired from a 21in torpedo tube or a rack, or

dropped by a helicopter. It tows a 300ft array consisting of a hydrophone, a projector (to simulate submarine sounds), and a magnetic source (to trigger MAD gear). Mod 1 speed is 7 kt (endurance 4 hr) to 30 kt (30 min); routine operating depth is 25–2000 ft (maximum depth 2500 ft). Turn rate is 0.25–8 deg/sec, depending on speed, and the target can climb at 2–20 deg. An acoustic link controls depth, course, speed, and shutdown to a maximum range of 5000 yd.

This program began in the late 1960s but was much delayed by deep budget cuts. Westinghouse delivered eleven Mod 0 (controlled by internal punched tape) beginning in 1970. Northrop received the Mod 1 contract; the first was delivered in June 1973. Unit cost rose from $895,833 (FY76) to $2,557,143 (FY77), partly because of a program which improved reliability from 30% to 65%, against a goal of 80%. Mk 30 was approved for service use in 1978. In 1976 the total stated requirement was 260, but this fell to 60 by 1981, the estimated unit cost then being $2.7M (FY82). The goal of 60 units by FY86 assumed 2400 runs per year. Goodyear (now Lockheed Martin Loral) is the current manufacturer.

The next versions are parts of the Advanced ASW Target program, comprising the Fast Deep Prototype Target (the faster Mk 30 Mod 2, for Mk 48 and Mk 50 torpedoes), the Advanced ASW Target (Mk 30 Mod 3), and the Mk 39 EMATT. Mod 3 uses the acoustic signal processor, power amplifier, and towed array developed for Mod 2, the guidance and control of Mod 1, and Mk 48 ADCAPS propulsion (selected in FY88).

◆ Mk 32

This fixed torpedo target, for Mk 37, 44, and 46 torpedoes, is suspended in the water at a preselected depth down to 500 ft (chosen in 50ft increments). It can be used with an SQQ-18A sonar transponder, suspended at 50ft depth; the latter provides returns for surface-ship sonars. Total weight is 95 lb.

◆ EMATT (Mk 39)

Sippican's Expendable Mobile ASW Training Target is an air- or ship-launched submarine simulator the size of an A-size sonobuoy (4 × 36 in, 21.1 lb). Run speed is 10 kt (duration 3 hr, programmed run), and maximum depth is 700 ft. EMATT acts as an echo repeater for active sonars and Mk 46 torpedoes and produces signals for passive sonars; it can tow a 100ft wire to produce a recognizable MAD signature.

◆ SPAT

Westinghouse's (formerly Gould's) Self-Propelled Acoustic Target submarine simulator is based partly on the BLQ-2 of the 1950s. Although normally a training device, SPAT might also be considered a long-lived decoy. The vehicle (10 × 129 in, 330 lb) tows an echo repeater (4–85 kHz, pulse width 1 msec–1 sec, PRI 1/3 sec or more) on a 12m coaxial cable. Apparent echo target size is 13–25 dB. The echo contains highlights, elongation, and self-Doppler. A broad-band noise generator simulates a submarine (800 Hz–85 kHz). Total radiated power is at least 160 dB. Run geometry (including snake, circular, and spiral patterns) can be programmed from the FCS launching SPAT or called up from the vehicle's preprogrammed memory. Total run time is 2 hr. Maximum speed is 11–13 kt (for up to 10 min), and cruising speed is 6–8 kt. Depth limits are 16–787 ft; maximum dive/climb angle is 15 deg.

SPAT entered production about 1980.

◆ SLAD

Lockheed Martin Hycor's list of decoys distributed at Euronavale 1996 included some new ship-launched mortar and rocket acoustic decoys (SLADs), to be fired from 112mm (RBOC) and 130mm (SRBOC) launchers. In each case, the deployed acoustic device is suspended from a float. Firing is controlled by Hycor's ALEX FCS (see the EW section).

MINES AND MINE COUNTER- MEASURES

The simplest contact mines are set off when a ship breaks the Hertz "horns" of the mine, releasing acid to activate a battery. The U.S. Mk 6 of World War I was a more sophisticated alternative: a ship touching an antenna formed one element of a simple battery, closing a firing circuit. The antenna greatly increased the lethal radius of the mine: a mine could destroy submarines passing well above or below it.

Because contact mines must be moored, the combination of mine body and mooring chain must be buoyant: the weight (length) of the mooring chain limits the weight of explosive. For example, Iranian contact (moored) mines in the Persian Gulf often broke their moorings because the Iranians tried to load them too heavily and therefore used chain that was too weak.

The mine lies or floats at its case depth. The anchor of a floating mine will lie at a far greater depth, the laying depth.

Influence weapons are triggered by a ship's signatures (e.g., magnetic and acoustic). Those on the sea bed were the first weapons attacking ships from under the keel; they can be effective in depths as great as 80 ft (greater if they attack deep-draft ships). Many influence weapons are moored.

World War II acoustic mines were triggered by an increase in broad-band sound. Like other sonars, they were subject to unwanted noise and also to multipath and other propagation problems. Like many modern passive sonars, many modern acoustic mines use fast Fourier transform (FFT) techniques to detect narrow frequency bands (tonals) and thus to attempt to recognize specific targets. This degree of discrimination may help protect them from countermining due to the broad-band noise created when a nearby mine (or countermeasures explosive) goes off.

A seismic mine senses the very low frequency (below about 10 Hz) vibration of the sea bed due to sound from a ship (water does not transmit much of this sound, but it travels efficiently in sediment). In effect, the area around the mine becomes its sensor array. Unlike a conventional acoustic mine, a seismic mine should continue to function even if it buries itself in seabed sediment. The sensor is entirely buried in the mine: it measures the mine's movement as the sea bed vibrates.

Early magnetic mines, which used an induction coil, measured the field (actually the change in the field as a ship passed) in one axis. Because they were quite insensitive (thus could be triggered only by a large ship), steel minesweepers remained usable even after the advent of such mines early in World War II. The much more sensitive mines introduced at the end of the war caused the construction of a new generation of nonmagnetic minesweepers and minehunters. Current mines can be so sensitive that remotely operated mine-clearance vehicles (ROVs) cannot safely approach closely enough to plant mine-neutralization charges directly against a mine, but instead must rely on the shock effect of such charges.

The induction-coil mine had to rest on the sea bottom, since motion (in the earth's magnetic field) up and down on the tide might trigger it. After World War II the U.S. Navy developed a three-axis magnetometer that could compensate tidal movement. A three-axis fluxgate magnetometer can separately detect the earth's field, the target's static field, and the target's alternating field. Usually the quasi-static field (5 mHz–5 Hz) is used, but it can be largely eliminated by degaussing. That leaves the mine with alternating fields due, for example, to shipboard machinery and even the ship's wake (since the water moved in the wake is a conducting medium). A typical detector operates in the 5–500-Hz band. Alternating fields are weak but they are relatively easy to detect and there is very little natural background noise.

Pressure mines sense the decrease in water pressure (suction) under a moving ship (about 0.1% of the static pressure). Lying on the bottom, they must be protected against mistaking the change due to the turn of the tide for the change due to the passage of a ship, often by providing a second (acoustic or magnetic) sensor. Alternatively, a microprocessor can discriminate between the slow change in the tide and the rapid change due to a ship; a really sophisticated sensor can measure the duration of the bow or stern pulses of a real target. Perhaps the most unpleasant MCM discovery of World War II was that no towed device could quite simulate a ship's pressure signature: in that sense, pressure mines were unsweepable. Pressure mines using auxiliary sensors can, in theory, be swept by using a towed noise-maker or magnetic field at the turn of the tide, but that has never been considered altogether satisfactory. The search for an effective pressure signature simulator therefore continues. The only protection against pressure mines is to move so slowly that the pressure change is not sufficient to trigger them. The maximum allowable speed depends on a ship's tonnage: the larger the slower.

Underwater electric potential (UEP) is generated by the corrosion current that runs between the ship's steel hull and her bronze propeller. UEP has both DC and AC components, the latter (ELFE, extremely low frequency electric field) due to propeller rotation and to rotating machinery. The static field propagates further than the alternating one, but the alternating one is easier to detect, competing against less background noise. Both fields are inherently short-ranged, and they are very difficult to silence. The U.S. World War I antenna mine (Mk 6) used a UEP-like mechanism, and full UEP was actively investigated by the British during World War II, both for mines and as a towed torpedo detector. Only the Russians seem to have applied it to operational weapons.

Many mines use multiple-influence sensors, to avoid being triggered by natural phenomena or simple countermeasures. Most work on the principle of search/target. When a long-range influence sensor detects a possible target, it opens a shorter-range influence sensor. The latter can trigger the mine or turn over its ship counter. Modern multi-influence mines detect a 2D ship signature, using a pair of influences of similar range.

For very deep water, there is a further category, the rising mine. The mine case may lie close to the bottom, but when it detects a passing ship or submarine it launches a projectile or torpedo. The U.S. Captor (Mk 60) is one example. Depending upon the speed and endurance of the projectile, a rising mine may be laid in extremely deep water. If it maneuvers on the way up, it may be able to hit a target at some distance. The passive search sensor may be acoustic or, perhaps, magnetic (MAD ranges are often about 1000 feet, comparable to the necessary range). Long range is important because there will be an appreciable time lag between the release of the rising device and its arrival at the target. Once a target has been recognized, the mine uses an active acoustic sensor for fire control. Because the mine, even if it is quite deep, is probably quite close to its target, it may be able to rely on an HF signature that is lost at normal ASW ranges. In the case of a rising projectile, the fire-control sensor sets a time fuze so that the weapon explodes near its target.

Case depth is fixed not only by crush depth but also by the time it takes the projectile to reach its target depth; if the depth is too great, the target will be gone by the time the projectile reaches its depth. In really deep water, then, the mine must be moored, and its case must be buoyant enough to support a considerable weight of cable. Consequently, the mine must be large, and the laying rate will be limited. In contrast, in shallower water, say down to 1000 feet or more, the mine case might well lie on the bottom.

Deep-water rising mines significantly extend the mineable area of the world. Countermeasures are very expensive because the mine may cover a substantial lethal area (the projectile may maneuver as it rises) and because any attempt to destroy mines or mine mooring requires very deep operations. Examples of such expensive countermeasures probably include not only the British extra-deep armed team sweep (EDATS) but also the U.S. Mine Neutralization System. However, because rising mines must probably use passive acoustic detectors, these mines are (at least in theory) subject to sweep by acoustic devices simulating target signatures.

During the Cold War, Soviet rising mines were considered a major threat to Western ballistic missile submarines. They could, at least in theory, be laid in the channels through which the submarines would have to pass when leaving their bases. With the end of the Cold War, British and French interest in such weapons declined dramatically, as only the Soviets could have mined their strategic submarine bases. However, rising mines are still a threat in deep straits. For example, reportedly Iran bought Chinese EM-52 rising mines, and can use them to threaten shipping through the Strait of Hormuz.

Finally, there are controlled mines, triggered from a shore station, for coast defense. They often carry sensors to indicate to the shore station which mine in the field a potential target has approached; alternatively, mine selection may be based on radar or other surface-sensor data.

Mine countermeasures fall into three categories: self-protection, mine reconnaissance, and mine clearance. Self-protection entails both neutralizing mines that the ship passes over (by paravane against moored contact mines, by degaussing, and by acoustic silencing) and mine avoidance using simple obstacle-detection sonars (such as the Kingfisher attachment to standard U.S. ASW sonars). Mine reconnaissance may be used to arrange wholesale mine avoidance. Mine clearance means either sweeping (wholesale clearance by cutting mooring cables or causing influence mines to explode harmlessly) or mine hunting, examining the bottom for suspicious objects and then dealing with them one by one. These methods are not mutually exclusive. For example, really effective mine reconnaissance would provide a map of the bottom, suspicious objects on which would then be examined and dealt with. At least as it is now done, hunting is inherently slow and difficult, but it is necessary to deal with unsweepable mines (such as pressure mines). Too, it may be used to recover sample mines, which can then be used as the basis for setting sweeps.

In the Persian Gulf, floating mines (mines whose mooring cables had broken) became a major threat to shipping. The usual countermeasure was some type of EO surface-search mechanism, such as the U.S. Mast-Mounted Sight.

Moored mines may be swept by a cable carrying small explosive-driven cutters. Mines whose cables have been cut float to the surface, where they can be destroyed or sunk by small-arms fire. Acoustic and magnetic mines are generally swept by towed acoustic or magnetic noisemakers. There are counter-countermeasures. A ship counter allows several ships to pass before the mine is armed. It may protect the mine against sweepers preceding a high-value target. Delayed arming forces influence sweepers to go back over a field. Similarly, the release of a moored mine from its anchor can be delayed. The ultimate counter-countermeasure is probably a mine-target detector keyed so precisely to a ship signature that it cannot easily be simulated.

Many current mines are microprocessor-controlled. They can be programmed to seek particular ship signatures, which can be extended in space (i.e., in time, as the ship passes over), and so will force the minesweeper to use more and more complex ship simulators. The French Sterne I exemplifies counters to this type of mine. Unlike earlier hard-wired mine sensors, a microprocessor can easily be reset to any desired set of target characteristics or counter-countermeasures.

Minehunting employs a high-definition (VHF) sonar to identify suspicious objects, and then some means of examining and destroying those objects. The simplest such system employs divers. Divers remain very important for examining and recovering hostile mines, but to clear minefields Western navies tend to employ remotely controlled submersibles, such as the French PAP 104 and the Honeywell MNS, equipped with even higher definition sonar and with underwater television. Unfortunately, many areas requiring clearance are covered by the detritus of industry (cars, refrigerators, bodies in concrete, etc.), much of it vaguely resembling mines. The very high false-target rate explains the need to examine each suspicious object, rather than destroying it immediately from the minehunter.

To the extent that friendly harbors must be protected against mining, detailed peacetime bottom surveys of the routes ("Q-routes") ships are expected to take can be used for comparison, to find out which suspicious objects are new. In theory, therefore, vital harbors should be surveyed periodically, and the results stored in electronic form for quick comparison with new surveys taken in an emergency. The new Egyptian MCM system, with its route survey craft and special archive, is a case in point.

Silty harbors are still a problem: mines bury themselves in the bottom. That may not make them less lethal.

MCM vessels tend to be small mainly in order to limit their signatures so as not to set off influence mines. Modern ones are quite expensive despite their size, because they need complex combat systems and because it is difficult to minimize their signature (while insuring against shock effects). They cannot, therefore, be built in very large numbers. Small size also usually implies low speed. These craft may be effective in home waters, but they cannot easily deploy with the fleet. If territorial waters are extensive, low speed may be a problem even at home. Hence current Norwegian interest in surface-effect (fast) sweepers and hunters. One alternative, adopted by the U.S. Navy, is the helicopter sweeper or hunter. Helicopters can be carried abroad with the fleet, and they can tow special sweeps or hunting sonars. At the least, they can deploy precursor sweeps to trigger the mines intended to attack more conventional hunters. Experience in the Persian Gulf seems to show that conventional surface sweepers and hunters are still essential.

One way to evade the high cost of sweepers or hunters is to keep the ship further from the mines, so that it need not be specially silenced or shock-proofed. There is, therefore, growing interest in placing minehunting sonars aboard self-propelled vehicles running ahead of the mother ship (the "dog on a leash"). There is also growing interest in antimine torpedoes, which can attack mines directly, even small charges probably causing them to explode sympathetically. That eliminates the problem of damage assessment that plagues other forms of minehunting. One problem is whether the high false target rate of current minehunting systems will make for an unacceptable rate of torpedo expenditure (the usual ROV is retrievable, and its simple charge is relatively cheap).

Small remotely controlled submersibles are used by the offshore oil drilling industry. Most of these devices may be too small to carry useful mine-disposal charges (or, for that matter, useful mine-classification sensors), but they may be usable under mobilization conditions.

Autonomous or unmanned underwater vehicles (AUVs or UUVs) present similar possibilities. They may also be used for covert minefield reconnaissance, for example, from submarines. In addition, truly autonomous vehicles (or, for that matter, airborne vehicles with towed sonar or laser systems) might be used to locate mines in a field without having to deal with them one by one.

Very precise navigational systems are essential to MCM because the sweeper must be able to identify the position of the cleared channel. Examples include the Racal Hyperfix (accuracy 5 m at 250 km) and the U.S. Precision Navigation System. Raydist, which was used to control the U.S. sweeping of Hanoi/Haiphong in 1973, was an extemporized civilian system using antennas on shore. U.S. MCM helicopters in the Gulf in 1991 used GPS (with ARN-151 receivers) rather than Hyperfix, to provide them with a common grid also used by EOD divers and by other MCM forces. Minesweeper navigation also requires high-definition surface-search radars, many of which are listed in the Antiaircraft Warfare section.

MINES

In 1988 the U.S. Office of Naval Intelligence stated that 21 countries could deploy mines capable of damaging major warships. The stated number in 1995 was 48, with 41 capable of making mines.

In 1996 ONI reported that three exporting countries made mobile mines (Russia, Sweden, and the United States), five made propelled-warhead mines (China, Norway, Russia, Sweden, and the United States), one made stealth mines (Sweden), six made vintage mines or copies (China, North Korea, Russia, the United Kingdom, the United States, and Yugoslavia), and twelve made advanced mines with pressure sensors (Argentina, China, Denmark, Finland, France, Germany, India, Italy, Russia, South Africa, the United Kingdom, and the United States). These lists

omit Brazil, Japan, South Korea, and Taiwan, all of which make sophisticated mines but do not export them, nor do they include Chile, which reportedly did export Cardoen mines. Of the advanced mine-makers, Finland and India are *not* represented in the entries below. Given the Finnish purchase of Stonefish, the Finnish reference is probably to license production of this weapon. India probably makes a derivative of the MRP-80 bought in the 1980s. The reference to Swedish and Norwegian rising mines is probably to the suspended coast defense program and the reference to a Swedish mobile mine probably refers to an aborted program. ONI reports that propelled-warhead mines have been exported to two countries (Iran and one other), vintage mines to 30, and advanced mines to 15. ONI also reported that more than 30 countries have submarine-laid mines. Typical prices are $20,000 or less for a vintage weapon or $200,000 or more for a rising mine.

Apparently an average Third World inventory is about 8,000. Numbers are small partly because storage and maintenance can be expensive. For example, explosive deteriorates, so ideally mines are stowed empty; a special mine-filling plant is needed. In some cases mine inventories have been destroyed because they have become too dangerous or too expensive to refill. Relatively few of the mines on hand may be influence mines. The few sales figures available are not large. For example, the Russian mine manufacturer Gidropribor estimates that no more than 10% of its post-1945 exports (about 300,000 mines) were influence types. On the other hand, Destructor kits (which convert standard bombs into influence mines) were made in very large numbers, and may have been exported widely.

Many mines of pre– or World War II origin may remain.

Deletions: Al-Muthena/35 and /45 (Iraq, apparently did not exist), Sigeel/400 (Iraq, apparently did not exist), TAR 6/TAR 16 (Italy, apparently long obsolete), VS-SM-600 (Italy, lost in 1978 competition, apparently not produced), AMG-1 (Russian, obsolete by 1950s), M-12 and M-26/KB (Russian, obsolete in 1945), MZh-26 (Russian, obsolete in 1945), PLT series (Russian, abandoned in favor of torpedo tube mines), Julia (Sweden, apparently obsolete), Telemine (Switzerland; apparently not manufactured), and mine modernization program (United Kingdom, abandoned with mine stocks).

ARGENTINA

Mines are made by Sociedad Argentina de Fabricacion de Sistemas Electronicos SRL (SAF), formed in the 1960s, under a SIMINA mine-development program. Most mines are designated in an MM series. The first letter of the suffix indicates the role (C is a deep-water [up to 50 m] mine, D a dummy practice mine, E a ground [ejercicio] mine, F a sensor mine); the second letter indicates the usual layer (A: aircraft or surface ships; B: boats or helicopters; G: submarines or submarines/surface ships; H: self-propelled for submarines alone; M: surface ships), and the third suffix indicates the mechanism (A and B: magnetic/acoustic/pressure; F: magnetic induction; L: Destructor magnetic mechanism; P: magnetic/acoustic).

◆ GAMA-1 (MM1-CBF)

This magnetic-induction anti-invasion mine can be laid by surface units and by helicopters. Claimed effectiveness (sinking factor) is 0.6 at depths between 2.6 and 6 m, using 14.6 kg of explosives. The sensor can detect 10 mOe/s (meter-Oerstads/sec) at a frequency of 0.5 to 4.0 Hz. Programmed arming delay time is 2 to 1000 hr; sterilization time is 2000 to 8000 hr.

◆ MIMBO (MM1-CAL and -DAL)

These are Destructor conversions of Mk 80–series bombs; -DAL is the practice version.

◆ Urania (MM2-CMP and -EMP)

Surface-launched magnetic-acoustic defensive mines.

◆ MM2-CGB, -EGB, -DGB, -CHB, -EHB, -DHB/Medusa

These magnetic-acoustic mines carry 580 kg of hex explosive. For the -CGB and -CHB versions, the manufacturer claims a sinking factor of 0.6 for water depths of 10 to 50 m. The magnetic-induction sensor can be adjusted between 0.1 and 40 mOe/s; the acoustic sensor employs selectable filters within 10 Hz–1 MHz. Arming delay is 4.5–2424 hr, and sterilization time can be 2 yr. The ship counter can be set at 1 to 99. All versions can be launched by submarine (-CHB, -EHB, and -DHB are self-propelled from torpedo tubes; they may also be called Medusa). -CGB and -EGB can also be launched by surface ships. -DGB and -DHB are recoverable practice versions.

◆ MM3-CGB, -EGB, -DGB, -CAP, -EAP, -DAP

These mines have microprocessor control to destroy particular targets. The associated signature recorder is Remina (MR3-FRF). Explosive charge and lethality match those of MM2. Sensors: magnetic (0.1 to 20 mOe/s, in a 35-deg cone around the vertical), acoustic (10–1000 Hz), pressure (which can detect variations of 10 mm in a 50m column of water, at a frequency of 0.1 to 0.02 Hz). Acoustic CCM features: rejects acoustic signals that rise at more than 10 dB/sec, has pass filters for bands at 10/20, 100/200, 200/400, 400/800, 100/1000 Hz. Magnetic: 4- and 8-sec random looks, looks for reverse polarity with 6–9–12-sec dead time and 20–30–40–60-sec live time, all being selectable. Arming delay is 1.5–4000 hr, and sterilization time can be 17,000 hr; the ship counter can be set between 1 and 99. The -CGB version can be laid in 10 to 50 m of water. MM3-CGB dimensions: 530 × 2200 mm (800 kg). -CGB and -EGB can be launched either by submarines or by surface ships. -DGB is the recoverable practice version. The other three are air-launched (-DAP is the recoverable practice version).

◆ Orca (M03-CAA, -EAA)

Surface-launched influence (magnetic, acoustic, pressure) mines.

◆ Overa (M03-CGB, -EGB)

Submarine-launched influence (magnetic, acoustic, pressure) mines.

BRAZIL

◆ MFC-01/100

This contact mine has been developed by Consub Equipamentos e Servicos Ltda of Rio de Janiero. The body is cylindrical, with domed top and bottom, with four horns protruding from the top. It is laid with its axis horizontal; the dimensions below include the anchor. Dimensions: 1.4 (L) × 1.02 (W) × 1.5 (H) m (770 kg, including 160-kg Trotyl charge); laying depth 10 to 100 m. Release from the anchor can be delayed. The Brazilian navy ordered 100 MFC-01/100 mines in August 1991.

MFC-01/100 is the first of a planned modular family of weapons, to carry up to three charges (presumably 160 kg each) and to use acoustic and magnetic sensors. The ground-mine version will be layable from submarine torpedo tubes, hence must have a smaller diameter.

CHILE

Cardoen Industries produces a clone of the British Marconi Stonefish, apparently with a broad- rather than a narrow-band acoustic trigger device. In August 1990 it was reported that some of these mines had been exported to Iraq.

◆ MS-L/MS-C

These magnetic ground mines are made by FAMAE (Fabricas & Maestranzas de Ejerato); MS-C is a shorter (1425- rather than 2060mm) air-droppable version of MS-L. Both are TT diameter (534.416 mm). The fuze seeks a sufficiently large change in polarity (through 0), within a set time window, to reject fields that vary either too slowly or too rapidly (e.g., to reject a magnetic object moving too slowly or too fast). The programmable parameters are the following: magnetometer sensitivity (2, 4, 8, 16, 32 mGauss), fuze arming time (2, 4, 16, 32, 64, 128, 256, 512 hr), inhibition time (32, 256, 512 sec), lower-limit window time (2 or 4 sec), upper-limit window time (16, 32, 64 sec), ship counter

(1–9), and sterilization time (2, 4, 8, 16, 32, 64 weeks). Inhibition time is a delay after the fuze has accepted a target as real, to protect the mine against multiple magnetic sweeps in combination.

CHINA

Chinese mine production began in 1958 with copies of Soviet large- and then medium-contact and antenna mines. In 1962 the large L-1 (L for Lao, moored) moored mine was standardized, followed in 1964 by the medium L-2 and in 1965 by the L-3 antenna mine. L-4 is an acoustic mine for deep water, standardized in November 1973. Work on an improved L-4A with better fuzing began in 1980 (it was standardized in November 1982); a solid-state L-4B appeared in December 1985.

The first bottom mine, C-1 (C for chen, sinking [to the bottom]), was standardized in 1966. C-2 was the first ground mine developed entirely in China, beginning with a proposal in 1956; sea tests followed in 1966. It used transistors rather than tubes. Improved in 1969–70, it entered production in 1975 as C-2A. Development of C-3 began in 1969; it entered production in 1974. This mine has antisweep features and can be laid in 6–50 m depth with a dual magnetic/acoustic pistol (or in 100 m with a single pistol). A recent Chinese account credits it with using the ship's secondary sound field ("infra-sonic," presumably seismic) as a way of solving the problem of reduced sensitivity caused by the siltiness of Chinese coastal waters. C-4 is a small noncontact modular bottom mine with combination or single pistol. It can be dissassembled for carriage by mule, and can be used for demolition. C-5 is a similar pressure mine (probably the first to be made in China); it can be drifted into position. It entered production in July 1975.

T-1 is the PRAM mine; work began in 1981 and was completed in 1987. Presumably it is the EM 52 described below. T-2-1 is a remotely controlled mine, using a combination of coded commands and a pistol (it has three modes: safe, armed, or command-detonated). Work began in 1978, and the design was frozen in December 1986. There are also floating mines and a riverine mine with a combined HF acoustic and remote pistol.

In 1985 China began marketing its versions of the Soviet AMD/KMD series as Type 500 or Type I (500 kg) and Type 1000 or Type II (1000 kg). Presumably these mines are the C-1 described above. Reported customers include Bangladesh.

◆ EM 52

This rocket-propelled rising mine, resembling a finned bomb, was displayed at Defense Asia 1991 (March 1991). Presumably it was inspired by the Russian rising mine. It is deployed in intermediate depths (max reported 110 m). It uses an acoustic sensor and a ship counter (1–99). 450 × 3700 mm (620 kg, including 140 kg explosive). Service life is 360 days. Reportedly this mine was exported to Iran.

DENMARK

Three types of modern mines have been or are being procured: two German (SGM 80 and SAI), and one Danish (MTP 19). Old types are being phased out as the new ones enter service. SAI replaces an earlier Danish Type 18.

◆ MTP-19

NEA Lindberg's controlled mine was first displayed at Defendory in October 1990. Dimensions: 878 (H) × 1000 × 1000; the lower part is configured as a trolley to ride the train rails in Danish ferries (which would be the primary minelayers in an emergency). With a buoyancy unit on top, the mine is 1128 mm high. Total weight is 500 kg including a 300-kg charge. Maximum laying depth is 20 m. The mine has two sections, the mine case proper (the 300-kg charge and a microcomputer) and the flotation unit. Because the flotation unit, carrying a marker buoy and 40 m of mine-control cable, rises to the surface for retrieval soon after the mine is laid, connection to the control cable is relatively easy; several mines can be linked to a single distribution box. The mine carries acoustic and magnetic sensors with microprocessor control. Minimum distance between mines is 50 m. The cables are linked on the surface to a system of distribution boxes and extension cables that sink to the sea bed. The boxes are microprocessor-controlled, so the system can configure automatically. The cables can be connected in random order, for rapid deployment. The weapons-control unit, up to 12 km from a mine, shows the entire minefield and the state of each mine. Operation is either under full control (which can be automatic, using a shore-based sensor) or auto-alarm (the mine uses its own sensors, based on criteria in its microprocessor). This mine may be designated M7/8 in Swedish service.

FRANCE

Thomson-CSF began work on mines in the late 1960s, beginning with exercise mines for surface ships and submarines.

Some of the standard prewar Breguet (B4, B4M, and B5B of the late 1930s) and Sauter-Harle (H5 and H5P of 1928 and H6 of 1935) surface-laid contact mines may still exist. B4/B4M were relatively small horned mines (1168 lb, including 176 lb of HE). B5B was an antenna ASW mine (2535 lb, including 485 lb of HE) analogous to the U.S. Mk 6, with 25m upper and 30m lower antennae, floating at 90 m (about 300 ft) with alternative mooring depths of 225, 300, or 400 m (respectively, about 740, 1000, and 1310 ft). The Sauter-Harles were horned mines with total weights of about 2550 lb (485 lb of TNT, 660 lb of TNT in H6).

◆ FG 26

Surface ship-laid mine.

◆ FG 29/FG 18

DCN's TT-laid FG 29 uses magnetic (high sensitivity), acoustic (several LF channels; resistant to broad-band explosion noise), and pressure sensors. There is a settable arming delay. Maximum case depth is 300 m, so it can be an ASW mine. Dimensions: 52 cm × 3 m; weight 1000 kg (600 kg of tritonal explosive). Development began in the early 1970s, and the first batch was delivered to the French navy in 1988. Thomson Sintra makes the sensors.

The earlier FG 18 was used on board *Daphne*-class submarines and may therefore have been exported with them (to Pakistan, Portugal, South Africa, and Spain).

MCC 23 (*above*) and MCT 15 (*below*). (Thomson Sintra)

◆ TSM 3510 (MCC 23)

Thomson Sintra's magnetic/acoustic TT-laid ground mine has a settable arming delay (up to 30 days) and a ship counter. The initial version (ca. 1978) was 530 × 2368 mm (20.9 x 93.2 in), with a 650-kg (1432-lb) warhead. The current version is 533.4 or 550 mm × 2.525 m (21 or 21.7 in × 99.4 in), 850 kg with a 530-kg warhead (1873/1168 lb). The mine is designed to attack any ship displacing over 1000 t.

This mine is or was made under license in Spain as MAE-10.

◆ TSM 3530 (MCT 15)

Thomson Sintra's air-dropped, parachute-retarded acoustic/magnetic mine is almost hemispherical. Dimensions: 1.2 (dia) × 1.1 m (47.2 × 43.3 in), 1500 kg, including a 1000-kg warhead (3306/2204 lb). This mine has a settable arming delay.

GERMANY

The postwar German navy used stocks of U.S. and British wartime and postwar mines. A new generation of ground and moored mines (and antisweep devices) developed under a Seemine 65 program included the FG 1 described below. Germany and Denmark collaborated in two later programs, Seegrundmine 80 (SGM 80) and Seemine Anti-Invasion (SAI).

◆ DM 11

550-kg moored mine.

◆ DM 41 (G1)

Faun-Werke's submarine-laid ground mine is built of nonmagnetic material and reportedly uses the sensors of the U.S. Mk 52 and Mk 55. Dimensions are 534 mm × 2310 mm: 710 mm for the control section, 1600 mm for the charge section (21 × 91 in; 28 in/63 in). Weight is 770.5 kg (1698 lb), with a 535-kg (1179-lb) warhead. Maximum effective depth is 60 m (197 ft). Reportedly this mine uses the sensors of the U.S.-supplied Mk 52 and Mk 55.

◆ DM 51 (SAI)

Seemine Anti-Invasion, a Danish-German project, is to be laid by landing craft. It was procured in 1982–90. Dimensions: 750 mm (dia) × 300 mm (110 kg, including 60 kg of HE). Fuzing is presumably magnetic, to destroy landing craft including hovercraft, as they cross the surf zone.

◆ DM 61 (G2/SGM 80/IGM 10)

This 750-kg cylindrical FAC-laid ground mine replaced U.S. Mk 25, 52, and 55 mines, drastically reducing maintenance load. The design requirement emphasized flexibility in target selection (with simplified setting), antisabotage and antisweep features, and minimum maintenance. The explosive and nonexplosive parts of the mine are coupled by a clamping ring, with the safing and arming device in the explosive section. The programmable microprocessor has acoustic (low or audio frequencies), magnetic, and hydrodynamic (pressure) signal-processing channels, which may be used either individually or in combination. The mine contains a library of ship signatures, corrected for local environmental conditions. The sensors estimate the range to the target, and the mine explodes when it comes within optimum range (for that type of target, as estimated from damage curves). A data-acquisition (measurement) version of the mine can be used to obtain the signatures of potential targets. Surveillance sensors filter out environmental effects, such as tides. The microprocessor program is divided into constant data (basic algorithms and signal-processing techniques) and mission data (preferred targets, choice of sensor combination, arming delay, ship count, etc.).

G2 is expected to require inspection every 4 yr, at which time operational inputs are fed into the microprocessor.

This joint Danish-German program began in 1980 (hence the initial Seegrundmine 80, or SGM 80, designation). Development was completed in 1986. KAE (now STN) won the production

SGM 80. (Dornier)

contract in 1987. Tests were completed at the end of 1989; as of 1996, 1058 had been made for the German navy during 1990–94, with another 2100 planned.

IGM 10 is a derivative, to be laid by submarines with external mine belts. It can be programmed immediately before leaving the ammunition depot.

There is also an exercise version.

♦ G3

This sea mine, now in the concept phase, is to neutralize new types of targets, such as surface-effect ships. Because they move so fast, they are probably best countered by a rising mine with a directional warhead, capable of attacking virtually at the surface.

IRAQ

Of about 1300 mines laid in the Persian Gulf before war broke out, about half were LUQM-145s (see below). Russian-supplied MYaMs accounted for about 7%, and KMD-500s about 3%. Mantas were about 5%. Another 16% were classified as unknown bottom mines, probably mainly Russian-supplied UMDs. Another 18% were beached/floating mines. The exotic weapons displayed at Bagdad in 1989 (described in the 1991/92 edition) apparently did not exist.

♦ LUQM-145

This "cheeseburger mine," encountered for the first time in the Gulf War, is a Russian-type contact mechanism (as in M-08) married to a larger floating body, an ovoid rather than a sphere, to carry more explosives.

ITALY

Sea mines are made by Whitehead Alenia (part of the Fincantieri group), which took over Misar (formed in 1977).

Whitehead is working on a CSM continental shelf rising mine with a guided warhead and also on a rising mine armed with the new Impact torpedo.

♦ EPR Series

Tecnovar's electronically fuzed anti-invasion mines, announced about 1981, are flat disks like land antitank mines. The number indicates the weight of explosive, 1.2, 3.6, or 6 kg (e.g., EPR 3.6). An EPR 2.5 limpet mine advertised in 1984 weighed about 6 kg (13 lb) and carried a 2.5-kg (5.5-lb) charge. Dimensions: 26 cm (dia) × 9 cm (H) (10.2 × 3.5 in). In tests, it blew a 250mm (9.8in)-dia hole in a steel plate 30 mm (1.2 in) thick.

♦ MAL/17 and MAS/22

Tecnovar's 22-kg (17-kg charge) anti-invasion mine, advertised in 1984, has three contact horns in its top and a stabilizer extending down from its spherical body. Dimensions: 38 × 110 cm (including stabilizer: 15 × 43 in). Case depth is about 3 m (10 ft). MAS/22 is an alternative version, virtually identical to the upper hemisphere of MAS/17, with three sharp stakes at its bottom so that it can be driven into a beach (just below the water line) or into a river bed. Height (including spikes) is 63 cm (24.8 in).

♦ Manta

Whitehead's magnetic/acoustic shallow-water (2.5–100 m) mine can be laid by ships, helicopters, or frogmen. Dimensions: 980 × 470 mm (38.6 x 18.5 in), weight about 220 kg or 240 kg depending on loading (the warhead is 140 kg of TNT or 170 kg of HBX-3, total weight 485 or 529 lb). The conical form of the casing is intended both to avoid movement due to currents and to avoid visual detection. Shelf life is 30 yr, and the mine will operate for 17 months after being laid. Export users included Iraq.

Manta, with MR-80 in the background. (Misar)

♦ MR-80/MP-80/MRP/Seppia

Whitehead's modular MR-80 ground mine can be laid at 5–300 m (15–1000 ft) by submarine, aircraft, or surface ship and can withstand the pressure of 500 m (1640 ft). Its fiberglass/epoxy resin casing carries explosives in the nose and the controls in the tail. Magnetic, acoustic (HF or LF), and pressure fuzes can be used in any desired combination. Arming and neutralization delays can be set up to 999 days, for a useful life of 500–1000 days. The 533mm mine can be built up with one, two, or three explosive sections (versions A, B, and C: lengths 1650, 2096, and 2750 mm, weights 656, 820, and 1070 kg, warheads 460, 630, and 870 kg).

MP-80/MRP is a digital version of MR-80/B (800 kg, 620 kg HBX-1); four microprocessors compare the target's signature (magnetic, pressure, and/or acoustic) with entries in a threat library. They also determine the moment of firing, based on target classification, and can set arming delay, armed life, and ship count. MP-80 is the Italian navy/NATO version; MRP (Misar's Advanced General-Purpose Sea Mine), with software not subject to NATO restrictions, is the export version.

Seppia is a moored version of MP-80 (660 × 1560 mm, 870 kg including 300 m of mooring wire and 200 kg of HBX-3). Mooring depth is 300–600 m. One version can be laid from a submarine's torpedo tube.

MR-80/I and MRP/I are training and trials variants of MR-80 and MRP.

First tested in the mid-1960s, MR-80 entered service in the late 1960s. Foreign sales began in the 1970s. Unit cost is between $30,000 and $35,000, and over 3400 MR-80s appear to have been made. Whitehead seems to have developed the digital TDD for Misar, and MP-80 was also advertised as its WP-900. It was the first Misar mine.

In mid-1985 Misar (now part of Whitehead) signed an agreement with Aerojet to market the U.S. Mk 65 Quickstrike mine with a Misar Target Detection Device (TDD) related to that of the MP-80/MRP. About a year later, at the request of the Italian navy, Misar studied modernization of Italian stocks of U.S. mines (Mk 13 Mod 6, Mk 52), proposing to install its TDD. It then offered similar modernization packages for U.S., European, and Russian mines. The Spanish MO-90 (initially MEB-90) also uses the Misar TDD.

Users:

MR-80: Greece (1970s), Italy, Norway (MR-80/1 exercise version, under 1984 contract), Turkey (1970s); at least one Third World country bought this mine in 1987. Sales were discussed with Argentina, Brazil, Chile, Iraq, Portugal, Venezuela, and several Middle Eastern and south Asian navies, but it is not clear which ones bought MR-80. Iraq reportedly undertook unlicensed production; a pair of MR-80s (or clones) apparently were responsible for the damage to USS *Princeton* during the Gulf War.

MP-80: At least India (MRP) and Italy; MP-80 won out over Valtec's VS-SM-600 in a 1978 Italian navy competition. Reportedly both Iran and Iraq bought MR-80 fuzing for Russian-type M-08 contact mines, converting them into influence mines. However, M-08s recovered in the Gulf (from both Iran and Iraq) were all contact weapons.

M-08-4 mines of Soviet design and North Korean manufacture, seized in the Persian Gulf in 1987 on board the Iranian ship *Iran Air.* (U.S. Navy)

◆ SB-81

Whitehead's (Misar's) 3.2-kg (2 kg HE) coastal mine/depth charge/countermining charge can shear a 35mm steel plate. Dimensions: 232 × 90 mm. It can be set to explode at a preset depth (by pressure) or mechanically fuzed. A helicopter magazine (the SY-AT system) is used to scatter it. The self-propelled C200 is the successor (it has an antimine version).

◆ SB-MV/1

Whitehead's (Misar's) 5-kg (2.6-kg charge) shaped-charge anti-invasion mine (displayed in 1980) can penetrate 150 mm of armor at a distance of 600 mm. A planned "extended range" shallow-water mine, P40, which projected a charge at a sensed target, apparently was never fully developed.

JAPAN

Mines are designated in a K-series (for the first letter of the Japanese word for mine) during development, after which they receive Type numbers. The United States encouraged Japan to build up a mining capability to block strategic straits through which the Russians would have had to pass between Vladivostok and the open Pacific.

The first lethal postwar mine was K-13 (Type 55), a seven-horned version of the wartime contact Type 93 (with four, seven, or nine Hertz horns), 50,000 of which were left. Stocks of the same mine held in Japanese-occupied territory probably survived the war and may still be in use. This principal wartime mine weighed 1543 or 1565 lb including its anchor (220 or 243 lb HE); diameter was 86 cm. Using thin cable, it could be laid in water as deep as 586 fathoms (3250 ft).

The U.S. Mk 6, received in 1954, was produced as Type 56 (K-15; an improved version is K-15B).

Japan received the U.S. Mk 25 and Mk 36, and made versions of these weapons: the 2000-lb K-1 through K-4 based on Mk 25, the 1000-lb K-21 through K-24 (Type 70: Mk 36); K-16 was a version of the U.S. Mk 18. Vacuum-tube mechanisms were magnetic pistol M-9, acoustic pistols A-3 and A-5, and the magnetic/pressure pistol A-6. Later Japanese versions of the U.S. Mk 52 (1000 lb) and Mk 55 (2000 lb) were made, probably as K-52 and K-55.

Then work began on Japanese mine designs, the first being the moored magnetic Type 71 (K-5). It (and modernized versions of earlier mines) incorporated integrated circuits and improved miniaturized electronics for better reliability.

K-33 is a moored contact mine.

A new air-dropped ground mine reached the hardware stage in 1989. Other new weapons are a rising mine and a new moored mine. Reportedly, Mitsubishi is modernizing some Japanese mines, presumably those manufactured under U.S. license.

Some Air Self-Defense Force C-130s can lay mines.

KOREA (NORTH)

North Korea made the Soviet-designed M08 mines used by Iran during the late 1980s. She received Soviet influence mines during the Korean War, and probably produces her own versions.

KOREA (SOUTH)

This model of the K-702 magnetic-acoustic ground mine is part of an exhibit of Korean-made weapons at the Korean national military museum. (D. Steigman)

NORWAY

Project Ida (formerly Project 6077) is the replacement of existing controlled minefields as part of the modernization of Norwegian coast defenses. It includes modernized Norwegian Mk 2 moored mines and U.S.-type Mk 51 controlled mines with new Safety, Arming, and Fuzing Unit (SAFU) using shore radars and EO for target detection. Test firings of mines and torpedoes took place in 1993. Bofors (ex-SA Marine) is supplying a new mine-sensor package (three-axis magnetometer, acoustic and pressure sensors, signal processing electronics, microprocessor, and lithium battery), a new safing/arming unit, and a new mine anchor. The development contract is to be completed during 1996. A new minefield planning system is based on SunSPARC workstations, using accurate seabed maps and current flow data.

Plans for a rising mine to attack both surface ships and submarines, the New Independent Mine (Project 6033), are in abeyance. It was to have been a guided weapon operating at twice the depth of a continental shelf mine, that is, about 2000 ft. In July 1994 18-month study contracts were awarded to three consortia:

BAeSEMA with Kvaerner Eureka of Norway (deep water aspects) and Alliant (rising mine subsystem)
Bofors Underwater Systems (Sweden)
NFT (Kongsberg), Raufoss, Simrad, GEC-Marconi

The planned 1997 contract award has now been deferred.

RUSSIA

A recent Russian account of postwar mine development breaks it down into four periods, 1945–55, 1956–65, 1966–85, and 1986–95, of which it gives details of major developments during the first three. The principal survivors of World War II types were the surface-laid AGSB, KB-3, KRAB, MIRAB, M-08, and M-39, and the aircraft-laid AMD-1 and AMD-2. New mines developed during the first period were the air-laid AMD-4-1000 (1951), AMD-2M (1955), and APM (1955); the ship-laid IGDM (1954); and the submarine-laid MDT (1953). There may also have been an MKB ship-laid contact mine.

During the second stage (1956–65) UEP and rising mines (active mines, in Russian terminology) were developed. The main new mines of this period were: the ship-laid GM (1956), KAM (1957), and KSM (1957), with unified versions UGM and UKSM (both 1960); submarine-laid PM-1 (1959) and PM-2 (1965); the first rising mine, RM-1 (1960), and the analogous RM-2 (1963); air-laid Lira (1956), Serpeiy (1957), and IGDM-500 (1958); and the first universal (ship/submarine/air-laid) mines, UDM (1961) and UDM-500 (1964). PLT-4 and -6 were developed for abortive special-purpose minelaying submarines. Pressure-firing sensors developed at this time were GDP-1, GDP-2, and GDP-G.

Mines entering service during the third stage (1966–85): rising mines PMR (1968), PMR-1 (1970), PMT-1 (a torpedo mine, 1972), and PMR-2 (all active type); and DM-1 (1973), UDM-2 (1979), and MDS (1979).

Gidropribor of St. Petersburg develops Russian mines. In designations, MD means bottom mine (Mina Donnaya).

◆ AMD Series

AMDs, initially air-laid ground mines, were adapted to ship-laying. From the AMD-1-500 and AMD-1-1000 of 1942 were derived the AMD-2-500 and AMD-2-1000 of 1945. AMD-4 appeared in 1951. Improved versions were AMD-500M, AMD-2-500M (AMD-2M), and AMD-4-500M. Charge weights were 300 kg for AMD-500 and 700 kg for AMD-1000, the figure indicating total weight; corresponding case depths were 30 m for AMD-1 and 50 m for AMD-2. All versions could be surface-laid.

AMD-1 used a magnetic-induction (two-impulse) sensor. The 1000-kg version was described as the air-dropped version of the MKD magnetic-induction ground mine, using a new mechanism based on that of the British A Mk 1, some of which were provided to the Soviets early that year. Compared to the British mine, AMD was considered more rugged and also more sensitive. Dimensions were 21 × 114 in (2167 lb with 1725 lb of modified torpex).

AMD-2 was magnetic-acoustic; the acoustic element could be HF or LF or a combination. AMD-2M was based on the FAB-1500 bomb (0.63 × 2.9m). AMD-2-500M (300 kg explosive) has a sensing range of about 50 m, and is laid in 8 to 50 m depth, with a lifetime of 10 days and a ship counter set at 1 to 20. It can be laid at a speed of up to 700 km/h, dropped from at least 500 m altitude. An Il-38 (May) carries four or eight. The early postwar submarine-laid MDT was developed from AMD-2.

AMD-4 is a magnetic-pressure mine. Case depth is 35 m (lethal radius 30 m for a 700-kg charge). Reported ship count is 1–21; reported arming delay is 12 hr to 10 days. The firing logic

takes three looks. These mines have anticountermine provisions.

For 500 and 1000 kg, respectively, maximum case depths (antiship) are reportedly 24.4 and 54.9 m (80 and 180 ft); charge weights 300 and 699 kg (660 and 1540 lb); and minimum distance between mines, 69 and 137 m (226 and 449 ft). If these mines are used against submarines, they may be laid at greater depths, up to 200 m (660 ft) for a -1000. Known influence mechanisms are (a) magnetic (horizontal or vertical component of target field), (b) acoustic (HF or LF), (c) pressure, and (d) combination.

NATO used the AMD designation to describe a wide variety of air-laid mines, as well as some projected (estimated as part of a future threat study) by U.S. Naval Intelligence, such as AMD-S, a remotely controlled mine (1970).

AMD-500 and -1000 could be laid by surface ships such as destroyers.

◆ APM

This aircraft-laid contact mine (with four horns) entered service in 1955. The charge weighs 260 kg. Case depth is 2–7 m, maximum laying depth 15 m.

◆ BPM-2

This swimmer-laid limpet mine (4 kg of HE) appeared in 1950.

◆ DM-1

This dual-purpose mine (laid by both surface ships and submarines) is effective at 50 m against a surfaced submarine and at 125 m against a submerged one. Dimensions: 533 × 2860 mm, weight 960 kg (746 kg explosives). DM-1 entered service in 1973.

◆ GM/UGM

This ship-laid influence mine, using the same mechanisms as KRAB, Lira, and AGSB (antenna), entered service in 1957. Its case floats at 10–30 m (mooring depth is up to 1500 m) and it carries 300 kg of HE. Lethal radius: 50–60 m with KRAB mechanism, 15–20 m with Lira mechanism. UGM (1960) is a unified version.

◆ IGDM and IGDM-500

IGDM (1954) is a ship-laid magnetic-induction/pressure ground mine. IGDM-500 (1957) is an air-laid equivalent with a 200-kg charge (lethal radius 30 m), to be laid in water 35 m deep.

◆ KAM

This ship-laid moored acoustic mine entered service in 1957. Lethal radius is 10 m (warhead 300 kg); the mine case floats at 20 to 40 m in up to 400 m of water.

◆ KB (NATO MKB)

KB (introduced 1940) was a new ("large") ship-launched five-horned contact mine, carrying twice the charge of M-08 (230 kg) and moorable at twice the depth (260 m); case depth was 2.4–9.1 m. MKB was apparently a NATO designation applied to KBs used postwar (probably KB-3s); there was a prewar MKB mine. As measured from specimens recovered in Korea, diameter matched that of M-08 (34.5 in), but the case was larger (length 52 in) and thicker. The charge was 506 lb of TNT; case weight was 984 lb, and the anchor weighed 1415 lb. Laying depths were 34–894 ft, and case depths 8–30 ft. Minimum separation was 138 ft. MKB-3 was similar, but with a shorter parallel midsection (length 47 in); charge weight (200 rather than 229 kg) and case weight were similar to those of the MKB. Minimum spacing was 35 m (115 ft) rather than 42 m (138 ft).

MKB mines were used in Korea (with AMD/KMD mines) and also in Vietnam (they were laid late in 1966 and found in January 1967 in the Long Tau Channel to Saigon). The Egyptians used MKB in 1967 to block the Straits of Tiran, and then in the Suez Canal.

◆ KPM

This surface-laid moored contact anti-invasion mine (three horns) entered service in 1957. Case depth is 0.5 to 2 m, and maximum laying depth is 20 m. The charge is 30 kg. A current version, advertised for export, weighs 745 kg (including anchor; charge is equivalent to 48 kg of TNT). KPM is made by the V. V. Kuibyshev Machine-Building Works of Petropavlovsk (Kazakhstan).

A KPM beach-defense contact mine. (Rozvoorouzhenie)

♦ KRAB

This moored ship-laid two-channel (reportedly 22.5 and 30–40 kHz, with two-look firing logic) acoustic mine entered service in 1944; it is essentially an acoustic device (which later itself became known as KRAB) inserted into a standard MKB ellipsoidal mine case. It may have incorporated captured German influence mechanisms. Mooring depth is 280 m, case depth is about 18 m, and the explosive charge is 230 kg. Minimum distance between mines is 41 m. KRAB means large ship-laid inshore acoustic mine (Korabelnaya Reydny Akusticheskaya Bol'shaya).

It seems unlikely that the reported Improved KRAB (1960) ever existed.

♦ KRM

The first Soviet rising mine is ship-laid in up to 100 m of water. The bomb-shaped mine is moored close to the bottom in an upright position, listening for a characteristic signature, then turning on its active pinger to determine target depth. KRM is propelled up by a rocket in its tail, stabilized by fixed fins; the entire weapon separates from its anchor. The weapon has proximity and hydrostatic fuzes. Lethal radius (300 kg charge) is 20 m. KRM was probably the basis for the Chinese EM 52.

♦ KSM/UKSM/AGSB

The ship-laid KSM (Korabelnaya Srednyaya Mina, 1957) carries (1957) a 150-kg charge, and can be moored in 500 m at a case depth of 10–210 m; lethal zone is 28 m wide and 36 m deep. UKSM (1960) is a unified version. KSM was developed from the World War II AGSB, which had two 35m steel antennae (above and below) and carried a 230-kg charge. It used a two-pulse operating circuit to overcome interference problems. Case depth is 2.4 to 91.4 m, and maximum mooring depth is about 500 m. Development began in the early 1930s, and AGSB entered combat early in World War II.

♦ Lira

This large air-laid moored acoustic influence mine, based on the FAB-1500 bomb, entered service in 1956. It could be laid in 25 to 250 m depth with a case depth of 2 to 25 m. As in the case of KRAB, the name Lira came to be associated with the mine's influence mechanism (see PM-1).

♦ M-08/M-39

This pre–World War I (1908) moored contact mine is manufactured in North Korea, and was used by Iran and Iraq in the Persian Gulf. The 34.5in spherical case carries five chemical (Hertz) horns. The filled case weighs 500 lb (charge 253 lb of TNT) and the anchor weighs about 700 lb. Case depth is 1.6 to 6.1 m, and mooring depth is down to 115 m. Minimum distance between mines (to avoid countermining) is 120 ft. M-39 is an improved version.

North Korean-made M-08 mines in the Persian Gulf sometimes broke from their moorings; probably the North Koreans (or the Iranians) used lighter, flimsier mooring chain so that the mine could carry a larger charge. Reportedly both Iran and Iraq bought Italian influence fuzes for their stocks of M-08 mines, converting them from contact to contact/influence weapons. However, all the M-08s encountered in the Gulf were contact-fuzed. The Iraqi LUQM-145 uses M-08 contact horns.

♦ MDM Series (NATO KMD and KMK)

Of these antisubmarine/antiship ground mines, MDM-1 and -6 are ship- or submarine-laid from 53cm torpedo tubes. Laid by ships at 4–15 kt and by submarines at 4–8 kt in, respectively, 12–120 and 20–120 m of water, it has both acoustic and magnetic (induction) channels. MDM-6 adds a pressure channel to MDM-1, and the upgrade can be supplied in kit form. Note that these mines are half torpedo length, so two can be accommodated on each skid. MDM-2 is for surface ships only. Laid in 12–35m water against surface ships or 12–125m water against submarines, it has a three-channel acoustic exploder (initial

MDM-5. A drawing published by Gidropribor shows a simpler cylindrical shape like that of a lengthened UDM-5; this may be a more modern version for higher-speed carriage. (Rozvoorouzhenie)

MDM-2. This mine releases a floating sensor once it has been planted. It has three acoustic channels, an early detector, and a pair of parallel channels (presumably the HF detector floating near the target and a guard channel detecting ambient noise away from the target). The outputs of the two parallel channels are compared to determine when to detonate the mine. Laying depth: 12 m minimum; maximum is 35 m against surface ships and 125 m against submarines. (Rozvoorouzhenie)

MDM-6 acoustic-magnetic-pressure mine. (D. Markov)

detector feeding a difference detector and a guard channel to avoid sweeps; the outputs of the two channels are compared to decide whether to explode). MDM-3, -4, and -5 can be laid by surface ships (MDM-3 in 8–35 m of water) at 4–15 kt or by aircraft (MDM-3 in 15–35 m of water) at 540 kt or (in the case of -5) by surface-effect craft at up to 100 kt. MDM-4 is to be laid in 15–50 m of water (to 250 m against submarines). All use combination acoustic/magnetic/hydrodynamic (pressure) exploders.

NATO called these mines KMD and KMK (for submarines). A Libyan "KMD," "995," probably an MDM-1, recovered in the Red Sea in 1984, showed a new type of influence mechanism (seismic in addition to the usual acoustic, pressure, and magnetic). It apparently had a modular electronic firing mechanism to replace the earlier plug-in type. This type of mine reportedly incorporates a ship counter (up to 11 ships) and a delayed-arming mechanism (up to 10 days). The charge cavity of the Libyan mine was not filled, but it would have been large enough to accommodate a 750-kg charge.

Characteristics (length and weight are for air/surface-laid versions):

	Depth (m)	Diameter (mm)	Length (mm)	Weight (kg)
MDM-1	12–125	533	2860	960
MDM-2	12–125	790	2200	1413
MDM-3	8–50	450	1580/1525	525/635
MDM-4	12–125	650	2785/2300	1370/1420
MDM-5	8–300	630	3055/2400	1500/1470
MDM-6	12–120	533	2860	960

◆ MDS/SMDM

Work began on this mobile mine, a converted 53-65KE with a two-channel (acoustic-magnetic induction) fuze, in the 1970s. Its lethal zone is about 50 m (480-kg warhead). It can travel up to 10 nm after leaving a torpedo tube, and is effective in depths of 4–150 m. Service life is 1–2 yr. SMDM is a 65cm equivalent with an 800-kg warhead and a standoff range of 25 nm. MDS is sometimes advertised as SMDM-1 (the 65cm version is then SMDM-2).

◆ MDT (NATO MKD) and KMD

The first postwar submarine-laid (TT) mine entered service in 1953, to equip first- and second-generation postwar diesel submarines. It was developed from AMD-2 and from the wartime PLT-3. With the appearance of the air-delivered Serpei and IGDM-500, it was standardized with the same sensors. MDT has a torpedo-shaped body with a smaller-diameter cylindrical head protruding from it; the head carries the safety device and the opening for hand-setting. Later versions had different lengths and weights, and were probably produced in ship-laid form. Derivatives include the ship-laid KMD series as well as DM-1 (1973) and MDM-1 and MDM-6.

Like MDT, KMDs were all 53cm weapons. KMD-2-500 and -1000, in East German service, were, respectively, 1905 and 2880 mm long (carrying 300 and 700 kg of explosives; total weights were 500 and 1000 kg). They could be laid in 50 m of water, and had acoustic and magnetic fuzes (to which a pressure sensor was

later added, at least by the East Germans). Ultimately these weapons had 21-ship counters and settable arming delays of 0.5 to 10 days. Exports of KMD-series mines began in the 1960s.

A Soviet TT-laid (i.e., 21in) mine recovered in the early 1950s, probably MDT, had a two-look magnetic fuze (interval 4–45 sec) to ensure that the object triggering it had some substantial size. However, the fuze tended to be more sensitive for the short period, so the mine was relatively easy to sweep. The mine also had a ship counter (0–11 ships) and a clock (0–10 days), as well as a hydrostatic safety. Its detection range was limited because of the limited length of its iron-dust (Sendust) core. The warhead was 1700 lb, equivalent to 2500 lb of TNT. Overall mine length was 114 in, of which 95.5 in was taken up by the charge.

◆ MIRAB

This magnetic-induction river ground mine is a half-teardrop in shape (40.5 [L] × 27.5 × 27.5 in, 616 lb with 141-lb charge). Effective range is 5 m or less against a 20t ship running at 2 kt or more. Minimum spacing is 200 ft. The mine was originally intended to be air-dropped (MIRAB means aircraft induction river mine, Mina Induktsionnaya Rechnaya Aviatsionnaya), but its case was not strong enough, and it was surface-laid. MIRAB originally used a vertical-field single-contact circuit, but it proved too easy to explode the mine by shock. The problem was solved by providing a directional condition. The final triggering circuit uses two looks but has no ship counter. This mine entered limited service in 1939.

◆ MShM

Thus far this submarine-laid sea-shelf rocket mine is the ultimate development of the rising mine concept. The guided rocket is much faster than a homing torpedo, albeit with less endur-

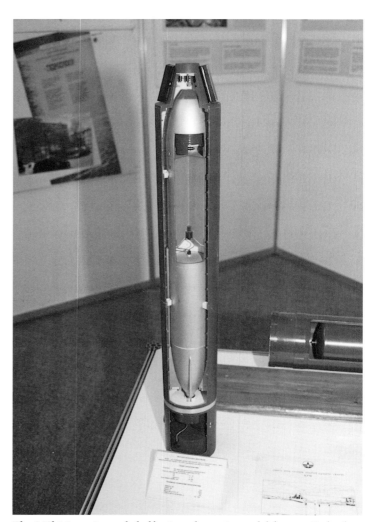

The MShM continental shelf mine, shown in model form at Defendory 1996. (D. Markov)

ance. A complete attack takes less than 25 sec. Dimensions: 533 × 4000 mm (820 kg with warhead equivalent to 250 kg of TNT); laying depth is 60–300 m. There are three independent safety mechanisms. See also PMR-2 below.

◆ MYaM (YaM)

This small ellipsoidal moored contact mine had three chemical horns. Dimensions were 21 in (dia) × 22.8 in. Weights were 44 lb of TNT, with a 142-lb case and a 243-lb anchor. Laying depth was 9–167 ft; case depth, 2–9 ft. Minimum distance between mines was 66 ft. MYaM was probably an antismall-craft mine (e.g., antisweeper). It was first reported in Korea in 1952, and both Iran and Iraq used MYaM in the Iran-Iraq War.

◆ PM-1

This submarine-laid acoustic moored mine, using a Lira sensor, could be laid in 400 m of water, the case floating at 10–25 m. Lethal radius (with a 230-kg charge) is 15–20 m. PM-1 entered service in 1959. It was designed to deal with both surface ships and submarines.

◆ PM-2 (NATO Cluster Gulf)

This UEP mine, which entered service in 1965, was developed specifically to counter submarines in ice. It consists of two cases (top and bottom) with three antennas (top, middle, and bottom), each with two electrodes. PM-2 may not have been the first Soviet UEP mine. Characteristics, as estimated by NATO intelligence, were: two charges (150 kg each) in the cases, case depth 100–200 m, bottom depth 600 m. The full array is 80 m long (262 ft), and the case weighs about 480 kg.

Reports of earlier UEP mines most likely refer to antenna weapons. For example, what NATO called the ship-laid KB-UEP of 1951 was most likely AGSB or KB-3; the supposed 1960 version was probably KSM.

◆ PMR-2/PMK-1

These third-generation submarine-laid rising mines (1975) use fast homing underwater rockets (rising at 80 m/sec) instead of torpedoes. PMR-2 dimensions: 534 × 7830 mm, 1850 kg. PMK-1 (534 × 7830 mm, 1850 kg, 350 kg HE) is an export version, firing a rocket-powered torpedo at 60 m/sec (about 120 kt) over a range of several hundred meters. The torpedo uses a combination of influence, contact, and time fuzes. Laying depth is 200–400 m. Laying speed is 4–15 kt for surface ships, 4–8 kt for submarines.

PMR-2. (Rozvoorouzhenie)

A model of PMK-1. (D. Markov)

◆ PMT-1 (NATO ATM, Autonomous Torpedo Mine)

This second-generation rising mine (1972) uses a lightweight torpedo payload to intercept a maneuvering target. Its design was inspired by the advent of the UMGT-1 torpedo. This mine was first seen (by Westerners) in 1984 when the Northern Fleet destroyer *Otlichnyy* was seen carrying four exercise examples.

◆ RM-1

The first air-laid rising mine entered service in 1960, work having begun in 1957. Like KRM, it rose toward the target as a unit. The difference was in propulsion; RM-1 used a water jet, with a water intake, and had no stabilizing fins. It had a hydrostatic fuze.

◆ RM-2 (NATO Cluster Bay)

The first submarine-laid rising mine entered service in 1963. It was equivalent to RM-1, the entire mine case rising, stabilized by retractable fins. Dimensions: 534 × 3850 mm (870 kg). The lethal radius of the mine is 20 m. It can be laid in depths as great as 450 m. The NATO code name indicates a recovered weapon examined by U.S. experts. Reportedly the mine listens at a typical submarine frequency (45 or 46 kHz), then pings at high frequency (158 kHz) to confirm the target's existence and measure its depth. The 220-kg warhead is equivalent to 600 lb of HBX. Maximum case depth is 1200 ft (mooring depth 2000 ft). Cluster Bay was impressive not only because it could attack deployed submarines, but also because it had the potential to close strategic straits such as the Sicilian Narrows. This weapon seems not to have been known to the West until about 1973, when it made a considerable impression. More than any other, it was responsible for Western interest in deep minesweeping.

◆ RMZ

This antihelicopter mine (to defeat helicopter sweepers) is probably a NATO-projected weapon rather than a Soviet-developed one. It was reported in 1980: 2 m long, weight about 700 kg (charge about 350 kg).

◆ RPM

This submarine-launched rising mine (1968) uses three attack elements on a common cable; each is 155 × 2545 mm, 110 kg with a 14-kg warhead. Mooring depth is 40–600 m.

◆ Serpei

This air-laid magnetic-acoustic ground mine entered service in 1957. With a 600-kg charge, it had a lethal radius of 50 m, and could be laid in water that deep. Setting delay is up to 10 days.

◆ TUM

This ship-laid controlled mine entered service in 1954. It carries 700 kg of exposive (lethal radius 50 m) and is laid in water up to 50 m deep.

◆ UDM

UDM (1961) and UDM-500 (1964) are universal (ship- and aircraft-laid) influence mines to attack ships and submarines. UDM and the modernized UDM-2 and -5 are based on older bombs with flat noses and air tails. UDM-3 and UDM-500 are cylindrical, with tail caps. UDM characteristics (ship/aircraft versions): 1420/1320 kg, 790/630 × 2100/2785 mm. UDM-2, 1470/1500 kg (800 kg explosive), 630/630 × 2400/3055 mm, laying depth 8–300 m. UDM-500: 635/575 kg, 600/450 × 1525/1500 mm. Minimum laying depth is 8 m. The lethal zone is about 50 m, depending on a ship's magnetic field. UDM-3 and -500 release a secondary magnetic sensor to float closer to the surface. This concept recalls the idea of the two-sensor rising mine. It brings the secondary sensor closer to low-signature targets such as MCM craft and surface-effect landing craft. This mine was used by the Iraqis during the 1991 Gulf War.

Models of Gidropribor mines on display at Defendory 1996: UDM-5 and -3 in the background (misidentified as UMDs), and the SMDM mobile mine in the foreground. MDM-4 and -5 are similar to UDM-5. (D. Markov)

UDM-5 at Defendory 1996. UDM-2 has much the same configuration. (D. Markov)

UDM-3 at Defendory 1996. UDM-500 has a similar configuration. (D. Markov)

UDM-500. MDM-3 is a somewhat similar cylindrical mine, but with a domed end. (Rozvoorouzhenie)

SOUTH AFRICA

It was reported in 1991 that Armscor had produced a number of mine designs originally sold by West Germany to Chile in the 1960s; presumably they are distantly related to the current SGM 80. Reportedly the principal mine can operate either by contact or by magnetic or acoustic fuzing, and can change its principal sensor after having been laid, for a period of up to 5 yr. The South African navy reportedly bought 2000, 500 were sold back to Chile, and 1020 to Iraq; 3000 more were sold to other users, possibly including Libya. Reportedly these mines proved particularly difficult to sweep during the 1991 Gulf War.

Northbend Instruments developed a modular Matrix mine in the early 1980s; it has been exported to several (unnamed) countries. There are 13 modules in all, including the TDD (magnetic, acoustic, other—presumably pressure and/or seismic), warhead (eight sizes), microprocessor, sinker, and chain. Claimed shelf life is 20 yr.

Reportedly, South Africa retains very large stocks of British mines built up during 1944–45 for use in the Indian Ocean and the Pacific, and retained postwar; few if any apparently were returned when the British naval presence at Simonstown ended in 1962.

Reportedly, Armscor modernizes some existing mines.

SPAIN

Inisel has manufactured the French MCC 23C under license as MAE-10. Spain may also manufacture the Italian Manta under

◆ UDME

This current dual-purpose mine is laid by surface ships in 12–125 m of water (12–50 m vs. both surface ships and submarines, 125 m vs. submerged submarines). Dimensions: 630 × 970 (height with bogie) × 2300 mm; weight 1413 kg including 645 kg of HE. Packed dimensions are 790 × 2300 mm.

◆ YaRM

This small shallow-water contact (anti-invasion) mine carries a 3-kg charge.

license. The Spanish navy also has 1500 Vickers-designed moored mines, which have been in storage since 1945, and are being upgraded.

MO-90 (Mina de Orinque) is a new magnetic-acoustic moored mine by SAES (of Grupo Indra)/Bazan/Explosivos Alaveses, first delivered in July 1993 (the program began in December 1990). Dimensions: 1180 mm (W) × 1090 mm (L) × 1690 mm (H), 1060 kg (300 kg HBX-3, equivalent to 480 kg TNT). The mine is programmed via IR sensor for depth (15–300 m, to within 1 m), fuzing, target characteristics, ship count, and sterilization period. The case is GRP, to make detection difficult. Underwater life is over 2 yr. This is probably the mine listed as MOM-90, with an "intelligent" magnetic sensor, a 3D acoustic sensor, and a glass-fiber mooring cable. Thomson-CSF may be involved in this project.

The SAES MO-90 mine on its laying trolley. (SAES)

SWEDEN

When Bofors absorbed SA Marine in 1994, that company was working on a hydropulse (gas generator rocket) rising mine, P85, developed from a General Dynamics design. Work was abandoned because there was no market. The Bofors proposal for the Norwegian rising mine was based on a torpedo rather than a rocket.

There is current interest in modernizing the large existing Swedish mine stocks with new safing/arming devices and some new electronics.

The FFV/Bofors/Ericsson project for a mobile mine (converted torpedo), announced in 1985, seems to have been abandoned.

◆ Bunny

Bofors's new submarine-laid bottom mine is laid from a saddle rather than a tube. It weighs 200 kg and uses the new 9SP180 sensor, described below, which is also being offered for mine upgrade programs. The saddle was developed by the German firm of Abeking & Rasmussen; it fits over the pressure hull of

the submarine, laying its mines vertically. Tests have shown that it is compatible with current Swedish submarines, but none has yet been bought by Sweden.

Bunny. (Bofors)

◆ GMI 100 Rockan

This anti-invasion ground mine, announced in 1984, can also be laid in deeper water as an ASW mine. The unusual shape causes the mine to glide through the water, typically to twice the depth of the water in which the mine is laid (5–100 m depth). The mine's low profile makes sonar detection difficult, and the irregular shape and GRP casing tend to camouflage Rockan's purpose. Dimensions are 1015 × 800 × 385 mm; weight is 190 kg (105 kg of explosive); minimum distance between mines is 25 m.

The Rockan sensor will not react to any sweep that creates a homogeneous magnetic field; this sensor is also being incorporated into the moored MMI 80.

Rockan shows its unusual shape. (Author)

◆ MMI 80

This moored influence mine, announced in 1984, has an operational depth of 20–200 m. The buoyant body is made of plastic, and the sensors are similar to those of the Rockan mine. Dimensions are 1125 × 660 × 1125 mm; total weight is 450 kg; charge is 80-kg hexotonal; sinker weight is 240 kg. Minimum distance between mines is 25 m.

◆ m/9 (GMI 600)

One of the main weapons of the Swedish amphibious coast-defense battalions, m/9 entered production about mid-1992. It was designed to be capable of either cable control or autonomous operation, and can be laid from fast raiding craft at up to 40 kt. The mine employs two, three, or four charge modules (each with

MMI 80, with Rockan at left and a model of Double Eagle at right. (Author)

100-kg charge), packaged with electronics in a rigid self-contained unit. A battery pack can be added. In the controlled mode, it is connected to a control station through four wire cassettes, each wound with 500 m of 6.5mm cable. This is a fully programmable multi-influence mine. The largest version is 1.7 m (L) × 0.6 m (W) × 0.7 m (H), 700 kg. Lifetime: 2 yr in water, 10 on the shelf.

The GMI 600 modular bottom mine. (Author)

◆ Type 74

This moored mine is made by SAB Industri AB. Total weight is 205 kg, and the body is cylindrical. It can be laid in depths as great as 110 m and operates over a radius of 3–70 m.

◆ Type 77

SAB's pressure mine weighs 470 kg. It is to be laid in depths from 20–200 m.

◆ 9SP180

BEAB's (formerly PEAB) mine sensor, announced in 1988, carries a BEAB PCHS-1 (Philips Combined Hydrosensor) and a three-axis magnetometer. The hydrosensor has separate channels for depth, dynamic pressure, and sound; all of the signals are filtered and evaluated against preprogrammed target criteria. Dimen-

sions: 320 × 350 mm (16 kg). Maximum depth is 150 m (490 ft). Operational lifetime (depending upon frequency of alerts) is about 12 months.

TAIWAN

Taiwan uses a variety of domestic and foreign-produced mines. There are still large stocks of ex-U.S. antenna and contact mines, as well as magnetic (and probably pressure) bottom influence mines. There are also air-dropped cylindrical bottom mines (WSM-110) and Manta-like anti-invasion mines (WSM-210). WSM-110 resembles World War II influence mines, with slight tapering at one end for an appropriate trajectory, and two holes in the side for sensors. It may be an adapted U.S. type.

WSM-210 bottom mine. (Fu S. Mei)

A Taiwanese-made influence mine, showing the setting panel. (Fu S. Mei)

UNITED KINGDOM

In mid-1993 the Royal Navy announced that all existing stocks of defensive mines (Mks 5 and 12) were being destroyed. Britain probably retains the ability to assemble bombs into Destructors for offensive mining. There is no known British standoff (torpedo) mine. The only new mine to be made in Britain, Stonefish, was made only for export.

◆ Older Mines

Many weapons probably survive in current and former British client-states such as India, Pakistan, and South Africa. These mines may also have been supplied to NATO navies.

There were three mine series: moored mines with Mk numbers, air-launched mines (A series), and magnetic ground mines

British Mk 5 bottom mine (in Australian service). (Klein)

British Mk 17 moored mines with Mk 18 bases (in Australian service). (Klein)

(M series). The principal mines, at and just after the end of World War II, were the following:

A Mk 6 was an aircraft-laid ground mine (1800 lb; 960- or 1040-lb charge; magnetic, acoustic, combination, or pressure). Minimum depth was 40 ft. Dimensions were 18.45 in × 8 ft 6 in (9 ft 4 in including parachute). In 1949, 5707 were on hand.

A Mk 7, 7*, and 7** were 1100-lb ground mines (555- or 610-lb charges). Fuzing was magnetic or acoustic. Minimum case depth was 40 ft. Dimensions were 15.8 in × 7 ft 6 in (6 ft 11 in without parachute). In 1949, 4502 were on hand.

A Mk 9 was an 1850-lb ground mine carrying a 960- or 1060-lb charge. Fuzing was magnetic, acoustic, combination, or pressure. Minimum case depth was 40 ft. Dimensions were 18.5 in × 8 ft 6 in (9 ft 4 in with parachute). In 1949, 1427 were on hand and another 400 were on order.

M Mk 1 was the standard buoyant magnetic mine, ship-laid in up to 1000 fathoms of water. It carried a 320- or 500-lb Amatol charge. A total of 8948 were on hand in 1949.

M Mk 2 was a 1760-lb ground mine (1020-lb Amatol charge), laid by submarine or coastal forces in 5–20 fathoms. 1310 were on hand in 1949.

M Mk 5 was running sea trials in 1949. It was a 1930-lb ground mine (1030-lb charge, with magnetic, acoustic, or combination fuzing) laid by submarines or coastal forces in 6.5–20 fathoms. This was presumably the Mk 5 mine retained until 1993.

S Mk 6 was a postwar-developed submarine-laid mine, discarded by the Royal Navy some time after 1959.

Mk 15 was a buoyant contact mine carrying 320 or 500 lb of Amatol; it could be laid in water as deep as 1000 fathoms. A total of 1972 were on hand in 1949.

Mk 17 was a similar buoyant mine, which could be laid in 500 fathoms of water; 14,933 were on hand.

A Type S and A Mk 12, developed in 1953–56, were air-delivered ASW ground mines. Weights were 1000 and 2000 lb, respectively. Both mines used combination acoustic-magnetic-pressure mechanisms. At the time of development, the standard air-drop requirements were 450 kt/5000 ft (Royal Navy) and 35,000 ft in altitude (RAF). Minimum water depths (which determined the shock level the mine had to survive during laying) were 12 and 40 ft.

Mk 10 was a postwar aircraft-laid buoyant contact ASW mine, development of which began during World War II. The length of the mooring cable had to be adjusted before flight. Mk 10 was intended to be as simple and as inexpensive as possible, and it was the only means of mining deep water not accessible to surface ships and submarines. Total weight was 810 lb (100 lb of Minol charge). Maximum case depth was 600 ft.

The three types in British service in 1993 were:

Mk 5 submarine- and ship-laid ground mine (M Mk 5)
Mk 12 air-laid ground mine (A Mk 12)
Mk 17 moored acoustic mine.

♦ **Dragonfish**

Marconi's 85-kg (80 kg of explosive) anti-invasion mine (for water depths of 30 m or less) uses Stonefish technology; it has two types of influence sensors. In-water life is 200 days.

♦ **Stonefish**

Marconi's medium-depth (30–200 m) modular magnetic/acoustic/pressure (single- or multiple-influence) mine is laid by airplane, ship, or submarine. Its microprocessor can be set for a particular target signature. Dimensions: 53 cm × 2.4 m (1.9 m training version); weight is 990 kg (600-kg Torpex warhead). In-water life is 700 days (shelf life is 20 yr). The training version (440 kg, in-water life 90 days) is laid only by surface ships. A shorter, lighter Mk 2 (500 kg of insensitive PBX in place of the original 700 kg of Torpex) has simplified firing circuitry (over 30 components eliminated). Finland was the first customer (1991).

Stonefish development began in 1981, a prototype was tested in 1983, and marketing began late in 1985.

Reported users: Australia (exercise version, probably 200 delivered), Chile, Finland (first customer, 1986), Pakistan, and Singapore. As many as 1250 Stonefish may have been made by 1993.

♦ **Versatile Exercise Mine System (VEMS)**

BAe's system is intended for exercises and to help develop new countermeasures. The 533mm × 2.71m (560 kg) VEMS body can be programmed to simulate any known mine firing device, and it can be recovered (and on-board test tapes removed) up to 6 months after laying, using a buoyant section the body releases. Service life is 20 yr.

Users: Australia, Thailand, United Kingdom, and United States (as Mine Mk 74).

UNITED STATES

According to a Mine Warfare Plan published in January 1992, the current Mk 60 (Captor) mine inventory is only 40% of the newly established post–Cold War (1999) requirement. Mk 67 (the submarine-launched mobile mine) is only 60% of the estimated 1999 requirement. These figures compare to the most recent Cold War assessments: 35% for Mk 60, and 40% for Mk 67. In 1990, Mk 52 and Mk 55 were up to requirement (they are not included in the post–Cold War plan), but Mk 56 amounted to only 50% of the required figure (but 110% of the 1999 figure). Destructors amounted to 300% of the Cold War figure, and 2150% of the post–Cold War estimate. Quickstrike amounted to 10% of the Cold War figure, but 85% of the post–Cold War estimate. These differences probably reflect an assumption that diesel submarines will be the primary mine targets in a post–Cold War conflict, and that the United States will have to mine only limited areas against surface targets. Even so, large numbers may be needed; about 300,000 Destructors were used in Vietnam (and 11,000 in North Vietnam in 1972).

Many existing mines are apparently impossible to use effectively. Mk 56, the only current U.S. medium-depth ASW mine, is considered inadequate because of its very limited actuation width (less than 2% that of Mk 60). Thus very large numbers are needed to mine substantial areas (e.g., 5000 P-3 sorties would have been required to execute the planned Cold War *defensive* mining mission around the continental United States). Presumably the planned medium-depth rising mine (Substrike) is still very attractive, since a few such weapons can replace large numbers of Mk 56.

Fleet commanders approved three new mine Mission Need Statements (MNS) at the end of 1993:

Upgrade of SLMM Mk 67 to improve accuracy and range; increase Mk 67 inventory.

Littoral Sea Mine, either a new program or an upgrade, to address the diesel submarine threat, provide wide area coverage.

A new high-volume air-dropped mine, to replace B-52 capability, with antiship and antisubmarine capability.

Mine-development funding has been scarce in recent years. Plans for a new ASW mine, at one time called Substrike, have been recast several times; now the weapon is called the Littoral Sea Mine (see below). Work on the improved Captor (Mk 60 Mod 2 with Mk 46 Mod 6 torpedo) was abandoned, and the torpedo version canceled. Funds for remote control of mines (RECO) were eliminated from the FY91 budget.

As part of the NATO buildup of the 1950s, the United States supplied mines and specially converted minelayers to Denmark, Greece, Norway, and Turkey, to close strategic straits in wartime. Germany, Italy, and Japan were also provided with large mine stocks. In each case a local production capability may have been developed, so that various countries have manufactured U.S. mines (perhaps in modified form) under local designations. The principal mines involved were probably Mk 6, Mk 13, Mk 16, Mk 18, Mk 25, Mk 36, Mk 49, Mk 51, and the postwar Mk 50 series.

♦ Destructors and Quickstrike

Destructors (DST) are standard streamlined bombs converted into shallow-water mines. Mks 36, 40, and 41 are, respectively, conversions of bombs Mks 82, 83, and 84; there is also a Destructor M117D Mk 59-0 (1985) for B-52s, using the standard Air Force 750-lb bomb (total weight 857 lb), using Arming Device Mk 32-1, battery, and firing mechanism Mk 42-4. Destructor Mods 0 (fixed arming delay and self-destruct) and 1 (selectable arming delay and probability actuator) require retarded delivery; Mods 2 (selectable arming delay and self-destruct and probability actuator) and 3 (adds sensitivity option for better countermeasures resistance) can be delivered unretarded against land targets. The arming delay allows the weapon to become physically stable in the presence of water currents and wave action and hence

Destructor Mk 40. (D. Steigman)

Destructor Mk 41. (D. Steigman)

allows its firing mechanism to become magnetically stable. Firing mechanism versions: Mod 3 is magnetic; Mod 4 is magnetic/seismic; and Mods 5, 6, and 7 are magnetic/seismic with K Tab Capability. As disclosed to the North Vietnamese in 1973 (as part of Operation End Sweep), the DST magnetic sensor is a thin-field magnetometer with selectable sensitivity. Presumably, the seismic sensor activates the magnetic sensor, so the mine cannot be exploded by a pure magnetic field. The bomb modification kit is Destructor Modification Kit Mk 75.

Destructor Mk 36 was developed beginning in August 1966, and first deployed in June 1967. Mk 40 was developed in 1968 for greater damage effectiveness against land targets. Development of both types ended in FY70, effort switching to Mks 41 and 42 (Quickstrike, see below) following recommendations of the NOL Minetech study, Mine Advisory Committee Nimrod study, and an Op-95 ASW R&D assessment. Plans initially called for 22,125 bomb conversion kits in FY67 and 20,250 for FY68, but in July 1967 the program was increased to 111,865 kits and in November 1967 to 148,998; by 1970, over 300,000 had been made. These mechanisms cannot have met the usual standards for reliability or shelf life: hence the development of the Quickstrike mines (Mks 62–65, see below). The Destructor firing mechanism was developed very rapidly, and at the end of the war it was stockpiled. It is not clear how many, if any, remain in U.S. war stocks. Many were probably exported. As of 1995, at least Australia, and probably many other countries, had Destructor mechanisms in stock.

The successor weapon, Quickstrike (Mines Mks 62, 63, 64, and 65), was to have entered service in 1976, replacing not only Destructors Mk 36 and 40, but also Mk 25, 36, 52, and 55 bottom mines. Initially plans called for a 500-lb air-deliverable weapon

Destructor Mk 36. (D. Steigman)

and a 2000-lb air/submarine-laid weapon, both derived from bombs (the submarine requirement was ultimately met by Mk 67). The program was justified on the basis that the Mk 52 and Destructor TDDs had all been compromised in Vietnam, and that existing TDDs were becoming difficult to maintain.

Mks 62–64 are conversions of standard Mk 82–84 bombs (500, 1000, 2000 lb); they replace the abortive Destructors EX-52 through -54. The two alternative target-detection devices (TDDs) are Mk 57 (magnetic-seismic) and Mk 58 (magnetic-seismic-pressure), for Mods 1 and 2, respectively. Mk 57 is being upgraded to deal with fast-attack boats (and, presumably, other craft likely to be encountered in littoral operations). Mks 57 and 58 are to be replaced by microprocessor-controlled (hence programmable) Mk 71 TDDs (an alternative Mk 70 was dropped) in Quickstrike Mod 3, which also has the new safing-arming device Mk 75. The FY93 program included completion of Mk 71 algorithms for UEP and enhanced pressure sensors. Work on improved pressure and magnetic sensors began in FY94 (the magnetic sensor work was to have been completed in FY96).

Mk 65 Quickstrike being prepared for flight. (U.S. Naval Institute)

Mine Mk 55. (D. Steigman)

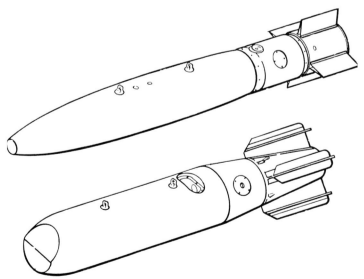

Quickstrike mines (Mk 64 above and 65 below).

Aerojet's Quickstrike Mk 65 is not converted from a bomb. It uses a special thin-walled casing and a special arming device. Dimensions: 29 (across fins) × 128 in (2390 lb). In 1985 Aerojet agreed to allow Misar to market Mk 65 in Europe. Misar's TDD replaces the U.S. Mk 58.

The universal laying mine project of the late 1980s probably bought adapters allowing for ship laying of Quickstrikes. The first 3500 kits were bought in FY86 for $3.7M, with 2400 planned

for FY88 and 3600 in FY89. This project may have been associated with purchases of new parachute flight gear Mk 16 for 500-lb mines.

Mk 62 was approved for service use in 1980. As of about 1986, plans called for procurement of 8000 Mk 57 and 2500 Mk 58. Actual TDD procurement: Mk 57: 1575 in FY83 and 1753 in FY84. Mk 58: 75 in FY84, 165 in FY85, 400 in FY87, 300 each in FY88 and FY89. Mk 65 was approved for service use in 1983. Procurement: 307 in FY82, 579 in FY83, 600 in FY84, 524 in FY85, 1445 in FY86, 500 in FY88, and 524 in FY89, for a total of 4479 against a planned total of 4500. As of 1986, a total of 39,804 Mk 70/71 TDDs were planned.

The next-generation Quickstrike will probably be based on the new JDAMS inertially aided bomb; JDAMS or JSOW may become the basis for an air-laid standoff mine. Work is also proceeding on a new generation of nonmagnetic lithium mine batteries, beginning with an AA-size cell in FY95, to replace the standard lithium batteries previously developed.

◆ Mk 6/16

This 34in spherical antenna mine (with supplementary Hertz horns), developed for the World War I North Sea antisubmarine barrage, later became the main U.S. surface-laid moored contact weapon. Weight, including sinker, is 1400 lb (300 lb TNT); maximum mooring depth is 3000 ft. Mod 3 had a 100ft lower antenna, Mod 4 a 50ft lower antenna, and Mods 14 and 15 (approved for service use in 1955 and 1964) have no antenna. All versions were withdrawn from U.S. service in 1970, but Mk 6 probably survives abroad.

The ovoid Mk 16 (2040 lb, including 600 lb of HBX-1) was designed as a successor. Mod 0 was a magnetic induction mine, Mod 1 an antenna/contact mine, and Mod 2 a moored acoustic mine.

◆ Mk 13/36

This aircraft-laid magnetic mine, delivered without a parachute, could also be used as a bomb. Total weight was 1048 lb, including 640 lb of TNT, or 1118 lb, including 710 lb of Torpex explosive. Mods 1 and 2 were redesignated Mk 26 Mods 0 and 1 (which was not produced); Mod 3 (with a parachute) was not issued; Mod 4 was designed for shallow water. Mod 5 (990 lb, including 640 lb of TNT, or 1060 lb, including 710 lb of TNT) had an acoustic exploder. Mod 6 (1020 lb, including 640 lb of TNT, or 1090 lb, including 710 lb of TPX) had an acoustic exploder and was fitted with a parachute.

Mk 36 might be considered a development of Mk 13, with a flat slanted nose for optimum underwater trajectory. Ship count: 1–10. Planting depth is 100–400 ft. Mods 0 and 1 were magnetic (induction) mines; Mod 2 was LF acoustic, and Mod 3 was pressure/magnetic. Magnetic version weights: 940 lb (including 570 lb of TNT) or 1008 lb (including 638 lb of TPX). Mod 2: 1024 lb (including 570 lb of TNT) or 1082 lb (including 638 lb of TPX). This mine was exported postwar to allied navies. It is no longer in U.S. service (Mods 1 and 3 were withdrawn in 1974, and Mod 2 in 1970).

Prior to development of the Mk 52 series, Mks 13/36 were the primary U.S. lightweight aircraft-laid bottom mines, and Mk 25 was the primary heavy equivalent. All were exported to U.S. allies postwar.

◆ Mk 18

This cylindrical surface-laid bottom magnetic mine has its axis vertical, with a prominent vertical post protruding from it. Wheels beneath the cylinder can run down a track on board the laying ship. Weight is 2140 lb (1440 lb of HBX-1). Dimensions: 42 in (dia) × 72 in (max height). Mk 18 was exported to U.S. allies in the 1950s.

◆ Mk 25

The standard U.S. World War II aircraft-laid bottom mine was exported postwar, and it was used during the Vietnam War. Weight was 2000 lb total (1234 lb of TPX or 1200 lb of HBX). Dimensions: 22.4 × 87.2–93 in (depending on flight gear), that is, roughly the size of the contemporary aerial torpedo Mk 13. In 1980 new flight gear was issued to permit this mine to be carried at high speeds. Mod 1 was acoustic, Mod 2 pressure/magnetic. It is no longer in U.S. service.

◆ Mk 49

This submarine-laid ground mine was designed to match the operational versatility of contemporary aircraft-laid mines (particularly Mk 25) at a lower cost than the earlier Mk 27. Dimensions: 20.8 × 120 in (2000 lb; Mod 1, 1890 lb including 1180 lb HBX-3; Mod 2, 1960 lb, including 1180 lb HBX). Versions: Mod 0 (magnetic induction with arming delay and ship counter), Mod 1 (LF acoustic with ship counter, arming delay, and sensitivity set automatically by sensed water depth), and Mod 2 (magnetic/pressure). Depths: Mods 0 and 1, 16–200 ft; Mod 2, 30–100 ft (can operate at 150 ft). Recommended spacing: 200 ft on hard bottom, 150 on mud (Mods 0 and 1); 300 ft for Mod 2. First tested in 1951, Mk 49 is no longer in U.S. service, but probably survives abroad.

◆ Mk 51

This controlled harbor defense mine, typically laid in groups of 13, is a vertical cylinder (62 × 37 in), carrying 3275 lb of TNT (total weight is 6200 lb). It resembles Mk 18, but is substantially larger. The mine carries a magnetic induction sensor; Mod 1 is used in conjunction with Acoustic System Mk 6, a line of hydrophones. The operator ashore, who can monitor 10 hydrophone channels (one per group), also has access to magnetic sensor outputs. The timing of mine firing is based partly on estimated target size, itself indicated partly by the number of mines responding to the target. Mod 0 was designed to counter conventional submarines; Mod 1 was intended to counter midgets down to a 30t displacement. Mk 51 was exported in the 1950s.

◆ Mk 52 and Mk 55

The 1000-lb-class and 2000-lb-class modular bottom mines have an instrument rack at one end carrying the firing and clock mechanisms, sterilizer, and associated batteries; the tail cover has three openings for TDDs open to the sea; and a separate well carries the hydrostatic arming device (in contrast, World War II mines had separate components plugged into the side of the mine). These weapons used new influence field detectors: pres-

Mine Mk 51 (practice version). The vertical tube is the magnetic-induction sensor. This and Mk 18 are the only U.S. mines in the form of upright cylinders. (U.S. Navy)

sure, acoustic, magnetic. Versions: Mod 0 (pressure), Mod 1 (acoustic, 1130 lb), Mod 2 (magnetic, 1170 lb), Mod 3 (pressure-magnetic, 1190 lb), Mod 4 (pressure-acoustic), Mod 5 (magnetic-acoustic, 1200 lb), and Mod 6 (pressure-acoustic-magnetic, 1235 lb), Mod 7 (improved dual-channel magnetic, abortive in Mk 52). Mod 8 (pressure-magnetic) was abortive. As disclosed to the North Vietnamese in 1973 (as part of Operation End Sweep), Mod 2 has a two-look, reverse polarity, magnetic-induction fuze, with selectable magnetic sensitivities, interlock, dead periods, and intership dead periods. Mod 1 was withdrawn about 1961, and Mod 4 in 1978. These weapons are sensitive enough to attack a submarine moving at only 3 kt and can be adjusted in sensitivity. Ship count is up to 30, and arming delay is 1 hr to 90 days.

Mines can be dropped either in cylindrical form with box fins (for internal carriage) or in streamlined form with a round nose and a pointed tail (with pop-out fins). They can be used as high-drag bombs. Dimensions: Mk 52: 18.8 × 70.2 in (625 lb of HBX-1). Mk 55: 23.38 × 89.875 in (142.625 in when faired for high-speed carriage). Weights (Mods 1–6): 2039, 2110, 2120, 2119,

Mine Mk 52. (D. Steigman)

2128, 2118 lb. Mk 55, and probably Mk 52, can be laid by surface ships using portable rails.

The corresponding training devices are Mks 70 and 73.

These weapons were part of the U.S. Long-Range Mine Program begun in 1948. Mk 52 was released for production in January 1954, followed by Mk 55 in November 1955; both became operational in 1961. In FY60 each of 2500 Mk 52 mines cost about $4900 and each of 1400 Mk 55 cost about $5500. Mk 52 was produced in West Germany and was probably exported to other allied navies. Both mines remain in U.S. service.

◆ Mk 53

This air-laid sweep-obstructor (to protect minefields against sweepers) fires when a sweep wire contacts the firing ring in the base of the mine case. It can be planted in water as shallow as 36 ft, with a case depth of 24–300 ft. Dimensions: 14.125 × 52.367 in (365 lb) in unstreamlined form (Mk 53 resembles an unstreamlined bomb with a box tail). For external carriage, it is faired at the ends, with a blunt nose and a pointed tail (which opens into stabilizing fins). Total length is 77.559 in (395 lb). Reportedly, the entire U.S. stock was transferred to Turkey in 1978.

◆ Mk 56/57

These aircraft- and submarine-laid magnetic moored mines use total-field sensors (adjustable to respond equally well to slow or fast targets). Ship count is 1–30. Dimensions: Mk 56, 22.4 × 114.3 in, about 2000 lb with 360 lb HBX-3. Mk 57, 21 × 121.1 in, 2059 lb, 340 lb HBX-3. The Mk 56 case is stainless steel, Mk 57 fiberglass. Planting depth is 150–600 ft. Mine release is settable. Modular design made for quicker assembly: 2 hr for Mk 56, compared to 8 hr for Mk 36.

Mine Mk 57. (D. Steigman)

The Mk 56 training device is Mk 72.

Both mines were part of the 1948 program. Mk 56 was released for production in 1960 and became operational in 1966; Mk 57, the submarine-laid version, was released for production at the same time and became operational in 1964. In each case, the delay was caused by a lack of production funding.

◆ Mk 60 (Captor)/Mk 66

Captor (the encapsulated torpedo) is a Mk 46 Mod 4 torpedo encapsulated in a mooring/sensing body that passively detects and tracks submarines passing overhead, using techniques developed for PUFFS (BQG-2/4). When a track is sufficiently attractive, Captor switches to active tracking and then launches the torpedo upward. The weapon utilizes reliable acoustic path (RAP) sound propagation. The mine body can be air-, surface-, or submarine- (TT) laid, in water at least 1000 ft deep. Lifetime is several weeks or months. Dimensions (weights) for the air/surface-launched versions are 21 × 145 in (2370 lb); for the submarine-launched version, 21 × 132 in (2056 lb).

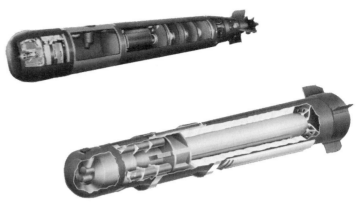

Mk 60 mine and its Mk 46 torpedo payload. (Goodyear)

This deep-water ASW mine was conceived about 1960 and developed at NSWC at White Oak. The name Captor was selected for a specific OR issued in May 1964. At that time it was hoped that Captor would reduce mine barrier costs by a factor of 100 (and barrier numbers by a factor of 400). A TechEval/OpEval production contract was awarded to Goodyear Aerospace (now a division of Lockheed Martin) in 1972. During TechEval (February in 1974–February 1975) the detection and classification system was unreliable and suffered from excessive false alarms. However, Captor showed sufficient potential to warrant provisional approval for service use (ASU) and for limited-rate (10/month) production (January 1976; procurement began in FY78). Full-scale production (15/month) was approved in March 1979 following 1978 tests with 10 Captors, but it was stopped in 1980 due to reliability problems (production resumed in FY82). Captor became operational in September 1979 (it was approved for service use in February 1980). This protracted development testifies to the complexity of the system.

In 1979 the objective was 5785 mines. Procurement: FY78–80, 1810; none in FY81; FY82, 400; FY83, 300; FY84, 300; FY85, 300; FY86, 150 (unrequested), a total of 3260. Unit cost in FY86 was about $377,000 (versus $113,000 in FY78).

Several Captor upgrade programs have proven abortive. A Captor Improvement OR was issued in March 1987, and later Captor and Substrike were amalgamated. Mod 1 was to have substituted a NEARTIP Mk 46 Mod 5 torpedo for Mod 4; Mod 2 was to have substituted a hybrid Mod 6 torpedo. A program for remote control (RECO) by acoustic signal died in FY91.

Mine Mk 66 is the practice version of Captor.

◆ Mk 67 (SLMM)

This submarine-launched mobile mine is a Mk 37 torpedo whose warhead has been replaced by a Mk 13 mine warhead, and whose acoustic panel has been replaced by an auxiliary controller. The remainder of the torpedo is slightly modified, to provide a longer run at low speed. The guidance and control section incorporates a modified depth setter, since the weapon must be guided into position on the bottom. Mk 67 uses Quickstrike-series TDDs. Like Mk 37, Mk 67 is an analog weapon, and thus requires some adaptation when fired by modern U.S. digital submarine FCS.

Engineering development began in FY77, and advanced development was completed in FY78. Mk 67 Mod 2 was approved for

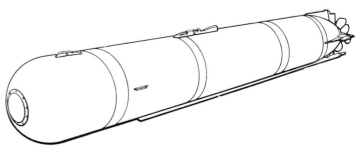

Mine Mk 67 (Submarine-Launched Mobile Mine).

service use in FY83. A submarine successfully launched a Mk 67 mine (using fire-control panel Mk 281) during FY87; this completed development and introduced the mine into the fleet. Procurement: 101 in FY82, 266 in FY83, 242 in FY84, 280 in FY85, for a total of 889, against a 1982 goal of 2421. Some further mines may have been made using torpedo-refurbishment funds.

In 1992–93 Alliant proposed replacing the mine's analog auxiliary controller with the programmable digital solid-state guidance and control (G&C) of its NT-37F torpedo (software control makes the same device applicable both to mine and to torpedo). In 1995 Alliant claimed that the new G&C unit would extend the usual maintenance cycle from 18 months to 6 yr. The existing cumbersome Mk 37 electromechanical enabler would be replaced by a simple rpm counter. The Alliant proposal was presumably prompted by the CinC MNS listed at the beginning of this section.

◆ Littoral Sea Mine

This is the latest in a long series of attempts to develop a relatively inexpensive rising mine for use on the continental shelf, that is, in water no more than about 600 ft deep. It supersedes Substrike, which replaced an earlier Intermediate Water Depth Mine (IWDM), and which in turn superseded PRAM (EX-68), the Propelled Ascent Mine. Substrike differed from most rising mines in using a combination of acoustics (with a volumetric array) and a magnetic sensor. The latter might be particularly valuable in noisy shallow water. These ideas apparently carried over to the new mine. The FY94 program included work on making the mine's HF sonar distinguish ships from the sea surface. The mine may use acoustic IFF signals to avoid attacking friendly ships, and thus to eliminate any need to maintain channels, which an enemy may detect, through our own minefields. The FY95 R&D program included work on an advanced gradient (presumably magnetic) influence sensor.

Some features probably carried over from earlier programs. They were to have been laid by submarines, surface ships, and aircraft, the need to carry two per skid limiting dimensions to 21 × 144 in and air delivery limiting weight to about 2000 lb (with a 500-lb warhead for sufficient lethality). PRAM range, about a mile, is probably still required. The Anglo-American competition to develop such a mine, the Advanced Sea Mine or Continental Shelf Mine (canceled 1989 when Britain withdrew) produced both rocket and torpedo solutions; some have argued that any mine traveling more than about 500 m requires some degree of mid-course guidance. The Anglo-American project gave way to Substrike.

As of 1995, plans called for beginning engineering development in FY97.

◆ Mk 69

Training shape for California sea lions used for ordnance recovery.

YUGOSLAVIA

Yugoslav mine stocks were presumably divided between Croatia and Serbia. In the mid-1960s Yugoslavia acquired Soviet ground mines (NATO designations KMD-500 and KMD-1000), presumably derivatives of MDT. The M-70 described below is a locally made version of the 1000-kg mine. In 1975 the Yugoslav government announced that two new acoustic mines were in production, *Koral* (coral) and *Biser* (pearl). Neither appears in a 1989 catalog of Yugoslav export naval weapons. A drawing in the catalog does show a river minelayer carrying Soviet-type river mines (YaRM), not the drifting river mine type described below. There are also PDM-1M and PDM-2 surf zone mines and PDM-3YA anti-invasion mines.

◆ Acoustic-Induction Mine M-70

This surface- and submarine-launched acoustic-magnetic bottom mine is an improved version of the Soviet MDT series. It is intended to be used against warships of up to 5000 t and merchant ships of up to 20,000 t, at depths as great as 50 m against

surface ships (150 m against submarines). Its electronics employs printed circuits. Dimensions: 534.4 mm × 2823 mm (21 × 111 in); weight 1000 kg (700 kg of explosive). Reportedly M-70 has been exported to Libya.

◆ PLRM-1A

This drifting river mine floats upright, suspended from a float carrying a circular wire bumper. Total draft is 500 mm. Dimensions: 260 × 370 mm (mine proper); weight 14 kg (10 kg explosive). Fuzing is mechanical (clockwork).

◆ SAG-2b

This locally produced contact mine, with a total weight of 600 kg (115 kg of explosive), can be laid in 110 m of water. The design must date to the 1950s or before.

MCM/MINEHUNTING SONARS

Deletions: Kiskii class (Finland: no longer robot boats, now operated only when manned), SSM (Italy, no sales), SH100 (Norway, no sales), EDATS (United Kingdom, presumably abandoned with the "River" class), Sea Serpent (United Kingdom, no known sales), ALQ-160 (U.S., not in service), ALQ-166 (U.S., work suspended 1990), AQS-17 (U.S., not adopted), ALARMS (U.S., not adopted), AMDAS (U.S., merged with Magic Lantern), SQQ-30 (U.S., all examples replaced by SQQ-32), WIMS (U.S., marketing abandoned, had been offered to Kuwait with LCAC platform).

AUSTRALIA

The Krupp-Atlas DSQS-11M (MWS 80-4) passed Australian trials after problems were encountered with the earlier version supplied for the RAN minehunters. This alternative, which ran 1991 trials, was the Thomson Sintra Ibis V Mk 2.

◆ VAP

Thomson Sintra Pacific's volumetric array processor uses a 100-kHz crossed array (vertical 64-element transmitter, horizontal 16-element receiver) to produce 3D beams for obstacle avoidance over a 60 × 12-deg sector at ranges up to 1000 m. The array is stabilized both mechanically and electronically. The vertical array produces eight 90 × 1.5-deg beams at different frequencies, which are depressed in 1.5-deg steps. The 11 receiving beams are about 5 deg wide, for a total of 88 beams. Repetition rate is about 1 Hz, and range resolution is about 1 m. Source level is 222 dB. A brassboard version was tested in a lake near Sydney in March 1995.

◆ AMASS

The ADI Minesweeping and Surveillance System (AMASS) was developed for the RAN COOP program, which was announced in November 1989. AMASS comprises a minesweeping control system, survey system, portable degaussing system, precursor sweep, influence sweep (acoustic and magnetic), and mechanical

Dyad magnetic elements are placed in the water to form part of a multi-influence sweep. For example, a frigate would be simulated by a string of nine such magnets, with two noisemakers to simulate machinery and the propeller. (ADI)

sweep. The route survey sensor is a Klein Type 595 side-looking sonar in a towfish. The associated navigational processor is QUILS II. Route survey data are processed by an ashore route survey database system (RSDS). Two drone precursor craft, operating at 6–8 kt, use mechanical and influence sweeps (the RAN found GRP drone boats more cost-effective than helicopters in this role). AMASS includes a degaussing system for the follow-up MCM craft.

The primary influence sweeps are built up from acoustic generators (adapted pipe noisemakers, for the LF, sonic, and HF ranges) and permanent magnets (dyads); the RAN uses up to eight dyads and two acoustic generators to simulate the largest ships. Dyad uses a 0.53 × 6.4m hollow mild steel pipe with strontium-ferrite inserts. The combination was suited to COOP use because it did not require electric power. There are also team, Oropesa, and bottom-following mechanical sweeps. The double Oropesa uses fishing-boat technology to save weight.

The influence and mechanical sweeps can operate in up to Sea State 4; claimed effective to depth of 180 m. The forward-support unit is containerized.

CANADA

Contrary to earlier reports, Trail Blazer and Manta were not bought by the Canadian navy.

The maritime coastal defense vessel (MCDV) is to conduct only coastal surveillance, route survey (with a towfish), mine inspection, and mechanical sweeping. Future elements may include remote hunting and neutralization. MacDonald Dettweiler is the prime contractor for ISIS, the integrated survey and inspection system, which comprises the route survey data analysis facility (RSDAF), route survey payload, mine warfare control system (MWCS), and inspection payload. Two RSDAF, one each coast, maintain the database; they share largely common hardware and software with the shipboard MWCS. There are three consoles at each RSDAF: mission planning, sonar data analysis, and system database/manager, maintaining the route survey database.

The high-speed sonar towfish for route survey, derived from AQS-20, is a new type with active control surfaces for bottom following, operating down to 200 m, close to the sea bed. The sonar is designed to cover a 400m swath (80% detection of a 0.5 × 1m object) at 10 kt (300 m in detection/classification mode, 150 m in classification mode). Image classification is based on a resolution of 12.5 × 12.5 cm in classification mode, 25 × 12.5 in detection/classification mode, and 37.5 × 12.5 cm in detection mode.

On shore, imagery is "mosaic-ed" together to form a continuous high-resolution map of the ocean floor; "mosaic-ing" fills in gaps with new mission data and drops duplicated data; it can make up for shadows in existing images. The system geocodes to register images precisely to map projections. It uses towfish speed, roll, pitch, yaw, MCDV location by GPS and gyro.

The MWCS uses a tactical console, a bridge console, two sonar data–analysis consoles, a mission-area specific copy of the route survey database, a system manager console, and a hull-mounted acoustic positioning system. Processors are based on 64-bit DEC 3000/6000 AXPs running at 175 MHz, with 1024 × 1028-pixel, 60-Hz, 19in color displays using Offshore Systems Ltd's Electronic Chart Precise Information Navigation System (ECPINS), Electronic Chart Display Information System (ECDIS), and Stanag 4420 symbology.

A Trailblazer submersible inspects objects, using sonar and video cameras. This ROV operates down to 300 m, with 600m standoff range at that depth, and a sonar range of 50 m.

In the minehunting phase a remotely controlled surface vehicle tows a sidescan sonar clear of the influence fields of the ship. The Canadians have tested the U.S. (Rockwell) Dolphin extensively, but are looking at others. Software development for the system was largely complete by the end of 1994, 18 months ahead of schedule.

The wire sweep is the BAJ Mk 9, for team sweeps to 200 m depth and single-vessel sweeps (single- and triple-wire double [port and starboard] Oropesa) to 90 m depth.

CHINA (PRC)

A recent Chinese account of military systems claims that a submarine mine-evasion sonar, TS-6, was developed in the mid-1960s as part of the nuclear submarine program.

◆ Type 312

This remotely controlled magnetic and acoustic minesweeper is similar in concept to the German Troika system. Type 312 can also operate manned. Displacement is 46.95 t fully loaded (dimensions 20.94 × 4.20 × 1.30 m), and propulsion is by a 300-BHP diesel. Another diesel drives a generator which energizes the magnetic sweep coils and runs the noisemaker. Radio control is effective to about 3 nm, and the craft is electrically driven at 1–5 kt. All equipment is shock-mounted, and the hull form is intended to reduce the shock effect of the mines the craft detonates. These craft have a laser-precision navigation system. They are limited to coastal waters because the hull form is not suited to heavy seas.

Type 312 became operational in 1984; by 1986, 60 were in service. Reportedly, this class was inspired by successful conversion of several 400t Lienyun-class auxiliary sweepers (trawler type) to remote control. This device has been exported to Thailand and Pakistan.

DENMARK

A Danyard GRP torpedo-recovery vessel was the basis for a two-boat drone minehunting system for the StanFlex 300s. Each robot boat tows its own TSM 2054 sonar. Boat dimensions: 18.2 × 4.75 × 1.20 m (32 t, 38 full load). For classification and disposal the StanFlex carries a tethered Bofors Double Eagle underwater vehicle (two per ship, selected mid-1992). Eight minehunting ship-sets and six ship-sets of Double Eagles (12 vehicles) are planned, though none had yet been funded as of late 1994. The second minehunting ship-set was delivered December 1991. The first drone, MRF 1, was completed March 1991.

DAMDIS (Danish Mine Disposal System), developed by Nordic Defence Industries of Sonderbord, is based on the Double Eagle ROV, with a special fasten and release mechanism for a 49-kg (31 kg Composition B HE) Danish mine disposal charge (DAMDIC), which it drops directly on the mine. The charge is detonated by cable from the minehunter, rather than by acoustic signal, which the Royal Danish Navy considers unreliable in coastal waters with complex acoustic layering (i.e., the Baltic).

◆ COOP System

At Brighton in March 1993, Eiva A/S displayed a COOP MCM system based on its Navipack navigational software system, which runs on an HP computer. An Ethernet LAN connects the Navipack data-acquisition and navigation system with an EG&G 272TD towed sidescan sonar and with a tactical and target display running on an 80486 computer. The system is packaged in a special low-magnetic signature aluminum and plywood container with its own diesel generator. One was sold in 1991 to the Royal Swedish Navy and another in 1992 to the German navy.

FINLAND

◆ Fiskars Sweeps

Fiskars Elesco's standard magnetic sweep, MRK-500, uses a 500m floating cable, from which three electrodes are suspended. There is also a more recent MRK-960 magnetic sweep. The MRK-400 acoustic sweep uses two towed pipe noisemakers (minimum tow speed 2–3 kt, 30 Hz–100 kHz) and two GRP floats with rudders. FIMS (Fiskars Integrated Minesweep System) combines MRK-400 and -500 (trailed from a single winch) controlled by a shipboard 80386-based SSCPU (shipboard sweep control and positioning unit). The system also monitors mine detonation (which shows whether the applied field is sufficient). The SSCPU uses sweep patterns stored ashore by another 80386-based computer, the TSCPU (tactical sweep coverage and planning unit), whose 1 Mbyte of memory suffices for 256 waveforms corresponding to different ships.

Magnetic sweep patterns are developed using a Fiskars computer program which calculates field shape and strength given electrode current and spacing, water depth, and other conditions. The program prints out equipotential curves for the three field components and provides the operator with the strength of the field at the sea bed. Mine detonations can be marked on the simulation curves so that the characteristics of enemy mines can be estimated in greater detail after sweeping.

FIMS uses a special small-diameter sweep cable to minimize the reel diameter (600mm dia) and to permit sharp turns by the sweeper so as to avoid coastal rocks. The system weighs 2.5 t. Fiskars claims that it is particularly simple to operate and can be launched by two people in 10 min.

Reportedly 11 sets of MRK-960 have been delivered since 1990.

Users: Finland, Indonesia (Tripartite sweepers), Pakistan (Tripartite sweepers [FIMS]), and Sweden. The Indonesian sweepers have Fiskars F82 magnetic sweeps, plus Swedish (SA Marine) AS.203 acoustic sweeps and the standard Tripartite Oropesa sweep (OD 3). The Swedish navy may use only the magnetic sweep.

FRANCE

The planned next-generation BAMO deep sweeper was canceled in the fall of 1991, although the first unit, *Narvik*, had already been launched. It is not clear to what extent hardware designed for the BAMO program was abandoned. The entry on the associated minehunting archive, CARDINAL, has been deleted from this edition.

At present the only French MCM craft carrying sweep gear are the *Eridan*-class (Tripartite) minehunters.

◆ Sweeps

Oropesa (Wire Sweeps) (OD): Lightweight OD 3 on Tripartite minehunters.

Magnetic (MB): MB 1 through MB 4 are symmetrical loops for coastal sweepers. MB 5 and MB 6 are asymmetrical loops for ocean and coastal sweepers. MB 5 uses a 225-kW or 364-kW sweep generator.

Acoustic (AM, AP, AE): AM 1 and AM 2 are hammer (marteau) sweeps. AM 3 and AM 4 are MF hammer sweeps for coastal sweepers. AM 3's dimensions are 856 × 520 × 340 mm; weight is 45 kg.

AP 1 and AP 2 are piston sweeps for LF. AP 1's dimensions are 1130 × 558 × 380 mm; weight is 105 kg.

The AP 4 acoustic sweep, announced in 1972, combines the capability of older LF and MF towed loop systems (band: a few Hz to 1 kHz) in a single body without any surface float. It can vary its signature to match that of a given ship (it has a 192-signature memory); it is synchronized with a magnetic sweep. It can be towed at 3–12 kt (8 kt nominal). Dimensions: 1.1 × 3.9 m (2350 kg). Compared to the British Osborn, AP 4 is said to cover a wider frequency range by using an electrodynamic (rather than hydraulic) noise generator. AP 4 was deployed aboard French Tripartite (*Eridan* class) minehunters beginning in 1985.

AP 4 acoustic sweep, covering both the low and intermediate frequency ranges. (Direction des Constructions Navales)

AP 5 extends maximum frequency to 10 kHz. It can generate over 30 spectral lines; programmed signals have a dynamic range of over 40 dB; AP 4 and 5 also have some directivity. Replaces Mk 4(V) MF and Mk 6(b) LF.

AE 1 is an explosive sweep.

◆ Minehunting Laser

Thomson Sintra is developing a blue-green minehunting laser. The prototype is reportedly effective to a depth of 50–200 m (160–660 ft), depending on water conditions. Resolution is reportedly several centimeters at a depth of 150 m.

◆ DUBM-20 (TSM 2020)

The first French minehunting sonar combines separate 100-kHz 7.5-kW search and 400-kHz 4.5-kW classification sonars in a single stabilized assembly. Its console can superimpose radar and sonar coordinates for accurate mine location. Typical performance: detection at 300 m, classification at 130 m.

A DUBM-20A upgrade program, announced in 1984, incorporated coherent processing (for better range in noisy conditions), sweep-to-sweep integration (for a clearer display), a performance indicator (to measure bottom reverberation), and a multi-image memory (to make classification easier).

Work began in 1963, and a DUBM-20X prototype was tested on board the ocean minesweeper *Narvik* in 1967. As a result of the success of these trials, the *Circe* class was built and equipped with DUBM-20A. The first such sonar was installed in 1970 (trials 1971).

◆ DUBM-21 (TSM 2021)

Derived from DUBM-20, DUBM-21 is the much smaller and more reliable successor sonar, also using a pair of stabilized arrays (against 15 deg of roll, 5 deg of pitch) for simultaneous detection and classification. This technology was adapted for the

DUBM-21B (TSM 2021) array (*Eridan* or Tripartite class). (Thomson Sintra)

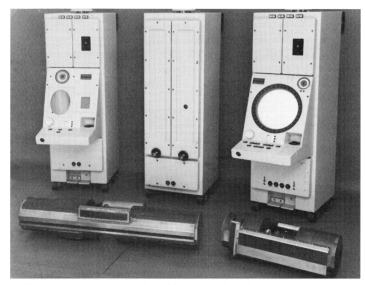

DUBM-21 arrays and consoles. (Thomson Sintra)

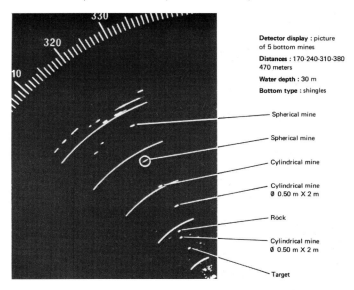

Detector display : picture of 5 bottom mines

Distances : 170-240-310-380 470 meters

Water depth : 30 m

Bottom type : shingles

— Spherical mine

— Spherical mine

— Cylindrical mine

— Cylindrical mine Ø 0.50 m X 2 m

— Rock

— Cylindrical mine Ø 0.50 m X 2 m

— Target

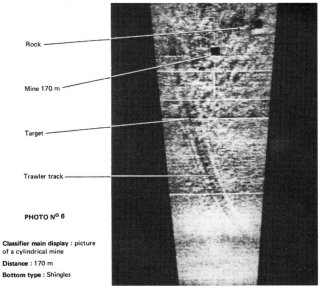

Rock —

Mine 170 m —

Target —

Trawler track —

PHOTO N° 6

Classifier main display : picture of a cylindrical mine

Distance : 170 m

Bottom type : Shingles

Detector and classifier displays (DUBM-21 sonar). (Thomson Sintra)

U.S. SQQ-32. Both transducers use preformed beams. The long-range 1.5 × 1.5-deg 100-kHz detection beam (0.2- or 0.5-msec FM pulses, modulated +/− 10 kHz) can sweep through 30-, 60-, or 90-deg sectors. Range scales are 400, 600, and 900 m. Source level is 110 dB (120 dB at maximum power). The 32-stave (six

elements/stave) array produces 20 preformed reception beams (total 30 deg). Their output is shown on a 16in PPI showing a 30-deg sector, with 100m range markers. Maximum detection speed is 6 kt. The 0.17 × 15-deg 420-kHz shadow (classifier) beam (FM pulses, widths as above, modulated at 15 kHz) covers either a 3.5- or 10-deg arc and can be depressed from −5 to −30 deg. Range scales are 200 and 300 m. Source level is 122 dB at maximum power. The 64-stave array (six transducers/stave) produces 80 preformed reception beams. Data are presented on a rectangular CRT, and the operator can mark mine images. Maximum classification speed is 2 kt. The transducers are not housed in a dome, to avoid distorting their beams; at low hunting speed (4 kt), cavitation around them would have only a limited effect.

Mines are classified both by shadow (effective range 100–170 m, providing some images at 200 m) and by direct echo (effective range 100–500/600 m). Thomson Sintra argues that echo is insufficient because the signatures of many mines are unknown (and the echo classifier generally does not provide an image immediately recognizable as a mine). Moreover, an irregular sea bed may mask the echoes of a small mine. Shadow classification can reveal the shape of a mine, even if it is nonreflective. On the other hand, it is not clear whether a shadow sonar can reliably detect deep ground mines.

As TSM 2021A, this sonar was first installed on board five French ocean minesweepers converted to minehunters, a program begun in 1974. TSM 2021B (with the TSM 5730 Doppler sonar log, for position keeping) is standard in the Tripartite (French, Belgian, Dutch) minehunter. The latest version, DUBM-21D, was made for the French minehunter *Sagittaire*, which replaces a ship transferred to Pakistan as PNS *Munsif*. DUBM-21D is an all-digital version of DUBM-21 with a new Mustang signal processor and high-definition displays. It will be installed on board the second and third Pakistani "Tripartite" minehunters. The corresponding tactical system is TSM 2061 Mk 2. Unit cost, including the associated minehunting system, is about $11.5–12.5M.

Users: Belgium (10 Tripartite class, of which three are for sale), France (10 Tripartite class, formerly in five other minehunters), Netherlands (15 Tripartite class), Pakistan (three Tripartite minehunters). Thomson Sintra reports that in all 60 DUBM 21–series sonars had been ordered as of 1992, but known installations amount only to 43.

♦ **PVDS/VERSUS**

Thomson Sintra's Propelled (mine-hunting) VDS places a TSM 2022 Mk III array in a Double Eagle vehicle running 200 to 500 m ahead of a ship. It was demonstrated at sea off Brest in the trials vessel *Thetis* in November 1994 and then on board *Landsort* in September 1995. VERSUS (VERSatile Underwater System) comprises a hull array, towed array, and PVDS, all integrated at the sonar level.

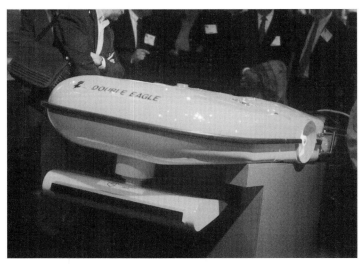

Thomson's PVDS, at Bourget Euronaval 1996. (Author)

◆ TSM 2022

Thomson Sintra's single-array hull-mounted commercial mine-hunting sonar was designed for smaller ships (hence the reversion to a single array). The roll- and pitch-stabilized linear array combines detection (165 Hz) and classification (400 kHz) elements. It can tilt vertically for depth finding, or turned to look down to profile the bottom. Beamwidth: 0.37 deg for search (14- or 28-deg sector, or mechanically scanned over 60 deg; the scanned sector can be steered 175 deg from the bow) or 0.17 deg for classification (7-deg sector, steerable 175 deg from the bow). Range scales: 50–500 or 50–1000 m for detection, 50–150 or 50–250 m for classification. The sonar can detect mines at 500 or 600 m and classify them at 250 m in water depths of 10–90 m. Mine position accuracy is 1 m. Resolution (classification mode): 0.16 deg, 0.15 m. With the array vertical, a moored mine 5 m (16.4 ft) below the surface can be detected at 300 m (about 330 yd). Objects as small as 0.5 m² (1.6 ft²) can be classified at up to 170 m (about 186 yd). Mines can be hunted at up to 6 kt and avoided at up to 10 kt.

TSM 2022 array. (Thomson Sintra)

Because all functions are concentrated in one array and its console, detection and classification must be consecutive. Classification is either by shadow or by direct echo.

Thomson Sintra considers TSM 2022 a fourth-generation minehunting sonar, counting from the DUBM 20 of about 1970 and including DUBM-21A and -21B (IBIS 41A and 41B). TSM 2022 Mk 2 is the current upgraded version. Thomson-CSF also offers TSM 2022NG Modular, with the suffixes PAR and SEQ. PAR (parallel) indicates simultaneous use of two arrays; SEQ indicates sequential use of one array. Different arrays and consoles are indicated by A1, A2, B1, B2, C, and D. Configurations: A1 SEQ B1, equivalent to TSM 2022 Mk 2 with one operator; A2 SEQ B2, a wide-field version with one operator; A2 PAR B2, a wide-field version with two operators; C SEQ D, with one operator.

Mk 3 is the PVDS version. It is about half the length of the ship versions (resolution: 0.7 deg detection, 0.3 deg detection).

Users: Egypt (three made by Thoray, a joint venture of Raytheon and Thomson, for coastal minehunters), Indonesia (two Tripartite minehunters, 1985), Korea (four MSC 289 class, as refitted), Malaysia (four *Lerici* class with TSM 2022 in IBIS II suite), Nigeria (two *Lerici*), Singapore (Mk 2 in four *Landsort* class), Sweden (seven *Landsort* class; last one canceled), Yugoslavia

(two delivered 1988, presumably to replace the Type 193M sonar on the French-built *Sirius*-class coastal minesweepers). This sonar may also have been sold to China (Thomson Sintra claimed a total sale of 31; the list above amounts to 29, including the canceled Swedish ship).

◆ TSM 2023

Thomson Sintra's new multiple-frequency system (simultaneous detection at 35 kHz with range scales of 400/600/900/1200 m and classification at three frequencies [250–525 kHz] with range scales of 200/300m) can be hull-mounted (up to 6 kt, up to 12 kt in side-looking mode), towed (down to 200 m, less than 150 m abaft the ship), or self-propelled (down to 300 m, up to 600 m ahead of the ship, at up to 6 kt). Classification is either by echo (image) or by shadow, and both detection and classification are computer-aided. Operating mode is selected with the assistance of a performance-prediction system. Long range makes the sonar a potential evasion aid in moored fields.

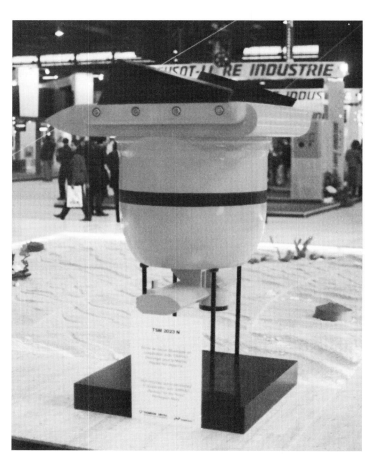

Thomson TSM 2023N minehunting sonar for the Norwegian navy, 1990. (Author)

This sonar combines a 256-stave electronically stabilized cylindrical detection array (six elements/stave, with electronically steered beams) and a 100-stave flat mechanically stabilized classification array (tiltable and trainable, working at three frequencies). Bearing resolution (classification) is 0.14 deg. Search sectors: 20/60/90 deg; classification sectors: 17.25/5 deg. The classification sonar can be used to confirm target detection, to select an object closest in size to that of a possible mine, among the objects detected. At low frequency and maximum range, its resolution is closest to the size of the smallest mine. Thomson Sintra argues that in bad bottom conditions detection range should be twice classification range to avoid having to change ship track to classify objects at the edge of a channel. The sonar can operate in sea states up to 5. Sonar fish course and depth are automatically controlled. It is integrated with a two-goniometer ROV tracker.

Two operators (each with a 19in raster-scan Colibri console) simultaneously detect and classify objects. Operator aids functions are CAD and CAC. CAD can process a 300m-deep sector; it draws a circle around the target it selects on ping-to-ping basis (with reference to reverberation ratio) and can maintain up to 60 such records. The operator decides whether a tracked echo is mine-like and must therefore be transferred to the tactical display. CAC highlights the shadow contours of the displayed object, eliminating distortion due to bottom contour, and measuring object size and indicating type. Each console has two trackballs (cursor and array azimuth/tilt). Each man/machine-intensive function (range, sector, transmit mode, etc.) has its own function key. Other functions are controlled via a menu. Screens are typically divided into three sections. The left-hand side shows sonar status, synthetic video of ship heading and sonar array azimuth and tilt, and performance monitoring/fault isolation. The main raw video sonar picture occupies the rectangle in the center of the screen. The magnifier display and stored images are presented on the right. Detection and classification screen arrangements are similar, for easy operator changes.

The system has a low magnetic signature.

TSM 2023 is based on R&D work done for the classification element of the U.S. SQQ-32. The displays are Colibri consoles.

User: Norway (*Oksoy*-class minehunters: 2023N version).

♦ TSM 2054

This high-resolution multibeam sidescan sonar is mounted in a fish towed at 4–15 kt, covering 5.4 km²/hr. The fish operates down to a depth of 200 m (660 ft), sweeping a 50m- or 100m-wide (55 or 110 yd) swath (resolution cells are 20 × 10 cm or 20 × 20 cm, depending on range). The operator programs the fish to fly at a fixed height above the sea bed, using its on-board echo sounder. The fish also carries an obstacle-avoidance sonar, which enables the fish to fly over 10m (33 ft) -high obstacles. It carries a Doppler sonar for precise speed measurement. The system automatically corrects the fish's speed, yaw, and pitch and computes the precise position of the towed body to an accuracy of better than 9 m. The system has two Colibri consoles, for sonar display and tactical control.

Users: Denmark (*Flyvefisken* class).

TSM 2054 on board a *Flyvefisken*-class multirole corvette, at IMDEX in London, 1995. (A. D. Baker III)

♦ FLAMS

Thomson Sintra's multifrequency Folding Light Airborne Mine-Avoidance Sonar replaces the FLASH fish with a different one, an operation possible in about half an hour. Software changes the sonar function. Thus the same helicopters can be used against both submarines and mines; the fleet deploys with an organic MCM capability. The keys to this capability are the fact that the sonar transmitter is in the fish, not in the fixed equipment on board the helicopter; new wide-band multifrequency transducers; new front-end miniaturization; and new signal-processing algorithms. Like FLASH, the new fish uses a folded array (in this case a linear multifrequency one, as in TSM 2022).

Unlike FLASH, it unfolds a pair of small motors to keep it steady and to rotate it as required. Like TSM 2023, it embodies CAD and CAC; it also has a real-time performance indicator. The LF detector (range scales 600/900 m) produces 1 × 3.2-deg beams covering a 90 × 16-deg sector (90 beamwidths across, 5 high) tiltable +/−20 deg to cover a 40-deg vertical sector. Range resolution is 6.25 cm. The HF detector (range scales 300/600 m) covers a 63-deg horizontal sector (beamwidth 0.7 deg). The classifier (range scales 200/300 m) covers a 12-deg horizontal sector (beamwidth 0.2 deg). A moored mine can be detected beyond 650 m and classified at 400 m; a bottom mine can be classified at 150 m.

The FLAMS fish, showing its sonar array (the dark horizontal bar) and its two little maneuvering propellers. (Author)

♦ DUBM-40A (TSM 5420)

This small 735-kHz (1-kW) mine-detection sonar is towed by standard 18t 14.87m naval launches on an 80m (262ft) cable. Pulses are 100 microsec long (range scales 40/80/120 m). Beam: 0.37 × 45 deg. The transducer rotates at 3, 6, or 9 deg/sec, either continuously or within 5-, 10-, or 15-deg sectors. The displays are panoramic (PPI) and rectangular. The fish and cable weigh 196 kg (432 lb), and the console inside the launch weighs another 185 kg (408 lb). Small seabed objects can be displayed and classified at depths as great as 300 m (984 ft).

DUBM-40B is a high-speed version.

♦ DUBM-41/42

This 735- and 785-Hz (750 W, 200-microsec pulses) towed sidescan sonar displays its data in real time on board a ship. The 15 × 35-deg beam sweeps a path 45 or 75 m to each side; two fish can sweep a 200m swath. A kite holds the 350-kg 3.7m fish to a depth of 5–60 m (16–197 ft) at 5 kt, on a 115- or 120m cable. The height of an object can be determined within 0.5 m. Typical mine classification range is 60 m. The display is either a persistent-image CRT (TEI) or a pen-marked paper (ALDEN).

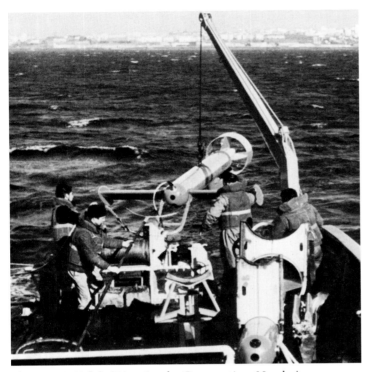

The DUBM-41 fish. (Direction des Constructions Navales)

DUBM-41B can be towed at 10 kt to cover a 400m swath, compared to 4 kt/50 m for DUBM-41.

This sonar is very similar to the U.S. Shadowgraph of the 1960s, except that it has three bottom-looking sonars to keep it clear of underwater obstacles. The French used it as a classification sonar, towed from U.S.-supplied MSO-class minesweepers equipped with the UQS-1D search sonar. They found the combination much inferior to a single integrated sonar such as SQQ-14 or DUBM-20.

The successor sonar, the preformed-beam DUBM-42 (TSM 2054), was to have equipped the abortive BAMO. It could be towed faster (12 kt) and deeper (300 vs. 100 m), covering a 200m track, and detecting mines at greater range (150 vs. 50 m). The search rate is almost 10 times that of DUBM-41. Beside TSM 2054, the towfish carries a TSM 2051 shadow-classification sonar.

◆ DUPM-1

This hand-held minehunting sonar enables a clearance diver to find a mine in disturbed or muddy water. It uses a conical reflector with the controls on its back. Power is provided by nickel-cadmium batteries (good for 50 hr), and range is about 200 m. Overall diameter is about 12 in, for a 9-deg beam (FM slides at 50–90 kHz). The operator listens to beats between the transmitted and received beams; the beat frequency is proportional to the time difference and, therefore, to the range, since the returning signal comes from a different portion of the FM slide. Range scales are 2–22 m, 20–90 m, and 60–200 m. In each case the audio-frequency range is 250–2500 Hz. This sonar can also listen for a 38-kHz sonar beacon that is laid to mark either an area to be cleared or a suspicious object (37–41 kHz, tuned manually). The beacon lasts for 500 hr and can be detected at 500–1000 m (550–1090 yd).

◆ Petrel (TSM 5424)

Thomson Sintra announced this surface-ship mine-avoidance system at Bourget Naval in October 1990. It uses the TSM 5424 preformed-beam mine-avoidance sonar, reportedly the only one in its class working in three dimensions. Petrel is designed for both major combatants, which may have to transit minefields,

and MCM/surveillance units employing towed sidescan sonars, which have no way of detecting mines in their path. It can also be used to evaluate mine density and risk, to mark safe channels, and to conduct preliminary operations prior to minehunting.

◆ PAP 104/SVDS/RECA

ECA's poisson auto-propulse, the first of the modern unmanned minehunting/minekilling ROVs, is held on course by a gyro and maneuvered by a pair of independent electric motors fed by internal batteries (sufficient for five 20-min missions). The 6-kt speed (which can also be set at 2 or 4 kt) was set by a requirement to work in a 4-kt current. The slight positive buoyancy of the fish is counterbalanced by the weight of a rope that it drags; when the rope hits bottom and begins to drag, the fish no longer supports its full weight, and it begins to rise. When the operation is over, the fish drops the rope and then surfaces. The original sensor was an underwater television camera with a floodlight. PAP 104 was designed to operate in water 10 to 100 m deep (the original French navy version could run at 80 m, but an alternative civil version could run at 300 m). It is tracked using a sonar transponder beacon in its sail, and it carries a 100-kg demolition charge. In very poor visibility the controlling sweeper can use her sonar to place the charge within 2 m. It is fired from deck, by acoustic signal (a small grenade), after the fish has been retrieved (typically 15–30 min after the charge had been laid). Launching takes about 5 min, and turnaround (replacement of guide rope, guidance wire, charge, and battery) takes about 15. Range, set by the length of the control cable, is 500 m; endurance is 3 hr at 2 kt. Dimensions, constant through the series: 1.2 × 2.7 × 1.3 m; weight is 700 kg (800 kg for Mk 5).

PAP 104. (Direction des Constructions Navales)

The Mk 2 initial production version was intended solely to attack ground mines; it had no cutters to deal with mine mooring cables. Production cost was reduced by using standard car-type batteries and a commercial television camera.

Mk 3, the first export version, was designed for reduced magnetic and acoustic signatures, as well as reduced corrosion. Royal Navy Mk 3s were built of nonmagnetic materials (other Mk 3s are degaussed). A PAP 104 Mk 3 LL (long life) announced in 1996 has a new video camera, cable, and console. The two other new versions are: Mk 3 I (identification) carrying a sonar that can acquire the target at 30m range; and Mk 3 PLS with nonmagnetic and silent propulsion (MG motors) and vertical thrusters, as in Mk 5.

PAP Mk 4 (1983), developed specifically for the Malaysian navy (to hunt at greater depth) has new electronically commutated 5-kt motors suitable for 300m depth (rather than the previous 120 m); the hull always had sufficient strength. This version has a high-data-rate cable developed for the German navy, which wanted to use a Krupp-Atlas AIS 11-104 high-resolution short-range sonar instead of the usual LLLTV, to acquire targets at up to 20 m, beyond television range. Although the Royal Navy also operates under conditions of low visibility in the water, it prefers LLLTV. Finally, Mk 4 introduced a cable-cutter, to attack deep-moored mines.

The current PAP Mk 5 (1986) was designed to meet a new Royal Navy requirement. Maximum speed is 6 kt, depth is 300 m, and range is 600 m. The modular fish carries alternative heads (user's sensors; a long-range reacquisition sonar; or a short-range classification sonar [AIS 11]); alternative payloads (two moored mine cutters, one on either side; the 100-kg mine-disposal charge; a manipulator with a TV; a high-capacity cutter; or ballast for mid-water navigation); alternative forms of propulsion (standard variable-pitch propellers or MG motors with electronic commutation, for increased power and depth and reduced acoustic/magnetic signature; or vertical thrusters); alternative control cables (standard 1000m [1090-yd] blue wire; a wider-band 1000m green wire; or a 2000m [2200-yd] red fiber-optic wire); alternative energy source (sealed battery; high-capacity storage battery; or power drawn through the control cable); and alternative means of depth control (guide cable with variable-length control or manipulator guide cable with variable-length control).

ECA offers three improvement kits: for increased depth, improved signature (magnetic and acoustic), new thrusters, and new batteries.

PAP was developed by ECA for the French navy, to a requirement set by GESMA (Groupe d'Études Sous-Marines de l'Atlantique). GESMA and ECA began their effort in 1968, and the first vehicles were delivered in 1970.

SVDS (self-propelled VDS) is an ECA/STN joint venture, a PAP 104 carrying the STN DSQS-11M sonar (see also the German MAS 90 system below). Development began in 1994, and trials on board the experimental ship *Schall* began in the summer of 1996.

Slung beneath PAP is the RECA (remote-controlled ammunition) mine-disposal torpedo, whose on-board sensor confirms that the target selected is indeed a mine (if it is not, RECA is recovered). Launched 10 m from the mine, RECA is command-detonated after the ROV has returned to the ship. Like a standard charge, it weighs 120 kg; maximum depth is 200 m. RECA was first tested in 1995, and a combat version should be available in the second quarter of 1997.

As of late 1994, 341 PAP vehicles had been sold. ECA claimed that over 30,000 operational runs had been made. PAP-104 has been used operationally in the Falklands War, in the Red Sea (1984), and in the Persian Gulf. In Royal Navy service, PAP 104

Mk 5 is designated RCMDS (remote-controlled mine-disposal system) Mk 2 (Mk 1 was an earlier PAP version).

Users (PAP 104): Australia (*Rushcutter* class), Belgium (Tripartite class), France (Tripartite class), Germany (Type 331), Indonesia, Japan (for new MSCs: license-built by Mitsubishi, presumably as S-9), Malaysia, Netherlands (Tripartite class), Norway (*Tana*), Pakistan (Tripartite class), Saudi Arabia (*Sandown* class), Singapore (*Landsort*), South Africa (*Umkomaas*-class inshore sweepers), United Kingdom, and Yugoslavia (*Sirius* class).

◆ Sterne I

Sterne I is a complex acoustic/magnetic sweep designed to mimic some of the detailed structure of a target's signature. It is analogous to FIMS. The sweep employs two magnetic bodies (solenoids) and one acoustic body (the standard French navy AP 4), the two solenoids lying to either side of, and slightly ahead of, the AP 4. Alternatively, a linear configuration, for example, six solenoids and one AP 4, can be used against mines so sophisticated that fidelity to the ship's signature is more important than

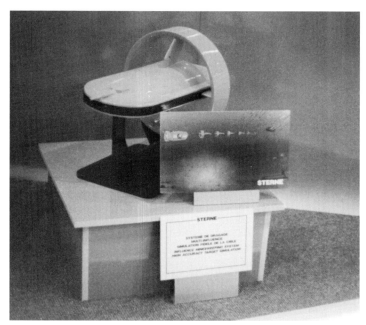

Sterne magnetic body, 1990. (Author)

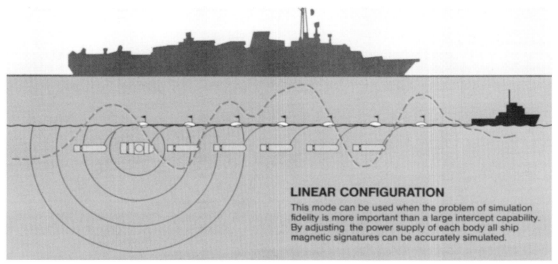

LINEAR CONFIGURATION

This mode can be used when the problem of simulation fidelity is more important than a large intercept capability. By adjusting the power supply of each body all ship magnetic signatures can be accurately simulated.

The linear Sterne I tow, intended to mimic a ship's detailed magnetic signature. (Thomson Sintra)

swept width. Solenoid power is supplied by an electronic amplifier that can adjust power to the level and shape of the desired signature. The manufacturer, Thomson Sintra, claims that it can achieve a large magnetic sweepwidth even using low electrical-power levels.

◆ KRAM

This French magnetic sweep was made under license in Yugoslavia for river minesweepers; it was exported (on board Yugoslav river sweepers) to Hungary and probably to Iraq. KRAM was also used to clear mines (laid clandestinely with U.S. assistance) from Nicaraguan waters. Hungarian river sweepers tow KRAM 200 m aft.

Presumably the wire sweeps used in Hungary are of Yugoslav origin, as are the river sweepers.

GERMANY

Current standard sweeps are SDG 31 (mechanical), HFG-G1 (acoustic), GBT-3, and GHA (acoustic). Pinguin A1 apparently never entered service, having been superseded by MA 2000. SDG 31 is also used by Thailand (M 48 class) and probably by Taiwan (MWW 50 class).

◆ MA 2000 (Minen-Abwehr 2000)/MJ 2000 (Minen-Jaeger 2000)

MCM 2000 (MA 2000) counters both "proud" (moored and visible ground mines) and buried mines. In an extension of the Troika concept, all minehunting and neutralization is to be by remote control. Each of five minehunters (converted MJ 332s) controls a pair of Seepferd (Seahorse) tugs with sonar towfish, whose sophisticated sonars are expected to eliminate false alarms, and thus to justify using expendable (one-shot) Seewolf antimine torpedoes rather than examining the suspicious objects before attacking them. Each hunter carries torpedoes. Another five hunters will be created by converting five SM 343s with DSQS-11M sonar and PAP 104 or Seefuchs antimine torpedoes. Three had already been equipped with a mine-avoidance version of DSQS-11 during the Gulf War; they will be brought up to -11M standard, and two more bought for other 343s. Each of five minesweepers (converted SM 343s) controls a next-generation Troika system, tows an improved SDG 31 mechanical sweep, and carries Seewolf. These SM 343s are no longer required to lay mines as a primary mission. That brings the MJ 2000 force to 15 hunters and sweepers (the five SM 343 hunters were ordered converted in December 1993).

The 340-kg towfish (0.3 × 3.5m) carries a 2.5m ProMiS (Proud Mine Sonar) linear array sidescan sonar slung beneath it, generating nine parallel 0.1-deg beams (resolution cell 10 × 20 cm at 100 m range); a buried-mine sonar, Sedis, developed by ELAC and Westinghouse, operates at relatively low frequency to penetrate the bottom. Its 1 × 0.5m linear array forms a fan of thirty 3 × 6-deg beams on 3-deg centers in both transmit and receive modes. The beams advance along the track as the vehicle moves. It is not clear whether the next step, to gain along-track resolution by synthetic aperture techniques, has as yet been demonstrated. Much depends on knowledge of bottom sediment; apparently the sonar uses a technique already used commercially in which sediment types can be classified according to their level of sound impedence. The gap between the two side swaths is filled by a sonar pointed downward and forward, integrated into the rear "wings" of the array. The Sedis array is mounted crosswise between the two gap-filler arrays.

The system's Westinghouse neural net CAD/CAC system uses the shape and size of shadow to classify objects as mines, which are highlighted on the operator's screen (scanning about 6 hectares/min). Objects classified as mines are highlighted on the screen. The operator can select enlargement, and hand the target over to the operations console.

The Abeking & Rasmussen/Lurssen Seepferd is about the size of a Troika boat (26 m long, 99 t) and carries its own 3D mine-avoidance sonar. Data are radioed back to the controlling ship at 3 GHz over 10 nm, the link carrying 4 Mbytes/sec with an-

tijam. The Seepferd remote-control system (an autonomous subsystem) will also be used for the German/Dutch next-generation Troika. The towfish is controlled using two depressors in the forward section. It has pitch and roll sensors, a bottom altitude sensor, and a Doppler log for movement over the bottom.

The Seewolf electric antimine torpedo (25 cm × 1.50 m, 70 kg, 30-kg PBX warhead, 7 kt, 10-min endurance) is controlled via a fiber-optic cable. It carries an HF sonar and LLLTV, and can also carry a range-gated laser camera. Individually controlled shrouds on top, bottom, and sides (to clear the control cable) carry its gearless electric motors and direct-drive propellers. Seefuchs (Seafox) is a much smaller version to attack moored mines, carrying a 2-kg shaped charge.

The German navy issued the MA 2000 Tactical Concept early in 1991; DASA–Daimler Benz won the contest and began work in mid-1992. Subcontractors include Abeking & Rasmussen, Lurssen, Atlas Elektronik (mine-avoidance sonar for Seepferd), Diehl, Rohde & Schwartz, Allied Signal (buried-mine sonar), Lockheed (joint development of expendable torpedoes with STN), and Westinghouse (sensor vehicle, sidescan sonar).

◆ GHA

This flow-driven but electromagnetically excited acoustic source (hence controllable [programmable] in frequency and in relative amplitude at different frequencies, whatever the tow speed), part of the new Ibak combined sweep, is towed 25 m aft, suspended about 8 m below the surface from a float. When used with a solenoid, GHA is suspended between the after end of the solenoid and the towing bridle of a float towed by the solenoid. It is 3 m long; weight is 500 kg in air, 250 kg in water. GHA has been in service on board Type 343 minesweepers since 1989.

◆ MAS 90

This STN Atlas mine-avoidance sonar is based on DSQS-11M. STN claims that it is the first 3D sonar to perform its processing and display in real time. It uses COTS hardware and an open architecture. The planar array carries vertical columns of LF and VLF elements side by side (they are not used simultaneously). Each ping period covers the entire vertical and horizontal sector (presumably the sonar transmits in SODT mode and preforms receiving beams [drawings in the current brochure suggest 32 × 17 beams]). Instantaneous horizontal search width is 110 deg. Targets are automatically detected and tracked. Pings use LPI waveforms. Typical ranges: LF mode: moored mine at 1100 m, obstacle at 1400 m, small submarine at 1600 m; VLF mode: small obstacle at 1500 m, large obstacle at 2300 m, very large obstacle at 2900 m. The standard display shows the sector in PPI form (detection display) with a classification/depth display of selected targets in the water column, which the sonar has estimated are mines. In an example shown, maximum range was set at 300 m and maximum depth as 60 m. MAS 90 was announced in 1995. Applications include the new German U212-class submarine and the upgraded Troika.

◆ Pinguin B3

MBB-VFW's mine identification-and-disposal vehicle (70 cm [dia]/1.45 m high/1.5 m span × 3.5 m [29.9/57.1/59.1 × 137.8 in], 1350 kg [2975 lb]) is part of the Type 343 minehunter (MWS 80) program. Like PAP 104, it is powered by batteries, in this case silver-zinc ones driving twin podded motors (6–8 kt, 150 min endurance). The gyrostabilized vehicle turns by controlling the thrust of the two motors, and it climbs and dives (and hovers) by manipulating elevons in the wash and by using a vertical propeller in a tunnel. It was given high speed to overcome the strong currents in German coastal waters. To reduce operator workload, Pinguin follows a preprogrammed path to a point selected by the minehunter's combat system, after which it hovers over the location of the presumed mine, using television (which looks both ahead and down) or a high-definition acoustic-lens sonar (2 MHz, range about 10 m) sonar. Alternatively, Pinguin can carry an STN high-definition (but lower frequency) sonar. The cable link with the controlling ship carries a two-way digital data link

Pinguin B3. (Messerschmitt-Bölkow-Blohm)

A Troika boat, *Seehund* 1. (L. van Ginderen)

for commands and feedback, a sonar link, and a television link. Pinguin B3 carries two 120-kg (264-lb) charges in tandem so that it can destroy two mines during a single mission. Alternatively, the forward charge can be replaced by a cutter or manipulator, or the ROV can be used for inspection/identification using standard TV and sonar sensors with a sidescan array slung below it. Range from the operating ship is 600–1000 m (660–1090 yd) and maximum depth is 200 m (which can be reached in less than a minute). For ease of recovery, the body is positively buoyant (but not enough so as to require strong control forces).

The first test vehicle was completed in 1979, a second following in 1982, with sea trials in September–October 1982.

Users: Germany (Type 343 minehunters), Taiwan (MWW 50 class).

◆ Troika

Krupp MaK's Troika influence sweep system uses a ship towing a moored sweep to control three drones with enhanced acoustic and magnetic signatures to trigger influence mines. The drones can tow two SDG-21 Oropesa (moored) sweeps. Each drone is fitted with a Luneberg Lens radar reflector (for the controller's TRS-N radar) atop its mast, and the control link (several miles' range) is UHF. The operator steers the drone along a track line visible on the radar scope. Courses for both drones and control ship are automatically corrected. The control ship carries her own mine-detection/avoidance sonar (DSQS-11A) to detect moored mines not swept by the drones, and tows a moored sweep.

Each drone (24 m [79 ft] long, 95 t, draft less than 2 m [6.6 ft]) has a blast-resistant steel core, around which a wooden hull is built. The diesel engine (using hydraulic drive for shock resistance), control, power supply, and remote controls are all shock-mounted within the core. Two coils wrapped around the core, one at each end, generate the strong magnetic field intended to explode magnetic mines. Each Troika also carries two MF sound sources in its bow and tows an LF source.

The new MCM-SDS (surface drone system) uses faster, longer-ranged, and more survivable 25m (90t) drones, which can be controlled from ship or shore. Each is self-guided through a series of preset navigational waypoints (using the new very accurate navigational aids), so that up to four can be controlled by a single operator. Each drone can carry four alternative mission kits: for route surveillance (towing a fish with side-looking sonar), for wire or magnetic sweeping, and for minelaying (the same control station is used for each mission). An alternative single-mission drone would displace 50 t.

Six Troika systems (6 ships, 18 drones) were ordered in the mid-1970s (the Type 351 controllers were converted in 1979–81). The successor system will be controlled by five converted Type 343 sweepers. The Royal Netherlands Navy adopted MCM-SDS, to be controlled by three converted *Alkmaar*-class minehunters (the first is to become operational at the end of 1998).

HUNGARY

The navy's major mission is to protect the Danube against mining. The main technique is countermining, using small mines on the river sweepers. The main mechanical sweep uses boats 100 m apart, and the sweep 100 m abaft the sterns. See also the French KRAM magnetic sweep.

INTERNATIONAL

In October 1991 France and Britain signed an MoU for a joint feasibility study of future MCM systems.

◆ NATO Mechanical Sweep Study

NATO Project Group 22 conducted a study of mechanical sweeping between September 1987 and May 1988. Maximum sweep depth was at least 600 m (about 2000 ft); 1000 m (about 3000 ft) was desired. Desired maximum sweep speed was 14 kt (compared to 8–10 kt now) with a 350m-swath width (currently 200–350 m, reduced to 50–100 m for bottom-contacting sweeps) capable of dealing with a bottom gradient of 7% (possible at present only with team sweeps). Separate volume and bottom sweeps were needed, the latter to deal with rising mines tethered within 1–3 m of the bottom (team sweeps can come only within about 15 m of the bottom). This close to the bottom, depth control becomes very difficult; reaction time may be too slow for the sweep to avoid obstacles. Deep sweeping requires a very powerful ship: a 350m sweep towed at 14 kt at 600m depth imposes a load of 1200 to 1400 t on the towing ship (2400 to 3700 t for a sweep contacting the bottom). Too, at great depth the towing winch must heave and veer at an enormous rate, about 130m/min for a 250m deep sweep at 14 kt. The group considered using decommissioned bulk carriers and other merchant ships. It recommended developing a flying sweep using existing types of cutters, and a rolling or sliding sweep to clear bottom mines.

In April 1992 France, Italy, and the Netherlands signed an MoU to begin a new program (within NATO PG 22) to mechanically sweep deep (100 m or more) and close-tethered mines. The United States later joined. The feasibility study was completed in 1994. It was conducted by a consortium of six companies, with TNO-FEL as system integrator (also for optimum positioning of cutters on the sweep). The others were: Raytheon (flow dynamics and sweep design), Whitehead (the cutter: a cable-launched A200 homing torpedo), Thomson Sintra, ACB, and De Regt Special Cables of the Netherlands (overall cable design). A triangular configuration with straight tail or leg would simplify location of the cutters/markers. The sweep would be "flown" by active depressors controlled from the ship on the basis of the ship's echo-soundings and the sweep's own obstacle avoidance sonar.

ITALY

The standard wire sweep is designated MIS.4. Whitehead has developed a mine disposal version of its A200 minitorpedo (1050 mm long, 13 kg with 3.6-kg charge, using one transmit and four receive beams). It was part of the NATO deep sweep concept. Unit cost is about $25,000.

◆ P2072 (SQQ-14/IT)

FIAR's version of the U.S. SQQ-14 has been completely redesigned, with a digital processor carrying up to four pictures in its memory, to be recalled, singly or together, for classification. Only the mechanical hoist of SQQ-14 has been retained; the transmitter electronics have been relocated into the towed body, and there are new consoles. The Plessey Speedscan (see the British Type 2048 in the ASW section) has been integrated with P2072 for route surveillance. P2072 is considered effective down to 350 m (i.e., down to the continental shelf). The associated minehunting combat system is SSN-714 (see below).

Users: Belgium (*Dash* class, in reserve), Italy (*Lerici*- and *Gaeta*-class and ex-U.S. minehunters).

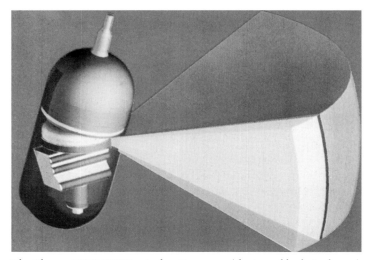

The Plessey-FIAR P2095 minehunting sonar (the towed body is shown). (FIAR)

◆ P2095

This FIAR/GE/Plessey development of the British Type 2093 is the P2072 successor, for use at greater depths (for oceanic minehunting). It is intended for the planned *Gaeta* follow-on class.

◆ MACTIS/SSN-714/IMICS

Datamat's Minehunting Action Information System (tactical-situation compilation and display) uses the same Rolm MSE 14 computer as the SACTIS submarine combat-data system, with a 16in circular CRT with a keyboard and tracker ball. IMICS (Integrated Minehunting Combat System) integrates MACTIS with the SPN-703 radar and with the SSN-715 precision navigation system. IMICS has two summary displays, one on the bridge and one in CIC.

Users: Italy (*Lerici* and *Gaeta* classes).

◆ MIN 77

SMIN's mine-disposal vehicle (105 cm [dia] × 3.5 m × 1.4 m [41.3 × 138 × 55.1 in], 1150 kg) is powered, at up to 6 kt, by a single ducted propeller, which can be oriented in two planes for steering. Paired (fore and aft) vertical and horizontal thrusters work in tunnels in the body of the vehicle. All motors are pneumatic (compressed nitrogen) rather than electric, to avoid magnetic signature; each is fed by an oil-nitrogen tank which can be topped up by an electric pump in the vehicle, powered by the on-board battery. Because the motors operate at variable speed, the propellers can be designed to minimize acoustic signature, operating at fixed pitch. Endurance is 40 min at 3 kt; MIN 77 can be recharged in 15 min and turned around for a second mission in 20 min. The umbilical is 1000 m long (maximum depth is 350 m and operational range is 400 m). MIN 77 can operate into a current of 3 kt and in sea states up to 4; it can maintain depth (hovering) to better than 0.5 m accuracy, and can measure bottom depth to better than 0.25 m accuracy. For minimum magnetic signature, MIN is GRP over an aluminum frame.

MIN Mk 2. (Whitehead Alenia)

Smaller than PAP 104 or Pinguin, MIN carries either an LLLTV (CCD with automatic iris, with underwater light) or a 400-kHz sonar mechanically scanning a 60-deg sector in about 2 sec. Sonar pulse widths are 0.05 and 0.70 msec (for, respectively, seabed or moored mines; typical ranges are 20 and 40 m). The TV and sonar are orientable 150 deg in vertical plane. Display modes are raw video (bottom mines), synthetic video (moored mines), or raw video with digital range (moored mines). MIN uses both an explosive charge and an explosive cutter. It floats to the surface after it drops its acoustically fired charge.

SMIN was formed in February 1978 by Elsag and Riva Calzoni, receiving a contract for four vehicles in June 1979. Tests began in 1983. Data above are for MIN Mk 2.

Users: Italy (*Gaeta* and *Lerici* classes, which carry one MIN 77 and a Pluto; MIN is used for mine location, Pluto for destruction).

◆ Pluto

Gaymarine's private-venture minehunting vehicle (0.6 × 1.68 × 0.63 m, 160 kg, including a 15-kg charge) has a fiberglass body mounted on a steel sled frame (for ease of handling). The forward section, carrying the sensors, can tilt up to 240 deg (the fixed after section carries batteries and electronics). There are five electric motors: two at about 45-deg angles behind the head, and three horizontal at the stern (one to turn, two to go forward or in reverse). The operator uses two joysticks. Maximum diving depth is 400 m, speed is 4 kt, and endurance is 1–2 hr. The umbilical control cable can be 500 m (copper) or 2000 m (fiber-optic) long, and there is also an umbilical power cable (500 m). The umbilical can carry 10 control and two telemetry (four-digit) channels. The sensors are a 200-kHz sonar (range 30 m, beamwidth 10 deg) and a television (monochrome LLLTV or color); a typical configuration shows two television windows and four underwater lights. Pluto carries either explosive cutters or a 15-kg mine-destruction charge.

Shown at Mostra Navale (May 1989), PlutoPlus is longer (1.95 m) and heavier (250 kg), and it can operate down to 400 m and at up to 7 kt (endurance is 10 hr). Sensors are a color TV camera and three sonars (navigation, medium-range search, and target identification).

Pluto is based on the FILIPPO underwater inspection device.

Users: Finland (one unit), Italy (all minehunters), Korea (SK5000 class), Nigeria (*Lerici* class), Spain (PlutoPlus was chosen for the CME minehunters early in 1996; Pluto is aboard the ex-U.S. minehunters), and Thailand (M 48 class). The U.S. Navy bought at least two Plutos.

JAPAN

The standard minehunting sonar, Hitachi's ZQS-2 (-2B in the *Hatsushima* class), is a license-built version of the British Type 193, used with the S-4 ROV. ZQS-3, a license-built Type 2093 used with the S-7 ROV, is carried by the *Uwajima* class. The *Yaeyama* class carries ZQS-4 (a license-built SQQ-32) to control S-8 (the U.S. SLQ-48). The new *Ayama* class, first authorized under the JFY95 budget, has the first Japanese integrated minewarfare system, a version of Nautis-M using ZQS-3, with the Australian dyad influence sweep. The old ZQS-1 (modified U.S. UQS-1) survives only aboard the support ship/minelayer *Hayase*. Hand-held diver sensors are the RQS-1 sonar (comparable to the U.S. PQS-1) and magnetic detectors (RSX-1 and -2, the latter analogous to the U.S. EOD Mk 4). The standard acoustic sweep is S-2. Japan also uses the U.S. A Mk 4(v) and A Mk 6(b) and the U.S. magnetic sweeps M Mk 5(a), M Mk 6(a), and M Mk 6(h). There are 11 MH-53E minesweeping helicopters.

S-4 (Type 75) mine-destruction vehicle. (*Ships of the World*)

◆ S-4

This saucer-shaped ROV has two thrusters with prominent motor housings, one at each side at the rear end, and a saucer-shaped nose with a flat dome on top. The destruction charge is carried in a tube in the center of the saucer. The associated sonar is ZQS-2B.

◆ S-7

Mitsubishi's mine-neutralization vehicle (1.5 m [W] × 1.2 m [H] × 2.8 m [L], 860 kg) has two 5.5-kW electric motors which can tilt up and down to steer, plus a vertical propulsor. S-7 is linked with the hunting ship by an umbilical (which provides both power and commands) and it carries a transponder for tracking. The vehicle carries an imaging sonar, a searchlight, and an LLLTV. The console on the hunting ship shows the images from these sensors; a smaller console maneuvers the device. S-7 carries one PAP-size explosive charge (detonated acoustically) and explosive cable cutter. The associated sonar is ZQS-3. S-7 is carried by the *Yaeyama* class and S-7 Mod 1 by the *Uwajima*-class coastal sweepers.

The new Japanese S-7 remotely operated underwater vehicle (ROV) for medium-depth sweeping. (*Ships of the World*)

NETHERLANDS

The *Alkmaar*-class sweeps are the French MDV/OD 3 wire sweep, the Finnish F82 magnetic sweep, and the Swedish AS.203 acoustic sweep. A planned Capability Upgrade Program comprises three Troika control conversions and 12 minehunter upgrades (eight with improved C² from 2001, four with self-propelled VDS).

Japanese mine-destruction charges used with the S-4 and S-7 ROVs. (*Ships of the World*)

NORWAY

◆ AGATE

Geco's Air Gun and Transducer Equipment uses air guns for high output in limited dimensions. Its digital signal processor generates the desired output waveform (preset or manually set), which is passed to the transducers (each with its own amplifier) in analog form. Each transducer uses three bandwidths to cover the range to 100 kHz: low (100 Hz, 10–20-kW input level), medium (3 kHz at 1–3-kW input), and high (0.1–1-kW input). The 12 air guns can be split into three lines with different frequency settings.

The prototype was completed in 1992. Production rights have been sold to CelsiusTech.

User: Norway (*Alta* class).

◆ EIMa

The magnetic element of the influence sweep system of the *Alta* class uses an improved "straight tail" sweep modified to provide either a conventional influence field or a detailed simulation of a ship signature (a target sweep). EIMa uses three electrodes (in fork arrangement) rather than the usual two. Each branch is separately controlled, using separate port and starboard generators, both connected to the common center electrode. In August 1995 GECO Defense received a contract to rebuild five existing magnetic sweeps to EIMa standard.

◆ SA950

Simrad's 95-kHz mine-detection and -avoidance sonar uses a retractable 64-stave hull transducer, transmitting a 45-deg-wide pulse and receiving with preformed beams (45-deg sector, thirty-two overlapping 1.7 × 10-deg beams). The sector is trainable (190 deg at 30 deg/sec) and tilts (between +10/−90 deg at 150 deg/sec). Pulses are CW (short, normal, and long: 0.2–12.8 msec, according to search range) and FM (0.8, 3.2, 12.8 msec, bandwidth 5 kHz: FM-0 [one pulse], FM-1 [two subpulses], FM-3 [eight subpulses], and auto, each subpulse being at a different frequency, so that in FM-3 each has a 625-Hz bandwidth). Range scales: 75, 150, 300, 600, 1200 m. The sonar can track targets. The display is a 20in color CRT (680 × 512 pixels in 8 bitplanes). Display modes are true motion (north-stabilized, with track history; current sector updated, data from sectors examined earlier persist; up to eight markers can be placed on the screen), sector (512 range arcs, 32 beams extrapolated to 64), and zoomed sector (only outer half of a sector shown, e.g., echoes from 600 to 1200 m). Maximum sonar operating speed is 12 kt.

SA950 is also used as a short-range ASW sonar.

Tests aboard the Norwegian "Bird"-class minesweeper *Kvina* began in February 1988.

Users: Finland (mine detection), Norway (mine avoidance for *Kvina* [ex-U.S. *Falcon* class] and *Alta*-class minesweepers), Sweden (*Hugin* class), Taiwan (minehunters), and Turkey (*Mercure* class and other sweepers). At least in the *Hugin* class, the search sector is adjustable to 60 deg. There may be other users.

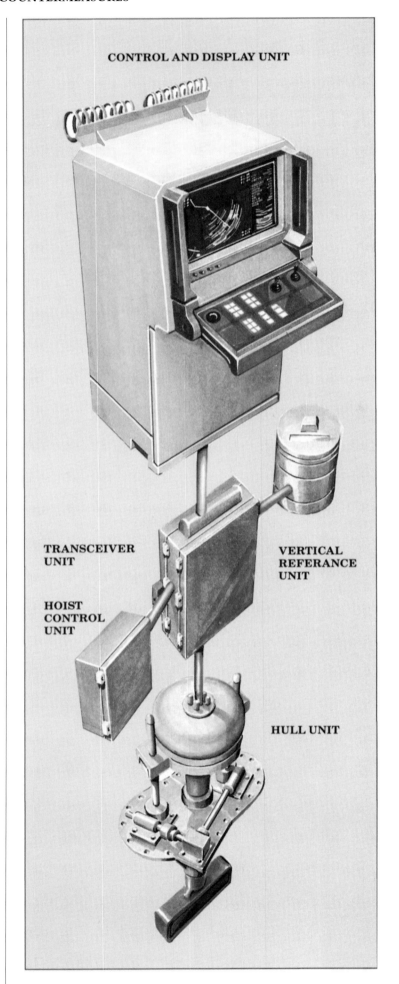

CONTROL AND DISPLAY UNIT

TRANSCEIVER UNIT

VERTICAL REFERANCE UNIT

HOIST CONTROL UNIT

HULL UNIT

SA950 in minesweeper configuration. (Simrad)

◆ MS 990 Series

Simrad announced these new ROV minehunting sonars in 1992. MS 992 combines 120-kHz medium-resolution search and 330-kHz high-resolution sidescan beams; the latter has a beamwidth of 0.2 deg and a range of 150 m. Suspicious objects are classified with a high-resolution scanning sonar (MS 997) mounted on the ROV, using a combination of multiple beams and mechanical scanning. Simrad proposes MS 992/997 for peacetime Q-route surveys, as well as for more general underwater-industry work.

◆ Minesniper

Bentech Subsea's antimine torpedo (150 × 1500 mm, 20 kg) is unique in that it has an inspection capability (hence can replace conventional ROVs) and it is recoverable if not used (despite its explosive content). Launched from a container under the ship, it is controlled by fiber-optic cable. Range is 4000 m at 6 kt (to overcome typical Norwegian coastal currents, 4–6 kt) using two midlength shrouded propellers. A glass nose covers an LLLTV, and there is also a scanning sonar. Maximum depth is 500 m (a deeper-running version is available) and range is 1 km. Minesniper uses the shaped-charge warhead of the Norwegian NM-72 antitank weapon.

Minesniper began sea trials, from the minehunter *Tana*, in the fall of 1994.

User: Norway (*Oksoy* class).

POLAND

◆ SHL 100 Flaming A

This retractable sonar, developed by the Centrum Techniki Morskiej of Gdansk, detects floating mines at 1600 m and bottom mines at 600 m; resolution is 7.5–25 cm (adjustable) and 4 deg. It covers a 60-deg search sector, which can be trained within +/− 120 deg of dead ahead. This is the mine-avoidance sonar of Polish "Notec" class (Project 207D, 207M, 207P) minehunter/sweepers.

◆ SHL 200 Flaming B

The 100-kHz side-looking mine-location sonar of Polish "Notec"-class minehunter/sweepers is towed at 2–6 kt up to 300 m astern. It operates at 100 kHz. Range is 150 or 300 m (swath on either side) with angular resolution 1 or 4 deg and range resolution 0.5 or 1.5 m; search depth is 5–100 m. The 90-kg body can drop up to 10 transponders to mark targets it detects. Both Flaming A and Flaming B use a standard console, except that Flaming B has an additional small CRT with a keypad to the right of the main CRT. Flaming A has a standard electronics cabinet in addition to its display (probably for array stabilization).

RUSSIA

The minehunting system in the "Gorya" class (Project 1260) was apparently inspired by Western rising mines, particularly Captor. A class of 20 units (to be built over 5 yr) was planned, but the program was deferred (more likely abandoned) as too expensive. The lead ship cost 41M rubles, of which only 5M went into the hull. It was intended to carry two submersibles (CTICH, meaning "self-propelled remote-controlled seeker-destructor" in Russian), each carrying two 100-kg demolition charges. A total of 20 such charges would have been embarked. Presumably the submersibles would have been launched by cranes extending out through the two sliding doors in the deckhouse. The planned outfit also included two special deep-water sweeps, Anaconda and Cobra, each employing a pair of old SET-40 torpedoes towing a sweep wire between them. Anaconda would have cut through mine cables; Cobra would have used cable-cutting charges.

There are several towed underwater televisions used for minehunting; they lay marker buoys for later investigation of suspected mines. The IT-3 television mine detector/exploder (hunt width 20 to 30 m, working depth 10 to 60 m, tow speed 3.5 to 6 kt, sweep-to-stern distance 70 m), can be used in water with white-disk transparency of 70 m. The IU-2 magnetic bottom mine detector-destructor is for harbor sweepers. Detection elements are towed 2–3 m above the bottom, with markers and antimine cluster bombs towed abaft them. The device searches at up to 6 kt in a zone 16 m wide. It can tow one or two strings (channels) of markers and bombs, each of which can mark four mines and destroy two, at depths of 6–20 m. Other current towed detector/destructors are KIU-1 in the Sonya class and Neva-1 in the Vanya class. MKT-210 is a towed underwater minehunter in the Natya class. The towed television marker was exported to India aboard the Yevgenya class.

Gidropribor's VNT helicopter sweep was described at Abu Dhabi in 1993. The 5 × 3 × 3m, 3t hydrofoil can be towed at up to 21.6 kt, producing a maximum sweep current of 1200 Amp. On-board generator fuel suffices for 4 hr. The active magnetic loop is 180 m long, and the electrode is 40 m long. It is probably based on the *Volga*-class sports hydrofoil.

Two views of the Russian VNT hydrofoil sled, taken from a Gidropribor video at Bourget Euronaval 1996. The generator is in the white box barely visible atop the sled. (Author)

Gidropribor is currently advertising a range of GRUNT mine-neutralization ROVs: PA-100 for small ships or helicopters, PA-300 to be used with hull sonar, and PA-500 combining forward-looking and sidescan swath sonars. PA-300 and -500 have twin motors.

Four or more Polnocny A– and B–class medium landing ships were converted to line-charge layers to clear beach defenses. These ships carry line charges in side troughs, with stern chutes to launch the two small remotely controlled motor boats that tow the charges into place.

Standard sweeps are:

AT-2: Acoustic sweep using sweep current 7.5–14 Amp, towed at up to 15 kt 550 m astern, requiring up to 4.2 kW power; the noisemaker proper weighs 370 kg. Total system weight is 2.2 t. In Vanya class (Project 257) and Yevgenya class (Project 1258).

AT-3 is in the "Zhenya" class (Project 1252), AT-5 in the Natya class (Project 266) and Sonya class (Project 1265), and AT-6 in the "Lida" class.

BAT-2: Towed acoustic sweep in T-43 class and in Olya-class roadstead sweeper.

BGAT: High-speed deep-water acoustic sweep in T-58 class.

BKT: Contact sweep in Natya class (Project 266); BKT-2 is in Sonya class (Project 1265).

GKT-2: Contact sweep: sweepwidth 260–280 m, sweep depth 10–200 m, towed at 9.5–10.5 kt. In Natya class (Project 266).

GKT-3M: Contact sweep: sweepwidth 50–120 m, sweep depth 2–120 m, towed at up to 12 kt. For the "Lida" and Vanya (GKT-3) classes.

MKT-1: Mechanical moored sweep in T-58 class.

MPT-3: Mechanical sweep in Indian Natyas.

MT-1: Moored sweep introduced 1944, towed at 5–10 kt at 7–32 m, sweepwidth 400 m. In the T-43 class.

MT-2G: Standard World War II moored sweep for large sweepers, towed at 8–12 kt at 70 or 80 m depth, for sweepwidth 200 or 100 m. MT-2P cartridge (patrone) version introduced 1950: 10–75 m depth, 220 to 110 m sweepwidth. In Zhenya (Project 1252) with one other sweep (AT-3). MT-2 (1944) towed at 5–10 kt at 7–32 m, sweepwidth 220 m.

MT-3G: Standard World War II small-sweeper moored sweep towed at 5–10 kt at 37–50 or 40–80 m depth for swept width 100 or 50 m; MT-3P cartridge-cutter version introduced 1948 (6–24 m depth, path 110 or 55 m). An MT-3U version (cutters and cartridges) was introduced in 1955 (4–12 kt, 4–26 m sweep depth, 120–135 m sweepwidth; special controlled version was towed at 30–76 m, sweepwidth 95–100 m). MT-3U is in Zhenya (Project 1252) class with AT-3 and PEMT-4. MT-3 (1944) towed at 4–10 kt at 4–18 m, sweepwidth 120 m.

OKT-2: Deep contact sweep with cutters and cartridges; it can also tow corner reflectors for use with acoustic sweeps.

PEMT-2: Magnetic loop sweep to counter highly sensitive needle and induction mines: 250 Amp, towed at 2 m depth (effective depth 7–35 m) at up to 4 kt 330–460 m astern, using a 424m three-core cable to which a 227.5m two-core feeder is connected; 5.4 t.

PEMT-4: Loop sweep for base sweepers: towed at up to 8 kt, 50 kW, current in sweep 250 Amp (750 Amp-turns), depth of sweep effect up to 60 m. In the Sonya class (Project 1265).

PMP-2: Magnetic sweep in Natya class (Project 266). This sweep is also listed as PMT.

PPT-1: Moored sweep (1947): towed at 4–6 km/hr, depth 10–100 m, sweepwidth 140 m.

PPT-2: Moored sweep: towed at 4–6 km/hr, sweep depth 20–100 m, sweepwidth 180 m.

RKT-1: Moored sweep (1951) towed at 7.5–18 kt at 2–12 m depth, sweepwidth 100/50 m. In Olya class (Project 1259) roadstead sweeper.

SEMP-3: Magnetic sweep in the Indian Natyas.

SEMT-1: Magnetic solenoid sweep for harbor (roadstead) sweepers introduced 1949, using one or two separated electromagnets (one, two, or three can be secured to one another by a log). The electromagnet weighs 12 t and produces a magnetic moment of up to 800 kAmp-m^2, effective down to 25–30 m. The sweep uses 23 floats. Tow speed is 4–8 kt, and minimum depth is 5 m. In "Lida," Olya, and Vanya classes.

ST-2: Solenoid sweep for coastal sweepers, to counter needle and induction mines; sweep current 200 Amp, towed at 5–12 kt, 300 m astern; minimum depth 10 m; total weight 2.24 t.

ST-2: Magnetic sweep in Sonya class (Project 1265).

TEM-2: Coil sweep in T-58 class.

TEM-3: Coil sweep with feeder cable length 455 m, minimum depth 15 to 20 m, towed at 10 kt in Sea State 4. Loop version: towed at up to 10 kt, 450 kW, current up to 1600 Amp, depth of sweep effect up to 150 m. Electrode version: towed at up to 14 kt, pulse power up to 900 kW, pulse current up to 3000 Amp, depth of sweep effect up to 150 m. Both versions are for ocean sweepers. In Natya class (Project 266).

TEM-4: Coil sweep in Natya class (Project 266).

TEM-52: Coil sweep (575 kW at 115 V) in T-43 class.

TS-1: Surface net sweep in Sonya class (Project 1265).

The Russians have drone minesweepers (analogous to the German Troikas), the Ilyusha class. There are also several dozen towed sweep craft.

◆ **MG-7**

High-frequency (300-kHz) small-object location sonar, dipped by large ships from davits to detect swimmers; it is used by some minesweepers as their principal hull sonar. In the Vanya class, the MG-7 sonar can be lowered to 30 m on stern crane. The mine-disposal weapon in this class is a seven-barrel MRG-1 grenade launcher.

◆ **MG-69 Lan**

The minehunting sonar in the Natya class is intended to detect moored mines. It uses a hull transducer with a swiveling head and a beamforming receiver (the full scanning sector is 70 deg). At 10 kt, it can detect a moored mine at 900 m; accuracy is 2 deg and 2% of range.

◆ **MG-79 Mizen**

The minehunting sonar in the Sonya class is intended to detect bottom mines. The scanning sector is 110 deg. At 8 kt own-ship speed, MG-79 detects a bottom mine at 100 m depth at 400 m. Accuracy is 1.5 deg and 1.5% of range.

◆ **MG-89 Serna**

Current MCM craft sonar (49 kHz) to detect both moored and bottom mines. The scanning sector is 180 deg. At an own-ship speed of 14 kt, it can detect a moored mine at 1500 m and a bottom mine at 500 m, with an accuracy of 1.5 deg and 1.5% of range. This sonar has a built-in trainer and BITE.

Users: India (Natya class) and Russia (Natya class).

◆ **Kabarga-A1**

Minehunting sonar of the new Project 10750 ("Lida" class) inshore sweeper. Operating range is 350–400 m.

SWEDEN

The Swedish Defense Research Establishment is working on underwater lasers, presumably for minehunting.

The U.S. Navy bought two SAM remotely controlled boats just before the Gulf War for $7M; they performed well. A follow-on Remote Influence Sweep (RIS), the Swedish-U.S. SAM II, will be a fast SES.

◆ **IMAIS**

Bofors's (formerly SA Marine's) integrated magnetic and acoustic influence sweep combines a buoyant cable with three aluminum electrodes with a low-drag noisemaker (a few Hz to hundreds of Hz: a drum for low frequency and a turbine for higher frequency) held down by a kite. The three electrodes provide a safety zone (less than 5 nT) at every depth below the towing ship, 200 m forward of the first electrode, but still offer an extensive swept width against modern sensitive mines (against a 100-nT mine sweptwidths are 560/520/440 m for depths of 30/60/100 m). This type of sweep can maintain a constant magnetic field and configuration independent of varying water conductivity. The acoustic source level exceeds 150 dB up to 40 Hz, and 160–170 dB for the rest of band. Total weight including inboard equipment is 2800 kg. The power requirement is about 200 kW. The system's microprocessor holds numerous ship signatures; any signature can be programmed using a memory card or the keyboard. The system displays instantaneous values of output voltage and current in the sweeps (both graphic and numeric formats) and mine-detonation positions on the waveform curves (so that mine characteristics can be estimated).

IMAIS was announced in 1991 as the successor to the company's SA Marine Combined Influence Sweep (using the magnetic MG 204 and the parallel-towed acoustic AS 203).

◆ 9TS700

BEAB's acoustic sweep combines two magnetostrictive and five ceramic transducers in a 2m body (835 kg) to cover four bands, the relative intensities of which are controlled by a single console which also controls the associated magnetic sweep. Propeller modulation can be superimposed on the transmitted signature. 9TS700 is the standard Swedish navy acoustic sweep.

◆ SAM/SAM II

Karlskronavarvet's precursor-sweep ROV is a pair of foam-filled GRP pontoons covered by an 18 × 6.1m aluminum-girder platform, on which sits the casing of the 150-kW Volvo Penta TAMD 70D engine with Schottel propulsion unit (up to 8 kt, endurance up to 330 nm). Draft is 0.7 m (1.6 m over propeller). The magnetic sweep is integral; the acoustic sweep is towed. SAM carries eight Dan buoys to mark a cleared channel. The SAMs were delivered in 1983–86.

SAM unmanned craft. (SUTEC)

Karlskronavarvet's SAM II air-cushion platform (20 [22.5 over skirt] × 5.2 [on-cushion beam 11.7] m; height on cushion 6.22 m; light displacement 30.6 t, with 5.1 t of mission equipment, 20.4 t fuel; full load 56.1 t) is powered by two TF-40B gas turbines (22,871 kW at 16,100 rpm; two ducted air props at either end on raised structures). Transit speed is 40 kt and sweep speed 25 kt. CelsiusTech is prime contractor. One controller will be able to handle three vehicles. Sweden and the United States signed an MoU for joint development (each country supplying its own sweep systems) in the spring of 1993, but the program was terminated by Congress in FY95; the U.S. Navy is apparently buying MCAC instead.

The Swedish systems are probably Acoustic Sweep 88 and Karlskrona magnetic and UEP sweeps. A new FMV acoustic sweep may use air guns and Terfenol transducers.

The U.S. version was to have used the advanced lightweight influence sweep system (ALISS). See the U.S. section below.

◆ Sea Eagle/Double Eagle

This ROV (76 cm × 1.45 × 0.58 m, 90 kg) is powered through the same umbilical which carries control instructions and data. Four horizontal thrusters (two athwartships, two lengthwise) power Sea Eagle at 2.5 kt; there are also three vertical thrusters. Range is 350 m; maximum depth is 250 m. The main sensor is a television camera on a 10m telescopic arm, which also carries the mine-destruction charge (allowing the ROV to place the

Double Eagle. (SUTEC)

Double Eagle (in the background) on board a Danish *Flyvefisken*-class multirole corvette at IMDEX, London, 1995. In the foreground are the extra buoyancy tanks which allow the ROV to lift a heavy DAMDIC mine-disposal charge (the Sea Eagle in the background is mated to its tanks). The netting abaft the Sea Eagle seems to contain DAMDIC charges. A *Flyvefisken* on mine-disposal duty has this type of rail only on the port side (this photo looks aft), the ROVs being handled by a crane aft. (A. D. Baker III)

charge closer to the mine without being destroyed by a sensitive magnetic sensor). The closer the mine, the smaller it can be. It is detonated by acoustic signal at 350–1000 m.

Double Eagle (1.3 × 2.05 × 0.45 m, 300 kg) weighs twice as much as Eagle but is much more capable (more than 5 kt forward speed to operate in strong currents, 3 kt backward, 2 kt laterally, 1 kt vertically, turning 180 deg rather than 40 deg). Maximum operating depth is 300 m (about 1000 ft), and the vehicle is gyrostabilized to within 2 deg. The tether is 600 m long (a greater length can, however, be supplied). Payload, normally 30 kg, can be increased by adding buoyancy modules. Each of four fiberoptic links can carry two video/sonar channels and spare serial data channels. The standard system includes a sonar and a tiltable color CCD camera with remote focus plus a connector for an additional color or black-and-white camera. Double Eagle is controlled by two joysticks (forward/back, lateral, yaw; and up/down, roll, pitch) and three mode-control switches (power, selection of axis along which joysticks operate, and reference adjustment, to balance current or cable drag).

Recent improvements: increased motor power (5 kW rather than 3 kW, for 250-kg thrust rather than 160 kg, 1995) and reduced tether diameter (10 vice 12 mm, 1996; a battery-powered version has a 3.5mm tether). The new version of Double Eagle ran trials early in 1996. It can maintain track in a 3-kt transverse current, and maintain 5 kt while hunting.

In 1996 BAeSEMA announced a new shaped-charge mine-disposal system, in which a Double Eagle would use its telescopic arm to place a small weapon (0.1 × 0.4 m, 6 kg) on the mine; the weapon has a "unique attachment facility" to hold it to the mine until commanded to explode. The weapon can also be used as the warhead of a one-shot disposal device.

Eagle and Double Eagle were developed by the Scandinavian Underwater Technology Group (SUTEC) from the earlier commercial Sea Owl. The Swedish navy used Sea Owl and underwrote half the development cost of Sea Eagle. Double Eagle is used in Thomson Sintra and GEC-Marconi propelled VDS minehunting sonars.

Users: Australia (*Huon* class, two per ship), Denmark (*Flyvefisken* class, first bought June 1992; uses a Danish Reson sonar), and Sweden (*Landsort* class).

UNITED KINGDOM

In April 1996 the Royal Navy concluded that the planned 15-yr life extension, which would have included a CDS upgrade, was not practicable. Instead, the ships will receive HMU (Hunt-class Minimum Upgrade) to extend their lives by 5–10 yr. It will include installation of wide-band sonar (see below). Although the CDS will not be upgraded as such, "spend to save" measures such as installation of more reliable color consoles may be taken. The MS14 and MSSA 1 influence sweeps will be upgraded for better reliability/maintainability. Reportedly the feasibility report on the planned upgrade also concluded that antimine torpedo technology was not yet mature enough to be worth buying (the hope had been positive mine destruction, a single shaped charge on the mine causing it to detonate rather than merely neutralizing it). Nor did it endorse the new "dog on a leash" propelled VDS concept. However, it did support remote sweeping (as in the German Troika) as a preferred alternative to a new influence sweep. Hunts and *Sandowns* could be the control ships.

With the end of the Cold War, the "River"-class deep sweepers were disposed of or shifted to other duties.

Towed Sweeps

Below are listed wire and magnetic sweeps in service since after World War II. Wire lengths are in fathoms (6 ft each), and other distances are in cables (120 fathoms). Since the wires are not straight, swept paths are much narrower than the lengths of the streamed wires. Type O is Oropesa, the sweep to cut mine moorings; Type A is acoustic; and Type M is magnetic. A double O sweep (towed by one sweeper, double because it uses a wire on each side) runs about 30 m deep and sweeps out a 265m (290 yd) path. A two-ship team sweep (A sweep) runs 90 m deep (300 ft) and sweeps a path 350 m (380 yd) wide. A typical magnetic loop sweep clears a path 75 m (80 yd) wide, 400 m (about 1300 ft) abaft the sweeper. In the mid-1950s loop sweeps replaced wartime electrode (magnetic) sweeps because they could be towed at relatively high speed and were easier to stream and recover. However, because the loops swept out to both sides of the sweeper, they tended to place a higher magnetic field under the sweeper. Moreover, it was relatively difficult to place an LF acoustic sweep inside a loop to trigger combined magnetic/acoustic mines. Wartime acoustic sweeps used broad-band noisemakers covering the usual ship frequencies. The postwar

Osborn can be tuned more precisely to the expected mine-triggering frequencies.

The current standard British sweeps are the Oropesa Mk 8, the MM Mk 11 magnetic loop sweep, and the Osborn acoustic sweep.

◆ Oropesa Sweeps

Mk 1: Ocean sweepers. O sweep 300 fathoms (kite to otter), 8/8.5 kt; A sweep (two sweepers, two cables apart), 400–450 fathoms between kite blocks, 8/8.5 kt.

Mk 2*: Coastal sweepers. O sweep 300 fathoms, 6–9 kt; A sweep, 300 fathoms, 5–7 kt.

Mk 3*: Coastal sweepers. O sweep 250 fathoms, 7–8 kt; A sweep, 300 fathoms, 5–6 kt. Mk 3*, rather than Mk 1, is the standard "Hunt"-class sweep.

Mk 7: Inshore sweepers. O sweep only 60 fathoms, 9–10 kt. This sweep was used by postwar inshore craft ("Ham" class).

Mk 8: Nonmagnetic version of Mk 3, for the "Hunt" class.

Mk 9: Deep wire sweep (EDATS) introduced 1981; for discarded "River" class.

These wire sweeps may be prefixed W, as in W Mk 2 for coastal sweepers.

◆ Magnetic Sweeps

LL means double longitudinal.

LL Mk 3: For coastal sweeper. Long leg 525 yd, short leg 200 yd, maximum sweep speed 7 kt, 300 yd wide in P formation (108-kW sweep current). Cycle 4.5 sec, double cycle 60 sec.

LL Mk 6*: For ocean sweeper. Long leg 575 yd, short leg 225 yd, maximum sweep speed 12 kt, path 300 yd wide in P formation (220-kW sweep power). Cycle normally 3.5–7 sec, special 10 sec, double cycle 28–60 sec.

LL Mk 8: For inshore sweeper. Long leg 500 yd, short leg 175 yd, 7 kt, 200 yd wide (sweep power 35 kW using batteries).

Mod L: Modified loop sweep. Three legs (575, 325, 185 yd), maximum speed 12 kt for ocean sweepers, 10 kt for coastal sweepers, 8 kt for trawlers; 125-yd-wide path.

ME means electrode sweep (this series probably superseded the earlier LL designations).

ME Mk 103: For motor minesweepers (MMS), using a 108-kW generator/battery outfit. Maximum pulse current is 1500 Amp, maximum sweep speed is 10 kt.

ME Mk 106: For *Algerine*-class steel ocean sweepers, using a 220-kW diesel generator to provide the sweep impulse, with a maximum pulse current of 1500 amps and a maximum sweep speed of 12 kt.

ME Mk 107: Alternative for *Coniston*-class coastal sweepers, using a 375-kW diesel generator; maximum sweep current is 2500 amps; maximum sweep speed is 12 kt.

ME Mk 108: For minesweeping motor launches, alternative for inshore sweepers ("Ham" class), using a 35-kW generator (340-kW inshore sweepers); maximum sweep current is 1200 amps; maximum sweep speed is 12 kt.

ML means loop sweep. As of 1959, the loop sweeps were standard, but some sweepers retained electrode sweeps, pending development of a convertible sweep.

ML Mk 3: For inshore sweepers ("Ham" class), using a 340-kW generator; maximum sweep current is 1500 amps, and maximum sweep speed is 6 kt.

ML Mk 4: For *Algerine*-class steel ocean sweepers, using a 220-kW generator; maximum sweep current is 2500 amps, and maximum sweep speed is 10 kt.

ML Mk 4-1: For coastal sweepers ("Ton" class), using a 375-kW generator; maximum sweep current is 2500 amps, and maximum sweep speed is 10 kt.

The current standard magnetic sweep is MM Mk 2.

♦ Acoustic Sweeps

Explosives sweeps were intended to deal with mines that could distinguish between the steady buildup of noise from a noise-making sweep and the relatively sharp buildup of the noise of a real ship.

AD (Acoustic Displacer): Uses ship's 220V DC current to produce LF noise (10–30 Hz) in two ranges (10–16 and 16–30 Hz). This device was used on board ocean, coastal, and inshore sweepers.

AH Mk 4 (Hammer): Uses ship's power (220 V) to drive two alternative diaphragms, either 19 in (150–1000) versus RN mines or 27 in (60–1000) versus German mines (during postwar mine clearance in European waters; but the Soviet KRAB was probably based on German practice).

AO Mk 4 (Acoustic Oscillator): Uses a 5-kVA motor alternator to provide high-intensity narrow-band noise (235–245 Hz) against coarse mines.

AX Mk 3 (Explosive Sweep): Produces broad-band noise from 100 Hz up, suitable for all sweepers, including small craft.

Osborn: See below.

♦ Wide-band Sonar

DRA's developmental sonar uses wide-band (band-time product over 1000) pulse compression to deal with both reverberation and noise simultaneously. High overall energy overcomes background noise, and pulse compression yields an effective pulse length short enough to overcome fading due to multipath (and also offers very fine target resolution). FM techniques had not previously been used in minehunting because it is relatively difficult at high frequencies; the problems were not worth solving against deep-water mines. Shallow water is very different. Trials have shown that the echo contains so much information that it can be used for classification, so that a single sonar can locate and classify simultaneously, at relatively long range.

♦ Type 193/193M

This hull sonar searches at 100 kHz (16 × 1-deg beam, range 600 yd) and classifies at 300 kHz (6 × 0.3-deg beam, range 300 yd). The array is stabilized and steerable both in train (270 deg to either side) and in elevation. To deal with the wide variety of objects on the sea floor (a dynamic range of 120 dB) using conventional 20-dB displays, the sonar has a variety of modes: shadow, target shape (direct mode), and echo structure classification (using a very short 50-microsec pulse). The shadow mode

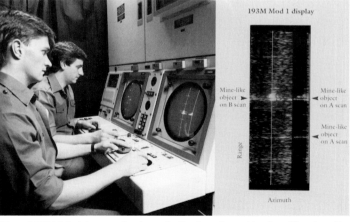

Type 193M Mod 1 consoles (search display alongside classification display) and a typical classification display, a magnified 27m section of the search display. It shows a B-scan alongside an A-scan of the same area. (GEC-Marconi)

is useful only if the background reflects strongly. Target shape is most useful against a mine with a rough surface (a smooth mine is a poor reflector). Echo structure uses discontinuities in the mine's projected surface.

The modernized solid-state Type 193M entered production in 1976. It is both much more compact and much more reliable than the original Type 193. It has a better beam pattern and introduced a long-range scale (600 yd). Mod 1, in the British "Hunt" class, adds LF elements to detect self-burying mines. Eight RN Type 193s have MUSL's Mills Cross add-ons, which improve long-range performance against small moored mines. Up to four views of a target can be stored and compared for classification. These devices are intended for mine avoidance; the Mills Cross was used on U.S. frigates in the Persian Gulf in 1987.

Mod 1 saves about 3000 kg on wet end weight by redesign of the directing gear and reduction in the volume of water in the dome. Other new features are CAC, history search (the four views of the target, shown flicker-free), processed search (digital processing and flicker-free presentation using a digitally refreshed display), and new classification display formats (A- and B-scan shown together, the A-scan allowing the full dynamic range to be seen).

Users: Argentina (two "Ton" class), Australia (one "Ton" class), Germany (Type 331A minehunting boats [with Mk 20(G) plotting table]), Korea (SK5000 class, based on *Lerici*), Japan (ZQS-2 is a license-made Type 193), Norway (*Tana*), South Africa (*Kimberly*), United Kingdom (Mod 1 in "Hunt" class), Yugoslavia (two of four *Sirius* class). The Korean boats have the Racal-Decca MAINS system. The Dutch "Ton"-class mine-sweepers converted to hunters in 1968–73 with Type 193M have been disposed of.

♦ Type 2034/2053

See the ASW section and Waverley 3010, below.

♦ Type 2093

This Marconi (ex-Plessey)/General Electric VDS or hull sonar reportedly searches at 80 kHz (90 × 1.5-deg beam, range 1200 m; this is the VLF element) and classifies at about 350 kHz (20 × 0.3-deg beam, range 300 m; there are actually two different classification frequencies, denoted HF and VHF, to deal with different bottom and sea conditions). A separate LF height-finder seeks moored mines while the rest of the system concentrates on ground mines. The towed body (1.054 [excluding vanes] × 2.521 m, 2900 kg) carries an LF ring array, a VLF ring receiver array, a VHF projector, an HF projector, a VLF projector, and an HF/VHF receiver, plus a VLF depth sounder on the underside. The HF and VHF classification sonars use separate transmitter arrays (producing wide or narrow beams as required) but share a common broad-band receiver. The LF height-finder uses a separate fixed-beamwidth array. The VLF transmitter uses its own array of six circular transducer layers, for vertical beamwidth control.

Each of two identical shipboard displays can conduct any of the sonar processing functions (for dual operation). CAC circuits take expanded HF or VHF range data and provide images directly to the display consoles.

Marconi claims at least twice the range of a conventional hull-mounted minehunting sonar and three times the detection depth, down to the continental shelf. Maximum speed of advance is 12 kt, compared to 3–4 kt for Type 193M. On the other hand, 2093 costs three times as much as 193M. This sonar was developed under a fixed-price contract at a total cost of £83M, including two preprototypes and 10 production units.

Users: Australia (*Huon* class), Japan (*Uwajima, Yaeyama,* MSC 07 classes), Saudi Arabia (*Sandown* class), and United Kingdom (*Sandown* class). The Nautis/2093 system in the Australian ships is called Mullauna.

♦ Archerfish

GEC-Marconi's antimine minitorpedo (104 × 880 mm, 6–7 kt, endurance 10 min) is controlled by fiber-optic link, has a shaped-charge warhead, and carries sonar and TV. Its pair of ducted

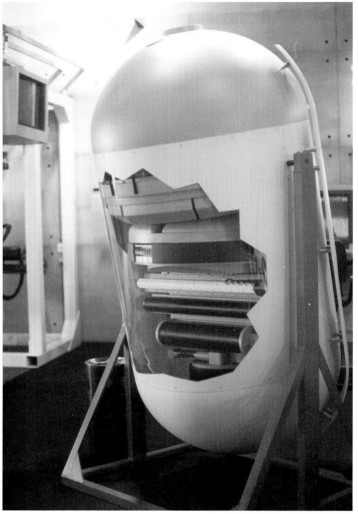

The Type 2093 towed body, showing its arrays and one of its stabilizing vanes, at Bourget Euronaval 1996. (Author)

mid-body propellers (run by a single motor) can turn vertical to hold Archerfish in a hover to identify the target. GEC-Marconi claims that Archerfish can clear mines at least four times as fast as a conventional ROV, and that existing magazines can carry up to 7 times as many Archerfish as conventional disposal charges (since it hits the mine directly, Archerfish is much smaller than a conventional charge). It would be launched from a cradle 8 m under a ship, oriented into the tidal stream, to protect the guidance wire from being caught in the propellers. Intended for integration with the Type 2093 sonar, Archerfish was announced in 1993.

Archerfish. (GEC-Marconi)

◆ Osborn (MSSA Mk 1)

BAe's acoustic sweep can simulate specific ship signatures. An acoustic monitor towed at greater depth insures that enough sound is supplied near the mine, despite surface layering. Osborn was part of a 1950s sweep program.

◆ Sea Witness (AMMS)

GEC-Marconi's HF mirror sonars employ a trainable reflector instead of a beam-preformer to focus reflections from a broad-beam projector. Because the mine target does not move and because distances are quite short, there is enough time to send and receive many narrow beams in succession. It is equivalent to the old searchlight ASW sonars, and its beam is narrow enough to image underwater objects. For example, an 875-kHz mirror sonar (24 or 48 transducers in a 50- or 100mm array, with a 75, 150, or 300mm mirror) on a boom 3 m below the surface, deployable at 2 kt, might be used for quick surveillance of the underwater hull of a ship to detect such illegal cargoes as drugs and arms. Range would be 10–50 m and resolution 0.2 m at 25 m; the sonar would normally observe a 5 × 1m area each sec at 25 m range. With 24/48 transducers, the 300mm mirror would offer a 10–12/20–25-deg FOV, with a resolution of 0.5/0.6 deg. Halving mirror size would double the field of view but halve resolution. A higher-frequency (2 MHz) version is offered for ROVs.

These sonars are derived from Plessey's mirror minehunting sonars (GEC-Marconi took over Plessey's sonar division). Under Project Kingfisher, Plessey packaged several such sonars into hull domes for use on board U.S. frigates for mine evasion in the Persian Gulf.

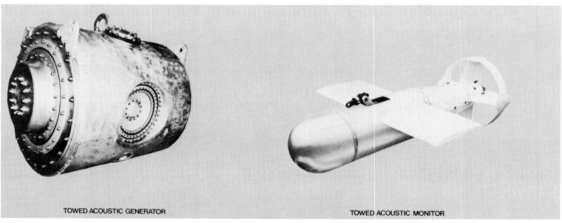

TOWED ACOUSTIC GENERATOR   TOWED ACOUSTIC MONITOR

Osborn. (British Aerospace)

This 250-kHz Sea Scout sonar, designed for small-craft mine avoidance and bottom object detection/classification, illustrates Marconi's mirror sonar concept. The small array scans its beam, focused to 0.6 deg width by the mirror, over a 20-deg sector which can itself be turned 30 deg to either side, for a total coverage of 80 deg. The 10-deg (vertical width) beam can be tilted to cover a range of +10/−45 deg. Range is better than 300 m. GEC-Marconi offers similar arrays, at different frequencies, for other roles, such as ship inspection (Sea Witness) and dockside swimmer detection. Because the sonar lacks a conventional fixed beam-forming transducer it is small enough to be made portable. (GEC-Marconi)

◆ Waverley 3010

This route survey (100 kHz) or mine detection (300 kHz) side-scan sonar uses both a high-resolution CRT and a thermal printer.

Users: Singapore (in the Integrated Route Surveillance System), United Kingdom (see 2034/2053), and United States (as SQQ-35, for COOP craft).

◆ NAUTIS-M (SYQ-15)

The minehunting version of the Plessey NAUTIS command/control system (see the Surveillance and Control section) is on board the *Sandown*-class single-role minehunters. A version of this system, SYQ-15, was adopted for the U.S. *Avenger* class.

NAUTIS-M is a three-console system (minehunting, operations, bridge, linked by a dual-redundant 1553 bus). As in other versions of NAUTIS, each console is modular, built up from five module types: a radar plot extractor, radar video module, graphics module, controller module, and power module. The display is a 16in circular CRT (which can be provided either in analog or in raster-scan format). The keyboard and tracker ball are a separate module. The controller is the computer for CIC functions. Each console is built around an Intel Minibus, which can support two or more processors per bus. Each carries the full system software in its bubble memory, so the system can continue to function after a console fails. Memory is dual-ported, so each processor can work independently.

As installed on board HMS *Sandown*, NAUTIS-M is combined with paired ROV (PAP 104) control consoles, the two one-operator NAUTIS consoles alternating with two-operator sonar and ROV-control consoles (each with two operators and square CRTs). The mine-warfare officer and the minehunt director each have their own NAUTIS consoles, and the sonar operators use two consoles for search and classification. The search operator and minehunt director have access to the ROV joystick and the ROV control display. The third NAUTIS console is on the bridge.

Users: Australia (*Huon* class), Saudi Arabia (*Sandown* class), United Kingdom (*Sandown* class), and United States (SYQ-15 in *Avenger* class).

UNITED STATES

The helicopter carrier *Inchon* has been converted into a command ship to support MCM helicopters; her NCCS-A/JMCIS system incorporates new MCM Decision Aids. Horizon Technology's MH-53E mission planning system prepares flight plans with up to 1000 navigational points. It is being integrated with EER Industries' on-board navigation and control system (NCS), which provides 6in horizontal situation display units (HSDUs) for pilot and copilot, showing navigation waypoints, Q-routes, sweep tracks, weight and balance, and systems data. The helicopter elements of both systems are on a 1553B bus. *Inchon* also has on board a module of EDO's modular airborne MCM C^2 system, the first real-time means of helicopter minesweeping control. Normally in van form, it was successfully demonstrated in December 1994. Two sets of vans will be provided for each MH-53E squadron. The van monitors paths swept by the Mk 105 sleds, and uses data from AQS-14 (and, in future, AQS-20) minehunting sonars. Helicopters communicate with it using a modified SH-2 TacNav data link, which EDO calls TLINK (Link 11 would not carry sufficient data, e.g., of path widths). The van communicates with the mine-warfare commander by Link 11.

MADOM, magnetic-acoustic detection of mines, used a cryogenic gradiometer and a synthetic aperture sonar to detect and classify buried mines. This ONR-sponsored ATD culminated in a successful December 1994 demonstration. The two sensors were to have been carried aboard a towed fish, but are now being proposed for UUVs under programs such as Near-Term Minefield Reconnaissance (see below). IBM displayed a MADOM system at the 1993 Navy League show, but the buried-mine project for which it was proposed was canceled in FY94 to provide funds for minehunting projects.

Laser-induced acoustics ("virtual array technology") is now in the exploratory research phase. A laser reaching out to its optical attenuation length measures water velocity, hence sound pressure, by the Doppler shift in reflected light. The outer boundary of the region it probes becomes a transducer (from sound to Doppler shift in light). A relatively small device, such as a UUV sonar, can have, in effect, a very large aperture.

About 1994 EDO was working with the Scripps Institute of Oceanography on a new concept of acoustic detection ("acoustic daylight"), using ambient ocean noise to illuminate objects, much as daylight illuminates objects on the earth. The concept may be particularly valuable for detecting objects, such as submarines, with anechoic coatings.

The three FY95 MCM advanced concept technology demonstrations were: NMRS (the UUV described below), Hamlet's Cove, and an advanced sensor. Hamlet's Cove sought to improve mine reconnaissance by using all-source information, including that from satellites. The advanced sensor program tested several 21in UUV sensors, including side-looking, synthetic-aperture, and toroidal sonars, in hopes of scanning the entire water column in a single pass. The toroidal volume search sensor (TVSS) was towed from a small boat and also tested in helicopter dipper form.

Since the early 1970s the U.S. Navy has used sea mammals to locate, mark, and neutralize mines. Marine Mammal Systems Mk 4 and Mk 7, which employ dolphins, are assigned to EOD (Explosive Ordnance Disposal) Mobile Unit Three in San Diego. At present only dolphins can reliably locate buried bottom mines and close-tethered mines in poor acoustic conditions, particularly in very shallow water. When deployed, dolphins live in special inflatable saltwater pools. For example, during the RIMPAC '94 exercise, they were accommodated on board USS

Juneau (LPD 10). Dolphins operated (with their handlers) one at a time, deployed on a small boat via the ship's stern well deck gate. Once in the MCM area, the dolphin swam alongside the boat, which moved between a series of way-points. At each, the dolphin was instructed to search, reporting mines by pushing a paddle on the side of the boat. It was then given a marker to be placed alongside the mine. Dolphins also participated in several 1995 exercises. According to a recent official account, "although free to swim away and join wild dolphins, these Navy mine-hunters choose to stay and work with their handlers and have proved extremely reliable."

Special Forces divers clear mines and obstacles from the surf zone to about 10 ft depth, using hand-held PQS-2 sonars. The R&D program includes an improved PQS-2A with a real-time correlator and spectral processor, a clandestine underwater UV mine imager, and a diver hand-held acoustic imager.

Explosive neutralization (EN) seems to be the only way to breach large beach minefields quickly enough, but the explosive weight must be properly distributed over the minefield. Two concepts in the ATD stage are Thunder Road and Flying Sword. Thunder Road, an air-dropped explosive array, is attractive because it does not expose the deploying craft to the minefield. An FY95 proof-of-concept test is to be followed by full-scale tests in FY97. Flying Sword is a large-caliber explosively formed projectile (EFP). Under the FY95 program, a single-plate EFP was demonstrated against a surf-zone mine, and a dual-plate EFP was designed to clear obstacles. Other surf-zone neutralization concepts include RAMICS (see below) and Power Blade, to clear anti-invasion mines from a beach.

During the Gulf War, the U.S. Navy used Swedish SAM unmanned craft. The follow-on HSRIS (High Speed Remote Influence Sweep) II program completed the project-definition stage but was terminated by congressional direction in FY95. It will presumably be replaced by MCAC, the drone air-cushion landing craft (LCAC) fitted with helicopter-type influence sweeps (Mk 104/105), and with a SABRE (shallow water assault breacher) line charge; it has also towed an AQS-14 helicopter minehunting sonar.

A new shallow-water mine threat, Cluster Pretzel, has been identified. The code name indicates a captured weapon, probably the Iraqi "cheeseburger" mine (LUQM-145).

◆ ALUV

Rockwell's Autonomous Legged Undersea Vehicle is a small crab-like six-legged crawler carrying an explosive charge developed under an ARPA contract. A UUV would eject them in large numbers; each would detect and classify objects of interest (mines and obstacles) and attach itself to a target. All would be blown up together on command. Because it remains submerged while searching, ALUV is covert; it requires only very limited and short-range comms with each other. The force exerted by water flowing across its body holds the ALUV in position; it resists wave forces by leaning into currents, and it can bury itself in sand by vibrating its legs. Phase 1 was completed February 1995 with a demonstration of ALUV target location and mobility in a simulated surf zone. Phase II, to be completed early in 1996, tests full group operation. A Phase III would bring the design up to production standard.

◆ Near-Term Mine Reconnaissance System (NMRS)/LMRS

This clandestine system uses a UUV launched from a submarine TT. The long-range follow-up (LMRS) is to be deployable from both submarines and surface ships. Exploratory programs for High Area Rate Reconnaissance (HARR) and Amphibious Operation Area Mine Reconnaissance/Hunting (MR/H) are developing UUV sensors. HARR uses a TVSS (toroidal volume search sonar) to hunt moored mines, a bottom-looking SLS (side-looking sonar) to find ground mines, and a gap filler to search the swath under the vehicle. The 68-kHz TVSS uses 120 receiving elements in a band around the UUV to form 120 3 × 3-deg beams. Range is 675 m, and search rate is 6 nm²/hr at 8 kt. The 400-kHz SLS uses a two-sided linear array 4 m long, with 38 × 10cm receiver elements. An unusual feature, full sampling in

Rockwell's ALUV mechanical crab. (Rockwell)

bandwidth, makes for more complete target analysis. In real aperture mode, SLS resolution is 10 cm out to 90 m, 20 cm at 180 m (5 cm in synthetic aperture mode). Range resolution is 4 cm. TVSS was tested successfully in the summer of 1994 in the Gulf of Mexico.

MR/H uses a high and low frequency (180 and 20 kHz) synthetic aperture sonar derived from the MADOM sonar. The HF element uses a linear array of 11 piezo-rubber receive elements, each 5 cm long with 2.5-deg azimuth resolution. A 30-kHz bandwidth ceramic projector with a 2.5cm range resolution is placed near the center of the receiving array. The corresponding LF sonar uses a 16-element array, each element 3.75 cm long (half a wavelength at 20 kHz) to allow beam steering through one radian. The projector has a 10-kHz bandwidth and 7.5cm range resolution. It is placed forward of the receive array. The entire sonar fits into a 90cm-long section, and consumes less than 400 W. Overall range is 40 m. The 20-kHz LF beam penetrates the bottom. The HF element comes close to identification capability.

The alternative Laser Visual Identification System (LVIS) for proud, partly buried, and moored mines should produce high-quality images, identifying mines at up to 40 ft range at a UUV speed of 4 kt. The laser would probably occupy a 32in long section of a 21in UUV, consuming 275 W of power. Effective range is likely to vary between less than 5 ft (turbid water) and 100 ft (clear water). Both line-scan and range-gated lasers have been tested, the former better overcoming blur/glow and forward scatter noise. It ran sea trials in the third quarter of 1995.

The UUV minehunting program consists of NMRS (requirement promulgated 9 March 1994, contract awarded to Westinghouse [now Northrop Grumman] 1994) and LMRS (contract awarded September 1996 to Lockheed Martin). The NMRS prototype is to appear in FY97, the system is to enter service in FY98, and to be withdrawn about FY03. LMRS is to enter service in FY04, after an FY96–FY00 demonstration/validation phase.

These programs build on earlier efforts, including the ARPA/ Navy mine surveillance system (MSS), which was tested at sea for about a year in 1992–93; and the abortive SOMSS (Submarine Offboard Mine Search System), which Congress terminated on the ground that it duplicated MSS. SOMSS was replaced by NMRS.

◆ Rapid Clearance (SABRE, BLNS, ENATD)

Problems encountered in Kuwait emphasize the need to clear boat lanes very quickly ahead of an amphibious assault. Approaches include surf-zone minehunting (AMDAS) and using line or other distributed charges or other explosives to neutralize or destroy very shallow anti-invasion mines. Large quantities of explosive may be needed, because mines are designed not to explode when nearby mines go off (i.e., to avoid countermining).

SABRE (shallow-water breach system) is complemented by BLNS (breached-lane navigational system). SABRE concept exploration and definition, begun in FY92, was completed at the end of FY93 (with demonstration/validation completed in the fall of 1994). It replaced an earlier Mk 58 line charge used to destroy land mines with an improved line charge (ILC) capable of clearing a 13 × 150-yd path. This type of system can destroy obstacles, such as barbed wire, as well as mines. Originally SABRE was to have been fired by helicopter-landed Marine Corps combat engineers, but late in 1994 OpNav decided that it would be launched by an LCAC approaching the beach. That delayed OT/DT from the end of FY94 to the third quarter of FY96.

An alternative is a rocket-drawn net carrying shaped charges at its vertices (DET, distributed explosive technology), to clear a 50-yd lane. An 18-month demonstration/validation phase began in FY92. The 100ft^2 net is being developed by Leigh Aerosystems. The pod enclosing the net is called Magic Carpet.

The shallow-water MCM Obstacle Breaching program uses air-dropped GBU-16 LGBs. Alternatives include wide-area explosives (binary liquids), directed projectiles (including guided shells and 2.75in rockets), and mechanical systems including rocket-launched grappling hooks, water cannon, and bridging.

The Breach Lane Navigation/Sector Light System (BLN/SLS) uses GPS to navigate landing craft to way-points, plus tricolor lights with 6-deg beams.

The goal of the next-generation ENATD (Explosive Neutralization ATD) is to clear a 50-yd-wide lane through the surf zone to about 100 yd inland. Begun in FY93, the ATD employs line charge arrays both for the surf zone (SZA) and for the beach zone further out to sea (BZA). The SZA, consisting of detonating cord, would be deployed by a pair of rocket motors; presumably it corresponds to the net system described below. A complementary linear array of discrete charges is carried by a single rocket. The BZA would be deployed by a GPS-guided glider, and would employ new shaped-charge antimine munitions (AMN). In a demonstration, a subscale BZA is to be released from a glider launched by a helicopter 24 km or more from the beach zone. A full demonstration is scheduled for FY97. It is not clear to what extent the ATD overlaps with the systems described below.

◆ Remote Minehunting System (RMS)/Dolphin

Lockheed Martin's system is intended to provide the fleet with organic protection. A radio-controlled diesel-powered semisubmersible (for low observability) tug, the RMV (remote minehunting vehicle) tows a modified AQS-14 sonar fish for bottom search, and the tug itself carries a forward-looking sonar (volume search and near-surface surveillance). Data from both sonars are relayed back to a ship via the control link. The 23ft torpedo-shaped tug, powered by a 370-HP Cummins 370B–series turbocharged diesel, weighs 12,000 lb. As in other unmanned vehicles, C^2 is a major issue. In this case, the containerized control station incorporates four standard dual-screen TAC-3/JMCIS consoles. Although not part of SQQ-89, it uses the same display formats and some of the same software, so it can later be integrated into that system. The data link uses a standard commercial OTH radio. The version now under contract is (V)3; the planned upgrade is (V)4.

Lockheed Martin won the RMS contract in September 1996. The RMS Operational Prototype (RMOP) used Rockwell's Dolphin (7.5 m long, 3500 kg, cruise speed 12 kt, sprint speed 16 kt). The Lockheed Martin RMV probably enjoys similar endurance (for Dolphin, 26 hr at 12 kt, or 325 nm at 16 kt).

The U.S. Navy concept exploration and definition phase began in September 1993. RMOP was successfully demonstrated in the Gulf of Mexico in October 1994, then embarked on board DD 973 *John Young* for the ''Kernel Blitz'' amphibious exercise near Camp Pendleton (24–27 March 1995). In February 1995 Dolphin

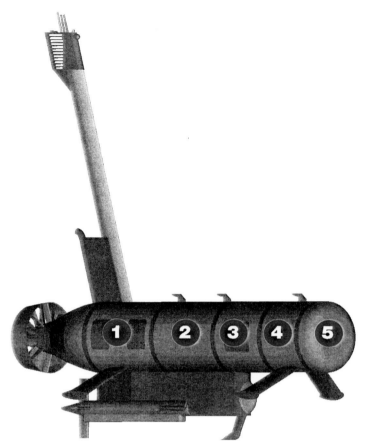

Lockheed Martin's RMS tug vehicle. Key: (1) propulsion module; (2) VDS winch and capture module, to tow the modified AQS-14; (3) fuel module (250-gal capacity); (4) electronics module (VME backplane); (5) nose module, including forward-looking sonar. (Lockheed Martin)

was ordered upgraded with control radios, a GPS-based navigation and control system, and C^2 software. Preplanned improvements (work on which is to begin in FY96) would add a synthetic aperture sonar, CAD and CAC, buried mine detection, and EO sensors for detection.

◆ COBRA

The Marine Corps Coastal Battlefield Reconnaissance and Analysis system uses a small UAV (Pioneer) to detect mines from the surf zone inland; its data are linked back to ships for processing via another UAV. The UAV carries two Xbion IMC-201 multispectral (400–900 nanometers) cameras, each with a six-filter wheel (turning every 1/30 sec, the frame rate) between the lens and imaging plane. An image intensifier makes short exposures (within the frame rate) possible but limits resolution. The COBRA Tactical Information Display System (CTIDS) comprises a real-time function (RTF) subsystem (using high-end PCs) and a postmission processing (PMP) subsystem using a Sun-SPARC-20 workstation. The RTF records, digitizes, and archives images, and can also be used for video-image review and analysis to assess flight effectiveness. It also displays aircraft position in real-time. PMP is the automatic minefield detector.

COBRA was derived from the exploratory FY91 Standoff Mine Detection Ground (SMDG) program, which demonstrated mine detection by processing video-based multispectral imaging sensors. Humans are needed to detect and locate obstacles, fortifications, and vehicles. COBRA began as an FY93 ATD, and completed its critical design review in January 1995.

TOWED SWEEPS

There are three types: A, acoustic; M, magnetic; and O, Oropesa (wire sweep). The principal versions are:

◆ **Acoustic Sweeps**

A Mk 2: Parallel pipes or bars, towed broadside-on, in different versions for different frequencies and different towing speeds (4–20 kt). A Mk 2(g) was used by helicopter minesweepers in North Vietnam in 1973. Suspended from a Size 5 O-float, it weighs 130 lb and consists of two parallel triangular plates connected by three pipes. Two other pipes are pivoted from one of these plates; as the device moves through the water, they strike each other and the other pipes. The faster the tow, the greater the noise level.

A U.S. acoustic sweep, photographed in 1987. It resembles but is not identical to the old A Mk 2. It is streamed suspended from an O-type float. (U.S. Navy)

A Mk 4 (TB-25): Towed hammer box (60–600 Hz), for small craft in restricted areas (later extended to all types). It consists of a hydraulically driven hammer in a streamlined box, driven by a gasoline engine on board the sweeper. Dimensions: 40 × 70 in (1300 lb). TB-27 (part of SLQ-37) is Towed Body 4(V), producing pulsed (duty cycle 0–100%) HF noise (40–600 Hz).

A Mk 5: Explosive sweep.

A Mk 4(V) acoustic sweep. (U.S. Navy)

A Mk 6: LF acoustic sweep (eccentric mechanism), usually towed about 1200 yd astern of a coastal sweeper. Its diaphragm is driven by pistons connected to an eccentric driven by an electric motor. Dimensions: 37.75 (dia) × 69 in (about 3500 lb). A Mk 6(B) Mod 5 is TB-24 (used in SLQ-37), operating at 10–35 or 10–22 Hz. Towed Body 6(B) (TB-26, also used in SLQ-37), 23 in (W) × 45 in (H) × 65 in (2800 lb) produces pulsed (20–100% duty cycle) LF noise at 6–40 Hz. During Operation End Sweep, the clearance of North Vietnamese waters, A Mk 2(g) was recommended to replace the A Mk 6(B) then in use by surface sweepers.

◆ **Magnetic Sweeps**

M Mk 1: Magnetized iron rail, which could be extemporized. It was not standard after World War II, but a device of this type was used in Vietnam (in the Cua Viet River, after magnetic-acoustic mines were found there). The MOP (see below) is reminiscent of this device.

M Mk 4(m): Small two-ship closed loop.

M Mk 4(i): Two-ship single-catenary small-craft sweep, using special tails, the short legs of which are connected by an insulated cable forming the catenary; the long legs stream aft. M Mk 4(V) was a postwar variation.

M Mk 5(c): Standard large-sweeper sweep, consisting of two legs (buoyant conducting cables) married together through the 675ft length of the shorter leg, with the longer leg streaming aft another 900 ft. In some arrangements two or more ships could sweep together, pulsing their tails synchronously. M Mk 5(a) is a straight-tail electrode version (I-sweep).

M Mk 6(a): J-sweep: the long leg curves around to meet a diverted line towed by the ship and connected to an Oropesa and a kite.

M Mk 6(b): Single-ship closed-loop sweep, using Oropesa floats to keep the legs apart. In M Mk 6(h), the two legs meet at a diverter line streamed from an Oropesa. The closed loop can be used in fresh water.

M Mk 7: Double diverted magnetic sweep, designed so that the fields cancel near the sweeper, so that a higher current can be used.

◆ **Oropesa (Wire) Sweeps**

All of these sweeps were designed to counter mines floating close to the surface, the only exception being antenna mines (which would probably be set off if a sweep wire brushed the vertical antenna).

O Size 1: Largest, for ocean sweepers (MSO and MCM), designated SLQ-38 in current MCM ships. When streamed with 300-fathom wires, the swept path is 500 yd wide (double sweep) at maximum speed, about 8.5 kt for an MSO. A single-side sweep clears a 250-yd path at 10 kt. Sweep depth is 5–35 fathoms (maximum 40 fathoms).

O Size 4: Modified, for coastal sweepers (MSC). With 300 fathoms of wire streamed on each side, the swept path is 420 yd at 8 kt; wire depth is 2–30 fathoms.

O Size 5: Small sweep, for minesweeping launches (MSL) and similar craft. Size 5-G, for adapted landing craft, was modified for MSBs and helicopters; it uses a different otter and depressor (for more precise depth control) so that it can be streamed at high speed (6–14 kt) in shallow water (1–7 fathoms). With 150 fathoms of wire streamed on one side, the swept path is 70 yd wide. Type 5 itself uses explosive cutters because the craft are too slow (maximum 7 kt) for the saw action of the wire to cut mine moorings. With 250 fathoms of wire streamed on one side, the swept path is 176 yd wide. This sweep can be used as an emergency or shallow-depth sweep, with a wire depth of 2 or 3 fathoms.

♦ Combined Sweeps

SLQ-37: The (V)2 version, in the *Avenger* class, combines A Mk 4(V), A Mk 6(B), and M Mks 5, 6, and 7; the first three were bought under the FY89 program.

ALISS: The Advanced Light Influence Sweeping System is part of a 1998 Joint Countermeasures ATD. With less drag than previous influence sweeps, ALISS combines a Navy-developed (with Raytheon and General Atomics inputs) closed-cycle-cooled superconducting magnetic countermeasure with Alliant's spark gap acoustics (to produce a fully controllable signal of sufficient strength, both broad- and narrow-band). ALISS was planned for the abortive U.S. version of the Swedish SAM II and will now probably appear on board converted LCACs. ALISS is to emulate landing craft signatures, to help clear mines near the landing zone.

♦ Helicopter Sweeps (Airborne MCM Systems)

Mk 104 and the other major helicopter-towed MCM were bought in quantity in response to Project SIXTY Decision 5 (1970, under Admiral Zumwalt), which ordered the MCM forces reorganized to emphasize helicopters. In 1971 the Navy borrowed 15 Marine Corps CH-53A helicopters to equip the first squadron, HM-12. This squadron swept North Vietnamese waters in 1972–73 and the Suez Canal in 1974–75. The CH-53As were replaced by RH-53Ds (six of which were exported to Iran in the 1970s). The current MCM helicopter is the three-engine MH-53E (exported to Japan as S-80M-1).

Mk 103: Boeing Vertol's helicopter-towed explosive-cutter moored sweep has a fixed sweeping depth. To deploy it, the helicopter streams the gear into the water while sitting at the end of the flight deck. Total weight is 1178 lb. Mk 103 was probably sold to Japan for use on board the now-discarded KV-107 MCM helicopters. It was probably also sold to Iran. A/N37U is the successor.

Mk 104: This helicopter-towed acoustic MCM consists of a cavitating disk within a venturi tube, driven by a water turbine. The helicopter supplies sweep power. Minimum sweep-water depth is 30 ft, compared to 15 ft for an MSL or MSB and 30 ft for an MSO or MSC. Dimensions (towed body): 26 in (W) × 35 in (H) × 49 in (L) (87 lb, 180 lb total).

Mk 105: EDO's helicopter-towed hydrofoil sled carries a power pack (gas-turbine generator) for magnetic sweeping. It is typically towed at 25 kt (becoming foilborne at 13 kt), about 450 ft behind the helicopter, the on-board gas turbine powering twin magnetic tails 600 ft long. Minimum sweep water depth is 12 ft.

A helicopter-towed acoustic countermeasure used during the clearance of the Red Sea in 1984. (U.S. Navy)

Total weight is 5200 lb. To launch, the sled is typically positioned (with its foils up) at the after end of an amphibious ship well deck, with the ship ballasted so that the ramp is about 18 in above water. The helicopter then picks up the tow cable from a small landing craft (LCVP) and pulls the sled down the ramp. An Engineering Change Proposal, mainly for reliability and maintainability, but providing a new higher-powered generator (75% more output) and a larger-diameter sweep wire (sweep current 3500 rather than 2000 Amp), was approved in February 1992 and the first modified units (Mod 4 conversions of Mod 2s) bought in 1996. EDO markets Model 819 MIMS (Modular Influence Minesweeping System), a shipboard derivative combining the magnetic tail with an acoustic fish. Plans to buy MIMS for the U.S. *Osprey* class have died. Mk 105 was approved for service use in 1970. The first production models were delivered on 1 July 1972, and Mk 105 was first used operationally during the Hanoi-Haiphong sweep at the end of the Vietnam War. This sled was exported to Iran before the fall of the Shah.

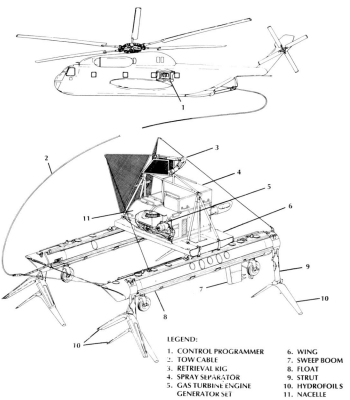

LEGEND:

1. CONTROL PROGRAMMER	6. WING
2. TOW CABLE	7. SWEEP BOOM
3. RETRIEVAL RIG	8. FLOAT
4. SPRAY SEPARATOR	9. STRUT
5. GAS TURBINE ENGINE	10. HYDROFOILS
GENERATOR SET	11. NACELLE

Mk 105 sled. (EDO)

Mk 106: Combined Mk 104 and Mk 105 acoustic/magnetic sweep, the Mk 104 being attached to one Mk 105 tail. Mk 106 was used extensively during the 1984 Red Sea sweep.

SPU-1/W (MOP)/SWIM: This magnetized pipe filled with styrofoam (MOP, Magnetized Orange Pipe) was used as a helicopter precursor sweep during the clearance of Haiphong harbor at the end of the Vietnam War (some of the mines were so sensitive that they would have destroyed sweep sleds). The MOP was also needed to sweep water too shallow for a sled and in places where open loops are ineffective; for example, the Baltic is not salty enough to close the circuit between the loop ends.

A modern version of the 1940 iron-rail sweep (M Mk 1[m]), MOP was a pipe long enough to provide magnetic mass and wide enough to be buoyant (30ft × 10in dia). MOP was sealed at each end, filled with styrofoam, fitted with towing lugs, and magnetized. A helicopter could tow as many as three in tandem; 150 were made by the Naval Coastal Systems Laboratory (Panama City). EDO's SWIM (Shallow Water Influence Minesweeping system, formerly EMSS, Enhanced Magnetic Sweep System) is an improved MOP with continuous power to keep it saturated,

A quarter-scale model of EDO's EMSS (now SWIM) was displayed at Navy League 1995. (Author)

AQS-14 helicopter-towed fish, with the towing helicopter in the background. (U.S. Naval Institute)

developed under a 1994 contract. As of mid-1996, procurement of 30 systems was planned for FY00, but it may move back to FY98. SWIM is being tested in the Baltic in 1996.

A/N37U: This controllable-depth mechanical sweep, usable at greater depths, replaces Mk 103. The helicopter crew monitors sweep depth and width, and can change depth while sweeping. Initial OpEval was conducted in FY90. Three EDMs were procured in FY91. General Systems Solutions received a contract for four test units in June 1992, plus seven production models (with an option for six more) to be delivered beginning in FY96. SLQ-53 (Modular Mechanical Single Ship Deep Sweep) is a shipborne version, an FY90 new start to meet an OR issued 8 March 1983. Two auxiliary depressors tow a single deep depressor, with a pair of sweep wires leading out to Otters on either side; another sweep wire leads from each of these wires to another Otter, making four in all. Each wire carries explosive cutters.

ALQ-141 (Double Alfa): Westinghouse's counter to rising mines, developed in the late 1970s, presumably produces two series of signals, one to activate the mine and the other to cause it to fire fruitlessly. EDO's ALQ-138 was probably the losing competitor. SLQ-35 is a ship-towed version of ALQ-141.

◆ AQS-14

Westinghouse's high-speed helicopter-towed minehunting sonar is actively controlled to keep the towed body clear of both the bottom and the surface; it can even right itself if it is launched upside down. The body (5.6 ft span × 10.7 ft, 550 lb) carries a Westinghouse-patented multibeam all-range focusing sonar, providing an operator with a continuous high-resolution television-like image of objects to either side. Objects it detects are marked by the towing helicopter for further investigation. AQS-14 is said to allow sweeping at a rate about 40% faster than can be achieved by conventional methods.

As of 1996, there is intense interest in a Northrop Grumman (ex-Westinghouse) proposal to add a laser linescanner to the AQS-14 fish, using a red laser. For some years Westinghouse has displayed very high-resolution underwater laser linescan photographs taken by this device. Money may not yet have been allocated, however.

AQS-14 production was approved in March 1980, OpEval having been completed in September 1979. As of March 1988, 29 had been made. AQS-14 was first used operationally during the Red Sea mine-clearance operation in 1984, and it was also used during Desert Storm in 1991. It is the towed vehicle of the LCAC minehunting system. This sonar operates with ALQ-141.

Users: United States (MH-53E and RH-53D helicopters). This sonar may have been sold to Japan as part of the S-80M (export MH-53) package (12 aircraft).

◆ AQS-20

Raytheon's helicopter-towed body (10 ft long, 5 ft span, 1000 lb) carries four sonars: ahead-looking, belly band (for volume search), sidescan, and gap-filler (for right below). Some data are processed in the tow body, with further processing in the helicopter. One mission control/display subsystem can handle three helicopters simultaneously via a UHF data link. Navigation is now so good that the AQS-20 map of a minefield can be used for follow-up attacks on individual mines by neutralization torpedoes. AQS-20 uses some SQQ-32 technology, especially for volume search (belly band), power amplification, and some SQQ-32 algorithms.

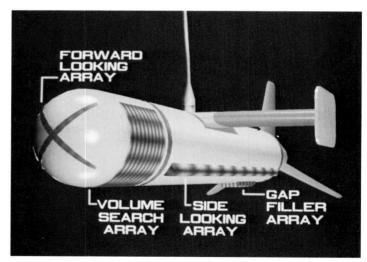

Raytheon's successful entry in the AQS-20 helicopter-minehunter competition. The 10ft-long towed body is 18 in in diameter and contains the beam-formers and signal processors for all four arrays. It maintains either a constant height above the bottom or a constant depth below the surface. (Raytheon)

AQS-20, formerly the Advanced Minehunting Reconnaissance System, replaces AQS-14. The AQS-20 Program Definition Document was issued in April 1986. A companion neutralization system (to use expendable vehicles) was abandoned but has now been revived (see AMNSYS below). The AQS-20 contract was awarded in the summer of 1992. AQS-20 is expected to complete OpEval (Milestone III) in FY97, and to enter production in FY98.

◆ Mk 24 Underwater Ordnance Locator/Klein 595

Klein Hydroscan's lightweight 100-kHz side-scanning sonar covers a 200m swath using a 0.75-deg beam. Klein offers several options: a 500-kHz version for super-high resolution, a 50-kHz fish (1.2 km swath) for large-area sonar sweeps, such as channel surveys, and a 3.5-kHz sub-bottom profiler to indicate bottom hardness and thus indicate whether buried mines are likely to be a problem. In the basic version, recorder and fish weigh about 150 lb, and range is selectable in 13 increments between 25 and 600 m. The fish can be operated down to 2300 m or, as an option, 12,000 m.

Mk 24 can be used on board virtually unmodified commercial helicopters and small craft, and it was adopted for the U.S. COOP program. It was used during the clearance of the Suez Canal after the 1973 Mideast war and has been used extensively since then by U.S. Navy explosive-ordnance-disposal teams and similar organizations.

Users: Australia (Model 595 bought 1988 for COOPs), Canada, Colombia, Germany, Greece, Indonesia, Japan (*Yaeyama* class deep sweepers), South Korea, the Netherlands, New Zealand, Norway, Pakistan, Portugal, South Africa (inshore sweepers: sole sensor), Sweden (seven bought 1984 for inshore ASW), Thailand, and United States (as EOD Object Locator Mk 24). *Yaeyama* class may have AQS-14 towfish. Note that most earlier U.S. EOD Object Locators (EODs) were magnetic.

◆ PQS-1 and PQS-1A

This hand-held continuous FM (30-kHz sweep between 50 and 90 kHz) diver sonar uses a 12in conical reflector, which forms a 9-deg beam at 70 kHz. Source level is 72 dB. The received beam beats against a sample of the transmitted beam to form a difference frequency in the audio range; minimum and maximum frequencies correspond to the minimum and maximum ranges of the range scale (20, 60, 120 yd) selected. The lower the tone, the closer the object. The set can also be used to detect a 40-kHz marker beacon; it indicates direction but not range.

PQS-1B in use. (U.S. Naval Institute)

PQS-2A is a nonmagnetic replacement operating in much the same way (6-deg beam, 12in object detected at 120 yd). The beacon frequency is 24–45 kHz; a 39-kHz beacon can be detected at 2000 yd. Maximum depth is 300 ft. Dimensions: 4.5 × 12.5 in (height, with handle, 9 in); 8 lb. PQS-2A was announced in 1986 by General Instruments Corp.

◆ SQQ-14

This minehunting VDS is unusual in that it is carried on a rigid retractable boom (maximum depth 45 m below the keel) rather than a flexible cable (on which it might swing back and forth above 5 kt, ruining its accuracy). Designers of later systems, such as the British Type 2093, tried to solve this problem using fins. SQQ-14 combines the 80-kHz search sonar of UQS-1 (1.5-deg beam, 100-deg FOV, 1.0-msec pulses, range resolution 1 m, 15 kW, 126 dB source level, scanning an 82-deg sector at 15 deg/sec

or more) with the 350-kHz classification sonar of Type 193 (0.3-deg beam, 0.1-msec pulses, range resolution 8 cm, 15 kW, 125 dB source level). Both the search and classification sonars can be tilted between +10 and −30 deg (elevation). There is a sidescan mode.

Data above apply to the Italian P2072 (SQQ-14[IT]) solid-state version but are probably accurate for U.S.-built SQQ-14s. Another solid-state version, SQQ-30, was fitted on an interim basis to U.S. MCM ships pending availability of SQQ-32; none is left in U.S. service. However, in 1995 Unisys announced that it was working on a refit for ex-U.S. MSOs (for Taiwan) to incorporate SQQ-30 and a version of its SYQ-12 using Differential GPS (dGPS) and Microfix for precision navigation. A new data link will allow the hunter to share information with a shore MCM command center. SQQ-30 is far easier to operate than -14. Thus it cuts alignment steps from over 400 to just 4. To seek deeper mines, it uses a cable (tow depth 400 ft) rather than the articulated strut of -14 (a new electronic compass provides orientation). The Taiwan navy will probably begin seeking funds for this upgrade in 1996.

SQQ-14 was standardized in 1960.

Users: Belgium (six *Dash* class), Saudi Arabia (four MSC 322 class), Spain (four *Aggressive* class), and Taiwan (ex-U.S. *Aggressive* class).

◆ SQQ-32

Raytheon/Thomson Sintra's VDS minehunting sonar searches at 35 kHz (60 × 3.1-deg beam) and classifies at 445–650 kHz (14 × 0.13-deg beam). Multibeam operation increases search rate. The low search frequency was adopted to achieve long range. Two identical display consoles display search and classification (direct and shadow modes) data or images simultaneously and interchangeably (the system can be operated from one console, although normally both are used). A computer helps classify the objects detected. The supervising computer is UYK-44. The towed body weighs 9977 lb, the processor 2265 lb, the control and display consoles 1310 lb, and the winch, the heaviest element, 20,480 lb. The sonar body can be retained in the hull to hunt in shallow water.

A P^{3}I version, to be completed in FY97, has improved detection/classification, a modified operator console with a color display, a TAC-series computer, and new system software. The

SQQ-32 towed body, showing the separate detection (belt of transducers) and classification (bar transducer at bottom) arrays. (Raytheon)

University of Texas Applied Research Lab received a sonar improvement contract in FY93. Raytheon received a November 1992 contract for console improvement and software modifications. NSWC and Panama City are improving the classification sonar.

In 1991 a developed SQQ-32, DS-OAS, was proposed as a mine-evasion sonar for submarines and surface ships.

Originally AMSS (Advanced Minehunting Sonar System), SQQ-32 uses Raytheon search sonar technology and Thomson Sintra classification sonar technology. Delivery of operational sets began in mid-1991, but an EDM equipped USS *Avenger* during and after Operation Desert Storm. It detected a Manta mine there at a range of 900 yd. Having completed TechEval, SQQ-32 was formally accepted for U.S. service on 30 September 1993 and was approved for full production in August 1994.

Users: Japan (*Yaeyama* class; first export sale approved 1989), Spain (new minehunters; decision to adopt SQQ-32 rather than 2093 announced fall 1994), United States (*Avenger* and *Cardinal* classes).

◆ UQS-1

This 100-kHz (10-kW pulses) short-pulse minehunting sonar scans a 2 × 10-deg beam over a 20-deg FOV, which can be tilted to cover +5/−50 deg and turned to cover a 90-deg or 360-deg sector (or oriented manually). Range scales: 200, 500, and 1000 yd; resolution about 6 yd; precision: 5 yd at 200, 25 yd at 500, and 50 yd at 1000. Bearing precision is 0.5 deg. Data refer to UQS-1D (2126 kg). UQS-1 is not stabilized, and it cannot provide the mine image required for classification. An 80-kHz version is combined with the Type 193 classification element to form the successor SQQ-14 sonar.

UQS-1 was derived from the World War II Underwater Object Locator Mk 4; about 150 were built in 1951–54.

Users: Denmark (two *Adjutant* class), Greece (nine *Falcon* class, five *Adjutant* class), Iran (two *Falcon*), Italy (may remain on four *Adjutant* class converted to patrol boats), Japan (as ZQS-1, on *Hayase*), Korea (five MSC 289 class, three MSC 268 class), Norway (three *Falcon* class), Pakistan (two *Falcon* class), Spain (eight *Adjutant* class), Taiwan (nine *Adjutant* class), Thailand (three MSC 289 class), and Turkey (12 *Adjutant* class, and probably four ex-U.S. Cape class).

◆ Mine Neutralization System (SLQ-48)

Alliant's minehunting ROV (3 × 12.5 ft, 2500 lb, 20 lb positive buoyancy, two 12-HP electric motors, 6 kt) is powered by the launching ship. The ROV maneuvers using two side thrusters. Compared to PAP 104, it is intended for much deeper hunting, to below 200 m (660 ft), to deal with rising mines; the umbilical is 3500 ft long. The onboard sensors are high-definition sonar and LLLTV. Weapons are MP-1 (Mk 26-0) cable cutters and an explosive mine-destruction charge (MP-2, Mk 57-0); the current

The Alliant Mine Neutralization System vehicle. (Alliant)

Mission Package 3 includes a device that positions a cutter against the mine mooring cable.

Including shipboard components, total weight is 26,000 lb and total power draw is 60 kW. Claimed MTBF is 120 hr (4 hr MTTR).

Prototypes were tested in 1971–77, and Honeywell (now Alliant) won the production prototype contract in 1978. EDM OpEval was completed in September 1982. As of 1994, 28 full systems and 57 vehicles (with 10 more on order) had been delivered. SLQ-48 is part of Mine Neutralization System Mk 116 Mod 0 (presumably in the same series as the Mk 104/105/106 sleds). The standard outfit is two SLQ-48 fish. Japan is the only export customer (numbers delivered are not known).

In 1994 Alliant announced an MNS II that would weigh one-third less and take up half the volume of SLQ-48, hence could be installed in smaller minehunters. Operating depth would increase to over 600 m, operating range to over 1000 m. The existing monitor and pair of consoles are replaced by a single console based on the TAC-3 computer, with a new navigation display for improved targeting, and a touch screen. An autotransit mode simplifies operation. Fiber-optic telemetry reduces cable diameter and thus the size and weight of the cable-handling system. It increases the number of video and data channels, reduces EMI, and makes it easier to vary ROV payload. The faster, more maneuverable, deeper-diving ROV has more powerful hydraulic thrusters, to operate against 8- rather than 5kt currents. It can be used for other roles. For example, the MNS might carry a minehunting sonar in "dog on a leash" mode, or it might carry a buried-mine package, a sidescan sonar, or a mine recovery package. Acoustic and magnetic signatures would be low enough to permit the ROV to operate very close to sophisticated mines.

◆ EMNS

Expendable Mine Neutralization System, formerly AMNSYS (Airborne Mine Neutralization System), uses minitorpedoes rather than ROV-delivered charges. It is now to be carried not only on MH-53Es but also on board surface combatants as an organic MCM. The helicopter (SH-60 or MH-53E) will use its sonar (perhaps a U.S. version of FLAMS in the SH-60) to identify a mine, and a minitorpedo will be guided into place (to reacquire the mine using its own sonar) by fiber-optic link. Early in 1995 representives of the OpNav mine warfare office and of Panama City visited European manufacturers of mine-disposal torpedoes. Plans currently call for a swim-off of existing weapons in FY98, with a low-rate initial production contract early in FY01. The minitorpedo may also complement SLQ-48.

EMNS replaces an earlier EMD (Expendable Mine Destructor) program canceled as unaffordable in FY94. Lockheed's LENS torpedo, using a two-beam homing sonar and a wire data link, would have been launched from an 8-rnd rack lowered from the ramp of an MH-53E helicopter towing an AQS-14 sonar. Since the link had very limited capacity, LENS needed considerable processing power. Lockheed delivered 25–30, but tests showed that the torpedo still had insufficient processing power. Then the Coastal Systems Station at Panama City provided a fiber-optic link, so the torpedo could fully exploit the processing power on board the helicopter; now a simpler, affordable torpedo would suffice. There was also some interest in providing the vehicle with a small camera for target identification.

◆ Focused Pressure Waves

This technology is now used for oil drilling in mud. A pressure shock wave might destroy the internal structure of the mine much as high-powered microwave weapons were once expected to destroy missile guidance and arming systems. Energy is transmitted by loading high electrical energy into a plasma in conductive saltwater, converting that energy into a pressure wave that is focused by phasing elements of the transducer array (probably 10 staves, 8 elements/stave). According to a 1996 brochure, pressure waves are to be generated at a 0.5-Hz repetition rate to clear an area 25 m wide and 8 m deep at a focal point 200 m from the transducer array, at a sweeper speed of 16 kt. Pulses are

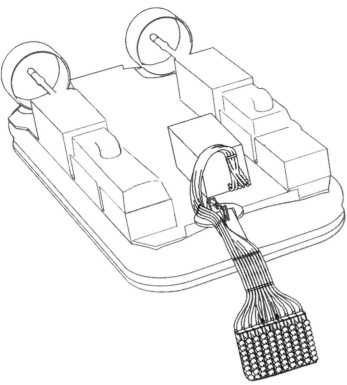

An LCAC is shown equipped with a focused pressure wave projector. (United Defense)

formed in a capacitor bank with an energy density of 8 MJ. The same device senses and destroys: once it detects a target, it turns up the power. As of mid-1995 this technology was in the ATD stage, for quick transition to development. Tetratech (an oil drilling firm) supplies the pressure wave generator; United Defense (which includes FMC) supplies the pulse-forming (energy supply) network originally developed for the ETG gun. A model system has been built and conceptually validated. Pressure wave technology is also being considered as an antitorpedo weapon.

♦ Magic Lantern/ALMDS/DEMON

Unlike other surface-piercing LIDARs (laser radars), Magic Lantern uses a large spot and a low repetition rate, in step-stare mode. The reflected light is range-gated (at a range corresponding to a depth below the surface) to eliminate surface reflection. Range gating limits the cross-path width per image because a greater width corresponds to a greater variety of slant ranges to the water surface. The current version therefore uses six electronically shuttered cameras, each separately range-gated, for a wider search swath. Objects at the set depth appear as bright spots; objects above are shadows. The current version uses automatic detection and a GPS-based system to aid in target reacquisition. In March 1991 Magic Lantern was credited with a 200ft search swath (65ft search depth) at a speed of advance of 40–50 kt, and with a potential for a 500–1000ft search swath if automatic detection could be used. The system uses a flash-pumped NdYAG laser (doubled) reportedly with an output of half a joule, operating at a pulse width of about 1 nsec.

Magic Lantern began in the fall of 1987 as a Kaman private venture. It was bought by the Navy under rapid prototyping procedures. Some may have been black money for nonacoustic ASW. In FY90 Congress provided money for a 2-yr development effort. Magic Lantern also received some U.S. Navy funding under Project Kingfisher and underwent a very successful 6-week demonstration. More funds were provided for further scientific work, which was completed in May 1990. A disassembled brass-board version of Magic Lantern (tested late 1990) was hurriedly reassembled (in 18 days) for deployment to the Gulf on 4 January 1991 on board an SH-2F. As of early 1991, Congress wanted Magic Lantern in all MH-53E MCM helicopters for rapid mine

search during exploratory sweeps and minehunting. The Naval Reserves wanted it in their helicopters and had adopted this requirement as an official position. Two ADMs ordered in November 1991 were delivered in FY92/93. Another was delivered during FY96 for OpEval/TechEval. In November 1994 Kaman made an unsolicited proposal to install Magic Lantern on board MH-53 minehunting helicopters. Early in 1995, however, an RFP for an Advanced Laser Mine Detection System (ALMD) was issued, calling for a system to be installed in MH-60 rather than MH-53 helicopters. The originally envisaged five units were replaced by 15. The original plan had been keyed specifically to Magic Lantern, but the new RFP was not. Magic Lantern performed very successfully in tests on board an SH-2F Seasprite, 15–21 June 1995; the results were described as a vast improvement over previous performance. As of late 1995, Magic Lantern was scheduled for initial operational capability in 1996 on board two Naval Reserve SH-2 helicopters. The first such helicopter was scheduled for rollout on 7 December 1996. Additional Magic Lanterns were scheduled for delivery for MH-53s.

Kaman developed a sonobuoy-size Terminator torpedo as the corresponding mine destroyer. Magic Lantern on board a helicopter would separately image both mine and Terminator, the latter being commanded to hit the mine.

Magic Lantern was combined with the Panama City/Lawrence Livermore Marine Corps Airborne Standoff Mine Detection (AMDAS) ATD at the behest of the FY91 Appropriations conference. The combination program emphasizes the surf zone because of its greater technical difficulty. AMDAS used a laser similar to that in Magic Lantern, promising a 1000ft swath width down to 40–50 ft depth at a speed of advance of 180 kt. An early version was tested, but the system was far less mature technically than Magic Lantern.

DEMON is another Navy laser detection program (no other details are available).

♦ MTDS

Mine Countermeasures Tactical Environment Data System responds to a CNO memorandum of 7 April 1986. The tactical environment includes background magnetic fields and tides.

♦ Project Kingfisher

This 1988 emergency project for mine detection and evasion was begun after the mining of the frigate *Roberts* and funded out of the JCS War Chest ($30M). Projects funded by Kingfisher were the mine-avoidance element of SQS-53/56 (tested four months after the *Roberts* mining), use of the Marconi (ex-Plessey) Mirror Sonar, the Magic Lantern test, the Hughes MMS thermal imager (primarily to detect floating mines), and Project Midnight. MMS and the Mirror Sonar were deployed to the Gulf. The mine evasion element of SQS-53/56 is now called Kingfisher.

Project Midnight was DRS's attempt to detect mines using SSQ-62 DICASS active sonobuoys. Two prototype buoys detected a small (-17dB) target at 400 yd; and predicted mine detection range was 1000 yd (PD 0.95). A prototype helicopter or small boat lightweight minehunting sonar used an SSQ-62 transducer. It would be sprint-and-dipped ahead of a moving force. Demonstrated range was up to 800 yd. Predicted range was up to 3000 yd.

The current Kingfisher sonar add-on emerged from the 1988 project. Although it suffered from a high false-alarm rate, it was placed in limited service. An improved very successful second-generation version appeared on six frigates, followed by a third-generation ECP-10 version on the CORT frigates. These ships all have SWAK (shallow water active kit), which provides additional display features and 90-deg (rather than the original 30-deg) coverage. A unique color-display format and GPS distinguish stationary from moving targets in the high-reverberation shallow-water environment. Kingfisher was installed in many SQS-53 sonars and became a formally required feature of SQS-53C. Because the SQS-53C transmitter is software-controlled, in this system Kingfisher is a software modification, providing a short-pulse wide-bandwidth sub-mode of variable-depression mode, covering 120 deg using three overlapping 45-deg sectors, each with nine beams. This mode allows for short range scales (2.5, 5, 10, 20 kyd).

◆ RAMICS

Hughes's Rapid Airborne Mine Countermeasures System fires supercavitating 20mm rounds from a conventional machine gun. Because it supercavitates (after its aerodynamic casing peels away), the bullet retains enough velocity 50 ft below the surface to penetrate the mine. As in Phalanx, the projectile is expected to transfer enough energy to the mine warhead to detonate it. If not, the mine is damaged by a powerful oxidant carried by the projectile. Hughes claims that a 50-rnd burst has a 95% chance

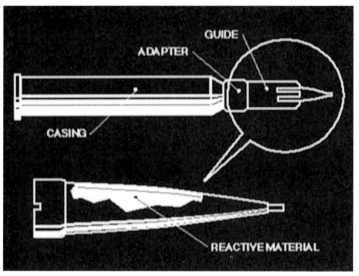

The RAMICS round, showing the casing that strips off as the bullet enters the water. Like a conventional bullet, the round is spin-stabilized in the air. It can keep its course even after entering the water at an oblique angle. (Hughes)

of killing a mine (it hopes to get the same effect with a 20-rnd burst). Estimated cost per round is about $30. Phase 2 of the program, completed in mid-1995, had been funded by the U.S. Navy since FY93; it demonstrated that the projectile was stable in both air and water at penetration angles from 90 to 20 deg. Phase 3 will integrate RAMICS with a laser minehunting system such as Magic Lantern. Should it prove successful, production may begin as early as FY97.

◆ AMDS

NUWC Newport is developing the advanced mine detection sonar for submarines, using transmitters under the chin and in the sail and a large-diameter cylindrical array (from the Applied Research Lab of the University of Texas). Lockheed Martin Federal Systems (formerly Loral Federal Systems, ex-IBM Federal Systems) is system integrator and is providing the receiver, beamformer, processors, controls, and displays. Northrop Grumman (ex-Westinghouse) provides outboard electronics and receiver sub-systems. AMDS will concurrently process signals from a wide aperture array such as BQG-5. Unlike BQS-14/15 or MIDAS, AMDS will not require the submarine to trim bow-down in order to detect mines, and it will be optimized to detect bottom mines. The ADM began trials in 1995.

◆ Model 260

EG&G Environmental Equipment's Image-Correcting sidescan sonar fish can be towed at up to 12.7 kt, covering a 600m swath on each side, with a resolution equal to 0.25% of range.
  Users: Egypt (route survey craft). The EG&G DF1000 towed side-looking sonar has been specified for the new Swedish YSB-class MCM ship.

YUGOSLAVIA

Yugoslavia has the following river sweeps: Type PEAM magnetic and acoustic; Type AEL-1 explosive; Types MDL-1 and -2 mechanical.
  Users: Hungary (six *Nestin*-type river sweepers), Iraq (*Nestin*-type river sweeper: PEAM, MDL-1 and -2), and Yugoslavia.

INDEX

SUBJECT	Page	SUBJECT	Page	SUBJECT	Page	SUBJECT	Page	SUBJECT	Page
A		ADAC	152	AIM-132	421	ALR-67ASR	64	Aparna	294
		ADACS (Korea)	542	AIMS IFF	370	ALR-68	544	APECS	564
A184	676	ADAD	361	AIMS MAD	662	ALR-71	545	APECS II	92
A200	678	Adams missile (Israel)	401	AIP	174	ALR-72	545	APFSDS	452
A244	670, 677	ADAP	10	Air Hawk	259	ALR-73	545	APG-63	176, 177, 178, 207
A244/S	677	ADAR sonobuoy	183, 657	Air-to-Air ARM	426	ALR-75	545	APG-66	176, 208
A290	670	ADATS	395	AIRBOC	538	ALR-76	541	APG-67	208
A Mk 2 sweep (U.S.)	754	ADAWS	1, 70, 71, 72, 92, 107, 110	AIRCMM	563	ALR-81	545	APG-68	208
A Mk 4 sweep (U.S.)	754			AIS	655	ALR-82	545	APG-71	178, 214
A Mk 5 sweep (U.S.)	754	ADAWS 2000	108	AIS Mk III	87	ALR-84	545	APG-73	14, 179, 191, 207
A Mk 6 mine (UK)	727	ADC EX-9	709	AIS-11	83	ALR-85	184, 541	APG-76	182, 183, 209
A Mk 6 sweep (U.S.)	754	ADC EX-11	711	AISYS	21	ALR-92	545	APG-77	182
A Mk 7 mine (UK)	727	ADC Mk 1	709	AIWS	251	ALR-93	541	Aphid	423
A Mk 7* mine (UK)	727	ADC Mk 2	709	AJ 37	200	ALR-300	517	APM	720
A Mk 7** mine (UK)	727	ADC Mk 3	709	Ajanta	491	ALR-310	517	APM-60 Orsha	169, 170
A Mk 9 mine (UK)	727	ADC Mk 4	709	Ajax	603	ALR-502	541	APN-215	215
A Mk 12 mine (UK)	727	ADC Mk 5	709	Akash	399	ALR-606	541	APP-50MA/-50MR	516
A Type S mine (UK)	727	ADC Mk 6	708	Akkord	146	ALR-730	501	APQ-104	193
A-7E	173	ADCAP torpedo	694	AKT-22	38, 181	ALR-735	501	APQ-126	173, 209
A-NEW	174	ADIMP	1, 5, 31, 32, 53, 107	Akula	604	ALR-801	545	APQ-156	209
A-RCI	618	ADLFP	655	Al-Muthena mines	715	ALR-2001	176, 472	APQ-173	193
A/N37U	756	ADLIPS	39, 74	ALADIN	595	ALSS program	472	APQ-183	193
AA-2	423	ADLIPS 90	48	Alamo	423	Altair	30	APQ-706	197
AA-8	423	ADM-141	573	ALARM missile	248	Altesse	479	APR-2E torpedo	168, 169, 684
AA-10	423	ADS (Advanced Display System)	121, 135	ALARMS laser minehunter	732	Alura	589		
AA-11	424			Albatros FCS	307	ALUV	752	APR-39	545
AA-12	424	ADS (Aegis Display System)	22	Albatros radar	330	AM-39	226	APR-50	181
AAAM	421			ALBATROS torpedo warning system	705	AMARTOF	437	April Showers	663
AAED	537, 572	ADS	22, 121, 135			AMASCOS	166, 216	APRN	271
AAP-400	660	ADSAMS	426	Alcor	103	AMASS	732	APS (Afloat Planning System)	219
AAP-640	660	ADT radars	84, 130	ALD-2	536	Amber Light	507		
AAPS	660	Advanced Digital Receiver	563	ALD-8	536	AMBL 1	484	APS series FCS	598
AAQ-10	207			ALD-9	536	AMBL 2A program	484	APS-20	193, 198
AAQ-13	204	Advanced Video Processor	134	Aldebaran	517	AMCGS program	465	APS-80A	209
AAQ-14	204			ALE-39	536	AMD decoy	562	APS-88	210
AAQ-16	181, 185, 204	Advanced White Cloud	19	ALE-40	536	AMD series mines	720	APS-115	175
AAQ-17	181	AEAS	24	ALE-47	16, 185, 537	AMDAS	732, 753	APS-116	176, 183, 209, 210
AAQ-21	204	AEB decoy	555	ALE-50	179, 537	AMDR	296	APS-124	211
AAQ-22	204	AECSP	535	ALEX	572	AMDS	623, 760	APS-127	211
AAR-47	536	AEER	655	ALF	601	Amelie Cristal	2	APS-128	211
AAR-50	204	Aegis system	6, 116, 411	ALFS	181, 617	Amethyst	663	APS-128PC	211
AAR-51	203	AEW radars	200	ALI	21	Ametyst LIDAR	169	APS-130	209
AAR-75	181	AFATDS	11, 180	ALICE	627	AMG-1	715	APS-131	212
AAS-36	176, 177, 205	AFDS	10	ALIS	119	AMH	12	APS-134	210
AAS-38	179, 205	AFSATCOM	18, 32, 35, 41	ALISS	755	AMMS	750	APS-135	212
AAS-40	206	AFTAS	615	Alligator	482	AMNSYS	758	APS-137	210
AAS-42	206	AGATE	744	Almaz	17	AMRAAM	178, 179, 180, 200, 426	APS-138	212
AAS-44	181, 206	Agave	194	ALMDS	759			APS-139	212
AAS-49	206	AGI	4	Alpha	244	AMSP/2	660	APS-140	193
AASM	228	AGIS	2, 82, 400	ALQ-39	538	AMSS	758	APS-143	211
AAT 52	434	AGM-12	253	ALQ-78	538	Amulet	708, 709	APS-145	212
Abbey Hill	524	AGM-62	261	ALQ-99	16, 538	AMW	136	APS-146	209
ABCAS	699	AGM-65	175, 258	ALQ-108	539	AN407	591	APS-147	211
ABCS	11	AGM-84	255	ALQ-126	539	AN410	591	APS-503	193
ABF (adaptive beam former)	24	AGM-84E	255	ALQ-141	756	An-12PPS	516	APS-504	193
		AGM-84E/H	259	ALQ-142	549	AN-52 bomb	187	APS-506	210
ABNCP	45	AGM-88	254	ALQ-144	540	AN/ASB-19	216	APS-705	197
ABRG 2	480	AGM-114	257	ALQ-149	16, 540	AN/BRT-1/2	44	APS-707	197
ACDS Block 1	71, 78, 118, 126	AGM-119	233	ALQ-156	472	AN/KAS-1	392	APS-717	198
		AGM-122A	259	ALQ-157	541	Anaconda array	92, 581	APS-784	198
ACDS chaff launcher	497	AGM-154	251	ALQ-160	732	Anaconda sweep	745	APS-SV/CP	210
ACDS combat system	8, 12, 57, 119, 125, 126	AGRION 15	194	ALQ-162	539	Andoga	146	APSET-95	684
		AGSB	721	ALQ-164	539	ANDVT	38	APSOH	596
ACIS	10	AH Mk 4 sweep (UK)	748	ALQ-165	178, 179, 540	Anemone	195	APTGD	223
ACORN	620	AH-1W Upgrade	174	ALQ-166	732	Angora-M	326	APX-111 CITs	394
ACOS	659	AHEAD ammunition	458	ALQ-167	541	ANL	223	APX-1000	393
Acoustic Data Link	45	AI-FCS	149	ALQ-190	538	ANNG	223	AQA-1	177
Acoustic sweeps (U.S.)	754	AICS	33	ALR-8	541	ANODE	645	AQA-3	658
Acoustic sweeps (UK)	749	Aidcomer	2, 78	ALR-44	541	ANR 360	203	AQA-4	658
Acoustic-Induction Mine M-70	732	AIDS	134	ALR-45	178, 179, 543	ANS	220	AQA-5	166, 177, 658
		AIEWS	549	ALR-47	541	Antennas	43	AQA-7	174, 177, 183, 658
ACS electronic system	8, 492	AIM-7	430	ALR-50	178, 179	Antiaircraft laser	471	AQA-801	648
		AIM-9	427	ALR-52	558	AO Mk 4 sweep (UK)	748	AQS-13	198, 616
ACTAS ASA 92	596	AIM-9L	200	ALR-60	541	AOCD	119	AQS-14	617, 756
ACTOR	320	AIM-9X	180	ALR-66	14, 181, 541	AOSP	54	AQS-18	173, 616
ACUTE	42	AIM-54	427	ALR-66B	176	APA-171 antenna	177	AQS-20	756
ACWS	136	AIM-120	179	ALR-67	16, 178, 179, 543	APA-172 console	177	AQS-22	181, 617
AD sweep (UK)	748	AIM-120A	426			APAR	93, 127, 319	AQS-23	617

SUBJECT	Page
AQS-901	53, 172, 653
AQS-902	166, 173, 653
AQS-903	654
AQS-920 series	653
AQS-930	654
AQS-950	614, 654
AQS-951	654
AQS-960	654
Aquacade	18
AR-700	184, 564
AR-730	566
AR-740	564
AR-900	566
AR-7000	566
Arabel	285
ARAMIS	228
ARAR 10	477
ARAR 13	477
ARBB 32	480
ARBB 33	481
ARBB 36	481
ARBG 1A	480
ARBR 10	482
ARBR 16	477
ARBR 17	477
ARBR 18	477
ARBR 21	477
ARBS	216
ARC-101	176
ARC-161	176
ARC-181	30
ARC-182	37, 176, 181
ARC-187	176
ARC-207	176
ARC-210	37, 179
Archer	424
Archerfish	749
Arcticsat	1
ARF (ex-STAR)	224
Arfa	606
Argentina:	
Mines	715
ARGO Phoenix I/II	566
Argonaute	582
Argos 73	303
Argument	336
Argun	606
ARI 5955	200
ARI 5980	202
ARI 18228	520
ARI 18240	522
ARI 18240/1	567
ARI 23491	522
Ariel	522
ARIES	560
ARIES/EP-3	176
ARINC 429	68
ARISE	361
Arktika	604
ARMAT	224
ARMOR	159
ARPA radar	115, 126
ARPA Submarine CDS	
Projects	159
ARQ-44	38
ARR-72	175
ARR-75	173, 180, 181
ARR-78	175
ARR-84	173, 181, 185
ARS (Advanced Rocket	
Systems)	265, 655
ARS-2	182
ARS-3	175
ARS-4	182
ARS-5	175, 546
ARTIST	319
ARTIVIS	642
ARUR 10	477
ARUR 11	477
ARUR 13	477
AS0 90	593
AS 12	228
AS 15TT	194, 224
AS 30	225
AS 30L	225
AS 34	228
AS 37	224
AS 40	641
AS C 17	641
AS C 18	641
AS-2	220

SUBJECT	Page
AS-4	234
AS-5	220
AS-6	199, 234
AS-7	234
AS-9	235
AS-10	235
AS-11	236
AS-12	235
AS-13	236
AS-14	236
AS-15	237
AS-16	237
AS-17	237
AS-18	236
AS-19	238
AS-228	697
AS-505	570
AS-1065	394
AS-1688	394
AS-2188	394
AS-3033	38
AS-3430	394
ASA-26B	181
ASA-66	175, 183
ASA-70	175
ASAP	660
ASAT weapons	39
ASC	9
ASCAC	12
ASCORE	286
ASDCS	387
ASDF	490
ASH data bus	68
ASIS	122
ASLP	188
ASM-1	232
ASM-2	232
ASMA	4
ASMP	187
ASN-116	177
ASN-123	38, 173
ASN-124	183
ASN-130	178
ASN-150	31, 33, 56, 166, 173, 181, 185
ASN-902	173, 184
ASN-903	173
ASN-990	171
ASO 80	592
ASOM	246
Aspide	401
ASPIS	541
ASPJ	540
ASQ	33
ASQ-10	664
ASQ-17	732
ASQ-81	175, 181, 664
ASQ-114	55, 175
ASQ-173	179, 213
ASQ-191	472
ASQ-197	191
ASQ-208	181, 664
ASQ-212	55
ASQ-504	173, 662
ASR	543
ASR 360	202
ASRAAM	421
Asroc	667
ASSAT	25
ASSESS	7
ASSTASS	576
ASTAB	117, 121
ASTARTE	26
ASTE	536, 548, 563
ASTECS	561
Aster	399
ASUTAA	646
ASUWC	130
ASV 21	171, 172, 200
ASW-27	177
ASW 600	700
ASW 601	700
ASW 604	700
ASWC	130
ASWDS	74, 577
ASWE	68
ASWM	10, 11, 12
ASWOC	11
ASWTA	580
AT-1	683
AT-2 torpedo	683

SUBJECT	Page
AT-2 sweep	745
AT-3	746
AT-24	683
AT-441	43
ATAC	44, 49
ATACMS	11, 272, 460
ATARS	33, 190
ATAS	597
ATC900 console	95
ATC-1	707
ATDS	177
ATES	120
ATHS	33, 165
ATIMS	15
ATIRCM	562
Atlantique Nouvelle	
Génération	166
ATLAPS	689
Atlas PP-10 sonar	596
ATM	723
ATOMS	615
ATP	9
ATRJ	548
ATTCS	11
ATW	12, 136
ATWCS	156, 220
AU-506	570
Australia:	
Airborne Sensors	193
Command Advice	
Systems	2
Electronic Warfare	472
MCM/Minehunting	
Sonars	732
Nonacoustic ASW	
Sensors	662
Shipboard Guns and Gun	
Systems	431
Signal Processors	647
Sonars and Underwater Fire-	
Control Systems	576
Sonobuoys	646
Surface Radar/ELINT	
(Electronics Intelligence)	
Systems	19
AUTO-ID	394
Autodin	15
AUTOLYCUS	662
Automatic Short-Range Air-	
Defense System	402
AUTSIG	460
AUUD-1	703
AV-8B Maintenance Data	
System	15, 177
Avitek-500 series	636
AVR-2	547
AVX-1	213
AWACS	30, 126
AWARE 3	522
AWARE 4	522
AWG-9	214
AWG-10	178
AWS-1	280, 355
AWS-2	280, 355
AWS-4	356
AWS-5	356
AWS-6	280, 356
AWS-9	352
AWW-13	257
AX Mk 3 sweep (UK)	748
AXX-1 camera	178, 214
AYA-8	55, 56
Ayaks	603
B	
B4/B4M mine	717
B5B mine	717
B-6D radar (China)	193
B-34 mount	442
B-ISDN	35
B.512	678
B.515	678
B.516	678
Backfire	199
Badger	515, 516
Bal (Whale)	244
Bald Head	507
Balkan	328
Ball End	325
Ballute	263

SUBJECT	Page
Baltic	408
BAMO	738
Band Stand	333
Bandfish	708
Barak FCS Radar	295
Barak I	401
Barem	479
Barra	646
Barracuda	220
Barricade (France)	486
Barricade (UK)	534
Base System 2000	105
Bass Tilt	334
Bastion	245
BAT	266
BAT-2	746
Baykal	169
Bazalt	241
BCAEFS	615
BCIS	393
BCIXS	34, 40
Beachcomber	460
Beamtrap	497
Bean Sticks	275
Bear F	168
BEARTRAP	661
BEFS	615
Bell Bash	508
Bell Clout	508
Bell Crown	31, 98, 99
Bell Hop	31
Bell Nest	508
Bell Nip	509
Bell Push	509
Bell Shroud	100, 509
Bell Slam	508
Bell Spike	31
Bell Squat	509
Bell Strike	31
Bell Tap	99, 510
Bell Thumb	31
Bell Thump	508
Bereg gun system	269
Berkut	169, 199, 200
Beryoza	516
BF	479
BFTT	118, 119
BGAAWC program	127
BGAT	746
BGL 400	227
BGL 1000	227
BGM-109	259
BGPHES	33, 138, 552
BGT	683
BI Series	650
Big Ball	99
Big Bird	17, 18
Big Bulge	31, 99, 198
Big Look program	542
Big Net	325
Bimilsat	32
Biryuza	244
Bizan'-4A	512
BKR-1	199
BLA-4	547
BLD-1	547
BLD-727	498
Blinder	199, 516
BLM/SLS	753
BLNS	752
Blowpipe	409
BLQ series	710
BLQ-355	517
BLQ-501	567
BLR-6	547
BLR-10	548
BLR-12	548
BLR-13	548
BLR-14	710
BLR-15	548
BLU series	265
BLU-110	263
BLU-111	263
Blue Fox radar	172, 201
Blue Kestrel	201
Blue Shark	679
Blue Vixen	165, 172, 201
BM 11	271
BM 14/17	271
BM 14/18	271

SUBJECT	Page
BM 21	271
BM 802	85
BM-1	200, 652
BM/HZ 8610	475, 510
BM/KZ 8608	475
Boa	428
Bofors 375mm rocket	
launcher	699
Bofors rockets	519
Bolide	408
Bombs (France)	261
Bombs (Russia)	262
Bombs (UK)	263
BOMSS	576
Bottle Cap	576
Box Office	428
BP-30 (Russia)	446
BPM-2	720
BPS-12	366
BPS-14	366
BPS-15	366
BPS-16	366
BPS-704	143, 298, 304
BQG-4	618
BQG-5	619
BQG-501	618
BQM-74E	126
BQM-145	192
BQN-33	153
BQQ-2	151
BQQ-5	152, 153, 620
BQQ-5E	154, 156
BQQ-6	620
BQQ-8	576
BQQ-9	138, 620
BQR-2B/21	622
BQR-7	151, 622
BQR-15	151, 622
BQR-19	622
BQR-20A	622
BQR-22	622
BQR-22A	622
BQR-23	622
BQR-501	577
BQS-4	151, 622
BQS-14	623
BQS-15	152, 623
BQS-24	44, 623
BRA-34	43
Brazil:	
Coast-Defense Guns and	
Rockets	267
Electronic Warfare	473
Mines	716
Missiles and Guided	
Bombs	220
Surface Ship Combat-	
Direction Systems	73
BRC-6	44
BRD-7	548
BRD-8	548
BRD-9	548
Breda 105mm multiple	
launcher	271
Breda 105mm rocket launchers	
(SCLAR)	502
Brest	605
Brick Bat	39
Brick Pulp	508
BRIGAND	553
Bronza	604
Broomstick	316
BRR-3	43
BRR-6	44
BRT-1	44
BRT-3 through -5	44
BRT-6	44
BS 19	641
BS 40	641
BSAWS	710
BSN-716	143
BSQ-6	44
BSS	707
BSTING	392
BSY-1	152, 156
BSY-2	154, 157
BSY-2 console	136
BSY-3(?)	158
BTI-IRCM	472
Bukhta	329

SUBJECT	Page
Bulgaria:	
Shipboard Radars and Fire-Control Systems	273
Bull Nose	605, 607
Bullpup	253
Bulls Eye	7, 20
Bunny	725
BURLAP	652
Burya	330, 608
Bushmaster (U.S.)	464
BX-132/164	305
BX-732/764	305
BYG-501	577
BYH-1	155

C

C2P	107, 119
C43	670
C303	707
C309	707
C310	707
C801	75
C-101	222
C-201	221
C-301	222
C-601	221
C-801	222
C-802	222
C-Pearl	492
C-SS-N-3	186
C/X-Band radar	342
CAAIS	52, 53, 71, 107, 108, 110
CACS	31, 53, 110, 114
CADAM program	432
CADS-N-1	407
CAE system	73
CAFMS	5
CAINS II	183
Calcuta	650
Calypso	284
CAMBS	653
CAMEL/BEL	483
CAMLAC	572
Canada:	
Airborne Sensors	193
Computers	48
Data Buses	67
Electronic Warfare	474
MCM/Minehunting Sonars	733
Nonacoustic ASW Sensors	662
Radars	274
Shipboard Radars and Fire-Control Systems	273
Signal Processors	648
Sonars and Underwater Fire-Control Systems	577
Sonobuoys	647
Strategic Underwater Sensor Systems	21
Surface Radar/ELINT (Electronics Intelligence) Systems	19
Surface Ship Combat-Direction Systems	73
CANDO	124, 385
CANE	51, 75, 107, 111, 130
CANEWS	73, 474
Canopus	78
CANTASS	577
CARDINAL	734
Cardion MCDS	130
CARMEN	532, 534
CARP	14
Carrier Bomb Light Stores (UK)	263
CARS	13
Cartridge Mk 234	473
CAS	5, 124
CASES	7
CASS	656
Cast Eyes	214
Cast Glance	214
Castor IIC system	49
Castor	79, 289
Caves	615
CAWCS	90
CBU series	265

SUBJECT	Page
CBU-15	261
CBU-59	179
CCA	5, 92, 107
CCC	37
CCD	16
CCIP	7
CCIS	31, 97, 104, 106
CCN	36
CCS system	10, 15
CCS Mk 1 (U.S.)	12, 152, 154, 156
CCS Mk 2 (U.S.)	12, 26, 27, 64, 131, 154, 159
CCS-2 (DF-3)	186
CCS-280	72, 73
CCSW	9
CD77	270
CD80	270
CDBS	12, 16
CDCS	128
CDDU	91
CDLMS	119
CDS (ex-NTDS)	119
CDS architecture	98
CDS/NTDS display systems	132
CDSC	157
CEC	125
CELTIC	473
CENTAC	12
Central Tactical System	171
CEPLO	72, 75, 104
Cerberus	487
CERAMIS	224
Cerise	17
CF 299	410
CGS-1	346
CH084	642
CH093	642
Chaff Charlie	532
Chaff Hotel	532
Chaff rockets	497
CHAFFBUOY	538
Chaffstar	565
Chaffstar II	575
Chalet	18
Challenge Athena	6, 13, 36
CHAMPS	15
Chang Feng III	130
Chang Feng series	519
CHBDL	33
Cheap Shot	251
Cheese Cake	325
Chelomei Alpha	171
CHESS	553
Chile:	
Electronic Warfare	474
Mines	716
Mortars and Depth Charges	697
Shipboard Radars and Fire-Control Systems	275
Sonars and Underwater Fire-Control Systems	579
Surface Ship Combat-Direction Systems	74
China:	
Airborne Sensors	193
Coastal Radars	279
Countermeasures	703
Electronic Warfare	474
Fire-Control Systems	278
MCM/Minehunting Sonars	733
Mines	716
Missiles	664
Missiles and Guided Bombs	220
Mortars and Depth Charges	697
Search Radars	275
Shipboard Guns and Gun Systems	431
Sonars and Underwater Fire-Control Systems	579
Sonobuoys and Signal Processors	648
Strategic Strike Systems	186

SUBJECT	Page
Strategic Underwater Sensor Systems	21
Surface Ship Combat-Direction Systems	75
Surface-to-Air Missiles	395
Torpedoes	670
CHIP	654
Chlio	184, 197
Chun Ma	396
CHURN	151
CIACIO-S	677
CIBS-M	16
CIDS	579
CIGARS	123, 133
CIGSS	13
CIRCE 2000	2
Circularly disposed array antennas	20
CIWS	123
CK034	642
CK040	642
CK043	642
CK/CH periscopes	641
CL 834	248
CLAMS	710
Classic Outboard	7, 554
Classic Salmon	559
Classic Wizard	7, 19
CLI	15
Clio	216
CLIP (U.S.)	465
Clipper Bow	19
CLOAC	566
Close Air Support Link	33
Close-In Weapons System Mk 15	467
Cluster Bay	723
Cluster bombs	265
Cluster Gulf	723
Cluster Lance	21
Cluster Nave	43
Cluster Pretzel	752
Cluster Ranger	176, 213
Cluster Sentinel	570
Cluster Spectator	560
CM010	642
CMR-85/90 radar	274
CMWS	562
Co-News	501
COAR	103
Coast Guard System	12
Coastal Protection System	390
Coastguard	356
COBRA	753
Cobra sweep	745
Cochin	295
Cockchafer	609
Cocoon	421
Colibri	500
COM	644
Combined sweeps (U.S.)	755
COMDAC	127
COMKAFS	150
Common Ring Laser Gyro	156
Compact 40mm (Italy)	438
Compass Sail Clockwise	540
Computer chips: DEC Alpha AXP, 62; **Hewlett-Packard PA-RISC Series**, 62; **Intel Chips (iAx86 series)**, 62; **Intel RISC Chips**, 63; **MIPS RISC Chips**, 64; **Motorola Chips (68000 series)**, 64; **Motorola RISC Chips (88000 series)**, 65; **Computers: 15M05**, 49; **15M125**, 49; **15M/05**, 49; **15M/125**, 49; **68040**, 112; **AAYK-14**, 54; **Argus M700**, 52, 111; **ASPRO**, 56; **ASQ**, 56; **ASQ-114**, 53, 55; **ASQ-212**, 53, 55; **AYK-10**, 53; **AYK-14**, 54; **AYK-502**, 48, 54; **BuOrd/NavOrd Computers**, 59; **CALISTO**, 49; **CDE**, 49; **CDG-3032**, 50;	

SUBJECT	Page
Censor 908, 52; **Censor 932**, 52; **Censor 932E**, 52; **CP-642B**, 54; **CP-848**, 55; **CP-855**, 55; **CP-901**, 55; **CP-901A**, 55; **CP-1469**, 56; **CP-1820**, 56; **CP-2044**, 55; **CP-2137**, 59; **CP-2184**, 60; **CP-2231**, 60; **CP-7010**, 50; **D80**, 52; **DTC I**, 59; **DTC II**, 59; **EL/S-8600 Series**, 50; **Elsag Computers**, 50; **F100-L**, 52, 111; **F200-L**, 52; **F2420**, 53, 111; **FM 1600B**, 52; **FM 1600D**, 52; **FM 1600E**, 53, 111; **GEC-Marconi 920ATC**, 53; **IRIS 35M**, 48; **IRIS 55M**, 49; **KS500**, 51, 111; **KS900**, 51; **L-304**, 61; **MARA series**, 50; **MDAU**, 61; **MECA 43**, 56; **Mk 152**, 55; **Mk 157**, 51; **MLX 32**, 49; **NDC-160/E**, 50; **Next-Generation Computer Resources**, 59; **OL-77**, 56; **OL-77**, 61; **P800**, 52; **Proteus**, 175; **RDP**, 53; **Rolm 1666**, 61; **Rolm 1666B**, 58; **SENIT 8 computer**, 49; **SM-3**, 51; **SMR**, 50; **SMR-4**, 50; **SMR-MU**, 51; **SMR-S1**, 51; **SMR-S**, 51; **System/4 Pi**, 61; **TAC-3**, 60; **TAC-4**, 60; **TADSTAND B**, 59; **TDP**, 61; **Transputer (T400/T800)**, 53; **Univac 1219B**, 55; **Univac 1230**, 55, 62; **Univac 1616**, 57; **Univac 1830A**, 55; **Univac 1830A/1830B**, 62; **Univac 1830B**, 55; **Univac 1832**, 53; **USQ-20**, 54; **USQ-69B**, 56; **UYK**, 55; **UYK-7**, 56; **UYK-15**, 57; **UYK-19**, 57; **UYK-20**, 57; **UYK-43**, 57; **UYK-44**, 58; **UYK-64(V)**, 58; **UYK-502**, 48; **UYK-505**, 48; **UYK-507**, 48; **UYQ-503**, 48; **UYQ-504**, 48; **UYQ-505**, 48; **UYS-1**, 175; **UYS-1/2**, 59; **UYS-2**, 59; **VAX**, 62, 112; **PowerPC**, 65; **Sun SPARC Series**, 65; **Texas Instruments TMS320C Series**, 66; **VisiBridge**, 66; **Zilog Z80/Z8000**, 67;	
CONAM	103, 124
CONDO-R	299
Condor EP-2060	176
CONTAC	74, 103
CONTRALTO	706
COOP system	105, 733
Copernicus architecture	6, 15, 16, 31, 33, 34, 36, 40
Copernicus Forward	5, 34, 40
Copernicus Links	36
Copernicus system	17
CORA	299
CORIS	597
Cormoran sonar	181
Corvus	533
Costas	25
CoSys	85
CoSys 200	72, 114
COTS	124
Coulverine II (France)	433
Counter Communications	562
CP-140	182
CP-1516	33
CR-2800	492
CR-UAV	193
CREM	149
CRESUS	706
CRIMSON	615
CRISP	654
Cross Fox	25
Cross Round (Positive)	325
Cross Sword	335
Crossbow	395
Crosseye	497
Crotale Naval	396
Crotale NG	396
Crouzet Mk III	166

SUBJECT	Page
Cruise Martel	248
CSA	112
CSA Mk 1	710
CSA Mk 2	710
CSA Mk 3	710
CSAS-80	579
CSCI	37
CSDS	36, 37
CSDTS	28
CSGE	2
CSS	33, 34, 43
CSS-80AS	579
CSSC gun-missile system	396
CSSCS	11
CSSX-6	222
CSS-NX-1 Scrubbrush	222
CSS-NX-4 Sardene	186, 222
CSS-NX-5 Sabbot	222
CSS-NX-8 Saccade	223
CST	5
CSU 3 series	591
CSU 90 sonar	142, 148, 593
CTAPS	5
CTC	115, 130
CTH	78
CTI	90
CTM	289
CTS	172
CTS-36 RDN	578
CTT	16, 38, 40
CTTLS	710
CUDIXS	12, 33, 35, 40, 67
Cuirasse	291, 482
Curl Stone-A	326
Cutlass	51, 527
CV-216	56
CV-2969	38
CWCS	16
CWDD	392
CWE-10N	600
CWE-610	634
CWS	73
CWS-1/2	280
CY-1	664
Cygnus	529
Cyrano	195

D

D3 data bus	68
D-5	189
D-7	236
D-8	235
D-9	188
D-9DU	188
D-9RM	188
D-19	188
D-100	598
D-102	598
DA-01	313
DA-02	313
DA-04	273
DA-05	130, 314
DA-08	130, 315
Daewoo 20mm ADS (U.S.)	469
Dagaie	114, 484
DAIL	67
DAISY	50, 90
DALAS	288
Dalia	477, 531
DAMA	34, 271
DAMDIC	733
DAMDIS	733
Damocles	266
DANCS	127
Danfish	357
Danish Coastal Radar	376
Dardo	307
DARIN	194
Dark Star	181, 192, 205
DAS	361
DASH	192
DASS 2000	567
Data buses	67
Data Links	31
DAVONET	67, 68
DBA	108
DBE	111
DBQS-40	593

SUBJECT	Page
DCB	149
DCC	150
DCG	149
DCH	576
DCJSS	472
DCM	150
DCR	342
DCS-2000	34
DDC 060	183
DDI	123
DDM	483
DDQS-11	83
DDSX-11	83
DDWCS	93
DE 1160	631
DE 1163	631
DE 1164	631
DE 1167	632
DE 1191	636
DEA	111
Decca 1226	281
Decca 1229	281
Decca 1629	280
Decca Hi-Fix	82
Deepwell	541
DEF-STAN 00-18	68
DEF-STAN 00-19 (ASH)	68
DELEX program	73
Delfin	188
Delilah	229
Deltic	658
DEMON	645, 759
Denezy	346
Denmark:	
Electronic Warfare	475
MCM/Minehunting	
Sonars	733
Mines	716
Radars	280
Radio Systems	25
Submarine Combat-Direction	
Systems	139
Surface Ship Combat-	
Direction Systems	75
DEPLO	104
Derkacz	507
Deseaver	497
Destructors	728
DFA	110
DFS	571
DFS 2000	472
DFTDS	72, 74, 112, 184
DHAX 1	166, 662
DHAX 3	662
DIANA	611
DIBC 1A	288
DIBC 2A	287
DIBV 10	287
DICASS	656
DIDON	79
DIFAR	645, 656
DIGIBUS	67
Digiraid	2
Digital ESM Receiver	567
Diodon	80, 586
DIP 12	588
Director Mk 46	390
Disopair	2
Dispenser (France)	261
DIWSA	12, 13, 15
DL-6T	475
DL-12T	475
DLA (EW)	533
DLA (UFCS)	590
DLB	533
DLC	533
DLE (EW)	533
DLE (data-link	
equipment)	32
DLF(1)	534
DLH	534
DLJ	533
DLK	534
DLPP	31
DLPS	31, 32, 108
DLT	590
DM1 Seeschlange	673
DM2A1 Seal	674
DM2A3 Seehecht	674
DM 11	717
DM 41	717

SUBJECT	Page
DM 51	717
DM 61	717
DM-1	720
DMC-34	14
DMS 2000	183
DMUX 20	141, 580
DMUX 80	581
DMZA4	674
DNA	113
Dolphin (AWS-6)	356
Dolphin (RMS)	753
Dolphin-1000 sonars	576
Don series	326
DORNA	342
Double Eagle	747
Down Beat	199
DPDS	183
DPEWS	549
DR 2000	477
DR 3000	477
DR 4000	477
DR-3000A ESM	166
DRAA-2	193
DRAA-2B radar	166
Dragon Eyes	22
Dragonfish	727
DRAKE	151
Drakon FCS	608
Drakon CIWS	434
DRBC 31	289
DRBC 32	289
DRBC 33	289
DRBI 10	281
DRBI 23	281
DRBJ 11	281
DRBN 32	281
DRBR 51	281
DRBV 15	282
DRBV 21A	282
DRBV 22	282
DRBV 23	282
DRBV 26	283
DRBV 26C	283
DRBV 26D	283
DRBV 50	283
DRBV 51	284
DRBV 52	285
DRUA-33	284
Drum Tilt	335
DS 30/SIGMA	459
DS-35	273, 297
DS-OAS	758
DSAX 1	650
DSBV 1	581
DSBV 61A	581
DSBV 62C	581
DSBX 1	581
DSCS	35
DSCS-2	148
DSM	140
DSMAC	13
DSP satellite	17, 18
DSPR	21
DSQS-11	83, 732
DSQS-21	84, 114, 130, 592
DSQS-23	593
DSSI	630
DST-92	679
DSTV 4L/M	648
DSTV 7	649
DSUV 2	582
DSUV 22	582
DSUV 61	583
DSUV 62	582
DSUX 20	580
DSVL	119
DTACS	212
DTS	38, 39
DUAV 4	583
DUBA 1	576
DUBA 2	576
DUBA 3	583
DUBA 25	583
DUBM 20	81, 734
DUBM 21	81, 734
DUBM 40A	737
DUBM 41	737
DUBM 42	737
Dubrava	327
DUBV 23	584
DUBV 24	585

SUBJECT	Page
DUBV 43	584
DUPM-1	738
Durandal	261
DUUA 1A/B/C	585
DUUA 2A/B/D	585
DUUG-1	703
DUUG-2	704
DUUG-6	705
DUUG-7	705
DUUV 23	585
DUUX 2A/B/C	585
DUUX 5	585
DWLC	153
E	
E40-65A	684
E40-75A	684
E45-70A	683
E45-75A	683
E53-72A	683
E53-79A	682
E 12	671
E 14	671
E 15	671
E 18	671
E-2C	177
EAGER	535
Eagle Eye	297
Eagle radar	273, 280
EAJ-1	703
EASY	90
EC-135s	176
ECCM	29
ECDIS	733
Echo	325
ECOS	659
ECP-510	544
ECPINS	733
EDATS	732
EDO 610 series	634
EDO 700	628
EDO 701	628
EDO 780	628
EDO 790 series	628
EDO 900	635
EDO 1102/1105	576
EDO 1110	635
EDO 1550	636
EDO Link 11 Consoles	39
EDO LRDS consoles	74
EFE	556
EFR-1	279
EGES FCS	400
Egg Cup	442
EH-101	167
EHF terminal	37
EIMa	744
Ekco AW 391	200
Ekran	326
EL/L-8300	492
EL/M-2022	171, 176, 197
EL/M-2028	86
EL/M-2032	197
EL/M-2035	197
EL/M-2207	295
EL/M-2208	295
EL/M-2216	296
EL/M-2221	296
EL/M-2226	296
EL/M-2228	296
Elbit AIO III	87
Elbit CDS Systems	86
Eledone	582
ELF	43, 44
ELINT	10, 17, 18
Elisra MPA system	176
Elk Tail	606
Elma	700
Elnath	517
ELSA	343
ELT 123	498
ELT 128	501
ELT 161	500
ELT 263	500
ELT/810 sonar	143
ELTA radar	176
EM 52	716
EMATT	712
EMCU	10

SUBJECT	Page
EMNS	758
EMP	26, 48
EMPAR	88, 300
EMSP	659
EMSS	755
ENATD	752
ENFCS	160
ENG-2 (China)	431
Enigme	480
Enot	681
Enot-2	681
ENTAD	753
EORSAT	4, 17, 30
EOS-400	344
EOS-450	344
EOS-500	344
EP 4220	532
EP-3	560
EPIC	627
EPLO	104
EPR series	718
ERADDS	127
ERAPS	646
ERASE program	255, 549
ERATO	231
ERC-1	475
Erieye radar	176
ERIMIS	105
ERWE	487
ES-3 Mission Planning	
System	15
ES-3A	552
ES-SDMS	69
ESGN	10
ESR-1	277
ESSFIVE	614
ESSFOUR	614
ESSMs	116, 118, 411
ET-80(50)	681
ET-80(67)	681
ET-80A(60)	681
ET-80A(76)	681
ET/SLQ-1	473
Ethernet	68
Ethernet 2	68
ETW	523
EU 90	675
Eumilsat	30, 32
EVEC	81
EVS	41, 43, 45
EW-1017 EMS	166, 567
EWAM	614
EWCM	8, 9, 548
EWCP	526
EWRRF	527
EWS 900	519
EWS 900CA	519
EWS 900E	519
EWS 905	517
EX-8	683
EX-10	708
EX-33	690
EX-39	460
EX-40	465
EX-41	464
EX-42	465
EX-68	732
EX-74	464
EX-89	466
EX-90	466
EX-91	466
EX-171	460
Excalibur	186, 227
Exocet	226
Eye Bowl	336
Eye Shield	275, 329
F	
F-14	178
F 17	671
F/A-18	179
F/A-18 program	54
FAAD	11
FAAMS	79, 399
FAAS	661
FaCS	132
FACT	125
FAGC	630
Falcon	377
FAMP	15

SUBJECT	Page
FAMS	89
Fanfare	710
Fantazmagoria	236
Farad	498
FARS	374, 531
FAS 3-1	592
Fasol	516
Fast Forty (Italy)	438
Fast Walker	18
Fasthawk	251
FASTT	34
FAW-70, -150, -200	240
FBCB2	11
FCC	6
FCCBMP	7
FCS-3	313
FDDI	89
FDDS	8, 9, 36, 53, 59, 60, 69
FDS	22, 23, 24
FDS-D arrays	22, 23
Felis Mk 3	342
FENELON	585
Feniks-M	604
FENRIS	97
Ferranti 500	83, 111, 116
Ferranti 700	107
FERRET	567
FESS	7
FEWSG	535
Fez	42
FFAR	265
FFISTS	59, 61, 127, 130, 185, 638
FFISTS 2	131
FFS	9
FG 18	717
FG 26	717
FG 29	717
FHS-900	21
FHS-2000	21
53-27L	680
53-38	680
53-38U	680
53-39	680
53-51	680
53-56	680
53-56V	680
53-56VA	680
53-57	680
53-61	680
53-65	681
53-68	681
53-71	682
53-83	682
56-SM	442
Fig Jar	31, 100
FILIPPO	743
FIM-92	417
FIMS	733
Fin Curve	278
Finland:	
Coast-Defense Guns and	
Rockets	267
MCM/Minehunting	
Sonars	733
Shipboard Guns and Gun	
Systems	432
Sonars and Underwater Fire-	
Control Systems	579
Strategic Underwater Sensor	
Systems	21
FISCS	576
Fish Bowl	31
Fiskars sweeps	733
FIST	12, 13, 34
5in/38 mounts (U.S.)	128, 130, 462
FIX-24	19
FL 400	472
FL 1800B	487
FL 1800H	487
FL 1800S	487
FL 1800U	487
FL-4	221
FLAG	19
Flag	330
FLAMS	737
Flap Lid	339
FLASH	587
Flat Screen	333

SUBJECT	Page
Flat Track	508
FlF-2	417
FLIRT	564
FLTSAT	41
FLTSATCOM	33, 36, 38, 40, 41, 43, 136
FLUTE	581
Fly's Eye	563
Flying Sword	752
FLYRT	574
FM-80	395
FMCW transmitters	20
FMPDS	441
FMS 12	614
FMS 13	614
FMS 15	614
FMS 52	614
FMSCS	32
Foal Tail	607
FOCON	68
FOCON-A	92
FOCSLE	4, 6, 137
Focused pressure waves	758
FODMS	69
Fog Lamp	279
FOG-MPM	220
Football	513
FORESEE	90
Fort S-300F	405
40-79	684
40mm grenade launcher Mk 19 (U.S.)	464
40mm/70 FCS (Sweden)	345
45-36ANU	683
45-36NU	683
FOSP	4
FOTC	8, 10, 14
FOTD	537
4K75DU	188
4K80	241
4K85	241
4P33	339
4R60 Grom	337
4R90 Yatagan	338
FPS 5	348
FQQ-1	23
FQX-3	661
France:	
Air Fire-Control Systems	216
Air-to-Air Missiles	421
Airborne Sensors	194
Aircraft Guns	266
Aircraft Tactical Data Systems	165
Command Advice Systems	2
Computers	48
Countermeasures	703
Data Buses	67
Electronic Warfare	475
Fire-Control Systems	288
MCM/Minehunting Sonars	734
Mines	717
Missiles	664
Missiles and Guided Bombs	223
Nonacoustic ASW Sensors	662
Optronic Systems	287
Radars	281
Radio Systems	26
Satellite Sensor Systems	16
Shipboard Guns and Gun Systems	432
Shipboard Radars and Fire-Control Systems	280
Signal Processors	649
Sonars	579
Sonobuoys	648
Strategic Strike Systems	186
Submarine Combat-Direction Systems	139
Surface Ship Combat-Direction Systems	76
Surface-to-Air Missiles	396

SUBJECT	Page
Torpedoes	671
Underwater Fire-Control Systems	590
Unguided Bombs and Air-Launched Rockets	261
Fregat-MR	331
FRESH	7
Frigate Bird	192
Front Dome	336
Front Door	336
FS 2000	105
FSAF	399
FSBS	43
FSK	25
FTAAS	647
FTAS	12, 661
FTC	711
FTEWA	125, 127
Furuno radars	312
Fut-B	331
Fut-B	338
Fut-N	329
G	
G1	717
G2	717
G3	718
G7e	675
G-100	472
GA35 35mm cannon	102
Gabriel	230
Gadfly	406
Gafel	512
Galiflir	198
GAMA-1	715
Gapfiller	36
Garpun	328
GAS-372	604
GASS	655
Gatekeeper	203
Gator	179, 265
GAU-13 (U.S.)	466
Gauntlet	404
GBS	33
GBU series	253
GBU-29/30	250
GCCS	4, 5, 7, 15
GCS-1	232
GD-53	208
GDS 3	71
GEC 30X Night Owl	181
GELA	238
Gemini	564
GEMMA	654
GEN-X	572
Generic Sonar	710
GENSER	40, 69
Geran	515
Germany:	
Air-to-Air Missiles	422
Aircraft Guns	266
Coast-Defense Guns and Rockets	268
Command Advice Systems	2
Countermeasures	706
Data Buses	67
Electronic Warfare	487
MCM/Minehunting Sonars	740
Mines	717
Missiles and Guided Bombs	228
Radio Systems	26
Shipboard Guns and Gun Systems	434
Shipboard Radars and Fire-Control Systems	293
Sonars	591
Strategic Underwater Sensor Systems	21
Submarine Combat-Direction Systems	141
Surface Ship Combat-Direction Systems	82
Torpedoes	673
UAVs (formerly RPVs)	192
Underwater Fire-Control Systems	596

SUBJECT	Page
GFCP	10, 14, 36
GFCS4	317
GFCS Model 1	312
GFCS Model 2	313
GHA	740
GHG	591
Giant (DM 19)	491
GII	608
Gimlet	404
GINABUS	67, 80
GIPSY	143
GKT	746
GKT-2/-3M	746
GLOBIXS	34, 36
GM mine (Russia)	720
GMI 100 Rockan	725
GMI 600	725
GMR	215
Goa	403
Goalkeeper	92, 114, 440
Goblet	403
God Eye radar	275
GOES satellite	8
Golden Dragon	208
GP 250	116
GPS	11, 14, 18, 30, 74, 97, 124
GPS Almanac	36
GPU-5 (U.S.)	466
Grail	404
Grand X	81
Granit	17, 242
Graseby G738	708
Graseby G750	609
Graseby G1732, 2008	42
Gray Wolf	183, 209
Griffin	529
Grifo	193
Grison	407
Grom	234
Grouse	405
Grumble	405
GRX series	678
GRX-2	678
GSA 7	364
GSA 8	364
Guardian	523
Guardian Star	567
Guardsman	356, 361
Gudgeon	588
Guided bombs (Russia)	238
Guided bombs (U.S.)	253
GUNAR	273
Guns: ADEN Mk 5, 267; AK-100, 442; AK-130, 441; AK-176, 443; AK-176M, 443; AK-230, 446; AK-306, 446; AK-630, 446; AK-630M, 446; AK-725, 444; AK-726, 443; AM-23, 267; Bofors 4.7in/46, 449; Bofors 4.7in/50, 449; Bofors 6in, 449; Bofors 40mm L60, 453; Bofors 40mm L70, 451; Bofors 57mm/70 Mk 2, 450; Bofors 75mm L60, 270; Bofors 76mm, 450; Bofors 155mm L39, 270; Bofors 254mm, 270; Breda 30mm, 439; Breda-Bofors 40mm, 49, 438; Breda-Oerlikon KBA, 440, 455; CADS-1 (Russia), 446; D-56TM (Russia), 444; DCN 25mm (France), 433; DEFA 552A, 266; 8in (UK), 270; 8in/55 (U.S.), 460; 81-K (Russia), 444; 81mm Mortar Mk 2 (U.S.), 463; 85mm (Russia), 269; 88mm (Germany), 268; Emerlec-30, 128, 464; ERSTA 120mm/62, 270; 15cm SCK/28 (Germany), 268; 15in/45 (UK), 270; 0.50-caliber machine gun (M2) (U.S.), 470; 5in/38 (U.S.), 271; 5in/54 ETG (U.S.), 460; 5in/54 Mk 42 (U.S.), 59, 114, 461; 5in/54 Mk 45 (U.S.), 461; 40mm (Germany), 434; 4.5in Mk 6 (UK), 458; 4.5in Mk 8	

SUBJECT	Page
(UK), 458; 4in (UK), 459; 14.5mm machine gun (Russia), 447; GAU-12/U Equalizer, 267; GIAT 20mm (France), 433; GSh-6-23, 267; GSh-301, 266; Karin 120mm L55, 270; M60 machine guns, 181; M60/Mk 43 (U.S.), 470; M61A1/M197, 267; M791, 266; Mauser BK 27, 266; Mk 8 (UK), 268; Mk 86 (U.S.), 71, 117, 118; NG15-2 (China), 432; NG15-2 (Russia), 445; 9.2in (UK), 270; 9A620, 267; 9A4071, 266; 90-K (Russia), 443; NR-23, 267; NR-30, 267; Oerlikon 20mm (Switzerland), 456, 457; Oerlikon 30mm, 49, 454, 455; Oerlikon (BMARC) 25mm (Switzerland), 455; Oerlikon/OTO 35mm (Italy), 439; 100mm (Russia), 268; 100mm gun, 67; 100mm KSM-65 (Russia), 268; 100mm/56 (Russia), 442; 100mm MLE 1953, 1964, 1968, and Compact (France), 432; 105mm (Germany), 268; 105mm/45, 434; 122mm (Russia), 269; 127mm (Germany), 268; 130mm (Finland), 267; 130mm (Russia), 268; 150mm (Portugal), 268; 152mm (Russia), 269; 152mm (Sweden), 270; 155mm (U.S.), 271; 180mm (Russia), 268; OTO-Melara 76mm, 49; OTO-Melara 76mm/62 Compact Mounting (Italy), 436; OTO-Melara 127mm/54 LW (Italy), 436; Sea Vulcan 30mm, 49; 7.62mm mini-gun (Mk 25) (U.S.), 470; 70-K (Russia), 445; 76.2mm/48 single mount (Russia), 444; 76mm, 128, 130; 6in, 268; 6in/47 (U.S.), 460; 6in/50, 270; SM-2-1 (Russia), 442; Steelet (Russia), 446; TAK 120 (Sweden), 449; 30mm (Type GCM) (UK), 459; 30mm twin mount (Russia), 446; 35mm Millennium (35/1000) (Switzerland), 455; 37mm (Russia), 445; 3in Mk 6 (UK), 459; 3in/50 (U.S.), 268, 463; 3in/62 Mk 75 (U.S.), 463; 305mm/52 (Russia), 269; 305mm/56 (Russia), 269; 12in/45 (U.S.), 270; 12in/50 (UK), 270; 20mm Mk 20 Rh202 (Germany), 268, 435; 25mm Automatic Cannon Mk 38 (U.S.), 464; 25mm Mauser E, 268; 25mm twin mount, 446; 2M-3M (Russia), 446; 2M-5 (Russia), 447; 2M-6 (Russia), 447; 2M-7 (Russia), 447; 210mm (Sweden), 270; 240mm (Taiwan), 271; Type 61 (Russia), 446; Type 66 (Russia), 444; Type 69 (Russia), 446; Type 76 (Russia), 444, 445; Type 82 (Russia), 447; Type 106 (Italy), 438; Type 107 (Italy), 438; Type 564 (Italy), 438; UTES-M (Russia), 448; V-11M (Russia), 445; V-47M (Russia), 445; Vickers 4in, 431; Vickers 6in/50, 269; Vickers 12in/50, 269, 270; Vickers 15in/45, 269; ZiF-31B (Russia), 444; ZiF-72 (Russia), 444; ZU-23-2 (Russia), 447	

SUBJECT	Page
Gvozdika	515
GWIS	37
GWS 1	410
GWS 20	409
GWS 21 radar (UK)	348
GWS 21 missile (UK)	409
GWS 22 radar (UK)	349
GWS 22 missile (UK)	409
GWS 24	409
GWS 25	411
GWS 26	411
GWS 30	410
H	
H930	57, 59, 71, 128
Hagenuk TFCS	596
Hai Ying radar	275
Half Cup	510
Half Hat	513
Half Plate	331
Hamlet's Cove	751
Hammerhead	251
HARD	342
Hard-Target Penetrator	264
HARM	167, 179, 183, 254
HARP	652
Harpoon	87, 92, 114, 121, 123, 139, 156, 161, 172, 178, 183, 255
Harpoon 2000	256
Harpoon II	220
Harpoon Shipboard Command Launch Control System	218
HARR	752
HATS	692
Have Gaze	18
Have Nap	250
Have Quick	28, 30, 35, 37, 41
Have Slick	220
Have Thrust	428
Hawk Link	38
Hawk missile	97
Hawk radar	235
Hawk Screech	336
Haze	170
HC 75 radar	128
HDS	580
Head Lights	337
Head Net C	326
Hedgehog FCS	636, 701
Helicopter sweeps (U.S.)	755
Helios	16, 26
Hellfire missile	181, 257
Hellfox	193
Helmet-mounted sight	214
Helos	216
HELRAS	617
Helstar	192
Heracles I, II	196
Hercules	604
Hermes	522
HESIS	341
HF surface-wave radar	366
HF/DF	19, 526
HFAJ	28
HFS-100	568
HFS-200	568
HHTI	361
HIDAR	652
Hinpads	166
HIPADS/HAP	646
HIPAS	576
HIRAM	574
HISAR	215
Hispano-Suiza 20mm guns (old) (Switzerland)	457
Hispasat	32
HISS	391
HISSAR	192
HN-5	405
HOMS	258
Horse Jaw	606
Horse Tail	606
Hot Dog	491
Hot Flash	337
Hour Glass	340
HPTS	45

SUBJECT	Page
HQS-102	599
HQS-103	599
HR-76	128, 130, 385
HS 12 sonar	173, 588
HS 71	583
HS 73	583
HS 312	588
HS 381	38
HS 601	41
HS 820	459
HS 831	459
HSBCA	44
HSCLCS	218
Hsiung Feng	247
HSL-42	181
HSL-46	181
HSL-48	181
HSQ-101	663
HSRIS	752
HSS-1	305
HSV-20NCS	390
Hughes Modular Combat System	57, 59
HUMINT	4
Hungary:	
MCM/Minehunting Sonars	741
Hunter	193
Hunter/SR-UAV	192
HUS-001	596
HUS-002	596
HUS-003	596
HY-1	220
HY-2	221
HY-3	222
HY-4	221
HY-5	222
HYCATS	73, 127
HYDAB	608
Hydra EO system	362
Hydra array	614
HYDROX	689
I	
IAD	24
IADT	84
IAS	9
IBIS system	614
Ibis	81
ICADS	59, 555
ICDC	157
ICES	127
IDAP	472
IDECM	548
IDLS	137, 184
IDM	33
IDPS-14	149
IDS-2000	30
IEEE 802.3	68
IFSAS	11
IGDM	720
IGDM-500	720
IGM 10	717
IGUANE radar	166, 194
IHS-6	501
Ikara	664
Il-20 Coot-A	516
ILAS-3	678
ILDS	409
IMAIS	746
IMICS	742
Impact	675
INCA	589
India:	
Countermeasures	706
Electronic Warfare	491
Missiles and Guided Bombs	229
Radio Systems	26
Shipboard Radars and Fire-Control Systems	294
Sonars and Underwater Fire-Control Systems	579
Sonobuoys and Signal Processors	650
Surface Ship Combat-Direction Systems	85
Surface-to-Air Missiles	399
Torpedoes	675

SUBJECT	Page
Indonesia	
Strategic Underwater Sensor Systems	21
Indra	294
Initsiyativa 2K radar	169
INMARSAT	31, 37, 126
Inmilsat	32
INS series	501
INSICOM	40
Integrated Maritime Surveillance System	19
INTELDATA	40
Intelink	9
Intelligence Broadcasts	38
INTELSAT	37, 40
International:	
Aircraft Tactical Data Systems	167
Command Advice Systems	3
Countermeasures	706
Electronic Warfare	492
Missiles	665
Missiles and Guided Bombs	229
Radio Systems	26
Surface-to-Air Missiles	399
Torpedoes	675
Iraq:	
Mines	718
IRDS	176, 183
Irida	19
IRIS-T	422
IRIX	94
IRSCAN	322
IRST	179, 391
IRSTS	206
Irytysh	603
ISAACS	139
ISABPS	40
ISAR	12, 14, 38, 181
ISDS	125
ISO 100	707
Israel:	
Airborne Sensors	197
Aircraft Tactical Data Systems	167
Computers	49
Countermeasures	707
Missiles and Guided Bombs	229
Optronic Systems	297
Radars	295
Shipboard Guns and Gun Systems	435
Surface Ship Combat-Direction Systems	86
Surface-to-Air Missiles	401
UAVs (formerly RPVs)	192
ISUS-83	141
ISUS-90	141
ITACS	130
ITALD	573
Italy:	
Airborne Sensors	197
Aircraft Tactical Data Systems	167
Bombardment Rockets	271
Computers	50
Countermeasures	707
Data Buses	68
Electronic Warfare	497
Fire-Control Systems	307
MCM/Minehunting Sonars	742
Mines	718
Missiles and Guided Bombs	230
Mortars and Depth Charges	697

SUBJECT	Page
Optronic Systems	305
Radars	298
Radio Systems	30
Shipboard Guns and Gun Systems	436
Sonars	598
Sonobuoys and Signal Processors	650
Submarine Combat-Direction Systems	143
Surface Ship Combat-Direction Systems	87
Surface-to-Air Missiles	401
Torpedoes	676
Underwater Fire-Control Systems	598
ITAS	383
ITATA	474
ITAWDS	10, 122
ITL/ITS 70	227
IUSS	5, 12, 23
IVIS	11
IWDM	732
J	
J-FOCSS	2
J-Hawk	261
JADDIN	16
Janet	482
Japan:	
Air-to-Air Missiles	423
Electronic Warfare	503
Fire-Control Systems	312
MCM/Minehunting Sonars	743
Mines	719
Missiles and Guided Bombs	232
Nonacoustic ASW Sensors	663
Radars	309
Radio Systems	30
Sonobuoys and Signal Processors	651
Strategic Underwater Sensor Systems	21
Submarine Sonar and Combat Systems	599
Surface Ship Combat-Direction Systems	90
Torpedoes	678
JASA	548
JASS	548
JASSM	250
JAST	182
JCAT	7
JCMS	7
JDAMS	15, 18, 179, 180, 250
JDISS	8, 37
JDS	1
JETS	548
Jezebel	645
JFACC	37
JHMCS	214
Jindalee	19
JINTACCS	136
JL-1	186
JM61MB (U.S.)	469
JMCIS	2, 5, 7, 8, 36, 43, 67
JMINI	35
JMOCC	10
JOCS	4
Joint Tactical UAV	192
JORN	19
JOTS	5, 6, 7, 8, 9, 36, 53, 59, 61
JPTDS	119
JSCAMPS	192
JSF	182
JSIPS	13
JSIPS-N	13, 14
JSOW	15, 18, 179, 251
JSTARS	38, 183
JTDS	84, 119, 124
JTIDS	15, 27, 29, 30, 36, 118, 179
JTT	16

SUBJECT	Page
JTUAV	193
Ju Lang 1	186
Jubilee Guardsman	203
Julia	715
Julie	45, 168, 169, 645
Jumpseat	18
Jupiter	282
Jupiter 08	283
Jupiter II	283
Jupiter IIS	283
JVIDS	61
JWICS	9
JWID-96	185
K	
K 66A	673
K 69	673
K-13 mine (Japan)	719
K-22M	216
K-26	216, 234
Ka-25/27	169
Ka-27PL CDS	169
KA-99 camera	191
KAB-250PL	667
KAB-500 bomb	238
KAB-1500 bomb	238
Kabarga-A1	746
KAE 7600	293
KAE 8600	293
KAE 9600	293
KAFS	150
KAFUS	21, 22
Kaira-24	239
Kaira-27	239
Kaliakra	273
Kalmar	170, 188
KAM mine (Russia)	720
Kanaris system	160
Karat	269
Karen	235
Kariwara	576
KAS 2000	700
Kasatka	17
Kashtan	407
Kaskad	269
KAST	153
Kastell	269
KATE	149
Katyusha	698
Kazoo	236
KB	720
KD 59	673
KDM-500	720
Kedge	236
Keflavik	12
Kegler	235
Kelvin-Hughes SCTD System	112
Kent	237
Kerch	605
Kerry	234
Kestrel	527
KG-84	14
Kh-15S	237
Kh-22	234
Kh-23	234
Kh-25	235, 244
Kh-25MR	235
Kh-28	235
Kh-29	236
Kh-31	171, 237
Kh-35	238
Kh-41	171, 243
Kh-55	237
Kh-58	236
Kh-59	236
Kh-59M	171, 236
Kh-65	237
Kh-65SE	171
Kh-66	234
Kh-101	238
KH-series optical systems	17
Khost	42
Kickback	237
Kilter	236
Kingbolt	236
Kingfish	234

SUBJECT	Page
Kingfisher OPV system	101, 119
Kingfisher (EW)	492
Kingfisher mine avoidance	631
Kinshal	404
Kinzhal	406
Kitchen	234
Kite Screech	337
Kivach 3	326
Klara	269
Klein 595	756
Klen-54	239
Klen-PS	239
Klinok	406
Kliver	325
KLON	217
KMC 9000 consoles	96, 97
KMD mines	721, 722
KMD-500/-1000	732
KMK mines	721
KN-NTDS	131
Kobra	344
Kolibri	269
Kollmorgen Model 975	273
Kolonka	340
KOLS radar	169
Kondensor	340
Kondor	269
Korea:	
Electronic Warfare	504
Mines	719
Sonobuoys and Signal Processors	651
Torpedoes	679
Korean Naval Command System	131
Kormoran	167, 228
Kormoran 2 missiles	196
Korrell	217
Korshun	168, 199
Kortik	407
Kosmos 1870	17
KPM mines	720
KR-75	294
KRAB	721
Krab-11	512
Krab-12	512
Krait	577
KRAM	740
Kremlin-2	510
KRIS	112
KRISS bomblets	224
KRM	721
KRUG and FIX series	19
Krypton	237
KS-1	395
KS-87B	191
KS-153	191
KS-172	425
KSM mine	721
KSM-65	269
KSR-2	216
KSR-5	234
KT44 torpedo	691
KT-216	514
Kursk	509
Kyle	235
L	
L7A2 gun (UK)	460
L 3	672
L 4	672
L 5	673
L-082 Mak	510
Lacrosse	18, 19
LADARs	662
Ladoga-P-670 FCS	146
LADS	496, 662
Lamb Tail	607
LAMPARO	649
Lamproie	583
LAMPS	54, 119, 180
LAMPS Data Links	38
LAMPS III	61, 110, 117, 123, 549
LAMS	400
Land Roll	339
LANDSAT	18

SUBJECT	Page
Lantirn	179
LAPADS	653
Laser Dazzle System	362
Laser-guided bomb	227
LASS	364
Lavi	295
LBVDS	633
LC 2000	474
LCAC Command/Surveillance System	127
LCAW	678
LEAD	712
LEASAT	32, 36, 38, 41
LEDS	28, 35, 127
Leevyen	667
LEIP	28
LEMF	28
Leningrad	604
Lev (Russia)	441
LEWA	142
LFA	24, 60, 576
LFATS	617
LFCS Mk 1	162
LHT	693
LIDAR	663
LIDS	321
LIFE	563
Lifeline	555
Light Bulb	31
Light Ship ESM	474
LIGHTHOUSE	615
Lightweight Sonar	576
Limbo	701
Link 1	26, 39
Link 2	26
Link 3	26
Link 4	26, 107
Link 4C	27
Link 5	27
Link 6	27
Link 7	27
Link 8	27
Link 9	27
Link 10	27, 32, 91, 107
Link 11	4, 8, 10, 12, 25, 26, 27, 28, 29, 32, 37, 61, 74, 78, 90, 91, 107, 123, 124, 184
Link 11 Data Terminal Sets	38
Link 11/16	126
Link 12	28
Link 13	28
Link 14	28, 32, 39, 61, 78, 90, 123, 184
Link 15	28
Link 16	29, 32, 39, 90, 118, 121, 179, 184
Link 22	30, 43, 78
Link America	1, 28, 41
Link Delta	28
Link G	32
Link Pi	28
Link R	32
Link Sigma	28
Link T (Taching)	31, 52
Link W	26, 75, 166
Link X	27, 32, 107
Link Y	27, 31, 32
Link Y Mk 2	26
Link Z	32
LIOD	321
Lira mine	721
LIROD-8	317, 321
LISA	26
LITDL	27
Little Look program	542
Littoral Sea Mine	732
LL Mk 3 sweep (UK)	748
LL Mk 6* sweep (UK)	748
LL Mk 8 sweep (UK)	748
LL Mk L sweep (UK)	748
LMAP	660
LMRS	752
LN-66	180, 274
LN-66HP radar	390
Locator	541
LOFAR	21, 23, 38, 645
LOFARgram	12, 23
Long Fold	651
Long Head	340

SUBJECT	Page
Long-Range Mine Program	731
Longlook	461
Lookout	273
LOPAS	596
LORA	629
Loral Surface Ship Integrated Combat Control System	131
Loral Surveillance System	25
LOROC	575
LOROP	191
Low Ball	3
Low-Drag Bombs (U.S.)	263
LQO-3	21
LQO-4	21
LR-100	568
LRAAM	408
LRDS	39
LSEOS	347
LTN-72	14
Lung Chin	22
LUQM-145	718
Lurch	30
LURES	555
Luz	230
LVIS	752
LW-02	315
LW-03	315
LW-04	273
LW-08	315
LW-09	316
LWI 1	689
LWS-20/30	576
LY-60N	395
Lynx	290
Lyutik	515

M	
M1 FCS	322
M2 FCS	322
M03-CAA	716
M03-CGB	716
M03-EAA	716
M03-EGB	716
M4 missile	187
M4 FCS	322
M5 missile	187
M5 FCS	600
M7/8 mine	717
M8 FCS	138, 141
M08 mine	719
M8 series	601
M8/7 FCS	144
M8/41	143
M9 series	602
M11	602
M20	186, 187
M40 series	323
M51	187
M Mk 1 mine (UK)	727
M Mk 1 sweep (U.S.)	754
M Mk 2 mine (UK)	727
M Mk 4(i) sweep (U.S.)	754
M Mk 4(m) sweep (U.S.)	754
M Mk 5 mine (UK)	727
M Mk 5(c) sweep (U.S.)	754
M Mk 6(a) sweep (U.S.)	754
M Mk 6(b) sweep (U.S.)	754
M Mk 7 sweep (U.S.)	754
M-1 sonar (Russian)	607
M-08	721
M-11	403
M-12	715
M-26/KB	715
M-39	721
M-46	346
m/9	725
MA 2000	740
MA 8530	21
MA 8560	21
Ma-3	238
MA-31	237
Machta	512
MACTIS	742
MAD Mk 3	662
MAD-SADE	663
MADOM	751

SUBJECT	Page
MAE-10 mine	717, 724
Magic	422
Magic Lantern	759
MAGICS	50, 73, 88, 89
Magnetic surveillance sensors	22
Magnetic sweeps (UK)	748
Magnetic sweeps (U.S.)	754
Magnum	18
Maigret	489
MAINS	107, 111
MAL/17	718
Malafon	664
Malakhit	241
MALD	573
Malin	700
Mangouste	650
Manta (EW)	529
Manta mine	718
MANTA ESM	26, 148
Manta	733
MAOC	12
MAPS	5, 12
Marconi 400 Series	273
Mare Tail	607
MAREC II	200
MAREX	294
MARIA	269
MARIL	31, 52, 104
Marine Target Simulator	706
Marisat	36, 38
Maritime Mission Support System	12
Maritime Patrol Suite	167
MARS	282
Mars-Passat	328
Marte	198, 230
MARTEL	224
MAS 90	740
MAS/22	718
MAST II	10
Mast-Mounted Sight	392
Master Pescador	220
Masurca	398
Matador	540
MATE	138, 151
MATES	563
Matilda	530
Matilde	530
MATT	16
Maverick missile	175, 179, 183, 258
MAWID	90
MBL-9	564, 574
MCAC	752
MCAR	630
MCC 23	717
MCOIN II	3
MCS	11, 116, 128
MCS 2000	128, 130
MCSS	655
MCT 15	717
MD 100/S	598
MD-103A	568
MDDS 1.X and 2.X	36
MDG-35	455
MDM series	721
MDS	36, 219, 722
MDT	722
ME Mk 103 sweep (UK)	748
ME Mk 106 sweep (UK)	748
ME Mk 107 sweep (UK)	748
ME Mk 108 sweep (UK)	748
Medusa	305, 715
Medvedka	667
MEECN	45
Menon	697
Mentor	759
MEOSS	362
Mermaid	527
Meroka CIWS	124, 448
MESAR	355
Metel	666
MEWS	562
MFC	116
MFC-01/100	716
MFCC	114
MG-7	605, 746
MG-10	604
MG-13	707

SUBJECT	Page
MG-15	604
MG-23	707
MG-26	42
MG-29	42
MG-35	607
MG-35E	42
MG-53	707
MG-69	746
MG-70	605
MG-79	746
MG-89	746
MG-100	604
MG-200	604
MG-311	607
MG-312	607
MG-322	607
MG-325	607
MG-332	607
MG-335	605
MG-335MS	605
MG-345	604
MG-519	606
MG/Mk 213C	266
MGK-100	605
MGK-300	605
MGK-400	606
MGK-500	607
MGK-540	606
MGK-607	22
MGM-140	272
MGP-86	404
MGT	684
MGT-2	684
MGT-3	684
MHIDAS	68
MHQ	2
MHT-500	19
Mi-14	170
MICA	422
MICE	67
MICFAC II	10
MICOS CDS	85
MICOS MCM	95
MicroPUFFS	577, 618
MIDAHS	167
MIDAS	158, 623
MIDAS (Germany)	434
MIDS	29, 30, 78, 179
MiG-29 and Su-27 Weapons Control System (SVU)	169
MIL-STD-1553B	69, 73
MIL-STD-1760	69
MIL-STD-1773B	69
MILAS	665
MILDS	563
Milestone I and II	22, 23
Milstar	32, 34, 35, 37, 39, 43, 45
MIMBO	715
MIN 77	742
Mine Modernization Program	715
Mine Neutralization System	758
Mine-type seismic sensors	22
Minehunting laser (France)	734
Minehunting systems	81
Minesniper	745
Mini-AIO	113
Mini-DAMA	34, 35
MIP	629
MIR-2	522
MIRAB	722
Mirage F1	166
MIRFS	182
Mirror Sonar	759
Mission Core System	167
Mistral	398
Mius	326
MIUW	657
MIUW Upgrade	25
MJ 2000	740
Mk 1 sweep (UK)	748
Mk 2 mine (Norway)	719
Mk 2* sweep (UK)	748
Mk 3 ASW sensor (France)	662
Mk 3* sweep (UK)	748

SUBJECT	Page
Mk 4 Marine Mammal System (U.S.)	751
Mk 5 guidance system (U.S.)	189
Mk 5 mine (UK)	726
Mk 6 depth charge (U.S.)	702
Mk 6 mine (U.S.)	713, 729
Mk 7 jammer (U.S.)	708
Mk 7 Marine Mammal System (U.S.)	751
Mk 7 sweep (UK)	748
Mk 8 sweep (UK)	748
Mk 8 torpedo (U.S.)	161
Mk 8 torpedo decoy (U.S.)	708
Mk 8** torpedo (UK)	686
Mk 9 depth charge (U.S.)	702
Mk 9 sweep (UK)	748
Mk 10 mine (UK)	727
Mk 10 MLS (U.S.)	418
Mk 11 air-launched depth charge (UK)	701
Mk 12 mine (UK)	726
Mk 13 launching system (U.S.)	125
Mk 13 mine (U.S.)	727, 729
Mk 13 MLS (U.S.)	418
Mk 13 radar (U.S.)	273
Mk 14 depth charge (U.S.)	702
Mk 14 launching system (U.S.)	125
Mk 14/23 series torpedoes (U.S.)	689
Mk 15 mine (UK)	727
Mk 15 torpedo (U.S.)	670
Mk 15/1 CIWS	123
Mk 16 mine (U.S.)	729
Mk 16 MLS (U.S.)	418
Mk 17 mine (UK)	727
Mk 18 mine (U.S.)	730
Mk 19 plotter (U.S.)	157
Mk 20 Rockeye bomblet	175
Mk 22 MLS (U.S.)	419
Mk 23 plotter (U.S.)	157
Mk 23 torpedo (U.S.)	161
Mk 24 target designation transmitter	389
Mk 24 torpedo (UK)	688
Mk 24 Underwater Ordnance Locator (U.S.)	756
Mk 25 mine (U.S.)	730
Mk 25 radar (U.S.)	377
Mk 25 torpedo launcher (U.S.)	696
Mk 26 FCS (U.S.)	273
Mk 26 MLS (U.S.)	419
Mk 28 (U.S.)	712
Mk 29 MLS (U.S.)	419
Mk 30 (U.S.)	712
Mk 32 (U.S.)	712
Mk 32 MLS (U.S.)	419
Mk 32 torpedo launcher (U.S.)	696
Mk 33 MLS (U.S.)	419
Mk 33/34 electronic system (U.S.)	574
Mk 34 radar (U.S.)	378
Mk 35 MLS (U.S.)	419
Mk 35 optical director	128, 130
Mk 35/H930 optronic sensor	390
Mk 36 electronic systems	574
Mk 36 mine (U.S.)	729
Mk 36 MLS (U.S.)	419
Mk 37 FCS (U.S.)	59, 377
Mk 37 MLS (U.S.)	419
Mk 37 series torpedoes (U.S.)	689
Mk 37 torpedo (Germany)	706
Mk 38 FCS (U.S.)	273
Mk 38 MLS (U.S.)	419
Mk 39 (U.S.)	712
Mk 39 MLS (U.S.)	419
Mk 40 mine (U.S.)	728
Mk 41 mine (U.S.)	728
Mk 41 MLS (U.S.)	420

SUBJECT	Page
Mk 42 mine (U.S.)	728
Mk 42 MLS (U.S.)	421
Mk 44 MLS (U.S.)	421
Mk 44 torpedo (Japan)	678
Mk 44 torpedo (U.S.)	691
Mk 45 MLS (U.S.)	421
Mk 45 torpedo (U.S.)	683
Mk 46 MLS (U.S.)	421
Mk 46 NEARTIP	691
Mk 46 SLEP program	692
Mk 46 torpedo (Japan)	678
Mk 46 torpedo (U.S.)	691
Mk 47 MLS (U.S.)	421
Mk 48 MLS (U.S.)	421
Mk 48 torpedo (U.S.)	152, 153, 156, 694
Mk 48-3 torpedo (U.S.)	161
Mk 49 mine (U.S.)	730
Mk 50 Barracuda (U.S.)	695
Mk 50 MLS (U.S.)	421
Mk 50 series mine (U.S.)	728
Mk 50 torpedo (U.S.)	54, 181
Mk 51 FCS (U.S.)	389
Mk 51 mine (U.S.)	730
Mk 52 FCS (U.S.)	273
Mk 52 mine (U.S.)	730
Mk 52 MLS (U.S.)	421
Mk 53 attack console	131
Mk 53 mine (U.S.)	731
Mk 53 MLS (U.S.)	421
Mk 54 depth bomb (U.S.)	702
Mk 55 mine (U.S.)	730
Mk 56 FCS (U.S.)	378
Mk 56 mine (U.S.)	731
Mk 57 mine (U.S.)	731
Mk 60 (Captor)	731
Mk 62 mine (U.S.)	728, 729
Mk 63 FCS (U.S.)	378
Mk 63 mine (U.S.)	728, 729
Mk 63 TT (U.S.)	697
Mk 64 mine (U.S.)	728, 729
Mk 65 mine (U.S.)	728
Mk 65 TT (U.S.)	697
Mk 66 (U.S.)	152
Mk 66 mine (U.S.)	731
Mk 67 (SLMM) mine (U.S.)	731
Mk 67 mine (U.S.)	727
Mk 67 TT (U.S.)	697
Mk 68 FCS (U.S.)	59, 379
Mk 68 TT (U.S.)	697
Mk 69 FCS (U.S.)	273
Mk 69 mine (U.S.)	732
Mk 69 TT (U.S.)	697
Mk 70 FCS (U.S.)	378
Mk 74 FCS (U.S.)	59, 126, 378
Mk 75 (Italy)	436
Mk 75 attack director (U.S.)	151, 152
Mk 76 FCS (U.S.)	59, 380
Mk 78 analyzer (U.S.)	151
Mk 80 series	263
Mk 81 WCC (U.S.)	152, 153
Mk 82 gun mount (U.S.)	465
Mk 82 Snakeye	701
Mk 86 FCS (U.S.)	380
Mk 90 launch-system console (U.S.)	125
Mk 91 FCS (U.S.)	51, 383
Mk 91 launch-system console (U.S.)	125
Mk 91 SAM system (U.S.)	84
Mk 92 ACC (U.S.)	152, 153, 156
Mk 92 FCS (U.S.)	127, 132
Mk 92 radar (U.S.)	384
Mk 93 FCS (U.S.)	128, 390
Mk 93 gun mount (U.S.)	465
Mk 94 gun mount (U.S.)	465
Mk 95 gun mount (U.S.)	465
Mk 95 radar (U.S.)	383
Mk 96 gun mount (U.S.)	465
Mk 96-0 WLC (U.S.)	153
Mk 98 FCS (U.S.)	189

SUBJECT	Page
Mk 99 FCS (U.S.)	117, 381
Mk 99 missile (U.S.)	117
Mk 101 FCS (U.S.)	636
Mk 103 sweep (U.S.)	755
Mk 104 sweep (U.S.)	755
Mk 105 FCS (U.S.)	636
Mk 105 sweep (U.S.)	755
Mk 106 FCS (U.S.)	636
Mk 106 sweep (U.S.)	755
Mk 111 FCS (U.S.)	636
Mk 113 FCS (U.S.)	146, 151, 153
Mk 114 FCS (U.S.)	84, 130, 131, 636
Mk 115 FCS (U.S.)	273
Mk 116 BRI (U.S.)	153
Mk 116 FCS (U.S.)	122, 117, 637
Mk 117 FCS (U.S.)	152, 153, 156
Mk 118 FCS (U.S.)	153
Mk 129 casualty battery-control unit (U.S.)	125
Mk 130 workstation (U.S.)	156
MK 171 chaff launcher (U.S.)	565
MK 182 chaff launcher (U.S.)	565
MK 186 chaff launcher (U.S.)	565
Mk 200X	73, 74
MK 214 chaff launcher (U.S.)	565
Mk 218 casualty weapons director (U.S.)	125
MK 245 chaff launcher (U.S.)	565
Mk 245 electronic system	491
Mk 309 fire-control panel	637
Mk A44 torpedo (U.S.)	691
MKB	720
MKD	722
MKD 600	297
MKT-1	746
MKT-210 minehunter	745
ML Mk 3 sweep (UK)	748
ML Mk 4 sweep (UK)	748
ML Mk 4-1 sweep (UK)	748
MLV satellites	33
MM1-CAL	715
MM1-CBF	715
MM1-DAL	715
MM2-CGB	715
MM2-CHB	715
MM2-CMP	715
MM2-DGB	715
MM2-DHB	715
MM2-EGB	715
MM2-EHB	715
MM2-EMP	715
MM3-CAP	716
MM3-CGB	716
MM3-DAP	716
MM3-DGB	716
MM3-EAP	716
MM3-EGB	716
MM 15TT	224
MM 38/40	226
MM-4 FCS	275
MM/SLQ-727	498
MM/SLQ-747	501
MM/SPS-768	301
MM/SPS-774	301
MM/SPY-790	300
MMD	711
MMI 80	725
MMIC	30
MMPM	45
MMRS	209
MN series (Germany)	434
MN-53	472
MNFEP	15
MO-90	725
MOC console	93
MOCC	10, 11
Model 76 periscope (U.S.)	644

SUBJECT	Page
Model 86 periscope (U.S.)	644
Model 90 periscope (U.S.)	644
Model 260 MCM (U.S.)	760
Model 985 director (U.S.)	390
MODEX	611
Modified Football	513
Modular FLIR	203
Modular Improvement Packages	131
Modular Propelled Bomb	227
Molniya	30
MOM-90	725
MOMS	15
Moose Jaw	605
Mortar Mk 10	701
Moskit	243
MOSS	153
MOSS Mk 57	711
Mouflon	650
Mouse Roar	603
Mousetrap	702
MP-80	718
MP-401	509
MP-403	511
MP-404	511
MP-405	513
MP-407	513
MPAvionics	183
MPDR-45	373
MPM	15
MPP	662
MPT-3	746
MPZ-301	339
MR-05	273
MR-80	718
MR-102	328
MR-103	338
MR-104	335
MR-105	334, 338
MR-114	337
MR-123	334
MR-145	337
MR-184	337
MR-201	327
MR-212	327
MR-302	331
MR-302M	331
MR-310U	326
MR-320	327
MR-500	325
MR-600	332
MR-700	331
MR-760	331
MR-800	332
MRCS	137
MRK series sweeps	733
MRK-50 Tobol	330
MRO-560 radar	339
MRP	718
MRR	286
MRS 3 radar	349
MS14	748
MS 500	697
MS 990 series	745
MS-C	716
MS-L	716
MSD-7001	73
MSDAU	61
MSDF	74
MSDHS	166
MShM	722
MSI-70U	95, 144
MSI-80S	95
MSI-90U	51, 97, 144, 145
MSI-340/350	97
MSI-3100	29, 51, 96, 97
MSIS	298
MSPS	483
MSR 810	648, 650
MSR 910	650
MSS	12, 24, 25
MSSA Mk 1	750
MSSE	141
MSTRAP	712
MT-1	746
MT-2G/-3G	746
MTDS	85, 125, 759

SUBJECT	Page
MTLS	689
MTP-19	716
MTRACS	710
MTST	12, 136
MTTR	316
Muff Cob	338
Mulloka	577
Multicast	33
Multifunction Workstation	137
MULTS	28, 39, 61
Murene	288, 670
MUROSS system	580
MUSAC	608
Mushroom	199
MUSIC	40
MUSICIAN	320
MUST	35
Mustang	650
MUTE	555
MW08 radar	114
MW-5 FCS	279
MW-5 radar	278
MW-08	317
MWCS	92, 733
MWS 80	83, 116
MWS 90	84
MX-512	38, 39
MX-512P	28, 29, 39
MX-902	275, 329
MYaM	723
Myriad (Italy)	440
MZh-26	715
N	
N001 Miech	200
N010 Zhuk	197, 199
N019 Sapfir-29	199
N 30 (Germany)	434
N-25	324
N-FOCSS	2
NA-9	307
NA-10	71, 86, 307
NA-18	306, 308
NA-21	308
NA-25	50, 309
NA-28	50, 309
NA-30	308
NAAWS	131
NACCIS	3
NADIR II	166
NADS	482
NAE	711
NAIS	87
NAJA	290
NAJIR	290
Nakat	512
Nakat-M	512
NAMFI	113
Napalm	265
Narama	576
Narrow-band secure voice channel	40
Nartsiss	169
Narval	273, 288
NASAMS	426
NATACS	493
NATO 4	26
NATO Data Links	26
NAUTIC	114
Nauticus	4, 71
Nautilus	150
NAUTIS	71, 108, 111, 114
NAUTIS-M	751
Naval Combat System Type 88C	396
Naval Integrated Bridge System	132
Naval Surface Fire Support Control System	11
Navalized Galix	487
NAVCAM	36
NAVFAC	23, 24
Navigator	203
NAVIPLOT	81, 82
NAVIXS	36
NAVKIS	51, 97
NAVMACS	33, 35, 40, 43
NavS	641

SUBJECT	Page
Navscon	87
NAVSPASUR	20
NAVSSI	156
Navstar	18
NAVTAC	102
NAWS	113
NCCS	6, 7
NCCS-A	6
NECC	37
NEDPS	149
Nemesis	563
Neptune	285
NESP	32
NEST terminal	32
Netherlands:	
Computers	50
Data Buses	68
Electronic Warfare	505
Fire-Control Systems	322
MCM/Minehunting Sonars	743
Optronic Systems	321
Radars	313
Radio Systems	30
Shipboard Guns and Gun Systems	440
Shipboard Radars and Fire-Control Systems	313
Sonars	600
Submarine Combat-Direction Systems	143
Surface Ship Combat-Direction Systems	90
Underwater Fire-Control Systems	601
Nettunel	124, 498
Nettuno	498
Neural-Net Signal Processor	662
New Attack Submarine Network	158
New Dipping Sonar	576
New Independent Mine (Norway)	720
New Threat Upgrade	386
NEWSY	482
Newton	498
NF-1	434
NFEP	6, 15
NFT armored turret	441
NGCR	69
NGDS	485
NIADS	28
NICE	500
NICS	26
NIEWS	9
Nighthawk	391
Nike Hercules	235
NILE	28
Nimrod MR.2	53
9CM series	518
9EW series	518
9GR600	343
9HCI 100 Hera	196
9KA100	344
9KA500	343
9KR400	343
9LV100 series	71, 345
9LV200 series	75, 79, 104, 105, 344, 345
9LV300 series	345
9LV 453 Mk 3	106
9LV Mk 2	52
9LV Mk 3 series	105
9LV search radar	343
9MCM200	106
9MJ400	82, 106, 111
9SCS Mk 3	148
9SP180	726
9TC302	609
9TCI210	149, 576
9TS700	747
NIPS	8, 10, 12, 13, 138
Nite Hawk	205
NITES	9
Nixie	711
NLCAW	665
NMRS	752
NOAH ARCS	97
NONAP	41

SUBJECT	Page	SUBJECT	Page	SUBJECT	Page	SUBJECT	Page	SUBJECT	Page
Norway:		**111SO/111SG/111SZ**		Ovod	236	Pinguin B3	740	Processor Mk 24	572
Coast-Defense Guns and		missiles	667	Ovod-M	236	Pioneer	192	Project 636	146
Rockets	268	ONGAR	688	Owl Screech	338	PIPRS	577	Project 877	146
Computers	51	Oniks	245	Ox Tail	607	Pirana	288	Project 941	188
Electronic Warfare	507	OP3A	291	Ox Yoke	607	Piranha	605	Project 5140	472
MCM/Minehunting		OPCON	2, 4, 6, 9	OYQ series	90, 124	Pirate	535	Project 6033	720
Sonars	744	OPERA	7			PISCES	161	Project Backscratch	23
Mines	719	Operation End Sweep	728	**P**		Pithon	605	Project Caesar	23
Missiles and Guided		OPINTEL	40			PIVAIR	639	Project Caliban	103
Bombs	233	OPS-1/2	273	P3T	248	PK-2	514	Project Embroidery	40
Mortars and Depth		OPS-9	309	P85 mine	725	PK-10	514	Project Horizon	79, 112
Charges	697	OPS-10	309	P2074	742	PK-16	515	Project Ida	268, 719
Shipboard Guns and Gun		OPS-11	309	P2095	742	PL-8	396	Project Indigo	18
Systems	441	OPS-12	310	P-3C	174	PL-9	396	Project JADE	615
Submarine Combat-Direction		OPS-14	310	P-5/6/35	241	PLANET	68	Project Kestrel	176
Systems	144	OPS-16	310	P-10 system	244	Plank Shave	31, 328	Project Kingfisher	759
Surface Ship Combat-		OPS-17	310	P-15/20/21/22	239	PLAT-1	683	Project Midnight	759
Direction Systems	95	OPS-18	310	P-70 Ametyst	241	Plate Steer	331	Project Orlan	684
Surface-to-Air		OPS-19	309	P-80	243	Platina	605	Project Sirius	171
Missiles	402	OPS-22	309	P-100	243	Plessey Torpedo		Project Teluma	613
Novator Alpha	245	OPS-24	311	P-120	241	Launchers	689	Projector Mk 15	701
NRWE	487	OPS-28	311	P-270	243	PLN 517	295	Projector Mk 20	702
NS-9000 series	493	OPS-29	309	P-500	241	PLRM-1A	732	Projectors Mk 10/11	701
NSGS	435	OPS-35	310	P-700	242	PLRS	9, 11	ProMiS sonar	740
NSIS/WLY-1	710	OPS-36	310	P-750	238	PLT series	715	Prophet	532
NSM missile	233	OPS-37	310	P-800	245	PLT-4	720	Protean	518
NSSMS	413	OPSMER	2	P-1000	246	PLT-6	720	Proteus	53
NT37 series torpedoes		Optoradar Mast	639	PA ROVs	745	Pluto minehunting vehicle		PRS 3 series	591
(U.S.)	689	OQA series	90	PAAMS	399	(Italy)	743	PRS-1 radar	267
NT-37	161	OQR series	90	PACCMS	7	Pluto radar (Italy)	301	PRSS	548
NTCCS	86, 87	OQS series	90, 599	PACIS	198	Pluto Plus	743	Przpiorka	507
NTCS	12	OR-89/AA	207	PADLOC	576, 629	PM-1 mine (Russia)	720,	PS-05/A	200
NTCS-A	6, 7, 8, 11, 156	OR-263/AA	207	PAE-1	600	723		PS-37/A	200
NTCSS	8	ORACLE	43	PAINTER	320	PM-2 mine (Russia)	720,	PS-46/A	200
NTDS	1, 8, 27, 28,	Orange Blossom	522	PAIR	629	723		PS-75	342
	48, 57, 68, 70	Orange Crop	522	PALANTIR	532	PMAWS-2000	562	PSBN-M-8 radar	193
NTIS	361	Orange Reaper	527	Palash	407	PMK-1	723	PSRS-2 Initsiyativa 2B	
NUAMP	657	ORB 31	196	PALIS	2, 84	PMP-2	746	radar	169
Nuclear Weapons		ORB 32	196	Palm Frond	327	PMR-2	723	PSTS	190
(Russia)	263	Orca mine (Argentina)	716	Panda	80, 290	PMS 26	610	PSU 1-2	595
Nulka	473	Orca CDS (South		PAON	290	PMS 27	610	PTA	579
NUR-25	324	Africa)	146	PAP 104	81, 738	PMS 46/56	576	PTW	14
NUR-27XA	324	ORDALT 6948	59	Parian	613	PMS 75	613	Puff Ball	199
NWS-1/2 radar	280	Orekh	336	PARIS	288, 704	PMT-1	723	PUFFS	618
NWS-1/3/4/5/6	280	ORESTES	35	Park Lamp	3, 42	PMTS	472	Punch Bowl	17
NWSS	7	Orion radar (Denmark)	376	Parus	403	PMTS 90	689	Purga	608, 683
NWTDB	8, 12	Orion radar (Italy)	303	Pathfinder 1500	376	PMW49A	689	PVDS	735
Nyada	327	Orion radar (Russia)	199	Paveway	253	PMW series	689		
		Orion sonar (Russia)	605	PAWS	167	PNS-24M	199	**Q**	
O		ORLO	507	PC EMSKED	7	Podberezovik	333		
		Oropesa sweeps (U.S.)	754	PCMS	549	POET	573	QBE-3	623
O Size 1 sweep (U.S.)	754	Oropesa sweeps (UK)	748	PDM	732	Poima	330	QCU-2	576
O Size 4 sweep (U.S.)	754	ORTS	117, 118, 130	PDS	75	**Poland:**		QH-50D	192
O Size 5 sweep (U.S.)	754	Osa-2M	339	Pea Sticks	275	Electronic Warfare	507	QRCC	386
OAB	5, 6, 18	Osa-M	403	Peace Bow	216	MCM/Minehunting		QTLHNR	710
OASIS	6, 12, 14	Osborn	750	Peace Peek	568	Sonars	745	Quick-Sat	40
OASIS III	176	OSCAD	4	Peel Cone	327	Shipboard Radars and Fire-		Quickstrike	728
OBIS	7	OSGP	7	Peel Group	338	Control Systems	324	QW-1	396
OBOE array	23	OSID 83	593	Peel Pair	327	Surface-to-Air		QX3	111
OBS	36	Osiris	17	Pegas	576	Missiles	402		
OBU	7, 36	OSIS	7, 9, 36	Pegaso	308	Polaris	186	**R**	
Ocean Master	195	Osminog	169	Pelamida	605	Polinom	606		
Ocean Venture 1993	37	Osprey	576	Pelican	171	Pollux	79, 290	R76	385
Octopus ESM	527	OSS	3, 6, 7, 9, 15	PEMT-2	746	Polypheme	229	R 550	422
Octopus sonar	582	OTCIXS	6, 8, 14, 15, 34,	PEMT-4	746	Pop Group	339	R-1 Rubin-1A	199
Odin	113		36, 37, 40, 156, 176	Penguin FCS (Norway)	51,	Porker	523	R-27	423
Odyssey	472	OTH Gold	2		95	Porpoise	527	R-29/4K75 missile	188
OE-207	43	OTH-T	1, 5, 7, 16, 37	Penguin missile (U.S.)	173,	**Portugal:**		R-29DU	188
OE-305/BRR	44	Otomach	231		181, 233	Coast-Defense Guns		R-29RM	188
OE-315	44	Otomat	88, 113, 231	Penguin Mk 4	233	and Rockets	268	R-39 Rif-M Missile	188
OE-315/BRC	44	Outboard	20, 36	Perch Gill	607	Poseidon	188	R-39UTTKh	188
OEPS-27	200	Outfit AZV	354	Pert Spring	3, 42	Poseidon C-3	186	R-60	423
OFD	363	Outfit DEC	362	Petrel	738	Positiv	327	R-72	425
OFLA-M	273	Outfit INB	7	PFAS	589	POST (Prototype Ocean		R-73	424
OG 20	306	Outfit JZZ	5, 107	PFCS 2	95	Surveillance Terminal)	8,	R-77	424
OG 30	306	Outfit RJJ	31	PFN 513	295	9, 10, 59, 120		R.440	396
OG.R7	86, 306	Outfit RTC	31	PFSS	4, 9	PoST (Portable Submarine		R.460	396
OJ-653	134	Outlaw Bandit	549	Phalanx	467	Terminal)	37	RACAL COMINT	
Oka-2 sonar	169, 170	Outlaw Hawk	16, 34, 36,	Phantom 2000 program	209	Pot Drum	328	system	531
OKT-2	746		57, 136	Philax	518	Pot Head	328	Racal navigational	
OL-76	177	Outlaw Hawkeye	14, 203	Phoenix	427	PPT-1	746	radars	357
OL-77	177	Outlaw Hunter	6, 12, 14	PHS-32	600	PPT-2	746	RACJAM	557
OL-82	659	Outlaw Prowler	203	PHS-36	600	PQ-826	517	Radamec 2400	84
OL-267	119	Outlaw Seahawk	14, 203	PIANIST	320	PQ-859	517	Radamec series	
OL-5004	659	Outlaw Shark	16, 34, 36,	Picador radar	281	PQS-1	757	1000/2000	363
Older mines (UK)	726		57, 136	Pike	607	PQS-1A	757	Radar displays	137
OLS-27 radar	170	Outlaw Story Teller	14, 203	Pike Jaw	604	PRAM	732	Radar plot extractors	
OMS	644	Outlaw Viking	14, 203	Pilot	342	PREBOR 6	101	(UK)	361
OMS-100	641	OUTPOST	44	Pilot Fish	615	PRISM	472	RADDS	9, 127, 130
ON-143	14, 36, 40, 66, 67	Outrigger	555	PIN 515	295	Privateer	568	Radiant Hail	33
1BV/2	596	Overa	716	Pinguin	83	Probe Alert	44	Radiant Ivory	33

SUBJECT	Page
Radiant Mercury	33
Radiant Mist	391
Radiant Outlaw	203
Radiant Snow	395
Radiant Tin	33
Radio Links	42
Radop	293
RADS	111
Raduga	31
Rafael MBAT	496
Ragep-Toran	81
RAIDS	387
RAINFORM	40
Rakurs	341
RAM	413
RAMICS	760
RAMPART	615
RAMS	172
Ramses	506
RAN missile destroyers	122
RAN-3L	301
RAN-10S	301
RAN-11 L/X	302
RAN-12 L/X	302
RAN-20S	303
RAN-30X	303
RAN-1010	496
Rangout	331
Rani	295
Rapid Clearance	752
Rapids	506
RAPLOC	619
RAS-2 Owl	492
RASCAR	132, 374
Rashmi	295
Rat Tail	606
RAT-10S/8S	305
RAT-33S/M	305
Rattler	496
RATTRAP	615
RAVAL	267
RAWL-2	295
RAWS (Role Adaptable Weapon System)	185
RAWS radar	295
Rayrider	408
Raytheon ICS	131
Raytheon ISCWS	164
Rb 04E/05A/08A	220
Rb 12	246
RBE-2	196
RBOC	574
RBOC II	574
RBP-3	200
RBS 15	105, 246
RBS 15F	200
RBS 17	257
RBS 70	408
RBS 73	200
RBU-900	697
RBU-1000	697
RBU-1200	697
RBU-2500	698
RBU-6000	31, 100, 667, 698
RBU-10000	667
RBU-12000	667
RC-134 program	136
RCM	530
RCMDS	738
RDA	24
RDC	196
RDL	531
RDR	492
RDR-1300	215
RDR-1400	215
RDR-1500	215
RDS-81 radar	215
RDSS	24
RDY	196
REALTO	706
RECA torpedo	738
Recital (ED.103)	67, 78
Redeye	418
Remena	716
Remora	479
REMSIG	460
Replica	534
Reporter	321
Reshet	86
RETORC II	695

SUBJECT	Page
REX II	97
Reya	328
RF-61	395
RGB-2	651
RGB-16/1	651
RGB-25	651
RGB-56	651
RGB-64	651
RGM-84	255
Rhyolite series	18
Rice Lamp	278
Rice Screen	278
Rim Hat	510
RIM-7	413
RIM-7M	51, 114
RIM-66A	414
RIM-66B	414
RIM-66C	416
RIM-67A	414
RIM-116A	401, 413
RIM-156A	417
RINS	111
Rivet Joint program	136, 176
RKT-1	746
RKV-500	237
RM-1	723
RM-2	723
RMES	576
RMS	753
RMZ	723
RN-231	325
RNSSIXS	67
RNTDES	132
RNTDS	119
Rocket Cruiser	99
Rocket Cutter	100
Rockets (France)	262
Rockets (Russia)	263
Rockets (UK)	263
Rockeye	179, 265
Rockwell ACS	161
ROLE (Link 11)	27, 29, 31, 40, 139, 143
Roquette LAT	703
RORSAT	4, 17
Ros sonar	169
ROTHR	6, 7, 20
Round Ball	279
RPB-2	199
RPB-4 Initsiyativa	199
RPK-1	683
RPK-2	666
RPK-3	666
RPK-5	667
RPK-6	667
RPK-7	667
RPK-8	667
RPLK-27	667
RPM	723
RQN series	501
RRASL	112
RSCES	118, 119
RSDAF	733
RSM-40	188
RSM-50	188
RSM-52	188
RSM-52M	188
RSM-54	188
RSM-54M	188
RTADS	16
RTB-92	652
RTIC	15
RTLOS	125
RTN-10X	86, 109, 303
RTN-20X	303
RTN-25X	303
RTN-30X	304
Rubba	331
Rubber Duck	534
Rubezh	240
Rubikon	606
Rubin	199
Rum Tub	511
RUM-139A	668
RUR-5A	667
Russia:	
Air Fire-Control Systems	216
Air-to-Air Missiles	423
Airborne Sensors	198

SUBJECT	Page
Aircraft Guns	266
Aircraft Tactical Data Systems	168
Bombardment Rockets	271
Coast-Defense Guns and Rockets	268
Command Advice Systems	3
Countermeasures	707
Electronic Warfare	507
Fire-Control Radars	333
Fire-Control Systems	341
MCM/Minehunting Sonars	745
Mines	720
Missiles	666
Missiles and Guided Bombs	234
Mortars and Depth Charges	697
Nonacoustic ASW Sensors	663
Optronic Systems	340
Radio Systems	30
Satellite Sensor Systems	17
Search Radars	325
Shipboard Guns and Gun Systems	441
Sonobuoys and Signal Processors	651
Strategic Strike Systems	188
Strategic Underwater Sensor Systems	21
Submarine Combat-Direction Systems	146
Submarine Communications Systems	42
Surface Missile Fire-Control Systems	217
Surface Radar/ELINT (Electronics Intelligence) Systems	19
Surface Ship Combat-Direction Systems	98
Surface-to-Air Missiles	403
Torpedoes	679
Unguided Bombs and Air-Launched Rockets	262
RVP	387
RVP/ADT	123, 124
RW-23-1	512
RX-740	526
RX-750	526
Ryf	325, 405
Rys	335

S

SUBJECT	Page
S3V	667
S123	20
S124	19
S810	358
S811	358
S1810	360
S1812	360
S1830	360
S1834	360
S1850L	360
S3000	525, 569
S Mk 6	727
S-2	239
S-3	207
S-3A	182
S-4	743
S-7	743
S-10	245
S-170M	102
SA950	744
Sa'ar V System	87
SA-15 (Tor)	407
SA-16	404
SA-N-1	403
SA-N-3	100, 403
SA-N-4	403
SA-N-5	404
SA-N-6	14, 98, 100, 405
SA-N-7	102, 406
SA-N-8	404

SUBJECT	Page
SA-N-9	404, 406
SA-N-10	405
SA-N-11	407
SA-N-12	407
SA-X-18	405
SAAM	399
SAAPS	577
SABER	394
SABRE	527, 752
SACC	7, 11
SACCS	33, 43
Sachem	2
SACMFCS	392
SACTIS	143
SAD	139
SADANG	650
SADANG 1000	166
SADE	139
SADIE	51
Sadie family	527
SADIS	572
SADOC 3	88, 89
SADOC series	50, 68, 70, 87, 124
Sadral	398
SADS	156, 158, 633
SAET-40	684
SAET-50	681
SAET-60	681
SAET-60M	681
SAFENET	7, 35, 69
SAFIRE	204
SAG-2b	732
Sagaie	484
SAGE	480
SAHV	408
SAI	717
SAIGON	480
SAIS	102
Salamandre	481
SALFAS	24
Salish	239
Salmon	586
Salt Pot	340
SALTO	706
SAM	747
SAM 204	701
SAM I	105
SAM II	105, 747
SAM-104	701
Samanta bomblets	224
SAMID	121
SAMIR	483
SAMPSON	355
Samson	573
Sandbox	241
SANDMAN	525
Sandpiper	569
Sanguine	44
Sapfir-27	200
SAPIENS	480
SAPOM	437
SAPOMER	437
Sapphire	113, 364
SAR	17, 27
SAR imagery	13, 14
SAR-8	273
SARA AA FCS (France)	291
SARA sonar (Italy)	598
Sardin (Spain)	448
SARIE	531
SARTIS	394
SAS 90	291
SASS	23, 24
SAT	139
SATAM	83, 116
Satan system	49
SATAR	705
SATCOMM	41
SATCOMM Link 11	28
Satellite Information Exchange System	40
SATIN	79
SATIR	71, 84, 87, 122, 124
Saturn 3S	32
SAVAAS	12
Sawfly	188
Sawhorse	222
SAWS	613, 710

SUBJECT	Page
SB-81	719
SB-MV/1	719
SBIR	17
SBP 1-1	648
SC-1005/1510/1525	305
SCALP	223
SCANS	571
SCATS	59
Sceptre	529
Scimitar	506
SCIP	572
SCORADS	321
SCORE	287
Scorpion	531
SCOT	32
Scout	92, 318
SCR-390	517
Scramshell	461
SCSS	33
Scutter	707
Scylla	580
SD-1	395
SDC	78
SDDU	91
SDMS	69, 400, 418
SDS	17, 23
SDV-1	392
SDWS	710
Sea Archer 1	364
Sea Archer 30	364
Sea Cat	109, 409
Sea Chaparral	128, 413
Sea Cobra	273
Sea Command	97
Sea Dart	75, 107, 108, 410
Sea Dragon FCS (U.S.)	393
Sea Dragon weapons system (Russia)	170
Sea Eagle missile (UK)	248
Sea Eagle radar (China)	278
Sea Eagle ROV (Sweden)	747
Sea Eagle weapons system	167
Sea Front System 2000	269
Sea Giraffe	74, 342
Sea Gnat	492, 533, 565
Sea Harrier	52, 165, 172
Sea Hawk	347
Sea Hunter (Switzerland)	79, 347
Sea Hunter (UK)	576
Sea Killer missile	198, 230
Sea Lance	157, 667
Sea Lion	527
Sea Lion ESM	161
Sea Nymph	557
Sea Owl (PID)	203
Sea Petrel	501
Sea Ray	259
Sea Saviour	532
Sea Searcher (UK)	201, 576
Sea Sentry ESM	570
Sea Sentry surveillance system	25
Sea Serpent	732
Sea Shield	455
Sea Skua	83, 248
Sea Slug Mk 2	410
Sea Sparrow	51, 67, 92, 106, 126, 131, 413
Sea Tiger antenna	79
Sea Tiger FCS	393
Sea Tiger radar	281
Sea Viking	105
Sea Vulcan 20/20P (U.S.)	469
Sea Witness	750
Sea Wolf	108, 411
Sea Zenith (Switzerland)	455
SEA-90 sonar	598
Sea-Eye	298
Sea-SLAM	257, 460
SeaAirSearch	375
Seabear	460
Seacom I	31
Seafox	740
Seagle	570
Seaguard	84, 347
Seahawk	181, 185, 372

SUBJECT	Page	SUBJECT	Page	SUBJECT	Page	SUBJECT	Page	SUBJECT	Page
Seahuntor	689	Sheksna	607	SLAM	12, 15, 118, 179, 181, 183, 255	SNW-10	273	Sphinx	506
Seaking	570	Shelon	606	SLAM ER	180	SOAS	159	Spider	483, 608
Seamos	192	Sherloc	167, 483	SLAMMR	184, 212	SOBIC	21	SPIDER	93
SEAO	2	SHF Links	40	SLAR	200	Soccam	517	SPIN	25
Search Mast	639	Shield	533	SLASM	581	SOLFERINO	26	Spin Trough	330
Searchlight	21, 22	Shields	549	SLAT	220, 705	Sonar 90	593	Spira	602
Searchwater	52, 172, 202	Shikari	295	SLATE	44	Sonar 3000 PLUS	613	SPN-35	388
Searchwater 2000	203	SHINMAX	73	Slava-class CDS	100	SonTak	608	SPN-42	389
Seaspray	201	SHINPADS	48, 67, 71, 73, 74	SLBMs	188	SOPELEM periscopes	640	SPN-43	388
Seaspray 4000	184	Shiploc	483	SLCM	16	Sopka	239	SPN-46	389
SEASTARS	183	Shipwreck	242	SLEP	121	Sorel	586	SPN-703	298, 304
Seawatch array	570	Shkval	683	SLEWS	472	SORTS	7	SPN-720	298
Seawatch OPV system	101	SHL 100 Flaming A	745	Slim Net	329	SOSS	4	SPN-728	298
SECBAT	649, 650	SHL 200 Flaming B	745	SLMM Mk 67	690	SOSUS	11, 12, 23	SPN-748	298
SECOMSAT	32	Short Horn	199	SLOT	44	South Africa:		SPN-749	298
Second Admiral	98	Shot Dome	31	Slot Back	199	Aircraft Tactical Data Systems	171	SPN-751	298
Second Captain	98	Shot Rock	31	Slow Walker	6, 18, 19	Electronic Warfare	516	SPN-753(V)	299
Sedis sonar	740	Shotgun	3	SLPRM	2	Mines	724	SPO-10	516
Seegrundmine 80	717	Shrike	220	SLQ-01	498	Missiles and Guided Bombs	246	SPO-15	516
Seehawk	206	Shtil missile	406	SLQ-17	562	Radio Systems	31	SPO-23	516
Seemine 65	717	Shtil series	188	SLQ-20	395, 549	Shipboard Guns and Gun Systems	448	Spot 1	18
Seewolf torpedo	740	Shtil' sonar	607	SLQ-20B	119	Shipboard Radars and Fire-Control Systems	341	Spot 4	16
SEMP-3	746	Shtorm	403	SLQ-22	472	Submarine Combat-Direction Systems	146	Spot Mk 2	17, 18
SEMT-1	746	Shtyk	199	SLQ-25	711	Surface Ship Combat-Direction Systems	101	SPQ-2	299
SEN-100/SER/TBA	73	SIASS sonar	144, 601	SLQ-26	472	Surface-to-Air Missiles	408	SPQ-3	299
Senior Blade	13	Siconta	73, 116	SLQ-29	562	Soviet Satellite Data Relay Network	30	SPQ-9	382
Senior Pennant	220	Side Globe	99, 511	SLQ-32	57, 118, 123, 124, 132, 138, 549	Sovremennyy-class CDS	100	SPQ-9B	382
Senior Span (U-2R)	38	Sidearm	259	SLQ-33	711	SP-100	74, 116	SPQ-12	127
SENIT	55, 70, 76, 77, 87, 122, 124	Sidekick	549	SLQ-34	552	SP-521	341	SPQ-701	299
SENIT 3	55	Sidewind	482	SLQ-36	711	SP-2060	556	SPR-02	523
SENIT 5	80	Sidewinder	165, 172, 179, 427	SLQ-37	755	SP-2110	576	SPR-06/00	505
SENIT 8	61, 62, 79	SIDS	387	SLQ-48	128, 758	SPA-4	137	SPR-A	498
Sentinel	361	SIEWS	545	SLQ-49	534	SPA-25	137	SPRINT	705
SEPA	598	SIFONET	68	SLQ-50	138, 552	SPA-25G	9, 120, 127, 130	Sprut	336
SEPACS	159	SIGHT	91, 92, 93	SLQ-380	517	SPA-50	137	SPS	639
Seppia	718	SIGMA	460	SLQ-501	474	SPA-50G	130	SPS 104	678
Sequoia	480	Sigma-670	146	SLQ-610	517	Spada	402	SPS 1000	661
Sergeant rocket	126	Sigma-Node	93	SLQ-620	517	Spain:		SPS-01	92, 316
Series 4	576	Sigma-Splice	93	SLQ-A	498	Coast-Defense Guns and Rockets	269	SPS-5	366, 516
Series 5 signal processor (UK)	654	Signaal Coastal Radar	321	SLQ-B	498	Electronic Warfare	516	SPS-6	367
Series 5 sonar (UK)	614	Signaal Mini- and Compact Combat Systems	94	SLQ-C	498	Mines	724	SPS-8	338
Series 800 system	472	Silex	666	SLQ-D	498	Mortars and Depth Charges	699	SPS-10	84, 132, 367
SERO 12	641	Silkworm	221	SLR-16	549	Shipboard Guns and Gun Systems	448	SPS-10/58	128, 130
SERO 14	641	SILO	395	SLR-21	472	Shipboard Radars and Fire-Control Systems	342	SPS-12	367
SERO 15	641	Silver Dog	491	SLR-22	549, 552	Surface Ship Combat-Direction Systems	103	SPS-29	86, 369
SERO 40	641	SIMAS	24, 59, 153, 633	SLR-23	549	Surface-to-Air Missiles	408	SPS-30	338
Serpei	723	Simbad	398	SLR-24	711	Spain:		SPS-37	369
Serpeiy mine (Russia)	720	SINBADS	141, 143	SLR-504	527			SPS-39	369
SES-210E	496	SINCGARS	37	SLR-600	541			SPS-40	74, 132, 370
SESIT	78	SINCOS	68	SLVR	43			SPS-42	369
SESTAS	577	SINCOS-1200	92	SM 39	226			SPS-48	126, 370
SESUB	148	Singer-Librascope SFCS Mk I/II	161	SM-1	130			SPS-49	114, 118, 123, 126, 371
SET-40	684	SINS	124	SM-1/2	124			SPS-52	369
SET-40-62	684	SINTAC	30	SM-1ER	59			SPS-52 through -52B	57
SET-53	681	Siren decoy (UK)	534	SM-1MR	59			SPS-53	366
SET-65	681	Siren missile (Russia)	241	SM-2 Aegis	417			SPS-55	114, 123, 128, 372
SET-65M	681	Sirena (SPB)	516	SM-2 Block IV	119, 417			SPS-58	128, 130, 132, 372
SET-72	682	Sirius	322	SM-2MR	88, 116			SPS-59	274
SET-73	684	SIRIUS IRST	93	SM-3	59			SPS-60	366
SET-80	682	SIRS	559	SM-4-1	269			SPS-64	373
SET-U	684	SISC	78, 89	SM-312 launcher	245			SPS-65	372
Setka-3	511	SISU-1 FCS	143	Small-Ship ESM	570			SPS-66	376
Setter	529	SIT	151	SMART	93, 135, 317			SPS-67	84, 132, 367
SEWACO	50, 71, 90, 141, 144	SIU	614	SMART-L	93, 317			SPS-69	374
SEWACO II	107	600 series	111	SMART-S	317			SPS-71	374
SEWACO VIII	141, 144	60mm Mortar (U.S.)	464	Smartello	360			SPS-72	374
SEWACO-FD	81, 93	65-73	679	SMASH	460			SPS-73?	374
SEWS	496	65-76	679	SMASHER	416			SPS-100	371
Sextant	2	65JD series	579	SMATCALS	273			SPS-130/140	515
SEXTET	591	Skanter 009	280	SMB	43			SPS-150	515
SFCS-6A	90	Skat	607	SMCS	31, 53, 113, 116, 150			SPS-160	515
SFMPL	10, 59, 156	Skiff	188	SMDG program	753			SPS-161/162	515
SGE-30 (Netherlands)	440	Skin Head	328	SMDM	722			SPS-702	299
SGM 80	717	SKIP	36	Spektr-F	510			SPS-768	300
SGR-103	317	Skipper	220	Smerch-1	698			SPS-774	300
SGRS	296	Skorpioen	246	Smerch-2	698			SPS-N 5000	489
SH100	732	Skubermor	81	Smerch-3	697			SPU-1/W	755
SH-2	180	Sky Flash	431	SMR-S	143			SPUD	654
SH-60B	180	Sky Guardian	520	SMS	639			SPWM	15
Shaddock	188, 241	Sky Guardian 300	184	SMTD	710			SPY-1	71, 116, 117, 118, 119, 126, 374
Shadowbox	540	Sky Shadow	224	Snake Eyes	209			SQ2 series	579
Shadowgraph	738	Sky Watch	328, 340	Snakeye	263			SQ series	602
Shark Fin	605	Skyflash	200	SNAPS	107, 149			SQC-1 sonar	579
Shark Gill	606, 607	Skyguard	402	SNG-21 FCS	275			SQK series	703
Shark Tail	605	Skynet	30, 32	Snoop Head	329			SQQ-14	623, 757
Shark Teeth	604, 605	SLAD	712	Snoop Pair	330			SQQ-14/IT	742
Sharpshooter	383			Snoop Plate	330			SQQ-23	623, 629
Shearwater	647			Snoop Slab	330			SQQ-25	623
				Snoop Tray	330			SQQ-28	123, 623
				Snowstorm	235				

SUBJECT	Page
SQQ-30	732
SQQ-32	58, 138, 757
SQQ-34	11, 12, 623
SQQ-89	58, 117, 118, 122, 130, 134, 156, 623
SQQ-89I/SQY-1	576
SQR-13	576
SQR-14	24
SQR-15	24
SQR-17	626
SQR-18	127, 180, 625
SQR-19	123, 181, 625
SQR-501	577
SQS-11	576
SQS-17	628
SQS-23	86, 629
SQS-26	127, 629
SQS-29 series	630
SQS-35	628
SQS-36	628
SQS-39 series	630
SQS-43 series	630
SQS-53	58, 117, 119, 629
SQS-54	180, 576
SQS-55	631
SQS-56	138, 164, 631
SQS-58	632
SQS-503	577
SQS-504	576
SQS-505	577
SQS-507	576
SQS-509	577
SQS-510	577
Square Head	340
Square Tie	331
Squeeze Box	340
Squid	697
Squid Arm	605
Squid Head	507
SQW-3 tracer	579
SQY-1	24
SR47 radar	275
SR-1A	507
SR-200	571
SR-UAV	193
SRBOC	92, 574
SRD-501	73
SRD-502	553
SRD-503	554
SRN-744	325
SRN-7453	325
SRQ-4	38
SRS-1	554
SS105	602
SS240 series	602
SS245 series	602
SS304	602
SS575	602
SS576	602
SS 12	588
SS 12M	228
SS 312	588
SS-2	366
SS-11	220
SS-C-1	241
SS-C-2	239
SS-C-3	239
SS-N-2	239
SS-N-3	99, 188, 198, 241
SS-N-4	188
SS-N-5	188
SS-N-6	186, 188
SS-N-8	188
SS-N-9	31, 100, 241
SS-N-11	240
SS-N-12	101, 198, 241
SS-N-14	21, 100, 666
SS-N-15	146, 683
SS-N-17	186, 188
SS-N-18	188
SS-N-19	17, 198, 242
SS-N-20	188
SS-N-21	188, 245
SS-N-22	31, 101, 243
SS-N-23	188
SS-N-24	186
SS-N-26	245
SS-N-27	245
SS-N-28	188
SS-NX-13	188
SS-NX-25	244

SUBJECT	Page
SSATS	576
SSCS	31, 43, 53, 71, 72, 85, 107, 112, 113
SSDS	121, 125, 126, 386
SSDS/QRCC program	473
SSES	10, 118
SSIPS	23
SSIXS	15, 35, 36, 40, 43, 44, 156
SSM	732
SSM-1	232
SSN-715	89
SSN-744	742
SSPA	43
SSPS	123
SSQ-33	33
SSQ-36	655
SSQ-41	656
SSQ-47	656
SSQ-47B	656
SSQ-50	656
SSQ-53	656
SSQ-57A	656
SSQ-58A	657
SSQ-62	181, 656
SSQ-70	554
SSQ-71	44
SSQ-72	554
SSQ-74	555
SSQ-75	646
SSQ-77	657
SSQ-79	646
SSQ-80A(V)	555
SSQ-82	555
SSQ-86	45
SSQ-89	123
SSQ-90	657
SSQ-93	9
SSQ-95	555
SSQ-101	657
SSQ-102	646
SSQ-103	646
SSQ-108	554
SSQ-109	128
SSQ-110	657
SSQ-113	657
SSQ-522	656
SSQ-801	646
SSQ-904	652
SSQ-905	652
SSQ-906	652
SSQ-907	652
SSQ-937	653
SSQ-954	653
SSQ-963	653
SSQ-981	646
SSR-1	40, 43
SSSB	26
SST-3	674
SST-4 Seal	674
SSTD program	702, 711
ST240	602
ST802	358
ST1802	359
ST-2	746
STACOS	50, 68, 90
Stag Hoof	607
Stag Horn	607
STAMO	119
STANAG 1241	29
STANAG 4153	69
STANAG 4246	37
STANAG 4254	79
STANAG 5030	43
STANAG 5511	27
Stand-Alone Link 11	32, 95
Standard ARM	220
Standard Missile	119, 259
Standard Missile-1	414
Standard Missile-2	416
Standard Sonar 80	592
Standard Strike	416
Standard U.S. chaff cartridges	575
StanFire	75, 76, 106
StanFlex 300 System	75, 106
STAP	141
Star of Siam	32
STAR-1	229

SUBJECT	Page
STARC 25 gun mount (U.S.)	465
STARKA	269
Starstreak	409
StaS C/3	641
STASS	634
Steer Hide	605
Sterne I	739
STIDAR	700
STIDAV	293
STIDR	700
STINA	4, 31
STING	320
Stinger	417
Stingray	188, 687
STIP	12
STIR	67, 73, 74, 92, 124, 130, 320
Stockade	534
Stonefish	727
Stop Light	512
Storm Shadow	248
Story Book	561
Story Classic	561
Story Teller	561
STOVL	182
STRAP	655
Strela 2/3	404
STRIC	106
STRIKA	4
Strike Plot	9
Strix	700
Strut Curve	31, 331
Strut Pair	331
STT	15, 16
Sturgeon	188, 670
STWS series	688
Styx	239
SU series	603
Su-24M	199, 236
Su-32FN	170
Sub-Exocet	141
SubACS	156
SUBCOMMS	36, 37
SUBICS	94, 139
SUBICS 900	161
Submarine Laser Communications	1
Subpack	614
SubRASS	155, 156
Substrike	731
SubTASS	614
SUBTICS	139
SUCCESSOR	113, 116
SUMP	4, 104
Sun Visor	273, 279
Sunburn	243
Super Anemone radar	167
Super Barricade	534
Super Étendard	166
Super R 530	421
Super Rapido	436
Super Searcher radar	173, 201
Super-Bird B	30
Super-Bs	183
Super-MAREC	200
Superbarricade	486
Surface-Launched Missiles	239
SURICATE	287
SURTASS	23, 24, 41, 60, 633
SUS	45
Susie	524
SUT	674
Sutec Eagle	105
SUW-N-1	683
SVDS	738
SVU-29	169
SWADC	615
SWAK	759
SWALAS	633, 656
Sweden:	
Airborne Sensors	200
Aircraft Tactical Data Systems	171
Coast Defense	344
Coast-Defense Guns and Rockets	269

SUBJECT	Page
Command Advice Systems	4
Computers	52
Countermeasures	708
Electronic Warfare	517
Fire-Control Systems	345
MCM/Minehunting Sonars	746
Mines	725
Missiles and Guided Bombs	246
Mortars and Depth Charges	699
Optronic Systems	344
Radars	342
Radio Systems	31
Shipboard Guns and Gun Systems	449
Sonars	608
Sonobuoys and Signal Processors	652
Strategic Underwater Sensor Systems	22
Submarine Combat-Direction Systems	148
Surface Ship Combat-Direction Systems	104
Surface-to-Air Missiles	408
Torpedoes	684
Underwater Fire-Control Systems	608
Sweeps (France)	734
SWG-1	218
SWG-1A	123
SWG-2/3	16, 219
SWIM	755
Switzerland:	
Shipboard Guns and Gun Systems	454
Shipboard Radars and Fire-Control Systems	346
SWPS program	258
SWR-503	19
SwRI Model 7401	571
SWS 35/40	576
SWS-23	84
SWY series	387
SWY-1	383
SY-1	222
SY-2	222
SYCOMOR	484
Syledis-Toran	82
Syllex	485
Sylver	399
SYQ-9	12, 138
SYQ-12	128
SYQ-13	128
SYQ-15	114, 751
SYQ-17	387
Syracuse	16, 26, 32
Syrinx	400
SYS series	74
SYS-1	104, 388
SYS-2	123, 124, 126, 388
SYS-3	388
SYSCOM NG	2
System 2000	204
SYTAC	139
SYTIT	590
SYVA	590

T	
T96 torpedo (Sweden)	686
T800 series	113, 116
T Mk 6 (U.S.)	710
TABIDU	620
TACAMO	26, 41, 42, 45
TACAN	15, 29, 30, 172
TACFIRE	11, 34
TACINTEL	8, 35, 36, 40
TACNAV	38, 61
TACNAVMOD	183
TACNET	41
TACSIT	158
Tactical Aegis LEAP	412
Tactical buoy simulator	555

SUBJECT	Page
Tactical Communications Systems	25
TACTICOS	76, 78, 93
TACTICS	139
TADIL-A	26, 27, 61
TADIL-B	26
TADIL-C	26, 27
TADIL-I	30
TADIL-J	29, 30, 38, 119
TADIXS	6, 15, 34, 36, 40
TADIXS A	10, 35, 156
TADIXS B	10, 38, 118, 156, 176
TADS	86
TAICOS	3
TAINS	260
Taiwan:	
Computers	52
Electronic Warfare	519
Mines	726
Missiles and Guided Bombs	247
Radio Systems	31
Shipboard Guns and Gun Systems	458
Shipboard Radars and Fire-Control Systems	348
Strategic Underwater Sensor Systems	22
Torpedoes	686
TALD	179, 573
Talisman	708
Talon Lance	15
Talon Sword	15
Talos	410
Tamir	607
Tamir-5L	607
Tamir-5LS	607
Tamir-5N	607
Tamir-5NS	607
Tamir-10	607
Tamir-11	607
Tamir-11M	607
TAMMS	15
TAMPS	12, 13, 15, 16, 36, 178, 181
TANS navigation system	173
Tantal-670 FCS	146
TAOM	30
Taran	517
Target Designation Assembly	103
Target Designation Systems	393
TARP	158, 634
Tarpon	600
TARPS	159, 178, 191
TARS	630
Tartar	59, 76, 122
TARTT	708
TAS	548
TAS 5-2	596
TAS 5-3	596
TAS 6-2	596
TAS 6-3	596
TAS 83-1	592
TAS 90	596
TAS Mk 23	126, 383
TAS-2019	625
TASD	273
Task Force XXI	11
TASPE	620
TASWIT	59
TATTIX	173, 653
TAU-2000	706
TAVITAC	49, 75, 77, 78
TAVITAC 2000	80, 93
TAVITAC-FD	80
TB-12X	634
TB-16/BQ	633
TB-23/BQ	634
TB-29	634
TBIP	119, 260
TBP	151
TCM-20 (Israel)	436
TCS	57, 214
TCSS Mk 9	615
TD-1135/A	166
TD-1271	34
TDASS	615

SUBJECT	Page
TDF-500 series	492
TDLT	26
TDM-200	33, 34
TDMA	30, 31, 35
TDPS	90
TDS 90	291
TDS (Target Designation Sight)	364
TDS (Terma)	25, 72, 75
TDS-2000	76
TDSS	638
TEAMS	12, 14, 15, 16
Tee Plinth	341
Telecom satellites	26
Telegon	490
Telemine	715
TEM-2/-3/-4/-52	746
TEMPEST	48
Temula	709
TENCAP	6, 7, 16, 17
TENet	33
TEP 200	105
TEPEE	8, 36, 59, 219
TEREC	16
Terma radars	280
Terma Reson	105
Terne attack sonar	603
Terne III	697
TERPES	12, 15
Terrier	59
TESEO	231
TESS	9, 12, 34
TEST-71	682
TEST-96	682
TFCC	6, 7, 34, 57, 61, 69, 120
TFDS	43
TFR	215
TGS	596
THAAD	418
THD 1040	285
THD 1077	282
THD 1280	290
Thetis ESM	143
30mm grenade launcher	446
3K10 Granat system	245
3K55	245
3M10	245
3M24	244
3M25	238
3M45	242
3M51	245
3M54	244
3M55	245
3M65	188
3M80	243
3M82	243
3RM series	304
Thunder Road	752
TIAPS	577
TIBS	16, 38
TICA	119
TICM MRT-S	184
TIDE	28
Tien Kung	52
"TIFLIR-49"	206
Tigerfish	688
TIGS	361
TILOS	559
Tilt Pot	341
TIMNEX 4 CH	496
Tin Man	341
TINS	204
TIOS	149
TIP	118
TIPS	10, 122
TISS EX-8 Mod 0	391
TITAC	139
Titan	18, 607
TM 1226	95
TMDS	34
TMK radar	347
TMMM	260
TMPCU	219
TMPS (TACAMO Message Processing System)	45
TMPS (Tomahawk Mission Planning System)	219
TMS (Track Management System)	388

SUBJECT	Page
TMS (Tactical Mission System)	173
TMS 2000	650
TMS320C25	35
TMV 026	477
TMV 430	477
TN-70 series warheads	187
TNR	215
Tobol	330
TOM	644
Tomahawk	259
Tomahawk APS	13
Tomahawk Block III	18, 156
Tomahawk FCS	117, 219
Tomahawk MDU	40
Tomahawk missile	5, 6, 14, 118, 151, 152, 259
Tomahawk/Mk 50	667
Tomahawk Weapons Control System (TWCS)	6, 8, 12, 36, 43, 138, 219
TOMS	664
Tooth Brush	340
Top Dome	339
Top Hat jammer (Russia)	512
Top Hat sonar (U.S.)	622
Top Hat black program	428
Top Pair	100, 332
Top Plate	331
Top Sail	98, 100, 332
Top Steer	98, 100, 331
Topaz radar	199, 327
Torch	565
TORCI	104, 608
Tornado	167
TOTED	706
Tp 46 (Grampus) torpedo	685
Tp 62 torpedo (Sweden)	686
TPN-30 MRAALS	388
TPS-44	375
TPS-66 radar	274
TPS-71 (XN-1)	20
TR47 radar	275
Trail Blazer	733
TRAM	629
TRANSIT	97
TRAP	16, 38
Trap Door	336
TRC 281	480
TRC 284	480
TRE	40, 43
Trebuzets	408
TRES	216
TREW	216
Tri-ASP	157, 659
Trident C-4	188
Trident II missile	153, 189
Trinity (Sweden)	451
Trishul	399
Tritan	71, 104, 124
Tritech 6000	105
Triton radar	79, 285
Triton sonar	162, 613
Triton tracker	341
Triton G	285
Triton II MTI	284
Triton IV	541
Triton S	286
TRIXS	16, 38
TRML-CS	293
Troika	741
Trout Cheek	604
TRS 2200	281
TRS 3001	282
TRS 3010	283
TRS 3015	282
TRS 3030	285
TRS 3033	286
TRS 3035	284, 285
TRS 3050	285
TRS 3220	290
TRS 3405	287
TRS 3410	287
TRS-3D	294
TRS-C	293
TRS-L	294
TRS-N	293
TS SM	220

SUBJECT	Page
TS-1	579, 746
TS-200	42
TS-510	42
TSC	9, 11, 12
TSC-125	16
TSCM	16
TSM 2020	734
TSM 2021	734
TSM 2022	82, 106, 736
TSM 2023	736
TSM 2026	82
TSM 2054	737
TSM 2060	81
TSM 2072	141, 590
TSM 2233	580
TSM 2233 Eledone	582
TSM 2243	704
TSM 2253	589
TSM 2255	585
TSM 2362	588
TSM 2400	583
TSM 2630	586
TSM 2633	589
TSM 2640	586
TSM 2681	597
TSM 2682	597
TSM 2683	597
TSM 2933	583
TSM 3510	717
TSM 3530	717
TSM 5420	590
TSM 5421	590
TSM 5423	590
TSM 5424	590, 738
TSM 5721	82
TSM 5730	82
TSM 8010	648
TSM 8030	649
TSM 8040	649
TSM 8050	649
TSM 8060	649
TSM 8210	650
TSM 8220	649
TSM 8230	650
TSM 8251 sonar (France)	583
TSM 8251 processor (France)	649
TSM 8252 sonar (France)	588
TSM 8252 processor (France)	649
TSM 8260	587
TSQ-129	11
TSQ-142	15
TSSAM	250
TSTAR	261
TSUNAMI	663
Tu-142	168
TUM	723
Turel	334
Turkey:	
Strategic Underwater Sensor Systems	22
TUUM-Z	42
TVT-300	344
TWCS. See Tomahawk Weapons Control System	
21HS	633
Twin Eyes	279
2.75in Folding-Fin Rockets	265
2KJ series	75
Two-Way Link 11	40
250mm rocket launcher	697
TWS-2000	711
Type 2 periscope (U.S.)	643
Type 8L Mod (T) periscope (U.S.)	643
Type 15L Mod (T) periscope (U.S.)	643
Type 18 mine (Denmark)	716
Type 18 periscope (U.S.)	643
Type 22 (NESSIE) periscope (U.S.)	643
Type 25 sonobuoy (Russia)	651

SUBJECT	Page
Type 42 series torpedo (Sweden)	685
Type 43X0 torpedo (Sweden)	685
Type 45 torpedo (Sweden)	685
Type 55 mine (Japan)	719
Type 56 mine (Japan)	719
Type 61 (Tp 61) torpedo (Sweden)	685
Type 62 AAM (Russia)	423
Type 64 (Italy)	438
Type 72 AAM (Russia)	424
Type 72 FCS (Japan)	312
Type 74 mine (Sweden)	726
Type 75 buoy (Russia)	168, 170
Type 75 sonobuoy (Russia)	651
Type 76 (China)	432
Type 77 missile (Russia)	237
Type 77 mine (Sweden)	726
Type 80 torpedo (Japan)	678
Type 88C FCS (China)	279
Type 89 torpedo (Japan)	678
Type 93 mine (Japan)	719
Type 93 missile (Russia)	235
Type 112 missile (Russia)	236
Type 133 electronic system	472
Type 162 sonar (UK)	609
Type 162M sonar (UK)	609
Type 164B sonar (UK)	576
Type 170 AAM (Russia)	424
Type 170B sonar (UK)	609
Type 172 AAM (Russia)	425
Type 174 sonar (UK)	576
Type 176 sonar (UK)	576
Type 177 sonar (UK)	609
Type 182 noisemaker (UK)	708
Type 183 (UK)	42
Type 184 sonar (UK)	609
Type 184M sonar (UK)	609
Type 185 (UK)	42
Type 187 sonar (UK)	610
Type 189 sonar (UK)	610
Type 193 sonar (UK)	610
Type 193 sweep (UK)	749
Type 193M sweep (UK)	749
Type 195 sonar (UK)	610
Type 197 sonar (France)	703
Type 241 radar (China)	193
Type 242 electronic system	527
Type 242 radar (China)	193
Type 244 radar (China)	193
Type 245 radar (China)	193
Type 262 radar (UK)	348
Type 275 radar (UK)	348
Type 277 radar (UK)	349
Type 278 radar (UK)	349
Type 312 MCM (China)	733
Type 331 radar (China)	278, 331
Type 341 FCS (China)	278
Type 342(?) FCS (China)	279
Type 343 FCS (China)	279
Type 347 radar (China)	278
Type 347(?) radar (China)	277
Type 352 radar (China)	75
Type 354 radar (China)	275
Type 360 radar (China)	275
Type 381 radar (China)	278
Type 404A radar (China)	279
Type 431 torpedo (Sweden)	685
Type 432 torpedo (Sweden)	685
Type 470 AAM (Russia)	423

SUBJECT	Page
Type 500/I mine (China)	716
Type 515(?) radar China)	275
Type 667 jammer (UK)	523
Type 668 jammer (UK)	523
Type 670 jammer (UK)	530
Type 675(2) jammer (UK)	523
Type 702 radar (China)	279
Type 756 radar (UK)	278
Type 901 radar (UK)	349
Type 903 radar (UK)	349
Type 904 radar (UK)	349
Type 909 radar (UK)	350
Type 910 radar (UK)	350
Type 911 radar (UK)	350
Type 912 radar (UK)	109
Type 921-A RWR (China)	512
Type 945PJ chaff/IR launching system (China)	475
Type 965 radar (UK)	351
Type 966 radar (UK)	351
Type 967 radar (UK)	351
Type 968 radar (UK)	351
Type 975 radar (UK)	352
Type 978 radar (UK)	352
Type 982 radar (UK)	273
Type 992 radar (UK)	71, 352
Type 993 radar (UK)	352
Type 994 radar (UK)	356
Type 996 radar (UK)	352
Type 1000/II mine (China)	716
Type 1006 radar (UK)	353
Type 1007 radar (UK)	353
Type 1008 radar (UK)	354
Type 1010 radar (UK)	354
Type 1011 radar (UK)	354
Type 1013 radar (UK)	354
Type 1022 radar (UK)	354
Type 1245 radar (India)	295
Type 2000 torpedo (Sweden)	686
Type 2001 sonar (UK)	139, 611
Type 2004 sonar (UK)	611
Type 2005 sonar (UK)	611
Type 2006 sonar (UK)	611
Type 2007 sonar (UK)	611
Type 2008 sonar (UK)	42
Type 2009 IFF (UK)	139
Type 2009 sonar (UK)	42
Type 2010 sonar (UK)	42, 139
Type 2012 sonar (UK)	611
Type 2013 sonar (UK)	611
Type 2015 sonar (UK)	611
Type 2016 sonar (UK)	107, 108, 611
Type 2018 sonar (UK)	611, 612
Type 2019 sonar (UK)	704
Type 2020 sonar (UK)	611
Type 2021 sonar (UK)	611
Type 2023 sonar (UK)	576
Type 2024 sonar (UK)	612
Type 2025 sonar (UK)	611
Type 2026 sonar (UK)	612
Type 2027 sonar (UK)	611
Type 2030 sonar (UK)	611
Type 2031 sonar (UK)	612
Type 2032 sonar (UK)	611
Type 2033 sonar (UK)	613
Type 2034 sonar (UK)	613
Type 2034 sweep (UK)	749
Type 2035 sonar (UK)	611
Type 2040 sonar (France)	582
Type 2040 sonar (UK)	613
Type 2041 sonar (U.S.)	618
Type 2041 sonar (UK)	613
Type 2042 countermeasure (UK)	708
Type 2046 sonar (UK)	151, 613
Type 2047 sonar (UK)	611
Type 2048 sonar (UK)	613
Type 2050 sonar (UK)	611

SUBJECT Page

Type 2051 sonar (UK) 162, 613
Type 2052 sonar (UK) 576
Type 2053 sonar (UK) 613
Type 2053 sweep (UK) 749
Type 2054 sonar (UK) 613
Type 2057 sonar (UK) 576
Type 2058 countermeasure (UK) 708
Type 2060 sonar (UK) 611
Type 2061 sonar (UK) 576
Type 2062 sonar (UK) 576
Type 2063 sonar (UK) 613
Type 2064 sonar (UK) 613
Type 2065 sonar (UK) 613
Type 2066 decoy (UK) 708
Type 2067 sonar (UK) 613
Type 2068 sonar (UK) 613
Type 2069 sonar (UK) 610
Type 2070 countermeasure (UK) 708
Type 2071 decoy (UK) 708
Type 2072 sonar (UK) 613
Type 2074 sonar (UK) 611
Type 2075 sonar (UK) 576
Type 2076 sonar (UK) 151, 613
Type 2077 sonar (UK) 613
Type 2078 sonar (UK) 576
Type 2081 sonar (UK) 614
Type 2082 sonar (UK) 151, 708
Type 2087 sonar (UK) 614
Type 2090 sonar (UK) 614
Type 2093 sonar (UK) 115, 614
Type 2093 sweep (UK) 749
Type 2094 sonar (UK) 614
Type 2095 sonar (UK) 614
Type 2459 radar (Spain) 115
Type 5051 sonar (Canada) 577
Type 5544 radar (U.S.) 375
Type A41A (Switzerland) 456
Type D-5 missile (Russia) 234
Type D-9 missile (Russia) 236
Type GAM-B01 (Switzerland) 456
Type GAM-C01 (Switzerland) 456
Type GBM-A01 (Switzerland) 455
Type GBM-B1Z (Switzerland) 455
Type GDM-A (Switzerland) 454
Type GDM-C (Italy) 439
Type GDM-C (Switzerland) 454
Typhoon gun system 435

U

UA-1/2 472
UA-3 523
UA-4 525
UA-8 523
UA-9 523
UA-10 523
UA-11 472
UA-12 472
UA-13 523
UA-14 472
UA-15 472
UAA 524
UAC 527
UAD 525
UAE 525
UAF 525
UAG 520
UAK 525
UAN 522
UAP 527
UAR 530
UARS 42
UAS(1) 526
UAT 529

SUBJECT Page

UAV Master Plan 192
UAVs 38
UBB 524
UCB 526
UCC-1 38
UCLAR 502
UDACS system 176
UDAV-1 667
UDICON 69
UDL 30
UDM 723
UDM mine (Russia) 720
UDM-500 720
UDME 724
UDWT 682
UEP 22
UFO 32, 36, 37, 38, 41
UGM mine (Russia) 720
UGM-84 255
UGM-96A 188
UGM-133 189
UGS 191
UGST 682
UKSM mine (Russia) 720
ULA-2 536
Ulisee 232
ULQ-6 73, 556
ULQ-11K 504
ULQ-12K 504
ULQ-16 556
ULQ-19 557
ULQ-20 552
UMGT-1 684
UMGT-1ME 684
Unifoxer 708
United Kingdom:
Airborne Sensors 200
Airborne Signal Processors 653
Aircraft Guns 267
Aircraft Tactical Data Systems 171
Coast-Defense Guns and Rockets 270
Command Advice Systems 4
Computers 52
Countermeasures 708
Data Buses 68
Electronic Warfare 520
Fire-Control Systems 364
MCM/Minehunting Sonars 748
Mines 726
Missiles and Guided Bombs 248
Mortars and Depth Charges 701
Optronic Systems 361
Radar Integration 361
Radars 348
Radio Systems 31
Shipboard Guns and Gun Systems 458
Sonars 609
Sonobuoys 652
Submarine Combat-Direction Systems 149
Submarine Communications Systems 42
Surface Radar/ELINT (Electronics Intelligence) Systems 19
Surface Ship Combat-Direction Systems 107
Surface-to-Air Missiles 409
Torpedoes 686
Underwater Fire-Control Systems 608
Unguided Bombs and Air-Launched Rockets 263
United States:
Air Fire-Control Systems 216
Air-to-Air Missiles 426
Air-Traffic-Control Radars 388
Airborne Sensors 203
Airborne Signal Processors 658

SUBJECT Page

Aircraft Guns 267
Aircraft Tactical Data Systems 173
Aircraft-Carried Sensors 190
Bombardment Rockets 272
Coast-Defense Guns and Rockets 270
Command Advice Systems 5
Computers 53
Countermeasures 709
Data Buses 68
Displays 132
Electronic Warfare 535
Fire-Control Radars 377
Helicopter Sonars 616
MCM/Minehunting Sonars 751
Mines 727
Missile Launching Systems 418
Missiles 667
Missiles and Guided Bombs 249
Mortars and Depth Charges 701
Naval Surface Fire Support Program 460
Nonacoustic ASW Sensors 663
Optronic Systems 389
Radar Integration 386
Radars 366
Radio Systems 32
Satellite Sensor Systems 17
Shipboard Guns and Gun Systems 460
Sonobuoys 654
Strategic Strike Systems 188
Strategic Underwater Sensor Systems 22
Submarine and Surface-Ship Sonars 618
Submarine Combat-Direction Systems 151
Submarine Communications Systems 43
Surface Missile Fire-Control Systems 218
Surface Radar/ELINT (Electronics Intelligence) Systems 20
Surface Ship Combat-Direction Systems 116
Surface-to-Air Missiles 411
Target Designation Systems 393
Torpedoes 689
UAVs (formerly RPVs) 192
Underwater Fire-Control Systems 636
Unguided Bombs and Air-Launched Rockets 263
Weapon Designation Equipment 393
Universal Modular Mast 644
UPD-4 191
UPD-8 191
UPD-9 191
UPD-501 472
Update IV 14, 184
Update programs 175
UPS-3 376
UPS-60/600 348
UPX-23 394
UPX-24 394
UPX-25 394
UPX-27 394
UPX-29 394
UPX-30 394
UPX-34 394
UQC-1 42
UQC-2A 42
UQQ-2 24, 633

SUBJECT Page

UQS-1 83, 758
Uragan M-22 406
Uragan system 697
Uran 244
Urania 715
URC-107 30
URDT-1 705
URN-30 111
URPK-3 666
URPK-4 666
URPK-6 684
URT-23 43
USC-13 45
USC-38 37
USC-40(V) 69
USC-42 34, 35
USET 684
USET-80 682
USET-95 684
USFCS 160
USK 800 487
USMTF 12
USQ-36 38
USQ-59 38
USQ-63 38
USQ-64 40, 136
USQ-69 39, 120
USQ-74 38
USQ-76 28, 29, 38, 39
USQ-79 27, 38
USQ-81 43, 57, 61
USQ-81(V) 16, 36
USQ-82 67, 69
USQ-83 38
USQ-101 40
USQ-111 28, 39
USQ-112 7
USQ-113(V) 557
USQ-119 7, 8, 9
USQ-123 33
USQ-125 28, 38, 39
USQ-132 638
Usta-670 FCS 146
UTSM 45
UTST-95 684
UUVs 634
UV26 516
UV-P1/UV-P2 516
UYA-4 11, 76, 77, 118, 122, 124
UYA-5 11
UYC-8 12
UYC-501 67, 73
UYH-2 155
UYQ-21 11, 107, 117, 118, 134
UYQ-23 12, 138
UYQ-25 24, 633
UYQ-31 138
UYQ-37 135
UYQ-61 41
UYQ-65 134
UYQ-70 49, 78, 118, 135
UYS-1 54, 181, 659
UYS-2 24, 54, 134, 659
UYS-5 660
UYS-501 648
UYS-502 646
UYS-503 181, 648
Uzel 606

V

V3800 364
V3900 364
VA-111 683
Valkyrie gun mount (U.S.) 465
VALLOR 43
Vampir 287
Vandal 416
Vanguard 318, 396
VAP 732
VARAN 194
Variant 319
Varo LWS 571
VAX4500 92
VCATS 215
Vee Cone 3, 99
Vega 26, 49, 71, 76, 77, 78, 79, 80, 83, 95, 607

SUBJECT Page

Velox 703
Velox M5 705
Velox M6 705
Velox M7 705
VEMS 727
VERDIN 10, 36, 41, 43, 45, 156
VERSUS 735
Vertical Launch Asroc 668
VESTA 30
VGS-3 607
VHSIC 30
VI-01 273
VIDS 36
Vierling (Germany) 434
Viggen 200
Vigil 193
VIGY 10 288
VIGY 50 273
VIGY 105 287
VIGY 200 287
Vikhr' 666
Viking 14
VINSON 40
VISION 288
Vision 2100M 132
VISTA 81
Vista Sabre 215
Vistar 1M 405 362
Viyoga 666
VLAD 657
VMS 1000 Voyage Management System 132
Volcan 273
Volna 188, 339, 403
Vortex 18
Voshkod 332
VPS-2 383
VR-1B/C 507
VS-SM-600 715
VSRAAD 409
VSRAD 395
VT-1 396
VTAS 214
VTG 120/N 307
VTG 240/N 307
Vulcano 231
VVFD 43
Vyaga 330
Vychegda 607
Vympel 334
Vyoga 683
Vysota missile 188
Vyuga 235

W

W87 warhead 189
W-120 128, 385
W-160 130, 208, 385
W-1200 73, 385
WAA 619
Walleye 261
WAM 266
WAMS 115
WAP 123
Warrant 472
WARSHIPS 460
Wasp Head 273, 341
Watch Dog 100, 512
Watchman 361
Waterboy 558
Waverley 3010 751
WBAR 24
WDS 119, 121
WDS Mk 11 389
WE177 bombs (UK) 189
Weapon Designation Equipment 393
Wet Eye 199, 200
White Cloud (Parcae) 7, 19
White Shark 679
Wide-band sonar (UK) 749
WIMS 732
Wine Flask 513
Wine Glass 513
Winnin 473
WJ 1140 559
WJ 8957 571
WJ 8958 571
WJ 32500 572

SUBJECT	Page	SUBJECT	Page	SUBJECT	Page	SUBJECT	Page	SUBJECT	Page
WJ 34901	572	WQC-2	42	**X**		Yezh	407	Zaliv-P	508
WLQ-4	557	WQC-501	42			YS 2000 system	518	ZALP-B (Long Bow)	269
WLR-1	557	Wrobel 2MR	402	XAAM-4	313, 423	Yu-1	670	ZAMBO	700
WLR-3	558	Wrobel II	402	XBT	655	Yu-2	670	Zapad	667
WLR-6	558	WRR-3	43	XSTAT	44	Yu-3	670	Zarechye	169
WLR-8	559	WRR-7	43			Yu-4	670	Zarnitsa	328
WLR-9A	712	WS 500	116			Yu-4A/-4B	670	Zenon	17
WLR-9B	712	WS-X-T torpedo	686	**Y**		Yu-5	670	Zeus	568
WLR-10	559	WSA 400	53, 107			Yugoslavia:		Zhuk radar	197
WLR-11	558	WSA 423	93	YAG	523	Coast-Defense Guns and		ZiF-121	514
WLR-12	712	WSA series	108	Yak-38 (Forger)	423	Rockets	271	ZIFRA	520
WLR-13	472	WSA-4	73	Yakhont	245	MCM/Minehunting		ZPS-4	312
WLR-14	559	WSC-3	37, 41, 43	Yakor'	336	Sonars	760	ZPS-6	312
WLR-17	712	WSC-5	41	YaM	723	Mines	732	ZQS series	743
WLR-18	559	WSC-6	35	YaRM	724			ZS-1015(S)	572
WM20 series	71	WSC-6(V)	41	Yashima	243			ZU-23–2MR	402
WM20/M20 series	79, 323	WSM series mines		YAW	524	**Z**		Zubr	243
WM25	92	(Taiwan)	726	YAZ	523			Zuni	266
WM-series FCS	94	WSQ-5	560	Yellow Gate	522	Z103B	84	Zvezda	607
Wok Wan	279	WSS	122	Yellow Veil	541	Z 13	673	ZW-01/3	316
Wolf Paw	604, 607	Wullenweber	20	Yen	199	Z 16	673	ZW-06	317
WP-900	719	WWMCCS	5, 6, 7	YeN radar	234	Zaliv	508	ZW-07	317

ADDENDUM

SURVEILLANCE AND CONTROL

Command Advice Systems

FRANCE

Aidcomer (AIDCOM) consists of a generic kernel plus applications. The kernel offers data servers (operational data, environmental data), Recognized Maritime Picture and Air Picture display, message handling (NATO ADAT-P3, GOLD, and other formats), software interfaces for applications, and communication interfaces (ACP 127 messaging network, X25/X400 data transmission networks), satellite transmissions (SYRACUSE, INMARSAT) via AIDCOM/SYGEDO.

Applications: AIDCOM/NHQ (naval HQ ashore for theater or world situation), AIDCOM/TFC (task force command), AIDCOM/NUC (naval unit command, for individual ship), AIDCOM/SW (submarine warfare), AIDCOM/ATD (air tasking definition), AIDCOM/AMP (air mission planning), AIDCOM/MPA (maritime patrol mission planning and analysis), AIDCOM/SATCOM (communication by satellite), AIDCOM/OBS (observation by satellite), AIDCOM/LOG (logistics). AIDCOM is interfaced with other systems such as shipboard CDS, EW systems, and JOTS.

Software is written in C++, operating on RISC/UNIX workstations on an Ethernet. In 1996 more than 30 ships and nine shore command facilities are equipped with AIDCOM: the two carriers (and later the *Charles de Gaulle*); 32 other combatants including frigates, destroyers (AAW and ASW), *Floreals*, amphibious ships, and submarines; five naval HQs ashore; one joint command center; two maritime air-operations centers; and three training and technical centers. The first installation was on board *Foch* in 1992.

CENTAC 2 is the host data-processing system in French navy maritime air-operations centers to update and present the Recognized Maritime Picture; to prepare missions; to monitor them; and to provide postmission data analysis. It is the specialized AIDCOM/MPA application of the AIDCOM core, providing generic AIDCOM features:

- Message processing
- Management of RMP operational data and specialized MPA functions
- Mission preparation and pre-flight data package insertion
- Mission following
- Mission retrieval (tactical mission extraction)

It is interfaced with numerous systems and command centers, using an Ethernet and with SYCOM 2 via the X25.N.WAN (Navy Wide Area Network). A dedicated front-end processor handles external (e.g., ACP 127 message handling system) and X25 communications.

UNITED KINGDOM

JCSI, the Joint Command System Initiative, creates a single unified command/control information system (CCIS) to supplant the usual separate service-oriented ones. It employs JOCS, the Joint Operational Command System. JCSI was created because after the Gulf War the British concluded that joint operations, which are inevitable in littoral warfare, require a single joint database (recognized tactical picture) shared by all three services, with clear lines of responsibility for information inserted into it. From the single picture appropriate maritime (RMP), land (LTP), and air situation (AS) products can be created at various levels of classification. A three-phase program began in 1994 with a Pilot Phase (1995–96) to create the Permanent Joint HQ (PJHQ) with its PJOCS system. Phase 2 (1997–2002) creates a common operating enviroment (COE) so that computer programs and systems can easily be transported between joint and single-service elements such as the Royal Navy's Command Support System. The use of JOCS elements in CSS simplifies the use of a British carrier as a JFHQ. This phase also develops Operational Intelligence data fusion procedures, in which the overall picture is compiled using national-level intelligence sources, as well as local information sent back from a deployed JFHQ. Phase 3 (1999–

2005) develops full system interoperability and communication integration among the British services, as well as links with the developing U.S. counterpart system, GCCS.

BAeSEMA's submarine maneuver decision aid, announced in 1995, is a hybrid between an expert-based system and an algorithmic processor. Taking the CDS-compiled current tactical situation, it uses expert rules to assess all possible maneuvers, giving a graphical projection of likely results. It offers advice, such as the best heading on which to use the towed array. This system has been bought by the U.S. Navy as a training aid.

UNITED STATES

Real-Time Support for Joint Power Projection Operations (RTS/JPP) is a SPAWAR (Space and Electronic Warfare) ATD, in effect a force-level complement to TAMPS begun in FY95 with demonstrations at NRL and at the Washington Planning Center as well as at operational and training sites (USACOM and the NSWC). It comprises two modules: a force-level rehearsal module (taking account of factors such as EW and radar terrain masking) for rapid collaborative planning; and target analysis. The rehearsal module connects with existing joint planning and execution systems such as the Tomahawk Strike Coordination Module (TSCM), Contingency Tactical Air Planning System, and JMCIS. The FY95 program included a lab demonstration of a high-performance LAN (155 Mbit/sec) for this system. The FY96 program included integration of RTS/JPP at Navy operational sites (including development of a shipboard equivalent of the high-speed LAN, ultimately with a capacity of 2.4 Gbit/sec) and real-time demonstrations of simulated optimized planning and routing of a strike coordinated by the ship's NTCCS-A/JMCIS.

As of fall 1996, the term JMCIS Afloat has formally superseded NTCS-A. The current JMCIS 22 was on board 34 ships as of late summer 1996, and is to be on board all ships by FY03. Version 2.2 completed OpEval on board USS *George Washington* in October 1995 and was released to the fleet in January 1996; it is the afloat terminal for the Defense Information Services Agency's (DISA's) GCCS. Version 2.2 replaces three earlier software versions. It includes space/electronic warfare applications and theater ballistic missile defense support for CEC. The next version, due in August 1997, will be built on the all-service Defense Information Infrastructure Common Operating Environment (DII COE) for easier integration with the other services. As of late 1996, plans called for installing Version 2.2 on 14 command ships and 45 unit-level ships during FY97, with another 11 following in FY98. This JMCIS Phase 1 program is to be completed in FY01. Phase 2 (FY98–03) increases communications capacity, enhances networking, and incorporates joint interoperable messaging. Wide-area networking will become possible due to the increased message capacity and interoperability. The COE will be made more robust, presumably partly to overcome the increased threat of information attack as more and more of a joint deployed force shares a single information environment.

JMCIS Ashore replaces the earlier OSS (Operations Support System). It has completed integration testing with GCCS and an operational field assessment to support DII COE. All the ashore sites use JMCIS LSDs, LANs, an integrated data server and briefing support. The next version will absorb the STTs that serve submarines as well as the ASW systems at shore ASW command centers, and will provide an upgrade to the information presentation and distribution LAN used by CINCUSNAVEUR.

JMCIS Tactical/Mobile (JTM) is the Tactical Support Center (TSC)/TSC Mobile Variant (TMV). It supports maritime sector commanders, including the mobile MOCC, the mobile integrated command center (MICFAC), and the mobile ashore support terminal (MAST). These centers are currently in use in Bahrein and Bosnia. There are 16 fixed TSCs and 16 mobile TMVs (the last was recently delivered). Like the other versions of JMCIS, JTM will be a GCCS terminal and will conform to DII COE.

NTCSS, the naval tactical command support system, uses JMCIS-type computers and absorbs a variety of nontactical shipboard systems, such as maintenance information systems. It provides the shipwide fiber-optic LANs used by JMCIS.

Surface Radar/ELINT Systems

UNITED STATES

A third ROTHR is being built in Puerto Rico to replace a military drug-traffic-detecting radar in Colombia, which was shut down in May 1994.

Strategic Underwater Sensor Systems

GERMANY

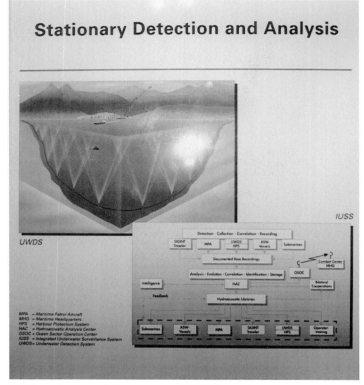

STN's underwater defense system (UWDS) was shown in poster form at Defendory, October 1996. Like the U.S. FDS, it is a distributed series of upward-looking sensors. (D. Markov)

ITALY

Societa Systemi Subacquei WELSE advertises an ASW Area System (ASWAS) integrating active/passive acoustics, seismic sensors, and magnetic sensors, using MAGICS-style dual-screen multifunction consoles.

RUSSIA

MGK-607 Dnestr is the low-frequency system code-named Cluster Lance by the U.S. Navy. MGK-407M is an older medium-frequency system, reportedly with about half the range.

UNITED STATES

The current SOSUS Consolidation Program includes replacing about 60% of dry-end equipment with COTS.

The FY97 R&D program includes a demonstration of bistatic operation of a deployable distributed array (ADS) and a deployable source, as well as rapid air deployment of a glider-deployed horizontal line array bottom system.

SURTASS is being improved with a COTS open architecture (fielded 1992). It accepted more powerful signal processors (500 MFLOPS) and a new beamformer that can adapt to the way in which the array changes shape as it is towed. To deal with an increased data rate and a larger number of beams, the system was provided with CAD and contact analysis, including detectors keyed to specific signature components. With many T-AGOS

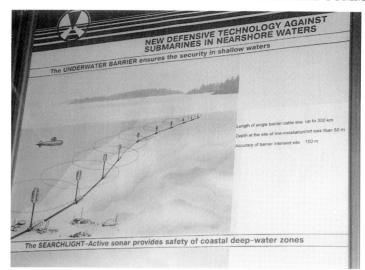

Okeanpribor's poster shows a passive sonar barrier probably similar in concept to the U.S. FDS, consisting of short-range sensors in a line up to 300 km long, each at a depth of at least 50 m. (Dave Markov)

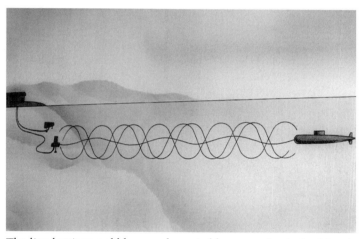

The line barrier would be complemented by seaward-pointing bistatic "Searchlight" sonars, each capable of detecting submarines out to 150 km (accuracy 3 km) over a 110-deg sector. The arrays can be located up to 40 km offshore. Projectors are at 1500 m depth, receivers at 300 m. (Dave Markov)

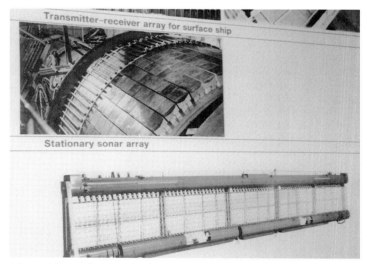

Okeanpribor's photograph of a static array probably shows the receiver of a Searchlight system. (Dave Markov)

ships retiring, their arrays have become surplus. Rebuilt with COTS telemetry instead of the earlier old hard-wired circuitry, these 180-channel arrays are designated A180R. They will be

retrofit into existing ships and installed in new ones. A new twin-line array was first deployed on USNS *Bold* (T-AGOS 12) in 1994. About a fifth the length of the standard array, it operates both passively and actively, forming separate left- and right-looking beams (the two lines maintain a constant separation through their length). The twin-line array consistently outperformed single-line arrays, even in high clutter (including Adriatic, East China Sea, Yellow Sea). At least four twin-line arrays will be cross-decked for ships assigned to littoral/shallow areas. This array developed out of a SPAWAR study begun in 1991.

On a lower level than ADS, MIUWs (Mobile Inshore Underwater Warfare units) are being modernized. The 28 MIUWs are distributed among two Groups (Group 1 in San Diego and Group 2 in Williamsburg, Virginia). Each has 12 officers and 60 enlisted personnel. IUWs were established in 1963 and were provided with the current TSQ-108 vans (which gave them their mobility) in the 1970s. The current System Upgrade Program provides each MIUW with JMCIS in the form of a MAST terminal (1997), a Mobile Sensor Platform (MSP), Portable Sensor Platform (PSP), strings of bottom acoustic sensors, and an upgraded main van. The MSP is a Humvee carrying a thermal/visual imager and an X-band Furuno radar; it can be up to 10 km from the van. The PSP, a quarter-ton trailer, carries another Furuno radar and an ALR-66(V), plus a microwave link to receive MSP data. The van contains an upgraded SQR-17 processor and a graphic data-fusion system that combines its picture with those from the deployed sensors and from lookouts. The underwater strings replace the SSQ-58 buoy.

TACTICAL COMMUNICATIONS SYSTEMS

Radio Systems

INTERNATIONAL

Further information on NATO Links 4 and 16 (JTIDS) has become available.

Link 4A (U.S. TADIL C) is used in air intercept control, strike attack vectoring (for F/A-18, S-3, and A-6), automatic carrier landing, air traffic control, and in setting the Carrier Aircraft Inertial Navigation System (CAINS). Some aircraft (EA-6B, A-6, S-3) have one-way Link 4A; the F-14A and F/A-18 have two-way links (the fighter downlinks can provide sensor tracks and fuel and weapons status). Many NATO fighters apparently have two-way Link 4A. The E-2C can control other aircraft using two-way Link 4A (U.S. AWACS aircraft have only one-way Link 4A, but NATO AWACS has the two-way link). Typically each air intercept controller has a Link 4A net, using a single frequency. A carrier may also use a net to provide waypoints, to land aircraft, and to set their CAINS systems.

All controlled platforms receive link addresses, by which they can recognize messages addressed to them. The control data terminal set (CDTS) transmits a control message every 32 msec, this interval being divided into a 14-msec transmit frame and an 18-msec reply frame (allowing 11.2 msec for the message and 6.8 msec for the message to go up from the ground station and back from the airplane over a distance as great as 550 nm). Aircraft transmit reply messages *only* on request, not on their own, in time slots after a later control message. Thus the net is time-division multiplexed by the CDTS, which can identify the replying aircraft by their time slots. Messages are built up of two 30-bit data words (frames), presumably related to 30-bit NTDS words. The 70-bit uplink message consists of 56 data bits prefaced by an 8-bit sync burst, a 5-bit guard interval, and a start bit, and ending with one guard bit (unkey signal). The 42-bit reply is prefaced and ended similarly, so it requires a total of 56 bits. Messages are not encrypted (to some extent, security is maintained by classifying message standards). The message rate is 31.25 messages/sec (data rate 5000 bps), except for CAINS, which is one-way and therefore operates at 62.5 messages/sec. The sync burst adjusts the receiver's automatic gain control and also synchronizes bit timing. Eight bits are used because the receiver may not pick up the entire string (one time slot is enough for the receiver to pick up both peak and trough).

The surface terminals are SSW-1 and USQ-118 (for CG 59-73 and DDG 51 and beyond). The E-2C uses ASW-25, the F-14 ASW-27, the F/A-18 the RT-1379 integrated transceiver/DTS, and the S-3 ASW-25B. The system operates in UHF (225–400 MHz).

Link 4C messages are not compatible with Link 4A. ASW-27B could communicate only over 4C; its successor, ASW-27C, can communicate over either link, but not over both simultaneously. Link 4C can connect up to four aircraft, one of which is designated master; each is assigned its own digital address and time slot. Each Link 4C aircraft can link up to four targets.

Link 16 uses 51 frequencies. Up to 20 nets can be stacked by allocating the same time slots to different users at different frequencies, each user hopping frequencies within its time slot (every 13 microsec) in a preset pseudo-random pattern. Each net is assigned a number (up to 128) indicating its hopping pattern; number 127 indicates a stacked net. Effective data rates are 26,880, or 53,760, or 107,520 bits/sec, depending on data packing (standard, Packed 2, or Packed 4, respectively). These rates translate to 28,800 or 57,600 or 115,200 bps if the 5 parity bits are included. The U.S. Navy uses the Packed 2 structure. In theory, Link 16 can carry 2 or 3 times as much information as Link 11, but in practice it is limited to about 50% more, partly because Link 16 adds non–Link 11 functions such as voice and air-traffic control, partly also because many slots must go unassigned. The number of time slots assigned to tactical data must be doubled to allow for relays.

Fixed-format messages are in a J-series (Link 4A is V-series uplink and R-series downlink; Link 11 uses the M-series) which includes equivalents to both Link 4A and Link 11 messages. Each J-message has a 5-bit label and a 3-bit sublabel, for a total of 256 different messages. Categories are: network management, precise participant location and identification (PPLI), surveillance (sets reference points, reports tracks), ASW, intelligence, information management (such as a data update request or a correlation), weapons coordination and management (including engagement status), control, platform/system status, EW, threat warning, national use, and miscellaneous. Each word is 70 bits (plus 4 parity bits and a spare), but a message can be several words long (typically 1, 2, or 3, although up to 40 can be sent). Fixed-format messages consist of an initial word, one or more extension words, and one or more continuation words. The initial word gives a label and sublabel, message length, and information. An extension word gives information only. A continuation word includes a continuation label. A variable-format message can vary in content and in length (though it consists of 75-bit words); fields within the message can cross word boundaries. The U.S. Army uses this format for its TADIL-B (Link 11) messages. There are also free-text messages, without any parity coding in a typical three-word block. There are also two voice channels, or ports, operating at 16 kbps (port 1 can also be connected to an external voice coder, or vocoder, operating at 2.4 or 4.8 kbps, but the U.S. Navy uses only 16 kbps). Both voice channels are encrypted, and are therefore considered secure.

Aboard ships, the C^2P processor converts all messages received over the links (11 and 16) into N-series messages for the CDS. The C^2P can also act as a gateway between Links 11 and 16. Link 4A messages pass through the C^2P untranslated.

Each participant in a net is assigned a unique five-digit octal number between 00001 and 77777 (Link 11 accommodates only three-digit octal addresses, which go up to 177); 77777 is the network manager. A JTIDS unit (JU) operating on several nets uses the same address on each. Track numbers are assigned five-character alphanumeric numbers (total 524,284 rather than the 4092 of Link 11). However, there is no pool mode; each unit assigns a track number to each target it sees. It is the responsibility of each participating CDS to eliminate duplication (as in Link 11).

Track identifiers are identity, platform, specific type, activity, and nationality rather than identity, primary amplification, and ID amplification; neutral and unknown categories are added. The former "assumed enemy" category is changed to "suspect." Aircraft status can include equipment status, exact ordnance inventory, radar and missile channels, fuel available for transfer,

gun capability, and ETA/ETD to/from station. A surface unit can report its inventory of specific types of missile. The precision (granularity) of track positions (32 ft vs. 500 yd), air track speeds (2 dmh [data mph] vs 28 dmh), altitudes, and lines of bearing increases compared to Link 11. Link 11 can report multisegmented lines and areas (Link 11 is limited to limited areas described as circles, ellipses, squares, or rectangles). Land (positions of objects such as buildings or tanks and reference points [waypoints]) is now a track category. EW information can be reported in greater detail. A Link 11 net cannot cover more than 512×512 nm, whereas Link 16 covers a worldwide area. Track quality can be specified as 0–15 rather than 0–7.

Net capacity is divided among network participating groups (NPGs), up to 512 of which can be formed (22 are currently defined, of which 16 are applicable to the U.S. Navy). One unit can participate in several NPG nets. NPG 7 is surveillance, NPG 9 is air control (two uplinks and 4, 8, or 16 fighters on the backlink [downlink]), NPG 10 is EW, NPG 18 is weapons coordination, and NPG 19 is a fighter-to-fighter link (for up to eight fighters; U.S. Navy F-14Ds cannot be active simultaneously on this net and on the air control backlink, but Air Force F-15s can operate on both). Plans call for all F-14Ds to be upgraded so that they can update their track files from the NPG 7 air picture.

The standard U.S. shipboard JTIDS transmitting antenna is AS-4127, 47×24 in (130 lb), mounted as a conical collar just below the TACAN antenna. The shipboard receiver is the conical AS-177B. DDG 72 and later ships have much smaller antennas (CA-3532 and -3627). The E-2C and F-14D JTIDS terminal is URC-107.

Current and planned Allied Link 16 ship platforms: France (*Charles de Gaulle* and *Cassard* class, also Project Horizon class); Italy (*Garibaldi* and *Maestrale* class), and United Kingdom (carriers, Type 42s).

UNITED STATES

As an interim step toward increasing effective satellite capacity, in 1990 the U.S. Navy planned installation of a new multiplexer for Channel 1 of its UHF satellites (in FY95), to provide a Single Integrated Satellite Broadcast (SISB) which would increase the capacity of the Fleet Broadcast more than thirtyfold. Channel 1 had been a 25-kHz wide-band channel (SHF uplink, UHF downlink) divided into 16 75-baud (bps) subchannels (total 1200 baud), one of which was typically used for the Fleet Broadcast. Alternatively, an entire channel can provide 2400-baud capacity without division.

The full 2.4 kbps are needed for the standard secure digitized voice communication system (the Satellite Voice Variant of the Advanced Narrowband Digital Voice Terminal [ANDVT], which replaced the earlier Navy Narrowband Secure Voice system). Note that the first U.S. digitized secure voice system was STEAMVALVE, an HF system deployed during the Vietnam War. ANDVT replaces the pseudo-digital Park Hill, which was widely used on HF and some satellite nets.

These long-haul systems should not be confused with short-range tactical systems, mainly the digital wide-band crypto VINSON (which replaces an earlier analog NESTOR). The usual VINSON terminal is a secure (scrambled) telephone (STU III). ANDVT and VINSON connect through gateways at the four NAVCAMs and at Naval Communications Station, Stockton, California.

Many operations showed that satellite voice capacity was insufficient, to the extent that some ships have used commercial cellular telephones, which of course are not encrypted. The stage beyond was to combine cellular operation with a STU III scrambler.

Due to its SHF uplink, Channel 1 is more jam-resistant than the other nine channels. The new multiplexer increases capacity to 9600 bps and provides twelve dynamically controlled (i.e., software-controlled) ports, as a step toward Copernicus. Of this capacity, 2400 baud is used for the High Speed Fleet Broadcast and 4800 is devoted to a new INTELCAST (providing intelligence narrative, imagery, and databases). Because the satellite has no SHF downlink, Channel 1 is one-way (simplex). The deployed FIST imagery processor already used a dedicated 2400 baud UHF channel, which was used for initial tests of INTELCAST in the Pacific Fleet. Plans call for placing an SISB-type multiplexer on a second (UHF-UHF) satellite channel to provide a duplex 9600-baud intelligence channel. Ultimately UHF satellites will have four high-capacity channels: the two existing DAMA (which configure a 25-kHz channel into four 2400-baud subchannels rather than one 2400-baud channel); the SISB Channel 1; and the 9600-baud INTELCAST channel.

These steps were nothing like sufficient. During the Gulf War, the carriers had to rely on air delivery of hard copy to receive the massive Air Tasking Order. An emergency program to improve satellite communications more than doubled the number of SATCOM media on board each carrier or large amphibious ship. Data rates were increased more than tenfold (the standard rose from 64 kbps to 2 Mbit/sec on a joint mission). The first step was to extend DSCS from shore to large-deck users, Air Force/Marine TSC-93 SHF vans carrying 4ft dishes being placed aboard ships in a "Quicksat" program (adding another 64 kbps of data rate). To accommodate the new tactical users, DSCS operation had to change. Current shipboard DSCS terminals, fed by 7ft dishes (to quadruple signal strength without requiring more satellite power), can handle up to 2 Mbits/sec, though typically only 64 kbps to 1 Mbits/sec are assigned to a carrier or LHA/LHD.

No parallel program for surface ships was pursued. For example, in 1996 modernization of WSC-3 (to allow access to the 5-kHz channels used by the other services) and improvements to USC-38 EHF terminals to surface combatants were either canceled or postponed, due to budget pressure.

The first Milstar medium data rate (MDR) satellite is due for launching in FY99; it will offer up to 1.5 Mbits/sec of protected (antijam) service per channel, which Navy EHF channels will receive at 512 or 1024 kbps, depending on ship size. Additional EHF packages are to be launched on board up to two satellites in highly elliptical orbits, to provide EHF service to units in northern waters.

To fill gaps in satellite capacity, the Navy also uses the commercial UHF INMARSAT system, which offers what amounts to on-demand telephone service (at 19.2 kbps) at about $5 per minute. The U.S. Navy is currently the largest INMARSAT user, at nearly 3 million minutes in 1995. A digital INMARSAT B will use 64 kbps channels, sharing them among users to cut the cost per minute to about $1.

With the success of Challenge Athena, commercial wide-band terminals are now (1996) programmed for all command ships. By 2003 there should be up to 12 space transponders serving 40 to 65 ships.

Currently there are several distinct satellite terminals. All using signals above 2 GHz are to coalesce under an Integrated Terminal Program (ITP); UHF terminals are to be replaced by SLICE. The new ADNS (see JMCOMS in this Addendum) will integrate satellite and LOS communications.

New communications systems now being fielded include JSIPS NIS (national input segment), the receive element of the Joint Defense Dissemination System, which provides tactical and strategic users with national (largely satellite) imagery. The Defense Information Support Network (DISN) offers tactical extensions of joint interoperable networks including JWICS (Joint Worldwide Intelligence Communications System, handling compartmented data), Secret Internet Protocol Router Network, and Internet Protocol Router Network (unclassified but sensitive information).

GBS (global broadcasting system), to begin operation in 1998, uses technology like that already used commercially for direct television broadcast via satellite. Capacity is 23.6 Mbits/sec spread over multiple channels to COTS receiving equipment. The Ku-band (SHF) system will use transmitters on the last three of the 10 UFO satellites. By 2005 every surface combatant will have a GBS dish, allowing reception of a spot beam. The Mission Need Statement (MNS) was approved in August 1995. Radiant Storm proved the GBS concept, including the necessary multi-level encryption. SP-95 demonstrated the full DBS (digital broadcasting system) waveform and conditional access (to limit access to compartmented information). ATM (asynchronous transmission mode) was demonstrated in AFC4A. The JWID 95 exercise expanded the use of ATM and addressed doctrinal issues and broadcast management.

GBS will remove simplex (one-way) traffic from existing two-way (duplex) systems, which can then be used more efficiently. Too, some high-data-rate duplex systems can transmit high-data-rate information, such as images, down to the network feeding GBS, which can then retransmit those images back to tactical users who have GBS terminals but lack high duplex capacity themselves.

A major driver for GBS is the need to send large numbers of images, each of which typically amounts to 100 Mbits. Older satellites are entirely inadequate: Inmarsat A (9.6 kbps) would require 3 hr to send a single image; even WSC-6, at 512 kbps (7ft antenna), requires 3.3 min. Challenge Athena (T-1) can send an image in 1 min, DSCS-E (3 Mbits/sec) in 30 sec, and GBS (12 Mbits/sec) in 8.4 sec.

JMCOMS, the Joint Maritime Communications System, is the Copernicus communications element. It will connect to the Army's Enterprise and the Air Force's Horizon systems. Hardware elements of JMCOMS are the SPEAKeasy digital radio (2 MHz–2 GHz, more capable and less costly), the integrated (satellite) terminal (allowing modular evolution to multiband terminals, in large- or small-deck form), and the automated digital network system (ADNS, for a fourfold increase in throughput efficiency). ADNS is the Copernicus switching system, allocating slices of different messages to different media as required for maximum efficiency. It is equivalent in theory to an asynchronous transmission message (ATM) system, as in the Internet. However, it adds a dynamic-assignment element. There is some skepticism that integrating time-urgent combat communications, such as the numbered Links, into JMCOMS might deny operators data at crucial moments. They may prefer the reliable low rates of Link 11 to the 9600-bps average rate offered by JMCOMS.

JMCOMS is being implemented in builds. Build 0 established a fleet baseline. It expanded land-based networks (NIPRNET, SIPRNET, JWICS) to sea. However, it provided no media management. Build 1 offers standard Internet services (HF E-Mail) and dynamic bandwidth allocation. Build 2 offers multicast and standard voice/video services, including the Army's SINCGARS and the Global Broadcast System (GBS). Control of selected radio room equipment is automated. Build 3 offers tactical voice/video services. It includes an expeditionary warfare module. The prototypes are in CG 48 and LHD 4, with Build 1 in one battle group (then in two more in FY97, and four in FY98). Build 2 will be in four battlegroups in FY99 and two in FY00, with Build 3 in two in FY00, four in each of FY01 and FY02, and the last in FY03. To deal with the growing bandwidth needed, ships are being fitted with multifunctioning electromagnetic radiating systems (MERS) masts and HF broadband (HFBB) antennas.

SPEAKeasy, a joint program led by the Air Force, produces a completely software-controlled multiband (2 MHz–2 GHz) multimode radio with a 5-kHz DAMA inside, using a very broadband antenna. Both hardware and software use open architectures. SPEAKeasy II is the core program. Model 1HW, developed July 1995–March 1997 for the Army's Task Force XXI, has two channels and can handle 9 waveforms and 10 network protocols. It can bridge voice signals from one network to another and embodies TRANSEC security. Model 2HW (October 1996–June 1998) has four channels and is extensively miniaturized (16 waveforms, 18 network protocols, voice and data bridging, all forms of information security). Model 3HW (July 1997–June 1999, for a tri-service demonstration) adds smart radio techniques (selecting a spectrum to minimize interference, adjusting transmitter power, data-link bit rate adaptation, LPI/AJ margin selection, and optimized network throughput), power management, and an improved cosite filter, to reduce interference. The radio included embedded GPS and a cellular phone, in addition to its normal channels.

The nine core waveforms are HF, SINCGARS, SINCGARS SIP, UHF SATCOM, GPS, Have Quick I/II, HF Modem, HFALE, and HFAJ. To these Model 2W adds Commercial Cellular (AMPS), Air Traffic Control, Wireless Packet (NTDR), UHF SATCOM DAMA, EPLRS VHSIC, Wireless T-1 (contractor specified), and LPI HF and VHF. The goal is to add Saturn, Law Enforcement, TRAP, TADIXS-B, TIBS, TADIL-A, TRIXS, and Link 16 (study). The first software-synthesized waveform was demonstrated in September 1996. A typical Navy four-channel SPEAKeasy might allocate channel 1 to HF (ship-to-shore, ship-to-ship primary voice), channel 2 to LOS UHF (ship-to-ship), channel 3 to UHF links (Link 11, Link 4A), and channel 4 to UHF SATCOM, which would include the bridge to Army radios.

The radio consists of four subsystems: RF, a modem (including the waveform processor), INFOSEC (key and crypto processors), and internetworking. Motorola sees SPEAKeasy development paralleling computer development, with generations of radio cores succeeding each other just as CPUs did. Current processors: RF, 68356; Modem, C40; INFOSEC, 68340 and CYPRIS; networking/multimedia, 80486 and C40; MMI, 80486 and C40 (for smart radio).

SPEAKeasy is being developed by Motorola, ITT, and Lockheed Martin Sanders.

Note the similarity (in concept) between the standard OTH-Gold formatted messages used in OTCIXS and TADIXS and Link 11 or 16, in that the messages are processed by computer to contribute to an operational picture. However, both the satellite links can also carry unformatted messages (which one operator called quite inefficient, as people use more bytes than necessary to communicate). CUDIXS carries only unformatted messages, the shipboard terminal for which is NAVMACS (Navy Modular Automated Communication System). The shore terminal is NAVCOMPARS (Navy Communications Processing and Routing System). In the 1980s, foreshadowing Copernicus, operators were ordered to tag administrative messages so that they could be held back to allow operational traffic to flow freely. Messages were also tagged with an expiration time, so that they could be rejected if not transmitted in time.

SPAWAR (naval TENCAP) projects (beside those listed in the text) are:

Radiant Beryllium: Develop and exploit strategic HSI sensors for tactical purposes; exploit unique signatures for "aided target identification."

Radiant Breeze: Provide operational intelligence and a common tactical picture to allies in coalition operations, using PC-based low-end loan assets; a JMCIS-like capability is a permanent equivalent.

Radiant Cirrus IV: Develop GENSER-level two-way comms for National Systems and collateral intelligence requests and products between theater CinCs, afloat commanders, and allies.

Radiant Clear: Exploit National Systems to form a common tactical picture of a littoral area, including local conditions. Classification and data quantity are to be scaleable.

Radiant Coal (USSOCOM Project Town Crier): Develops an SOF capability to inject intelligence data into tactical broadcasts such as TDDS in near real time.

Radiant Copper: Improves National Systems CW processing and mapping capabilities, transmitted over TDDS.

Radiant Crimson: Develops National Systems BRIGAND tracking capability, transmitted over TDDS.

Radiant ELM: Improves precision strike planning through more effective use of National Systems products, especially imagery. Subtasks: (a) enhance TOPSCENE mission planning system by using a wider range of images (EO, IR, SAR, etc); (b) improve Tomahawk mission planning through innovative use of National Systems data and redistribution of targeting effort; (c) improve NSWC (Fallon)'s capability to act as a center of excellence and to evaluate applicable new tactical image processing and mission planning technologies.

Radiant Frost: Develop new signal-processing technologies to improve the accuracy and timeliness of current automated ELINT processing, specifically to track currently unidentified emitters.

Radiant Gold: Improve support to ballistic missile defense: (a) refine Tactical Detection and Reporting System (TACDAR), (b) develop data sharing between TACDAR and JTaGs for better data fusion; (c) conduct Theater Event System (TES) operational assessments to improve TES reporting; (d) explore the potential of the developmental multispectral Cobra Brass sensor to support tactical operations; (e) develop Project Pinpoint (joint project) to improve the location accuracy of reports; (f) develop a ship-deployable theater missile defense (TMD) workstation testbed to receive, process, fuse, and disseminate TMD information to navy TMD assets; (g) explore using TES to improve Aegis cueing; (h) evaluate the potential use of ASW principles (such as wide-area surveillance, sensor cross-cueing, localization, data fusion) in TMD.

Radiant Jade (joint with Marines): Develop capability for tactical users to receive updated Electronic Order of Battle (EOB) for a specific area of interest from a theater Joint Intelligence Center; also insure a common EOB for the theater. Reports are transmitted over TDDS.

Radiant Mercury: Automated system to replace USQ-69/ESPRIT manual sanitizer.

Radiant Oak II: Real-time in cockpit (RTIC) demonstration using National Sensors.

Radiant Silver: Develop and maintain surface target emitters (STEs) for training; report over TDDS.

Radiant Storm: Demonstrate the technical and tactical feasibility of a direct broadcasting system (DBS) very large bandwidth simplex broadcast to remote or deployed naval forces.

Radiant Thunder: SPAWAR's general training and travel fund.

Radiant Topaz: Tests the operational utility of interactive and automated National System mission support tasking by afloat commanders using an "NSS-High" system mix.

Radiant White: Develops and demonstrates the tactical utility of GPS-based transportable Reference Emitters (REs) to improve National System targeting and relocation accuracy. In a test at Fallon, two prototype reference emitters were placed near a target emitter, a satellite making a correlation report. The goal is to narrow the geolocation error to 100 m. SOF would emplace the reference emitters.

Radiant Zinc (ended FY96): Developed user-controlled digital imagery browsing and acquisition capability from a central database using low-bandwidth communications with data compression. The goal is to disseminate the MSI (Multispectral Imagery) product, typically 85–300 Mbytes, electronically rather than by hard copy. This project uses a 25:1 compressor developed by Unitech Inc.

NRL has published details of a MATT it has developed, which is presumably typical of devices offered to support this requirement. MATT can simultaneously receive and process formatted TRAP, TIBS, and TADIXS-B intelligence reports, as well as messages from the future CTT. To do that, it has up to six separate 30–4000 MHz transmit/receive channels. The intelligence reports translate into series of updates of a current tactical picture. MATT can accommodate a correlation module that can be used to track a moving platform. In this sense it unites communication with some CDS functions. Each radio modem connects to a black (unclassified) LAN and to a TIBS/CTT processor module, which digitizes the waveforms received. The processor in turn feeds a KG-A module which decrypts the digital data for each channel, and which in turn feeds a message format/deformat module. This module feeds a Red (classified) LAN, to which the correlator module and an input-output processor module are attached.

Submarine Communications Systems

Note that there are significant distinctions among shore-to-submarine VLF/LF communication systems. Initially CW (on/off keying) was used; each pulse used the whole available channel width. It was replaced in the early to mid-1960s by frequency-shift keying (FSK), in which symbols are equated to pulses at different frequencies. Minimum FSK (MSK) uses smaller frequency shifts, so a given channel can support more message traffic. For the U.S. Navy, the transition to FSK and to MFSK was required to support a growing nuclear submarine force, the units of which rarely if ever came to or near the surface to receive messages (earlier diesel boats could receive HF more often).

FRANCE

Safare Crouzet's TUUM-4A/B is the new French navy underwater communications device, superseding TUUM-2C/D and WQC-501 of the Canadian navy; 150 of the previous generation are in service. Frequency range is 1.45–50 kHz; offers both NATO channels and WQC-2 LF channel. Modes are voice, passive (silent squelch key), responder, distance measurement, automatic transmission. Transmission can be directional or omni, depending on the transducer used. Range (14 km in NATO mode) can be extended to 20 km using an additional amplifier, or limited by reducing output power.

UNITED KINGDOM

Deep Siren is an RK Systems acoustic bellringer, presumably equivalent to the U.S. Probe Alert. As of mid-1996, it was soon to undergo evaluation on board a British frigate and an SSN, having recently undergone its sixth phase of at-sea development trials.

COMPUTERS

UNITED STATES

Analog Devices produces a 32-bit floating-point ADSP21060 Super Harvard Architecture Computer (SHARC) digital signal processor (26 million devices, 512 kB of on-chip SRAM) running at 40 MHz with peak throughput of 120 MFLOPS and 40 MIPS. Each chip has two serial ports and six link ports, and its 4-Gword address space makes it possible to link six such chips without external controllers. Analog Devices claims that SHARC is at least three times as fast as a TMS320C40. SHARC is in several new systems, in at least one case as a six-chip cluster. Integrated Computing Engines (ICE), an MIT spinoff, produces arrays of SHARCs, its Desktop RealTime Engines. A 32-SHARC array operates at 33 MHz (3.2 GFLOPS); a 64-chip 40-MHz array operates at 7.7 GFLOPS.

SPARCstations are made by Solaris of Anaheim, California. Clock rates: SPARCstation 10E (SPARC 10E processor), 60 MHz; SPARCstation 20, up to 70 MHz; SPARCstation 5, 70/85 MHz. Rugged Systems' R/SPARC20 (SuperSPARC II processor) runs at up to 125 MHz, and its R/SPARC5 at up to 110 MHz.

As of the fall of 1996, 200-MHz Pentium Pro chips are available.

TACTICAL DATA SYSTEMS

Surface-Ship Combat Direction Systems

CHINA

According to Thomson-CSF, only two TAVITAC were ever sold to China; any further production is unlicensed.

FRANCE

DCN won the contract to provide a new CDS for the upgraded Brazilian *Niteroi* class. The new system will incorporate some SENIT software, but will be compatible with the Siconta system on board the carrier *Minas Gerais*.

Thomson-CSF's Tavitac-NT has been sold for two shore sites and to Kuwait, for the PB37BRL-class patrol boats.

At Bourget Euronaval 1996, CMN, a fast-attack boat builder, advertised its plans to assemble an inexpensive FAC CDS, prob-

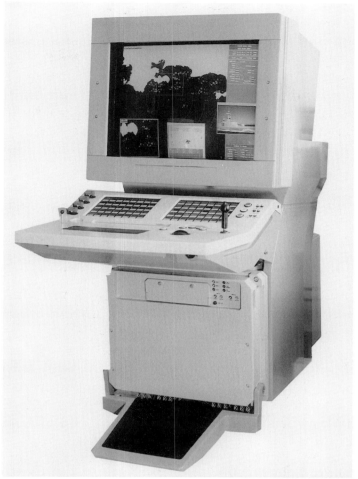

A Vista console, of the type used in TAVITAC. (Thomson-CSF)

ably with three consoles, out of existing elements with COTS components, on the ground that existing CDS were far too expensive. This system is to cost less than $10M.

GERMANY

The AGIS system aboard FAC is to be updated with COTS computers; the competitors are Loral and Signaal.

NETHERLANDS

At Bourget Euronaval in 1996, Signaal displayed a new CO tactical console built around a chair with an LCD screen on one side.

NORWAY

By mid-1996 the competition for the Norwegian fast patrol boat CDS had narrowed to Alenia versus DCN. The new class is to have a six-console system, with a four- or five-console variant for the modernized *Hauk* class.

RUSSIA

New information on a surface-ship CDS has become available. MVU-211 is the "second captain" system in a *Udaloy*. The central computer runs at 1 MOPS. Apparently it is separate from the radar processing/track management system. It accepts radar, sonar, ESM, and data-link data. The computer and consoles are on a bus that can carry up to 100 devices. MVU-211 feeds a UHF data link. The complete system weighs 30 t and requires 60 kW of power.

KRS-27 is the surface target acquisition system of the Moskit missile. It includes the Light Bulb data link and, probably, the directional antenna inside Band Stand. Light Bulb or the directional antenna probably communicates by uplink with the missile. The system also includes the downlink and processor to obtain data from an airborne observation platform (which prob-

ITALY

A CTI console, displayed at Bourget Euronaval 1996. (Author)

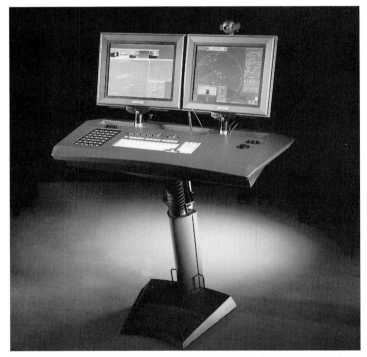

Signaal's CO tactical station (Command) and conference display (Presenter) were first shown at Euronaval 1996. Command shows its 38cm high-resolution flat-panel display, its quick-entry panel, and its 3D spaceball. Presenter's two flat screens can be replaced by LSDs. (Signaal)

ably includes ESM). The data link is also used to control ships in a force during the preparation and delivery of a missile strike (but apparently not to distribute defensive radar data, which is the province of Bell Crown). The active radar element of the system detects surface contacts out to 35–70 km. Rated ESM range, presumably using ducting, is 150–200 km. The system covers four passive radar bands. Rated MTBF is 6000 hr; the system weighs 8100 kg. A photograph of the system controls shows a double console, each element of which has two CRTs: round and square on left, two square on the right. The left element has a trackball, presumably for target designation.

SPAIN

On the *Santa Maria*–class frigates *Navarra* and *Canarias,* a Bazan-built CMC-1 CONAM console replaces earlier standard CIC consoles. It will be retrofitted to others of the class. Tritan was never installed in the *Descubiertas.*

SWEDEN

The Swedish government plans to buy a common C³I architecture for land and sea forces, so that all can easily share a common tactical picture. As in the U.S. JMCIS initiative, the key is common software standards. All systems in this LIM (Ledningessystem i Marinen) will be COTS-based. Major elements are STRIMA (Stridsledning i Marinen), which forms the tactical picture; MAST (Marinens Strabsstoed), a decision aid using the

STRIMA picture; MTS (Marinens Telesamband), the jam- and intercept-resistant communications link between platforms; and MSL (Marinens Systemstoed), a planning aid used to reconfigure the LIM infrastructure to meet particular tactical requirements. The first LIM-compatible CDS is MARIL 2000, replacing MARIL 880 on board six *Spica II*–class fast attack boats. It employs three workstations and a laptop PC to control missiles and torpedoes. This COTS system was chosen in favor of a MARIL 880 upgrade or TACTICOS or a system offered by Terma or Erisoft; it is made by YDAB, a CelsiusTech subsidiary.

The YS 2000 CDS is to be called CESTRIS. It will probably include control of air defense missiles (BAMSE, RBS 23).

CelsiusTech is now marketing 9LV Mk 3E (enhanced), a COTS version of 9LV Mk 3 using flat screen displays, an FDDI LAN,

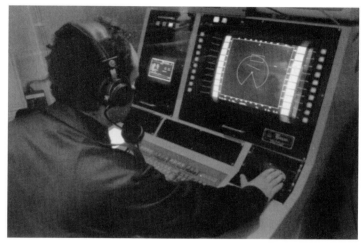

The console of Bazan's Alcor small-combatant CDS. This system was installed only on board the experimental fast-attack boat *Cormoran*, which has been sold to Colombia. (Bazan)

and Windows-style MMI. In a new ergonomically engineered workstation, the left arm of the operator's chair carries the trackball; the right arm carries a keypad and a touch-screen. Between the arms is a flat desk carrying a keyboard with special-action buttons above it. In front of the desk is a pair of flat LCD screens. At present Mk 3E retains the ADA code of the earlier 9LV. It adds underwater warfare capability (including MCM), and AAW performance is sufficiently improved to permit local area defense using a ship's gun. Planned future software modules include medium-range AAW missile control. As of late 1996, CelsiusTech hoped to sell Mk 3E for the Swedish YS 2000 corvette, or the Malaysian/Australian OPV, or the planned modernization of the Polish *Orkan* class (ex–East German *Sassnitz* class, to which end CelsiusTech displayed a version at the Polish Military Arms Exhibit at the Babie Doly naval air station in 1996).

UNITED KINGDOM

SSCS Phase 2 software, currently operational, is limited to navigation and picture compilation; ships equipped with it are restricted to low-intensity tasks such as guardship duty in the South Atlantic or the West Indies. Phase 3 integrates the ship's weapons: Harpoon, Seawolf, GSA 8/Mk 8 gun, UAF(1), Sea Gnat, and Type 1010 IFF (previously Seawolf required a stand-alone STAC launch control terminal). Phase 3 trials were completed on 18 October 1996 when a Certificate of Clearance for Use (CCU) was issued; live fire trials on board HMS *Somerset* are expected in 1997. The Phase 3 CCU was delayed by problems elsewhere in the ship's combat system, reportedly with the LFA track extractor/combiner (ADT), which sent raw radar data rather than processed tracks onto the ship's combat-system bus (combat-system highway in British parlance). To deal with the greater data flow, BAeSEMA had to install Pentium CPUs in the SSCS server nodes (which form the tactical picture) and also had to add data processing algorithms. The Phase 3 CCU was clearly crucial for any serious combat use of the class, but in the absence of a formal requirement for Type 23 system performance, the requirement levied for the CCU also became in effect the system staff requirement. Phase 4 (due for CCU in the second half of 1997) adds ASW and data-link capability. Phase 5 (1998) adds TDAs (including an equivalent to the destroyers' CCA) and embedded training. Although ships with Phase 3 software are officially described as capable of unrestricted deployment, it is not clear how they can function effectively without data links.

HMS *Edinburgh* was fitted with a color ADAWS 2000 console for user evaluation in May 1996; it will be supported by GEC-Marconi for 4 yr at own cost. The console incorporates a Sun-SPARC Station 10 board, Metheus integrated radar-scan converter and graphics engine (supporting X-Windows/Motif), and a 19in screen. A dual-redundant Ethernet connects it to ADAWS via an I/O gateway, which runs ADA and assembler language software. A fleetwide ADAWS 2000 color-console installation to add Link 16 to ADAWS Mod 1 is planned, to provide two consoles in a Type 42 and three in a carrier. A developmental private-venture GEC large-screen display may replace horizontal conference displays on ADAWS Mod 1 ships. ADAWS 2000 may replace ADAWS altogether in Type 42 Batch 2/3 and in at least one carrier. It would run existing ADAWS software (in Coral 66) under a UNIX operating system. The full four-console system is being installed in HMS *Ocean* and it will equip the LPDs.

UNITED STATES

Note that CEC includes the *illumination* of a target by an airborne platform. The airborne platform detects and tracks target, tracks missile, sends track data to surface ship, provides and schedules illumination. In the January 1996 Mountain Top exercise, the Kokee site on Kauai (3800 ft elevation) was a surrogate airborne platform, with an SPG-51D illuminator and an ADS-18 search radar. Participating ships were the cruisers *Anzio* (CG 68), *Lake Erie* (CG 70), and *Cape St. George* (CG 71). Also participating were Army Hawk and Patriot batteries, Air Force F-15 and F-16 fighters, an AWACS aircraft, ECM aircraft, and a Customs Service P-3 equipped with CEC. Four SM-2s fired by an Aegis cruiser hit targets beyond the ship's radar horizon. A CEC net is apparently currently limited to fewer than 24 users.

As of 1996, plans for installation were:

CG: 1 in FY93, 2 in FY97, 2 in FY99, 2 in FY00, 1 in FY01, 2 each in FY02-FY06 (total 18)
DDG 51 class: 2 in FY99, 1 in FY00, 3 in FY01, 6 in FY02, 7 in FY03, 8 in FY04, 7 each in FY05-06, 2 in FY07 (total 43)
DDG 993 class: 2 each in FY02-03 (total 4, whole class)
DD 963 class: 2 in FY02, 3 each in FY03-04, 4 in FY05 (total 12)
CV/CVN: 1 in FY97, 1 in FY99, 2 in each of FY00-01, 1 in FY02, 2 in each of FY03-04, 1 each in FY05-06 (total 13)
LPD 17: 1 in FY00, 2 each FY02-06, 1 in FY07 (total 12)
LHD/LHA: 1 in FY97, 1 in FY99, 2 in FY00, 1 in FY01, 2 each FY02-03, then 3 in FY04 (total 12)
LSD 41 class: 2 in FY03, 3 each FY04-06 (total 11)
E-2C: 2 in FY97, 5 in FY99, 6 in FY00, 7 in FY01, 8 each in FY02-04, 5 in FY05 (total 49)

CEC on board *Anzio* and *Cape St. George* was certified as having attained initial operating capability on 30 September 1996. Low-rate initial production (Milestone III) is scheduled for 1997.

The ACDS Block 1 interface with CEC (Level 2) will be tested in 1996–97 aboard the carrier *Eisenhower* and the LHD *Wasp*. Block 1 Level 1 was in the carrier *Constellation*. Two carriers already have Block 1 (but without CEC). Block 1 includes modifiable doctrine, two-way NTCS-A interface, and DMA-based maps. Planned installations of Block 1 (as of mid-1996): 1 in FY96, 1 LHD Block 1 in FY96, 2 LHA Block 0 in FY97, first DDG 993 (OJ-194) in FY97.

FCDISSA (Fleet Combat Direction Systems Support Activity)'s Port Hueneme Division (East Coast Operations) has developed an ACDS Command Station for non-Aegis warships. It provides the ship's CO with his own tactical display. Each user can control two independent displays, such as a workstation and an LSD or Amplified Local Display Screen. The first version was hosted on a DTC-II computer, it uses a Solaris real-time operating system running X-Windows and MOTIF graphics. An upgraded version, running on a UYQ-70 (with HP-743 processor), uses the HP-UX and HP-RT operating systems. A tactical data communications processor (TDCP) acts as interface between the ship's CDS and the system. The Command Support Station contains it plus a Geographic Server (holding the system's map and other geographical data) and a Network Archive and Playback Server (NAPS). The station in turn is connected to an FDDI LAN, which is also connected to a UYQ-70 (an OJ-451 emulator), a UYQ-70 command table (carrying two OJ-451 emulators with Geographic Display Capability [GDC] and the command station display system [CSDS]), and one or more LSD control stations (also with CSDS software).

In the LHA, the command table is a two-operator horizontal arrangement of five 19in monitors with two keyboards and two trackballs, with two LSDs above and behind it. The monitors and human-computer interfaces are shared between the tactical systems via a Display Device Control Processor (DDCP), which directs video from any source to any monitor or LSD at the table. The system displays the current tactical picture (taken from the CDS) and can display up to 200 planned tracks (PIM tracks). Formations can be defined for widely dispersed ships. Screens can be defined. A doctrine capability allows the user to define different filters (with type, identification, speed, altitude, range, bearing, course, track movement relative to own ship) for each display surface. Alternatively, one screen can be used to replay recent activity (24 hours of tactical data can be recorded) while another shows the current tactical picture. The tactical picture uses standard NTDS symbology. It includes SYS-2, Link 11, and WDS tracks; EW and acoustic data; ACDS weapons system status and inventories; weapons engagement status; controlled aircraft status; ACDS UYK-43 interface status; nonfiring zones; weapons tracking sectors and zones; and WSN-5 nav data. Color geographic displays include the world vector shoreline and digital terrain/elevation data. Advanced Graphics Displays to aid Flag/CO/TAO decisionmaking include Track Display Doctrine, Track Profile Plot, Overlays for OP Areas and Areas of Concern, Geographic Grids, Air and Surface Track Auto Tagging, 4-W Grid, Screen K Grid, and multileg PIMs. This software works with 1280×1024 accelerated graphics.

The DTC-II Level 1 Phase 1 ACDS Command Station was first deployed to the Mediterranean on board USS *Wainwright*, then installed on board the cruisers *South Carolina* and *Arkansas* and on the *Kidd* class. The upgraded version, being installed during the LHA modernizations, includes special displays for Mine Danger Area, Fire Support Areas, Beach Assault, Amphibious Objective Area, Vertical Assault, and Miscellaneous Zones/Areas. Command stations will be installed in CIC, TACC, Flag, and LFOC spaces on these ships.

The LHA Command Table. (NSWC)

Submarine Combat-Direction Systems

FRANCE

SUBTICS, the system planned for the Pakistani Agosta 90B submarines, can control two wire-guided torpedoes while firing two antiship missiles or a missile and a free-running torpedo.

RUSSIA

New information on submarine CDS has become available. The MVU-133 system in a Delta II–class submarine is built around a central computer (capacity 500 KOPS, 320 kwords of memory) which can process information on 10 targets and direct fire against two of them. It employs a pair of side-by-side workstations connected to a digital computer and to an interface to ship

systems. The system automatically evaluates the threat represented by various targets and distributes fire among them. This system weighs 9.1 t and requires 17 kW of power.

SWEDEN

The 9SCS Mk 3 system on board the submarine *Gotland* has a reported capacity of 95 tracks.

UNITED KINGDOM

The original 16-bit PDP-11/44 version of DCG had a 48-Mbyte hard disk, Fortran software, and four operator positions with 768 $\times$ 574-pixel displays (three for operators, one a maintainer/operator position). It could time-share several tasks simultaneously, all sharing access to its 2-Mbyte memory. Upgrades through 1992 for new TMA algorithms and new weapons required three times the source code, twice the memory, and a 312-Mbyte hard disk, using COTS equipment inside a protective enclosure. After 1993 the manufacturer no longer supported the computer (production of which had ended in 1986), and failures increased fourfold between 1986 and 1992. Hence the COTS upgrade, using distributed workstations (four SunSPARC 5/110, chosen 6 months before their commercial release to ensure that the system was still current when it entered service). One workstation acted as server, with shared peripherals. About 400 kloc of Fortran code was ported into the new UNIX environment. The new version implemented DRA's ITMA algorithm, an alternative approach in which a stream of observations is evaluated before determining a final TMA solution. It can also detect target maneuvers. SMCS implements maneuver detection and checks for bad data.

UNITED STATES

As of late 1996, it was reported that *Collins*-class software development was well behind schedule, and that it would not be completely ready by the target date, early 1998. One unofficial report suggested that the interim system would suffice only for surveillance and not for weapons control. However, according to the submarine project director, by 1998 all weapons and sensors will be operable. Hardware and software-controlled functions have been tested successfully, but apparently they have not yet been integrated, so data from some separate sensor and processor systems must be fused manually. Too, the development program is beginning to incorporate features not originally envisaged, partly as a result of lessons learned from the ship's sea trials since October 1994. The ship is to be equipped with an extra standalone processor and display console. This statement suggests that computing power did not suffice for passive LF signal processing from the submarine's flank and towed arrays.

Aircraft Tactical Data Systems

RUSSIA

In June 1996 Ilyushin announced an MPA version of its Il-114 airliner, Il-114P, as part of a larger martime surveillance system developed by the Proton-Service scientific research center, NPO Geophisics, NPO Poliat, VNII Radiotechniki "Skala," NII Sistemotechniki, and NII Pribornoi Automatiki. The after cabin of the airplane houses the Strizh maritime-surveillance system, including two crew workstations. It uses an IIR/TV system, a nose search radar, a satellite navigation system, and a data link. A typical weapons load would be a pair of gun pods under the fuselage and four stores under wing hard points. The airplane would form part of a network including coastal radar stations and regional command centers. Il-114P may be a rival to the An-72P previously announced.

New information has become available concerning the CDS of the Il-38 May. The prototype (without full mission equipment) flew in 1961, but the full system may not have entered service until 1971. That suggests that Il-38 was part of the same anti-SSBN program that produced the AT-1 ASW torpedo, Shkval, and several ASW missiles. The system operators, the TACCO and the acoustics operator, occupy a short mission compartment abaft the flight deck. They sit next to each other facing aft, with the acoustics station next to the side of the airplane. The TACCO apparently has two circular CRTs, possibly with a third between and below them. Apparently there is no acoustic display. This arrangement would be consistent with the use of the BM-series buoys of the early 1960s: one CRT would be for the radar and the buoy transponders (buoys report on the radar when they detect a sufficiently strong signal), the other for tactical computations. Aircraft often operate in pairs, which suggests that one maintains contact while the second descends to attack. Of 57 aircraft built, in 1996 it was estimated that 16 were in service in the Northern Fleet at Severomorsk, and 20 in the Pacific Fleet at Petropavlovsk, plus 5 in Indian navy service at Goa.

UNITED KINGDOM

In June 1996 the British government chose Nimrod 2000, with the Boeing CDS, as the Nimrod replacement. However, it also announced that Boeing would have to form a "strategic alliance" with GEC-Marconi, the losing CDS contractor.

The Racal RAMS 4000 Central Tactical System is being installed in German navy Lynx helicpters, which are being brought up to Royal Navy HMA.8 standard, including Sea Skua capability. Due to delays in the NH90 program, they are expected to remain in service through 2015. For the same helicopter, Westland is promoting a glass cockpit based on work done on the EH 101, including a FLIR display integrated with the cockpit display.

UNITED STATES

Japan has bought both APS-137 and the ASQ-212 computer for P-3 upgrades, and is expected to buy other elements of the AIP package. Under a 1996 contract, Fujitsu is supplying new high-resolution displays.

STRATEGIC STRIKE WARFARE

RUSSIA

The NATO designator SS-NX-28 has been assigned to the SS-N-20 successor, for modernized Typhoon-class submarines. SS-NX-29 is the NATO designation for the Medvedka ASW weapon.

UNITED STATES

Late in 1996 NAVSEA asked for proposals for a launch controller for nuclear Tomahawks, to control missiles in two submarine torpedo tubes simultaneously. In the past, Tomahawks have been controlled by the submarine's CDS. Nuclear control places special certification requirements on the CDS, and so presumably makes transition to COTS difficult. The situation is much simplified by separating out the nuclear element. The system is to be installed on board *Los Angeles* and New Attack Submarine–class units. Planned procurement: one in FY98, 7 in FY99, 14 in FY00, 15 in FY01, 18 in FY02.

STRIKE WARFARE

CHINA

Some J-8-II fighters (over 400 of which the Chinese reported in naval service in mid-1996) carry C-801/802 missiles.

According to a 1996 ONI report, China is likely to have a submerged-launch tactical missile by the turn of the century.

FRANCE

A contract for full-scale developed of an ANNG airframe/engine testbed, VESTA (Vecteur Statoreacteur), was announced at Bourget Euronaval in October 1996. The Franco-German staff requirement for ANNG was signed in April 1995. Its development contract is expected in the last quarter of 1998 following system studies in 1996-98. VESTA/ANNG are being developed by a Franco-German consortium led by Aerospatiale; DASA is responsible for navigation, the warhead, and the firing unit; Aerospatiale is responsible for the airframe, engine, and mid-course and terminal guidance. ANNG should first fly in September 2001, with two test flights in 2002, five ship firings, and entry into service in mid-2005.

Apache, with its wings spread, at Farnborough 1996. (S. Zaloga)

At Bourget Euronaval, Thomson-CSF displayed a light helicopter UAV, Vigilant F 2000C (2.3 × 0.5 × 0.6 m, 32 kg, speed up to 100 km/hr, ceiling 3000 m, endurance 1 to 2 hr).

The alternative warheads for Aerospatiale's modular AASM are a Mk 82 or Mk 84 bomb, a 250-kg penetrator, or a submunitions dispenser. The head can carry a laser or IR seeker (or no seeker at all); the guidance section behind the head can be GPS/inertial or inertial only. The weapon can glide or it can have a rocket motor.

GERMANY

The German government has withdrawn from the Apache program, citing its high cost, and is trying to interest the British in a German alternative. As of mid-1996, the French planned to buy 300 missiles, the British 800 or 900. Germany is trying to interest other countries, including Italy, in its Aramis ARM.

Aramis is shown at Farnborough, 1996. (S. Zaloga)

INDIA

The submarine-launched weapon is Sagrika (Oceanic), with a range of about 160 nm (300 km). It may use commercial GPS (CEP 50–100 m) plus a terminal seeker. Work began in 1991 for completion about 2000.

INTERNATIONAL

The current NATO UAV program (administered by Project Group 35) envisages three levels of operation of another ship's UAV: (i) a ship's ability to receive data from the UAV; (ii) adding the ability to take over control of the UAV); and (iii) adding the ability to land, fuel, service, and relaunch the UAV. The Project Group hopes to build on the common open-architecture tactical control system (TCS) being developed by the United States to control all U.S. UAVs (such as Predator). Its program envisages:

1. The United Kingdom is to fund an interface between the U.S. TCS and the German SEAMOS for trials in 1997–98.

2. The UK review of digital UAV data links is to be completed at the end of 1996, and the NATO NIAG is to produce a STANAG for U.S./UK/German integration in a demonstration using the SEAMOS avionics package.

3. Land trials with U.S. (and possibly other) UAVs are expected in 2000–2002. Sea trials should follow.

As a submarine surface-attack weapon, Polypheme can be carried in tandem pairs in torpedo tubes, a total of four per tube. Reports of German interest have apparently been exaggerated; as of November 1996 the BWB had not yet approved any tests. A 30km flight test may still be planned for December 1996. The U.S. agent is Northrop Grumman; the U.S. Navy is considering buying Polypheme rather than Raytheon's ACID army FOG-M missile (15km range vs. 60 km for Polypheme). ACID is to be tested in mid-1997. The Northrop Grumman version is 10 in × 9 ft, 240 lb, with GPS/INS mid-course guidance and IIR dual-FOV terminal guidance.

IRAN

Iran has reported an indigenously developed Tondar (Thunder) missile in service in the Northern Gulf as well as a Piroozi-75 (Victory-75), probably on a missile boat. Tondar is probably HY-2, and Piroozi-75 is probably the C-802 bought from China.

ITALY

Work on the 250-km TESEO Mk 3 began in 1996 using tri-service funds. It uses a data link and a GPS receiver. Otomat Mk 3 range is 180 km versus 160 km for Mk 2. It has obstacle avoidance capability, three waypoints, and sea-skimming or pop-up attack modes. Single missiles can be fired at 20-sec intervals, and a salvo of three at 3-sec intervals. The refit of the Saudi *Al Madinah* class reportedly includes an Otomat software upgrade to include enhanced search patterns to reattack missed targets. That may mean substitution of Mk 3 missiles for Mk 2s.

A surface version of Marte Mk 2 is in development. The new Marte Mk 2/A is an aircraft version of the existing Mk 2, without the rocket booster. Length without the booster is 3789 mm (with the booster, 4796.5 mm). Two or four can be carried. A Mk 2 version with additional boosters can be fired by a hovering helicopter.

The AEW version of APS-784 is designated HEW-784; it occupies a 3m radome, compared to the 1.8 m required for APS-784. The AEW version of the EH-101 helicopter is expected to operate about 50 nm from the ship, orbiting at 10,000 ft and sending all sensor data to the controlling ship by data link. The ship correlates all tracks and assigns fighters or missiles to targets. The maritime utility version of the helicopter is to have an APS-705B search/weather radar taken from a discarded AB-212 helicopter.

EH-101 is to have a FLIR, probably the stabilized dual-FOV (narrow with 4× magnification) 8–12-micron Galileo GaliFLIR Astro, which uses a SPRITE detector. The turret is slaved to other sensors.

NORWAY

The preliminary NSM startup contract was awarded in June 1996 (the full development contract is expected by the end of 1996). The coast defense version (to replace 150mm guns), suspended late in 1995, may resume development at the end of 1996. Kongsberg is looking for a foreign partner. Reportedly Matra is interested; some computer designs for NSM resemble its Apache. Design requirements include a range of at least 100 km and that eight be stowable on below-decks launchers on the new FAC. The turbojet missile will follow terrain near fjords.

RUSSIA

Ship-launched antiship missile systems (at least from SS-N-9 onwards) are integrated by NPO Granit (formed in 1921 to develop FCS).

New information clarifies the guidance system of the SS-N-19 (Granit) missile. It is a fire-and-forget weapon. The missiles in a salvo communicate as they approach the target, presumably comparing RCS in the narrow slices they see to decide which target is largest or most important and to distribute their fire over the target array. The missile has a three-channel seeker (passive and 3cm and 8mm active). It uses the LPI (spread-spectrum) 3cm element in a high-altitude search, then dives to low altitude before turning on the 8mm element in the terminal phase. Work on a laser terminal seeker, using a focusing mirror, is progressing. Granit entered service in 1980.

A video of SS-N-19 suggests that it is an extrapolation of SS-N-3 with an air scoop under its fuselage.

Bazalt (SS-N-12) was the final development of the SS-N-3 concept, in which externally supplied data were matched with a missile's radar picture of the target area. It seems likely that Bazalt needed very high speed to get to the target area quickly enough to match the radar picture seen before launch, whereas Granit can operate at lower speed.

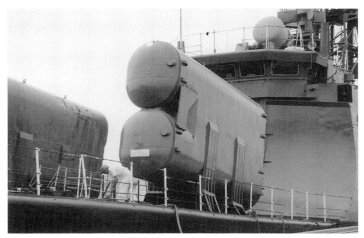

Styx (P-21/22) launchers on the Indian corvette *Khanjar*, Dubai, 1995. (S. Zaloga)

Chelomei's P-35 is the sole surviving version of SS-N-3. (D. Markov)

Both Alfa and Yakhont are being developed, Yakhont being further advanced. Flight tests have validated its performance to Mach 2.5.

Kh-22 (AS-4) and Styx both use Inhibited Red Fuming Nitric Acid as oxidizer; the fuel is kerosene. The combination is quite dangerous. Several Blinders (for which Kh-22 was designed) were destroyed when they belly-landed on fueled missiles. Similarly, the Finnish navy abandoned Styx for fear of explosions of fueled missiles (attack boats have no fueling arrangements, so the missiles must be loaded in fueled condition).

Early in 1997 it was reported that Russia had sold two existing *Sovremennyy*-class destroyers, carrying 3M80 missiles, to

China; the Chinese claimed that the 1996 Taiwan Straits confrontation had shown that their own weapons were an insufficient deterrent to U.S. carrier operations in the Straits. Note, however, that in 1995 the Russians reported having sold 3M80 to China.

The current U.S. Foreign Comparative Test Program includes money to extend MA-31 (target version of Kh-31) range from 17 to 45 nm by lengthening the missile by about 0.5 m (for extra fuel); two missiles are to be modified by McDonnell-Douglas during 1997. In addition, 12 more MA-31s are being bought for tests.

Reportedly the air-launched version of Maschinostroyeniye's Alfa differs from the ship-launched version, partly in being propelled by a turbojet rather than by a ramjet.

Data on major antiship missiles given in a recent unofficial Russian book:

> Oniks (for the new submarine *Severodvinsk*): range 320 km, speed Mach 2.3, length 10 m. This missile is launched from either a 65cm torpedo tube or a slightly inclined nearly vertical 65cm tube abaft the submarine's sail; the submarine carries 12 missiles.
> Vulkan is 3M70/P-1000: 4.5 t with 1000-kg warhead, range 700 km, speed Mach 2.3, length 11.6 m; minimum flight altitude 40 m.
> SS-N-19 is P-700; 5 t with 1000-kg or 500-kT warhead, range 555 km, speed Mach 2.5; length 10.5 m. SS-N-12 is P-500/4K80: 4.8 t, warhead 1000 kg or 500 kT, range 550 km, speed Mach 2.9, length 11.7 m. By way of comparison, according to this account P-35 (SS-N-3B) weighs 5.3 t with 930-kg or 20-kT warhead; range is 350 km at Mach 1.2; length is 10.2 m.
> SS-N-9 is 4K85/P-120: 3.18 t, 1000-kg warhead, range 150 km, speed Mach 1, length 8.9 m. This book lists SS-N-7 as 4K66/P-20M.

SWEDEN

RBS 15 Mk 2 (converted from 15M shipboard and 15K coastal missiles) is expected to enter service in 1999 (under a 1994 contract). Saab is discussing a similar upgrade with the Finnish navy (which operates the SF1 shipboard and SF2 coastal versions; SF3 would be the upgraded version). RBS 15F is to be upgraded separately. Mk 3 is a private venture aimed primarily at the British Horizon frigate project. The Swedish navy is now interested in a land-attack version, and may buy a submarine version sometime after 2010 (if it is stealthier; this interest is linked to land-attack capability). There is also some interest in a terminal supersonic capability.

New information gives Mk 3 range as 200 km; the 200-kg warhead is of a new type; and the seeker is a Ku-band radar. Waypoints are programmed in both elevation and in azimuth. As of mid-1996, Saab planned test firings from the new launcher by end of 1996, live launchings by late 1997/early 1998, and a proven product by 1999.

Reportedly over 120 RBS 15 were sold to Yugoslavia, of which 24 are in Serbia/Montenegro, the rest in Croatia.

Sweden is currently examining alternative self-propelled coast defense guns. The requirement is apparently to be able to hit a 4 × 4 m target moving at 50 kts at a range of 3–20 km. Reportedly the only successful gun was the new German PzH 2000 155mm/52, which is to enter German service in 1998.

UNITED KINGDOM

Racal-Thorn won the Sea King AEW (AEW.7 version) upgrade contract with the Searchwater 2000 AEW radar. The upgrade will include a new central tactical system and Link 16 (using Rockwell's IDS-2000). In a different version, Searchwater 2000 was selected for the Nimrod 2000 MPA.

At Bourget Euronaval, Vosper-Thornycroft displayed a corvette armed with a naval version of Royal Ordnance's RAYO launcher (a joint venture with Chile and South Africa), currently used only in 12-rocket form on trucks. Range is 45 km, and the warhead weighs 45 kg.

All RAF Tornadoes will be able to fire Sea Eagle after having been upgraded to GR.4 standard under the MLU program. This probably involves installation of a 1760A weapons data bus and changes to the airplane's flight control program (with additional computer capacity) and to its stores management system. Reportedly all aircraft have already had their ground mapping radars (GMRs) upgraded, new features including ISAR for target classification.

UNITED STATES

The Tier II + UAV has been renamed Global Hawk. The Predator UAV ran successful carrier trials in 1995 and in 1996 was tested by the nuclear submarine *Chicago*. It was used to conn SEALs onto an island, and it helped the submarine recover them. However, late in 1996 a Navy study showed that adapting Predator to shipboard operation might be quite expensive, since the UAV would have to be fitted with a heavy-oil engine and the ships fitted not only with the necessary radios but also with arresting gear and some means of launching the UAV. A less expensive option might be to retain the UAV's gasoline engine and launch it from land, controlling it (and using its sensors) from ships offshore, in littoral operations. As of the fall of 1996, these options were due to be briefed to Congress by the end of the year.

On 23 November 1996 Rockwell received a three year FY97 ATD contract for Fasthawk (previously Cheap Shot). The missile is to be wingless, steered by angling the exhaust nozzle of its continuous-bleed afterburning turbojet, reportedly related to the engine used in the SR-71. The annular air intake surrounds a nose shock cone. Maximum speed is to be Mach 4, and the missile is to be capable of attacking targets as much as 12 ft underground. With a 750-lb warhead, the missile is to weigh 1960 lb, with a range of 500 nm. With a 450-lb warhead, range is to be about 1000 nm. Fasthawk is to be launchable from standard VLS cells. Unit cost is to be held to $300,000.

According to new information, Harpoon 1D (AGM-84F) has completed OpEval, but is not in production (10 missiles were upgraded from 1C to 1D for tests). Although the U.S. Navy has not yet bought the 1G version, FY96 and later foreign sales are of that model. SLAM production ended in FY96; SLAM-ER is to become operational in 1997.

Harpoon 2000 is now called Harpoon Block 2 (some in industry call it Block 1J). Funds are being sought in the FY98 budget for an upgrade to incorporate the most affordable littoral enhancements. There is again official interest in adapting Harpoon to the VLS, now that antiship Tomahawk is gone. A data link may be added for man-in-the-loop assistance in littoral areas. In 1996 the Harpoon project office issued an RFI for new seekers adapted to littoral requirements. Replies included IIR, mm-wave radar, enhanced radar, and LADAR. A more accurate clock in the missile may offer better simultaneity. McDonnell-Douglas is studying a new signal processor that could improve target discrimination and ECCM, as well as a new seeker.

JSOW at Farnborough, 1996, with its wings folded and a BLU-108 anti-armor submunition underneath. (S. Zaloga)

JDAMS low-rate initial production is to begin in April rather than December 1997 with 937 kits ($23M) for the Air Force. The decision for full-rate production was moved up from July 1999 to April 1998. Unit price is now $18,000. The planned Hammerhead terminal sensor did not survive the FY97 budget review. JDAMS first flew successfully on 22 October 1996 (a Mk 84 inertial version was dropped by an F-16). An early November flight using GPS to aid the inertial system apparently failed. As of late 1996, about 87,000 JDAMS kits were planned.

Development of an improved version of the GBU-28/B hard-target killer began in August 1993. This weapon carries a one-piece 2270-kg National Forge BLU-113A/B penetrator in place of the original reworked gun barrel. Production: 161 in FY97 for $18.4M. Note that the projected boosted kinetic energy penetrator (BKEP), BLU-106, was never bought; BLU-109 was bought instead.

McDonnell-Douglas has begun work on a Small Smart Bomb (15.2 × 182.8 cm, including 30.4cm control and GPS/INS guidance; the case weighs 72.4 kg, the explosive 22.6 kg, for a total of 113.2 kg) for the Air Force, to arm future stealthy aircraft with limited internal bay space. The objective, to be reached by 2005, is a bomb capable of penetrating 1.8 m of concrete and of attacking 80% of targets now requiring a BLU-109. Work began under a mid-1995 Miniaturized Munitions Techology Demonstration (MMTD) contract. Innovations include a biconic nose and a length:diameter ratio of 12:1. Phase I is to use repackaged JDAM guidance; Phase II is to use antijam GPS and LIDAR. Drop tests from an F-16 are scheduled for November 1996–March 1997. There is also interest (U.S./British) in a larger 450-kg Dense Metal Case Penetrating Weapon (DMCPW), to be developed under a 3-yr program, entering EDM in FY00. The weapon's tungsten case should double hard-target penetration compared to steel. Finally, a 1020-kg boosted weapon compatible with the F/A-18 and with Air Force fighters is to be developed (to be completed FY01). Meanwhile, Motorola has developed a hard target smart fuze (HTSF) which can survive penetration of one layer of concrete, sense the void, then go off. The Air Force bought 150 to be used on GBU-27s and -28s.

The submarine force is showing increasing interest in UAVs. In December 1996 USS *Asheville* simulated the launch of an Army Ferret from a Harpoon canister, using UHF (LOS) control, and then transferring control to Special Forces on the ground. The UAV was used for simulated strike reconnaissance and poststrike damage assessment. This test follows the use of a Predator UAV by USS *Chicago* earlier in 1996.

The first operational ATWCS was installed on board USS *Peterson* in 1996 and is to become operational in 1997 (the launch control group element enters service in 1998). It replaces TWCS Block III. Evolution is staged. The FY97 version replaces the Tomahawk track control group (TCG) with an open-architecture TCG employing four TAC-X (currently TAC-4) workstations on a LAN. This version is still limited to Tomahawk, because it retains the original LCG, which communicates with the vertical launcher. The FY98 version adds four more TAC-X elements to the LAN, to replace the separate LCG. It still communicates with the VLS and thence with Tomahawks. Finally ATWCS becomes the Advanced *Tactical* Weapons Control System: two more TAC-X workstations are added, and the LAN connects to other naval weapons, such as the 5in gun firing ERGM shells and Harpoon/SLAM. The vertical launcher now fires not only Tomahawk but also Block IV (TBIP), with its two-way data link, and other missiles such as the future naval shore fire-support weapon (in 1996 ATWCS was selected as the foundation of the planned NSFS Warfare Control System, NWCS, controlling the 5in guided shell). The LAN (bus) is the key to this growth. ATWCS to be installed on board 28 DDG 51, 22 CG 47, and 24 DD 963.

The next version of Harpoon control software is to halve the minimum distance between a target and the shore. Though currently unfunded, a GPS/INS upgrade to Harpoon (proposed by McDonnell-Douglas) seems likely because it will greatly improve the missile's performance near land. At present Harpoon has no mid-course guidance; it dead-reckons its position between launch and the programmed activation of its radar. The radar scan width has to be broad enough to take account of drift during the dead-reckoning phase of flight, and it may therefore detect more than the desired target. The closer to shore, the more nontargets.

JSOW (AGM-154A) production plans have been cut as unit price has risen. When JSOW was conceived, Secretary of the Navy John Lehman imposed a unit price of $50,000. When the contract was awarded in FY90, planned unit price was $79,900 for the 6300th missile. The current estimate, for early units, is $439,000, but late in 1996 an attempt was being made to cut it to $150,000 for late production. As of late 1996 LRIP was extended from one year (FY97) to two, with numbers reduced from 300 in FY97 and 740 in FY98 to 100 and 186, respectively. To some extent this was a vote in favor of the developed versions of the missile, carrying unitary or BLU-108 warheads. However, it also reflected a tightening budget. The proposed POM cut FY98 production to 164 and planned for 374 missiles in FY99, 844 in FY00, 1151 in FY01, 1459 in FY02, and 1486 in FY03. However, later in the year the Navy's Budget Estimate Submission (BES) cut 1084 missiles from the planned total of 5578. It increased the projected FY99 purchase to 463, then cut the later purchases to 776, 823, 1059, and 1109 missiles. At that time the FY98 program was uncertain because although 100 missiles had been requested in FY97, money had been appropriated for 150. Some of the changes may reflect the decision to slip production of the two improved versions a year.

Under a small-business research program begun in 1991, Science and Applied Technology of San Diego has developed a dual-mode seeker for a next-generation antiradar missile. It adds a mm-wave radar which can select a target within the battery indicated by the missile's passive seeker. The program, AARGM (advanced antiradar guided missile), will test the seeker on board up to six HARM bodies, and may lead to low-rate production by 2002 or 2003.

In the fall of 1996 Greece bought 84 HARM (and 50 AMRAAM) to equip F-16s, joining Germany, Spain, and Turkey in Europe. Note that German HARMs equip naval strike and air force EW Tornadoes; Spanish missiles equip EF-18s.

A new Air Force submunition, Loral Vought's LOCAAS (low-cost antiarmor submunition), may have important future naval applications. LOCAAS is winged (for greater gliding range) and, more important, its mmwave-LADAR sensor is intended to classify targets so that its warhead can operate in alternative modes: shaped charge versus armored vehicles, or self-forging fragments versus softer targets. The seeker and target recognition algorithms have already been tested. The LOCAAS program began in September 1990 and guided flights began early in 1994. The program was funded by ARPA under BTI.

ANTIAIRCRAFT WARFARE

CHINA

LY-60 is a copied Aspide, examples of which were imported under a secret 1988–89 agreement with Italy, terminated in 1990, after the Tiananmen Square Massacre. The air-to-air version, CY-60, is probably designated PL-11. PL-10 was an attempted Chinese copy of AIM-7E, which LY-60 superseded. As of late 1996, the Chinese military had not yet bought PL-11. Work on an active version of LY-60 is proceeding.

FRANCE

Jupiter II, the solid-state transmitter version, uses sixteen 300W transmitters, for a peak power of 4.8 kW. This radar, using an LW-08 antenna, was ordered by both Saudi Arabia and Taiwan for their *La Fayette*–class frigates. The version in the carrier *Charles de Gaulle* uses 32 transmitters (9.6 kW). In brochures distributed at Bourget Euronaval 1996, this version was designated Jupiter-ER (extended range). A new Jupiter-LA (light antenna) has a planar array antenna and a 16-module transmitter. Instrumented ranges are 340 km in the air channel and 90 km in the surface channel (compared to 370 and 140 km for the parabolic-antenna version). Scan rates are 6 and 12 rpm, and an-

Arabel occupies the radome on board the test ship *Ile d'Oléron*, at Toulon in May 1996. (A. Preston)

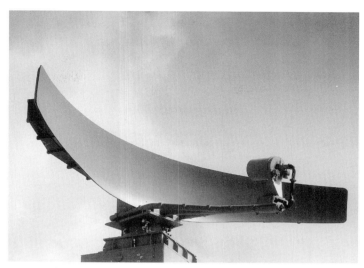

Suricate. (Thomson-CSF)

TRS 3405 is shown at Cap Gris-Nez, for vessel traffic control. (Thomson-CSF)

VAMPIR MB, with VIGY 10 on the platform above it, at Bourget Euronaval 1996. The device on the platform to the left is probably VIGY 20, with its two large widely separated windows. (Author)

The Najir 2000 optronic FCS carries a CCD TV camera and two IR cameras (3–5 and 8–12 microns) as well as a laser ranger (1.54-micron eyesafe type). Elevation limits are +85/−35 deg. Maximum train rate is 120 deg/sec. Swept radius is 0.53 m, and the sensor head weighs 200 kg (the processor below decks weighs 295 kg). (CS Defense)

Najir Mk 2 moves the Najir operator below decks, leaving its sensors on a new lightweight LOS-stabilized mounting with better tracking performance (train rate 90 deg/sec) and better reaction time through a better operator interface. The mount weighs 550 kg, the processor 560 kg, and the control console 300 kg. Elevation limits are +67/−18 deg. (CS Defense)

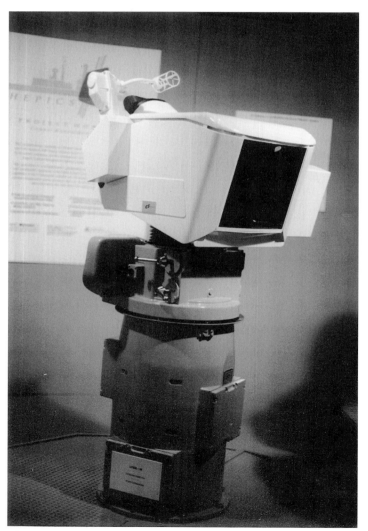

The Lynx IR optronic director carries a height-adjustable optronic unit (CCD TV with 4 to 16 deg FOV, 8–12-micron IR camera with 4-deg FOV, and operator's monitor) with an elevation pick-off to transmit data to the ship's CDS. Elevation limits are +40/−15 deg; the director trains at 1 rad/sec. It weighs 205 kg. The first deliveries were in 1996. A 3–5-micron IR camera is available as an option. (Author)

TDS 90. Elevation limits are +65/−20 deg, and designation accuracy is 3 mrad. Dimensions: 382mm diameter, height 1.7 m (weight 77 kg). (Author)

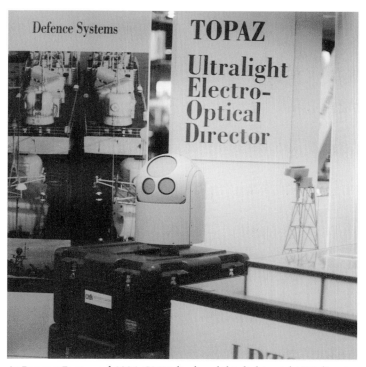

At Bourget Euronaval 1996, CMN displayed this lightweight EO director as part of a proposed fast-attack combat system, which also included an MRR radar (model at right). (Author)

NAJIR Mk 2 at Bourget Euronaval 1996. (Author)

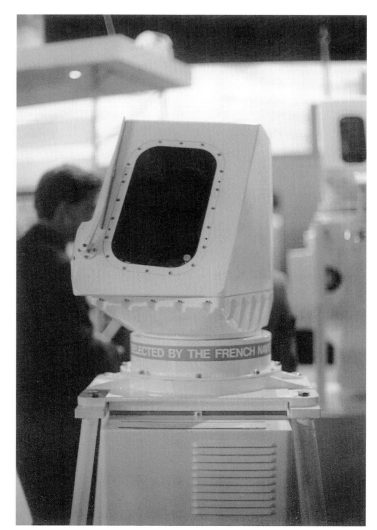

VIGY 105 at Bourget Euronaval 1996. (Author)

CS Defense's model of NAJIR Mk 1. (Author)

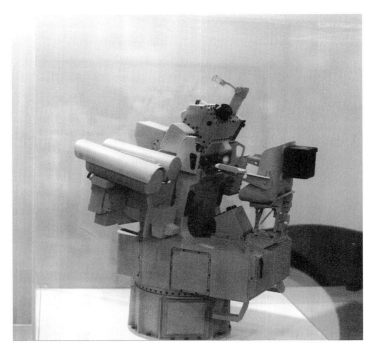

CS Defense's model of NAJIR Mk 1. (Author)

Coulverine carrying a 27mm Mauser MN 27 gun, at Bourget Euronaval, 1996. The control console is in the foreground. The same mounting can take Mauser's 30mm MK 30 (800 rnd/min, 1100 m/sec [1450 m/sec sabot round], with 120 ready-use rounds on the mount). Effective range is 3 km (4 km for sabot rounds). The 27mm version achieves 1025 m/sec (1100 m/sec for sabot round); effective range is 2.7 km (4 km sabot). Training radius is 1630 mm for the 27mm version, 2255 mm for the 30mm version. Elevation limits in both versions are +60/−15 deg; the gun trains at 1 mrad/sec to 55 deg/sec. It is gyrostabilized and points with better than 1 mrad accuracy. Dispersion is less than 2.5 mrad. Both versions carry 120 rounds of ready-service ammunition on the mount. (Author)

tenna weight is 700 kg (as in Mars 05; the original parabolic antenna weighs 1500 kg and scans at 7.5 or 15 rpm).

Arabel uses a lens to reduce the number of phase shifters to about 100. The beam elevates from 2 to 70 deg.

At Bourget Euronaval 1996 Thomson-CSF displayed a model of a vertically launched (cold-launched) version of Crotale NG. Reportedly the Royal Navy has shown some interest. The scheme is apparently being discouraged officially because of possible conflict with the PAAMS program, and Thomson-CSF has described it as an exploratory development using Russian cold-launch technology. Similar difficulties apparently arose over DCNI's development of a version of the *La Fayette*–class frigate armed with Standard Missiles, to meet a particular navy's requirements.

CS Defense's model of Lynx. (Author)

GIAT is now responsible for the 100mm gun, Creusot-Loire having withdrawn from gun-making.

New details of the X-band Suricate are now available. Peak power is 6 kW (pulse-compressed: 40-, 10-, or 0.2-microsec pulses at 400, 800/1600, 3200 pps). Antenna tilt angle is adjust-

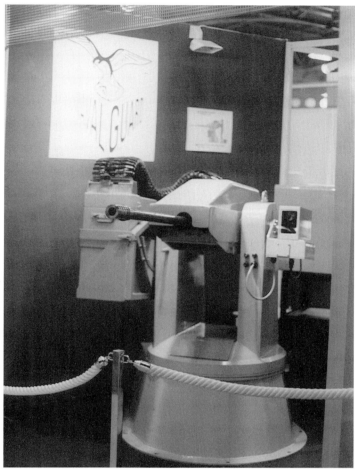

The Coulverine 20mm mount, at Bourget Euronaval 1996. Note the sensor at right, at trunnion level. (Author)

able (+5/−5 deg) and gain is 40 dB (4.4m antenna). In long-range mode (instrumented range 333 km) the radar can detect a 2.5m² air target at 82 km and a 10m² target at 112 km; in normal (anti-clutter) mode (instrumented range 157 km) the corresponding figures are 66 and 90 km. The radar can handle 400 tracks. Resolution is 1.3 deg, 48 m (accuracy is 0.1 deg and 7m).

Brochure photographs show Thomson-CSF surveillance radars in Canada (Les Escoumins), France (Cap Griz-Nez, Mont St. Frieux, Ushant), Indonesia (Batam), and Saudi Arabia (Jubail).

Naval Guard received the contract to adapt Coulverine to the Mauser gun on 1 November 1995, and the gun was delivered on 7 March 1996.

At Bourget Euronaval 1996 SAGEM announced CSR, a compact X-band (9.4 GHz) navigational radar for submarines using the Kelvin-Hughes Type 1007 console (ARPA, with a capacity of up to 50 tracks) and an enclosed slotted waveguide antenna with co-located transceiver, the latter being linked by cable to the below-decks processor. That reduces power demand from 25 to 5 kW.

SAGEM also showed VIGY 105EOMS (EO multifunction system), an enhanced version of VIGY 105 with a single-spectrum IRST (3–5 or 8–12 microns) with autodetection and 2D tracking and director functions. Sea-skimmer missiles are detected beyond 10 km. Elevation range +65/−20 deg. FOVs: 3 × 4 and 9 × 12 deg. The head contains an IR channel, a monochrome or color TV channel, and an eye-safe laser ranger with high PRF. The IRIS thermal imager uses a 288 × 4 FPA. VIGY 105 itself slews to a designated bearing in less than 1 sec. Dimensions: diameter 480 mm, height 1.48 m (weight less than 150 kg).

GERMANY

Mauser is now marketing an EO version of its quadruple 27mm Drakon, using a Najir 2000 FCS and a below-decks Calisto console. Targets would be detected by a Vampir ML 11 IRST.

ITALY

GIAT's Affut 15 (Mount 15) for small combatants, at Bourget Euronaval 1996. (Author)

A Myriad FCS radar at Bourget Euronaval 1996. (Author)

Medusa Mk 3 at Bourget Euronaval 1996. NA-18L is Medusa with extra processing power to operate as an FCS, and with a laser ranger (1.54 micron, instrumented range up to 10 km), typically carried below the TV camera visible at left. The sensor on the right is an IR camera (8–12 microns, two FOVs). Some Medusas lack the IR camera. (Author)

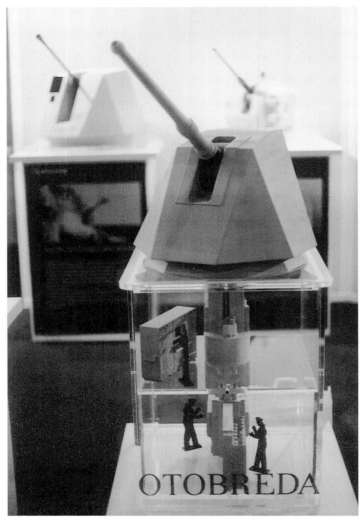

OTOBreda's next-generation 5in/54. (Author)

Aspide 2000 at Bourget Euronaval 1996. (Author)

OTOBreda's nondeck-penetrating version of its 76mm gun. (Author)

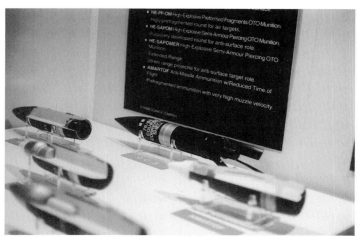

OTOBreda's course-corrected 76mm shell, showing its stabilizing fins folded down. (Author)

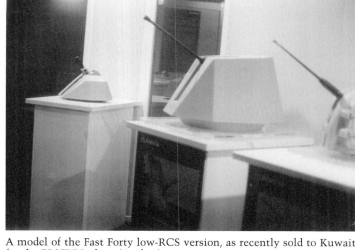

A model of the Fast Forty low-RCS version, as recently sold to Kuwait for the PB37BRL class. (Author)

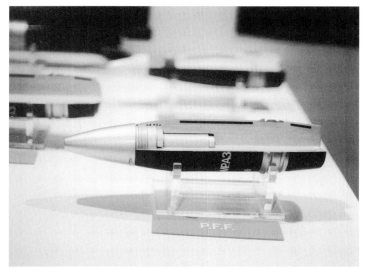

A 76mm prefragmented shell. (Author)

Myriad in model form. (Author)

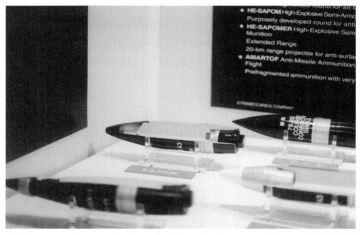

A 76mm semiarmor-piercing shell. In the foreground is an AMARTOF shell (antimissile ammunition with reduced time of flight) and, to its right, a high-explosive multirole shell (MOM). (Author)

ISRAEL

EL/M-2228X has been bought for the Singaporean *Fearless* class. EL/M-2228S is for the *Eilat* (*Sa'ar* 5) class. A two-dimensional version of EL/M-2228S, using the same transmitter but the antenna of the earlier EL/M-2208, is already reportedly in Israeli and Chilean service, as the target acquisition radar of the Barak missile system.

NETHERLANDS

At Bourget Euronaval 1996 Signaal announced Mirador, a COTS IR tracker/FCS to replace LIOD and fill the low-end market, mainly for small combatants and as a secondary system for larger ones. The goal was to cut price by $\frac{2}{3}$ to $\frac{3}{4}$, to improve accuracy by a factor of 20 to 40, to reduce weight by $\frac{2}{3}$, and to reduce delivery time by $\frac{2}{3}$ to $\frac{3}{4}$. The buyer can install this plug-and-play system without assistance from Signaal. The key to all of this improvement was to adopt COTS components, including sensors (the eye-safe laser is still expensive, and sensors amount to 60% of system cost). Mirador uses a single-card 400–500-MFLOPS processor (MPC860-36860-SHARC). Its sensors are carried in a carbon-fiber turret (for stealth: RCS is reduced from the usual 1–20 m² to 0.01–0.1 m²), which can train at 340 deg/sec (accuracy

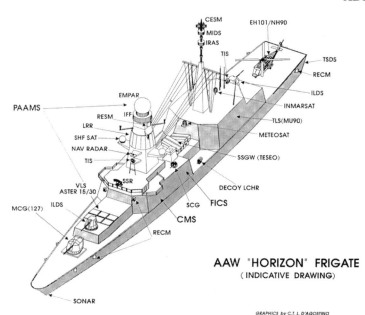

AAW "HORIZON" FRIGATE
(INDICATIVE DRAWING)

GRAPHICS by C.T. L. D'AGOSTINO

A recent sketch of the Italian version of the Project Horizon trinational frigate shows some of the new Italian naval systems. The gun forward is the low-RCS version of OTOBreda's 127/54. ILDS (inner-layer missile defense) is the new version of the OTOBreda 76/62, presumably firing a course-corrected shell. Note the spaced countermeasures transmitters (RECM) along the hull and superstructure, and the corresponding mast ESM array (RESM), for Alenia's new Cross-Eye antimonopulse countermeasure. The small-caliber gun (SCG) is presumably OTOBreda's 30mm, in its new low-RCS gunhouse. Note the phased-array long-range radar (LRR) wrapped around the tower foremast; this ship does not carry the SMARTELLO planned for the British and French ships. The main-mast carries a communications ESM (CESM) array (including HF/DF), a microwave identification system (MIDS), and an IR acquisition system (IRAS); note that the latter seems to be an array rather than a scanner. The small tubes running up the mast are probably transmitting antennas. TSDS indicated aft is a torpedo self-defense system. Note the absence of any separate set of launchers for MILAS, so that the total of MILAS plus the antiship TESEO is only eight weapons; note that the lightweight launcher for MU 90 Impact torpedoes is buried in the after superstructure. The visible indication of attention to radar cross-section is that all flat surfaces are angled to avoid creating square corner radar reflectors. (Italian Navy)

JAPAN

A remote-controlled Gatling gun (JM 61) is shown aboard a Japanese hydrofoil missile boat. Note the EO sensor atop the housing. (*Ships of the World*)

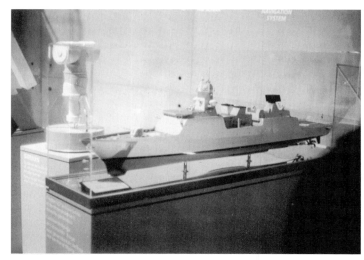

This model of the Dutch LCF frigate shows the APAR forward and SMART-L aft. The big foremast domes are for satellite dishes. In the background is a model of the Sirius IRST. (Author)

This model of the LCF foremast shows the depth of the APAR arrays. The small object on top is Sirius. (Author)

APAR on the foremast of the LCF model. On top of the mast are Sirius (at the fore end) and two ESM arrays. (Author)

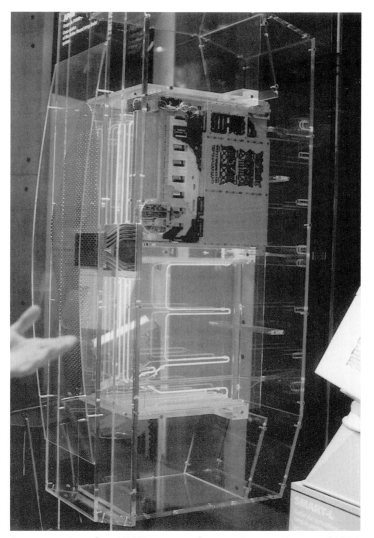

A cross-section of an APAR array, as shown at Bourget Euronaval 1996. (Author)

10^{-5}, fixed-focus (2.2-deg FOV) tracker, thermal imager (8–13 microns, FOV 10×5 deg), and an eye-safe laser ranger (1.54 microns, NdYaG, instrumented range 20 km, divergence 0.6 microrad, repetition rate 3 Hz [8-Hz burst]). Above-decks weight is 55 kg. Functions: surveillance, auto-acquisition (a new capability), autotracking, ballistics/FCS, gunfire support, splash-spotting. Range: Mirador detects a small ship at 20 km and can direct gunfire against shore targets at 10 km. Maximum target tracking speed is 1000 m/sec.

Mirador at Bourget Euronaval 1996. (Author)

The current AAW upgrade of the *van Heemskerck*–class frigates includes installation of CWI in the STIR 1.8 director, to provide a third missile control channel (missiles are currently controlled by the two STIR 2.4s). The upgrade also includes Scout, JMCIS, and a bulk reloader for Goalkeeper.

Data on the SCORADS (Signaal Coastal Radar System) C-band coastal radar are now available. Peak power is 2 kW (using 24-microsec medium PRF air mode or 10-microsec low PRF surface mode pulses compressed to 550 nsec). There are 64 channels. The carbon fiber reflector antenna forms a 0.75×2.75-deg ($\csc^2$ to 30 deg) beam (gain 40 dB, sidelobes average -40 dB). Maximum range is 120 km on air targets and 105 km (horizon) on surface targets; maximum altitude is 10,000 ft. Minimum range is 1 km. Accuracy (resolution): 100 (100) m, 0.25 (2) deg. Scan rate is 10 rpm. Track capacity is 400 per scan. Many modules within the radar are adapted from other Signaal products.

better than 10 microrad) and elevate at 340 deg/sec (limits $+120/-30$ deg) using a brushless direct-drive motor (to eliminate the need for maintenance). The turret carries up to five sensors: a zoom color TV for observation (FOV 5.5–61.6 deg [diagonal], dynamic range 5–300,000 lux), an LLLTV (400–900 nm, FOV 6.2–62 deg [diagonal] with $10\times$ zoom, dynamic range down to

Signaal's SCORADS. (Signaal)

RUSSIA

The cruiser *Petr Velikiy*, the last of the *Kirov* class, reportedly has a land-type planar array antenna in place of her after Top Dome (3R41 Volna). This radar, probably 36N85 (NATO Flap Lid), folds down when not in use. Like Top Dome, it can engage six targets simultaneously (two missiles each); it has alternative scan modes optimized for low-fliers (90 × 1 deg), medium/high-fliers (64 × 5 and 64 × 13 deg), and ballistic missiles (32 × 10 deg). In automatic tracking or missile guidance modes, scans cover 4 × 4 or 2 × 2 deg. Peak power is 130 kW. Given that this radar is unlikely to have been marinized, it was presumably installed because a second Top Dome was not available.

Kilo-class submarines (and probably others) carry a surfacing-security radar, MPRK-60. It incorporates both an active radar and an ESM system (with analysis), all in a small radome. This may be the device nicknamed Amber Light (see the EW section). It gives the close-range surface picture for safety of navigation and warns of ASW helos and ships. MTBF: active 8 hr (5 min warm-up), passive 24 hr.

Versions of Fregat (NATO Top Plate) on current surface units are: MR-710 (*Kuznetzov*, two *Kirov* class, one *Slava* class, *Udaloy* class), MR-750 (*Sovremennyy* class), and MR-755 (*Krivak* class).

SOUTH AFRICA

Reutech Radar of Stellenbosch developed a sea-skimmer detection radar (RSR-1050) and a naval FCS (RTS-6400), both for the projected South African navy corvette and for export. Under a late 1996 agreement, DASA will market RTS-6600 (possibly as ETS-6600), an evolved RTS-6400, as part of its proposal for the German navy Type 130 corvette, the search radar for which is TRS-3D/16. Reutech will offer TRS-3D/16 (and RTS-6400) to the South African navy for the projected Project Sitron corvette. RSR-1050 had been developed to meet a separate South African requirement for a missile detection radar (i.e., a target acquisition radar), but under the agreement with DASA the company now claims that TRS-3D can perform both search and target-acquisition tasks.

The X-band RSR-1050 uses a lightweight composite-material stabilized offset Gregorian feed antenna (similar in concept to a Cassegrain, using a subreflector and a main reflector) scanning at 12/24/30/60 rpm (programmable optimized rates), to detect a fighter beyond 30 km or a missile beyond 20 km; nominal instrumented range is 30 km (i.e., slightly beyond the horizon). Its ADT memory can handle 100 target tracks. Accuracy is better than 30 m/0.1 deg. The frequency-agile very broad-band TWT transmitter offers programmable pulse compression (i.e., variable ratios) and scenario-adaptive Doppler processing (which suggests software-controlled PRF). ECCM features include random PRF stagger and PRF jitter as well as a large instantaneous dy-namic range. As in other current pulse-compression radars, peak power is low to limit probability of intercept. The company claims a very high level of ECM immunity and excellent clutter rejection for all-weather operation. The radar's data processor uses standard processing boards and the software includes adaptive tracking filters with motion compensation. There are separate track and search color displays. Reutech offers as options a solid-state transmitter, additional ECCM features, an Ethernet interface (the system is designed to use FDDI), customized displays, and remote diagnostics (the radar has BITE features).

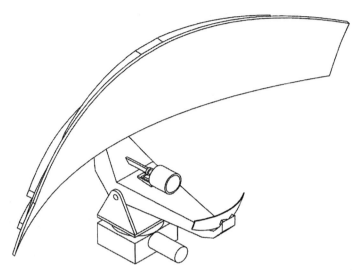

The antenna of Reutech Radar's RSR-1050 missile detector shows both a secondary (*front*) and a primary reflector. (Reutech Radar)

RTS-6400, one of a family of tracking systems, is the complementary X-band/EO FCS tracker, connected to a combat systems bus. It compiles a track file, which is sent via the bus to an external fire-control computer or computers. As with RSR-1050, the bus is either FDDI or, as an option, an Ethernet. Normally RTS-6400 receives external target designation, but it can also perform a limited autonomous search. It can also use only its passive optronics (see below) for search.

As in RSR-1050, RTS-6400 uses a coherent X-band digital (software-controlled) pulse compression monopulse (three-channel) radar for clutter rejection (up to 50 dB against stationary clutter), all-weather performance (up to Sea State 5, 25mm/hr rain), and ECCM. The software-controlled waveform is optimized for target range. Reutech claims that the system's broad-band frequency agility offers both ECM immunity and superior low-level (antimultipath) tracking. Presumably the transmitter is the same as that in RSR-1050. As in that system, limited peak power makes for some degree of stealth. Reutech claims that the tracker benefits from using a high-performance positioner for extremely fast reaction and excellent stabilization and pointing accuracy. Elevation limits: +81/−25 deg. The platform uses direct-drive DC motors.

As in RSR-1050, the usual transmitter is a wide-band TWT; a solid-state transmitter can be substituted at some cost in range. Pulses are digitally generated (software controlled); compression uses programmable pulse codes. Two pulse widths (long coded or short uncoded) are automatically selected, based on target range. Frequency is generated by a fast-switching synthesizer. PRF changes on a pulse-to-pulse or batch basis. Tracking is by range Doppler.

The tracker can carry control elements for semi-active or command-guided (to LOS) missiles.

The complete radar (receiver/synthesizer) is housed in a sealed container above decks. It is provided with power and with a few timing signals; its output, sent below decks along low-power coaxials, are three IF signals (sum, azimuth, elevation). The latter signals are digitized and processed below decks (Doppler-processed in both the detection channel [full range] and in up to two radar and two command missile tracking gates). Instrumented range is 60 km in surface mode and 25 km (programmable) in air mode. Bad-weather range is better than 24 km on a fighter and better than 16 km on a missile. Tracking accuracy is better than 5 m/0.6 mrad (1.5 mrad including multipath). Overall acquisition time is better than 3 sec (1.5 sec typical). Slew rate is greater than 5 rad/sec (acceleration greater than 6 rad/sec^2). The radar can track on jam.

The tracker also carries a 10-micron thermal imager (FOVs 2.2 × 1.5 and 7.9 × 5.4 deg), TV (FOVs 1.8 × 1.4 and 7.3 × 5.6 deg, exposure range 2 lux [narrow FOV] or 8 lux [wide FOV] to 100,000 lux), and laser ranger (PRF less than 20 Hz), whose signals are handled by a dedicated optronics autotracker before being sent to the main RTS-6400 single-board COTS data processor for data fusion (the autotracker provides confidence estimates).

As currently planned, RTS-6400 uses a 1.2m dish with an offset feed (at its bottom), and with an optronics package on its left side. Options include a 5-micron FLIR and a Ka-band radar channel.

SPAIN

The DORNA director shows optics (high-definition TV, IR camera, and laser ranger) alongside its K-band radar on a gyrostabilized pedestal. DORNA autotracks in both EO and radar. Its distributed architecture is built around an IEE 802.3 LAN; it includes some C^2 functions for small ships.

Bazan's EO surveillance system for the *Serviola* class. (Bazan)

Bazan's DORNA. (Bazan)

SWEDEN

The ANZAC frigates have a new Ceros 200 director using a 1m Cassegrain antenna, incorporating both a J-band radar and an I-band CWI for the Standard Missile. The director also carries a

daylight TV, IR imager, and laser ranger. Later RAN ships will have solid-state illuminator transmitters rather than the current Raytheon magnetrons.

SWITZERLAND

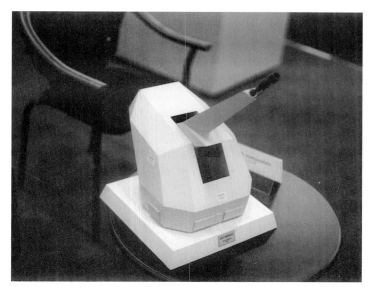

A model of Millennium shows the velocity-measuring and fuze-setting coils at the muzzle required by the gun's AHEAD ammunition. The faceted gun house and barrel cover are intended to reduce radar cross-section. (Author)

UNITED KINGDOM

Two proposed ships shown at Bourget Euronaval 1996 were equipped with Spectar, a projected single-face version of Siemens-Plessey's Sampson. As of October 1996, Spectar was to have become available in about 18 months.

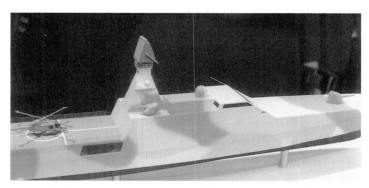

Spectar is shown on a model of BAe's Cougar corvette, at Bourget Euronaval 1996. The guns are all in low-RCS housings, which include the barrels. The two small ones are Millenium 35mm guns; the bow gun is a 76mm. (Author)

A new track extractor, LFE, is to replace the current LFA of the Type 996 radar, which is unable to deal with the volume of data the radar produces (raw data rather than plots are output onto the combat data bus). As an interim measure, LFA is being modified.

Factory trials of AWS-9(2D) were completed in September 1996, with sea trials aboard *Trondheim* due for completion in December 1996.

The two *Fort*-class AORs are being fitted "for but not with" Phalanx at their next refits; they were originally to have had VL Seawolf.

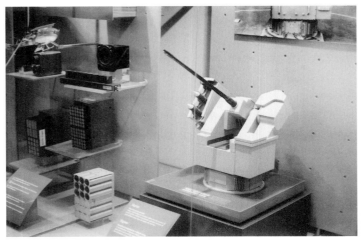

MSI's model shows SIGMA, its gun-missile combination, in this case carrying three Mistrals. (Author)

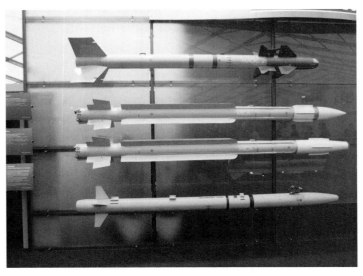

UNITED STATES

The pulse-Doppler upgrade of SPS-48E reportedly provides the three lowest beams of the bottom beam group with a PRF of 2778 pps. A $1m^2$ target can be detected at 17 nm.

Further details of the Lockheed Martin Sanders HF surface wave radar are now available. Testing on board the Self-Defense Test Ship (ex-DDG 31 *Decatur*), originally planned for June––August 1997, have now been set back to February–April 1998 due to budget cuts. The test on an LSD is now also scheduled for 1998. Frequency range is 15–25 MHz, the best range for performance being 15–18 MHz (best for ballistic missile detection is about 20–25 MHz), but the best to avoid interference from shore users being around 18–19 MHz. The radar uses phase-coded, digitally synthesized pulses (225 microsec long, PRF 2000, each pulse containing 16 subpulses, each 12.5 microsec wide). In addition to sea-skimmers (beyond 37 km) and aircraft (beyond 75 km), it is expected to detect surface targets beyond 150 km and ballistic missiles beyond 500 km. The 24 small (1 × 1 × 3 ft) deck-edge antennas feed a digital beam-former. The transmitter antenna is a pair of vertically stacked meander-line antennas. The signal processor uses i860 CPUs, and the track processor is a TAC-4.

HFSSW was an FY95 ATD. Late in 1996 it was announced that the concluding FY97 funds would not be available. It is not clear whether funding from earlier years will support the planned demonstration.

On 13 December 1996 Hughes was named winner of the AIM-9X competition, with a missile using the existing Sidewinder motor. Many observers considered this choice a victory of economics over a more innovative approach; reportedly the U.S. Air Force had not been particularly impressed by ASRAAM, the basis of the Hughes proposal. Ironically, the U.S. government had withdrawn from the ASRAAM program (which then envisaged a rather different missile) some years earlier, on the ground of insufficient performance. It may be that the helmet-mounted sight and high-angle-of-attack software contribute by far the largest improvement in system performance, and thus that it is unwise to invest too much in the missile itself.

In the fall of 1996 the British government demanded that the Mk 41 VLS be considered as an alternative to Sylva in Project Horizon. It was soon apparent that Mk 41 could launch the Aster missiles planned for the new ship, but it was also clear that adoption might be the initial step toward substituting the Standard Missile for Aster. There was, indeed, talk of abandoning any (expensive) TBMD role for Aster in favor of adopting a projected SM-X TMD weapon, which will probably be developed by the Dutch-German frigate consortium. Both Hughes and Raytheon offered baseline and enhanced versions of AIM-9X, all using 3–5-micron InSb focal plane arrays with two-color discrimination to reject false targets. The Hughes baseline is an evolved Sidewinder (Box Office II with small canards) using Hughes's 128 ×

ASRAAM, showing its seeker and its size compared to the French Magic (*top*) and Mica (*second and third missiles down*). (S. Zaloga)

128-pixel ASRAAM sensor, but with a wider gimbal angle and an extended dome. Thrust vectoring vanes are mechanically coupled to the tail fins. The 5in Mk 36 Sidewinder motor is retained. The enhanced missile is a P^3I version of the British ASRAAM with thrust-vectoring and with a bigger blast-fragmentation warhead, but with the existing proximity fuze, seeker, inertial measurement unit, electronics, power unit, and rocket motor; Hughes argued that the sale of about 2000 ASRAAMs to Britain would cut overall price (ASRAAM is to enter production in 1997 and to enter service in 1998). Although ASRAAM is 6.5 in in diameter, it can fit Sidewinder pylons. Raytheon used a 256 × 256-pixel sensor (already in production, and baseline for the Israeli Arrow ABM) and thrust-vectoring. The 188-lb baseline version was 119 in long ($9.9in^2$ fin box size). The enhanced version used a 6.3in-dia Israeli Python 4 motor, integrated with the warhead.

It provided 2.25 sec of initial high thrust, then sustainer thrust, then a third high pulse at the end of the 8-sec burn for terminal maneuvers. The alternative engines in the enhanced versions were allowed into the competition in April 1996, when the requirement that the motor be an insensitive munition was dropped.

By late 1996, the official U.S. Air Force view was that AIM-9X was urgent because the existing AIM-9M was already outclassed by the Russian AA-11, Israeli Python 4, later versions of the French Mica, and by the British ASRAAM (which is not yet in service). Too, the view is now that in future about 25% of air combat will be short-range, compared to 5% based on studies of the Gulf War against Iraq. Reportedly, contact simulations showed that aircraft armed with AIM-9M won only 1 out of 50 dogfights against those armed with AA-11, whereas AIM-9X (with a Sidewinder engine) would reverse the odds to 6:1, and a larger engine might achieve 60:1 odds. Presumably much of the difference can be traced to adoption of a helmet-mounted sight.

Late in 1996 plans called for completion of EMD by October 2002, followed by low-rate production of 1000 missiles in three lots, then 500 missiles per year for a total of about 10,000.

The 5in/62 will probably be designated Mod 4; Mod 3 would have been the existing gun with a new adaptable control system. It is unlikely to appear.

There is current interest in a twin-barrel vertical 155mm gun, VGAS (vertical gun for advanced ship), a FY97 new start. It is to be buried in the deck of the Arsenal Ship. Although such a gun would not provide any initial guidance to the shell, it would offer about a fourfold advantage over a missile launcher in boost efficiency per unit ammunition volume. Much then depends on how cleverly the guidance unit in the shell can use that initial boost. It may be possible to make guided shells inexpensively using the gyroscopes and accelerometers now being manufactured in very large quantities for cars, for their antiskid braking systems (the main current difference is that military versions, unlike car versions, must be calibrated). The VGAS goal is to exceed a range of 250 nm with a CEP of 5–10 m. Initial R&D funds are included in the FY97 budget.

Texas Instruments won the contest to build the EX-171 Extended Range Guided Munition (ERGM) with a contract for 70 test rounds and an option for up to 500 more, to be produced in FY00. First test firings are scheduled for 1998. The stated unit cost goal is $2000, but as of late 1996 conventional 5in rounds cost $4000. The contract was awarded 13 September 1996. Development is to be completed by September 2000, and the shell is to enter service by FY01. As of late 1996, it appeared that as many as 8000 rounds might be bought by FY02, given the number of 5in/62 guns expected in the fleet. Each shell carries 72 submunitions in a 35-lb cargo space.

As of late 1996 the Marines were calling for development of a guided shell for counterbattery fire, in hopes that more of their artillery needs could be met by the fleet offshore.

An additional optical sensor has been proposed for the Phalanx surface upgrade. One advantage of the pair of EO sensors is that the gun can now track targets in the low-altitude radar multipath zone. As of late 1996, with funding tight, there was fear that the ASuW upgrade would be canceled altogether. One possibility was that the new barrels would be bought but the EO elements deferred. That would maintain a capability to fire the compressed-powder round, which is still under development. Proponents of continued Phalanx development have pointed out that the Phalanx radar (in a doubled-range mode) is the main engagement radar sensor of SSDS. Unless Phalanx is retained in service, then, SSDS may lose much of its capability.

SABER is being used as a joint situational-awareness system, because a wide variety of platforms (including tanks and helicopters) can receive its data, transmitted via a 25-kHz satellite channel, which can report 60,000 GPS positions per hour. Exercises showed that one of its advantages was that units such as helicopters could report position without unmasking themselves, since their signals had to go vertically but not horizontally. Aegis cruisers used SABER while returning to a force without using conventional IFF, and for controlling their helicopters

The SSDS Command Table. The Sensor Supervisor, responsible for the detection phase, controls sensor contributions to the track picture. The Weapons Supervisor schedules weapons and reviews the system's engagement recommendations. The Weapons Supervisor approves semi-automatic engagements, and can always manually control the system. The TAO approves system response to tracks through identification and engagement doctrine approval and activation. The TAO decides whether the system operates in automatic, semiautomatic, or manual mode, or in a combination of the three. The TAO controls the Batteries Release/System Hold Fire safety key. (Hughes)

The four antenna panels of the Phalanx Block I tracker are shown in model form. (Author)

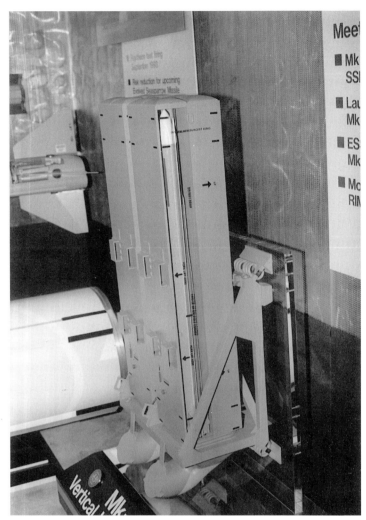

A model of a Mk 48 launcher shows the paired exhausts under the vertical cells. (Author)

A model of the long-barrel version of the 5in/54, displayed by British Aerospace at Bourget Euronaval 1996. In the background is a model of Millenium; the missile models between the guns show the effect of Millenium's AHEAD ammunition. One end of a Stonefish mine is in the foreground. (Author)

without TACAN. Since all SABER tracks were converted to other standard formats (Links 11 and 16 and OTCIXS [Gold]), the SABER tactical picture was available to all Link 16 terminals, including some ashore. SABER was first used operationally during the April 1996 evacuation of civilians from Monrovia by the 22nd Marine Expeditionary Unit (MEU) aboard USS *Guam*; the Marines had 24 SABER beacons.

Comparative models of long-barrel and conventional 5in/54s at Navy League 1995. (Author)

The Mk 96 Mod 0 stabilized 25mm gun/40mm grenade launcher mount is shown with its side plating removed. Elevation limits are +55/−5 deg (train rate 20 deg/sec, elevation rate 25 deg/sec, in each case using the control grip trigger). The mount weighs 1430 kg loaded. MTBF is 9360 hr (mean rounds between failure: 25mm, 5000; 40mm, 1100). (United Defense)

Valkyrie under test in manned configuration. (SEI)

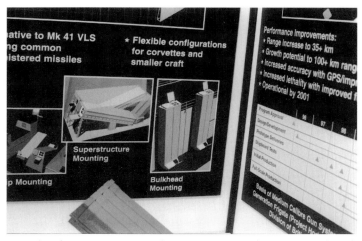

United Defense's 1996 poster shows Cocoon, its alternative to the Mk 41 vertical launcher, in both cross-deck and vertical formats. The panel visible at right advertises the improved Mk 45 gun. (Author)

Current improved versions of AMRAAM (AIM-120) are AIM-120B (producibility enhancement) and AIM-120C (preplanned product improvement [P³I]). AIM-120B offers an improved inertial unit, an improved RF processor and transmitter, and an interim digital range correlator. It entered full-scale production with Lot 7 in October 1994, the first preproduction missiles having become operational in the second half of 1994. AIM-120C Phase I is the current clipped-wing version (to fit in the F-22 weapons bay). Phase II provides ECCM upgrades, a new or improved warhead (presumably directional), and motor improvements. It is to enter production in FY97. Phase III will be larger and will offer more range; to some extent it will offer the Navy the capability lost when AAAM was canceled (and when Phoenix is withdrawn from service). As of 1996, no production date had been set. A parallel Air Force program, Have Yak, developed anticruise missile improvements for AIM-120. Current (1996)

production goals for AIM-120 are 8600 for the Air Force and 2436 for the Navy, but they may not include AIM-120C. This is a drop of about 2000 compared to 1992 estimates. About 7700 missiles, including those for export, have been produced to date. The latest export customer is Greece, for use on board F-16s.

Standard Block IVA is expected to enter service in 1999. Block IV was approved for low-rate initial production in 1995, with full production to follow in 1996–97.

The LEAP version of Standard is now being called SM-X. Its LEAP kinetic kill weapon is now being termed a kinetic warhead (KW). Lockheed Martin has proposed an alternative in which a THAAD kinetic warhead (which is heavier than LEAP) would be carried atop an advanced second-stage/extended length vectorable nozzle motor. A modified Standard with a second-stage motor is to be tested during 1997.

ESSMS: The FY96 POM (as of mid-1996) envisaged low-rate initial production beginning late in 1998 or early in 1999, with 35 missiles bought through FY99, followed by 135 in FY00, 157 in FY01, 136 in FY02, and 188 in FY03, a slight increase over earlier plans. Hughes expects to sell about 3000 missiles in all, at a unit cost of $420,000.

Firebox is a new CIWS project under development by the Office of Naval Research. It will use multiple composite barrels to fire semi-actively guided rocket rounds, each soft-launched to protect its electronics. Firebox is to fit within a Phalanx footprint.

The water barrier currently under development uses a line charge to produce a wall of water 300 to 400 ft from a ship, 5 to 6 ft thick, primarily to stop fragments of a missile destroyed at greater range, but also as a last-ditch antimissile defense.

ELECTRONIC WARFARE

FRANCE

Dassault Electronics advertises ESM-99, a lightweight naval or airborne E-J band (expandable to C, D, and K-bands) ELINT set using a 6–8 element antenna and an IFM, with a 68020 CPU.

ISRAEL

NATACS uses a Pentium processor.

Sa'ar 4.5 boats are being refitted with a 72-rnd DESEAVER launcher capable of firing up to 12 different rounds packaged in groups of 6 (2 × 3). Boxes on either side of the mounting each carry four such groups (2 × 2); a third box on top carries another four (groups tilted sideways). The boxes are covered with RAM and angled sides reduce radar RCS. Decoy types include long range chaff, Beamtrap, and a previously undisclosed Heatrap (IR seduction).

A recent list of expendables includes a 0.385-kg 3.33cm rocket- or cannon-fired Chaff Muffin round covering 4–7 GHz.

ITALY

The EH-101 helicopter will use the ALR-735(V)3 RWR. Note that there are two monopulse DF channels, coarse and fine. The maritime utility version will have ELT 156X(V)2 as well as a Marconi RALM/01 laser warner.

SWEDEN

At Farnborough 1996 CelsiusTech announced a new 55mm BOP expendable towed decoy for the J-37 (BOP/A) and JAS-39 (BOP/B). The body carries both receiver and transmitter, the towing cable carrying power and some commands. Work began in 1990–91 and the company hopes for a full-scale development contract in 1997. A planned version may be towable from existing BOZ chaff pods.

UNITED KINGDOM

The June 1994 GEC-Marconi Siren (DLH) contract covers over 700 rounds to fit 21 ships, beginning in 1998.

PIRATE is used by Turkey and by at least one other NATO navy, and it is produced under license by Nissan Aerospace for the JMSDF. It is based on Mk 214 (chaff round) hardware, the canister releasing nine payloads (three air-burst at intervals of 1,

3, and 4.5 sec plus six floating phosphor pots). The air-burst lasts about 20 sec, after which the floating pots last another 60 sec.

UNITED STATES

The Maryland congressional delegation managed to insert $50M into the FY97 budget to restart ALQ-165 (ASPJ) production, adding 36 sets. All F-14Ds and all F/A-18s operating over Bosnia are being equipped with ALQ-165, and late in 1996 the F/A-18Cs of a carrier air wing en route to the Western Pacific had the jammer.

Increasing confidence in ASPJ has led to questions about the need for IDECM, its planned successor (which is to enter service in FY02). The response is that the ASPJ jammer can handle threats such as SA-6. However, it cannot deal with monopulse radars such as those used in SA-8. For that a towed decoy, which is planned for IDECM, is needed. The GAO has now raised the question of whether the ALE-50 decoy can be added to non-IDECM aircraft such as the F-14 and F/A-18.

The EA-6B upgrade is likely to be called ICAP III; the baseline will be Block 89A with embedded GPS/INS, USQ-113, low- and high-band transmitters, and the universal exciter upgrade (UEU). The request for information (RFI) asked for new Band 1–10 receivers with sufficient frequency accuracy and discrimination to assign narrow-band jammers, and with the ability to detect frequency changes by a limited number of emitters being jammed so that jammers can be reassigned to follow. Direction of arrival would have to be accurate enough (with sufficient discrimination) to classify emitters and manage jammers, and would provide geolocation accurate enough to target HARMs in range-known mode. The airplane would perform electronic support and HARM-targeting functions while jamming. A goal, but not a requirement, is SEI. The RFI also envisaged situational awareness improvements to aid jamming and lethal suppression (HARM) by integrating on-board and external data (the latter to come from the TRAP, TADIXS-B, and TIBS intelligence links and from Link 16). A new display is to show both on-board and external data. The program envisages upgrading 126 aircraft at a unit price of $2.5–$3.5M. Responses to the RFI were received on 13 September 1996, at which time the program was due for execution in FY99–01, aircraft entering service in FY03. However, Congress pressed for a faster schedule, and the RFI included a provision that, should a contract be awarded in the third quarter of FY97 rather than in FY99, the upgrade should enter service in FY01.

Northrop Grumman is developing a submarine version of Litton's LR-100. The Egyptian army has selected it as baseline equipment in its planned UAV program, and it equips the F-16U being proposed to (but not yet bought by) the UAE.

ALR-801 can reportedly handle 1024 emitters simultaneously.

The Navy has contracted with Israel Military Industries (IMI) to convert up to 150 TALDs to powered ITALDS (ADM-141C); the first 100 were ordered converted in September 1996, and money was added to the FY97 budget for more.

MINE WARFARE

FRANCE

Sterne (TSM 3850) can be towed at 5–10 kt (submerged at 5 to 10 m) 200 m abaft a sweeper, using a combination of one magnetic and one wide-band acoustic sweep, and can resist the explosion of 1000 kg of TNT at 30 m. It can reproduce the magnetic signatures of ships from tankers down to patrol boats.

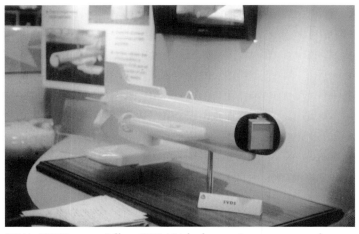

ECA's SVDS, essentially a PAP 104 body carrying a nose search sonar and an underslung classification sonar, as displayed in model form at Bourget Euronaval 1996. (Author)

GERMANY

G1 was originally SGM65, the first joint Danish-German mine project. Denmark planned to buy 2300 G2, of which 2100 had been ordered by 1994. SAI is G4. AIM (anti-invasion mine) is a reported STN project for a non-NATO derivative. The G3 program has apparently been dropped due to the end of the Cold War.

NORWAY

The Mk 1 moored controlled mines are reportedly ex-British, presumably the wartime L Mk II (1180 lb with 500-lb charge, moored in up to 25 fathoms [150 ft]). Norway also has U.S.-supplied Mk 51 controlled bottom mines.

Simrad's Minesniper as displayed at Bourget Euronaval 1996. (Author)

Date	UGDM 1954	Serpei 1957	UGDM-500 1958	UDM-E 1961	UDM-500 1964	UDM-2 1979
Weight (kg)	1150	1300	525	1413	575	1500
Warhead (kg)	620	750	200	645	300	800
Length (mm)	2855	2855	1585	2200	1500	2850
Width (mm)	630	630	450	630	450	650
Mine Interval (m)	150	150	80	125	—	—
Fuzing	IH	MA or IH	IH	A	—	IH

Fuze types: A, acoustic; H, hydrodynamic (pressure); I, induction; M, magnetic

RUSSIA

Further information on Soviet-era mines has appeared. KMD-1, -2, and -4 were based on AMD-1, -2, and -4. Data for some air-delivered bottom mines are tabulated on the previous page.

Details of the Lira air-delivered moored mine (contact/non-contact versions): 630 × 2855/3510 mm, 925/985 kg (250 kg of TGAG-5 explosive), water depth 20–250 m, mine interval 50/100 m, case depth 2, 3, 4, 5, or 6 m; or 10, 15, 20, 25 m; layable in 0.6–0.7 or 0.4–0.6 m/sec current.

An MDM-3 ground mine displayed by Gidropribor, 1995. (S. Zaloga)

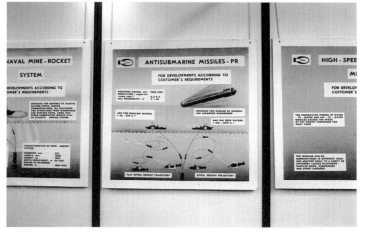

A 1995 Gidropribor poster suggests that the payload of the current rising mine is related to the APR-series rocket torpedo. The panel partly visible to the right advertises Shkval. (S. Zaloga)

UNITED STATES

The B-1B and B-2 are being certified to lay the Mk 62 Quickstrike mine (in the last quarter of FY96 and the third quarter of FY97, respectively), to supplement existing B-52 aerial minelaying capability. However, given the very limited numbers of these aircraft, it seems unlikely that this capability will be used.

Interest in using national (i.e., satellite) sensors for mine and obstacle reconnaissance continues as littoral remote sensing (LRS). Radiant Clear is a planned Navy/Marine Corps test of this TENCAP concept. It includes remote meteorological and environmental sensing.

The current surf-zone assault breaching system is the Mk 1-0 Mine Clearance System (MCS) using three M59 linear demolition charges (LDCs) deployed by three Mk 22-3 or -4 rockets fired

Gidropribor's 1995 poster shows the series of Grunt ROVs. The panel to the right shows the VNT helicopter-drawn sweep. (S. Zaloga)

UNITED KINGDOM

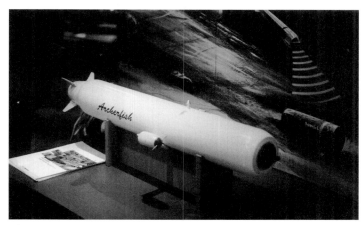

The current Archerfish configuration, displayed at Bourget Euronaval 1996. (Author)

from a Mk 154 launcher on board an amphibious vehicle (AAV). The LDCs are designed to breach land minefields, and in fact 75 MCS were used to clear Iraqi minefields in 1991. The LCAC-carried interim replacement, MCS Mk 5, uses the M58 LDC (developed in the 1950s) deployed by a Mk 22-4 rocket. An LCAC typically carries 12 Mk 5s arranged three abreast.

The planned replacement is a combination of SABRE (MCS EX-9) and DET (EX number not yet assigned); an LCAC carries nine multiple SABRE launchers abaft two twin DET launchers. SABRE uses a 405ft line carrying 130 discrete charges (10 lb of PBXN-103 each), each charge being connected to the next by a 3ft nylon harness. The charge is carried in a modified M58A3 container and deployed by a Mk 22-4 rocket. It flies a preset distance and automatically arms and delay-detonates (the delay allows the charge to settle to the bottom). Developed by NSWCs Dahlgren, Panama City, and Indian Head, SABRE has been successfully demonstrated, including a full detonation shot in a special pond at Eglin Air Force Base. DET is a 180 × 180ft explosive net made out of parallel lines of SX-2 detonation cord linked by inert cross elements. It is deployed by a pair of Mk 22-4 rockets firing simultaneously, parachutes pulling back the trailing edge to make the array spread out in flight. As with SABRE, range is preset (the rockets fire at a 25-deg angle) and delayed detonation is automatic. As with SABRE, DET has been demonstrated successfully; both systems have passed their Milestone II tests.

Plans call for SABRE to be used against anti-invasion mines in 10 to 3 ft of water, followed by DET to deal with mines from 3 ft to high water. A single LCAC would clear a 50yd path, first firing two-SABRE salvoes. Three firings more or less abreast would clear a 400ft × 50yd swath. Moving up the swath, the LCAC could fire again; in an example, the two 400ft swaths overlap, so the total cleared path is 750 ft long. From positions in the shoreward swath, the LCAC then fires two two-DET salvoes, each pattern canted to one side.

RMS: The current AQS-14 search sonar is to be replaced by a unit giving a search rate of 6nm^2/hr in deep water at a search rate of 8–12 kt.

ALISS is to be tested in FY98 on board a standard QST-35A target boat.

A planned upgrade to the SLQ-53 sweep adds a mine-marking capability (so the mines can be recovered and examined), a bottom-following capability, and a single-sided sweep version for the *Avenger* and *Osprey* classes.